HELLENISTIC

CIVILIZATION

AND THE

JEWS

by
Victor Tcherikover

translated by
S. Applebaum

HELLENISTIC CIVILIZATION AND THE JEWS

Philadelphia 1959

The Jewish Publication Society of America
The Magnes Press, The Hebrew University

Jerusalem 5719

ACKNOWLEDGMENTS

The Jewish Publication Society gratefully acknowledges the help it has received in the preparation and publication of this volume: Doctor M. Amit of the Hebrew University graciously came to our aid when the untimely death of the author faced us with very serious problems in seeing the book through the press. He asked us to acknowledge his debt to Dr. M. Stern and Prof. A. Fuks of the Hebrew University for their advice on many points. The Magnes Press of the Hebrew University in Jerusalem participated in planning the English version of this important work. The Littauer Foundation has cooperated in making the publication of this book possible. We are grateful also to S. Applebaum, D. Phil. (Oxon.), for his translation of the book from the original Hebrew manuscript.

CONTENTS

HELLENISTIC

CIVILIZATION

AND THE

JEWS

INTRODUCTION

In spring 334 B.C.E. Alexander of Macedon crossed the narrow sea that divides Europe from Asia, and went to war with the King of Persia. In a few years he had successfully dealt the Persian army its deathblow and had put an end to the rule of the Achaemenid royal house of Persia. On the ruins of the mighty kingdom which he had destroyed, Alexander established his own realm. Those eleven years (334-323 B.C.E.) began a new chapter in the history of the ancient world, the so-called Hellenistic Period, chronologically set between Alexander the Great and the coming of the Romans to the countries of the East.

The war with Persia did not come as a sudden decision on the part of the young king; Alexander's father, King Philip, had already made all necessary preparations for it and had even sent to Asia a small force under the leadership of Parmenion, one of his best generals. Philip would without doubt have attacked the Persians himself had he lived. Macedon, which under his rule had been transformed from an unimportant petty kingdom into a strong state, had become, thanks to the conquest of Thrace, a next-door neighbor of the lands of Asia Minor which were subject to Persia, and the Persians had begun to be openly hostile to the sudden flowering of the new kingdom. The king of Macedon was compelled to defend the frontiers of his realm and to anticipate the danger that threatened him from the east. But in the midst of the

1

preparations for war, Philip fell by the sword of one of his courtiers (336), and the task of carrying out his ideas passed to his son Alexander, a young man of twenty, who succeeded to the throne.

The kingdom of Macedonia, which had emerged into the light of history in Philip's day, constituted in several respects a glaring contradiction to what was normally accepted in Greek politics. The monarchical regime, which in Greece had been preserved only as a vague reminiscence of olden times, had continued uninterrupted in Macedon during the entire period of the state's development, and was still the form of government when the state reached the peak of its prosperity in Philip's day. The king was the principal factor in the state; though not a divine personage after the manner of the oriental countries, he acted in the capacity of a military and political leader, and as head of the nobility, after the fashion current in Homeric Greece. Next to the king stood the nobles, the courtiers and the owners of large estates. Most of the people belonged to the small peasantry, legally free men who composed the Macedonian army. Experience showed that these peasants were excellent military material; thus the military organization became the center of gravity of the new state. The discipline of the Macedonian forces met every test, and in Macedon those revolutionary elements were entirely absent which so frequently disturbed the orderly life of Greece: for Macedon lacked that live and fermenting public institution till then typical of Hellas, namely, the Greek *polis*, with its developing and unstable regime, its touchy and excitable *demos* (the common people), its party-strife and class-struggle, which turned Greece for hundreds of years into a cockpit of revolution and warfare.

The kingdom of Persia, which Alexander was about to conquer, extended over an area some fifty times larger than tiny Macedon, but the kingdom's strength was not commensurate with its size. The huge empire lacked a solid national basis; dozens of different nations lay under the Achaemenid royal scepter, and outnumbered the Persians several times over. It included peoples of high culture, such as the Egyptians and the Babylonians, as well as some which were utterly uncivilized, such as the mountain tribes who acknowledged no public regime whatsoever and called no man their master. The kingdom as a whole was divided into provinces or satrapies. The satraps, who stood at their head, had been originally officials obeying the king's orders, but in course of time had become independent princes, sometimes rebelling against their king, and the position itself frequently passed hereditarily from father to son. Nor was the Persian army an effective fighting force, being in greater part recruited from units of the peoples subject to the Persian kings, or from mercenaries among whom the Greeks played the chief part. But no state can base its existence on mercenary forces alone, still less on foreign mercenaries. Thus the gigantic kingdom, which ruled from India to the southernmost parts of Egypt, stood on a frail foundation, lacking a solid internal authority, national feeling and a proper means of self-defense. No wonder Persia did not muster the strength to stand up to the Macedonian army, which was small but reliable, disciplined and commanded by experienced and courageous commanders.

The very first encounter between the Persians and the Macedonians proved the superiority of the latter: near the River Granicus (in northern Asia Minor, by the ancient town of Troy) the Persians were defeated and some of them taken prisoner by Alexander. The Persian forces at the Granicus were not large, but it was characteristic of Persia's ineptness that, apart from this small force, it had no other army in Asia Minor at all. (The towns, such as Miletus and Halicarnassus, held only insignificant garrisons and it was not hard for Alexander to take them.) All the western part of Asia Minor fell into Alexander's hands soon after Granicus, and its center and south a little later. Having taken Asia Minor, Alexander passed on to Syria. Near Issus, in the narrow defile among the Taurus Mountains on the road from Cilicia to Syria, he met the Persian king Darius at the head of a great host.

The place of encounter was not favorable to the Persians: the narrow pass between the sea and the hills prevented Darius from deploying his forces to the full, while Alexander's small force easily retained its maneuverability in the restricted space. The outcome of the encounter could have been foreseen: Alexander inflicted upon the Persians a decisive defeat and Darius, abandoning the battlefield, fled for his life. Alexander decided not to pursue him before he had taken the lands about the Mediterranean, so he went down to Phoenicia, whose great and wealthy towns opened their gates to him, only Tyre resisting. Alexander laid siege to the city. The struggle about its walls lasted seven months and, when the city was taken, Alexander leveled it to its foundations.

3

From here he advanced upon Palestine. The governor of Gaza closed the city's gates to him and Alexander captured it after a two months' siege. The next step was Egypt. The Egyptians had never respected the Persians and welcomed Alexander joyfully. The Persian satrap at Memphis abandoned the defense of the city and handed it over to Alexander without bloodshed.

Alexander's sojourn in Egypt reveals several features of the coming epoch. Chief of these to be noted is the founding of Alexandria, the first and most important city in a series of some thirty founded by Alexander in the countries of the East. What impelled Alexander to found the new city just here, by the small Egyptian village of Rhakotis —and who advised him to do so—we do not clearly know, but at any rate the choice of the spot was most fortunate. The future showed that Alexander's advisers were not mistaken in their calculations, and the city flourished and grew till it became the most important in the Hellenistic world, thus creating a vital center of Greek culture in a country of ancient oriental civilization. Secondly, Alexander displayed publicly his respect and admiration for the religion of the country, sacrificing to the gods of Egypt (among the rest, to Apis, the sacred bull of Egypt), visiting the temples and even ordering the erection in Greek Alexandria of shrines to the Egyptian deities. But at the same time, in the same Memphis where he had honored Apis with sacrifices, he held Greek athletic contests, without questioning the significance of such Greek sports in the land of the pyramids. History has supplied these facts with its own interpretation: here began for the first time that fusion of the religions of the Orient with the rites of Greece, which set its stamp, not only on the Hellenistic epoch, but upon all the subsequent epochs down to our own.

After the conquest of the lands on the Mediterranean coast, Alexander, hastening to encounter Darius and to put an end to his rule, went up to Syria and thence, traversing Mesopotamia, to the countries of central Asia. Across the Tigris, by Gaugamela, near the city of Arbela, Darius awaited him at the head of a huge host, which outnumbered even his first force at Issus. Here too Alexander was victorious: Darius again fled for his life and all his baggage fell into the hands of the victors. Alexander did not hasten to follow him: he had decided first to subdue the neighboring countries. Wealthy cities, full of oriental majesty and splendor, such as Babylon, Susa, Persepolis, Pasargadai, Persian imperial centers and royal residences of yore, opened their gates to him and huge treasures of silver and gold fell into his hands. Only after a year had passed did Alexander turn north to pursue Darius. On the way he learned that the Persian notables had rebelled against Darius and put him under guard. This news spurred the pursuers to greater speed, for Alexander wanted to seize the king while he was still alive. But without avail: the Persian princes, when they learned of Alexander's approach, killed Darius and fled. Alexander found the king's body where it had been flung onto the road, and nothing remained for him but to celebrate the last solemn rites for the last king of the Persians.

The year which passed between the victory of Gaugamela and the death of Darius was a year of crisis in Alexander's life. Immediately after the victory of Gaugamela, Alexander declared himself "King of Asia," thus stressing that the authority of the Achaemenids in Asia was at an end and that he, Alexander, now took the place of the "Great King." As long as Darius was alive, Alexander's rule was not sufficiently assured; but after Darius' fall by the swords of the rebels, the question was automatically solved. Darius was dead and left no lawful heirs. Availing himself of the right of the victor, Alexander ascended the royal throne and became lawful king of Persia and successor to the sovereigns of the Achaemenid house.

The Orient swiftly cast its magic veil over him. The ways of the Macedonian royal court were simple, and the king did not hold himself aloof from the people who surrounded him. Not so with the kings of Persia. Although they were not likened to descendants of the gods, as were the kings of Egypt and Babylon, neither were they mere mortals. The mighty power gathered in their hands made them almost supernatural beings in their subjects' eyes. A rigid etiquette prevailed at the royal court where, surrounded by slaves, servants and eunuchs, the king lived his life far from the masses of his subjects, and only on great feast days did he appear before the people in all his dazzling splendor. In this fashion had the Persians been accustomed to honor their kings since ancient times, and in this fashion they now honored Alexander.

It does not seem that Alexander had intended to demand all this adulation from his Persian subjects; the honor was paid of itself. But as it was paid, it became *de rigueur,* and Alexander easily accustomed himself to his new circumstances. He put on Persian dress and surrounded himself with Persian servants. His devotion to Persian customs grew from day to day and expressed itself, not only in matters of court etiquette, but also in more important things, as, for example, when he ceased to dismiss the Persians satraps from their posts, leaving them at the head of the countries which they had formerly governed, and even began to appoint new officials from among the Persians, bestowing upon them important positions. This change in the king's behavior aroused opposition among the Macedonians; more than once affairs came to a sharp clash between him and the more prominent of his courtiers, compelling Alexander to take very severe measures against the leaders of the disgruntled.

Meanwhile the war had not yet ended. Alexander as king of Persia was not prepared to be content with the half of the kingdom which he had won; all the lands which had lain beneath the Persian scepter must yield to him. He advanced eastward to Aria and Arachosia (Afghanistan), Bactria and Sogdiana (Turkestan), and even to far India. After overrunning the valley of the Indus (today Punjab), Alexander wanted to continue eastward, but here he encountered the opposition of the army, which for the first time during the war threw off discipline and refused to follow its leader; in the soldiers' view, they had had enough of conquering the world and the hour had come to go home. In vain Alexander pleaded with them; in vain he threatened; they obstinately held their ground. In the end, the king had to give in: he retraced his steps. There remained for him but to fortify the frontier of the huge kingdom which he had won by the sword.

The war was at an end. The last year of Alexander's life was a tranquil one. He set himself with energy to build his kingdom. He did not think of returning to Macedon—at least not immediately. The king of Macedon seemed to have forgotten that he had come from there. Persia and Mesopotamia, Babylon, Susa and Ecbatana were the countries and cities where Alexander spent the year, Babylon being more especially a center of his work. There is reason to think that he regarded Babylon as his capital. He ordered the old canals of Mesopotamia repaired in order to restore to the country its former economic value. His inclination to Persian manners grew from day to day, and he began to demand also of his Macedonian companions the same respect for the conquered which he himself accorded them.

In order to bring the Macedonians nearer to the Persians, Alexander held a great wedding at Susa, in which at his command eighty eminent Macedonians married noble women of Persia. It is worth noting that the ceremony was according to Persian custom. Besides, 10,000 Macedonian troops who had wedded foreign wives also received gifts from the king. His desire to merge the peoples affected even the Macedonian holy of holies—the organization of the army. Before the very eyes of the Macedonians, and despite them, he appointed generals from among the Persians, made Persians his bodyguards and even bestowed upon some of them the honorary title of "kinsmen of the king." The Macedonians tried to oppose him, but at last saw that they were incapable of breaking the king's will and gave in. Alexander, to celebrate peace and concord, held a splendid banquet in which Persians and Macedonians alike took part, while priests of Greece and Persian Magi poured libations and prayed for the welfare of those gathered. Thus did Alexander display at various opportunities his determination to efface the difference between victors and vanquished and to fuse westerners and easterners into a single nation.

Alexander died suddenly at Babylon, in the summer of 323 B.C.E., before he had lived to be thirty-three. What he would have done in the world had he continued to live is an idle question; but the work which he had succeeded in carrying out was sufficient to give the course of history a new direction. By destroying the Persian kingdom Alexander had abolished the frontier between the East and the West and opened the countries of the Orient to the Greeks, from the Mediterranean Sea to the frontiers of India. He had also shown to future generations the direction in which he desired the historical process to develop—the merging of the East and the West into one cultural body. History, indeed, confirmed the great king's dream: the fusion of peoples and cultures became a fact, although it was not realized at the pace that Alexander had hoped for, nor exactly in the form he had dreamed. The penetration of Greek culture to the Orient and the Orient's influence on the Greeks are the basic themes of the history of the centuries between Alexander's death and the conquest of the eastern lands by Rome.

After the death of Alexander there was a period of prolonged and violent warfare. Alexander left no legal heirs capable of taking the reins of power, which thus passed into the hands of a small group of Macedonians of high birth, Alexander's captains and companions in arms. Among them Perdiccas held one of the most distinguished positions. The Macedonian captains appointed Perdiccas to the high post of regent of the state, thereby demonstrating, at least outwardly, their desire to maintain the unity of the kingdom. But simultaneously a number of the high-born captains were appointed as viceroys of the kingdom's various countries, and each viewed the land which fell to his lot as his own portion of Alexander's legacy. Perdiccas made strenuous efforts to preserve the unity of the kingdom, but the centrifugal forces grew from day to day, till he could no longer control them. In 321, he fell before the arms of the generals who had risen against him, and from that moment Alexander's empire began progressively to break up. Power passed to the satraps, that is, the viceroys of the individual countries.

These were all Macedonian aristocrats, men of practical energy, leaders by nature and by virtue of the training they had received in Macedon and in Alexander's camp. In principle opposed to the policy of international fusion which had been Alexander's dream, they at once abolished the innovations introduced by him into the army and divorced the Persian wives whom they had unwillingly espoused. The Macedonians were now the conquerors, and the eastern peoples the conquered, and the link which had begun to be forged between the two in Alexander's day was broken. A small group of Macedonians ruled over an immense area of the eastern lands from Egypt to India; and, as each wished to increase his power at the expense of his fellow, the world became the cockpit of a prolonged and ruthless struggle. Countries passed from hand to hand in rapid succession and made impossible the growth of an internal bond between governor and territory. Only an insignificant section of the Macedonians ever returned to Europe; most of the commanders remained in the rich oriental countries, remembering their lands of origin only when they needed new recruits for their armies or when the conquest of Macedon and Greece became important for the strengthening of their political position as a whole.

The period of the Diadochi (as the Macedonian generals who succeeded Alexander are called) introduced new political principles into the life of the ancient world, the main motive factor being the unrestricted strength of a forceful personality aspiring to power. The Macedonian people produced within a brief space a large number of aggressive characters, who used the confusion of the period to make themselves absolute rulers. The central aggressive personality was Antigonus, who had been satrap of Phrygia in Asia Minor while Alexander was alive. In 316 he extended his control not only over all of Asia Minor, but also over Syria, Palestine, Mesopotamia, Persia and Media, and, regarding himself as supreme ruler of all Alexander's heritage, demanded that others yield completely to his power. Seleucus, satrap of Babylon since 321, fled before him to Egypt, where he was favorably received by Ptolemy, who since 323 had governed that country, and a treaty was signed between them and the other satraps for the purpose of waging common war against Antigonus.

In 312 Ptolemy defeated Demetrius, Antigonus' son, near Gaza, and overran the whole of Palestine; Seleucus returned to Babylon the same year, and reestablished his rule there.

Antigonus, indeed, drove Ptolemy out of Palestine, but found himself unable to defeat his many opponents decisively. In 311 the enemies signed a treaty of peace, and the fighting ceased for a short time. It was renewed in 307; Antigonus sent Demetrius to "liberate" the cities of Greece from the control of Cassander, the governor of Macedon, that is, to bring them under his own control. Demetrius "liberated" some of them and chose Athens as his base. After a year he left Greece and with his great fleet attacked Cyprus, which was under Ptolemy. Ptolemy was defeated by Demetrius, and after this victory Antigonus placed the crown upon his own head (306). By this act he openly expressed his intention of becoming Alexander's sole heir; his aim was to gather beneath his crown all the lands ruled by the Macedonians. The other rulers, however, would not tolerate such aspirations. After an interval they imitated him, and four Macedonian generals—Ptolemy in Egypt, Seleucus in Babylon, Cassander in Macedon and Lysimachus in Thrace—declared themselves kings. Antigonus attempted to conquer Egypt, but failed. The city of Rhodes, an important commercial center closely connected with Ptolemy, was besieged by Demetrius but defended itself stoutly, till Demetrius was forced to give up the idea of capturing it. The war died down again, and once more flared up in 302, when Antigonus was attacked by his enemies on every side. Finally the old warrior fell on the battlefield of Ipsus (Phrygia). His great kingdom passed to his opponents (301); Lysimachus took the western part of Asia Minor; Ptolemy took Palestine; and Seleucus the remaining lands from Syria to Babylon.

The battle of Ipsus ended the stormy period of the wars of the Diadochi. Peace, indeed, did not come to the political world, for Demetrius remained alive; he was crowned king of Macedon in 293 and prepared, like Alexander, to attack the eastern lands with a large army. But the time of easy conquests was over. The Hellenistic monarchies, which had developed from the ephemeral rule of the Macedonian generals, were now consolidated, and Seleucus did not find it hard to put an end to the outdated ambitions of Demetrius. Two men—Ptolemy and Seleucus—at length emerged victors from the hurly-burly of the period of the Diadochi, and their names have remained associated in history with the kingdoms which they established. They were not the greatest men of the epoch, but they were wary statesmen who knew how to pick their moment and to be content with part instead of aiming at the whole.

Seleucus obtained the largest portion of Alexander's empire; all the countries of Asia from the frontiers of India to the Mediterranean littoral were under his rule. In 281 he defeated Lysimachus and annexed Asia Minor to his kingdom. Only Palestine and the islands of the Mediterranean remained subject to Ptolemy. The oriental lands under the rule of Seleucus differed among themselves politically, economically and culturally; it was possible to bring them under one central authority, as the Persians and Alexander had done, but it was impossible to make of them a homogeneous state; hence the Seleucid kingdom was constantly threatened with disintegration. Ptolemy, however, was free of such an anxiety, since his kingdom was much smaller than that of the Seleucids and was centered on one country, and that country—Egypt—composed of a single national and cultural body. Its strategic position, moreover, was one of the best, for while all the oriental lands in the period of the Diadochi were the victims of long wars, Egypt saw no enemy within her borders. Egypt, further, possessed great economic importance, serving as the granary of the Mediterranean lands. All the other countries which Ptolemy conquered—North Africa (Cyrene), Coele-Syria, the Aegean Islands, and the islands along the Red Sea coast, were dependent on Egypt, and apart from their economic value they also possessed a strategic value as defense positions on the roads leading to her.

The epoch of the Diadochi opened with a Macedonian reaction against the oriental aspirations of Alexander; but after the Hellenistic kingdoms had been founded, the Orient began once again little by little to permeate the environment of the conquerors. The influence of the East was recognizable in many and various ways. First, in the function of the king in the state: in Persian and Babylonian eyes the Seleucids and their descendants took the place of the monarchs of the Achaemenid house, while the Egyptians saw in the Ptolemies the heirs of the Pharaohs. And, in fact, the political position of the Macedonian kings in their new kingdoms was more or less a repetition of the position of the former oriental monarchs. The king was theoretically the sole ruler of the country, his will was law to all his subjects, and he was the legislator, judge and supreme magistrate of his realm. The Ptolemies were also regarded in principle as the owners of all the soil of Egypt. As the most outstanding expression of their absolute power the Hellenistic kings devised their own deification. Alexander in the last year before his death demanded of the Greeks that they render him honor as a god, and his divinity was actually recognized by several Greek cities, including Athens. After his death Alexander was recognized as a god in all the lands of the Diadochi, and an official cult was set up in his honor at various places in Asia and Egypt.

In the period of the Diadochi several rulers received divine honors; the inhabitants of the Greek cities consecrated altars and offered sacrifices to them and appointed priests to tend the new cult. In Egypt, Ptolemy II Philadelphus was the first to give the royal cult an official character. Thereafter the royal cult of Egypt assumed the form of a permanent institution. The kings chose for themselves names borrowed from the religious world (Soter—savior; Euergetes—benefactor; Epiphanes—the god manifest, etc.), or such as displayed the king's devotion to his family (Philadelphus—lover of his sister; Philopator—lover of his father; Philometor—lover of his mother). Statues of the Ptolemies were set up in all the temples of Egypt, where the kings joined the company of the Egyptian deities. With the Seleucids we find more or less the same situation: sometimes they went even farther than the Ptolemies in self-deification, for while the latter were content with divine titles, the Seleucids definitely put themselves on the same footing as the ancient gods of Greece; thus Seleucus I was known by the name of Zeus, and Antiochus I as Apollo.

The Hellenistic kingdoms were organized on bureaucratic lines, in which respect also the oriental tradition exercised great influence. Classical Greece had never recognized officials as professionals. The officials of the Greek cities were citizens, elected for a term to carry on the city's affairs and relieved by other citizens after fresh elections. In eastern countries, on the other hand, there existed a large and important class of "scribes" in whose hands lay the whole work of administration; and the Hellenistic kingdoms followed in the footsteps of the kingdoms which had preceded them. The sources for the Seleucid kingdom are regrettably few, and we cannot restore a clear picture of the administrative structure of the state.

The soil of Egypt, by contrast, has bequeathed to us a large number of Greek papyri of the Hellenistic age, from which we are able to explore the bureaucratic authority of the Ptolemaic period in all its exact details. A very large number of officials appears in the papyri, from the high state officials resident in Alexandria (among whom the *dioiketes,* or minister of finance, occupied the chief position) to the petty officials in the villages and provincial towns. In spite of certain deficiencies (wasted time, lack of consideration for the individual, and the like) it can be stated that the technique of the bureaucracy's work was of the required level, perhaps no less so than the official business of our own time. Every high official kept a special journal in which he noted the events of the day; the documents received by the office or sent by it were marked with the appropriate dates and a brief summary of their contents noted on their backs; obsolete documents were kept in archives and could be extracted therefrom, if need was, even after decades. The postal service facilitated intercommunication between the offices in various towns and the government center in Alexandria; in the king's service a rapid post was organized on the model of the Persian *angaria.* The bureaucratic machine, from the king down to the lowest village official, worked tirelessly, rapidly and diligently, as it had worked previously under the Pharaohs, and as it was to continue to work under the Romans and the Byzantines. The names changed from period to period, but the machinery itself remained unaltered.

The treasury was chief among the institutions of state; the minister of finance (the *dioiketes*) sometimes discharged the task of king's deputy. The great majority of the state officials worked in the various branches of the treasury, and the whole bureaucratic machine stood permanently at the disposal of the *dioiketes*. The Ptolemies had one aim throughout their domination in Egypt—to wring from the country's inhabitants as much as they could in money and labor. The chief wealth of Egypt lay in its abundance of corn; the government kept a careful eye on this wealth, in order to prevent it from slipping through its fingers and to secure its arrival in the royal granaries, for the trade in grain was one of the kingdom's main sources of income.

As had already been the practice under the Pharaohs, the royal officials carried out, from time to time, a precise registration, following a regular order: the name of the owner of the estate, the area and quality of the land, the changes that took place from year to year following the Nile inundations, and so on. The whole land of Egypt (which theoretically was regarded as the king's private property) was divided into "royal land," leased to native tenants of the country ("royal peasants"), and into "grant land" made over by the king in temporary or perpetual usufruct to temples ("sacred land"), to soldier-settlers ("cleruchic land"), or to private persons ("gift land"). The "royal peasants" paid rent directly to the government officials, whereas the peasants settled on "grant land" paid their dues to the priests, the *cleruchs* or the estate-owners, according to the type of land on which they dwelt. But the priests, the military settlers and the owners of "gift land" were also subject to taxes, and part of the rent which they received from the peasants was transmitted by them to the king.

All the land taxes (rents and other dues) were paid in agricultural produce, which the payer had to deliver to the "royal granaries." The government also derived a large income from trade. The king drew especially large profits from a system of monopolies. Nearly all edibles, such as salt, olive oil, honey and fish, as well as woolens and flax, blankets, cushions, towels and linens, all sorts of drugs and cosmetics, gold and silver ornaments, papyrus and the like—all were made and sold under the supervision of government officials, and a severe penalty threatened anyone daring to infringe upon the king's profits. The government fixed the prices of the commodities sold in the market, and vigilantly supervised the merchants to prevent them from raising prices above the rates fixed. The royal treasury also derived no mean profit from farming out the taxes, a normal procedure under the Ptolemies. The farmers paid the government a fixed sum in exchange for permission to collect a given tax in a certain place and, although theoretically they were regarded as private individuals, actually they too were under the strict control of the government officials. Such were the elements of the Ptolemaic kingdom, which may therefore justly be described in modern terms as a "totalitarian state."

The whole burden of taxation was a heavy yoke upon the natives of the country. The Greeks and Macedonians were not affected by it in the same measure as the Egyptians, for they were the conquerors and the Egyptians were the conquered. Throughout the third century, under the first four kings of the house of Ptolemy, the difference between the two sides was very marked. Nearly all the government officials, both in Alexandria and in the provincial towns, were Macedonians or Greeks; only the petty village officials were generally recruited from the Egyptians. The official language in which all documents and petitions were written, and which was used in the offices and the law-courts, was Greek; the Egyptians were forced to learn this foreign tongue if they desired to come into contact with the government.

The Ptolemaic army was composed of Macedonians and other mercenaries brought from abroad; the Egyptians took part in warfare only in exceptional instances, and then chiefly as porters, while heavy compulsory labor such as the repair of canals, the paving of roads and the construction of dykes, fell upon them alone. The natives were thus degraded to the level of people without rights, while the aliens ruled their country with a high hand. During the third century the Egyptian people bore the foreign yoke patiently and submissively, till at last the spirit of revolt awoke in its midst and the nationalist movement raised its head.

The beginning of the Egyptian nationalist movement was associated with an episode which belongs to the political sphere. In 219, Antiochus III of Syria attacked Egypt; Ptolemy IV Philopator went out to meet him at the head of his army of mercenaries; and in order to expand his forces he also recruited 20,000 men of the native population. Ptolemy defeated Antiochus at Raphia (217) and this victory, in which Egyptians also participated, served as the starting point for the reawakening of the Egyptian nationalist spirit.

When the war ended, risings took place in Egypt and did not cease for a long time. Among the Egyptians there arose nationalist leaders who declared themselves the heirs of the Pharaohs. Moral and perhaps also material support for these uprisings was apparently forthcoming from the priests, who were the most educated and self-confident part of the native population. The kings, beginning with Ptolemy I, had attempted to find a *modus vivendi* with the priesthood in order to avoid clashing with them. The absolute rule of the Ptolemies, however, affected them also; their economic life (their income from the "sacred lands," the organization of their temple industries, etc.) was strictly supervised by the officialdom, as was the life of every other member of the population. The revolts showed the government that the priests were not to be underestimated, and that not every ruler of the country was inevitably regarded as its sovereign.

Under Ptolemy V Epiphanes a change took place in the attitude of the Ptolemies to their Egyptian subjects. It seems probable that an alliance was formed between the king and the priesthood—the former undertaking to favor the latter's interests, and the priests giving up all propaganda against the government. From that time on, the Egyptian element grew progressively in strength in the Ptolemaic state, penetrating the royal court and occupying important government positions. Ptolemy VIII (Euergetes II) was especially outstanding in his concern for the Egyptians; he went to the extent of expressing this concern by a negative attitude to the Greek population of Alexandria.

Thus the Egyptians forced the Macedonians to recognize their nationality and to make them partners in the state. The Ptolemies gradually drew closer to the spirit of the people which they ruled. The Egyptian priests had always looked upon them as Pharaohs, and from the time of Epiphanes the Ptolemies also began to regard themselves as such. Their solemn crowning at Memphis was carried out according to the ancient rites of Egypt and under the strict supervision of the clergy. The Egyptian deities ceased to be alien to the Ptolemies, and to this day the temples which they built in Upper Egypt bear witness to their reverence for the Egyptian religion. Among the Egyptian practices which penetrated their house, the marriage of brother and sister may be especially noted. Philadelphus was the first to wed his sister Arsinoë (it made a strange impression on the Greeks), and he was imitated by most of the kings after him. The custom was in fact widespread among the oriental kings of various countries, originating in their desire to preserve the purity of the family blood, and as such was a pronouncedly oriental institution unknown to the Greeks in their land of origin; its assimilation by the Ptolemies symbolizes the extent to which they were influenced by the Orient.

Nevertheless the broad function of the Ptolemies as standard-bearers of Hellenism in the East cannot be denied. The process of the "barbarization" of the dynasty never brought it to deliberate rejection of its Macedonian origin, and the Ptolemies always appeared as very prominent patrons of Greek culture. As early as the reign of Ptolemy I and especially under his son, Ptolemy II Philadelphus, Alexandria became the established center of Hellenism. With the name of the Greek philosopher Demetrius of Phaleron, who came to Egypt under Ptolemy I, is associated the Ptolemies' great undertaking, the founding of the Museum and Library of Alexandria. By the term "museum" was meant a temple of the Muses; but that was merely its superficial signification, its real function being to serve as a center for scientists and artists, an institution of the sort today known as an academy.

The library became famous throughout the Hellenistic world as possessing special importance, for it was the largest known and, when founded, the first public library; even in Athens no municipal library existed and books there were in possession of private individuals only. This great cultural enterprise gave a considerable impulse to the development of Greek civilization in Alexandria; and men of learning, writers and artists, streamed from all corners of the Hellenistic world to enjoy the advantages which the Ptolemies were ready to grant them. In the reign of Philadelphus the royal court at Alexandria was a permanent center of Greek men of intellect, in this respect resembling the court of the French sovereigns in the seventeenth and eighteenth centuries.

The same dualism—the tendency to Hellenism on the one hand and the influence of the Orient on the other—distinguished the monarchy of the Seleucid family. At first the Seleucids possessed a stronger inner bond with the East than the Ptolemies. While the Macedonian generals had divorced their Persian wives after the death of Alexander, Seleucus had remained faithful to his wife, and thus Apama, a Persian woman, became the mother of the dynasty even as Seleucus, the Macedonian, was its father. Persian blood, therefore, flowed in the veins of the Seleucid kings from the beginning of the dynasty; and subsequently also instances of intermarriage occurred between the Seleucids and the daughters of barbarian kings. It is therefore probable that the Seleucids were more oriental in their appearance than the Ptolemies. Brother-sister marriages, customary among the Ptolemies, also crept into the Seleucid family: Antiochus II married his sister Laodice, and in 196 Antiochus III solemnized the nuptials of his daughter and his son Antiochus. In Babylon, the Seleucids played the same role as the Ptolemies at Memphis; here they appeared as the legitimate heirs of the former kings, and it may be surmised that, had they remained at Babylon, the influence of the East would have become increasingly stronger.

But the Seleucids always inclined to the western part of their dominions and aspired to control the Mediterranean. From Antiochus II's time (261-246) they neglected their territories farther east and transferred their center of activity to Syria and Asia Minor. Here the Greek element was stronger, particularly in Asia Minor; and the Seleucids, who stood in direct contact with the Greek cities, found in them support for their Hellenic ambitions. Greece itself was not far off, and the frequent revolutions at the royal court had the effect that, from time to time, men ascended the throne whose education had been that of private individuals in Greece, in the cities of Asia Minor, or at Rome. This situation explains the interesting coincidence that, precisely when the Ptolemies were submitting to Egyptian civilization, the Seleucid throne was ascended by Antiochus IV who had absorbed western culture more thoroughly than any Seleucid monarch before him.

The oriental reaction which we have observed in Egypt arose and gained strength in the Seleucid empire also, but its external expression differed in accordance with the special conditions of historical development in that realm. As has been indicated, the Seleucid kingdom comprehended dozens of different peoples, and centrifugal forces found wide scope for action. The break-up of the kingdom began almost from the day it was founded. Even before his victory over Antigonus, Seleucus had given up his power in India, so that all Alexander the Great's successes in that country were thus erased. Nor was the other end of the empire, Asia Minor, ever organically bound up with the Seleucid kingdom. In the middle of the third century B.C.E. a great crisis passed over the eastern portion of the Seleucid empire: Arsaces, a native of central Asia, rebelled against Seleucus and entrenched himself in Parthia, founding the Arsacid dynasty of the Parthians, which ruled in the East till the third century C.E. The Parthian rulers soon took the offensive in their endeavor to extend the frontiers of their kingdom, and gradually the wealthy lands across the Euphrates fell into their hands, among them Mesopotamia with its great Greek city of Seleuceia-on-Tigris. Still earlier than Arsaces' revolt, the Greek Diodotus had founded an independent kingdom in Bactria, and his heirs even ruled western India for a time.

Thus the Seleucids, little by little, lost the great heritage which they had taken over from Alexander and were forced to restrict themselves to the countries west of the Euphrates. But here too the oriental reaction was powerfully at work, and in 167 there began in Palestine, which thirty years before had passed from the Ptolemies into Seleucid hands, a nationalist movement which led in a short time to the establishment of the kingdom of the Hasmoneans. Among the Arabs, also, nationalist leaders arose who set up independent principalities. The Seleucid kingdom, unable to stand before the combined assault of all the forces of the Orient, tottered steadily to collapse. Its last sovereigns, deprived of power and influence, rapidly replaced one another on the throne. In 83, King Tigranes of Armenia overran the whole of Syria; but it was the Romans who put an end to the house of the Seleucids when, in 64, Pompey annexed Syria to the Roman dominions.

Even the foregoing brief survey will have sufficed to reveal the difference between the oriental reaction in Egypt and that which took place in the Asiatic countries. In Egypt the movement took the form of a national-cultural protest; in Asia it was chiefly political. In Egypt the movement was directed against the Greeks and hence also against Hellenism; in Asia the peoples fought for their liberty against the rule of the Seleucid dynasty, but not against Hellenism as such—hence Greeks also were able to take part in the movement. It is notable that several small kingdoms, such as Bithynia, Cappadocia and Armenia, set themselves up of their own accord as Hellenistic states after they had broken away from the Seleucids, and that even the Parthians, the Seleucids' most dangerous enemies, regarded Hellenism favorably, for under their rule the city of Seleuceia-on-Tigris retained its independent existence and Greek tragedies were even performed at the royal court.

The common factor in the nationalist movements in Egypt and Asia can be perceived in their social coloring. The Egyptian soldiers, whose part in the battle of Raphia gave the first impulse to the outbreak of disturbances, had no prospect of receiving from the government allotments of more than five or seven *arourai* (one Egyptian *aroura* was the equivalent of 2750 square meters), as this was the regular scale for local servicemen, while the foreign-born soldiery (Macedonians, Thracians, etc.) obtained allotments of 24 to 100 *arourai*. This discrimination created much bitterness among the Egyptian peasants who were conscripted into the army and shed their blood for the government of King Ptolemy. The sore yoke which oppressed the Egyptian peasant, the high taxes, the *corvées*, the arbitrary attitude of the officialdom—all these inflamed the fellahin to revolt, and made it hard for the Ptolemies to put down the risings, which were supported by the majority of the villages of Egypt.

It is probable that the concessions made by the government to the priests were intended to drive a wedge among the rebels and to attach to the government those elements which were socially more interested in political peace and quiet than in the victory of the nationalist idea. And, in fact, it can be deduced from several isolated fragments of information that the rebels also attacked the temples, in other words, that they turned against the wealthy and aristocratic elements among the Egyptians themselves. It is more difficult, on account of the meagerness of the sources, to trace the social lines of the nationalist movements in the Seleucid kingdom, but one fact is beyond all doubt: the Seleucids found allies among the urban population, while the people of the countryside remained hostile to the government and readily supported the revolutionary movements. And when we speak of the urban population, we are not referring to the urban proletariat, but to the wealthy merchants, the city fathers and providers of its funds, who were interested in the unity of the great kingdom and in the security of its routes in order that their commerce should flourish. It would not be wrong to say, therefore, that in Asia also, as in Egypt, the nationalist movement was concentrated chiefly in the villagers, and that the factor which drove the poverty-stricken peasant into the ranks of the militants was as much social as it was political and national.

The Hellenistic kingdoms absorbed a large number of Greeks who left their country and went to eastern lands to settle. These brought to the Orient the style of public life customary in Greece, and more particularly the urban way of living. As to the Macedonians, they settled mainly in military colonies, as did the remaining nations who composed a considerable part of the armies of the Hellenistic kingdoms (Thracians, Moesians, Galatians, etc.). These colonies were founded for the most part in the earliest Hellenistic period, when the Macedonian army was playing a decisive role in the wars of the Diadochi; they were called *katoikiai* or *cleruchies,* and they were juridically classifiable as villages. The inhabitants of the *katoikiai* called their colonies by names that reminded them of their home-countries, usually after the native city where the majority among them had originated.

In the Seleucid kingdom the *katoikiai* were founded chiefly in Asia Minor, where for a long time they fulfilled an important military task, but finally became ordinary villages. Their internal organization and the size of their populations are unknown to us; on the other hand, the papyri have yielded us very rich material on the development of the military colonies of Ptolemaic Egypt. In the Pharaonic epoch it had already been governmental practice to distribute land allotments for soldiers to settle on, in order to provide the military class with a firm economic basis. The Ptolemies also pursued this course, and founded agricultural colonies whose inhabitants were recruited from the army. The new settlers belonged to various nations, many being Macedonians or natives of Thrace, Thessaly, Asia Minor and other lands. The large allotments which they received from the king endowed them with the character of landowners rather than that of real farmers; nor did they work the land themselves, but leased it to native tenants.

Although the number of settlers was considerable, it was insignificant compared to the seven million indigenous Egyptians, and they had to struggle stoutly with the alien environment to preserve their national character. Whether or not the will thus to struggle existed, cannot be said: at all events, even if they desired to defend their national heritage, they were not the victors. Mixed marriages were the main factor in the process of assimilation, for the soldiers married women of the local population, and with the women Egyptian names, language, religion and customs entered into their family life. The children of such mixed families normally followed the mother; the Egyptian religion exercised a strong attraction upon the Greeks and gave them something that was absent in their own cults, namely, a mystic closeness to divinity, inner confidence, and a share in a future life. The Egyptian gods, indeed, now frequently received Greek names, in accordance with the Greek habit of identifying their gods with those of other peoples, but the gods themselves did not become Greek with the change of name; it is of particular interest that, precisely in the Hellenistic period, the cult of the sacred animals spread on a scale hitherto unprecedented in Egypt. In the temples of Egypt the Egyptian priests reigned unchallenged, and the Egyptian language prevailed officially, assuming the form of a holy tongue. As a spoken language, too, Egyptian did not give way to the official language; not only in Upper Egypt (the Thebais), whither Hellenism hardly penetrated, but even in the Hellenized Fayûm, the natives frequently resorted to the assistance of interpreters when they had need of contact with the authorities.

All these factors—mixed marriage, the influence of religion, and language—produced the result that the Greek inhabitants of the villages and provincial towns became assimilated to the Egyptians, and a new mixed stock, derived from both nations, replaced the first Greeks who had settled in Egypt in the third century. When the Romans reached Egypt from Greece and Rome, they found in its villages, not the Greek type known to them in those former places, but Graeco-Egyptians, whose names, customs and ways of life were oriental. The fate of the military settlers in Egypt demonstrated decisively that the oriental village was not only uninfluenced by people of Greek culture who settled in or near it, but possessed the power of fusing the strangers with itself and of obliterating their intellectual and national character. And if Hellenism, despite the effect of environment, struck roots of some depth in the eastern countries, the reason must be sought, not in agricultural colonization, but in the foundation of Greek cities in the Hellenistic empires.

Alexander was the first of the Hellenistic kings to build Greek cities in the eastern countries. He founded Alexandria of Egypt with the intention of creating an important commercial city which would serve as a bridge between Greece and the land of the Pharaohs. In the countries of central Asia and in western India, he built a large number of "Alexandrias" in order to fortify the frontier of his empire. After his death, the Diadochi, especially Seleucus I and his son Antiochus I, continued this activity, founding a large number of Greek cities in Asia Minor, Syria, Mesopotamia, Persia, Media and Afghanistan. Side by side with the "Alexandrias" there arose flourishing "Antiochs," "Seleuceias," "Laodiceias," and "Apameias," among them extensive and important cities, such as Antioch-on-the-Orontes (or "by Daphne") and Seleuceia-on-Tigris.

The Ptolemies also built Greek cities outside Egypt: on the Mediterranean islands, in Asia Minor, in Palestine and on the Red Sea coast. We know in all of over 350 cities founded in the Hellenistic period, but many others are still covered by deep drifts of desert sand and their very names are unknown. This great building activity introduced into the Orient a political institution with a Greek style of life foreign to the local inhabitants but destined to play a decisive part in the Hellenization process of the eastern lands.

The most prominent feature of the Greek cities of the classical period was their independence. The Greeks took it for granted that no city (*polis*) could exist except under conditions of liberty. Two terms were the constant watchword of the cities in all their struggles against one another: "autonomy"—the right to conduct the city's affairs according to its own laws, and "liberty"—non-subjection to any power whatever outside the city. The Greek *polis* was not a city in our sense of the term, but a petty state. Questions of war and peace, the making of alliances with other cities, monetary arrangements, the drafting of laws and statutes, the internal authority—all these were conducted by the members of the city with complete freedom and without coercion from outside.

In those cities which were conducted according to the rules of democracy (such as Athens), the whole people (the *demos*) participated in the exercise of power, and everyone had the right to express his opinion in the general assembly (the *ecclesia*) of the city. The citizens elected a city council (*boulé*) which decided all questions on the agenda. This right to self-government constituted the outstanding superiority of the town over the village. Yet from the economic point of view the city itself was a sort of large village; not only merchants and craftsmen but also landowners and working farmers dwelt there as citizens, and most of the lands about it were the private property of its members. Thus, in the economic sense, the town did not cease outside its own gates, but extended over a wide area round about, so that its borders touched the borders of the next city.

Every Greek city was surrounded by a wall, and this fortification symbolized its independence. The greatest catastrophe and disgrace that could befall it was to be deprived of its rights, as a sequel to an unsuccessful war or an internal revolution. In such case the town was humiliated and deposed from its political eminence, its walls were dismantled, and it became a village. Such occurrences the Greeks called "the destruction of the city," although at times the town itself, that is, its houses and buildings, were not completely destroyed and remained where they had always been. For, in the Greek view, not buildings distinguished a city, but the citizen body which endowed it with life. The Greek *polis* was not a geographical, but a political-social concept.

In the classical period cities were erected by a certain group of people who constituted the city's initial body of citizens. After Alexander the Great the initiative passed to the kings and, naturally enough, city rights suffered severely from the royal surveillance. First and foremost, the kings took away from them their political rights, that is, their authority to make war and to sign peace treaties, and the like. Officials appointed by the king's government to supervise their economic life also appeared frequently in the Hellenistic towns. Yet in spite of this, the towns continued even in that epoch to live a free life, albeit within a more restricted framework, and to enjoy several privileges which they had possessed previously.

Theoretically the Greek cities were regarded as "allies" of the king; their relation to them was not that of subjects to their lord, but that of one of two political powers possessing equal rights. The defense of city rights, of their "freedom" and "autonomy," was a matter of honor in the eyes of the kings and an attribute of civilized political behavior. Hence the kings accorded license to the ancient cities (such as those of Asia Minor or the Aegean Islands) "to live according to their ancestral laws," that is, they confirmed the traditional constitutions of the cities; but they also permitted new ones to conduct their internal affairs freely, to elect a council and officials, to strike coins, to hold athletic contests, and so on. Each city possessed laws of its own, according to which its officials conducted its public life; it had its permanent religious center and all its citizens took part in the common festivals in honor of the city god or goddess. Even the cities most completely subject to the kings remained nominally free and did not miss any opportunity to convert theory into fact; at the end of the Seleucid domination the Greek towns exploited the weaknesses of the kings and obtained virtual independence.

The chief possession of the Greek cities, therefore, was not their buildings, but their men and citizens. The kings' first concern, then, when a new city was founded, was the formation of a citizen body. Sometimes they found new citizens among the Greek towns round about, as, for example, in Asia Minor; but when the town was being built in a remote country, they had to bring the inhabitants from a distance. There were instances when the kings compelled the inhabitants of ancient cities to settle in the new one against their will, and the emigrants had to abandon their beloved native towns and move far afield at the royal command. The second feature in the foundation of a city was the building of the city itself, that is, the erection of houses, the laying out of roads, the digging of drains, and so on. This work occupied a prominent place in the establishment of Greek towns, especially if the town was intended to discharge an important function politically or economically. Frequently the kings supervised the work in person, and the best architects directed the construction.

Every new city needed a name, and its endowment with such was in the Hellenistic period an act of importance to which political value also might attach. The vast majority of the names belonging to Greek cities were dynastic in origin and proclaimed their founders, who named them either after themselves or after their forebears, wives or mothers. The dynastic name witnessed to the inner bond between the city and the king who founded it, a father-daughter relationship, as it were, since but for the royal builder the town would not have existed. The tomb of the *ktistes*, or founder, was the most important spot in the city, and generally the founder-monarch was buried in one of the towns which bore his name.

Not all the cities of the oriental countries, however, were called after their founders. Not a few were named after some city in northern Greece or Macedon; and these too were genuine *poleis*, like those which bore dynastic appellations. Such cities were founded, not as a result of the whim of a monarch, but developed gradually from small colonies into towns of large population. We have seen that among the first Greek immigrants the Macedonian troops occupied a very important place, being settled by the kings in *katoikiai* with the object of enabling them to support themselves in agriculture. The *katoikiai* usually remained villages unpossessed of privileges; but sometimes they grew, owing to the addition of new settlers, till they became real *poleis*. Although we have no detailed information on the subject, it is to be assumed that most of the towns known as Europus, Pella, Dion, Edessa, Larissa, and the like, took their origin from Macedonian military colonies in the days of Alexander or of his early successors.

    The policy of the Ptolemies and Seleucids in founding Greek cities exhibits two contrasting approaches to the problem. Except for one city, Ptolemais in Upper Egypt, founded by Ptolemy I, the Ptolemies did not establish Greek cities in Egypt, while the Seleucids built them by dozens in their realm. This historical fact calls for an explanation, especially as on it modern scholars base assumptions which have no direct bearing on the question itself. It is customary to see in the building of the Greek cities a pronounced symptom of the kings' Hellenistic aspirations, and on these grounds the Seleucid monarchs are described as bearers of Greek culture in contrast to the Ptolemies who, it is held, compromised with oriental civilization and betrayed Hellenism. This view is based on the simple syllogism that the Greek cities served as centers of Greek civilization; the Seleucids built Greek cities; and therefore the Seleucids were bearers of Greek civilization. But the building of cities or the abstention therefrom is an independent question, not to be identified with this or that attitude toward Greek culture; it is easy to discover the reasons for city-building entirely in political conditions.

    The bureaucratic government of the Ptolemies in Egypt has been discussed above, and Egypt's integrated political, economic and cultural character was there emphasized. Within this bureaucratic machine there was no room for the Greek cities and their dangerous demands for "freedom," "autonomy" and the like. To found them here would have been to weaken the central power, to restrict the area of the "royal land" and to diminish the tax-quota; clearly the Ptolemies had no desire to adopt this course and so undermine their own authority. On the other hand, in countries where the bureaucratic system of the Pharaohs did not prevail, as in the conquered lands beyond the frontiers of Egypt, the Ptolemies appeared as founders of Greek cities no less than the Seleucids. We know in all of some thirty-five founded by them in Palestine, Asia Minor, on the Red Sea coast, on the Mediterranean islands and in Cyrenaica, most of them under Ptolemy II Philadelphus. These cities, more especially those of Asia Minor, were in part organized as Greek *poleis,* and only those founded on the Red Sea coast rather resembled *katoikiai.*

The political conditions which determined the attitude of the Seleucids to Greek cities were quite different; for, while the Ptolemies found in Egypt only two cities, Alexandria and Naucratis, whose foundations preceded them, the Seleucids found a multitude of ancient Hellenic towns in Asia Minor, besides those built by Alexander in central Asia. From the beginning of their rule in the East the Seleucids were forced to take these into account as an existing fact, and they had to choose one of two policies: to fight them or to make them their allies. They easily perceived that only the latter policy could benefit their state. Dozens of different peoples lay beneath Seleucid rule, and they were not easily governed; hence the Seleucids were in need of allies to support them in their conflicts with the indigenous population. Such allies they found in the Greek cities. Through them the kings could dispose of an organized force of manpower possessed of good military training, who knew they were a minority among the multitude of Orientals, and whose very existence in foreign lands therefore depended on the royal favor. Hence they willingly supported the government when it was endangered by the surrounding peoples. Every new city founded by the kings in the Orient served simultaneously as a stronghold of the kings and of Hellenism, and it is not surprising that these two forces joined hands as long as they were faced by a common foe.

Let us now turn to the inner life of the Greek town in the East. The urban population was divided juridically into two parts: citizens and mere inhabitants. The bearer of the juridical conception of the *polis* was the citizen body, which in the Hellenistic period was organized by the king's order when the city was founded. After the formation of the urban body there were only two ways of becoming a citizen: by being the son of a citizen, or by obtaining citizen rights through a special act of the city council and the popular assembly. The number of citizens in a town was not especially large, and when we read in our sources about the great populations of Alexandria and Seleuceia-on-Tigris, we have to remember that among this vast number of people were also included simple residents whose number sometimes exceeded that of the enfranchised citizens. The residents were known by various Greek terms, such as *metoikoi, paroikoi, katoikoi, synoikoi,* words which meant dwellers "by," "at," or "with." Only the citizens enjoyed all civic rights, while the residents were regarded as foreign-born natives, although they might have been born in the city and have grown up there.

The rights and duties of a citizen were many and varied: he took part in the general assembly of the civic body, participated in debates, decided all the city's affairs, and elected its council and its officials. If he was elected a member of the council or a magistrate, he discharged a given function in the city for a year and took an active part in the conduct of its political, financial, economic and religious business. Sometimes the posts involved expense; if the citizen was comfortably off, the city would impose upon him for a stipulated period the expenditure involved in the holding of athletic contests, the urban corn supply, the conduct of the affairs of the gymnasium, or the like. These "public tasks" (*liturgiai* in Greek) cost, indeed, a great deal of money, but also bestowed honor on the person who undertook to be a "benefactor" of the city.

The citizen educated his sons in the municipal educational institutions—the *gymnasion* and the *ephebeion,* which were the very embodiment of the spirit of Hellenism. Here the young citizens received their Hellenic education, developed their strength and agility by physical exercise, and learned poetry and music; and if such an education was not imposed on the citizens as an absolute duty, no one deliberately avoided it. The oriental peoples were ignorant of this gymnastic education, and physical culture was generally alien to their outlook; hence the gymnasia became the symbols of Hellenism as a whole, and whoever could prove his membership in one thereby confirmed his Greek origin. The gymnasiarch, the citizen upon whom had been imposed the conduct of the gymnasium and the satisfaction of its monetary requirements, was regarded by the citizens as one of the most honored men in the city. An inner connection existed, moreover, between the gymnasia and the athletic contests which were held in the large cities every four years and were participated in by the representatives of various towns. The large crowds which attended the contests imparted to them the character of immense demonstrations in honor of Hellenism; these athletic assemblies were for the Greeks not simply amusements, but affairs of the greatest gravity and moment, not only culturally but also politically. During the festivals the Greeks were sensible of the living bond between themselves and all their fellow Greeks scattered over the world, a bond that bound them to ancient Greek tradition and to their mother-country.

Religion occupied an important place in the life of the Greek city; it is possible to state without exaggeration that its entire public life revolved within the framework of Greek religion. Every *polis* had its particular god who was its guardian and whose cult was the focus of the religious life of the citizen body. The participation of citizens in this official cult was taken for granted, and desire to abstain from it would have been regarded by the city as an insult to its dignity and as a political offense. Beside the official deity the citizens also worshiped the other gods of Greece, built temples in their honor, and celebrated their festivals, which excelled in their beauty and pomp, drawing the eager participation of the entire urban populace. Several inscriptions from the cities of Asia Minor inform us that the presence of citizens at festivals was not a privilege but a duty.

The athletic contests which were invariably held in honor of the deities (or of the deified rulers) also possessed a religious value, while the municipal posts were equally associated with the carrying out of certain religious rites, and no official would deliberately have shunned the city's divine cult or shirked participation in the festivals. The modern concept of the separation of Church and State was unknown to the Greeks; in Greek eyes both were merged in the supreme concept of the *polis*, which was at once a political and a religious institution.

The Greeks introduced into the Orient their science, philosophy, literature and art; but not all the Greek towns bore the standard of Greek culture in equal measure. While Alexandria of Egypt absorbed the whole wealth of Greek civilization, the small cities of Syria and Mesopotamia left not the least historical trace in the cultural sphere. Among the natives of these cities, indeed, we sometimes encounter isolated names of Greek writers or scholars, but these cases are rare and it is to be remarked that most of them belong to the Roman period, when eastern Hellenism was strongly supported by Rome.

Greek was predominant in the Greek towns, and together with the language, books written in Greek were also used, implying the reading of classical literature from Homer to Demosthenes. Egyptian papyri have preserved several copies of Greek poetic works, of Plato and Aristotle, and of tragic and comic authors. But precisely the example of Egypt is convincing evidence that Greek books were one thing and pure Greek culture was another; we have already seen that the Greeks of Egypt did not prove strong enough to stand against the influence of the Orient and that they ended by being assimilated into the country's population. The overwhelming majority of the Greeks of Egypt, however, were settled in the countryside; what then was the cultural function of the Greek city? Was the *polis* of the Orient a stronghold of Hellenism, which shed its light upon its oriental surroundings and diffused Greek civilization on a liberal scale among the local inhabitants, or was it merely an isolated Greek island amid a strange and hostile environment, preserving its cultural originality with difficulty, till it capitulated and sank into the vast ocean of the East?

Let us first set down certain facts characterizing the external conditions of the oriental Greek city's existence. So far we have spoken of the foundation of Greek cities and have not touched upon the relations of the new towns to the ancient centers of settlement; but it was not our intention to suggest that the new towns were built in uninhabited or abandoned desert localities. On the contrary, it is to be observed that every Greek town in eastern lands was erected in the vicinity of some ancient city. We invariably find either a large oriental town which had received into it a new Greek colony; an ancient village in whose proximity the new settlement had developed; or (especially in Asia Minor) small Greek towns, originating in the classical period, which had joined forces to found a large and important city. This phenomenon was neither haphazard nor the result of a subjective decision on the part of the founders, but natural and inevitable. A city by its very nature cannot exist in a vacuum. Every town develops as the economic center of its surroundings, especially from the commercial point of view, and without an appropriate environment there is no place for urban settlement.

The ancient cities of the Orient also discharged an economic function; either they were situated on the seacoast, or near a river, or along the caravan routes leading from one country to another. The city-builder of the Hellenistic period was compelled to take account of the fact that economic centers had long existed in those lands and could not be abolished or transferred elsewhere. If, therefore, the kings desired the Greek cities to become wealthy and develop into economic centers themselves, they had no alternative but to found the new town hard by the ancient one and *to make the Greek polis the heir of the oriental town.* And as the two towns, the old and the new, stood next to one another, they resembled one city. This indeed is what happened: every newly founded Greek city in the oriental lands was in effect a refoundation or enlargement of an ancient town. Even the largest Greek cities were originally associated with some ancient settlement or other. Alexandria of Egypt was founded by Alexander near the Egyptian village of Rhakotis, which later became a quarter of that huge city; Seleuceia-on-Tigris, whose population in the Roman period exceeded 600,000 souls, was established near the ancient town of Opis; and on the site of the Syrian Antioch had stood ancient villages whose original names have not come down to us.

This fact, that the Greek cities were invariably associated with ancient settlements, is very important for our estimate of the cultural level of the Greek *polis* in the Orient. The Greeks of the Hellenistic period did not go out to unsettled and uninhabited localities to transform the desert to settled ground and to bring culture to places which hitherto had possessed none. The contrary was the case: they went out to countries of rich and ancient civilization, and settled among peoples who had lived their historical lives for millennia and created important cultural values, including those which were fundamental to Greek culture itself. The Greeks established their towns within the areas of ancient cities or near them, in other words, in places which had served as permanent centers of political and cultural life. It need occasion no surprise, therefore, that this life eventually influenced the Greeks no less than it was influenced by them.

Greek sources do not always distinguish between racial Greek and Hellenized Oriental; and there was a reason for this, since sometimes they themselves did not notice the difference. In the Hellenistic period the term "Greek" ceased to be a purely ethnic, and became also a cultural, concept. The Greeks did not always make a distinction between a Greek who had come from Greece to settle in oriental lands, and an Oriental who had learned Greek and acquired Greek culture. A "Greek city," as it is mentioned in the sources, means a city organized in the form of a Greek *polis*, not a city whose inhabitants were racial Greeks; and this fact must be remembered when we come to discuss the cultural problems associated with the flowering of Hellenism in oriental lands. Today also we are sensible of the difference between original inner culture and culture which is borrowed and imitated, and this can be exemplified by the difference between genuine Europeans and "Europeans" of Levantine type. The question of national origin is therefore extremely important, and we must understand the nature of the human material of the Greek cities if we wish to know what was the cultural standard created by it.

Every Greek city stood in the proximity of some ancient oriental urban community. This fact alone could under certain conditions bring about a mixture of oriental population with the Greeks, by intermarriage, mingling of language, and similar factors. However, it was not sufficient to overwhelm the Greek *polis*, which was a citadel closed to aliens; only as citizens possessed of full rights and privileges could the oriental inhabitants gain a place worthy of consideration so that their influence on their Greek neighbors might be felt. The question therefore is: was the citizenship of Greek cities granted to oriental inhabitants? This question is not easily answered, on account of the meagerness of our sources. Everything depended on the location of the *polis* and on the period of its foundation. Ancient Greek cities, founded before Alexander, kept a strict guard over the purity of their Hellenic origin: at Naucratis in Lower Egypt, for example, intermarriage between citizens and local inhabitants was prohibited, and it is to be assumed that the ancient towns of Asia Minor, such as Miletus, Ephesus and Pergamum, were also very strict in the acceptance of new members into the ranks of their citizenry.

But the situation was different in the newly founded Hellenistic towns. Alexander constituted the populations of the towns which he built in the Far East from three elements: Macedonian veterans, Greek mercenaries and local inhabitants. In this composition can be perceived his ambition to bring about an international fusion. The very fact that he invited the local population to participate in the life of the new towns evidences their receipt of citizen rights: local inhabitants were in any case to be found near the Greek cities and would have needed no individual invitation, had not equality of rights been promised to them. Seleucus I also transferred part of the population of ancient Babylon to Seleuceia-on-Tigris, which he was about to found, and Josephus witnesses that the Syrians took part in the public life of that city with the Greeks and Macedonians (*Ant.* XVIII, 372 ff.). In Alexandria the royal officials kept a close watch on the citizen body, and cases occurred in which at the king's order it was extended by the introduction of a large number of new citizens. Since several kings, such as Ptolemy VIII (Euergetes II), had no love of the Greeks and sympathized with the Egyptians, there is reason to believe that these new citizens were for the most part drawn from among the natives of the country. It is equally clear that those Greek cities founded by kings of barbarian origin (in Bithynia and Armenia) received a mixed population from the first. Even the Greek cities themselves were ready in times of difficulty to grant civic rights to soldiers of the garrisons quartered on them, although they were not Greeks by race.

Not only individual native inhabitants, but an entire oriental town might on occasion be converted into a *polis*. We find the most convincing such case in Phoenicia. The citizens of the Phoenician towns (Tyre, Sidon, Arados, Byblos) placed on their coins, not only Greek, but also Semitic inscriptions, which tells us that the ancient population of Phoenicia composed the majority of the citizens in the new *poleis,* for it is hard to imagine that it would occur to Greeks to strike their coins with inscriptions in a foreign language.

Another indication of the conversion of an oriental city to a Greek *polis* is provided by a change of the old town's name. The granting of a Greek city constitution to an oriental town was regarded as equivalent to "founding" a new city. This act therefore was generally associated with the bestowal upon it of a new name, which was almost without exception dynastic, advertising the bond between the oriental city and the king, its new "founder." When we hear, for instance, that Antiochus Epiphanes founded a Greek city of Epiphaneia at Ḥamat (Syria) and another at Ecbatana (Media), or that Damascus was also known as Demetrias, we need not doubt that these Greek *poleis* were just ancient oriental cities whose names were changed when they received Greek constitutions from the king.

To obtain the privileges of a *polis* was very beneficial to the economic development of a city: it received the right to strike bronze coins for the local market and to take part in international Hellenist undertakings (such as the athletic contests) which constituted a convenient means of creating political and economic connections with other countries. The city could further anticipate that the favor of the sovereign founder whose name, or alternatively whose father's or mother's name, it had received, would not be withheld in an hour of need. The wealthy bourgeoisie of the Orient, and the upper strata of the landed aristocracy and of the priesthood, were interested in the conversion of their towns to *poleis,* and were prepared to purchase the valued privileges even at the price of some concessions in respect of the elements of their traditional regimes, since every conversion of an oriental town into a Greek *polis* was bound up with the Hellenization of its social life. The king, for his part, was interested in the Hellenization of the eastern cities, since in this way he gained loyal friends among the local population. Thus an alliance was formed between the wealthy bourgeoisie of the ancient oriental towns and the Hellenistic kings, an alliance whose external mark was the exchange of the city's traditional constitution for the new constitution of a Greek *polis.*

Let us now glance at the Greek immigrants who settled in the eastern lands from the time of Alexander onwards. Here too we have to beware of the usual associations involved in the name "Greek," for they are apt to be utterly misleading. With this name we are accustomed to associate the conception of a rich and lofty culture. When we pronounce the word "Greek" we think of Herodotus and Thucydides, Sophocles and Euripides, Plato and Aristotle. It was not, however, the great men of the nation, the creators of Greek culture, who went to the "Diaspora." Who were the early emigrants to the oriental countries? First, soldiers, most of them Macedonians. These were still at a very low cultural level, and there is no need to stress that these simple peasants could not appear in the eastern countries as "bearers of civilization." Together with the Macedonians came the Thessalians, who were also noted warriors, especially as horsemen, but they too were among the backward portion of the Greek population; Thessaly had appeared as an organized political force on the stage of history only some decades before Alexander.

In their footsteps came a mixed company from every corner of Greece: mercenaries, peasants, traders and undefined persons without fixed occupations, sometimes also adventurers who hoped to find wealth and an easy livelihood in the lands of the Orient. Without stating that these people stood absolutely at the lowest cultural level, or that there were not among them some educated men—the example of Alexandria proves that there were—we must admit that the overwhelming majority of them were clearly neither the creators of culture nor its patrons, and it is doubtful if they were capable of shouldering the great task of diffusing Hellenism among the eastern nations.

This fact explains the ease with which the Orient influenced the Greeks. Our archaeological and epigraphical sources afford evidence that the Greek cities were unable to shield the Greeks from the influence of the oriental environment. The oriental religious cults especially penetrated deep into Greek life, and the Greeks swiftly assimilated the cults of the eastern peoples; for, although they were attached to the worship of their own gods, they saw no lack of reverence toward them in according to other deities the right to exist. They felt, moreover, a vital need to appease the local deity in order to avoid his wrath, for he was master of the land. In several instances sources testify that the eastern god, the ruler of the locality of yore, became the official god of the new *polis*, whether he retained his own nature or changed his name and assumed a superficial Hellenistic garb.

The ancient sacred places, among them entire cities, were also sanctified by the Greeks. Three of them, in Cilicia, Phrygia and Syria, received the Greek name Hierapolis, meaning "sacred town," although the deity that ruled them was not a Greek god but rather that of their pre-Greek inhabitants. Thus the oriental cults attached the Greeks to the customs of the foreign land and undermined the cultural integrity of the *polis*, with the result that the Greek *polis* in eastern lands ceased in the course of time to be racially a Greek town and remained so only in political conception, and, but for the Greek language predominating in it, would have been indistinguishable from its oriental predecessor at the same spot.

Nor could the Greek tongue hold its ground in the Greek towns and prevail over the oriental language which dominated the neighborhood. In Syria, for example, Aramaic did not give way before Greek and survived in the Greek towns, not only as a spoken language, but even as a literary tongue. We have already mentioned above that the Phoenician cities were not content with Greek inscriptions on their coins, but felt the need to inscribe the name of the city in Semitic letters also. From these legends we learn that the national tongue had not lost its value before Greek even as a language of administration. If this was so in the Greek cities, how much more did it apply in the villages and smaller towns.

While the oriental names of cities and villages have been preserved with slight modification down to modern times, nearly all the Greek names have vanished without trace among the inhabitants. There are few places which are today known as Antioch, Alexandria, or that bear similar names; yet how many hamlets or remote towns of Syria and Palestine, by contrast, are still known by Semitic names which preceded the Greeks by two thousands years or more. It should be further stressed that the great oriental cities such as Tyre and Sidon, although they became Greek *poleis* in the Hellenistic period, did not change their names at all, and even those of them that acquired Greek names (Damascus-Demetrias; Beirut-Laodiceia) soon discarded them; and the Greeks themselves did not apply the Greek names to them. The Byzantine author Malalas relates that the city of Antioch-Edessa in Mesopotamia received from its founder, Seleucus I, the name of Ἀντιόχεια ἡ μιξοβάρβαρος, "Antioch the town mixed with barbarians"; and it can be easily supposed that the same title could be applied to the majority of the cities founded in the lands of the Orient in the Hellenistic period.

The Greek urban organization, therefore, did not save the towns from the influence of the East, and the Greek *polis* was unable to withstand the constant offensive of the local inhabitants, carried out sometimes by peaceful methods, sometimes by violence. The Greek towns could not Hellenize the East, but the East was strong enough to "barbarize" them. Yet, despite this, their Greek citizens did not sink to the low level of their kindred who dwelt in the villages of Egypt. Greek, although it was not the only language spoken in the towns, nevertheless served as the official and spoken tongue among the upper levels of the public; the gods of the East, although they did not change their oriental nature, received Greek names and took on external Hellenic garb which made them kin to the ancient gods of Greece; Greek education, although it did not penetrate social life to any depth and left untouched the foundations of family and class, gave to young citizens some notion of the cultural loftiness of Hellenism and developed their physique and agility and also the aesthetic sense associated with physical culture.

But the most important thing which raised the Greeks above their eastern neighbors was the Greek city itself, that same free and autonomous institution previously unknown in the Orient which was the most complete expression of the spirit of Hellenism. Even the eastern potentates (for example, the Parthians) respected this political institution, and upon it the Roman conquerors based their power in the countries of the East. The local inhabitants who mingled with the citizens altered the human material of which the Greek *polis* was composed, but the political and juridical form remained unmodified by them. In the Roman period, thanks to the frequent support of the emperors, the towns awoke to new life, and only when the Empire began to collapse did the economic decline affect the Greek cities as well and destroy their external form simultaneously with their economic basis and their cultural content.

In the Byzantine period the cities lost their former value, becoming progressively impoverished, till they were reduced to small villages devoid of significance and influence. In this condition the Arabs found them. The sands of the desert covered the ruined houses and palaces, and only recently has archaeological excavation revealed to us here and there the city's streets, the foundations of ruined dwellings, remains of a Greek shrine, or the broken stone tablets with half-obliterated Greek inscriptions—all that survived of the rich and colorful life that had once flowered here, whose special cultural character set its stamp on the development of the eastern lands for a thousand years.

part **I**

HELLENISTIC
CIVILIZATION
IN
PALESTINE

chapter **1**

POLITICAL
EVENTS
DOWN TO
THE TIME OF
ANTIOCHUS IV EPIPHANES

At a time when important political events were occurring in Europe, and Philip of Macedon was extending his power over the whole of the Balkan peninsula to include Greece, Palestine lay quietly under the rule of the kings of Persia and no historical event of special importance disturbed its regular and slow-moving manner of life. The Persian yoke was not especially heavy, and the central government at Susa placed no obstacle in the way of the natural development of the numerous peoples under its sway; hence the Jews also enjoyed a certain autonomy under their national heads, the High Priests. It is to be regretted that we largely lack historical sources for Jewish life in the Persian period. Nor can we establish either the limits of Jewish autonomy or the scope of the High Priests' authority. It is, however, very probable that the Persians did not interfere with the conduct of Jewish spiritual affairs once they had confirmed in principle the Law of Moses as the basis of the national life of those exiles who had returned to Zion.[1]

It is not to be assumed, however, that they also granted to the Jews such political and economic autonomy as would have been implied by free intercourse with their neighbors: the right to levy troops, to strike coins, and the like; according to all our sources, the chief person in Judaea was not the High Priest but the satrap appointed by the king.[2] For this reason the Persian period was for the Jews a time of concentration of intellectual, rather than the development of material, forces, although there is of course no indication that the Jews ceased to be a nation and became a religious community, as most of the theologians have thought. Ezra's religious reform itself arose from the need to strengthen the national group; and facts such as the building of the wall of Jerusalem, the dispute with the Samaritans, and the attempts to strengthen the power of the High Priests, evidence very clear political aspirations among those who had returned to Zion.

But the very political situation in which the Jews were placed to a large extent resulted in cultural concentration at the expense of political development. The small country of Judaea was surrounded on all sides by diverse peoples who shut it off from the wide world and denied it the ability to develop freely, especially from the economic viewpoint. The seacoast and the fertile belt of country near it, the Shephelah of Philistia and the Plain of Sharon, were in the possession of the Syrian cities, and all the trade of the maritime states was gathered in the same hands or in those of the Phoenicians. The latter ruled the waves through the power of their large navy, and in the Persian period enjoyed almost complete independence, controlling also the Palestinian coast, as the sources testify.[3]

The north of the country was in the hands of various indigenous peoples, the Jews' nearest neighbors on this side being the Samaritans, who were the offspring of intermarriage between the Israelites and other peoples settled there by Sargon of Assyria; they accepted Jewish religious laws, but did not recognize the nation's religious center at Jerusalem and had built their own temple to the God of Israel on Mount Gerizim. The disputes between the Samaritans and the Jews run like a continuous thread through Jewish history from the period of Nehemiah down to the Jewish rebellion against Rome. In Transjordan dwelt the Nabataeans, a strong Arab tribe engaged in commerce; while the south of the country was in the hands of the Idumaeans. Thus Judaea was surrounded on every side by various peoples who barred the tiny Jewish population from access to the broad world of international relations.

Palestine had known the Greeks long before Alexander the Great appeared there at the head of his host of Greeks and Macedonians. The excavations carried out during the last thirty years at various places in the country and in Transjordan have revealed that Greek influence began to penetrate as early as the seventh century B.C.E., while in the fifth and fourth centuries it reached very wide proportions. Greek commerce embraced the whole Near East, and as the trade-routes between Greece and South Arabia (the source of the spice and incense trade) passed through southern Palestine, it is not surprising to find Greek remains even at Elat.[4] Demosthenes evidences a settlement of Greek merchants from Athens at Acco in the middle of the fourth century,[5] and sherds of Greek pottery, sometimes painted in the Greek style, have been found in a large number of excavations and even in localities in the Jerusalem area.[6] Athenian coins bearing the figure of an owl were current throughout the country, and under their influence the local authorities also began to strike coins on the Athenian model.[7] Various Greek myths were also known in Palestine, and as early as the middle of the fourth century the city of Jaffa is mentioned in Greek literature in connection with the well-known Greek legend of Perseus and Andromeda.[8] The name of the Greeks was therefore familiar to the inhabitants of Palestine, especially to those of them who dwelt on the seacoast, but there existed as yet no reciprocal influence between the two peoples and their brief encounters led to no cultural fusion. The new period began in the summer of 332, when Alexander the Great entered Palestine on his way from Tyre to Egypt.

The Greek and Roman writers who relate the life and deeds of Alexander—Arrian, Diodorus, Plutarch and Curtius—pass over the short period which Alexander spent in Palestine in almost complete silence; they mention only his hostilities with the city of Gaza, which was under the command of a Persian general and resisted Alexander continuously for two months (Diod.XVII,48,7; Arrian II,26-7; Curt. IV, 6,7ff.). This silence reflects historical reality. Alexander did not linger in Palestine, but went down to Egypt immediately after he had taken Gaza (Arrian III,1,1). Nor on his return from Egypt did he stay long in the country, but went straight from Egypt to Tyre and thence to North Syria and to Mesopotamia.[9] Palestine itself did not arouse his special interest; he considered one thing only as important, namely, that the country should remain under his control; and this he secured by placing Macedonian garrisons at Gaza and, perhaps, in other coastal cities. The conquest of the country itself was carried out by his commanders, probably by Parmenion, who was sent to Syria after the battle of Issus and brought Damascus under Macedonian dominion (Arrian II,11,10). No close relationship was created between Alexander and Palestine, and it is doubtful whether the king even remembered the country. But neither the country nor the Jews who dwelt there were prepared to forego a place in their imaginations for the poetic figure of the hero-king who had visited their towns. Legend filled the vacuum which history had left, and such legend we must scrutinize to discover whether or not it contains some germ of history.[10]

Flavius Josephus has a detailed account of Alexander's visit to Jerusalem (*Ant*.XI,304ff.). He begins by describing the quarrel between the Jews and the Samaritans. Menasseh, brother of the High Priest Yadoa, had married the daughter of Sanballat, satrap of Samaria, an action which aroused much bitterness among the people of Jerusalem. The people demanded that Menasseh divorce his foreign wife or give up the priesthood; Yadoa also joined them and forebade his brother to approach the altar. Menasseh sought help from his father-in-law Sanballat, who promised him not only the high priesthood, but also the rule of Samaria after his death, taking upon himself to obtain from Darius a permit to build a special temple on Mount Gerizim at Samaria. Sanballat's promise made a great impression in Jerusalem and caused a stir among the priests.

In the meantime Darius was defeated by Alexander at Issus. Sanballat at once went over to the victorious side, bringing Alexander, who was then before Tyre, 8000 warriors. Alexander received him favorably and gave him the permit to build the temple at Samaria. Thereupon Sanballat returned home and built it, but died shortly afterwards, before Gaza had surrendered to Alexander. Alexander's first meeting with the Samaritans, therefore, took place in peaceful fashion. But the case with the Jews was different. During his seige of Gaza, Alexander sent a letter to the Jews demanding that the High Priest despatch auxiliary troops and corn for his host; but Yadoa would not dishonor his oath of allegiance to Darius and refused Alexander's demands. The king, filled with rage at this insolence, determined to punish the Jews severely and, after capturing Tyre and Gaza, went up to Jerusalem. Fear and perplexity prevailed in the city; the people gathered in the Temple to pray to God to save them from the king's wrath, whereupon God appeared to Yadoa in a dream and encouraged him, saying that no harm would befall the Jews, but that the city-gates should be opened and that the multitude should go out to meet the king in white festal garments, the priests in their sacred vestments. This they did. On Mount Scopus they encountered Alexander. When he saw the Jews from afar, he hastened to be the first to meet the High Priest and fell upon his face before the Ineffable Name which was inscribed upon the latter's headdress. When Parmenion asked the king why he had prostrated himself before this priest, when all mortals prostrated themselves before the king, Alexander replied: "This man, clad in those garments, I beheld in a dream when I was in Macedon; and I know that his God will give me victory over my foes." With these words Alexander entered Jerusalem accompanied by the High Priest and offered up a sacrifice in the Temple to the God of Israel. The priests showed him the Book of Daniel, in which was written that a Greek king would come and destroy the kingdom of the Persians, and Alexander heard the words of prophecy with joy. He gave the Jews permission to live according to their laws and customs and exempted them from taxation in the sabbatical year. The Jews begged him to permit the Jews of Babylon and Media to live according to their own laws, and to this request also Alexander willingly consented.

When Alexander left Jerusalem he was met by the Samaritans, who had heard of his favorable attitude to the Jews and now sought to be counted among them. "For such," remarks Josephus, "was the habit of the Samaritans: when the Jews were in distress, they held aloof from them; and when their lot was good, they remembered their descent from Joseph, Menasseh and Ephraim." The Samaritans besought Alexander to visit their shrine at Samaria, and he promised to fulfill their request when the war was over. Thereupon the Samaritans begged him to exempt them from taxes in the sabbatical years. Alexander asked them who they were, and they replied that they were Hebrews known as "Sidonians from Sichem." Alexander asked them again whether they were Jews: and to this question they were forced to give a negative reply. Alexander then said: "This privilege I have given to the Jews; when I return from the war I shall sift your complaints and see what is to be done." Thus frustrated, the Samaritans left Alexander, and the king continued on his way, having attached to his army the force of Samaritan warriors which Sanballat had brought.

Let us attempt to analyze this story. It is clear that we have here two different narratives which have been linked together by Josephus: the first dealing with the disputes between the Jews and Samaritans and the erection of the temple at Samaria; the second with Alexander's visit to Jerusalem and his negative attitude to the Samaritans. Behind the first, historical events can be discerned: the building of the Samaria temple is a historical fact, and Sanballat, satrap of Samaria, is known to us from the Book of Nehemiah, while the Elephantine papyri also mention his name.[11] The incident of the Jewish priest who married Sanballat's daughter is also compatible with truth (Neh. 13.28).

Yet the tale loses half its historical value on account of the chronological error it involves, since Sanballat lived in the period of Nehemiah, that is, in the second half of the fifth century, not in that of Alexander the Great. Many attempts have been made by modern historians to rescue Josephus' chronology, but they cannot be regarded as especially successful.[12] It is to be assumed that the fable of Sanballat's meeting with Alexander was composed in Samaria, although Josephus uses its Jewish version.[13] Josephus attached to it the second narrative which he had before him, and the combination had two curious results, namely, the sudden death of Sanballat, quite unjustified by the course of events, and the amazing speed with which the Samaritan temple was built. Sanballat was the central figure of the first tale, but was unmentioned in the second; Josephus, therefore, had to remove him in the middle of the account in order to explain to his readers why he was missing from the end of the narrative. In the first story Sanballat obtains from Alexander the permit to build the shrine, whereas in the second it has been standing for a long time, and the Samaritans invite Alexander to visit it. When both narratives were combined the result was that the temple appeared to be constructed within a few months.

This contradiction between the two accounts also stands out in the description of the meeting between Alexander and the Samaritans at the end of Josephus' account: Alexander asks the Samaritans who they are, as if he were seeing them for the first time, whereas he had already met Sanballat, who had brought him Samaritan auxiliary troops when he was at Tyre. These contradictions prove that Josephus was unsuccessful in fusing the two narratives into one, and that he contented himself with giving one after the other, changing only one or two features in order to make the tale easier to understand; in effect he only made it more complicated.

The whole story is full of legendary traits, as all scholars admit. The picture of Alexander which the author had before him is apposite not to Alexander King of Macedon (as he was in the year 332 when he entered Palestine), but to Alexander King of Persia, as he became after he had defeated Darius in central Asia. Parmenion refers to the custom of kneeling before Alexander, but this custom was Persian and was not yet accepted in Alexander's court.[14] Josephus also refers to Chaldeans among his train: but these dwelt not in Palestine but in Babylonia, whither Alexander had not yet journeyed.[15] The High Priest's request to permit the Jews of Babylonia and Media to enjoy their own laws and customs, is further based on the assumption that those lands were already under Macedonian dominion. It is obvious that the author was ignorant of the chronological order of Alexander's campaigns and described the king as ruler of the whole world according to the accepted contemporary version. Nor was the length of time spent by Alexander in Palestine known to the narrator. Josephus relates that he visited Jerusalem after he had captured Gaza, and we know (Arrian III,1,1; Curtius IV,2,7) that Alexander accomplished the journey from Gaza to Pelusium in Egypt in a week; and he could not, therefore, have gone up to Jerusalem in so short a time.

One more chronological error reveals the historical unreliability of the narrative, and this is that the Jews read the Book of Daniel to Alexander, in whose time the book was not yet in existence, since it was written more than 150 years afterwards. If we mention further decidedly legendary features, such, for example, as the dreams of Yadoa and Alexander,[16] we shall have no difficulty in realizing that Josephus' narrative is not to be regarded as a serious historical source. Alexander's visit to Jerusalem is not a historical episode which the Greek writers "forgot" to relate and which has "by chance" been preserved in Josephus; it is a historical myth designed to bring the king into direct contact with the Jews, and to speak of both in laudatory terms. Here is material for research worthy not of the historian, but of the student of literature.[17]

Various stories of Alexander have also come down to us in talmudic literature, most of them mere anecdotes without any historical value. Thus the Egyptians and the Jews appear before Alexander to dispute on questions connected with the Exodus; Alexander reaches the Mountains of Darkness and enters a city inhabited entirely by women; he bandies sophistries with the old men of the South, and even flies on eagles' wings.[18] These tales resemble most of those composed about Alexander by the peoples of East and West in the Middle Ages; their origin goes back to Alexandrian literature of the Hellenistic period.[19] This is no place to examine them, but it is advisable to consider one such item which resembles Josephus' narrative in several particulars.

This runs as follows, according to the "Scholion," or commentary, on *Megillat Ta'anit*:

The 21st of the month (Kislev) is the day of Mount Gerizim, when mourning is forbidden. On this day the Samaritans begged a temple from Alexander of Macedon and said to him: Sell us five *kurs* of earth on Mount Moriah. He gave it to them. When they came, the inhabitants of Jerusalem came out and drove them away with sticks and told Simon the Just. He put on priestly vestments and the head men of Jerusalem with him and a thousand councillors clothed themselves in white and the priestly neophytes clashed the sacred vessels. And as they went among the hills they saw torches of light. The King said: What is that? The informers said to him: Those are Jews who have revolted against you. When they came to Antipatris, the sun shone. They came to the first sentry-post. They said to them: Who are you? They said: We are people of Jerusalem and we have come to welcome the King. When Alexander of Macedon saw Simon the Just, he alighted from his chariot and knelt to him. They said to him: Do you know this man? He is a mere mortal. He said: I behold the image of this man when I go to war and conquer. He (Alexander) said: What do you seek? He (Simon) replied: Gentiles have misled you and you have given to them the house in which we pray for your kingdom. He asked: Who are they who have deceived me? He replied: The Samaritans who stand before you. He said: I hand them over to you. They pierced their heels and hung them on the tails of their horses and dragged them over thorns and thistles till they reached Mount Gerizim. They ploughed and sowed it with horse-beans as (the Samaritans) had thought to do to the Temple. And the day they did this they made into a festival.[20]

This talmudic story greatly resembles Josephus' story; only the name of the High Priest Yadoa is here replaced by that of Simon the Just, and the drama is transferred from Jerusalem to Antipatris. The mention of Simon the Just has provided some scholars with grounds for seeing in the encounter between this High Priest and Antiochus III, King of Syria, a historical event under whose influence the folk-story described the alleged meeting between Alexander and Yadoa.[21] However, the imagination of the author was probably not so feeble that he needed the aid of some particular event in order to describe the meeting between Alexander and the High Priest; and where the details are concerned, Antiochus III certainly no more knelt to the Jewish High Priest than did Alexander.[22]

The political negotiations between Simon the Just and Antiochus did not, so far as we know, concern the Samaritan question, whereas the talmudic story emphasizes precisely this: the dispute between the Jews and the Samaritans ("Kutim" in the Talmud) here ends with the destruction of the temple on Mount Gerizim, that is, with events that took place in the period of John Hyrcanus, when the city of Samaria was captured by the Jews and utterly destroyed. A historical element is therefore no more to be sought in the talmudic story than in that of Josephus, and we must agree that in this instance also the task of inquiry belongs rather to the literary man than to the historian.

Nevertheless, even in legends, there are some individual features which invite the historian's investigation. One such feature occurs in the story of Alexander, namely, his relationship with the Samaritans, and of this more may be profitably said.

Alexander's negative attitude to the Samaritans is stressed both in Josephus and in the Talmud (despite Alexander's peaceful first meeting with Sanballat). We possess one other source which links Alexander with the Samaritans in a manner not to their advantage, and this is an extract from the Greek writer Hecataeus cited by Josephus (C. Ap. II, 43). "Alexander," writes Josephus, "honored our people, and of this Hecataeus speaks in his book on the Jews; he relates that Alexander gave the Jews the land of Samaria free of tax, in exchange for the friendship and loyalty which they elicited." Here too, therefore, we see the hostility between Alexander and the Samaritans; to our regret we cannot judge whether this information is likely to have been true or not.[23] The pronounced accentuation of this antagonism, repeated in three sources, one of them at least (Hecataeus) independent of the others, makes us aware that a nucleus of historical truth exists hidden behind the literary embellishments of the story. This is to be detected if we compare the foregoing narratives with the brief notice in Curtius (IV, 8, 9) telling us that, when Alexander returned from Egypt through Palestine, rumor reached him of a Samaritan revolt, in which the Samaritans had captured the governor of Syria[24] and burned him alive. On hearing this, Alexander hastened against the Samaritans and wrought havoc among them. According to the Christian writer Eusebius, he also established a Macedonian colony in the city.

Here, then, is the historical occurrence which served as a foundation for the tales about the conflict between Alexander and the Samaritans. There is reason to believe that not Alexander himself but Perdiccas punished the Samaritans and settled Macedonians in Samaria (see below, ch. II), but this modification does not negate Curtius' account of the Samaritan revolt and its suppression. It may be supposed that the course of events was somewhat as follows: Alexander was on his way from Egypt to Tyre, when news came to him of the Samaritan rising, and he immediately sent Perdiccas to put it down; the Jews naturally rejoiced at their enemies' prospective discomfiture and perhaps also afforded Perdiccas substantial aid. Whether they received on this occasion part of the territory of Samaria, as Hecataeus relates, we do not know, but apparently they remained on excellent terms with the Macedonian rulers, a fact preserved by popular memory and expressed in legends and folk-stories concerning Alexander.

In the talmudic story, Antipatris is mentioned as the place where Alexander met the Jews. The name betrays chronological inaccuracy, as the city of Antipatris was founded by Herod and was nonexistent in Alexander's day; nevertheless, Hellenistic towns were not built on vacant sites, and we know the name of the previous nearby settlement, which was K'far Saba.[25] As this is near the shore, and Alexander traveled along the coast on his way from Tyre to Gaza and back, he passed by K'far Saba, and it might be conjectured that the talmudic story preserved an important local tradition on the historic meeting between Alexander and the Jews. However, the same *Megillat Ta'anit*, which contains the story of Alexander and the Jews, also recounts the Emperor Caligula's order to place an image in the Temple, and in this tale too Antipatris appears as a station on the route between Caesarea and Jerusalem.[26] We learn from this that here the north-south coast-road crossed another from Jerusalem to the Shephelah, and the town's mention in the tale is purely a matter of convention.[27]

We may now abandon legend and attempt to solve the problem of Alexander's meeting with the Jews inductively. Is it likely that Alexander would have traversed Palestine twice without the Jews appearing before him to "welcome the king" as the talmudic tale puts it? Their appearance before their new sovereign was not only their right but their duty, and failure to appear would have been interpreted as lack of political tact or as deliberate opposition to the new authority. There is no doubt that all the peoples of Palestine made submission to Alexander as the kings of Phoenicia and Cyprus had done (Arrian II, 20, 1-3); why then should the Jews have been an exception? We do not know where and when the Jews presented themselves before the king, but the meeting itself appears to me a certainty.

This being so, we can guess what was the subject of discussion at the meeting. If it took place after Alexander's return from Egypt, the Jewish-Samaritan dispute may well have been discussed, as the Samaritan rising would have created a political atmosphere favorable to Jewish complaints. There was, however, another more general question of principle certainly mentioned in the discussion, namely, the Jews' privilege to live according to their ancestral tradition. The Persian kings had in their time ratified Jewish autonomy within certain limits, and the situation now required confirmation at the hands of the Macedonian authorities. That such confirmation was without doubt forthcoming we can deduce from the fact that the High Priest continued to rule as before and that the Mosaic Law remained in force among the Jews as it had always been.[28]

Several documents have survived from the time of Antiochus III and the Roman period, in which the rulers pledged the Jews permission "to live according to their ancestral Law," and there are sufficient grounds for the assumption that Alexander the Great was the first Hellenistic ruler who published a pronouncement worded in this way. No special sympathy for the Jews need be perceived in such a political declaration, for such was his behavior everywhere in relation to all peoples, and it would be a matter for surprise had he refused to act in this manner only in respect of the Jews.[29] We are not in a position to say whether he made a solemn declaration addressed to the High Priest himself as representative of the nation, or whether he acted with less publicity by sending a letter to the Macedonian official in charge of the affairs of Palestine. The latter was the usual manner of making declarations of this sort in subsequent generations.[30]

49

The Greek cities which were founded in Palestine in the Hellenistic period also told unfounded tales about Alexander the Great; thus, for example, three cities in Transjordan associated their establishment with Alexander. These tales, however, are historically worthless. We have just seen that even Alexander's visit to Jerusalem has no foundation in the sources; how much less so, then, his visits to Transjordan, a country which lay entirely off his path.[31] Generally, it must be remembered that every Greek city was ready to boast that the great hero was its personal founder, and various fables were composed in the oriental countries to prove that he had visited given places and issued an order to found this or that city. The truth is that Alexander built his cities (with the exception of Alexandria in Egypt) only in the last years of his life, when he was active in the countries of central Asia,[32] and among the cities of Palestine there was only one with which he had come into direct contact, namely, Gaza, which had closed its gates before the king and had been captured by him after a two months' siege. Alexander gave the order to found the city anew, fortified it and granted its new inhabitants permission to settle there. Thus the ruined town rose again and became in course of time a large and important Greek city.[33]

We have no information on the fate of Palestine in the years during which Alexander was fighting in the East. Only the names of the governors of Syria have been preserved by the Greek historians, and those not completely.[34] After Alexander's death (323) Syria fell into the hands of Laomedon, and remained under his control in 321, on the second partition of territories after the death of Perdiccas.[35] These years were doubtless years of peace for the country; the war of the Diadochi had not yet flared up with full violence, nor had Palestine become a battlefield of the rival forces. There are grounds for supposing that in the period when Perdiccas was at the helm, some of the country's Macedonian colonies were founded (see below, ch. 2). The situation changed in 320, when Ptolemy, satrap of Egypt, invaded Coele-Syria[36] with the aim of bringing it under his control and annexing it to Egypt. "He perceived," says Diodorus, explaining Ptolemy's attack (XVIII, 43, 1), "that the geographical situation of the countries of Phoenicia and Coele-Syria was excellent in relation to Egypt and therefore threw all his energy into the endeavor to gain control of those places."

By this action Ptolemy was unconsciously continuing the old policy of the Pharaohs, who had also aspired to bring Syria under their control. Whoever ruled the Phoenician ports also controlled the trade-routes in the western Mediterranean, and as trade in ancient times was conducted coastwise, the Syrian lands and the island of Cyprus played the part of the trade links between Egypt. It should be further added that the cedars of Lebanon provided the somewhat rare raw material needed for the building of fleets. The country was conquered without great difficulty. Nicanor, one of Ptolemy's generals, traversed the Syrian mainland to the Phoenician towns, while Ptolemy in person delivered an attack from the sea. Laomedon was taken prisoner by Ptolemy, having refused to accept from him a gift of silver in compensation for his rule of Syria; some time afterwards he succeeded in slaying his guards and in escaping to Asia Minor. Ptolemy consolidated his dominion in Syria, by placing garrisons in the conquered cities, and returned to Egypt. Thus Palestine was annexed to Egypt for the first time (Diod. XVIII, 43; Appian *Syr.* 52).

Ptolemy ruled Syria for five years. Meanwhile Antigonus had founded his great kingdom, which constituted a constant danger to the other Macedonian generals (see above, p. 9). They made an alliance among themselves, and laid their demands before Antigonus. Among other things they demanded that Antigonus agree to Ptolemy's government of the whole of Syria (Diod. XIX, 57, 1). Antigonus refused their demands and the war began. In 315 Antigonus invaded Syria and Palestine and apparently met with little resistance from Ptolemy: Diodorus (XIX, 59, 2) mentions only two towns—Jaffa and Gaza—which refused to open their gates to Antigonus and were taken by him by force. The latter attached to his own army the Ptolemaic troops whom he found in the country, and strengthened the cities he had captured by garrisons.

Ptolemy, however, had not given up his power in Syria, and in the course of three years (in 312) seized the opportunity, when Antigonus was engaged in warfare outside Syria and the country had been left under the management of his young son Demetrius, to invade Palestine in Seleucus' company with a strong army. They met Demetrius near Gaza: the fight was long and obstinate, but Ptolemy and Seleucus were ultimately victorious and Demetrius abandoned the field and fled northward (Diod. XIX, 80ff.). The whole of

Palestine as far as the Phoenician cities fell into Ptolemy's hands, but his domination did not last for long. Several months after the battle Antigonus prepared to enter Syria in person, and Ptolemy, not daring to face the old and tried field marshal, destroyed the fortresses of Acco, Jaffa, Samaria and Gaza, and returned to Egypt (Diod. XIX, 93, 4-7). Palestine again passed, apparently without resistance on the part of its inhabitants, into Antigonus' possession.

On the fortunes of Palestine under Antigonus there is little information. Antigonus fought against the Arabian tribes which dwelt about the Dead Sea, and sought to take up positions in those localities in order to commence the exploitation of the sea's natural wealth (the production of asphalt), but without success (Diod. XIX, 94ff.). The silence of our sources is the more regrettable because presumably it was in this period that Hellenism began to strike root in the country. Alexander had had no intention of Hellenizing it: as long as the kingdom of Persia still existed he could not afford to waste his energy on settling Macedonian troops in the conquered localities. Antigonus' situation was different. After many years of warfare, a short period of peace supervened in 311. Antigonus now had to solve several problems created by immediate circumstances; it was necessary to look to the welfare of the new Greek population which had migrated to Syria, to build new towns, to fortify those already in existence, to discharge troops whose period of service was up, and to allot them land on which to settle. Antigonus carried out his tasks energetically, among other things building a number of towns in Asia Minor and Syria.[37] It is to be assumed that he also paid attention to Palestine, for its strategical importance in case of war with Egypt was unquestionable. We may surmise that he continued Perdiccas' activity and erected several Macedonian colonies in the country; to this question we shall return in the next chapter.

In 302 the Macedonian generals (meantime turned kings) again leagued together for a common war against Antigonus. The part played by Ptolemy in this war, and his great caution, set their stamp on the whole history of the Syrian lands in the Hellenistic period, and even in the time of Antiochus Epiphanes, 130 years later, we hear echoes of the events of those days. At the beginning of the war, Ptolemy overran Palestine for the third time and reached Sidon; but on hearing a rumor (later proved false) of Antigonus' victory and of his early arrival in Syria, Ptolemy evacuated the places he had occupied and returned hastily to Egypt (Diod. XX, 113, 1-2). As a result he took no part in the campaign of the Macedonian kings at Ipsus and thus lost his share of the vast spoil which fell to the victors after Antigonus' death (301). The sovereigns struck his name from the list of the confederates and gave the whole of Syria to Seleucus; but Ptolemy had no intention of giving up Coele-Syria, and when Seleucus went to Phoenicia to establish his authority in a country his by decision, he found Coele-Syria again in Ptolemy's hands.

Diodorus (XXI, 1, 5) relates that in the conflict which flared up between the two kings over the question of the rule of this territory, Ptolemy accused his ally, friend and companion of intending to rob him of a country in his possession, after the kings had affronted him and taken from him his portion of the spoil, although he too had participated in the war against Antigonus. To these complaints Seleucus replied that "it was just that the conquered territory should belong to those who had defeated the foe in battle, and as to Coele-Syria, he did not intend raising the matter for the moment because of his friendship for Ptolemy, but in due time he would return and attend to it and would then decide what course he should adopt toward friends who came with exaggerated demands."

It is therefore clear that, according to Diodorus, Seleucus in effect conceded dominion over Palestine to Ptolemy, and I see no grounds for doubting the statement.[38] Nevertheless, in contradiction to Diodorus' plain language, many scholars believe that Seleucus ruled Palestine, and that the Ptolemies occupied the country only after a certain period. Niese thinks that part of southern Syria came into Egyptian hands perhaps in 295/4, and Bouché-Leclercq even conjectured that the conquest of the country was carried out in 280 by Ptolemy II Philadelphus, who took advantage of the confusion which arose in Syria after the death of Seleucus I. This is also the opinion of Eduard Meyer. Abel thinks that in 295 Seleucus was ruling Judaea and also imposing a regular tax upon the Jews. Hölscher attributes to Seleucus the building of most of the Greek cities of Palestine, and Schwartz sees in the erection of the Greek cities of the Decapolis a result of the policy of Seleucus I and Antiochus I.[39] It would be well therefore to treat of this question in order to ascertain if grounds can be discovered in the sources for these scholars' views.

We have learned from Diodorus that Coele-Syria belonged *de iure* to Seleucus, and was *de facto* in the hands of Ptolemy.[40] The same political situation is indicated in the account of Polybius (V, 67), who speaks of diplomatic negotiations between Antiochus III and Ptolemy IV Philopator, in 218, in connection with the question of Coele-Syria. Both sides based their right to rule the country on the events of 301, Antiochus claiming that Coele-Syria belonged to the Seleucids because Seleucus I had ruled it; Ptolemy, he said, had gone to war with Antigonus to conquer this territory on behalf of Seleucus and not on his own behalf, the decision of the kings whereby Syria was given to Seleucus being especially important.[41] Antiochus III's statement here betrays the diplomatic activity carried out in the third century at Antiochus' court, with the object of interpreting the events of 301 to the advantage of the Seleucids. The Antiochan politicians could not deny the fact that Coele-Syria was conquered by Ptolemy, but they sought to belittle the political and juridical value of the occupation by declaring that it had been carried out by Ptolemy on behalf of Seleucus. This view is based on the assumption that Ptolemy was a vassal of Seleucus—a situation quite inappropriate to the historical reality.

Antiochus, on the other hand, rightly interpreted the decision of the Macedonian kings after the campaign of Ipsus to hand the whole of Syria to Seleucus as a *juridical* basis for Seleucid rule in Syria. The representatives of Ptolemy Philopator did not, of course, agree to Antiochus' view, and claimed that the country's occupation by Ptolemy I was sufficient juridical basis for Ptolemaic authority in Coele-Syria, and that Ptolemy had joined the war alongside Seleucus on condition that all Asia should fall to Seleucus, while Coele-Syria and Phoenicia went to himself. The Alexandrian diplomats did not seek, therefore, to deny the official value of the kings' agreement, but argued that previous to it there had existed another agreement between Ptolemy and Seleucus, according to which Coele-Syria belonged to Ptolemy.

Here too we can trace the diplomatic activity which alters events according to existing needs; even if we suppose that such an agreement had been made between Ptolemy and Seleucus before the war, it is clear that Ptolemy had lost his right to use it as authority after he had voluntarily given up participation in the final conflict and thus quitted the sovereigns' joint enterprise. What concerns us at present, however, is not the explanation applied at this later period to the events of 301; what is important for us is only the fact that, at the end of the third century, both sides knew that, immediately after the battle of Ipsus, Coele-Syria had in fact fallen into the hands of Ptolemy, while the formal right of authority had remained in the hands of Seleucus. Polybius' words are decidedly consistent with the information furnished by Diodorus.[42]

                    Two other proofs are adduced by scholars in favor of their view on the rule of Seleucus in Coele-Syria: the Seleucid names of the Greek cities of Palestine and the Seleucid dating which is alleged to appear on the city coinage of Coele-Syria in the period under discussion. But the Seleucid city-names appear in Palestine at a late period, after the conquest of the country by Antiochus III; and on the matter of coinage, scholars are now known to have been in error in supposing that the various calendars current in the Greek cities represented the official Seleucid era.[43] Neither of these proofs, then, can stand up to criticism or cancel the evidence of Diodorus and Polybius. Hence the outcome of our present inquiry is that Palestine after Antigonus' defeat passed directly into Ptolemy's hands, while Seleucus in effect gave up his authority over the country which belonged to him by legal decision.[44]

                    Among the cities of Palestine occupied by Ptolemy was Jerusalem. The sources have preserved various contradictory statements on Ptolemy's attitude to the Jews. We can distinguish two threads of historiographical tradition, one describing Ptolemy as their enemy and the other as their friend. The first tradition is represented by Agatharchides, a Greek historian of the second century B.C.E., who wrote on the period of the Diadochi. Josephus, basing himself on Agatharchides, writes: "He (Ptolemy) captured Jerusalem by deceit and treachery; he entered the city on the Sabbath as if desiring to offer a sacrifice, and the Jews did not prevent him, as they did not suspect that he was an enemy" (*Ant.* XII, 4). Agatharchides mocks at the Jews who had "out of negligence" got themselves a "hard master" on the Sabbath day, and Josephus says that the king ruled Jerusalem "with a high hand" and that his acts in Palestine proved the contrary to what was indicated by his title "Savior" (*Ant.* XII, 3-6; cf. *C. Ap.* I, 209ff.). Appian also (*Syr.* 50) refers briefly to the destruction of Jerusalem by Ptolemy. As a result of the capture,

55

many Jews who were taken prisoner by Ptolemy were transported by him to Egypt and sold as slaves.[45]

The second tradition has been
preserved in Hecataeus of Abdera, a Greek writer who was a
contemporary of Ptolemy I. According to Hecataeus, Syria fell
into Ptolemy's hands after the battle of Gaza (312), when many
people accompanied Ptolemy and even followed him to Egypt,
as they had heard of his lofty virtues—"his kindness and love
of mankind." Among these people was also a Jewish High Priest
Hezekiah, a man of sixty-six, one of the notables of the Jewish
population, prominent for his eloquence and his administrative
abilities (*C. Ap.* I, 186ff.; cf. *Ant.* XII, 9). Hecataeus' story did
not gain the credence of modern scholars of a former generation, but we now have sufficient basis for evaluating his accounts
as preserved in Josephus, more especially the story of the priest
Hezekiah, by means of a criterion other than that current in the
nineteenth century, and of seeing in many of them genuine historical reminiscences.[46] The inquirer, therefore, faces no easy
task if he wishes to reconcile two differing traditions and to
discover the appropriate political situation for each of them.
Since Ptolemy conquered Palestine four times (in 320, 312, 302
and 301) and most details of the conquests are unknown to
us, while Ptolemy's policy toward the country's population in
peacetime is still less known, there is no prospect of reaching
a confident conclusion, and the results of the inquiry are more
dependent on conjectures and guesses than on a strict analysis
of the historical facts. With these remarks in mind, we shall
venture to reconstruct events as follows.

Ptolemy overran Palestine
for the first time in 320, but Agatharchides' story of the capture
of Jerusalem is not to be ascribed to this year, as some scholars
have thought.[47] Appian (*Syr.* 52) evidences explicitly that
Ptolemy came to Syria by sea and returned the same way, and
Diodorus (XVIII, 43) relates that the conquest of the country
was carried out by Nicanor, his general. In that year, therefore,
Ptolemy was not in Jerusalem in person, whereas Agatharchides'
account notes his personal presence there. Nor can the political
situation explain why Jerusalem was obliged to close its gates
to Ptolemy; that year the fiction of the great united kingdom
founded by Alexander still existed, and neither Laomedon, the
former Syrian governor, nor Ptolemy, its new ruler, was officially more than satrap of the central authority; they were not
independent rulers. It can hardly be assumed that the Jews

opposed Nicanor or any other official who had come to them on behalf of Ptolemy, and it is very probable that Ptolemy's seizure of the control of Judaea was carried out peacefully.

In 312 the political situation was quite different: the central power had long lapsed, the country was in Antigonus' hands, and Ptolemy entered it as a foreign conqueror. For this reason most scholars incline to ascribe Agatharchides' narrative to this year,[48] but once again among the events of 312 there are certain details which do not suit this supposition. First, immediately after his victory at Gaza, Ptolemy went up to Phoenicia (Diod. XIX, 85, 4); and since the conquest of the coastal towns was important to him, it is to be supposed that he marched thither by way of Jaffa and Acco, without turning aside to Judaea; and if he did not capture Jerusalem at the beginning of the campaign, it is doubtful whether he found time to do so at all, since he spent only a short time in the country. Secondly, among the towns destroyed by Ptolemy when he left the country (Acco, Jaffa, Samaria and Gaza), we do not find Jerusalem. Thirdly, in this year Hecataeus places his story of the inhabitants of Syria, including Hezekiah, who accompanied Ptolemy. It may be supposed that Ptolemy's rule, which lasted five years (320-315) became popular among the population, including the Jews, whereas Antigonus was a hard man and a stern ruler and certainly gained small sympathy for himself or for his government. It may therefore have occurred that at the beginning of 311, when Ptolemy was compelled to leave Palestine, those of the Jewish leaders accompanied him who were known for their sympathy for Ptolemy and feared Antigonus' vengeance: the High Priest Hezekiah, apparently, was at their head.

Jerusalem again passed under Antigonus' rule, this time for a long period of about a decade. We do not know whether during this time the Jews managed to form ties of friendship with Antigonus; at all events, in 302, important changes again occurred in the political world, and the Jews had to decide whether it would be well for them to support Antigonus (who was then in Asia Minor preparing for the decisive encounter with his enemies), or whether it would be more worthwhile again to associate themselves with Ptolemy. As usual in such instances, there were certainly two opposing parties in Jerusalem, one supporting Antigonus and the other Ptolemy, and Agatharchides' story excellently suits this unstable political situation. According to this account (in Josephus' paraphrase) Ptolemy took advantage, not only of the Jews' abstention from fighting on the Sabbath, but employed a ruse; he feigned friendship and made his way into the city on the pretext of wishing to offer a sacrifice (naturally, to the God of Israel).

But if the Sabbath repose explains why the Jews did not resist the king when he was already within the city, it does not in the least explain why they allowed Ptolemy to enter the city at all or why they believed his false declarations. Clearly he had friends within the city, who hastened to open the gates for him, so that after the Sabbath was over, the Jews found Jerusalem in the King of Egypt's hands, which, it seems, was not to the liking of many of the population. Things came to a collision, and Ptolemy showed a strong hand, wrought havoc among his opponents, treated the city sternly, took captives, and sent them to Egypt. Some time later he was again forced to evacuate the country, and then "destroyed" the city, in other words, breached its walls, in order that it should not serve Antigonus as a fortress. When he entered the country again for the fourth and last time he probably found the city walls still breached and had no difficulty in bringing both it and the whole of Judaea under his control. These are more or less the lines along which I would reconstruct the course of events in harmony with the meager information preserved in various writings: but clearly there is no absolute certainty in the matter, and other reconstructions are equally possible.

The internal life of the Jews during this primeval period of Hellenism in Palestine is described by Hecataeus of Abdera, whom we have already mentioned twice in connection with individual events of the epoch.[49] We shall dwell entirely on the political features of the very substantial description devoted by Hecataeus to the Jews.[50] Hecataeus had heard nothing whatsoever of the rule of kings in Israel; he thought that it was Moses who had transmitted justice and the supervision of laws and customs to the priests: "Therefore a king has never ruled over the Jews, but the people's representation (τοῦ πλήθους προστασία) is given to that priest who excels over the others in his understanding and lofty qualities. Him they call the High Priest" (Diod. XL, 3, 5). This sentence proves very clearly that in Hecataeus' time the High Priest was the central personality in Judaea and that the historic process of the transfer of the traditional authority from the king to the High Priest, which began in the time of Zerubbabel ben Shealtiel of royal descent, and of Joshua ben Jehozadak the High Priest, had ended with the decisive victory of the High Priest.[51]

Not only, however, had Hecataeus heard nothing of the kings of Israel, but he did not know of the satraps either. The *prostasia*, or people's representation, was vested, according to him, in the High Priest. We shall see below that in the third century, under Ptolemaic rule, the *prostasia* was a permanent position, generally in the hands of the High Priest, its task being to represent the people before the sovereign. There is every reason to assume that Hecataeus is using this term in the same sense, that is, in his time the post of "vice-satrap" or "assistant satrap," which had existed under Persian rule[52] as intermediary between the king and the local population, was no longer in existence. The political reality of the period of the Diadochi confirms this supposition. We do not hear from any source of the existence of the post of "assistant satrap" as the permanent governor of a given country, and with reason, since the growing power of the satrap-in-chief was not to the advantage of the independent positions of the small satraps. The results of this historical process were very important for Judaea. She ceased to be subordinated to a special official placed over her, and the only mediator between her and the king was now the High Priest. Judaea's autonomy, which had been purely cultural and intellectual in the Persian period, made in the early Hellenistic epoch the first steps towards political independence, and the High Priest at the head of the people assumed the aspect of a petty monarch.

The Ptolemies ruled Palestine for a hundred years. Politically these were years of peace and quiet. Apart from the destruction of Samaria by Demetrius in 296, we hear of no military or political event (prior to 219) which involved the country directly. The wars between the Ptolemies and the Seleucids, which continued at intervals from 275 to 240, approximately, were waged at various places in the great empire and did not penetrate the interior of the country. It is indeed difficult to express this opinion with complete confidence, since we know scarcely anything whatever of these hundred years; mutilated fragments of information preserved in Josephus and in Alexandrian literature do not provide sufficient material for an account of the period, and what they do provide is very suspect in the eyes of the modern scholar. Thus, for example, Josephus says (*C. Ap.* II, 48) of Ptolemy III Euergetes, that he visited the Temple at Jerusalem to render thanks to

God for his victory in the war against the Seleucids, and Josephus explains explicitly why he poured out his heart to the God of Israel and not to the gods of Egypt. Naturally such statements have to be treated with the utmost caution. Nor does what Josephus relates of Joseph son of Tobiah and his son Hyrcanus always bear scientific criticism (see below, ch. 3).

But luckily we now have another source at hand, whose historical trustworthiness is beyond doubt, namely, the Zenon papyri, part of which concerns the affairs of Palestine in the period of Ptolemy II Philadelphus. This Zenon, whose extensive archives were discovered in Egypt in 1915 in the territory of the ancient village of Philadelpheia in the Fayûm, was one of the most diligent and dexterous officials of Philadelphus' time. He stood under the orders of the *dioiketes* (finance minister) Apollonius, himself a man of great energy and one of the best administrators of Ptolemaic Egypt. Zenon's chief task involved the management of Apollonius' large estate near Philadelpheia in the Fayûm; but prior to obtaining it, he had discharged several missions on behalf of Apollonius, and among them in the year 259 had visited Palestine and stayed there a whole year. He brought back with him from this journey various documents and letters which were preserved among his records; and after his return to Egypt maintained touch with Palestine for some time and kept the various letters that arrived from there for Apollonius and his officials. The total number of papyri concerning Palestine is very small compared with the immense number belonging to the Zenon archives as a whole— in all, some forty notes, accounts, letters and memoranda out of a grand total of approximately 1200. Nevertheless, their value for the historical study of Palestine in the third century is very great, as this period—from 300 to 220 or thereabouts—is otherwise completely lacking in sources.[53]

In addition to the Zenon papyri we now have another important papyrus published in 1936 from the great collection of papyri at Vienna; it contains two orders of King Ptolemy Philadelphus: one for the registration of flocks and herds in Ptolemaic Syria, the other settling the question of slaves (or, more correctly, of free men and women who had been unlawfully enslaved) in the same country. On several points this Vienna papyrus fills out our information derived from the Zenon papyri.[54]

Southern Syria, when it was in the hands of the Ptolemies, was known in the official language of the Egyptian offices as "Syria and Phoenicia," and popularly simply as "Syria."[55] The Zenon papyri enable us to determine the frontiers of the country, if not with strict precision, at least on general lines. Three points mentioned in the Zenon archives fix the northern frontier between Ptolemaic and Seleucid Syria; these are the city of Tripolis (*PSI* 495); the Plain of Masyas, that is, the valley between the Lebanon and the Anti-Lebanon (*PCZ* 59093); and Damascus (*PCZ* 59006). The boundary itself is not precisely known. According to Strabo (XVI, 756), Arethusa was the frontier between Seleucid and Phoenician Syria in the Roman period. This town stood several kilometers north of Tripolis; possibly therefore the frontier passed by here in the Hellenistic period also. From Arethusa it crossed obliquely in a southeasterly direction to Baalbek, thence to Damascus, and on to the desert.[56]

        As regards the eastern frontier, there is no doubt that the whole of Transjordan as far as the desert was in Ptolemaic hands. The papyri of Zenon refer to Ḥauran (*PSI* 406; *PCZ* 59008), Ammon (*C. P. Jud.* 1) and to the Nabataeans (*PSI* 406), that is, to all the central and southern part of Transjordan; but it is clear, if the Ptolemies held Damascus on the one side and Ḥauran on the other, that they also ruled Trachonitis and Batanea.[57] Concerning the administrative divisions, we learn from the Vienna papyrus that the country was divided into hyparchies; the smallest administrative unit was the village, as in Egypt.[58] The royal concern for the Syrian province was expressed in the publication of several orders, regulations, statutes and rescripts which are all referred to in the Vienna papyrus, hence it is clear that the government at Alexandria paid special attention to the welfare and economic development of Syria.[59]

        We do not know whether Ptolemaic Syria was organized as a proper "province," to use the term in its Roman sense—that is, whether it was under a special governor and lived under laws peculiar to itself, for such a governor is not mentioned in our sources. According to the account in the Zenon papyri, the contacts between Alexandria and Palestine were so lively and direct that the post of a governor as intermediary seems to have been unnecessary.[60] The great interest shown by Apollonius in the Syrian countries makes one think that Ptolemaic Syria was under the special supervision of the *dioiketes* at Alexandria. On the other hand, there was also a special *dioiketes* in Syria, as we learn from the Vienna papyrus, and he was perhaps the most important official in the country. In every hyparchy there resided an *oikonomos*, a special official in charge of economic life; moreover, we hear of a very large number of officials, high and low, who attended chiefly to matters of administration and economy.[61]

We can judge the number of government officials in Palestine from one of the Zenon papyri, which contains drafts of five letters sent by Zenon to the officials of Marissa in Idumaea. In all five Zenon refers to the same matter: when he was in Marissa he had purchased young slaves who had escaped from him and returned to their former masters. The masters now demand 500 drachmae compensation for the return of the slaves to Zenon, who therefore applies to the various officials at Marissa requesting them to aid his emissary to recover them. Two of the letters are very politely written, being sent evidently to the head of the civil administration and to the city police chief respectively. In two more of the letters Zenon requests the officials (whom he apparently knew personally) to use their good offices with other officials not to impose "liturgical" labor on his emissary as this would interfere with his search for the slaves.[62]

We have here, therefore, a miniature of the Egyptian officialdom, and it may be legitimate to suppose that they had transferred to Palestine the whole Egyptian bureaucracy with all the defects which we know so well from the papyri of that country. This had brought not only the defects, however; we also detect among the Ptolemaic officials of Palestine the great diligence of the Ptolemaic government offices, the same enforcement of the law of the state in the remotest corners, the same strict official surveillance over the life of the private individual. Thus, for example, the Vienna papyrus mentions certain dates by which people concerned must fulfill government demands, the fines imposed on offenders, annual registrations of property (in one case—of sheep and cattle), and the like.[63] Anyone who is acquainted with the elements of the Ptolemaic administration of Egypt will have no difficulty in recognizing the same method and the same practices now transferred almost without change to the province of Syria.[64]

A special position was held in Syria by the agents of the finance minister Apollonius. They did not belong to the regular government officialdom, but acted as special emissaries of Apollonius and called themselves "the people of Apollonius the *Dioiketes*."[65] These agents were scattered over the whole country and were especially active in the coastal cities of Gaza, Jaffa, Acco, Sidon and Beirut. There they supervised the trade in grain and olive oil, despatched ships laden with merchandise to Pelusium, and also had to carry out all the private orders of the minister of finance, buying slaves for him and sending him "gifts." Possibly not all Apollonius' agents did their duty honestly and legally; nevertheless, it cannot be denied that their activity was extensive and productive, if judged from the point of view of the Egyptian authority: with their help was organized the commercial connection between the two countries so profitable to the Alexandrian government.

There are grounds for thinking that the year 259, the year in which Zenon visited Palestine, was that in which Apollonius decided to turn his attention to the Syrian countries in particular: he sent a large group of his agents (perhaps under Zenon's management) to tour the country, to examine its economic situation and to set up a liaison between it and Egypt. These agents made numerous journeys throughout the country and were joined both by resident Greeks and by natives, till the group became a caravan of some hundred or more people which traversed the whole land of Palestine, including Transjordan, creating contacts with the inhabitants in every locality. In subsequent years we find many of Apollonius' agents who had been members of this large convoy, permanently settled in the country's large towns, such as Jaffa, or carrying on the affairs of Apollonius' estate at Bet-Anat and at other places. The long lists of the travelers' names preserved in Zenon's archives are reliable evidence of the activity of Apollonius in the year 259.[66]

The unstable equilibrium of Palestine's political situation faced the Egyptian kings with the grave problem of the country's defense; it should not be forgotten that from a military point of view southern Syria served as the first line of defense to Egypt itself; from the Zenon papyri we learn the methods employed by the Ptolemies to attain this object, namely, the founding of *cleruchies* and the stationing of garrisons in the Syrian cities. In one of the papyri (*PSI* 495) troops are referred to at Tripolis, evidently the Ptolemaic garrison protecting the northern frontier of Ptolemaic Syria. The mobile group of Apollonius' agents was joined by several high-ranking officers whose military titles evidence that they belonged to the garrisons of fortresses.[67] The Vienna papyrus speaks of "the soldiers and other settlers in Syria and Phoenicia" who had taken wives from among the local women;[68] these mixed marriages show that the king's reference was not to troops who were visiting the country for a short time, but to garrison troops who were quartered in Syria permanently.

The most interesting information preserved by the Zenon papyri concerns the *cleruchy* of the Ptolemaic troops in Transjordan. Papyrus *C. P. Jud.* 1 (*PCZ* 59003) contains a deed of sale passing between a Greek, a native of Cnidos in Caria, and Zenon; the Greek describes himself as "one of Tobiah's people," and the name of the place where the deed has been drawn up is "the citadel of the Land of the Ammonites." The contract is signed by six witnesses, two of them "*cleruchs* of the cavalry of Tobiah," and four members of Zenon's retinue ("of the people of Apollonius the *Dioiketes*"). One other person signed the deed as guarantor; he too was one of Tobiah's *cleruchs*. This papyrus is evidence that the Ptolemies had also transferred to Palestine their practice of distributing land-holdings to their troops and of settling them in *cleruchies* (see above, p. 20). The aim of the founding of the *cleruchy* in Transjordan was the defense of the country against the attacks of Bedouin from the desert; the citadel mentioned in the papyrus was the center of the *cleruchy*, and the troops who had settled there belonged in part to the cavalry and in part to the infantry.[69]

One detail in the above papyrus demands special emphasis: at the head of the *cleruchy* stands not a Greek or Macedonian officer, but a local native prince, Tobiah. This man is mentioned in several other papyri: he writes letters to Apollonius and to King Ptolemy Philadelphus himself and sends them gifts—to the king, rare animals (perhaps for the zoological garden of Philadelphus at Alexandria) and to Apollonius, four young slaves accompanied by a eunuch (*C. P. Jud.* 4-5). In one of the papyri Tobiah's residence (apparently the above-mentioned *cleruchy*, including the citadel) is described as "Tobiah's land"; this name evidences that Tobiah was a wealthy "Sheikh" known throughout the region.[70] It is not difficult to discover his origin: he was without doubt one of the descendants of "Tobiah the Ammonite slave" mentioned several times in Nehemiah as one of the opponents of the Jewish national policy of Nehemiah; and his genealogy can be scrutinized in even more ancient times.[71] Nor is there any doubt but that this Tobiah was the father of Joseph son of Tobiah, the famous tax-gatherer, who played such an important role in Jewish society in the third century (see below, ch. 3).

We therefore have before us a unique political phenomenon: the appointment of a local "sheikh," a man of great influence among the local population, to a high rank in the Ptolemaic army. The Ptolemies in Egypt were careful not to assign high posts to native Egyptians, and till the middle of the second century we do not find Egyptians in key positions in the Ptolemaic army. But in Palestine the Ptolemies had to take account of local conditions; their rule of the country could not be placed on a firm footing without gaining the sympathies of people of influence there. It was very important in the eyes of the Egyptian government to win to its side powerful princes such as Tobiah and to make them its allies in case of war against the kings of Syria. Tobiah, in fact, did not disappoint the hopes reposed in him by the kings of Egypt: his loyalty to the Ptolemies was transmitted to his son Joseph, who throughout his life kept a careful eye on Jewish loyalty to the Ptolemies.[72]

Tobiah was not the only powerful person with whom the Ptolemies had to reckon; the papyri of Zenon mention several other people in Syria who, although they held no official positions, were also men of independent standing. One was Jeddous, evidently a Jew, who owed Zenon a certain sum of money but had not paid the debt at the appointed time; and when the government officials appeared at the village with Zenon's representative to collect the debt or to impound Jeddous' property, the latter paid no heed to the officials' demands "but raised his hand against them and drove them out of the village" (*C. P. Jud.* 6 = *PCZ* 59018). Jeddous' behavior astounds us by its effrontery; incidents of this sort would hardly have been possible in an Egyptian village. If Jeddous dared to expel the officials from the village, it must be supposed that he found people to aid him, and probably the whole village was on his land.

We have here once again a rich "sheikh" who is not afraid of the royal officials and will not permit them to do as they like with his home. Another instance of powerful individuals is provided by *PCZ* 59015 *verso*, to which we have already referred: these are two brothers of Idumaea, Zaidel and Colochoutos, from whom Zenon had purchased young slaves. He had bought them ἐκ τῶν Ζαιδήλου—

65

"from among Zaidel's people"—an indication that Zaidel had numerous other slaves. He was evidently a wealthy man, as was also his brother. Their strength and influence is shown by the fact that Zenon has to write five letters to recover from them the slaves whom he has purchased. The size of the compensation is also somewhat unexpected: for 100 drachmae two young servant-girls could be purchased (see below, n. 88). We get the impression that Zaidel and his brother were taking advantage of the opportunity (the escape of the slaves back to them) again to demand of Zenon part of the money which he had already paid them. Such behavior is additional evidence of the independent standing of the local sheikhs; they had scant respect for the high Egyptian official, and for his master the finance minister, for whom the slaves had been purchased.

The economic and social basis of the wealthy sheikhs' independence is to be seen in their control of the soil. We have again before us a social phenomenon alien to Ptolemaic Egypt, but whose reality in Syria is well attested. The example of Tobiah informs us that the influential people in Syria were the members of ancient aristocratic families who were settled on land which had been their permanent and long-standing possession. It might not have been hard for the king to confiscate these lands; but then he would have raised against him the whole local aristocracy, and this would have cost him dear in the event of war. For these reasons the Ptolemaic monarch was prepared to make several concessions on the question of the proprietorship of the soil.

In Egypt, as we have seen above (p. 13), the whole land belonged theoretically to the king. This principle was very hard to realize in Syria, not merely because of the land of the wealthy sheikhs, but also because the coast had been studded since ancient times with cities (those of the Phoenicians and Philistians) which now demanded recognition as "Greek" cities, that is, as urban communities organized on the model of Greek *poleis*. Every *polis*, as is well known, controlled the land of the villages around it, and this was also the case in Palestine (see the next chapter). The king therefore was forced to recognize the authority of the towns over their territory —again a phenomenon foreign to the spirit of the bureaucratic administration of Ptolemaic Egypt. We do not know what was the fate of the land belonging to the ancient temples, but there is every ground for the assumption that here too the king confirmed the existing situation and did not attempt to lay hands on the sacred lands or the income enjoyed by the priests.

On the other hand, we find hints in the Zenon papyri of the new situation created in Syria by the Ptolemaic conquest. According to the political theory of the Hellenistic period, a conquered country belonged to the conqueror as his private property, and therefore theoretically the whole land of southern Syria belonged to Ptolemy. And if for political reasons the king conceded his control of the soil to the rich landlords, the cities and the priests, there is no proof that he gave up all the areas of the conquered territory. From several papyri we discover that Apollonius was possessor of an estate at Bet Anat where existed a mixed farm consisting of a vineyard and cornfields.[73] One of Apollonius' agents was in charge of this estate, but beside him we find there another official, referred to in the papyrus as a "village lessee," by which is apparently meant a man who had leased the collection of taxes from the village in question. According to the Vienna papyrus, there were in Syria special officials engaged in leasing the villages, that is, in collecting their taxes on behalf of the royal treasury;[74] hence it must be supposed that the village of Bet Anat was under the constant supervision of the treasury officials.

If we ask in what manner had Apollonius acquired his estate at Bet Anat, the simplest answer is that he had received the land as a gift from the king, since his large estate in the Fayûm was likewise a gift from the king. These lands, according to the practice in Hellenistic Egypt, were not the private property of the estate-owner, and the king reserved the right to confiscate them any time he wished (see above, p. 13). From this we learn that certain parts of Palestine (perhaps very extensive tracts, to judge from the position in Egypt) were in the king's hands as "royal land" and that the peasants settled on them were "royal peasants," in other words, they were small tenants who paid their dues to the "village lessee" appointed by the king to collect its taxes. In this respect the Macedonian kings appeared in Palestine—as everywhere else—as successors of the Persian sovereigns. The "royal lands," previously in the possession of the latter, now passed by inheritance to the Macedonian kings. Many references inform us of the Persian royal estates in Syria, especially of the *pardessim,* that is, timber plantations, orchards, and vineyards.[75] It may therefore be assumed that Apollonius' estate at Bet Anat also constituted a direct continuation of such a Persian royal *pardes;* its peasants had merely changed masters.[76]

The Zenon papyri have yielded us rich material also on the question of trade between

Syria and Egypt. Two types of people participated in this trade: government officials (including Apollonius' agents) and merchants. The latter's function was not very important. Ptolemaic "totalitarianism" did not recognize free trade any more than it recognized free economic life as a whole, and private initiative stood permanently under the strict supervision of the government. We notice this policy especially in the corn and olive oil trade. Two papyri, which contain the same version of a letter from Apollonius to his agents in Palestine, evidence that the import of Syrian wheat to Egypt was not in private hands but was an organized affair and a government enterprise: Apollonius' agents supervised the traffic and received payments in money from the corn-merchants, the bills of sale together with the names of the traders and the sums paid by them being sent to Alexandria to the officers of the minister of finance.[77]

A similar picture emerges concerning the import of olive oil. Special government officials also supervised the trade in perfumes and incense.[78] The traffic itself did not involve much danger, since the voyage from Pelusium (the Egyptian harbor nearest to the frontier of Syria) to Gaza hardly lasted more than two days, and for trade it was possible to use small craft built for the Nile traffic.[79] Among the coastal towns of Palestine and Phoenicia, Gaza, Tyre and Acco were the most important harbors of export.[80] It is worth mentioning that the papyri of Zenon describe only the export trade from Syria to Egypt and not the import trade from Egypt to Syria, although Ptolemaic Egypt was known throughout the world as an exporting country.[81] The explanation of this peculiar phenomenon is to be sought in the special character of the Zenon papyri: they reflect the interests of the minister of finance, who derived direct advantage from the consignment of Syrian wares to his own private house and estate in Egypt.

Among the various exports from Syria to Egypt slaves especially should be mentioned. The slave trade was evidently freer than any other; export of slaves from Egypt was prohibited, but not their import into the country, and government control was not particularly burdensome.[82] We encounter Syrian slaves in Egypt with frequency; it was worth a merchant's while to buy them in Syria and sell them in Egypt, since the number of slaves in the latter country was not large, while their price in Syria was very low.[83] Part of those bought in Syria by Zenon and Apollonius' other agents were destined not for hard labor in the fields but for the lighter tasks of household slavery; the girls were perhaps destined for work in Apollonius' weaving mill in one of the villages of the Fayûm.[84] Hence most of the slaves purchased by his agents were of very tender age, nor did those sent by Tobiah as a gift to the finance minister include any over the age of ten.

A chapter for itself was the trade in *paidiskai,* in other words, in young serving maids. One memorandum sent to Zenon by a wagoner (*PSI* 406) tells of two boys (one also a wagoner, the other possibly) who devoted themselves seriously to this business; the memorandum mentions five girls who had fallen into their hands. They were dragging their living merchandise from one end of the country to the other, from Ammon to Acco and from Palestine to Hauran. One of the girls found her home with a "frontier guard" at Pegai, and, though we do not know for certain which frontier passed this place, all frontiers are points where traders gather, pay customs duties, or prepare for some reason or other to cross, and we may surmise that the "frontier guard" was also the owner of an inn in which the girl was to earn her livelihood.[85] Another girl is referred to in a memorandum as a "priestess"; the seller had brought her to Jaffa for the fourth time, and she evidently performed the duty of a sacred prostitute in one of the temples of Ashtoret-Aphrodite.[86] From this papyrus it is clear that Syria offered a broad field for the activities of unscrupulous people from Egypt, and also perhaps of people locally born, who took no thought of morality or of any other law in the prosecution of their infamous activities, and doubtless also sometimes infringed the rights of free people. Manhunting was apparently so widespread in Syria that King Philadelphus found it necessary to intervene and by a special order prohibit attempts on anybody's part to enslave free men and women among the population of the country; this order has been preserved in the Vienna papyrus.[87]

Second in order of importance may be mentioned the trade in foodstuffs, especially in grain. Even before the discovery of the Zenon papyri, scholars knew that the Egyptian population in the Hellenistic and Roman periods used a special variety of wheat, called "Syrian wheat." The reason for its importation was not easy to discover; Egypt herself was a land of abundant corn and served as granary to other countries of the Mediterranean basin. In times of drought, indeed, wheat was imported from Syria and other countries, but exceptional instances could not lead to the spread of Syrian wheat in Egypt or to experiments to acclimatize it there. The papyri of Zenon show that Syrian wheat was common in Egypt as early as the period of Ptolemy Philadelphus, its purchase in Syria and its importation into Egypt being organized by officials of the government and by the minister of finance, and the reason was evidently that Syrian wheat ripened in a shorter time than the other sorts of wheat in Egypt.[88]

The importation of olive oil from Syria to Egypt is mentioned more than once in the papyri.[89] We hear nothing whatever about the importation of wine, but the fact that Apollonius owned a vineyard at Bet Anat and that one of his agents sent him "Syrian wine" from there (*PSI* 594) bears evidence that wine from Palestine was common in Egypt, and it is merely chance that it finds no explicit mention in our sources.[90] Other foodstuffs, such as smoked fish, cheese, meat, dried figs, fruit, honey, dates, etc., are referred to among the imports from Syria to Egypt (*PCZ* 59012-14). But the Syrians sent to Egypt not only their own home-produce; the land acted as a transit-station for trade with more distant countries, such as Greece, Asia Minor, and the Aegean Islands. The Zenon papyri mention the importation of honey, wine, cheese and nuts from Greece and the Aegean Islands into Egypt, and a curious "merchant" is described who visited several cities of Asia Minor and Syria (Miletus, Kaunus, Halicarnassus, Gaza, Rabbat-Ammon and Acco) specializing in the purchase of cushions, blankets, mattresses, sheets, and such-like; all this queer "merchandise" ultimately reached the "merchant's" wife in Alexandria (*PSI* 616). Southern Syria, especially Gaza, also acted as a very important intermediate station of the perfume between south Arabia and Egypt.[91]

The papyri have preserved slight but valuable information on the fusion of the western and oriental populations and on the initial process of the Hellenization of the people of the country. The army was the chief melting-pot. The Vienna papyrus (line 49ff.) mentions "the soldiers and the other settlers in Syria and Phoenicia who have married native women," and the fact that the king saw need to allude to these marriages specifically evidences that they were a regular occurrence in the country. *C. P. Jud.* 1 tells of the composition of the *cleruchy* of Tobiah in Ammon: of four men whose nationality is known, one is a Greek from Cnidos (Asia Minor), one a Macedonian, and two are Persians, and since the name of the father of one of the "Persians" is Ḥananyah, it is clear that he is a Jew.[92] The Ptolemaic *cleruchy* in Transjordan, then, was

composed of Greeks, Macedonians and Jews, a make-up characteristic of the process of international fusion in the Hellenistic
period. A second source of contact between the local population
and the Greeks were the groups of Ptolemaic officials who visited
the country in large numbers and settled in various places in the
Syrian province. Among the members of the large caravan of
Apollonius' agents mentioned above, we find several names of
local personnel who accompanied it in the various capacities of
mule drivers, wagoners, servants, and so on.

                     This proximity of the local
people to the Greeks no doubt induced the first steps toward the
superficial external Hellenization of some of the local population.
From the fragmentary *PCZ* 59009 we learn that the natives had
already begun to adopt Greek names.[93] Most interesting from
this point of view is Tobiah's letter to Apollonius (*C. P. Jud.* 4):
in the formula of greeting at its beginning we encounter the
usual Greek expression πολλὴ χάρις τοῖς Θεοῖς, "many thanks to the
gods." This plural is surprising in a letter of a Jew. It is written,
indeed, not in Tobiah's own hand, but by his secretary, who was
certainly a Greek; nevertheless it is hard to assume that a strict
Jew would have permitted such a letter to be sent from his own
home signed with his own name. This small detail sheds light on
the intellectual atmosphere prevailing in Tobiah's home where
Joseph was brought up: Tobiah was too devoted to his high
protectors in Egypt not to acquire something of the external rind
of Hellenism. Hellenization begins with the "contamination" of
the Tobiad family by things of no importance, such as pagan
formulae in correspondence, probably with the changing of
names, the learning of Greek, and the like, and leads in the third
generation (the sons of Joseph) to a spurning of tradition and
an attempt to introduce a thoroughgoing Hellenistic reform.

                     We may summarize the in-
formation which we have derived from the papyri of Zenon and
from the orders of Ptolemy Philadelphus preserved in the Vienna
papyrus. Ptolemaic policy in Palestine was conducted in two
contradictory directions. On the one hand, the Ptolemies saw
that it was impossible to rule the country according to the principles of complete absolutism prevalent in Egypt. Instead of the
monotonous uniformity of a peasant population inured to a life
of servitude—a picture characteristic of Ptolemaic Egypt—they
found in Syria numerous peoples and tribes each holding to an
ancestral tradition (sometimes a tradition both rich and ancient)
and aspiring to an independent development. The wealthy

HELLENISTIC CIVILIZATION AND THE JEWS

"sheikhs" performed an important function in the lives of these peoples and were not prepared to give it up. The cities along the coast, whose livelihood was commerce, demanded municipal autonomy within certain limits. These aspirations to liberty and independence could be suppressed, but in case of war the peoples subject to such suppression could easily go over to the enemy's side. The Ptolemies decided to choose the path of concession. They assisted the development of independent city-life, left the sheikhs their lands and even permitted some of them to discharge a political function in the country. This statesmanship approximated in the main to the political method of the Seleucids in Asia, which arose from much the same cause.

However, the Ptolemies did not follow this road to its conclusion. Palestine was too near Egypt not to be infected by the spirit of servitude that prevailed there. From an administrative point of view "Syria and Phoenicia" were only part of Egypt, like the Fayûm or any other Egyptian district, and clearly it would have been difficult to conduct part of the state according to special laws mainly antagonistic to the general spirit of the country's regime. For this reason the effective policy of the Ptolemies in Palestine approximated to the normal method of subjection. A network of officials was spread over the whole Syrian province; the ownership of the lands, indeed, remained in possession of the local people or passed to the Greek cities, but alongside of them stretched the "royal lands" which perhaps occupied the lion's share of the country's area, and on them dwelt the small tenants whose duty it was to pay taxes to their new masters and to hold their tongues. Trade was in government hands and private enterprise stood under the constant supervision of the officials; it is not to be thought, therefore, that the population derived much advantage from the trade with Egypt. Thus did reality efface the fine principles of liberty and autonomy. The conditions of Syria did not permit the kings to base their power there on enslavement, and the political reality of Egypt could not accord with a government based on liberty. Ptolemaic statesmanship in Palestine was essentially equivocal.

No less equivocal was the reaction of the local population. Polybius evidences that the inhabitants of Syria were devoted to the Ptolemaic government (V, 86, 10), but the same writer himself says (ib. 86, 9) that there was no country whose inhabitants changed their political sympathies so easily as those of Syria. The aspirations to liberty

72

and autonomy, whose development was assisted by Ptolemaic policy, ultimately turned against the Ptolemies themselves, as this policy was not sufficiently consistent to attract the population for many generations. It may be said, therefore, that the Ptolemies prepared the soil for the great national movements which arose in the second century and caused the destruction of Hellenism in Palestine. Naturally the Ptolemies are not to be accused of an anti-Hellenistic policy; on the contrary, in the following chapter we shall see that they set up many Greek cities in Syria and so gave an enormous impulse to the development of Hellenism in the country. It is also to be remarked that Tobiah stood under the special patronage of the Ptolemaic government, and his family subsequently sponsored a strong Hellenistic movement. Yet despite all this, the government which could permit the village sheikh Jeddous to expel its officials from the village was unwittingly assisting the development of a historical process which in course of time transformed Jeddous into Judah the Maccabee.

In 219 the period of peace came to an end. Antiochus III, a young and energetic king, again raised the question of the sovereignty of Coele-Syria. As early as 221 he had attempted to invade Palestine, but had encountered two strong fortresses in the Lebanon valley and had had to give up his design (Polyb. V, 45-6). Within two years he renewed the war, and thanks to the treason of the Egyptian generals easily captured the towns of Tyre and Acco, and laid siege to Dor. The Egyptians, who were not ready for the war, sought pretexts for delaying Antiochus' attack in order to gain time to organize the defense. They proposed to Antiochus to open diplomatic negotiations, and Antiochus consented. We have referred above (p. 54) to the complaints and demands of both sides. The negotiations led to no positive result, and in 218 Antiochus renewed his offensive; he passed down the Phoenician coast and invaded Upper Galilee. The cities of Philoteria (Bet Yeraḥ on the shore of Lake Kinneret) and Scythopolis (Bet Shean) fell into his hands without resistance, and he took the strong fortress on the summit of Mount Tabor by cunning. Antiochus rejoiced to find himself ruler and commander of this rich and grain-fertile land, and continued his offensive. The city of Pella and others in its proximity were easily taken; he crossed the Jordan and was readily received by the Arab inhabitants. The fortresses of Abila, Gadara and Rabbat-Ammon barred his way, but he captured them and also sent a small force to get possession of Samaria. He returned to winter at Ptolemais (Polyb. V, 70-1).

Meanwhile Ptolemy IV Philopator had gathered a huge army and entered Palestine; Antiochus hastened to meet him; and the two met at Raphia, in the south of the country (217). The battle was one of the hardest fought of the Hellenistic period; Antiochus was decisively defeated and had to abandon the field.[94] All his opponents in Asia Minor and the Orient now reared their heads. In order to stand up to the foes that surrounded him, Antiochus hastened to sign a peace with Ptolemy and to restore to him everything he had won in Coele-Syria during the war. Ptolemy, accompanied by his wife Arsinoë, visited the towns of Palestine and spent some three weeks in the country, where the inhabitants greeted him with ovations of goodwill. Polybius (V, 86,10) testifies that the reason was not only their natural striving to curry favor with the ruler, but genuine devotion to the Ptolemaic rule of the country.

Did Ptolemy Philopator visit Jerusalem during his tour of Syria? Polybius says nothing about any such visit, and a Graeco-Egyptian inscription found in 1924, whose contents are devoted to the events of the year 217, also maintains silence on the question that interests us.[95] On the other hand, the Jewish book written in Greek, known as the *Third Book of Maccabees*, contains a detailed narrative of Philopator's visit to Jerusalem; but to our regret the book is not to be depended on, as it is simply fiction. It opens, indeed, with an account of the battle of Raphia, and this account is similar in its basic lines to that of Polybius;[96] but this is merely a historical introduction to a story composed on the model of the historical romances of the Hellenistic period. According to the author of *III Maccabees*, Ptolemy Philopator sought to break into the Holy of Holies, and his intention awoke great perplexity in the city, so that the High Priest prayed to God to defend the sanctity of the place. And a miracle occurred: God dashed the proud king to the ground, paralyzed in all his limbs; his friends bore him from the Temple and he left the city with angry threats. There is no need to seek a historical nucleus in this tale, which was deliberately composed with the intention of demonstrating how immeasurably the power of the God of Israel exceeded that of mortal kings.[97]

From the literary point of view there is no doubt that the story is influenced by the parallel description in II Maccabees, where Heliodorus, envoy of the

Syrian king, Seleucus IV Philopator, plays the part of Ptolemy. Not only the same order of events but even the same words and expressions are found in both places.[98] The fact of Ptolemy Philopator's visit to Jerusalem, nevertheless, is decidedly within the bounds of possibility, and there are no grounds for assuming that the king did not do in relation to the Jews what he did everywhere else. Jerusalem was quite well known as a religious center of importance, and if Philopator visited the city, he certainly did there what every Greek king would have done in his place, namely, sacrificed to the local god and behaved favorably toward the priests. If then the author of *III Maccabees* selected Philopator in order to describe a thorough anti-Semite, we have to seek the reason, not in historical events connected with Palestine, but in the general motive of the book, which was written in Egypt and was influenced by events connected with that country.[99]

Antiochus evacuated Coele-Syria, but his defeat did not cause him to despair; he waited at a distance for an opportune moment to test his powers afresh. Events in Egypt prepared the ground for him. In 204 Ptolemy IV Philopator died and Ptolemy V Epiphanes, a child of five, ascended the throne.[100] The power passed to the king's guardians, and when their rule was unsuccessful, there began a growing popular ferment among the Egyptians, especially among the citizens of Alexandria. Antiochus exploited these disturbances to carry out his designs; in 201 he invaded Coele-Syria, and obtained possession of the whole country without much difficulty, only Gaza maintaining its alliance with the Ptolemies and closing its gates before him (Polyb. XVI, 40, 1ff.; *ib.* XVIII, 2).

Of the happenings of the subsequent years our sources have preserved only fragmentary information which does not add up to a complete picture. So far as we can judge, the Ptolemaic general Scopas succeeded in reconquering the whole of Palestine in 200, but the encounter with Antiochus in the north of the country, near Panion, ended in his decisive defeat. Scopas fled with the remnants of his army and was besieged in Sidon; Ptolemy's attempt to bring aid to him was unsuccessful and the city was captured by Antiochus. Following this, in the years 199-8, Antiochus captured all the fortified cities of Coele-Syria, and the Egyptians evacuated the country, this time for good, so that it passed decisively under the rule of the Seleucids.[101]

Just as we do not know the details of the events during the conquest of the country as a whole, so we are without details on the individual fate of Judaea and Jerusalem. The capture of Jerusalem by Antiochus in 201 was carried out, apparently, without resistance on the part of the Jews.[102] The succeeding year, during the winter months, the city was taken by Scopas, on the evidence of Polybius (in Jos. *Ant.* XII, 135), and that author again witnesses (*ib.* 136) that Jerusalem passed into Antiochus' hands after the victory of Panion, when he had overrun Batanea, Samaria, Abila and Gadara. From this brief information it is impossible to decide what the orientation of the Jews was in these stormy years, or if they had any permanent orientation at all. On this question other sources come to our aid, in part contemporary (Antiochus' letter to Ptolemy, his official, to be treated in detail later), in part late (Jerome's commentary on the Book of Daniel). Jerome states one general fact, that "when Antiochus the Great and Ptolemy's generals were at grips, the land of Judah was drawn in two opposite directions, some supporting Antiochus and some Ptolemy."[103] This statement, even if it is only the result of general considerations, without particular support in the sources, is precisely to the point, for this is the fate of a small country situated between two great powers, that it leans now in one direction, now in the other.

Further material is supplied by Jerome, when he says in his account of the conquest of Judaea by Scopas and his retreat to Egypt, that "he took with him the heads of Ptolemy's party."[104] This information is not as accurate as it might be: Judaea was conquered by Scopas before the battle of Panion, that is, in the year 200, while his retreat into Egypt took place only after Sidon had fallen into the hands of Antiochus, when Scopas was not in Jerusalem; it is to be assumed, therefore, that the heads of the pro-Ptolemaic party in Jerusalem were interned in Egypt not by him, but by other Ptolemaic commanders who were in charge of the occupied city.[105] From Antiochus' letter to Ptolemy we know that a Ptolemaic garrison remained in the citadel of Jerusalem until Antiochus appeared before the town (evidently in 198) and that the Jews helped Antiochus to expel Ptolemy's men from it (*Ant.* XII, 138). From this we learn that the Ptolemaic party controlled Jerusalem as long as Ptolemy's generals held power in Judaea, but that when their power began to collapse as a result of the defeat at Panion and the fall of Sidon, the Seleucid faction prevailed and cooperated with Antiochus as he drew near the city. It is therefore not surprising to read in Antiochus' letter that the Jews received him with extraordinary acclamation and that the "council of elders" (*Gerousia*) also came out to receive him (*ib.* 138). Such oscillations of political orientation are natural in time of war and no conclusion is to be drawn from them concerning the true sympathies or antipathies of the Jews.

Have we any means of penetrating more deeply into the minds of the Jewish people and of establishing in which direction the hidden aspirations of the nation inclined in those fateful years? This question has been asked more than once in modern literature, but no clear answer has been given, nor can it be provided as the outcome of a scientific analysis of reputable historical sources, since it depends on the interpretations, more or less daring, of one obscure passage in the Book of Daniel. The nature of this book is such that it poses riddles rather than illuminates historical events, and it must be used with great caution, for the modern scholar may easily discover in it any idea that he chooses to put there.[106] The sentence which provokes the scholar's itch to solve the riddle is Daniel 11.14: "And in those times many shall stand up against the King of the South; also the children of the violent among thy people shall lift themselves up to establish the vision; but they shall stumble."

In modern times this passage has been the subject of a comprehensive inquiry by Täubler, who investigated not only the quotation itself but also all the sources bearing on the occurrences of the years 201-198, and we have already availed ourselves of the results of this excellent study above, in regard to the chronological question and the order of events (see n. 105). However, not even a scholar such as Täubler was able to avoid subjectivity in the interpretation of the above-mentioned passage, for it contains hardly a word which cannot be explained in several ways. First and foremost, we do not, for instance, know how to explain the "vision" mentioned here; is some biblical prophecy meant, or some "vision" which the "violent" themselves entertained (that is, some political program)? Is the failure of the violent the failure of their vision, or is the failure itself the realization of the vision?[107] And who are the violent—simply brigands, or revolutionaries, or people of power and influence in public life?[108] Does the sentence "and the sons of the violent among thy people . . ." elaborate the preceding sentence "many shall stand up against the King of the South" (if so, the revolt was directed against the Ptolemies on behalf of the Seleucids), or did the author of the Book of Daniel use the conjunction "and" to link two sentences unpossessed of any internal connection with one another, as was his method throughout chapter 11 (in which case the insurgents may have been members of the pro-Ptolemaic party)?

Clearly, any interpretation set upon each individual word will influence the interpretation of the whole passage; but, on the other hand, it is clear that every scholar has approached the work of interpretation with a preconception concerning the passage as a whole, hence we are caught in a vicious circle. Generally two principal interpretations have been proposed for Daniel 11.14: we shall call them briefly the interpretation of Eduard Meyer and that of Täubler. According to Eduard Meyer, the insurgents were the pro-Seleucid or Hellenizing party, and their revolt was suppressed by Scopas.[109] This view rests on the general assumption that the Seleucids were active Hellenists (that their aim was the Hellenization of the Orient), while the Ptolemies were indifferent to Hellenization; hence any party which supported the Seleucids was of necessity a party of Hellenizers. We have already dwelt above (p. 16f.) on the question of the Hellenization of the Orient and have seen that there are no grounds for seeing in the Seleucids conscious Hellenizers, any more than the Ptolemies are to be regarded as opponents of the principle of Hellenization. We have no hint in the sources that a "Hellenistic" party already existed among the Jews in 200, and the pro-Seleucid orientation of the High Priest Simon the Just (see below) is sufficient assurance that the party supporting Antiochus lacked all Hellenistic coloring.

This does not mean, however, that Meyer's view must inevitably be wrong; if we interpret the rebellion of the "violent" as a rising against the rule of the Ptolemies, the most natural idea is to assume that the insurgents supported the Seleucids. The negative attitude of the author of the Book of Daniel to the rebels (see p. 436, n. 108) is conveniently explained on the assumption that everyone who had once supported the Seleucids was regarded by him as a criminal, on the strength of his experience in the period of Antiochus Epiphanes. Now Täubler thought that the insurgent movement was "messianic," that its aim was to liberate the people from any foreign yoke. He interprets the "vision" as a political program for the carrying out of some promise, and he

sees the "violent" as "political activists." He places the time of the rising in the short period between Antiochus' retreat from Gaza and the reconquest of Jerusalem by Scopas in the winter of 201/200; Antiochus' sudden retreat from Gaza looked to contemporaries like the finger of God and appeared to portend the fall of mighty powers.[110]
It is not to be denied that this interpretation is attractive in its clarity and in the way in which it can be coordinated with the other historical phenomena of the period; but Täubler did well to state the episode in general terms only; had he sought to discover details, he would inevitably have become involved in numerous difficulties. For we may ask: What was the character of this messianic movement? Was it directed against the Ptolemies and Seleucids simultaneously? If the aim of the revolt was full political independence, did the rebels think of establishing a theocracy with the High Priest at the head of the State, or was their intention the restoration of the royal house of David? In the first case we should expect to see the High Priest at the head of the revolt; but Simon the Just was apparently a supporter of Antiochus, and it is in any case hard to imagine that he would have remained in power after the suppression of the revolt in which he had been involved. If, however, the dream was of the throne of David, who was the pretender to the kingship? For a "messianic movement" cannot exist without a "messiah." If the movement was indeed one of national liberation and was remembered by the folk down to Daniel's day, why is Daniel's attitude to it negative? It is of course easy to say that we cannot answer these questions adequately, since we lack sources for the period; but are the sources sufficient to establish the mere fact of a "messianic movement"? We have, after all, only one passage in the Book of Daniel, and anyone who desires to build a complete system on it is suspending his inquiry by a hair. In my view, therefore, we must be very cautious in our interpretation of vague sentences of this sort, and must avoid drawing far-reaching conclusions from them. We may not extend our historical knowledge by these cautious methods, but at least we shall avoid errors.[111]
I now pass to the question of the composition of the pro-Seleucid party which supported Antiochus in 198 and helped him to capture the citadel of the city. From Antiochus' letter to Ptolemy the official we have learned that the council of elders (the *Gerousia*) came out to

receive the king; and, as we have remarked above, no conclusion is to be drawn from this fact, as it would have been
natural for the Jews to receive the victorious sovereign on
whose favor their fate depended. We shall see below, notwithstanding, that Antiochus in his letter announced several favors
towards the priests and the Temple, which proves that he was
interested in creating good relations with the aristocracy of
Jerusalem. On the other hand, in Antiochus' letter to Ptolemy
two actions carried out by the Jews for Antiochus' benefit are
alluded to, namely, military aid and the supply of foodstuffs
for the royal troops and elephants; and clearly these exceeded
normal courtesy, being valuable demonstrations of sympathy
towards the king on the part of the pro-Seleucid faction. There
is every ground for supposing that the High Priest Simon the
Just in person stood at the head of the pro-Seleucid party.[112]
This we may conclude by comparing the account of his actions
by his contemporary Ben Sira with what is referred to in Antiochus' letter to Ptolemy. Ben Sira devoted a complete chapter
of his book to an account of the High Priest (although he does
not generally mention his contemporaries who played a part
in the political life of the country). With great admiration Ben
Sira describes Simon the Just as he appears before the people
in the Temple on the Day of Atonement:

> How glorious was he when he looked forth from the Tent,
>   And when he came out from the sanctuary.
> Like a morning-star from between the clouds,
>   And like the full moon on the feast-days;
> Like the sun shining upon the Temple of the Most High,
>   And like the rainbow becoming visible in the cloud;
> Like a flower on the branches in the days of the first fruits,[113]
>   And as a lily by the water-brooks . . .

Ben Sira makes special allu-
sion to Simon's fruitful activity for the benefit of the people:
in Simon's time the ruins of the Temple were repaired, flowing
water was conducted into the city, and the wall was built. This
note shows that in Simon the Just's time Jerusalem was in a
state of ruin, and Simon undertook the task of rebuilding the
town and the Temple. Now the ruin of the town is referred to
also in Antiochus' letter, where the king expresses his desire
to restore it and details the works of building and reconstruction
to be carried out in the Temple (*Ant.* XII, 139-141). It is impossible not to perceive a certain connection between the work

of Simon the Just and the building program in Antiochus'
declaration, and as Simon was a contemporary of Antiochus III,
and as it is hard to suppose that in so short a time Jerusalem
was twice destroyed and twice rebuilt, I believe that in the
activity of these two men we must see the same historical event:
Simon the Just carried out what Antiochus had promised the
Jews in his manifesto.

Hence we learn that Simon
the Just was recognized by the king as chief of the Jews and
as their official representative to the authorities. If we take into
account that the High Priest was in any event a central personality in the *Gerousia* (its "chairman" in modern terminology)
and that the *Gerousia* received the king when he entered the
city, we shall not be mistaken if we suppose that even before
the city's capture Simon the Just stood at the head of the party
which inclined to the Seleucids. This surmise is confirmed by
Josephus: when he speaks of the feud between Hyrcanus son
of Tobiah and his elder brothers, he stresses that most of the
people backed the latter, and the High Priest Simon followed
suit. Hyrcanus' pro-Ptolemaic orientation is beyond all doubt,
hence we know that his elder brothers, supported by Simon
the Just, were on the side of the Seleucids. Unfortunately we
do not know precisely when Joseph son of Tobiah died, or when
the fratricidal struggle broke out among his sons, but for several
reasons it may be supposed that this happened at the end of
the period of Ptolemaic rule in Palestine, perhaps at the very
time of the transference of power.[114]

We now have learned two
things of importance: (1) that the pro-Seleucid party in Jerusalem was composed of representatives of the upper stratum
of the priestly class (the High Priest himself), of the Jerusalem
aristocracy (members of the *Gerousia*) and the wealthy (the
sons of Joseph ben Tobiah); (2) that this party possessed no
particular cultural, that is, Hellenistic colorings, as Eduard
Meyer and others thought, since Hyrcanus son of Tobiah was
no less a Hellenizer than his elder brothers, and Simon the Just
who attracted the profound and sincere admiration of a scholar
so pious as Ben Sira, clearly never headed a Hellenizing party.
The breach between the two sections of the Jewish community
in the years 201-198 possessed not a cultural and theoretical,
but a political and practical background; the greater part of the
Jewish aristocracy sensed the growing weakness of the Ptolemies

and put its trust in the new power which had appeared in the country, and most of the people followed the aristocracy.

Josephus gives us three documents issued by Antiochus III for the benefit of the Jews. It is worth studying them with special attention since they are vital for the determination of the juridical position of the Jews in the Hellenistic period.

The first document (*Ant.* XII, 138ff.) represents Antiochus' letter to an official named Ptolemy, appointed, it seems, by the king to govern Coele-Syria.[115] In this letter Antiochus describes the excellent reception accorded to him by the Jews and the aid which they had rendered him in his operations against the Ptolemaic garrison of Jerusalem. This has already been referred to above and need not be discussed again. In return for the benefits received from the Jews, Antiochus announces a long series of privileges and projects of assistance to their advantage, these being: aiding in the rebuilding of the city, which had been destroyed during the war; enabling those inhabitants who had fled to return to the town; allotting a considerable sum of money for supplying the Temple with sacrifices, wine, oil, incense, and the like; permitting the importation into Jerusalem of timber from the Lebanon and other places free of duty, for the repair of the ruins of the Temple; granting the people permission to live according to their ancestral laws; exempting the members of the council of elders (the *Gerousia*), the priests, "the Temple scribes" and the singers (*hieropsaltai*) from the poll-tax, from the "coronation tax" and from the salt gabelle;[116] exempting the inhabitants of Jerusalem from all taxation for three years and reducing their taxes by one-third permanently thereafter;[117] redeeming all those who had become prisoners during the war and been sold as slaves, and restoring to them their property. Here Josephus ends the text of the letter.

Many scholars of the past generation—among them Niese, Willrich, Schubart and Büchler—have seen in this letter a Jewish forgery of a later period. It is not incumbent upon the writer to refute them, since others have already done so, especially Bickermann, who is the first and only scholar to have devoted to the analysis of the document a profound and detailed commentary.[118] I wish to dwell here on only one sentence of the document, which seems to me to be the most important. Antiochus gave the Jews permission to live "according to their ancestral laws." This is one of the two documents of the Hellenistic period where this right is referred to explicitly (for the second document see *Ant.* XII, 150), but we have several Roman documents containing the same formula, and it has already been remarked above (p. 49) that this permission was without doubt accorded to the Jews by Alexander also. We may add that the Ptolemies certainly confirmed Jewish autonomy by a formal pronouncement, for had they not done so the authority of the High Priest and *Gerousia* in Judaea would have been devoid of all juridical basis.[119]

The question, however, is: What was the nature of these ancestral laws? Antiochus did not invent the expression: Hellenistic offices always used this formula in a conventional manner and the "ancestral laws" are mentioned not only in relation to the Jews, but also in relation to other peoples and to Greek cities, the content of the laws differing from place to place.[120] What did the expression imply for the Jews? Bickermann (*op. cit.*, p. 27) says that the Law of Moses is meant. There is no doubt that he is right: but what is the "Law of Moses"? Is only the Written Law meant, the laws and regulations of the Pentateuch; or must we include in the conception also the "Oral Law"? So far as is known to the writer, no study has yet been made of the "ancestral laws" of the Jews, although the question is important in respect of Jewish juridical status under the Hellenistic monarchies. This is not the place to engage in a detailed investigation; the intention here is to make such observations as seem most fundamental to the question.

There is no doubt that the concept of "ancestral laws," where it concerns the Jews, is much broader than the Law of Moses, and includes, not only the elements of the Jewish religion, but the maintenance of political institutions, the form of the regime, the methods of social organization, and the like. The "theocracy" of Jerusalem, for example, with the authority of the High Priest, and the priestly class grouped about the Temple, all rested on the right of the Jews "to live according to their ancestral laws"; the Mosaic Law, however, knows nothing of the High Priest as head of the nation, nor of the Temple at Jerusalem. To take another example, every Jewish community in the Diaspora set up synagogues for itself and sometimes even courts of justice, and these activities too were carried out in accordance with the Jewish privilege

"to live according to their ancestral laws"; the synagogue, however, is a late institution without any authority either in the
Pentateuch or in the Bible as a whole.

If therefore we accept the
assumption that the ancestral laws were the Torah of Moses,
we must agree that the concept has to be made to include in
"Torah" much more than was given in the Written Law. Nor
was this difficult for the Jews, since, from Ezra's day on, the
Oral Law had begun to develop among the scribes, and a very
ancient legal fiction held that the whole of this Law had also
been given to Moses on Sinai.[121] It is not to be supposed that
Antiochus or any other Hellenistic king knew what the Mosaic
Law was, or what was written in it and what was not, and he
was certainly not familiar with the difference between the written and oral codes. Not he, but the Jews themselves imbued
the dry juridical formula "the ancestral laws" with a living
practical content. And by "the Jews," we mean the authorized
representatives of the Jewish people and, in the case under
discussion, the heads of the theocracy of Jerusalem, and the
class of scribes who were recognized as the official interpreters
of the Torah (see below, ch. 3). The real content of Antiochus'
declaration thus lay in his confirmation of the political situation which he found in Judaea and in his acknowledgment of
the rule of the High Priest and his assistants over Judaea and
Jerusalem. Whether or not this rule was to be in accordance with
the Torah of Moses depended on the Jews themselves; the
king's function consisted solely in according supreme royal ratification of Jewish autonomous life in Judaea.

If this was the case, there
is no paradox in the fact that the laws of the Sabbath, for
instance, were imposed on the Jewish population by the Greek
king, for not the king imposed them, but the Jewish authority
in Jerusalem and the former only gave his consent as he gave
prior consent to any law promulgated in Judaea by the authorized Jewish instances; but when he gave his consent to the laws
of Israel, he also in effect undertook their defense, so that henceforward Jewish autonomy was protected by the military and
administrative apparatus of the Seleucid state.[122]

The second document (*Ant.*
XII, 145ff.) reproduces two examples of the king's orders issued
in pursuance of his general confirmation of Jewish autonomy.
The first contains the prohibition against any non-Jew entering
the interior of the Temple, "even as it is prohibited to Jews,

unless they have purified themselves as is customary according to their ancestral law." The second order prohibits the introduction into the city of the flesh of unclean animals, such as horses, mules, donkeys (wild and tame), panthers, foxes, hares, "and any animals prohibited to the Jews"; the order also forbids the introduction of the skins of these animals, and, further, their rearing within the town; contraveners of these orders will pay fines to the priests. Bickermann devoted a special article to this document also,[123] but even his great erudition in the lore of Hellenistic documents has not sufficed to explain away all the difficulties involved in its interpretation. The external form of the document is that of a proclamation, and Josephus is in error where he says that the king published it "in the whole kingdom" (*Ant.* XII, 145). Bickermann rightly observes that Josephus confused the Seleucid *programma* with a Roman "edict," which was published in an entire province, while the Seleucid *programma* was exhibited for view at the appropriate place (in our case, at the gates of the city of Jerusalem). Nor is it difficult to explain why the king published a special proclamation dealing with certain details (not the most important ones) of the Jewish cult, since he had already ratified Jewish autonomy as a whole in his letter to Ptolemy: this time there was no need for such a publication, as the proclamation was intended not for the Jews, but for aliens, as is specifically stressed in its first paragraph; aliens were not subject to the orders of the High Priest, nor were they obliged to fulfill the duties of the Torah. But in this case also the king acts in harmony with his general confirmation, and this is clear from the way he cites the authority of the "ancestral law" on the question of the purification of those Jews who wish to enter the interior of the Temple.

As to the first order, it evokes no doubt on our part: for scholars have long known the text of an inscription of the Roman period forbidding strangers to enter the Temple, and this prohibition has parallels in the Greek world.[124] It is not surprising, then, that a similar prohibition existed under the Seleucids, just as it had no doubt existed under the Ptolemies. Doubts arise when we come to the second order. We can understand the prohibition against bringing the flesh of unclean animals or their skins into the city by foreigners, but why was the rearing of such animals also prohibited within the city? Such a prohibition, it is to be assumed, did not affect the Jews; for what would have been the animals used by the inhabitants of the people of Jerusalem for their daily needs, if not donkeys, mules and horses? The use of unclean animals was not forbidden to Jews, only the corpse being a source of pollution (M. Kelim, I, 2). Bickermann endeavors to remove the difficulty by pointing to the fact that, not the entry of the beasts was forbidden, but their rearing in the city; if an unclean animal were to be reared in the town, the danger existed that it might die and its corpse would cause pollution.

According to Bickermann, no such danger existed in respect of permitted animals, as they might be eaten and sacrificed, and might therefore be slaughtered properly. This answer, however, is not relevant, since a permitted animal could also die a natural death or be killed by another animal, and any unclean beast introduced into the city for a short time might also happen to die. Had the legislator wished to avoid the danger of pollution by corpses within the city, he would have had to prohibit the entry of any animals whatsoever—which was impossible. I see only two ways of solving the problem; either we must assume that the text of the document has been corrupted by Josephus (or by the writer from whom he copied it), or we must conjecture that the word "city" does not indicate the *entire* built-up area of Jerusalem, but only its center, that is, the Temple and its immediate neighborhood. The first method is the easier, but from the methodological point of view should not be used unless all hope has failed of finding a satisfactory solution on the basis of the existing text of the document.[125]

As regards the second supposition, several details in the document are clear evidence, in the writer's opinion, that the legislator was, in fact, referring to the Temple, for (1) The clause forbidding the introduction of the meat of unclean animals into "the city" follows immediately after the clause prohibiting the entry of aliens into the Temple; the two sentences are, moreover, linked grammatically. Naturally the *programma* which forbade entry into the Temple was hung on the gate at the entrance to the Temple or to that part of the city directly associated with it; and if this was so, the prohibition in regard to unclean beasts would have been hung in the same place, and not at the gates of the entire city of Jerusalem. (2) The legislator speaks of unclean animals, and immediately afterwards remarks that only such traditional sacrificial animals may be used as are customarily sacrificed to God. The composer of the document, then, is thinking of animals from the cultic point of view, whether they are permitted or forbidden for sacrifice, and this outlook is, I think, more justified if we restrict its area of applicability to the localities nearest the Temple.

(3) The fine for contravention is paid to the *priests*. They here fulfill the function, apparently, of the officials of the treasury, and although in a "theocratic" state the priest might interfere in simple matters of government, the most reasonable assumption is that his function is here bound up with his activity as intermediary between God and man, and that he atones for the human transgression in accordance with the commandment in Leviticus 5.14ff.; Numbers 5.5ff.[126] This conjecture is of considerable help to us in understanding the document, although it must be confessed that the investigation is not yet at an end and that we are still far from an authoritative interpretation of all its finer details.

The third document which contains Antiochus' letter to the official Zeuxis, discusses the transfer of a certain number of Jews to the lands of Phrygia and Lydia. This question is associated with that of the Jewish population in the Diaspora and will be dealt with in the second part of the present work.

Antiochus' documents do not yield sufficient historical material for the study of the political position of Judaea within the Seleucid state. They nevertheless contain very important details. Antiochus permitted the Jews "to live according to their ancestral laws," that is, he did not disturb the political-religious foundation of Jewish tradition on which the whole public life of the Jewish people was based. Antiochus refers twice to the *Gerousia*, and the members of this institution appear together with the priests as people possessed of certain privileges in matters of tax-payment. There is no doubt that the *Gerousia* was the supreme administrative institution in Jerusalem, which assisted the High Priest in a permanent capacity. What was the relationship between the High Priest and the *Gerousia* on the one hand, and the royal officials on the other? The first document of Antiochus is addressed to Ptolemy, and this official had to carry out all the pledges Antiochus had made to the Jews. But we have learned from Ben Sira that it was not the king's officials, but the High Priest Simon who rebuilt Jerusalem and repaired the ruins of the Temple; hence we must conclude that the Seleucid government saw in the High Priest the supreme ruler of Judaea and Jerusalem; in other words, Judaea entered the Seleucid state as a distinct political unit possessed of wide autonomy, which was decidedly in keeping with the spirit of Seleucid tradition. The great kingdom recognized three kinds of self-contained political organization under its control: cities, peoples and princes. The "peoples" enjoyed a certain degree of home-rule and obeyed their national leaders; the Jews obviously were included in this class.[127] The government officials of course possessed the authority to interfere in the internal affairs of Judaea whenever there was need, but all our information on the Seleucid regime in the country in connection with the Hasmonean revolt evidences that they were content to pay more or less brief visits to Jerusalem, and had no desire to stay there for long. It may further be supposed that politically the transfer of power from the Ptolemies to the Seleucids constituted a certain alleviation for the Jews, since the Ptolemies strove (as we have learned from the Zenon papyri), though not with complete success, to introduce the Egyptian bureaucratic regime into Palestine; the Seleucids, who did not know this regime to the same exaggerated extent characteristic of Egypt, doubtless avoided excess in this respect.

The documents of Antiochus evidence explicitly that the king had no intention of changing the traditional way of life of Judaea by imposing Greek tendencies. On the contrary, Antiochus by his orders strengthened the priests' power, exempted them from taxes and gave to the commandments of the Torah the validity of official law. To this period doubtless belongs the activity of a certain Johanan, whose name is mentioned in II Maccabees. This Johanan had obtained from the king certain privileges for the Jews and as these were abolished by the Hellenizers in the time of Antiochus Epiphanes, it may be supposed that they were dictated in harmony with Jewish religious tradition and had the aim of securing the maintenance of Jewish religious customs in Judaea.[128] The striving to Hellenization which awoke among the Jews of Jerusalem about this time, has therefore no direct connection with the change of rule, and we must seek other reasons in order to explain its appearance. Nor did Seleucus IV Philopator who occupied the throne after the death of Antiochus III seek to Hellenize the Jews; the pious author of II Maccabees even praises this monarch for his favors to the Temple of Jerusalem.[129] Under the Seleucid kings the Jews felt absolutely no external pressure to change their ways of life, just as they had felt none under the rule of the Ptolemies. The storm that broke over their heads came in consequence of the natural development of the Jews themselves, part of whom inclined to Hellenism as a spontaneous aspiration; but this phenomenon took the form of a national catastrophe on account of the fact that just at the time of the political and cultural crisis in Judaea, a grave political crisis was taking place in the Seleucid empire, which created a new approach to the problems of the land of Judaea and its population.

With this we conclude the account of the political events which took place in Palestine during the rule of the Macedonian kings. The history of the Seleucid monarchs from Seleucus IV Philopator onwards involves the political events in Judaea itself and may be described only in association with the process of the Hellenization of the Jews. But before we pass to the investigation of this process, we must devote attention to the Greek cities which were founded in Palestine in the Hellenistic period and performed a very important function in the political, economic and cultural life of the country.

chapter 2

THE GREEK
TOWNS OF PALESTINE

Palestine has always been a country of transit, which has never ceased to absorb the cultural influences of the neighboring lands and to adapt them, successfully or otherwise, to its own original culture. This was the situation also in the Hellenistic period.

Hellenization encompassed Palestine on every side. To the south lay the mighty kingdom of the Ptolemies, which ruled Palestine for a century and whose rulers, officials and soldiers were Greeks or Macedonians, and the language of whose government-offices and culture was Greek. Eastward and southeastward on the desert-border itself, dwelt the strong Arab tribe of the Nabataeans, who controlled the trade-routes from southern Arabia to Egypt; modern scholars are following with interest the excavations and explorations being carried out in their area of occupation, excavations which are revealing a very high level of Hellenization in building, sculpture, painting and the like.[1] To the north, along the Mediterranean coast, lay the ancient Phoenician towns, whose inscriptions and coins evidence how very rapid was the process of the conversion of these oriental cities into Greek *poleis*. They acquired the Greek political organization, participated in the international life of Greek athletics, held athletic contests, adorned themselves with gymnasia, theaters, and stadia, and, in short, exchanged their traditional oriental appearance for a new Hellenistic aspect.[2]

Especially successful in adapting themselves to the new cultural life were the cities of Tyre, Sidon and Beirut, not far from the frontiers of Palestine,[3] and there are grounds for thinking that Damascus also took on a Greek appearance as early as the time of Ptolemy II Philadelphus.[4] Palestine stood in live and constant contact with all her neighbors, and if proofs for this assumption were formerly lacking for the Hellenistic period, the papyri of Zenon have now made good the deficiency (cf. above, p. 60ff.). Convenient routes crossed the entire length and breadth of the country, and hundreds of Greeks visited it as officials, merchants and tourists; the estates of Hellenistic kings and their high officials were scattered here and there, and these facts alone suffice to indicate how Hellenism spread through the land. But the most important channel through which Hellenism penetrated into Palestine was furnished by the Greek cities.

The question of the Greek cities founded in Palestine may be investigated from three angles. It can be asked: (1) Where were these cities founded? (2) What remains of them? (3) What was their value in history? The first question is a subject for the Palestinographer; the second for the archaeologist, the third for the historian. It may be said at once that the following survey concerns itself with the third question only—with the historical and cultural problems of the Greek cities of Palestine.

These were concentrated in two groups: one strung out in a line along the Mediterranean coast from the Egyptian frontier to Tyre; the second located in Transjordan, especially in the region of the sea of Tiberias. Apart from these cities there were isolated Greek towns in Galilee, Samaria and Idumaea. We know of only some thirty towns which were founded in Palestine in the Hellenistic period, or which exchanged their oriental for Hellenistic exteriors.[5] Let us take them in order and see when they were founded, by whom, and what were their fortunes in the Hellenistic period. We shall commence with those located on the Mediterranean coast.

(1) The city of Acco stood on the northern frontier of Palestine.[6] Its name is mentioned in the Tel el-Amarna letters, in inscriptions of the kings of Egypt and Assyria, and in the Bible (Ju. 1. 31).[7] Acco saw Greeks before Alexander's time, and here resided, on the testimony of

Demosthenes (LII, 20), the representatives of Greek merchants from Athens. At the beginning of the Ptolemaic period Acco was an important fortress; Ptolemy I destroyed it when he evacuated the country before Antigonus in 312 (Diod. XIX, 93, 7). Ptolemy II Philadelphus converted it into a Greek town and named it Ptolemais, as is evidenced by Aristeas (Aristeas' letter, 115), and also by the coins bearing the image of Ptolemy Philadelphus minted there.[8] In the Zenon papyri the city already appears under its new name.[9] According to Demetrius of Magnesia, who lived in the first century B.C.E., the citadel (*akropolis*) of Ptolemais had previously been called Acco,[10] whence it may be deduced that the new town of Ptolemais exceeded old Acco in area. The city's enlargement may have been associated with its refoundation by Philadelphus.[11] Under Antiochus IV Epiphanes, Acco again changed its name to Antiocheia, and on the coins struck by the city under that king and his successors the legend appears: "The Antiocheans at Ptolemais."[12] The new name did not take root among the local population, and even the name Ptolemais, which is repeated several times in Greek literature in the Hellenistic period, did not survive among the inhabitants; the Jews always called the town Acco, and this has also been its Arab name down to the present day.

(2) Dor, like Acco, was an ancient town. In the Persian period it belonged to Sidon (below, p. 417, n. 3), hence the mistaken view that it was founded by the Phoenicians.[13] In 219 the city was besieged by Antiochus III, who did not succeed in capturing it (Polyb. V, 66); it also held out in the face of hostile attacks in the war between Tryphon and Antiochus Sidetes (*Ant.* XIII, 223ff.; I Macc. 14.11f.), from which it may be deduced that Dor was a fortress which commanded respect, although not, apparently, a large town. The Greeks knew it as early as the classical period,[14] although there are no grounds for believing that it was under Athenian control in the fifth century.[15] In the Hellenistic period it was a Greek *polis*, as is evidenced by the fact that under Pompey it obtained self-government when the latter reestablished the Greek towns of Palestine which had lost their independence to the Hasmoneans.[16] The excavations carried out here in 1950 revealed pottery of the Persian and Hellenistic periods and remains of a Roman theater.[17]

(3) The city of Straton's Tower was not, apparently, an ancient one; its name is absent from the Greek geographer Scylax and we hear nothing of it

prior to the Hellenistic period.[18] It is first referred to in a papyrus of the Zenon archives of the year 259 B.C.E. (*PCZ* 59004), and in literature by the Greek writer Artemidorus in approximately 100 B.C.E. (see Stephanus *s. v. Doros*). Under Pompey, Straton's Tower also obtained independence (*Ant.* XIV, 76). It was rebuilt by Herod, who renamed it Caesarea; from this time begins its flourishing period as an important commercial town and as center of the Roman administration in Palestine.[19] A Jewish population began to take root in the city at the same time, Jews not having settled previously, it seems, at Straton's Tower.[20] According to a late notice[21] the city had been founded by a Greek named Straton, while Stark[22] also believes that the founder was a Greek general of the Ptolemies in the third century B.C.E. More correct is the supposition that the city was built by one of the two Sidonian kings (the first at the beginning of the fourth century, the second a contemporary of Alexander the Great), who also bore the name Straton (Phoenician—"servant of Ashtoret").[23]

(4) Between Caesarea and Jaffa stood the Greek town of Apollonia, mentioned by Pliny, by the geographer Ptolemy and by Stephanus.[24] The place is now called Arsuf, which helps us to explain the city's Hellenistic name, as Arsuf is derived from the root *Reshef*, a Phoenician deity equated by the Greeks with Apollo.[25] The city's chief god in the Hellenistic period therefore became Apollo, the city accordingly changing its name to Apollonia. We have no reason to think, consequently, that the city was founded by Seleucus I[26] or by Apollonius, the Seleucid general under Demetrius II mentioned in I Maccabees (X, 69ff.).[27] Under the Hasmoneans the town belonged to the Jews (*Ant.* XIII, 395); it was rebuilt by Gabinius as a Greek city (*War* I, 166). Excavations in 1950 revealed remains of buildings of the Byzantine period which evidenced among other things a glass industry of that epoch.[28]

(5) Jaffa, one of the most ancient Palestinian cities, whose name is referred to in inscriptions of Egypt and Assyria,[29] also became a Greek city in the Hellenistic period. Jaffa was then distinguished not only as an important port, but also as a strong fortress. Ptolemy I, after he had conquered the country for the first time, placed here a Macedonian garrison; in 315 Antigonus captured the city and attached Ptolemy's troops to his own army (Diod. XIX, 59, 2). It was among the towns destroyed by Ptolemy in 312 (Diod. XIX, 93, 7). Under the Ptolemies the city developed into a large

and important port where Greek merchants and officials resided permanently, as the Zenon papyri witness,[30] while Jaffa's connection with maritime trade is also demonstrated by the image of the sea-god Poseidon which appears on its coins.[31] The Hasmoneans, ambitious to strengthen their hold on the seacoast, set their hearts first on the capture of Jaffa, and under their rule the town was Judaized. The process ceased under Pompey, who reestablished Jaffa as an autonomous town, but a large Jewish population remained there even after Pompey and was probably only destroyed in the war against Vespasian.

(6) Yavneh, the Greek Iamnia, is always remembered as a Jewish town and as the center of the activity of Jewish scholars after the war of 70 C.E.; but in the Hellenistic period its population was predominantly non-Jewish; Judah the Maccabee attacked it, destroyed its harbor and burned its ships (II Macc. 12. 8-9). In the Hasmonean epoch it too was Judaized, and in Philo's day most of its inhabitants were Jews.[32] Pompey restored it to self-government, and Gabinius rebuilt it (see below, p. 443, n. 5); thus it is obvious that Yavneh in the Hellenistic period had possessed the organization of a Greek *polis*.

(7) The fate of Ashdod in the Hellenistic epoch is unknown. This Philistine city is mentioned frequently in Assyrian inscriptions from the eighth century onwards.[33] The Hasmoneans destroyed it; Pompey and Gabinius restored it. The author of I Maccabees related that Jonathan the Maccabee destroyed the temple of Dagon at Ashdod (I Macc. 10.84; 11.4), indicating that the old Philistine cult survived in the city in the Hellenistic period.

(8) We have more detailed information on Ascalon, the ancient Philistine city. Its name appears in Egyptian and Assyrian inscriptions[34] and frequently in the Bible. In the Persian period the city was apparently under the Tyrians, as Scylax calls it "Ascalon city of the Tyrians";[35] it was then a great mercantile town which maintained constant links with Egypt, as may be deduced from the large number of statues of Egyptian gods found there in excavations.[36] These excavations have uncovered remains of various periods from the eighteenth dynasty of the Pharaohs down to the Arab epoch, including remains of public buildings of the Seleucid period.[37] The Hasmonean domination left the city untouched and in 104 B.C.E. its citizens even succeeded in obtaining autonomy,

as is evidenced by the city's calendar, which begins in that year.[38] This is probably the reason why we do not find its name among those towns founded and restored by Pompey and Gabinius. At the beginning of the Roman period Ascalon occupied an important place in the world of Greek culture, several Greek authors being born there.[39] The names of Greek gods appear on its coins, and it was especially noted for its cult of the goddess Ashtoret, who became Aphrodite in the Hellenistic period.[40] In talmudic literature Ascalon is regarded as a city situated on the country's borders, and there were different opinions on the question whether it was within the territory of the Land of Israel or not.[41] In the Roman period the city was known for its hatred of the Jews (*War* III, 10; Philo *Leg. ad Gaium*, 205).

(9) Between Ascalon and Gaza lay the Greek town of Anthedon, now the ruins of Teda, near el-Blachiya, northwest of Gaza. The city is referred to in most of the sources as a coastal town,[42] and only Pliny (*NH* V, 13, 68) mistakenly places it far from the shore. We find the name Anthedon among the cities of Boeotia, hence it is possible that the Greeks who settled at the Palestinian Anthedon originated in the Greek town; but it is more probable that the name is merely an adaptation to Greek nomenclature of some ancient local name.[43] Under the Hasmoneans the city was in Jewish hands and was restored by Gabinius. Herod rebuilt it again and changed its name to Agrippias (*Ant.* XIII, 357; *War* I, 416), which did not take root among the inhabitants; and Ptolemy (V, 16,2), Stephanus (*s. v. Anthedon*), Sozomenos (*Hist. Eccl.* V, 9) and others refer to the city by its former name.

(10) Gaza, the ancient Philistine city,[44] was a very large town in Alexander's time, perhaps the largest in the country, as is observed by Arrian (II, 26, 1) and Plutarch (*Alex.* 25). Herodotus (III, 5), who visited it in the Persian period, says that Gaza was not much smaller than Sardis in Asia Minor. As a commercial city it was known to the Greeks before Alexander and its coins of the Persian period give evidence of Athenian influence.[45] Alexander took the city after a two months' siege and destroyed it; according to Hegesias of Magnesia, he wrought a frightful massacre among its inhabitants,[46] but later ordered its restoration and its settlement with inhabitants from the neighborhood (Arr. II, 27, 7). In the Hellenistic period Gaza was known as a strong fortress, resisting

Antigonus in 315 and being captured by him by force (Diod. XIX, 59, 2). Three years later it fell into the hands of Ptolemy after the battle between him and Demetrius near the town (312); and some time afterwards it was destroyed by the former (Diod. XIX, 93, 7). Antiochus III also encountered powerful resistance from the city when he overran the country in 200.[47] The fact that Gaza resisted kings coming from the north on three occasions (Alexander, Antigonus, and Antiochus) shows that her economic life was bound up with the lands of the south, and Ed. Meyer was certainly correct in ascribing the reason to the desire of its citizens to retain possession of the perfume trade with southern Arabia.[48] Gaza's trade with the maritime countries was also doubtless highly developed; Diodorus' story (XX, 73/4) tells us that a port existed at the town as early as Antigonus' time.

Under the Ptolemies Gaza stood in regular commercial communication with Egypt and her name is mentioned frequently in the papyri of Zenon.[49] Josephus (*Ant.* XVII, 320; *War* II, 97) designates Gaza as "a Greek city," and on its coins the images of Greek gods generally appear. A temple of Apollo existed there under Alexander Jannaeus (*Ant.* XIII, 364), but in the Roman period and possibly in the Hellenistic period too, the city's chief god was the Syrian deity Marnas.[50] In the second century B.C.E. the town changed its name to Seleuceia, evidently in honor of Seleucus IV Philopator, and struck coins with the legend Δήμου Σελευκέων τῶν ἐν Γάζᾳ.[51] The sources mention old and new Gaza, and according to Strabo (XVI, 759), Alexander the Great destroyed (old) Gaza "and since then the city has remained in ruins"; but he is here inaccurate, as Diodorus witnesses (XIX, 80, 5) that in 312 old Gaza was still standing. It is therefore more correct to suppose that the new town was built by Gabinius after the old city had been completely destroyed by Alexander Jannaeus.[52]

(11) The last city on the coast as the Egyptian frontier was reached from the north, was Raphia, whose name appears in Egyptian and Assyrian inscriptions,[53] and is frequently mentioned in the Hellenistic and Roman periods, becoming especially renowned after the great battle between Ptolemy IV Philopator and Antiochus III in the year 217 (see above, p. 14). Alexander Jannaeus captured the town (*Ant.* XIII, 357; *War* I, 87); Gabinius restored it, and the city reckoned its years from a date commencing with the year of restoration by Gabinius.[54] On its coins of the Roman period appear the images of the Greek deities Apollo and Artemis.

We now turn to the second center of Hellenism in Palestine—Transjordan. In the Roman period (perhaps from Pompey's time) Greek Transjordan was known as Decapolis, that is, the Ten Cities, according to the number of Greek cities existent there. Their names are given by Pliny (*NH* V, 18, 74), these being Damascus, Philadelpheia, Raphana, Scythopolis, Gadara, Hippos, Dion, Pella, Gerasa and Canatha. But Pliny himself says that this list was not the only one, and that other writers reckoned different towns among the cities of the Decapolis.[55] We are not obliged to follow only Pliny therefore, and may, for example, include among them the city of Abila, which was without doubt a Greek town and whose membership of the Decapolis is confirmed by the geographer Ptolemy and by an inscription (see below, p. 444). Possibly the numerical name of "ten cities" was appropriate only when the Decapolis was first organized (perhaps in the time of Pompey), but afterwards other towns also joined the league, as, for example, Damascus.[56] In a book discussing the Hellenistic period, the number of members of the Decapolis is not so very important, since this city-league was in any case unknown in that epoch. Its cities nevertheless existed before Pompey, and like the coastal towns, should be individually investigated.

(12) We lack information on the town of Canatha in the Hellenistic period. But since it is mentioned by Pliny as a member of the Decapolis and its citizens reckoned their years according to the Pompeian era, it is to be assumed that this ancient city[57] had become a Greek *polis* in the Hellenistic period. In talmudic literature Canatha is referred to as one of the towns on the frontier of the Land of Israel.[58] The ruins surviving today belong to the Roman period, as do the inscriptions which mention the names of various municipal magistrates. In Greek the town was sometimes called Kanata, and on the basis of this slight change of spelling, and on archaeological grounds, too, some scholars have decided that there were two towns called Canatha in Transjordan: one the modern Kanwat, the other, not far away at Kerak. This conjecture is improbable, and it is to be supposed that the ancient Canatha stood where Kanwat is today.[59]

(13) We know very little of the city of Raphana, which is mentioned once in literature— by Pliny (*NH* V, 18, 74)—as one of the cities of the Decapolis. It is apparently identical with the town of Raphion in I Maccabees (V. 37), which stood in the vicinity of the town of Karnaim (cf. also *Ant.* XII, 243). According to Klausner[60]

Raphana was the ancient Ashtoret (today Tel Ashtara), also near Karnaim.

(14) The town of Susita changed its name in the Hellenistic period to Hippos (or, to be precise, translated it from Aramaic into Greek). Under this title it appears twice in Pliny (V, 15, 71; 18, 74), and it is also mentioned by Josephus, with others, in the list of Greek cities (*Ant.* XVII, 320; *War* II, 97).[61] On the city's coinage we read the legend "The Antiocheians of Hippos,"[62] which informs us that under the Seleucid regime the city called itself Antiocheia. In talmudic literature Susita appears as a Gentile town constituting an enclave within the Land of Israel; its inhabitants are exempt from tithe and from the sabbatical year.[63] The remains of the city are located on the hill of el-Hösn near the east shore of the sea of Tiberias, and the name of Susita is preserved today in that of the abandoned site of Susiya near Kal'at el-Hösn.

(15) Gadara was known in the Hellenistic period as a strong fortress—"exceeding in strength all the towns of this region" according to Polybius (V, 71, 3). Antiochus III captured it twice: in the year 218 before the Raphia campaign (Polyb. *loc. cit.*) and in 200, after the victory of Paneas (Polyb. XVI, 39); Alexander Jannaeus took it after a ten months' siege (*Ant.* XIII, 356). Stephanus (*s.v. Gadara*) asserts that the city was also called Antiocheia and Seleuceia, and this is credible although not yet confirmed by coins. Josephus terms Gadara "a Greek city" (*Ant.* XVII, 320; *War* II, 97), but it was not merely this: it gained a reputation as a town of Greek culture, particularly in the Roman period.[64] Its remains survive at Um-Keis, southeast of the sea of Tiberias.[65]

(16) East of Gadara lay Abila,[66] now Tel Abil, which was also a fortress in the Hellenistic period; together with Gadara it was twice taken by Antiochus III. Although unmentioned by Pliny among the towns of the Decapolis, we know from Ptolemy (V, 14, 18) and from an inscription of the period of Hadrian (*OGIS* 631), that it was also included in that League. During the Seleucid domination of the country Abila was called Seleuceia, as its coins witness.[67]

(17) Pella, today Fahil, is mentioned in the Talmud by its Aramaic name Pehal, this being the town's original name as early as the second millennium B.C.E., on the evidence of inscriptions of Thuthmose III and Seti I.[68] The Greeks slightly modified the sound of the name in honor of the Macedonian Pella, where Alexander the Great was

born, whence it may be deduced that the Greek settlement here consisted more especially of Macedonians. Stephanus (*s.v. Dion*) writes of the town of Dion in Palestine (see below): "The city was founded by Alexander," and an anonymous reader added "Pella also."[69] This hasty remark need not, of course, be considered, for as we know, there is no proof that Alexander visited Transjordan (see above, p. 50).[70] Appian (*Syr.* 57) mentions Pella among the towns founded by Seleucus I, but this king no more came to Transjordan than Alexander, and Appian's information must be attributed to Pella in Syria, that is, Apameia-on-the-Orontes.[71]

It is to be supposed that Palestinian Pella was founded at the very beginning of the Hellenistic period; this is shown first by the town's Macedonian name, and secondly by the fact that it already existed under the Ptolemies and was then known as Berenice.[72] The name Berenice appears twice in the Ptolemaic royal family during the third century, being that of two queens, the wives of Ptolemy I Soter, and of Ptolemy III Euergetes, respectively. It cannot be determined which of these two kings rebuilt Pella, but the writer inclines to Ptolemy Euergetes, as by his time Hellenism had struck fair roots in the country. In 218 Antiochus III captured the city (Polyb. V, 70, 12), and it was no doubt on this occasion that Pella-Berenice lost its Ptolemaic name and reassumed its former Macedonian title. Alexander Jannaeus destroyed the city after its inhabitants had refused to become converted (*Ant.* XIII, 397); it was rehabilitated by Pompey. According to Stephanus (*s.v. Pella*) Pella had another name—Boutis—which, according to Schumacher, perhaps survives in Beit Idis, an Arab village near Pella.[73]

(18) Dion was also a Macedonian colony; this was the name of a large city in Macedon and of several other towns in northern Greece (see Stephanus, *s.v. Dion*). As we have just seen, Stephanus attributed the town's foundation to Alexander the Great: we may discredit this information on the same grounds as those stated above in connection with Pella. The town was captured by Alexander Jannaeus, and obtained self-government from Pompey, and this is all that Josephus relates of its fortunes in the Hellenistic period (*Ant.* XIII, 393; XIV, 75). The precise site is unknown and various conjectures have been expressed; most scholars incline to place the town at Tel el-Asha'ri.[74]

(19) One other city associated its foundation with Alexander the Great, namely Geresh (Gerasa), the modern Jerash, whose famous ruins hold first place among the relics of Greek antiquity in Transjordan.[75] Iamblichus, a neo-Platonist philosopher of the fourth century C.E., writes of Gerasa: "Gerasa is named after the old men (*gerontes*) who set out to war with Alexander, and as they were not fit for warfare, established a colony in that place."[76] The Greek author here attempts to explain the word Gerasa by its phonic resemblance to the Greek word *gerontes;* this is of course a folk etymology without any scientific foundation. The word's root is not clear and it may be Semitic. Although the inscriptions, coins and building remains at Gerasa all originated in the Roman period, there is no doubt that the town was founded in the Hellenistic epoch, and apparently at its beginning, as is evidenced by the cult of Perdiccas which already existed there in the third century B.C.E., likewise by the existence of a group of people who called themselves Macedonians even in the Roman period.[77] Under Seleucid rule the city bore the name of "Antiocheia-on-the-River Chrysorroas," on the evidence of inscriptions and coins, and this name was also in use in the late Roman age.[78] The town was captured by Alexander Jannaeus (*War* I, 104), and undoubtedly obtained its liberty from Pompey. The inscriptions of the Roman period include names of municipal magistrates, which demonstrates the city's development in imperial times. The splendid ruins of Gerasa also witness the opulent life which was lived there in the Roman epoch.

(20) The southernmost city of the Decapolis was Philadelpheia, the ancient Rabbat-Ammon, today Amman, which became a Greek town in the days of Ptolemy II Philadelphus, as Stephanus (*s.v. Philadelpheia*) and Jerome (*ad Ezek.* 25), as well as its name, witness. According to Stephanus the town was also called Ashtoret; this ancient goddess was here apparently identified with Asteria and this was the name of the city goddess as we learn from coins.[79] Asteria was the mother of the Tyrian Heracles (Melkart) and both had a special cult in the town.[80] It is clear then that the Hellenistic city of Philadelpheia was linked by both religion and cult with Tyre, and as new settlers were accustomed to take their country's gods with them to their new abode, it may perhaps be conjectured that Ptolemy Philadelphus used Hellenized inhabitants of Tyre to constitute the citizen body of the new *polis* in Transjordan. Although the city is frequently referred to by its new name of

Philadelpheia, the Greek name was unable to obliterate the ancient title completely; Polybius (V, 71, 4) calls the town Rabbat-Amman (*Rabbat-amana*), as do also the Zenon papyri.[81] At the time of Antiochus III, Philadelpheia was a notable stronghold, and Antiochus only captured it thanks to treachery (Polyb. V, 71). In the fourth century C.E. Ammianus Marcellinus (XIV, 8, 13) still refers to the city in company with Gerasa as one of the strongest fortresses in Arabia.

(21) Apart from the coastal cities and those of the Decapolis, there were several other Greek cities in the country. On the northern frontier lay Paneas (פניאס or פמייס in the Talmud, *Paneas* in Greek, today Banias). The city's name was borrowed from that of the cave sacred to the Greek god Pan,[82] and the same name was applied to the whole district. We do not know what was the town's oriental name, but according to the Talmud, Paneas stood on the site of the ancient Dan.[83] We encounter the Greek name first in the year 200, when Antiochus III defeated Ptolemy's general Scopas near Paneas (Polyb. XVI, 18, 2). In the Hellenistic period the town was apparently of no importance; it underwent a revival under Philip son of Herod, who rebuilt it and changed its name to Caesarea (*Ant.* XVIII, 28).[84] The new name did not take root among the inhabitants, for in the Middle Ages the town was again known as Paneas, which title survives among the Arabs down to the present day.

(22) Among the towns captured by Alexander Jannaeus, Josephus mentions Seleuceia on the shore of the Semechonitis Lake (*Ant.* XIII, 393; *War* I, 105; IV, 2). In the Roman period Seleuceia was regarded as a village (Jos. *Vita*, 37); but it is not to be imagined that this was its situation in the previous period, since the dynastic name evidences that the settlement was organized as a Greek *polis*.[85] Hölscher sees Seleucus I as the founder,[86] but we have already seen that Seleucus I did not rule Palestine. Kahrstedt[87] thinks the town was founded by the Seleucid kings about the middle of the third century, but produces no evidence for this conjecture. The town could only have been founded after the country had been conquered by Antiochus III; it is to be assumed that it was called after Seleucus IV Philopator (187-175). The Greek name has survived down to the present in that of Siluk, southeast of the Semechonitis Lake.[88]

(23) In the same vicinity must also be sought Antiocheia in Ḥuleh. The vale near it is

referred to in the Talmud as "Ḥulat Antiocheia" or "Ḥulata of Antiocheia" (Tos., Dem., II, I; Jer. Dem., II, 22d; Jer. Horayot, III, 48a, etc.), and in Josephus (*War* I, 105; *Ant.* XIII, 394) as Ἀντίοχου φάραγξ. The city itself is mentioned by Josephus as "Antiocheia of Syria" (*Ant.* XV, 359; XVII, 23ff.); but as Schlatter shows,[89] this is an error, and the connection between the town and the Vale of the Ḥuleh proves convincingly that Antiocheia near Lake Semechonitis is meant. The city was no doubt founded by Antiochus III to commemorate his victory over the Ptolemaic general Scopas in 200 B.C.E., and Schlatter thinks (*op. cit.*, 319) that it may have been built at one end of the actual battlefield.

(24) The city of Philoteria on the shore of the sea of Tiberias is mentioned by Polybius in the year 218, when the town handed itself over voluntarily to Antiochus III (Polyb. V, 70, 3-5). In the first century B.C.E. it was captured and destroyed by Alexander Jannaeus. The name points to Ptolemy II Philadelphus as founder of the city, for Philotera was the sister of Philadelphus, and another city by the Red Sea is called by the same name.[90] Philoteria is generally identified with Ḥirbat el-Kerak to the south of the sea of Tiberias, the site of the ancient Bet Yeraḥ or Sinnabris of the talmudic period, but the excavations have not yet yielded decisive proof for this conjecture.[91] The finding of a small hoard of coins of Alexander and his successor, Philip III Arrhidaeus at Bet Yeraḥ may perhaps be taken to prove the existence of a Hellenistic settlement in this part of the sea of Tiberias as early as the opening of the Hellenistic period.[92]

(25) The ancient Bet Shean[93] became the Greek Scythopolis in the Hellenistic epoch. It appears under this name under Ptolemaic administration (*Ant.* XII, 183), and in 218 the city transferred itself voluntarily to Antiochus III (Polyb. V, 70, 5). Alexander Jannaeus ruled it; Pompey restored its independence; and Gabinius rebuilt it. Although Scythopolis stood to the west of the Jordan, it was reckoned among the towns of the Decapolis: Josephus (*War* III, 446) calls it "the largest city of the cities of the Decapolis." Its official deity was Dionysus, as evidenced by the name Nysa which appears on the city's coinage and in authors (Nysa was the mythological birthplace of Dionysus, the god's foster-mother bearing the same name), further by the remains of the temple of Dionysus discovered in the excavations at Bet Shean.[94]

If it is remembered that Dionysus was the principal god of the Ptolemies,[95] it is easy to conclude that Bet Shean received its Greek aspect while the Ptolemies were ruling the country. The town's name, Scythopolis, poses scholars a question of considerable difficulty. According to Hölscher (*Palestine*, 43ff.) and Schürer (II, 171), who follow Synkellos (I, 405, ed. Bonn), its interpretation is "the city of the Scythians," and their view is that the city was called after the Scythians who invaded Palestine in the seventh century B.C.E. (Herod. I, 105). This supposition is hardly acceptable. How did the Greeks know in the fourth century (they were not in the country before that) that 300 years earlier the Scythians had camped just at Bet Shean? Herodotus in his narrative of the Scythians does not mention Bet Shean, and it is hard to suppose that the Greeks learned of it from the local inhabitants. Even if we assume that there remained among the inhabitants of Bet Shean a faint memory of the savage folk from afar who had ruled here in ancient times, they could hardly have known that they had been called Scythians: the name was current only among the Greeks, and connoted all the northern peoples from South Russia to Turkestan; the Scythians of course called themselves by a different name (or names) and these only could the population have learned from their temporary rulers.[96] It may be plausibly suggested that the name "city of the Scythians" (*Skython polis*) was an attempt at an interpretation of the city's name (Skythopolis); in this manner the Greek scholars wished to explain this strange appellation whose origin is, however, evidently not Greek.

The question therefore remains, whence did Bet Shean receive this curious name? Some scholars have sought to derive the name from "Succot" mentioned in Amos 5.26;[97] others have thought that Bet Shean was also called Bet Shekket, a name with the same meaning,[98] but none of these conjectures rests on a firm basis. We must admit that we cannot solve the problem satisfactorily, but it is permissible to determine the direction the inquiry should take: Malalas (V, 139-140) says that the city was also known as Trikomia—"three villages"—which informs us that the town was founded by the unification (synoecism) of three centers of settlement. The name of one of these villages was probably Bet Shean; the names of the other two are unknown, and it may be that the name Scythopolis was derived from one of them.

(26) The rising at Samaria in the time of Alexander the Great, related by Curtius IV, 8, 9 (see p. 47), has been referred to above. Eusebius[99] adds to this account: "Alexander gave the conquered city to the Mace-

donians to inhabit." But in another place[100] Eusebius names
Perdiccas as founder of the city of Samaria, and since he was
not as famous as Alexander, his mention as founder is probably
historically accurate. It may be supposed that Perdiccas founded
it during Alexander's lifetime and on his orders; this is Willrich's
supposition, entertained also by Schürer (II, 195). It may also
be conjectured that Perdiccas, who was supreme ruler in the
years 323-321, elevated the Macedonian colony at Samaria,
which had been in existence under Alexander, to the rank of
a city. In 312 Ptolemy destroyed the place when he evacuated
the country before Antigonus (Diod. XIX, 93, 7). It was destroyed again by Demetrius.[101] The excavations carried out in
Samaria uncovered remains of fortifications—round towers and
a wall.[102] Samaria did not play an important role in the country,
nor do we know if the Macedonians succeeded in striking root
in the town and in developing a large settlement there. Under
John Hyrcanus Samaria was destroyed by the Jews, but restored
under Pompey and Gabinius. Under Herodian rule a new epoch
began in the life of the town, when Herod founded his city of
Sebaste on its site, and henceforward it developed with great
rapidity and played an important part in the life of Roman
Palestine.

      (27) Josephus mentions Are-
thusa only once among the towns of the interior of the country
which were restored by Pompey.[103] He refers to it immediately
after Ashdod and Yavneh, hence there are grounds for thinking
that it too stood in the south of the Philistine Shephelah. Various
attempts have been made to identify the place, partly on topographical grounds,[104] partly on the basis of the resemblance of
the name Arethusa to one of the modern Arab place names,[105]
but none emerges from the realm of conjecture. In my opinion,
that absence of information prevents the satisfactory solution
of the problem; but one thing is beyond doubt: we have to seek
the town near some stream or spring, since Arethusa was the
name of a source-goddess or water nymph in Greek mythology,
and it was applied by the Greeks to many springs and also to
several cities that were built by streams.[106]

      (28-29). I conclude the list
of Greek cities of Palestine with two towns in Idumaea, Marissa
and Adora. Marissa is mentioned by Josephus among the towns
which received their independence from Pompey and were rebuilt by Gabinius, Adora being mentioned among those rebuilt;[107] and this proves that in the Hellenistic period, too, they

were organized as Greek cities. There are further proofs of the diffusion of Hellenism in these cities; the citizens of Adora worshiped Apollo,[108] and at Marissa in the second century B.C.E. dwelt Hellenized Sidonians.[109] From the Zenon papyri it is evident that the towns of Idumaea were in lively commercial contact with Egypt, for Zenon visited Idumaea in the course of his Palestinian journey and purchased slaves there, as has been mentioned above (p. 66).

Some thirty Greek cities, then, were established in Palestine in the Hellenistic period on the orders of the Macedonian kings, and we can determine the approximate chronological order in which they were founded. Gaza was the first Palestinian city to exchange its oriental for a Greek form: Alexander the Great himself issued the order to re-erect it after its destruction in the course of the war. Samaria also received a Macedonian colony as early as Alexander's time and at his order. Perdiccas' term of government and the period of the wars of the Diadochi against the rule of Antigonus (323-301 B.C.E.) left few traces among the cities of Palestine, and the sources are also silent on this period; but we know that besides Samaria and Gaza, Jaffa and Acco too were considerable fortresses in which, without doubt, Macedonian garrisons were permanently stationed. It is therefore possible that even in this early period these towns had begun to draw closer to the customs of the conquerors and to Hellenize. The founder of the Greek city of Gerasa was Perdiccas, his name being also associated with the city of Samaria, so that it is credible that he was the first among the successors of Alexander who sought to plant a Macedonian population in Palestine. Pella and Dion were also perhaps founded in his time, or in that of Antigonus; their Macedonian names, at any rate, point to the early period of the spread of Hellenism in the country. The chief factors impelling the foundation of these Macedonian settlements was probably the desire to safeguard the loyalty of the country's population to Macedonian rulers and the need to settle on the soil soldiers who had completed their term of service in the regular army. Thus Hellenism began to strike root among the Palestinian population even before power passed to the Ptolemies.

But only under the latter (301-200 B.C.E.) did the prosperous period of the Greek towns of the country begin. Ptolemais, Philoteria and Philadelpheia bear witness to the extensive activity of Ptolemy II Philadelphus in Palestine. Two towns called Arsinoë are mentioned by Stephanus in his gazetteer, one in Syria and the other in Coele-Syria; one can be identified, in the writer's opinion, with Damascus (below, p. 442, note 4); the other we probably have to seek among the cities of Palestine. They too were doubtless founded by Philadelphus, for Arsinoë was his much beloved wife and sister. His successor, Ptolemy III Euergetes, also left a memento in the country, as it must have been under him that Pella changed its name to Berenice. The Dionysus cult at Scythopolis testifies to the Ptolemaic influence in that city; and Gaza too was devoted to the dynasty, as can be seen from its resistance to Antiochus III. Not only did these individual towns become Greek *poleis* under the Ptolemies, but all the coastal cities certainly developed in this period and acquired their Greek form, since their life was based on commerce and their geographical situation tied them to the maritime countries, primarily to Ptolemaic Egypt. Nor did the Ptolemies ignore the towns of the Decapolis; the foundation of Philadelpheia and Berenice (Pella) shows their interest in Transjordan, and it would not be an error to ascribe to them the Hellenization of some other towns of the Decapolis, whose strategic value left no room for doubt. Schwartz[110] sees the cities of the Decapolis as a great system of fortifications set up by Seleucus I and Antiochus I against the Ptolemies; but in the writer's opinion the contrary was the case: these towns were constructed by the Ptolemies as defense-points against the Seleucids. They did, indeed, play an important strategic role under the Ptolemies, and when Antiochus III invaded Palestine the Decapolis towns were the strongest fortresses standing in his way; he was unable to press home his attack till he had captured Abila, Gadara and Philadelpheia. Between the years 200 and 198 the Palestinian cities fell under Seleucid rule, but not for long, as only three Seleucid dynasts—Antiochus III (198-187), Seleucus IV Philopator (187-175), and Antiochus IV Epiphanes (175-164)—were active in the country as absolute rulers. After the rebellion of Judah the Maccabee, the kings of Syria could no longer do as they chose there, and the point was finally reached where they had to abandon the country entirely. Even those years left their traces in the city-life of Palestine, although the work of the Seleucids is hardly comparable with that of the Ptolemies in this respect. The Ptolemies came to Palestine when Hellenism had not yet spread through the country, and were able to found new Greek cities by the side of Syrian towns, or to transform Syrian towns into Greek ones. The Syrian kings were in different case; it was their historical fate in Palestine to continue the work commenced by others, since they found the most convenient sites for city-foundations occupied by their predecessors, and nothing remained for them but to change the names of towns long since Hellenized, so setting the Seleucid seal upon them in a purely token fashion. Thus under Antiochus Epiphanes, Ptolemais-Acco became Antiocheia, although the town had been Hellenized a hundred years before. The activity of the Seleucids is especially recognizable in the Decapolis towns, where Susita, Gerasa and Gadara were now renamed Antiocheia after Antiochus (III?), and Abila became Seleuceia, which was also an alternative title of Gadara. Here too the Seleucids were not the first to Hellenize the eastern population, for there had been a century of Ptolemaic rule in Transjordan. If we mention further the city of Seleuceia on the shore of Lake Semechonitis and Gaza, which changed its name to Seleuceia, we shall have exhausted the list of cities founded in Palestine by the Seleucids.

It goes without saying that the Greek cities of Palestine were established according to the same rules as held good in the other countries of the Orient, and most of what has been stated above (p. 21ff.) may therefore be applied to the subject of the Greek cities of that country. Here too the Greek town was first and foremost a *polis* from the juridical point of view—an independent urban community with a council (*boulé*) and magistrates appointed by the people, with authority to conduct its own financial, public and religious affairs in complete freedom. So characteristic was this "autonomy" of the Greek city in Palestine, that we sometimes find the Talmud designating the town itself as *avtonit*,[111] or *boulé*.[112] There exists no historical evidence on the internal organization of the Greek cities of Palestine, and only isolated notices survive here and there, as for example, when Josephus tells us in passing that when Alexander Jannaeus attacked Gaza, the city had a council of 500 members (*Ant.* XIII, 364). We must therefore fall back on parallels from the Roman period; and their use is permissible, since the Romans hardly changed anything in the internal arrangements of the Greek towns, merely restoring to them the home-rule which had been

denied to them in the Hasmonean period. A few examples
will suffice. In the inscriptions of the city of Gerasa, the holders
of municipal magistracies are mentioned, such as the agoranomos, the gymnasiarch, the archons, and so on; the same posts
are alluded to in the inscriptions of the town of Canatha. We
sometimes further read in inscriptions, such as at Gerasa, the
permanent formula "the council and the people" ($\dot{\eta}$ $\beta o v\lambda\dot{\eta}$ $\kappa\alpha\dot{\iota}$ $\dot{o}$
$\delta\hat{\eta}\mu os$) so characteristic of the Greek *polis*.[113] Like all Greek
cities, those of Palestine were also authorized to strike coins,
and the coins of several of them have been preserved.[114] Important parallel material is also provided by the Greek cities
founded in Palestine by Herod and his sons on the model of
those urban communities existent in the country from the
Hellenistic epoch; as in particular the foundation of the city
of Tiberias with its popular assembly, its council of 600 members
its archons, and the rest.[115] The internal organization of the
coastal towns of Phoenicia and Syria, which was that of typical
Greek *poleis*,[116] may serve as an additional parallel for the
organization of the Palestine communities.

As in the other lands, so in
Palestine, the Greek towns served both as a fortress and as an
economic center. Gaza, Jaffa, Dor, Acco, Samaria, Abila, Gadara
and Rabbat-Ammon in the Hellenistic period, all fulfilled a military role as strong fortresses; Gaza and Gadara were outstanding
in this respect. Both these and the other Greek towns were certainly surrounded by walls, as these symbolized civic independence. Not the whole inhabited town, indeed, was so enclosed;
as time went on the inhabitants settled also outside the wall
and the old town remained standing as a fortress and civic
center; so, for example, old Acco served as the citadel of the
new Greek town of Ptolemais.

The city's population was
engaged chiefly in agriculture and commerce. Like every other
Greek city, the Palestinian Greek town controlled the land about
it, and each had its territory, all of whose villages were its
dependents. Here again we have to seek proofs in the Roman
period. Josephus (*Vita* 9) mentions "the villages of the inhabitants of Gadara and Hippos," which impinged on the territories of Tiberias and Scythopolis; this informs us that the
territories of Susita (Hippos), Gadara and Tiberias bordered
one upon the other, and that all the land around the sea of
Tiberias (and the same may have been the case throughout
Transjordan) was in the Roman period divided among the

Greek urban communities.[117] It is true that we should not refer the limits of the territories of the Roman epoch to the Hellenistic period, since the settlement of boundaries, the inclusion of isolated villages within a given territory, and similar operations were the outcome of the work of local rulers and were apt to change from one generation to the next; but in a general way it may be said that the beginning of this process belongs to the Hellenistic period. The majority of the citizens were engaged in agriculture, whether as simple peasants or as the owners of large estates. The tillers of the soil occupied, I believe, an especially important place in the towns of the Decapolis, as the soil of Transjordan was always noted for its quality. It is certainly not by chance that precisely here we find three colonies of Macedonian veterans—at Dion, Pella, and Gerasa.

The commercial function of the Greek cities requires no special emphasis; it is sufficient to recall the Mediterranean coast, which was completely lined with Greek towns from Raphia to Acco. Acco and Gaza were, as stated, important harbor towns, and Jaffa too was then known as a commercial city, although then as now no proper harbor existed there and ships had to anchor off-shore, a risky operation (*War* III, 419f.). It is supposed that Straton's Tower also concentrated on trade, as the place was chosen by Herod in which to found a great city (Caesarea). As time passed, the Decapolis towns likewise developed into commercial communities, for here passed the caravan route from Palestine to Syria (to Damascus, thence through Abila, Baalbek, Emesa, Ḥamat, and Apameia to Antioch) and to Mesopotamia (from Damascus through the Syrian towns to Ḥauran, Edessa and Nisibis, or straight across the desert to the Euphrates).

As in the other oriental countries, the Greek colonies of Palestine were founded on the sites of ancient settlements; here too the Greeks chose to settle in the ancient towns and to make them the centers of their life in the country. Ammonite Rabbat changed its name to Philadelpheia, Acco became Ptolemais and afterwards Antiocheia, Bet Shean—Scythopolis, Bet Yeraḥ—Philoteria, Abel—Seleuceia, Peḥal —Pella, Gerasa—Antiocheia, Susita—Antiocheia, Hippos, and so on. And if there were in Palestine towns whose Greek names alone are known to us (such as Seleuceia and Antiocheia on the shore of Lake Semechonitis, Paneas, Dion, Arethusa and Anthedon), this does not mean that these towns were built on vacant sites, but rather that absence of information prevents us from identifying with sufficient certainty those ancient villages which stood on the same sites before the cities were founded.

What was the external appearance of the Greek city in Palestine in the Hellenistic period? We cannot discuss this question, since the remains discovered in the country during excavations belong in most cases to the Roman period, nor does literature provide material to solve the problem.[118] No doubt the kings assisted in building the towns when they were founded, as they did in several other places; but it is not to be assumed that they supervised the work in person: Ptolemy Philadelphus, for instance, in whose time important towns were founded in the country, did not visit it at all, and the building was doubtless carried out by officials appointed for the purpose by the sovereign.[119] A large number of cities in Palestine received dynastic names, which possessed a purely official value, and there are very few (like Ptolemais) whose dynastic name actually took root: both the oriental population and the Greeks themselves used the ancient titles.[120] In course of time the dynastic and, indeed, the Greek names as a whole, vanished from the memory of the population, and the old appellations again resumed their place. Except for Paneas, Seleuceia (on the shore of Lake Semechonitis) and Anthedon, which are today still known respectively as Banias, Seluk and Teda in Arabic, I do not know a single Greek city-name which has been preserved in the country from the Hellenistic period,[121] while the names Acca (Acco), Amman (Rabbat of the Ammonites) Beisan (Bet-Shean), Jerash (Gerasa), Paḥil (Pahel), Tel Abil (Abel), Susiya (Susita), Jadar (Gadara), Canwat (Canatha), Rapha (Raphia), and others, witness to the vitality of the ancient names. Here too the ancient town prevailed over the Greek city, and in this respect also Palestine was no exception to the rule among the lands of the Orient.

Who were the inhabitants of the Palestinian Greek towns? Let us begin with the alien elements who had come from abroad—the Greeks and Macedonians. Their number cannot be determined, for statistical information has not been preserved, if it ever existed. Nor can we say from which cities and districts in Greece the Greeks came to Palestine; only short and mutilated notices survive, which are not such as to add up to a complete picture. If the coastal town of Anthedon was named, indeed, after Anthedon in Boeotia, it would be possible that the immigrants who settled there came from that country. In Acco dwelt merchants from

Athens even before Alexander and possibly they attracted
further immigrants from that city. In Gadara there also lived
Greeks from Attica.[122] These hints apart, there is no information
in literature on the Greek immigration to Palestine; but that
does not of course mean that they resided only in the afore-
mentioned towns; there were certainly Greeks in most of them,
for a Greek city could neither be created nor strike root in the
country unless Greeks came to it. Possibly Palestine received
its Greek population not directly from Greece, but more particularly from Egypt. The Zenon papyri have revealed the
frequent commercial and administrative links between the two
lands, and probably a certain number of traders and officials
from Egypt who had come to Palestine on chance business
settled down permanently in the country's Greek towns.

We have more information
on the Macedonians. These played a dual role in Palestine as
in all the eastern lands, appearing as soldiers and farmers, and
the two Decapolis towns of Pella and Dion, which were so
called after the corresponding Macedonian cities, were apparently agricultural colonies. The fact that the inhabitants of Pella
refused to Judaize in Alexander Jannaeus' time (*Ant.* XIII, 397),
the city being destroyed by the Jews, informs us that the
Macedonian peasants stoutly maintained their independence and
did not yield their life of freedom lightly. Gerasa and Samaria
too were Macedonian colonies founded at the beginning of the
Hellenistic period, as we have seen above. Besides these four
colonies there were certainly other Macedonian settlements in
Palestine, or mixed settlements of Macedonians and members
of other peoples (like the military cleruchy in the land of
Ammon ruled by Tobiah), but these have left no trace in history.
As to Macedonian garrisons, it is to be assumed that at the beginning of the period there were Macedonians in every large
city of the country, particularly in those which served as fortresses in wartime, such as Gaza and Acco. As under the Ptolemies peaceful conditions generally prevailed, it is not to be supposed that the number of these troops was very large. We also
encounter individual Macedonians at various places, probably
government officials.

The third element among the
population of the Greek towns was constituted by the local inhabitants, the Syrians.[123] Here we are affected by lack of information and have to collect stray references in order to form
a more or less complete picture. Before we go on to study the de-

tails, let us mention the three general facts of which we spoke above (see p. 29ff.): (1) Every Greek town was in the vicinity of some ancient oriental urban center; (2) Local inhabitants also received permission to join the citizen body of the Greek town and to take part in its public life as citizens possessed of equal rights with the Greeks; (3) A complete oriental town could organize itself as a Greek *polis* and obtain all the privileges enjoyed by Greek cities. If we bear in mind these three things, we shall easily see that genuine Greek cities, that is, cities whose populations consisted solely of Greeks, never existed in the country, and that those designated as such were Syrian towns which had become Hellenized, or towns whose populations were of Greeks and Syrians intermingled.

Let us here take note of one phenomenon which had few parallels in other countries, namely, the fact that there were in Palestine many towns which had not changed their ancient names, but must nevertheless be regarded as Greek cities. These were the coastal communities of Raphia, Ascalon, Ashdod, Jaffa, Yavneh, Straton's Tower and Dor, to which may be added the Phoenician coastal towns of Tyre, Sidon, Gebal and the rest. This fact requires an explanation, for the Greek kings were in the habit of changing the names of the smallest towns to Antioch and Seleuceia. Why then did they leave the ancient names unaltered just here, despite the great importance which they attached to the coastal towns as commercial communities? The explanation is probably this: every Greek name indicates the foundation of a Greek city—the creation of an urban society organized as a *polis*—but here such societies did not have to be created, since the coast-towns had already been long organized in a manner similar to the Greek *poleis* and their histories had evolved essentially in an urban setting. After their submission to Alexander little had changed in their internal lives, and under the rule of the Greek monarchs throughout the Hellenistic epoch they retained the same autonomy. They had merely changed their external garb, and become "Greek" cities without modifying their form of life in any respect. These cities remained the Syrian centers they had been before, and beside the Greeks who settled in them in the Hellenistic period, the Syrian inhabitants of the ancient cities remained as citizens possessed of equal rights, composing without doubt the majority within these communities.

We may now examine the historical material to be found in the sources. Let us consider

Gaza, which Josephus calls a "Greek city" (*Ant.* XVII, 320). We know how this "Greek" city was formed; Alexander destroyed it because it had not submitted to him voluntarily, and after he had annihilated or sold into slavery its ancient inhabitants, he gave orders to restore the town and to settle it with people drawn from the surrounding population. Thus these villagers, by race the products of intermixture between Philistines, Arabs and other peoples, became the first citizens of the new *polis*. Apollonia was without doubt a "Greek city": its name was pure Greek. Yet we have seen above that, not the Greek Apollo, but the Phoenician god Reshef ruled the city; and since he remained (in his Hellenistic guise) the chief deity of the new town as well, it is to be concluded that his former worshipers also remained in the town as enfranchised citizens. The ancient deities did not in any sense give way before new competitors from Greece, for Dagon continued to be the principal god of Ashdod, Ashtoret remained in power at Ascalon, and the same was the case in the other urban centers. As time went on, the Syrians acquired Greek customs and the Greek language, and were regarded as Greeks in every respect.

In Caesarea-on-the-Sea, under the Emperor Nero, a feud broke out between the Syrian and Jewish populations, the former seeking to prove to the Jews that they (the Syrians) alone had the authority to be counted as citizens, and claiming that before Caesarea's foundation by Herod (in the Hellenistic period, when on the site of Caesarea stood the Graeco-Phoenician town of Straton's Tower) there had been no Jewish inhabitants at all, the Syrians being the only residents. Hence even though the city had been refounded by a Jew, King Herod, this proved nothing whatever, since the "city itself was of Greeks" (*War* II, 266; cf. *Ant.* XX, 173). Here therefore the Hellenized Syrians are explicitly designated as Greeks, and if in another place Josephus writes (*War* III, 409) that most of the inhabitants of Caesarea were "Greeks," we can easily understand that he means not racial Greeks but Syrians, whose external manner of life had now taken on a Greek coloring. If, moreover, we consider the conflicts between the Jews and the populations of the Greek cities during the great war against Rome, we shall see that in Transjordan, too, it was the Syrians and not the Greeks who were the real enemies of the Jews, and that it was they who constituted the majority of the inhabitants of the Decapolis towns.[124] Having made clear to ourselves the fundamental features of the character of the Greek towns, we must ask: what was their cultural function in Palestine?

It is doubtful that a positive answer can be given to this question. Thirty is a considerable number of towns in a small country like Palestine; but we must not forget that, in a geographical sense, only part of it (the coast, Transjordan on the north, and the regions about the sea of Tiberias and Lake Semechonitis) stood under the direct influence of the towns; in Judaea not a single Greek urban community was founded, nor did Hellenism become deeply rooted in Samaria or Idumaea: it is doubtful if the Macedonian colony at Samaria, or the small towns of Marissa and Adoraim, could modify local habits of life to any considerable degree. But neither could the large Greek towns such as Gaza, Ptolemais and Philadelpheia, for their Hellenism was too feeble to fill a great cultural role.

This does not mean, of course, that they had no cultural influence at all. The Greek *polis* exercised an influence, first, as a political institution, awakening among the Syrian towns the desire to resemble it in internal organization, and spurring them to form their public life in the Greek fashion. Secondly, it could transmit to the population the externals of Greek culture; the populous Hellenic town adorned and beautified by fine buildings and shrines, with its athletic contests and its theaters, made a great impression on the simple villagers who visited it, and perhaps also awoke in them a desire to take part in its interesting and colorful mode of life. Thirdly, the Greek city acted as a permanent center of the Greek language (which was, if nothing more, the official language, and no doubt the spoken tongue among the citizens of the upper classes) and, as literature is linked with speech, the inhabitants of Palestine also could, if they chose, acquire the inner content of Hellenic culture. The works of the Greek poets and philosophers were certainly to be found in the Greek towns, and possibly philosophers and scholars from Greece or the new centers of Hellenic culture such as Alexandria of Egypt sometimes visited Palestine.[125] The man who wished to acquire Greek learning could probably achieve his object to a certain degree in the Greek towns of the country. But when we speak of cultural influence, the reference is not to isolated instances, but to a broad influence working of its own accord and imperceptibly on everyone who came into contact with it. In this sense the Palestinian Greek city was not capable of winning either the country's inhabitants as a whole, or the Jews in particular, for the inner aspect of Hellenism in sufficient measure to achieve the genuine Hellenization of the country, first because the cities there did not act as versatile cultural centers, and secondly because their civilization was not pure Greek civilization, but was intermingled with foreign oriental elements.

        We have already dwelt on the fact (p. 33f.) that the Greek immigrants who came to the oriental countries did not belong to the Greek intelligentsia, but were derived from the lower social strata, generally bringing to the new lands where they settled little beyond the strength of their hands. In this sense presumably Palestine was no exception. Strabo and Stephanus, it is true, mention the names of some philosophers, authors and scholars who originated in the towns of Palestine—Gadara, Gerasa, and Ascalon[126]—but most of these prominent men belong to the Roman period which, as stated, infused new life into Greek culture in the oriental countries; apart from which there was not among them a single one of genuine greatness.[127] Of the cultural activity of the Greek cities of Palestine in the Hellenistic period we hear absolutely nothing. Nor can they be compared with the Hellenistic cultural centers of Egypt or Asia Minor, such as Alexandria or Pergamum. Palestine was a remote corner from the Greek cultural point of view, and when we have said this we have exhausted the issue. The Greeks came thither neither as professors of learning nor as the standard-bearers of art and culture, nor did they rear their towns to promote the Hellenic cultural spirit. They came as soldiers, farmers and merchants, to create a new life for themselves outside their impoverished home-country which could no longer support them. Of course, they organized their lives in the Orient in the style to which they had been accustomed in Greece; but simultaneously they themselves became assimilated to the local inhabitants, who influenced the Greeks no less than the Greeks influenced them. These mixed populations swiftly became the bearers of culture in the Greek towns. It has already been observed (p. 100) that the first inhabitants of the Greek *polis* of Philadelpheia were apparently Hellenized Tyrians, not true Greeks. But the most instructive example is the Idumaean town of Marissa, which was conquered by John Hyrcanus, who forced its population to adopt Judaism (*Ant.* XIII, 257). Later Pompey restored the town, and since he was interested in rehabilitating the Greek towns only, this means that Marissa had been reckoned as such before the Hasmoneans (see above,

p. 104f.). And, in fact, fifty years ago an ancient burial-place was found there with Greek inscriptions and paintings on its walls, whose subjects were in part borrowed from Greek mythology. A number of Greek names were also found inscribed on the tombstones; their bearers, however, were not genuine Greeks, but Hellenizing Sidonians who had settled here in the Hellenistic period. It is quite clear that Hellenism had not penetrated deeply among them, since both Sidonian and Idumaean names are also inscribed on the tombs.[128] Marissa, indeed, was a small and unimportant town, but there is no guarantee that the situation was different in Jaffa, Gaza and Ascalon, for there too the majority of the inhabitants were Syrians who had acquired with facility the external Greek culture, but remained internally as oriental as they had ever been. The people of the Greek city offered their sacrifices and incense not to Apollo and Aphrodite, but to Reshef and Ashtoret, although they called their gods by Greek names. In Palestine we behold the same historical spectacle so familiar in all the other ancient lands from Egypt to India, namely, the fusion of oriental and Greek elements and the gradual prevailing of the former over the latter. In this hybrid culture, which was very far from classical Hellenic civilization, the external garb—speech, nomenclature, and architecture—was generally Greek; the content—religious customs, art, opinion and *Weltanschauung*—remained oriental in origin. This is not the place to examine the foundations of Hellenic culture, but we must be careful not to set too high an estimate on the cultural value of the Greek towns of Palestine and on their influence over the country's population. It must be emphasized that when modern historians describe the Greek Palestinian cities as points radiating the light of Greek culture in the Orient, their view does not fit historical reality; and Greek names do not always constitute evidence of the Greek content of a civilization.

Chapter **3**

JERUSALEM
ON THE EVE
OF THE HELLENISTIC REFORM

Antiochus III's victory over the Ptolemies in the years 200-198 brought the Jews under Seleucid rule. We have seen above that this political change was not associated with any cultural change among the Jews and that the traditional mode of life of the people of Jerusalem lost nothing by the substitution of Syrian Antioch for Egyptian Alexandria as ruler of Judaea. But in course of time the situation altered and in the seventies of the second century there arose among the inhabitants of Jerusalem a new faction composed of Hellenizing Jews, which for several years held power in Judaea and became noted for its strong adherence to Hellenism and for its unconcealed contempt for Jewish tradition. The Hellenizers converted Jerusalem into a Greek town, introduced Greek customs into Jewish life, built a gymnasium and did not even oppose the spread of the Greek gods in Judaea. This group found its shield and patron in the Syrian king Antiochus IV Epiphanes, who intervened in the internal affairs of the land of Judaea and threw the weight of his sword onto the scales of the party struggle. With his aid the Hellenizers were for a time in control of Jerusalem, until another sword, the sword of Judah the Maccabee, put an end to their aspirations and restored the old form of national life.

Nevertheless, if Antiochus intervened with a strong hand in Jewish affairs and created perplexity and demoralization among the people, it should not

117

be forgotten that he had not begun the business, but had merely come to Judaea when he found the way prepared for him by the Jews themselves. Hellenism was not introduced into Israel by the forces outside; part of the Jewish public itself developed an attachment to alien customs and became eager for Hellenistic modes of life to obtain a foothold in Jerusalem. Now if the aspiration to Hellenization arose among the Jews as a result of the internal development of Jewish history, it devolves upon us to investigate the factors which led part of the Jewish community to Hellenization, and we have to ask, first of all, what was the motive of those who inclined in this direction? The obvious and simple answer is that their aim was the spread of Greek culture and that for them Hellenization was based on their consciousness of the advantages of Hellenism over Judaism.

Cultural sympathies and antipathies have, however, a certain social basis. It is a fact that the bearers of the idea of Hellenization among the Jews were not distributed among various classes of Jewish society, but were entirely confined to one class, namely, the ruling aristocracy of Jerusalem. This being the case, the study of the question shifts from the purely cultural to the historical and social spheres, and we may ask what was the reason why the Jewish aristocracy at a given historical moment (that is, in the time of the rule of Antiochus Epiphanes) decided to lead the Jewish people along the road of Hellenization? The more deeply we probe the social structure of the Jewish people in the Hellenistic period, the clearer becomes the fact that Hellenization was only an external expression of an inner historical process, which in reality bore no direct relation to cultural questions. This process has to be studied for the correct appreciation of the "philo-Hellenic" movement in the brief period before the rebellion of Judah the Maccabee.

Our sources of information on the social and cultural situation in Judaea during the decades preceding the flowering of Hellenism in Jerusalem are very meager. Material is provided by two literary works only, namely, Josephus' story of Joseph son of Tobiah and his son Hyrcanus; and Ben Sira's *Book of Wisdom*. But it must be remembered that it was not the intention of these authors to transmit exact historical facts. The motive of Josephus' narrative was to praise the activities of Joseph son of Tobiah and his son Hyrcanus, hence it is full of legendary features which frequently arouse doubts as to their historical truth. As for Ben Sira (Sirach), he was not a historian at all, but a moral preacher who was instructing his disciples in wisdom and understanding. Nevertheless, these books contain several important details which can furnish valuable material for the clarification of the following questions: what was the social environment in which Hellenism began to strike root, and who were the first Jews to pave the way for Greek culture?

Before we proceed to a detailed analysis of these sources, it would be well to glean any hint we can from other sources likely to aid the historian's understanding of the social situation of the Jewish people in the period under discussion.

Hecataeus of Abdera says that the Jewish people was "very populous"; he estimates the inhabitants of Jerusalem at 120,000 people and the area of the city at fifty stades.[1] There is no need to accept these figures as strictly historical; the inaccuracy of the ancient writers where figures were concerned is sufficiently well known, and Hecataeus was certainly no exception. However, the size of the city is further confirmed by Agatharchides, and the figures on the city's area to be found in other authors fall little short of that of Hecataeus.[2] One thing seems certain; Hecataeus would not have emphasized the size of the city and its population without any support from the facts. Whether he had seen the city himself or had heard of it from eyewitnesses, he gained the impression that it was a large and populous town.[3] This evidence, given by a Greek historian around the year 300, has considerable importance for the fundamental problems of the Hellenistic period. The development of the Jewish people in the pre-Hasmonean epoch, the attempted Hellenistic reform, the foundation of the Hasmonean state, the nation's expansion over the whole of Palestine and the neighboring lands—none of these things can be understood unless attention is paid to the principal fact, namely, that at the beginning of the Hellenistic era the Jews were already a numerous people, the natural frontiers of whose country were too narrow to hold them.

Among the classes of Jewish society in Jerusalem and Judaea, the priestly class held chief place. Hecataeus puts the number of priests in his time at some 1500 (*C. Ap.* I, 188), which is inconsistent with the much higher figure (4289) given by Nehemiah (7.39-42), and scholars have offered various conjectures in order to reconcile the contradiction.[4] This is no place to discuss the question in full; what is important is that, of the entire Jerusalem population, Hecataeus takes note of only the priests, which means that in a stranger's eyes this class occupied the most important position in the city's society. Another outsider, a Jew from the Alexandrian Diaspora who composed the *Letter of Aristeas*, confirms Hecataeus' impression: although Aristeas' account of Palestine is much more detailed than that of Hecataeus, his interest too was almost entirely confined to the Temple, to the High Priest's splendid appearance before the people, and to the priestly class that worshiped and served in the shrine.[5] Ben Sira, as we have seen (p. 80), also devoted phrases full of poetic enthusiasm to the account of the magnificent appearance of the High Priest Simon. It is therefore with some justification that scholars are in the habit of calling the social regime in Judaea a "theocracy," or a "hierocracy," for not merely was the spiritual leadership of the people in the hands of the priests, but their class was the strongest and the wealthiest among the classes of Jerusalem from the political and social viewpoints.

We shall see below that the Temple also served at this period as a deposit-bank of considerable importance, and its association with this treasury gave a solid financial basis to the power of the priestly class. It is not of course to be supposed that all the priests were rich and highly connected. In the Roman period the difference between the richer and poorer priests was very considerable and even created actual class-hatred between the two sections,[6] and it is not to be assumed that the situation was different in the Hellenistic period. The list of those who had returned from the Babylonian exile preserved in the books of Ezra and Nehemiah indicates that the priests, like the rest of the people, were divided into kinship groups (Ezra 2.36-38; Neh. 7.39-41), while the division of the class into families was a regular occurrence at a later period.[7] It is therefore clear that in the Hellenistic period also the priestly class was divided into families, and among them were rich and highly connected families that controlled the Temple, the city and the whole country, while others had to be content with little. Among all these, that of the Oniads, who held the hereditary post of High Priest, was the noblest and the wealthiest.[8]

The sources are silent on the secular aristocracy; nevertheless, there is no doubt that they were the strongest class after the priests. In a certain sense the secular aristocracy was older than that of the priests: the Jerusalem "theocracy" was not created in a day, but had developed gradually, as authority was slowly transferred from the satrap or vice-satrap to the High Priest; this process was complete, as we have seen above (p. 58), only in the period of Alexander. In the Persian period, not the priests, but the "nobles" (*horim*) and the "rulers" (*s'ganim*), who are frequently referred to in Nehemiah, ruled the people. As the latter on its return from Exile was divided into families, it is to be assumed that inequality prevailed among them from the first, according to what had been the material situation of each in exile. Nor had land-distribution in Judaea been carried out on the principle of strict equality, and this also was apt to accentuate the class differences between rich and poor. It will certainly be no error to suppose that the *horim* and *s'ganim* were the heads of the wealthy kinship groups who governed the people by virtue of their position as owners of large estates.[9] The dependence of the small peasants on these rich men is proved by Nehemiah's agrarian reform, which was directed against the *horim* and the *s'ganim*: Nehemiah reports how the people "cried to him" concerning the peasants' agricultural property (fields, vineyards, olive-groves and homesteads) which had passed in mortgage to the rich in return for the money given to them as loans; the peasants' plight had become depressed to the point where their sons and daughters were enslaved to the wealthy (Neh. 5.1ff.). Nehemiah was compelled to "contend" with the *horim* and *s'ganim* (*ib.* 7) in order to compel them to agree to the reform, namely, the cancellation of debts and the restoration of all the confiscated property to its former owners (*ib.* 11).

Nehemiah's testimony therefore makes it plain that in his time large estates had begun to develop in Judaea, and although his reform was likely to have altered the situation to a considerable extent, the very fact of the reform bears witness to the existence of an entire class of large landowners. The secular aristocratic group in Judaea, therefore, was based economically on two sources of livelihood, both generally characteristic of the nobility of the ancient world (especially in Roman Italy), namely, income derived from agricultural holdings, and high posts in the administration. We do not know how this class developed after Nehemiah's time, but it may be assumed with complete confidence that the division into families or kinship groups continued to exist as before, since important families are frequently mentioned in the Hellenistic and Roman periods. Unfortunately we are unable to distinguish between priestly families and those of the secular nobility—the sources are not always concerned to make the situation clear by such a distinction—and we shall see below that even the origin of an important family like that of the Tobiads is not as clear as we could wish. We know even less about other families whose names have been discovered in excavations or are mentioned incidentally in the literature of the period,[10] and a detailed study of the high-born families of Judaea in the Hellenistic-Roman era has still to be written; it would be of great value for the investigation of the social life of the period.

When Nehemiah speaks of the classes in Jerusalem, in one place he names them as follows: "Jews, priests, *ḥorim* and *s'ganim*" (2.16). The "Jews" are evidently the simple people, the small peasants of the countryside, the laborers and city craftsmen. Under Nehemiah the countryside far exceeded the town: "Now the city was wide and large but the people were few therein, and the houses were not builded" (7.4). Not only the small peasants, but also the *ḥorim*, *s'ganim* and even part of the priests lived outside the city, on their estates, appearing in the city purely for business purposes. Nehemiah improved matters as far as he was able, by organizing a census, assembling the people "to be reckoned by genealogy," and as a result "the captains of the people" came to live in Jerusalem, the people drew lots "to bring one of ten to dwell in Jerusalem the holy city, and the nine others dwelt in the other cities," that is, in the provincial towns of Judaea (11.1). From this we learn that in Nehemiah's time the Jerusalem community had not yet outgrown the framework of a small rural community whose economic interests were entirely restricted to its farms, its vineyards and its olive groves.

Even after Nehemiah, the small peasant continued to constitute the majority of the Jewish people in Judaea. One important piece of information has been preserved by Hecataeus, who says that a law existed in Judaea prohibiting private individuals from selling their estates, in order to prevent the wealthy from concentrating land in their hands.[11] This law was a natural continuation of the social reform of Nehemiah, who had ordered the cancellation of debts and the return of agricultural property to its former owners, while the law mentioned by Hecataeus aimed at preventing a reversion to the original situation and checked the future growth of large holdings at the expense of the small holdings of the humble peasant.[12] Although it is not to be assumed that this law completely put an end to the development of the large estate,[13] it was able to preserve the small holdings for many generations and saved the Jewish peasant from the fate which befell his brother in Italy in the second century B.C.E. Hence the Jerusalem community retained its agricultural character throughout the Hellenistic period. Aristeas, in his account of the country, dwells first and foremost on its agriculture (107ff.), speaking of the fields of wheat and the other grain, of the olive plantations, vineyards and honey, the dates and the other fruits, finally alluding to the excellent grazing for livestock (*ib*. 113). The evidence for the various agricultural branches of the countryside is plentiful also in the Roman period.[14]

Although Nehemiah spoke of Jerusalem as a "wide and large city," and deplored its small population (7.4), Hecataeus found it well populated (cf. above, p. 119). From this we may conclude that the city developed very rapidly at the end of the Persian period till, at the commencement of the Hellenistic epoch, it was both large and important. Without considering those classes which dwelt there and were simultaneously bound up with their country estates (the secular aristocracy and part of the priestly class), the original city populace was composed of craftsmen, merchants and people concerned in finance, such as tax-collectors, moneylenders and the like. Of these three classes, only the first could be regarded as old, established in the town since the time of the return from exile. Nehemiah himself refers to the craftsmen of various kinds organized in their craft-guilds: metal-workers, herbalists, peddlers, bakers and "medicine men" (physicians), and several other types of craftsmen should no doubt be added.[15] As in every ancient city, the craftsmen of Jerusalem constituted the chief part of the urban "proletariat" that earned its living by diligent and hard work, but was also alert, nervous and quick to blaze up, and hence the first in line to take part in any political disturbance or social revolution, whereas the rural population, sluggish in thought and deed, was much less prone to swift and hasty action. The merchant class, for its part, developed slowly and had but shallow roots in Jewish history in Palestine.

In Nehemiah's time trade was conducted chiefly in foodstuffs and was in the hands of the surrounding peasants who brought their produce to the city (13. 15); the fish trade, on the other hand, was in Tyrian hands (*ib*. 16), whence it may be deduced that a Jewish trading class had not yet been created in Jerusalem to undertake journeys to distant countries. This is not surprising in view of the fact that the trade in all valuable products was conducted in ancient times by sea, an element remote from the hill-dwellers of Judaea and alien to their outlook. The situation changed little in the Hellenistic period. Aristeas indicates that it was the Arabs who imported into Judaea spices, precious stones and gold—luxuries from afar (114). As we have seen in the previous chapter, the seacoast in the Hellenistic period was lined with Hellenized towns, and clearly all the trade between Palestine and the maritime countries passed through them, irrespective of whether their own citizens were merchants or whether the towns merely served as the residence of commercial agents from overseas. There would not, therefore, have been a developed merchant class in Jerusalem in the early Hellenistic period,[16] still less would there have been financiers. All such groups were the result of the Jewish people's development during the Hellenistic epoch itself, and their appearance in considerable numbers is good evidence for the beginning of the new era in Judaea and Jerusalem. Of this more below.

Another very important class, qualitatively if not quantitatively, must be mentioned here, namely, the scribes or interpreters of the Law. The beginning of this class goes back to the time of the return from the Exile, or at any rate to that of Ezra and Nehemiah, and the name itself is borrowed from Persian officialdom.[17] According to the biblical tradition, the interpretation of the commandments of the Torah in all matters of law and justice was entrusted to the priests,[18] and indeed Ezra, the scribe *par excellence*, belonged to that class. However, for many reasons, the priests were unable to retain this important authority for more than a certain number of generations, although it is to be assumed that at the commencement of the Second Temple period they had been the official interpreters of law.

The Jerusalem theocracy gradually transformed the priests into an exclusive caste, superior to the people, sometimes oppressing it with a high hand; they constituted the Jewish aristocracy, the wealthy landed group, and quite naturally drew away from the poor and their troubles. The urban population sought other intellectual leaders who lived and thought in a manner more akin to themselves. Hence rose the class of scribes, the flesh and bone of the broad city populace, which took upon itself the task of interpreting the Torah neglected by the priests.[19] Thus was created the Oral Law as a continuation, interpretation and supplementation of the Written

Law. Presumably the opposition between the priests and the scribes arose initially not from the fact that the priests recognized the written word only, while the scribes interpreted it and made a number of new laws (the written word also required a certain interpretation if it was to be applied to actual life), but from the readiness of the priests to be satisfied with a brief *official* interpretation, while the scribes carried out a profounder investigation, extending it to every sphere of public life; the scribal interpretations later became inestimably richer and deeper than those of the priests, till the official interpretations lost all importance.

Possibly the new scribal interpretations were delivered in the synagogues which had now for the first time risen and spread in Judaea, and thus was created the important opposition between the Temple and the Synagogue.[20] At all events (we must eschew dogmatism, since lack of evidence permits only conjecture), in the early Hellenistic period the class of scribes held a respected place among the various classes of the capital, and the nation's entire brains—its intelligentsia, to use a modern term, was concentrated among the men of this class. And as it was natural for this intelligentsia, engaged permanently and professionally in questions of law and justice, customs, religion and observance, to acquire a certain ideology, it is not surprising to find a special sect among the scribes, the sect of the Ḥasidim, who constituted its external expression.[21]

The Ḥasidim are mentioned for the first time in historical literature in the period of Judah the Maccabee as an already established sect (I Macc. II, 42); hence it is clear that they originated at an earlier period. There are some grounds for the supposition that the sect was first organized under Simon the Just—at the beginning of the second century B.C.E.[22] An important change took place among the scribes under his rule: Simon the Just himself belonged, apparently, to the Ḥasidim and, as he was chief and leader of the theocratic commonwealth, the scribal interpretations were accepted by the priesthood, and the Oral Law fostered by the scribes was declared by the Jerusalem community to be the official authoritative interpretation of the Mosaic Law.[23] If it is recalled that just at that time the Jewish "ancestral laws" were officially ratified by King Antiochus III as the fundamental constitution of the Jewish community of Judaea and Jerusalem (above, p. 83), it will be easily understood how great was the social and cultural importance of the silent revolution which took place in the capital under Simon the Just. The scribal class, chiefly represented by the Ḥasidic sect, was elevated to a position of authority in every matter of law and justice, and thus became part of the ruling group in the Jewish theocracy.[24] We have reviewed the various classes existing in Judaea and Jerusalem at the beginning of the Hellenistic period and we may now return to the main question which concerns us, namely, that of the emergence of the Hellenizing movement and its development among the Jewish community. The social basis of this movement will now be easier to discover and the behavior of the various kinds of Hellenizers will be more comprehensible. We may begin with the story of Josephus about Joseph son of Tobiah and his son Hyrcanus.

The residence of the Tobiads and the family's origin have been discussed above (p. 64), and something may be added on the latter subject. From the Book of Nehemiah it may be deduced that Tobiah "the Ammonite" was no stranger in Jerusalem, but stood in frequent contact with the prominent men of Judaea, being the son-in-law of one of them. His son Jonathan, moreover, married a daughter of one of Jerusalem's prominent men (Neh. 6.18). He also had access to the Temple, since Elyashiv the Priest made a special chamber in the Temple court for him (Neh. 13.4-8). His name, Tobiah, and that of his son, Jonathan (Yeho-natan), are sufficient evidence that he belonged to the cult of the Jewish God in Jerusalem. All these facts justify the question, whether Tobiah was not of priestly descent: his links with the priesthood are beyond doubt, for Elyashiv the Priest was his relative (Neh. *ib.*) and we shall see below that Joseph son of Tobiah was the nephew of Onias II, the High Priest. In view of the fact that the leaders and representatives of the nation to the foreign authorities belonged at this period to the priests, it may be conjectured that the brilliant career of Joseph son of Tobiah at the royal court of Egypt was possible chiefly because he belonged to the ruling group, the priests. Tobiah the contemporary of Zerubbabel—one of the family's forebears, if Maisler's conjecture is correct—may have been a priest, since he is mentioned together with Jedaiah, one of the prominent priests of the time.[25] The silence of the sources, however, does not permit definite conclusions on this question.

In his *Antiquities* Josephus relates the biographies of Joseph and his son Hyrcanus in great detail.[26] Not every detail need be dwelt on; scholars have more than once pointed out the legendary aspect of the narrative and the untrustworthiness of several features of it. Nevertheless we need not follow Wellhausen in rejecting the historical value of the story completely,[27] and if we put aside the fabulous element in Josephus' narrative, a short account remains which is more or less consonant with historical reality. Under King Ptolemy of Egypt (we shall see below which Ptolemy Josephus meant) the High Priest Onias II refused to deliver the large tribute which he paid annually to the Egyptian sovereign. The king, angered, sent his envoy to Jerusalem with a severe message and the threat that, if Onias did not pay, he would divide Jewish territory into cleruchies and send troops to Jerusalem as military settlers. Despite these threats Onias refused to yield and maintained his former decision.

Then arose Joseph, the youthful son of Tobiah and of Onias' sister, called the people together to an assembly in the Temple, and proposed himself as emissary to the king to effect a compromise in the dispute. The people agreed to his proposal, and after he had honored the Egyptian envoy with fine gifts and borrowed money for the journey from friends in Samaria, he went down to Egypt, appearing there before the king as chief (*prostates*) of the Jews. He succeeded not only in softening the king's wrath, but also in negotiating a successful deal in his own favor, by leasing from Ptolemy the taxes imposed by the king on Syria; from this time his wealth increased steadily, till he became one of the richest men of his generation. He acted as tax-gatherer for twenty-two years, and bequeathed his wealth to his numerous sons.

Josephus' story of Joseph the son of Tobiah dovetails into his narrative of Hyrcanus son of Joseph. If we divest this story also of its legendary elements, we get an historical picture whose essence is as follows: Hyrcanus was clever and energetic, loved by his father and envied by his brothers, and jealousy led to hatred. When on one occasion Hyrcanus was sent by his aged father to Egypt to congratulate the king on the birth of a son, he was able to gain the king's favor, but in so doing spent much money from his father's funds in Egypt, so that on his return to Jerusalem a quarrel broke out between him and his father and brothers, which compelled him to seek refuge across the Jordan. There he built a strong fortress, which served also as a resort for his many pleasures, and passed the time fighting the Arabs. These wars were not to the liking of the Syrian government, although under Seleucus IV it did nothing to prevent them; but after the accession of Antiochus Epiphanes, Hyrcanus saw that he could not stand up to the new king and committed suicide. His entire property passed to Antiochus.

Such are the few details of the life of Joseph and Hyrcanus which may be regarded as appropriate to historical reality. We may now examine some of the details of the story and deal with the chronological problem.

Scholars have already demonstrated Josephus' error in placing his story of Joseph *after* his account of the conquest of the country by Antiochus III. According to the same writer Palestine in Joseph's time was in Seleucus' hands, but Antiochus III gave the country's revenues to Ptolemy V Epiphanes as a dowry granted to his daughter Cleopatra when she married the latter (*Ant.* XII, 154): by this supposition Josephus sought to explain the strange fact that Joseph son of Tobiah negotiated with Ptolemy when the country was already subject to the Seleucids. This explanation cannot stand up to criticism. Although Antiochus III did actually promise Ptolemy Epiphanes his share in the revenues of Coele-Syria,[28] we do not know whether or not the pledge was official, and it is clear that he never kept it; Polybius (XXVIII, 1.3) says clearly that from the time of the Paneas campaign Coele-Syria remained in Seleucid hands. The main point is that the question concerned solely Ptolemy's right to enjoy the revenues and not Antiochus' authority to rule the country, which Josephus specifically negates in his story, when he depicts Ptolemy as ruling the country with unlimited power and threatening to drive Jews from their land.[29] It is clear that all the events described by Josephus occurred when the country was really subject to Egypt—before 200 B.C.E.—since after that year the rule of Coele-Syria passed into Seleucid hands.

We are still far from solving the chronological question. Ptolemaic rule in Palestine lasted a century; to which period are we to attribute Josephus' story? Some scholars put the appearance of Joseph the son of Tobiah in the year 219 and think he was active from that year to 198.[30] But if Joseph was son of Tobiah, the contemporary of Philadelphus, it is hard to imagine that he had begun his activity only in 219, especially as he was then, on Josephus' evidence, a young man.[31] His activity must be ascribed to the epoch of Ptolemy III Euergetes (246-221), a conjecture which finds authority in Josephus' own account, for on one occasion he calls the king Ptolemy Euergetes (*Ant.* XII, 158), although at the time to which he assigns Joseph's activity, Ptolemy Epiphanes, not Euergetes, was ruling Egypt. This was probably what he found in his source and he copied the name without noticing the contradiction between it and what he himself had previously written.[32] He calls the king's wife Cleopatra, whereas Euergetes' queen was Berenice; but the error can easily be explained: at the beginning of the second century, after Cleopatra, daughter of Antiochus III, had entered the family of the Ptolemies, the name persisted there and nearly all the queens of Egypt were so named, hence it is not surprising that Josephus replaced the rarer name Berenice with that of Cleopatra to which he was well accustomed.

The year of Joseph's appearance may be tentatively fixed with greater precision. Büchler describes Onias' refusal to pay the tribute as an act of hostility against the Ptolemies and evidence of sympathy for the Seleucids; he associates the event with a war between the Ptolemies and the Seleucids. He was certainly right, but was only mistaken in thinking that the war was that of Antiochus III against Ptolemy Philopator in 218: we have already seen that Joseph was a contemporary of Euergetes and not of Philopator. In Euergetes' time, however, there was also war between Egypt and Syria; and with many other scholars we may link the unrest in Jerusalem with the events of this earlier conflict.[33] The year 242 would have been the most suitable for Onias' attempt to break off his connections with Egypt and to go over to Syria. That year Seleucus II Callinicus gathered his scattered forces, which had been defeated by Ptolemy Euergetes at the beginning of the campaign, and took the offensive against Egypt; he was able to beat Ptolemy's forces on several occasions and drive them back on Damascus. These victories may have aroused Onias to hope that Seleucus would be the victor, hence he refused to pay Ptolemy the customary tribute, in the belief that his rule was at an end. However, he encountered resistance from the supporters of Egypt whose most prominent representative was Joseph the son of Tobiah; Seleucus' successes were short-lived and Onias' attempt remained an isolated incident which brought no change in the Jewish political situation.

This chronological conjecture enables the further approximate determination of the other dates in the narrative. When Hyrcanus made his journey to Egypt his father was an old man; hence he made it at the end of the third century, a short time before the Seleucids conquered the country. Hyrcanus was then a young man, and he died in 175, or shortly after,[34] being therefore about fifty at his death. None of these dates contradicts the other; but Josephus gives one more piece of information which can throw the whole chronological order of the narrative into confusion: this is that Joseph son of Tobiah held his post of tax-collector for twenty-two years, and if we assume that he obtained it on his first journey to Egypt, as Josephus thinks, presumably in 242, he must have resigned it about the year 220. However, from Josephus' story of Hyrcanus' journey to Egypt it emerges that Joseph then still retained his post[35] and was of advanced age, whereas in 220, at least, he was not yet so. Josephus' chronology as a whole contains a pronounced contradiction, in that these three items of information—first, that Joseph was a youth when he obtained the post of tax-collector; second, that he served in the post twenty-two years; and third, that he retained it in old age—are mutually irreconcilable.

There seems to be only one solution to the problem, namely, to suppose that Josephus was mistaken in thinking that Joseph obtained his post on his first journey to Egypt. Josephus' error is evidenced by one detail in his narrative: Joseph visited Egypt to settle the conflict that had broken out between Ptolemy and Onias, that is, he went as envoy of the people of Jerusalem, with a clearly defined objective: How are we to explain that he returned to Palestine as tax-collector? Can such matters have been arranged incidentally, as if they were of secondary importance? Clearly there was no direct connection between the political question which Joseph had to solve in Egypt, and his private affairs, and the two activities must therefore be distinguished. Since Joseph visited Egypt more than once (cf. *Ant.* XII, 187), the leasing of the taxes may legitimately be ascribed to another journey. This supposition removes the chronological difficulty in Josephus.[36] The precise dates cannot in any case be determined, but the approximate order of events may be described as follows:

Birth of Joseph	270-260
Onias' clash with Ptolemy	242-240
Joseph appointed tax-collector	230-220
Hyrcanus visits Egypt	205-200
Death of Hyrcanus	175-170

We may now pass to the internal analysis of the historical material preserved in Josephus' narrative. This is a legend, and we may ask with some surprise, what was it that caused the transformation of the life of Joseph the Tobiad into a hero tale? He was neither a general nor a great statesman, much less a man of intellect; yet his name has survived in Jewish history, in contrast to several important men who headed public life in Judaea, whose names are lost to us for good, and even the High Priests of the period have left no clear memory. This curious fact can be rightly interpreted only on the assumption that Joseph introduced new principles into the Jewish society of his time. What were they and what was the innovation made by Joseph in the Land of Judaea?

To answer this question it is essential to survey Joseph's entire career. His father Tobiah was perhaps the first of the Tobiads not to see himself confined to the narrow frontiers of his estate in Transjordan and to dream of a more important political role. As a member of a noble house, he wedded the High Priest's daughter and so obtained a foothold in Jerusalem, coming into contact with the Ptolemaic administration and acquiring recognition as its military representative in Transjordan. He was bound by ties of business and perhaps friendship with Apollonius, the all-powerful finance minister of Philadelphus. His son Joseph knew well how to exploit his father's connections and, as the High Priest's nephew, was one of the respected residents of Jerusalem; the estate where he was born and which had apparently been acquired by his father, was near the city.[37] Yet it is to be doubted whether this family, whose origin was linked with Transjordan, found it easy to acquire the entire ancient tradition of the Jews of Jerusalem. Josephus relates that, before his journey to Alexandria, Joseph borrowed money from his "friends in Samaria" (*Ant.* XII, 168), and anyone knowing the eternal hostility and detestation prevailing since Nehemiah's day between the Jewish community of Jerusalem and the Samaritans will quickly grasp that no loyal and patriotic Jew could have had "friends" at Samaria.[38] As remarked above (p. 71), the cultural atmosphere in Tobiah's home was "Greek," and this atmosphere Joseph had breathed from his childhood on.

From the beginning of his career Joseph appears as an "international" figure standing above the "petty" interests of his native country. This "internationalism" was based mainly on money. Just as he had friends at Samaria ready to grant him loans in the hour of need, so he stood in communication with powerful people at the court of Alexandria who were also prepared to aid him (*Ant.* XII, 180, 185), and these connections were especially important to him, since here was the financial center of the world and here the supreme administration of Palestine was focused. His journey to Alexandria after the Onias affair may not have been his first visit, and possibly from his youth on he had discharged a certain fiscal function as representative of the Ptolemaic government in Jerusalem, initially perhaps merely as his father's assistant. This would enable us to understand his political position vis-à-vis Onias: as an Egyptian official Joseph was closely bound to Egypt, for there lay all his prospects of future success. His relatives supported him and aided him to strengthen his position: Josephus tells us that when Onias refused to pay tribute to Ptolemy, Joseph was not in Jerusalem; but that his mother, Onias' sister, immediately informed him of the matter as if to warn him that his affairs were in danger. He at once returned to Jerusalem, frustrated Onias' intention and restored the people to its former loyalty to Egypt. This was the beginning of his career. He appeared before Ptolemy as "head" (*prostates*) of the Jews. To our regret we have no clear information on the character of this position; as we have seen above (p. 59), the post of the *prostasia* was in the hands of the High Priest at the beginning of the Hellenistic period, on the evidence of Hecataeus, and evidently carried with it considerable profits. Joseph accused Onias of retaining the *prostasia* out of greed for gain (*Ant.* XII, 162); it is therefore to be assumed that the tax collection in Judaea was concentrated wholly or partly in the hands of the *prostates*, who could hardly have enjoyed any other opportunity of enriching himself from his position.[39] It is at any rate clear that the post of *prostates* was of high financial and administrative character, apparently the highest in Judaea, and it now passed to Joseph. Thus occurred the first breach in the edifice of the theocracy of Jerusalem: the responsibility for the levying of taxes and their transmission to the king was removed from the High Priest and handed to a professional financier.

Joseph the son of Tobiah became, in Hellenistic terminology, the *dioiketes* of the High Priest; but the responsible tax-collector was also liable for the country's allegiance to the government, hence he was not just a financial official but the people's political representative to the king. The manner of Josephus' account of the transfer of power from Onias to Joseph is quite idyllic: Onias resigning his post voluntarily, as it were, the people empowering Joseph to appear before the king as its delegate or *prostates*. It is improbable that Joseph's victory was so easily won; there was doubtless a conflict between the parties at Jerusalem before the Jews agreed to hand over power to a *novus homo* and to alter the ancient political tradition in such an off-handed manner. The fact was, at any rate, that there now arose, alongside the traditional theocratic authority, a new power based on the personal financial skill and experience of a private individual who was closely bound up with the broad international field.

This field was more important to Joseph than the tiny land of Judaea. Hence his second act, namely, to lease from the king the collection of the taxes "from all Coele-Syria, Phoenicia, Judaea and Samaria" (*Ant.* XII, 175).[40] This activity had no bearing on the internal development of Judaea; it was undertaken on his own initiative. Josephus' story of the negotiations between Joseph and the king at Alexandria is full of legendary traits, although its core is in harmony with historical reality, for the annual leasing of the taxes was a permanent practice in Egypt, and there are grounds for thinking that those abroad were also leased by the kings to private individuals, as Josephus relates.[41]

As *prostates* of the Jews, Joseph would certainly have appeared from time to time at Alexandria to renew his lease on the taxes of Judaea, and simultaneously would have appeared the representatives of the Greek cities, each of whom leased the taxes of his own town. Joseph's financial ability apparently was much superior to that of the Syrians; at any rate the program of financial reform which he proposed to the king was his own invention, and was simple: why should the king negotiate with various people, work out the conditions of lease and demand a guarantee from each one? Let him hand over the lease of the whole of the province of Syria to one man, and not only would the royal treasury not suffer from the change, but would profit from it. At the same meeting Joseph proposed himself for the task and promised to remit to the king double the sum he had received till then.[42] The king agreed to his proposal, and thus a fundamental change took place in the system of leasing the taxes of Ptolemaic Syria.

No other Jew had ever attained so high a rank; and clearly his authority grew also in the eyes of his compatriots, before whom he now stood as a man successful in a peculiar field, possessing a unique importance; they could be proud of him. Not so the Syrians and the citizens of Greek cities, who were compelled to notice that a stranger was performing an important function in their internal life. Attempts were made to resist him, and the cities of Ascalon and Scythopolis refused to pay the taxes which he imposed. But as a government tax-gatherer Joseph was a powerful person, supported by the army of Ptolemy. He punished both towns severely and executed some of their most respected citizens; his action was confirmed by the king.[43] After this display of force the Syrian towns submitted to Joseph; nor do we hear of any further rebellion or insubordination.

The principles introduced by Joseph the Tobiad into Judaea are now clear. They were the principles of the Hellenistic epoch as a whole, dominated by the striving of the strong personality to make its way in life. Joseph's character manifests those basic traits so typical of a number of Greeks of the period: immense willpower, rapidity of action, self-confidence and, resulting from them, undisguised contempt for ancestral tradition. Through quiet unchanging Jerusalem new winds were suddenly blowing, as if a window had been suddenly thrown open to reveal all the wealth and splendor of the wide world, a world where power and money reigned supreme, annulling religious, national and moral tradition. Samaritans might be negotiated with if profits were to be gained from the business; it was permissible to live at the king's court, to eat forbidden food at his table, and to pursue Greek dancing girls, if thereby a man could gain entry to the society necessary to his career; it was ethical to attack peaceful cities and to slay their citizens, if it was likely to strengthen a man's position as royal official. But all these things which were "permitted" in the Greek world were in complete contradiction to the spirit of Jewish tradition.[44] A Jew of the type of Joseph the Tobiad had no alternative but to quit the narrow framework of Jewish tradition or even to encounter it in head-on collision, and although we hear nothing of such a clash, the fact that from Joseph's family originated the "sons of Tobiah," the politicians who under Antiochus Epiphanes headed the Hellenistic movement in Jerusalem, itself suffices to explain in which direction the sympathies of Joseph and the members of his family inclined.

Joseph

One of his sons was Hyrcanus, whose life also became a legend, and here too the question is apposite: why? It is extremely difficult to discover the answer, as the legendary in Josephus has blurred Hyrcanus' real life-story by its false details. The only way is to analyze the story and to seek the historical nucleus hidden in it, commencing with his journey to Egypt.

Why did he go to Egypt and what did he do there? In the story as related by Josephus details are given, most of which are incredible. Moreover, the narrative seems to stop in the middle and its point becomes incomprehensible. Hyrcanus is a clever and capable young man, loved by his father in preference to his other sons; and for this reason his brothers are jealous of him. His father sends him to Egypt, where he wastes his father's money, a thousand silver talents, amounting to a third of Joseph's total capital, in order to bestow upon the king and queen rare and beautiful gifts unusual in the royal court. This waste transforms his father's love into hatred. When the king asks Hyrcanus what gift he desires to receive from him, Hyrcanus replies that he asks no gift, but that the king should speak well of him in his letters to his father and brothers. The king does as he asks, but in vain; the brothers attack Hyrcanus on the road, while at Jerusalem both the brothers and father oppose him and prevent him from entering the city. What does all this mean? Why were Hyrcanus' gifts to the king so much more valuable than the other gifts on the same occasion? (Cf. *Ant.* XII, 215ff.)

As the favorite son of Joseph, Hyrcanus could be confident of a favorable reception at the royal court even without presenting the king with exceptional gifts. To obtain this great sum he had thrown Arion, Joseph's agent in Egypt, into prison, and he knew that such an act, added to the waste of money, would bring upon him his father's wrath. If we accept the version of the story as it stands, we shall have to confess that Hyrcanus' doings in Egypt display no wisdom whatever and that there are no grounds for making him the hero of the tale. But the very fact that he became this, and that everything Josephus tells of his childhood cleverness (*Ant.* XII, 190ff.) prepares the reader for some derring-do or other in Egypt, shows us that some unknown factor here lies concealed and that we must read between the lines in order to understand the motive of Hyrcanus' action. That he did what he did without a definite aim is inconceivable, and I think that this aim was to depose his father from his position as tax-collector and to purchase it for himself (or at least to obtain the king's promise that the post would be given to him after his father's death). His reasons were sufficiently clear. Hyrcanus was the youngest in the family, and his enemies spoke of improprieties connected with his birth.[45] It was therefore well known that not he but his elder brothers would inherit Joseph's immense property; and being a clever and energetic person, he determined to purchase his father's position, in order to prevent his brothers from holding it after his father's death.

This supposition satisfactorily explains the obscurer details of Josephus' narrative. The expensive presents were not simply prodigality, but a means of purchasing the king's consent and of influencing him to grant Hyrcanus' requests. He also gave presents to the courtiers, whose sympathy had to be acquired, especially as they constituted a great danger to him, since his brothers had sent them letters requesting them to slay him (*Ant.* XII, 218). This formidable hostility on the part of the brothers receives its logical interpretation, since they detested Hyrcanus not for his superior wits, as the story explains (*Ant.* XII, 190), but because they noted his success at the royal court and feared it. They also won old Joseph to their side; but it is interesting that he did not venture to pour his wrath on Hyrcanus openly "for he feared the king" (*Ant.* XII, 221). These words show that Hyrcanus had gained his objective and obtained from the king what he had asked. We do not know if he really purchased his father's position in his lifetime, or only obtained the king's permission that it should be given to him after Joseph's death, and the matter is not particularly important. The main point is that Hyrcanus had closed the door to his brothers, had secured for himself the collection of the taxes, and had thus become an Egyptian official. According to his request, the king addressed to his father, brothers and the high officers[46] official letters whose text has not survived, but in which the king doubtless praised Hyrcanus fulsomely and indicated his new standing in the state.

It is therefore no wonder that Hyrcanus' brothers attacked their younger brother and attempted to murder him; they were unsuccessful and two of them fell before his sword. But Hyrcanus himself was not strong enough to hold his own at Jerusalem and was compelled to cross to Transjordan, where his father had long had his estate. "There," writes Josephus (*Ant.* XII, 222), "he dwelt and levied taxes upon the barbarians," that is, he at once set about employing the rights which he had obtained in Egypt, and continued to discharge in Transjordan the function which till then had belonged to his father Joseph. It is hard to establish whether he succeeded in utilizing his privilege in the other lands of Syria, since the story says nothing on that score. Political events may have prevented him from so doing, for in 198 came the great upheaval in the life of the country: Syria passed into Seleucid hands, and the whole political situation changed completely.

After his father's death, Hyrcanus returned and attempted to penetrate Jerusalem, but his brothers barred his way and the struggle broke out anew (*Ant.* XII, 228ff.). As far as can be judged from Josephus' brief account, it now exceeded the bounds of a family quarrel and took on political garb; the whole people was divided into two camps, the majority siding with the elder brothers, while Simon the High Priest also supported them. The interest taken by the people and the chief of the Jewish community in this struggle proves that important political issues hung on its outcome. Unfortunately we do not know precisely when the conflict blazed up between Hyrcanus and his brothers; but it is reasonable to believe that it occurred some time before the country was conquered by Antiochus III or even at the time of the conquest itself (on the chronological question, see above, p. 128ff.). The pro-Seleucid orientation of the High Priest Simon is already known to us (above, p. 80); we learn that the elder sons of Joseph also belonged to the same party. It is to be assumed that Hyrcanus' success in Egypt had bedeviled the good relations between Joseph's elder sons and the Ptolemies, and the former hoped to obtain from the king of Syria those privileges that their father Joseph had once obtained from the kings of Egypt. Hyrcanus, on the contrary, as an Egyptian official, supported the Ptolemies and did all he could to strengthen their government in the country, or (if the quarrel broke out after the year 200) to restore Palestine to Egyptian rule. Whichever was the case, Hyrcanus' attempt failed and he was forced to return to Transjordan.

There he resided till his death. Josephus gives a brief account of his activity in Jordan: he fought successfully against the Arabs, slaying and capturing many of them and building himself a fortress not far from Ḥeshbon, at a place called Tyros, Tzur or Tirah. He adorned this castle with marble blocks and with paintings of various animals; in it he built chambers for banquets, installed water-pipes, planted groves about it, and so forth.[47] He ruled seven years in those regions; and he put an end to his own life on the appearance of Antiochus Epiphanes, fearing "to be punished by the king for what he had done against the Arabs." All this information shows that Hyrcanus did not reside in Transjordan as a simple landowner, but as a politically independent prince. His wars against the Arabs, the building of the fortress, the edifice's wealth and magnificence, clearly prove that Hyrcanus was a petty king, and there is no doubt that he wielded great influence across the Jordan. We are not in a position to determine whether he stood in contact with the kings of Egypt; it is possible that his previous relations with the Ptolemies did not cease at this period, although he could no longer discharge an official function for the Egyptian government. For seven years Hyrcanus ruled his small state,[48] which might have developed and performed an important task for the Jews, had not the course of world history led to its destruction. An independent Transjordanian state did not suit the views of Antiochus Epiphanes, least of all when he was plotting to make war on Egypt, and any independent political power constituted a danger to his plans. We have no notion what occurred between Antiochus and Hyrcanus, whether the latter attempted to fight the king and suffered military defeat, or whether he saw beforehand that no such attempt could succeed and decided to accept his fate. He committed suicide and with him his little kingdom came to an end.

Although Hyrcanus spent some twenty-five years over the Jordan, he did not give up his desire to return to Jerusalem, and there are grounds for supposing that he had lived there for some time and had acquired friends in the city. The author of II Maccabees has preserved a very important piece of information, to the effect that when Heliodorus, the minister of Seleucus IV, came to Jerusalem to confiscate the Temple funds (see below, ch. 4), money belonging to "Hyrcanus son of Tobiah" was lying in the Temple treasury (II Macc. 3.11).[49] At this time Onias III was High Priest in Jerusalem, and in conversation with Heliodorus he alluded to Hyrcanus, designating him as "a man of very important standing" (*ib.*). Had Onias been one of Hyrcanus' opponents, as the High Priest Simon, his predecessor, had been, he certainly would not have referred to Hyrcanus with such respect; hence we learn that Onias was his friend. Nor is this surprising, if we consider that Onias was opposed to Tobiah's sons, that is, Hyrcanus' brothers (see below). The fact that Hyrcanus' money was lying in the Temple treasury proves that he had confidence in those at the head of the Temple, and particularly in the High Priest Onias. It may well be therefore that he was in the habit of coming to Jerusalem personally and of meeting his friends there; and it may be believed that these meetings also possessed a political significance, since Hyrcanus, who was a supporter of Egypt, certainly would not have regarded the Syrian sovereign with favor and would have dreamed of the restoration of Palestine to the Ptolemies.

Hyrcanus, like his father Joseph, appears as a characteristic personality of the Hellenistic period, symbolizing the strong, self-reliant man. His aspirations, however, differed from those of his father, for Joseph was chiefly a financier and, if he also discharged a political function by the way, this was only insofar as this function helped him to establish his private position. Hyrcanus, on the other hand, was a politician, maintaining an opinion and a permanent stand on questions of state, and in different circumstances might have become renowned as a great statesman. But it was his tragic lot to fight a losing battle from the start. He charted his political path on devotion to Egypt, which was at that time a broken reed not to be leaned on. A career in Jerusalem was closed to him from the outset, and there, under the protection of the Seleucids, his brothers kept wary watch. Against them he fought all his life without avail, for he lacked the support of the people, who apparently did not see in him a national leader. He thereupon followed the example of many Hellenistic princes and established his own state. But if his relation to Egypt was outdated, the establishment of an independent state between Syria and Egypt was premature, anticipating the historical development of the Jewish people and of Palestine by some fifty years. Here too he was fighting a losing battle. He was unsupported, and his great energy, which found no worthy cause in politics, was wasted; Hyrcanus exhausted his powers in drinking bouts and pleasures, resembling several Hellenistic princes and kings in this respect as well. It is easy to imagine him overcome by despair; he died in solitude, and his tragic end was a sad but logical termination of his unsuccessful life-story.[50]

What was the attitude of Joseph the Tobiad and his son Hyrcanus to that same striving to Hellenization which in course of time, under Antiochus Epiphanes, came to occupy so important a place in the life of the population of Jerusalem? There can be no doubt that Hellenism was not alien to them; but they cannot be reckoned among the deliberate Hellenizers who sought Hellenism through a thoroughly prepared and premeditated program. Their Hellenism was the outcome of imitation; they were the first Jews to maintain frequent contact with the Greeks, and the life which they witnessed in Alexandria influenced them chiefly in externals. Some details of the lives of Joseph and Hyrcanus indicate that they were not strict in the maintenance of practical Jewish observances, since they ate at the king's table and took part in the drinking parties of the Alexandrian court; Hyrcanus, moreover, adorned his fortress with the pictures of animals.

Contact with the Greeks brought them wealth and the opportunity of playing an important part in the life of their land; they had no grounds for a negative attitude to the Greeks and doubtless saw no need for such an attitude, since in the time of Joseph the question of Hellenization was not yet the acute question which it became under Antiochus Epiphanes. We may therefore suppose—and lack of information permits no more than conjecture—that Joseph and Hyrcanus adopted Greek habits in daily life, learned Greek, gave their children Greek names, and so on. It was not, of course, Greek philosophy or art which they picked up in Alexandria; the anecdote of Joseph and an Egyptian dancing girl (below, p. 460, note 45) shows convincingly that they were influenced mainly by the external aspects of Hellenism, by its physical rather than by its intellectual freedom. But it is a well known rule in the lives of peoples, that the culture of a more civilized nation influences its backward neighbor first of all by its externals, which are sometimes not worthy of the name of culture; understanding of the internal aspects comes later— if at all.

Who composed the story about Joseph the son of Tobiah and his son Hyrcanus? Scholars are unanimous that at the basis of Josephus' tale lies a fragment of some particular literary creation lacking any connection with the historical events of the period, its sole object being to praise the house of Tobiah. Scholars, however, are divided on the question from which circles—Jewish or Gentile—the story comes. Some, particularly those not distinguished for their affection for Jews and Judaism (Eduard Meyer for example), ascribe the tale to a Jewish author, and as Joseph's moral character is not especially praiseworthy, they use the narrative to draw anti-Semitic conclusions.[51] J. Klausner, on the other hand, writes that the details of the Joseph and Hyrcanus story "come for the most part from non-Hebrew sources and elicit an attitude of hatred or mockery towards the Jews, containing nothing of the severe Jewish outlook in respect of the irregular conduct which characterized the tax-collecting father and his son."[52] Büchler, too, thinks that the story was written by a non-Jew, and seeks the author in Samaria.[53]

To solve the problem, the author's motive must be more precisely determined. In the entire story not a single sentence indicates any interest on the part of the writer in the fate of the Jewish people as a whole; the personalities of Joseph and Hyrcanus hold the center of the tale throughout and the historical details are purely incidental, serving merely as a framework for the adventures of the "heroes." The belief then is justifiable that the story found in Josephus was derived from the family chronicle of the House of Tobiah, a chronicle which could only have been written by the family's official historian on the basis of the tales and anecdotes handed down orally in the family from generation to generation. Since Hyrcanus holds pride of place in the chronicle, and the author in his account of the war between him and his brothers clearly sides with the former, it is to be supposed that the writer was near to that branch of the family and was a member of the household of Hyrcanus or of Hyrcanus' descendants.

The historical and moral level of family chronicles of this sort was naturally not apt to be very lofty, since the author's whole aim was to eulogize the family heroes for their successors to boast about. Hyrcanus' permanent residence was in Transjordan and his heirs probably remained on the scene of their father's great exploits. The description of Hyrcanus' stronghold in *Ant.* XII, 230ff. is so detailed that only an eyewitness could have written those lines. Hence the legend of the House of Tobiah was created in Transjordan, in an environment remote from the spirit of the national rebirth awakened among the Jews by the Hasmoneans, in surroundings exposed to no direct influence from indigenous Judaism. Accordingly, the story is devoid of the more religious attitudes of Judaism so prominent in all the other books of the period. But this is no proof that the author was a non-Jew. A Greek or a Hellenized Syrian would never have described the clashes between Joseph and the representatives of the Greek cities with such unconcealed sympathy for Joseph's actions, nor would he have stressed with such peculiar pleasure the cutting rejoinders which Hyrcanus made to the Greeks who mocked him before Ptolemy. The author was neither a Greek nor a Jewish nationalist, but a Hellenizing Jew, for only a writer of the latter group would have been capable of describing the family affairs of the Tobiads with enthusiasm, and only Jews of this type could have found edification in reading the doings of Joseph son of Tobiah whose exploits consisted entirely in his talent for business and money-making.[54]

Joseph the son of Tobiah "brought the Jewish people from a situation of poverty and indigence to more brilliant conditions of life" (*Ant.* XII, 224). With these words Josephus concludes his account of Joseph the Tobiad. Whether he took these words from the same source whence he derived his information on the Tobiads, or whether they express his own viewpoint, the opinion is only partly true. Joseph was indeed one of the first to show the Jews the way to a broader and more brilliant way of life than that accepted in Judaea, but in actual fact the Jewish people derived no benefit whatsoever from his activity. Joseph created new conditions of life chiefly for himself and the members of his family, and these could set an example only to the upper circles of the Jewish community, not to the whole people. Another thing emerges clearly from Josephus' story: Hellenism, from its first appearance in Judaea, was internally bound up with one particular social class—with the wealthy families of the Jerusalem aristocracy. The crafty and resourceful tax-collector, the powerful and unscrupulous businessman, was the spiritual father of the Jewish Hellenizing movement, and throughout the entire brief period of the flourishing of Hellenism in Jerusalem, lust for profit and pursuit of power were among the most pronounced marks of the new movement.

Rich and colorful material on the life of the period prior to the efflorescence of Hellenism in Jerusalem is furnished by the great book of Ben Sira (Sirach). His activity can be chronologically determined with relative accuracy. His grandson, who translated his book into Greek, went to Egypt in 132 B.C.E., and published his translation after 118 B.C.E.[55] Ben Sira therefore was at work some seventy-five years earlier, approximately during the first twenty years of the century. The book itself contains support for this dating, for in one place (10.8) Ben Sira alludes, apparently, to the change of rule in Palestine in the year 200 ("Sovereignty is transferred from nation to nation on account of violence of pride") and, on the other hand, the book contains no reference to the obstinate struggle which broke out in Jerusalem about the year 175 and caused the Antiochan persecution and the Hasmonean revolt.[56] His book was written, therefore, between 200 and 180, the life of the period reflected in it being still peaceful, and only from time to time does the reader notice the gathering of the heavy storm clouds which foretell the coming tempest. Ben Sira was no politician, but a scholar who dedicated his life to educating the youth and preaching morality; nevertheless his book contains hints that bear witness to his endeavors to fulfill a certain task in the political world as well. He speaks of the great tribulations which he encountered in his life, of people who slandered him to the king, and of the danger of death which faced him and from which he was saved by the help of God (51.2-5).

On the basis of these brief allusions no complete picture can be drawn of his political activity, which was doubtless neither important nor prolonged, yet probably with it was bound up the great experience which Ben Sira acquired in life, of which he frequently speaks. He emphasizes chiefly the experience he had acquired from his frequent journeys during his youth (cf. 51.13), and it is interesting that in long journeys (and in many-sided experiences of life generally) Ben Sira sees a condition for acquiring the "wisdom" which is his supreme ideal of intellectual achievement. This outlook witnesses to the widening of the intellectual horizon of the people of Jerusalem in Ben Sira's time. Although Ben Sira opposes the spirit of free Hellenism, as we shall shortly see, he cannot find satisfaction in the restricted conditions of life in the tiny land of Judaea, and he feels a need to leave its borders, to wander over the wide world, to see other lands, and to experience diverse things; nor does he recoil from the sufferings inseparable from such wanderings. In this sense Ben Sira may be considered to represent the new generation, and may be compared with Joseph the Tobiad and his son Hyrcanus. But the experiences acquired in foreign countries differ from one person to the next; while Joseph and Hyrcanus were influenced by Greek culture and adopted the life which they saw at the royal court of Alexandria, Ben Sira returned to

Jerusalem the orthodox Jew he had been before, and in vain do we seek in his book symptoms of Greek culture.

Actually the contrary was the case: Ben Sira fought against the spirit of Greek civilization all his life, for he understood the danger threatening Judaism from Hellenism. Free inquiry which was not afraid to ask questions about nature and morality, or to answer them by the power of the human mind alone, Greek wisdom, unassociated with fear of God, aroused the fear of Ben Sira, who saw in them a contradiction to the spirit of Judaism and warned his pupils from treading this path.

> Seek not (to understand) what is too wonderful for thee,
>   And search not out that which is hid from thee.
> Meditate upon that which thou must grasp,
>   And be not occupied with that which is hid.
> Have naught to do with that which is beyond thee,
>   For more has been shown to thee than thou canst understand.
> For many are the conceits of the sons of men,
>   And evil imaginations lead astray. (3.21-24)[57]

In contrast to Greek wisdom and in the tradition of the Bible (the Book of Proverbs) Ben Sira declares that fear of God is the foundation of all wisdom and understanding; fear of the Lord and the observance of the commandments are the real beginning of wisdom (19.20); a little wisdom with fear of God is better than much wisdom without it (19.24). Even in the world of statesmanship, piety occupies the foremost place:

> Prince, ruler and governor are honored—
> But none is greater than he that feareth God. (10.24)

The wisdom of which Ben Sira speaks with such enthusiasm is not the wisdom of human reason: in his eyes it assumes the semblance of a universal divine power of God's creation in the six days of Genesis (24.1-6; cf. Prov. 13.22-32). Simultaneously wisdom assumes a religious national form in the spirit of Jewish tradition: she dwells among the people of Israel; Zion and Jerusalem are her abode; her sole expression is the Law of Moses (24.8-23). The praise of wisdom is associated for Ben Sira with the preaching of the doctrine of Jewish morality and with accented stress on the observance of the commandments. With fury Ben Sira flings himself upon those of his people who have cast aside the ways of Judaism:

> Woe to you, ungodly men,
> Who have forsaken the Law of the Most High God!
> If ye increase, (it will be) for mischief,
> And if ye bear children, (it will be) for sighing;
> If ye stumble, (it will be) for everlasting joy,
> And if ye die, (it will be) for a curse!   (41.8-9)

He wages war on those Jews who have begun to be ashamed of "the Law of the Most High and the statute" (42.2); transgressors of the commandments are in his eyes "a despicable race."

> An honorable race is what? the race of men!
>   An honorable race is that which feareth God.
> A despicable race is what? the race of men!
>   A despicable race is that which transgresseth
>   the commandments. (10.19)

Ben Sira stresses not merely the internal aspect of Jewish tradition—the Mosaic Law and its commandments; the external historical aspect, the priestly government of Jerusalem, is also sacred in his eyes. Among the portraits of the Jewish national heroes which Ben Sira paints in chapters 44-50 (from Enoch to Simon the Just), Aaron, the ideal symbol of the High Priest, holds virtually the most important place. Ben Sira devoted five verses to the description of Moses, and seventeen to that of Aaron. He addresses his hearers with these words of rebuke:

> Fear God with all thy heart,
>   And reverence His priests.
> With all thy strength love Him that made thee
>   And forsake not His ministers.
> Glorify God and honor the priests,
>   And give (them) their portion as it is commanded (thee).
>   (7.29-31)

These, very briefly, are the views of Ben Sira on traditional Judaism and Greek culture. A detailed analysis of his moral doctrine is not the subject of this survey,[58] since our account concerns only matters which directly affect the social life of the period. On this question Ben Sira has some very interesting things to tell us, which are of particular importance as they occur in his book quite incidentally and are not therefore dependent on the writer's declared motive.[59]

Ben Sira speaks frequently of the rich and the poor and of the relations between them. Although he is largely under the influence of the Bible both in his style and frequently in his thought, the independent value of his descriptions cannot be denied insofar as they concern the public life of the period. For Ben Sira describes rich and poor, not in the conventional formulae known to him in literature, but as an artist who draws the material he needs direct from life. Ben Sira knew the rich men of his generation very well; he speaks of their pride (5.1-2), of their hard attitude to their fellow men (13.19), of their pursuit of money (27.1-2; 31.5-7); relates their talent for exploiting men for their own benefit and tells of their attitude of contempt and mockery to those same people when they are no longer needed (13.4-7). He knew the wealthy man's constant concern for his capital and the pleasure seeking that went with wealth:

> Watchful care over wealth wasteth the flesh,
> And anxiety about it dissipateth slumber. (31.7; 4.7)

The wealthy man holds an honored place in public life, possessing friends and companions and a large group of henchmen to do his bidding. The humble man is in different case: he is solitary, without shield or shelter from hatred and contempt, or any support but his natural abilities:

A rich man when he is shaken is supported by a friend,
But the poor man when he is shaken is thrust away by a friend.
A rich man speaketh, and his helpers are many;
And though his words be unseemly, they are pronounced lovely.
A poor man speaketh, and they jeer at him;
Yea, though he speak with wisdom, there is no place for him.
When the rich man speaketh, all keep silence,
And they extol his intelligence to the clouds.
When the poor man speaketh: "Who is this?" say they;
And if he stumble they will assist his overthrow. (13.21-23) [60]

Ben Sira counsels the poor man to comport himself with the rich; he must not approach too near him—let the rich man seek the poor man if he needs him. To depart from him completely is, however, also very dangerous, as the rich man might forget him. "Do not thyself draw near, lest thou be put at a distance; and keep not too far away, lest (thou be forgotten)" (13.10).[61] The poor man must speak cautiously before the rich man, nor be outspoken to him; nor should he trust in his promises, since he may be testing the poor man and wishing to draw something from him (13.9-13). But in fact all this advice is profitless: Ben Sira knows that there is neither understanding nor common ground between the wealthy and the humble; nor can they be reconciled. The poor man is in continual danger from the rich man, and he may as well abandon all hope of associating with him:

> Contend not with a mighty man,
>> Lest thou fall into his hands.
> Strive not against the man that is rich,
>> Lest he weigh thy price, and thou be destroyed. (8.1-2a)

> What is too heavy for thee do not lift,
>> And with one that is richer than thyself associate not.
> What association can jar and kettle have in common
>> When, if the one smite, the other is smashed? (13.2)

There is not yet in these words what we now term "class conflict"; the poor in Ben Sira's account are too weak and have not the strength to fight or to defend themselves. But if there is no struggle, there is hatred, and Ben Sira speaks of it in clear and emphatic terms:

> All flesh loveth its kind,
>> And every man his like.
> All flesh consorteth according to its kind,
>> And with his kind man associateth.
> What association can wolf have with lamb?
>> Even so is the ungodly that consorteth with the righteous.
> What peace can the hyena have with the dog?
>> Or what peace rich with poor?
> Food for the lion are the wild asses of the desert:
>> Even so the pasture of the rich are the poor.
> An abomination to pride is humility;
>> Even so an abomination to the rich are the poor. (13.15-20)

As can be perceived from these words, Ben Sira sees no remedy for the state of everlasting hostility between the two parts of the people; riches and poverty are natural things in his eyes, and rooted in man is his striving to associate with those like him. It is the will of God that humanity should be divided into two in respect of its economic position, after the manner of the world of morality: "Good and evil, life and death, poverty and wealth come from God" (11.14). It is not worth seeking ways to correct the situation, therefore, or at least no remedy will come by revolution; in another place (26.5) Ben Sira denounces the popular revolts and conspiracies in the city, and is here perhaps alluding to some event well known to his pupils but subsequently forgotten by the nation and not preserved in historical literature. Only one way is open to the poor man who wishes to escape the straits he is in: individual self-education and principally the learning of "wisdom." Peasants and craftsmen are needed each according to his sort, to work the fields and so forth; but their voices are not heard in popular assemblies, nor should they occupy the judge's seat (38.25ff.); a man of wisdom and understanding, however, will always find his way in life; his intelligence will gain him a reputation, he will stand before the prominent and the powerful, will receive a post from the king, occupy an important place in public life, and so on.[62] Ben Sira frequently emphasizes the importance of learning wisdom to those who desire to get on in life; and, in the writer's view, in this emphasis an allusion may be seen to Ben Sira's own career; he may well have been born and educated in poverty and have gradually climbed to prominence by force of his natural intelligence and of his devotion to the study of Torah and practical wisdom.

Ben Sira speaks frequently of "rulers," "philanthropists" and "great ones." By reading his book we become familiar with the governors, judges and representatives of the Jerusalem community (synagogue).[63] Ben Sira's attitude to them is one of great respect; but he does not ignore the fact that they too, as rich men, are far from the people, the poor and the humble. He demands of the people complete humility towards authority:

> Make thyself be loved in the assembly,
> And to the ruler of the city bow thy head. (4.7)

Yet in several places in his book we feel that behind this humility lies a feeling of fear of the powerful rather than respect for authority. Ben Sira knows, indeed, that there are good kings and judges who care for the welfare of the state (10.1ff.), but generally he sees only the negative side of the people in authority, their tyranny, their pursuit of gain, and the like. And he counsels his pupils

Seek not to be a judge,
  Lest thou be not able to put down presumption
(And) lest thou be in fear in the presence of a mighty man,
  And thou put a stumbling-block in (the way of) thy uprightness.
                                                            (7.6)

Go not to law with a judge,
  For he will judge according to his good pleasure. (8.14)

Keep far from the man that hath power to kill,
  And so thou needest have no dread of death's terrors. (9.13)

Expressions of this sort prove conclusively that the men in power in Jerusalem did not possess the requisite moral standards, and that it was taken for granted that a poor man without influence must keep far from them if he were not to stumble. It cannot of course be stated that this period was exceptional for its corruption among men of authority; there has been no period or state whose rulers have been guiltless of violence, its judges guiltless of perverting justice, or its officials guiltless of greed. But it should be remembered that in the smaller towns and places of limited population where the powerful men in charge are a restricted and select circle, the enmity between the ruler and the man in the street takes a sharper form than in large states. Here an offended man knows his foe personally and by name, and social conflict assumes the shape of private enmity. This was the position, no doubt, in Jerusalem, and it may be surmised that there too the antagonism between the two parts of the community assumed the character of prolonged conflicts between families and individuals.

Although Ben Sira is usually addressing the broad sections of the population, sometimes he turns to the wealthy, and it may be conjectured that the sons of communal leaders also came to hear his instruction. Ben Sira teaches them how to behave toward members of their families, their slaves, etc. and he also dwells on money matters. He counsels his hearers to watch their property carefully and not to waste money frivolously (33.19 = 30.28); he speaks at length of loans and the need to recover debts on time (29.2ff.), of security and the dangers it involves, on account of the untrustworthiness of debtors (29.14ff.). Ben Sira frequently mentions merchants and their pursuit of profits, and these passages again reflect the new period which began in Judaea under Greek rule, when the money economy, the opportunity to invest one's means in profitable enterprises, and lively and absorbing commercial traffic had begun to develop. Here, too, as in the passages dealing with the need for ample experience of life, we feel the new free spirit which had begun to move among the Jews, and the broad horizons which were opening before the private initiative of active men. Again we are reminded of Joseph the Tobiad and his sons, the most characteristic representatives of the age.

It was not people of this sort, however, that Ben Sira wanted. If there were also wealthy men among his pupils, he modified his moral views not a whit in their favor. The new spirit noticeable in Ben Sira crept into his book without the author's intending that it should; for he opposed it, knowing that numerous commercial preoccupations, pursuit of profit and the development of trade could not raise the moral level of public life. The opposite was the case: life of this sort was inevitably bound up with injustice and dishonesty and in the world of commerce particularly a trader of integrity was an impossibility; many sinned for gain: "A nail sticketh fast between the joinings of stones, and sin will thrust itself in between buyer and seller" (27.1-2). Wealth is good if it is without wrongdoing (13.24), but Ben Sira knows that such cases are rare:

> He that loveth gold shall not go unpunished,
>   And he that pursueth hire erreth thereby.
> Many there are that have bound themselves to gold
>   And have put their trust in corals.
> It is a stumbling-block for the foolish
>   And whoso is simple is snared thereby.
> Happy is the rich man that is found blameless,
>   And that hath not gone astray following mammon!
> Who is he? that we may felicitate him—
>   For he has done wondrously among his people. (31.5-9)

Gold influences and sweeps men off their feet, leads their minds astray and terrorizes the multitude (8.2). It would be well, therefore, to forego a life of commerce completely and so be free from transgression.

> My son, why multiply thy business (unduly)?
> But if thou so doest thou shalt not go unpunished. (9.10)

Ben Sira particularly detests the wealthy and aggressively prominent who place all their trust in their wealth and power, and do as they want in life without remembering God and His Law. This pride will avail them nought in the day of their calamity:

> Trust not in unrighteous gains
> For they shall profit thee nothing in the day of wrath. (5.8)

> Trust not in thy wealth,
> And say not: I have power. (5.1)

Riches lead to pride, licentiousness and religious transgression; a wealthy man can with difficulty avoid infringement of the commandments or apostasy from the fundamentals of Judaism; this is the conclusion to be drawn from the book of Ben Sira. Ben Sira recognizes a threefold antagonism which existed in his time in the Jewish community: the social antagonism between rich and poor; the moral antagonism between sinners and righteous; and the religious antagonism between unbelievers and the pious. These three antagonisms naturally tended to combine into one all-inclusive antagonism; on one side the wealthy, morally transgressing in their oppression of the poor, their perversion of justice and their dishonesty, also rejecting the fundamentals of Judaism; opposed to them stands the great mass of the poor and the humble, who are morally "righteous" and religiously "devout." In Ben Sira we do not yet find this contrast as clearly emphasized as it is in the *Book of Enoch* about a hundred years later.[64] Ben Sira hesitates to return a negative verdict on the entire comfortable class, and still wishes to believe that there is wealth free from offense (13.24), that there are governors and rulers concerned for the people's welfare (10.1ff.). The idea of solving the problem by violence is alien to his outlook, and he sees in philanthropy and charity, on the one hand, and modest behavior and courtesy, on the other, the way to understanding between the two classes.

This unstable attitude is appropriate to the situation in the Jewish community of Jerusalem before the Hasmonean rebellion. The social antagonisms existed among the people and could not be ignored, and the contrast between the zealots of the traditional faith and the freethinking Hellenizers was also outstanding in public life; but the antagonisms had not yet found their external expression in the organization of political parties, the devising of slogans, programs of action and the like. The powerful moneyed men were sympathetic to Greek customs and drawn to the new mode of life from abroad, but the men had not yet appeared who saw in the Hellenization of the Jews an instrument for seizing power and creating for themselves a brilliant political career. The broad masses of the poor and the humble, on the other hand, naturally inclined to the traditional religious way of life; but the leaders had not yet appeared to give to religious observance the character of a national program. Ben Sira faithfully described this period of transition and it is not difficult to note in his book the sharpening of the spirit of hostility between the two sections of the public and the slow preparation for the coming conflict. We do not find signs of the conflict itself in the work, which was written before the outbreak of civil war in Jerusalem, nor do we know whether Ben Sira took part in the war or not. His personal fate was forgotten by the people and only his book remained as a trustworthy document for the short and important period preceding the bursting forth of the Jewish people's native forces, which prepared the soil for a basic change in the course of Jewish history.

chapter 4

THE HELLENISTIC REFORM

We come to the account of the events which occurred in Jerusalem in the seventies of the second century B.C.E. (180-167). This short space of time during which the aspirations to Hellenization, covertly evolved in the previous period, emerged into the open, has found no full expression in historical literature. In vain do we seek an account of the epoch in the Greek authors of the second century: various portions of their books have been preserved down to our time, but they contain no allusion to the questions we are discussing here, and it is to be doubted whether they ever dealt at length with this chapter of Jewish history. The author of Daniel is important as an eyewitness of events, but he speaks of them with extreme brevity, and scholars have not always been successful in solving his riddles or in translating his allusive style into the language of precise scientific research. Josephus is almost completely silent on this period, and his silence shows that he took no interest in the events which preceded the Hasmonean revolt; when he touches on them in passing, he frequently makes mistakes in names, dates and the order of events, and not only is of no assistance to historical inquiry, but frequently impedes it.

The author of I Maccabees has by his work raised a magnificent memorial to the first days of the Hasmonean dynasty; but he was no more interested than the other in events preceding the appearance of Mattathias the Hasmonean, devoting to them only one chapter, which constitutes an introduction to his main theme and deals with events in a very superficial fashion. Only in chapters 3-4 of II Maccabees do we find a more or less detailed account of the people who headed the Hellenizing party and their internecine strife, of their attitude to the people, their political policy and the like. But for these chapters, we should know nothing of the prolonged ferment among the population of Jerusalem and the party struggle which finally led to civil war and to the Antiochan persecution.

The historical trustworthiness of II Maccabees has been frequently questioned by modern scholars, and we do in fact find in it information that sometimes contradicts our knowledge gained from other sources. The inquirer is therefore obliged to commence with a critique of the sources, to determine which of them may properly serve as a basis for an account of the period, and in what way they may be reconciled when they contradict one another. In order that these detailed inquiries should not interrupt the course of the systematic historical account, they are relegated to Appendix I at the end of the book, and it is enough to remark here that the following exposition is based mainly on II Maccabees, which, despite its numerous deficiencies, is the only work to give a detailed historical picture of approximate authenticity.

The flourishing period of Hellenism in Jerusalem is associated with the political activity of the Tobiad family, who had stood constantly at the center of events and may be assumed to have been the main instigators of the Hellenistic reform in Jerusalem. The family's origins have been treated above (pp. 126f.; 457, n. 25) where we dwelt on the wealth which accumulated in the hands of Joseph the son of Tobiah on account of his prolonged activity as tax-collector. After Joseph's death his property was inherited by his sons; of these he had begotten eight: the youngest, Hyrcanus, being resident in Transjordan; two had been killed in the fratricidal strife between Hyrcanus and his brothers, and the remaining five dwelt in Jerusalem. When we encounter the term "Tobiads" in the sources, we must ascribe the name to the sons of Joseph and their descendants, who were no doubt numerous.[1]

The name appears twice in the sources; once in the *Antiquities* (XII, 237ff.) of Josephus and once in his *War* (1, 31ff.). From these passages, to which we shall return, two conclusions may be drawn: first, that the Tobiads were people of great influence with power to control the course of things as they chose; second, that they stood at the head of the Hellenizing party. This of course has been insufficient to satisfy the historical curiosity of scholars who, not content with this brief information, have sought to enroll among the Tobiads the three men who at this period headed political affairs in Judaea, and of whom sources give a detailed report: namely, Menelaus, High Priest under Antiochus Epiphanes, and his two brothers Simon and Lysimachus.

In the opinion of Wellhausen, Büchler and E. Meyer, there is no doubt that these three brothers were of the Tobiad family, or to be precise, sons of Joseph. Schürer, on the other hand, denies this possibility and in this is followed by the majority of modern writers: Bickermann, Bévenot, Abel, Momigliano and others.² The present writer does not hesitate to associate himself with the second group of scholars: proofs built on a comparison of extracts from the sources, each individual extract of which evokes grave doubts, cannot serve as a basis for far-reaching conclusions.³ Josephus says in the *Antiquities* (XII, 239) that the Tobiads sided with Menelaus, from which it is to be concluded that the Tobiads and Menelaus belonged to one party, but not that Menelaus was a member of the family. However, if not related by blood, they were of kindred outlook, and in this respect scholars have been right in describing Simon, Menelaus and Lysimachus as representatives of this important family.

Wherein lay the power of the Tobiads? According to all the information surviving on Joseph the Tobiad, it may be said that their power lay in their great wealth. It is possible (although this is unmentioned in the sources) that under Seleucus IV (187-175) the sons of Tobiah had discharged the same function at the Syrian court which Joseph had discharged in his time for the kings of Egypt: they were tax-collectors and fiscal officers of the crown. But it is not to be assumed that they also inherited the post of the *prostasia;* we have seen above (p. 80) that the High Priest Simon the Just led the pro-Seleucid party under Antiochus III and also held in his hands the internal power, including the work of rebuilding damaged Jerusalem. Hence it may reasonably be supposed that the official representation of the people to the king (which was the *prostasia*) had reverted to the High Priest in his time.

The Tobiads' influence therefore was not in the political sphere in the narrow sense of the term, but in the social; but when great wealth falls into the hands of one man or is concentrated within the narrow circle of one family, these people will inevitably begin to be interested in political issues and to develop ambitions to power; for capitalists cannot remain indifferent to any and every political system, but must seek to obtain control of political developments in order to give them the direction desirable to themselves. Such was the case with the Tobiads, and their first step in this direction was to seize a strong position in the management of the Temple.

The Temple was first and foremost the religious center of Judaism; but besides its religious value it had considerable economic importance. Among ancient peoples every temple served as a financial as well as a religious center; this was the case in Babylonia and Egypt, Greece and Rome.[4] Every temple had a regular income, its treasuries were full of silver and gold, and the Jerusalem Temple was no exception.[5] Great wealth accumulated in its store rooms; the half-shekel which the Jews paid each year to the cult probably covered most of the daily rites, and in the course of generations this income grew and amounted to a considerable sum.[6] "It is no matter for wonder," says Josephus, "that great wealth was concentrated in our Temple, for all the Jews and God-fearers of the whole world, both Asia and Europe, had been sending their contributions ever since ancient times" (*Ant.* XIV, 110). These treasures, besides their main duty of furnishing the needs of worship, also performed a practical function. "We have no public resources apart from the sacred funds," says Josephus (*Ant. ib.* 113).[7] The Temple treasury, therefore, played the part of a state exchequer, which was otherwise lacking in Judaea, and this was the direct outcome of the fact that the government of Judaea was "theocratic" or "hierocratic" (above, p. 120), that is, the priests who stood at the head of the cult also held the secular power. In addition to the public moneys, the money of private individuals was also kept in the Temple treasury on deposit, since this was the safest place in Jerusalem and acted as a sort of bank in the modern sense (*War* VI, 282; II Macc. 3.10-12). This fact alone is not such as to cast suspicion on the management of public funds in the Temple; but it does permit the assumption that a danger existed of confusing public with private money, especially when the majority of the owners of the deposits belonged to the same limited circle of Jerusalem aristocracy of which the governing priesthood were also members. If an owner of capital could place his means in the Temple treasury on deposit, why could he not also obtain from it sums of money in the form of loans? And who could have distinguished precisely between the Temple expenditures made in the public interest, and those expenditures bound up with the interests of private people? In the Persian period, when economic life was not yet developed and great wealth had not yet accumulated in the hands of individuals, the danger was not great, but in the Hellenistic period, and especially after the activity of Joseph the Tobiad, the situation became entirely different, and the Temple treasury was in danger of becoming the private fund of a few highly-placed families that wielded power in the city.

Among these families the Tobiads occupied the most prominent place. Joseph the son of Tobiah was the son of Onias II's sister, and Simon the Just supported Joseph's sons during their war with Hyrcanus "because he was related to them."[8] The Tobiads themselves may have been priests, as has been suggested above (p. 126); there is no doubt, at any rate, that they were close to the Temple, just as Tobiah the Ammonite had been in the time of Nehemiah (Neh. 13.7ff.). If the money of Hyrcanus was deposited in the Temple when Onias III was High Priest, it goes without saying that his elder brothers' money would have been deposited there when Simon the Just headed affairs. Relatives of the Tobiad family probably held the most important posts in the Temple, and as long as Simon the Just was High Priest the Tobiads continued in undisturbed enjoyment of their great wealth and their influence upon public affairs.

Then Simon died and was succeeded by his son, Onias III. What were his character and aims? The author of II Maccabees describes him as a good man who pursued justice and was concerned for the public welfare, but this does not explain what made Onias alter the direction of his foreign policy and the course followed by Simon his father. Under Onias, Hyrcanus' money was deposited in the Temple, and Onias himself spoke of him with much respect. Hyrcanus was known as a supporter of the Ptolemies; this being so, it is to be supposed that Onias too had gone over to the pro-Ptolemaic party. It was not indeed wartime, and Onias' new policy did not therefore bear the character of open rebellion against Seleucid rule, but if there was no rebellion there was certainly a change of attitude not merely toward the Seleucids but also toward their supporters, the Tobiads. Naturally, these powerful men could not permit their opponent to rise to prominence and to acquire outstanding influence over the Temple treasury. Hence civil strife broke out in the city.

Simon was the first to take the offensive. He was a member of an influential family,[9] and designated in II Maccabees as "the Overseer of the Temple."[10] He demanded of Onias, in addition to his previous post, the function of the *agoranomia* of the city. What the character of this function was we do not exactly know; the *agoranomos* may have exercised supervision over the market (the city's economic life), and also over the police; or it may have been predominantly a juridical and administrative post.[11] Since Onias refused his demand, Simon resorted to the foreign power then ruling Judaea, the Syrian government. The author of II Maccabees relates that he appeared before Apollonius, the governor of Coele-Syria and Phoenicia, and told him that in the Temple treasury lay much wealth, which exceeded what was needed for the cult, and that it would be well for this great wealth to come into the possession of King Seleucus (II Macc. 3.5-6). This report, as we read it in the source, is not as clear as it might be, for we may well ask why Simon should have been interested in handing over the Temple treasures to the King?[12] He probably did not mean the entire money in the treasury, but intended to emphasize the political direction of the High Priest and, as an example of Onias' Egyptian sympathies, cited the fact that in the treasury was deposited the money of Hyrcanus, which required confiscation to prevent its use by Onias against the king.

The course of events as related in the sources, indeed indicates that the question of confiscation chiefly involved those moneys kept in the Temple on deposit, and not the Temple treasures.[13] When Seleucus heard from Apollonius about the Temple's wealth, he sent Heliodorus, one of his chief ministers,[14] to inquire into the matter and to confiscate the money; for, having to pay tribute to the Romans, he was constantly short of means. Onias received Heliodorus with due respect, but refused to hand over the Temple treasures, telling him that the moneys there were deposits belonging to widows and orphans; there was further the money of Hyrcanus the Tobiad, "an important and influential person," the whole sum amounting to 400 talents of silver and 200 of gold; he was unable to hand over the money to anyone, for what would the people say who had reposed their confidence in the sanctuary and placed their deposits there?

Heliodorus, of course, refused to believe Onias and broke into the Temple at the head of his troops. What happened then is far from clear. The author of II Maccabees relates that a mounted man accompanied by two youths appeared to Heliodorus, and that the two youths seized him and beat him till he fell senseless. This is, of course, a legend of the usual Hellenistic type, and I do not think it worthwhile to look for a historical germ in the story.[15] It is nevertheless a fact that Heliodorus gave up his intention to obtain the Temple money. It is hard to decide what was the real reason for this concession; he may have reached an agreement with Onias acceptable to both. He returned to Seleucus, and in Jerusalem all remained as it had been before: Simon's first attempt to overthrow Onias was unsuccessful.

But Simon was an energetic man, reluctant to abandon the field. He again turned informer, reporting that Onias had comported himself toward Heliodorus in an undesirable manner, and that he was plotting against authority. The second accusation was dangerous and Onias was compelled to take notice of it, for his position as supreme ruler was tottering. A civil war was about to break out in the city; clashes and assassinations had already begun there, while Apollonius the governor of Coele-Syria and Phoenicia was preparing to intervene in the affairs of Judaea. Onias then determined to go to Seleucus personally to reinforce his position, and the author of II Maccabees explains his journey in these words: "He went to the king, not to make accusations against the people of the city, but to benefit the entire nation; he saw that without the king's supervision peace could not be restored" (II Macc. 4.5-6). These words carry in them a hint of apology; evidently another opinion prevailed concerning Onias' journey, and his enemies were saying that its object was to improve his personal position and to return to Jerusalem at the head of a Syrian force to wreak havoc among his foes. It is difficult to decide which view was right; but even if we assume that such were Onias' intentions, he did not succeed in carrying them out, perhaps because just then Seleucus IV died, and his brother Antiochus Epiphanes ascended the throne.

Before continuing the account, let us determine the chief motivations at work within the Jewish body politic in this brief period preceding the Hellenistic reform. Two things emerge clearly from the narrative in our sources: first, that the movement began as a dispute between two families of power and influence among the Jewish aristocracy; and secondly, that the dispute possessed international political significance. The first fact arose from the internal structure of Jewish society in the Second Temple period, for, as we have seen above, since the return from Babylon the upper orders of the nation, including the priests, had been divided into families and it was natural for each to assume a certain stand on political and social questions, which stand became hereditary and imposed itself on individual members of each family as a tradition developed over generations.[16]

It must nevertheless also be emphasized that the Hellenistic period was a period of revolution, which all over the world broke up the fixed frameworks of tribe, *polis*, and family, and put in their place the will of the strong individual. Hence in Judaea, too, we behold the infringement of family tradition by one or another of its members; thus Hyrcanus broke with his father and brothers, and a similar fratricidal struggle blazed up in the Oniad clan, as we shall shortly see. Political orientation also now ceased to be constant and permanent in a given family, for while the Tobiads as a whole inclined to Syria, Hyrcanus kept faith with Egypt; and while Simon the Just cooperated with the Seleucids, his son Onias III obviously supported a pro-Ptolemaic policy. Thus parallel with family tradition developed personal ambitions antagonistic to it, and a man's success in life frequently depended, not on the support he obtained from his relatives, but on his own personal talents and characteristics.

This generalization applied equally to cultural sympathies and antipathies. Although the sources tell us nothing of the Hellenizing movement before the year 175, it is clear that the Hellenistic reform did not occur all of a sudden and that it had been preceded by a more or less lengthy period during which Greek culture had become rooted among the population of Judaea and Jerusalem. The Tobiads developed this sympathy for Hellenism by family tradition. We have already observed the beginning of the process in the home of Tobiah and his son Joseph; nor is it surprising that these two, who were in touch with the wide world, were attracted to Greek civilization as being that of the people who ruled the world. Joseph's sons, brought into frequent contact with aliens owing to their great wealth, continued to foster the Hellenistic tradition. This aspiration to Greek culture accorded well with their pro-Seleucid orientation, not because the Seleucids sought to

Hellenize their subjects, but because they saw in the Greek element of their kingdom the strongest prop of their rule over the indigenous populations (see above, p. 26). Thus aspirations to power and a steady political cultural orientation were fused among the Tobiads and their faction, and this fusion set its stamp on the entire course of events during the seventies and the early sixties of the second century in Judaea and Jerusalem.

We may now return to our account of events. Onias' departure from Jerusalem was in effect a flight from the front. The power passed automatically to his opponents, and the hour had arrived for them to carry out the political program whose general outline had probably been long prepared. But first it was necessary to scotch the danger threatening from Onias, for as long as he was High Priest with the approval of the government, nothing permanent could be built up; a new candidate must be found for his post. The revolutionaries proceeded cautiously, for apparently it was difficult to abolish at one swoop the ancient tradition which accorded to the Oniads the monopoly of the High Priesthood; a change could, however, be made within the family itself. The needed man was found, namely, Joshua, Onias' brother, who had changed his Hebrew name to the Greek name of Jason. Jason may not have been the person most desired by the Tobiads, and we shall see below that in the end he was cast aside by his confederates, but for the moment the High Priest's brother was the most suitable man for the priesthood.[17]

To seize the post, Jason had to depose Onias, and this was impossible without the king's permission; so Jason journeyed to see Antiochus. We do not know how he managed to discredit Onias—the latter's pro-Egyptian tendencies probably played a primary role—we only hear of the results. Jason promised the king, in addition to the 300 talents which were evidently the usual tribute (cf. below, p. 459, n. 39) another 60, and a further 80 "of another revenue" (II Macc. 4.8); by this payment he purchased the High Priesthood from Antiochus. This act of Jason introduced an important innovation in the character of the High Priest's function: whereas till now the post had been hereditary and the king had been in the habit of only granting or withholding his ratification in respect of the new candidate—henceforth the candidate paid the king the price of the position, so that in consequence the High Priesthood became a normal official post and the High Priest a

Seleucid royal official utterly dependent on the king's favor. The way to political reform was now open to the members of the party which was rising to power. II Maccabees (4.9) reports that Jason promised to pay Antiochus another 150 talents if the latter granted him permission to build a *gymnasion* and *ephebeion* in Jerusalem and to "register the people of Jerusalem as Antiochenes." Many interpretations have been set upon this sentence; some have thought that Jason obtained for the people of Jerusalem the privileges of Antioch, the capital of Syria; others have seen in the "Antiochenes" a sort of corporation called after the king and centered on the gymnasium.[18] None of these interpretations can stand up to criticism, and the only correct one (which, indeed, many scholars have proposed) is that Jason received from Antiochus permission to convert Jerusalem into a Greek *polis* called Antioch. Thus were laid the foundations of a comprehensive Hellenistic reform.

The sources furnish only a few allusions on this reform by Jason and each one has to be interpreted if we wish to understand the main lines of the project. We may begin with the interpretation of the passage from II Maccabees cited above. Jason had obtained permission from the king "to register the people of Jerusalem as Antiochenes." In other words, he had to draw up a list of those people who were in his estimation worthy of being citizens of the city of Antioch. It is not to be imagined that all the inhabitants of Jerusalem became Antiochenes automatically. Every Greek *polis* recognized the difference in principle between citizens and mere inhabitants (see above, p. 26f.), and even a democratic city like Athens rigorously insisted on this distinction; how much more an oriental city which had no knowledge of the nature of democracy. Even among the ancient Greek cities there were many which preferred the aristocratic regime to the democratic in the Hellenistic period; the rich town of Rhodes may serve as an example of this type.[19] As the reform was in Jason's hands, which meant in the hands of the representative of the ruling aristocracy, it is not to be supposed that all of Jerusalem's "hewers of wood and drawers of water" were introduced into the citizen body.

In harmony with the basic features of the constitution of the *polis*, Jason had first and foremost to organize the *demos*, the citizen body—and he no doubt fulfilled his task by introducing into his register the nobles and wealthy men of the city. The establishment of the *gymnasion* and *ephebeion* was also in harmony with the city's aristocratic character; it is true that the *gymnasion* was an educational institution typical of every Greek city, but education in the *ephebeion* was bound up with no small expense and therefore became in the Hellenistic period more or less the monopoly of the sons of the wealthy.[20] The fact that, together with the opening of the *gymnasion*, Jason built an *ephebeion*, shows with complete clarity which were the classes among the people of the new *polis* for whose education he was providing. Naturally we have no means of determining the number of new citizens, but a surmise is permissible. II Maccabees (4.40) relates that, in the absence of the High Priest Menelaus from Jerusalem, his brother Lysimachus armed 3000 men whose task was to defend the Hellenizers' regime against the rebellious people (see below). As the citizens of every Greek *polis* were only men of military age (that is, from the age of 18 upwards, approximately), it is a reasonable assumption that in an emergency, when serious danger was threatening the city of Antioch, Lysimachus mobilized the entire manpower at his disposal, namely, all the citizens of the *polis*. The figure of 3000 is also more or less in line with the number of citizens usual in an aristocratic *polis* in Greece.[21]

The *boulé* and the *demos*—the council and the people—were the two main pillars of the political organization of every Greek city. While the constitution of the *demos* in Antioch-Jerusalem was probably attended by several difficulties, the setting up of a council was an easy matter. The council of Jerusalem is already mentioned under Antiochus III under the title of *gerousia*, namely, the "council of elders" (see above, p. 82), and we encounter this institution again in the time of Menelaus (II Macc. 4.44), that is, immediately after the destruction of Jason's rule; from this we learn that the *gerousia* had acted as a supreme administrative institution also in the intervening period, when Jason was High Priest. This is not surprising, for the council of elders was always an aristocratic institution, whether in an oriental city or in a Greek *polis*, and as the Hellenistic reform at Jerusalem was carried out by the aristocracy, there was no need to replace the existing institution by another. It is possible, of course, that isolated individuals were replaced who were not suitable, on account of their political and religious views, to administer a Greek *polis*, but the function of the institution itself remained unchanged.[22]

Simultaneously with the establishment of the *polis*, Jason set up at Antioch-Jerusalem two establishments which were the chief educational institutions of every Greek town—the *gymnasion* and the *ephebeion*. Of all the institutions of the new *polis*, these were the only ones which attracted the special attention of our sources, and this is easy to understand, for their establishment in Jerusalem symbolized in a tangible and visible fashion the entire immense change in the life of the city which took place in consequence of the Hellenistic reform. The author of II Maccabees relates that the license to build a *gymnasion* and *ephebeion* was granted to Jason by Antiochus together with the license to found the city, as if the establishment of these institutions was virtually identical with the reform itself. The *gymnasion* was built "under the fortress," on the Temple hill itself, and the youthful heirs of the Jerusalem aristocracy hastened to don the *petasos*, the broad-brimmed hat of the god Hermes, patron of the *epheboi*, so characteristic of the Greek student youth of the *gymnasia* (II Macc. 4.12).

Crowds of young men streamed to the *gymnasion*, among them many priests who abandoned their service in the Temple to take part in the athletic sports (*ib.* 14). II Maccabees sees in the practice of Greek athletics, which had penetrated so suddenly into Jerusalem, the "peak of Hellenism and the high point of foreign customs" (*ib.* 13). I Maccabees also, although not particularly interested in the history of the Hellenistic reform, refers to the establishment of the *gymnasion* and even transmits one very characteristic detail in connection with the Jews who exercised there, that they sought overnight to become Greeks: they grew ashamed of the seal of the covenant of circumcision that was revealed to the gathering when they were naked during the games, and employed artificial means to efface it (I Macc. 1.15; cf. Jos. *Ant.* XII, 241).

However, the setting up of the *gymnasion* and *ephebeion* at Jerusalem is not to be regarded as a cultural project and nothing more; their building is to be evaluated as a political and juridical precondition essential to the city's Hellenistic constitution; for in every Greek city the gymnastic education, and especially the ephebate, was a prerequisite for the reception of the young man into the citizen corporation.[23] Jason, therefore, had a purpose when he set up these institutions at one and the same time as the *polis* itself:

he himself determined the list of first citizens, but in future it would be the *gymnasion* which would be the mode of admission to citizenship.

Jason's reform is described in II Maccabees not as a superficial attempt to introduce a few changes into the customary political and religious constitution of Jerusalem, but as the complete abolition of the existing constitution and its replacement by a new one. We have spoken above (p. 82) of Antiochus III's manifesto of the year 198, whereby he granted to the Jews of Jerusalem the permission to order their public affairs "in accordance with their ancestral laws." By virtue of this license the traditional theocratic regime of Jerusalem became the fundamental law of the Jewish people under government auspices.

II Maccabees designates these privileges granted to the Jews by Antiochus with the term "beneficent laws" and mentions the name of a certain Johanan who had been, apparently, the mediator between the king and the Jews. Now came Jason "and abolished the king's beneficent laws which had been customary among the Jews . . . and made new and wicked customs by destroying the lawful (customs) of the state" (II Macc. 4.11). I Maccabees (1.13) also emphasizes the constitutional nature of Jason's reform without mentioning the name of the High Priest: "And the king gave them (namely, the Hellenizers) permission to do according to the laws of the Gentiles." It is clear then that the abolition of the former regime, which had been based on the Mosaic Law and the ancestral tradition, and the setting up of a new regime in its place, were two aspects of one undertaking, carried out simultaneously and with great energy.[24] Jason may be considered quite correctly as the founder of the Greek city of Antioch-at-Jerusalem.

The theoretical founder, however, was not Jason but Antiochus, for the town was called after him. According to Hellenistic tradition, the city named after the sovereign was bound to him by an inner bond, for he was its "divine" guardian, was entitled to a special cult there in his capacity of *ktistes* (founder), and sometimes even found his last resting place within the city-bounds.[25] It is to be assumed that in Jerusalem at least part of these honors was paid to Antiochus Epiphanes as royal founder. II Maccabees (4.21) relates that on one occasion (perhaps in the year 172, perhaps earlier)[26] Antiochus chanced to come to Palestine on affairs of state, and visited Jerusalem. He was received with great shouting and rejoicing and with torches "by Jason and the city."

It may well be that this mention of the "city" (the Greek *polis* of Antioch) is not by chance, but possesses a deeper significance; possibly the visit of Antiochus and the festivities associated with it marked the actual juridical foundation of the *polis*, for in 175 the license had been given to Jason only "to register the people of Jerusalem as Antiochenes," that is, only the first steps were taken to establish the civic roll, and probably some time elapsed before Jason was able to inform Antiochus that the new city was organized in due legal form and that its institutions were established. It may be assumed without difficulty that the work of "founding" the city took some two years, and that Antiochus' visit to Jerusalem formed a suitable pretext for proclaiming officially and with great pomp the foundation of the Greek city "Antioch-at-Jerusalem."

The new city was identical with Jerusalem; it did not stand "near" Jerusalem, nor "within" it, as some scholars think;[27] it was Jerusalem itself in a new form. This follows from the fact that the founders of the town were the priests, led by the High Priest. The Temple belonged to the new *polis*, not to the old city, and without the Temple Jerusalem had neither a religious nor an economic basis. Nor are Antioch and Jerusalem to be distinguished topographically, for the *gymnasion*, the principal institution of the new town, stood directly "under the fortress," that is, on the Temple mount, in the very center of old Jerusalem. The *gerousia* also belonged to "Antioch," for it was an aristocratic institution, and it was the aristocracy which had carried the reform through.[28]

The fact that the masses of the people of Jerusalem possessed no citizen rights in the new city cannot be used against this assumption: they doubtless became metics or *katoikoi*, retaining their houses and estates, though these economic rights accorded them no political rights in the city. In the view of the Syrian government Jerusalem no longer existed, since it was represented by no public institution; the name remained merely a designation of locality, whereby the new Antioch was indicated and distinguished from the numerous remaining Antiochs.

Yet another question requires clarification. In what measure did the reform of Jason infringe traditional religious customs? Did the conversion of the theocracy to a *polis* entail the abolition of the Jewish religion, or at least far-reaching modifications of the cult? The sources give a negative answer to this query. The very fact that the author of II Maccabees, who found such sharp words of denunciation to utter of Jason as initiator of the reform and the man who introduced Gentile customs into Jerusalem, found not the smallest accusation to make against him of offenses against the Jewish faith, shows definitely that such offenses did not exist. The abolition of the former constitution based on the Mosaic Law did not mean the automatic abolition of the Law itself. The reform said only one thing, that from now on the *polis*, the citizen body organized as an urban *demos*, was the supreme arbiter and maker of decisions in religious matters, just as it was the arbiter in every other matter. The *demos* had the authority to abolish the Mosaic Law, but no clause of the new constitution obliged it to do so. The introduction of foreign customs such as athletic games and physical exercises, though alien to the national spirit, was not a religious offense in the exact sense of the term: the Law of Moses had never forbidden them explicitly.[29] The *petasos* was, indeed, the hat of the god Hermes, but it is questionable whether his statue or that of any other Greek god stood in the *gymnasion* building, as was customary in Greece, and even if they did, this offense against the commandment "Thou shalt not make unto thee any graven image or any likeness . . ." was not yet real paganism, for the statues standing in the *gymnasion* (that is, not in a place consecrated by the local religious tradition) had no special cult significance.

As to the sacred place itself, it is not to be conceived that any changes took place there. Even the Greeks reverenced the local deities at every place and honored them with sacrifices and offerings, and the Hellenized Orientals all the more so. The Hellenization of the gods of the East nowhere caused a change in the local cultic customs. The God of Israel was neither identified with any other divinity nor did He receive a Greek name, and the fact that His identification with Zeus Olympius is reported only in connection with the persecution of Antiochus—and the account emphasizes that this was a great and terrible change—is sufficient guarantee of the fact that under Jason nothing of the sort occurred.

One hint preserved in our sources confirms the assumption that Jason's reform did not affect traditional religious life. Being now a Greek city, Antioch-at-Jerusalem sent envoys to the athletic games which were held at Tyre every fifth year in the presence of the king himself. The delegates brought with them 300 silver drachmae and should, according to custom, have handed over the money for sacrifices to the city-god (Melkart-Heracles); but instead they requested that the money be donated toward ship-building (II Macc. 4.18-20). Scholars see in this "strange" behavior of the Antiochenes a contradiction to their new status as citizens of a Greek city; but there was here no such contradiction, for Jason's reform was not a religious one, and no law bound the citizens of Antioch-at-Jerusalem to make sacrifices to the gods. The Law of Moses which had ceased to apply as the law of the state approved by the government, had not been abolished by the Jews themselves, although their political organization had taken on a different form. Religious reforms were still a matter of the future. If then Jason's reform was not religious, what were its leading motives?

The author of I Maccabees reports the program of the Hellenizing reformers in these words: "Let us make a covenant with the Gentiles about us; for since we have been different from them we have found many evils" (1.11). The end of self-differentiation from the Gentiles, which had been the tradition of generations ever since Ezra's time, was therefore the slogan of the authors of the reform. With the end of the differentiation the gates were opened to the wide world, a world imbued with the spirit of Hellenistic civilization; hence the reform had inevitably to assume the form of Hellenization. According to Josephus (*Ant.* XII, 240), Menelaus and the Tobiads fled to Antiochus[30] and proposed the following program of reform: They did not desire the laws of their fathers and the former regime, and it was desirable that they should live according to the king's laws, "and that they should have a Greek form of government" (Ἑλληνικὴν πολιτείαν ἔχειν).

Modern history-writing, influenced by theology, has seen in this program of the reformists predominantly an aspiration to religious reform, or at any rate a change in the traditional way of life. However, the Greek *politeia* ("way of government") was not a religious concept, but a political one, and Josephus' sentence says no more than that the reformers wished to obtain for Jerusalem the status of a Greek city. To get it, the previous constitution, based on the "ancestral laws," had to be abolished. Now, the "ancestral laws"

in the language of the Seleucid kings—and the Jews when negotiating with them had perforce to use their terms, that is, the
terminology of the Seleucid bureaucracy—included not merely
the confirmation of the Mosaic Law (a subject in no sense
familiar to the king), but also several matters politically very
important, in particular the entire organization of the Jewish
nation as an *ethnos* (see above, p. 84). The conversion of Jerusalem into Antioch meant first of all the transfer of the Jewish
state from one political category to another: from *ethnos* to *polis.*
Some scholars[31] have asked in surprise why there was need to
pay money to a Greek king, and of all kings to Antiochus
Epiphanes, to obtain a permit to Hellenize the Jews and to
build a hall for physical training at Jerusalem. For this of course
there was no need for bribery; but that was not the question.
The establishment of Greek institutions was but the outer
aspect of the transformation of the *ethnos* into a *polis,* and this,
associated with the change of status of the Jewish people vis-à-
vis the central authority at Antioch, unquestionably required
government approval.

The privileges which were
to fall to the lot of Jerusalem as a result of the reform were
many and varied. The "cities" occupied quite a different position in the Seleucid empire from that of the "peoples," for they
served as supports of the central power in its relation to the
indigenous populations, were regarded as allies, enjoyed municipal self-government, and had the right to strike bronze coins of
their own—a very important privilege for the development of
the city's local trade.[32] Moreover, thanks to their common Hellenic basis, the cities of every state, and also those beyond it,
were linked among themselves by bonds of friendship which
were expressed by participation in general cultural projects
such as athletic celebrations, also by the commerce which developed both between cities and various countries. The *ethnos,*
by contrast, was a people distinct from others which lived its
traditional life according to its "ancestral laws," far from the
main road of world culture and without hope of developing
and flourishing economically. This then was the true significance
of the Hellenizers' slogan "Let us make a covenant with the
Gentiles"—entry into the commonwealth of Hellenic peoples
as a member with equal rights in order to enjoy all the privileges
which the status of Greek *polis* granted to those that controlled it.

All the other details of the
reform, such as the establishment of Greek educational insti-

tutions, the introduction of Greek customs into the daily life of Jerusalem, and perhaps also public belittlement of the Jewish religious customs existent since the days of Ezra—all these were only the logical results of the basic reform. The changes in the spheres of religion and culture were not the reason for the reform, but its consequences, and they involved no principles, although very probably they were apt to cause grave offense to the men of the older generation and hence might easily become the "watchwords" of reform, so evoking, simultaneously, a strong anti-reform movement.

Thus, motives of great political and economic importance impelled the members of the Jerusalem aristocracy to reform. On the other side, Antiochus for his part was ready to aid in every attempt to convert an oriental city into a Greek *polis*. Below we shall dwell in greater detail on the principles of Antiochus' policy; here it is sufficient to emphasize the fact that the period of the building of authentic Greek cities was already over, and if Antiochus desired to acquire friends and loyal allies who would aid him in war with the natives, he had no alternative but to create Greek cities artificially, that is, to Hellenize oriental towns and to attract them by awarding them numerous privileges. Just as the "Macedonians" who served in the army of Antiochus were not Macedonians by race, but Syrians who had received military training in the Macedonian fashion, so the "Greek" cities of Antiochus were merely Syrian towns that had assumed the shape of *poleis*.

By granting rights to these towns Antiochus deepened the gulf between the wealthy urban population and the backward oriental countryside; he anticipated that in the decisive struggle that was to break out between the Seleucid kingdom and the awakening Orient, the wealthy *bourgeoisie* would stand by him. The Hellenization of a city like Jerusalem, lying in the vicinity of the southern frontier of the realm, on the road to Egypt, was likely to be extremely advantageous to him, especially in the event of war with his Ptolemaic rival. Thus the interests of both sides met—the striving of the Jerusalem aristocracy for economic and political growth and the king's endeavor to acquire a friendly power in this part of his kingdom—and the outcome of the meeting of interests was Jason's Hellenistic reform.

We lack details of the course of political and social events in the new Antioch during the three years (175/4-172/1) when Jason ruled the city. The participation of the young aristocrats, including priests, in the physical exercises of the *gymnasion,* the sending of *theoroi* to Tyre to the athletic games,[33] the visit of Antiochus to the city— these are the few events known to us in this period, and they have already been referred to. In the meantime, political affairs developed as they always do in such cases; like every party which rises to power amid the confusions of its period and by unconstitutional means, the Hellenizing party contained both moderate and extremist elements, and little by little the extremist elements grew stronger.

If at the beginning of the revolution the idea of electing a High Priest not of the House of Onias was still strange to the Hellenists themselves, now, when the "ancestral laws" had been officially abolished, and the citizen body was the supreme deciding body in every matter of internal government, the public began to become accustomed to the idea that the High Priest was no more than a municipal official (after the fashion of the priests in Greek towns),[34] and did not have to belong to a certain definite family. Jason, for all the important part he had played in carrying out the reform, could not be *persona grata* to the Tobiads; despite everything he belonged to a family for whom the Mosaic religion was an ancestral tradition, and he could not therefore be completely relied on. An external factor of some importance may have been decisive here. Antiochus was constantly in need of money, for from the day that his father had been defeated at Magnesia by the Romans (190 B.C.E.) the Seleucid kingdom had become involved in a recurring financial crisis. The wealthy temples fulfilled, as already mentioned, the function of banks in ancient times, and Antiochus III, Epiphanes' father, had already coveted their treasures.[35] Antiochus may have demanded of Jason free access to the Temple treasure just as Seleucus IV had demanded it through his emissary Heliodorus (above, p. 157f.). Jason could not comply with this demand without forfeiting the confidence of those classes in Jerusalem which had placed their trust in the High Priest; the plundering of the Temple was also apt to infuriate the masses of the people.

The Tobiads, who were interested in maintaining good relations with the king at all costs, determined to oust Jason from the High Priesthood and to hand the post to a man who would be more loyal to themselves, namely to Menelaus, brother of the Simon already mentioned. According to Josephus (*Ant.* XII, 239) Menelaus' asso-

THE HELLENISTIC REFORM

ciation with the Tobiads was particularly close, and on the other hand he was connected with the Temple, since his brother Simon held there the high position of Overseer of the Temple. He was therefore the most suitable candidate for the post of High Priest. Jason, however, was not prepared to yield his place without a fight. So serious civil strife broke out in Jerusalem. The details of what happened are insufficiently known; each side had its own story. In the *Antiquities* (XII, 237ff.) Josephus relates that Antiochus was angered with Jason and gave the High Priesthood to Menelaus; but since Jason was unwilling to surrender it to him, civil war broke out, Menelaus being supported by the Tobiads and Jason by the majority of the people. The latter gained the upper hand and Menelaus and the Tobiads were forced to escape to Antiochus.

Josephus relates nothing of the results of this conflict,[36] but luckily we find a clearer narrative in II Maccabees, according to which Jason sent Menelaus to Antiochus to pay the taxes, and Menelaus exploited the opportunity to gain power, giving Antiochus a sum of money exceeding by 300 talents the sum Jason paid for his priestly position, so purchasing the post for himself. He returned to Jerusalem as High Priest and Jason was compelled to flee before him to the Land of Ammon (II Macc. 4.25-6).[37] From these contradictory reports we may conclude that Jason did not yield his place without attempting to defend it, that a civil war broke out twice[38] in Jerusalem and that in this struggle the Tobiads, the most important Hellenizers, were on the side of Menelaus.

Menelaus was victorious (perhaps with the assistance of the Syrian garrison), but the victory brought little profit to the Hellenizing party. In Jason's time, under the rule of the moderate Hellenizers, Hellenism had begun to strike root among the people, whereas now, once the extremists had seized power, it began to collapse. Josephus indicates that most of the people supported Jason, while Menelaus had attained power against the will of the Jerusalem population and could only maintain himself by brute force. In the words of II Maccabees (4.25) he was an unparalleled tyrant, "like a beast of prey in his wrath," which means that he was forced to conduct his rule by means of terror in order to protect himself and his party. His position was difficult: the people hated him and he did not receive sufficient support from the king of Syria. To the latter he had promised a large sum of money in a short time, but this he found it difficult to raise rapidly, and the Greek official Sostratos, who held the citadel for the government, demanded the discharge of the debt.

Menelaus traveled to Syria to excuse himself before the king, who, however, was not at Antioch, his deputy being the high official Andronicus. Menelaus won him over to his side by a bribe of several gold vessels from the Temple, a fact proving clearly that the danger of the confusion of private and public money that had always threatened the Temple funds (above, p. 155) had now fully materialized; the Temple treasury had now become the private treasury of the powerful men and the rulers of Jerusalem. The spoliation of the plate was hard to conceal from the gaze of the community, and became known to Onias, the former High Priest, then resident at Antioch. Onias issued a rebuke against Menelaus, thereby doubtless making a considerable impression upon the Jewish community of the city. Thus he involved himself in political strife, and to save his life took refuge at Daphne near Antioch.[39]

Onias' sojourn near Antioch could not be welcome to Menelaus, who suspected the intentions of the legitimate High Priest among the Greeks; clearly he was awaiting a suitable moment to turn the king against Menelaus and to attempt a return to Jerusalem in order to seize the power which was lawfully his. Obviously no time could be more promising for such an attempt than the present, when Menelaus had become financially involved in that he had not paid the king on time. These possibilities doubtless weighed on Menelaus, and he determined to rid himself of his dangerous enemy. He found the needed assistance in Andronicus, who lured Onias from his refuge by cunning and put him to death.[40] The murder was ill-timed and cost Andronicus his life (II Macc. 4.32-8). Menelaus apparently escaped, but immediately afterwards other events occurred which caused the renewed deterioration of his position.

These events were of an entirely new kind. Till now the civil war had been a struggle for power waged between two powerful families. The Hellenization of the Jews as a means of strengthening political positions was used by both sides and the hostility between the Tobiads and Onias was not an antagonism in principle. Onias himself, indeed, was loyal to the tradition of his fathers, but his family undisguisedly followed the road of Hellenization.[41] The broad masses of the Jewish population had not yet been able to take up a clear position in the confusion of the time, and during the conflict between Jason and Menelaus had stood, as Josephus testifies, on Jason's side, but not, of course, for national or religious reasons: Jason, too, was known as a leader of the Hellenizers in Jerusalem, and the religious question in its full scope was not yet central.

But gradually the situation changed. Menelaus' activities gave a strong impulse to a mass awakening of the people. While he was in Syria there had remained in Jerusalem as his deputy, his brother Lysimachus, and it was he who had carried out the spoliation from the Temple treasury of the vessels which Menelaus needed. This lawless deed aroused the ire of the population of Jerusalem; the Temple treasure, accumulated over generations, was the property of all Israel, and it was hard to tolerate the fact of a small group of people disposing of it as if it were their own. The Temple, moreover, this national and religious center, was now in the hands of men who had cast off the restraints of religion and followed strange customs belonging to other peoples. The plundering of the Temple plate made good material for religious propaganda among the masses, and the people came out openly against the Hellenizers. Lysimachus armed some 3000 men and a battle took place in the streets of Jerusalem. The people was victorious: Lysimachus' men gave way and he himself was killed near the Temple (II Macc. 4.39-42).

The subsequent events are not sufficiently clear. II Maccabees relates immediately after the account of Lysimachus' death that "because of these things Menelaus was indicted in court" by the king. This is somewhat curious, since for Lysimachus' murder it would have been proper to indict his slayers rather than Menelaus. Both in Judaea and at the royal court the political position had evidently altered to the disadvantage of the extreme Hellenizers, a change also demonstrated by the fact that there appeared before the king three men of Jerusalem who "had been sent by the Council of Elders" in order to accuse Menelaus (II Macc. 4.44).[42] Menelaus was brought up for trial, and the verdict pending boded him no good. Yet here too bribery availed him in his plight, and by giving money to one of the king's relatives, the latter was induced to influence the sovereign in his favor. The three elders were found guilty in his stead and condemned to death. Menelaus remained High Priest as before (II Macc. 4.50), no doubt successfully suppressing the popular revolt in Jerusalem, wreak-ing havoc among his foes and consolidating afresh his power and that of his party in the city.

Thus two strong forces confronted one another, both the product of the natural development of Jewish history: the Jerusalem aristocracy, organized in the Hellenizing party, and the people, who had not yet found their leaders and could only express their bitterness in risings and abortive demonstrations. We cannot say which force would have been ultimately victorious, or whether they might have reached some compromise, had Jewish history continued to develop solely according to the laws of its own inner life. But the process of inner development was checked midway by the intervention of Antiochus Epiphanes.

chapter 5

ANTIOCHUS'
PERSECUTION OF JUDAISM

The persecution of the Jewish religion known as "the *Gezerot* [= evil decrees] of Antiochus" has puzzled the scholars of our time. What caused the Greek king, a man who had been reared and educated in the atmosphere of religious tolerance so characteristic of Graeco-Roman culture, to attack the Mosaic Law by force of arms, to substitute the cult of the Olympian Zeus for that of the monotheistic cult of Jerusalem, and to prohibit circumcision, the observance of the Sabbath and the other Jewish practices, as if they were the customs of a nation both criminal and corrupt?

Many attempts have been made to explain the reasons and motives of the decree, and we must familiarize ourselves with them before we describe what occurred or seek our own solution. The results of research on this question can be summarized under five headings, each of which reflects a certain method of exposition, but it should be said at once that this classification is somewhat schematic, as in effect all these methods overlap and the method favored by most scholars has been syncretistic.[1]

1. First, let us dwell upon the method which links the Antiochan decrees with the character of the king. No one of course sees in Antiochus' character the sole reason for the persecution, but nearly all scholars have been sensible of those elements in his make-up which lent the final impulse to the execution of the decrees. There is a certain

sense in this emphasis: even in the ancient world Antiochus' strange traits of character attracted the attention of historians. As the Hellenistic authors reflect him, Antiochus appears as a person in whom the positive and negative were mingled in equal proportion. Jewish historiography has made him "the evil one," a tyrant of unparalleled brutality; but clearly this distorted picture cannot be used to characterize him, for justice and impartiality are not to be looked for from foes. Nor is there, on the other hand, an adequate basis for an idealization of Antiochus.

Besides the Jewish books, Greek sources exist which describe Antiochus' personality: Polybius devotes to him a detailed description, from which Livy and Diodorus derived their accounts. The verdict passed by Polybius on Antiochus is in no sense such as to arouse admiration. Polybius has strange things to tell of him. He lacked political tact and did not understand how to behave as befitted a king. Sometimes he would leave his palace and wander through the streets of his capital with two or three of his courtiers, enter shops and the craftsmen's places of work and converse at length with these insignificant people. Once, during one of his habitual visits to the public baths he poured a jar full of perfumed ointment over the heads of the bathers and enjoyed the sight of the people rolling on the slippery floor, unable to rise or to keep their balance, himself among them. Particularly fond of taking part in the carousings of common folk, he was more than once seen in the shady company of aliens of unknown origin and identity. If he heard of some drinking party that was being held by young people, he would appear suddenly among the guests accompanied by an orchestra, making so strange an impression on the participants that fear fell upon them and many would make their escape. Sometimes he walked the streets of Antioch splendidly garbed and crowned with roses, showering upon those he met now rings of gold, now simple stones.

Like Nero two hundred years after him, he liked to participate personally in theater performances; once during a magnificent festival which he was holding at Antioch, he appeared on the stage before the audience as an actor, and began to dance with the other players. The Greeks had never seen their king in such a role, and many left the banqueting hall in shame. His behavior toward other people was full of contradictions and sudden surprises, for he was silent in the company of his best friends and talkative with strangers;

Biography

to some he gave precious gifts such as silver and gold, and to others, without clear reason, worthless objects such as dates and dice. Irritable and nervous, full of profound inner contradictions, ever striving to do something extraordinary and to astound the world—this was the figure cut by King Antiochus in the eyes of his Greek contemporaries. Hence it is not to be wondered at that humorists mocked him and called him in jest *Epimanes* ("mad") instead of *Epiphanes* ("the god manifest").[2]

On the other hand, in Polybius we sometimes find a more sympathetic attitude, while a positive portrait of the king emerges especially from what the sources relate of his political activities. His endeavors to restore the Seleucid kingdom and to rescue it from decline, as expressed in the granting of rights to Greek or to Hellenized cities and in the strengthening of the armed forces of the state; his desire to enlarge the state's frontiers which found its expression in his two wars in Egypt, his cautious attitude to Rome which testifies to his shrewd judgment in the field of international politics—these are not easily reconciled with the strange qualities to be discerned in his nervous character; on the contrary, they give evidence that he was a ruler with realistic and logical political aspirations.

This also explains the diverse accounts of his character to be read in the literature on the subject. If all the scholars utilize the same sources, the interpretation set upon them differs from one author to the next, hence the king's figure varies according to each scholar's particular conception of him. While in Klausner's view Antiochus is simply a "degenerate" and Bouché-Leclercq compares his strange conduct to that of Caligula and Nero, Ed. Meyer and Rostovtzeff regard him as one of the most important figures of the Seleucid dynasty. Thus we see that each scholar forms his own picture of Antiochus.[3]

All the interesting traits of Antiochus' strange character which Polybius relates might serve as supremely important source-material for a historical novel, were we writing one; but as we are concerned not with novels but with history, we may ask to what degree an inquiry into Antiochus' character can assist in solving the problem before us. It is clear that nervousness, hysteria, degeneracy and the like, cannot explain the causes of the persecution of the Jewish religion, since this or that attitude to religious questions does not depend on a man's human type, but on his views. Even

Caligula's "insane" order to set up his statue in the Temple of Jerusalem was not the result of his "madness," but of the fact that this "madness" expressed itself in a certain theory, and the theory, not the madness, was the reason for the order. At most one may agree that Antiochus' ample energy and nervous temperament did something to hasten the process which led to the persecution, but the reasons for the persecution itself have to be sought elsewhere.

2. The view which prevailed in the nineteenth century, and still finds its disciples today, holds that the main motive for Antiochus' policy was his great devotion to the Hellenic spirit and culture. Many scholars see in Antiochus the Hellenizer *par excellence,* who was determined to spread Hellenic culture among all his subjects in order to make it an instrument for uniting all the inhabitants of his huge empire into a single body. In contrast to all the rest of the population, who accepted Hellenization, however, the Jews alone resisted it. In Palestine Antiochus' Hellenistic tradition encountered another tradition, deeply rooted in the soil, and scholars offer differing evaluations of the fierce clash between Greek culture and Jewish monotheism—each scholar according to his general views on Hellenism and Judaism respectively.[4]

If we turn to the sources, we shall find in them many facts which appear to support this manner of thinking. Antiochus was renowned in the ancient world as an enthusiastic Hellenist. The leaders of the Greek people explicitly emphasized that he was the first and only Seleucid king to bestow benefactions upon the Greek people and to concern himself with their many needs (Polyb. XXIX, 9, 13). His generosity to the Greeks knew no bounds. He built a splendid temple to Zeus Olympius at Athens, set up statues and altars of the gods at Delos, made a donation to the citizens of Megalopolis to build their city wall, laid the foundations of a marble theater at Tegea, gave gold vessels to the citizens of Cyzikus, and more besides (Livy XLI, 20). No less well known was his work on behalf of Hellenism within the frontiers of the Seleucid kingdom itself. Like the great founders of the Seleucid dynasty, Seleucus I and Antiochus I, Antiochus Epiphanes also strove to be a founder of Greek cities, and if his work cannot be compared with that of the first kings of the line, this was not for lack of will but because he was born at least a century after his time.

The diffusion of Hellenism throughout the oriental countries by means of Greek cities was a thing of the past; the Seleucids had lost the lands of the Far East and only a small part of the great kingdom—Syria and Mesopotamia, precisely the most Hellenized portion—remained in their hands. It was not easy to continue the propagation of Hellenism in these countries, since many important Greek towns, such as Syrian Antioch and Seleuceia-on-Tigris, had long existed there. Hence the novel character of Antiochus' activity: his design was not to build new Greek cities, but to intensify the Hellenism of those that already existed, also to turn the ancient oriental towns which had not yet been Hellenized into Greek *poleis,* by granting them special political privileges. Some eighteen cities were linked by name to that of the philhellenic king.[5] The great political importance of the Hellenization of these oriental towns is not to be denied, for this policy created for Antiochus friends among the wealthy *bourgeoisie* of those communities and so considerably strengthening the entire state. It has already been observed that Antioch-at-Jerusalem also was intended as a link in the long chain of strongholds of the new Hellenism in the Seleucid empire.

And if we ask what had this pro-Hellenic policy to do with the persecution of Judaism, here too the view under discussion can find authority in the sources, and precisely in the best of them, namely, in the documents. In Antiochus' letter to Nicanor on the Samaritans, the king writes: "As their envoys (those of the Samaritans) have appeared before my council and have declared that the allegations against the Jews do not apply to themselves, as they (the Samaritans) have preferred to live according to the customs of the Greeks. . . ."[6] This letter testifies, then, that the reason for the decrees against the Jews was that they showed no inclination to live "according to the customs of the Greeks." II Maccabees relates that at the beginning of the persecutions an order was published by the king to extend the persecution to the Jewish population of the Greek cities of Syria; in it the king ordered the execution of those Jews "who do not wish to go over to Greek ways of life."[7] The declaration of Antiochus V, Epiphanes' son, in 162, was written in the same spirit: "We have heard that the Jews did not consent to go over to Greek customs as our father (wished), but preferred their own . . ."[8] From all these passages the fact emerges clearly that Epiphanes' contemporaries, and the king himself, saw the reason for the persecutions in the Jews' obstinate refusal to exchange their traditional way of life for Greek ways. The forcible Hellenization of the Jews was the reason for the persecution.

This view, which is to all appearances supported by such convincing proofs, cannot in fact stand up to criticism, for the following reasons. Scholars see in Antiochus Epiphanes the sovereign who continued the Seleucids' traditional policy of Hellenizing their subjects. But as already observed (p. 25ff.), the Seleucids were never "bearers of culture" and never intended to Hellenize the populations of the Orient on profound spiritual matters, Hellenization expressing itself in a purely external political form, that of the transformation of oriental towns into Greek *poleis*. There are no grounds for supposing that the "philhellenism" of Antiochus was expressed in any other form; he saw in Hellenism a *political* means of strengthening his state; but it never occurred to him to abolish local culture and to substitute for it the Greek.[9]

One detail, at any rate, of Antiochus' activity may be noted which casts doubt on his special devotion to Greek culture, namely, his unquestionable devotion to Roman civilization.[10] Just as his pro-Roman policy arose from his desire to strengthen his kingdom by maintaining good relations with Rome, so his Hellenistic policy was also designed to strengthen his realm, not to spread the ideas of Greek civilization. The way to Hellenization was political—the granting of the rights of Greek *poleis* to oriental towns, and this is what was done at Jerusalem at the demand of the Hellenizing Jews themselves. And here we come to the second reason. As early as 175, Jerusalem had become a Greek *polis* and we have seen above that this had caused no change in the city's religious life; the cult of the God of Israel remained as before and the traditional rites of the faith were not abolished, even if their legal basis was denied. The persecution was not therefore bound up with the conversion of Jerusalem to a Greek *polis*. Something happened in the period between 175 and 167 that changed the situation fundamentally and imparted to the Hellenization of the Jews the character of a command from above. It is clear then that it was this same "something" which caused the persecution, not Hellenization as such. We shall see below that only a detailed analysis of the events during this period can provide us with the clue to an understanding of the origin of the persecution and its peculiar character.

3. The weakness of the foregoing theory has resulted in its substitution by another, which

may be called the doctrine of "unification." This doctrine holds that Antiochus sought to strengthen his crumbling kingdom by political centralization and cultural unification. The establishment of one religion for all the people of the state was part of his plan of reform.[11] This explanation too finds authority in the sources. I Maccabees (1.41) relates: "And the king wrote to all his kingdom that all should be one people and that each people should abandon its customs; and all the peoples did as the king commanded."[12]

Scholars find a second authority in Daniel, 11.36ff.: "And the king shall do according to his will; and he shalt exalt himself, and magnify himself above every god, and shall speak marvellous things against the God of gods. . . . Neither shall he regard the god of his fathers, nor the desire of women, nor regard any god, for he shall magnify himself above all." In these obscure lines scholars have discovered an allusion to a far-reaching religious reform. Antiochus, they allege, turned his back on the official cult till then existing in his kingdom and introduced another that would have been strange to his ancestors; this cult was associated to a certain degree with his own deification. This interpretation has found unexpected support in numismatics; coins afford evidence that under Antiochus Epiphanes the cult of Zeus Olympius took root in his dominions, being especially fostered by the king and replacing the traditional cult of Apollo, the divine guardian of the Seleucid dynasty.[13]

Specialists further point to coins of Antiochus on which the image of Zeus resembles the king's features. From this they conclude that the king's ultimate aim was to introduce into his realm the worship of himself in the form of Zeus Olympius, and that this also was the cult which was to prevail on the Temple hill at Jerusalem.

This doctrine looks much better founded than the preceding, and the syncretistic form of the new cult has proved especially attractive to scholars. Zeus Olympius was actually an original Greek deity, but could easily be identified with any "chief" god of the oriental pantheon, and particularly with the Syrian "Baal Shamin." The God of Israel could also (in Antiochus' view, at least) be readily identified with Zeus. But, we may ask, was the period of Antiochus Epiphanes ripe for a syncretistic reform? If the report in I Maccabees (1.41) is correct, and if it is true that Antiochus sought to introduce the cult of the Olympian Zeus throughout his realm in place of the local cults, this means that he wished to set up a "pagan monotheism," a thing unparalleled in the Graeco-Roman world before the third century C.E. The emperors of the Severan dynasty perhaps dreamed of such a reform; but what was comprehensible at the time of the decline of the Roman Empire was without historical foundation under Antiochus.

The fusion between East and West had not yet reached the stage of a comprehensive religious synthesis, the Greek philosophical idea of one principle ruling in the world had not yet gained substance from material borrowed from the religious cults of the East, nor do we find any hint in the spiritual development of the period which permits us to see in Antiochus Epiphanes a religious reformer of far-reaching aspirations. There is no doubt that Antiochus for some reason possessed a special leaning to Zeus Olympius and endeavored to spread his cult in his kingdom. It is credible, of course, that he wished to set up some sort of worship of himself in the form of Zeus. But this was no new aspiration. Where deification was concerned, Seleucus I had long been worshiped as "Zeus Nicator," as had Antiochus I under the form of "Apollo Soter."[14] And if the Jews, like the author of I Maccabees and Daniel, saw in the propagation of the cult of Zeus a monotheistic policy, their conception is clearly understandable from the fact that they were themselves monotheists and that they saw in every tendency to prefer one cult over others an attempt to set up a uniform religion with the aim of abolishing the rest.[15] Nor is there any connection between the worship of the Olympian Zeus and the persecution of the Jewish religion. Even if it is correct that the God of Israel could, in Antiochus' view, be merged with Zeus, the fusion was carried out at the time of the persecution itself as one of its numerous legal provisions, and was not one of its motivations. We shall see below that it was not the Olympian Zeus but the Syrian Baal Shamin who actually prevailed on the Temple mount. There are then no grounds for supposing that the Jews fell victims to Antiochus' policy of "religious unification," since the very existence of this policy is only a theory held by modern scholars.

4. The above doctrine has an inner connection with the theory which accounts for Antiochus' decrees by political motives. The policy of unification in the religious field was merely a partial expression of Antiochus' general policy of reconstituting the decaying power of his king-

dom. This is the spirit of the view expressed by Rostovtzeff, Otto, Kölbe, Tarn, Jansen and many others.[16] The theory is no doubt correct insofar as it explains the reasons for the conflict between Antiochus and the Jews, for according to all the sources the tension between them originated from purely political complications, and the anti-religious decrees arose in the final phase of a long development. However, this method cannot answer for the central question, namely, how did the political conflict become religious enmity, and it cannot ultimately avoid utilizing the reasons offered by the two preceding theories—the theories of "Hellenization" and "unification." Nevertheless, had scholars extracted the utmost from all the information in the sources on the political clashes between Antiochus and the Jews, they might have come nearer to a solution of the problem than any of those who have followed other methods of explanation.

5. Bickermann seeks to account for the persecution of Antiochus in a new way. His book *Der Gott der Makkabäer* is an important study, and some of its conclusions may be accepted as fundamental to all further inquiry (see below, p. 195). But precisely the central idea of the book evokes numerous doubts. Bickermann's basic assumption is that Antiochus, a king of Greek education and a pupil of the Epicureans, could not have been the initiator of the persecution, since it meant, not simply an abolition of the existing law, but the imposition of a new religious law in a way which implies religious fanaticism, whereas in the entire ancient world there is no example of religious fanaticism of this sort, if the Pharaoh Akhenaton be excepted. It would never have occurred to the king to order the burning of the Torah, to prohibit circumcision, compel people to eat pork, and the like. But all this is comprehensible if we assume that not Antiochus but the Hellenistic reformers of Jerusalem, the High Priest Menelaus and his group, were the real initiators of the decrees. Antiochus' function was merely the abolition of the rule of the Torah in Judaea, and it was the Jewish Hellenizers who filled the formal abolition with real content. What was their aim? They sought to abolish Jewish particularism and to come to terms with the peoples around them. In this they were influenced by Greek views, since in Greek eyes all exclusiveness was barbarism. The Jews therefore faced the alternative of being thought barbarians or of joining

the Hellenistic world, which meant recognizing the existence of other deities besides the Jewish God.

It was not hard for the Jewish Hellenists to give up the Torah, because they did not believe in its divine origin. Greek religious research had already reached the conclusion that many legislators, from Zarathustra to Lycurgus, had, like Moses, relied on divine inspiration. In addition, the educated Greeks saw several features of the Jewish religion (such as self-seclusion, the prohibition of certain foods, etc.) as symptomatic of a late degeneration contrasting with the situation at the time when Judaism still preserved its freshness and upheld the sole principle of the worship of God without image or representation, which Greek philosophers regarded as a very positive phenomenon. A Hellenizing Jew could not ignore this philosophical opinion, hence Philo's symbolical interpretation of the Torah, without which he could not have justified its commandments. "It is sufficient to follow the trend of thought of these Jewish Hellenists (Philo, and the other Alexandrian commentators), in order to understand an ideology of the sort held by Jason and Menelaus in Palestine. They desired to reform Judaism by abolishing the barbaric exclusiveness which had infected it with time, and to return to an original worship of God free of all distortion" (*Gott der Makk.*, 132).

Bickermann, then, shifts the onus from Antiochus to the Hellenizing Jews. For this he finds authority in the sources; as is well known, all of them ascribe the attempt to Hellenize the Jews not to Antiochus but to the Hellenizers among the Jews themselves, and this has been emphasized more than once by modern writers.[17] Bickermann's innovation is in seeing the Hellenizers, not only as the initiators of the reform, but also as the initiators of the persecution. And here many doubts arise. Paramount among them is the association of the persecution with Antiochus' name alone in our sources, which contain not a word about Jason and Menelaus as religious persecutors. The conversion of Jerusalem into the Greek *polis* of Antioch, the building of the *gymnasion* and *ephebeion* and the whole reform of 175 were not associated with any act against the prevailing faith, as has already been noted (p. 66).

The reform did not begin under an anti-religious slogan, and it is therefore clear that the idea of persecuting Judaism arose as a result of the development of affairs at Jerusalem, not as a preconceived plan. Secondly, it is an error to describe the Jewish Hellenists of Jerusalem as the bearers of Greek philosophical ideas. Such a conception is in contradiction to the superficial "levantine" character of Hellenistic culture in the oriental countries generally and in Palestine in particular (see above, p. 31). The parallel with Philo cannot stand up to criticism, for what was natural to Philo, a pupil of Greek philosophers and a citizen of the most highly civilized and Hellenized city of the entire Hellenistic dispersion, was in no sense natural to the political and public leaders of an oriental town, whose Hellenism had not yet emerged from the first phase of the superficial aping of foreign customs.

How much stronger, then, do our doubts become as to the correctness of Bickermann's theory, when he not merely attributes to the Jerusalem reformers a general knowledge of Greek philosophy, but even makes them conversant with complex specialized questions such as the evolution of religion, the nature of culture, and the like. For according to Bickermann it was precisely the profound knowledge of these questions which exercised the main influence on the program of reform in Jerusalem.[18] And if Jason and Menelaus were really so profoundly imbued with the spirit of Greek philosophy, why was it that they had not acquired the Greek skepticism in religious matters or the broadminded tolerance of every strange and curious cult? Bickermann rightly believes that Antiochus, a Greek king and a disciple of the Epicureans, was incapable of being a religious fanatic; but if so, why did Jason and Menelaus become fanatics, having received the same education and breathed the same atmosphere of lofty liberal culture as Antiochus?

Thus we have reviewed the various theories proposed by modern scholars as solutions for the riddle of Antiochus' decrees and have not found a single one which supplies a satisfactory answer to the problem before us. Nevertheless, the above survey cannot be said to have been superfluous: we have seen that each view relies on certain sources and from this we conclude that each one must contain part of the truth. A mere syncretistic method, however, such as is followed by a number of scholars, cannot produce a solution, for the mechanical assembly of various factors is not a correct method of understanding complex historical processes. We must seek the key which will enable us to understand the organic link between the various phenomena associated with the decrees of Antiochus. And although an account of the happenings of the years 170-167 has been given more than once in learned literature, I believe that scholars have ignored a very vital link in the chain of events, namely, the Jewish rebellion which preceded the persecution. And if we endeavor to determine the reasons, the extent and the ideological bases of this rebellion, we shall perhaps also discover the solution to the riddle of Antiochus' persecution.

The events in Judaea which led to the persecution are bound up with Antiochus' Egyptian campaigns. The establishment of the chronology of these campaigns and also their number, has long been a subject of controversy among scholars, but the studies of Otto and Bickermann make it virtually certain that Antiochus' first expedition to Egypt fell in the year 169, and the second in 168.[19] More important for the present discussion is the question, how many times did he visit Jerusalem? The account of the occurrences connected with these visits is far from clear in the sources; I Maccabees speaks of only one visit—after the first campaign (1.2); while in II Maccabees, although Antiochus also appears only once at Jerusalem, he does so after the second campaign (5.11). The general view of modern scholars is that Antiochus visited Jerusalem once only—after his first campaign in the autumn of 169, whereas after his second he did not come in person, but empowered his general Apollonius to ravage Judaea. We cannot accept this view, since the Book of Daniel speaks explicitly of two visits by Antiochus to Jerusalem.[20] The political situation in Jerusalem in 168 was so dangerous that it necessitated the king's personal presence; yet, as we shall see shortly, this fact in no way detracts from Apollonius' function as the executor of Antiochus' orders. We may now describe the course of events as reflected in the various sources, in the following order.

Antiochus reached Jerusalem for the first time when he was returning from Egypt at the end of 169. That year his relations with Jerusalem, in other words with the *polis* of "Antioch-at-Jerusalem," were friendly. Josephus testifies on the evidence of important Greek authors that the Jews were then looked upon as "the king's helpers and friends," but the same writers indicate that on this visit Antiochus laid hands on the Temple treasures and looted them.[21] I Maccabees (1.20ff.) also gives a detailed account of the spoliation of the Temple vessels and speaks of the way the place was desecrated.

Naturally this left a feeling of violent hatred for Antiochus among the people, and as it was a time of war, this inevitably assumed a political coloring.

The inclination to favor Egypt grew among the people, only the Tobiads and the other Hellenizers remaining loyal to the Syrian king. In the course of a year this trend took on a clearer form, for a false rumor reached Jerusalem from Egypt that Antiochus was dead. Jason, who had been High Priest in the years 175-172 and had been deposed by Menelaus, left his hiding-place in Transjordan and attacked Jerusalem at the head of a small body of some thousand men. Menelaus attempted to defend the city, but without success, being forced to retire and fortify himself in the city's citadel. Jerusalem fell into Jason's hands. There is no clear report on what he did there, but II Maccabees relates that he wrought great slaughter among the citizens (5.6), and another passage reports that he and his men "burnt the gate and shed innocent blood" (*ib.* 1.8), one of the gates of the Temple apparently being meant.

From all these hints it may be deduced that civil war broke out in the city; and the main question is who was fighting against whom? At first glance the simple assumption is that the fighting was between Jason and Menelaus, who was supported by the Tobiads and their party; but the account in II Maccabees is against this. The writer accuses Jason of brutality to his fellow citizens and is full of sympathy for his victims, and it is hard to imagine that he would have pitied them and denounced Jason so fiercely had he known that Jason's foes were the Tobiads whom he so detested. Moreover, II Maccabees says that Jason, unable to retain control, was forced to evacuate the city and to escape back to the country of the Ammonites (5.7); as the story of his expulsion precedes that of Antiochus' arrival in the city and is quite unconnected with the king's activities, it is obvious that it was not the king who drove Jason from Jerusalem. In that case, who did so? If we suppose that it was Menelaus, the entire course of subsequent events ceases to be comprehensible. Antiochus, seeing in the happenings at Jerusalem a rebellion against his royal authority, came to put it down with a strong hand; but had Menelaus regained control of the city in the meantime, there would have been no occasion for such extreme measures, for with Menelaus' assistance the city would have returned to its previous allegiance to Syria.

Logic demands the conclusion that, after Jason's failure, the control of the city passed to the opponents of the king—the enemies of the Hellenizers. This means that a very significant thing had occurred in Jerusalem, namely, a people's revolt against Jason and the overthrow of the rule of the Hellenizers in the city: Antioch-at-Jerusalem was liquidated and the people was preparing to return to its traditional form of government. Simultaneously, the rising was a demonstration of hostility toward Syria and of sympathy for Egypt, for only from Egypt could the rebels hope to receive support for the liberation movement. As a dissident movement arose also in other parts of Syria at this time,[22] Antiochus perceived that his kingdom was in considerable danger and that he must put down the Jewish rising with a strong hand. According to II Maccabees (5.11ff.) the king, gripped by the fury of a wild animal, took the city by storm and gave his troops the order to put its inhabitants to the sword; some 40,000 people were slain and an equal number was sold into slavery. These figures are of course exaggerated, but it is clear that Antiochus now regarded Jerusalem as a hostile city and behaved toward it accordingly.

We can imagine the course of events roughly in this wise: Antiochus released the beleaguered Menelaus from the citadel; annihilated part of his opponents in the course of street-fighting, while another section fled or sought refuge in hiding; handed over the administration of the town to the Hellenizers and reestablished the *polis* of "Antioch." Antiochus did not, it seems, have time to complete his punitive action, and perhaps believed that he had suppressed the rising completely, for he departed from the city, leaving Philip, the commander of the Phrygian mercenaries, in charge (II Macc. 5.22). He was mistaken, however, for when he had departed, the rebellion blazed up afresh and Jerusalem again passed into the hands of the insurgents. Although the renewal of the rising is nowhere referred to, it cannot be doubted, for according to all our sources Apollonius, head of the Moesian mercenaries ($\mu\nu\sigma\acute{\alpha}\rho\chi\eta\varsigma$), was compelled to capture the city by trickery on a Sabbath, a sign that once again it was not in the hands of the Syrian forces. Apollonius had received from Antiochus the assignment of putting an end once and for all to the danger threatening the peace of the kingdom from the rebellious Jews; his authority was very wide and, as he was acting for the king, our sources, very naturally, do not always distinguish between his actions and those of the sovereign.[23]

II Maccabees is silent on Apollonius' activities, whereas I Maccabees has preserved very important information on the events of 168. Daniel also adds valuable details of the same events. According to I Maccabees, the king's commissioner (that is, Apollonius), having captured the city and punished the rebels, fortified the "City of David" with a wall and towers and converted it into a strong fortress, the Akra, which was occupied by the Jewish Hellenizers and so became the new center of the Greek *polis*. But not only Hellenizers settled in the Akra. I Maccabees says that Antiochus settled there "people of pollution, sons of Belial, who brought thither spoil from the whole of Jerusalem and shed innocent blood about the Temple" (I Macc. 1.35-36); as a result, the inhabitants of Jerusalem abandoned the city, and it became an "abode of aliens" (*ib.* 35). In another passage (3.45) I Maccabees again speaks of Jerusalem as having become a waste and of "the sons of the aliens in the Akra." Daniel also (11.39) tells of the strangers in the Akra: "And he shall make fortresses of strength with the people of a foreign god, whom he shall acknowledge, shall increase glory; and he shall cause them to rule over many, and shall divide the land for a price."[24]

From all these passages it is quite clear what means were adopted by Apollonius to punish the rebellious city: he settled in it "a nation of a foreign god," that is, new settlers drawn from among the Gentiles, who were, of course, soldiers; every *cleruchy* or *katoikia* in the Hellenistic period was military in its membership and organization, and earlier Ptolemy Euergetes had threatened the Jews that he would divide up the land of Jerusalem among *cleruchs* and would send thither military settlers (*Ant.* XII, 159). Thus Jerusalem became "an abode of aliens."

Scholars of the present day have not realized the importance of this fact and mention it merely in passing. But such an important event should not be passed over lightly, for we know the meaning of the establishment of a *katoikia* in an inhabited place. It meant confiscation of the agricultural property of the citizens, the introduction of new settlers into their homes, deeds of violence and rape upon the former inhabitants, the imposition of taxes upon them and sometimes even their expulsion from the town.[25] The earlier threat of Ptolemy Euergetes and later of Lysias (I Macc. 3.37) to turn Jerusalem into a military *cleruchy* itself testifies that this punishment was the severest that could be imposed on civilians, and if I Maccabees perhaps exaggerates when it describes Jerusalem as a wilderness completely abandoned by its inhabitants (1.38; 3.48), its story of the flight of masses of people from the town is certainly authentic. It would be hard to imagine that the people would react to Apollonius' penal order in any other way.[26] And the question must be asked whether this reaction was entirely passive.

Our general outlook on the Antiochan persecution and the Hasmonean revolt has usually been formed under the influences of our sources for the events of the epoch. According to the books of the Maccabees the events developed in the following order: (1) Collisions between parties or personalities among the Jews; (2) the military intervention of Antiochus in the affairs of Judaea; (3) the persecution; (4) the rebellion of the Hasmoneans. According to this order, the rebellion came as an answer to the persecution. This interpretation of our sources is quite understandable. The author of I Maccabees is merely an official historian of the Hasmonean dynasty whose task is to describe the rise to power of the great family. He is not interested in the history of the time prior to the dynasty's rise, and performs his duty as historian by giving the briefest possible account of events in the year 167. Nor is he concerned to praise those who fought the people's struggle before the Hasmoneans, for by so doing he would be detracting from the claim of the Hasmoneans to be the people's saviors and sole leaders.

As to II Maccabees, its author, not being a historian of the dynasty, is much freer in his account of the period preceding the rising; but he sees the Temple as the nation's center, and therefore describes Judah the Maccabee, purifier of the shrine from Gentile profanation, as the great hero who rescued Israel from enslavement to the pagans; and in his eyes, too, the entire long period before the persecution is only a prelude to the appearance of Judah. He does indeed give a much more detailed account of the events down to 167 than I Maccabees, but he too is not concerned in speaking at length of the insurgent movement prior to Judah, because he desires to bestow upon his hero the exclusive honor of being the initiator of the liberation movement and the chief realizer of its aspirations. Thus, thanks to the influence of the sources, the well known picture of the order of events has been determined in this wise: the party-struggle in Jerusalem; Antiochus' intervention; the persecution; the revolt.

Yet the reality was different. It was not the revolt which came as a response to the persecution, but the persecution which came as a response to the revolt. Only on this assumption can we understand Antiochus' decrees and their political purpose.

It requires but little consideration to understand that from the moment Menelaus was appointed High Priest (172/1) the ferment among the Jerusalem community had progressively grown, and that from 168 onwards the Jewish people was virtually in a state of open war with Antiochus. These facts were recorded by II Maccabees and if we take into account that book's general direction, as just discussed, it will be clear, not only that the author was not exaggerating, but that he was playing down as much as possible the account of the popular revolt before the appearance of Judah the Maccabee.

Modern historians interpret all the political events which preceded the Hasmonean revolt as a feud between the two great families of the Tobiads and the Oniads. This view is somewhat one-sided, and we have remarked above (p. 159) that the Hellenistic period burst the confined framework of family tradition and opened up a broad field for individual talents. The family feud, therefore, should not be made into a key to all problems. Several important episodes of the period cannot possibly be explained on the hypothesis of the family feud. Who, for example, was responsible for the slaying of Lysimachus; against whom had Lysimachus gathered the large force of 3000 men, and against whom was he fighting? With the Oniads? Onias himself was no longer alive, and Jason was a fugitive in the land of Ammon. It is clear that here was no inter-family feud, but a clash between the Hellenizers' government of the *polis* and the population of Jerusalem. Nor can the events of 168 be described as a conflict between two families and nothing more. Jason, it is true, invaded Jerusalem and Menelaus fled before him to be besieged in the town's citadel; this, then, at first sight, is a collision between Oniads and Tobiads. But we have seen above that it was not Menelaus but another force which drove Jason from Jerusalem, and this informs us that the family feud was merely a prelude to a much more momentous collision of forces.

The key to an understanding of the events of the entire period has to be sought not in inter-family quarrels among the aristocracy, but in the conflict of interests between the aristocracy and the people, interpreted as the broad sections of the lower urban populace, composed of craftsmen, day-laborers, shopkeepers, petty vendors, and the rest. Of the deep gulf between these elements and the Jerusalem aristocracy, even before the Hellenistic reform, we have spoken at length above (p. 151). The Hellenistic reform of 175, which placed the poorer sections of the people outside the *polis*, could only make this gulf more profound. The *plebs urbana* of Jerusalem, if we may use the Roman terminology, was interested neither in diplomatic relations with the Hellenistic world, nor in the conduct of high policy at the royal court of Antioch, nor even in the development of commercial relations with other states. It knew one thing clearly, that as a result of the Hellenistic reform all the affairs of the city were gathered in the hands of the rich and well-connected in even greater measure than hitherto. The urban *plebs* was doubtless also linked with the agricultural population of the villages around the city, for both classes had a common enemy, the large estate owners permanently resident in the town, although their liveli-hood was derived from the villages of the Judaean countryside. It may be supposed that the lower priesthood also joined the popular movement (as more than once in history the inferior clergy has joined the opponents of the dominant upper ten). It is not difficult to recognize that the movement of opposition to the Hellenistic authorities in Jerusalem had existed from the beginning of the reform, but had not found the right tactics of struggle just so long as the situation had not forced open re-sistance. Only when Menelaus seized the High Priesthood and began the unconcealed plundering of the Temple treasure, did the opposition arise for the first time as an organized force and win its first victory by slaying Menelaus' brother Lysimachus (above, p. 173). It won its second victory by expelling Jason from the city, thereby declaring open war on Antiochus. Apol-lonius' persecution came in reply to this declaration, the Hellen-izers received a military center in the Akra and the city became an "abode of strangers."

What was the reaction of the Jerusalem population to these measures? Our sources report the mass flight of Jews from the town; but they mention it generally as if it happened *after* Antiochus' decrees; they do this, however, because from that moment begins their real interest in the course of events. Actually it is clear that the flight had begun immediately after Apollonius' actions, without any connection with Antiochus' decrees; the sources themselves witness this when they speak candidly.[27] The flight can hardly be interpreted as a quiet retirement from the city to the country, conducted out of a desire to shun the abominations being perpetrated in the city (cf. II Macc. 5.27); such an account involves idealization and lack of consideration for the real state of affairs. The largest percentage of the refugees were doubtless those whose property had been confiscated by the government; but, on the other hand, the direct result of flight was the confiscation of further property in the town. The fugitives, who had lost their livelihood, if they wished to subsist, had no alternative but to organize themselves in bands and to live the life of guerrillas. And as the flight was from the town to the country, the villagers also joined the insurgent movement, and the whole of Judaea became a cauldron. This is the real picture of Judah and Jerusalem in the year 168/7 before the decrees of Antiochus.[28]

So far, we have not transcended the limits of the political events of the period. What part then did religion play in the revolutionary movement before the promulgation of the decrees?

The Hellenistic reform had from the beginning offended the religious susceptibilities of the broad sections of the Jerusalem public. The alien customs of Greece, the belittlement of the sanctities of Judaism on the part of the high-born priests, the program "to be like all the Gentiles" which doubtless despised the prohibition to eat at the tables of non-Jews and perhaps even to intermarry with them, all ran openly counter to the foundations of traditional Judaism as they had been accepted from the days of Ezra onward. The abolition of the constitution of Antiochus III by Jason and the handing over of all affairs, including those of religion, to the *polis,* even if it had not caused an immediate change in the people's customs, carried within it the danger of such changes in the future, as the commandments of God henceforth depended on the general assembly of the *demos* of "Antioch," meaning the high-born and wealthy citizens of the new city. Yet so long as the right of the common people to live according to the Law of Moses remained uninfringed, relative quiet reigned in Jerusalem. The change of principle in the situation was created by the establishment of the Akra and the absorption of foreign settlers among the citizens of "Antioch."

It is surprising that modern scholars, who are perfectly familiar with the fact of the establishment of a *katoikia* of foreign troops on the territory of Jerusalem, have not asked the question: what was likely to be the effect of this fact on the cult of the God of Israel upon the Temple mount? For these troops were settled in the Akra and were part of the *polis,* and clearly they had the right to express an opinion on questions of religion and worship, as on every other question. What was their attitude to Judaism and what was their influence on the cult arrangements in their new place of residence? And above all, who were these new colonists and to what nation did they belong? The reply is not difficult to give. The soldiers who were settled in the Akra were neither Greeks nor Macedonians, since in the time of Antiochus Epiphanes the Syrian kings had no foothold in the lands of Greece and Macedon, nor any opportunity of recruiting new mercenaries for their army there; and as for the Macedonians born in the military *katoikiai* founded by Alexander and the first Seleucids, they had long since mingled with the local inhabitants and lost their racial purity. By Antiochus' time the term "Macedonian" had come to denote a soldier who had received his military training in a Macedonian fashion, and all the numerous units of "Macedonians" at this epoch were simply "natives" who had been trained in this way.[29]

As regards the troops settled in Jerusalem, it is clear that they were local Syrians, just as most of the Seleucid armies subsequently encountered by the Hasmoneans were of Syrian origin (see below, ch. 7). These Syrian troops, who by the royal will had become settlers of the city of Antioch-at-Jerusalem, brought with them the cults of their native country. It is not indeed to be imagined that they intended to abolish the cult of the God of Israel, for the local god was always the chief deity in the eyes of alien settlers and his cult had to be respected. It was nevertheless natural that in the local deity the Syrians should look to one of the gods known to themselves, so uniting the local cult with that of their homeland; and as the Jewish God was "the Supreme God," a God of Heaven, His identification with "Baal Shamin" ("the Lord of Heaven"), the chief god of the Syrian pantheon, was taken for granted. They worshiped not only him, but also other deities, such as Dushara, the god of wine, who was identified by the

Greeks with Dionysus, and the great Syrian goddess, queen of heaven, who had many names and could be equated with Aphrodite, Athene, or any other Greek goddess. The importance of Bickermann's discovery of, and emphasis on, the oriental Syrian character of the divine cults on the Temple hill during the persecutions of Antiochus may be understood and estimated in the light of these facts: it is his opinion that these were not the Greek gods, Olympian Zeus, Dionysus, or Athene, as they are called in the sources, but Syrian deities in Hellenistic garb.[30] The wanton women, moreover, whose presence in the Temple is referred to by the sources, were simply the sacred prostitutes so characteristic of the cults of Syria, and so utterly foreign to any Greek cult.[31] But Bickermann himself could not prove his own innovation completely, because he had no logical explanation for the sudden victory of the Syrian cults; the Jewish Hellenists, if they had sought, as Bickermann believed, to convert the Jews to another faith, would have imposed upon them not a Syrian but a Greek form of worship, in accordance with the education which they are alleged to have received. Yet the solution is simple: the Syrian cults prevailed on the Temple mount because the population of the *polis* of Antioch-at-Jerusalem was now partly Syrian. The result could have been foreseen; a temple in which Syrians ruled and made their sacrifices to the God of Israel under the form of the Syrian Baal and to other Syrian gods as well—a temple in which Syrian prostitutes sported with Syrian soldiers—could not serve the needs of the Jewish religion, and it was abandoned by the Jews, doubtless after conflict and bloodshed both grave and prolonged. Only the Hellenizers, who were now a mere worthless appendage to the *katoikia* of Syrian troops, continued to serve in the shrine, and it is to be assumed that Menelaus still performed his function as official High Priest of the Jewish God. But the Jewish masses neither acknowledged nor could possibly acknowledge what was being done in the Temple. The Temple of the Lord had been polluted by Gentiles and by a pagan rite.[32] Our account has reached events at the end of the year 168; yet we have still heard absolutely nothing of a religious persecution. The order of Antiochus prohibiting the Jewish faith was promulgated about a year after Apollonius' political measures.[33] According to II Maccabees (6.1) Antiochus sent a special emissary to Judaea to carry out the decree: "in order to force the Jews to transgress the laws of their fathers and not to live according to God's commandments."[34] The Temple was renamed after Zeus Olympius, the observance of Sabbath and circumcision was prohibited, and the Jews were forced to celebrate the king's birthday every month and to participate in the festal procession in honor of Dionysus.

The author of I Maccabees paints a more detailed picture: the king sent an order to his emissaries at Jerusalem and in the towns of Judaea prohibiting Sabbath observance, the festivals and the rite of circumcision. He further ordered the erection of high places and altars on which swine and other animals were to be sacrificed. Upon the altar of the Temple was set up the "abomination of desolation"; books of the Law were burnt and inspectors were appointed by the king to make sure that his order was being carried out in all the towns of Judaea (I Macc. 1.44ff.). The Book of Daniel also mentions the profanation of the Temple, the cessation of the permanent sacrifice, and the setting up of the "abomination of desolation" (11.31). It is clear then that our sources distinguish plainly between the political measures of the year 168 taken by Apollonius, and the religious persecution of 167 carried out in pursuance of the king's order by his special emissary. What was it, then, that occurred during that year, which spurred the king to take such severe action?

After all that has been said above it is not hard to answer this question. Apollonius' acts had created a rebellion, and the introduction of the Syrian cults onto the Temple mount had lent a religious odor to the rising. The Jewish faith was faced, not *after* Antiochus' decree, but *before* it, with the alternative of renouncing its existence or of fighting for its life. The Jewish rising, which had first broken out in natural resistance to Apollonius' acts, during the year 168/7 took on the form of a religious movement.

It will not be a mistake to suppose that the rebellious folk had already found its leaders. These were the Ḥasidim.

What was the political and religious function of the members of this group? We are not in a position to determine precisely when the sect was organized, but, as we have seen above (p. 125), this took place apparently at the time of Simon the Just. In I Maccabees the Ḥasidim are alluded to immediately after the revolt of Mattathias the Has-

monean: "And he gathered unto him a congregation of Ḥasidim, a great force in Israel, every man that obeyed the Law" (I Macc. 2.42). In this passage I Maccabees stresses the influence of the masses of the folk ("a great force in Israel") and their devotion to the Mosaic Law.
We have said above (p. 125f.) that the Ḥasidim were the chief scribes and authoritative interpreters of the regulations and commandments of the Torah. The attitude of the scribes in general and of the Ḥasidim in particular to the Hellenizers is quite plain. The abolition of the "ancestral laws" by Jason made their entire class superfluous; if the Law of Moses was no longer to be the prevailing law in Israel, what point would there be in interpreting it? Naturally, isolated individuals might go on resorting to the scribes with their queries, but the *polis* of Antioch took no account of them and had no need of them. Hence the struggle of the Ḥasidim against the Hellenizers was not merely an ideological struggle for the maintenance of the commandments of the Law, but also the struggle of an entire class for its existence. This class did not live in a social vacuum, but was supported by the broad sections of the urban population of Jerusalem, that is, by the mass of the people consisting of craftsmen, laborers, petty traders and kindred elements (see above, p. 123). The Law of Moses, therefore, became the war-cry of the masses, just as Greek culture was the watchword of the aristocracy. When the urban *plebs* took up arms to oppose the Hellenizing government with force, it was natural that the Ḥasidim, meaning the scribes and their leaders, should be the popular directors and leaders of the insurrection.
This assumption is not mere conjecture, and its correctness can be proved on the authority of the sources. I Maccabees (7.12) says that "the congregation of the scribes" came to Alcimus "to seek justice,"[35] and uses the same expressions to denote those people who had fled to the desert from the persecution of Antiochus, to "seek justice and judgment" (2.29). This tells us that these two groups were akin to one another, and scholars have undoubtedly been correct in identifying the fugitives to the desert with the Ḥasidim or their disciples. There is additional proof in that these people refrained from bearing arms on the Sabbath day and thereby permitted themselves to be butchered like sheep, which demonstrates their exceptional devotion to the commandments of the Law.

But scholars have erred in making these Ḥasidim harmless and peaceful people, deliberate, conscientious pacifists, for besides the Sabbath there are six other days in the week, and the very fact that the soldiers saw fit to attack them on the seventh proves convincingly that on any other day they could have expected sturdy resistance. I Maccabees witnesses that these men fled "to the desert hiding places" (2.31), and we have already seen that this flight cannot be explained as an attempt to avoid contact with the corruption of the world, but as the first organization of the forces of national resistance. The further fact that the Ḥasidim joined the Hasmoneans immediately after Mattathias raised the standard of rebellion, indicates that they were organized as a fighting community.[36] II Maccabees looks upon Judah the Maccabee as the leader of the Ḥasidim (14.6), an indication that even after the outbreak of the revolt of the Hasmoneans the Ḥasidim composed a strong independent nucleus in the freedom-fighters' camp.

The Book of Daniel also speaks of the important role of the Ḥasidim in the insurgent movement, calling them "the enlightened" or "enlighteners of the people," that is, he sees in them the intellectual leaders, who "shall stumble by sword and flame, by captivity and by spoil many days" (11.33), meaning that they had suffered greatly during Antiochus' persecution. Daniel witnesses to the aid that they received (evidently from the Hasmoneans) and to the multitudes of people that joined them;[37] he therefore regards them rather than the Hasmoneans, who had not yet been able to reveal the full extent of their strength, as the true leaders of the nation. From all these passages it is to be concluded that the popular revolt had broken out on a large scale before the evil decrees of Antiochus, and that the acknowledged leaders of the people in revolt were the Ḥasidim.

We are now in a position to understand the reasons for the decrees of Antiochus. If the revolt was led by the Ḥasidim, for whom the commandments of the Torah were of the utmost sanctity, and if devotion to the Mosaic Law was the watchword of the uprising, then that Law had to be extirpated if the rebellion was to be put down. This was the conclusion drawn by Antiochus from what was occurring in Judaea.

Many factors contributed to this decision. First, not all the Jewish people had joined the rebels. The Hellenizers continued to be devoted to the king even after the popular rising against Antiochus, who was under no obligation to carry out statistical research to determine what was the real percentage of Hellenizers. He too may have thought, like most modern scholars, that the entire Jewish people was on the road to complete Hellenization, and that only a tiny group of obstinate fanatics still held to their ancestral faith.[38] Secondly, although it was true that the Graeco-Roman world was very liberal in matters of religion and did not know what religious persecutions were, even this liberalism had certain limits.

It is true that the ancient world did not experience religious persecutions such as occur where the monotheistic religions prevail, like the persecutions of "false beliefs" by "true faiths," for the conceptions of "truth" and "falsehood" were not the criteria of religious value in the ancient world. But there were other criteria: a religion (or a philosophy) could be regarded as a danger to the state's welfare insofar as it offended the existing gods of the *polis* and so undermined the foundations of the state's political and social life. The religion of a subject people could be dangerous to the ruling people, if its priests placed themselves at the head of a national movement against the foreign power; in such case the authorities might declare the religion in question to be a "barbarous superstition" (*barbara superstitio*). Athens, the cultured and enlightened, provided the world with several famous instances of inquisitorial trials of the first type;[39] and Rome's attitude to the religion of the Druids may serve as an instructive example of the second type of persecution.[40]

As to Judaism, it might easily have seemed dangerous to the welfare of the Seleucid kingdom once its commandments had become slogans in the mouths of the national leaders; and if it did not appear savage and injurious in its customs, the avoidance of all work on the Sabbath, or self-seclusion from Gentiles at meals, doubtless served as clear proofs of a *barbara superstitio*. The anti-Semitic literature, indeed, which developed at the end of the Hellenistic period and in the Roman epoch, declared the Jewish religion to be a barbaric superstition and was even able to invent proofs of the savagery and cruelty of its various observances.[41] All these grounds were sufficient to make Antiochus issue his famous order prohibiting the Jews from performing the commandments of the Torah and imposing severe penalties on those who persisted in living according to their ancestral tradition. So began the period of the *Gezerot*, the persecutory decrees.

We know little of their details. On the 15th Kislev (roughly December) of the year 167, the "abomination of desolation" was erected on the altar of the Lord (I Macc. 1.54), meaning that royal approval was officially given to the Syrian cult of Baal Shamin which had been unofficially introduced onto the Temple mount about a year before. The innovation consisted entirely in that the god was henceforth called by his Greek name Zeus Olympius, in harmony with Antiochus' special devotion to this deity. Clearly Antiochus saw no profanation in this action, for the local god, Yahweh, could easily be identified with the Greek deity. The other cults (of Dionysus and Athene—see above, p. 194f.) now also received the official seal of approval. Special inspectors toured the villages to make certain that the prohibition of the Jewish observances had been accepted without demur, for the measure was important insofar as the revolt was being supported in force by the country population. It is a controversial question whether the king's order related only to Judaea, or whether it also affected Jewish populations beyond its frontiers; from certain hints in our sources it can be deduced that Antiochus' order applied only to the area infected by rebellion—Jerusalem and Judaea—but on the initiative of the inhabitants of Syria and perhaps with the aid of the royal officials, it might have been extended to the Jewish settlements in the whole of Palestine.[42]

We cannot determine to what extent the persecution was brutal and prolonged; the tales about the old man Eleazar and the mother and her seven sons who died martyrs' deaths (II Macc. 6.18-7.42) are hardly more than fables originating at the time of the persecution, or a short time after it, to satisfy the needs of religious and national propaganda. The figure of Antiochus conducting the inquisitorial trial in person contains, of course, no vestige of historical truth. A short time after the publication of the decrees he had left Syria on his way eastward, for he faced the task of fortifying the vulnerable frontiers of the Seleucid kingdom in those remote places. It is quite possible therefore that he was not in Palestine at all during the period when the decrees were being put into effect.

This ends the account of the Antiochan persecutions. If we recall all the methods of historical analysis that have been used to clarify its origins, we can say that each one contains something of the truth. The "political" theory (above, p. 182f.) more especially rests on a certain solid basis: the Jewish people was in a state of open war with Antiochus from 168 on, and the struggle developed against a pronounced political background. There is also some justification for the views which describe Antiochus as a Hellenizer or as a "unifier" of his kingdom, as the persecutions resulted from the special favor shown by him to the Hellenizers whom he regarded as loyal allies; nor should we forget that the god on the Temple hill received the name "Zeus Olympius" (above, p. 181). Antiochus' irate temper can in some measure explain the swiftness with which he resorted to the promulgation of the decrees, without troubling first to make clear to himself the character of the Jewish people or the number of the population who desired to remain loyal to their "ancestral laws." But all these explanations remain bereft of interconnection or solid basis without one fundamental assumption, to wit, that the persecution did not anticipate the uprising, but rather that the uprising anticipated the persecution. This assumption alone can account for the true character of the persecution as a means of pressure upon a nation, part of which had dared to defy the king's will on the authority of its ancestral religion.

What was the attitude of the Tobiads and their faction to the *Gezerot* of Antiochus? Were they satisfied with his acts or not? Probably not, for this had not been their intention. They had aimed to rule Jerusalem themselves, and as it turned out, not they but the Seleucid officials now held the reins of power; on the site of Jerusalem a new city was being built whose inhabitants were half Syrian, while a "Macedonian" force entrenched in the Akra protected them. They were, it is true, very remote from the devotion to Judaism prevailing among the Ḥasidim, and their ambition was to introduce Greek customs into Jewish public life; but religious persecution had been no part of their program; they knew the popular devotion to the Mosaic Law perfectly well, and it could be of little advantage to them to convert into enemies the majority of the people whom it was their intention to rule.

But whether they wished it or not, the process of history had made them the protégés of Antiochus. They had paved the king's way into Jerusalem and now had no alternative but to support him. The great honor which the heads of the Hellenizers had shown to him during his visit in Jason's time, and also on his visit in 169, when Menelaus had guided him into the Temple treasury, permitted Antiochus to regard himself as the protector of Greek Antioch-at-Jerusalem. Nor is it surprising that he despatched a large force to Judah when peril threatened the existence of a city that bore his name.

As to the inner character of the Hellenizing party, their devotion to Greece and its civilization should not be exaggerated. Eduard Meyer called the Tobiads and their party "representatives of enlightened reform Judaism" (*aufgeklärtes Reformjudentum*) and evaluated their appearance as a protest against petrified religious formalism. Bickermann also regards them as religious reformers, even making them enthusiasts for Hellenism, as we have seen.[43] This approach only touches the external aspect of the movement and does not adequately explain its inner character. It is true that among the wealthy and powerful men of Jerusalem frequent contact with the Greeks had engendered an urge to rid themselves of the austere laws of Judaism and to create for themselves easier and more attractive conditions of life than those enjoyed by the greater part of the people. But these urges did not exceed the bounds of the cultural sympathies of private persons and cannot effectively explain how this external Hellenism became a war-cry under which a large party embarked on a struggle for power.[44]

The details of this struggle have been dwelt on above: we have seen that in it political and financial questions figured far more prominently than those of a "cultural" nature. From the day of its birth to its demise the Hellenizing party was bound up with the restricted group of Jerusalem capitalists, and the Tobiads were permanently at the center of its activities. The considerable wealth concentrated in their hands confronted them with important problems; and just as Jewish tradition seemed to them narrow compared with the Greek way of life to which the Tobiads had adapted themselves, so was Judaea too narrow for the aspirations bred by much wealth. The Tobiads sought to become rich, to attain greatness, and to rule over others; they saw the wide Greek world, the royal court of Syria, and the opulence of the Greek cities, and conceived a keen desire to have a part in such a life. Jerusalem must overcome its miserable poverty and turn into a Greek *polis*, and in this new shape was destined, in their view, to develop economically. The people of Israel was to participate in the course of world history as an ally of the Seleucid kingdom and to be "like all the peoples."

In this new state of affairs the Tobiads and their circle were to rule Judaea as the people's leaders and High Priests. This was a fine broad program, yet nothing whatever came of it. The Tobiads had failed to take into account the strength of the nation's resistance to their political plans, for the people had no love for them, and this was no mere chance. The social enmity between the two sections of society, of which Ben Sira had spoken in his time, did not come to an end just because the Tobiads replaced Onias and his family at the head of the government. On the contrary, the Tobiads were men of wealth *par excellence,* the very symbols of power and possession, and had nothing in common with the people. As we have already seen, exactly as Hellenism became the watchword of the influential, so Jewish tradition became the slogan of the populace. Thus the hostility between the two sections of the Jewish community found its way into various branches of public life, both political and cultural, and Antiochus' heavy hand underwrote the nation's cleavage.

chapter **6**

THE WAR OF LIBERATION

Of the beginning of the Hasmonean rebellion we read in I Maccabees; and that well-told stirring account is known to every Jew. It is the story of a company of Syrian troops that came to the village of Modiin to compel the inhabitants to bow down to the pagan gods. Then up rose old Mattathias, priest of the order of Joarib, and slew the Hellenizing Jew as he was about to obey the Syrian command; then he slew the king's commissioner who had been appointed to carry out the royal decree, and fled with his sons to the hills. And so the uprising began.

From what has been said in the preceding chapter it will be clear that this picture is not quite authentic. There is of course no reason for doubting the actual fact of the bloody clash between Syrian troops and the inhabitants of the village of Modiin. Even the details of the story (the slaying of the Hellenizing Jew and the royal commissioner) may be true, and it is certainly true that from that moment the Hasmonean family made its appearance on the stage of history. What is not true is that this was the commencement of the rising. The movement of rebellion had been in progress for a year and was led by the Ḥasidim; but they had not been able to produce among themselves a leader of note who could give to the guerrilla struggle the character of a regular planned war. The refusal to fight on the Sabbath further weakened the rebels to a considerable extent. The innovation introduced by the Hasmoneans affected these two important points: they abolished the prohibition of self-defense on the Sabbath (I Macc. 2.39ff.) and they gave the liberation movement its leader. With the appearance of Judah the Maccabee the rising put off its haphazard form and took on the shape of an organized war.

I Maccabees plays down to a considerable degree the part of Judah the Maccabee, and attributes not to him but to his father Mattathias the honor of being the initiator of the revolutionary movement. It associates with Mattathias all the events at Modiin and a series of further events, such as the decision to fight on the Sabbath, the entry of the Ḥasidim into the ranks of the fighters for freedom and the spread of the rising over the countryside of Judaea.

The account thus denies to Judah first place as creator of the movement. He was one of the five heroic brothers, and not even the eldest, for Simon was older than he both in years and counsel.[1] According to Niese,[2] this picture was influenced by the general approach to the history of the period on the part of the author of I Maccabees, who was the Hasmonean court historian, wrote his book under John Hyrcanus, and desired to underline as strongly as possible the personality of Simon, John's father, in preference to that of Judah, who had died without sons. Hence the great role of Mattathias, father of the dynasty, and of Simon in I Maccabees.

This modern historian's view finds support in the second source at our disposal, II Maccabees. According to this source Judah fled from Jerusalem with nine other men even before Antiochus' persecution, and hid in the desert (5.27), whence he returned by by-ways to the villages of Judaea to gather some 6000 men under his banner (8.1). This short narrative, lacking all legendary and rhetorical embellishments, is probably nearer historical reality than the artistic and patriotic story of I Maccabees. As to Mattathias, no doubt need be entertained that he was a real person, for he is mentioned in an official document as Simon's father (I Macc. 14.29), but the attractive figure in I Maccabees belongs rather to the world of fiction than to historical reality, and it should be remarked that II Maccabees does not refer to him at all.[3]

To what extent the author of I Maccabees was influenced by the political situation prevailing many years after the rebellion may be judged from the course of events during the rebellion as he himself relates them. As

long as Judah was alive his brothers were of no independent value in either the military or political sphere; and they occupied an important place at the head of the nation after Judah's death only because the people saw them as the continuators of the movement which he had initiated.
Let us now examine the rebellion itself. Scholars have pointed to one phenomenon in the progress of the movement which has struck them as very important. The rising, which at its beginning was entirely religious, aiming to defend freedom of worship, became in course of time a political movement, in other words, a struggle for power on the part of Judah and his brothers. Scholars emphasize this new direction especially from the year 162 onwards; in 162, Antiochus V Eupator rescinded the decrees of his father Antiochus Epiphanes and restored to the Jews the right to live "according to their own laws." The movement now had no further religious or cultural *raison d'être;* yet despite this it did not come to an end, but made great progress.[4] Scholars generally content themselves with mentioning this fact without seeking to explain it appropriately, or sometimes give explanations of slight value bearing only on the superficial aspects of the movement. It is not easy, indeed, to find the correct explanation of this phenomenon if we retain the opinion of most present-day scholars that the revolt in Judaea came solely in reply to Antiochus' persecution and that, without the persecution, no national movement would have developed among the Jews at all.[5]
We have seen in the preceding chapter that the Hasmonean rising was a continuation of the revolt of the Ḥasidim, which had already broken out, and that revolt itself was a natural consequence of the whole complex of political affairs which had been created in the land of Judaea as a result of the internal rift in the nation and of Antiochus' intervention in Jewish affairs. The theologians (who have arrogated to themselves a monopoly of the study of Jewish history) entirely dismiss this whole prolonged and complicated process, involving the spread of Hellenization among the upper circles of the Jerusalem public from the days of Joseph ben Tobiah, the social antagonism between the wealthy aristocratic Hellenizers and the common people, the frequent disturbances in Jerusalem which had been taking place as early as the day of Onias and led to open civil war under Menelaus and, above all, the natural generation-long development of the country and

population of Judaea coupled with their striving to break out of the narrow confines of Jerusalem and its immediate surroundings. If we take all these things into account, it becomes clear that Antiochus' decrees were only the trigger which set off the explosion of forces, the push needed to release the avalanche, but not the sole nor even the basic reason for the Hasmonean movement. And if this is the case, there are no grounds for describing the movement as purely religious in its inception, or as purely political at a later stage. In all the doings of Judah the Maccabee and his brothers, the political and religious aspects were equally involved, and any distinction between them can only be artificial.

Not only these elements, but a further social element played an important part in the Hasmonean movement. The sources do not, unfortunately, treat of this question, modern scholars even less so, but here it must be remembered that the Maccabean revolt was from a broader point of view only one link in a long series of uprisings on the part of the oriental countries against their western rulers. These uprisings manifested the deep social antagonism between the towns, which supported the central power and compromised with Hellenism, and the countryside, which upheld ancestral tradition and fought the foreign power and the local aristocracy simultaneously (cf. above, p. 19). If we consider the profound social antagonism between the Hellenizers and the people, which formed the general background of everything that occurred in Jerusalem from 175 on, we shall easily realize that the Hasmonean movement, insofar as it was both religious and political, was also religious and social, and this aspect too was bound up with the Maccabean movement from the outset.[6]

Let us here try to emphasize the basic lines of the rising of Judah the Maccabee in its initial stage. The course of events is well known from the sources.[7] We first read of the Syrian general Apollonius and his attempt to suppress the rebellion. Judah defeated his force and Apollonius himself fell in action.[8] He was followed by Seron, who was also defeated by Judah.[9] These victories revealed to the Syrian government at Antioch that the Jewish rebellion was not to be despised; so Lysias, who was Antiochus Epiphanes' viceroy over the western part of the State while Epiphanes himself was at war with the Parthians, sent to the land of Judaea a large force under Ptolemy, Nicanor and Gorgias. This force, however, failed before the strategic abilities of Judah the Maccabee and was defeated by him twice. Finally Lysias himself had to come to Palestine; he sought to invade the country from the south, but here too Judah anticipated him and forced him to give up the attack. Lysias returned to Antioch, and Judah the Maccabee, now master of the entire country of Judaea, captured Jerusalem, with the exception of the fortress of the Akra, purified the Temple and restored the cult of the God of Israel. This took place some three years after the commencement of Antiochus' persecution, and with it the first period of the war for independence came to an end.[10]

Even in the early stage of the rising certain lines stand out which later developed and became characteristic of its "political" period. It had not yet acquired the character of a broad national movement, yet the entire Greek population of Palestine was taking part in its suppression and aiding the forces of the government to fight the Jews. Certain facts mentioned in the books of the Maccabees are worthy of attention; Apollonius' army was composed of various peoples ($\xi\theta\nu\eta$) and especially of the people of Samaria (I Macc. 3.10), while the forces of Nicanor and his comrades were also of variegated ethnic composition (II Macc. 8.9); and when Nicanor and his associates entered Palestine they were accompanied by an auxiliary force from Idumaea[11] and Philistia (I Macc. 3.41). The "Greek" army against which Judah the Maccabee was fighting was not therefore racially Graeco-Macedonian, but Syrian, and the troops recruited to suppress the rising were mostly volunteers native to the country (see p. 210).

The Graeco-Syrian population of the Hellenized cities was quick to welcome the Greek commanders and joyfully anticipated a Jewish defeat. When Nicanor invited the citizens of the maritime towns (that is, the Hellenized cities) to meet him with money in hand for acquiring slaves (Nicanor intended to sell cheaply the Jews who fell into his hands), the wealthy were quick to throng to him from every place, bringing not only money but also fetters for the slaves.[12] The Greek cities also took part in the persecution of the Jewish religion, in accordance with the invitation of the government to Hellenize the Jews residing in the Palestinian towns.[13] There is no doubt that these persecutions swiftly created general hatred against the Jews and ruined them economically. The second period of the rising, opening with Judah the Maccabee's attack on the Graeco-Syrian population in Palestine, was a natural out-

come of the situation created immediately after the beginning of the insurrection.
This situation calls for an explanation. What was the reason for the Palestinian population's negative attitude to the Jews? A simple answer would seem to be that the Syrians and the Greeks saw a seasonable opportunity to enrich themselves at Jewish expense, as restraints had been relaxed and the government itself was amenable. But this explanation is inadequate. The antagonism between the Syrians and the Jews, manifested to the world for the first time on this occasion, did not cease with the calling off of the persecution; it runs like a thread through the whole of Jewish history, from the time of Judah the Maccabee down to the great war with Rome. The reason, then, was not fortuitous, but was bound up with an internal state of affairs. It can be discovered by paying attention to the general direction of Jewish history in the Hasmonean age. In that period, as is well known, the Jews were expanding over the entire land of Palestine and were bringing the Syrian population under their control. This too was no sudden phenomenon, but a continuation and conclusion of a prolonged process which had begun long before the Hasmoneans.
The expansion of the Jews over Palestine had begun along with the initiation of the Diaspora outside the country, in other words, about the year 300. Hecataeus had already testified to the large population of Judaea at that time (see above, p. 119). The country could not ultimately support the whole growing population, so the Jews sought to issue from the narrow frame of the hills of Judaea and to take up positions in other territories—first, of course, in Palestine itself. The new mood introduced by Joseph ben Tobiah into Jewish life helped to strengthen their aspiration, for developing commerce urgently required that the Jews should have representatives of their own in the various countries of Syria. Thus the Jews began to settle in various localities of Palestine and to create for themselves footholds in the Syrian and Greek areas of settlement. The books of the Maccabees have preserved some information on the Jewish population of Palestine before Judah the Maccabee. We find the Jews in such coastal towns as Jaffa (II Macc. 12.3) and Yavneh (ib. 12.8), in various places in Galilee (I Macc. 5.14; ib. 21), and in the north-western portion of Samaria,[14] in Gilead (ib. 9) and in the "land of Tov" (ib. 13).[15] Jews also dwelt in Ammon; there were Jews among the mixed population of the cleruchy of Tobiah (cf. above,

p. 64), while the force with which Hyrcanus son of Joseph fought the Arabs was also doubtless a Jewish force.

The number of Jews living in all these territories cannot be determined. I Maccabees relates that Judah the Maccabee and his brother Simon transferred all the Jews of Galilee and Gilead to Jerusalem (5.23; *ib*. 45); but this statement is probably an exaggeration, for it is doubtful that the land of Judaea was rich enough to support all these immigrants, even if we assume that their number was not large. Probably only part of the Jews of Galilee and Gilead was transferred—the women and children and those who feared attacks from their neighbors. According to I Maccabees, a thousand Jews were killed in the Land of Tov (5.13), and here too doubtless the writer was exaggerating; yet it must be supposed that the size of the Jewish population in that country was not small, otherwise he would not have adopted so large a figure. Thus the Jews gradually penetrated the various regions of Palestine. Clearly the local people would not have welcomed them, for the population of the country was pretty dense and areas vacant for settlement were few and far between. In Galilee and Transjordan the Jews had to reckon with the opposition of the peasants; in the coastal cities, with that of the merchants.

From the psychological point of view, moreover, the new neighbors did not suit the Syrians, for the Jews were not just strangers; it was common knowledge that, once upon a time, the whole country had been theirs and, what was more, the Jews themselves remembered the fact. They were not simply sojourners abroad, but arrivals in places which had once belonged to them. And if the idea of national and political revival was formulated clearly only under the Hasmoneans, there can be no doubt that the national idea was secretly at work among the Jewish population of Palestine in an earlier period. The Jewish communities were sensible of a strong inner bond with the people's national center at Jerusalem and had no desire to assimilate among the Syrians or to give up an independent position. This independent stand no doubt irritated the Syrians, especially as the Jewish communities grew continually with the constant arrival of new immigrants from Judaea. Thus hatred of the Jews increased among the Palestinian population and, the moment the government declared a persecution of Judaism, the Syrians willingly joined the army and helped it to fight against the Jews in order to exterminate them.

We return to the course of the rebellion itself. Antiochus had decreed the outlawing of the Jewish religion, the propagation of Hellenism by force, the desecration of everything sacred to the Jews, the cessation of worship in the Temple, and the burning of Scrolls of the Law. Such were the methods whereby his will was to be put into effect. But it is not hard to see that the decrees constituted not simply a religious persecution, but a great peril to the existence of the entire Jewish nation. The propagation of Hellenism and religious persecution, in fact, soon ceased to be the sole object of the Greek government at Antioch. The objective was accompanied by several other aspirations; nor is this surprising, for the "cultural" objective of propagating Hellenism was in place as long as the Jews were still more or less loyal subjects of the regime, but after open war had begun the Jews became simply "rebels," and in such a situation more "material" questions became relevant. Nicanor's intention of selling into slavery the Jews who were taken prisoner, has been noted, and there was a special reason for this, for by this sale he hoped to earn thousands of talents in order to facilitate the payment of Antiochus' debt to the Romans (II Macc. 8.10).

These then were the new hopes which the Syrian authorities set upon the suppression of the rising, and it is obvious that they had no connection with the propagation of Hellenism. But the gravest danger which threatened the Jews was the confiscation of lands in favor of new immigrants whom the Syrian government was proposing to send to Judaea. This threat—the dispatch of Greek inhabitants to Judaea and Jerusalem and the reallotment of the land—is twice mentioned in the sources. According to I Maccabees (3.36) Antiochus Epiphanes, prior to his departure to the lands of the East, ordered Lysias "to settle aliens in all their borders (that is, of Judaea) and to divide their land into allotments" (κατακληρονομῆσαι), while according to II Maccabees (11.2), Lysias intended "to make the city (Jerusalem) a place of Greek settlement," to levy taxes on the Temple, as was done in relation to other (pagan) sacred places, and to convert the High Priesthood into a post open to annual auction. These two sources are here discussing the same program, apparently worked out at Antioch at the end of the year 165 and at the beginning of 164; it devolved upon Lysias to carry it out when he went to Judaea in the spring of 164.

There is no reason for doubting the truth of this information, for it implies a logical continuation of the same measures of suppression and coercion adopted by Apollonius as early as 168. To the plan of new settlement were added far-reaching plans of reform in the spirit of extreme Hellenism, including the imposition of taxes on the Temple and the conversion of the High Priesthood into an official Seleucid post. These two reforms possessed a clear fiscal motive; for in this way, after their execution, the *polis* of "Antioch-at-Jerusalem" was to assume the form of a model Hellenistic city. No wonder Judah the Maccabee and his allies swiftly realized that not only the nation's intellectual, but also its material heritage stood in danger: not simply its religion, but its very homeland. It must be supposed that rumors about the impending confiscation of land influenced chiefly the rural population, in whose minds religious zeal combined with a stout determination to defend the existence of their individual holdings, and it may be assumed that many of them entered the ranks of the rebellion.

Besides the Graeco-Syrians, Judah the Maccabee had other enemies, namely, the Hellenizing Jews. Our sources term them "criminals" and "transgressors" (ἀσεβεῖς), and praise Judah the Maccabee fulsomely for his ruthless fight against them. The sources relate Judah's frequent attacks on towns and villages and the extermination of their Hellenizing inhabitants (I Macc. 3.8; II Macc. 8.6), and from these brief reports it emerges clearly that the civil war which had begun in Jerusalem under the government of the Tobiads had now spread and embraced the whole of Judaea. We know from previous chapters who these people were whom Judah persecuted with such hatred; they were the high-born and wealthy, the rulers of the nation, people who saw in the Hellenization of the Jews an easy way of attaining prominence. They now stood defenseless before multitudes of insurgents filled with a spirit of religious fanaticism and detestation of their oppressors. Small wonder that the Hellenizers sought protection and shelter from the Syrians and became their loyal confederates. When Seron marched against Judah he was accompanied by a large company of Hellenizers (I Macc. 3.15), and when Gorgias invaded the country of Judaea to attack Judah the Maccabee, these ("the people of the Akra") acted as guides to the Seleucid army (I Macc. 4.2).

Unfortunately the sources are not interested in the internal aspect of Jewish history during the

Hasmonean revolt and, as their entire attention is devoted to
the external events of political history, namely, to Judah the
Maccabee's struggle with the Syrian armies, they frequently
forget that side by side with the external conflict a civil war
was going on, which was no less important to Jewish history.
However, even isolated hints tell us that the religious hatred
which inflamed the enthusiasts of traditional Judaism sometimes
assumed the color of social class hatred. It may be conjectured
that the civil war in Judah and Jerusalem took the form usual
in civil war, in which social-religious pathos and exaggerated
cruelty to enemies were equally mingled. A custom in the ancient
world gave the victors the right to enrich themselves at the expense of the conquered. This was so in every political war, and
much more in a social conflict. The Jews were no exception to
the rule: II Maccabees says that the warriors of Judah the
Maccabee shared the spoil among themselves after their victory
over the enemy,[16] nor is there any doubt that this statement is
correct, not only in relation to the Syrian camps which fell into
Jewish hands after battle, but also in relation to the private
property of wealthy people. This can be demonstrated: in the
year 162 the Hellenizers complained to the Syrian government
at Antioch that Judah the Maccabee and his faction were killing
their allies when they fell into their hands, and looting their
property—and the estates of the Hellenizers were apparently
meant.[17]

What occurred among the
Hellenizing party during the first three years of the revolt? The
authors of the books of the Maccabees report nothing on this subject. Only one thing is known, namely, that the Hellenizers converted the Akra into their operational headquarters and thence
controlled Jerusalem till Judah the Maccabee captured the city.[18]
But there is another source, which, though within the books of the
Maccabees, originates from the official bureaus of the period,
namely, the documents cited in II Maccabees, chapter 11. Mis-
understanding has been rife among scholars concerning these
documents. The chief difficulty connected with their study has
been chronological. Of four, three were written in the spring of
the year 164 B.C.E., as their date testifies; scholars have thought
that the fourth document also (the second in the order of documents in II Maccabees), which is undated, was composed together with the rest, and this supposition, which was without
sufficient basis, has introduced much confusion into the study
of the question. The second document speaks of the death of

Antiochus Epiphanes, who died at the end of 164, hence it could not on the face of it be imagined that it was drawn up in the spring of 164, when the king was still alive. Scholars have sought to resolve this chronological difficulty by making various conjectures: assuming, for instance, that part of the second document is a forgery, or that all the documents are forgeries. All these surmises, however, were unsuccessful in solving the problem till Laqueur[19] showed that the chronological difficulty vanishes if we separate the second document from the rest. It was composed, of course, after Antiochus' death, and Laqueur ascribes it, quite correctly, to the year 162. The others belong to the year 164, as their date shows, and there are no grounds for suspecting their historical authenticity. We may therefore utilize this important source for the study of the period now under discussion.

The documents are as follows: *Document 1* (II Macc. 11.16-21).

Lysias greets the Jewish people ($\tau\hat{\omega}$ $\pi\lambda\acute{\eta}\theta\epsilon\iota$ $\tau\hat{\omega}\nu$ Ἰουδαίων). Johanan and Absalom, who were sent by you, have delivered to us the memorandum subjoined and have requested of us a reply on the matters indicated in it. What it has been necessary to refer to the King also, I have proposed to him, and what (I personally) have been able to approve, I have approved. If you retain your devotion to the Government, I also shall endeavor in the future to care for your welfare. As to the details of the matter, I have empowered your representatives and my own to enter into negotiations with you. Farewell. Written in the year 148, on the 24th of the month of Dioskorinthios.

Document 2, see below, p. 225f.

Document 3 (II Macc. 11.27-33).

King Antiochus greets the Council of Elders ($\tau\hat{\eta}$ $\gamma\epsilon\rho o\nu\sigma\acute{\iota}\alpha$) of the Jews and the rest of the Jews. We hope that you are well; we too are well. Menelaus has revealed to us that you desire to return to your homes and also to devote yourselves to your private affairs. Whoever departs up to the 30th of the month of Xandikos, may go under safe escort and may be certain that the Jews will receive permission to use their foods and their laws as originally; nor will any one of them suffer any interference whatsoever on account of former offenses. I have sent Menelaus to you to make peace with you. Farewell! Written in the year 148, on the 15th of the month of Xandikos.

Document 4 (II. Macc. 11.34-38).

Quintus Mummius and Titus Manlius, the Roman ambassadors, greet the Jewish people ($\tau\hat{\omega}$ $\delta\acute{\eta}\mu\omega$). We also agree to everything to which Lysias, the King's kinsman, has consented. As to those matters which he has decided to bring before the King, do you yourselves discuss them and send someone swiftly, that we may express our opinion as befits your affairs. We are on our way to Antioch, therefore send several envoys quickly that we also may know what you think. Farewell! Written in the year 148, on the 15th of the month of Xandikos.

Before passing to an analysis of the documents, let us briefly sketch the chronological problem. The third document was written in the month of Xandikos of the year 148 of the Seleucid calendar—in April 164 B.C.E. The fourth document was composed, at first sight, on the same day, for its date resembles word for word that of the third document. This is impossible, for its contents show that number 4 preceded 3 (see below). It is clear that the real date of the fourth document has not survived and in its place the date of the earlier document was erroneously inscribed.[20] The date of the first document is also a problem: the month of Dioskorinthios is unknown to us, or at any rate is lacking among the names of the Macedonian months.[21]

The third document is therefore the only one whose time of composition is known to us; but it also settles the time of composition of the others. It is clear that 3 was written after numbers 1 and 4, as in number 1 Lysias promises the Jews that he would lay their affairs before the king (Antiochus); and further, in 4, the Romans write that they are on their way to Antioch. Number 3, written at Antioch and signed by the king, completes the diplomatic negotiations begun in numbers 1 and 4. It will not be erroneous, then, to ascribe the composition of number 1 to the first campaign of Lysias against Judah the Maccabee. It transpires clearly from the text of the document that Lysias is not in the king's proximity, hence he is not at Antioch; and as in 164 he was in Palestine, it may be reasonably supposed that he there met the Jewish representatives.[22] If so, the negotiations between the Jews and the Syrian government opened in Palestine and were concluded at Antioch in the spring of 164—six months before Judah the Maccabee's capture of Jerusalem.[23]

The documents may now be analyzed. Who are the Jews who have sent representatives to Lysias and the Romans and are addressed by the king in his letter? All scholars agree that they are Judah the Maccabee and his allies, an opinion logically associated with their general view of the documents, and anyone not distinguishing between number 2 and the others is bound to conclude that all of them are directed to Judah the Maccabee and his faction, as the king's letter in number 2 (see below), mentioning "the Jews," obviously refers to that party. The first to make this mistake was the author of II Maccabees himself, who collected all the documents in one place and cited them as evidence of negotiations between the government and Judah the Maccabee. But now, after the above-mentioned article of Laqueur, we may avoid following the author of II Maccabees, and it is surprising that modern scholars who have read Laqueur's article and adopted his chronological assumptions, have not drawn all the conclusions arising from them.

A detailed analysis of the third document shows that it has no connection whatever with Judah the Maccabee. The king addresses the letter to the *gerousia* of the Jews, and we have seen above (p. 162) that that body was the official council of the *polis* of Antioch-at-Jerusalem, not the representative body of traditional Jewry. At the beginning of the letter, the king mentions Menelaus, who had appeared before him as a mediator between the Jews and the government. It can hardly be supposed that Menelaus would have gone to Antioch as the representative of Judah the Maccabee, for each was then heading his own party, and each was fighting the other with bitter hostility. Nor is the petition of the Jews which was submitted to the king by Menelaus appropriate to the spirit of the rebels. Menelaus reported to the king that the Jews wanted "to return home and devote themselves to their affairs"; was this the longing of Judah the Maccabee and his warriors—yearnings for a peaceful life and nothing more? It should not be forgotten that Judah had already successfully beaten the Syrians three times, and now was about to attack Jerusalem; his army's mood was certainly not now inclined to concessions.

Nor does the attitude of the Jews to Lysias correspond to that of Judah the Maccabee: they appear before Lysias as seekers of peace, and Lysias pledges them his good offices on condition that they "retain their devotion to the government in the future also." What would such a "devotion to the government" be on the part of Judah the Maccabee? In 164 the national party, despite all its victories, was still regarded by the Syrian government as a gang of rebels, and no diplomatic negotiations between the two forces were possible. It is further extremely difficult to imagine that the Romans would have undertaken the defense of the insurgents as long as they did not constitute a political force of some weight. Only after the capture of Jerusalem and the series of campaigns against the peoples of Palestine and Transjordan, did real political power come to be concentrated in the hands of the national party, and only then did the opportunity present itself to the Syrian government to create contact with them without damaging its own prestige in the eyes of the international world.[24]

Hence it was not Judah the Maccabee and his faction but the Hellenizers at Jerusalem, who despatched their emissaries to Lysias, and Menelaus to Antioch, and requested the Romans to undertake the function of mediators between the Jews and the government. What, then, was their aim?

Document number 3 is the only one that furnishes certain historical material, but unfortunately this is not such as to enable a detailed study of the question. Menelaus has requested of the king permission for the Jews to return to their homes.[25] Who are the Jews to whom Menelaus is referring? They need not be regarded as loyal supporters of the Hellenizers, on the ground that the Hellenizers mentioned them in the document. It is to be assumed that large numbers of people all over the land of Judah had suffered severely from the war without regarding themselves as bound to any political party; life on the countryside was unsafe and many of the peasants had left their former abodes and had sought secret asylum in the mountains or had sent their families thither; others had been driven from their lands by the Syrian forces, and perhaps also by the insurgents.

These masses, who had done nothing and were bearing the brunt of the suffering of the civil war without taking part in it, were very dangerous to the authority of the Hellenizers, for these peasants were suffering chiefly from the religious persecution and might easily join the forces of the fighters for freedom. The Hellenizers quickly thought of a way of winning this unorganized section of the people over to their side: it was necessary to enable them to return to their homes and to insure them a peaceful life in their villages. But this could not be done without totally altering the official policy; as long as the Syrian forces were hounding those Jews who were devoted to the customs of their fathers, the way to compromise was completely barred. So the Hellenizers came to a decision, namely, that the rescinding of the laws against Judaism would strengthen their political position and bring the people over to them. This decision did not contradict their principles, for as we have seen above, Antiochus' decrees were not at all what they had wanted (see p. 201).

The new political step was extremely dangerous to the fighters for freedom, for should Menelaus and his friends succeed in obtaining the annulment of Antiochus' decrees, Judah the Maccabee and the Hasidim would lose their most inspiring slogan—defense of religion. It should not be forgotten that Judah's supporters too would now be able to return to their villages. The plan was a good one, and the Hellenizers invested much energy in its realization. They sent two emissaries to Lysias, who was then apparently in the land of Judah, and presumably these were members of the *gerousia* and highly respected men.[26] The details of the negotiations are unknown. In document number 1, Lysias writes that he has confirmed some of the delegates' demands and has written to the king concerning the other matters. Among the latter was no doubt the question of principle involved in the annulment of the persecution; and this had to be dealt with at Antioch. Thither went Menelaus. Meanwhile the Hellenizers heard of the Roman ambassadors who were going to Antioch on political business;[27] as the Roman influence on the Hellenistic states was then very great, the Hellenizers sought to exploit the favorable opportunity to secure for themselves important advocates at the royal court. The Romans gave a positive reply (document number 4), which constituted a great success, enabling the Hellenizers to hope that the negotiations at Antioch would end in their favor.

This indeed occurred, but it is very doubtful that all their demands were fulfilled. The Syrian government's attitude on the Jewish question was not sufficiently consistent. On the one hand, it was clear that Antiochus Epiphanes' harsh policy had not led to the looked-for results, for instead of binding the Jews to Syria it had aroused among them a strong movement of revolt. The persecution of religion as such was not likely to find supporters within the

Syrian government, as it was opposed to the political tradition of the Seleucids, who were not inclined to suppress the faiths of the peoples over whom they ruled. The Syrian officials who sought to rescind Antiochus' decrees may have been led by Ptolemy son of Makron, a Ptolemaic general who had gone over to Antiochus, for II Maccabees remarks (10.12) that he was friendly to the Jews and sought to help them.[28] But on the other hand, the decree could not be completely rescinded, without admitting to the utter failure of the entire policy of Antiochus Epiphanes toward the Jews; and, at any rate, it was dangerous to change his policy in his absence.

In the end, a compromise was reached. The government permitted the Jews to return to their homes and to devote themselves to their normal affairs, which meant agriculture, and promised to those who wished to use this permission, armed escort, religious freedom and an amnesty. But it added one important rider, that the permission could be used only until the 30th of the month of Xandikos—for a period of a fortnight.[29] This restriction converted the permission into an order, directed to Jews who had taken part in the rising; the government made a show of placing their fate in their own hands. They now had the alternative of either leaving the rebel camp forthwith, to throw away their arms and to return to their villages—in which case the government annulled Antiochus' decrees in regard to them; or to persist in the revolt—in which case the government would continue the persecution of the Jewish religion and the suppression of the national movement. It was clear from the start that not all would be able to exploit the license, even if they wanted to; hence would arise of its own accord the compromise situation desired by the government: Antiochus' decrees would cease to apply to "good" and "honest" subjects, and would continue in force in respect of those Jews who persisted in their "evil" ways.

What impression was created by the order in Jerusalem is unknown. The Hellenizers may have succeeded in interpreting it as a complete annulment of the persecution, and many of the "non-party" Jews may have exploited the permission to leave Jerusalem to return to their villages. But in the rebel camp the order did not, it seems, make any impression, perhaps because its members did not believe in the "benefits" obtained for the Jews by Menelaus, perhaps because the victorious army had no inclination to compromise. The clever diplomacy of the Hellenizers brought no profit to their party, and about six months later Judah the Maccabee appeared before the walls of Jerusalem and took the city. With this capture began a new chapter in the progress of the war of liberation.

            The capture of Jerusalem fundamentally altered the position of the rival parties. The Hellenizers, who had till now held the power, were compelled to yield their place to their opponents, to evacuate the town and to fortify themselves in the Akra. Part of them took refuge with the peoples in the vicinity of Judah, such as the Idumaeans (II Macc. 10.15). Judah the Maccabee and his faction now controlled Jerusalem and the country. We do not know what his official title was—he was not at any rate High Priest—perhaps because Menelaus was still officially regarded as such.[30] His first objective was to abolish Antiochus' decrees and to restore the cult of the God of Israel to its rightful place. On the 25th Kislev of the year 164, the Jews of Jerusalem celebrated the festival of the dedication of the Temple, after the shrine and the entire city had been purified from the remnants of the worship of the Greek deities.[31] Then came the internal reform. The Hellenizers had abolished the "ancestral laws" as the legal foundation of Jewish political and social life. It is clear that Judah's chief task was to procure the restoration of the Torah to its former place of primacy.

            According to *Megillat Ta'anit*, on the 24th of the month of Av the Jewish courts were set up afresh and "once again judged according to the laws of Israel."[32] This reform is probably to be related to the information in II Maccabees (2.14) on the gathering in of the scrolls of the Torah by Judah the Maccabee; if we recall that the decree of Antiochus had condemned the Torah-scrolls to be burnt (I Macc. 1.56), it will easily be understood that the decision to collect the copies of the books of the Law saved from the persecution was not a mere demonstration.[33] The restoration of the Torah to its former position doubtless also restored its interpreters to their previous duties, and although there is no allusion to this in the sources, we shall not be mistaken if we state that the Ḥasidim, Judah the Maccabee's loyal allies, now obtained full satisfaction and once again took over the monopoly of interpreting the commandments of the Torah and of building national life in accordance with the "ancestral code" as they understood it. As to the service in the Temple, Judah the Maccabee selected priests devoted to the Law of Judaism (I Macc. 4.42). If it is remembered that precisely the priests had been carried away by the current of Hellenization, it will be understood that the victory of the national party led to a far-reaching purge among them. Presumably the families who had till then stood at the head of the Temple cult, those who had held the leadership, were forced to leave their permanent posts (part no doubt were in the beleaguered Akra), and other families—perhaps belonging to the priestly democracy resident in the provincial towns, whence also the Hasmoneans were derived—rose to prominence and occupied the chief positions.

Important changes were also of course made in the council of elders (*gerousia*), and it must be supposed that here, too, members of humbler families took the places of the previous communal elders; unfortunately the sources tell us absolutely nothing about this.[34] Judah the Maccabee's victory over the Hellenizers was the victory of small peasants and the "urban *plebs*" over a small group of high-born and wealthy people, and if this victory did not cause a social revolution, as occurred two hundred and thirty years later during the Jewish war against Rome, it may nevertheless be assumed that it caused an important democratization of the public life of Jerusalem and perhaps also deprived the wealthy of part of the economic basis on which their lives had been built.

Judah the Maccabee became leader of the nation, and the nation immediately had reason to know it. From every corner of Palestine—from Idumaea, Ammon, Gilead and Galilee, as well as from the maritime cities— messengers sped to Jerusalem bringing evil tidings, that the Syrians and the Greeks were attacking the Jews and plundering their property. The Idumaeans, who had received the refugee Hellenizers from Jerusalem in a favorable manner, had invaded and plundered the land of Judaea; the Ammonites, under the leadership of their commander Timotheos, were preparing to go to war with the Jews; in Gilead the inhabitants were attempting to annihilate them and had forced them to seek refuge in fortresses; the people of Acco (Ptolemais), Tyre and Sidon, with the inhabitants of Galilee, were attacking the Jews of Galilee with the intention of wiping them out; in Jaffa the citizens had put them into small boats and drowned them in the sea.[35] This was a sudden outburst of the forces of hatred which had been accumulating for generations among the Syrian population. The Jews sought the protection of Judah the Maccabee, who naturally did not reject their appeal, but countered the Syrians in prolonged campaigns conducted in all corners of the country. He fought the Idumaeans and the Ammonites, fortified Bet Zur against Idumaea, crossed the Jordan to destroy several towns of Gilead, captured Hebron and Marissa in the South, broke into Ashdod and looted it, attacked Jaffa and Yavneh and burned their harbors. His brother Simon traversed Galilee and rescued the Jews who dwelt there from fear of pogroms.

This was not yet offensive war; Judah was merely avenging his people's sufferings at the hands of Syrian animosity, nor did any single town which he ravaged and burned remain in his hands for any length of time. Nevertheless, in these campaigns appear certain symptoms heralding a new period. Judah, for instance, attacked Yavneh, which had not yet openly assaulted its Jewish inhabitants and had only been preparing to do so (II Macc. 12.8); when he returned from Gilead he prepared to move against Bet Shean, and only when the Jews of that town had testified that their fellow-citizens were not among the enemies of their people, did Judah leave the city unmolested (II Macc. 12.29-31). The unsuccessful offensive of two commanders of Judah's army against Yavneh, I Maccabees relates as follows: "Seeing the success of Judah in Transjordan, they said: Let us also make a name for ourselves and go out to wage war on the Gentiles in our neighborhood" (5.57).

From these instances it may be deduced that the offensives of Judah the Maccabee and his subordinates did not everywhere or invariably arise from the need of protecting their fellow-Jews. They regarded the entire Syrian population of Palestine as hostile; nor was it important if some city or other had not yet managed to express its enmity to the Jews openly. A further detail is worthy of the scholar's attention: Judah and his brothers regarded the Syro-Greeks not simply as enemies, but as "the worshippers of heathen gods." During the persecution of Antiochus, the Syrians had sought to convert the Jews by force, and now Judah took vengeance not only on the Syrians but also on their deities, burning the temple of the Syrian goddess Atargatis (Ashtoreth) over the heads of those who had taken refuge in it (I Macc. 5.44; II Macc. 12.26) and destroying the high places and statues of the gods at Ashdod (I Macc. 5.68). Thus did Judah's campaigns against the Syrians assume the character of religious wars. They were not merely campaigns in defense of Judaism; they were offensives against the local cults.

One of the most important
results of the wars of Judah the Maccabee for Jewish history
was that they created the Hasmonean dynasty. For the first
time after an interval of hundreds of years there had appeared
among the Jews an organized military force, a fact which
had its repercussions both on the Jewish world and on other
peoples. Till now Judah the Maccabee had been only a leader
of the rebels; with the capture of Jerusalem, he became a national leader, and the peasant force which had accompanied
him at the beginning of the rising now assumed the form of a
real army, which could be used not only for attacks on villages
but also for organized warfare against strong enemies. Judah's
army was never, of course, a professional force; in periods of
peace the soldiers returned to their villages and resumed the
working of their land.

Nevertheless, it must be sup-
posed that the prolonged campaigns had their effect on these
countrymen, so that many of them became accustomed to the
life of camp and grew to resemble the normal military type.
This type was not one of the loftiest, least of all in the Hellenistic period; its basic characteristics were brutality to the foe and
a predisposition to plunder his property and to share it with
comrades. Hence it is not surprising to hear that in some localities Judah's assaults on the Syrian population were accompanied
by the total extermination of all the male inhabitants.[36] This
ruthlessness was no doubt justified in the eyes of the fighters for
freedom, for they were fighting for their religion and for the
sanctities of Judaism against pagans; hence the conduct of the
war was accompanied by religious ceremonies and religious
slogans.[37] This was the role of the Ḥasidim—to foster the religious zeal of Judah's warriors. We do not know what the former's
relation was to Judah the Maccabee, but there is no doubt that
the simple soldiers loved and worshiped their leader, seeing in
him a hero and trusting him implicitly. The admiration communi-
cated itself from Judah's camp to the broad sections of the
people, and to this day we feel, as we read the books of the
Maccabees, the tremendous impression made by Judah the Maccabee on his contemporaries. This impression was also strong
beyond the frontiers of Judah, since for the first time the Jews
had dared to cross the borders of their little country and to
appear among other nations, not as peasants or traders, but
as warriors fighting for their people and their country. This

fact placed the Jews on the same level with the other peoples of the Orient who had long waged wars on their own account. Judah the Maccabee can be compared with Zipoetes of Bithynia, Mithradates of Pontus, Arsaces of Parthia and Ariarathes of Cappadocia, all leaders who fought the Seleucids for an independent position and founded royal dynasties, just as Judah was destined to do.

Meanwhile the civil war also continued. The Hellenizers had suffered much from the power of the national party, and when Judah passed to the offensive against their last refuge and laid siege to the Akra, some of them fled to Antiochus and sought aid from the Syrian government. Two years had passed since the day when Lysias had sought to remedy the situation in the land of Judah by a partial annulment of Antiochus' decree, and since then the Syrian government had taken no steps to intervene in Jewish affairs. I Maccabees does indeed report that immediately after his failure in Judah (164), Lysias returned to Antioch and began to recruit troops for a new attack on the Jews (4.35). But it is difficult to imagine that the recruiting took two years, especially as the renewed attack (in the year 162) came, not as a result of Lysias' decision, but in response to the demands of the Hellenizers.[38] The official policy of the government to the Jews was being carried out at this time, apparently, by Ptolemy son of Makron, who favored the Jews and had opposed the Antiochus decree (II Macc. 10.12). It was a peace policy whose consequences were very dangerous to the authority of the Syrian power: the two years gave Judah the opportunity of holding Jerusalem and of showing his strength to the peoples of Palestine.

At the end of 163, important changes took place at Antioch. Antiochus Epiphanes had died in the East and his son Antiochus V Eupator had ascended the throne. Lysias was now the king's guardian and the supreme ruler of the state. He brooked no rivals, and Ptolemy son of Makron, who evidently wielded great influence in Antioch, was executed at his order. This caused a change of policy toward the Jews; Lysias now lent an attentive ear to the refugee Hellenizers and accompanied by his young king went to Palestine. Thus the civil war again brought about the intervention of foreign powers in the course of the internal history of the Jews.

This time the Syrian forces were very large: I Maccabees reports 100,000 infantry, 20,000 cavalry and 32 war-elephants (6.30), and if it is clear that these

numbers are exaggerated, the participation of the king and
the head of the state in the campaign is an assurance that special
importance was attached to the undertaking. The aim seems
to have been to put an end once and for all to the movement
of rebellion and to reassert Seleucid rule. The beginning was
reasonably successful. Judah had not sufficient force to fight
so large an army; he was defeated by Lysias and compelled to
hand over the fortress of Bet Zur to the Syrians. The Jews fortified themselves in Jerusalem and Lysias laid siege to the city.
The Jewish situation was dif-
ficult, for the sabbatical year had diminished the city's corn
supply, while the Jewish refugees who had found shelter in
Jerusalem swelled the number of the hungry. Salvation came
from an unexpected quarter. Before his death Antiochus Epiphanes had appointed Philip, one of the royal ministers, as regent
of the state in place of Lysias, and he now appeared in Syria
at the head of a strong army to demand the government's recognition. Lysias, unwilling to share power with another, hastened
to terminate the Jewish war and to return to Antioch to meet
Philip on the field of battle. But the war could not be wound
up without arriving at a compromise with Judah the Maccabee,
so negotiations were set afoot. Their details are unknown, but
a document exists, written in 162, in which the results of the
negotiations are recorded. This is the second document in II
Maccabees (11.22-26), which the author erroneously added to
the other documents, as mentioned above.[39] It contains the
letter of King Antiochus Eupator to Lysias; the Hellenistic sovereigns were in the habit of making their pronouncements on
political principles in the form of such letters, sent as an order
to one of their prominent ministers.[40]
The document was drafted
in conformity with certain court rules of procedure, and it is
clear enough that not the young king drafted the rescript, but
someone in the office of Lysias, the chief minister of state, or
Lysias himself. This was, then, an official document in which
the government defined its attitude on the Jewish question. This
is the text of the letter:
Antiochus the King greets his brother Lysias. Now that our
father has ascended to the gods,[41] we desire that all the
inhabitants of the state should devote themselves quietly
and peacefully to their affairs, and as we have heard that
the Jews are not in accord with our father's command compelling them to live in the spirit of the Greeks, but prefer

their own life and therefore ask that permission be given to them to live according to their laws, it is our desire that this nation too should live in tranquillity. Therefore our decision is: To restore to them the Temple and to permit them to live according to the customs of their fathers. You will do well therefore to send emissaries to them to make an agreement with them, in order that their spirits be raised up when they learn of our goodwill and that they turn joyfully to their affairs.

It may be asked what was the innovation in the king's letter, when the Antiochus decree had in fact become void by force of events and the Temple had been for a long time in Jewish hands? The answer is that the letter's importance lies, not in its practical value, but in its theoretical intention. The decree of Antiochus had indeed been annulled by Judah the Maccabee, but the government had not yet confirmed this new situation. The Temple, too, had passed into Jewish hands without the government's official sanction. Only now did ratification come in clear language, the Syrian government undertaking to recognize once again the "ancestral laws" of the Jews, reverting to the legal position created in Judaea in consequence of the solemn declaration of Antiochus III which had become void with the foundation of the Greek *polis* in the year 175.[42] In other words, the government abolished the *polis* of Antioch-at-Jerusalem after it had existed for thirteen years. This was a very valuable achievement on the part of Judah the Maccabee and his party. Their second achievement was the official restoration of the Temple to "the Jews," that is, the cancellation of the right of the Syrian colonists of the Akra to participate in the cult of the God of Israel on the Temple mount, or to set up Syrian cults there.

We may ask, indeed, what was the fate of the Syrian *cleruchy* which had been introduced into Jerusalem by Apollonius? Did it continue to exist? This is hard to assume, for during the siege laid to the Akra by Judah the Maccabee all the holdings of the colonists had unquestionably been plundered and their lands probably restored to their former owners. It should not be forgotten that from the year 168 the Akra had been the virtual center of the *polis* of Antioch; and now, with the abolition of the *polis*, its existence too should have terminated. As is known, the Akra nevertheless continued to exist till 142 and to serve for the whole period as the last and only refuge of the Hellenizers. The solution will probably

be found if we cease to think of the Akra as a political unit and
see it as a purely military strongpoint. As a town and center
of the *polis* of Antioch the Akra came to an end in 162; but the
Akra as a fortress continued to be very important in the view
of the Syrian government. The latter's concessions to the Jews
did not include political independence, and indeed no one in
the land of Judaea dreamed of independence at this time; the
suzerainty of the Seleucid house over the country and Jerusalem was still taken for granted. When Lysias saw the fortress
built by Judah the Maccabee on Mount Zion, he ordered it
to be destroyed, and it is to be assumed that this was a self-
understood precondition of the signing of the treaty.[43]
It also went without saying
that the Jerusalem fortress, the Akra, should remain in the king's
hands. It may therefore be supposed that the Syrian troops
continued in occupation there, though not as military settlers
but as a normal garrison. In the Akra, under their protection,
also dwelt the Hellenizers, and their appearance in the streets
of Jerusalem, or on their estates in the country of Judaea, insofar
as the latter had not been completely despoiled by Judah the
Maccabee (cf. I Macc. 6.24), depended on each occasion on
the general political situation; if the official Jewish government
did not oppose the Hellenizers, they could appear in the city
and take a hand in political affairs; when the power in Judaea
passed to Judah the Maccabee and his brothers, their situation
in the city was dangerous and it was better for them to remain
quietly behind the strong ramparts of the Akra.
The making of peace be-
tween the Syrian government and Judah the Maccabee led
therefore to the liquidation of the bitter legacy of the past: the
Hellenistic reform was abolished and the Jews again received
permission to live according to their laws. But this peace neither
could nor did abolish all the profound antagonisms in the Jewish
body politic which had arisen in the course of many generations.
The Syrian government, now in command of the situation, had
to decide on which sections of Jerusalem society it would base
its authority in the future. The Hellenizers, indeed, had disappointed their hopes, and Hellenism was not the road to
political stability in Judaea. Lysias poured out his wrath on
Menelaus, who was selected as the scapegoat, taken to Antioch
and thence sent to the city of Beroea where he was executed on
the king's order in the most brutal fashion.[44]

But this did not mean that the sympathies of the Antioch government were on the side of Judah the Maccabee, who was in their eyes a successful robber chief and nothing more; it was feasible to take account of his strength and to come to terms with him, but it was not possible to put him in power and so make him the head of the nation. Moreover, the government had to consider its former allies. Menelaus' political mistakes could not be allowed to obscure the fact that the Hellenizers represented the wealthy and well-connected elements of Jerusalem society and therefore were still fitter than any other class to serve as the reliable prop of Syrian rule in Judaea. Lysias' first concern now was to select a suitable man for the post of High Priest. He chose Alcimus (Jakim, Jehoiakim), a man "who of his own will had contaminated himself in the period of disturbances," in the words of II Maccabees (14.3), that is, he was a Hellenizer, but, apparently, not one of their extremists.[45]

According to Josephus he did not belong to the Oniads; Lysias purposely took the High Priesthood from the House of Onias and transferred it to another family (*Ant.* XII, 387; XX, 235). II Maccabees, on the other hand (14.7), says that Alcimus saw the High Priesthood as an ancestral inheritance ($\pi\rho o\gamma o\nu\iota\kappa\dot\eta$ $\delta\acute o\xi\alpha$), in other words, that he belonged to the Oniad family, and there seems no reason to doubt this view. Thus Lysias sought to find a compromise which would be acceptable to both the hostile camps: the abolition of the Hellenistic reform and the restoration of the Temple to the entire nation were meant to appease the nationalists gathered about Judah the Maccabee, whereas the authority was to return to the wealthy and well born, in other words, to the Hellenizers, and the High Priest himself was to be one of them.

Were Judah and his party prepared to accept this compromise? There are grounds for believing that for a time they hesitated and did not at once discover the correct attitude to adopt. Judah's first reaction was negative, for the restoration of the High Priesthood to a Hellenizer provided no guarantee that his reforms would not at once be put aside. II Maccabees (14.3) says that Alcimus was not even allowed to reach Jerusalem to take up office as High Priest, and sought the aid of the Syrian government. In 162 Demetrius, son of Seleucus Philopator, ascended the Syrian throne, and Alcimus appeared before him in the company of "the wicked and the sinners of Israel" (I Macc. 7.5) to make his bitter plaint

that Judah the Maccabee had driven him from the priesthood
and had not ceased to persecute the Jews with military violence;
as long as he was alive, peace and quiet would not return to
the land (II Macc. 14.3ff.). Demetrius confirmed Alcimus' claim
to the High Priesthood and sent him to Judaea with a Syrian
army led by Bacchides.

Once again Judah the Mac-
cabee and his party faced the question how to react to a fresh
hostile attack; and this time profound differences of opinion
arose in the camp of the fighters for freedom. Till now Judah
and the Ḥasidim had acted together and we hear nothing of
disagreements between them; the outer world still regarded
Judah the Maccabee as the leader of the Ḥasidim (II Macc.
14.6). But now the latter decided to act on their own and to try
the way of *rapprochement* with Alcimus. Scholars see in this a
profound ideological rift: for while Judah the Maccabee made
no distinction between religious questions and other questions
bound up with national existence, the Ḥasidim (it is alleged)
were concerned entirely with religious matters, and after Antiochus' decree had been officially rescinded saw no further need
to participate in the war of liberation.[46]

This outlook appears too
modern. We have already seen that religious, political and social
questions composed one integral unit, and it is doubtful if the
people of that period could distinguish between one question
and the other with such clarity as we exercise today. It would
be more accurate to suppose that the question which interested
the Ḥasidim was a decidedly practical one, namely, was Alcimus
prepared to see in them the official interpreters of "the ancestral
laws"—in other words, would he agree to cooperate with them
and to share the power with them? The question of the interpretation of the Law was the central problem over which the
negotiations were conducted between Alcimus and the Ḥasidim.
I Maccabees describes the "assembly of scribes" which presented
itself before Alcimus and Bacchides to "demand justice," and
immediately afterwards reports the readiness of the Ḥasidim to
compromise with the former, since he was "a man of the priesthood of the seed of Aaron" (I Macc. 7.14). If further supporting
evidence is needed that the scribes and Ḥasidim were identical
in the time of Judah the Maccabee, one of the most prominent
scholars of the period according to the Talmud was Yose ben
Yoezer, "a Ḥasid among the priests."[47]

The question of the interpretation of the Torah was not exclusively one of religion, for it embraced law, everyday customs, the ceremonies of the national festivals, and the order of service in the Temple—in short, the whole life of Jewish society. Till 175 the scribes had conducted national affairs, since they held the monopoly of expounding the Torah. When the *polis* was founded their influence had been abolished and it has already been stressed that their struggle against Antiochus and the Hellenizers was the struggle of an entire class for its existence (above, p. 197). Judah had restored to them their central position in the nation, but the Syrian government had not confirmed Judah as the nation's head and had chosen another man, who was a priest of the legitimate Oniad family and had perhaps given certain pledges to the Ḥasidim, as indeed I Maccabees (7.15) hints.

The practical question facing the Ḥasidim was, therefore, whether it was worth entering into negotiations with Alcimus and forcing him to hand over to them what they regarded as the scribes' monopoly. We do not know what Judah the Maccabee's attitude was to this step; he may not have been opposed to it in any way, although it is more probable that, as a military man and activist, he was less prepared for compromises than the jurists and lawyers. Whatever the case, the attempt ended in utter failure; for reasons not clear a quarrel broke out between the Ḥasidim and Alcimus, and sixty of them were executed by order of the High Priest. There is every reason to suppose that after this political reverse the Ḥasidim returned to Judah's camp; and if there had been differences of opinion between them at any time, they vanished completely before the Syrian policy which had again given the power in Judaea to the Hellenizers, the enemies of the Ḥasidim and Judah the Maccabee alike.

The renewal of the rule of the Hellenizers brought in its train the resumption of the civil war. Judah the Maccabee continued to harass the Hellenizers, and Alcimus again appealed to Antioch for help against him. Demetrius sent Nicanor at the head of a strong army. But instead of pursuing Judah, Nicanor entered into peace negotiations with him. It cannot be determined whether this was a ruse on his part, his real object being to capture Judah secretly and to execute him (as I Macc. 7.29 thinks), or whether he discovered that the real strength was on Judah's side and that it was profitable to negotiate with him (thus II Macc. 14.23ff.). Whatever the case, the peace did not last and the "treaty" was easily broken, perhaps under the influence of Alcimus (II Macc., *ib.*).[48] Nicanor marched out against the Jewish force and for the last time fortune favored Judah. The Greek host was defeated and Nicanor himself fell on the field of battle.

This was an important victory for the nationalist party, but its last. Alcimus fled to Syria, and after an interval Demetrius again sent Bacchides, accompanied by the High Priest, to wreak havoc among the Jews. This time Judah had insufficient force to meet the foe; his army was small and this, too, scattered when it heard of Bacchides' great host; Judah made his last stand before Bacchides with 800 men. The Syrians had the upper hand, and Judah himself fell in battle (160). The strength of the nationalist party was broken, and power passed to Alcimus and his faction.

The Syrians and the Hellenizers again ruled the country. Bacchides appointed the "criminals" as rulers and violently persecuted the supporters of Judah (I Macc. 9.23ff.). The nationalist group had lost its leader and with him its energy; but neither the Syrian power nor the terror of Alcimus and his associates could bring peace to the land. The followers of Judah the Maccabee rallied round Jonathan his brother, and chose him as their leader. Civil war blazed forth afresh, and Jonathan's small bands gave no rest to their opponents. Bacchides marched out against Jonathan, who retired before him. The movement grew and seized the whole country, so that the Hellenizers found need to establish a number of forts to support them in their struggle with Jonathan and to take hostages from the country's gentry.

But none of these operations remedied the situation, since the Hellenizers lacked an army of their own and could carry out no operations without Syrian aid. After Alcimus' death no single man of their party was found able to hold power, and the post of High Priest remained vacant for seven years. As long as Bacchides stayed in the country the Hellenizers retained the advantage, but the Syrian general could not remain in Judaea permanently, and after Alcimus' death he returned to Antioch. The Hellenizers made an attempt to capture Jonathan; but as a result themselves lost fifty of their confederates, who fell into Jonathan's hands and were put to death by his order (I Macc. 9.61). Once again the Hellenizers appealed to Bacchides; he came to Judaea and conducted a campaign against Jonathan, but without success, his force being defeated, and his efforts came to nothing. Finally Bacchides' patience gave out; it hardly seemed worthwhile to come to Judaea every year to expend men and money in abundance merely to strengthen the Hellenizers' party, which could not defend itself for even a short time and was continually in need of help from outside. Could such a party serve the needs of the king of Syria satisfactorily? Bacchides opened negotiations with Jonathan, restored to him those of his allies who had been taken prisoner and took an oath not to injure him for the rest of his life (I Macc. 9.71). Having concluded this treaty, he returned to Syria and Jonathan moved on Michmash. "And he began to judge his people and put an end to the wrongdoers of Israel"; so I Maccabees (9.73) concludes its account of the beginning of Jonathan's acts.

Ten years had passed from the day that Judah the Maccabee raised the standard of rebellion, and eighteen years from the day that the Hellenizers had exchanged the traditional regime in Jerusalem for the new regime of a Greek *polis* and thereby set ablaze the fury of a civil war—yet the two parties, the Hellenizers and the nationalists, still faced each other with drawn swords. But the situation had altered enormously during that time, and many far-reaching conclusions could be drawn from the experience of these stormy years. While the nationalist party, despite all its grave failures, was still firmly established and could point with pride to its many successes (the abolition of the decree of Antiochus, the democratic reform in Jerusalem, the war of revenge against the Syrian inhabitants of Palestine), the Hellenizing party's internal weakness and inability to rule were patent to all. The Hellenizers had never beaten their opponents with their own strength; the Syrians had always had to come to their assistance, no less in the case of Alcimus and his followers than in that of the Tobiads and their faction. The Hasmonean movement was solidly grounded among the people, for the country population was openly in sympathy with Judah the Maccabee and his comrades, giving him substantial support when he needed it,[49] whereas the Hellenizers fought in isolation, surrounded by a vacuum. Ultimately the Syrians perceived this and drew the logical conclusion from the situation created in Judaea. In the year 152 war broke out between Demetrius I of Syria and Alexander Balas, who sought to depose Demetrius from the throne of his kingdom and to take his place. Both mobilized their forces, and both sought allies and helpers. Judaea, as a relatively independent part of the kingdom, was important in their estimation. But it was hardly feasible to invite the assistance of the Hellenizers, for this party had no genuine power, and, moreover, the post of High Priest had been vacant for seven years.

There was only one man in Judaea with energy and military experience capable of supporting one or the other of the warring sovereigns, and that was Jonathan. Demetrius was the first to understand the situation, and so invited Jonathan to make an alliance with him, gave him permission to enroll military forces and to equip himself with arms, and also ordered the hostages in the Akra to be delivered to him. Alexander Balas went further, appointing Jonathan as High Priest. Jonathan was not slow to accept the favors thus showered upon him. On the festival of Tabernacles of the year 152, he appeared for the first time before the public of Jerusalem garbed in the robes of the High Priesthood, and thus ended the prolonged period of civil war in Judaea and Jerusalem. It had lasted as long as it did on account of the support obtained by the Hellenizers from the kings of Syria, and the moment the Syrians withdrew their hand from them, the war ended with the victory of the Hasmoneans.

The victory was of great importance in relation to the past, as a final conclusion of the civil struggle, and no less in respect of the future. A military force not hitherto known to the Jews had grown up in the confusion of the period; on numerous occasions the civil struggle had assumed the form of open war against the kings of Syria, and many times the Jews had gained the upper hand. Judaea was now a political power which had to be reckoned with. The Tobiads had dreamed that Judaea might play an independent role in the Hellenistic world, and now the dream was fulfilled, but in quite a different fashion. The land of Judaea was to take part in the international life of the epoch, not as a Greek city subject to Syria, but as an independent state controlled by its national kings. The dynastic principle was linked by an inner link with the course of events, for in the ancient world the democratic movement was generally conducted by strong men— the "tyrants" of Greek political terminology.

Judah the Maccabee had also been a "tyrant" of this sort, that is, a military leader who fought against the government of the aristocracy on his own responsibility and was supported by the masses. He himself did not reach the point of founding the state, but he showed the people the way to the objective, namely, a concentration of national forces about a single central personality. After his death, the people rallied round Jonathan and thereby laid the foundation of the Hasmonean dynasty.

chapter **7**

THE HASMONEAN PERIOD

The hundred years that passed from the time of Judah the Maccabee to the appearance of Pompey in Palestine—the period of the Hasmoneans—left a profound impression on the life of the Jewish people. In this period the national aspirations which had matured during the revolt found their satisfaction; the Jewish nation spread across the narrow frontiers of Judaea over the whole of Palestine, attained its independence and founded a strong state. The national and political renascence led to a rich development of cultural life, and to the creation of new values in literature and religion which profoundly influenced the beliefs and opinions of succeeding epochs. The Hasmonean period breathed a new spirit into all branches of the national life of the Jewish people.

It is not our intention to enter here into a detailed study of the period: it is so rich that it might well form the subject of an independent book, nor should it be treated cursorily, or as an epilogue to the study of the preceding period. Only the questions directly affecting our topic—Hellenism in Palestine—will be considered, these being: (1) The relationship between the Hasmoneans and the Seleucids; (2) the Jewish wars against the Greek cities; and (3) the influence of Greek culture on the Hasmoneans. The first question is political, the second mainly economic, and the third cultural.

We begin with an account of the political events which made Judaea independent.

After Alexander Balas had acknowledged the independence of Jonathan, the latter became a Syrian official. He was appointed "*strategos* and governor (*meridarches*)" of Judaea, and was enrolled among "the chief friends" of the king (I Macc. 10.65). As a high official of the state, Jonathan took part in the splendid celebration held in the year 150 at Acco-Ptolemais in honor of the marriage of Alexander with the Egyptian Cleopatra. When Demetrius II appeared as a new candidate for the royal throne of Syria, Jonathan remained loyal to Alexander. In 145, Demetrius II was crowned king. Although he had grounds for finding fault with Jonathan's previous policy, he saw no need to voice complaints against him; he not only confirmed him in his post in Judaea, but gave him leave to annex three districts of Samaria—Ephraim, Lydda and Ramatayim—to his territory.

As the loyal vassal of the king of Syria, Jonathan on one occasion hastened to his lord's aid, when the citizens of Antioch had revolted against Demetrius, and with 3000 of his own troops put down the disturbances in the capital. After some time, Demetrius was defeated by Tryphon, who was fighting for the crown in the name of the infant son of Antiochus VI. Jonathan, having sufficient reason for complaint against Demetrius (who had not kept his promise of removing the Syrian garrison from the Akra), went over to Tryphon and was confirmed by him in his official position. His brother Simon also received an official post, being appointed *strategos* of the entire Palestinian coast, from Tyre to the "River of Egypt" (Wadi el-Arish). As Tryphon's general, Jonathan fought against Demetrius and in the course of these campaigns traversed the entire country, also visiting Damascus and operating near the Syrian town of Emesa. The alliance between Jonathan and Tryphon did not, however, last for a long time. For some unknown reason Tryphon decided to get rid of Jonathan, lured him by trickery to Ptolemais, imprisoned him and later put him to death.

Simon, Jonathan's brother, succeeding to the High Priesthood, joined Demetrius II, who exempted Judaea from payment of taxes to Syria, in other words, acknowledged her independence completely and finally. The same year (142), Simon captured the Akra, which had been uninterruptedly in the possession of a Syrian garrison since the time of Antiochus Epiphanes. Thus were loosed the chains which had fettered Judaea to the Syrian kingdom for some sixty years, and the people of Israel won its political liberty.[1]

In this early period of Hasmonean rule the Jewish princes appear as Seleucid royal officials. To understand this fact more precisely we must notice the titles granted to Jonathan and Simon by the Syrian kings. Alexander appointed Jonathan *meridarch* of Judaea. Kahrstedt[2] looked upon the *meridarch* as a representative of the local population (on the analogy of the post of ethnarch); but it would be more correct to suppose that the post was an official position in the Seleucid state. Josephus (*Ant.* XII, 261) calls Apollonius, governor of Samaria, by the name of *meridarch,* and this shows that the *meridarchs* governed certain parts of a large political unit, as may be perceived from the word itself.[3] In our present context the large unit is Coele-Syria and Phoenicia, at whose head stood a high official, "the *strategos* of Coele-Syria and Phoenicia," the subsections being Samaria, Judaea and the rest.[4] In the preceding period Judaea had been under the authority of the High Priests, but that position was not a government post, and over the High Priests stood government officials who held the real power in their hands.

Alexander now appointed Jonathan as *meridarch* of Judaea, that is, he handed over to the High Priest the official control, and this converted Jonathan into a civil servant of the Seleucid state, a valuable step forward on the path of the struggle for political independence. Not less important was the position obtained by Simon from Tryphon: he was appointed *strategos* of the area between the "Ladder of Tyre"[5] and the frontier of Egypt (I Macc. 11.59). The title of *strategos* does not afford a clear conception of the nature of the post, since every military commander and every official with military authority could be so termed in the Hellenistic period.[6] But the position itself was not a temporary one, for in the year 162 Lysias gave to the Greek official Hegemonides the post of *strategos* of the localities "from Ptolemais to Gerar" (II Macc. 13.24)[7] and under Antiochus Sidetes "the *epistrategos* of the seacoast" (I Macc. 15.38) is again mentioned; hence we know that the coast was in charge of a special official, and this post now passed to Simon. The Hasmonean brothers, therefore, as officials of the Syrian kings, controlled a considerable part of Palestine. But the most important aspect was that no other official now intervened between the Hasmonean princes and the king of Syria.

The position of "*strategos* of Coele-Syria," a regular post under the Seleucids down to Judah the Maccabee's time, was now abolished, Bacchides being the last to hold it (in 161: I Macc. 7.5).[8] The Hasmonean revolt, then, caused important changes in the administration of the country: the large administrative unit of "Coele-Syria and Phoenicia" was abolished, and instead, officials were appointed over the country's various divisions, two of these divisions being handed over to the Hasmoneans. The High Priest of Jerusalem in particular gained in importance, since he was simultaneously a Syrian official and the representative of the Jewish people, a status which enhanced the value of the High Priesthood with both sides and pointed the way to independence.

Complete political independence was obtained under Simon, when the High Priest ceased to be a Syrian official and became a free ruler of his people and his country. Three important changes which occurred under Simon indicate the new situation which had come about in Judaea: namely, the exemption of the Jews from the payment of taxes to the Syrian sovereign, the liquidation of the Syrian garrisons in the fortresses of Judaea, and the laying of a legal foundation for the rule of the new dynasty of the Hasmonean house. The tax-exemption was proclaimed in the rescript of Demetrius II to Simon (I Macc. 13.39), a similar exemption having already been referred to in Jonathan's time (*ib.* 11.35; cf. 10.29). The act of exemption was published on the 27th of Iyyar of 142, and the author of I Maccabees accompanies the information with the triumphant observation: "In the year 170 (of the Seleucid area) the yoke of the Gentiles was taken away from Israel" (*ib.* 13.41).[9] He was indeed right in his estimate of the event, for the payment of tribute was always regarded as a sign of subjection, and in the Hellenistic period every Greek city dreamed of being ἀφορολόγητος, that is, exempt from dues, and only if she was so did she regard herself as really "free."

Not less important was the peaceful occupation of the Akra; on the 23rd of Iyyar of the same year the Syrian garrison surrendered to Simon and received permission to march out of the fortress.[10] This meant also the liquidation of the Hellenizers' party which had played such an important role under Antiochus Epiphanes. Its last activities belong to the days of the reign of Jonathan, when in 150 the

Hellenizers appeared before Alexander Balas at Acco seeking to slander Jonathan to the king, but were unsuccessful in their designs (I Macc. 10.61); they renewed their attempt several years later before Demetrius II, again without success (*ib.* 11.21ff.). After Jonathan had fallen into Tryphon's hands, the "men of the Akra" besought the Syrians to hasten to their assistance, and Tryphon was preparing to do so, but was delayed by severe weather (*Ant.* XIII, 208). That was the end of their role in Jewish history. Besides the Akra, the important fortress of Bet Zur in the south of Judaea also passed into Jonathan's hands with the remainder of the country's fortified places.[11]

More important than any of the above was the foundation of the Hasmonean dynasty. Jonathan had received the High Priesthood from the king of Syria, just as Jason, Menelaus and Alcimus had received their posts from the kings of Syria; but such an appointment was not sufficient to create a legitimate basis for Hasmonean rule. In the eyes of the people the High Priesthood was the ancestral inheritance of the Oniad family. But the Oniad house had come to an end, and its last representative had built himself a temple of his own in Egypt; so it devolved upon the people to ratify Simon's rule and thus create a new legal basis for the political situation which had been created in Judaea. This ratification was accorded by "the Great Assembly (*Keneset*) of the Priests and the People, of the rulers of the people and elders of the land" which gathered on the 18th of Elul of the third year of Simon's reign (140).[12]

By decision of the Assembly, Simon was elected High Priest ($\dot{\alpha}\rho\chi\iota\epsilon\rho\epsilon\acute{\upsilon}s$) military leader ($\dot{\eta}\gamma o\acute{\upsilon}\mu\epsilon\nu os$, $\sigma\tau\rho\alpha\tau\eta\gamma\acute{o}s$) and leader of the people ($\dot{\epsilon}\theta\nu\acute{\alpha}\rho\chi\eta s$), which meant that the people placed solely in his hands the traditional rule of the nation, previously in the hands of the Oniads, together with the political authority as head of the nation (ethnarch, *prostates*), whose function was to represent it before external powers; and to these two forms of authority was added the military power which had grown up among the Jews as a result of the troubled times, from the time of Judah the Maccabee on. Moreover, the Assembly granted the entire scope of this power to Simon in perpetuity (I Macc. 14.41), a conception involving the right of the new ruler to bequeath his authority hereditarily to his son. Thus Simon gathered into his hands powers of a genuinely monarchical character, and the new dynasty was established on a strong legal basis which was far broader than that which had been the foundation of the power of the High Priests of the house of Onias.

The years of Simon's reign passed in peace and tranquillity. In his time the frontiers of the land were extended and the important harbor of Jaffa passed into Jewish hands. But Simon's position was not secure as long as Antiochus had not conclusively confirmed the political change which had come about in Judaea. The Seleucid government, in fact, did not invariably incline to concessions. In 138, Antiochus VII Sidetes ascended the throne; he was the last Syrian king whose name is worthy of historical record, for he was a man of energy and dreamed of reestablishing the Seleucid state. He disliked Judaea's independent status and was especially angered by Simon's attempt to enlarge the country's borders. He demanded of him the restoration to Syria of the towns of Jaffa and Gezer, also of the Akra fortress (involving the control of Jerusalem), or the payment of a sum of money in exchange for them. He did not, however, demand of Simon complete capitulation—a fact which testifies to Antiochus' theoretical admission of Jewish independence—requiring only that Simon should not overstep his country's frontiers.

Simon refused his demands and Antiochus despatched his general Kendebaios to fight the Jews; Kendebaios' campaign was unsuccessful and he was defeated by Simon's sons, so that Antiochus determined to go to Palestine in person. In the meantime Simon fell by the sword of a member of his own family, and after a short war against the assassin, Simon's son, John Hyrcanus, assumed the rank of High Priest (135). Antiochus continued the war, invading Judaea himself and laying siege to Jerusalem, so that John was forced to yield. The peace-terms were extremely severe, John restoring to Syria his father's conquests (the towns of Jaffa and Gezer), paying a large indemnity, giving Antiochus hostages, and undertaking to raise a large annual tribute. To all appearances Antiochus had succeeded in reestablishing Seleucid rule in Judaea. But this was actually not the case.

There was a great difference between the positions of Jonathan and Hyrcanus: Jonathan had been a Syrian official while John was an independent prince who had lost a war. Antiochus gave up his intention of placing a permanent garrison in the Akra, and acknowledged the independent status of the Jewish High Priest, while the fact that John was forced to take part in Antiochus' Parthian expedition shows conclusively that the former saw the Jews as a respectable military power which could be useful in an emergency. The juridical foundation of the Hasmonean state was not annulled by this reverse; only its political situation became bad. But this too soon altered. In 129, Antiochus Sidetes fell in battle, and from that time the kingdom of Syria lost all importance in the political world, while John exploited the Seleucid weakness to extend his country's frontiers and laid the foundations of Jewish domination throughout Palestine. His son Aristobulus drew the final conclusion from the dynasty's new situation, by taking the title of king. Under his brother, Alexander Jannaeus, the Hasmonean kingdom reached its peak of development by controlling the whole of Palestine, from Lake Semechonitis (Huleh) in the North to the Egyptian frontier in the South.

The Maccabean struggle against the Seleucids and the founding of the independent Jewish state have been variously evaluated in modern learned literature. Few scholars have viewed the Hasmonean cause with affection, and we shall have further occasion to allude to this negative attitude when we touch upon the question of the war of the Maccabees against the Greek cities. The intention here is to treat of only one assumption of modern scholarship, commonly accepted as an authoritative view, namely, that the Jewish state was not the product of the inner strength of the Jews, but was rendered possible by the weakness of the Seleucids. The most important historians[13] lay special emphasis upon this fact, and for that reason a brief discussion of its truth may be worthwhile.

What do scholars mean when they dwell at length on the weakness of the Seleucids? They generally refer to the period after Antiochus Epiphanes, when the throne had begun to pass from hand to hand and the men who held power were not capable of conducting the state's affairs. From this time, it is alleged, the small nations, including the Jews, began to strive for independence and the power of the central authority was inadequate to put an end to their aspirations. According to this view, the breakup of the kingdom came as a result of the weakness of its administrative center and, but for the struggle of rivals at Antioch and the lack of capacity of the last kings, the Seleucid state would not have lost its strength nor would the peoples of the Orient have rebelled successfully.

This view is a superficial treatment of the question. We may ask, what were the reasons for the decay of the central state? Was it mere chance that the throne began to pass from hand to hand? And is it true that before Antiochus Epiphanes the Seleucid kingdom was a strong state which was fighting successfully against the eastern peoples? We have dwelt above (p. 17f.) on the internal organization of the Seleucid empire, and have seen that as an organization it was never strong enough to bring the conquered peoples under the yoke of political discipline. Asia Minor remained a land of independent states, and in central Asia the Parthians and the Bactrians rose to weaken the state's unity. Under Antiochus III the state was near to complete disintegration and only the ample energy of the king for some time checked the development of this natural process. Antiochus spent some seven years in the countries of the East, and on his return home received from his subjects the title of "the Great," but his military victory could not conceal his political failure. After an obstinate war against Xerxes of Armenia, Arsaces of Parthia and Euthydemos of Bactria, Antiochus was compelled to acknowledge their independence officially and to be content with empty promises of the payment of tribute and the like. What is more, Antiochus gave Xerxes his sister in marriage, and promised Demetrius, son of Euthydemos, the hand of his daughter.[14]

The success of Antiochus' wars against the kings of the East, was therefore purely superficial; in point of fact, in his reign the Seleucid state became a federation, and it was clear from the start that such a situation could not last. Not many years passed before Bactria cast off the royal yoke, and the Parthians extended their power at the expense of the Seleucids. What else then was the Seleucids' weakness but the strength of the Orient? It is hardly legitimate to differentiate between these two phenomena, and to see one as the cause and the other as the effect; we have before us two sides of the same coin. All the other factors—the feuds at the royal court, the contemptible character of the reigning kings, and so on—may be regarded as subordinate factors which indeed hastened the disintegration of the State, but which amounted to virtually nothing compared with the fundamental cause—the great strength of the Orient.

Looked at from this angle—the struggle of the Hasmoneans against the Seleucids, however important to the Jewish people's movement to liberate itself from foreign rule, was only one link in the long chain of conflicts between East and West. In those days the East was the attacking party, since the oriental peoples were fighting for political liberty, and for the right to organize their lives on a national basis, while the West was defending the positions which it had captured in the time of Alexander. As the oriental offensive was being mounted simultaneously on various fronts, one front protected the other without even knowing of its existence; and this was the case in Judaea as well. Three times the Hasmonean national cause was in danger of destruction—in the time of Lysias (162), in that of Bacchides (160), and in that of Antiochus Sidetes (135); on each occasion quite unlooked-for salvation came from an unexpected quarter.

Although in all these instances the military advantage was on the side of the Seleucids, the victors were compelled to admit their inability to annihilate the enemy. They could control Judaea only with the aid of the Jews and, in order to associate them with the government, they were forced to acknowledge their national demands. Bacchides' relation to Jonathan and Antiochus Sidetes' relation to John Hyrcanus were no different from that of Antiochus III to Xerxes, Arsaces and Euthydemos. Here too the kings gave up the attempt to force the enemy into submission and recognized the independence of parts of the state. Palestine too was to become part of the federal state, yet there also, as in central Asia, this compromise could not save the Seleucid state from its predicament; the end was complete capitulation to the independent forces of the Orient.[15]

We return to the affairs of Palestine: The rise of the Hasmonean government's political power had a direct impact upon the existence of the Greek cities of Palestine. We have seen above that as early as the time of Judah the Maccabee these two forces—the Syro-Greek population of the country and the national movement in Judaea—stood face to face, and their first encounter was not a peaceful one. After the death of Judah the Maccabee this hostility assumed the form of an obstinate war. The conquest of the coastal towns in particular became the standing object of Hasmonean policy, for on their capture depended the fate of the economic development of the land of Judaea, which needed to break a way through the motley population of the lowland towns in order to capture an outlet to the sea. In Jonathan's time this objective was not entirely clear, and other reasons drew him to the maritime plain.

When Demetrius II went to war with Alexander Balas, Jonathan supported the latter, and Demetrius despatched his general Apollonius against him. Apollonius, encamped at Iamnia (Yavneh), sent a challenge to Jonathan to come and fight in the Shephelah, and the letter, which was intentionally couched in insulting phrases, achieved its purpose. Jonathan descended to the lowland plain and encamped near Jaffa. The Greek cities were supporting Apollonius (I Macc. 10.61) and the citizens of Jaffa shut their gates to Jonathan; when the latter attacked, the citizens, fearing he would destroy their town, opened their gates, and Jonathan became master of Jaffa. Apollonius had encamped at Ashdod, where the encounter took place; the Greeks, routed by the Jews, escaped into the city and sought refuge in the Temple of Dagon. Jonathan burned Ashdod, its surrounding villages, and likewise Dagon's temple over the heads of those who had fled into it. Thence he marched against Ascalon, whose citizens met him with high respect, so that he left the town unharmed and returned home with much booty. When Alexander Balas heard of Jonathan's loyalty to him, he gave Ekron and its territory to him as a present. Thus, for the first time, the Jews had seized a position in the Philistine Shephelah (I Macc. 10.67-99; *Ant.* XIII, 91ff.).

Jonathan appeared in the region for a second time as an official of Tryphon at the head of a Syrian force, with the purpose of compelling the towns of Palestine to desert Demetrius II and go over to Tryphon's side. At Ascalon he was received with great honor, but Gaza refused to obey him and closed its gates against him. He laid siege to the city, wasting its territory, whereupon it surrendered and sent hostages from among its highborn citizens (I Macc. 11.60-62). Simon also, when appointed by Tryphon as *strategos* of the coast, kept a careful eye on the maritime towns lest they rebel against Tryphon; and when he heard that the citizens of Jaffa intended to surrender their city to Demetrius, he occupied it and garrisoned it with his own troops. Thus the Hasmonean brothers ruled the coastland as royal Syrian officials. But the situation was short-lived, for under Simon an independent Hasmonean policy began to take shape.

Immediately on his accession
to the High Priesthood, Simon sent his commander to Jaffa to
capture the city and to expel its inhabitants (I Macc. 13.11).
Josephus, seeking for an excuse for this violent action, says:
"He feared lest the citizens hand over the city to Tryphon"
(*Ant.* XIII, 202). This reason may have influenced Simon among
others; but in effect from that time Jaffa remained in Jewish
hands. The expulsion of the inhabitants, which was the first step
in the Judaization of the town, was repeated in the other Greek
towns which fell under Hasmonean sway. After a time Simon
captured Gezer, which lay on the road between Jaffa and Jerusalem, so that its occupation secured the Jews the way to the
coast. The citizens begged Simon to have mercy on them and
not to put them to the sword; he granted their plea, but drove
them from the city, purified the dwellings in which had stood
images of the gods, and settled there "people who kept the Law"
(I Macc. 12.43-48).

Besides Jaffa and Gezer, Yav-
neh also fell into Jewish hands at the same time, apparently after
Simon's sons had defeated Kendebaios, general of Antiochus
Sidetes.[16] The conquest of Jaffa and Gezer was the first expression of an independent Hasmonean political policy, and both
Jews and Greeks saw it as such. I Maccabees praises Simon for
converting Jaffa to a Jewish port, so securing for the Jews an
outlet to "the islands of the sea" (I Macc. 14.5). Antiochus
Sidetes, on the other hand, demanded of the Jews that they
restore to him these two towns, which had belonged to his
kingdom, and we have already seen that Simon's refusal brought
upon Judaea an unsuccessful war. Only after Antiochus Sidetes'
death did these towns fall—this time for good—into the hands of
the Hasmoneans.

Not only the Philistine She-
phelah, but the other regions of the country were swiftly affected
by the change that had taken place in Judaea. Judah the Maccabee had fought against the Idumaeans and the Ammonites
and had attacked the towns of Transjordan, while his brother
Simon was fighting in Galilee. Jonathan, as a Syrian official, had
marched the length and breadth of the country more than
once. But this was not yet offensive warfare. The systematic
and planned conquest of the country began only under John
Hyrcanus. Immediately after the death of Antiochus Sidetes,
John went to war with the peoples surrounding Judaea, taking
two cities of Transjordan, also capturing Sichem and destroying

the Samaritan temple on Mount Gerizim. His war in the south was especially productive of results, for he overran the entire country of Idumaea with its Hellenistic towns of Adora and Marissa, and compelled the Idumaeans to proselytize (*Ant.* XIII, 257). In this way the frequent danger of sudden raids that had threatened Judaea from the south, became a thing of the past.

Later, John also eliminated the second foe which from time to time had harassed the Jews from the north, namely, the Samaritans. His army, under the command of his sons Antigonus and Aristobulus, encamped about Samaria for a whole year, and even the intervention of Antiochus Kyzikenos of Syria brought no profit to the Samaritans. John captured the city and razed it to its foundations (*Ant.* XIII, 275ff.). The Greek city of Scythopolis also passed into Jewish control at this time, it seems (*Ant.* XIII, 280; *War* I, 66), and probably part of Galilee as well, for Josephus reports that Alexander Jannaeus, the younger son of John, grew up and was educated in Galilee (*Ant.* XIII, 322). Thus the Hasmonean power under John Hyrcanus was extended over almost the entire country of Palestine. Aristobulus I and Alexander Jannaeus, his sons, rounded off this historic process. Aristobulus conquered the Ituraean people, who dwelt near the Lebanon, and forced them to become Jews, but this conquest, it seems, was not adequately secured, for in the first place we do not hear anything whatever about the Ituraeans as Jews at a later date, and secondly, Upper Galilee and northern Transjordan were not then in Hasmonean hands, and these two regions stood between the Ituraeans and Palestine. These districts were subdued only by Alexander Jannaeus.

Jannaeus took the towns of Gadara, Pella, Gerasa and Gamala in Transjordan, and Seleuceia together with the place called "Hulata of Antioch" in the north of the country, near Lake Semechonitis. Gadara held out against him for ten months (*Ant.* XIII, 356), and Pella was destroyed by him because its citizens refused to obey his order to become Jews (*Ant.* XIII, 397). Alexander also fought against the Greek cities of the coast, capturing Raphia and Anthedon and destroying Gaza after she had put up a prolonged resistance (*Ant.* XIII, 358ff.; *War* I, 87). Apollonia and Straton's Tower are also mentioned by Josephus as towns which belonged to Alexander, and only three—Acco-Ptolemais in the north, Ascalon in the south and Philadelpheia in Transjordan retained their independent existence. Under Alexander Jannaeus the Hasmonean state expanded to the frontiers of Palestine; and the Greek cities, losing their independence, were included in the Jewish political entity.

As can be seen from the above outline, the Hasmoneans showed the Greek cities no mercy and, not only deprived them of liberty, but destroyed several of them, expelled and annihilated their inhabitants, or forced them to Judaize. Among the Greeks this severe policy aroused fierce hostility to the Jews as a whole and to the Hasmonean state in particular,[17] and the echoes of this hostility can still be heard in the harsh censures of some scholars, who look upon the work of the Hasmoneans as an outburst of the forces of barbarism and of religious fanaticism, whose aim was to destroy Greek culture in Palestine. This view, which is partly influenced by admiration for Greek culture, and partly by a theologian's approach to the Jewish people and its function in history, evaluates the political achievements of the Hasmoneans by their destructive acts, and ignores their constructive achievements.[18]

Historical events, however, require a historical evaluation, and the political process of the rise of a state cannot be judged from a religious, cultural or humanitarian point of view alone; for if we judge it in this way, we are likely to condemn not only the Hasmonean kingdom, but several other larger and mightier states as well. The war of the Hasmoneans against the Greek cities was internally bound up with the foundation of the Jewish state and with its economic development. The capture of Jaffa was the first step in the encouragement of a Jewish commerce as well as the first attack on a Greek town. It was clear from the outset that every attempt to enlarge the frontiers would bring about a severe clash with the Greek towns, for it endangered their mercantile monopoly; their fear of the Jews was a fear of new competitors, and the Greek urban communities mustered their entire strength to defend the *status quo*. It was on the whole a struggle between equal forces, and it would be incorrect to describe it as an assault of strong military formations upon the feeble and unarmed. The cities had as many weapons as they needed, they were protected by garrisons composed of citizens, and sometimes the defense was in the hands of a professional who governed the city as a "tyrant."[19] Many of the towns were effective fortresses capable of holding out against hostile attack for ten to twelve months, apart from which they frequently received fairly substantial aid from the kings of Syria. Thus Antiochus Kyzikenos came to Palestine to assist the Samaritans in their struggle with Hyrcanus. The capture of the Greek towns was no small matter, therefore; Acco-Ptolemais, for example, did not yield to the Hasmoneans at all, although Alexander Jannaeus sought to make war on her early in his reign.

Nor should the responsibility for the conflict be placed on the Jews alone, for the truth was that, while under the Hasmoneans, it assumed the form of ceaseless attacks on the part of the Jews, it should not be forgotten that they had not in fact begun the affair. The hatred exhibited by the population of Palestine to the Jews in Judah the Maccabee's time has been stressed above (p. 210), likewise the assistance which the former rendered to Antiochus Epiphanes and his generals. The Greek cities stood prepared to suppress and eliminate the national movement in Judaea even before it had begun to develop. The Hasmonean war against the Greek urban communities was thus a continuation of the Syrians' war against the Jews in the time of Antiochus, but now the Jews were the stronger side. Yet even under the Hasmoneans the cities might have compromised with the new situation. The city of Ascalon, for example, cheerfully accepted the new regime and saw no need of resisting the Hasmoneans, so that in the end she remained uninjured and her autonomy unimpaired. From 104 B.C.E. Ascalon began to reckon her years according to her own special era.[20]

To sum up, the struggle between the Hasmoneans and the Greek towns was not for or against culture, but the rivalry between two political powers, one of which was striving for economic development, while the other was defending the positions which it had long enjoyed. The character of the struggle was severe and brutal, like all wars of the period, but the Hasmoneans did not act as they did out of hatred of Greek culture or out of overweening zeal for Judaism. We shall see below that they did not hate Greek culture at all, and Alexander Jannaeus, who fought continuously for six years against the Pharisees, was certainly no religious fanatic. The state constructed by the Hasmoneans was a secular state, a fact which alone suffices to explain their policy toward the Greek towns; nor was the ideology which they upheld one of blind religious fanaticism, but a broad nationalist outlook based on knowledge of Jewish history. When Antiochus Sidetes demanded of Simon the return of the towns of Jaffa and Gezer, Simon replied: "We have not taken foreign soil, but the inheritance of our fathers, which fell into the hands of our foes unjustly, and now the land has returned to its first owners" (I Macc. 15.33-34). According to this view, the whole of Palestine was to be united under the rule of the Hasmoneans, and its inhabitants were again to be Jews, as they had been under the kings of the house of David.

The Judaization of the Syrian population of the Greek cities was part of the political program of the Hasmoneans and not an ambition to engage in religious propaganda. It is true that, from the point of view of the Syrian urban population, the Hasmoneans' reasons were not particularly important, for the plight of the conquered was in any case very bad, and the Judaization of a town marked the end of its civic autonomy, while if the inhabitants refused to accept the Jewish religion they were doomed to the sword. Yet even here care must be taken not to link the fate of the Greek cities with the fate of Hellenism as a whole; it has already been observed (p. 111ff.) that the populations of the Greek towns of Palestine were not racially Greek; they were Syrians who had become Hellenized. It is very doubtful if the destruction of these cities caused much damage to the condition of Greek civilization in the Orient; it was the Syrian population which suffered in the Hasmonean wars, not Greek culture. Hellenism did not come to an end in Palestine owing to the destruction of the cities—it merely lost its political importance. Moreover, the same state which had destroyed the Greek urban communities was itself prepared to follow in the footsteps of the conquered and to adopt the superficial Hellenic customs of the Orient, and the Hellenism of the Hasmoneans may have been no whit inferior to that of the Syrian population of the Greek cities.

While the course of the establishment of the national state produced a persecution of Hellenism outside Judaea, this same process led to the opposite results within the country. From the time of Simon onward the sources are silent on the Hellenizers in Judaea; their history ended with the fall of the Akra, as has been noted (p. 239). This does not, however, mean that Hellenism thereby ceased to exist in the country. It ceased to exist as the political program of a party, but it remained a cultural phenomenon and the process of political organization itself served as an important factor in its diffusion. As long as the Jews had not issued from the confines of the Judaean hills, they were of no importance in the world of politics. Now, after the Hasmonean state had been founded, it was inevitable that the new power should come into political and cultural contact with the wide world—with Rome, Egypt, Syria and the rest. That world was a Hellenistic world, hence the Hasmonean kingdom was destined to become a Hellenistic state.

The reign of Simon already reveals the lines of a new epoch. The coronation decree of Simon (I Macc. 13.27ff.), although it was a decision of "the Great Assembly," bears the stamp of a pronouncedly Hellenistic influence. It is sufficient to draw attention to the external splendor bestowed upon the High Priest ("he shall put on purple and cloth of gold"), and to the reckoning of the era by the year of his priesthood ("and let all the bills of the country be registered in his name": *ib.* 14.43). It is of special interest that Simon earned the praise of the Keneset because he "had spent much money of his own and had armed the warriors of his nation and given them fee" (*ib.* 32)—the typical praise accorded to a Hellenistic king who stands above the state and extends aid to his subjects out of his generosity and humanitarian feelings.[21]

In the eyes of the outer world, too, Simon was an independent prince of Hellenistic type; Antiochus VII of Syria granted him permission to mint coins of his own (I Macc. 15.6), a right given only to free Greek cities and to vassal princes of independent standing. It is to be remarked, indeed, that Simon was not actually able to utilize this privilege, if we may judge from the negative evidence of numismatics.[22] Simon's great wealth, the gold and silver utensils which were appointed for use at his court, and the entire brilliance of his new state, amazed the envoy of Antiochus not a little and angered the king himself (*ib.* 32ff.). Not only Simon, but his family were known for their wealth; thus it is reported of Ptolemy son of Ḥabub, Simon's general, that he possessed an abundance of silver and gold plate, "for he was the son-in-law of the High Priest"—as I Maccabees naïvely remarks (16.11). It is clear then that the sons of the Hasmoneans had no sooner ceased to be leaders of the nation in rebellion, or officials of the Seleucids, than they drew all the political conclusions arising from their independent status and appeared before their subjects crowned with Hellenistic splendor, just as did most of the petty monarchs who set up their kingdoms on the ruins of the disintegrating Seleucid empire.[23]

The following details will make the situation a good deal clearer. John Hyrcanus was the first to import mercenaries from abroad for his army (*Ant.* XIII, 249). This was characteristic of the epoch; with the exception of Rome, all the states of those days utilized mercenary troops. The practice did not arise from lack of local forces, since the Jewish population of Palestine, although it was small, could furnish Hyrcanus with some thousands of troops, and the wars of Judah the Maccabee showed conclusively that the peasants of Judaea were not inferior in military prowess to the Syrians. The need of bringing mercenaries from abroad arose from the desire of the rulers to bind the army with strong and direct bonds to their own persons. This was the practice everywhere. In the Hellenistic world the ruler stood above the state which he ruled, as a personal power independent of the population, and this power was based mainly on formations of mercenaries who received permanent pay from the ruler and were alien to the local people and to the affairs of the state.

Josephus reports (*Ant. ib.*) that Hyrcanus obtained the money to pay his army in a strange way: by opening the tomb of King David and taking from it 3000 talents of silver. It is hard to know what this treasure really was, but it is at any rate clear that this was not regular money received by the ruler from the people in the form of taxes or other revenue, but some peculiar source concealed from general knowledge, of which Hyrcanus had gained control by force or fraud. This manner of finding money was also typical of the period, for Hellenistic rulers took money whenever they could, not always in lawful fashion.

By these two acts—the hiring of foreign troops and the plundering of David's tomb—Hyrcanus marked the beginning of the rift between himself and the people. The rule of Judah the Maccabee and his brothers had sprung directly from the national awakening which had swept the nation during the persecution of Antiochus and the government of the Hellenizers. The first Hasmoneans were national leaders and part of the people itself. Now the dynasty faced the people as an independent power, and the question was whether the two could find a common language.

Alexander Jannaeus continued his father's policy. He took natives of Pisidia and Cilicia as mercenaries (*Ant.* XIII, 374), and as their military training—and perhaps also their language—was Greek, it looked as if a Greek army was commanded by the Jewish High Priest. Josephus, in telling of the war between Alexander Jannaeus and King Demetrius Eukairos, mentions the Syrian king's attempt to bring Alexander's mercenaries over to his side "because they were Greeks" (*Ant.* XIII, 387). Thus the army of the Hasmoneans developed the normal Hellenistic character, and probably the local Jewish force at their disposal was also armed on the Greek model; while war was waged by them according to the military theory accepted in that period throughout the Hellenistic world.

The life of the court was also fashioned on the model of the court life of the Hellenistic monarchies. In their private lives the Hasmoneans were very far from the austerity and stateliness befitting a Jewish High Priest. Nor is this surprising, for they were primarily military leaders who spent most of their time fighting, and the life of the camp neither was nor could be austere or stately. The Hasmoneans did the same as all the other monarchs of their time, having drinking parties, taking mistresses in addition to their lawful wives, and persecuting those of their relatives whom they suspected for personal or political reasons. Simon was killed by a member of his family during a banquet when he and his sons were drunk (I Macc. 16.15); Aristobulus confined his mother and brother in prison, and his mother perished there of hunger (*Ant.* XIII, 302); his brother Antigonus was put to death on his orders (*ib.* XIII, 303ff.). Alexander Jannaeus, according to the same account, sat at a banquet with his mistresses while the executioners were crucifying his vanquished opponents in front of him (*Ant.* XIII, 380). If some of the details of these stories can be doubted, the picture as a whole is certainly authentic: the Hasmonean rule was a secular rule, hence the life of the court was secular also, possessing no higher a level than that of the courts of Antioch or of the kings of Asia Minor.

Furthermore, the first coins of the Hasmoneans bear only a Hebrew inscription; but from the time of Alexander Jannaeus a Greek inscription also appears on the coins along with the Hebrew.[24] The Hasmoneans possessed double names: besides their Jewish, they had Greek names, and these—Hyrcanus, Aristobulus, Alexander and Antigonus—prevailed over the Hebrew appellations even in the memory of the Jewish people itself. The followers of the Hasmoneans also adopted them: Simon's son-in-law, who murdered him, was called Ptolemy, and the envoys sent by Jonathan to Rome were Numenius son of Antiochus and Antipater son of Jason (I Macc. 12.16). Aristobulus, the first to call himself king,[25] also copied the Hellenistic sovereigns by choosing a special soubriquet for himself, and it is characteristic that this king, who forced the Ituraeans to become converted to Judaism, called himself *Philhellen*—lover of the Greeks.[26]

Thus the Hasmoneans went the way of Hellenization and began to resemble the normal type of Hellenistic monarch; Herod later trod the same road and trod it to the end. It may be assumed that the Hasmoneans too might have played down the nationalist side of their policy in favor of international Hellenism, had they been free to act as they chose, but they were not, for from the time of John Hyrcanus they encountered strong opposition from the Pharisees, whose party fought obdurately against the secular monarchy of Alexander Jannaeus and finally, under Queen Salome Alexandra, victoriously put an end to the Hellenistic aspirations of the Hasmoneans.

This is not the place for a detailed discussion of the two parties of the Pharisees and the Sadducees, an important subject which demands a special study. Many have treated the question, yet even today it is hard to state that all the problems associated with the struggle of sects in Israel have been solved.[27] The sources describe the conflict between them in various ways. Josephus on one occasion speaks of them as philosophical schools preoccupied with questions of religion and ethics; on another as political-social parties struggling for power.[28] In talmudic literature (the Mishnah and Tosephta), the conflict assumes the character of differences of opinion between scholars on various questions of religion and law.[29]

These accounts do not in fact contradict one another; for this sectarian strife lasted more than two hundred years and quite naturally took various forms at various periods. Under the Hasmoneans the quarrel between the Pharisees and Sadducees was mainly political, and two strong parties, each supported by certain social strata, fought for power in the state. Herod put an end to the independent political life of the Jewish community, and henceforward anyone desiring to engage in politics was forced to tread the path of revolution. This road was taken by the "left" wing of the Pharisees, the Zealots, who under Herod split off from the former and founded an independent sect, while the Pharisees themselves gave up interfering in affairs of state and restricted themselves to activity within the walls of the schools. The Sadducees also, whose political power had been broken under the last Hasmoneans by Rome and Herod, now turned their attention to questions of religion and law. The parties appeared again as political forces for the last time during the Jewish war with Rome (66-70 C.E.), but their role was restricted and, after the end of the struggle, the Sadducees quit the stage of history for good. Nor did the Pharisees reconstitute their sect as such, but were lost among the general body of scholars and interpreters of the Torah.

Our sources (Josephus, the Mishnah and Tosephta, the Gospels) are familiar with the sects only in their last period, so that the entire well-known account of their characteristics to be found in there belongs to the first century of the present era. What was the character of the Pharisees and Sadducees under the Hasmoneans, and whether their late features may also be ascribed to the earlier period, are questions which still await solution. We should therefore be extremely cautious in utilizing late information, and adopt as our basic source only those reports which treat directly of the Hasmonean era.

Josephus alludes to these parties for the first time under Jonathan (*Ant.* XIII, 171), when they appear without connection with any particular historical event, nor is it clear why Josephus introduces them into his narrative.[30] The first detailed account of the sectarian dispute belongs to the period of John Hyrcanus (*Ant.* XIII, 288-298): the Jews, relates Josephus, were jealous of Jonathan's great success, the Pharisees in particular regarding him unfavorably. John himself was a pupil of the Pharisees, who held him in affection at the beginning of his reign. He once invited them to a banquet, during which he requested them to outline to him all his errors and transgressions. All praised him highly, and only one of the Pharisees, named Eleazar, rose and said: "If you desire to pursue the path of righteousness, you should give up the High Priesthood and content yourself with ruling the nation only." On John inquiring what the reason for this demand was, Eleazar replied: "We have heard from the old men that you were born while your mother was a captive in the days of Antiochus." This was a falsehood, and John, enraged with Eleazar, demanded of the Pharisees that they punish him. The latter sentenced Eleazar to stripes, a sentence which Hyrcanus thought too light, for in his view it should have been that of death. The Sadducees, who had long hated the Pharisees, exploited the quarrel to alienate Hyrcanus from the Pharisees, proving to the king, from the fact that they had not seen fit to punish him as he desired, that Eleazar had expressed the opinion of all the Pharisees. Hyrcanus, enraged against the Pharisees, drew away from them and went over to the Sadducees.

The same story is told again in the Talmud (Kidd. 66a). It resembles Josephus' account in its main lines, except that John Hyrcanus' name is here replaced by that of Jannaeus, the leader of the Pharisees being called not Eleazar but Judah, and Eleazar being named as the leader of the Sadducees. The talmudic tale, like that of Josephus, is connected with a banquet held by the king for his guests. "And there was there a jester with an evil heart, a masterless man, called Eleazar ben Poirah. And he said to King Jannaeus: "O King! The Pharisees have set their hearts against thee!"—"And what should I do?"—"Rise up against them with the blossom that is between thine eyes" (meaning, test their loyalty with the symbol of the High Priesthood which the High Priest wore on his forehead). This he did. There was present an old man called Judah ben Yedidyah, who said to King Jannaeus: "King Jannaeus! Thou hast enough with the royal crown, leave the crown of priesthood to the seed of Aaron!"—For they said that his mother had been a captive at Modiin, and this was inquired into and not found (true), and the scholars of Israel were furious in their disagreement. And Eleazar ben Poirah said to King Jannaeus: "This is the sentence when a simple Jew in Israel is offended, but thou art king and High Priest, is this then a fit sentence?"—"And what shall I do?"—"If thou wilt hearken to my council, trample them under foot!"—"And what will happen to the Torah?"—"It will be wrapped up and laid in a corner, and all who wish to study it, let them come and study."[31]

The story transmits the important historical event in the form of an interesting anecdote. We are not in a position to judge how far its details are authentic, but the fact of the rift between Hyrcanus and the Pharisees is not itself in doubt. Josephus relates that, immediately after the split, Hyrcanus abolished all the laws which the Pharisees had given to the people. Josephus takes the opportunity of explaining to his readers the basic differences between the Phari-

sees and the Sadducees: "The Pharisees had given many laws
to the nation, based on ancestral tradition which had not been
written in the laws of Moses; whereas the Sadducean sect
opposed this, saying that only the written laws should be observed, not those arising from ancestral tradition." Josephus
adds that on this issue great conflicts took place between the two
groups, and only the wealthy followed the Sadducees, whereas
the people joined the Pharisees.

These observations provide
a profound explanation of what is related in the anecdote, showing that here was no chance quarrel which had broken out at
the royal court owing to the discourtesy of a guest at a banquet,
but the perpetuation of the ancient feud between the priests
and the scribes, whose social character we have discussed in
previous chapters.[32]

What did the Pharisees de-
mand of Hyrcanus? According to the accounts in Josephus and
the Talmud, the Pharisees asked him to give up the High Priesthood and to be content with the secular power which he possessed. They based their demand on the pretext that he had
been born to his mother when she was in captivity. "This was
a falsehood," says Josephus, and we may concur.[33] What then
was the real reason for their strange demand? According to
Aptowitzer, one of the reasons was that Hyrcanus had taken
the crown, and many could not countenance this because the
Jewish throne belonged to the house of David.[34]

But had this been so, the
Pharisees would have demanded that Hyrcanus give up the
secular power and remain High Priest as before, whereas they
demanded just the opposite. Aptowitzer also argues that the
Pharisees could not consent that the High Priesthood be held
by men whose hands were stained with blood.[35] But the Law
of Moses had never prohibited offensive war against idolators,
however cruel, while the forcible Judaization of the Palestinian
population which had been carried out by the Hasmoneans,
is likely to have won nothing but approbation from the Pharisees.
It seems that we have to seek other reasons to account for their
political stand and for their negative attitude to the Hasmonean
methods of government.

Josephus indicates that the
people sided with the Pharisees; nor need this information be
doubted, for it is confirmed by the whole course of events in
the Hasmonean period. The first rift between the Pharisees and

the Hasmoneans under Hyrcanus apparently caused a popular rebellion: Josephus mentions very briefly that Hyrcanus suppressed the rising, but gives no details of the facts (*Ant.* XIII, 299; cf. *War* I, 67).

The dissident movement spread under Alexander Jannaeus and finally assumed the form of a prolonged and obstinate war. On one occasion when the king appeared at the Feast of Tabernacles at the Temple, those assembled pelted him with their *ethrogim*, shouting that he was unworthy to be High Priest. Alexander put down the rising and slew 6000 people. Some time afterward a rebellion again broke out, and Alexander fought for six years against his own countrymen, the number of slain—if we may believe Josephus' figures—exceeding 50,000. The rebels appealed to the Syrian king Demetrius, thus converting the internal struggle into a foreign war in which the Syrians participated. Alexander was defeated, his entire political fortunes were in jeopardy. With difficulty he was able to effect a recovery and to punish the insurgents. But even when he was victorious, it was a profitless victory. Before his death he realized that the dynasty could not maintain its position if the masses were to support its foes; he counseled his wife Salome Alexandra to come to terms with the Pharisees, and after his decease the queen carried out his advice, so that the Pharisees again obtained control of matters of religion and law and, in consequence, the opportunity of directly influencing the course of affairs in the state.

It is thus a historical fact that fifty to sixty years, approximately, after Judah the Maccabee, the alliance between the people and the Hasmoneans broke down. What caused the nation to transfer its allegiance to the foes of the dynasty, and why did it sympathize with the Pharisees who fought against it, and not with the Sadducees who were its supporters? The answer is not difficult to give, if we transfer the question from a political to a social setting. Unfortunately we lack historical sources reporting the economic situation of the broad sectors of the people and the social relationships between the various categories of the Jewish community under the Hasmoneans. We know nothing of the scale of taxation, of the condition of the rural population of Judaea, or of the commercial development of the country. Nevertheless, we can conjecture that the Hasmonean conquests furnished the men of capital with an easy opportunity for enrichment: for the generals grew wealthy on booty and plunder, the landowners by acquiring more land, the moneylenders by investing their capital, and the merchants from the trade which began to develop between the Jews and the Greek world.

But it is an open question how far the lower orders of the nation profited from the new policy of the Hasmoneans. In Herod's reign things were to reach the point where the state authority weighed grievously upon the people, taxation grew intolerable, the small man's property was destroyed and the peasants fled to the hills, where robber-bands had their refuge.

We may well believe that the beginning of the process can be traced back to the period of the last Hasmonean kings. The policy of territorial acquisition exacted a heavy price, and if part of the outlay was obviously covered by the war itself (the plundering of enemy property, the selling of prisoners into slavery, and so on), it may be surmised that the other part of it fell upon the common people. About the Hasmoneans gathered the Jewish aristocracy, composed of the priests, high military officers, officials, large landowners, the men of wealth and influence. These enjoyed all the benefits of wealth, and it was they who governed the people. The distance between them and the small peasants of Judaea was no smaller than the distance between the wealthy and the humble in the days of Ben Sira. The foundation of the Jewish state brought about a very important change in the political position of the Jewish nation, but from the social point of view nothing had changed; or, if there was a change, it was for the worse.

As a century earlier, so now the Jewish public was divided into two sections, into the "wealthy" and the "humble," between whom enmity was daily growing. There is a work which furnishes us with an opportunity of gauging this enmity, for certain chapters of the *Book of Enoch* (84-95) date from the Hasmonean period, or, to be precise, from that of Alexander Jannaeus, and in these chapters the social hatreds of the epoch find their sharpest expression.[36] The writer speaks with fury of the wealthy who accumulate their wealth unrighteously, who oppress the poor and persecute the just (85:7; 86:8; 87:8-10); they trust in their riches, but their trust is in vain, for they are doomed to destruction on the day of judgment and God himself will rejoice at the fall of the wealthy (84:7-8; *ib.* 10). The evil mock the righteous, but on judgment day the just will ascend to heaven, while the evil will go down to hell (103:1ff.; 100:1ff.). God will wreak havoc among the wicked, and the righteous too will take part in the vengeance and slaughter their persecutors ruthlessly (88:12). The wealthy are also the evil and the "unbelievers." They transgress the laws of the Torah of Moses (89:2), and the author of this section has no hesitation in accusing his foes of actual idolatry (89:9; *ib.* 14).

If we compare these chapters of the *Book of Enoch* with the utterances of Ben Sira (see above, p. 142ff.), we shall see that in the course of a century class hatred had made huge strides. Ben Sira speaks of the negative attitude—an attitude of contempt and mockery—of the rich to the humble; Enoch speaks of persecution. Ben Sira counsels the humble man not to seek the society of the rich man; but Enoch advocates actual warfare. Ben Sira is still ready to believe that there is wealth that is free from crime; but in Enoch's eyes the wealthy and the criminal are identical. Ben Sira is apprehensive lest wealth lead the individual to religious transgression; whereas Enoch regards the rich as heathens who are fated to be destroyed by the sword. Ben Sira seeks ways of compromise; while Enoch only perceives the antagonisms. And if in Ben Sira's time it was still possible to hope that the inner feud between the two sections of the Jewish community might somehow be ended by peaceful accord, it was now clear that only open warfare could solve the problem.

The slogan chosen by the Pharisees testifies to their great skill in political tactics. "The royal crown is sufficient to you, leave the priestly diadem to the seed of Aaron!"—in these words the Talmud defines the Pharisean demands upon King Jannaeus. At first sight this demand did not detract from the power of the dynasty, for the Pharisees were ready to leave the royal crown—the army, foreign affairs, the court and the administration—in its hands; it was to concede only the Temple. In the eyes of the common man, far from the mysterious ways of high politics, this demand might well have been justified. Since the suspicion existed concerning the legitimate origin of the High Priest, and this infringed the commandments of the Law (Levit. 21.4; cf. M. Pesah. II, 9; *Ant.* III, 275; *C. Ap.* I, 35), it was not permissible to leave the Temple and its service in the hands of men who were unacceptable to God. The Pharisees here appeared in their customary guise—as interpreters of the Law and nothing more.

As to the secular power of the Hasmoneans, it is to be assumed that the brilliant victories of John Hyrcanus and Alexander Jannaeus found a sympathetic echo among the broad population, hence the Pharisees took care not to touch on that side of the question. But they knew very well that, if the Hasmoneans gave up the High Priesthood, they would forfeit their key position of authority over the people—the Temple, its treasures, its great revenues and its tremendous psychological influence over popular faith and imagination. For the Hasmonean state was a theocratic state, in which the royal title was in the nature of an ornament to impress foreigners and no more, a late emergence imitating Hellenistic practices, rather than the outcome of an internal popular development.

The historical tradition which formed the basis on which the Maccabees had established their rule was not the royal throne of the house of David, but the robes of the High Priesthood of the house of Zaddok. The Pharisees struck at precisely this vital point, declaring that the Hasmoneans did not belong to the Zaddokite family,[37] and thereby cut the historic ground from under their feet. For what profit would there be in the royal power, if the head of the nation could not appear in the Temple, garbed in the brilliant traditional splendor of the High Priest, as the authoritative and lawful intermediary between the nation and the Divinity? And how could "the King of the Jews" wage his wars if all the Temple revenues were to be controlled by someone else, or to be more precise, by the Pharisees? It should be remembered that in a theocratic polity the Temple treasure was also the treasure of the State.[38] The Hasmoneans, therefore, would have lost all their power and influence, both morally and materially, had they agreed to the Pharisee demand to give up the High Priesthood and "to be satisfied" with the royal crown.

We have to acknowledge the high political wisdom of the Pharisees in selecting a slogan which seemed to recognize the right of the Hasmoneans to rule the nation, yet constituted a potential death-blow to the new dynasty. It is clear that John Hyrcanus was aware from the outset what lay behind the Pharisees' insulting slogan, and was not prepared to countenance the destruction of the edifice raised by his father and by himself. He broke off his connections with the Pharisees and joined their enemies, the Sadducees. Thereby he renewed in Judaea the situation which had existed under the rule of the Hellenizers: the scribes (then the Hasidim, now the Pharisees) again ceased to be the authorized interpreters of the Law under the auspices of the government. And as a result the traditional bases of the Oral Law and the Written Law—on which the life of Judaea and Jerusalem was based in respect of law, justice, religious customs and actual mode of living—were undermined. The question of the "ancestral laws" again became topical.

Just as the Pharisees headed the people and guided them toward a definite political aim, so the Sadducees headed the other group and gathered about them the forces of the Jewish aristocracy. This group was chiefly political, supporting the Hasmoneans in their foreign policy, and the thirty years (from the end of the reign of John Hyrcanus to the beginning of the reign of Queen Salome Alexandra) during which they headed the government, were years of warfare and conquest. The national "imperialism" of the young state had their material and theoretical support. From this point of view Wellhausen was right when he remarked that of the two rival parties it was the Sadducees who deserved the name of the "national" party.[39]

The social basis of this party is fairly obvious. On several occasions Josephus mentions that only the wealthy and the aristocratic followed them, while the *Book of Enoch* also emphasizes their great wealth. Thus, they were great landowners, the priests, the courtiers and men of similar standing. No wonder that they supported foreign conquests, for the development of the state, the expansion of its frontiers, the capture of the seacoast which opened the way to trade, warfare itself, all brought substantial profit to the wealthy aristocratic class. Their social position resembled that of the Tobiads before them, and if it is true that the word "Sadducees" itself meant "sons of Zaddok,"[40] this is the external token linking the Sadducees with the Jerusalem aristocracy of the time prior to the Hasmonean revolt. The question in any case arises whether they did not resemble that aristocracy also in their attitude to Hellenism; they too may well have aspired to Hellenize the Jews.

The sources do not furnish sufficient material to enable us to say definitely whether or not this was the case; moreover, on this question they are apt to be misleading. Josephus in his books set forth the characteristics of the three sects; but he was writing for a Greek public and therefore endeavored to impart to them the character of philosophical schools. He compared the Pharisees to the Stoics (*Vita* 2) and the Essenes to the disciples of Pythagoras (*Ant.* XV, 371).

Thus it was bound to result that the third sect—that of the Sadducees—would resemble the followers of Epicurus.

The Sadducees appear as men without religion or morality in later talmudic literature, and in Enoch's eyes they were simply pagans. If these sources are to be relied on, it must be admitted that the Sadducees were Hellenists, even extreme Hellenists; and this view, indeed, sometimes appears in the literature on the subject.[41] However, the same sources themselves point in the opposite direction. The Sadducees, according to Josephus, did not acknowledge the Oral Law and recognized the authority of the Mosaic Law alone, showing that the Torah was sacred in their view probably no less than it was in the eyes of the Pharisees. Moreover, the rejection of all the laws not to be found in the Torah should logically have led to a special emphasis on the Mosaic Laws themselves. This was, in fact, the case: the Sadducees were rigorous in their application of the Law and their legal decisions were nearer to the written word of the Torah than were the views expressed by the Pharisees.[42]

The disputations between the Sadducees and the Pharisees in the Mishnah testify that the Sadducees (at least in the Roman period) knew the Pentateuchal commandments just as well as the Pharisees, and the fact that most of the priests of high family, in whose hands lay the whole Temple worship, belonged to the Sadducees is additional proof of the familiarity of the latter with questions of religion and cult. Hence there are insufficient grounds for regarding the Sadducees as freethinkers, *Apikursim* or Hellenists, and those scholars are correct who evaluate both parties as phenomena peculiar to Jewish historical development.

This does not mean, however, that the Sadducee sect arose out of a religious movement; belief in the Torah might have developed among them equally for other reasons, and it would be well briefly to examine how this development took place.

We have seen above (p. 124) that at the beginning of the period of the Second Temple the official interpretation of the Torah was in the hands of the priests, until for various reasons the monopoly of interpretation passed to the scribes. From the time of Simon the Just, the priests too recognized the scribal interpretations, and as a result completely neglected this activity. Even the Temple rites were now conducted under the supervision of the scribes. The Hellenistic reform for a time removed the scribes from power, but no other group took upon itself the task of legal interpretation, because the Torah itself ceased to be the fundamental law of the new *polis*. The first Hasmoneans restored the *status quo,* and the scribes (now the Pharisees) regained their important position as teachers and leaders of the people. The Jewish aristocracy, still suspected of sympathy with Hellenism, stood aside and took no part in the political policies of the High Priests.

And then came the great change: the Hasmoneans took the road of monarchy; the power of the High Priest became a secular authority; between the royal court and the Jerusalem aristocracy a *rapprochement* took place and consequently the Pharisees went over to the opposition. The new force to which the Pharisees turned to find support in their struggle with the dynasty was the people, which knew from experience the hardships involved in the organization of a new state and was ready to support any political force that promised it some improvement and relief in its economic life. The daily religious and legal life of the people was built on the Mosaic Law, and the Mosaic code was entirely in the hands of the Pharisees, who governed the broad sections of the population on the strength of it. How then could the Pharisees and the people be separated from one another?

In the view of the Sadducees the only way to do this was to wrest the Mosaic code from their opponents and thus abolish the Pharisaic monopoly of legal interpretation. This they did. Josephus relates that immediately after the dispute between the Pharisees and John Hyrcanus, John abolished the Pharisaic laws (*Ant.* XIII, 296). This was a dangerous action, for the abolition of the authoritative Pharisaic interpretations was apt to throw the religious and legal life of the nation into chaos. The Pharisees, indeed, made a mock of the Sadducees by pointing out that according to their proposal anyone was qualified to undertake the work of interpretation.[43] This, however, could not have been what the Sadducees really intended, since chaos in Torah-interpretation would have created chaos in political life and would ultimately have endangered the welfare of the kingdom. On the other hand, they could not undertake the work of interpretation themselves since they were not skilled in it. The way out of the dilemma was to declare the Mosaic Law to be a legal code that required no interpretation, as all had been said in it and everything in it was clear. Thus was born the new ideology: The Written as opposed to the Oral Law.[44]

Hence the positive attitude of the Sadducees to the Mosaic Law rose, not from any special religious feeling, but from political opposition to the legislative activity of the Pharisees. And the great difference between the two periods should be stated: a century before, in the time of the Tobiads, the aristocratic movement in Jerusalem had given rise to the aspiration to Hellenize the Jews and to abolish the Mosaic Law as the basis of national culture; now a movement of the same social groups had brought about the supreme acknowledgment of the Torah and thereby a strengthening of the national elements. There is, in fact, no resemblance between the Tobiads and the Sadducees. It is possible, of course, that the Sadducees, like the Hasmoneans, had adopted the superficial Hellenism of the Orient, called themselves by Greek names, spoke and read Greek and were prepared to associate with the Greeks during commercial or diplomatic intercourse. But there are no grounds for thinking that they intended a Hellenistic reform or sought to introduce Greek customs into Israel, nor did they see any need for this.

The Tobiads had dreamed that Judaea and Jerusalem would enjoy a spacious political future and had seen no other way of realizing their ambitions than by Hellenizing the Jews. The Sadducees worked in a different environment, in which it was clear that a "barbarian" state could also participate in the political life of the world at large without having to modify the bases of its traditional life. Every state of this sort, indeed, was apt to assume the form of a Hellenistic state; but this was a purely external garb, which had no effect on the people's real culture. To all appearances the two could be combined, and this may have been the Sadducee policy. They assisted the Hasmoneans in developing the secular elements of the young state and simultaneously decreed that the Mosaic Law was the eternal foundation of the nation's life and culture. Rallying round the Hasmonean sovereigns, who were not afraid to call themselves "Philhellenes," they nevertheless helped them fight the Greeks and to unite the country of the Jews. Their aim was *to build a Hellenistic state on a Jewish national foundation.*

This, however, was to prove impossible. Judaism and Hellenism were, as forces, each too peculiar to itself to be able to compromise within one country. A Hellenistic state could not be founded on the Jerusalem theocracy. A Jewish High Priest could not be a Hellenistic king, and the two conceptions had to be separated. This operation was carried out by Herod, who separated the monarchy from the priesthood and established a Hellenistic state; yet this state did not rest on a national foundation. The Pharisees also wished to make a distinction between the secular power and religious life; from Herod's time began the great work of the scholars which aimed to set the people's life on a solid basis of Hebrew tradition. They thus created the national foundation, but the life constructed on it was not political.

We have reached the end of the period which is the subject of this inquiry. In the year 64 B.C.E., Pompey came to Syria, and from the next year on begins the Roman period of Jewish history. But historical life knows no stops. The movements and aspirations which had arisen and developed among the Jewish people during the Hasmonean period continued to live their own lives in the new epoch as well, one element only being added to the complex of existing elements, namely, the strong and heavy hand of Rome. Hellenism persisted in the country also in the Roman period, flourishing anew in Syria and Palestine under Roman tutelage. Pompey, followed by Gabinius, rebuilt the Greek cities destroyed by the Hasmoneans and restored to them their autonomy. Herod erected his state on the ruins of that of the Hasmoneans; it was organized on a strictly Hellenistic model in every detail. New Greek towns were built in the country, and within the old Jewish cities—especially Jerusalem—rose theaters, amphitheaters and gymnasia in the Greek style. Power was gathered in the hands of Greeks and Hellenizing Jews; but simultaneously Hellenism ceased to be a problem of inner Jewish history; Hellenization assumed an individual form and no single Jewish party or group sought to draw Jews from their religion or propagate Hellenism among them by force.

The political period of Hellenization had passed and gone for good, only the cultural influence of Hellenism remaining. Generations of proximity to the Greeks had not passed over the Jews of Palestine without leaving considerable traces in their literature, language, law and all other aspects of their civilization. These questions, however, are beyond the theme of the present work and require a special study—or, to be exact, special studies. Since our aim has been to inquire into the material bases of Jewish history in the Hellenistic period, we may here conclude our survey of the Greeks and Hellenizers of Palestine.

part **II**

HELLENISTIC
CIVILIZATION
IN THE
DIASPORA

Part II

HELLENISTIC
CIVILIZATION
IN THE
DIASPORA

chapter **1**

POLITICAL HISTORY

"One country cannot support the Jews, because they are so numerous."[1] In this sentence Philo seeks to explain to his readers the reason for the great expansion of the Jews over the Graeco-Roman world in his day. There is no doubt that he had found the correct answer: even before the Hasmonean revolt Judaea was too small to contain the Jewish people, and in Philo's time, that is to say, in the first century of the present era, the Jewish inhabitants filled the whole of Palestine, and the country could not support them. But Philo's answer, which is correct for his period and explains the development of the Diaspora as the result of continual emigration from Palestine, does not resolve the question in respect of an earlier period and does not furnish the reasons for the Diaspora's origin and formation. The density of the population in Judaea was probably not felt before the third century,[2] whereas the Diaspora communities had existed long before that. The Aramaic papyri from Elephantine, a small fortress in Upper Egypt, which were discovered at the beginning of the present century, testify that even before the conquest of Egypt by the Persians (525 B.C.E.) a small colony of Jewish troops existed at that place and continued its independent life for generations, still existing in approximately the year 400.[3]

The discovery of these papyri has thrown a new light on one piece of literary information, whose value scholars had not previously properly estimated.

269

I refer to a passage in the *Letter of Aristeas*, which speaks of Jews who had come to Egypt in the time of the Egyptian King Psamtik, to aid him in his wars with the Ethiopians, and of other Jews who later arrived with the Persians.[4] This Psamtik (the second of the name, as the first did not fight the Ethiopians) reigned from 594 to 589 B.C.E.; a Greek inscription from Abu Simbel (not far from Elephantine) shows that the king's force was composed of Greeks, Egyptians and other peoples recorded in the inscriptions under the term of *alloglossoi*, "speakers of foreign languages." These foreign peoples were Semites, and names incised on the stone near the Greek inscription are written in Phoenician letters.[5] If we assemble these three pieces of information—the Semitic peoples in Psamtik's force, Aristeas' remark on the Jews who helped Psamtik to fight the Ethiopians, and the existence of a military colony of Jews at Elephantine—we shall probably not be wrong in assuming that the colony at Elephantine was founded by the Jews who had fought in Psamtik's army, and that its object was to protect the southern frontier of Egypt against Ethiopian invasion. The beginning of the Egyptian diaspora therefore goes back to the years 594-589, that is, to the stormy period which preceded the destruction of the kingdom of Judaea, when conditions of life in Judaea probably changed for the worse and caused many young Jews to leave the country to seek their fortune and livelihood in mercenary service.

The national catastrophe itself awakened a new wave of migration to Egypt. Jeremiah (41.16) tells of the "remnants of the nation"—"mighty men of war, women, children and eunuchs"—who were preparing to go down to Egypt. As is well known, they carried out their intention, although Jeremiah opposed the migration on principle (41-44). The emigrants settled at Migdal and Taḥpanḥes (Lower Egypt) and at Patros (in Upper Egypt) (Jer. 44.1). Thus Jews spread over the whole of the country of Egypt from the frontier of Egypt to the Mediterranean coast. Their number was probably not large, and there are grounds for thinking that most of them became assimilated with the Egyptians.[6] In those days Egypt was not yet the center of the Diaspora, which was of course Babylonia, whence came the third wave of migration. If Aristeas' first report on the Jews under Psamtik's command has received confirmation from inscriptions, there is no reason to suspect his second, on the Jews who came to Egypt with the Persians. This may have been in the year 525, when Cambyses conquered Egypt and annexed it to the Persian kingdom. The details of this migration are unknown to us; Aristeas says that the migrants were "numerous," which may also be true.[7]

If we sum up the above information, we shall see that the western diaspora of Egypt originated approximately at the same time as the eastern of Babylonia, and both for the same reason, namely, the destruction of the Jewish state. All the other causes (including the one mentioned by Philo, which was the most important) began to operate only as time went on, after the soil had already been prepared for Jewish emigration by the first and fundamental cause. On the other hand, it should be remembered that the Jewish diaspora in Egypt before the Hellenistic period was small and had no cultural value in the Jewish world. These small military colonies are not to be compared with the large and dense population of the Jews of Babylonia, among whom original cultural forces were at work and whence went out the call "to establish the land; to cause to inherit the desolate heritages" (Isaiah 49.8).

Even before Judaea became a place from which Jews emigrated to other countries, Babylonia had fulfilled this task: apart from the Babylonian Jews who went down to Egypt with the Persians, there were the two thousand Jewish families transferred by Antiochus III from Babylon to Asia Minor (see below). The situation changed only gradually. During the fifth century, Judaea filled up with Jewish inhabitants who had returned from Babylonia, and in the Hellenistic period Palestinian Jews came into frequent contact with the western countries. From that time on the western Diaspora began to expand with great rapidity and, together with Palestine, Jewish Egypt occupied an important place in the cultural life of the Jewish people, while the Babylonian exile dropped out of sight for a long time, to reappear on the stage of history only in the talmudic era, after the state of Israel had lost the last remnants of liberty and independence.

In keeping with the theme of the present book, we shall describe the Jewish Diaspora in the Hellenistic countries only. Western Europe—Italy, Sicily, Spain, etc.—will remain outside the geographical limits set for this work, as also will the oriental lands of Babylonia, Persia and the rest, excepting the Greek cities founded there in the Hellenistic epoch. Here, as in the foregoing section, we shall endeavor not to transgress the chronological limits of the Hellenistic period. But in the Diaspora the transition from one period to the next was not associated with an important historical event, as it was in Palestine, where it was marked by the destruction of the Hasmonean state; hence the historian may legitimately derive the information he needs from the early Roman period as well (down to the end of the first century C.E.), insofar as conclusions may be drawn from it concerning the preceding epoch.

We will commence with Egypt. There is no clear information on the first stages of Jewish emigration from Palestine to Egypt in the Hellenistic period. Josephus ascribes the beginning of the process to the time of Alexander himself, who in his opinion gave the Jews permission to settle in Alexandria on a basis of equality of rights with the Greeks; this favor they received in return for their loyalty to him (*War* II, 487; *C. Ap.* II, 35). We shall see below that these reports of Josephus are not to be relied on, for they have a clear apologetic motive, and were composed at a late period without a basis in exact historical sources.

Two important sources of the Hellenistic period—Aristeas and Hecataeus—know nothing of Jewish migration to Egypt under Alexander. Aristeas relates that the Jews came to Egypt (a) under Psamtik, (b) with the Persians and (c) under Ptolemy I; he passes over Alexander's period in silence, whence a conclusion may be drawn in respect of Hecataeus also, since Aristeas had read Hecataeus (Arist. 31), and if he nevertheless knew nothing of the Jewish immigration into Egypt under Alexander, it is a sign that he did not find it in his source. The citations preserved from Hecataeus in Josephus also confirm this assumption.[8] Juster believed that various inscriptions definitely proved the existence of a Jewish settlement in Alexandria at the time of the foundation of the city and that they confirmed Josephus' assumptions.[9] But this is not the case; the inscriptions do indeed date from an early period in the city's existence, but there is no clear proof that they are of Alexander's time.[10] The idea of connecting Alexander and the Jews served the apologetic motive excellently, but had no real historical foundation. Josephus' report (*Ant.* XI, 345) that the Samaritans accompanied Alexander to Egypt and were settled there as troops and farmers in the Thebais is equally without basis, being derived from the Samaritan story about Alexander and Sanballat, which is devoid of any historical value.[11] Greater importance attaches to the Jewish immigration to Egypt under Ptolemy I (323-283). We have seen above

(p. 55f.) that two different traditions existed concerning the conquest of Palestine by Ptolemy. According to the one preserved by Hecataeus, the Jews, headed by their High Priest Hezekiah, followed Ptolemy voluntarily; according to the second (that of Agatharchides and Aristeas) Ptolemy was a "hard master" to the Jews and brought to Egypt multitudes of captives from Jerusalem. Of these two traditions, only the second is important for the question of the mass migration of Jews into Egypt.[12]

Aristeas (12-14) tells of 100,000 Jewish captives brought to Egypt in the time of Ptolemy I; 30,000 of these, men of military age, Ptolemy placed in fortresses, and the rest (old men and children) he gave to his soldiers as slaves. Ptolemy II Philadelphus, on ascending the throne, freed them from slavery. There are no grounds for doubting the historical trustworthiness of this tale, and it is very credible that as a result of his wars in Palestine—especially after the capture of Jerusalem—Ptolemy took numerous Jews prisoner and brought them to Egypt as slaves. The information that some of them were placed in fortresses to protect the country now evokes no skepticism.[13] There are, however, sufficient grounds for doubting the large figure of 100,000 captives, for such a large number of prisoners would have meant the complete destruction of Palestinian Jewry.[14] It may therefore be accepted as a historical fact that the Jewish diaspora in Hellenistic Egypt began under Ptolemy I, and that the vast majority of the Jews left their native country not of their free will but under compulsion.

Under Ptolemy II Philadelphus (283-246) the Egyptian priest Manetho wrote his book on Egyptian history. In it he also touched on the Jews, in a not very sympathetic manner, and his book is justly regarded as the first expression of literary anti-Semitism. To write of the Jews the author must have known both them and the Jewish tradition concerning the Exodus;[15] so it follows that at that time the Jews of Egypt were already numerous. According to Aristeas a very important event had occurred in the life of the Jewish population of the country under Philadelphus: the king purchased from their owners the Jews who had been taken prisoner in the days of his father Ptolemy I and set them free. Those Jews who had come to Egypt before the Hellenistic period now also obtained their liberty. To validate this statement Aristeas furnishes a copy of the royal order officially setting forth the details of the project (22-24). This order was regarded by scholars of the last generation as a forgery, but comparison of the text with papyrological documents has revolutionized the appreciation of the order (as it has revolutionized the appreciation of a number of other documents) and scholars of standing, such as Wilcken and Wilhelm, have expressed views in favor of its authenticity.[16] Indeed, several details in the document itself testify to its genuineness, such as its language, which is typical of the Ptolemaic government offices, the reference to Ptolemaic Syria by its correct title—"Syria and Phoenicia" (see below, p. 428, n. 55)—the fixing of a definite date for the submission of the list of prisoners, and more.[17] On the other hand, there are details in the order that arouse suspicion of falsification, such as Philadelphus' open rebuke of the acts of his late father's troops, the special mention of the liberation of those Jews brought to Egypt after Ptolemy I's reign, and particularly the huge number of Jewish prisoners who were liberated.[18]

Probably, therefore, in this instance, as in several others, scholars have gone too far in declaring the absolute authenticity of the document (in healthy reaction to those who had declared it to be a complete forgery); the correct solution lies in between; the document is basically genuine, but has probably been worked over here and there and by a Jewish forger.[19] If this approach is adopted, we may regard the liberation of the Jewish captives by Philadelphus as a historical fact, although we shall not accept Aristeas' figures as approximating the truth. The document is evidence of the growing influence of Egyptian Jewry—particularly, one may suppose, of the Jewish community of Alexandria—and of the relations of sympathy that had begun to spring up between the Jews and the royal court. These relationships were to bear full fruit in the reign of Ptolemy VI Philometor, some hundred years after Philadelphus' day.

No literary sources survive from the time of Ptolemy III Euergetes (246-221). The *Third Book of Maccabees* ascribes to his son's, Ptolemy IV Philopator's, time (221-205) the attempt to carry out a pogrom with regard to the Jews of Alexandria. This book has already been referred to in connection with the events in Palestine after the battle of Raphia (above, p. 74), and we have seen that it is merely a historical romance whose aims are very far from those of a historical document designed to tell the truth. Ptolemy Philopator is here described as an irascible sovereign who decided, come what might, to enter the Holy of Holies, and was punished for this sin by God. The romance, continuing, takes its readers to Egypt, where Philopator, angry with the Jews of Jerusalem, decided to vent his wrath on the Jews of his own country. He issued a command obliging them to acknowledge the cult of Dionysus, and whoever refused to obey was to be enslaved. The Jews, of course, refused to bow down to the gods.[20]

Thereupon the king assembled all the Jews of Egypt into the stadium of Alexandria and determined to cast them at the feet of drunken elephants. He first sought to ascertain the number of Jews, but found this to be impossible; for forty days the scribes recorded the names of the imprisoned Jews and could not complete the work because there were no more pens left in Egypt. For three days and three nights the Jews in the stadium awaited their day of tribulation. Finally the elephants were brought out, while the king and his court prepared to enjoy the gory spectacle. But at the last moment a miracle occurred: the elephants turned from the victims and fell upon the spectators. Thus the evil decree was annulled; the king repented of his design; and the Jews, having taken vengeance upon those of their brethren who had proved disloyal, returned to their homes with merrymaking and rejoicing and made the day of their salvation a festival for future generations.

Scholars differ on the question whether or not there is a grain of historical truth in this tale.[21] Most of them have rightly discovered the historical nucleus in the persecution of the Jews by Ptolemy VIII Euergetes II, a report of which is preserved by Josephus. We shall see later that Euergetes II had sufficient grounds not to love his Jewish subjects, and since the story in Josephus resembles our story here in one important detail (the sending of drunken elephants against the Jews), it is reasonable to assume that this historical episode served the author of the book as a model. The events in *III Maccabees* do not belong, then, to the time of Ptolemy IV Philopator, and the time of the book's composition indicates that its author was not familiar with events of the third century, the book apparently having been written at the beginning of the Roman period, when the question of civic rights discussed in it was acutely and particularly current. To this question we shall return in the next chapter.[22]

We may pass over the period of Ptolemy V Epiphanes (205-181), which left no trace in Jewish annals, and turn to the reign of Ptolemy VI Philometor (181-145) in whose days began the flourishing period of Jewish history in Egypt. One event—the building of the Temple of Onias—

275

is looked upon by scholars as the central event of the epoch and all historians, from Josephus down to the modern scholars, devote some attention to it. This event should therefore be examined with a view to ascertaining how far it deserves such special notice.

Josephus mentions the building of this Temple four times, and it is a pity that he did not do so only once, but with sufficient clarity and without contradicting himself. The principal contradiction is that, according to the account in his *War* (I, 33; VII, 423), the Temple was founded by Onias III, the High Priest of Jerusalem, who allegedly fled to Egypt during the persecution by Antiochus, whereas according to the account in *Antiquities* (XIII, 62ff.; XII, 387), this was the work, not of Onias III, but of his son Onias IV. The latter stayed in Judaea throughout the rule of the Hellenizers in the hope that a day would ultimately come when he would be appointed High Priest. When he saw Alcimus appointed after the death of Menelaus, he despaired of his hope and removed to Egypt. This happened in the years 162-160. The views of modern scholars differ according to which of these different versions they favor. Willrich constructs his account solely on the narrative in the *War*,[23] regarding Onias III as a statesman and soldier who, seeing the desecration of the Jerusalem Temple by Antiochus Epiphanes, determined to found another shrine in Egypt to replace it. His flight to Egypt was a political act, as he brought Ptolemy troops and dreamed of a military alliance between the Jews and the king of Egypt. Only Onias III, then in the prime of life—thinks Willrich—could have played so important a part in the political world, as opposed to his son Onias IV, who was then a young boy lacking all experience in politics. Although Willrich's view has not won general agreement, some scholars of repute still follow him.[24]

Against Willrich and his supporters it should first be stated that this view utterly rejects the historical worth of II Maccabees, according to which Onias III was killed at Daphne near Antioch and did not flee to Egypt.[25] Secondly, Josephus himself, in his *Antiquities*, describes Onias IV as the founder of the shrine, and as he wrote that book after he had written the *War*, it is to be supposed that he was purposely correcting his previous error. Thirdly, no conclusion may be drawn from the ages of the father and son, since we do not know how old they were when the shrine was built: Onias III may have been an old man, and his son not young at all, as

Josephus says, but actually in the prime of life. It is worth remembering that Onias appears as an Egyptian general after the death of Philometor in 145, in other words, some twenty years after his arrival in Egypt. This is more appropriate to the age of the younger Onias. Fourthly, Willrich is confident that Onias fled to Egypt with the full intention of founding a new shrine to take the place of the one that had been desecrated, the whole affair being of political significance. This is only true on condition that the founder of the temple was really Onias III the High Priest, and a man wielding political influence—but this fact remains to be proved.

To sum up, Willrich's conjectures cannot stand up under criticism, and the inquiry into the question of the Temple of Onias must be based, not on the corrupt reports in the *War*, but on the clearer account in the *Antiquities*.[26]

Even there not everything is clear. According to *Antiquities* XII, 387, Onias fled to Egypt after Menelaus' death, in other words, between 162 and 160 approximately. In those years the Temple of Jerusalem was again the religious center of Judaism, the worship therein being in the traditional form, and even the Ḥasidim acknowledged Alcimus as the official High Priest (see above, p. 229f.). The desecration of the Jerusalem shrine could not, therefore, have been Onias' reason for building a second shrine. Josephus, understanding this, gives two other reasons in the *Antiquities*, namely, that Onias decided to build the temple because he desired to acquire a reputation and in order that his memory should be perpetuated; further, "that the Jews of Egypt should be able to pray for the welfare of the king when they gathered in this temple, with a feeling of mutual solidarity . . ." (*Ant.* XIII, 63, 67).

Let us first examine the second motive. Josephus introduces it into Onias' forged letter to Philometor (*ib.* 66-68) and if we remove from the aforementioned sentence the reference to the king made for reasons of political etiquette, we shall find that Onias' object was to set up a temple for the needs of Egyptian Jewry, so that they should have a religious center of their own.

At first sight there is nothing impossible in this reason; but if we examine the details of the matter and the general historical situation, we shall see that it is not in keeping with historical reality. If Onias had wanted to set up a religious center for Egyptian Jewry, he would inevitably have done so at Alexandria, the place of the largest Jewish population, or at least at Memphis, but not at Leontopolis, a remote village of the Heliopolite nome, 180 stades (about 22 miles) from Memphis, and never a center of Egyptian Jewry.[27] Moreover, if we assume that Onias founded the shrine for them, this means that they had need of it; yet all we know of the Jewish diaspora in Egypt points in the opposite direction. In the whole of Judaeo-Alexandrian literature there is no trace of Onias' temple;[28] even the name is found only in Josephus. On the other hand, several pages full of enthusiastic admiration are devoted to the Temple of Jerusalem, it being sufficient to mention the *Letter of Aristeas, III Maccabees,* Philo's writings, and other works. Throughout the Hellenistic period the Jews of Egypt visited the Jerusalem Temple as pilgrims, and this was the case also, without doubt, in Onias' time, after the annulment of the decrees of Antiochus and the restoration of the divine cult at Jerusalem. It cannot be assumed that Onias did not know of this attitude on the part of Egyptian Jewry, which reverenced the tradition of its fathers, and it is hard to imagine that he found support among the broad sections of the Jews of Egypt when he was about to do something so obviously opposed to Jewish tradition.

A further fact should be noted: the Temple of Onias was built on the site of the shrine of the Egyptian goddess Bubastis, or, more correctly, within this ancient sanctuary itself, after it had been repaired and rearranged for the needs of the new cult—a place quite unsuited for the needs of the worship of the God of Israel.[29] Are we really to believe that a temple such as this was welcome to the Jews of the Egyptian diaspora and was built at their demand?

If Onias did not intend to build a temple to compete with that of Jerusalem, nor to create a religious center for the Jews of Egypt—why did he build it?

Let us endeavor to solve this riddle by analyzing the sources. In Onias' forged letter to Philometor the former refers to his participation in war on the king's side.[30] After Philometor's death (145), Cleopatra being threatened by Euergetes and the people of Alexandria, Onias entered the city "at the head of a small force" to bring aid to the queen; this is testified to by Apion, who is mentioned by Josephus (*C. Ap.* II, 50). Josephus says in passing that Onias built a fortress in the Leontopolitan district (where the temple had also been set up), the land about the shrine being called "Onias' territory" (*War* I, 190; *Ant.* XIV, 131). The inhabitants of the region were Jews who also fulfilled a military role later, in the time of Julius Caesar. They guarded the route from Pelusium to Memphis; and when Antipater, father of Herod, was hastening to Caesar's help, he had to enter into diplomatic negotiations with these Jews in order to bring them over to his side (*War, ib.; Ant., ib.*). In the vicinity was a place known as "the Jewish camp" (*War* I, 191; *Ant.* XIV, 133), probably the *castra Iudaeorum* mentioned in late sources.[31]

All these reports add up to one picture: Onias was a warrior and a general of the Ptolemies; a Jewish force of some size was under his command and was permanently encamped in the Leontopolis district, where the troops dwelt as *katoikoi* when they were not needed for a campaign. When was this *katoikia* founded? Two answers are possible: either this occurred immediately after Onias' arrival in Egypt, the settlers being people who had come to the country with him, or the settlement was carried out several years later, when Onias had gained a reputation as a good general and had successfully gathered about him a Jewish force of a certain military value.

The second possibility seems more acceptable to the writer. For, as we have already seen, the Jewish colony at Leontopolis possessed an outstandingly military character, and even if we assume further that a certain number of men who followed Onias from Palestine were of military age, it is hard to imagine that they constituted a force ready and trained in all the rules of combat of the Hellenistic period. A force of this type, capable of awakening the interest of King Philometor and his court, was then nonexistent among the Jews of Palestine, where Jewish forces only began to be organized under the leadership and guidance of Judah the Maccabee. Those who accompanied Onias were probably priests and supporters of the lawful dynasty of the High Priests of the "House of Onias," Onias' own relatives, and probably also various dependents of that great family (its "clients," to use Roman terminology).

There may also have been young men among them who knew how to wield sword and lance, and perhaps they later constituted the nucleus of the military colony on Onias' land after they had received the necessary military training on Egyptian territory. If we accept this conjecture, we shall not be far wrong in fixing the date of the founding of the *katoikia* round about 145, some time before the king's death. The temple also was built then. Its erection was internally bound up with the military colony at Leontopolis, and but for the latter it would never have occurred to Onias to select this deserted locality for a shrine. If not for the colony, moreover, the temple would never have existed.

We have seen above that the idea of founding a temple as a religious center for the entire Jewish diaspora of Egypt cannot be ascribed to Onias; the shrine possessed a purely local significance, being the temple of the military colony of Leontopolis. This assumption resolves a number of questions without creating difficulties—the selection of a locality remote from centers of Jewish life, the silence of Jewish-Hellenistic literature, and to a certain extent also the flouting of Jewish sacred values. The problem of the foundation indeed remains—why was Onias not content to build an ordinary synagogue, and why did he have to build a temple in the style of the Temple of Jerusalem? I see two possible answers, which are not mutually contradictory and may easily be combined. It has already been mentioned that Josephus saw, as one of the motives for the erection of the temple, Onias' desire "to acquire a reputation and in order that his memory should be perpetuated"—in other words, his personal ambition. He no doubt never forgot that he was son of the High Priest, and a scion of the dynasty of the lawful High Priests of Jerusalem, hence he sought to create for himself the atmosphere of the High Priesthood, to garb himself in its mantle and to enjoy all the splendor and magnificence befitting that high position. In his temple he no doubt discharged the function of High Priest and the entire style of life in the Land of Onias may have been organized on the model of that of the traditional Jerusalemite aristocracy.[32]

On the other hand it may well be that the foundation of the Temple suited the desires of those who directed foreign policy at the royal court of Alexandria. Egypt had never given up her claim to the countries of southern Syria which she had ruled for the long period of a hundred years, and when signs of decay appeared in the Seleucid dynasty and the throne began to pass from hand to hand, Egyptian policy assumed an aggressive form to the point of direct intervention in Syria's internal affairs. Philometor himself waged a prolonged war with Syria and even succeeded in having the crown offered him by the people of Antioch. He met his death during the same war, in battle against Alexander Balas.[33]

The political situation of Palestine was decidedly obscure at this time, for the Hasmonean kingdom had not yet crystallized, and the High Priest Jonathan was only a Seleucid official appointed on behalf of the king over certain regions of southern Syria (see above, p. 236ff.). A rival candidate for the throne of the High Priest, whose rights to govern Jerusalem were beyond cavil and who was simultaneously dependent on Egyptian royal favor, was very desirable to Philometor. It was worthwhile fostering Onias' aspirations to power and awaiting an opportunity when he could be used as an important pawn in the political game for power in Syria.[34] Thus Egypt's political aspirations to expansion in Syria and the private ambitions of the last member of the lawful priestly family of Jerusalem found a common meeting point, and the result was the setting up of the Temple of Onias at Leontopolis.

There is no doubt that the "House of Onias" awoke the curiosity of the Jews of Egypt; it was an interesting phenomenon in Diaspora life, characteristic of those Jews who had abandoned Palestinian tradition and were seeking new ways of expressing the religious feeling at work within them. But the phenomenon should not be accorded more importance than it really possessed, nor should Onias' temple be regarded as "the temple of the Jews of Egypt." Egyptian Jewry never officially recognized the shrine, and as long as the Temple of Jerusalem remained intact their gaze was directed toward it.

More important than the building of the temple was Onias' position in the state. Even on the assumption that Josephus was exaggerating when he said that Philometor and Cleopatra entrusted the whole of the land of Egypt to Onias, it is a fact that Onias and his friend Dositheos were Egyptian *strategoi*, that is, men of great influence in the affairs of the state. Especially important was Onias' role after the death of Philometor. The latter's widow Cleopatra faced two foes: Ptolemy VIII Euergetes, who had throughout his life fought against his brother Philometor, and the Alexandrian populace, always ready to vent its revolutionary inclinations in risings. Onias remained loyal to Cleopatra, entering the city "at the head of a small force," in Apion's words, with the evident object of suppressing the rising (see above). Thus the Jews took part in the political life of the Egyptian state, which shows the growth of the Jewish population of Egypt and its flourishing condition in the middle of the second century B.C.E.

The intervention of the Jews in the life of the state, however, did not go well. Cleopatra could not long withstand Euergetes, and this hard and brutal man[35] ultimately became king of Egypt (145-116). No wonder his attitude to the Jews, the allies of his deceased brother, was unfavorable; and the first attempt to perpetrate pogroms on the Jews is associated with his name. Josephus relates that the king decided to exterminate the Jews of the country and prepared to throw them naked and fettered at the feet of drunken elephants, which, however, left the Jews untouched and attacked the king's companions. Affected by the sight, and as a result of the prayers of his mistress Ithaca (or Irene), he repented of his evil intent; and the Jews instituted a festival in memory of the day of salvation (*C. Ap.* II, 53-55). We have already encountered this story (p. 274f.), of which approximately the same events are attributed by *III Maccabees* to Ptolemy IV Philopator. But the historical value of these two sources is not equal; an event quite unjustified in the period of Philopator takes on the character of historical authenticity in the time of Euergetes II (a brutal tyrant who was reported to have ordered his army to surround the gymnasium and put all its pupils to the sword).[36] He hated the Jews because he regarded them as his political opponents, hence it is not surprising that he determined to get rid of them, or at least to punish them. I do not therefore agree with those scholars who deny the historical value of this story,[37] although this does not mean that we are obliged to believe such fabulous details as, for example, the appearance of the drunken elephants.

The festival celebrated by the Jews of Alexandria in memory of that day shows that they were really saved from some serious danger, and this sudden rescue was experienced by them, it seems, as a result of a change in Euergetes' policy. Instead of pressing the war with Cleopatra, he compromised with her and made her his wife, as a result of which festal event, an amnesty was probably granted to all the queen's previous supporters. There are grounds for believing that in course of time the king and the Jews made their peace, for two inscriptions from Xenephyris and Nitriai (in Lower Egypt), respectively, contain the regular formula of the dedication of a new synagogue in honor of the king. This would have been impossible if the latter had persisted in the same hatred of the Jews which he had shown at the beginning of his reign.[38]

The high position and important posts which fell to Onias' lot passed hereditarily to his sons. In the reign of Cleopatra III (116-102), Onias' sons Helkias and Hananiah gained distinction as Egyptian commanders. Cleopatra was fighting her son, Ptolemy IX Lathyrus, who was compelled to evacuate Alexandria and to fortify himself in Cyprus. Strabo transmits an interesting detail of the role of the Jewish commanders in this war, for all those generals sent by Cleopatra to Cyprus quickly went over to Lathyrus, and only the Jews drawn from Onias' territory remained loyal to the queen, "because their citizens Helkias and Hananiah were held in very high esteem by the queen."[39]

We learn from this sentence, not only the fact that Helkias and Hananiah were Egyptian generals, but also that a Jewish force, the *katoikoi* of Onias' territory, was under their command as one of the sections of the Egyptian army. The Jewish commanders therefore had a substantial force under them and knew how to use it to influence the course of Egyptian policy. In the years 104-102, when the fighting shifted from Cyprus to Coele-Syria and Palestine, Cleopatra herself accompanied her army, which was commanded by Helkias and Hananiah.[40] Among her allies was the young Alexander Jannaeus, who had recently acceded to the throne, and some of the queen's intimates counseled her to take no account of the young king and to overrun his country. At this Hananiah[41] gave his opinion that the queen would behave unjustly if she permitted her young ally to be denied the rule which was lawfully his: "I would have you know, that this wrong to the king will turn all the Jews who dwell in your kingdom into your foes" (*Ant.* XIII, 354). Here Hananiah appears as a strong man who is in a position to menace the queen with serious threats, for he has behind him the entire Jewish population of Egypt, including its armed forces.

Another important piece of information is to be derived from Hananiah's speech, namely, the internal bond between the Egyptian diaspora and the Jews of Palestine. If, some fifty years before, Onias had really dreamed of gaining control of Judaea and of restoring the crown of the Oniads to its former state, the foundation of the Hasmonean kingdom had revealed to all whither the sympathy of the Jewish population of Palestine was directed and how vain were all hopes of turning back the wheel of history. The Hasmonean monarchy was a historical fact and, even if it had been created by the Jews of Palestine, it was not alien to the Jews of Egypt, who saw themselves morally bound to defend it in its hour of peril to the utmost of their ability.

Moreover, they sometimes obeyed orders originating from Palestine. Josephus relates two instances of this sort belonging to the last period of Ptolemaic rule in Egypt. In 55 B.C.E. the Roman proconsul of Syria, Gabinius, came to Egypt to restore Ptolemy XI Auletes to his throne. The guarding of the ford at Pelusium was in Jewish hands, and it was not known whether the Jews would allow the Roman army to break into Egypt. The Romans, however, possessed a loyal friend in Antipater the Idumaean, who was then at the head of the Jewish state (Hyrcanus II, the state's official ruler, was entirely in his power). The Jews who guarded the passage obeyed Antipater and allowed the Romans to enter the country (*Ant.* XIV, 131; *War* I, 190).

The second incident has already been mentioned above (p. 279) in passing: in the year 48, Julius Caesar was at Alexandria, in a far from desirable predicament, while a small force of his allies, including Antipater, was hastening from Syria through Pelusium with help for the Roman *imperator*. On the way from Pelusium to Memphis, they encountered the Jewish troops settled in Onias' territory, who were unwilling to yield passage to the foreign army. Once again Antipater did his political duty, by showing the Jews letters from the High Priest Hyrcanus, the "friend" of Julius Caesar, and commanded them, not merely not to impede the army's transit through Onias' territory, but to furnish it with supplies for the journey. The Jews acted accordingly. From these instances we learn that even Hyrcanus II, a ruler of no power or influence whatever, was a man of great authority in the eyes of the Jews of the Diaspora, since he was High Priest and symbol of the Jewish power in Palestine.

We have reached the end of our account of the history of the Jews of Egypt in the Hellenistic period. A few words may be added on the location of the Jewish settlements in that country.[42]

The center of Egyptian Jewry was Alexandria, and inscriptions testify to Jewish settlement in that city from the beginning of the third century, perhaps under Ptolemy I.[43] In Philo's day two quarters of the city were full of Jews,[44] but there was no ghetto, for Philo testifies that Jewish synagogues were scattered throughout the whole town (*Leg. ad Gaium* 132). The Jewish place of residence was more especially by the seashore, not far from the royal palace. In the words of Josephus (*C. Ap.* 35), Alexander himself gave this place to the Jews to settle in—a report devoid of historical value (see above, ch. 2). The Jews lived also in the areas surrounding the city, as is clear from the building of a synagogue at Schedia under Ptolemy III Euergetes.[45]

In Lower Egypt we encounter Jews in various places. They had dwelt at Migdal and Tahpanhes as early as the days of Jeremiah.[46] The military colony of the Jews of Pelusium has been alluded to above, likewise the Jewish *katoikia* in the Land of Onias, and late sources refer in this neighborhood to a *vicus Iudaeorum*, or "Jewish village," perhaps so called as early as the Hellenistic period.[47] An Augustan papyrus alludes to an estate at Bousiris belonging to a Jew.[48] An inscription from Athribis tells of the building of a synagogue at that place in the Ptolemaic period.

Two other inscriptions indicate Jewish settlements respectively at Xenephyris and Nitriai.[49] Another papyrus speaks of three Jews from the "Syrian village."[50] At Memphis, Jews had been settled since the days of Jeremiah, and fragments of Aramaic papyri testify to a Jewish settlement near the town in the Persian period.[51] This large city, the center of political and religious life in the epoch of the Pharaohs, certainly contained Jews within its walls in the Hellenistic period also, although there is no clear information on the subject. Southwest of Memphis stretched the great province of the Fayûm, part of which was converted to settled country under Ptolemy II Philadelphus. The Jewish population there was very highly developed. In the large villages, such as Arsinoë, Philadelpheia, Theadelpheia, Psenyris and Tebtynis, and also in some of the smaller villages, papyri have been discovered mentioning Jewish names;[52] in the Heracleopolite nome also a Jewish community is alluded to.[53]

In Upper Egypt Jews were settled by the sixth century B.C.E. (p. 269, above). Numerous ostraca have been found in the vicinity of Thebes with Hebrew names inscribed on them;[54] a Jewish quarter existed at Apollinopolis Magna (Edfu) in the Roman period, but the beginning of the Jewish settlement here goes back to the Hellenistic period.[55] Thus the Jewish population extended over the entire land of Egypt, "from the Ladder of Libya (Sollum) to the frontiers of Ethiopia," as Philo says (*Flacc.* 43).

The number of Egyptian Jews was not small, but we have no means of determining it precisely. According to Philo (*ib.*), they numbered a million souls in his time, and this report is generally accepted by scholars as genuine. However, we are bound to ask whence Philo derived this figure, and whether he was able to avail himself of official documents? The reply, I think, must be in the negative, for although Egypt was a country of frequent censuses, organized by the government for fiscal purposes, and although the government always knew the exact number of tax-payers in each nome, the separate numbering of the Jews was not practiced either under the Ptolemies or in Philo's time; the appropriate background for it was created only from the reign of Vespasian, when the payment of a special tax was imposed upon the Jews. Hence there are no grounds for thinking that Philo used official material and it would be more correct to suppose that he selected as "round" a figure as possible in order to arouse the imagination of his readers. We must not forget that the use of exaggerated figures was usual among ancient writers from Herodotus onwards, and very few historians practiced caution in this matter.

According to Josephus (*War* II, 385) the number of inhabitants of Egypt, excluding Alexandria, amounted to seven and a half million souls,[56] and it is hard to suppose that every eighth person in the country was a Jew, if we consider the density of the Egyptian village-population, which barred the way to the unrestricted mass expansion of any foreign folk. Nor do the other figures preserved in Hellenistic literature arouse our confidence. Aristeas tells of the 100,000 Jewish soldiers who were freed from slavery under Philadelphus; but we have seen above (p. 273) that this figure is not to be trusted. *III Maccabees* reports the huge number of Egyptian Jews under Ptolemy Philometor who could not be counted because the pens ran out; but this is the figment of an unfettered oriental imagination, out of all touch with reality. Josephus says that, in the year 66, 50,000 people were killed in Alexandria (*War* II, 497—cf. 60,000 *ib. War* VII, 369), and although we have no means of checking this figure, it is the only one that might be accepted. Apart from the criticism to which the above figures have been subjected, the very fact that all the writers insistently emphasize the large number of the

Jewish inhabitants of Egypt, proves convincingly that their number was really large and that their influence was felt in the various branches of the public life of the kingdom. It was possible to live at peace with the Jews or to oppose them, but it was impossible to close one's eyes to them or to leave them out of account.

A more or less complete account of the Jewish Diaspora can be rendered in respect of Egypt alone; as to the other countries, we must content ourselves with brief and isolated items of information preserved by chance in contemporary writings, or discovered in excavations. Most of the information belongs to the Roman period, and we shall only use such part of it as derives from the Upper Empire, not later than the end of the first century C.E.

The first report on the Jews in Asia Minor belongs to the middle of the fourth century B.C.E. Clearchus, the pupil of Aristotle, relates that his master, when he was in Asia Minor (347-345), met a Jew who had come to the seashore "from the mountainous regions,"[57] "and was a Greek not only in speech, but also in spirit." We shall see below (ch. 4) that this figure of a learned Hellenizing Jew belongs to the world of imagination, hence the historic basis of the meeting between this Jew and Aristotle also collapses. Even were we to assume that a Jew from Palestine visited Asia Minor in the middle of the fourth century, this would be no proof that Jewish settlements existed then in those places, since Clearchus' anecdote, even if we admit its truth, concerns an isolated and exceptional case.[58]

We encounter Jewish emigration to Asia Minor for the first time in the period of Antiochus III.[59] Josephus (*Ant.* XII, 148-153) has preserved Antiochus' letter to the official Zeuxis, in which the king orders the transfer of two thousand Jewish families from Mesopotamia and Babylonia to Lydia and Phrygia; he had heard of the rebellions in those countries and believed that the Jews would do good duty as soldiers and keepers of the fortresses on behalf of the king. This letter has received various appraisals in historical literature, for, while some scholars admit its authenticity, others regard it as a Jewish forgery of a late period.[60]

In the writer's opinion there are no grounds for doubting the genuineness of the letter. Willrich found symptoms of falsification in the failure of the letter to list explicitly the names of the fortresses and localities designated for Jewish settlement, and he thinks that such detailed information would never have been missing from an official document of this nature. However, Antiochus wrote his order when he was in the East,[61] without an exhaustive knowledge of all the details of the risings in Asia Minor, and Zeuxis himself could have fixed the Jews' places of settlement in conformity with the situation. The fact that Antiochus III decided to use Jews as troops now arouses no suspicion, since several instances of Jews serving in the army have been discovered in the documents. The end of the letter, which relates the details of the Jewish settlement (including the cancellation of taxes for a given period and similar provisions), is also appropriate to the historical information concerning the settlement of soldier-peasants on the soil.[62]

It may therefore be accepted as a historical fact that 2000 Jewish families were transferred from Babylonia to Asia Minor in approximately the years 210-205. These families, which settled in Lydia and Phrygia as military *katoikoi,* laid the foundation of the Jewish diaspora in Asia Minor.[63] This diaspora continued to expand with rapidity. In the time of Simon the Hasmonean, the Roman consul published a proclamation in favor of the Jews, sending it to various lands and to the Greek cities where Jews resided.[64] Among the various localities, the regions and cities of Asia Minor are mentioned, these being Caria, Pamphylia, Lycia, Halicarnassus, Myndos, Cnidus, Phaselis, Sidé, Amysos, and the islands of Delos, Samos, Cos and Rhodes. In the year 62 B.C.E., Flaccus, the governor of the Roman province of Asia, confiscated Jewish money at Apameia, Laodiceia, Adramyttium and Pergamum, as is related by Cicero.[65] Josephus cites several documents drafted by Romans (from Julius Caesar to Augustus), also resolutions taken by Greek cities, which relate to the Jews, and mention the Jewish populations in the towns of Miletus, Pergamum, Halicarnassus, Tralles, Laodiceia, Sardis and Ephesus, and on the islands of Paros, Delos and Cos (*Ant.* XIV, 213, 225-264; XVI, 6).

We can extend this list by information drawn from the books of the New Testament (Smyrna, Philadelpheia, Antioch in Pisidia, Tarsus and Iconium) and from inscriptions (Phocaia in Ionia, Magnesia by Syplos, Iasos by Miletus, Hierapolis in Lydia, Tlos in Lycia).[66] Philo indicates that Jews dwelt even in the remotest places of Asia Minor—in Bithynia and Pontus on the Black Sea coast (*Leg. ad*

Gaium 281). In another place he says that there was no city of Asia or Syria which did not contain Jews (*ib.* 245).[67] Thus, in the course of 200 or 300 years, Jewish settlement spread and expanded over the whole of Asia Minor.

The Syrian dispersion was no less numerous than that of Asia Minor; Josephus says that here the Jews were more numerous than in any other country because of their proximity to Palestine (*War* VII, 43). The Jews of Syria are alluded to frequently in talmudical literature;[68] they settled especially in Antioch, which attracted foreigners by its size and populousness (*War* VII, 43). The beginnings of Jewish settlement in the city are related by Josephus, who states that the Jews received citizen rights there as early as the time of Seleucus Nicator (*Ant.* XII, 119). We shall see later that this report is not reliable. In another passage (*War* VII, 43) Josephus says that the Jewish population of Antioch grew particularly "in the days of the kings who followed Antiochus," and he apparently means Antiochus Epiphanes.[69] This information is credible, for the civil war probably caused many inhabitants of Judaea to remove to Syria.

But even prior to this, in the period of the Hellenizing regime, the High Priests frequently made the journey to the Syrian capital, and Onias III dwelt there and was slain at Daphne near Antioch (above, p. 172). II Maccabees (4.36) testifies that in Onias' time a Jewish settlement already existed at Antioch. It may be supposed that regular connections between Judaea and Antioch began round about the year 200, after Palestine had fallen into the hands of Antiochus III; and to this period, it would seem, must be attributed the beginning of the Jewish population in the city.[70]

We have only isolated reports on the other towns. The Jews of Apameia are referred to by Josephus, in the Talmud and in inscriptions.[71] The pogroms against the Jews of Damascus in the year 70 are related by Josephus (*War* II, 559-561). Here the mysterious sect, which had fled from Judaea on account of persecution, found refuge. Other refugees settled in the city of Chalcis.[72] The citizens of Tyre and Sidon knew the Jews as early as the time of Judah the Maccabee, for otherwise they would hardly have taken part in the persecution of the Galilean Jews (I Macc. 5.15). Jews also dwelt at Arados, at least from the time of Simon Maccabee (I Macc. 15.23). These isolated notices do not furnish a complete picture, and it is not of course possible to judge the scope of

the Jewish diaspora in Syria, least of all in the lands bordering on Palestine, such as Phoenicia and the Lebanon, which were full of Jewish inhabitants, as Philo indicates when he says that Jews resided in every town of Syria and Asia (*Leg. ad Gaium* 245).
In Babylon and Mesopotamia Jews had lived since the period of the Babylonian Exile. Philo and Josephus bear witness that in their time the diaspora there was very numerous indeed.[73] Under Tiberius Caesar, two Jews, the brothers Hasinai and Hanilai, attempted to set up a small principality in Babylonia (*Ant.* XVIII, 310ff.). Jewish influence was also strong in Adiabene, across the River Tigris; in the first century C.E., its kings accepted Judaism (*Ant.* XX, 2ff.). For us only the information on Jewish settlement in the Greek cities founded here in the Hellenistic period is important. Unfortunately only one item on this subject has survived. Josephus tells of the Jews of Babylon who escaped in large numbers to Seleuceia-on-Tigris, after the attempt of Hasinai and Hanilai to found a Jewish principality had failed and had aroused the hatred of the Babylonians for the Jews.
There were two sections in the population of Seleuceia—Greeks and Syrians (the original natives)—who were rivals for local power. The Jews joined the Syrians, and both peoples together defeated the Greeks; but the situation changed suddenly, when the Greeks made secret contact with the Syrians and entered into an alliance with them, as a result of which terrible riots broke out against the Jews. If we may credit Josephus, 50,000 Jews fell during these pogroms, and their remnants found asylum in Ctesiphon.[74] This is all we know of the Babylonian Jews in the Greek cities.[75] Josephus, indeed, says that they obtained citizen rights in all the towns founded by Seleucus Nicator (*Ant.* XII, 119); but we shall see later what the historian's words are really worth when they concern Jewish privileges. It is of course possible that during the Hellenistic period Jews settled also in many Greek towns of Babylonia and Mesopotamia founded by the Seleucids, but details of this historical process are unknown to us.
The Jews arrived in Cyrene from Egypt. According to Josephus, they were sent thither by Ptolemy I when he conquered the country (*C. Ap.* II, 44). Cyrene is mentioned several times in the letter of the Roman consul referred to above (I Macc. 15.23). Strabo (ap. Jos., *Ant.* XIV, 115) mentions the Jews of Cyrene during the first half of the first century B.C.E. as a special group distinct from

the other resident sections. Numerous inscriptions, especially from Teucheira-Arsinoë, testify to a large Jewish population in the cities of Cyrene; some places retain among the Arabs, even today, the name of Ḥirbet el-Jahud.[76]

The fact that the Hellenistic author Jason, whose narrative was the basis of the Second Book of the Maccabees, was a native of Cyrene, is some indication of the high cultural level of the Jewish community in that country. In the Roman period the Jewish population in Cyrene developed considerable strength, and at the end of the reign of the Emperor Trajan made its desperate attempt to rebel against Rome, a rebellion which brought destruction not only on the Jewish population of the country but also on the Jews of Egypt and Cyprus.[77]

Jews also reached Greece and Macedonia. In Philo's time they lived in Thessaly, Boeotia, Macedonia, Aetolia and Attica, and in the towns of Argos and Corinth, as well as "in the best places of the Peloponnesus," likewise on the islands of Euboea, Cyprus and Crete (*Leg. ad. Gaium* 281-282). The *Acts of the Apostles* mention Jewish communities at Philippi, Thessalonica, Beroia, Athens and Corinth. In many places in Greece, moreover, inscriptions have been found evidencing Jewish settlements.[78] Two of them, discovered at Delphi, report the emancipation of Jewish slaves. They belong to the years 170-157, which was the period of the Hasmonean revolt, and it is possible that the Jews referred to there were taken prisoner and sold as slaves during the war.[79] The Roman proclamation under Simon Maccabee alludes to the Jews in Sparta, Sicyon, on the island of Crete (in the town of Gortyn) and on the island of Cyprus (I Macc. 15.23). The Jews of Cyprus are also mentioned by Josephus in the reign of Cleopatra III of Egypt (*Ant.* XIII, 284), and Jewish coins of the Maccabean epoch have been found on the island.[80]

These notices show that the Jewish dispersion in Greece was already in existence in the middle of the second century B.C.E., but it was not very important even in the Roman period, and it is hard to imagine that the number of Jews in the lands of the Balkan Peninsula went on growing, since the local inhabitants themselves had for generations been rapidly abandoning their native country, which had been progressively impoverished and could no longer hold them even at the end of the classical period.

Thus, in the course of the Hellenistic period, the Jews became dispersed over the whole Greek world. As early as 140 B.C.E. approximately, the author of the *Sibylline Oracles* testifies "that the whole land and sea are full of Jews."[81] Strabo's assertion, that the Jew "had reached every town, and it is hard to find a place in the world whither this race has not penetrated and where it has not obtained a hold,"[82] refers to the period of Sulla, about the year 85 B.C.E. Josephus speaks in the same language of the Diaspora communities: "There is no people in the world among whom part of our brethren is not to be found" (*War* II, 398), and elsewhere he writes: "The Jewish race is scattered over the entire world among the local inhabitants" (*ib.* VII, 43). Philo speaks of the wide expansion of the Jews throughout the world and of Jerusalem as the center of that scattered and sundered nation (*Flacc.* 46; *Leg.* 281ff.).

The Jewish Diaspora was a considerable power among the indigenous peoples, and it is to be regretted that we are unable to determine the precise number of Jews outside Palestine. The only writer who has given (or thought he had given) the over-all figure of Jews in the Roman Empire in the reign of Claudius, belongs to a very late period and his information is not to be relied on; he is the Christian author known as Bar Hebraeus, the son of a converted Jew, who lived in the thirteenth century of the Christian era. He speaks of a grand total of seven million Jews in the Empire.[83] This, however, is merely an error on his part, as he was confusing the number of Jews with the number of Roman citizens according to the Roman census made by Claudius in the year 48.[84] As to the partial figures of the Jews of Palestine or Egypt, preserved by Josephus and Philo, they must be used with great caution, since they are generally highly exaggerated.[85]

Many attempts have been made by modern scholars to determine the number of Jews in the Roman Empire, but without much success. Relying on the figures of ancient writers, some scholars have arrived at the over-all number of six, seven or eight million Jews in the Empire. Other scholars, by estimating the number of Jews in Palestine by the number of its inhabitants in Turkish times or under the British mandate, reach the small figure of half a million or 600,000 inhabitants in that country, only part of these constituting the Jewish population. Some think that the majority of the Jewish nation lived in Palestine, and others estimate the number of the Jews of the Diaspora as four times that of the Jews of Palestine. Some regard the large number of Jews as a result of their natural increase, whereas others think that the proselytes were the main reason for the Jewish people's surprising increase.[86]

It is not difficult to grasp how greatly the approach of these writers to the problem of the size of the Jewish population in the Graeco-Roman world has been influenced by their general outlooks. In order to avoid the mistakes made by others, I do not wish to adopt any hard and fast figure, which must inevitably be as arbitrary as any other. By this I do not mean that we should despair of any attempt to investigate the possible size of the Jewish population in the ancient world, but such an inquiry must in my view be conducted not by the laying down of *a priori* principles, nor under the influence of ancient historiography—which is to be suspected of falsification—nor again by superficial comparison with population-densities in modern times—but chiefly by a cautious and accurate analysis of the documentary material, and further, by a comparison of the life of the Jewish people with that of other peoples of ancient times.

Those who place their reliance on the figure of a million Jews in Egypt according to Philo's view (above, p. 286), might do well to take notice of the fact that of some 1300 papyri found in the archives of Zenon at Philadelpheia in the Fayûm (see above, p. 60), less than fifteen (one percent!) relate to Jews and Judaism. To those who think that the growth of the Jewish population was due to the refusal of the Jews to expose their children, in contrast to the practice of the remaining peoples of the Roman Empire, it should be remarked that at the only place in Egypt where we have fairly detailed documentary information on the Jewish population— the town of Apollinopolis Magna (Edfu) in Upper Egypt— there is no trace of families burdened by numerous children, and insofar as the matter can be examined, there is no family the number of whose children exceeds three.[87]

Those who think that the Jewish people increased through proselytization, should be reminded that the instances of *complete* conversion are not numerous in our records, whereas the larger number of half-proselytes ("God-fearers," sabbatarians and the like) remained officially outside the framework of the organized Jewish communities.[88] Nor should it be forgotten, of course, that as opposed to the

Judaizing movement among the Gentiles, there existed no less strong a movement among Jews to assimilate among the Gentiles, and it is quite impossible to know which of the two was the stronger.

If we desire to determine the approximate number of Jews in the Graeco-Roman world, we must compare the Jews with the remaining peoples of the world in the same period. We should not regard the Jews as a people exempt from the general laws of historical development, any more than we should look at Palestine as a country standing outside the influence of climate and soil conditions. If the Egyptian fellah made do with five or seven *arourai* (3-4 acres) to support his family on the fertile soil of Egypt, which renews its productivity annually thanks to the Nile floods, it is for agricultural experts to determine what must have been the size of the Jewish peasant's holdings in the hills of Judaea, in the Shephelah and in Galilee, if he was to feed his family; and if Egypt, the most fertile of the Mediterranean countries, did not support more than seven and a half million inhabitants, or with the population of Alexandria, some eight million—what must have been the size of the population of Palestine, which is chiefly a mountainous country and whose area is smaller than the Nile Delta? And if it is stated that the Jewish population in the world was mainly urban, it must be replied that other peoples also lived in cities and engaged in commerce, and the average number of inhabitants of the medium-sized Greek city is more or less known. And as the Jewish community was only a small part of the Greek urban population, or at least a permanent minority in it, it is not very difficult to settle approximately the size of the medium-sized Jewish community in the medium-sized Greek city. Only calculations such as these, both detailed and cautious, can bring us somewhere near a solution of the statistical question, and there is every reason to believe that the results of the examination would be more in favor of those who adopt small figures than of their opponents. As long as an investigation of this sort has not been carried out—and it should not be undertaken perfunctorily, as it demands much knowledge and patience—the adoption of any figures at all must be unfounded guesswork without adequate historical basis, and this should be avoided as far as possible.

But whatever the results of the inquiry, it is at any rate clear that the Jewish population was quite considerable in the Graeco-Roman world, especially in the eastern half of the Mediterranean. Greeks and Jews met at every turn, especially in the large cities, but also on the countryside, in the camps of the armed forces, in the small provincial towns, and elsewhere. This common life confronted both peoples with many questions whose solution was frequently difficult. It may be stated that "the Jewish question" faced the Greeks, and later the Romans, with the same urgency that it faces the cultured world of our own day.

chapter **2**

JEWISH COMMUNITY AND
GREEK CITY

Scattered and dispersed among the nations, the Jews could maintain their existence and national features only as long as the organization of their internal life was of sufficient strength to serve as a barrier against the influence of the alien environment. The Jews were not facing this question for the first time in their history, for the Babylonian Exile had already tested their national strength. We do not know how the Jews solved the problem of internal national organization in Babylon, but it is clear that they found the correct solution, for not only did their strength suffice them to send repatriates to Palestine and to reconstitute their national life in their home country, but they were able to preserve their national identity in the exile too, and to bring about the blossoming of Babylonian Judaism in the talmudic period. The small colony of the Jews of Elephantine, which lived its independent life in a remote corner of Egypt, also discovered the correct solution, and could look back proudly upon two centuries of existence, its Jews having for generations retained their language, religion and national customs. The Jews of Babylonia and Palestine had examples of this sort before them at the beginning of the Hellenistic period when migration began to the western countries; but even without such specific models, it was clear to every Jew that he could build a new life in a foreign land only together with his brethren and with their aid. Thus in every land of the West where Jews lived, organized Jewish communities were founded, and a form of public life was created which gave the people of Israel the strength to resist assimilation and which has survived—naturally with great changes—down to our own day.[1]

Theoretically the Jewish community was open to every Jew who had come from another country to settle in the place where that community existed. But the continual emigration from Palestine, which caused the flourishing of the communities in various countries, also caused a division in the community itself. The civic status of the Jews in the Greek world was not the same for all the members of the community; those that had come first enjoyed certain rights, while the new immigrants were looked upon as foreigners. Within the community existed aristocratic groups which constituted the upper stratum of society, and side by side with them the broad sections of the population, including chiefly those immigrants who had arrived later. Sometimes several communities existed in one city, the reason for whose separateness from one another cannot now be determined.[2]

These divisions and disputes within the community did not, however, affect the existence of the community itself, and probably no single Jew remained outside the bounds of its organization, except those who had voluntarily excluded themselves from the generality and had abandoned both the Jewish community and Judaism in order to become assimilated among the Greeks. Hellenizing Jews of this type were to be found in every locality and we have no means of determining their number. We shall see further that Hellenization did not make departure from the Jewish community obligatory, the less so because as a rule it brought few real benefits; the Jews enjoyed many privileges and it was not always worthwhile giving them up in order to enter Greek society, which was not at all inclined to welcome Jews readily.

To the outside world the Jewish community appeared as a legally independent unit. There was no special juridical term in Greek for the Jewish communal organizations, but frequently the Jews of the city were designated simply as "Jews," or as "Jews resident in the city."[3] More important was the term *politeuma*, which is encountered in the *Letter of Aristeas* (§310) in connection with the Alexandrian community, and in two inscriptions from Berenice in Cyrenaica.[4] The interpretation of the word is quite complex, as we shall presently see. A slightly more accurate term was *katoikia*, used of colonies of people of foreign birth, especially of troops, in other countries; these enjoyed a measure of self-administration, but had no urban privileges and from the legal point of view were classified as villages (see above, p. 25).

An inscription from Hierapolis in Phrygia indicates that the Jewish community there was organized as a *katoikia*.[5] At a later period various other terms—*laós, synodos, synagogé*—were in use to denote the Jewish communities. The terms had very broad meanings, nor can any conclusion be drawn from them on the internal organization of the communities and their political position in the Greek world. However, we learn two things from this variegated terminology: first, that the Jews were classified by the Greeks with aliens and people born abroad; and, secondly, that the Greeks officially acknowledged the autonomous organization of the Jewish communities.

These conclusions deserve more detailed elaboration. Was the Jewish community a unique organization, calling for an exceptional attitude on the part of the Hellenistic world, or did its existence involve no contradiction of the political principles of that world and no breach in the universally accepted framework? The Jewish historian, influenced by the originality of Jewish culture and more particularly by its monotheistic religion, which differed from every other religion in the ancient world, tends to see the Jewish community as a political organization *sui generis*, unable to exist in an alien environment without a special attitude toward it on the part of the authorities.

We shall see below that this approach is partly justified, but only partly; we must not ignore the simple fact that the Hellenistic world (and, quite naturally, the subsequent Hellenistic-Roman world even more so) lived and developed in an atmosphere which was international in the widest sense of the word. There was no corner of it in which various peoples did not meet and where antagonisms did not arise between various parts of the population. What should be the attitude of permanent residents to foreigners; what was the legal and political framework in which aliens could live in accordance with their own customs and at the same time obey the laws of the country; what was the precise definition of "foreigner," and when precisely did a "foreigner" cease to be one and become a permanent resident? This entire complex of problems had faced the Hellenistic monarchies and likewise the citizens of the Greek cities long before the Jews from Palestine appeared before them with their claims and their wishes. Clearly, then, it was not for the Jews alone that the Graeco-Roman world made special arrangements whose function was to steer the existence of alien communities in a defined legal channel. We can distinguish two different ways of resolving the question: the establishment of ethnic communities on the one hand, and the organization of religious corporations on the other. The first method was expressed chiefly in the organization of the *politeuma*, as has been mentioned. The interpretation of the concept is rather complicated, for sometimes it denotes a normal Greek city, sometimes the entirety of the inhabitants of a locality (or city), sometimes—and this is the interpretation we require—a community of aliens within a Greek city or a Hellenistic kingdom.[6] Thus, for example, *politeumata* of mercenaries from the towns of Asia Minor (Kaunus, Termessos, etc.) existed at Sidon and in Italy;[7] not less important are examples from Hellenistic Egypt.[8] With regard to the second type of organization, corporations concentrated about the cult of a given deity were scattered over the entire Hellenistic world.[9] As every group of foreigners coming to a place from another country brought with it the cult of its native land, it was natural that every *politeuma* should also be a group of peculiar religious complexion, and if the ethnic group had many members and much influence, it was normal that its religious observances should be widely known among the local inhabitants.[10] We see then that the Jews found the way prepared for them and were able to enter the Hellenistic world without their appearance causing a breach in the existing framework or the creation of novel political and religious organizations. Nor did the attitude of the Hellenistic authorities towards the Jewish community differ in principle from their attitude to every political or religious organization. It requires little explanation to understand that in an autocratic country like Egypt no *politeuma* was an independent power, for even a Greek *polis* like Alexandria or Ptolemais was not independent (see above, p. 25). It may be taken for granted (although no document survives on the question) that no *politeuma* could be organized without the special permission of the king, or of a high official representing him. No more could the Jewish communities, of course, be formed solely on their own initiative. It is to be remarked that precisely in relation to the organization of Jewish communities we possess, not a document, but a literary quotation interpretable as the account of the granting of a special "charter," under royal auspices, to the founder of the community. I refer to the words of Hecataeus cited by Josephus in his *Contra Apionem* (I, 189). Speaking of the High Priest Hezekiah, who joined Ptolemy I after the battle of Gaza (cf. above, p. 56f.), Hecataeus relates that this High Priest gathered a number of people among the Jews, who were prepared to follow him to Egypt, and read to them an extract from a certain writing: "For he possessed (the conditions) of their settlement and their political constitution (drawn up) in writing."

Various interpretations have been set upon this sentence, and it may be confessed that it is not as clear as it might be.[11] Nevertheless, it seems certain that we have here an allusion to an official document issued to Hezekiah in Ptolemy's name, perhaps in the form of a letter signed by the king, which fixed in advance the type of settlement of the group of Jews in Egypt and also their political status in their new country of residence.[12] If this interpretation is sound, it suggests the way the first organized community of Jews was founded in Hellenistic Egypt—perhaps in Alexandria or perhaps somewhere along the Egyptian frontier with the object of protecting it, on the model of the Jewish communities founded in Egypt in the Persian period. It will not be an error to state that this was the usual manner of setting up a *politeuma,* and every new Jewish community that arose in Ptolemaic Egypt needed a special "charter" on the pattern of that granted to Hezekiah by Ptolemy I.[13]

What is the meaning of the words "written political constitution" ($\pi o \lambda \iota \tau \epsilon \acute{\iota} a$ $\gamma \epsilon \gamma \rho a \mu \mu \acute{\epsilon} \nu \eta$)? Are we to believe that Ptolemy went into every detail of the Jewish community which was to be set up and settled precisely what was to be permitted and what was to be prohibited? A municipal constitution is a document of many clauses, and so doubtless was the law of the *politeuma,* yet there is no instance where the royal license for the founding of a city or community is accompanied by detailed codes.[14]

The document in possession of Hezekiah probably contained only the main principles of the act of settlement; and if we wish to know what they were, we must again turn to examples from the Hellenistic world at large. In every act of the foundation of a city or colony under royal patronage certain details were determined pertaining to the process of the foundation itself, such as the number of inhabitants, the location, the aim of the settlement, its exemption from taxes, and the like;[15] such details doubtless appeared also in Ptolemy's writ to Hezekiah, but they are not the ones that interest us. The word *politeia* points to more important matters, for hereby a permanent legal status received the sanction of the ruler. By analogy with Antiochus III's letter to Ptolemy and his other rescript to Zeuxis (see above, p. 82ff.), it may be concluded that here too permission was granted to the Jews "to live according to their ancestral laws," or "to use their own laws." It should be reemphasized that the Hellenistic and Roman periods have preserved for us several examples of the granting of this right to various cities and peoples, and the Jews were not exceptional from this point of view.[16]

What was the actual content of this privilege? We have seen above that the Jews' right "to live according to their ancestral laws" in Judaea was identical with the conception of the Law of Moses in the broad sense of the term: not only the Written Law, but also the new decisions and observances introduced among the Jews by the oral tradition were implied (above, p. 83f.). Our statement concerning the Jews of Palestine applies equally to those of the Diaspora. The permission to live according to their ancestral laws meant *the internal autonomy of the organized Jewish community in the Diaspora.* It is clear, indeed, that the same restrictions affecting a Greek city affected the Jewish community; its autonomy was not political but religious and social only. It is not to be thought, for instance, that the entire Jewish diaspora in Egypt was organized in a *single* communal organization, for such an organization would of necessity have taken the form of a state within a state and could have constituted a danger to the royal power. Nor is it to be assumed that the representatives of the various communities met together on regular occasions to take counsel on current affairs, for a supra-communal organization of this type would again have been a potential danger to the peace of the state.

The Jewish community did not exceed the restricted limits of the city or village, and therefore lacked any political power, because it was too small. Yet within these restricted bounds it enjoyed complete freedom in all matters of religion, observance and law. The right "to live according to its ancestral laws" meant the right to build synagogues, to maintain independent courts of justice, to educate the youth in the spirit of the Torah, to set up communal institutions and to elect officials, and the like. The Jewish community with its officials and institutions, its synagogues and courts, its economic and social life, was a miniature kingdom; and if, from the point of view of the Hellenistic state, its case was no different from that of every other *politeuma*, from an internal point of view it was more like the autonomous Greek *polis* than an ephemeral group of foreigners from abroad.

Literature and epigraphy have preserved some information on the internal organization of the Jewish community. Strabo relates that the ethnarch, who stood at the head of the Jewish community of Alexandria, "ruled the people, judged its cases and supervised the implementation of contracts and orders, like the ruler of an independent state."[17] From this we learn that the ethnarch had charge of the supervision of the court of justice and the registry of the community. The post of ethnarch, however, appears to have been no more than a transitory phenomenon in the life of the Alexandrian community. Aristeas, who in his book reflects the position of the community about a century before Strabo,[18] has no knowledge of the ethnarch and speaks of the "leaders" of the community.[19] The former's post, on the other hand, was abolished a short time after Strabo. In the years 12-10 B.C.E., Augustus substituted for the ethnarch's position that of a council of elders, the *gerousia*. This is reported by Philo (*Flacc.* 74) and, although another report exists contradicting his words, we may credit them, since we encounter the *gerousia* on several occasions during the first century, while we hear nothing whatever of the ethnarch.[20] According to the information of the Talmud (Tos. Sukk., IV, 6; Sukk. 51b) the number of the *gerousia*'s members was seventy-one;[21] Philo mentions 38 of them, who were flogged during the pogroms in Alexandria under Gaius Caligula. Philo calls the members "archons," and this title may have denoted only the most important members of the council, known to Josephus as "the heads of the *gerousia*" (*War* VII, 412), rather than all its members. The archons had in their hands all the affairs of the community.

The post of archon was widespread among the Jews of the Diaspora, being found at Antioch (*War* VII, 47), Berenice (see above, p. 296), at the city of Tlos in Asia Minor, at Arsinoë in Fayûm, and particularly at Rome.[22] The character of the post is insufficiently known to us. The inscription from Berenice shows that in that city the Jewish community had nine archons, and that the decisions adopted by the community were taken in common by the archontes and the *politeuma*, meaning the (general ?) meeting of the members of the community. This is evidence, on the face of it, of the democratic spirit of the Jewish communities; but I do not think that the power of the archons was restricted to any considerable extent by the general meeting. True democracy did not fit the situation in Jewish communities. It is, for example, a fact that in the course of time the post of archon acquired the character of an honorary position, well-born families occupying the vacant places as a matter of course and keeping them for their sons. This can be seen from the inscriptions at Rome, in which appear the names of small children who are termed "little archon," or "future archon."[23] This fact throws light on the internal structure of the Jewish community, at whose head stand well-born families that hold the reins of power and take good care that the rule should not pass to the broad sections of the public. We shall see later, indeed, that the social antagonisms within the community were pretty strong and that the rise to power of Jewish "democracy" boded no good for the rich wardens of the community.

Besides the archons there were other posts in the Jewish community—the head of the *gerousia (gerousiárches)*, the head of the synagogue *(archisynagogos)*, the overseer *(phrontistés)*, the secretary *(grammateus)* and others. We have scarcely any information on these posts.[24] Of the communal institutions, likewise, we hear only rarely. Wherever Jews dwelt there was of course a synagogue which served as the communal center, place of prayer, of instruction and justice, and even for lodging Jews who had come from afar. Its official name in Egypt was *proseuché*, or "prayer-place."[25] Synagogues are frequently mentioned in the inscriptions and the papyri of Egypt during the Hellenistic-Roman period.[26] One inscription relates that Ptolemy Euergetes (whether the first or the second is uncertain) granted to a Jewish synagogue *asylia*, meaning that he made it a place of refuge after the manner of the Egyptian temples.[27] This evidences the respect in which the kings held the Jewish cult. The Jews, for their part, did not refrain from expressing their respect for the monarchs, dedicating synagogues to "the king's welfare," just as the other peoples dedicated their temples.[28] An Alexandrian papyrus refers to a Jewish records office,[29] and another such existed at Hierapolis.[30]

The communities also had their special courts, for in the Tosephta (Ketub. III, 1; Peah IV, 6) a Jewish court at Alexandria is mentioned, and we find another court in the city of Sardis in Asia Minor (*Ant.* XIV, 235). There is no need for special proofs of the existence of courts in the communities, for such institutions were bound up with the very existence of the Jewish community and with its freedom to live according to its ancestral laws. Disputes between one Jew and another were undoubtedly sifted within the community itself. Various juridical acts (such as the emancipation of slaves) were also carried out in the community, sometimes in the synagogue.[31] Despite all this, the papyri have shown that the Jews of Egypt frequently appealed to the government courts and offices, and were also influenced in their mode of living by the general Hellenistic legal system; on this question we shall speak below in chapter 4.

The ghetto, in the late sense of the term, that is, as a special compulsory Jewish place of residence, was unknown to the Diaspora Jews of the Hellenistic and Roman epochs. Nevertheless, it may be said that at this time began the process which later led to the organization of Jewish life within the walls of the ghetto. There was here no external coercion; the Jews settled voluntarily in each other's vicinity, as they have been accustomed to do down to the present day. In Alexandria two quarters of the city were regarded as Jewish, and in Apollinopolis Magna (Upper Egypt) one quarter was full of Jews.[32] In Halicarnassus the Jewish population was concentrated by the seashore (or at least that was where their synagogue stood).[33]

At Sardis the Jews themselves requested the city to give them a special place to settle "so that they would be able to gather there with their women and children for prayer and traditional worship of God"; and the city consented, giving them "a place to build houses and to settle in."[34] Here the Jews themselves appear as the founders of the ghetto, the chief reason for their action being their desire to preserve their national and religious mode of life. Josephus uses approximately the same reason when he seeks to explain to anti-Semites why the Jews in Alexandria settled in one permanent locality. In his words, the kings (the *diadochi*) granted the place to the Jews in order to enable them to lead a pure life and avoid being forced to assimilate among their neighbors (*War* II, 488). It is clear enough that not the kings but the

Jews themselves saw to this; like the Jews of Sardis, those of Alexandria aspired to concentrate their settlement within a fixed area of land in order to create for themselves their traditional life and atmosphere. And this was the practice, no doubt, in other cities as well.[35]

So far we have spoken of the Jewish community as a normal *politeuma*, and have stressed the fact that its existence was not opposed in practice to the general Hellenistic procedure. However, we said above that those scholars who saw the Jewish communities as organizations *sui generis* were also right. Indeed, not all the questions connected with the existence of the Jewish communities can be solved in the normal way. The main point is that the Jewish religion could not exist in the Graeco-Roman world without certain privileges. The first and most important condition was for the Jews not to be obliged to take part in the cult of the gods. It is true that the ancient world was unacquainted with religious persecutions and no one cared what deity reigned in his neighbor's home. But religion was an organic part of the political system of the Greek city, and we have shown above (p. 28) that the Greeks knew nothing of the modern principle of the separation of Church and State. One might (with the consent of the citizens) introduce new deities into the city; but to despise the old gods, especially the chief of them who was guardian of the urban community, was forbidden.

Nor, naturally, might one abandon the official cult of the state, which in the Hellenistic and Roman period took on the permanent form of the deification of the kings and emperors. All these things were accepted by the Syrians, Tyrians, Sidonians, Egyptians and others who received the Grecian gods into their pantheons without opposition; but they could not be accepted by the Jews. The God of Israel acknowledged no rivals, nor could one pray to Him and simultaneously offer sacrifices to another deity. The cult of the gods was in Jewish eyes the complete negation of Judaism. The existence of the Jewish communities was therefore bound up with the exemption of the Jews by the authorities from participation in the cult of the Greek deities, and this was its negative condition. But there were also positive conditions. In order to enable the Jews to retain their customs and live "according to their ancestral laws," the external world had to show consideration for the fundamentals of the Jewish religion and avoid coercing the Jews—intentionally or otherwise—into transgressing the commandments of the Torah. It was difficult to observe the Sabbath rest if there was need to appear in a Greek court on that day or to serve in the forces. The Jewish communities, therefore, demanded that an exceptional legal status be introduced on their behalf, and that this status be guaranteed to them by privileges under the auspices of the authorities.[36]

The character of these privileges can be judged only on the basis of examples from the Roman period. Josephus has preserved in the *Antiquities* a large number of official documents in favor of the Jews from the time of Julius Caesar to that of Claudius, and fortunately these documents are free from suspicion of forgery.[37] They may therefore be utilized; and as the Romans made no important innovations in the countries which they conquered, but generally confirmed the *status quo*, we may relate the results of our inquiry to the Hellenistic period which we are discussing in the present work.

Before we proceed to an analysis of the documents, let us remark on the fact that there exists no document which exempts the Jews from the duty of participating in the worship of the gods. Precisely this privilege, the most important of them all, on which the actual existence of Jewry in the Greek world depended, is nowhere mentioned in the documents. It might be thought that the non-survival of such documents is due to chance, but this is not the case; if we look into the question more deeply, we shall see that the exemption of the Jews from the cult of the gods could not be stated in an official document. For could anyone—whether Greek king, Roman governor or Greek city—write the words: "I permit the Jews not to respect the gods"? No one could demand of the Greeks that they emphasize this point. The same was true in respect of the cult of the kings and emperors: only once do we find, in an official document, a trace of the exemption of the Jews from the worship of the divine Caesar, but this emphasis had a special reason connected with contemporary events;[38] generally the documents pass over this question in complete silence.

The government affected not to have heard anything of the Jewish refusal to honor the gods and the kings, thereby confirming the *status quo* and protecting Jewish liberty of worship. There was, however, a certain danger in this silence. When the anti-Semites began to undermine the privileges of the Jews, the latter could proudly point to the official documents of the emperors in which all their rights were recorded. But when the Jew-haters accused the Jews of lack of reverence for the gods, the Jews could not answer their enemies: "*By law* we are exempted from pagan worship," and the religious and moral replies which they did make had no influence on the Greeks. It should be observed that reverence for the gods proved the stumbling-block to the Jews in their struggle for civic rights in the Greek states.

The observance of the Sabbath and festivals was an integral part of the right of the Jewish community "to live according to its ancestral laws," hence it needed no special confirmation. We nevertheless read in the documents that the Romans accorded special recognition to the sanctity of the Sabbath and granted the Jews permission to celebrate it according to the commandments of Judaism, while the Greek cities also, on Roman demand, acknowledged this Jewish privilege.[39] The reason for this special confirmation was the fact that the Jews refused to appear on Sabbaths at official offices on business which also concerned Greeks. The latter were not always considerate about this refusal on the part of the Jews,[40] hence there was need for separate documentary emphasis of the right to celebrate the Sabbath, and thus we find it in the document of Augustus.[41]

Another important privilege was connected with Sabbath observance, namely, exemption from military service. In the year 43 B.C.E., Dolabella freed the Jews of Asia Minor from military service in accordance with the request of Hyrcanus the High Priest (*Ant.* XIV, 223ff.). We learn from Dolabella's rescript that the Jews had enjoyed this privilege previously,[42] perhaps by order of Julius Caesar, and there is reason to think that it was given only to Jews who were Roman citizens.[43] The connection between the release of Jews from army service and the keeping of the Sabbath was well emphasized in Dolabella's letter: Hyrcanus wrote to him that the Jews "cannot serve in the army because they are forbidden to bear arms on the Sabbath days, or to march."

How far this was true can be seen from the case of John Hyrcanus when he accompanied Antiochus Sidetes on his campaign against the Parthians: the entire Greek army was compelled to wait two days till the Jewish holidays were over (on Josephus' conjecture, the Sabbath and the Festival of Pentecost which fell on a Sunday) and John Hyrcanus' force could continue its journey (*Ant.* XIII, 251-2).

Nevertheless, there is no need to exaggerate the importance of this privilege; we have seen above (p. 279), and shall see again later, that in the Hellenistic period the Jews served willingly in the armed forces, especially as fortress garrison-troops or in special Jewish battalions such as that of the *katoikoi* of the territory of Onias in Egypt; and it is therefore to be supposed that the release of Jews mentioned in the Roman documents had some special reason.[44]

One of the most important privileges in Jewish eyes was the permission to collect money and to send it to Jerusalem. Augustus stressed this in the clearest possible fashion (*Ant.* XVI, 162ff.), not being satisfied with mere permission, but also classifying the money as "sacred funds": anyone who stole it was liable to the death-penalty as a *hierosylos*, one guilty of sacrilege. Agrippa made the penalty inflicted on the robbers even severer: according to his letter to the citizens of Ephesus (*Ant.* XVI, 167/8), the accused could even be taken from sanctuary and must be handed over to the Jews. This privilege was much resented by the Greek cities, hence the Romans saw need to reemphasize its importance in various rescripts sent to them.[45] We cannot say what the judicial position of the dispatch of moneys in the Hellenistic period was and whether the Ptolemies and Seleucids also assisted the undertaking. On the basis of analogy we may suppose that this privilege also found legal expression as early as the Hellenistic period. The sums of money collected among the Jews were not small, and this fact was apt to tempt the Greeks to confiscate the money and to use it for the needs of their cities.[46]

These were the chief privileges enjoyed by the Jews at the beginning of the Roman period, and most probably also in the Hellenistic period. They were an essential condition to the existence of the Jewish communities; without them the Jews could not have exercised their right to live according to their ancestral laws and would have been in danger of assimilation among the Greeks. However, the days of the ghetto were not yet. The Hellenistic and Roman period was a period of the association of peoples, of the fusion of East and West. The tempo of public life was swift; developing commerce drew remote elements together and destroyed barriers between countries and peoples. The large cities founded in this period, Alexandria, Antioch and the rest, swiftly took on an international aspect both in the composition of their inhabitants and in the mixed culture which was created and developed there. It was impossible to live amid this tumultuous life without taking part in it.

The Jews, too, could not remain within the frame of their communities; they also saw need to draw near to the Greeks and to participate in the vigorous life of the cities and states. But that life, which was international from the cultural and racial points of view, was from a legal point of view internally bound up with the traditional Greek outlook; both under the Hellenistic monarchs and in the Roman period the Greek city continued to be the supreme institution of political life, despite the fact that new historical conditions had destroyed its former liberty. Anyone who desired to participate in the cultural and public life of this environment, and to play any part whatever in the world at large, had first to be a citizen of a Greek city. The question therefore is whether or not the Jews possessed citizen-rights in the Greek cities.

The question of the civic rights of the Jews in the Greek cities has attracted special attention among scholars and caused prolonged controversy in learned literature. While some scholars—Schürer, Juster, Klausner, De Sanctis and Momigliano[47]—believe that the Jews in Greek towns enjoyed equality of rights, others[48] reject this supposition entirely, or accept it with certain limitations.

There is good reason for these differences of opinion, arising out of the inconsistency prevailing in our sources. Every scholar can find authority for his views in the writings of Josephus or Philo, and can adduce proofs to strengthen his theories from some papyrus or Greek inscription or from the apocryphal books of the period. Nor are these contradictions in the sources due to chance: the question of the acquisition of citizenship became a "burning question" at the beginning of the Roman period, and created enmity between the Jews and Greeks; hence it is not surprising that the literary sources of the period do not excel in neutrality and tend to exaggerate—sometimes even to falsify—the state of affairs in regard to it. I refer particularly to the writings of Josephus, on which all those scholars rely who argue that Jews and Greeks possessed equal rights. We shall see later that on this question Josephus is to be estimated, in the main, not as a historian but as a Jewish apologist, which of course diminishes the historical value of his accounts.

The investigation of the question, then, has to be based first of all on historical sources whose authenticity is undoubted, that is, on official documents. Only after the situation has been made clear by these sources, may we turn to the literary sources also. In regard to the latter, one must remember that they are not strict in their use of legal terms, a fact which makes historical inquiry much more difficult. In the classical period the Greeks created a detailed terminology for juridical concepts and used it with great precision. In the Hellenistic period, and much more so in the Roman, these concepts to a large degree lost their legal refinement and precision. In popular language, for example, every inhabitant of Alexandria was "an Alexandrian," although from a legal point of view this appellation denoted only citizens of the city, and not simple residents. In official documents, indeed, the ancient concepts are preserved in their exact meaning, but this is not so in the works of authors, most of whom followed the popular language of the masses. We cannot depend on them, therefore, when we seek to solve the problem of Jewish rights in the Greek cities, since the problem is mainly a legal one.

Before we study the question itself, let us try to define precisely what it is, in order that we ourselves should not confuse the legal concepts. The question is: Did the Jews possess *civic* rights in the Greek cities, that is, those same rights which the citizens of the Greek city possessed? I have especially emphasized the word "civic," because the difficulty of the question turns on this word. There is no doubt that the Jews had rights, namely, those national rights and privileges which have been discussed above. The question is whether, besides these, the Jews had all those municipal rights which every Greek member of the city had; in other words, whether the Jewish community took part in the town's public life, for example, in the conduct of municipal affairs, the election of magistrates, and the like.

It must further be remembered that the question concerns communities, or at least large groups within the community, and not isolated individuals. The latter could obtain citizen-rights by special resolution of the *demos* of the city, especially where Hellenizing Jews were concerned. But the matter is not so simple in regard to entire communities. Here we may ask: could the Greek town have granted citizen-rights to people who did not acknowledge the city's official cult? Could the whole Jewish community as a peculiar collective have received citizen franchise, although this was given only by special decision of the municipal assembly, and generally individually? Is it possible that every Jew, insofar as he was a member of the organized Jewish community, was also a member of the Greek *polis*, and if this was not possible, where was the demarcation between Jews who were citizens of the *polis* and Jews who were simple residents?

Historical inquiry is generally conducted in chronological order; but in our case this is not the method to be followed. The best sources come from the Roman period (the first century C.E.), while the Hellenistic period has left only isolated and deficient notices. In our inquiry, then, we shall proceed in reverse chronological order and pass to the ancient period only after we have clarified the state of the problem in the Roman epoch.

It is no coincidence that the beginning of the Roman period yields rich material on the civic rights of the Jews. From the time of Augustus on, an important change took place in the situation of the Jews of Egypt, chiefly of the Jews of Alexandria, and the question of Jewish citizenship in the Greek city ceased to be simply a question of honor, and assumed the form of a decidedly practical problem. Augustus differentiated clearly between the Greeks and the other inhabitants of Egypt: the former enjoyed various privileges, were made partners in the institutions of local government and were regarded as civilized people; the latter were classed as simple subjects and the whole weight of taxation fell upon them.

The external sign which distinguished the two sections of the population from one another was the payment of the poll-tax (known in Egypt as the *laographia*); this had not existed under the Ptolemies, but was introduced into Egypt by Augustus.[49] The payment of the tax signified not merely a grievous monetary burden, but personal human degradation; the citizen of a Greek town was exempt from it, whereas the inhabitants of the native villages paid it.[50] This situation, created in Egypt as a result of Augustus' financial reforms, was a heavy blow to the Jews, particularly to the Jews of Alexandria. The upper classes of the Jewish population of the city were profoundly imbued with Greek culture, and to be made to pay the poll-tax was for them a grave effront. The question was not merely financial; it was much more cultural: where did a cultivated Jew belong—among the cultured Greeks who enjoyed all the privileges bestowed by citizenship in a Greek city, or among the Egyptian fellahin who paid the poll-tax as members of a subject people inured to endless stripes? The Jews of Alexandria could not consent to their own degradation in Greek society and began a desperate struggle for citizen rights in the city. We may term this struggle, in modern language, a struggle for emancipation.[51]

No wonder then that this period, full of severe clashes with the Greeks, left important traces in contemporary documents and literature. Let us first analyze the documents, as they introduce us into the actual process of the struggle, unaccompanied by any attempt to distort the facts.

A papyrus of the time of Augustus contains a petition addressed to the Roman governor of Egypt, Gaius Turannius. The petition was written by a man calling himself an "Alexandrian"; but this word is canceled in the papyrus and in its stead, between the lines, are written the words "a Jew from Alexandria." Whether the Jew himself corrected the error, or whether it was done by an official who revised the petition, the meaning of the correction is quite clear. This Jew thought that he was an "Alexandrian," that is, a citizen of the city of Alexandria; but when he tendered his petition it was ascertained that he was unable to prove his civic status, and he was forced to designate himself by the humble and civically insignificant title of "Jew from Alexandria."

In the papyrus (which is unfortunately quite torn and almost indecipherable) the word *laographia* (poll-tax) is mentioned three times, and this explains the reason for the petition. Apparently the Jew was complaining to the governor because he had been subjected—unjustly in his view—to the poll-tax, and was requesting exemption from the obligation. He may have had some special reason for requesting this exemption, for it is clear from the petition that his father had been an Alexandrian citizen. We do not know whether this Jew gained a hearing from the governor, but the petition itself evidences the strenuous struggle of the Jews of Alexandria for civic rights in their town, a struggle carried on individually by everyone who was hit by the *laographia* decree.[52]

Another papyrological document, also of the Augustan period, reflects the Greek resistance to this "struggle for emancipation." An anonymous person, speaking in the name of the citizens of Alexandria, petitions the Emperor Augustus to permit the Alexandrians to have their own council. A council of this sort, claims the writer, will benefit Rome and Alexandria equally, taking care that people owing payment of the *laographia* should not enter their names on the list of the *epheboi*, thereby exempting themselves from payment of the poll-tax, an act apt to injure the state-treasury; and it will, on the other hand, prevent people without culture and education from contaminating the purity of the city of Alexandria by enter-ing the list of citizens.[53] Although the Jews are not alluded to explicitly, it is clear that it is they and the Egyptians who are meant, since these are the people "without culture and educa-tion" who, against the will of the Alexandrians, are unscrup-ulously daring to penetrate the ranks of the citizens, for this purpose registering themselves or their sons as pupils of the gymnasia (for such registration opened to the young Greek the way to citizenship).[54] The Alexandrian spokesman, therefore, requests protection from the Emperor against these undesirables.

Still another papyrus takes the reader into the most fateful year of the struggle for emanci-pation, the year 41 C.E., when the "Jewish question" came up for arbitration at Rome before the Emperor Claudius, and dele-gations from both sides, citizens of Alexandrians on the one hand and Jewish residents of the city on the other, appeared before him to defend their positions.[55] One of the leaders of the Alexandrian anti-Semites, the *gymnasiarch* Isidoros, disput-ing with the Jewish King Agrippa before the throne of the Emperor, utters these words about the Jews of the city: "They are not like the Alexandrians, but in their way of life (they resemble) the Egyptians. Are they not like those who pay tribute (the poll-tax)?" Here again we have the emphasis on the remoteness of the Jews from the Greeks, and on their affinity, where civic status is concerned, to the Egyptians who pay the hated tribute.

I conclude the survey of the documents with the famous letter of the Emperor Claudius to the Alexandrians in the year 41, one of the most interesting documents in papyrological literature.[56] This is not the place to enter into the details of this rescript; we shall only indi-cate the points which directly concern our subject. Claudius addresses "the Alexandrians" on the one hand and "the Jews" on the other, which shows that he does not consider the Jews as belonging to "the Alexandrians," that is, as citizens of the city. He prohibits the Jews from participating in the athletic con-tests held by the city magistrates (the *gymnasiarchs* and *kos-*

metes), in other words, he withholds from them permission to receive a gymnasium education. This prohibition is especially interesting in view of the fact that a few lines earlier Claudius has confirmed the entry into the citizen body of all those registered as *epheboi* prior to his accession; in other words, he has officially established the inner connection between gymnasium education and admission into the citizen body.

In conclusion, Claudius warns the Jews of Alexandria not to dare to aspire to additional rights, but to be satisfied with the abundant benefits which their sojourn "in a foreign city" can bestow upon them. If the Emperor Claudius, who that year had investigated the problem of the Jews of Alexandria in all its details, reached the conclusion (and published it in an official document) that, to the Jews, Alexandria was a foreign city, although the Jewish community had existed there for hundreds of years, there is no doubt that in the view of the authorized interpreters of the law at Rome, just as in that of the authorities of the *polis* of Alexandria itself, the Jews were not citizens of the town. Claudius' letter set an official stamp on the claims of the anti-Semites and ended the struggle of the Alexandrian Jews for emancipation once and for all. The Jewish attempt to take up a position in Greek society, as people possessing equal rights with the citizens of the town, ended in utter defeat.[57]

The papyrological documents of the period of Augustus and Claudius, therefore, throw a clear light on the civic position of the Jews of Alexandria and solve the problem in a negative sense. But still more important, they introduce the reader into the heated atmosphere of the period and show the Jews pursuing the citizen-rights which the Greeks refuse to grant them. Claudius saw need to stop the Jews penetrating the select circle of Greek youth which was studying in the gymnasia, a sign that in actual fact Jews had penetrated thither in order to prepare the ground for the acquisition of citizen-rights. Nor is there doubt that there were Jews who had attained their aim and finally joined the ranks of the citizens. This fact doubtless caused much bitterness among the Greeks, hence Claudius prohibited the Jews from aspiring to additional rights and ordered them to be satisfied with what they had, namely, the traditional rights of the Jewish community.

However, the Jews were not prepared so easily to forego their position in Greek society and to sink to the level of the Egyptian fellahin. All possible

literary means were brought into play to prove to their antag-
onists the justness of their claims. This propaganda literature,
like all literature created for political purposes, was chiefly one-
sided and did not shrink from exaggerations, distortions of fact
or even from falsification of documents. We have to bear in
mind these characteristics of Jewish Alexandrian literature at the
beginning of the Roman period when we turn to its works with
the object of studying the question of Jewish rights in Alexandria and the other Greek towns. It is clear at the outset that we
have to exercise the most stringent caution with regard to it.
We will begin with two
works by Philo, *Against Flaccus* and *The Delegation to Gaius,*
written a short time after the riots against the Jews of the year
37, with the aim of denouncing to the Roman authorities those
guilty of their perpetration: that is, the leaders of Alexandrian
anti-Semitism, the Roman governor of Egypt, Flaccus, and the
mad Emperor Gaius Caligula.[58] Those scholars who hold that
the Greeks and Jews had equal rights endeavor to find in these
books authority for their view;[59] but we shall soon see that
theories cannot be based on isolated expressions of Philo, and
the only place that speaks of their rights in more or less clear
fashion proves the opposite of what these scholars have sought
to find in it. Of primary importance is the fact that Philo
employs legal terms in the same way as the people of Alexandria, that is, without dwelling on their precise juridical significance. Once (*Flacc.* 47) he calls the Jews who dwelt in the
Greek cities *politai* (citizens) and on another occasion (*ib.* 172)
designates the Jews of Alexandria as *katoikoi,* though these terms
are mutually contradictory. The name "Alexandrians" is also
applied by Philo to the Jews of the city (*Leg.* 183, 350), without any connection with its legal meaning.
Philo speaks frequently of
the civic organization of the Jews of Alexandria and calls it
a *politeia,* but does not interpret this complicated term.[60] He
tells of Flaccus' attempt to destroy the internal organization of
the Jewish community of Alexandria and to deny to it its share
of political rights (*Flacc.* 53); but what was the real content of
the term "political rights" we do not know; at any rate, there is
no reason to see in them an allusion to citizen rights, since the
term *dikaia* also denoted Jewish privileges.[61] In the same place
Philo accuses Flaccus of an attempt to declare the Jews "strangers and aliens" in Alexandria, which informs us that the Jews
were not regarded there as "strangers."[62] This was never in

315

doubt, but it cannot be concluded from this that they were citizens of the city, since *katoikoi* without rights also frequently belonged to the permanent residents.

On one occasion Philo had the opportunity of speaking at length of Jewish rights; but it was an unlucky hour. As he stood before Gaius, the Emperor said to him: "I want to know what are the legal bases of your political organization?"[63] Philo was prepared to reply to this important question, but at that moment Gaius turned his back upon him; the planning of the great building which he was in the act of visiting, and the question which color was more suitable for the windowpanes, engaged him much more than the speech of an Alexandrian philosopher concerning Jewish rights. Thus we too have lost an excellent opportunity of hearing Philo speak on "the Jewish question."

There is only one place in Philo's writings which is really important for us, and is relied on by the supporters of the theory of equal rights; but it can easily be shown that it actually disproves the theory. In his book on the pogroms in Alexandria, Philo mentions the acts of violence wrought against the members of the Jewish *gerousia:* thirty-eight of them were taken to the theater and there flogged. Philo voices his indignation, not only against this brutal act itself, but also against the way the punishment was carried out. The members of the *gerousia* were beaten with the whip, a punishment reserved solely for Egyptians, while citizens of Alexandria had the privilege of being beaten with rods, and by special constables. "This custom," adds Philo, "the governors preceding Flaccus observed *also with regard to ourselves,* and Flaccus too observed it at the beginning of his activity" (*Flacc.* 79).

From this passage scholars have sought to deduce that the Jews of Alexandria possessed equal rights with the Greeks, but the words "also with regard to ourselves" point to just the opposite: Philo is stressing equality of rights in the matter of corporal punishment precisely because it was not a normal thing.[64] Had the Jews belonged among the citizens of Alexandria, he would have had no need of this emphasis, since it would have been in any case clear that what was proper for the Greeks was also proper for the Jews. There is here, then, no evidence of equality of rights.

Nevertheless one thing of importance is to be learned from this passage: although the juridical position of the Jews of Alexandria obligated no special attitude to them, such an attitude had in course of time grown up at least in respect of isolated questions such as forms of corporal punishment. From this we deduce that the Alexandrian Jews, in their claim to be citizens, could point to certain practices established in relation to themselves during the Ptolemaic period in order to bridge the gap between the Jews and the Greeks. This unstable situation was upset at the beginning of the Roman period when the imposition of the poll-tax on the entire non-Greek population put an end to any attempt to efface the difference between one and the other. The new situation gave the anti-Semites a pretext to call in question even those rights which had been the foundation of the autonomous life of the Jewish community from the beginning of its existence in Alexandria and had no connection whatever with civic rights.[65]

This conclusion from the books of Philo is also in harmony with our information from another source of nearly contemporary composition, namely, the *Third Book of the Maccabees*. The book's historical value has been discussed above (p. 274f.), and we have seen that it is not to be regarded as a serious historical source. However, its lack of historical worth does not mean that individual bits of information within it are not true; for writers of fiction also describe the historical environment, in accordance with the actual conditions of the period, in order that the story itself should make on the reader an impression of authenticity, and it is even more important when such writers do so unintentionally and inadvertently. As a result, valuable information can be derived even from books of the type of *III Maccabees*.

For us the most important item of information preserved in the book is the story about Ptolemy Philopator's desire to compel the Jews to worship Dionysus. He threatened to class them with those inhabitants of Egypt who paid the poll-tax (*laographia*) and to make them all slaves if they refused to obey him (2.28). But to those who obeyed, he promised equality of rights with the Alexandrians (2.30). These two sentences settle the date of the book's composition with sufficient accuracy. We are in the period when the levying of the poll-tax divided the entire population of Egypt into two blocs—those that paid the *laographia* on the one hand, and the citizens of the Greek cities on the other. The Jews did not belong to the second bloc, but apparently their adherence to the first was also a new phenomenon, since the author of *III Maccabees* identifies the payment of the *laographia* with a position of slavery and sees in the census carried out to determine the number of taxpayers an atrocity against the Jewish people.

But we can learn from *III Maccabees* more than simply what a depressing effect the imposition of the poll-tax in Augustus' time had upon the Jews. It is a fact of great importance that the granting of civic rights is bound up, according to the author, with the condition of the Jews acknowledging the official cult of the god Dionysus. Here the author was using a real historical detail: Ptolemy IV Philopator was a great devotee of that god.[66] It is not indeed to be concluded from this that *III Maccabees*' entire story of Philopator's attempt to compel the Jews to worship Dionysus is true, as some scholars think.[67] The historical worth of the story lies in that the obtaining of civic rights was bound up with the Hellenization of the Jews, in other words, with their participation in the cult of the Greek gods, and not for nothing did the anti-Semite Apion emphasize this religious question.[68]

Especially interesting is *III Maccabees*' attitude to the question of the acquisition of citizenship. He puts into Ptolemy Philopator's mouth an account of the events in the form of an official letter to his officials (3.12-29). The king writes that he had intended to grant the Jews citizen rights in Alexandria, but the latter refused to listen to him, not only rejecting "this citizenship whose value is so great," but also seeking to turn against the king those who were ready to obey him (3.21-23). In another passage (2.31), the writer speaks with much bitterness of the Jews who had betrayed "the city of righteousness" for privileges in "the city" (of Alexandria).

The author's intention is quite clear. He wishes to tell his readers: "Do not betray your religion! You do not, indeed, possess citizen rights, but they are not worth the betrayal of the God of your fathers. Look how evil is the lot of the traitors and how great God's providence for those who remain loyal to His Covenant." This literary warfare is directed against those Jews to whom Claudius wrote: "Do not pursue additional rights and know to be content with the abundant benefits which the alien city can bestow upon you." Concerning the assimilating Jews, the Roman Emperor and the orthodox Jewish writer used the same language.

Next comes the testimony of Josephus. We have already more than once had occasion to use the great legacy of that historian, and frequently found cause to know that not everything he says can be accepted as scientific history. It should be remembered even more especially that he is incapable of giving correct answers to legal questions, for he did not possess sufficient Greek education for this purpose (as, for example, Philo did). He did not even know the Greek language thoroughly,[69] much less was he expert in Greek law or in the correct use of Greek legal terms. Secondly, it were well to remark that Josephus, like most ancient historians, had no clear notion of what we now call criticism of the sources. He generally copied his sources without troubling about the worth of the book before him, whether it was a respectable historical source, like I Maccabees, or a tendentious romance or historical legend, like the *Letter of Aristeas* and the annals of Joseph the Tobiad. Thirdly, and this is the main point, Josephus was not just a historian, but also a Jewish apologist, his aim being to raise the prestige of the Jewish nation in the eyes of the Greeks and to emphasize its finer characteristics.

In this respect he was following those Jewish writers who, at the beginning of the Roman period, created the polemical literature of whose low level we spoke above (p. 309). The struggle against anti-Semitism had shown these authors the best way of influencing the Greeks: it was necessary, not only to praise the Jews, but also to demonstrate to the Gentiles that they themselves, that is, their greatest and most honored representatives, had held the Jewish people in affection and esteem. This method provided the Jewish apologists with an excellent weapon in their disputes with the anti-Semites. What do the Greeks say? That the Jewish people are base and knavish, hating the gods and humankind alike, and that their customs are outlandish and strange? Yet Alexander the Great himself, Ptolemy Soter, Seleucus Nicator, Julius Caesar and many others, honored the Jews, worshiped their God, employed Jews as soldiers, invited them to settle in the towns which they were about to found, granted them civic rights in those cities on a generous scale, and so forth. And if the Greeks refused to believe all these tales, the apologists would invite them to visit Jewish record-offices to be shown the documents drawn up by the kings and ministers, recording all these Jewish rights and privileges.

The Jews, indeed, really possessed such documents, but whether they were the same documents which the Jews had received from the kings themselves, whether their wording had not been slightly altered in the course of years and generations, or whether other documents had not been drawn up in the past whose contents contradicted those extant—is unknown to us, and in the first century C.E. was perhaps unknown even to the apologists themselves. But what they knew very well was the situation of the Jews in their own time, and since that situation did not satisfy Jewish demands and requirements from a juridical point of view, the apologists, including Josephus, endeavored to conceal its deficiencies and to represent it in brighter colors. The outcome of their work was that historical reality was in large measure distorted by them and that we stand helpless before their literary creations, unable to distinguish between historical truth and their gratuitous apologetic exaggerations.

After this brief foreword, we can approach the subject at hand, commencing with Jewish rights in Alexandria, to which Josephus devoted special attention.

"In the city of Alexandria," says Josephus in *War* (II, 487ff.), "there was a long-standing quarrel between the Jews and the inhabitants, from the time that Alexander had utilized the bravery of the Jews in his war in Egypt and gave them, in return for their loyalty as allies, permission to settle in the city on the basis of equal rights with the Greeks. And in the days of his successors this right was retained by the Jews, and the kings also allotted a special place to them, in order that they should be able to lead their own life in greater purity and not mingle with aliens, also permitting them to be called Macedonians. And after the Romans had conquered the land of Egypt, neither the first emperor nor any of those that rose after him permitted detraction from the Jewish rights granted to them by Alexander."

In this extract there are three assumptions which deserve attention: (a) that the Jews had settled as early as the time of Alexander and had received their rights from him; (b) that these rights were equal to those of the Greeks, that is, that the Jews were citizens of the city; (c) that the Ptolemies gave the Jews equal legal standing with the Macedonians. These same three assumptions recur in other passages of Josephus' writings. In *Ant.* (XII, 8), he writes of Ptolemy I: "The king settled many Jews in the fortresses of Egypt and also in Alexandria and gave them equality of rights with the Macedonians." In *Contra Apionem* (II, 35), Josephus ascribes, not to Ptolemy, but to Alexander himself the granting of Macedonian rights to the Jews, and adds, "And to this day their contingent (*phylé*) is called by the name of Macedonians."

In the same passage Josephus speaks with much bitterness of Apion, who has dared to cast doubt upon the full privileges of the Jews of Alexandria. "If Apion has read the letters of King Alexander and Ptolemy son of Lagos and if he has seen the documents of the kings of Egypt who rose after Alexander, and the stele which stands in Alexandria and contains the privileges which the great Julius Caesar granted to the Jews—if, I repeat, he has read all this and, notwithstanding, has dared to write the contrary (to what he found written there), he is a knave; and if he has not heard anything at all of these things—then he is a man of no education. And if he is surprised that the Jews can be called Alexandrians, it is merely the same lack of education. For all those invited to take part in the foundation of any new settlement, even though they are entirely different from one another, are called after the founders. And why seek examples among others? The Jews who reside in Antioch are called Antiochians, since the founder Seleucus gave them their civic constitution. The Jews who reside in Ephesus and the rest of Ionia are also known by the same names as the citizens born there, because the Diadochi gave them permission to be so" (*ib*. 37-39).

Let us consider Josephus' first assumption, that the Jews took part in the foundation of the city of Alexandria and received civic rights in the town from Alexander. This assumption lacks historical foundation, and without doubt Josephus was here using an Alexandrian legend, whose apologetic aim was to raise the prestige of the Jews of the city in the eyes of the Greeks.[70] The reason produced by Josephus for the receipt of rights from Alexander should be noted: that the Jews obtained them in return for their loyalty to the former as allies in his Egyptian war. From this it follows that the Jews accompanied Alexander to Egypt and aided him to conquer the country. But the truth is that Alexander never "fought" in Egypt and never "conquered" the country by force; it came into his possession without any resistance on the part of the inhabitants (cf. above, p. 4). Even if we assume that in this early period there were in his army auxiliary contingents recruited from the conquered peoples, we cannot believe that there were Jews among them, since the latter were then entirely unknown as a warlike people.

It is not difficult to discover the apologetic basis of the story. Josephus (or the source from which he drew his information) wished to show that the Jews had come to Egypt together with the Greeks and had aided Alexander to conquer the ignorant Egyptian natives; hence it was only right that they (the Jews) should be counted among the superior circles of the conquerors and not be equated with the conquered. This outlook had a basis in the conditions of public life in Egypt at the beginning of the Roman period. As we have seen above, the difference between the Greeks and the Egyptians from a juridical point of view became very sharp from the time of Augustus onward. It is to be noted that the Jews used every means to explain to the Romans and the Greeks that they were completely different from the Egyptian native population.[71] We see, therefore, that Josephus' information on Alexander and the Jews in Egypt is built on late political attitudes; hence the story of Jewish settlement in Alexandria as citizens in Alexander's time is entirely baseless.[72]

Josephus' two other assumptions—that the Jews possessed rights like the Macedonians', and that they had civic rights equal to those of the Greeks—require closer consideration. For a long time scholars failed to notice the contradiction between the two suppositions, since the Macedonians were also "Greeks."[73] Only after the appearance of Schubart's article,[74] which utilized new material from the papyri, did scholars begin to distinguish between these two different concepts. And, indeed, if we suppose that there was no difference between the Greeks and the Macedonians as to the scope of their civic rights, why should Josephus have stressed in four places that the Jews possessed equal privileges with the Macedonians?

The over-all name of the citizens of Alexandria was Alexandrians, and the citizens were generally known as "Greeks," not as Macedonians. There is no doubt that "Macedonians" is here a definite legal term, and not simply an ethnic group. We have already seen (p. 320) that in course of time the adjective lost its ethnic content and became a military term, by which certain formations were indicated irrespective of the ethnic origin of each individual soldier. This change of concepts explains the curious fact that in Josephus' time there was a Jewish contingent (*phylé*) of Macedonians in Alexandria (*C. Ap.* II, 36). The existence of this *phylé* has been placed beyond doubt by the publication in Berlin of a papyrus of the time of the Emperor Augustus.[75] Here two persons are mentioned who in another papyrus are termed "Macedonians";[76] they are applying to the Jewish records office for confirmation of their documents. It cannot be supposed, of course, that these "Macedonians" were racially such, for what business would such people have had with a Jewish office? We thus have two Jews known as "Macedonians," and they are apparently members of the Jewish-Macedonian "contingent" of Alexandria. Jews such as these were, according to Josephus, "equal in rights to the Macedonians"; this is quite possible, but the question is whether those rights were identical with those of the Greek citizens of Alexandria, as Josephus thought, and as some modern scholars have thought with him. The papyrological material furnishes a negative reply to this question. The soldiers called "Macedonians" in the papyrological documents are dispersed over the whole of Egypt, fulfill important duties in the army, and sometimes at the royal court, but have no connection with Alexandrian citizenship.[77]

The Macedonians might have been citizens of Alexandria if they were among the first inhabitants, but everything that we know of the town's foundation and early organization proves that the first settlers were Greeks and Egyptians, not Macedonians (see p. 513, n. 72). However, there was undoubtedly in the city a Macedonian garrison which grew in the course of time as the city developed, and especially when Alexandria became the capital of the Ptolemies.[78] At some period (perhaps under the "philo-Semitic" Philopator), a group of Jewish soldiers seems to have been accepted into this garrison, and their *phylé* survived down to Josephus' time as an independent unit within the Jewish community of Alexandria. The internal organization of this *phylé* was probably military, but no information on the subject has been preserved. Information on the scope of these Jews' rights has also been lost, and only one negative assumption can be accepted with complete confidence: that they were never citizens of Alexandria.[79]

Josephus, however, not content with declaring the equality of privileges of Jews and Macedonians, says that the Jews also possessed equality of rights with the Greeks, that is to say, with the citizens of the city. How can we explain this statement, which stands in clear contradiction to what is known to us from the documents? I do not think that Josephus is to be suspected of deliberate deception. He says what he says because he sincerely believes it. In the first place, like most modern scholars, he did not realize the difference between "Macedonians" and "Greeks," and gave to the legal term "Macedonian" a racial signification. He considered them to be "citizens of Alexandria in the full sense of the word" (Schürer). Secondly, in his time there certainly were Jews in Alexandria who possessed civic rights, and there were others who called themselves "Alexandrians" although not authorized to do so, and their limited number grew considerably in Josephus' imagination.[80] Thirdly, Josephus himself was not an Alexandrian, and his information on the city depended on what others told him, and their accounts, derived from apologetic circles of the Jews of Egypt, did not excel in historical accuracy. The consequence was that Josephus transmitted certain assumptions with complete definiteness, although he had no means of proving them. He says that the Jews had obtained rights equal to the Greeks' from Alexander (*War* II, 487) and hints that they had documents and letters from that ruler himself, or from his successors, that testified to this.

But it is interesting that, while he quotes several documents of the Roman governors (*Ant.* XIV, 190ff., etc.), he does not cite a single one by Alexander or his first successors, although as a historian of repute he would certainly have utilized such papers had they really been available in the archives. Josephus accuses Apion of "lack of education" because he had not interested himself in these documents (*C. Ap.* II, 37), but in another passage (*Ant.* XIV, 187) Josephus himself admits that they were extremely difficult to utilize, because they were not to be found in the public records-offices (why?), but were kept only by the Jews, "and some barbarian peoples." But if it was hard for Apion to obtain these "buried" documents, Josephus, as Jew and historian, had certainly seen them, so why did he not keep copies of such important papers? Josephus, apparently, was no more expert in the matter than Apion. He hastens, therefore, to pass over this complicated question and points with satisfaction to the monument which Julius Caesar ("Augustus" should here be read[81]) erected in Alexandria and on which he wrote "that the Jews are citizens of Alexandria" (*Ant.* XIV, 188).

Even these plain words evoke skepticism. Why did not Josephus reproduce the text of the inscription on the monument verbatim? This he could certainly have done quite easily. And if we are to believe Josephus, that the statement was really inscribed on the monument, how could Apion have asked his question, on what authority the Jews were called Alexandrians? (*C. Ap.* II, 38). How could he, as an Alexandrian, not have seen the stele standing in the town where he lived? And how could the Emperor Claudius have prohibited the Jews their share in gymnasium education if they had possessed citizenship based on a permit from Augustus? Here too, it seems, Josephus was confusing juridical terms. In another passage (*C. Ap.* II, 37) he calls the privileges bestowed by Julius Caesar (read "Augustus") on the Jews *dikaiomata*, a term of many meanings used to denote, *inter alia*, also the Jewish national privileges; and there is no doubt that Augustus' monument contained precisely those privileges, and not the civic rights.[82] Here too there is no need to suspect Josephus of deliberate distortion of the truth; it is highly probable that he had not read the inscription on the stele himself, or that he had read it at a time when he was not interested in it as a historical source, and later reported on it at second hand when he was unable to authenticate how far the reports were accurate.[83]

In his exposition on the history of the Jews of Alexandria Josephus mentions in passing two events which may be useful for the study of the problem under discussion. During the famine which affected Egypt, in the time of the last Cleopatra, the Jews did not receive wheat from the government granaries (*C. Ap.* II, 60). Much the same occurred again in 19 C.E., when Germanicus distributed supplies of bread to the entire population except the Jews (*ib.* II, 63). Josephus attempts to justify Germanicus by pointing to the shortage of bread in the town. He may have been right; but in this case we may ask why did the insufficiency affect precisely the Jews? It is to be supposed that had the Jews been citizens, they too would have shared in the distribution of bread by lot, along with the rest of the citizens. No far-reaching conclusions can of course be drawn from these isolated items of information; but it cannot be ignored that their evidence speaks against Josephus' theory of Jewish rights of citizenship.

We have reviewed all the sources at our disposal, and we may now summarize our conclusions. The documents testify to the struggle which went on between the Jews and the Greeks (who were supported by the Roman authorities) for civic rights in Alexandria, and to the defeat of the Jews; in the year 41 C.E. they were told authoritatively that they must be content with their national privileges and not aspire to additional rights "in an alien city." Philo, who himself lived through the period of the struggle and devoted two books to an account of the Jewish situation in his day, does not say that the Jews enjoyed civic rights in Alexandria, but is content with vague general expressions in speaking of Jewish rights.

From Philo's books the conclusion may be drawn that, although certain rules of procedure had been fixed in relation to the Jews, derived from the civic procedure of Alexandria, these rules lacked the official seal of approval and remained permanently custom rather than law. The *Third Book of the Maccabees* indicates that the Jews lacked citizenship rights, but adds that these could be obtained by a complete surrender of Jewish tradition. Josephus is the only writer who states with confidence that the Jews enjoyed equality of rights with the Greeks; but his apologetic approach and legal inaccuracy deprive his conclusions of all historical value.

The sources of the early Roman period, it thus appears, solve the problem of civic rights in a negative fashion. In what measure may we utilize the results of our inquiry also with reference to the Hellenistic period? It is to be observed that no document or literary source of that period touches the question under discussion. This silence is, of course, very regrettable, but it is also instructive. If the documents and literary sources of the beginning of the Roman period speak a great deal of Jewish civic rights, the reason is that the question of obtaining them had become a burning one at that time, as a result of the imposition of the poll-tax on the Jews. Hence we conclude that in the Ptolemaic period when the poll-tax was nonexistent, the question was entirely absent from the agenda; at any rate, it was neither acute nor painful. Moreover, in the Roman period citizenship in the Greek towns became a preliminary stage for obtaining Roman privileges. And if this reason is not to be regarded as decisive, since the number of Alexandrian Jews who could hope to obtain Roman citizenship was not large, its value should not be underestimated as concerning a small group of Jews of wealth and political influence.[84]

When we turn to the Ptolemaic period we find ourselves in a much quieter atmosphere; the pursuit of citizen-rights is much more the result of Jewish development in the area of culture and in his way of life, than of a desire to gain genuine advantages from a juridical point of view. The citizens of Alexandria, like those of every Greek city, enjoyed a constitution of their own,[85] but the Jewish community also enjoyed the right "to live according to its ancestral laws" and possessed autonomy in the organization of its social, cultural and religious life. The citizens of every Greek town had their own municipal institutions and an elaborate system of officials; so did the Jewish community. Furthermore, while Greek Alexandria did not receive the privilege of a council either at the beginning of the Roman period or, apparently, in the late Hellenistic era, the Jewish community was the proud possessor of a council of elders of seventy-one members, a magnificent body which might well arouse the justifiable envy of every Greek![86]

The Alexandrians, indeed, enjoyed several privileges throughout the Ptolemaic state, as, for example, exemption from the labor service imposed upon the native Egyptians. But we have seen above that privileges of this sort were also given to the Jews, and if they were exempted from the baser form of corporal punishment in Alexandria, it may be assumed that they were also exempt from the *sordida munera* to which the Egyptians were subject. Why then should they have wanted to obtain civic privileges? Only one reason seems of special importance: the cultivated and assimilated Jew of Alexandria desired to be accepted in a Greek environment, and for this reason it suited him to be a citizen. It must be supposed, however, that such a Jew obtained citizenship individually, without the affair assuming any general public importance. He might do so by a special resolution of the Alexandrian people, in return for certain favors which he had bestowed upon the city;[87] alternatively he might be made a citizen by decision of one of the kings,[88] or he might "infiltrate" into the citizen-body illegally by finding his way into the gymnasium as a youth and later, as a graduate of this Greek institution, be regarded as a Greek and a citizen in every respect.[89] In most of these instances the Jew who aspired to the franchise was a man of wealth, respected also by the Greeks and accepted in government circles. His reception as a citizen of Alexandria bestowed upon him the last honor which he had till then lacked in the eyes of the Greek world.

We see then that the juridical status of the Jews of Alexandria was not a uniform one, and the question of civic rights is not to be solved by a simple positive or negative. We can distinguish three groups: 1. Jews who were citizens, that is, those individual Jews who had succeeded in acquiring the franchise personally. There is no doubt as to their existence, as this is confirmed by official documents,[90] and also by the general fact that there were assimilated Jews in the town to whom the question of the franchise was one of dignity. 2. Jews who had "infiltrated" in an unauthorized manner. Jews of this type no doubt became more numerous mainly at the end of the Ptolemaic period, when much confusion prevailed in Alexandria and political and civic order was frequently disturbed by riots and revolts. Their number grew even more at the beginning of the Roman period, when the obtaining of Alexandrian citizenship acquired particular importance. 3. The masses who were ordinary members of the Jewish community. These could not, of course, dream of belonging to the Greek *polis,* and for many of them such membership was undesirable, as it would have seemed like betrayal of ancestral tradition.

Having made clear the civic position of the Jews of Alexandria, we may turn to the other countries where Jews dwelt. We lack sources almost entirely, and Josephus is the only one who gives some information on the Jewish status in Asia Minor and Syria. Here too we have to be careful and not place complete reliance in his reports, since in this field also his books display the same deficiencies which have been remarked on above.

We have already alluded to Josephus' sentence concerning the Jews of Syrian Antioch: they were called "Antiochians" because Seleucus I, founder of the city, granted them civic status (*C. Ap.* II, 39). The same idea appears again (in *Ant.* XII, 119): "Seleucus Nicator gave them citizenship in the towns founded by him in Asia and Lower Syria, also in the capital Antioch itself, and made them equal in rights to the Macedonians and Greeks who were settled there; and this civic status exists to the present day." This distinction was obtained by the Jews from the kings of Asia because "they had accompanied them in their wars."

Here is the same erroneous outlook, recognizable by its apologetic stamp, which we have already observed in Josephus' writings concerning the Jews of Egypt: the Jews "assist" the kings of Macedonia to conquer the countries of the East, and in return for this favor they receive citizenship rights from them. No single document confirms Jewish settlement in the Hellenistic cities under Seleucus I, or their participation in the campaigns of the first Seleucid kings (see above, p. 319). The Jews of Palestine could have played no part in the history of the Syrian monarchs before the year 200 B.C.E. approximately. This did not apply to the Jews of Babylonia, who were under Seleucid rule from the beginning of their reign; but Josephus was barely interested in that part of the Diaspora and possessed no respectable sources on Jewish life in the Orient. As to his reports on Jewish equality of rights in Antioch and the other towns of Asia, they are clearly derived, not from official documents, but from the same source which he used in connection with the Jews of Alexandria, that is, some anonymous apologetic work.

It is interesting that Josephus himself sees need to strengthen his theory by some striking proof in order to make it more plausible to his readers. The proof which he furnishes for this purpose is, however, both feeble and irrelevant. Josephus says (*Ant.* XII, 120) that those Antiochian Jews who did not wish to use the olive oil of the Greeks received from the gymnasiarch a sum of money equivalent to the cost of the oil; and this aroused ill will among the Greeks. From this report it can only be inferred that the Jews had permission to use the municipal olive oil jointly with the citizens, not that they themselves were citizens.[91] (Analogous is the Alexandrian Jews' exemption from the more humiliating form of corporal punishment in common with the Greeks, although they were not citizens.) How obscure were the origins of Jewish privileges in Antioch in Josephus' time can be realized from the fact that even Josephus, when writing his *War,* had heard nothing whatever of the acquisition of these rights from Seleucus Nicator and thought that the kings who succeeded Antiochus Epiphanes (some 150 years after Seleucus) had bestowed equality of franchise upon the Jews (*War* VII, 44; cf. above, p. 321). But this report too is unsatisfactory; the expression "equality of rights" is too broad, and Josephus does not define the rights enjoyed by the Antiochian Jews with any precision. The fact that such rights were inscribed on bronze tablets (*War* VII, 110) says nothing concerning their legal contents. Josephus did not copy their texts, just as he did not copy the text of Augustus' monument at Alexandria. On one occasion he calls the Jewish rights at Antioch *dikaiomata* (*War, ib.*), and it has been remarked above that this term was normally applied to Jewish autonomous privileges. It may therefore be supposed that here too Josephus was confusing Jewish national and civic privileges. We encounter the same confusion of concepts on Josephus' part in those passages of his books which discuss the Jews of Ionia. In the extract from *Contra Apionem* (II, 39) referred to above, Josephus says that the Jews resident in the Ionian towns were called after the cities like the rest of the citizens, which, to all appearances, evidences equality of rights between them and the Greeks. In *Antiquities* (XII, 125ff.), Josephus underlines this idea with greater emphasis. He here refers to the endeavors of the Greeks of Ionia to abolish Jewish rights and to the intervention of Agrippa, Augustus' general, in favor of the Jews. "The Greeks," relates Josephus, "requested Agrippa that he grant to themselves exclusively permission to enjoy the citizen status granted to them[92] by Antiochus, the grandson of Seleucus, known by the Greeks as *Theos* (God)." In the lawsuit tried before Agrippa, the Jews won, owing to the pleading of Nicolaus of Damascus, and obtained permission "to live according to their customs." Josephus failed to notice the contradiction between the beginning of the narrative and its end, for the Greeks had asked Agrippa to abolish Jewish *civic rights*, such as they themselves had acquired from Antiochus II; yet after the Jewish victory it emerged that the whole affair concerned only whether the Jews might live according to their customs, in other words, according to the *autonomous privileges of the Jewish community*.

What, then, was the real cause of the dispute? Josephus supplies his own answer in another passage of the *Antiquities* (XVI, 27ff.). Here he relates at length the Jewish complaints to Agrippa, that the Greeks were not permitting them to live according to their ancestral customs, were forcing them to appear in court on the Sabbath, were confiscating the sacred moneys earmarked for dispatch to Jerusalem, and so forth. We see that, not the civic rights of the Jews, but their specific privileges were the object of a violent Greek attack, such as occurred also in other cities. This account, then, cannot serve as a basis for the study of the civic status of the Jews in Ionia.

It may be supposed that the situation was no less un-uniform in the cities of Ionia than it was in Alexandria. We know from the documents preserved in Josephus that at the beginning of the Roman period there was in Asia Minor a certain number of Jews who were Roman citizens (*Ant.* XIV, 228ff.). Although civic enfranchisement in Greek towns was not the sole condition of acquiring Roman privileges (below, n. 84), it must be supposed that some of these Jews possessed citizenship rights which they had acquired individually. Other information on Jewish membership in citizen-groups in the Ionian towns has not survived.[93] On the other hand, the Jews of Paros are in one document termed *paroikoi* (*Ant.* XIV, 213), and the Jewish community of Hierapolis calls itself by the name of *katoikia* (above, p. 298). The civic status of the Jews of Ionia, therefore, cannot be defined by one brief fixed formula; everything depended on when the Jews had settled in a given town, how the community had developed, what the number was of new immigrants compared with the Jews of long standing, and similar factors.

Of the Jews of Cyrene, Josephus relates what he reports of the Jews generally, namely, that they had obtained equality of rights (*isonomia*) from the first kings (*Ant.* XVI, 160). We have already learned what attitude to adopt to this report. More important is the testimony of Strabo, preserved in Josephus (*Ant.* XIV, 115). He says that during Sulla's war against Mithradates (85 B.C.E.) there were four groups of inhabitants in Cyrene—citizens, peasants, metics (μέτοικοι) and Jews. This information is not as clear as it might be; was it, for instance, impossible for an agriculturalist to be a member of the city? Strabo evidently excludes this possibility; thus we have to assume that the "peasants" were native Libyans reduced to serfdom by the Greek population of the towns.[94]

The Jews, who reached Cyrene only in the Hellenistic period, could not of course be accepted into the first group of citizens of the town, which was probably composed of the municipal aristocracy, that is, the descendants of the first Greek immigrants who founded Cyrene. The fact that Strabo lists the Jews as a special group among the rest, shows that they were organized in an independent community, which is confirmed by the great inscription from the Cyrenaican city of Berenice, where the Jewish community is termed *politeuma*, indicating its independent position in a more or less broad sense (above, p. 297).

This is what is known to the historian of the civic status of the Jews of the Diaspora. There is no other information available, and what there is does not add up to a complete picture. Three conclusions may be drawn from all this historical material: 1. The civic status of Diaspora Jewry was not uniform, and the extent of their rights depended on when, how, and for what purpose the Jews came to a given country outside Palestine. 2. The organized Jewish community as a whole stood juridically outside the Greek city, and the Jews who lived in it had no civic rights there. 3. Isolated Jews could acquire civic rights individually.

These three statements describe more or less precisely the Jewish civic position in the

Diaspora. All other assumptions—particularly those of Josephus —which assert that the Jews shared equal rights with the Greeks, can only confuse the issue. We learn one other important thing from the sources: not citizen rights in the Greek towns, but the privileges of the Jewish communities were the focus of Jewish life in the Diaspora. These privileges were very great indeed, and they frequently aroused the envy and hatred of the Greeks. We shall see below that the existence of the Jewish community with its own authority, side by side with the Greek city, frequently caused a collision between the two forces and contributed not a little to fostering anti-Semitism among the Greeks.

chapter **3**

ECONOMICS AND SOCIETY

What was the economic basis of Jewish life in the Diaspora? What were the Jewish occupations and sources of livelihood?

No judgment should be formed on the Hellenistic-Roman period which is derived from the experience of Jewish Diaspora life in modern times. Many scholars have made the mistake of applying the elements of Jewish life today to a description of life outside Palestine in the Hellenistic and Roman epochs. Speck writes: "Even at that time the basic occupation of those Jews who lived far from their native land was commerce. . . . Capital accumulated in the hands of the Jewish merchants to the same extent that it accumulated in the hands of the Roman."[1] Herzfeld also thought that the Jews of the Diaspora engaged more especially in trade, and saw in commerce the most important factor which impelled the Jews to leave Palestine and Babylonia to migrate to western lands. In his opinion, no external reason existed in the Hellenistic period compelling the Jews of Palestine to abandon their homeland; they left it of their own free will in search of a livelihood, and as they could not hope to succeed in acquiring land in foreign countries or in devoting themselves to agriculture among the Gentiles, they placed their chief hope in commerce.

To back his views, Herzfeld pointed to the fact that the Jews settled in the large towns, which played an important part in the commercial life of the Hellenistic and Roman periods.[2] Even today several other writers have a great deal to say on the commercial preoccupations of the Jews of the Diaspora and on the great wealth which they derived from them.[3] This view, which lacks sufficient basis in the sources, cannot be accepted, especially now that new sources such as papyri and ostraca have been discovered which testify to the participation of the Jews in a variety of branches of economic life in their countries of residence, and not solely in commerce. As against the long list of large towns containing Jewish populations drawn up by Herzfeld, a list of no lesser length can be compiled of the Egyptian villages and provincial towns of Asia Minor where likewise Jewish communities existed. This is not to deny completely the role of trade in Jewish life in the Hellenistic period; our intention is merely to utter a warning against the one-sidedness which has prevailed and continues to prevail among scholars on this question.

As we begin our survey of the social situation of the Jews in the Diaspora, we must consider one group of people which has no parallel in Jewish Diaspora life in our own day. I refer to the Jewish soldier class. Anti-Semitic scholars of the type of Willrich adopted an attitude of skepticism and even of mockery toward the sources mentioning military service by Jews in the Greek kingdoms. They cast doubt on the information of Aristeas on the Jewish prisoners settled by Ptolemy I in Egyptian fortresses, and on Josephus' report about the two thousand Jewish families transferred by Antiochus III to Asia Minor to discharge military duties. It has already been emphasized (p. 287) that these reports evoke no doubt among scholars today, because they are supported by the impartial testimony of the papyri. Since the publication of the Elephantine papyri scholars can no longer question the military role of Jews in Egypt. The Jews of Elephantine call themselves "the Jewish force" (חילא יהודיא), they live in "the fortress" (בירתא) and are divided into "standards" (דגלים), special battalions—and their entire life bears the stamp of military organization.[4]

If the Jews could serve as troops in the Egyptian fortresses in the Persian period, why should their military fitness in the Hellenistic epoch be doubted? We have seen some facts relating to this subject, such as the participation of a Jewish military force in the wars of the Ptolemies under the leadership of the Jewish commanders, Onias and his sons Helkias and Hananiah; the Jews of the territory of Onias who were about to prevent a foreign force from bringing aid to Julius Caesar; and the other Jewish troops who were in charge of the ford at Pelusium. These are reports from Josephus which reflect the real situation from 150 B.C.E. on. No less important is the papyrological information derived from an earlier period (from the middle of the third to the middle of the second century B.C.E.). The papyri describe Jewish soldiers against the background of the Ptolemaic army as a whole. This army was composed of a regular force and a reserve (the *Epigoné*), and contained cavalry and infantry. The cavalry were organized either on the national principle (*hyparchies* of Thracians, Thessalians, Moesians, etc.), or in mixed squadrons designated by numbers: the first, the second *hyparchies*, and so on. The infantry was also divided into battalions named after their commanders. The characteristic feature of the Ptolemaic army was its foreign origin, since the Ptolemies were careful not to introduce native Egyptians into their forces and used natives in exceptional cases only, their entire army being recruited from Macedonians, Greeks, natives of Asia Minor and members of other peoples, as well as from the younger generation of these nations, born and bred in Egypt. In order to bind this foreign army to the soil of Egypt, the Ptolemies distributed plots of land among the troops, each soldier having his allotment (see above, p. 20).[5]

The Jews mentioned in the papyri served in the Macedonian army on an equal footing with all the other peoples, though they never ranked among the warlike nations, such as Macedonians, Galatians, etc. We find among them simple soldiers and officers,[6] men of the regular army and of the *Epigoné*,[7] cavalrymen and infantrymen.[8] Allotments were distributed among them as among the other foreign troops. From the papyrological material it can be gathered that the Jews served in mixed units (such as the *hyparchies*) and among them were some called "Persians" or "Macedonians," who belonged to the "pseudo-ethnic" groups of the Ptolemaic army.[9] The existence of a purely Jewish unit is not mentioned in the documents and probably no such unit existed till the time of Onias. Thus in Egypt we see quite a large number of Jews serving in the various branches of the Ptolemaic forces equally with the other Greek and "barbarian" peoples, in harmony with the practice of the Hellenistic period of entrusting the defense of the state to formations of foreign mercenaries.[10]

From soldiers we pass to peasants. According to the practice prevailing in the ancient world in many countries, especially under the Ptolemies and Seleucids, lands were distributed by the government for settling those troops who had completed their terms of active service, or had been settled on the soil in order to serve as a nucleus around which a future army might be maintained. The Jews were no exception from this viewpoint. The papyri have yielded several items of information on Jewish servicemen who held considerable allotments of land. These soldiers almost certainly did not work the soil themselves, but leased it to Egyptian "fellahin" as was the usual practice in Egypt.[11] In one papyrus there has been preserved a list of sheep and goats belonging to members of a military colony at Samaria in the Fayûm; most of the names of the members of the colony are Hebrew.[12] According to the letter of Antiochus III to Zeuxis (above, p. 287f.), every Jewish soldier about to settle in Lydia and Phrygia was to receive a "plot on which to build a house and also soil for cultivation and the planting of a vineyard" (*Ant.* XII, 151). The Jewish colony at Hierapolis (above, p. 298) was called a *katoikia,* that is, it was also essentially a military colony, and it may be supposed that its members also engaged in agriculture. Again, military settlers were probably the first Jewish emigrants who came to Cyrene from Egypt at the beginning of the Ptolemaic period; and we have some evidence that a military settlement of Jews from the Trachonitis was founded in Cyrene in Herod's reign.[13] The papyri inform us that the plots given to soldiers for settlement in Egypt were regarded as royal land and in the third century might at any time (and certainly after the death of the settler) revert to the king; but during the second century they became in effect the private property of the settlers, who had the right to bequeath them hereditarily.[14] Thus military service in the Hellenistic kingdoms aided the Jews to strike root in foreign soil and to take possession of land which became in course of time family property descending from father to son.

Military service was not the only origin of Jewish land-holding. The ostraca in Upper Egypt testify to a large number of Jews who from time to time "measured" quantities of corn into the royal granaries, or, in other words, paid the government the land-tax on their holdings. The quantities of corn "measured" by them are quite varied and these variations (although this is uncertain) may reflect the differences in the sizes of their estates.[15] We do not know to which class of peasants these Jews belonged, but the most likely supposition is that they were "royal peasants" settled on royal land which they worked according to certain conditions (see above, p. 13). In one document "the land of Helkias" is mentioned in the neighborhood of Alexandria, but we do not know whether Helkias was a big landlord, a military settler, or a man who had received his holding as a gift from the king.[16]

The Jews also included agricultural laborers who worked the land of others for wages. In a papyrus from Fayûm we read of "peasants receiving wages" who were working the land of a wealthy estate-owner; one of the peasants bears the Hebrew name of Joab.[17] The papyri of Zenon mention two Jewish vintners who had leased a vineyard of 60 *arourai* from Zenon,[18] and in various other documents Jewish shepherds appear.[19] Thus Jews found their way into various branches of agricultural work, as military settlers, landholders, small peasants, agricultural workers and so on, and if we ask what was the reason for this striving to live a rural life, the answer is simple: in their native country, among the hills of Judaea, they had also practiced agriculture, and it was natural for them, when abroad, to engage in the same types of work to which they had been accustomed from their youth.

It is surprising that the papyrological documents hardly mention Jewish craftsmen at all. In one papyrus two Jewish potters from "the Syrian Village" in the Fayûm are referred to, who lease a pottery-factory jointly with an Egyptian family, and Jewish weavers appear in other documents. But this is all, or nearly all.[20] This lack of official sources is especially regrettable because there are grounds for thinking that craftsmen held a very important place in Jewish Diaspora life. For Alexandria several reports have been preserved in talmudic literature, the most important being in Sukkah, 51b:

> R. Judah says: He who has never seen the Diploston of Alexandria in Egypt has never seen the glory of Israel. They said: It was a sort of great basilica, stoa in front of stoa; that at times it held twice as many as left Egypt . . . And they did not sit intermingled, but the goldsmiths by themselves, the silversmiths by themselves, the blacksmiths by themselves, the carpet-weavers by themselves, and the weavers by themselves; and when a poor man entered, he recognized the members of his own craft and applied to

them, whence he derived his livelihood and that of his family.[21]

Even if we do not credit all the legendary details of this description, we learn two things from the passage: first, that the Jewish craftsmen of Alexandria occupied an important place in the Alexandrian community, and second, that they were organized in special societies on the model of the professional organizations (*collegia*) of the Hellenistic and Roman world. Instances are mentioned in the Talmud in which craftsmen had to be brought from Alexandria to Jerusalem to make necessary repairs to Temple vessels.[22] It seems that in Jewish Alexandria were to be found specialists in every type of handicraft. Philo also mentions Jewish craftsmen in the city (*Flacc.* 57).

There is no detailed information on Jewish commerce. Although, as already stated, this was not the only occupation of Jews in the Diaspora, it undoubtedly had an important place in their life. Jewish traders are to be looked for, of course, in the large towns, and above all in Alexandria. Philo has preserved valuable information. When speaking of the paralysis of economic life in Jewish Alexandria after the pogroms of the year 38 C.E., he lists (*Flacc.* 57) various classes of the wealthy population of the city, namely, owners of property, merchants owning their own ships and simple merchants.

Philo says that the members of the first group "had lost their investments" on account of the riots; hence we learn that these were "capitalists" who, while not taking part in trade personally, financed it by investing sums of money in business transactions. The second class, the ship-owning merchants, must be assumed to have been pretty numerous in Alexandria, since the city was the export-harbor of Egypt and the entire produce of the various branches of that wealthy country, above all, grain, passed through the port of Alexandria on its way to Rome and to all other Mediterranean localities.[23] The third group, the *emporoi,* or simple traders, must be assumed to have composed the majority of the Jewish middle class of the city, the difference between them and the craftsmen, who are also mentioned by Philo, being probably not very considerable, since at this period, as in medieval Europe, the craftsman was also the dealer who sold his products.[24] Other sources add a few details to the picture drawn by Philo. An inscription from Upper Egypt speaks of the Jew Theodotos who thanked the gods for rescuing him from peril at sea.[25] It must be assumed that he was a merchant accustomed to sea voyages. The *Third Book of Maccabees* (iii. 4), telling about the mob's attacks on the Jews in the time of Ptolemy IV, refers to the good attitude of some Greeks toward persecuted Jews who were "their partners in business." This is more or less all we know about the commerce of the Jews of the Diaspora.

With this commerce must be connected the great wealth of individual Jews who also lent their money on interest. The immense resources of Joseph the Tobiad were kept in Egypt, and Arion, his representative, took care of them (above, p. 135). It is easy to imagine that such money did not lie idle in the safe, unused by its owners for profitable purposes. The *alabarchs* were also renowned bankers and the richest Jews in Alexandria. Scholars identify them with the *arabarchs*, the officials in charge of the trade between Egypt and Arabia.[26] It may be assumed that their great wealth did not depend directly on their official position, which could not have brought them much profit (see below), and its source has to be sought in commerce and banking.

Josephus alludes with respect to two *arabarchs*—Alexander (*Ant.* XVIII, 159, 259; XIX, 276; XX, 100), Philo's brother, and Demetrius (*ib.* XX, 147). Of the former he relates that he lent a large sum of money to the Jewish King Agrippa when he was traveling to Rome, giving him part of the money in cash in Alexandria and promising the rest when he arrived at Puteoli-Dikaiarchia (in Italy, near Naples). This informs us that part of Alexander's money was deposited in Italy and that his business was not confined to Egypt alone, but embraced numerous countries. There were rich Jews also in Cyrene, as we are told by Josephus (*War* VII, 442, 445).

Interesting evidence on Jews lending at interest is to be found in a papyrus of the year 41 C.E.[27] This papyrus contains the letter of a Greek merchant Serapion to his friend Heracleides in Alexandria. Heracleides has apparently become involved in unsuccessful business dealings and is at a loss how to get out of his perplexing situation. Serapion advises his friend to seek a loan and adds the characteristic words: "but do you, like us all, beware of the Jews!"[28] Scholars are divided on the question whether in these words is to be seen "the most ancient evidence of business anti-Semitism," or just a caution to a Greek not to enter the Jewish quarter at a time when the relationships between the two peoples were strained to the utmost.[29]

But whatever the interpretation set upon these words, it is at least clear that we have here objective evidence of the existence among the Jews of money-lenders advancing loans on interest, and, further, of the wide reputation enjoyed by them in the Greek community. Thus there were Jews in the Diaspora who grew wealthy by lending money at interest and from trade, but it is doubtful that these were characteristic of Jewish Diaspora life as a whole. A number of papyri from Alexandria of the period of Augustus speak of Jews belonging to the lower orders of the community who are in search of loans, and the picture furnished by these documents in large measure corrects the bright picture of Philo who was only interested in the wealthy.[30] Apion gibes at the Jews of Alexandria for living by the seashore where the sea threw up its jetsom (*C. Ap.* II, 33), and in the Roman period Jewish poverty was a byword among the anti-Semitic writers.[31] We shall see below that "Jewish wealth" was never a subject for anti-Semitic propaganda.

The Jews also distinguished themselves as government officials, especially under the Egyptian Ptolemies, occupying various posts in the administration, from the lowest to those of ministers next to the throne.[32] As military service was bound up with the preservation of public security in remote places, it differed little from service in the police, hence there were policemen among the Jews. One (*phylakítes*) is mentioned in the middle of the second century B.C.E. in a papyrus;[33] approximately contemporary is the inscription from Athribis in Lower Egypt, reading: "In honor of King Ptolemy and Queen Cleopatra, Ptolemy son of Epicides, police-chief, and the Jews at Athribis built this synagogue to the Supreme God."

I see no grounds for doubting that this Ptolemy was a Jew, although the inscription does not say so explicitly.[34] Josephus writes that the kings and later the Romans entrusted the Jews with the policing of the Nile (*C. Ap.* II, 64: *fluminis custodiam*); the report is probably incorrect in its sweeping form, but from it it may be inferred that the Jews, too, served among the Nile police.[35] The arabarchs also were government officials. Schürer calls them "the supreme superintendents of the customs in Arab territory across the Nile."[36] Wilcken made a detailed investigation of the tax collected by the arabarchs, which was known as the *apostolion* and was levied on travelers who crossed from Egypt to the Red Sea by way of Koptos and Berenice.[37] From the account given by Wilcken it is to be concluded that this tax was not especially high, and it is difficult to suppose that the Alexandrian arabarchs grew as rich as they did from its collection. The post of arabarch, which was for some time in the hands of Alexander and Demetrius, wealthy Jews of Alexandria, was perhaps rather an honorary position than a profitable business. Naturally these rich bankers did not themselves collect the customs from the caravans which crossed the desert from the Nile to the Red Sea, but were assisted by lower officials dependent upon them.

Among the petty customs-collectors was also a considerable number of Jews, as we learn from the ostraca of Upper Egypt.[38] Several of them are known to us by name: Shabbatai, who leased the transport taxes in the Thebais (he is mentioned frequently on the ostraca); Simon son of Lazarus (Joezer), who collected the customs from the fishermen; Aviel, who collected the shoemakers' tax; Simon son of Aviel, who collected the chaff from the estate-owners, and others.[39] Tax-collectors were hated by the Egyptian population as they were hated by every population everywhere else.[40] It is hard to know why just these posts fell to the lot of Jews, for the profit from tax-gathering in Ptolemaic Egypt was not particularly large and the danger of severe punishment constantly hung over the heads of those collectors who did not meet their obligations.[41] Their relatively large number in Upper Egypt may be explained on the assumption that the post of collector, despite the disadvantages involved, conferred upon its possessor a position of respect among the rural population.

A few more words on the lower officialdom. On a few ostraca from Upper Egypt we find Hebrew names (or Greek theophoric names characteristic of Jews) among the employees of the τράπεζαι (banks) or the ἀχυροθῆκαι (the barns where the chaff was collected).[42] A papyrus of the Roman period gives the names of Jews who were *sitologoi*—government officials who supervised the delivery of grain to the royal granaries.[43] Another papyrus of the end of the Ptolemaic period mentions the "scribe" or "clerk" (*grammateus*) Onias, who was, it seems, the assistant of the government official in charge of a toparchy in the Heracleopolite nome.[44] All these men were minor officials living on salaries like thousands of other government officials among the Greeks and Egyptians. We know nothing at all of how they lived, and we must suppose that they led the austere and parsimonious lives characteristic of small people in Ptolemaic Egypt.

Slaves were not very common among the Jews, for the Jewish community regarded it as a charitable act to redeem their distressed brethren from slavery. Only rarely do we hear of Jewish slaves in Egypt and in other lands. The most important information on the subject has been preserved by Aristeas, on whose evidence the Jews taken prisoner in Palestine by Ptolemy I were given as slaves to the Macedonian soldiers and later freed by order of King Philadelphus (above, p. 273). There is no other information on Jewish slaves in Egypt in the Ptolemaic period.[45]

The wars of the Hasmoneans no doubt put a considerable number of Jewish prisoners on the slave-market of the Hellenistic world, especially at the beginning of the rebellion. We have seen above (p. 208) that the Greek cities of Palestine anticipated this as an excellent opportunity of acquiring slaves cheaply from the Macedonians and of selling them at a high profit; and although their hopes of an easy Syrian victory were disappointed, there is no doubt that numerous Jews fell into their hands and were sold as slaves. There exist, in fact, two inscriptions of this period (170-157 B.C.E.) which mention Jewish slaves at Delphi in Greece.[46] Another inscription of the end of the first century B.C.E. indicates that there were Jewish slaves even in remote places such as the city of Pantikapaion (Kerch) on the north coast of the Black Sea.[47]

The added fact that at the beginning of the Roman period there was in Asia Minor a considerable group of Jews who were Roman citizens, permits the supposition that at least part of them were the descendants of Jewish slaves emancipated by their Roman masters. The Jewish family of Antonius Rufus at Edfu, in Upper Egypt, also doubtless originated as freedmen.[48] Thus we find isolated Jews in various places in a condition of slavery; but it should be noted that nearly all the sources—including the official documents—mention Jewish slaves precisely at the time of their emancipation, which is a definite sign of how strongly the Jews desired to free themselves from this humiliating station and to create for themselves a position in life.

If we sum up the above material we shall easily see that the Jewish Diaspora in the

Hellenistic period was very far from the one-sidedness of ghetto life. The Jews had not yet lost the natural tie between the people and the land; in foreign countries, under new and difficult conditions, they reestablished the mode of life to which they had been accustomed in their native place. Apart from the priests, there was no single social class in Palestine which did not exist in the Diaspora.[49] Generals, soldiers, policemen, officials, tax-farmers, estate-owners, agricultural laborers, slaves, craftsmen, merchants, moneylenders, and doubtless also members of the free professions such as physicians, scribes and the like—all these types of people were to be found in the Diaspora, and if we had more numerous sources at our disposal we should certainly discover a still greater variety.

In the Middle Ages and in modern times the Jews frequently played a special part in the life of the state where they settled. In a feudal society living mainly on agriculture they developed trade and finance and thus supplied what was lacking till the indigenous people matured sufficiently to take over the initiative in these branches of the state's economy. This was not the case in the ancient world. It is quite wrong to suppose that Jewish interests in the Hellenistic Diaspora were concentrated in any single branch of life, that Jews subsisted only on trade or handicrafts, or that they were all wealthy or all poor. Residents in the large towns were naturally more devoted to trade, finance and the crafts; but dwellers in the countryside and in provincial towns engaged in agriculture or held government posts. Wealth was gathered in the hands of exceptional individuals who had been successful in their commercial dealings or in tax-collecting, and the vast majority lived humbly by the sweat of their brows. In short, from the economic point of view there was no difference between the Jews and the other peoples among whom they lived, and no single economic branch constituted a monopoly for Jewish activity. And if, notwithstanding, the Jews and the Gentiles alike were aware of the great distance which separated them, the reason for the differences has to be sought, not in the economic situation, but elsewhere.

chapter 4

THE CULTURAL CLIMATE

A full and comprehensive account of the cultural position of the Jews of the Diaspora cannot be the subject of this study, which concerns the material and not the intellectual questions of Jewish history. The latter found their expression in the Jewish Hellenistic literature created mainly by the Jews of Egypt. This literature exhibits an interesting and valuable fusion of Greek ideas and Jewish tradition, a process which reached its apogee in the writings of Philo, whose philosophical ideas set their stamp on the intellectual development of the peoples of Europe for many generations. M. Friedländer, in his numerous books,[1] put forward the thesis that the Jews of the Diaspora were entirely different from the Jews of Palestine. While the latter followed the Pharisees and enclosed themselves within the four walls of Jewish tradition, Hellenistic Jewry was imbued with the spirit of inner liberty, and Jewish religion and ethics evolved within it into a universalistic spiritual legacy. This outlook, based on an exaggerated estimate of the Greek elements in Jewish Alexandrian literature and on an ignoring of its traditional Jewish elements, has now been abandoned, and rightly so, for it is easily demonstrable that the difference between Palestinian Jewry and the Jews of the Diaspora was not a difference of principle but only of degree. Obviously the Hellenizing movement struck deeper roots among the Jews of Alexandria than it did in Jerusalem; but we have seen above that in Jerusalem too a strong Hellenizing movement had arisen which left its decisive impress on the course of Jewish history.[2] On the other hand, while it is true that the center of Jewish tradition was Jerusalem, the Jewish community of the Diaspora also stood four square on tradition, and this was officially recognized by the authorities.

Nevertheless, it cannot be denied that the problems of Hellenization and tradition faced Diaspora Jews in a much more acute form than these currents faced the Jews of Palestine. The crisis thrust upon Jerusalem by the Hellenizing faction was temporary, and after it had passed, national life again took its traditional course. Although in Palestine as a whole, with its numerous Greek cities, Hellenization became general and penetrated by numerous byways even into Hasmonean Jerusalem, Jerusalem Jewry was strong enough to defend itself, to counter force with force, and intellect with intellect. This was not the case with Diaspora Jewry, which, internally much weaker and exposed to immeasurably greater forces from without, was compelled to struggle with external influences not by a one-time mobilization of national forces, but by a ceaseless, stubborn, day-by-day and hour-by-hour defense of its national heritage. The will to this constant and wearisome struggle was not always present, and not every Jew in the Diaspora shared it. The lot of Hellenistic Jewry outside Palestine was the lot of every Diaspora Jewish group down to our own time. Nor is it disputable that the plight of the Jews as a distinct alien body among the peoples has exercised a decisive influence on the molding of Diaspora Jewry itself. To exist in the alien environment, the Jew is forced to develop his spiritual powers and to exert his uttermost endeavors, for he is assisted neither by local tradition, personal contacts, language nor national customs, which in fact impede his efforts to succeed. Hence the methods of his struggle for existence are frequently quite different from those practiced among the "host nation" (in German terminology—the *Wirtsvolk*).

This struggle for existence may be conducted, and actually is conducted, in two opposite ways. Sometimes the will to succeed induces in the Jew a decision to imitate local manners and customs and to make himself like the "host people" in every respect. This is the way of assimilation, which leads the Jew to repudiate his ancestral customs and sometimes even makes him an unconcealed enemy of the Jewish people. The second way, quite opposed to the first, is equally obvious: in his struggle for existence in a foreign country the Jew naturally resorts to his own people for encouragement and aid, whence the maintenance of organized Jewish communities in every locality of the Diaspora and the obstinate adherence of the solitary Jew to his community. Now, the community signifies tradition, for it must be based on the principles of the original national culture, otherwise it possesses a *raison d'être* neither in the eyes of the "host nation" nor in those of the Jews themselves. Thus Jewish history in the Diaspora fluctuates between two mutually contradictory principles: between the ambition to assimilate arising from the Jew's desire to exist among strangers by his individual powers, and the adherence to tradition, induced in the struggle for existence by the need of support from the strong collective organization represented by the community. This general axiom was as valid in relation to Hellenistic Jewry as it is in relation to modern Jewry.

Let us now examine the various forms assumed among the Jews of the Hellenistic Diaspora by the two aspirations just described, and dwell first on the various manifestations of the Hellenizing trend among Jews outside Palestine.

In the Diaspora, as in Palestine, Hellenization found its first external expression in the changing of personal names. The papyri and inscriptions provide ample material on this subject.[3] Although Hebrew and Semitic names as a whole did not disappear throughout the Hellenistic period,[4] by their side appears a multitude of Greek names such as Alexander, Ptolemy, Antipater, Demetrius, Jason and the like. Sometimes the Jews translated their Hebrew names into Greek (Mattathias, for instance, became Theodotos), and they were especially fond of using names compounded with the Greek word for "God," ($\theta\epsilon\delta s$), examples being Dositheos, Theophilos, Theodotos and Dorotheos.[5] The Jews did not even hesitate to use names derived from those of Greek deities, such as Apollonius, Heracleides and Dionysus. Sometimes they took two names, Greek and Semitic, together: thus we find in papyri "Apollonius whose Syrian name is Jonathan," "Heras also called Ezekiel," and so on.[6] The Jews acquired, not only Greek, but also Egyptian appellations, as, for instance, the popular name Horus.[7]

It is hard to tell which sections of the public used foreign names so frequently—the poor or the urban upper class. The tendency to take Greek names is first noticeable among the Jewish soldiers settled in the Fayûm.[8] Numerous Greek names are also encountered among the tenants of estates and the tax-collectors in Upper Egypt; further, among members of the Jewish settlement-region of the territory of Onias.[9] On the other hand, the Jewish aristocracy was also fond of Greek names. Thus, for example, of the nine archons of Berenice (in Cyrenaica) eight bore Greek names, and so did their fathers; the ninth, although his name was Joseph, was the son of a man with the Greek name of Straton.[10] The arabarchs of Alexandria were known as Alexander and Demetrius, the brother of Alexander being the philosopher Philo, and among the Jewish writers in Egypt were men with names like Aristobulus, Demetrius, Eupolemos and Jason (of Cyrene). Thus this superficial symptom of Hellenization took root among various sections of the Jewish public of the Diaspora. The reasons which induced the Jews to change their names no doubt resembled those operating today among American and European Jews: habituation to the names of the natives of the country, greater facility in dealing with non-Jews, and the desire "to be like all the peoples." Although this phenomenon must inevitably be regarded as a symptom of assimilation, great importance should not be attached to it, nor should every instance of a change of name be interpreted as an act of hostility to Judaism. Jason of Cyrene, Philo and the Hasmonean kings cannot be suspected of deficient national feeling or of estrangement from the elements of Jewish tradition.

More important was the fact of change of language. The Jews outside Palestine spoke, wrote and generally thought in Greek. The Semitic languages—Hebrew and Aramaic—did not vanish, or at any rate not all at once, for ostraca inscribed in Aramaic testify to the existence of that tongue in Egypt at least down to the middle of the second century B.C.E.[11] However, the importance of these potsherds is negligible compared with the abundant works of Jewish Hellenistic literature, written entirely in Greek, although the overwhelming majority of its readers were Jews. To what degree Greek was the current language of the Jewish intelligentsia of Alexandria can be deduced, for instance, from the fact that Philo regards it as "our language" and has no qualms about attributing to the heroes of the Bible a knowledge of Greek etymology.[12]

The cornerstone on which the entire edifice of Jewish Alexandrian literature rested was the Greek translation of the Scriptures, known as the Septuagint or "Translation of the Seventy." Aristeas, who relates in detail how, when and by whom this great project was carried out, seeks to prove that its aim was to enable the Greeks to become acquainted with the Jewish Scriptures, and that the initiative for the translating of the Pentateuch came from the Greek courtiers of Ptolemy Philadelphus. Modern scholars do not concur with Aristeas. There is little doubt that the translation was carried out for the benefit of the Jews themselves for the simple reason that the Egyptian Jews had ceased to understand Hebrew and it was necessary to provide them with the Pentateuch in the language which they spoke.[13] Greek prevailed in the synagogue (the inscriptions there were composed in that tongue), in the official assemblies of the communities (their resolutions were in Greek), in literature and in daily life. The vitality of Greek among those Jews who had been cut off for long periods from a Greek environment is remarkable, for most of the inscriptions in the Jewish cemeteries of Rome were written in that language and not in Latin.[14] The Greek spoken by the Jews was not, indeed, invariably of the purest and least corrupt: the Hebraisms of the Septuagint are known to every Bible scholar, while the learned Greek, Cleomedes, gibes at the rude folk-dialect used in the synagogues.[15] There may also have been Jews who were illiterate in Greek (some instances are known to us from Egypt); but they may, for ought we know, have been illiterate in every other language.[16] It is clear, then, that the Greek language won a decisive victory over Hebrew and Aramaic among the Jews of the Diaspora, and this victory was won in the Hellenistic period, since in the Roman and Byzantine epoch the reawakening of the national spirit caused a considerable revival of Hebrew.[17]

In the organization of their communities and in the external style of their public life, the Jews took as models the political institutions of the Greeks.[18] All the public positions in the community were known by Greek terms, examples being the *archon, gerousiarch* and the like. Even the post of *hazzan* in the synagogue of one of the villages of the Fayûm was called *nakoros*, a priestly title borrowed from pagan temples.[19] The Greek word *prostatai*, which denoted the leaders of the congregation, also entered Hebrew and is found written in Hebrew letters as *prostatin* in a Hebrew papyrus of the

Byzantine period.[20] The resolutions of the communities were known as *psephismata* and were drafted exactly on the model of the resolutions of the popular assemblies of the Greek cities: "In such and such a year, in such and such a month, under the archons so and so. Inasmuch as . . . (the content of the resolution), it seemed good to the archons . . . etc.[21] The Greek custom of honoring people who had merited it by the bestowing of wreaths (*stephanoi*) and by the *prohedria* (the assignment of a prominent place at assemblies and games, etc.) was also customary among the Jews, as was the practice of inscribing these resolutions on a stone and placing it in a prominent public place.[22] The Greeks dedicated their temples to kings; the Jews did the same with their synagogues.[23] In short, the entire external frame of organized communal life was modeled on the public life of the Greek *polis*.

From the external frame we pass to deeper phenomena. The Jewish community was based on its right to live according to its ancestral law, and it possessed its own judicial institutions, and also Jewish "archives," that is, offices where official papers pertaining to Jews were composed and drafted. This general situation is undoubted and is confirmed by much evidence (see above, p. 301). We may, however, ask whether every individual Jew in every instance resorted to his communal institutions, or whether Jews did not also utilize the institutions of the government. Egyptian papyri have furnished an unexpected reply to this question. They have preserved several business transactions between individual Jews and have proved to us that these were carried out, not according to the principles of Mosaic Law, nor before the representatives of the Jewish community, but in accordance with the principles of general Hellenistic law, before the officials of the Ptolemaic government and through their mediation. The documents were written in the usual Hellenistic form, the reference to the "divine" sovereign appearing in them to indicate the date;[24] they were written in the general Hellenistic office and the name of the Egyptian or Greek official appears upon them.[25] The laws and ordinances cited by the Jews as authority are the royal laws and ordinances;[26] the court before which they come to be judged is Greek.[27]

If the entire judicial framework was Hellenistic, it was natural that the principles of Hellenistic law itself should have penetrated Jewish life. Thus we find instances when the marriage and divorce of Jews in Alexandria under Augustus were conducted in the municipal office in accordance with normal Hellenistic notarial procedure.[28] The life of the Jewish woman in Hellenistic and Roman Egypt bore a closer resemblance to that of the Greek woman than to that of the Jewish woman of Palestine; for, while by Jewish law a woman's sole guardian was her father, and then only till she attained the age of twelve, the Jewish woman in Egypt was subject to guardians throughout her life in accordance with the custom prevalent in Greece.[29] Financial transactions between Egyptian Jews were also conducted according to Hellenistic law and Jews had no compunction about charging interest to their fellow-Jews, despite the specific prohibition in Exodus (22.24) and Deuteronomy (23.20).[30] If, then, Jewish family-life and financial business were conducted according to Hellenistic law, it is clear that the Jews of Egypt were very highly assimilated, and that even the community did not save many of them from being swallowed up among the Greeks.[31]

Greek education also cast its spell upon the Jews. We have already seen (p. 312) that, at the beginning of the Roman period, the Jews made various efforts to penetrate the citizen-class, and one of their ways of doing this was to obtain an education in the gymnasium. Greek athletic life, however, was carried on in a Greek religious setting, and was saturated with memories of Greek mythology and Greek classical literature; and not for nothing did II Maccabees regard the establishment of the gymnasium at Jerusalem as "the acme of Hellenism" (4.13). But Diaspora Jewry thought differently. Philo saw the life of athletics, with its physical exercises and various agonistic sports, as an everyday phenomenon and found no fault with it.[32] At the town of Iasos in Asia Minor a list of epheboi of the early Roman period has been preserved on which names such as Judah, Dositheos and Theophilos indicate that among these young men were many Jews.[33] At Miletus a special place was reserved in the theater for the Jews,[34] and at Hypaipa (near Sardis in Lydia) a group of young Jews called themselves *neoteroi*, following the usual system of grouping the *ephebes* into juniors, intermediates and seniors.[35] All these examples indicate the keen ambition of the Diaspora Jews to emulate the Greeks in the most important branches of original Greek cultural life, and there is no doubt that the education of young Jews in the gymnasia opened to them the way to a deeper understanding of Greek culture as a whole.

All this goes far to explain the flourishing state of Jewish Hellenistic literature. The translation of the Pentateuch into Hebrew was itself an impressive literary undertaking unexampled in the ancient world,[36] but it was only a beginning. The translation created the language, concepts and general background on which a Jewish literature could be constructed in Greek. Its beginnings were feeble and unpretentious; the first literary works did not venture beyond the imitation of classical compositions of Greek literature, and this imitation was generally unsuccessful.[37] But in course of time the Jewish writers learned to express all their aspirations and hopes in Greek literary style, and literature became a powerful instrument in their hands for influencing the Jewish reading public, later also serving as a means of systematic warfare against anti-Semitism.[38] The problem of assimilation and tradition was also more than once discussed in Alexandrian literature.

Especially interesting from this point of view was the attempt of the author of the *Letter of Aristeas* to bridge the gulf between Jews and Greeks. Aristeas conceives of Judaism as mainly identical with Greek philosophy, with the addition of the belief in one God. From this point of view there was no internal antagonism between Judaism and Hellenism; all had one God, known to different peoples by different names, and to the Greeks as Zeus. The Jews must acquire a Greek education and abandon the barbarous features of their character, but simultaneously must cleave with all their hearts to the Law of Moses (in its Greek garb in the Septuagint) which contains lofty philosophical elements. In everyday life also the two peoples must draw closer to one another.[39] The ideas voiced for the first time by Aristeas in the second century B.C.E.[40] were repeated at the beginning of the Roman period with special emphasis and with much profounder arguments by the greatest of Jewish philosophers, Philo. He, too, saw as his chief task the bridging of the gulf between Hellenism and Judaism, and he also regarded Judaism as a lofty philosophy which could compromise with Hellenism without difficulty.[41] Alexandrian literature, however, is not our present theme, our intention being merely to observe that there existed in that literature a strong ideological current which sought a synthesis between Judaism and Hellenism and saw in the propagation of Jewish "philosophy," which it regarded as comprehensible to every people and in every tongue, the justification of the Jewish nation's existence in the dispersion.

The outcome of this desire to live with the Greeks, and to discover a synthesis between Hellenism and Judaism, was that even on the central question which divided the two cultures, that of monotheism and polytheism, Jews were prepared to compromise. The Jewish attitude to polytheism was always negative in principle, but not consistently aggressive. It may be observed that the passage in Exodus 22.27 (*elohim lo teqallel*) was translated in the Septuagint (*ib.* 22.27): "Thou shalt not revile the gods." The translators here retained the plural form of *elohim*, although generally they were not strict in this matter, and the verse thereby acquired a completely new content. In this the Septuagint was followed by Philo and Josephus.[42] We have seen above that Aristeas speaks of the Greek Zeus as the one, unique deity identical with the God of Israel. The Jewish author Artaphanos went even farther than Aristeas, making Jacob and his sons the builders of pagan temples and Moses the founder of the cult of the sacred animals in Egypt.[43]

Inscriptions also furnish some material on the question under discussion. An inscription from the town of Iasos in Asia Minor mentions a man called Niketas son of Jason the Jerusalemite "who donated a sum of a hundred drachmas to the festival of the God Dionysus."[44] The inscription belongs to the middle of the second century B.C.E. that is, the flourishing period of Hellenization in Jerusalem, when the "Antiochians" of the town were sending their contribution to the festival of the Tyrian Heracles (above, p. 167); hence there is nothing surprising if a Hellenizing Jew who happened to be staying at Iasos took part in the fete of the Greek god. A case is known to us in Egypt, too. I have referred above (p. 338f.) to the inscription at Thebes, in which a Jewish merchant "thanks God" for his rescue from peril at sea. Near this inscription is another of a second Jew, who also "thanks God."[45] These two stones stood in the temple of the god Pan; who then was the "God" praised and thanked by these two Jews? Even if they meant the God of Israel, they did not say so openly, perhaps deliberately, and visitors to the temple no doubt received the impression that the god recorded in the inscription was the lord of the shrine, Pan.

Such cases are, of course, very rare, and far-reaching conclusions should not be drawn from them. Nevertheless, if we observe them against the general background of the aspiration of certain Jewish circles to compromise with the Greeks, they too acquire (at least in principle) a certain value.

If we survey the numerous roads to assimilation just recounted, we shall not be surprised to discover Jews who had openly betrayed their ancestral tradition and completely abandoned their nation and religion. One case is known to us at the end of the third century B.C.E. *III Maccabees* tells of a Jew, Dositheos son of Drimylos, courtier of King Ptolemy IV Philopator, who "changed his faith and became a stranger to the laws of his fathers" (I, 3). Dositheos distinguished himself as a royal official in various posts and was even priest of the cult of Alexander and the Divine Ptolemies, as papyri witness.[46] Two other cases are known to us in the Roman period. These are Tiberius Julius Alexander, the nephew of Philo, who left Judaism and in a short time achieved a brilliant "career" as a high Roman official,[47] and Antiochus, a Jew of Syrian Antioch, the son of a Jewish archon, who not only abandoned Judaism, but conducted fierce propaganda against it and sought, with the aid of a Roman force, to abolish the observance of the Sabbath and to compel the Jews to accept Greek customs.[48]

III Maccabees (vii, 10ff.) speaks bitterly of such traitors to their people and describes with much satisfaction the vengeance exacted upon them by the Jews after the danger of the persecution by Ptolemy Philopator had passed. Philo too refers in harsh terms to those Jews who had strayed from the path and left the religion of Moses.[49] We know nothing of the number of these assimilators or of the basic factors which led them to betray their people. There are grounds for thinking that mixed marriages constituted then, as now, an important factor making for assimilation. Philo, speaking of the Exodus, says that with the Jews there left Egypt a mixed mob of various people born of marriages between Hebrews and Egyptian women;[50] he may be describing the conditions of his own time. In another place he stresses the prohibition against such marriages in the Mosaic Law.[51] We shall not be far wrong in stating that intermarriage was frequent, particularly among the rural population, which lived in direct proximity to the natives; here, perhaps, the Egyptian element attracted the Jews more strongly than did the Greek.[52] In the cities other additional motives influenced the Jews, especially the wealthy among them: for example, the gay and liberal life of the Greek youth, careerism, shame at differing from Greek friends and acquaintances in matters of religion, and the like.[53] There is no special need to study the various causes of the assimilationist movement in the ancient world, for they have not altered with time and we all know them from present day life in the Diaspora.

All the material which we have reviewed effectively shows that the Jews of the dispersion were strongly influenced by Hellenism and sometimes did not muster the strength to overcome the temptation "to be like all the peoples." But if instead of the isolated instances of Hellenization, we note the entire trend of Jewish life outside Palestine, and if we take into account the existence of organized Jewish communities for many generations in given localities, and the synagogues scattered over the whole world, we shall easily see that the Diaspora Jews were closely attached to their nationality and that the overwhelming majority of them did not incline to assimilation. Jewish tradition was the foundation on which the Jewish communities were built, and without it Jews would not have had the right to demand protection of their privileges from the kings, nor would the latter have found special reason for making exceptions of the Jews from the juridical point of view. It is sufficiently clear from anti-Semitic literature that Jewish religious customs—circumcision, the Sabbath, the festivals and the dietary laws—were the first things to attract the attention of the Gentiles, serving as signs which made the Jew immediately recognizable. If we recall, for example, the importance ascribed by the Romans in their documents to the question of the Sabbath, we shall at once see that the demand for governmental protection of the Sabbath rest arose from a profound need on the part of the Jewish population.[54]

There were undoubtedly synagogues in every town that had a Jewish population,[55] and inscriptions and papyri mention nine synagogues in Egypt,[56] apart from Alexandria, where such were scattered all over the city, as Philo testifies (*Legat.* 132). The Talmud extols the stateliness and wealth of the Alexandrian synagogue;[57] the *Acts of the Apostles* refer to synagogues in Asia Minor (Antioch, Pisidia, Iconium, Ephesus), in Syria (Damascus), in Macedonia (Philippi, Thessalonica, Beroia), in Greece (Athens Corinth), and on the island of the Cyprus (Salamis). Even in distant Pantikapaion (Kerch) a synagogue existed in the first century of the present era.[58] The meetings in these buildings for common prayer and reading of the Torah were the normal expression of religious feeling, and Philo frequently speaks of them with deep reverence.[59] The festivals celebrated in Palestine were also brought to the Diaspora, and these included not only the traditional celebrations such as Passover and Tabernacles, but also the new festivals of Purim and Hannukah.[60]

In connection with the last subject, it is to be stressed that the diffusion of the new festivals outside Palestine did not take place of its own accord, but as the result of organized propaganda emanating from Hasmonean Palestine.[61] This question, namely, the regular contacts between Palestine and the Diaspora and the influence of Palestinian Jewry on that of the Dispersion, is of great importance; it has not yet been sufficiently investigated and deserves the special attention of scholars. Examples of the political influence of Palestine on the Egyptian Diaspora have been alluded to above (p. 283f.); but Palestinian influence had very many aspects and was not confined to isolated instances in the political field. It was largely cultural and expressed itself primarily in the export of the new Palestinian literature and in its translation into Greek.[62]

Together with the new works, such as the Book of Esther and the Book of Judith, there reached the Diaspora a different spirit, completely opposed to the compromising pro-Greek aspirations of Aristeas or Philo. This was the aggressive national spirit of Hasmonean Israel, born with the rebellion of Judah the Maccabee, which found its political expression in a stubborn struggle against the Greek cities of that country. This spirit desired no compromise with the Greeks, and still less with those Jews who inclined to them. Jason of Cyrene was the first Jewish author in the Diaspora to extol the great religious and national cause of Judah the Maccabee and to voice in his book the acute bitterness prevailing among the fighters for freedom towards the Hellenizing Jews. He was followed by other Diaspora writers; and this branch of Alexandrian literature acquired increasing importance at the beginning of the Roman period when the relations between Jews and Greeks grew sharper in the political sphere. There are excellent grounds for supposing that books such as *III Maccabees* and *The Wisdom of Solomon* were composed in this stormy period.[63] This literature is much more superficial and much less interesting than the literary trends of Aristeas and Philo, but it is more sincere and consistent and closer to the spirit of the masses. The philosophical works of Philo and the *Letter of Aristeas* reflect, after all, only the views of restricted groups of wealthy people in Alexandria and of the Jewish intelligentsia influenced by Hellenism, while literature of the type of the *Third Book of the Maccabees* faithfully reflect the trend of thinking prevailing among broad sections of the Jewish population on the Egyptian diaspora and probably in other diaspora centers as well.

To sum up: despite the great influence of Hellenism on the Jews of the Diaspora, Jewish tradition did not give way to Greek culture and was able to defend itself. The ancestral customs had struck deep root in the Jewish psyche and could not be abolished under the influence of peoples whose spirit was alien to them. But the main reason for the existence of a Jewish Diaspora culture was the vital strength of the Jewish communities. Just as the civic organization of the Greeks in the Greek cities secured the preservation of Greek culture outside Hellas, so the organization of Jews in independent communities safeguarded Jewish tradition. The Greeks who settled in the countryside quickly lost their national characteristics and merged with the natives, while the urban Greeks remained people of Greek culture for generations.[64] The Jews, too, when they appeared as isolated individuals among the great mass of foreigners, could not overcome the influence of their environment or retain the elements of Jewish culture, and the fate of Egyptian Jewry after the year 117 C.E. proves this.[65]

But such cases were exceptional; the Jews always settled in groups, and the communal organization bound all the Jews of the locality into one body. The synagogues were the property of the communities; just as the temples belonged to the Greek cities, and just as the cult of the city god was obligatory on every member of the city, so the worship of the God of Israel was the bounden duty of every member of the Jewish congregation. As long as the Greek city existed in the Orient, the Greek deities continued to exist in one form or another; as long as the organized Jewish community stood firm, Jewish tradition—the belief in one God, circumcision, the Sabbath and the festivals—remained solidly grounded. The public life of the Greek cities was based on the statutes of Hellenic law, and as long as the Greek city functioned, Greek law also performed its public function.

The Jewish community was based on the Mosaic Law; and as long as the former survived, the Jewish religion was bound up with Jewish public life, and whoever wanted to abandon Judaism had also to quit the organized community. This was not so easy, for before he left the community the Jew had to be sure that the Greeks would accept him into their society as a citizen, which was by no means a foregone conclusion. At times the Jews' common sense told them that it was not worthwhile leaving the Jewish community, with which so many privileges were associated, in order to be citizens of a Greek city the scope of whose rights did not always exceed those of their own congregation.[66] Membership in the Jewish community also brought considerable advantage from an economic point of view. It was convenient for a Jewish trader to know that wherever in the world he took his wares he would find his brethren and co-nationals, people like himself, to help him in his hour of need and furnish him with necessary information on the state of the local market, being at the same time, moreover, eager to do business with him. Not only the trader, but also the Jewish craftsman needed this close tie which bound all the Jewish communities into one international body. Above (p. 337f.) have been cited the words of the Talmud concerning the poor craftsmen who, on entering the synagogue in Alexandria, immediately discovered their fellow craftsmen, "whence they found their livelihood and that of their families." From a practical point of view, therefore, there was little advantage to be gained from leaving the community.

Only those people who wanted to achieve an administrative career on a grand scale, such as Dositheos son of Drimylos or Tiberius Julius Alexander, or those quite uninterested in questions of livelihood because they possessed great wealth, saw no special need to remain within the community. People such as these were not, of course, either usual or common. The broad sections of the Jewish public had no desire to exclude themselves from the generality even in cases where civic rights could be purchased at that price. Indeed, we have seen above that the pursuit of civic privileges in the cities was not connected with departure from the Jewish congregation, since the Jews desired to be members of the cities and of their own communities simultaneously. This duality greatly irritated the Greek public, and was potential material for anti-Semitic propaganda, as we shall see.

Very few phenomena of human history have a history of approximately two thousand years. Anti-Semitism is one of them. We here behold an uninterrupted evolution of hatred for Jews and Judaism from the moment that Jews quit, or were forcibly ejected from, their country, down to our own day. On its long historical journey, anti-Semitism has assumed various forms, sometimes upholding political or racialist ideas, sometimes disguising itself in the habit of economic and social hatred, most frequently appearing under the mask of religious faith; but always and everywhere remaining true to itself in its hatred of the Jewish people. Its activities have also varied, from literary polemics conducted with specious scientific and philosophical objectivity, to the perpetration of pogroms and the installation of gas-chambers.

When the historian proceeds to investigate anti-Semitism in a given epoch, he sometimes finds himself at a loss before this puzzling and complex picture; nor does he always discover the correct method of distinguishing between the essential and the irrelevant, between cause and effect, between truth and falsehood. The main danger that lies in wait for him is a confusion between the inner quality of anti-Semitism, which is always and everywhere the same, and its various manifestations, which alter according to place and circumstance. The inner quality of anti-Semitism arises from the very existence of the Jewish people as an alien body among the nations. The alien character of the Jews is the central cause of the origin of anti-Semitism, and this alien character has two aspects: The Jews are alien to other peoples because they are foreigners derived from another land, and they are alien because of their foreign customs which are strange and outlandish in the eyes of the local inhabitants.

The road to hatred is not at all difficult and the Jews have no means of barring it, for the very fact of their alien quality creates the setting for its development. But the manifestations of anti-Semitism are very diverse and their study throws light on the social and political situation and intellectual lineaments of the "host'" people on the one hand, and of the Jewish communities of the Diaspora on the other. This, then, will be our own angle of approach to the study of anti-Semitism in the ancient world.

Anti-Semitism originated in Egypt. The Egyptian priest Manetho was the first to speak of the Jews with detestation. Such detestation had been unknown to the Greeks previously. Their first encounter with the Jews had aroused no antipathy among them; on the contrary, they looked upon the Jews as members of a unique people entirely

devoted to philosophic observation. I have referred above
(p. 287) to Clearchus of Soli's story of the meeting of Aristotle
with a Jew who was a Greek "not only in language, but also in
spirit." This Jew, relates Clearchus, made the acquaintance of
Aristotle and his pupils because he was interested in their philosophy; but in the end they learned from him and not he from
them. Clearchus reveals *en passant* his knowledge of the Jews:
"The Jews are the descendants of the philosophers of India.
They say that the philosophers are called Kalanoi among the
Indians, Jews among the Syrians; the name is derived from
their place of habitation, Judah. The name of their town, which
is very strange, is Hierousaleme."[67]

The same estimate of the
Jews as philosophers is found also in Megasthenes, one of the
intimates of Seleucus I, who visited India on the occasion of
diplomatic negotiations and wrote a book on that country.
"Everything recorded by the wise men of ancient times about
nature," writes Megasthenes, "is to be found also among the
philosophers outside Greece, part among the Brahmans in India,
part in Syria among the people known as Jews."[68] Even more
interesting is the opinion about Jews expressed by Theophrastus,
a pupil of Aristotle. He tells of the sacrifices offered by them to
God and adds: "Throughout this time they discourse together
about the Divine, because they are philosophers by nature, and
at night they observe the stars, watching them and addressing
them in their prayers."[69] Thus, the Greek intelligentsia of the
period of Alexander the Great, and some time after him, regarded
the Jews as philosophers, men of intellect and religious speculation. The reason for their view is to be sought, not in the impression made by the Jews on the Greeks (it is doubtful whether
any one of the above three writers had ever seen a Jew), but
in a certain trend of Greek thought itself.

Among the Greeks as among
every people of high culture, there awoke at times the aspiration
to seek the loftiest intellectual possessions of mankind among
remote "exotic" peoples, and even among savage tribes that had
no culture at all. Thus the ideal healthy life was envisaged by
Tacitus, the pampered Roman, among the savage Germans, and
the authors of the modern European "Utopias" have sought their
ideal system of public life across the ocean far from "corrupt"
European civilization. The conquest of Asia by Alexander opened
to the Greeks a broad field for such fantasies, and it is precisely
at this period that the Greek "Utopias" appear.[70] Among the new

peoples that suddenly emerged before their curious gaze, were some which were not savage at all and whose religious customs, veiled in the tenuous glamor of oriental mysticism, caught the Greek imagination. Among these peoples the Greeks numbered, for example, the Indians, and also the Jews, perhaps because they had heard from soldiers or travelers of the Jewish refusal to worship the gods, which could be explained as resulting from philosophical thought, and of the Sabbath repose, which the Greeks believed arose from the need for devotion to religious speculation. Thus there originated among them the legend of the peculiar philosophical characteristics of the Jewish people.[71] The first Greek writer to write more or less realistically about the Jews was Hecataeus of Abdera, a contemporary of Ptolemy I.[72] Hecataeus had not read Jewish literature (in his time the Bible had not been translated into Greek), but he had heard something of the Exodus, of Moses and the High Priests, and assembled these items of information into a complete narrative, not all of which agrees with the biblical account. In Hecataeus' story, for example, Moses did not merely enter Palestine, but also founded Jerusalem and other towns and, further, built the Temple. Hecataeus had heard nothing whatever of the kings of Israel; with him an unbroken dynasty of High Priests begins in Moses' time and continues till his own day. Especially interesting is his story of the Exodus. A severe epidemic began to spread over Egypt and the Egyptian population ascribed the cause to the wrath of the gods; for the country was full of all sorts of aliens who had brought from abroad the cults of strange deities, on account of whom the shrines of the local gods stood empty and forsaken. To appease the gods of Egypt, the Egyptians resolved to expel all foreigners, and they carried out their decision. The stronger and cleverer among those expelled formed contingents which crossed to Greece, and the remainder of the exiles, the vast mass of them, departed to the land of Judaea, then a desert.[73] Thus the Jews became a people. In this story there are not yet signs of anti-Semitism; the fact that Hecataeus prefers the Greeks to the Jews is natural in a Greek writer. The narrative is important to us because it furnishes for the first time the Egyptian version of the Exodus which was later "enriched" in several details by Manetho and others.[74] A hint of anti-Semitism can nevertheless be found in Hecataeus. When he tells of the religious and political institutions founded by Moses, he remarks that Moses initiated a form of life encouraging seclusion from humankind and hatred of aliens (Diod. 40, 3, 4). Hecataeus may have heard—or have known from experience—of the Jewish refusal to eat at Gentile tables, and this may have impressed him as incomprehensible pride and hatred of aliens. Apart from this sentence I do not find any negative attitude to the Jews in Hecataeus; on the contrary, he speaks with respect of Moses' legislative work and emphasizes several positive details in the laws which he gave to the people of Israel.

Under Ptolemy II, the Egyptian priest Manetho published his Egyptian history, which he wrote for the Greeks in their own language. Of this great literary work Josephus has preserved two extracts of very great importance for the present question. Their interpretation is beset with difficulties, as Manetho's actual words and Josephus' personal opinion cannot always be distinguished, while the genuineness of individual passages is open to doubt. For this reason Manetho's attitude to the Jews is difficult to determine. While some scholars regard him as an anti-Semite, others doubt whether he ever touched on the Jewish question at all. Indeed, the first extract[75] concerns other matters. Manetho tells of the Hyksos nation which attacked Egypt and ruled it for over five hundred years. Forced out of Egypt, they turned toward Syria, and on their way there, founded the city of Jerusalem in the land of Judaea. This is far from clear.

The second passage is more important and much more complicated.[76] Manetho here deviates from the path of scientific learning to recount the hearsay and legends which he seems to have collected among the Egyptian priesthood. King Amenhotep (Amenophis) desired to behold the gods and received an oracle that he would attain his wish if he purified the land of lepers. The king gathered them and sent them to forced labor in the quarries, then gave them the city of Avaris as their territory, their number amounting to eighty thousand. After they had fortified themselves in Avaris, they rebelled against the king and elected a priest of Heliopolis by the name of Osarseph as their leader. Osarseph commanded the lepers to cease worshiping the gods, also ordering them to slaughter and eat the sacred animals of the Egyptians. He further forbade them to associate with people not of their persuasion. He fortified Avaris with walls and sent an invitation to the descendants of the Hyksos who lived in Jerusalem to come to his aid in the conquest of Egypt. They obeyed him willingly and came to Egypt to the number of 200,000. King Amenophis fled in fear to Ethiopia, taking with him the sacred animals, and stayed there thirteen years, as long as the lepers ruled Egypt. This rule was of unparalleled cruelty; the lepers burned down towns and villages, plundered temples, defiled the images of the gods, converted shrines into shambles and roasted the flesh of the sacred beasts. Ultimately, Amenophis gathered courage to fight the lepers, attacking them with a great host, slaying many of them and pursuing the survivors as far as the frontiers of Syria.

                 After this passage we read in Josephus: "They say that these laws and statutes were given to them by a priest born in Heliopolis called Osarseph (after the god Osiris of Heliopolis), who after going over to this people (that is, to the Hyksos and the lepers) changed his name and called himself Moses" (*C. Ap.* I, 250). Laqueur[77] sought to prove that these words were never in Manetho's book and that they were a late interpolation by an anti-Semitic writer. If we erase this paragraph, we shall be eliminating, in Laqueur's view, two important things from Manetho's writings, namely, the identification of Osarseph and Moses and the assimilation of the Jews to the lepers. On the basis of Laqueur's study, Heinemann[78] concluded that what Manetho said had no bearing on the Jews; the story of the destruction of the Egyptian temples by the lepers merely preserved a memory of the religious persecution of the monotheistic Pharaoh Amenhotep IV (Akhenaten). This story became associated with the Hyksos invasion, and only later, after Manetho's time, were stories of the Jews added. I do not regard this explanation as acceptable. Manetho's narrative, of course, may be based on ancient Egyptian legends, but their association with Jewish questions already existed in his writings. Even if we erase from the story paragraph 250, which refers to Moses, sufficient ground still remains for charging Manetho with anti-Semitism. For who are the Hyksos who came from Jerusalem, if not Jews? Manetho does not call them so specifically, it is true, contenting himself with the unclear term "Jerusalemites," but all his contemporaries knew very well that the Jews lived in Jerusalem. Manetho refrains from mentioning the name "Jews" for the simple reason that in his opinion they were not yet in existence at that ancient time. His account of the Hyksos and the lepers explains to the reader the Jews' origin. Amenophis expels the Jerusalemites and the lepers from Egypt and pursues them "to the frontiers of Syria," and it is clear that the Hyksos returned whence they had come, to Jerusalem, and the lepers went with them.

Laqueur thus appears to be mistaken in thinking that the idea of the Jews intermingling with the lepers is contained only in paragraph 250. Even without this passage it emerges clearly from Manetho's narrative that the Jews who lived in Jerusalem were the descendants of the Hyksos and the Egyptian lepers. Hence the description given by Manetho of the activity of the lepers in Egypt is also undoubtedly directed against the Jews. Manetho wanted to show his readers that the Jews' ancestors, the lepers, had already publicly manifested the negative characteristics later inherited by their descendants: cruelty, hatred of the customs of other religions, the striving to seclude themselves from others and to find associates only among themselves. This anti-Semitic motive cannot be eliminated from Manetho's account, unless we cast doubt on the genuineness of the entire story; but there are no adequate grounds for doing anything of the kind.

What was the cause of Manetho's anti-Semitism? The reason is probably to be sought in the fact of his being an Egyptian priest. Josephus says on one occasion that the Egyptians were the real foes of the Jewish people, and that the relations between the Jews and Greeks were good till the Egyptians interfered and incited the Greeks against them (cf. p. 523, n. 71). This view originated from apologetic motives, and cannot be depended on. But there was one question which interested the Egyptians more than it did the Greeks, and that was the Exodus. The Egyptian priests saw need to reply to the biblical story which, as is well known, is not distinguished for its sympathy for the Egyptians.[79] Manetho did not invent the reply himself, but only collected the legends and stories (some of which preserved genuine historical remiscences from very ancient times) used by the Egyptian priests as material in their disputations with the Jews. The name Osarseph is too like Joseph[80] to be regarded as a normal Egyptian name. The Jews told stories of Joseph as a wise governor of Egypt, whereas Manetho replied that he had ruined the country, polluted the shrines and persecuted religion. The Jews regarded themselves as a people, whereas Manetho related that they were derived from a degraded mob of lepers. The Jews claimed that God had brought them out of Egypt, while Manetho asserted that they had been expelled from the country after they had ruled it brutally for thirteen years. Thus was created the first anti-Semitic book. The Greeks later took over what the Egyptian priests had written, and the Egyptian version of the Exodus took deep root in Hellenistic literature, remaining there for generations.

It is not our intention to dwell on the details of the anti-Semitic literature which flourished at the end of the Hellenistic period and at the beginning of the Roman period. Only its basic features will be noted. First, the religious question. All agreed in viewing the Jewish religion as nothing but a "barbarous superstition" (*barbara superstitio*), to use Cicero's definition.[81] The respect awakened among the Greeks by the first reports of Jewish "philosophy" was swiftly dissipated, only one more-or-less serious attempt being made to distinguish between the essential and the unessential in Jewish religion. Poseidonius, one of the great Greek philosophers of the Hellenistic period, gave the following picture of the development of Judaism.[82] Moses, who was an Egyptian priest (the origins of this theory are now familiar to us), openly attacked the Egyptian animal cult and also the endeavor to describe divinity in human form; he taught that God is "that which surrounds us all, also the earth and the sea; we call Him the heavens, or the world, or the nature, of the whole universe." The elements of Judaism were determined by this pantheistic outlook—imageless worship, the revelation of divine will in a modest shrine—in brief, a religion befitting people of wisdom and righteousness. This was the work of Moses. But those who came after him did not preserve the principles of the pure religion, and in its place came superstitions, so that the commandments of circumcision, forbidden foods and so on, were established. On this theory, then, Judaism had undergone a long development from a lofty philosophical doctrine, worthy of acceptance by every thinking person, to a form of popular faith that was merely a superstition.

But this endeavor to explain the Jewish religion in its historical development remained isolated; the anti-Semites did not set themselves such complicated aims. Most of them regarded the rejection of idols as the rejection of the gods altogether, and thus the paradoxical situation was created that the Jews, the only people of the ancient world who upheld the idea of the unity of God, were accused of the offense of "atheism." The approach of the anti-Semites is not difficult to understand: If the Jews refused, with incomprehensible obstinacy, to worship the gods, while their own God could not be seen or heard—and there was neither point nor profit in praying to "the heavens"—what was Judaism but a religion without a divinity? The anti-Semites, therefore, failed to discover in Judaism its main point: the idea of the oneness of God; and what remained was simply a collection of curious customs. On these customs—circumcision, the keeping of Sabbath, forbidden foods (especially swine's flesh)—the anti-Semites poured unstinting mockery. Sabbath observance, for example, was nothing but a desire to be lazy; the Jews had become so fond of a life of idleness, that they even suffered defeats on its account, as their enemies exploited their sloth to capture Jerusalem on the Sabbath. Jokes of this sort were also heard on the subject of circumcision and the dietary laws. There is no point in considering them in detail, but we may dwell upon some of the most characteristic features of ancient anti-Semitism. In the writings of Mnaseas of Patara, pupil of the famous Alexandrian scholar Eratosthenes, is found the first account of the cult of the ass in the Temple of Jerusalem. Mnaseas tells of a man who had penetrated into the interior of the Temple and stolen from it the ass's head, which was made of gold.[83] Poseidonius tells that when Antiochus Epiphanes entered the Holy of Holies, he saw there the statue of a bearded man riding on an ass and holding a book; this was Moses, who gave the Jews laws of hatred toward all mankind.[84] Damocritos wrote in his book *On the Jews* that they worshiped a golden ass's head,[85] and Apion, the well-known anti-Semite of the time of Gaius Caligula and Claudius, related that the head was worth a great deal of money.[86] Scholars are divided on the origin of this strange slander, most connecting it with the Egyptian myth of the deity Typhon or Set, god of evil, the steady opponent of Osiris, god of good. His sacred animal was the ass, and he was himself sometimes described as an ass-headed man.[87] Plutarch relates that, after a battle Typhon fled on an ass for seven days and, having been saved from death, begot two sons, Jerusalem and Judah.[88] In this myth Typhon appears as the ancestor of the Jews, and if we recall that Moses in Poseidonius' story is also described as an old man riding on an ass, we may suppose that the anti-Semites equated Moses with Typhon, symbol of evil. This legend too would appear to have originated among the circles close to the Egyptian priesthood, like Manetho's story of the lepers. Bickermann was of a different opinion,[89] believing that it was unnecessary to look for profound reasons for the origin of the slander; the anti-Semites merely needed mocking tales concerning the Jews, and that was all, hence they made up the story that the Jews worshiped an ass, taking the details from an old Idumaean tale about the theft of a golden ass's head from an enemy shrine—a tale originally quite unrelated to the Jews. This explanation is very simple, but also involves difficulties. We may ask: was the ass-cult really more ridiculous to the Greeks than that of the crocodile or the cat, so usual in Egyptian religious life? The anti-Semites wished to emphasize, not the foolishness of the Jews, but their knavery, and for this reason chose the ass, the animal sacred to Typhon, who symbolized evil. The usual explanation, then, seems closer to the mark than Bickermann's theory, though admittedly it too does not clear up all the details of the problem.

It is no less difficult to establish the origin of another story in Damocritos and in particular in Apion, namely the blood-libel. Damocritos says that the Jews made a practice once every seven years of kidnaping a foreigner, killing him, and cutting his flesh into small pieces.[90] Apion (Josephus, *C. Ap.* II, 91ff.) has a more detailed version. When Antiochus Epiphanes entered the Temple he found a Greek lying in bed, and by him a table loaded with good food. Seeing the king, the Greek fell on his face before him and begged him to save his life; from his story the king learned that the Greek, who had been innocently touring the country, had been suddenly made captive by unknown people and brought hither. Here they had begun to fatten him up with all sorts of dishes; this had pleased him at first, but then he had become afraid, for the Temple servants had revealed to him the secret that each year the Jews seized a Greek tourist, fattened him for a year and later, taking him to a wood, murdered him. After this ceremonial murder they tasted the entrails of the slain man and swore an oath to nurture hatred of the Greeks in their hearts. This is Apion's story. It is of special interest as the first of a long series of tales of this kind, whose tragic role in Jewish history is all too well known.

Whence came this story and what was its motive? Bickermann has found an excellent explanation for the literary derivation of the tale and he cites several examples from Hellenistic and Roman literature to account for its style.[91] But the historical reasons which he adduces for its origin do not, in the writer's opinion, get to the bottom of the problem. Bickermann believes that the myth arose among Greek literary groups that were close to Antiochus Epiphanes. Antiochus had desecrated the Temple of Jerusalem, and such sacrilege was regarded by the Greeks as a great and unforgivable sin. The Greek authors were therefore set on the aim of "whitewashing" the king. They performed their duty by pointing to the crimes and murders which they alleged had been committed in the Temple. If the House of God at Jerusalem had become a den of robbers, Antiochus had done well to stop this evil-doing and to desecrate what was no longer in any sense holy.[92]

But it is hard to assume that this was the real origin of the legend. In the reign of Antiochus Epiphanes the hostility to the Jews was so strong among the Greeks that the writers had no need at all to acquit the king of the crime of sacrilege, for the Greek public had not seen his act as such in any real sense.[93] It is interesting that Polybius (XXXI, 11), relating the death of Antiochus, explains that he met his death deservedly in punishment for profaning the temple of Artemis-Nanaiah in Elam; he makes no mention whatever of Antiochus' additional desecration of the house of God at Jerusalem. The story was not composed to justify the king, but out of a desire to make a direct attack upon the Jews. Its center of gravity is at the end, in the Jews' solemn oath "to nurture hatred for the Greeks" (*ut inimicitias contra Graecos haberent*). The eating of the entrails of the victim associated with the oath is indeed part and parcel of the literary genre, but the oath itself has a genuine significance. The Greek author's real meaning is: "Beware of the Jews! They hate and detest us. Look at their brutal custom, whose aim is to give solemn expression to that hatred!" If this is the case, there is no need to seek the author among the circles of Antiochus' friends. The king appears in the story only because he had once entered the interior of the Temple, and it was therefore convenient to link his name with the account of the crimes alleged to have been committed in that secret place. It would be more correct to assume that the tale originated in Alexandria, where its composition can probably be dated in the flourishing period of Alexandrian anti-Semitism, namely, in the decades preceding the pogrom under Caligula. Apion may have been the first to put the story into literary form.

Closely connected with the blood-libel is the charge leveled against the Jews of misanthropy, *misoxenia*, meaning hatred of mankind, loathing of strangers, or *amixia*, unwillingness to merge with others—an idea already encountered in Hecataeus and Manetho. Diodorus, citing

Poseidonius, relates that when Antiochus Sidetes attacked Jerusalem, his courtiers advised him to exterminate the Jews completely, arguing that they alone of all the peoples refused to come into contact with other peoples and regarded all of them as enemies.[94] Apollonius Molon wrote of the Jews: "They do not accept among themselves people who entertain different outlooks on God, nor do they wish to come into contact with those whose customs differ from their own."[95]

Lysimachus ascribes to Moses the following injunctions: not to receive any man favorably, only to give bad counsel and to destroy all the temples of the gods.[96] Apion describes the solemn oath as sworn "in the name of God the Creator of the heavens," to hate every foreigner, and especially the Greeks.[97]

At a late period (in the third century C.E.) Philostratus wrote: "These people mingle with others neither for common meals nor in prosperity, prayer, or sacrifice; they are farther away from us than are Susa, Bactria or India . . ."[98] This was the Greeks' explanation of the obstinate Jewish observance of the commandments; they did not look deeper to find the real reasons and saw only the superficial aspect of the phenomenon, of "Touch me not, lest I be contaminated!" From this they drew their permanent conclusions, based not on the peculiar character of the Jewish religion, as they might have done had they thought logically, but on the suppressed hatred that they believed burned in the Jew against every non-Jew. This accusation was later transferred, as is well known, to the Christians.[99]

Reinach correctly observes: "Once hatred for a certain class of people becomes rooted in man's heart for some reason or other, everything associated with that class begins to be detestable."[100] Together with the frequent "grave" charges repeatedly leveled in anti-Semitic literature—hatred of mankind and irreverent contempt of the gods—unimportant and sometimes ludicrous accusations grew up. Apollonius Molon wrote that the Jews were both cowardly and insolent, and were the only barbarians who had not made any useful invention, because they were a people without ability.[101] Lysimachus related that the name of Jerusalem was at first Hierosyla, meaning sacrilege, and was devised by the founders of the city who had come to Palestine after they had desecrated the temples of Egypt.[102] Apion, seeking an answer to the question why the Jews sanctified the seventh day, gave the answer as follows, that after they had journeyed for six days, they suffered pains owing to the swelling of their stomachs and therefore rested on the seventh, naming it the Sabbath, because swelling of the stomach was known in Egyptian as *sabbatósis*.[103]

The Exodus in particular furnished abundant material to the anti-Semites, who one and all copied Manetho but added several offensive details to his original story. The canard about the lepers who had been expelled from Egypt because of their disease appealed to the Greek writers, and Lysimachus, Chairemon, Apion and others, each elaborated it in a new version. There is no point in devoting time to an account of these tales or in studying every small detail of ancient anti-Semitism; its peculiar nature will be apparent from what has already been said. It remains to deal with the question: what were the causes for the appearance and popular spread of anti-Semitism in the Greek world?

To the modern anti-Semites the question is no question at all. E. Meyer writes: "After the Greeks had come to know the Jews more intimately, their first idealization was inevitably bound to give place to the opposite opinion." And again: "This special (Jewish) character was bound to arouse hatred of the Jews."[104] Here anti-Semitism oversimplifies by seizing upon the antipathetic character of the Jews as a solution, and it goes without saying that no scientific basis need be sought for this view.

If we turn to more serious explanations, we shall see that most of them can be divided into three schools of thought: economic, religious and political. The first type seeks the reasons for anti-Semitism in the economic position of the Jews, in their function in the ancient world as traders, moneylenders, tax-collectors and the like. This doctrine has been especially developed in the books of Stahelin and Bludau, who have not only stressed the Jews' great wealth but have pointed to the dishonesty and unscrupulousness of their business conduct. The "explanation" rests on the hypothesis that the Jews in the ancient world performed the same functions of traders and financiers as they afterwards performed in the Middle Ages and in modern times. It has already been pointed out above (p. 343) that this approach is fundamentally erroneous,[105] and it were well to observe that Bludau himself is forced to admit that he finds no complaint in ancient anti-Semitic literature against Jews who lent money at interest.[106] As to Jewish speculation, this assumption rests on an arbitrary interpretation of several papyri which have won the particular affection of modern anti-Semites. These papyri, however, prove absolutely nothing, or at most bear witness to the fact that there were frauds and thieves among the Jews as well.[107]

The second school of thought emphasizes the religious and public self-segregation of the Jews and regards it as the sole cause of the flourishing of anti-Semitism (Reinach). This thinking approximates the truth more closely, but does not solve the problem completely. It is quite true that Jewish religious segregation repelled the Greeks, and even Hecataeus, who is not to be suspected of anti-Semitism, regarded it as the result of their hatred of foreigners. But it must be asked: did every people with strange customs evoke a similar reaction on the part of the Greeks? Were not the Egyptians, who worshiped crocodiles and cats, for instance, regarded by the Greeks as a strange people? Were not laws of purity and contamination normal in several oriental cults, and—which is of particular importance—in the cults of Greece itself?[108]

As to the fanatical devotion of the Jews to their faith, had not the Egyptians of Alexandria publicly executed a Roman soldier because he had dared to harm a cat?[109] And why should the custom of observing the Sabbath, so full of dignity and calm, have aroused contempt and mockery? Had self-segregation been the sole cause for anti-Semitism, it might have been supposed that the Greeks would have welcomed those Jews who wished to free themselves from it and become like Greeks. But actually the opposite was the case: the Greeks fought obdurately against the striving of the Hellenized Jews of Alexandria to take part in the physical training of the gymnasia, and even obtained an imperial prohibition against their doing so, as we have seen (p. 313f.). It is clear, then, that the mode of thought which sees the cause of anti-Semitism in religious factors does not solve the problem completely.

The third line of thinking emphasizes the political antagonism between the Jews and the other peoples. Heinemann[110] lists three "centers" of conflict (*Konfliktsherde*), namely, Syria (from the time of Antiochus Epiphanes), Egypt (from the end of the second century B.C.E.), and Rome (the conflicts between the Jews and the Roman state), apart from smaller centers dispersed everywhere. Lurié offers a more general formula for the political antagonism between the Jews and the Greeks.[111] In his view the Jews remained a political and national unit even outside their country, and this the Greeks were unwilling to recognize. The political theory sometimes correctly solves isolated problems of the growth of anti-Semitism in various places, but cannot explain the origin of anti-Semitism in its entire scope. Most scholars are not themselves content with the political theory alone, and Heinemann, for instance, adds to his study of the political causes a short account of "the intellectual grounds" which spurred the Greeks in their struggle against the Jews. This, indeed, may well be the right method; anti-Semitism, like many other broad historical phenomena, took various forms according to conditions of time and place, and cannot by its nature find an exact definition in one brief formula.

On the other hand, the solution cannot be found by a mechanical combination of all the "reasons" and "causes" which assisted the appearance and spread of anti-Semitism. Such an inquiry may explain the spread of anti-Semitism in a certain country, but not what it was in principle. This latter aspect can perhaps be brought into relief by ignoring the imaginary accusations of anti-Semitic literature and paying attention to the position held by the Jews in the Greek world as a strange nation whose features were novel both from a religious and a political viewpoint. The Jewish community, a political institution with a religious basis, was the completest expression and emphasis of these novel characteristics. The Greek *polis*, on the other hand, was also a political institution closely bound up with religious elements (see above, p. 28), and perhaps we shall be able to understand the profound reasons for ancient anti-Semitism if we can answer the question: what was the relationship between these two forces?

The material is not ample. In two passages (*Ant.* XII, 125ff.; XVI, 27ff.) Josephus tells of the Greeks of Asia Minor (Ionia) who wished to prevent the Jews living in their cities from observing their customs, forced them to desecrate the Sabbath by summoning them to their offices on that day, confiscated the sacred money earmarked to be sent to Jerusalem, and imposed upon the Jews the defrayal of urban taxes—a military service tax and "liturgies"—from the same sums. Their claim was this: "If the Jews are really of our community, let them honor the gods whom we honor." The case was tried before M. Agrippa, the counselor of Augustus, and won by the Jews thanks to the influence and intervention of Nicolaus of Damascus who

appeared in their defense. About the same time, the Greek
cities of Cyrenaica attacked their Jewish residents, also confiscating the sacred money, on the pretext that the Jews had not
paid their taxes. M. Agrippa abrogated this discriminatory measure and reconfirmed to the Jews of Cyrene the privileges which
they had received from Augustus (*Ant.* XVI, 160; *ib.* 169f.).
Several rescripts of Roman magistrates to Greek cities in Asia
Minor, belonging to the second half of the first century B.C.E.,
show that at that time also the cities were not reconciled to
Jewish privileges, and that the Jews were able to protect their
rights only thanks to Roman intervention.

Thus, for instance, the citi-
zens of Miletus prohibited the Jews from celebrating the Sabbath
or carrying out the commandments properly (*Ant.* XIV, 245).
The people of Tralles also refused to acknowledge Jewish privileges (*ib.* 242). The citizens of Paros even passed a special
resolution abolishing Jewish customs, and only thanks to the
Roman praetor did the Jews regain their license to live according
to their own laws (*ib.* 213ff.). If we possessed the records of the
Greek towns of Asia Minor and the other countries, we should
certainly find in them many resolutions of this sort and numerous
letters from kings or Roman officials canceling them. The hostility between the citizens of Alexandria and the Jews, which
ended with the disorders of the year 37 C.E., is also a striking
example of a severe clash between the Greek *polis* and the organized Jewish community.[112] The struggle against the Jews was
not therefore simply a literary manifestation, but a common
phenomenon of everyday life: literature merely gave a theoretical form to the hostile feelings which were growing among the
Greek population.

What impelled the Greeks
to oppose the Jews? National hatred in the modern sense did
not exist in the ancient world, and much less religious hatred.
The Greeks were familiar with many foreigners from abroad who
had settled in their cities, but had found no need to carry on
a violent attack against them. Why did they hate the Jews of
all people?

The answer is that the Jews
did not resemble the other aliens. Strangeness is always apt to
arouse mockery and hostility; but as long as the strangers are
not numerous and live unobtrusively, without making demands
and claims, there is no special reason for hating them, and the
"host people" may even accord them courtesy and recognition.

This was the position of the *katoikoi* or metics in the Greek cities, people without political rights who willingly bore the burden of civic duties, since the city gave them permission to enjoy its cultured life, and they had to pay for the favor.[113]
This was not the case with the Jews, who enjoyed numerous privileges yet were exempt from duties. This situation was the result of the fact that the Jews were not dependent on the favors of the Greek city, but had received their privileges directly from the kings, later from the emperors. It must be conceded that this was the right way: for the Greek city, which was based on Greek law, recognizing only two classes of people—citizens with rights and mere residents without rights—could not create an exceptional juridical position for the Jews. The kings were in different case. The Hellenistic kingdoms, with their variegated basis of diverse peoples, juridical principles and faiths, were ready to welcome the Jews as an additional element among those already to be found in the state.

In the Hellenistic period the Greek cities were also dependent on the favor of the kings, and consequently both the Greek city and the Jewish community stood side by side as forces of equal importance. The Greeks had great difficulty in defending their own autonomy and on several occasions were forced to surrender some part or other of their liberty to perform the king's orders and to preserve at least the outer semblance of traditional freedom. At the same time the Jews, under the protection of the same monarchs, enjoyed all the advantages of an internal autonomy the scope of whose rights was not inferior to that of Greeks. What was more, the Jews demanded of the Greek city that it recognize this privilege and take them into consideration, and such demands the Greeks had never heard from metics. The Jews required that they should not be forced to desecrate the Sabbath, that they be exempted from military service and from the associated taxes, that the city-taxes (liturgies) should not be levied from them, and that they be permitted to collect money and send it to Jerusalem.

The last privilege in particular was apt to arouse the anger of the Greeks, for the Greek cities were generally in need of money and could not reconcile themselves with the fact that part of the inhabitants should be legally exempt from liturgies although they possessed means. How great therefore was the temptation to confiscate this money for the needs of the city and to put an end to the anomalous situation of a corporation possessing privileges which in Greek eyes were entirely unjustified. The Jews, however, could not surrender their status, for with these privileges was bound up the very existence of the Jewish community. The Jews did not assume the most important liturgies of the city, the supplying of the needs of the gymnasia, the organization of the athletic games and the building of temples, because all these things were associated with the Greek religion. Nor did they hold municipal posts, because every such post was connected with the recognition of the city's official cult. They could not be good citizens even if they wished to be, because religion sundered them from the Greeks.

We have seen above that the observances of the Jewish religion itself were not such as to produce anti-Semitism among the Greeks. The latter knew many peoples and, far from taking up negative attitudes to their cults, respected them and voluntarily participated in them. Circumcision and the prohibition of certain foods were nothing new to the Greeks, for such customs were to be found in Egypt. Sabbath observance could be explained by the Jews' strange "philosophy," nor was there anything shameful in such a practice. Even the fundamental of Judaism, monotheism, was not strange to the Greek mind, for the epoch of naïve religion was long passed, the philosophers having undermined traditional Greek polytheism and prepared the soil for a deeper understanding of divinity. The various gods served only to symbolize the forces of nature or were likened to isolated manifestations of the universal divine power ruling the world.

But if the Greek intelligentsia had abolished polytheism in theory, this did not mean that it was prepared to give it up in everyday life, least of all when the masses were firmly attached to it. Innovations (such as new cults) might be introduced into religion, but what existed must not be abolished. The Greeks were prepared to accept the God of Israel into their Pantheon, but here they were faced with a riddle. The gods of Greece could easily compromise with the God of Israel, but He could not compromise with them. This was hard to understand. It was taken for granted that every nation reverenced its deity, but that did not mean that it had to despise the gods of its neighbors. The Greeks neither knew, nor could they know, the peculiar character of the Jewish faith, the faith in one, unique God, Creator of the heavens and earth, who denied by His very nature the existence of all other divinities. The Jews neither could nor did surrender this belief, for their entire national culture was based on it. Moreover, in monotheism they saw their intellectual superiority to all the other nations, and the entire Alexandrian literature is a hymn in praise of the one, unique and supreme God. Only He was God, and the other deities were "idols." And if the Jews sometimes endeavored, out of politeness or for political considerations, to conceal their detestation and contempt of the "idols," naturally the Greeks could not always be deceived, and they knew perfectly well what was the true Jewish attitude to their deities.

This attitude they might perhaps have pardoned if it had expressed itself only in abstract questions, for they knew plenty of atheist thinkers in their own country. But the Jewish contempt of the gods was bound up with contempt of the Greek *polis*. We have seen above that religion played a very important part in the latter's life, and the city itself was from a certain point of view a religious concept. Whoever did not acknowledge the official cult of the city withheld recognition of the city's sanctity and of its independent power as a political unit, and this undermined its autonomy. The Jewish refusal to worship the gods was in Greek eyes a sign of their hatred of the Greeks as a whole. "If the Jews are really of our community," claimed the Ionians, "let them also honor the gods whom we honor." "If the Jews belong to the citizenry," asked Apion, "why do they not respect the gods whom the Alexandrians respect?"[114] The Greeks could not forgive the Jews this insult, and naturally were never ready to accept into the civic body a people who with incomprehensible obstinacy refused to fulfill the easiest and simplest demands of public etiquette.

The acquisition of citizenship by a Jew in a Greek city seemed impossible so long as he remained loyal to his religion. The Jews were intellectually strangers to the Greeks, and this strangeness was felt by both sides at every step. Nor did the Greeks seek the proximity of the Jews, for what could they gain from such a *rapprochement*? The Jews, on the contrary, had no desire to be aliens, for it should not be forgotten that in many cities the Jewish communities had existed for centuries, and could not regard themselves as simple metics. They participated in the town's economic life, acquired the Greek language, names, and customs; the wealthy and well-born among them desired to be citizens, seeking to be Greeks and Jews at one and the same time. This "double-facedness" more especially was apt to anger the Greeks, for who could accept the strange situation in which a person was both a member of the city, enjoying all the city's rights as a Greek, yet was exempt from its duties as a Jew?[115] The Jews themselves were sometimes aware of the abnormality of the situation, and men such as the author of the *Third Book of the Maccabees* knew that one could not enjoy both worlds, and that one had to choose one of two ways: either to be a Jew, or to assimilate among the Greeks. Jews of this sort, however, did not come into constant contact with the Greeks; those who did were the wealthy men of good family who were the wardens and leaders of the community. These had drawn near to Greek culture and wanted to be like the Greeks, without being compelled to abandon their Judaism. They strove after civic rights, and the result was an unyielding refusal on the part of the Greeks to accept them into their society. The result was reciprocal hatred and grave clashes in the city streets.

Thus the two peoples faced each other without being able to achieve mutal understanding. Anti-Semitism was the external expression of this lack of understanding. Its growth was not coincidental, but was bound up with the Jews' actual situation outside their homeland, since they had built their public life on the basis of Jewish tradition and neither desired nor were able—even had they wished—to reconcile Jewish monotheistic doctrine with Greek culture based on polytheism. The two fundamental anti-Semitic accusations—atheism (contempt of the gods) and misanthropy (hatred of mankind)—grew directly from this fundamental antagonism. And after hatred of the Jews had taken root among the Greeks, it was not difficult to interpret all Jewish observance in a malicious manner and make Jews frauds, knaves and shedders of innocent blood.

The political position in the East added fuel to anti-Semitic propaganda. The persecution of Antiochus raised the populations of the Greek cities of Palestine against the Jews, and the Hasmonean war against the same cities intensified hatred for the Jews, not only among the Palestinian population, but throughout the Hellenistic world. The peculiar anti-Semitism of the Egyptian clergy (which rose, as we have seen, in answer to the biblical story of the Exodus) joined hands with Greek hatred, and from all these factors sprang the anti-Semitic literature which itself influenced the development of the movement and created fixed and formulated charges against the Jews, formulae which have not lost their propaganda power down to this very day.

It goes without saying that the Jews did not suffer the attacks of the anti-Semites in silence. They were capable of defending themselves by force when opposition assumed the character of open warfare, and also by diplomatic negotiations with the representatives of the authorities. But their strongest weapon was literature and religious propaganda. The apologetic trend in the rich Alexandrian literature developed chiefly at the beginning of the Roman period, that is, in the time when the anti-Semitic movement reached its zenith. We are acquainted with this trend from the writings of Josephus and Philo. The anti-Semites charged the Jews with atheism, and the Jews countered by stressing their belief in one God, demonstrating the philosophical and moral superiority of monotheism over polytheism. The Greeks mocked the strange customs of the Jewish people, whereupon the Jews described them as moral and social institutions in complete harmony with the laws of nature and the dictates of good sense. The Greeks spoke of Moses with hatred and contempt, and the apologetic writers made Moses and the other heroes of Jewish history into the perfect ideal of the "sage" of Greek type, and the Greeks into the pupils of the Jews in philosophy and science. The anti-Semites stressed the "misanthropy" of the Jews; the Jews threw open the doors of their synagogues and invited all the Gentiles to come and worship the one God, Creator of heaven and earth, in their company.

But religious and literary questions overstep the limits set to the present work, whose aim has been to investigate the material foundation of Jewish life in the Hellenistic period, and the political, economic and public bases of Jewish life in the Greek world. It has, indeed, been impossible to discuss these topics without sometimes touching on cultural questions, but the intellectual development of the Jewish people in the Hellenistic period, and not less in the Roman epoch, should form the subject of a separate study.

APPENDICES

NOTES

BIBLIOGRAPHY

INDEX

APPENDIX I

The Sources

for the Period of the Hellenizers' Rule in Jerusalem

1. II Maccabees

The Second Book of Macca-
bees is the only source furnishing the historian with more or less
orderly material on the period of the Hellenizers' rule in Jerusalem before the revolt of Judah the Maccabee. The attitudes
of scholars to the historical value of the book vary widely. In
the nineteenth century the attitude was generally negative; II
Maccabees was thought to be a tendentious work by a Pharisee
author, who sought to give a religious account of the events of
the time of Judah the Maccabee (in contrast to the political
nationalist account of I Maccabees) and to this end distorted
historical truth. According to Wellhausen "the book is unreliable
in every passage where it can be checked (against other sources),
hence it is not to be relied on in relation to passages that cannot be checked."[1] This too is the opinion of Willrich.[2] Out of a
desire to controvert this negative attitude, Niese in 1900 published his study of the two books of the Maccabees, in which
he sought to bring into relief the great historical value of II Maccabees and to attribute to it greater importance than to I Maccabees.[3] After Niese's study, scholars were compelled to pay
more attention to the second book; Laqueur, Kolbe and Eduard
Meyer, as well as scholars of our own day, such as Gutberlet,
Bévenot, Bickermann and Abel,[4] estimate II Maccabees as a

reputable historical source, although they do not go so far as Niese.

Although many articles and books have been written on II Maccabees, it cannot be claimed even today that all the difficulties associated with the study of this source have been successfully solved. The first difficult problem is the chronological question. In chapter 2.23, the author says that in his book he intends to transmit a précis of the words of Jason of Cyrene, who described the events in five books. This informs us that II Maccabees is not an original work, but an abbreviation of another writer whose writings have not survived, and whose name is not mentioned at all in history or literature. The chronological question therefore falls into two parts, namely, when did Jason of Cyrene live, and when was II Maccabees written?

We shall commence with the second question. At the beginning of II Maccabees the reader finds a letter from the Jews of Palestine to their brethren in Egypt, bearing the date "the year 188" (of the dating of bills), that is, the year 125/4 B.C.E.[5] This date, indeed, belongs only to the letter mentioned and bears no apparent relation to the work itself (to the abbreviation of Jason's book), which begins at the opening of chapter 3. However, the object of the letter is to urge the Jews of Egypt to celebrate the new festival of the Hasmoneans—the rededication of the Temple, in memory of the events which occurred in the days of Judah the Maccabee; this event is described at length in the body of the book. This informs us that the connection between the letter opening II Maccabees and the book itself is not merely superficial, but is profoundly internal: the detailed story of the events in Palestine under Judah the Maccabee was to serve, in the writer's view, as historical material capable of convincing the Jews of Egypt that they should accept the proposal of the Jews of Palestine to celebrate the festival of Hannukah (the Dedication) in Egypt. The date of the year 125/4 constitutes, therefore, not only the *terminus post quem* for the completion of II Maccabees, but also more or less indicates the actual time it was written; for it is difficult to assume that the author extracted an old letter from the records, since the fact of its being old would have diminished its value for the Jews of Egypt to whom it was directed. It must also be remembered that the Hasmonean propaganda in the Diaspora countries was especially strong at the beginning of the dynasty's existence, as is proved by the letter of 143/42.[6]

Hence there is every ground for assuming that II Maccabees was composed about the year 120, when the establishment of the Jewish state was still a fairly new phenomenon and still able to fire the imagination of Diaspora Jewry. The Egyptian Jews no doubt read with greater enthusiasm the account of the heroic deeds done in Palestine under Judah the Maccabee, and willingly opened their synagogues to the new festivals originating from the events of the war of independence.[7] Further, although the author of II Maccabees is not to be regarded as a Pharisee writer, as most scholars think,[8] it is not to be denied that he was a strict Jew devoted to the religious tradition with all his heart, and it is hard to suppose that a Jew of this type would have described the events leading to the establishment of the Hasmonean dynasty with such enthusiasm, had he known that the dynasty had ultimately deviated from the ancestral path and mounted a persecution of the interpreters of the Torah and of its loyal adherents. The rift between John Hyrcanus and the Pharisees may therefore be seen as the *terminus ante quem* for the writing of II Maccabees. The years 124-110 B.C.E., therefore, are the most appropriate years for the book's composition.[9]

If the "Epitomator," the "abbreviator" (the author of II Maccabees is generally called by this name, because he carried out the *epitoma*, or abbreviation, of Jason of Cyrene), lived in the years of 124-110, then it is clear that Jason lived some time before him and wrote his work between 160 (the date of the death of Judah the Maccabee) and 124. Is there any possibility of determining his date more closely?

1. II Maccabees tells his readers (2.19ff.) what the events are which he intends to relate: the events which occurred in the time of Judah the Maccabee and his brothers, the dedication of the Temple and altar, the wars against Antiochus Epiphanes and his son Eupator, and the miracles and heroic deeds that occurred in that time—"all those things which were related by Jason of Cyrene in five books, I will attempt to abbreviate into one discourse." From this we learn that Jason's work did not cover a longer period than that treated by the Epitomator.[10]

As is known, II Maccabees does not even reach the death of Judah the Maccabee and ends with an account of the victory of Judah over Nicanor. It may be assumed, of course, that Jason extended his account of events another year or two and included in his description the death of Judah, but there are no grounds for thinking that he also described the period of Jonathan and Simon, as such a supposition would be contrary to the explicit words of the Epitomator.[11] We therefore conclude from II Maccabees 2.19ff. that the five books of Jason were entirely devoted to an account of the events down to approximately the year 160.

2. The very fact that he fixed the chronological limit of his work in the year 160, or near it, indicates that he had no interest in describing the Hasmonean dynasty. Indeed, Mattathias is not to be found in II Macc. and, as the Hasmonean tradition associated the first deeds of heroism of the fighters for freedom with Mattathias, it is hard to suppose that the Epitomator would have omitted such wonderful tales had he found them in Jason. We have already said (p. 205) that the figure of Mattathias was very important to the author of I Macc., as Mattathias was father of the dynasty; his absence from Jason proves the contrary, namely, Jason's lack of interest in the history of the dynasty.

The same thing becomes clear from the allusions to Judah's brothers in II Macc.: Jason assigns to them no independent role and on occasion relates things not to the credit of Simon.[12] Jason has before him only Judah the Maccabee and it is only his deeds and heroism that he describes. The simplest explanation for this approach is that Jason wrote his work immediately after Judah had fallen, when the historical roles of Jonathan and Simon were not yet well known to their contemporaries. The year 152, when Jonathan was appointed High Priest at Jerusalem, may perhaps serve as a *terminus ante quem* for the writing of Jason of Cyrene's book.

3. In Jason's view, Judah the Maccabee is still "leader of the Ḥasidim" (II Macc. 14.6). This outlook belongs to the beginning of the revolt, and is comprehensible in a man who had witnessed the beginning of the liberation movement under the leadership of the Ḥasidim and saw in the appearance of Judah simply a change of personnel in the upper leadership.[13] The familiarity of Jason with the events preceding the rising testifies to his nearness to them, for they possessed nothing to attract a Jewish historian living many decades later.

4. In II Macc. 4.11, John, who obtained from Antiochus III a confirmation of Jewish autonomous rights (cf. above, p. 82ff.) is designated as the father of Eupolemus, "the one who took part in an embassy to Rome

concerning an alliance of friendship." It is unusual to designate a father by his son's name, though the opposite method is normal. If nevertheless Jason used so unusual a method, it can only be because Eupolemus' name was known to his readers; whence we learn that Jason and his readers were contemporaries of Eupolemus, that is, of Judah the Maccabee.

From all these arguments it may be concluded—if not with absolute assurance, at least with a very high degree of certainty—that Jason of Cyrene was a contemporary of Judah the Maccabee and saw most of the events which he described with his own eyes. The surmise has more than once been voiced in learned literature that Jason is perhaps to be identified with Jason son of Eleazar who is mentioned in I Macc. 8.17, as Eupolemus' companion in the embassy to Rome; but scholars have rightly been careful to avoid dogmatism on the point.[14] Nor of course can the present writer produce any convincing proof in favor of this conjecture, but it cannot be denied that this Jason son of Eleazar admirably suits the role of historian: his relationship to Judah, his political function, his Hellenistic education (it is not to be supposed that Judah would have sent a man to Rome who did not know Greek fluently)— all these mark his personality as that of a man thoroughly versed in the events of the epoch and therefore suitable to be its authoritative interpreter in writing. However, as we have said, this is mere conjecture.

If Jason of Cyrene was a contemporary of Judah the Maccabee, it is clear that he described the events of the time as an eyewitness who himself took part in them, and not as a historian working from written sources (and this assumption is valid also in relation to the short period described by Jason as the "prehistory" of the revolt). What attitude, then, should we take to the claim of Bickermann, who says that Jason, when he describes the events preceding Judah's revolt, used a "Seleucid" source?[15] I must confess that I have not been convinced by the proofs adduced by Bickermann for his idea.

Bickermann proceeds from the assumption that a Jew cannot write "pragmatic history"; a Jew is capable of describing history only on the biblical pattern of: "And he did evil—or good—in the eyes of God—and reward and punishment are meted out to the good and the evil." And as Jason—like Josephus after him—wrote for the Greek reader, who demanded of the historian a pragmatic account of events, he had no alternative but to borrow such an account from the Greek historians—in our case, from Seleucid historiography. This approach of Bickermann would be justified if the subject were the books of the Kings on the one hand and Thucydides on the other, but as we approach the Hellenistic period, the boundaries between the two worlds become fainter and the extremes approach one another. Hellenistic historiography admits the dominance of chance in the world, and is not afraid to introduce the gods into pragmatic history—and it was not for nothing that Polybius, the great rationalist, fought against historiography of this type.[16]

On the other hand, Bickermann himself says (with a certain amount of exaggeration) that only two peoples of the ancient world became Greek in the full sense of the term—the Jews and the Romans[17]—and, if this was so, why should we deny to them the ability to write historical works in the spirit of Hellenism? Is the pragmatic approach to the events of history so hard to understand that a Hellenizing Jew educated in the spirit of Hellenism would never have been able to adapt himself to it? And if writers such as Jason and Josephus could embody pragmatic descriptions borrowed from Greek writers in their works, why could they not also create pragmatic history, even if it was only an imitation of the Greek authors? Nor am I certain that the biblical outlook completely contradicts the pragmatic approach to history: for it leaves the alternative with man to choose good or evil as he sees fit, and thus retains the possibility of giving rational explanations for man's acts and aspirations.[18]

Finally it should also be mentioned that Bickermann cannot cite by name a single "Seleucid" historian and does not point to any one relic of "Seleucid historiography" in any author except Jason and Josephus.[19] On the strength of the above arguments we are permitted to rule that there is no compulsion to assume that Jason used an unknown Seleucid historian—or any other historian—the most reasonable supposition being that he wrote his work as an eyewitness of events.

Who was Jason of Cyrene? Was he a native of Cyrene, a Jew from one of the Diaspora communities, who was visiting Jerusalem on business or because he wished to see the Temple, and, filled with a spirit of religious and nationalist zeal when he beheld the profanation of Israel's holy places by Antiochus, joined the liberation movement and spent long years in the proximity of Judah the Maccabee? Or was he a native of Palestine and son of a well-born family who gave him an education at once traditional and Hellenist, a man who beheld personally all the sufferings that came upon his people and country from the beginning of the Hellenist reform movement till the rising in which he took active part, and the death in battle of his great hero Judah the Maccabee; and then, despairing of the prospects of the conflict, migrated to the Diaspora and found a new homeland with the Jewish community of Cyrene?

We are not in a position to answer this question. The personality of Jason will remain forever wrapped in obscurity, unless some quite unlooked-for papyrological discovery comes to tell us something about him. One thing is clear: a large-scale historical work, written by an educated man in the international language of the period for the Greek-reading Jews of the Diaspora, was certainly written according to the rules of Hellenistic historiography and served as a first rate source for the study of the epoch. Jason of Cyrene should not of course be imagined as a second Polybius, and it would be more correct to suppose that he resembled those authors so sharply criticized by the latter. He probably belonged to the "pathetic" trend of Hellenistic historiography, which deliberately attempted to impress the reader by describing atrocities and crimes on the one hand, and acts of bravery and lofty traits of character on the other, and was not afraid to introduce the gods, with all the miracles and wonders involved in their appearance, into the course of history.[20]

All this, however, was no more than the rhetorical embellishment normal to the period, and does not adversely affect the actual historical narrative, based on political understanding, the knowledge of the facts and a genuine desire to tell the truth. Were we to possess Jason's book, we should know the period of the Hellenizers in Jerusalem and the Maccabean rebellion as well as we know the history of the Jewish war with Rome of the years 66-70 C.E., and quite possibly Jason of Cyrene would prove to be no whit inferior as author and historian, to Josephus—and what would we know of the Jewish war with Rome but for Josephus' great book?

However, Jason's book has not come down to us, and we possess only a résumé of his work in II Maccabees. What is the relation between Jason and the Epitomator? Have we any guarantee that what Jason wrote has been faithfully transmitted to us by the abbreviator? Who, for example, was interested in placing the fate of the Temple at the center of the narrative of events? Who introduced the exaggerated religious tendency (in contrast to I Maccabees) into the book? In what measure are the legends (such as that of the torturing of Eleazar or of the mother and her seven sons) the work of Jason, and what here was the interpolation of the Epitomator?

There is no answer to all these questions, nor shall we ever discover one, for both Jason and the Epitomator belonged to that type of Jewish Hellenistic historian who, writing in Greek, addressed himself to the Jewish reader in the Diaspora; and this being so, their approach to most of the problems of Judaism was the same. How, therefore, are we to distinguish between them? One thing certainly is clear: II Maccabees is not a complete literary and artistic creation, as Jason's book certainly was; the author introduced into Jason's historical discourse several things necessary to his own special motives; and more than he introduced he expunged and abbreviated, for he converted Jason's five books into one.[21] All these changes in Jason's text caused a disturbance in the chronological order of the narrative. Particular confusion was created by the writer's error in regard to the documents in chapter 11. This question has been treated above (p. 214ff.), and here I again briefly summarize the matter.

Among the four documents in chapter 11, one belongs to the year 162; it evidences negotiations between the Syrian government and Judah the Maccabee. The remaining documents belong to the year 164 and their subject is the negotiations between the Syrians and the representatives of the Hellenizers. The Epitomator, in abbreviating Jason, merges all four documents into one unit, thus making two mistakes: he thought that all of them belonged to the year 164, and that the Jews referred to in all the documents were Judah the Maccabee and his party. After making these errors he drew the logical conclusions from the political situation indicated in the documents. If the second document, in which the King wrote about Jewish freedom of religion, belonged to 164, this meant that the first war between Lysias and the Jews ended with the signing of a peace-treaty and not with the defeat of Lysias, as in fact occurred: hence he saw need to rework the story of Lysias' war in Judaea. In the same document is mentioned the death of Antiochus Epiphanes. The author, who assigned the document to the year 164, saw need to tell of Antiochus' death before that year, although Antiochus actually died in 163. In this way much confusion was introduced into the book, and for this reason II Maccabees makes the impression of an unfinished literary work, and scholars have been chary of placing reliance on its information.

Now, however, scholars approach the book with another object, no longer seeking errors, but attempting to make a reconstruction of Jason's original account. The results are very interesting: if we remove from II Maccabees the abbreviator's errors and correct the small mistakes made to embellish the narrative, or which rose from the need to give a certain satisfaction to religious and patriotic feelings, we find that the original scheme of II Maccabees is decidedly like that of I Maccabees. Both books relate the same events in the same order.[22] This informs us that the scholar may trust II Maccabees no less than he trusts I Maccabees. We may say in opposition to Wellhausen, that II Maccabees is reliable in every passage which can be checked, hence it may be trusted also in passages which we cannot check.

Among such portions are chapters 3-4, which are particularly important for us. In them the author gives a detailed account of the events preceding the revolt of Judah the Maccabee. I Maccabees tells hardly anything of this period; this does not prove that he did not know the same events, but it is clear that he was not interested in them (cf. above, p. 152). On the other hand the author of II Maccabees gives a full and logical account of this development, and Jason of Cyrene undoubtedly devoted at least one complete book to them.[23]

We find here the feud between Onias and Simon, the visit of Heliodorus to Jerusalem, Onias' journey to Antioch, the accession of his brother Jason to the High Priesthood, Jason's Hellenistic reform, the war between him and Menelaus, Menelaus' victory, the disorders in Jerusalem in connection with the plundering of money from the Temple, the murder of Onias at Daphne, Jason's attack on Jerusalem, the appearance of Antiochus in Judaea—in short, all the complicated history of the Hellenizers' government in Jerusalem, which found a description in no other place in the historical sources of the period.

It is not our intention to claim that we are bound to credit every detail of the account—

as, for example, the characterizations of the historical figures, the number of slain in Jerusalem, or the mythical details associated with the appearance of Heliodorus at the Temple. These are the rhetorical embellishments so typical of Hellenistic historiography in general and of Jewish historical writings in particular. These embellishments cannot, in our view, negate the great importance of the historical account itself, which evolves logically and sometimes gives such a detailed description that it cannot in any sense be regarded as a fabrication or as the fruit of the author's fertile imagination.

Among those details is also the story of the murder of Onias at Daphne. If we believe everything told in chapters 3-4, there are no grounds for thinking this passage to be fabricated. On this question see page 469, n. 40. I mention this detail here because it has great importance for the criticism of the extract in Josephus (*War* I, 31ff.), which will be discussed below.

2. *IV Maccabees.*

This book as a whole is not a historical source; it treats of religious and philosophical questions, and the examples cited by the author from history serve only to give validity to his abstract ideas.[24] Only one extract discusses the historical situation in the period of the Hellenizers. This is chapter 4, which forms a transition from the exposition on general philosophical subjects to the historical examples. The contents of the chapter are parallel to chapters 3-4 of II Maccabees; it contains the feud between Onias and Simon, Simon's delation, the visit of the Syrian official to Jerusalem and his unsuccessful attempt to plunder the Temple moneys, Jason's purchase of the High Priesthood, his Hellenistic reform, the false rumor of Antiochus' death in Egypt and the Jews' rejoicing thereat, Antiochus in Jerusalem and his persecution.

All is narrated with great brevity, and many important things, such as Menelaus' rule, are not related at all. The parallel to the account in II Maccabees is clear, but there are also differences between the two descriptions, and these are: (a) Onias is termed High Priest "for life"; (b) Simon flees to Apollonius and returns together with him; (c) the Syrian official who visits the Temple is termed "the representative of Syria, Phoenicia and Cilicia"; (d) Simon's delation concerns the private money deposited in the Temple; (e) Apollonius comes to Jerusalem "at the head of a strong force"; (f) his function is to confiscate private moneys; (g) he enters the Temple with his entire force; (h) angels appear to him in the shape of horsemen; (i) he himself begs "the Hebrews" to have pity on him; (j) Antiochus Epiphanes is the son of Seleucus (formerly called Seleucus Nicator); (k) Jason pays Antiochus 3660 talents yearly; (1) the gymnasium is built over the citadel.

These differences tend to produce the conjecture that the author of *IV Maccabees* was drawing directly on Jason of Cyrene without using II Maccabees, and this conjecture has indeed been expressed in learned literature.[25] However, nearly all the above differences can be interpreted either as simple errors (the result of the desire to shorten the text of II Maccabees), or as arbitrary rhetorical additions. Jason of Cyrene would never have called Antiochus "son of Seleucus Nicator" (that is, Nicator, founder of the Seleucid dynasty) and this addition merely evidences the ignorance of the author. Nor is it to be assumed that Jason called the official sent to Jerusalem Apollonius, for then it would be inexplicable why II Maccabees called him Heliodorus; on the other hand *IV Maccabees'* error is easily understood, as Apollonius is mentioned in II Maccabees (4.4), as governor of Coele-Syria and Phoenicia. Nor does the surprising addition of "Cilicia" to Coele-Syria originate from Jason, but reflects the administrative reality in the Roman Orient in the first half of the first century C.E., as Bickermann has remarked.[26] Even the special emphasis on the confiscation of the moneys of private people (as opposed to the plundering of the treasury money—which is not mentioned) requires the use of no other source apart from II Maccabees, as the matter is mentioned there twice (4.10; 4.66). The bribe of 3660 talents allegedly promised to Antiochus by Jason is beyond all possible proportion, and it is clear that it originates from the fertile imagination of the author of *IV Maccabees,* and not from Jason's book. The remaining changes are simple historical embellishments. Therefore there is no basis for seeing in *IV Maccabees* a parallel source to II Maccabees, which derives, as it were, from Jason of Cyrene; the most correct probable assumption (adopted by most scholars) is that the author of *IV Maccabees* drew the historical material he needed direct from II Maccabees. And if this is so, *IV Maccabees* has no independent value for the study of the Jewish history of the period of Hellenizing rule in Jerusalem.

3. *War* I, 31-33.

The writer has made a study of this passage elsewhere.[27] Here only a résumé of that study will be given. The passage is as follows:

"When Antiochus known as Epiphanes was fighting Ptolemy VI over Coele-Syria,[28] a feud took place among the Jewish dignitaries (jealousy existed between them on the matter of power, because no one of the important men would suffer subordination to his fellows), and Onias, one of the High Priests, prevailed, and drove the sons of Tobiah from the city. They fled to Antiochus and besought him to invade the Land of Judaea, and to use them as guides. The king, who had long been plotting to do so, agreed; he came in person with a great army and captured the city by force. He slew a great multitude of those who favored Ptolemy, and gave permission to the troops to plunder unrestrainedly. He himself despoiled the Temple and abolished the permanent sacrifice for three years and six months. And the High Priest Onias fled to Ptolemy; he received a territory from him in the district of Heliopolis and built a small town in the semblance of Jerusalem and also set up a Temple there resembling (that in Jerusalem). Of this we shall speak in the appropriate place."

The evaluation of this passage depends on the evaluation of II Maccabees. If we accept as a historical fact the account of II Maccabees of the murder of Onias at Daphne, we shall be unable to agree with Josephus' view that Onias fled to Egypt and there founded the well known temple. We have seen above that no doubt can be attached to the historical trustworthiness of the author of II Maccabees; moreover above (p. 276ff.) I have advanced arguments in favor of the supposition that not Onias III but his son Onias IV established the temple in Egypt. So the end of the passage, at least, is incorrect.

Let us see whether the name of Onias is appropriate to the historical situation indicated at the beginning of the extract. "When Antiochus known as Epiphanes was fighting Ptolemy VI . . . a feud took place between the Jewish dignitaries . . . and Onias . . . prevailed, and he drove the sons of Tobiah from the city. . . ." Antiochus fought in Egypt twice, in the years 169 and 168, and Onias was killed at Daphne some time before, in 171 or 170. This also, then, is not true. Did Josephus make the chronological error of ascribing to the time of Antiochus' war in Egypt events that had occurred previously? But when, if at all, did Onias fight against the Tobiads and expel them from the city? From 175 onwards he lived at Daphne (or at least, outside Judaea), and before that he fought against Simon brother of Menelaus, but it was not he who expelled his opponents from the city; he had to quit Jerusalem because his enemies prevailed over him. It is clear, therefore, that the beginning of the passage no more belongs to historical reality than does its end.

If we rest content with this criticism, we have to erase completely the passage *War* I, 31-33 from the list of historical sources of the Hellenistic period. But a possibility exists of rescuing it. Let us make the experiment of reading Jason instead of Onias; then we shall see that the whole extract takes on a different form.[29]

Jason fought against the Tobiads twice; first in 171 (above, p. 171), and the second time in 168 (above, p. 187). In 171 he expelled the Tobiads from the city and they sought aid from Antiochus; this Josephus relates in *Antiquities* XII, 237ff. In 168 Jason attacked Jerusalem from Transjordan with a contingent of a thousand men; Menelaus retreated and fortified himself in the city (II Macc. 5.5-10). Which war does Josephus mean in our extract? He apparently confused these two conflicts. The end of the extract is better suited to the events of 168; Josephus describes Antiochus' appearance in Jerusalem as the result of intestine strife among the Jews, and this was the case in 168.

But the beginning of the passage makes a different impression. Josephus speaks of the feud between the Jerusalem dignitaries as of a prolonged affair originating from the reluctance of each to give way to the rest, and not as of a sudden attack of one of them upon the city. Nor is the expulsion of the Tobiads from the city appropriate to the year 168; Menelaus did not leave the town then, but fortified himself in the Akra, and it is possible that the Tobiads did likewise. The idea that Antiochus had "long been plotting" to attack Jerusalem also stands in contradiction to the political situation in 168; Antiochus, while in Egypt, heard of the rebellion and at once decided to put it down. It may then be concluded that the passage is based on the events of 171, but Josephus, desiring to shorten the story and to pass on quickly to the account of the persecutions of Antiochus, embodied them

393

in the second war of Jason and transferred the whole affair to the time of Antiochus' Egyptian campaign.

But Josephus says that Onias fled to Egypt and there set up his temple, and this cannot be ascribed to Jason. This is an important argument, but it cannot negate our supposition, since Jason also fled to Egypt, as II Maccabees testifies (5.5). It was not he, of course, who built the House of Onias, but after Josephus had confused Jason with Onias, and taken him to Egypt, it was a natural thing for him to make Onias builder of the shrine which was called by his name. Thus one error led to another, and Josephus repeats it elsewhere in his *War* (VII, 7, 2). Only in the *Antiquities* did Josephus correct his mistake, writing that not Onias III but his son Onias IV built the temple in Egypt.

In this way the importance of *War* I, 31-33 as a historical source can be restored. Indeed, even after emendation, the passage does not become a very important one; Josephus has here written too briefly, stressing only the political aspect of events; it were as well to mention that he makes no allusion at all to the Hellenistic reform of the Tobiads, and the reader asks in surprise what need had Antiochus to suspend the perpetual sacrifice in the Temple, if the war had no other aim than a political one?

Scholars generally think that behind *War* I, 31-33 lies a Greek source, either Nicolaus of Damascus or Alexander Polyhistor. This is not the present writer's opinion. Josephus, it is true, says that the war between Antiochus and Ptolemy broke out "on account of Coele-Syria"; as Polybius writes (XXVIII, 1; *ib.* 15). But on the other hand, he relates that Antiochus suspended the perpetual sacrifice for three and a half years, this number being taken from the Book of Daniel. It results, to all appearances, that not only a Greek, but also a Hebrew source lies behind the passage. However, few would be ready to agree that Josephus read and studied a number of sources to write these two or three lines. In the *War* Josephus' object was to relate the great war between Rome and the Jews in the years 66-70 C.E. In order to explain to his readers the reasons for the revolt, he wrote a long preface, in which he narrated the events in Palestine from the time of Antiochus Epiphanes down to the rebellion. He introduced this preface with several additional lines, in which very briefly he gave the reasons which brought Antiochus to Jerusalem, and this is the passage which we are now discussing.

For this short passage it was not worth searching the sources exhaustively, and Josephus wrote what he remembered from the books he had read previously and what he knew as a man of general historical education. Certain things he remembered, and certain things he forgot. He remembered, for instance, the occurrence of a quarrel between the dignitaries of Jerusalem during Antiochus Epiphanes' wars in Egypt, but forgot that it had begun before that. The names of famous people of the period remained in his memory, but he forgot who had fought against whom, and confused Jason with Onias. But most important of all, he touched only upon the political aspect of the events, because otherwise he would have been unable to solve the problem: why did Antiochus come to Jerusalem? But he did not go into the life of the period profoundly, because he had no special interest in it. The passage in *War* I, 31-33, may therefore serve as an additional source for the study of the epoch, but it contains nothing that can enrich our knowledge to any considerable degree.

4. *Antiquities* XII, 237ff.

In the *Antiquities of the Jews* also, Josephus did not do all he might have done with respect to the period of the Hellenizers in Jerusalem. From the time of Judah the Maccabee onwards, Josephus felt solid ground beneath his feet; he followed I Maccabees and afterwards, generally, Nicolaus of Damascus. He described the most ancient period, using as his sources the biblical books. But from the time of Nehemiah down to that of Judah the Maccabee he had no reputable sources at hand. He endeavored to fill the vacuum with various stories which he found everywhere—with the story of Alexander's visit to Jerusalem, with extracts from the family chronicle of the Tobiads, with Aristeas' book and with others. We cannot tell clearly which source he used to describe the period under discussion; here too, as in the *War*, he did not go deeply into the study of the period, which did not interest him for its own sake, but merely served as a preface to the account of the events which came after it. Several errors which he made in the *War* he corrected in the *Antiquities*, as, for example, on the subject of Onias and his erection of the temple in Egypt. He also found it necessary to touch on the internal aspect of events and referred to the Hellenistic reform of the Tobiads. But instead he made further mistakes: thus, for instance, he made Menelaus the brother of Jason. According to the account in the *Antiquities*, Antiochus, after Onias' death, gave the High Priesthood to Joshua, whose Greek name was Jason; subsequently the king became angry at Jason and gave the priesthood to his younger brother Onias, whose Greek name was Menelaus. War breaks out between Jason and Menelaus, and Jason drives the Tobiads from Jerusalem. The Tobiads appear before Antiochus and propose to him the program of the Hellenistic reform. Then comes the account of the wars of Antiochus in Egypt and his persecutions.

We have only one way of authenticating the truth of this story, namely, by comparing it with II Maccabees. No one doubts that the detailed narrative of II Maccabees, written a short time after the events, is historically more trustworthy than that related in the *Antiquities*. The scholar is therefore permitted to eliminate from the *Antiquities* everything which contradicts II Maccabees, and confirm as historical information those things which are in harmony with, or at least do not contradict, the same work. According to II Maccabees, Jason obtained the High Priesthood not after the death of Onias, but during his lifetime, and Onias did not die a natural death (as Josephus seems to think), but was slain at Daphne. The information in *Antiquities*, then, is not historical.

According to II Maccabees Menelaus was brother of Simon, who was "of the tribe of Benjamin," or, according to scholarly emendation, of the watch of the priests of Minjamin or Belgea (see below, App. II); he did not, at any rate, belong to the family of the previous Oniad priests, and could not have been the brother of Onias and Jason, as Josephus thinks. Josephus' remark that Menelaus' Hebrew name was Onias also contradicts his account, for it is not to be assumed that two brothers would have borne the same name. Josephus then informs us of the war between Jason and Menelaus over the High Priesthood. II Maccabees also relates this war, but in that book the struggle ends swiftly with Menelaus' victory, while Josephus tells of Jason's victory and of the expulsion of the Tobiads from Jerusalem. Josephus here can of course be corrected according to II Maccabees, but in *War* also Josephus speaks of the expulsion of the Tobiads from the town, and if information occurs twice in the sources, we are bound to take it into account.

The expulsion of the Tobiads is apparently a historical fact; the only question is who expelled them and when did it occur? In the *War* Onias drove them out: in the *Antiquities* it was Jason; but we have seen above that the story in *War* openly contradicts II Maccabees and we have proposed that the name Onias be substituted by that of Jason. If this emendation is accepted, the account in *War* and II Maccabees can easily be reconciled by the supposition that Jason's conflict with Menelaus continued for some time, Jason being successful at the beginning and driving Menelaus from the city, but that subsequently Menelaus returned to Jerusalem at the head of a force which he received from Antiochus, and defeated Jason. This occurred in 171, since in 168 Menelaus did not leave Jerusalem (cf. above, p. 393). If this conjecture is accepted, we can further rescue for history the information that the Tobiads supported Menelaus. This fact is especially important, because II Maccabees does not mention the Tobiads at all and passes in silence over their considerable role in Jewish history.

Farther on, Josephus' narrative again contradicts II Maccabees: the Tobiads propose to the King the plan of Hellenistic reform. It is known that not they, but Jason, proposed this plan and was the first to Hellenize the Jews. Here too, however, the necessary compromise can be found. The fact cannot be denied that the Tobiads were decided Hellenists in their tendencies, a trait which they inherited from their forebears, and it may be believed that Jason's reform was the result of their political plan. Josephus forgot who was High Priest in Jerusalem during the reform and remembered only the fact that it was connected with the policy of the Tobiads. They later destroyed Jason and joined Menelaus. Josephus thought it was in the latter's time that they began to carry out their designs. Here he made a chronological error, but was right in his actual approach to the events; the tendency to Hellenism actually did develop among the restricted circle of the Jerusalem aristocracy, among which the Tobiads occupied the most important place. This is the great importance for the historian of the passage *Antiquities* XII, 23ff., since it emphasizes the internal connection between Hellenism and the Tobiads which was not correctly expressed in the remaining sources of the period. We should very much like to know whence Josephus derived this information, but, as we have said, Josephus' sources for this passage are obscure.

5. I Maccabees

The great value of I Macca-
bees for historical study of the Hasmonean period is beyond
doubt; even the critics of Niese have been unable to annul
its importance in the eyes of scholars. If we remove certain
details from the book which were inserted into it to flatter the
dynasty, we have a simple practical narrative of the events of
the period, from the appearance of Judah the Maccabee down
to the death of Simon. But the first chapter in which the writer
tells of the events preceding Judah the Maccabee, suffers from
several deficiencies: it is too brief and written here and there
in a poetic style. The writer cannot control his religious and
patriotic emotions and gives sharp expression to his wrath and
bitterness toward Antiochus and the Hellenizers. Nor does he
mention the names of the Hellenistic reformers; the expressions
"criminals" and "transgressors" are enough in his view. He has
not gone deeply into political questions, for there is for him no
internal link between Antiochus' Egyptian wars and the events
in Jerusalem.

Notwithstanding, there are
several items of great value which he relates as it were *en
passant*, such as his details on the Hellenistic reform, the looting
of the vessels from the Temple by Antiochus, the establishment
of the Akra and the founding of a colony of aliens on the land
of Jerusalem. Very important for us also is the information on
the flight of the Jerusalem population prior to Antiochus' persecution and on the desertion of the Temple (cf. above, p. 189).
On the other hand some of his reports, such as that on Antiochus'
proclamation, that all peoples in his state should become one
nation (I, 41-42), are not credible. In general it may be stated
that in chapter I of I Maccabees several important items of
information have been preserved which add material to the
study of the period of Hellenization in Jerusalem, but they do
not give a full picture, and each individual report attains its full
value only after comparison with the historical material derived
from other sources, chiefly the II Maccabees.

6. Daniel

The Book of Daniel derives
from the actual period of the events under discussion. The
author knows of Antiochus' two Egyptian wars (11.28; *ib*. 30),
but has not heard of his expedition to the East and of his death;

he anticipates his third expedition to Egypt (*ib.* 40). This being so, the book was composed some time after the year 160, but before the capture of Jerusalem by Judah the Maccabee; were this not the case, we should expect to find in the book some allusion or other to Judah and to the dedication of the Temple. A book of this sort, written during the actual events, might have been one of the finest historical sources. However, the author of Daniel had no intention of writing history; for him prophecy and vision took the place of a factual account of events.

Anyone desiring to utilize Daniel as a historical source must first discover the key to its allusive language. This is not easy, for we do not know all the fine details of the period to an extent enabling us to understand every reference in the book with the same facility as Daniel's contemporaries. Can we say with certainty that by the words "now when they shall fall, they shall be helped with a little help" (*ib.* 34), the Hasmoneans are meant, or that the words "the robbers of thy people shall exalt themselves to establish the vision, but they shall fall" (*ib.* 14) are directed to a certain political party?[30] What guarantee is there that the messiah in chapter 11.26, and "the prince of the covenant" in chapter 11.22, is Onias III, as scholars think?[31]

All these allusions can only find their solutions after we have compared each individual verse of Daniel with reports on the events of the period in other sources. Hence, Daniel cannot explain the period for us; but the events of the period reported by other sources will assist us in solving the riddles of the Book of Daniel. In such a situation we cannot hope that the book will furnish much material for the historian; generally the scholar himself first inserts his explanations into the book, and then utilizes them as if they were certified historical material. At most we are permitted to say that Daniel sometimes provides the scholar with additional authentication of what is known from another source. Thus, for example, had we not known of the murder of Onias at Daphne from II Maccabees, it would not have occurred to us to relate verses 9.26 and 11.22 in Daniel to this occurrence and to see in Onias the messiah and the "prince of the Covenant." But once this is known to us, the conjecture may be entertained, and thus the scholar obtains a supplementary picture to the report in II Maccabees.

Another example can be cited: it is known from I and II Maccabees that Antiochus and his successors intended to divide the land of the Jews among their troops (see above, p. 189); now Daniel also tells of "the people of a foreign god" who had settled in citadels, and of land which Antiochus divided among them at a price (11.39). Here too the historian obtains a very important additional authentication concerning reports derived from other sources. Daniel's story of Antiochus' second visit to Jerusalem also finds support in the combination of reports from I and II Maccabees. But where we cannot compare Daniel with another source, we stand helpless before his riddles, and all our conjectures will lack any solid basis.

And perhaps Daniel's greatest importance does not lie in the establishment of certain historical facts, but in his preserving for us the spirit of the period. He speaks of those "who leave the Covenant of Holiness" and of the "betrayers of the Covenant" on the one hand, and of the "enlighteners of the people" and "holy ones" on the other, and we find ourselves in the midst of the sore struggle between the Hellenizers and the Ḥasidim, and learn from his book of the persecutions, the tortures and of the mutual hatred between the two camps. How far we may use the first six chapters of the book as a characterization of the period of Antiochus is a separate question. It is the writer's impression that these chapters also contain clear references to the period under discussion, but many scholars incline to a different view, nor can the question be solved perfunctorily.[32]

7. The "Dead Sea Scrolls"

What has been said above about the Book of Daniel may be said equally about the "Dead Sea Scrolls," whose discovery in recent years constitutes one of the most important discoveries for Jewish history in the Hellenistic and Roman period.[33] From one point of view the study of the "Dead Sea Scrolls" is much more difficult than that of the Book of Daniel, since we know the date of the composition of the latter, whereas we do not know that of the scrolls, and the chronological question is in the nature of a riddle which has to be solved before the scholar can proceed to exploit the historical material buried in them. Various chronological solutions have been proposed by scholars, ranging from the third century B.C.E. down to the third century C.E.,[34] and each inquirer produces "certain" proofs from the analysis of the texts to prove that he is right. And in proportion as theories multiply, the prospects of discovering the solution diminish. Nor is this surprising; the scrolls are written in the same allusive language as Daniel. Their authors refrain from using personal names and historical dates and are careful not to mention certain events, but on the other hand use numerous flowery expressions characteristic of the biblical style, nor can one know precisely what each reference refers to, or if events occurring at a given time and at a given place are intended, rather than an eschatological vision deriving from the imagination of the author.

If we accept the prevailing opinion, which holds that the allusions refer to historical events and are susceptible of solution—then we have here the history of a religious sect, the "Yaḥad" sect, which was akin in its *Weltanschauung* to the Essenes, and was founded by an unnamed person known as the "Teacher of Righteousness," who was persecuted, suffered tortures, and was perhaps also put to death, by the "wicked Priest," the entire sect being persecuted by wicked men. Against the setting of the persecution an actual war developed, the war between the "sons of the light" and the "sons of darkness," and as a consequence of this war part of the sect, or its entirety, was forced to migrate from Palestine and to seek a refuge in Damascus. When did all this happen? Some hold that the foundation of the sect belongs to the pre-Hasmonean epoch, and that the Teacher of Righteousness died under the regime of the Hellenizers (the High Priest Onias III being possibly the Teacher while the wicked Priest was one of the agents of the Hellenistic reform)—Jason, Menelaus or Alcimus, the war of the sons of light and the sons of darkness being the conflict of the Ḥasidim and Judah the Maccabee against the forces of the Syrians and the Hellenizers.[35]

Others hold that we have here the struggle of the sect with Alexander Jannaeus, who is the Wicked Priest, before whom the members of the sect fled to Damascus to settle.[36] Others seek the historical setting for the events at the beginning of the Roman period, or in the complex political strife during the great war of the Jews against Rome, or even later.[37] Besides the "Teacher of Righteousness" and the "Wicked Priest" several other names provoke the curiosity of scholars, such as those of the "Khattim" and the "House of Absalom." As for the "Khattim," some think the Macedonians are meant, others the Romans,[38] and to identify "the House of Absalom" a search has been made among all the men of that name in the Hellenistic-Roman period. Others hold that no actual man, but Absalom son of David, a historical and legendary figure who became a symbol of treason and transgression, is meant.[39]

How is one to find a certain line among all this chaos? The writer confesses that at the beginning of his work on the present book he intended to utilize the "Dead Sea Scrolls" for the account of the period, as he thought that the war of the sons of light and the sons of darkness was "undoubtedly" the struggle between the Ḥasidim and the Hellenizers and therefore bore directly on the subject of his book. But after the writer had gone more deeply into the problems involved in the study of the scrolls, he realized that although he could erect a certain theory, it would be subjective and no more solidly based than any other theory, and even if he could perhaps successfully rebut the opinions of others, he would never be able to prove his own view with the same absolute certainty that alone would justify the use of the scroll material for the aims of historical research. New material may furnish us with fresh data and at last produce the necessary certainty; but as long as this certainty is remote, we shall do well to be content with the dictum "ignoramus."

The condition of research on the "Dead Sea Scrolls" for the time being resembles the situation already noted with reference to the Book of Daniel: rather than the scrolls explaining the period to us, the events of the epoch, insofar as they are known to us from other sources, can show us the way to decipher the allusions contained in the scrolls. And once again what has been stated in relation to Daniel applies equally to the scrolls; it is very dangerous to form definite conclusions concerning *the facts* mentioned in the scrolls, but *the spirit* pervading these tattered parchments is very important for historical study. If, indeed, the view of those who ascribe the composition of the scrolls to the Roman period turns out to be correct, they have nothing in common with the subject of the present book, but if they were composed in the time of Alexander Jannaeus, or even at the end of the Hasmonean period, the spirit animating them is still the same which inspired the first Ḥasidim and Judah the Maccabee to their stubborn struggle against the armies of the Syrians and the Hellenizers; for the roots of the sect were deep, and its spiritual features did not alter much in the course of that century.

APPENDIX **II**

The Origin of the Family of Simon, Menelaus and Lysimachus
see pp. 154, 157, 170ff.

According to II Maccabees
(3.4), Simon was "of the tribe of Benjamin" (ἐκ τῆς βενιαμεὶν
φυλῆς). Scholars have invariably found difficulty in accepting
this report at its face value; if Simon was of the tribe of Benjamin,
then his brother Menelaus was of the same tribe, that is, not of
a priestly family; how then did it happen that he held the post
of High Priest? Menelaus, indeed, belonged to the Hellenizers,
and the epoch was generally one of contempt for Jewish tradition; however, had Menelaus not been of priestly blood, the
sources would certainly have stressed the fact, which itself would
have caused anger and bitterness among the Ḥasidim. Furthermore, the period described in chapter III of *IV Maccabees* precedes the Hellenistic reform, when life was still being conducted
traditionally, so how could it have occurred that the high post
of "ruler of the Temple" (προστάτης τοῦ ἱεροῦ) was held by a man
not of the seed of Aaron? For these reasons scholars have endeavored to amend the text, and have indeed easily found a slight
and plausible emendation, namely, that the writer did not mean
one of the Jewish tribes, but one of the priestly watches, בנימין
or מנימין, mentioned more than once in the Bible (II Chron.
15; Neh. 12.17; *ib.* 14; I Chron. 24.9; Neh. 10.6; 12.5).

The alteration of one letter
of the manuscript needs no special justification,[40] and the Greek
word *phylé* can equally denote "tribe" and "watch." In the first
(Hebrew) edition of the present book, the writer also followed

the accepted view. However, another solution now seems more acceptable. In the Latin translation of II Maccabees we read that Simon was of the "tribe of Belgea,"[41] this being the name of one of the priestly families also mentioned in the Bible (Neh. 12.5; *ib.* 18). As it is not to be assumed that the translator himself substituted the rare name of "Belgea" for the well known name of "Benjamin," he must have found it written in the Greek manuscript from which he was translating the text.[42] Hence we learn that there existed in the Greek manuscripts of II Maccabees two different traditions, and we have to choose between them. According to the well known philological rule, in cases of differing versions the "more difficult reading" (*lectio difficilior*) should be followed. It is indeed easy to understand the thought-process of the copyist, who found ἐκ φυλῆς Βαλγεα in his manuscript, understood the word *phylé* as "tribe," and knowing that no Jewish tribe of this name existed, "emended" the error by altering the curious name "Belgea" to that of "Benjamin" which begins with the same letter. If on the other hand we assume that "Benjamin" was really written in the manuscript, we cannot explain the copyist's reason for exchanging the well known name for the uncommon name "Belgea."[43] The writer thinks, then, that the three brothers Simon, Menelaus and Lysimachus belonged to the priestly family of Belgea,[44] or at any rate were members of the priestly class.

APPENDIX **III**

Antioch at Jerusalem

see pp. 161ff.

In his book *The God of the Maccabees*, pp. 59ff., Bickermann has dealt in detail with verse 4.9 of II Maccabees: τοὺς ἐν Ἱεροσολύμοις Ἀντιοχεῖς ἀναγράψαι, and as he is an expert textual commentator, familiar with Hellen-

istic law in all its exact details, we are bound to weigh all his observations, whether philological or juridical, with due attention. We shall concur at the outset that Bickermann has used the right method, by interpreting the above passage in the light of the Hellenistic law and by a strict examination of the Greek wording and style. But the question is whether his conclusions are as correct as is his method.

In Bickermann's view, scholars are in the habit of interpreting the word *Antiocheis* in the above sentence as an accusative of the predicate, translating the sentence as follows: "And (Jason received permission) to register the people of Jerusalem as Antiochenes." This permission is interpreted by scholars either as the granting of the privileges of the Seleucid capital town of Antioch to Jerusalem, or as the formation of a new city of Antioch on the site of (or near) Jerusalem. These two conceptions Bickermann thinks are erroneous, first for linguistic reasons: in his view *anagraphein* with a double accusative means "to enter (a person's name) onto a public list (which is to be published)"[45] and this work was not the concern of the High Priest, but was in the hands of a normal municipal official.

Bickermann proposes to interpret the denotation of the place *Hierosolymois* as a relative clause connected with *Antiocheis,* translating "And (Jason received permission) to register the Antiochenes who were in Jerusalem." In order to justify his use of *anagraphein* with a simple accusative in the sense of "to draw up a list," Bickermann cites two examples—one from the papyri of Zenon[46] and one from inscriptions.[47] As a result of this "registration" a sort of Greek society (corporation) was founded in Jerusalem, called after King Antiochus and centered on the gymnasium. The foundation of such a society did not mean the foundation of a city, hence Jerusalem's own existence did not come to an end. Its actual abolition took place only in the year 168, when the Greek city was founded at the Akra, simultaneously with the commencement of the hard days of Antiochus' persecution.

Several arguments can be leveled against Bickermann's view. Let us begin with questions of language. The verb *anagrapsai* with a simple accusative is found on countless occasions in inscriptions in the sense of "inscribe on stone"; this is not the interpretation which fits the present passage. Bickermann seeks a different content, namely, to register, or draw up a list. This meaning of *anagrapsai* is found

HELLENISTIC CIVILIZATION AND THE JEWS

fairly frequently in papyri. I give below the two examples cited by Bickermann (nos. 1, 2) with the addition of another three passages from the papyri chosen without intention of exhausting the material.

1. *Ann. Brit. School of Athens*, 1905/6, 452 A: Τοὺς δὲ νικήσαντας ἀναγράψουσιν οἱ γραμματεῖς.
2. *PCZ* 59166 ἀναγραψάμε[νος ἡμῖν πάντα τὰ ὑπ]άρχοντα ζεύ[γη].
3. *PCZ* 59493: οὐκ ἀναγράφουσιν τὸν γόνον.
4. *P. Tebt.* 1000: ἀπὸ τον . . . ἀναγραφομένον ἐν κληρουχίαι.
5. *BGU.* 1199: κελεύω ἀναγράφεσθαι τοὺς . . . ἱερεῖς καὶ παστοφόρους.

From these examples two conclusions may be drawn: (1) The list is invariably drawn up by officials (cf. no. 1) and minor civil servants, and not by ministers of government. Bickermann's argument against the use of *anagraphein* with a double accusative, meaning that this interpretation forces us to ascribe to the High Priest work which is beneath his dignity, falls to the ground, as Bickermann's own interpretation encounters exactly the same argument.[48] (2) In all the above examples existent objects are counted and listed—yokes of cattle, priests, members of colonies, etc. It follows therefore that "Antiochenes" existed in Jerusalem before Jason decided to register them. This, of course, is impossible: *Antiocheus* means a member of a certain organized community who does not exist independent of that community.[49] This alleged registration of individual existent Antiochenes, without connection with an existent community, could only have taken place provided we were to interpret "Antiochenes" as people "holding citizen rights of the Syrian city of Antioch"; but Bickermann rightly rejects this supposition, which is in principle opposed to the basic elements of Hellenistic law.[50]

We therefore return to the usual interpretation: *anagraphein* with double accusative. Where does Bickermann get his translation "to enter up (a person's name) on a public list"? It is true that this interpretation also exists (in inscriptions), but it is one of the rarest. The normal meaning is that in classical literature: "to recognize someone as something, to proclaim someone as something, to make someone something." Whoever wants proof of this may consult Liddel and Scott's *Greek-English Lexicon* and there will find examples from Isocrates, Demosthenes, Herodotus, Plato and other writers. In all these cases, the exact content of the verb *anagraphein*—"to register," is merely a symbolical expression for a deeper content meaning to recognize, proclaim, etc. And this is its significance in the passage under discussion: Jason received permission from the King "to register the people of Jerusalem as Antiochenes," that is, to proclaim them as "Antiochenes." Henceforward they are not to be called "Jerusalemites" but "Antiochenes."

What does this signify? We pass to the analysis of the sentence from the historical point of view. Bickermann argues that the Antiochenes constituted a "corporation." He himself however admits that this is not a Greek corporation in the usual sense of the word, for were this so, the society's name would be formed in a different way.[51] He compares the society of Antiochenes in Jerusalem to a *politeuma* or *demos* (in the Hellenistic period non-urban organizations also sometimes called themselves *demoi*). The result is therefore that the "corporation" of the Antiochenes at Jerusalem was not a city, nor a Greek society in the usual sense of the term, but something in between. This assumption is acceptable only if it is sufficiently fortified by instances. Bickermann produces two: the coins of Gaza and Ptolemais-Acco of the second century B.C.E. These have been discussed (p. 443, n. 12; p. 447, n. 51); we have seen that they refer, not to corporations, but to normal Greek cities. As to "politeuma," usually this word serves as a *terminus technicus* to indicate an ethnic community living amid a population of different derivation (see above, p. 299ff.), whereas the Hellenizers of Jerusalem did not differ in their racial origin from the rest of the inhabitants.

Nor has the example of the "Greek quarter" at Memphis (Bickermann, *op. cit.*, p. 61) any bearing whatever on the question at issue; a quarter of this sort, known by the name of *hellenion*, existed not only at Memphis but also in other towns of the Orient.[52] These quarters were erected as a result of the desire of the Greek inhabitants to live separate from the local population, whereas the Hellenizers of Jerusalem were not Greeks. The very fact that the High Priest himself stood at the head of the Hellenizers, and that the Temple, the cult-center of the entire nation, was under their control, proves conclusively that the Hellenizing faction neither thought of segregating itself from the people which it governed, nor could have done so.

All these proofs may be summarized in one sentence: The "Antiochenes in Jerusalem" were not a Greek "society" in the normal sense (*synodos, syllogos, thiasos*), nor a village *demos*, a *politeuma* or *hellenion;* they were a Greek city (*polis*), just as all the Antiochs, Seleuceias, Laodiceias and Apameias, so numerous in the Seleucid Empire, were cities.[53] This assumption is not simply a conjecture, but is confirmed by our chief source, II Maccabees, which describes the reform of Jason not as a superficial attempt to introduce a few changes into the political and religious constitution in force in Jerusalem, but as its complete abolition and replacement by another constitution. (On this question see above p. 164ff.)

With the dismissal of the idea of the "corporation," Bickermann's second idea of the "life in mutual proximity" (symbiosis) of the Greek and the previous city, must also be dismissed. Bickermann cites proofs from the Orient that a "symbiosis" of this sort between a *polis* and a "temple state" (Tempelstaat) was possible, but he does not note the fact that in none of those places did there exist any hostility between the *polis* and the "temple state": the Hellenization of the cult encountered no opposition from the inhabitants of the ancient oriental town. The situation in Jerusalem was entirely different. I have noted above (p. 165) that the foundation of the *polis* of Antioch did not create a new city near the old town; the new city absorbed into itself the whole of Jerusalem, and the chief thing was that the Temple, the nation's religious center, remained in the hands of the *polis*. So long as the Hellenistic reform did not directly affect the religious life of the people, the Temple continued to serve as the cult-place of the entire land of Judaea; but the situation changed with the foundation of the Akra and the settling of Syrian troops in Jerusalem.

Bickermann writes that the foundation of the Akra "did not in any sense oblige the abolition of the Jewish nation. It could go on existing as a federation of Jewish villages: Jerusalem, Modiin, Bet Horon and so on, about the *Temple*" [italics ours] (*God of the Maccabees*, p. 77). But the Jewish villages could not concentrate "about the Temple," since the latter had been profaned by the Syrian cults and since officially it no longer belonged to the Jews, as is stated explicitly in the document of Antiochus V Eupator (II Macc. 11.25: cf. above, p. 226), and as Bickermann himself emphasizes (*ib.* 74, etc.). Hence no "symbiosis" between the *polis* of "Antioch-Akra" and Jerusalem was possible. Jerusalem revived only after the abolition of the *polis:* this happened, *de facto,* at the end of 164, when the city fell into the hands of Judah the Maccabee, and *de lege* in 162, when the Syrian government confirmed the exist-

ing situation. The problem of the "symbiosis" between Jerusalem and the Akra begins, in point of fact, only after that year.
I have observed above (p. 226f.) that the Akra after 162 is no longer a city but simply a fortress; but it is under constant siege during almost the entire rule of Jonathan, and it is difficult to see how its inhabitants could have existed in such conditions. It is to be assumed that in periods of peace, and especially when a man like Alcimus governed Jerusalem, the people of the Akra could emerge without fear from their hiding place and even appear in the streets of Jerusalem; at other times they lived on the food supply they had accumulated in times of calm, and from time to time they doubtless took into the fortress a new supply under a strong guard of Syrian troops who broke the investment. But we have no information on these questions.

APPENDIX IV

Claudius' Edict in
Antiquities, XIX, 280ff.

In *Antiquities* XIX, 280-285, Josephus cites the edict of the Emperor Claudius which touches on the affairs of the Jews of Alexandria. This edict is not generally suspect of falsification in the eyes of scholars. Even Wilcken, who doubted the reliability of most of the documents preserved in Jewish authors of the Hellenistic period,[54] found nothing to criticize in this document. Notwithstanding, Claudius' edict is a stumbling block to everyone studying the civic status of the Jews in Greek cities, and the question became even more complicated after Claudius' rescript to the citizens of Alexandria had been published in Bell's book.[55] This rescript proves decisively that the Jews of Alexandria were not among the citizens of the city (cf. above, p. 313f.). Claudius' edict, by contrast, writes explicitly that the Jews possessed equality of rights with the Greeks. Several attempts have been made to compromise between the edict and the rescript in one way or another. Bell himself wished to reconcile the two documents by a new interpretation of some juridical expressions in the edict (see below) whereby the contradiction would fall away of itself;[56] Engers found the solution to the question by postulating a change in Claudius' outlook on the Jewish question.[57] We shall see later that none of these attempts solves the question completely. Let us now turn to the edict itself. *Antiquities* XIX, 280ff. says:

> As it has been long known to me, that the Jews of Alexandria called Alexandrians ('Αλεξανδρεῖς λεγομένους) took up settlement in [the city] together with the Alexandrians in the most ancient times, and the kings granted them equal citizen status [with the Alexandrians], as has been made clear [to me] by documents to be found in their possession and from the edicts; and after Alexandria came under our authority in the time of Augustus, their rights were preserved by the governors sent at various times [to Egypt], nor did the Jews have any dispute concerning these rights; and when Aquila was [governor] in Alexandria, and the Ethnarch of the Jews died, Augustus did not prevent there being ethnarchs [subsequently also], as he desired that every man standing under his authority should remain loyal to his customs and not be compelled to transgress his ancestral religion; but the Alexandrians offended the Jews who dwelt with them, in the time of the Emperor Gaius, who persecuted the Jews owing to his great madness and want of understanding, because the Jewish people did not wish to transgress their ancestral religion and to call him [by the name] of a god; [and now] it is my will, that nothing should detract from the rights of the Jewish people on account of Gaius' lack of understanding, and that they should also retain for themselves the privileges which they had previously, and that the Jews should remain devoted to their customs, and I order both sides to take good heed that no disorder occur [between them] after this edict has been promulgated.

Even a superficial reading of this edict reveals the contradiction between it and the letter.

What is the interpretation of the words: "The Jews of Alexandria called Alexandrians"? Who called them by this name? If this was an accepted term among the people, and it meant simply inhabitants of Alexandria, how did this popular expression find its way into an official document? And if its interpretation is "citizens of the city," how can we reconcile the edict with the rescript, which denies that the Jews were among the citizens of the town, and how are we to interpret the bitterness of Apion, who could not understand by what right the Jews had arrogated this term to themselves (*C. Ap.* II, 38)?

It is hard to imagine that Claudius would have touched perfunctorily upon this important question, which for many years had been a subject of controversy between two sections of the population, especially when drafting an official document designed for wide publication. It is even more difficult to imagine that Claudius would have attributed this term not to the entire Jewish population of Alexandria but only to one section of it.[58] In that case the edict would have lost all its political value; for could Claudius have confined the rights to only one section of the Jewish population of Alexandria, forgetting the rest of them?

Let us consider the interpretation of the term "equal citizen status" ($\iota\sigma\eta\ \pi o\lambda\iota\tau\epsilon\iota a$). If we assume that this expression denotes the scope of the rights of the private person, it results that every individual Jew had rights equal to those of every individual Greek, in other words—that he was a citizen of the city. If we accept this explanation, we again face the obvious contradiction between Claudius' edict and his rescript. Bell, understanding this, desired to eliminate the contradiction by a new interpretation of the term *isopoliteia*. In his view Claudius was referring not to the individual Jew but to the entire Jewish community, the scope of whose rights was so great that it was possible to speak of equality of rights between it and the Greek city (Bell, *op. cit.*, 16). It is difficult to accept this view. Did the Jewish community really possess all the rights possessed by a Greek city, for instance—the right to strike coins? Clearly not; the Jewish community never fulfilled the functions of the town and its juridical basis was completely different from that of a Greek city. Apart from this, the term "isopoliteia" does not possess the meaning in Greek juridical language which Bell sought to ascribe to it.[59]

Reinach proposed to eliminate the suspect sentence on "equality of rights" from the document. He was correct in this, but was mistaken in thinking that we can do away with all the difficulties by this operation. We have seen that the expression "called Alexandrians" does not suit an official document, and there is another further detail in the first sentence which arouses grave doubts. Claudius writes that the Jews "took up settlement together with the Alexandrians from the most ancient times," or in other words, that they had settled in Alexandria in the period of Alexander the Great, at the actual time of the city's founding. We find this idea in Josephus, nor is it difficult to detect in it the odor of Alexandrian apologetic literature (cf. above, p. 320). In his letter Claudius says that the Jews had dwelt in Alexandria "for a long time" (ἐκ πολλῶν χρόνων), which is decidedly appropriate to reality. Here too, therefore, comparison between the edict and the rescript reveals the falsification executed on the text of the document in Josephus.

Another suspect sentence in the edict is that in which the Alexandrian ethnarch is mentioned. Claudius writes that in the time of the governor Aquila, when the Jewish ethnarch died, Augustus did not hinder the continued existence of ethnarchs. If this was so, it may be supposed that the ethnarch who died under Aquila was succeeded by others, and that therefore nothing occurred to modify Jewish civic status. However, if this was true, why was it necessary to mention Aquila and the date of the death of one particular Jewish ethnarch at all? Apparently this was not the case in reality: the Jewish ethnarch who died under Aquila was actually the last of the line, and after his decease Augustus did not permit another to be elected. This is proved by Philo, who relates that under the governor Magius Maximus, Augustus abolished the post and substituted for it a council of elders or *Gerousia*.[60]

No doubt need be entertained, therefore, that the post of ethnarch was really abolished, and we have to ask with some surprise how Claudius reached the point of finding it necessary to emphasize the opposite in an official document? In the writer's view this sentence cannot be understood so long as we regard it as having been written by the Emperor. The question will be solved automatically if we assume that we are faced with a Jewish forgery. It was very important to the Jews to show their anti-Semitic enemies that the civil status which they had received from the kings remained unmodified under Augustus, for Augustus was the first Caesar to rule Egypt and all his acts set an example for the emperors who succeeded him. But under him something had occurred which was a potential cue for anti-Semites; the post of ethnarch had been abolished by his order. The unpleasant impression so created had to be neutralized, hence controversial matter was inserted in a camouflaged fashion into Claudius' edict, with the object of "correcting" reality in harmony with the demands of apologetic literature. With Augustus' edict, Josephus cites another of the same Emperor, the aim of which is to treat of the political situation of the Jewish population throughout the Empire (*Ant.* XIX, 287, etc.). This edict also reveals sympathy towards the Jews, but it does not exaggerate on the subject, and the words reminding the Jews "not to behave with contempt toward the gods of other peoples" evidence the trustworthiness of the document. Bell thinks that this second document "stands or falls" with the first, and that if it is genuine, the first is genuine too.[61] He brings no convincing proof of this view and I do not see what his authority for it is. In this second edict Claudius mentions his two Jewish friends, the kings Agrippa I and Herod (Agrippa's brother), who had requested him to grant to all the Jews of the Empire the rights which he had granted to the Jews of Alexandria; the Emperor willingly fulfilled this request. From this we learn only that Claudius promulgated an edict in favor of the Jews of Alexandria, but not that the text of this edict was exactly like that in Josephus. What is more, it can be seen from the second edict that Claudius' edict in favor of the Jews of Alexandria was drafted differently from the version given in *Ant.* XIX, 280ff. The version in Josephus says explicitly that Claudius confirmed to the Jews of the city their civic rights (that is, gave them equality of rights with the Greeks); it follows therefore that in the second order he made all the Jews of the Empire citizens of the Greek cities, or, to be precise—citizens of Alexandria.[62] I do not think that this conclusion is credible. It is clear then that there is no inner connection between the first edict (in its version as given by Josephus) and the second, and each requires a special study to itself. We still have to consider the view of those scholars (Willrich, Engers and others) who endeavor to rescue the trustworthiness of the first edict by the conjecture that Claudius drafted it under the influence of the Jewish King Agrippa. The latter was the Emperor's friend and without his aid Claudius might not have ascended the imperial throne as easily as he did. Agrippa was staying in Rome at the beginning of the new Emperor's reign, and then went to Palestine. The edict in favor of the Alexandrian Jews was composed while Agrippa was still in Rome, whereas the rescript was written when Agrippa was already in Palestine.[63] The scholars therefore suppose that what Agrippa told the Emperor about Jewish citizen status in Alexandria was baseless, and that he perhaps also showed him forged documents, so that the Emperor fulfilled his request without hesitation or too much questioning and wrote what Agrippa put into his mouth. After Agrippa had departed from Palestine the Emperor's eyes were suddenly opened, and he then wrote the opposite to what he had first written.

However, official documents are not composed in this personal manner, nor generally by the sovereign himself, but by his secretaries, the sovereign merely making emendations in the written text. In addition to this general reason, we have clear proof that the first edict of Claudius was not written in haste or under the influence of one man, but was composed after investigation of and inquiry into the question. In his letter Claudius addresses the Alexandrians and commands them to respect the Jewish customs confirmed by Augustus "and which I also confirmed *after listening to both sides.*"[64] The reference here, of course, is to the edict written at the beginning of Claudius' reign, and from this we learn that immediately after Claudius ascended the imperial throne, the representatives of both sides had appeared before him and debated the Jewish status in Alexandria.[65] There is no doubt therefore that he had already then heard from the Greeks everything he was to know some six months later, so how are we to believe that notwithstanding he wrote of Jewish and Greek equality of rights?

Every attempt therefore to evaluate the document in *Antiquities* XIX, 280-285 as a genuine edict of Claudius, encounters numerous difficulties, and the question is simply this: Is the document entirely forged or has it merely been worked over by forgers? The second answer is probably nearer the truth. The end of the document in particular gives the impression of genuineness: Claudius here confirms the privileges ($\delta\iota\kappa\alpha\iota\acute{\omega}\mu\alpha\tau\alpha$) of the Jews, permits them to live according to their national customs and appeals to both sides with the good advice to maintain public order and to refrain from disturbing it. The mention of both sides connects this passage of the edict with the similar passage in Claudius' rescript, which is an important proof in favor of the genuineness of the edict. There are other places in the document which need not be regarded as forged, such as the mention of the persecution of the Jews under Gaius, or the report of the confirmation of Jewish privileges by Augustus.

It is to be assumed, therefore, that at the basis of the document in *Antiquities* XIX, 280ff. lies Claudius' genuine edict, which was no different in content from the documents of the other Roman emperors, its aim being to confirm to the Jews of Alexandria the privileges they had received from the Ptolemaic kings, later confirmed by Augustus. The Jewish forger converted the privileges into civic rights, interpolated into the document the term "Alexandrians" and also "corrected" history with respect to one fact in the period of Augustus. By this elaboration the document took on a new form, which in those times could bring a certain advantage to the Jews in their struggle for civic rights, but destroyed its present importance as a reputable historical source for the study of Jewish civic status in Alexandria.

LIST OF ABBREVIATIONS

Abh. Bayr. Ak.	Abhandlungen der bayerischen Akad. der Wissenschaften
AJP	American Journal of Philology
ARAST	Atti d. reale Accademia di scienze di Torino
BASOR	Bulletin of American Schools of Oriental Research
BSAA	Bulletin de la société archéologique d'Alexandrie
CAH	Cambridge Ancient History
CIJ	Corpus inscriptionum Judaicarum
FHG	Müller's Fragmenta Historicum Graecorum
HTR	Harvard Theological Review
HUCA	Hebrew Union College Annual
JBL	Journal of Biblical Literature
JPOS	Journal of the Palestine Oriental Society
JQR	Jewish Quarterly Review
MGWJ	Monatschrift für Geschichte und Wissenschaft des Judentums
MNDPV	Mitteilungen und Nachrichten des Deutschen Palästina Vereins
OGIS	Orientis Graeci Inscriptiones selectae
PCZ	Zenon Papyri (Musée de Caire)
P.Col.Zen.	Zenon Papyri (Columbia University Press)
PSI	Publicazioni della Società Italiana
QDAP	Quarterly of the Department of Antiquities in Palestine
RB	Revue Biblique internationale
REJ	Revue des études juives
SEG	Supplementum epigraphicum Graecum
SEHHW	Rostovtzeff's Social and Economic History of the Hellenistic World
SRHJ	Baron's Social and Religious History of the Jews
ZDPV	Zeitschrift des Deutschen Palästina-Vereins
ZNTW	Zeitschrift für die neutestamentlicher Wissenschaft

1   On the Persian kings' ratification of Jewish autonomy, see, for example, E. Auerbach, *Wüste und Gelobtes Land*, 2, 1936, 238, 399. For Jewish history under Persian rule, see J. Klausner, *History of the Period of the Second Temple* (Heb.), 1949, I, 131ff.; II, 9ff.; R. Kittel, *Geschichte des Volkes Israel*, III, 2, 1929; A. T. Olmstead, *History of Palestine and Syria to the Macedonian Conquest*, 1931, p. 553ff.; W. Oesterley, *A History of Israel*, II, 1932, 63ff.; Auerbach, *op. cit.*, 223ff.

2   It should not be forgotten that the policy of Nehemiah was based on the fact that he was the king's deputy, and not the representative of the local Jewish population. The Persian satrap who came after him, Bagoas, also ruled Judaea autocratically (*Ant.* XI, 298ff.). The coins with the inscriptions "Yahud" on them cannot serve as a proof of the political autonomy of Judaea, as some scholars assume (see E. L. Sukenik, *JPOS*, 14, 1934, 178ff.; *id.* 15, 341ff.; W. F. Albright, *BASOR*, 53, Feb. 1934, 20ff., and, following them, with certain reservations, Reifenberg, *Jewish Coins* (Heb.), 1947, 10; Shalit, in the *Commentationes in memoriam Johannis Lewy* (Heb.), 1949, 263, n. 22: autonomous minting in the Persian Empire was generally rare and this permission was granted either to great commercial towns (such as those of Phoenicia), or to "dynasts" (local princes of political or military influence in their districts, *e.g.*, in Caria, Lydia, Cilicia, etc. Cf. Babelon, *Les Perses Achéménides*, 1893, p. xxiff.). Jerusalem was not a city of commercial importance, nor was the political influence of the High Priest felt beyond the borders of Judah. It is therefore much more likely that the above-mentioned coins were minted by the satraps, like those which they issued in west Asia Minor, in Cilicia, Caria, Babylon and Persia (Head, *Historia Num.*, 596, 628, 715, 816, 829). This is also the view of Narkiss, *Coins of Eretz Yisrael* (Heb.), II, 1936, 14ff. It is especially hard to assume that the High Priest selected as a model for his "autonomous issue" a Cilician coin representing a winged god seated in a chariot (who, Narkiss [*ib.* 25] thinks, is the Cilician god Baal-Tarz). Would such contempt of the Mosaic Law have been possible after Ezra?

3   Scylax, the Greek geographer of the fourth century B.C.E., calls Dor "a Sidonian town" (Müller, *Geog. graeci minor.*, I, 79). The inscription of Eshmon-Ezer, King of Sidon, relates that the Sidonians received two towns, Dor and Jaffa, as a gift from the King of Persia (*C. I. Sem.*, I, 9-20). Migdal Sharshon (Straton's Tower—later Caesarea) was also founded by a Sidonian king—cf. Schürer, *Gesch. d. jüd. Volkes*, II, 4, 134.

4   Nelson Glueck's explorations in the south of the Negev have revealed numerous Attic sherds at Elat from the fifth and fourth centuries. The town apparently served as a transit-station for the perfume

trade with Southern Arabia. See N. Glueck, *BASOR*, 80, Dec. 1940, 3ff., *id.*, *BASOR*, 82, Apr. 1941, 3ff., *id.*, *The Other Side of the Jordan*, 112.

5 Demosth. 52, 20; cf. Isaios, 4, 7.

6 See Watzinger, *Denkmäler Palästinas*, 2, 1935, 5ff.; Iliffe, *QDAP*, VI, 1936, 61ff.; D. V. Bothmer, *BASOR*, 83, Oct. 1941, 25; Albright, *From the Stone Age to Christianity*, 1940, 259. Attic sherds of the fifth century B.C.E. have been found in the recent excavations carried out by the Israel government's Department of Antiquities, as, for example, at Tel el-Kasile; see the archaeological etc. studies *Eretz Yisrael* (Heb.), I, 1951, 68; *Isr. Expl. Jnl.*, I, 212, 249; *Bull. Dept. Antiqs.* (Heb.), III, 1951, 6ff.

7 These are the well known coins bearing the figure of an owl. Cf. Narkiss, *Coins* etc. (Heb.), II, 85ff.; Reifenberg, *Jewish Coins* (Heb.), 8ff.; G. F. Hill, *Cat. of the Greek Coins of Palest.*, 1914, LXXXIII, 176ff.; Sellers, *The Citadel of Beth Zur*, 1933, 69ff.; *QDAP*, 2, 1933, 1ff.

8 See Scylax, 104 (Müller, *Geog. graeci minor.*, 1, 79).

9 On his visit to Samaria, related by Curtius, see p. 43.

10 The literature on Alexander's visit to Jerusalem, and to Palestine generally, is abundant. Cf. Klausner, *History* (Heb.), II, 95ff.; Gutmann, "Alexander of Macedonia in Palestine," *Tarbitz* (Heb.), XI, 271ff.; Willrich, *Juden und Griechen*, 1895, 1ff.; Spak, *Der Bericht des Josephus über Alex. den Grossen*, 1911; Büchler, *REJ*, 36, 1898, 1ff.; Abrahams, *Campaigns in Palestine from Alexander the Great*, 1927, 7ff.; Abel, *RB*, 44, 1935, 48ff.; R. Marcus, in Loeb's *Josephus*, VI, p. 512ff.

11 Cowley, *Aram. Pap.*, 30, 1.29; 31, 1.28; cf. on these papyri, Kraeling, *The Brooklyn Museum Aramaic Papyri*, 1953, 104ff. Josephus explicitly calls Sanballat "Satrap of Samaria" (*Ant.* XI, 302), a term confirmed by the Elephantine papyri (30, 1.29). Nehemiah does not mention this fact. The title "satrap" in relation to such officials as Sanballat and Nehemiah has to be treated with some reserve. The Persian Empire was divided, according to Herod. III, 89, into 20 satrapies (Darius himself gives the numbers 21, 23, and 29 in his inscriptions). These were the large ones. However, Dan. 6.2 speaks of 120 "satrapies" (*ahasjdrapiya*), and the Book of Esther (1.1) of 127 "states" (*medinah*). These were the small administrative units, the men in charge of them also being called satraps, or pashas, but a governor of this type is more correctly called a "vice-" or "assistant-" satrap. Cf. Bengston, in *Gnomon*, 13, 1937, 122. The states of "Yahud" and Samaria were small parts of the large satrapy of Ever-Nahara, which embraced all the countries between the Taurus Mountains on the north, the River Euphrates on the east, and the frontier of Egypt on the south. Cf. on the question of the Satrapies, Lehmann-Haupt, *RE*, *s.v.* Satrap, II; Reihe, 1923, 136ff.; Abel, *Géog. de la Pal.*, 1938, 115ff.

12 Spak (*loc. cit.*, 2ff.) would justify Josephus' chronology on the supposition that there were two Sanballats, one in Nehemiah's time and the second under Alexander. So also Gutman, *loc. cit.*, 290. If this were so, we would have to assume that there were also two Jewish priests who married daughters of governors of Samaria, one in Nehemiah's time, the son of Yoyada who became the son-in-law of the first Sanballat (Neh. 13.28), the second under Alexander, Yadoa's brother who became the son-in-law of the second Sanballat (*Ant.* XI, 302ff.). I do not think that we can accept this strange repetition of events as historical fact; scholars, indeed, do not generally endorse Spak's conjecture (cf. *e.g.*, Motzo, *Saggi di storia e letteratura Giudeo-Ellenistica*, 204). Gutman, *op. cit.*, 294, n. 44, and prior to him, Oesterley, *op. cit.*, 156, rely on the information in Josephus, *Ant.* XIII, 256, that the temple on Mount Gerizim stood for 200 years before it was destroyed by John Hyrcanus, as a proof that the shrine was built at the end of the fourth century (that is, under Alexander or shortly afterwards). They ignore, however, that Josephus is here using no new sources, but is repeating his former story of Alexander, Yadoa and Sanballat in the self-same paragraph, and has made a simple calculation in "round" figures of the years which intervened, in his view, between Alexander and John Hyrcanus. Another and more plausible conjecture holds that a distinction must be made between the first Jewish-Samaritan dispute and the building of the Temple; the first took place under Nehemiah, but did not mark a complete break; whereas the construction of the shrine was carried out only in Alexander's time, when all hope of healing the breach between the two camps had gone. See Motzo, *op. cit.*, 203; Gutman, *op. cit.*, 292; Alt, *PJB*, 1935, 31, 107. Klausner, *Hist.*, II, 49, also thinks that the "complete break" between Jews and Samaritans took place under Alexander, although he does not believe that the Temple was built then. It is difficult to bring decisive arguments against this conjecture, but it is also hard to prove; it is at any rate clear that those who transfer the building of the Temple to Alexander's period must sunder the link between Sanballat and its erection, whereas the link is well stressed by Josephus. In my view the problem can only be solved if we place the question of the building of the Temple on Mount Gerizim within the broader framework of the general relations between Judaea and Samaria, simultaneously analyzing in detail the events in Judaea itself. Such an analysis has been carried out with thoroughness by A. Shalit in his article, "A Chapter in the History of the Party Conflict in Jerusalem at the End of the Fifth Century and at the Beginning of the Fourth Century B.C." in the *Commentationes in memoriam Johannis Lewy*, 252ff. Shalit concludes that the building of the Temple was carried out round about the year 400, as a result of a prolonged struggle between two parties in Judaea, that of Nehemiah and Ezra on the one hand, and the pro-Samaritan faction on the other. I have nothing to add to the result of this study, which I regard as well-founded in all its basic ideas.

13 Like the Jews, the Samaritans also composed stories about Alexander; thus, for example, they described the meeting between Alexander and Hezekiah, their High Priest, in much the same way as Josephus (Montgomery, *The Samaritans*, 1907, 69, 302; Gaster, *The Samaritans*, 1925, 33). Sanballat was also a sort of Samaritan "national hero," as his resistance to Nehemiah was well known. The Samaritan origin of the story is evidenced by the good relationship between Alexander and Sanballat at its beginning; the information that Sanballat brought Alexander 8000 fighting men as auxiliaries for his campaign can only be a Samaritan fable. It were well to remark, by the way, that nearly all the historians regard this information as historical, and have failed to perceive that Alexander never relied on the troops of conquered peoples (Curtius, IV, 6, 31) and did not use native auxiliaries till he reached the countries of central Asia; cf. Berve, *Das Alexanderreich*, I, 1926, 150ff. The Jewish working over of the story is evidenced by the fact that in the end the Samaritans depart from Alexander frustrated. On the "anti-Samaritan" source in this story, see Motzo, *op. cit.*, 201ff.

14 When he was in the remote lands of Asia, Alexander sought to introduce this practice also among his Macedonian and Greek courtiers, but without success; see the story of the philosopher Callisthenes' opposition to it in Arrian (IV, 9-14); Curtius VIII, 5-8; Plut. *Vit. Alex.*, 53-55. The custom was regarded by the Greeks as the symbol of baseness when practiced toward mortals.

15 It is possible, indeed, that the name Chaldeans (*Haldaioi*) here appears, not in reference to Babylonian priests (see below, Arrian VII, 16, 5, etc.) but as a synonym for astrologers and soothsayers generally, in conformity with the use of the term in the Roman period. It is possible, too, that Χαλδαίων is a misspelling for Χοναίων (Samaritans).

16 Dreams are mentioned frequently by the historians who tell of Alexander, and usually an ancient hero appears in his dream to make some announcement to him. Thus Heracles appears to him before the capture of Tyre (Arrian II, 18, 1) and Homer before the foundation of Alexandria (Plut. *Vit. Alex.*, XXVI, 3).

17 Without entering into a detailed literary analysis of the narrative, I would merely make some isolated remarks. The story is in my view fundamentally a Palestinian folk-story; this is evidenced by the fact that it is repeated, with some changes, in the Talmud. The Samaritan story of the encounter between Alexander and Hezekiah (cf. n. 13) is also a Palestinian folk-story, but reached Josephus in its literary version. This literary form was given to it, apparently, in Alexandria in the first century C.E., as is shown by certain apologetic features characteristic of the period. Alexandria was in general a center for the composition of stories about Alexander (see below, n. 19), and it may be observed that the Jews also did not refrain from participating in the composition of such tales (cf. F. Pfister, "Eine jüdische Gründungsgeschichte Alexandrias," *Stzb. Heidelb. Akad.*, 1914, 11, 23ff.; R. Marcus in Loeb's *Josephus*, VI, 514ff.). The story, then, had experienced many vicissitudes before it reached Josephus.

18 The discussion on the Exodus: Sanhedrin, 91a; cf. Gen. Rabb. 41, 5; see on this controversy Levy's article in *REJ*, 63, 1912, 211ff. The Mountains of Darkness, etc.: Tamid, 32a; Levit. Rabb. 27. The old men of the south: Tamid, 32a; the conversation with these is influenced by the Greek tradition: cf. the ten questions asked by Alexander of the Indian sages (Plut. *Vit. Alex.* 64); cf. also the story of Onesicritos, one of Alexander's companions, about the Indian sages (Strab. XV, 715). Alexander's flight in the air: the Midrash of the Ten Kings, see Eisenstein, *Otzar Midrashim* (Heb.), II, p. 463.

19 Alexandria was the place of composition of the first historical romance about Alexander, known to scholars as the Pseudo-Callisthenes. See on this Ausfeld, *Der griechische Alexanderroman*, 1907. Mythological features have found their way into the serious historical literature concerning Alexander, as, for example, the stories on his contacts with the Amazons; see Diod. XVII, 77, 1-3; Arrian VII, 13, 2; Curt. VI, 5, 24ff.

20 *Meg. Ta'an.*, ed. Lichtenstein in *HUCA*, VIII-IX, 1931-2, 339; cf. Yoma 69a; Levit. Rabb., XIII, 5. Gutman, *loc. cit.*, 281, wishes to explain the brutality exercised toward the Samaritans as a literary motif borrowed from the Greek stories of Alexander's cruelty at the capture of Gaza. The parallel is not convincing.

21 See Zeitlin, "Simon the Just and Kenesset Ha-gedolah," in *Ner Maaravi*, 1925, 137ff. (I regret that I have been unable to obtain this article) and, following him, G. F. Moore's article on Simon the Just in *Jewish Stud. in Mem. of Israel Abrahams*, 1927, 357, also in his book *Judaism*, I, 35, n. 1. Cf. further Lichtenstein, in *HUCA*, VIII-IX, 304.

22 Scholars have unintentionally followed Willrich (*Jud. u. Griech.*, 13), who saw Agrippa's visit to Jerusalem in the time of Herod (*Ant.* XVI, 14) as the historical event which was the model for the author of the Alexander story. On Simon the Just and Antiochus III, see below, at the end of this chapter.

23 Not, at any rate, in its full extent: it cannot be supposed that Alexander gave the Jews the whole of the land of Samaria; the question is whether they received from him a part of it, that is, the part bordering on Judaea. Even this is open to doubt. The Jews received the districts of Aphairema, Lydda, and Ramatayim, bordering on Judaea, from the Syrian king Demetrius II (II Macc. 1, 11, 34), and not from Alexander. If Hecataeus was right, we must suppose that the Jews had subsequently lost the districts received from Alexander and obtained them again from Demetrius. We have no authority in the sources for such a supposition.

24 Coele-Syria is meant. See n. 34.

25 See Schürer, II, 202, who cites authorities from Greek and talmudic literature.

26 *Meg. Ta'an.*, 22 Shevat (ed. Lichtenstein, 344), The "Scholion" tells of Caligula's envoy (*legatus*) who visits the towns of the country and sees Jews everywhere who have come to beg him to rescind the decree. "He had scarcely arrived at Antipatris when the rumor reached him that Caligula had been slain." Cf. also *Mid. Proverbs* and *Yalkut Shim. to Proverbs* IX, 2; *Acta Apost.*, XXIII, 31ff.

27 Antipatris (today Rosh Ha-Ayin) took the place of the Hellenistic Pegai, the town standing by the "frontier" (see below, p. 433, n. 85); we learn from this that as early as the Ptolemaic period the place was known as a crossroads; it retained its importance in the Roman period.

28 This is evidenced by Hecataeus, who wrote on the Jews in the period of the Diadochi; on him see in this chapter, p. 58.

29 A few examples may be desirable. Alexander restored their laws to the Greek cities of Asia Minor after he had abolished the oligarchies set up by the Persians (Arrian I, 18, 2); he permitted the Lydians the use of their ancient laws (*ib.* I, 17, 4); he gave to the Arabs their "traditional autonomy" (Strab. XVI, 741). Similarly as regards the Indians (Arrian VII, 20, 1), and so everywhere.

30 The idea that the Jews obtained confirmation of their national rights from Alexander is not new; we find it in Radet's book on Alexander (Radet, *Alexandre le Grand*, 1931, 134), and he is followed by Abel (*RB*, 44, 1935, 48ff.).

31 The only hint that Alexander sojourned in the Jordan Valley is an extract from Pliny where the learned Roman speaks of the balsam groves of Jericho, *N.H.* XII, 25, 117. But the sentence *Alexandro Magno res ibi gerente* may be interpreted as referring to Alexander's stay in Syria as a whole.

32 See the author in his *Hellenistische Städtegründungen*, 140.

33 On Gaza, see ch. 2.

34 Our sources distinguish between the governors of Syria and the governors of Coele-Syria. The first governor of Syria was Arimmas (Arrian III, 6, 8); after him came Asclepiodorus (Arrian, *ib.*). As governors of Coele-Syria are recorded Parmenion (Curt. IV, 1, 4, doubtless only temporarily), Andromachus (*ib.* IV, 5, 9) and Menon (*ib.* IV, 8, 11; cf. Arrian II, 13, 7). However, this distinction is not valid everywhere: thus, for instance, Andromachus is once recorded as governor of Coele-Syria (as above), and once as governor of Syria (Curt. IV, 8, 9). The chronological order of their governorships is also not entirely clear. See Gutman in his above-mentioned article, p. 275ff.: Kahrstedt, *Syrische Territorien in Hellen. Zeit*, 1926, 9ff.; Berve, *Das Alexanderreich*, 1926, 2, pp. 38, 60, 88, 259, 302; Abel, *Hist. de la Palestine*, 1952, 12ff.

35 Diod. XVIII, 3; *ib.* 39, 6; Curt. X, 10, 2; Justin. XIII, 4.

36 The geographical conception of Coele-Syria (ἡ Κοίλη Συρία) differed from period to period. At first the name indicated the Persian satrapy of Ever-Nahara ("across the river"); at the beginning of the Hellenistic period Coele-Syria included all southern Syria from the mountains of Lebanon to the Egyptian frontier, and the whole of Palestine; the Ptolemies were in the habit of calling these countries "Syria and Phoenicia" (as below, n. 55), while the Seleucids called them Coele-Syria. At the end of the period the name was used to denote only the Vale of Lebanon and the localities about Damascus. The etymology of the name is not clear. Some think it an ordinary Greek name meaning "Hollow Syria"—the depression between the mountains of Lebanon and Anti-Lebanon which is continued southward in the Jordan Valley and the Dead Sea (thus former scholars, and among the more recent, Bickermann); some look for a Semitic root, *Ḥilata* or *Ḥulata* (valley or rift, in Aramaic), or Kol-Syria (Heb.—"the whole of Syria"). See Kahrstedt, *op. cit.* 1ff.; Bickermann, in *RB*, 54, 1947, 256ff.; A. Schlatter, *Zur Topographie u. Gesch. Palästinas*, 1893, 315; Galling, in *ZDPV*, 61, 1938, 85ff.; A. Shalit, *Scripta Hier.* I, 64ff.

37 Among the most important of them were Antigoneia Troas in Asia Minor and Antigoneia in Syria. See the present author, *Hellenistische Städtegründungen*, 154ff.; cf. on Antigonus' activity generally, Köhler, "Das asiatische Reich des Antigonos," *Stzb. Preuss. Akad.*, 1898, 11, 824ff.; W. W. Tarn, in *CAH*, VI, 489ff.

38 It is permissible, of course, to question the reason given by Diodorus for this retirement (feelings of friendship), but the fact itself is certainly historical, and it is not difficult to discover more substantial motives for Seleucus' readiness to make the concession. The rule of Coele-Syria was not a matter of great importance to him, since he controlled northern Syria, that is, the exit to the Mediterranean Sea. He also perceived that, were he to insist on his demand, he would have to fight Ptolemy, and such a war was certainly not to be taken lightly, after he had just concluded the arduous campaign against Antigonus.

39 Niese, *Gesch. der griech. u. Maked. Stäaten*, 1, 387; Bouché-Leclercq, *Hist. des Lagides*, I, 154; Ed. Meyer, *Urspr. d. Christent.*,

II, 3; Hölscher, *Palästina in pers. u. hellen. Zeit*, 58ff.: Schwarz, *Nachr. d. Gott. Ges. Wiss.*, 1906, 374; Abel, *Hist. de Pal.*, 1952, 42.

40 Diodorus (XXI, 1, 5) stresses that Seleucus came to Syria to conquer the country "in accordance with terms which had been made" by the kings. Palestine therefore belonged to Seleucus by legal decision.

41 Antiochus IV Epiphanes, also, when he was at war with Egypt (169), justified Seleucid rule in Syria on the basis of the decision of the kings after the battle of Ipsus (Polyb. XXVII, 17, 7; cf. Diod. XXX, 2).

42 According to Ed. Meyer, Palestine (or at least its northern part) passed to Demetrius, son of Antigonus, after the Ipsus campaign, and in 296 Seleucus took the country from him. It is hard to see what basis Ed. Meyer finds for this supposition. On Seleucus' war with Demetrius over Coele-Syria, sources say nothing, and they are equally silent concerning Demetrius' rule of Palestine. Demetrius' name is mentioned only once in connection with the events there: Eusebius has preserved a short notice on the destruction of the city of Samaria in 296 by Demetrius (see above, ch. 2). This information cannot serve as authority for Meyer's view; on the contrary, if Demetrius destroyed the city, it is a sign that it did not belong to him and that he had invaded Palestine as an enemy. It is important that in the same year we find Demetrius in Greece; he did not stay long in Palestine, therefore, and his attack on Samaria (if Eusebius' information is chronologically correct) must have been in the nature of a "reconnaissance in force" only.

43 Babelon (*Rois de Syrie*, LXXXV) found the Seleucid era in the dates which appear on the coins of Acco (of years 5-46) and Tyre (of year 2), and failed to notice that in the years 2 and 5 of the Seleucid era, in 310 and 307, the towns of Palestine and Phoenicia were under the rule of Antigonus and could not therefore have reckoned their years according to the Seleucid date. In Babylon itself the Seleucid dating appears first only in 305, and as regards Syria there are reasons for thinking that it was not adopted till the time of Antiochus III. It is clear that Babelon was in error and took for Seleucid dates others which appear on the coins of the Phoenician cities. On this question see Abel, "L'Ere des Séleucides," *RB*, 47, 1938, 198ff.

44 On the question of the conquest of Palestine by Ptolemy in 301, see Beloch, *Griech. Gesch.* IV, 2, 319ff.; Bevan, *A Hist. of Egypt under the Ptolemaic Dynasty*, 35ff.

45 This is related by Josephus, *Ant.* XII, 7, citing the order of Ptolemy II Philadelphus, preserved in the Aristeas letter. Many scholars now admit the authenticity of the order; see Wilhelm's article in *Arch. f. Papyrusforschung*, XIV, 1941, 30ff.; cf. Wilcken, *ib.* XII,

1937, 222ff. It is to be concluded that the behavior of Ptolemy's troops toward the Jewish prisoners was pretty brutal (Arist. 23). The number of 100,000 prisoners given by Aristeas (12) is doubtless exaggerated; a reduction of population on this scale would have meant the complete destruction of Judaea and the depopulation of Jerusalem, which is in contradiction to Hecataeus' account of the city's large population. See above, p. 119.

46 On the new attitude to the fragments of Hecataeus preserved by Josephus, see below, n. 49. Hecataeus' story of Hezekiah has evoked the suspicion of scholars, since it was difficult to understand the reason why a high priest should leave his post in Jerusalem to migrate to Egypt. But the real existence of Hezekiah has now received possible confirmation by the finding of a coin in the excavations at Bet Zur (Sellers, *The Citadel of Beth Zur*, 1933, 73ff.). It bears two inscriptions, one, first read "Yehohan(an)," the second, "Hizkiyahu" (Hezekiah). On the basis of the erroneous reading "Yehohanan," Sellers and after him Olmstead (*JAOS*, 56, 1936, 244) thought that Yehohanan was the High Priest Onias, and that Hezekiah was his treasurer. Scholars now know that the correct reading of the first inscription is Y-h-d (Yahud), the name of the Satrapy of Judaea under Persian rule. (See Sukenik, *JPOS*, 14, 178ff.) However, were this so, we should expect to find in the second inscription the name of a Persian satrap, not of a Jewish High Priest (see above, p. 417, n. 2). According to Sukenik in his above-mentioned article, p. 181, the inscription is not as clear as it might be, and it is not certain, therefore, that the name is Hezekiah: thus it is possible that we have the name of some Persian satrap which happens to resemble Hezekiah. Narkiss (*Coins*, I, 28) also considers that the inscription "Hezekiah" "still requires clarification"; in his view the coin does not belong to the Ptolemaic period, as at that time coins of the Attic standard (with the owl figure) were no longer being minted in Palestine; he voices the conjecture that the above coin was minted under Persia, and that, if the inscription is really "Hezekiah," nothing prevents us attributing the activity of this High Priest to the Persian period, as according to Hecataeus, Hezekiah was in 312 an elderly man of 66 (cf. *ib.* II, 38, 86).

From these contradictory opinions it is to be concluded that Sellers' coin complicates the question instead of solving it. I see three possible solutions: 1. "Hezekiah" is not the correct reading. In this case the coin belongs to the Persian period and has no connection with Hecataeus' account (which does not of course mean that the latter is untrue). 2. The reading is "Hezekiah" and the coin belongs to the Persian period (as Narkiss believes); if so, we have to admit that the High Priests under Persian rule had permission to strike coins, that is, that the Jews enjoyed a considerable breadth of political autonomy, and with this it is very hard to agree (see above, p. 39). 3. The coin was minted between 332 and 312, Hezekiah being High Priest some time during that period. This supposition seems reasonable; as we shall see below. The power of the small "satraps" in Judaea comes to an end at this time, and the High Priest assumes the aspect of the chief ruler of Judaea responsible directly to the king. The political autonomy within certain limits, which can with difficulty be accepted for the Persian period, can be easily admitted for the Hellenistic epoch. The silence of the sources concerning Hezekiah can also be easily reconciled; his term may not have been prolonged (perhaps only a few years shortly before 312), hence the absence of any memory of him in late writers. Even the strange fact of a High Priest deciding to leave his post and to migrate to Egypt can be explained by his Ptolemaic political stand (see below). Some writers have sought to see in Hezekiah's title of *Archiereus,* not the High Priest, but one of the priests of the high priestly family, in conformity with the use of this title by Josephus and in the New Testament (cf. Büchler, *Tobiaden u. Oniaden,* 33; Thackeray, in Loeb's *Josephus,* I, 238). Hecataeus, however, uses the title *Archiereus* only for the High Priest, as can be seen in the passages in Diodorus.

47 Cf. for example Droysen, *Gesch. d. Hellenismus,* 2, 105.

48 Thus, for example, Bouché-Leclercq, I, 50; Willrich, *Jud. u. Gr.,* 23ff.; Abel, *Hist. de Pal,* 31.

49 In the nineteenth century, historians were in the habit of distinguishing between the authentic Hecataeus, extracts from whose writings have been preserved in Diodorus (XL, 3), and Pseudo-Hecataeus, a Jewish forger, whose writings were used by Josephus (*C. Ap.* I, 183ff.) for apologetic purposes. This distinction was regarded as unimpeachable, and only a few scholars (Wendland, Schlatter) dared to take issue with the majority. Today several scholars still follow this old method and perceive in Josephus' extracts from Hecataeus a Jewish apologetic motive; see, for instance, M. Stein's article "The Pseudo-Hecataeus, the date and purpose of his book on the Jews and their country," in the periodical *Zion* (Heb.), VI, 1934, 1ff. A new chapter in the investigation of Hecataeus was opened by the article of Hans Lewy in ZNTW, 31, 1932, 117ff. Lewy analyzes most of the information preserved in Josephus and proves—in this writer's view convincingly—that this is not the work of a Jewish forger, but information derived from the work of the authentic Hecataeus. This does not, of course, prove that all Hecataeus' information is historical truth: he also could make mistakes; his intention was not to give a precise description of Jewish life, but to write a kind of "Journey to the Land of the Jews" in the spirit of the travelogues and "utopias" which were so common in the Greek literature of the period (cf. Lewy's article, 130ff.). In the first edition of the present book (Heb.) the writer also followed the majority view, but now believes that Lewy's approach is the correct one, and that we may use the Hecataeus fragments preserved in Josephus as valuable historical material, although, of course, each of his accounts requires strict scrutiny, as they include several plain falsehoods intended for the Greek taste of that period.

50 On the social classes in Hecataeus, see ch. 3.

51 According to Bickermann, *Gott d. Makkabäer,* 57, the High Priests attained their great power in Judaea only in the third century. This assumption is based on another, that the High Priest was not only chief of the Jewish priests, "but also first and foremost the deputy of the Seleucid sovereign" (*ib.*). This last supposition can find support in some facts of the Seleucid period when the reform carried out by the Hellenizers introduced new practices and ideas into the Jewish people's political life. But we have not the slightest hint in the sources that the High Priest in the Persian or Ptolemaic period was appointed by the royal authorities, as Bickermann thinks (*ib.* 58). We can suppose, of course, that the king, as the supreme ruler of his kingdom, could interfere in the affairs of Jerusalem, confirm or reject the election of a given High Priest, and demand the election of another in his place, if he had transgressed against the king; but this is no proof that the High Priest was an official appointed by the Persians or the Ptolemies. The High Priesthood had developed as an ancient tradition of the Jewish people itself, and this tradition demanded that it remain permanently within the family of Zaddok. Every king who confirmed to the Jews their right "to live according to their ancestral laws" (see above, p. 49) would in any case have also ratified their right to elect the High Priest from the family of Zaddok. Bickermann emphasizes the paradoxical position created in Judaea by the situation in which a pagan ruler appointed the Jewish High Priest: "Stellen wir uns vor, dass der Grostürk den römichen Papst zu ernennen hatte: so paradox war die Situation in Jerusalem." This is, indeed, a very paradoxical situation, but it was created by Bickermann himself and has no support in history. Only under Antiochus Epiphanes, when the High Priesthood had lost its true content, was the High Priest transformed into the political official of the Seleucid sovereign. On this see ch. 4.

52 See above, p. 418, n. 11.

53 The Zenon papyri have so far appeared in the following publications: *Pubblicazioni della Società Italiana (PSI),* IV-VII; C. C. Edgar, *Zenon Papyri* (Catal. général des antiquités égypt. du Musée de Caire = PCZ), I-V; C. C. Edgar, *Zenon Papyri in the University of Michigan Collection* (P. Zen. Mich.); Westermann and others, *Zenon Papyri,* Columbia University Press (P. Col. Zen.), I-II. The following books may be mentioned among the considerable literature devoted to the Zenon archives: Rostovtzeff, *A Large Estate in Egypt in the Third Century, B.C.,* 1922; Viereck, *Philadelpheia,* 1928; Edgar, *P. Zen. Mich.,* Introduction; Cl. Préaux, *Les Grecs en Egypte d'après les archives de Zénon,* 1947. On Palestine in the Zenon papyri, see the

HELLENISTIC CIVILIZATION AND THE JEWS

present writer's article "Palestine in the Light of the Zenon Papyri," *Tarbitz* (Heb.) IV, 226ff., 354ff.; cf. *ibid.*, "Palestine under the Ptolemies," *Mizraim* (Heb.) IV-V, 1937, 9ff.; O. McLean Harper, Jr., "A Study in the Commercial Relations between Egypt and Syria in the Third Century B.C.," *A.J.P.*, 49, 1928, 1ff.

54 This papyrus (P. Rainer inv. 24552 gr.) was first published by Liebesny in the papyrological journal *Aegyptus*, 16, 1936, 257ff.; see now *SB*. 8008. The papyrus originates from the twenty-fourth or twenty-fifth year of Ptolemy II Philadelphus, that is, 261 B.C.E. See on this papyrus, Rostovtzeff, *SEHHW*, 340ff.

55 The official name "Syria and Phoenicia" is mentioned three times in *SB* 8008 (lines 33 and 51, and the fragment b + c); cf. also Ezra III (= Ezra I in the Septuagint, 6.3; 6.7; 6.27), and the Aristeas letter, 22. The popular use of the name "Syria" instead of "Syria and Phoenicia" is very usual in the papyri of Zenon; cf. *P. Zen. Mich.*, 2; *PCZ* 59012, 59093; cf. also *C. P. Jud.* 1, p. 5, n. 13.

56 The question of the frontier between Ptolemaic and Seleucid Syria is discussed in detail by Kahrstedt, *Syrische Territorien*, 22ff., but most of his suppositions are unacceptable; see my above-mentioned article in *Mizraim*, 32ff.; cf. W. Otto, "Beiträge z. Seleukidengesch. des III Jahr. v. Chr.," *Abh. Bayr. Ak.*, 34, 1.

57 On the eastern frontier of Ptolemaic Syria, especially the attachment of Damascus to the Seleucid kingdom, see my above-mentioned article in *Tarbitz*, IV, 360; *Mizraim*, 34ff.

58 Hyparchia: *SB* 8008, lines 1, 38; villages: *ib.* 18, 19; cf. *C. P. Jud.* 6.

59 Orders (προστάγματα): *SB* 8008, lines 3, 8, 33, 38; regulations (διαγράματα): *ib.* 6ff., 26, 30, 31; laws, *ib.* (ἐν τῶι νόμωι τῶι ἐπὶ τῆς μισθώσεως): letters: *ib.* 25 (ἐν τῇ παρὰ τοῦ βασιλέως ἐπιστολῇ). Possibly part of the above legislative activity was directed not to Syria alone; but we hear of it, at any rate, only in that connection.

60 Cf. *Tarbitz*, V, 38; *Mizraim*, 38ff.; Rostovtzeff (*SEHHW*, I, 344) and Bengtson (*Die Strategie in der hellenistischen Zeit*, 166ff.) assume that the king was represented in Syria and Phoenicia by a *strategos*, but this assumption is hard to prove. It is indeed true that in other provinces (such as Thrace and Cyprus) there were *strategoi* who were deputies of Ptolemy (cf. Cohen, *De magistratibus Aegyptiis externas Lagidarum regni provincias administrantibus*, 2ff.; 7ff.); but these were distant provinces demanding the concentration of power in the hands of one high official, while Syria could easily be managed directly from Alexandria. As for the *strategoi* mentioned by Polybius during the war between Antiochus III and the Ptolemies, these may not have been permanent officials at all, but military commanders to whom authority had been delegated in a time of emergency. Polybius is here using the administrative terminology of the

Seleucid empire, as may be deduced from the title τεταγμένος ἐπὶ Κοίλης Συρίας (V, 40, 1), which would have been impossible under the Ptolemies, and this casts doubt on his acquaintance with the Ptolemaic provinces in general. I would therefore leave the question open for the time being.

61 The Syrian *dioiketes: SB* 8008, line 55 (the subject is public sales held ὑπὸ τοῦ διοικοῦντος τὰς κατὰ Συριαν καὶ Φοινίκην προσοδόυς). The *oikonomoi: ib.* 1, 37; the *komarchs* (village headmen): *ib.* 18. The Zenon papyri mention several government officials by their private names but do not give their titles. Among these officials may be mentioned Menekles (perhaps the chief of the customs office at Tyre), Alexis (perhaps the police-chief at Jaffa), Orias and (Alexan)dros (the latter apparently a village headman, the former perhaps a higher official in the *hyparchy*); see *PCZ* 59018, 59077, 59093. Among the officials engaged in economic affairs we know of "Diodorus in charge of the incense trade" at Gaza (*PSI* 628).

62 *PCZ* 59015 *verso.* Cf. *Tarbitz* IV, 238; *Mizraim,* 40ff.

63 Registration of property must be carried out in every *hyparchy* during the sixty days following the publication of the order; in case of non-obedience to the order, the offender will be fined in accordance with regulations: *SB* 8008, 1ff.; registration of flocks and herds liable to tax or exempt from it: *ib.* 17ff.; such registrations to be carried out annually: *ib.* 23; declarations on acquisition of slaves within twenty days: *ib.* 33ff.; fines imposed on those not declaring their slaves: *ib.* 39ff.

64 On the Ptolemaic administrative organization in Egypt, see Bouché-Leclercq, III, 1906, 123ff.; Jouguet, *L'Impérialisme macédonien et l'hellénisation de l'Orient,* 1926, 332ff.; Bevan, *A Hist. of Egypt,* 132ff.; Rostovtzeff, *CAH* VII, 116ff.

65 *C.P. Jud.* 1, line 21: τῶν περὶ Ἀπολλώνιον τὸν διοικητήν.

66 See my article in *Mizraim,* 57ff. on the large caravan of Apollonius' agents in 259; I have there investigated the composition of the group of travelers, whose 66 members, all of Greek origin, are known to us by their personal names. As the activity of Apollonius' agents in Syria had two aspects—their service for the state and their private service for the finance minister, it is very hard to establish in every instance what was the purpose of their activity—for the benefit of the state or for the private benefit of the *dioiketes.* Cf. *Mizraim,* 30ff. Sometimes Apollonius' agents used their power and influence to carry out activity on their own initiative, for their own private advantage; thus, for example, one of the agents wanted to bring slaves out of Syria and sell them abroad (*PCZ* 59093), which was illegal (cf. *Mizraim,* 68, also *Tarbitz,* IV, 244). The hero of *PSI* 616 is also under grave suspicion of carrying out illegal transactions. This behavior on the part of Apollonius' agents caused Rostovtzeff to pass a negative verdict on their operations in Syria (cf. *Large Estate*, 34). However, crimes and frauds were the deeds of isolated individuals only, and they were not so numerous as to justify the condemnation of the acts of all the *dioiketes'* agents. Their wide function as organizers of trade relations between Syria and Egypt is beyond all doubt.

67 In *PCZ* 59004 and 59006, the following posts are referred to: *hegemon* (evidently garrison commandant), *akrophylax* (chief of the citadel), *phylakarches* (chief of police), *archyperetes* (perhaps an official in charge of military pay). On these posts cf. *Mizraim*, 37ff.

68 *SB* 8008, 1.49ff.: τῶν δὲ στρατευομένων καὶ τῶν ἄλλων τῶν κατοικούντων ἐν Συρίαι καὶ Φοινίκηι.

69 Tobiah's fortress is evidently identical with the place in Transjordan known today as 'Arak el-Emir; on the remains of a large building near this place the name of Tobiah is incised twice. Whether the head of the Ptolemaic *cleruchy* is here meant, or Hyrcanus "son of Tobiah," his grandson, or one of Tobiah's ancestors (all of these opinions have been expressed in modern literature), it is clear that we have here the remains of the ancient palace which was the family seat. For the topographical question and an account of the ruins, cf. M. C. Butler, *The Princeton Univ. Arch. Exped. to Syria in 1904-05*, Div. II, Sect. A, 1ff.: Dalman, *Palästina Jhrb.*, 1920, 33ff.; Watzinger, *Die Denkmäler Palästinas*, 2, 1935, 13ff.; Vincent, *JPOS*, 3, 55ff.

70 The "land of Tobiah" is mentioned in an unpublished papyrus of the Zenon archives: *P. Lon. inv.* 2358(A). In this papyrus a group of travelers is described which visited two places on the same day, namely Abila and Sourabitt(ois), arriving the following day in "the territory of Tobiah." Abila and Sourabitt are also mentioned in *PCZ* 59004: Abila is "Abel Ha-Shittim in the steppes of Moab" of Num. 33.49, opposite Jericho; the second place (? = Zur bet Tobiah) is probably in Wadi es-Sir near 'Arak el-Emir. On the list in *PCZ* 59004 (= *C.P. Jud.* 2a) see Abel's article in *RB*, 32, 1923, 409ff., and Alt's remarks in *Arch. Pap.* VII, 293. Abel has identified Abila with Abila of the Decapolis, and "Bet Zur . . ." with Imm es-Surab. These conjectures have been disproved by the above London papyrus. The question as to whether the "territory of Tobiah" is to be identified with the *Eretz Tov* mentioned in I Macc. 5.13 (cf. II Macc. 12.17) as Klein and others think (*Jew. Pal. Expl. Soc. Bull.* [Heb.], III, 115) is not easily soluble, as *Eretz Tov* is mentioned elsewhere in the Bible: Ju. 11.3-5; II Sam. 10.6-8. Cf. Abel, *Les Livres des Maccabées*, 1949, 93.

71 On the origin of the Tobiah family see Maisler's article, "The House of Tobiah," *Tarbitz* (Heb.), XII, 109ff. (cf. *id.*, *Eretz Israel*, IV, 249ff.). Maisler ascribes to the family not only "Tobiah the Ammonite" of the time of Nehemiah, but also the Tobiah mentioned in the year 519 (approximately) in Zechariah (6.9ff.) as one of the heads of the people, and also Tobiah the contemporary of Zedekiah, whose name was discovered among the Lachisch documents. The results of Maisler's study seem reasonable. We have before us, then, a very ancient family whose roots go back to the period of the kings. This study has solved the problem which long engaged scholars: were the Tobiads Ammonites who had joined the Jews, or were they Israelites who had settled among the Ammonites? Nehemiah's evidence could be used in favor of the first possibility, since he not only consistently calls Tobiah an "Ammonite," but aims against him the passage that "an Ammonite and a Moabite shall not enter the congregation of the Lord" (Deut. 23.4). However, hard and fast conclusions are not to be drawn from Nehemiah's words, since the latter thoroughly detested Tobiah, and may therefore have deliberately confounded his geographical with his national origin in order to keep him away from Jerusalem as one alien to the Jews. Maisler's researches have shown that the Tobiads were already a well-connected Israelite family in the days of the kings, and went into exile in Babylon with the rest of the Jerusalem aristocracy. (They are referred to in cuneiform texts of the time of Darius II at Nippur; see Maisler, *loc. cit.*, 118.) As to the family estates in Transjordan, these may have come into their hands after they had returned from Babylon, or possibly, as Maisler supposes, the Tobiads had ruled those parts from the days of the First Temple, or even before the conquest of Transjordan by Tiglathpileser III (in the eighth century B.C.E.); cf. *Eretz Israel*, *loc. cit.*

72 The literature on the Tobiads written since the publication of the Zenon papyri is very extensive. Cf. Vincent, *RB*, 29, 1920, 161ff.; Wilcken, *Arch. f. Pap.* 6, 449ff.; Gressmann, *Stzb. Berl. Ak.*, 1921, 663ff.; Ed. Meyer, *Ursprung u. Anfänge d. Christ.* II, 1921, 128ff.; 462; Rostovtzeff, *SEHHW*, 111, 1746 (Index); Momigliano, *Atti della Reale Accad. d. scienza di Torino* 67, 1931-32, 165ff.; *C. P. Jud.* I, p. 115ff.

73 Bet Anat is mentioned several times in the Papyri of Zenon: *PSI* 594, *PCZ* 59004, *P. Lond.* inv. 2661 (the last as yet unpublished). The letter in *PSI* 554 also discusses Apollonius' estate at Bet Anat, although the name of Bet Anat is not referred to in it; cf. *Tarbitz* IV, 234ff.; *Mizraim*, 45ff. On the topographical question see the last-mentioned article by the present writer, 84, n. 80. Cf. Abel, *RB* 32, 1923, 409ff.; *id.*, *Geog.*, 265ff.; Alt, *Pal. Jahrb.* 1926, 55ff.; Saarisalo, "The Boundary between Issachar and Naphtali," *Ann. Acad. Sc. Fennicae*, 1927/28, 118f. Apollonius' estate at Bet Anat is called a *ktema*, this word denoting in the Hellenistic period not simply an estate, but a vineyard or orchard. In *PSI* 594, and in the London papyrus, wine from Bet Anat is spoken of, and in *PSI* 554 the preparation of currants is referred to. The measure of a *kur* mentioned in *PSI*

554 evidences the cereal-growing branch; in the mishnaic period this unit served principally as a dry measure: "Forty *seah* liquid are two *kurs* dry" (Kelim XV, 1; Ohalot, VIII, 3); cf. *Tarbitz*, IV, 237, n. 2.

74 *SB* 8008, 1.17f.: $\tau[o\grave{v}\varsigma]$ $\pi\epsilon\pi\iota\sigma\theta\omega\mu\acute{\epsilon}\nu o\upsilon\varsigma$ $\tau\grave{a}\varsigma$ $\kappa[\acute{\omega}\mu]a\varsigma$. On these officials and their work in Syria see Rostovtzeff, *SEHHW*, I, 344ff.

75 Villages of the Queen of Persia in Syria, Xen. *Anab.* I, 4, 9; *Pardesim: ib.* I, 4, 10; Neh. 2.8; Diod. XVI, 41, 5 (at Sidon). A place called *Pardes* is mentioned by Strabo (XVI, 756), and another Triparadeisus, by Diodorus (XIX, 12, 2; XVIII, 39, 1).

76 In comparison with Ptolemaic Egypt, the Syrian situation exhibits a much greater variety in the proprietorship of land, and approximates more to the situation under the Seleucids. On land tenure in Asia Minor and in the Seleucid Empire generally, cf. Rostovtzeff, *Stud. z. Gesch. d. römischen Kolonates*, 247; *id., SEHHW*, 472ff.; 502ff.

77 *PSI* 324/325. Cf. *Tarbitz*, IV, 229ff.

78 *PCZ* 59077. Cf. *Tarbitz*, IV, 242ff. Thus for example, *PSI* 628 mentions an official called Diodorus who "is in charge of the trade in incense."

79 These small craft were called *keletes* and *kybaiai*. Their use for travel on the Nile is evidenced by *P. Zen. Mich.* 22, and *PCZ* 59110, 59054, 59320. The same craft also undertook the voyage to Palestine: *PCZ* 59012, 59015 *recto*, 59077. From *PSI* 594 we learn that these boats, when they reached Egypt from Syria, entered the Nile and brought their cargo straight to Memphis, and if needful could continue their voyage from there northward to Alexandria. Cf. *Tarbitz*, IV, 241.

80 Gaza was the most important port in southern Palestine. Here was concentrated the trade in perfumes (*PSI* 628); from here one of Apollonius' agents brought slaves and other merchandise to Tyre (*PCZ* 59093); here Zenon waited for the ship which was to take him to Egypt (*PSI* 322). Gaza's function in the north of the country was discharged by Tyre: there was here a customs house (*PCZ* 59093), and here wares were transferred from vessel to vessel on the outward trip (*ib.*); hither came people from Cyprus to make various purchases (*PCZ* 59016); from here slaves were exported abroad. (This is evidenced by the Greek poet Herodas who reports a conversation between travelers: "I have brought wheat from Acco," says one; "And I—prostitutes from Tyre," responds his friend. See Herodas, *Pornoboskos*, 16ff.) Acco is also mentioned on several occasions in the Zenon papyri; from here, for instance, Zenon sent his "gifts" to Pelusium (*P. Lond.* inv. 2358 B). Cf. also Herodas' reference to Acco in the above quotation. One of Apollonius' agents was permanently resident there (*PSI* 495).

81 On this question, see my article in *Mizraim*, 15ff.

82 One papyrus (*P. Lille*, 29 = M. *Chr.* 369) mentions the prohibition to sell slaves outside Egypt explicitly: "It is forbidden for
anyone to sell slaves for export abroad." A prohibition to import slaves
into Egypt is nowhere mentioned. Rostovtzeff wanted to see such a
prohibition in a Zenon papyrus (*PCZ* 59093); against this view see
my arguments in *Tarbitz* IV, 245; *Mizraim*, 18ff.

83 Syrian slaves in Egypt, *P. Cornell* 1, *PSI* 648, *P. Col. Zen.* II, 87;
cf. for the Roman period: *BGU* 155, 178, 618, 816. The price of
slaves: a girl of seven—50 drachmae (*C. P. Jud.* 1); two young girls—
150 and 300 drachmae respectively (*PSI* 406); a young slave—112
drachmae (*PCZ* 59010). On the price of slaves in Egypt see *Mizraim*,
75, n. 15.

84 Cf. *PCZ* 59142, 59295. A seven-year-old girl bought by Zenon
in the *katoikia* of Tobiah was called Sphragis (*C. P. Jud.* 1), and this
is also the name of one of the servant girls of Apollonius at Fayûm
(*PCZ* 59145). This may be the same serving girl in both cases.

85 Pegai ("springs"), later Antipatris, is near the modern Rosh
Ha-'ayin; the name is mentioned in talmudic literature (M. Parah,
VIII, 10; B. Sanhedr. 5b; B. Bat. 74b). It perhaps survived in that of
the small Arab village of Fedsha, southeast of Petaḥ Tikvah. As may
be seen from the function of Antipatris as a crossing point of the
north-south *Via Maritima* ("the way of the sea") and that linking
the Shephelah with Jerusalem (see above, p. 48), Hellenistic Pegai
also filled the role of a frontier town or fortress. On this frontier at
Pegai various conjectures have been voiced; Kahrstedt in his *Syrische
Territorien*, 44, believes that the administrative boundary between
the Jaffa district and Samaria passed here; the late Professor Klein,
in a private communication to the writer, thought it was the boundary
of the district of Narbatta (cf. his article in *MGWJ*, 1930, 36ff.). According to Avi-Yonah (*Hist. Geog. of Eretz Yisrael* [Heb.], 1950, 20)
the boundary between the district of Ashdod and those of Samaria
and the Sharon coastal zone is meant. The division of Ptolemaic Syria
into *hyparchies* (as we have now learned to know it from the Vienna
papyrus) favors the belief that the boundary at Pegai was between
administrative districts, whichever these were. It may be surmised,
on the other hand, that the Pegai boundary marked the division
between the urban territory of Jaffa (if we assume that Jaffa had
already obtained the status of a Greek *polis* in this period) and
"royal land." On the topographical question and that of the Pegai
frontier, see Alt, "Pegai," *ZDPV*, 45, 1922, 220ff.; Abel, *RB* 36, 1927,
400 = *Géog. de Palest.* 1, 472f.

86 We have no information on the temple of Ashtoret-Aphrodite at
Jaffa, but the cult existed in several Palestinian cities. Herodotus (I,
105) mentions the temple of Aphrodite at Ascalon. The image of

HELLENISTIC CIVILIZATION AND THE JEWS

Ashtoret appears on the coins of numerous cities in the Roman period, *e.g.* Anthedon, Dor, Caesarea.

87 *SB* 8008, 11. 33ff. The royal order prohibits any enslavement of free persons among the population of the country bought or acquired in any other fashion except by purchase at a public auction held under government auspices. On the question of personal enslavement (for debt and similar reasons) associated with the contents of this order, see the above-mentioned article of Liebesny in *Aegyptus*, 16, 257ff.; cf. Gutman, *Dinaburg Anniversary Book* (Heb.), 77ff.; B. Welles, "Manumission and Adoption," *Mélanges de Vissher*, II, 512, n. 20.

88 Cf. *Tarbitz* IV, 229ff.; Schnebel, *Die Landwirtschaft in hellenistischen Ägypten*, 1925, 45; Thompson, *Arch. f. Pap.*, 9, 213.

89 *PCZ* 59012, 59013, 59015 *recto*, 59077. Cf. *Tarbitz* IV, 242; *Mizraim*, 22.

90 Strabo relates the importation of Syrian wine into Egypt in the Roman period (XVI, 752); the city of Laodiceia had the reputation of being πολύοινος and sent most of its produce to Alexandria.

91 On Palestine as a country of transit trade, see *Mizraim*, 24ff. Strabo discusses the question of the importation of *aromata* from Arabia to Egypt through Palestine (XVI, 776). Cf. on this, Glueck, *The Other Side of the Jordan*, pp. 107, 112, 158 and *passim*; Kortenbeutel, *Der ägyptische Süd-und Osthandel*, 1931, 31; Rostovtzeff, *SEHHW*, 386ff.

92 In the Ptolemaic period the "Persians" in Egypt became a pseudo-ethnic group; the term denotes not a people, but a military unit. See Part II, ch. 2; cf. *C. P. Jud.* I, p. 14.

93 In this papyrus we read the words: *para Zenodorou patros Abbaiou*—from Zenodorus father of Abba. The father, an adult, has already adopted a Greek name; the child still bears a local one; when he grew up he probably followed his father's example as a matter of course. The sentence is evidence of the custom (still prevalent among the Arabs) of calling the father after the son.

94 See Polybius' account of the battle (V, 79-86). Cf. Abel's article in *RB*, 48, 1939, 225ff.

95 See, on this inscription, Gauthier and Sottas, "Un décret trilingue en l'honneur de Ptol. IV," *Service des Antiquités de l'Egypte*, 1925; Spiegelberg, *Stzb. Bayr. Ak.*, 1925, IV; Sottas, "Notes complém. sur le décret en l'honneur de Ptol. IV," *Revue de l'Egypte ancienne*, 1, 1927, 230ff.; Momigliano, *Aegyptus*, X, 1929, 180ff.; Lehmann-Haupt, *Klio*, 21, 107f. The inscription contains a declaration by the priests of Egypt in honor of Ptolemy Philopator after the battle of Raphia. The declaration gives a short survey of the course of the campaign in Coele-Syria, mentions the king's great victory and also states that he visited the conquered cities and various temples of

Coele-Syria after the battle. Especially interesting are lines 23ff. of
the Demotic text, which relate the resistance encountered by the king
in one place in Syria, the waging of the war with these enemies, and
the signing of a peace-treaty with them; these lines are not as clear as
they might be and have been the source of various translations and
interpretations (cf. below, n. 97).

96 See my article "The Third Book of the Maccabees as a Historical
Source of the Augustan Period," *Zion*, X, 2ff.

97 In line 23 of the above-mentioned (n. 95) Demotic inscription,
Sottas read: "Eléazar et ses partisans," thus providing the grounds
for the supposition that those rebelling against the king were Jews.
Cf. Abel, *Histoire de la Palestine*, 83. Spiegelberg, however, translates
the text differently, and no trace of Eleazar appears in his rendering.
Momigliano also concurs with his translation and remarks that Sottas
took the name Eleazar from *III Macc.* (6.1). Nevertheless, Momigliano believes that the revolt mentioned in the inscription was a
Jewish one, but that these were "minor disorders" (*piccoli disordini*)
rather than a real rebellion. However, with the erasure of the name
Eleazar, the only link associating the revolt with the Jews is lost, and
III Macc. is not a reputable historical source which can serve as an
authority. To our regret, no single sentence on the rising has survived
in the Greek version of the inscription (*SB.* 7172) and the doubtful
Demotic text is the only source at our disposal.

98 See above, ch. 4, on Heliodorus' visit to the Temple. The
possibility that the story about Ptolemy in *III Macc.* influenced the
author of II Macc. to describe Heliodorus' visit in the same language,
cannot be considered, as the comparison between the two stories evidences the originality of II Macc.; cf. my above-mentioned article,
p. 4, n. 16.

99 Cf. Part II.

100 See Bickermann, "L'avènement de Ptolemy V Epiphane,"
Chron. d'Egypte, 15, 1940, 124ff., on the chronological question in
connection with the succession of Ptolemy V Epiphanes.

101 In settling the chronological order of events, I have followed
E. Täubler, "Jerusalem 201 to 199 B.C.E. On the history of the
Messianic Movement," *JQR* 37, 1946, 47, p. 1ff. On the difficult question of the date of the battle of Panion, Täubler decides in favor of
the year 200 as against 198; he was anticipated in this dating by
Eduard Meyer, *Ursp. d. Christ.*, II, 123, n. 2; cf. B. Niese, *GGMS*,
II, 578, n. 6. The most important proof in favor of this date is the fact
that Polybius described the battle of Panion in the sixteenth book of
his history, and this book ended with an account of the events of the
year 200.

102 Josephus (*Ant.* XII, 131) writes: "After Antiochus had defeated
Ptolemy, he brought Judaea over to his side"; then he describes the

death of Ptolemy Philopator; it follows that Antiochus conquered Judaea in Philopator's time, that is, during his first war for Coele-Syria (221-217). This, however, is a slip of the pen; the context makes it clear that Josephus was referring to the events of the year 201 and not to the battle of Raphia.

103 *"Pugnantibus contra se Magno Antiocho et ducibus Ptolemaei, in medio Judaea posita in contraria studia scindebatur, aliis Antiocho aliis Ptolemaeo faventibus"* (Hieron., in Daniel, 11. 14 = *P. L.* 25, 562).

104 *"Cumque Antiochus teneret Judaeam, missus Scopas Aetolus . . . adversus Antiochum fortiter dimicavit cepitque Judaeam et optimates Ptolemaei partium secum abducens in Aegyptum reversus est"* (*ib.*).

105 Cf. Täubler's article already mentioned, 14ff.

106 On the Book of Daniel as a historical source, see Appendix I at the end of this book.

107 All these explanations have been proposed by various scholars. Cf. Marti, *Kurzer Hand-Commentar zum A. T.: Das Buch Daniel*, 1901, 80; Montgomery, *A Crit. and Exegetical Commentary on the Book of Daniel*, 1927, 439; Charles, *A Crit. and Exegetical Commentary on the Book of Daniel*, 1929, 288; Baeck, *Das Danielbuch*, 1935, 78.

108 All these various interpretations have also been offered by various scholars. It appears to me certain that the attitude of the author of the Book of Daniel to the "men of violence" is negative, whatever the word means: the significance of the word in the Prophets (see Jer. 7.11: "a den of robbers"; Ezek. 7.22: "And violent men entered it and desecrated it") does not permit any sort of positive conception of the notion. Täubler (in his above-mentioned article, 24ff.) sees in "the men of violence" revolutionaries who used violence for their ends. His authority is the Greek translation of Theodotion οἱ υἱοὶ τῶν λοιμῶν, and also a citation in *Acta Apost.* XXIV, 5, where the apostle Paul is called Λοιμός, a person who brings about revolutions. But it is quite clear that, wherever the expression *loimos* means "revolutionary," the intention of the user (in *Acta* the users are Paul's opponents, who are accusing him before the procurator) is not to praise the revolutionary, but to describe him as a dangerous and injurious person. The word νόσος, sickness, is used in exactly the same way to denote political or religious movements which constitute a danger to the public peace. Cf. Lösch, *Epistula Claudiana*, 1930, 24ff.; Janne, *Mélanges Cumont*, 1936, 280ff. There is no doubt, therefore, that Daniel too saw in the "men of violence" dangerous people whose activity was apt to cause (or actually had caused) damage to the nation.

109 "Es ist die seleukidische oder, wie wir sogleich sagen können,

die zum Hellenismus neigende Partei, die sich erhebt, aber dann dem
Skopas erliegt" (*Ursp. d. Christ.*, II, 127). Cf. Marti, *op. cit.*, 81;
". . . בני פריצים sind die Tobiaden und ihr Anhang." Charles, *op. cit.*,
288; Bickermann, *REJ*, 100, 1935, 24.

110 Täubler, *ibid.*, 22, mentioned some of the scholars who anticipated him in this view (A. A. Bevan, Smend, Herzfeld, Hitzig), but
stressed that he had arrived at the idea quite independently of them.
Cf. among previous scholars E. Bevan, *Jerusalem under the High
Priests*, 1904, 30. The time assigned by Täubler to the rising of "the
men of violence" is not particularly satisfactory; if the reason for the
movement was the sudden withdrawal of Antiochus from Gaza, which
was interpreted as a supernatural omen, it would have been directed
against Antiochus, as Jerusalem was still in his hands. Why then was
the rising suppressed by Scopas, as Täubler says on p. 30? Whatever
were its aims, any attempt to revolt from the Seleucids would have
found support from the Ptolemaic general, especially in war-time,
when all allies were assured of a sympathetic welcome.

111 The certain facts for which authority can be found in the details
of Daniel 11.14 are very few: 1. The revolt of the "men of violence"
occurred during Antiochus III's war with Ptolemy V (that is, during
201-198); this emerges clearly from the context. 2. It is possible (but
not essential) to suppose that the movement of the "men of violence"
in Judaea was only part of the movement of the "many" who then
came out against "the King of the South"—the Ptolemies. 3. Daniel's
attitude to "the men of violence" is negative. 4. It may be assumed
that the insurgent movement originated from a group whose members were not numerous, but which was influential and possessed a
strong military organization: the description applied by Daniel to the
rebels as "the men of violence of your people" is most appropriate to
such a character. 5. The movement failed, and we do not know if the
failure was internal (lack of support from the people) or external
(suppression of the revolt by foreign forces). The reader may judge
for himself whether or not these few data are sufficient for the framing
of conjectures with wide implications.

112 Scholars differ on the question, which Simon was "the Just," the
first (beginning of the third century) or the second (end of the third
century and beginning of the second). The problem appears to me
to have been solved by Moore, who has presented convincing proofs
in favor of the identification of the second Simon with Simon the Just.
See his article "Simon the Just," *Jewish Stud. in Mem. of I. Abrahams*,
1927, 348ff. Cf. Klausner, *History*, II, 163; L. Finkelstein, *JBL*, 59,
1940, 455f.; *id. The Pharisees*, 576ff.

113 A corrupt text of the Hebrew original; I cite according to the
translation of Holmes in R. H. Charles' *Apocrypha and Pseudepigrapha*, I, p. 508.

114 On Joseph son of Tobiah and his sons, see below, ch. 3.

115 This Ptolemy is apparently identical with the Ptolemy son of Thrasyas mentioned in an inscription of the beginning of the second century as *"strategos* and High Priest of Coele-Syria and Phoenicia" (*OGIS*, 230). Cf. Bengston, *Strategie*, II, 166ff.

116 A crown or coronation tax, regarded theoretically as a freely-made payment for the king's benefit, but actually collected by the royal officials like any other tax.

117 Our information on the Seleucid taxes is not sufficient to establish the character and weight of the taxes mentioned by Josephus. See Bickermann, *Institutions des Séleucides,* 111ff.; Mittwoch, in *Biblica* 36, 1955, 352ff.; Rostovtzeff, *SEHHW,* 469ff. The poll-tax is referred to in "The Economics," a work attributed to Aristotle but composed during the period of the Diadochi (Van Groningen, *Aristote, le second livre de l'économique,* 1933, 1346a, 4, p. 4.40); the Seleucids therefore may have taken the tax from the Diadochi, who themselves took it from the Persians. If Ptolemaic Egypt, on the other hand, was not acquainted with the poll-tax in its severe form, many taxes existed there which were levied personally on the inhabitants (capitation taxes); cf. the present writer's article "Syntaxis and Laographia," *Journ. Jur. Pap.,* IV, 1950, 183ff. The salt-gabelle was also customary under both the Ptolemies and the Seleucids; cf. *SEHHW,* 470; *ib.* 309; Cl. Préaux, *L'économie royale des Lagides,* 249ff. We may therefore explain the existence of the above-mentioned taxes in Jerusalem under Antiochus III in one of two ways: 1. As a continuation of the Ptolemaic imposts; 2. As the imposition of Seleucid taxes on Palestine.

118 Niese, *GGMS,* II, 579, Anm. 3; Willrich, *Urkündenfälschung in d. hellen.-jüdischen Literatur,* 1924, 18ff.; Schubart, in *Arch. f. Pap.,* 6, 343ff.; Büchler, *Tobiaden u. Oniaden,* 143ff.; Bickermann, "La Charte séleucide de Jérusalem," *REJ,* 197/8, 1935, 4ff. Bickermann has analyzed the document clause by clause and cited many parallels from the Hellenistic world for each individual detail, as, for example, the king's assistance to a city which has been destroyed or is in process of being built, support of the local cult, permission for refugees to return up to a certain date, etc.

119 Bickermann also believes that the permission to live according to their ancestral laws was already granted to the Jews by Alexander and the Ptolemies (see his above-mentioned article, 27). I would not however rely on *Ant.* XI, 338 (the conversation between the High Priest Yadoa and Alexander) as an authority, the story of Alexander's visit to Jerusalem being a mere fable, as we have seen above (p. 42).

120 Cf. Bickermann, *Instit. des Sél.,* 135ff. The Romans followed the example of the Hellenistic kings and confirmed the traditional autonomy of the peoples and Greek cities of the Orient; cf. *OGIS,* 441,

11.45f.; 442, 449; Abbott and Johnson, *Municipal Administration in the Roman Empire,* nos. 15, 19, 40, 52, 67.

121. Cf. Moore, *Judaism,* I, 251ff.

122 Bickermann interpreted Antiochus' manifesto as an order given to the Jews to live according to their laws: "Pour les Juifs de Jérusalem l'édit d'Antiochos III exprimait leur devoir d'observer le sabbat, par exemple. Je dis le devoir, car le roi ordonne: ce peuple vivra selon les lois de ses ancêtres" (*op. cit.,* 27). Heinemann in a review of Bickermann's book *Der Gott der Makkabäer* (*MGWJ,* 82, 156) remarks that obligations are not imposed as a reward of gratitude for loyal sentiments ("Zum Lohn für Loyalität legt man keine Verpflichtungen auf"); he interprets Antiochus' proclamation, not as an order to the Jews, but as a defense of the Jewish cult obligating aliens only but not Jews themselves ("Die Urkünde . . . bindet zwar Andergläubige, soweit es der Schutz der jüdischen Religion erforderte, bindet aber nicht *der* jüdische Gesamtheit"); the imperative πολιτευέσθωσαν used by the king to the Jews, Heinemann interprets as a pledge, not as a command. Bickermann replied to Heinemann's observations in a short note (*Syria,* 25, 1946-8, 74, n. 1) saying that this imperative, being in an official document, could only denote an order. The controversy, however, cannot be settled by grammatical analysis alone; we must pay attention to the legal situation resulting from the publication of the "order." Bickermann was right from the formal point of view: the royal order clearly obligated the Jews first and foremost, and not merely aliens, as Heinemann thinks; it can hardly be supposed that the king would punish foreigners for infringing laws which the Jews themselves were not obliged to keep. On the other hand, there is here no coercion whatsoever, since the granting of autonomy by the king was in answer to the Jews' own petition. The prisoner who enjoys an amnesty is also released "by order," but it cannot be claimed that freedom is imposed upon him against his will. The granting of permission "to live according to ancestral laws" is no more than a ratification of autonomy; it is not the king who settles the real content of "the ancestral laws," but the authorized representatives of the Jews themselves. To take an instance, the "order" to preserve the sanctity of the Sabbath is simply the royal pledge to the Jewish authorities to protect the Sabbath rest by force in the event of this being demanded by the Jews themselves; and as long as the Jews did not appeal to the king with such a request the safeguarding of the Sabbath was entirely their own internal affair. It is in this fashion that the difficulties associated with the document's interpretation must, in the present writer's view, be resolved.

123 Bickermann, "Une proclamation séleucide rélative au temple de Jérusalem," *Syria,* 25, 1946/8, 67ff.

124 *OGIS,* 598. Cf. Iliffe, *QDAP,* VI, 1936, 1ff. = *SEG,* 8, 169; Bickermann, *JQR,* 37, 1946/7, 387ff. Examples of similar prohibitions in Greek temples are given in Bickermann's article in *JQR*, 390. Cf. now a temple inscription at Samothrace: *Hesperia*, 22, 1953, 14.

125 In the first (Hebrew) edition of the present book the writer referred to "the bad condition in which the document is preserved in Josephus," and he was of the opinion that Josephus had not transmitted the complete document, but had transcribed only a part of it. The document, however, is not a personal letter, like Antiochus' letter to Ptolemy, but a *programma,* and as such seems to be complete. Of course, that is no proof that there are no errors in the text. Heinemann writes: "The document has apparently been transmitted inaccurately. It is not to be supposed that the king prohibited the keeping of donkeys and panthers; doubtless he merely prohibited the rearing of swine" (*MGWJ*, 82, 155, n. 21). But precisely swine find no mention, and if we accept Heinemann's conjecture, we have to assume the occurrence of not one but numerous errors in the body of the document. The silence of the latter concerning swine occasions surprise. Bickermann has sought to remove the difficulty by supposing that the document was directed to foreigners—principally sightseers—who were not to be suspected of rearing swine. However, Bickermann himself also mentions the members of the Seleucid garrison of the city as possible visitors to Jerusalem, and these might have reared swine; it were well therefore to seek another explanation, unless we are to suppose that the word "swine" has accidentally dropped out of the main text. Ralph Marcus (in the Loeb Classical Library's edition of *Josephus,* VII, p. 763) expresses two conjectures aimed at explaining the obscurities of the document: 1. The text was composed according to Antiochus' instructions by a Seleucid official who used a document of one of the Greek temples (many of which strictly observed laws of contamination and purity), and applied it without alterations to Jerusalem. 2. The original was directed only to the introduction of unclean animals on the Sabbath, but the word "Sabbath" had later dropped out of the body of the text. As regards the first conjecture, while it is correct that many temples, and even complete cities, strictly observed laws of contamination and purity (cf. for example, the prohibition against keeping various animals such as dogs, goats, etc. at Ialysos, on the island of Heracleia, and on the island of Delos: see the above-cited article of Bickermann in *Syria,* 76ff.; on Heracleia, cf. L. Robert in *Hellenica,* VII, 1949, 161ff.), it is difficult to imagine that the responsible official did not know the difference between one cult and another and did not take into consideration the simple fact that every place had its own tradition, so that the religious customs of one could not be applied automatically to another. As regards Ralph Marcus' second conjecture, the writer does not see how it would have been possible to prohibit the rearing of unclean beasts precisely on Sabbath for it is of the *rearing* of animals within the city, not only of their introduction into it, that the document specifically speaks.

126   It need evoke no surprise that the word *polis* in this case denotes, not the entire town, but only its central part: it is a normal phenomenon, found both in ancient and modern history, for the city to grow beyond its original walls and for the old town to be termed by long-standing habit simply "the city." Information on the growth of Jerusalem beyond its walls has been preserved from the Roman period (Jos., *War* V, 148), and it is not hard to suppose that this phenomenon already existed in the period of Antiochus. It is for the archaeologists to determine what area around the Temple could have been called "the city" in that epoch.

127   Cf. Bickermann, *Inst. des Séleucides*, 164.

128   II Macc. 4.11. The author of II Macc. calls him the father of Eupolemos. This Eupolemos is mentioned in I Macc. 8.17; he lived in the time of Judah the Maccabee. It is therefore reasonable to believe that Johanan his father lived in the time of Antiochus III. For the concept *philanthropia* see Bell, "Philanthropia," *Hommages à J. Bidez et à F. Cumont*, 31ff.; Schubart, in *Arch. f. Pap.*, XII, 10f.

129   II Macc. 3.3; Seleucus IV took upon himself all the expenses involved in the sacrifices in the Temple. On the relationships between Seleucus and the Jews, see ch. 4.

NOTES   *part* **I**   *chapter* **2**

1   Nelson Glueck, *The Other Side of the Jordan*, p. 158ff.; Iliffe, "Nabataean Pottery from the Negeb," in *QDAP*, VI, 6ff.; VIII, 87; IX, 105ff., etc.

2   On the question of the Hellenization of the cities of Syria and Phoenicia see especially Rostovtzeff, *CAH*, VII, 190ff.; *SEHHW*, 478ff.; A.H.M. Jones, *The Cities of the Eastern Roman Provinces*, 1937, 246ff.

3   Tyre was destroyed completely by Alexander, but we find the city figuring as a fortress only two years after his death (Diod. XVIII, 37, 3-4), and in 315 the city was strong enough to withstand attack by Antigonus for fifteen months (*ib.* XIX, 61, 5). During the century that the Ptolemies ruled there, Tyre became a Greek town. In 274 the royal dynasty of Tyre apparently came to an end, and from that year its citizens begin to reckon the years according to a calendar peculiar to the city (cf. Beloch, *Griechische Geschichte*, II, 2, p. 328). Like every Greek city Tyre struck coins with Greek legends, but Phoenician inscriptions also appear on them, as they appear on the coins of other Phoenician towns. The city god Melkart was now called Heracles, and the Greek athletic games were celebrated in the town with great pomp every fourth year (in 173 B.C.E. they were held in the presence of King Antiochus IV himself—cf.

II Macc. 4.18). The Hellenism of Sidon is evidenced by an inscription of the year 200 approximately, which speaks of the participation of the people of the city in the Nemean games held in Greece under the auspices of the people of Argos. In 270 the representatives of Sidon and Byblos were victorious in the athletic contests of Delos. It is to be concluded, then, that in Sidon as in other Phoenician towns, the youth received the Greek athletic training normal in the educational institutions of Greek cities. For the above inscription on athletics in Sidon and the other Phoenician cities, cf. Bickermann's article in *Mélanges Dussaud*, 1939, 91ff. Under the Seleucids, Beirut changed its name to Laodiceia; see the present writer's book *Hellenistische Städtegründungen*, 68.

4 Damascus was captured by Parmenion after the battle of Issus and thenceforward remained in Macedonian hands till the Roman period. Jerome (in his commentary on Isa. 28) witnesses that in "the time of the Macedonians and the Ptolemies" the city's life revived (*donec sub Macedonibus et Ptolemaeis rursum instauraretur*). This report is too general to serve as a basis for conjecture; nevertheless, it may be concluded that the Ptolemies played a certain part in restoring the town. There are grounds for thinking that under Ptolemy II Philadelphus, Damascus was called Arsinoë: Stephanus mentions an Arsinoë in Syria, which was situated "in a valley" and Strabo (XVI, 756) says that the Greeks called the valley near Damascus Aulon. It is also to be deduced from Stephanus that this town was a large one, and as there were no large towns near Damascus, he may mean Damascus itself (cf. the present writer, *op. cit.*, 65ff.). In one of the Zenon papyri (*PCZ* 59079) of the year 257, a city is mentioned called "Arsinoë of Dion." This may be Dion, a general of Ptolemy, who was expelled from Damascus by "Antiochus son of Seleucus," as Polyaenus (IV, 15) relates. In this instance the identity of Arsinoë with Damascus received additional confirmation. It is possible therefore that Damascus had changed its oriental appearance for a Greek one and became a *polis* as early as the time of Philadelphus. There is, at any rate, no doubt that this happened under the Seleucid King Demetrius III Eukairos (95-88), as the coins indicate that under this king Damascus was renamed Demetrias (cf. the writer, *op. cit.*, 66). The archaeologists have revealed the building plan of ancient Damascus in the Roman period, and there are grounds for believing that this corresponds in the main to the original town plan of the Hellenistic epoch (see Watzinger and Walzinger, *Damaskos, die antike Stadt*, 63ff.).

5 In the Roman period additional Greek cities were founded in Palestine, more particularly by Herod; the detailed treatment of these has been omitted here in order not to overstep the chronological limits of the present work. For the Hellenistic period Josephus has preserved a very important list of Greek cities, rehabilitated by Pompey, which had been destroyed by the Hasmoneans or had lost their independence during their time. These were Gadara, Hippos, Pehal (Pella), Dion, Scythopolis, Samaria, Marissa, Gaza, Ashdod, Yavneh, Jaffa, Arethusa, Dor, Straton's Tower (*Ant.* XIV, 75ff.; *War* I, 155ff.). The list does not include all the towns freed by Pompey, for there were other Greek cities in the country which obtained their liberty, as can be seen from the "Pompeian" era adopted by them in the Roman period (cf. Schürer, II, 102; Jones, *Cities*, 454, n. 42). Some of the towns which were reduced to ruins during their war with the Hasmoneans were restored by Gabinius (in the years 57-55), these being Samaria, Scythopolis, Raphia, Anthedon, Yavneh, Apollonia, Marissa, Adora, Gaza, and Ashdod (*Ant.* XIV, 88; *War* I, 166).

6 In talmudic literature Acco is sometimes considered in the same category as towns outside the country. "R. Judah said: Acco and the country north of Acco count as the north" (M. Gitt., I, 2). Cf. Hildesheimer, *Beiträge z. Geographie Palästinas*, 11; S. Klein, *Galiläa von der Makkabäerzeit bis 67*, p. 51ff.

7 Cf. J. B. Pritchard, *Ancient Near Eastern Texts Relating to the Old Testament*, 1950, pp. 242, 256, 287, 484ff.

8 *Catalogue of Greek Coins in the British Museum, Ptolemies*, p. 33f.

9 *PSI* 406, 495, 616; *PCZ* 59004, 59008.

10 Harpocration, *s.v.* Ἄκη.

11 The territory of Acco-Ptolemais in the Roman period extended from the "Ladder of Tyre" on the north to the mountains of Carmel on the south, and from the sea to the hills eastward (*War* II, 188). We do not know whether the whole of this extensive area belonged to Acco as early as the Hellenistic period. Acco governed all the rural area surrounding it, like every other Greek city, but the extent of its territory may have changed from period to period. On the city-land of Acco in the Roman period, see Avi-Yonah, *Historical Geography of Eretz Yisrael* (Heb.), 1950, 134ff.

12 Some scholars (Babelon, *Rois de Syrie*, CIII; Rouvier, *RB*, 1899, 395) have seen in these "Antiochians" a colony of Syrian Antioch at Ptolemais. Schürer (II, 145, n. 205) rightly objects to this supposition and suggests his own explanation: "The term *Antiocheis* must be linked directly with the name of the king. The 'Antiochians' are those pledged to be loyal to the king." According to Bickermann (*Der Gott der Makkabäer*, 62), the Antiochians composed a corporation which enjoyed certain privileges received from King Antiochus IV Epiphanes, and was located in the city of Ptolemais; similar corporations Bickermann finds in the "Seleuceians of Gaza" and in similarly termed bodies. All these explanations do little more than complicate the question. The solution is fairly simple, and has, indeed, been put for-

ward by many scholars: the "Antiochians" are simply citizens of the
city called Antiocheia. It is common knowledge among Greek
numismatists that the Greeks inscribed on their coins not the city-
name, but the name of its citizens: "Antiochians," not "Antiocheia."
If proof is required, we know
several towns whose coins carry the inscription "Antiocheis" or
"Seleuceis," and we know from other sources that their names were in
fact Antiocheia or Seleuceia (see on Edessa [= Antiocheia on
Callirhoe] Polyb. V, 21; Malalas XVII, 418; on Nisibis [= Antiocheia
in Mygdonia], Strabo, XVI, 747; Plut. *Lucull.*, 32; Polyb., V, 51). A
further proof is that the citizens of Gerasa, Susita and Abila call themselves "Antiocheians" and "Seleuceians" on their coins and inscriptions *in the second century C.E.*; to which Antiochus or Seleucus
could these people have been "loyal" at that period, and what value
could a "corporation" of anonymous people who had once received
certain privileges from some Seleucid king or other have had in the
Roman period? And are we to believe that the kings gave the right
of striking coins to these corporations? Bickermann himself does not
believe so, for in his book *Les Institutions des Séleucides*, which was
published a year after the book *Der Gott der Makkabäer*, he includes
the "Antiocheians of Ptolemais" and "the Seleuceians of Gaza" in the
list of cities (pp. 231, 234). He rightly states that the right of striking
coins was the sole monopoly of the king, who sometimes conceded it
to *cities and dynasts* (*ib.* 228); it is clear that the corporations, which
belonged to neither class, could not strike their own money. Only one
difficulty is created by the association of the words "Antiocheians in
Ptolemais"; for Ptolemais was also a Greek town—and would it have
been possible for one Greek town to be within another? Surely the
formula ought to have been "Antiocheians in Acco."
However, this difficulty can
also be solved. As every new Greek name needed an additional
qualification (for there were numerous Antiochs, Seleuceias, Alexandrias, etc.), it was usual to select such from among the local names.
The local name was usually Semitic, although there were also Greek
names that took rapid root among the inhabitants. The city of Nisibis,
for example, called itself "Antioch in Mygdonia," and Mygdonia is not
an oriental but a Macedonian name. A century had elapsed since the
city of Ptolemais had been founded on the site of Acco and during
that time the inhabitants had grown used to calling the whole surrounding countryside "Ptolemais," and it was *de rigueur* to use the
name at least for all official business. Hence when Ptolemais changed
its name to Antioch, the name of Ptolemais was used to denote that
the new town belonged to a certain locality.

13 See Stephanus, *s.v.* Δῶρος. Josephus also calls Dor "a Phoenician
city" (*Vita* 8). The town is also mentioned in the voyage of Wen-
Amun (Pritchard, *op. cit.*, 26), and in the Bible, Josh. 17.11; I Ki.
4.11. Cf. Abel, *Géog. Pal.*, 308.

14   Hecataeus of Miletus, who lived about the year 500 B.C.E., mentions it in his geography books. See Stephanus, *ibid.*

15   This assumption is based on the notice naming among the towns of Caria a city called Doros which paid tribute to Athens in the fifth century (Craterus *ap.* Steph., *ibid.*). As there is no town in Caria of this name, Köhler (see his book, *Urkunden und Untersuchungen z. Gesch. d. delisch-attischen Bundes*, 1869, p. 121; 207) and later the present-day scholars who have studied the Athenian tribute-lists of the fifth century (see Meritt, Wade-Gery, McGregor, *The Athenian Tribute Lists*, I, 1939, p. 154; 483) have thought that Dor in Palestine was meant, and have associated Athenian authority at Dor with her war with Egypt in 460 (*ib.*, III, 9ff.). But they ignored the fact that there is another Dor, whose geographical position is more appropriate to the solution of the problem: this is Doron in Cilicia, mentioned by Pliny (*NH* V, 27, 92). Craterus mentions Doros together with Phaselis, which too is not in Caria but in the eastern part of Lycia, near Cilicia. Athens' influence on the towns of Cilicia is beyond doubt; on the other hand, we have not the smallest hint of Athenian authority in Syria in the fifth century.

16   See above, n. 5.

17   The place el Burj, north of the Arab village of Tantura, marks the site of the ancient Dor. The excavations carried out near here in 1950 revealed pottery of the Hellenistic and Roman periods and remains of a Roman theater. See the *Bull. of the Dept. of Antqs.* (Heb.), III, 38.

18   See Galling's article in *ZDPV*, 61, 1938, 83.

19   The literature on Caesarea is very rich. See now Reifenberg's article in the *Israel Expln. Journ.*, I, 1950-1, 20ff.

20   In 61 C.E., during the conflict between Jews and Syrians at Caesarea, the latter claimed that in ancient times, when the town was still called Straton's Tower, not a single Jew lived there (*Ant.* XX, 173).

21   *Corp. Iur. Civ.*, III, Justiniani Novellae, 103, *praefatio.*

22   Stark, *Gaza und die philistäische Küste*, 1852, 450.

23   The Semitic name of these kings of Sidon was 'Abd-Ashtoret (cf. Jones, *op. cit.*, 231, 249), and could easily change, when pronounced by Greeks, into Straton, or when pronounced by Jews, into Sharshon.

24   Plin. V, 13, 69; Ptol. V, 16, 2; Steph., *s.v. Apollonia*, no. 13: "near Jaffa."

25   Schürer II, 133; n. 159; Jones, 231.

26   This is the opinion of Hölscher (*Palästina in persisch. u. hellenist. Zeit*, 60); he cites proof from Appian (*Syr.* 47) who mentions Apollonia among the towns of Seleucus; but there were many Apollonias in the Orient, and there are no grounds for thinking that Appian meant just this one. We have already seen above (p. 54) that Seleucus did not rule Palestine at all.

27 Smith, *Historical Geog. of the Holy Land*, 129.

28 *Bull. of the Dept. of Antqs.* (Heb.), III, 41ff.

29 Pritchard 22-3, 287; cf. S. Tolkovsky, *Hist. of Jaffa* (Heb.), 1926, 11. In the Persian period Jaffa and Dor were given as a gift to the Sidonians; see above, p. 417, n. 3.

30 *PCZ* 59011; 59093.

31 Head, *op. cit.*, p. 803.

32 Philo, *Leg. ad Gaium*, 200.

33 Pritchard, 284ff. (cf. Index).

34 Pritchard, Index.

35 Müller, *Geog. graeci minor.*, I, 79.

36 Iliffe, *QDAP*, VI, 1936, p. 61ff.

37 See Albright's article, *BASOR* 6, May 1922, p. 11ff.

38 Head, *op. cit.*, p. 804.

39 Stephanus lists four famous men among the natives of Ascalon, *s.v. Ascalon;* cf. Schürer, II, 53.

40 Herodotus (I, 105) calls the goddess of Ascalon "Aphrodite Queen of Heaven." The goddess' Greek and oriental name is referred to in a Greek inscription from Ascalon: Ἀστάρτη Παλαιστίνη Ἀφροδίτη Οὐρανία (see ZDPV, 1913, 233).

41 "R. Judah said: Ascalon and the country south of Ascalon count as the south" (M. Gitt., I, 2). Another view is found in Tos. Oholot XVIII, 4. Cf. S. Klein, *Das tannäitische Grenzverzeichnis Palästinas*, 30ff.

42 Thus, for example, in *Ant.* XIII, 395, and especially in the Greek geographer Scymnos of Chios, 500.

43 Thus Jones, 448, n. 16.

44 Mentioned in the Tel el-Amarna letters and in Egyptian and Assyrian inscriptions; cf. Pritchard, Index; Abel. *Géog. Pal.*, 327.

45 According to the view prevailing among numismatists, Gaza struck coins on the Attic standard with the Semitic inscription עז on them. See, for example, Head, *op. cit.*, p. 805. But cf. against this view the opinion of Narkiss, *Coins of Eretz Israel* (Heb.), II, 30ff.

46 Jacoby, *Frag. Griech. Hist.*, B, no. 142, p. 807. Cf. for this pasage Gutmann's article *Tarbitz* (Heb.), XI, 281.

47 Polyb. XVI, 40, 6; 18, 2. Cf. above, p. 75.

48 *Urspr. des Christent.* II, 122.

49 *PCZ* 59001, 59006, 59009, 59093; *PSJ* 322; *P. Col. Zen.* 3; Cf. Abel in *RB*, 49, 1940, 64ff.

50 See Schürer II, 28.

51 G. F. Hill, *Catalogue of the Greek Coins of Palestine*, LXIX, p. 143. Bickermann sees in the *demos* of "the Seleuceians of Gaza" a "corporation" on the model of the "Antiocheians in Ptolemais" (see above, p. 443, n. 12). It is correct that *demos* may sometimes also denote a village body, but the principal meaning of the word is of course the people organized in an urban society. In this sense the word *demos* is used by the cities of Seleucid Syria, *viz.* Seleuceia, Antioch, Laodiceia and Apameia when in the second century B.C.E. they strike coins inscribed ἀδελφοὶ δῆμοι (Head, *op. cit.*, p. 778; cf. Bickermann, *Inst. des Sél.*, 234). It should once again be remarked that no "corporation" had permission to mint.

52 On the topographical question, see Avi-Yonah, *Geogr.*, 107ff.

53 Pritchard, 254, 284, 285, 292.

54 Head, p. 806.

55 Plin. *NH.*, V, 18, 74; *Decapolitana regio a numero oppidorum, in quo non omnes eadem observant.*

56 Ptolemy (V, 15, 22-3) lists eighteen cities among those of Coele-Syria-Decapolis, including those in the Vale of Lebanon; but there are grounds for thinking that the word "Decapolis" has here been inserted in error and is to be erased, so that "Coele-Syria" alone should be read. See Schürer, II, 149. Cf. on the question of the cities of the Decapolis, Jones, 260ff.; Avi-Yonah, *Geogr.*, 42ff.

57 Its name is referred to in the Bible, Num. 32.42; I Chron. 2.23.

58 Tos. Shev. IV, 10: Jer. Shev., VI, 36c.

59 See on the topographical question, Schürer, II, 164ff.

60 J. Klausner, "Raphana, one of the ten cities," in *Journal of the Jewish Palestine Exploration Society* (Heb.), II, 134ff.

61 On the topographical question, cf. Gutmann in *The Epstein Jubilee Volume* (Heb.), 70; Avi-Yonah, *Geogr.*, 142; Albright, *BASOR*, 1925, 16; Abel, *Géog. Pal.*, 432.

62 Head, p. 786: Ἀντιοχέων τῶν πρὸς ῞Ιππῳ, cf. Avi-Yonah, *Georg.*, 146.

63 Tos. Ahil., XVIII, 4: "Smaller towns that are enclaves in the Land of Israel, such as Susita and her companions, Ascalon and her companions, although they are exempt from tithe and the seventh year fallow, contain no Gentile territory."

64 Schürer, II, 161.

HELLENISTIC CIVILIZATION AND THE JEWS

65 The ruins are described by Schumacher, *Northern Ajlun*, 1890, 46ff. The ancient name "Geder" (in its Arabic pronunciation *Jedar*) has survived in the eastern part of the town down to the present day. The warm springs near Geder (Ḥamei Geder, Ḥamat Geder, Ḥamatah) are frequently referred to in talmudic literature; see Sukenik, *JPOS* 15, 1935, 109ff.

66 Not to be confused with Abel-Bet-Ma'acha, Abel ha-K'ramim and Abel ha-Shittim, all mentioned in the Bible. The name was very frequent in Palestine. Cf. Abel, *Géog.*, 233ff.

67 Head, p. 786. The ruins of the town at Tel Abil are described in detail by Schumacher in his work, *Abila of the Decapolis*, 1889.

68 Pritchard, 243, 253.

69 Schürer, II, 175, n. 334.

70 In the author's book *Hellenistische Städtegründ.*, 61, 75.

71 It has been remarked above (p. 25) that the Greek cities of the east, whose names resemble those of the Macedonian towns, were founded in the early period of the spread of Hellenism in the Orient.

72 Stephanus, *s.v.* βερενίκαι: "There is another Berenike in Syria, called Pella." This statement cannot be ascribed to Pella-Apameia in Syria, as the town was never under Ptolemaic rule.

73 Schumacher, *Pella*, 1895, 66. The name of the place today is Ḥirbat Tabkat Fahil (Avi-Yonah, *Geogr.*, 148; Abel, *Géog. Pal.*, 405.

74 Avi-Yonah, *Geogr.*, 145; Abel, *Géog.*, 306.

75 The excavations at Jerash were carried out by Yale University, together with the British School of Archaeology at Jerusalem, in the years 1928-1930; they were continued in 1930-34 by Yale University jointly with the American Schools of Oriental Research. The results were summarized by Kraeling in his book *Gerasa, City of the Decapolis*, 1938. On pp. 353-494 a full collection is given of all the inscriptions from Jerash, edited by Welles. On the former literature on Jerash see Schumacher, "Dscherasch," *ZDPV*, 1902, 109-177; Адаялекъ Лазоревъ Джерошь, 1897.

76 Iamblichus, commentary on the *Arithmetics* of Nicomachus; cf. *Etymologicum Magnum, s.v.* Γερασενός: "Alexander captured the city, killed all the warriors and spared the old men; these joined together to found the city."

77 An inscription mentioning Perdiccas—no. 137 in Kraeling's collection (p. 423). Ἀυρ(ήλιος) Σερῆνος Ἀουίτου τὸν Περδίκκαν τῇ κυρίᾳ πατ[ρίδι] [ἐ]φιλοτι [μήσατο]. Welles is correct in his observation that the mention of the name Perdiccas with the definite article shows that he was founder of the city. According to Kraeling (p. 29) this inscription does not prove more than that he was thought to be so in the third century B.C.E., nor is it to be concluded that he really founded the city, as Jones thinks (*op. cit.*, 239). However, Perdiccas' name was not as famous as that of Alexander, and it would not have occurred to the citizens of Jerash in the Roman period to associate the town's foundation with his name, unless a memory had survived there of his historical function as its founder. Jones' remark therefore seems to the writer acceptable. The Macedonians are referred to in inscription no. 78 (second half of the second century C.E.).

78   Head, 787; Kraeling, inscriptions nos. 56-8; 69, 143-45, 147, 153, 192 (from the time of Trajan to the year 211). Cf. *ZDPV*, 18, 147; 36, 1913, 260; *MNDPV*, 1901, 57, 68, 75; *RB*, 1927, 250.

79   Hill, *Catal. of the Greek Coins of Brit. Mus., Arabia,* XXXIX.

80   Schürer, II, 40ff.

81   *PSI* 406, 616.

82   The cave of Panion from which the Jordan issued, is described by Josephus, *Ant.* XV, 364; *War* I, 404. Cf. Tos. Bekhor. VII, 4: "The stream that issues from the cave of Pamias."

83   *Pirkei d'Rabbi Eliezer,* XXVII: ". . . Dan is Pamias." Cf. Meg. 6a.

84   "Kisareion" in talmudic language, to distinguish it from Kis'rin (Caesarea) on Sea. (See Krauss, *Lehnwörter* II, 536.) In Greek the city was called Caesarea of Philip or Caesarea-Panias. On the territory of Caesarea in the Roman period, see Avi-Yonah, *Geogr.,* 138.

85   See above, p. 32. Only in Egypt were villages also known by dynastic names, chiefly in the Fayûm in the Hellenistic period.

86   Hölscher, *Palästina,* 64.

87   Kahrstedt, *Syr. Terr.,* 23ff.

88   *ZDPV,* IX, 347.

89   A. Schlatter, *Zur Topographie u. Geschichte Palästinas,* 1893, 314ff.; cf. Avi-Yonah, *Geogr.,* 140.

90   See the author's *Hell. Städtegr.,* 13, 72.

91   See in favor of the identification of Philoteria with Bet Yeraḥ, Sukenik, *JPOS,* 2, 1922, 101ff.; Abel, *Géog. Pal.,* 284; against the identification, Avi-Yonah, *Geogr.,* 127, n. 12. As to the question whether Khirbet el-Kerak is to be identified with Bet Yeraḥ, or with Senabris, cf. the article of Bar-Adon in "Archeological etc. Studies," *Eretz Israel,* IV, 1956, 50ff. The excavations have uncovered remains of various periods, including those of the Hellenistic epoch; see *Bull. Jew. Pal. Expl. Soc.* (Heb.), XI, 1944-5, 77ff.; *ib.,* XIII, 1946-7, 53ff.; *Bull. Dept. Antqs.* (Heb.), III, 1951, 32ff.; Bar-Adon, *op. cit.,* 52.

92   See Baramki, "Coin Hoards from Palestine," *QDAP,* 11 (1944), 86.

93   Bet Shean was a Pharaonic fortress in Palestine as early as the middle of the second millennium, as the American excavations on the

HELLENISTIC CIVILIZATION AND THE JEWS

site have revealed. See *The Museum Journal*, 1923, 5ff. The city is mentioned in Egyptian inscriptions and in the Tel el-Amarna Letters: Pritchard, 242, 486, 489.

94 Cf. Head, p. 803; Plin. *NH*. V, 18, 74; Steph. *s.v. Skythopolis.* The Temple of Dionysus, *The Museum Journ.*, 1923, 239. Jones (p. 252) and following him, Avi-Yonah (p. 27) think the city was called Nysa in honor of the niece of King Antiochus IV; but Scythopolis was not the only town so called, and everywhere the name is associated with the cult of Dionysus and the chthonic deities. (Cf. the author's *Hell. Städtegr.*, 27, 107.) There are no grounds for believing that Scythopolis was an exception.

95 Ptolemy III was descended from Heracles on his father's side and from Dionysus on his mother's (*OGIS*, 54). Ptolemy IV Philopator particularly distinguished himself by his devotion to the Dionysiac cult, and even branded the god's symbol on his body. From papyrus *BGU* 1211 = *SP* 208, we hear that Philopator sought to plant the mysteries of Dionysus in Egypt under government auspices. See on these questions J. Tondriau, "Tatouage, Lierre et Syncrétismes," *Aegyptus*, 30, 1950, 57ff.; *id.*, in *Chron. d'Egypte*, 50, 1950, 293.

96 Plin. *N.H.* V, 18, 74, also sought to connect the significance of the name with the Scythians; not, however, with the seventh-century invaders of Palestine, but with those that accompanied the god Dionysus on his travels: *Scythopolin, antea Nysam, a Libero patre . . . Scythis deductis.* He thus transfers the town's foundation and the origin of its name to the mythological age. An attempt has recently been made to explain the name by the supposition that at the beginning of the Hellenistic period the town harbored Scythian horsemen, since such served among Alexander's army (Abel, *Hist. Pal.*, 57). But we know nothing whatever of a Scythian garrison at Bet Shean in this period, nor is it easy to conceive that a Hellenistic town would call itself after a temporary garrison, least of all when the word "Scythian" was synonymous with cruelty and barbarism.

97 See Schürer, II, 171; cf. Jones, 449, n. 20. Authority for the identity of Scythopolis and Succot can be found in Jerome: *est autem usque hodie civitas trans Jordanem hoc vocabulo inter partes Scythopoleos.* On the site of Succot see Nelson Glueck's article, *BASOR*, 90, April 1943, 14ff.

98 See Smith, *Hist. Geog. of the Holy Land*, 364. In the author's *Hell. Städtegr.*, 72, the opinion was expressed that there might be some truth in this conjecture, but he now sees that it has no solid basis and may be given up.

99 Euseb. *Chron.*, trans. Jerome, 123. Cf. also Syncellus, I, p. 496 (ed. Dindorf).

100 Jerome, *ib.*, p. 127.

101 See p. 424, n. 42. Eusebius transmits the information in the following words: "Demetrius king of Asia . . . destroyed the city of the Samaritans which had formerly been built by Perdiccas" (*Chron.*, trans. Jerome, p. 127). He forgot that "the city . . . built . . . by Perdiccas" had already been destroyed in 312 by Ptolemy. The town destroyed by Demetrius was built after 312, not, of course, by Perdiccas, who had been killed in 321. Josippon too has preserved a reminiscence of the destruction of Samaria by Demetrius: "And Iptolis Olgis died and Demetrius Philiocritus, which means 'warrior,' reigned in his place, and he captured Samaria" (p. 112, ed. Baron Ginzberg, 1896-1913).

102 *QDAP*, 5, 1936, p. 203; *Excav. in Palestine*, 1934-5; Crowfoot, Kenyon, Sukenik, *The Buildings of Samaria*, 1942, 24ff.

103 *War* I, 156; cf. *Ant.* XIV, 75-6.

104 Stark (*Gaza u. die philist. Küste*, 434) thought that Arethusa was the ancient Gaza; Hölscher (*Pal.*, 61) wished to see it as Ekron, and Avi-Yonah (*Bull. Pal. Jew. Expl. Soc.* [Heb.], 1943/4, 18ff.) regards it as the Hellenistic Pegai—the Herodian Antipatris.

105 Schlatter (*Gesch. Israels*, 3, 2, 13) and following him Klein (*BPJES*, III, 109ff.) have placed Arethusa at Artas, on the road from Jerusalem to Hebron, and Press (*Eretz Yisrael, Enc. Topog.-Hist.*, I, 53) puts it at Artuf (Hartuv) in the hills of Judaea. Clearly these identifications, which remove Arethusa from the Shephelah, cannot be regarded as successful.

106 Besides Arethusa in Palestine, we know of two further towns in the Orient with this name: one in Syria on the River Orontes (Strab. XVI, 753; Steph. *s.v.* Ἀρέθουσα), the other in Arabia (Plin. *N.H.* I, 23, 159), cf. Appian, *Hist. Syr.*, 57.

107 See above, p. 442, n. 5. In the mss. of the *Antiquities*, we find the version "Dor" instead of "Adora," but the town is mentioned together with Marissa and scholars have therefore been correct in emending "Dor" to "Adora." In the *War*, the word is correctly written. See Schürer II, 7, n. 10.

108 *C. Ap.* II, 112; here too "Adora" should be read in place of "Dor"; see Schürer II, 5ff.

109 On the Sidonian colony at Marissa see below, p. 453, n. 128. Remains of a wall from the Hellenistic Age were revealed in excavations; cf. Avi-Yonah and Yeivin, *Kadmoniot Artzenu* (Heb.), 1956, 317.

110 *Nachr. d. Ges. d. Wiss. Göttingen*, 1906, 374f.

111 Jer., Meg., I, 70a; Jer. B. B., III, 14a; cf. Krauss, *Talmud. Arch.*, I, i, 28 (Heb.); S. Klein, *Jewish Transjordan* (Heb.), 10.

112 Jer. Ned., III, 58a; Jer. Shev., III, 34d; cf. Krauss, *Talmud. Arch.*, I, i, 47 (Heb.).

113 See Schürer, II, 181; the same formula is found on the inscriptions at Ascalon of the Roman period, *Pal. Expl. F. Q. St.*, 1922, 22; cf. also Beresh. Rabba., VI, 4:בולי ודימוס

114 Head, p. 786ff.

115 See Avi-Yonah, "The Foundation of Tiberias," *Isr. Expl. Journ.*, I, 160ff.

116 Cf. Jones, 246ff. Especially interesting is an inscription of the Syrian town of Seleuceia (for the year 186 B.C.E.) which contains the conventional formula δεδόχθαι τῶι δήμωι and mentions the "archontes" of the city and its division into *phylai* and *demoi*. Cf. Seyrig, "Décret de Séleucie et ordonnance de Séleucus IV," *Syria*, 13, 1932, 255ff.

117 The division of the whole country into city territories in the Roman and Byzantine period is given by Avi-Yonah, *Geogr.*, 87ff.

118 The remains of Bet-Zur, as revealed by excavation, belong, indeed, to the Hellenistic period, but Bet-Zur was not a Greek city. See Sellers, *The Citadel of Beth Zur*, 1933.

119 This was the Ptolemaic practice also in regard to cities founded on the coast of the Red Sea: Philoteira was founded by Satyros (Strab. XVI, 769), Ptolemais Theron by Eumedes (*ib.* XVI, 770).

120 Polybius calls Philadelpheia by the old name of Rabbat-Amman, and so also the Zenon papyri. Gadara is also referred to in literature (by Josephus and Polybius) as Gadara, although it had Greek names, Antioch and Seleuceia. The citizens of Abila refer to themselves by two names on their coins, *Seleuceis Abilenoi* (Head, p. 786), nor do the citizens of Antioch-Gerasa forget their oriental name, but call themselves "citizens of Antioch of Chrysoroas, who were citizens of Gerasa."

121 The modern name "Teda" may perpetuate some oriental name from which Anthedon was also derived; see above, p. 95. Besides Greek city-names, some isolated Greek village-names have also survived, such as the name of Fedsha; cf. above, p. 449, n. 86. Many more Graeco-Roman names have survived from the Roman period—Caesarea, Tiberias, Nablus (Neapolis), and others.

122 Cf. Schürer, II, p. 161.

123 I designate as "Syrians" all the populations of Palestine apart from Judaea, although of course from a scientific point of view the various peoples—Syrians, Phoenicians, Samaritans, Edomites and Philistines, including some in no sense Semites, must be distinguished.

124 In *War* II, 458ff., Josephus relates the Jewish attack on the Greek cities, and immediately afterwards (461) says: "But the *Syrians* also slew not a few Jews." It is worth noting that Alexander Jannaeus did not use Syrian mercenaries "because of their hatred for the Jews" (*War* I, 88).

125 To these Greek men of culture we owe the interesting fact that Palestine's various cities and localities found their way into the cycle of Greek myths. Concerning Jaffa, Gaza, Ascalon and many other towns, legends were told which were linked with the lives of the Greek heroes of old. Frequently a chance resemblance of the sound of a name supplied the decisive pretext for the "Hellenization" of the city. Cf. Abel, *Hist. Pal.*, 270ff.

126 For a list of these names, see Schürer, II, 53.

127 Rostovtzeff (*CAH* VII, 195) emphasizes the low standard of the men of repute among the natives of Seleucid Syria, and, apart from Poseidonius, cannot discover among them a single person of cultural stature.

128 On the Marissa tombs, see Peters and Thiersch, *The Painted Tombs of the Necropolis of Marissa*, 1905; Watzinger, *Denkmäler Palästinas*, 2, 1935, 17ff.; Albright, *BASOR*, 85, Feb. 1942, 18ff. The colony was founded about the year 257 or a few years later; cf. the article of Vincent in *RB*, 1920, 177ff. The founder, Apollonius, was an official of Ptolemy II Philadelphus. The paintings in tomb 1 present an appearance of syncretistic Greek-oriental culture. The bearers of the Greek names (including the founder of the colony himself) were Sidonians or Edomites. Apart from isolated Macedonians, there was nobody of Greek racial origin among the colonists; hence it is not surprising that the oriental elements here swiftly gained the upper hand over the not very pronounced Greek cultural elements (see Peters and Thiersch, *op. cit.*, 13). The large number of Edomite names confronts the scholar with the question, whether the "Sidonians" at Marissa were really from the neighborhood of Tyre and Sidon, or whether they were "Canaanites" in the broad sense of the term; as is well known, the term "Sidonians" could be used also in the latter sense, as may be concluded from the example of the Samaritans who called themselves "Sidonians of Shechem" (*Ant.* XII, 258ff.). Probably only a small part of the colonists were born in Sidon or in its district, and the remainder were recruited from the local people: here too, therefore, as at Philadelpheia, the Hellenized Sidonians were the bearers of Greek culture in the new "Greek'" towns. On the fusion of various ethnic elements at Marissa, see Abel, *Hist. Pal.*, 55.

NOTES part I chapter 3

1 Diodorus, XL, 3, 8; γένος πολυάνθρωπον; *C. Ap.* I, 194; πολυαν-θρωπότατον . . . τὸ ἔθνος; for the figures of the population and the extent of the city; cf. *C. Ap.* I, 197.

2 Agatharchides ap. Jos. *Ant.* XII, 6. According to Timochares (ap. Eus. *Praep. Evang.* IX, 35) the size of the city was 40 *stades*, and the same figure is given by Aristeas, 105. On other figures cf. the article of M. Stein in *Zion*, 6, 1934, p. 10, n. 2 (Hebrew). None of these figures is certain.

3 It is obvious, therefore, that the number of 20-25,000 inhabitants, as suggested by Jeremias, *ZDPV*, 66 (1943), 24ff. is too small, since it does not fit the impression gained by Hecataeus.

4 According to Stein, in his above-mentioned article, p. 8ff., the small number of 1500 people reflects the situation created in Judaea at the end of the second century B.C.E., after the Hasmoneans had "purged" the priestly class of Hellenizers. However, if we assume that the figures in Neh. 7.39ff. are authentic, the number of priests in the second century would have been so large that its decline to 1500 would have meant not a "purge" but the virtual annihilation of the class. For other conjectures see Schürer, II, 287, n. 29.

5 Of thirty-two sentences devoted by Aristeas to an account of the journey to Palestine, seven concern the description of the city, and twenty-one an account of the Temple (including the fortress guarding it). Aristeas reports with genuine enthusiasm the magnificent exterior of the Temple, its walls and towers, the curtain before the entrance to the shrine, the thousands of sacrifices at festivals, and especially the internal discipline and the quiet activity of the priests, when 700 worked without sound or bustle (84-95). See the commentary on the passages by R. Tramontano, *La Lettera di Aristea e Filocrate*, 1931; cf. also Vincent's article in *RB*, 17, 1908, 520ff.; 18, 1909, 555ff. On the Aristeas letter generally cf. below, in part II, ch. IV.

6 Cf. for example, Josephus' story, *Ant.* XX, 180; 206: The High Priests sent their slaves to the threshing-floors to confiscate for their own benefit the tithes to which the rank-and-file priests were entitled.

7 On the highly connected priestly families much information has been preserved from the period of the Herods and the Roman procurators. Of twenty-eight High Priests who replaced one another in the post from the year 37 B.C.E. to 66 C.E., twenty-two belonged to four families only: eight to the family of Boethos (including that of Kanthiras), eight to that of Ḥanan, three to that of Fiabi and three to that of Kimḥit (Schürer, II, 275). Cf. the well known *baraita* in Pesaḥim, 57a = Tos. Menaḥ. 13, 21. On the Kohanic families generally see Schürer, II, 286ff.

8 "The family of Onias" is merely a modern name applied by scholars to the priestly dynasty from Onias I onwards, or to the family of Onias III only. The official name of the dynasty was "the sons of Zaddok," although these (the descendants of Zaddok, the High Priest under Solomon) in fact included all the priests of Jerusalem as well as the dynasty of the High Priests. Cf. Schürer, II, 479ff.

9 These heads of kinship groups in Nehemiah are also called the heads of the people (10.15), the captains of the people (11.1), and the heads of the State (11.3); they signed the pact after the Priests and the Levites (10.15ff.). From passages such as 13.11ff., 13.17ff., it is to be supposed that the *horim* and the *s'ganim* were high officials in charge of the general administration of the country, since it is from them that Nehemiah demands a report and with them he "contends" when it is known that they have not faithfully carried out their obligations. The further fact that many of the *s'ganim* ate at the satrap's table (5.17) shows the high official rank of the members of this class.

10 In excavations about Jerusalem several cemeteries of wealthy families have been discovered, which preferred to bury their dead in separate rock-cut tomb-chambers. In these have been found niches with ossuaries for the preservation of the bones of the dead. Such was the private burial-place of the priestly family of the B'ne Ḥazir (see *CIJ,* 1394). Another tomb-chamber was discovered on the slopes of Mount Scopus; according to Sukenik's conjecture this was the burial-place of the priestly family of the house of Boethos (Sukenik, "A Jewish Tomb on the Slopes of Mount Scopus," *Journal of the Jew. Pal. Explor. Soc.,* 1934, 62ff.). These are priestly tombs; did the high-born families of the secular aristocracy possess similar burial-places? This possibility cannot be dismissed *a priori.* The famous building near Jerusalem known as "The Monument of Absalom" also stands in the burial-place of some unknown family. There may be some connection between this family and the "house of Absalom" mentioned in the *Pesher Habbakuk,* 5.9. The monument is apparently called after Absalom, son of David, but this is a very late legend composed to explain the name Absalom which is associated with the building, evidently from the time it was built, that is, from the Hellenistic period. The name Absalom is mentioned on several occasions in that epoch (I Macc. 11.70; 13.11; II Macc. 11.17), but the passages in question give no means of determining the origin of the family.

11 Diod. XL, 3, 7.

12 Tiberius Gracchus in his struggle against the Roman *latifundia* likewise prohibited the small peasants from selling their holdings which they had received under his *Lex Agraria* (App. *Bell. Civ.* I, 27). The Senate's struggle against the Gracchan laws expressed itself first and foremost by the annulment of the prohibition to sell lands, and as a result the growth of *latifundia* recommenced (App. *loc. cit.*).

13 From the period of Judah the Maccabee onwards the large estates are frequently encountered.

14 See Klausner, *Hist.*, IV, 59ff. On the small holder as the central figure of Jewish society in the period of the Second Temple, see especially Schwalm, *Le type social du paysan juif à l'époque de Jésus Christ*, 1908.

15 *Neh.* 3.8, 11, 12, 31-33; the tower of furnaces, 12.38. Ben Sira lists among the craftsmen of Jerusalem the builders, smiths, and potters (XXXVIII). Cf. Mendelssohn's article in *BASOR*, 80, 1940, 17.

16 According to Klausner (*Hist.*, II, 27ff.) the Jews were engaged in commerce, and even in overseas trade, as early as the Persian period. His account is based on isolated statements in the books of Proverbs and Psalms, and in the writer's opinion is not convincing. Possibly adventurous individuals among the young men of Jerusalem from time to time took service in Phoenician ships, and thus accounts of the sea found their way into Hebrew literature; but this is no evidence that these people were genuine professional merchants.

17 On the beginning of this class in the time of Ezra, see H. H. Schaeder, *Esra der Schreiber* (1930), 39ff.

18 Levit. 13.2ff.; Deut. 17.9ff.; 33.10; Jerem. 18.18; Ezek. 44.23ff.; Malachi 2.7; II Chron. 19.8.

19 Many scholars have expressed the correct opinion that the scribes were the representatives of the urban middle class and were supported by it; cf. for example, L. Finkelstein, *The Pharisees*, 1946, I, 7ff., 101ff., and many other passages in the same work; G. F. Moore, *Judaism*, 1944, I, 67; S. Baron, *A Social and Religious History of the Jews*, 2nd ed., I, 237; II, 343. The social basis of the scribal class, and of the Ḥasidic and Pharisaic sects, has been discussed chiefly by Finkelstein both in his above-mentioned work and also in his article in *HTR*, 22, 1929, 185ff. In his view the scribes (= the Pharisees) represented the urban population, whereas the priests (= the Zaddokites) depended on the rural elements; he interprets several ancient rulings in the light of this view. Finkelstein's attempt to explain these rulings entirely from a social angle must be treated with some reserve, but the main idea (the social antagonism between the priests and the scribes, corresponding to the antagonism between town and country) deserves special note.

20 The antagonism between Temple and Synagogue is stressed chiefly by L. Baeck in his book *Die Pharisäer*, 1927, 43ff. On the beginning of the synagogues, cf. S. Krauss, *Synagogale Altertümer*, 1922, 52ff.

21 The ideology of the scribal sect cannot be precisely defined, as it is not anywhere described in detail; but it would not be erroneous to say that the term "Ḥasidism" (the quality of being pious or devout) does not imply the aspiration to moral perfection, involving physical asceticism, directed to the correction of the soul (after the manner of similar terms in Christianity), although possibly such tendencies were not absent in Ḥasidism. The center of gravity was here, not in the realization of an abstract religious moral ideal, but in the performance of the commandments of the Law in everyday life, as was demanded of the Ḥasidim in their capacity as the authorized interpreters of the Pentateuch. The adherence to the Mosaic Law, the desire to fulfill every single jot of it and even to overdo the severity of the commandment—such were the foundations of Ḥasidism as understood by the members of the sect. If "the first Ḥasidim" mentioned in talmudic literature (M. Ber., V, 1; Tos. B. Kam., II, 6) were the Ḥasidim of this period, their aspirations were in harmony with the above definition. It was natural that the strict fulfillment of the commandments, principally the commandments relating to ritual purity, was bound to produce a certain segregation of the Ḥasidim from the masses of the people, as occurred later with the Pharisees; hence the foundation of the sect. If the Essenic sect and the Yaḥad sect (the latter known to us from the Dead Sea Scrolls) constituted late stages of the development of the same Ḥasidic group, there are grounds for assuming that some of the customs known to us from these late sects already existed among the Ḥasidim. The latter are frequently referred to in the Psalms (see, for example, 4.4; 12.2; 16.10; 17.7, and a number of other passages), but this is not the place to go into the complicated question of the date of the composition of the Psalms, which demands a special inquiry.

22 This is the opinion of Foerster; see his article "Der Ursprung des Pharisäismus," ZNTW, 34, 1935, 41. On Finkelstein's view, see the following note.

23 In the Tractate Abot, Simon the Just is designated as one "of the last of the Great Assembly"; hence his retention in historic memory as a scholar skilled in the Law. He and his pupil Antigonus of Socho were links between the Great Assembly and the "pairs" (Zugot) of scholars. It is therefore clear that the talmudic scholars saw in Simon the Just one of the pillars of the Law of the past. Finkelstein (in his book The Pharisees and the Men of the Great Assembly, 1941, 40ff.) regards Simon (correctly, the present writer thinks) as the head of the Ḥasidim of his time, although he believes that the formation of the sect belongs to a more remote period.

24 This new position attained by the Ḥasidim in the public life of Jerusalem considerably influenced the political part they played when the Hellenizers were in power and under the first Hasmoneans; see chapters 5 and 6. As nearly every scholar writing of the Pharisees begins his exposition with an account of the Ḥasidim, the literature on them is in effect part and parcel of the abundant literature devoted to the Pharisees, see ch. 7, note 27.

25 Maisler, "The House of Tobiah," Tarbitz, XII, 116.

26 Ant. XII, 154-222, 224, 228-236.

27 See Wellhausen, *Israelitische und jüdische Gesch.*, 7 ed., p. 231.

28 This is testified by Appian (*Syr.* 5). Ptolemy VI Philometor based his claims to Coele-Syria on this promise while waging war against Antiochus Epiphanes (Polyb. XXVIII, 17, 9). Antiochus, of course, took no notice of Ptolemy's claims and cast doubt on the whole affair (*ib.*).

29 This fact was not taken into account by Cuq (see *Syria*, 8, 1927, 143ff.) one of the few modern scholars to recognize the chronological reliability of the above story of Josephus. The simple chronological calculation is sufficient to controvert this view. The marriage between Ptolemy Epiphanes and Cleopatra took place in the year 193/2, and if we assume that Joseph leased the taxes in the same year, his term ended in 171 (twenty-two years, according to Josephus!), which is impossible. Furthermore, in the excavations of Samaria and Bet Zur, coins of the first four Ptolemies were found in considerable numbers; the Ptolemaic coins stop after 200, a sign that the Egyptian kings had no foothold in Palestine from that year. See Sellers, *The Citadel of Beth Zur*, 81; Bickermann, *Inst. des Sél.*, 211ff.

30 Büchler, *Die Tobiaden und Oniaden*, 62, 70; Oesterley, *Hist. of Israel*, II, 1932, 211.

31 Bickermann, *op. cit.*, 29ff., supposes that there were two men called Joseph the Tobiad, one of whom died under Seleucus IV, and the other, probably his grandfather, who lived under the Ptolemies. This assumption certainly solves the chronological difficulty but seems too arbitrary.

32 Several scholars (such as, Bouché-Leclercq, I, 386, n. 1; Ralph Marcus, in Loeb's *Josephus*, VII, p. 82, n. C) think that the sentence "Euergetes, who was father of Philopator" was an interpolation inserted in Josephus' text by an anonymous reader, who recalled that Syria under Epiphanes no longer belonged to the Ptolemies, and therefore transferred the story to the time of Euergetes. It would however be wrong to ascribe to an interpolator words that have no particular point. Josephus satisfactorily explained the payment of tribute to the Ptolemies instead of to the Seleucids by his story of Cleopatra's dowry (*Ant.* XII, 154-5) and the pointless addition of the name "Euergetes" can change nothing in this narrative. The interpolation, if it exists at all, can apply only to the words "who was father of Philopator"; this addition was perhaps made by a reader who did not understand how Euergetes' name had found its way into a story dealing with Epiphanes, and desired to explain who he was.

33 Cf. Graetz, II, 2, p. 243; Momigliano, "I Tobiadi nella prehistoria del moto maccabaico," *Atti d. reale Accad. di scienze di Torino*, 67, 1931/2, 176; Klausner, *History*, II, 132.

34 There is no need to attribute Hyrcanus' death to the year 175, as most scholars do. Probably some time elapsed before he perceived the character of the new regime and understood that he was not in a position to stand up to Antiochus. We may place his death between 175 and 170.

35 He was then connected with Egypt: his money was deposited there, and Arion, his *oikonomos,* paid the necessary sums into the royal treasury from time to time in pursuance of Joseph's orders.

36 It may be held that the dispute between Ptolemy and Onias also broke out against a financial background. However, the sum of money mentioned here and paid by the High Priests from their private incomes, is very small (20 talents) (see below, n. 39), whereas Joseph's leasing of the tribute included the whole of Ptolemaic Syria. On the first journey Joseph appeared before the king as guarantor of the money paid by the High Priest; he thereby became representative (*prostates*) of the people. The financial abilities which he displayed during the time he held this post afforded the king the assurance that he would succeed also in a broader field of activity.

37 Joseph was born in the village of Phichola (*Ant.* XII, 160), whose location is unknown. According to Maisler's conjecture (*op. cit.,* 109, n. 4) this may be Wadi Fukhin near Bethlehem.

38 Cf. Ben Sira, L, 26: "That foolish nation that dwelleth in Sichem." It were well to observe that, some time before Joseph's appearance, the Samaritans had attacked the Jews and ravaged Judaea (*Ant.* XII, 156).

39 Josephus relates that the sum of money amounted to 20 talents (*Ant.* XII, 158). This sum is too small to satisfy the assumption that this was all the Jews paid to Egypt. According to Josephus (*ib.*) the High Priests paid this tax from their private property; it is possible therefore that these twenty talents did not belong to the regular taxes of the land of Judaea, but were a special tax paid by the High Priests with which they purchased the *prostasia.* As for the general taxes, the sum may have been 300 talents (Bickermann, *Inst. des Sél.,* 108), although the passages cited to support this supposition (II Macc. 4.8; 24; I Macc. 11.28; Sulp. Sev. II, 17, 5) are open to several different interpretations.

40 The geographical designation is not appropriate to the administrative terminology current in the Ptolemaic offices. The official name here ought to be "Syria and Phoenicia" (cf. above, p. 61). Josephus here links the terminology of the Seleucid offices (Coele-Syria and Phoenicia) to the traditional Jewish division of Palestine into Judaea and Samaria.

41 We find authority for this conjecture in a papyrus of the year 201 B.C.E. (*P. Tebt.* 8 = W. *Chrest.* 2), which speaks of the sale of the taxes of the country of Lycia, then under Ptolemaic rule. Cf. on

459

the method of auctioning the taxes in Ptolemaic Egypt generally, Rostovtzeff, *CAH*, VII, 129ff.; *SEHHW*, 328ff.; C. Préaux, *L'économie royale des Lagides*, 450ff.

42 The figures given by Josephus cannot stand up to criticism: the countries of Ptolemaic Syria paid, allegedly, 8,000 talents (*Ant.* XII, 175), and Joseph doubled this huge sum. We know that the fifth Satrapy of Darius—Ever-Nahara—which extended from the frontiers of Cilicia to Egypt, paid only 350 talents (*Herod.* III, 91); the incomes from all the lands ruled by Antigonus amounted to 11,000 talents (Diod. XIX, 56, 5) and those from Ptolemaic Egypt under Philadelphus, to 14,800 talents (Jerome, *Comment. ad Daniel*, XI, 5; cf. Cl. Préaux, *op. cit.*, 424).

43 Josephus reports this confirmation in very naïve language: The king permitted Joseph "to do everything his heart desired" (*Ant.* XII, 182). If we credit Josephus' story in all its minor details, we shall have to believe that the entire control of the economic and administrative affairs of Syria as known from the decrees of Philadelphus (*SB* 8008; cf. p. 428, n. 54) was suspended under Euergetes. This is very hard to believe, although it is apparently a fact that Euergetes introduced into Syria a more concentrated method of tax-collecting, which was also stricter, and that Joseph played the most prominent part in this reform.

44 The following are the words of a traditional writer on the subject of forbidden foods: "And Daniel purposed in his heart that he would not defile himself with the portion of the king's meat, nor with the wine which he drank" (Dan. 1.8f.). Without going into the complicated question, when the first six chapters of the Book of Daniel were written (cf. for example M. A. Beek's *Das Danielbuch*, 1935, 7ff.), I would merely remark that verses 1.8ff. sound like a direct reply to the anti-traditional behavior of Joseph the Tobiad at the Egyptian royal court.

45 Josephus (*Ant.* XII, 186) relates that when Joseph was in Egypt, he fell in love with a dancing girl and wished to possess her. He asked his brother to aid him; but the latter tricked him by sending him his own daughter by night in place of the dancing girl, in order to keep Joseph from sinning. After the event, Joseph's brother told him of the whole affair, and Joseph, who had been apprehensive of the king's anger because of the dancing girl, was overjoyed that all had ended well and took the niece in question in marriage, it being she who bore him Hyrcanus. All this may have been true, but it is also credible that Hyrcanus was really the son of a Gentile woman, and that the afore-mentioned events were related fictitiously in order to conceal his illegitimate origin and to make him a genuine legitimate son of Joseph.

46 The king wrote πᾶσι τοῖς ἡγεμόσιν αὐτοῦ καὶ ἐπιτρόποις. This terminology is not Ptolemaic, but more in harmony with the Roman period:

the title *hegemon* was the term with which the Prefect of Egypt was addressed, and the *epitropos* was the Roman "procurator." In the Ptolemaic period *hegemon* was a military rank, and the title *epitropos* is not found at all. May it then be concluded that Josephus used the story of the House of Tobiah in its last edition made during the Roman period? Or did he himself substitute the Ptolemaic titles, which were no longer current, by Roman titles to which he was more accustomed?

47 On 'Arak el-Emir and the residence of Hyrcanus, see above, p. 430, n. 69. Representations of an eagle and a lion are still preserved on the walls of the fortress. See Butler, *Princeton Expedition,* IIA, i, p. 21, fig. 12; *ib.* II, pl. i.

48 Josephus' words: "He ruled seven years in those places" (*Ant.* XII, 234) immediately follow the account of the building of the fortress "not far from Ḥeshbon." It is clear that by the words "those places," not the whole of Transjordan is meant, but the district around the fortress only, that is, the small state which Hyrcanus established and ruled for seven successive years. He spent in all twenty-five years in Transjordan.

49 "Ben Tobiah" is here Hyrcanus' surname; all his brothers were known as "B'nei Tobiah," although they were actually sons of Joseph ben Tobiah. Those scholars may be right who have supposed that Hyrcanus' Hebrew name was Tobiah, so that we ought to read Ὑρκανοῦ τοῦ καὶ Τωβίου, "Hyrcanus also called Tobiah." The custom of calling the grandson after the grandfather was common among the Jews.

50 Hyrcanus' personality has always attracted scholars. Our few sources are such as to arouse historical curiosity without furnishing the material to satisfy it. Hence the endeavors of inquirers to extend our knowledge by diverse conjectures. Klausner (*Ha-shiloaḥ,* XLII Heb.; *History* II, 230) saw in Hyrcanus the author of the Book of Ecclesiastes (a hint of a similar view may also be found in Renan, *Hist. du peuple d'Israel,* IV, 275). According to Gressmann, Hyrcanus regarded himself as a messiah, and his tragic end formed the basis of the legend of "the Messiah son of Joseph" (Gressmann, *Die ammonitischen Tobiaden,* 668). A realistic historical approach free of far-reaching conjecture is found in Momigliano, in his above-mentioned article (cf. above, n. 33), pp. 170ff. In the writer's view, a closer understanding of Hyrcanus' personal life could be obtained if those who seek it, were to pay attention to the lives of the Greeks of the period, instead of restricting themselves to the narrow confines of Jewry. The lives of Eumenes, Demetrius and Pyrrhus as told by Plutarch may perhaps help us to understand Hyrcanus' psychology and character.

51 Cf. E. Meyer, *Ursp. u. Anf. d. Christentums,* II, 32, 129.

52 "The author of the Book of Ecclesiastes" (Heb.), in *Ha-Shiloah*, XLII, 49.

53 *Tobiaden und Oniaden*, 87. Büchler even makes Joseph the Tobiad a Samaritan; but this opinion is based on no evidence. Willrich (*Juden und Griechen*, 99ff.) also thinks that the Joseph legend originated in Samaria.

54 A few words should be added on the question of the criticism of the source. Whoever reads Josephus' story of Joseph and his son Hyrcanus with attention will doubtless discover a certain contrast between paragraphs 154-222 and paragraphs 228-236 (*Ant*. XII): in the former paragraphs the narrative is detailed and full of popular anecdotes; in the later paragraphs it is brief and dry and not at all like a legend. These two sections also differ in external form: between 222 and 228 there are passages without relevance to the Tobiads, and in 228 Josephus begins his account afresh and states that Hyrcanus was the "youngest of the brothers," as if he had not reported this already. On the basis of these inconsistencies some scholars think that Josephus has here worked over two sources on the life of Joseph, one of which was detailed and full of legend and anecdote, and contained the adventures of the young Hyrcanus in Egypt, the other brief and historical, concerning Hyrcanus' conflicts with his brothers and his life in Transjordan. See, for example, Walter Otto, cited in B. Motzo, *Saggi di Storia e Letteratura Giudeo-Ellenistica*, 191, and also Klausner, *History*, II, 140. I do not think that this conjecture has sufficient foundation; precisely in paragraphs 228-236 occurs the detailed account of Hyrcanus' fortress in Transjordan, which informs us that this chapter too comes from the family chronicle of the House of Tobiah, and from that branch of the family with which Hyrcanus was connected. It can hardly be supposed that this family chronicle was written twice by two different people, and it would be more correct to assume that Josephus used one source, but gave its first part at length, while taking only a few items from the second. Cf. the remarks of Motzo on Otto's theory, *op. cit.*, 191ff. The whole mélange was caused by Josephus' decision to interrupt the narrative for chronological reasons in the middle, and to tell the reader what happened in the reign of Seleucus IV and in the time of the High Priest Simon, the son of Onias. This sudden interruption in the course of the story caused a change in the style of the reporting. It may well be, too, that Hyrcanus' last years afforded less material for romancing than his early ones, hence the dry practical nature of the end of the narrative.

55 This date is now accepted by most scholars; see Ryssel in Kautzsch's *Apokryph. u. Pseudepigr*. I, 235; Smend, *Die Weisheit des Jesus Sirach*, 1906, p. xv; Schürer, III, 216; Pfeiffer, *History of NT Times*, 1949, 364.

56 Smend (*op. cit.*, preface, p. xx, and in various places in the body of his commentary), indeed, notes several passages in Ben Sira which appear to allude to the struggle between the Tobiads and the Zaddokite priests, or to the ferment among the priestly group itself; but I do not find in these passages sufficient grounds for his theory. It is particularly incomprehensible how it is possible to deduce from ch. L that in Ben Sira's time the High Priest did not fulfill his task on the Day of Atonement (*ib.* 477); there is no hint of this in the source.

57 All the quotations are according to the translation of Box and Oesterley in Charles' *Apocrypha and Pseudepigrapha,* I, 1913, 268ff.

58 See on Ben Sira generally Segal, *Sefer Ben-Sira ha-shalem* (Hebrew), 1953, 22ff.; Klausner, *Hist.,* II, 233ff.; Schürer, III, 212ff.; E. Bevan, *Jerusalem under the High Priests,* 1904, 49ff.; Pfeiffer, *Hist. of NT Times,* 359ff.

59 On Jewish social life in the time of Ben Sira, cf. Schechter's article in his book *Studies in Judaism,* Second Series, 1908, 55ff.; on social questions in the Second Temple period generally cf. Finkelstein, *The Pharisees,* 1946, 1ff.; J. Jeremias, *Jerusalem zur Zeit Jesu,* 1929, *passim.*

60 Cf. Prov. 14.20; 19.4.

61 In the Hebrew version "lest thou hate," which is to be read (as in the Greek translation) "lest thou be forgotten."

62 Cf. for example, 8.8; 11.1; 20.27; 38.3; 39.4.

63 Smend sees in these "great men" (in the Greek translation, μεγιστάνες), the Greek rulers (see his commentary on verses 8.8; 20.27, etc.); he quotes no proof of this view and it is hard to know what his authority is. In the present writer's opinion Ben Sira means the Jewish leaders of Jerusalem; he sees in the study of "wisdom" the means to rise to greatness and to "stand before the leaders," and his wisdom is traditional Jewish learning bound up with fear of God; what would this have to do with Greek rulers?

64 The writer's reference is to ch. 94-105 of the *Book of Enoch;* cf. especially 94.7ff.; 96.7ff.; 97.8ff.; 99.12ff. See below ch. VII.

NOTES *part* I *chapter* 4

1 I emphasize the word "their descendants"; we cannot say with certainty that the Tobiads were the sons of Joseph himself. Possibly in the sixties the sons of Joseph were already elderly men, and not they but their sons headed the movement.

2 Wellhausen, *Israel. u. jud. Gesch.,* 7 ed., 236; Büchler, *Tobiaden und Oniaden,* 9ff., 80; E. Meyer, *Urspr. u. Anf. des Christent.,* II,

133; Schürer, I, 195, n. 28; Bickermann, *Gott der Makk.*, 65, n. 1; H. Bévenot, *Die beiden Makkabäerbücher*, 1931, 181ff.; F. M. Abel, *Les livres des Maccabées*, 1949, 316; Momigliano, *ARAST*, 67, 189.

3 At the center of these comparisons stands the passage *War* I, 31ff.; but this is to be used with the greatest caution. See Appendix I.

4 On the activity of temples as banks in Sumer, Akkad and Babylonia, see T. Mendelssohn, *Slavery in the Ancient Near East*, 99ff.; Cl. Préaux, *L'économie royale des Lagides*, 293ff. On the parallel function of temples in Greece, see Andreades, *A History of Greek Public Finance*, 1933, 190ff.

5 A. Schwarz (in his article on the Jerusalem Temple treasury in *MGWJ*, 63, 1919, 225), stresses the fact that where its treasury was concerned, the Temple of Jerusalem resembled all the other temples of the ancient world.

6 See Schwarz, *loc. cit.*, 234ff.; cf. Schürer, II, 314ff.; Baron, *SRHJ*, 2, I, 215, 392, n. 6. Bickermann, in his article on Heliodorus' visit to the Temple of Jerusalem (see below, n. 12), p. 14, seeks to belittle the value of the half-shekel: he thinks that the half-shekel became a general tax only from the time of the Maccabees, since the latter were interested in it and it is nowhere mentioned before the Roman period. This view of Bickermann's is not the result of any special research on the half-shekel, but follows from his general assumption that the Temple funds were subsidized by the Seleucid state treasury (cf. below, n. 12). As the main assumption is open to doubt, the view on the half-shekel also lacks adequate basis. The silence of the sources does not prove anything, as no source of the Hellenistic period deals with the specific question of the Temple's income.

7 In this sentence, indeed, Josephus is referring to the Roman period, but it applies equally to the previous epoch, since the theocratic character of Judaea had not altered in the meantime.

8 *Ant.* XII, 229. The reason given is somewhat curious, for was not Simon related to Hyrcanus as much as he was to his brothers? These words are in the writer's opinion an echo of the gossip rife among Hyrcanus' enemies concerning his improper origin (cf. above, p. 460, n. 45). In Simon's eyes only Hyrcanus' brothers were legitimate Tobiads.

9 On the origin of Simon and his brothers, Menelaus and Lysimachus, see App. II.

10 II Macc. 3.4: προστάτης τοῦ ἱεροῦ. Momigliano (*ARAST*, 67, 1931/2, 188ff.) interprets this title as if προστάτης τοῦ λαοῦ had been written, and sees in Simon one who held the secular *prostasia* under the auspices of the Seleucid sovereign. The original text, however, speaks explicitly of Simon as *prostates* of the Temple and not of the whole nation, and we have already remarked (p. 81) that under Simon the Just the authority to represent the people before the king had probably reverted to the High Priest. We therefore have to look for the post among the high positions connected with the Temple. In Neh. 11.11 is mentioned the post of "the President of the House of God," and this title seems to suit excellently the Greek term προστάτης τοῦ ἱεροῦ mentioned in II Macc. It is to be assumed that the general administration of all the affairs of the Temple was in the hands of the holder of this post. With it should be compared the *prostasia* of the Temples in Ptolemaic Egypt (P. Tebt. 781, and others) and in Hellenistic cities (*e.g.*, *OGIS*, 531).

11 The post of *agoranomos* of the first category is found in Greek cities in the classical and Hellenistic period; cf. Andreades, *A History of Greek Public Finance*, 213; A. H. M. Jones, *The Greek City*, 215ff. It is mentioned in the second sense in Ptolemaic Egypt; here the *agoranomos* performed the function of the modern notary: in his office official papers were drafted, documents signed, etc. Cf. Bouché-Leclercq, *Hist. des Lagides*, IV, 134ff.; E. Bevan, *A History of Egypt Under the Ptolemaic Dynasty*, 295.

12 According to Bickermann ("Héliodore au Temple de Jérusalem," *Annuaire de l'Institut de Philol. et d'Hist. Orient.*, VII, 1939-44, 5ff.) the Temple of Jerusalem had no money except that granted to it officially by the Seleucid king to support the sacrifices. Simon was a royal official, and informed the king that the government's money was being expended only partly for sacrificial needs, while the surplus (τὰ διάφορα) remained in the treasury unused; this he regarded as an injury done to the royal money by the priests of Jerusalem. Against this reasoning of Bickermann's several objections can be urged. (1) τὰ διάφορα does not mean the surplus created by the difference between income and expenditure, but "money" generally, as may be concluded from II Macc. 1.35 and *ib.* 4.28: on this meaning of the word see Liddel and Scott's Greek dictionary, *ad voc.* For this reason Bickermann's idea on the surplus money remaining in the Temple treasury cannot stand; Simon's intention was simply to tell the king of "the huge amount of money" in the treasury, "which had not been entered up to the sacrificial account," meaning, it was not necessary for the daily expenditure of the Temple. (2) It is true that both in the Persian and in the Hellenistic periods the kings allotted a special budget for the Temple from the state funds—cf., for example, the allotment fixed by Antiochus III (*Ant.* XII, 140). However, it is not stated anywhere that this was meant to cover *all* the Temple expenses and that the Temple of Jerusalem had no other financial income. The very fact that the allotment was made for the sacrifices alone indicates that it was not the only one, for, besides the sacrifices, the Temple had several other items of expenditure, such as the maintenance of the edifice, the holding of festivals, the support and clothing of the priests, etc. Bickermann's supposition, then, that the Temple fund was subsidized only by the government, is baseless. Hence his view is also baseless that the half-shekel was non-existent at this period (see above, n. 6). (3) The supposition that Simon was a royal official is entirely conjectural. It would be acceptable only if his post of the *prostasia* could be interpreted as "representation of the people" in Momigliano's manner (above, n. 10); but we have seen that this interpretation is not acceptable, Simon's post being connected with the Temple and not with the general administration. The existence of a permanent Seleucid official post within the Temple of Jerusalem would have destroyed the foundations of Jewish autonomy as confirmed by Antiochus III, since the Temple was not merely a religious institution, but also the center of the theocratic government of Judaea.

13 Cf. II Macc. 3.15; *ib.* 3.22. It were well to remark that the author of *IV Macc.*, who took the material for his historical account from II Macc. (see App. I, at end), sees in the mission of Apollonius (who here plays the part of Heliodorus in II Macc.) one aim only, "to confiscate the private money (τὰ ἰδιωτικά) of the treasury" (IV, 6).

14 An inscription (*OGIS* 247) describes Heliodorus as ἐπὶ τῶν πραγμάτων τεταγμένος—supreme minister of affairs of state, or "prime minister" in modern language.

15 On the conventional form of the Hellenistic tales describing the "appearance" (ἐπιφάνεια) of gods, and the like, see Bickermann's above-mentioned article, 18ff.

16 In this matter Jewish history is far from unique: family authority was a common phenomenon in ancient times, and republican Rome provides the most convincing examples of it.

17 It is to be assumed that, in his brother's absence, Jason automatically took his place, just as Lysimachus later took the place of his brother Menelaus when he was absent from Jerusalem.

18 On the foundation of "Antioch-at-Jerusalem," see App. III.

19 On the aristocratic character of Rhodes, see Strab. XIV, 652/3; cf. Rostovtzeff, *CAH*, VIII, 632ff.; *SEHHW*, II, 684ff.

20 See A. H. M. Jones, *The Greek City*, 224.

21 The number of citizens in Rhodes, in the Hellenistic period one of the richest Greek cities, was some 6,000 people (Diod. XX, 84, 2). In the two oligarchic revolutions at Athens (in the years 411 and 404) the number of citizens was restricted to 5,000 and 3,000 people respectively. A medium-sized Greek city was of course much smaller than Athens, and if its regime was aristocratic the number of its citizens certainly did not exceed 3,000.

22 The *gerousia* was a fairly common institution in Greek cities;

the best known example in the classical period is Sparta. The "elders" (γέροντες) are frequently mentioned in Greek cities in the Hellenistic period and very frequently in the inscriptions of Thrace, Asia Minor, and the Aegean Islands in the Roman period (cf. *RE., s.v. Gerontes, Gerousia*). An aristocratic council also existed in the city of Laodiceia-on-Sea in Syria, as we know from an inscription of the year 175 B.C.E. (see Roussell's article in *Syria*, 23, 21ff.). It is not therefore surprising that Antioch-at-Jerusalem saw no need to exchange its *gerousia* for some other institution. Klausner (*History*, II, 185) thinks that the *gerousia* continued to exist after Jason's reform as the supreme instance in Jerusalem, while the new *polis* received the *boulé*. But we hear nothing of the *boulé* at Antioch-at-Jerusalem; and as to the possible existence of two towns (Jerusalem and Antioch) side by side, see p. 165.

23 On the connection between *gymnasion* education and reception into the citizen-body, see the inscription *SEG* VIII, 641, of the year 104 B.C.E. from an Egyptian town (evidently Ptolemais in Upper Egypt). Emperor Claudius' famous rescript to the citizens of Alexandria (*SP.* 212,ll.53ff.) gives proof of the reception of *epheboi* into the citizen ranks in the Roman period.

24 Bickermann, in his book *Der Gott der Makkabäer*, seeks to distinguish between two stages in the Hellenistic reform: the foundation of the corporation of "the Antiochenes in Jerusalem" by Jason in 175, and the foundation of the Hellenistic city in the Akra in 168. He writes of the constitution drawn up by Antiochus III for the Jews: *Das privileg wurde durch die Gründung der Korporation der "Antiochener in Jerusalem" durchbrochen; es wurde im Jahre 168 von Epiphanes ganz aufgehoben.* It is surprising that Bickermann, a scholar of highly developed juridical intuition, should use such hazy expressions to describe the character of the reform of 175. What sort of juridical term is *durchbrochen?* Either Antiochus III's constitution remained in force after Jason's reform, in which case the whole reform, including the building of the *gymnasion* and the *ephebeion*, was unconstitutional, since it was in contradiction to the "ancestral laws," or the reform was carried out by special permission of the king, a permission including the abolition of the previous constitution and the granting of powers to the High Priest to draw up a new one. The writer sees no middle road between the two possibilities. On the corporation of the Antiochenes see App. III.

25 On the connection between the new city and its royal founder, see the present writer's book *Hellenistische Städtegründungen*, 132. If the city was called after the king, the latter took a special interest in its fortunes; thus the city of "Antioch in Persia" testifies more particularly to the will of its founder, Antiochus I Soter, to enlarge the number of its inhabitants, "since it bore his name" (*OGIS* 233, line 15). The cult of the *ktistes* persisted in the cities under Roman rule; cf.

for example the cult of Ptolemy I at Ptolemais in Egypt in the second century C.E. (*BIFAO* 41, 43ff.) and the cult of Perdiccas at Samaria (above, p. 443, n. 77).

26 On the chronological question see Bouché-Leclercq, *Hist. des Lag.*, II, 5ff.; Bevan, *History*, 233ff. In contradiction to the accepted opinion which places the date of Antiochus' visit to Jerusalem in 172, Otto, *Gesch. der Zeit des 6. Ptolemäers*, 15ff., thinks it was in 175/4.

27 Cf. Motzo, *Saggi*, 125ff.; Klausner, *Hist.*, II, 185. See App. III.

28 See above, n. 22.

29 Cf. Heinemann, *MGWJ*, 82, 146ff.

30 According to Josephus, Menelaus, not Jason, was the initiator of the reform.

31 *E.g.*, Willrich, *Juden und Griechen*, 86. Cf. Abel, *Livres des Macc.*, 331.

32 On the rights of the Greek cities in the Seleucid state, see Bickermann, *Instit. des Sél.*, 141ff.; 157ff.; on their right to strike coins, see *ib.* 228ff. The importance of independent coinage is emphasized in the letter of Antiochus Sidetes to Simon the Maccabee (I Macc. 15.6); cf. Narkiss, *Coins of Eretz Yisrael*, I, 17.

33 II Macc. 4.19. The envoys who appeared before the deity or who attended the athletic games which were also consecrated to one of the gods, were known in Greece as *theoroi*.

34 The priest in a Greek city was a magistrate like any other magistrate and usually elected for one year. In some cities the name of the High Priest served to distinguish the year, as did that of the Chief Archon at Athens or the consuls at Rome. It is worth mentioning that in 164 Lysias threatened the Jews that he would make the High Priesthood an annual auctionable post: this was a logical consequence of Jerusalem's conversion to a Greek *polis*.

35 He died while endeavoring to plunder the treasures of the god Bel (evidently the chief deity) of Elam; see Strabo XV, 744; Diod. XXVIII, 3; XXIX, 15. Cf. Bouché-Leclercq, *Hist. des Séleucides*, I, 223.

36 Josephus' account as a whole is extremely confused. According to *Ant.* XII, 239, Menelaus was Jason's brother, his Hebrew name being Onias; scholars have long remarked on the impossibility of this assumption, as in this case Jason would have had two brothers both named Onias. Nor is Josephus' account in *War* I, 31ff. about Onias' expulsion of the Tobiads credible, for here he confuses Onias with Jason. See for details, App. I at the end.

37 According to Abel, *Livres d. Macc.*, 339, Jason may well have fled to 'Arak el-Emir, the former residence of Hyrcanus. Cf. also Bévenot,

Macc., 190; Klausner, *History*, 189. This is conceivable, for Hyrcanus represented the pro-Egyptian trend, and Jason also appears later (in 168) as the opponent of Antiochus Epiphanes, that is, as a supporter of Egypt, and moreover flees to Egypt after his failure in Jerusalem. Probably a certain pro-Egyptian tradition survived at 'Arak el-Emir after Hyrcanus' death.

38 On the first occasion Jason was the victor and on the second Menelaus; in this way it may be possible to compromise between the two reports (in Josephus and in II Macc.).

39 Daphne was the suburb of Antioch famous as the cult-center of the god Apollo and as the pleasure-resort of the masses of the Syrian capital's population. According to II Macc. 4.33, Onias fled to a place of refuge at Daphne, which report is generally interpreted to mean that Onias fled to Apollo's shrine. (Cf. Bévenot and Abel in their commentaries, *ad loc.*) But the existence of a Jewish synagogue at Daphne is referred to in sources of the Roman period (see below, Pt. II, ch. I, end), and it may therefore have existed as early as the Hellenistic period; the synagogues, as is well known, also enjoyed the right of ἀσυλία (asylum or refuge)—cf. *OGIS*, 129. The flight of a Jewish High Priest to a synagogue is more credible than an attempt on his part to seek shelter with Greek deities. It should be remembered that Onias was not a Hellenizer and was known as one devoted to the ancestral faith (see n. 41).

40 According to Wellhausen (*Israel. u. jud. Gesch.*, 235) and Willrich (*Juden und Griechen*, 77ff.), the story of Onias' murder is not reconcilable with historical reality; some present-day scholars (such as Momigliano, *ARAST*, 67, 190; Zeitlin, *The Second Jewish Commonwealth*, 26ff.; Seeligmann, *The Septuagint Version of Isaiah*, 91ff.) also incline to this view. The opinion of Wellhausen and Willrich was based on their negative attitude to II Macc. as a historical source; on this see App. I at the end. One of the proofs of these scholars rests on the assumption that the author of II Macc. transferred to Onias the story of the tragic death of Seleucus' son who was killed by the same high official Andronicus, according to Diod. XXX, 7, 2, cf. John of Antioch, frag. 58 ap. Müller, *FHG*, IV, p. 558. The account of the prince's murder is, however, too brief to enable the establishment of precise parallels with the narrative of II Macc., and both may be true. II Macc. may have adorned the story of Onias' death with certain details taken from that of the prince's murder not preserved in our sources, for example, Antiochus' anger against Andronicus and the mourning among the inhabitants of Antioch, but this is no proof that Onias was not slain by Andronicus as well. Onias' tragic death seems to have contributed to his idealization: in II Macc. 15.12ff., Onias appears to Judah the Maccabee in a dream in company with the prophet Jeremiah. It should be mentioned as the accepted view of scholars that Daniel 9.26 is referring to Onias' death when it says:

"an anointed one shall be cut off"; cf. the commentaries of Montgomery (p. 393), and Charles (p. 246ff.), *ad loc.*

41 On the struggle between the Oniads and the Tobiads, Tarn
writes: "Both Oniads and Tobiads were hellenizers, and their quarrel
had no religious import" (*Hell. Civilization*, 3rd ed., 214). "The High
Priest and his following . . . were no less hellenistic than the Tobiads,
though perhaps their interest in the Temple made them less extreme"
(L. Finkelstein, *The Pharisees*, II, 585). As to Jason, his Hellenistic
tendencies are sufficiently well known; nor can Onias III's son, Onias
IV, the founder of the well known temple in Egypt ("the House of
Onias") be regarded as one devoted to his fathers' customs, since the
foundation of a temple beyond the borders of Jerusalem was an
undertaking opposed to tradition. But Onias III himself is not to be
regarded as a Hellenizer, for had he been so, it would be hard to
understand his idealization in II Macc. (see *e.g.*, II Macc. 3.1; 4.2;
15.12).

42 This anti-Hellenist stand of the *gerousia* need not occasion surprise; it has already been observed that the Hellenistic reform was no
infringement of the religious or cultic fundamentals, hence nothing
prevents us assuming that the members of the *gerousia* were devoted
to the Jewish religion. They supported Jason, the moderate Hellenizer,
but could not support Menelaus and his government by terror. On the
gerousia, see above, n. 22.

NOTES *part* **I** *chapter* **5**

1 In the investigation of the Antiochan persecution the following
works have been consulted: J. Klausner, *History of the Period of the
Second Temple* (Heb.), II, 1949; E. R. Bevan, *The House of
Seleucus*, II, 1902; *Camb. Anc. Hist.*, VIII, 497ff.; Niese, *Gesch. d.
griech. und maked. Staaten*, III, 1903; Bouché-Leclercq, *Histoire des
Séleucides*, I, 1913; Ed. Meyer, *Ursprung und Anfänge d. Christen-
tums*, II, 1921; Wilcken, *Pauly-Wissowa Realenz.* I, 2, 2470ff. (*s.v.*
Antiochus IV); Kolbe, *Beiträge z. griechischen und jüdischen
Geschichte*, 1926; Oesterley, *A History of Israel II*, 1932; W. Otto,
Zur Geschichte der Zeit des 6 Ptolemäers, 1934; Bickermann, *Der
Gott der Makkabäer*, 1937; E. Reuter, *Beiträge zur Beurteilung des
Königs Antiochos Epiphanes*, 1938; Rostovtzeff, *Soc. and Econ. Hist.
of the Hellenistic World*, II, 1941; *id. Mélanges Dussaud*, 293ff.;
Seyrig, in *Syria* 20, 1939, 298ff.; Ludin Jansen, *Die Politik Antiochos
des IV*, 1943; Abel, *Histoire de la Palestine*, I, 1952. These works are
henceforth referred to by the names of their authors only.

2 Polybius XXVI, 10; XXXI, 3-4; Livy XLI, 19-20; Diod. XXIX, 32;
XXXI, 16, 1-2; Polybius' account is evidently suspect in the eyes of
several scholars, who have accused the Greek historian of prejudice

and hostility toward the king. These accusations are without solid basis. Antiochus' pro-Roman policy and the gifts made by him to the cities of Greece, including Polybius' birthplace of Megalopolis, could have aroused in Polybius only admiration for the king. If, despite this, he stressed the negative aspects of his character, it must have been because he saw this as the true picture. Against the above view, cf. Reuter, 19ff.

3 Klausner, 177ff.; Bouché-Leclercq, 279; Meyer, 139ff.: *ein echter Seleukide, vielseitig begabt und voll Energie und Rührigkeit, eine der bedeutsamsten Gestalten der Dynastie.* Rostovtzeff, *SEHHW*, 738: "The last great Seleucid"; cf. Niese, 96: *tatenlustig und ehrgeizig, zugleich aber unbeständig, launenhaft und auschweifend.;* Bevan, *CAH*, VII, 498: "a Bohemian curiosity to experience life in its diverse kinds . . ."; Otto, 84: *ein innerlich zerissiner, nervöser Mensch.*

4 According to Meyer, 140, the only element which gave the Seleucid kingdom internal unity was Hellenism. According to Bevan, *The House of Seleucus*, II, 153, the Hellenism of Antiochus did not content itself with propagating certain political forms: "It extended to the sphere of social and private life, to the manner of thought and speech, to religious practice." See also Wilcken, 2474, who emphasizes that at the very beginning of his political career Antiochus revealed the same trend of thought that later brought him to the attempt to Hellenize the Jews. He certainly inherited the aspiration to Hellenize from his forebears, the first Seleucids; *Dass er aber die Geduld verlor und glaubte, die hellenistische Kultur durch einen Schwerthieb einführen zu können, war allerdings töricht.* Cf. further Niese, 94ff.

5 Among the towns which Antiochus "founded" may be mentioned six ancient cities of Cilicia which were undoubtedly already Hellenized at the beginning of the Hellenistic period. Edessa and Nisibis, which under Antiochus became "Antiochs," had known Greeks since the time of Seleucus I, as also had Ecbatana-Epiphaneia in Media, which was surrounded by Greek towns on all sides a century before Antiochus. Alexandria-Charax, founded by Alexander and subsequently destroyed, was restored by Antiochus and renamed Antioch. In Babylon also Antiochus founded a Greek city, that is, he organized the Greek population of Babylon as a *polis*. On Antiochus Epiphanes as city-founder, see the present writer's *Hellenistische Städtegründungen*, 176ff.: cf. A. H. M. Jones, *Cities of the Eastern Roman Provinces*, 250ff.

6 *Ant.* XII, 263: τοῖς Ἑλληνικοῖς ἔθεσιν αἱροῦνται χρώμενοι ζῆν.

7 II Macc. 6.9.

8 II Macc. 11.24.

9 Cf. Bickermann, *Gott der Makk.*, 90ff., who rightly remarks that while oriental cities regarded as sacred towns under Antiochus received the status of Greek *poleis,* in none of them did this cause the abolition of the local cult. It may even be supposed that Antiochus' philhellenism in relation to the Greek cities of Greece itself did not arise from purely cultural motives, but was conditioned by calculations of *Realpolitik.* Cf. Otto, 33.

10 In 189 after Antiochus' defeat by Rome, his son Antiochus was sent to Rome as a hostage and remained resident there some thirteen years. Rome made a great impression upon him, and after he ascended the throne he endeavored to provide a foothold for Roman culture in Syria. He built a temple to Jupiter Capitolinus at Antioch, introduced gladiatorial games, which were not at all in the Greek spirit, armed part of his army on the Roman model, and so on. He further attempted to introduce into the monarchical regime of the Seleucid kingdom the democratic spirit of the Roman political institutions without asking himself if these diverse elements could be grafted together and if the oriental masses would be capable of understanding the spirit of the reform. At Antioch he introduced the posts of *aedilis* and *tribunus plebis,* which were quite inappropriate to the life of the oriental city, and himself appeared as candidate for these posts, and following the Roman custom went about the market-places of the city courting the citizens, embracing them and begging them to vote for him. The inhabitants of Antioch entirely failed to understand the business and some thought he was insane (Polyb. XXVI, 10, 6-8). Cf. on Antiochus' pro-Roman policy, Reuter, 38ff.

11 Rostovtzeff (*Mél. Dussaud,* 294ff.) formulated the principles of this ideology in these words: "(Antiochus') dominating idea was—the unity of his empire. . . . His religious policy was similar. His ideal was a religion common to his whole empire and acceptable to all, Greeks and orientals alike. . . . He offered to the empire a synthesis of deities as an official religion." Several other scholars have expressed similar opinions; cf. for example Abel, 126, who sums up Antiochus' views in these words: *unifier les croyances des parties disparates de son empire en abolissant les usages et rites particuliers.*

12 This sentence has been variously interpreted, some entirely denying its historical value, some accepting it as it stands. Otto, 85, thinks Antiochus' order was authentic; so also Kolbe, 153. E. Meyer thinks that the contents of the order as transmitted in I Macc. reflect the genuine opinion of the king, but that although he expressed some such idea, he had no basis for publishing such an ordinance for his whole kingdom, since he encountered resistance only among the Jews (143ff.). Heinemann also (161ff.) regards the order, but not its verbal formulation in I Macc., as genuine: the king expressed a certain desire, but did not order the peoples to give up their traditional customs. Bickermann, 127, rejects the ordinance's authenticity completely.

13 On the coins with the representation of Zeus Olympius, see Seyrig's article in *Syria*, 20, 298ff. Cf. Bouché-Leclercq, 283; Bevan, 150ff.; Abel, 124ff.

14 *OGIS*, 245; cf. Bickermann, *Inst. des Sél.*, 242ff.

15 This is the explanation of most of those scholars who see the order of I Macc. 1.41 as historical, but as worded in accordance with the outlook of the author of I Macc.

16 Rostovtzeff, *SEHHW*, 64; Otto, 34; Kölbe, 153; Tarn, *Hell. Civil.*, 186; cf. Oesterley, 222, and Niese, 232ff. This mode of thought has found its completest and most consistent formulation in Jansen's work. In that author's view, Antiochus' main mission was "the welfare of his kingdom, the checking of its disintegration, and the restoration of its internal unity both materially and intellectually" (*ib.* 31). The chief cause of the persecution of the Jewish religion was "the Jewish religion's anti-Syrian character" (*ib.* 37)—the Ptolemaic, anti-Seleucid, orientation of the Jewish masses who were loyal to their ancestral tradition. On the general lines of Antiochus' policy see Reuter, 30ff.

17 Cf. I Macc. 1.11ff.; II Macc. 4.7ff.; *ib.* 13.4. The function of the Jewish Hellenizers is stressed by all scholars; particularly sharp emphasis is laid on it by Bevan, 168, and by Oesterley, 224. In the account of the events of the years 175-168 in the first edition of the present work also, emphasis was laid on the activities of the Jewish Hellenizers.

18 Bickermann, 128ff. Cf. the arguments correctly marshaled against him by Heinemann, 156ff.

19 This view may be regarded as accepted among historians. Fresh papyrological data, however, have confronted scholars with new questions such as are likely to undermine previous conclusions. *Pap. Ryl.*, IV, 583 informs us that in November 170 the calendar of Egypt had already been fixed according to the years of the co-rule of the two sovereigns Philometor and Euergetes II, whereas on the accepted view the brothers' co-rule began only after the end of Antiochus' first Egyptian expedition. This expedition must then be ascribed to 170 and not to 169. See C. Préaux, in *Chron. d'Egypte*, 47, 1949, 134; Aymard, in *Aegyptus*, 32, 1952, 85; but Bickermann in his article in *Chron. d'Eg.*, 54, 1952, 396ff. seeks to strengthen the previous view by new proofs in spite of the information deriving from the above-mentioned papyrus, and some of his reasons seem sound. We shall do well, therefore, to retain the accepted view for the time being, until scholarly research illumines the problem in all its details and reaches confident conclusions.

20 His first visit, in 169: "And he shall return to his land with great substance, and his heart shall be against the Holy Covenant, and he shall do his pleasure and return to his own land" (Dan. 11.28). In

168: "And he shall return and shall have indignation against the Holy Covenant and shall do his pleasure, and shall return and have regard unto them that forsake the Holy Covenant" (*ib.* 30). Anyone reading these two passages without prejudice must perforce admit that we have here a brief report of two similar operations, nor can it be proved that the subject of the first passage is the personal visit of Antiochus to Jerusalem, whereas that of the second is the mission of his official, Apollonius (so Bickermann, 161ff.). The scholars who reject Apollonius' second visit "amend" Daniel by I Macc. (cf. for example, Montgomery, *Comm. to Dan.*, 449), that is, they correct an eye-witness according to a book written some fifty years after the events. This method seems wrong to the writer. It is indeed hard to utilize Daniel as an authority, on account of his picturesque and obscure style (see App. I), but in those passages where he is clear (and this is one of them), Daniel is a historical source of the highest importance.

21 *C. Apion* II, 83; Antiochus plundered the Temple treasure: *cum non esset hostis, et super nos, auxiliatores suos et amicos, adgressus est.* Josephus reports the same act in the following words: *Omnes dicunt pecuniis indigentem Antiochum transgressum foedera Judaeorum expoliasse templum auro argentoque plenum.* For this his authorities are Polybius, Strabo, Nicolaus of Damascus, and other historians. The looting of the treasure need not surprise us, since Antiochus III, as remarked above, had long ago seen in the temple treasures of his realm an unfailing source for the improvement of the depressed financial situation of the state.

22 In the city of Arad in Phoenicia, according to Jerome's commentary on Daniel 11.44; cf. Otto, 66, n. 4.

23 Thus, for example, Jos. *Ant.* XII, 248ff., attributes all Apollonius' operations (he does not mention him by name) to the king himself, including the detail of the capture of the city by deception.

24 The reading עַם אֵלֹהַּ נֵכָר, instead of עַם אֵלֹהַּ נֵכָר, has been accepted by all scholars. Montgomery reads the sentence וְעָשָׂה לְמִבְצְרֵי מָעוּזִים וכ'ו (p. 463). Charles (*Commentary to Daniel,* 316) leaves the usual vocalization of מִבְצָרֵי, and translates the sentence: "He shall use for the strongest fortresses the people of a strange god."

25 The establishment of the *cleruchies* of Athens under Pericles frequently involved the expulsion of the former inhabitants; cf. Thuc. I, 114, 3; II, 70, 4; IV, 102, 3. In other cases the inhabitants became tributary subjects (*ib.* III, 50, 2). The settlement of Roman legionary troops on the soil of the Italian cities under the Second Triumvirate caused a grave social revolution and finally even an attempt to fight back on the part of Italy, thrown on the defensive against the soldiers led by Octavian (App. *Bell. Civ.* V, 3, 12; cf. R. Syme, *The Roman Revolution,* 207ff.). The evidence of Daniel "and shall divide the land for a price" means that the land of Jerusalem (till then in Jewish possession) was partitioned, in entirety or in part, among the new population, as occurred in Italy.

26 Many scholars would restrict the extent of the flight, or even discount it completely; cf., for example, J. S. Dancy, *A Commentary on I Maccabees*, 1954, who calls the report in I Macc. 1.38, "pure fantasy." We suggest that these scholars study Appian, *Bell. Civ.*, V, 12: the Italians came to Rome in crowds and claimed that they, guilty of no crime, had been "driven from their land and from their homes as if they had been conquered in war." Only if one rejects Apollonius' order as a historical fact, is one permitted to reject the flight of the inhabitants of Jerusalem from the city. But so far as I know no one has cast doubt on the order of Apollonius or on the establishment of a military colony of Antiochus' troops at Jerusalem.

27 I Macc. (1.38) reports the flight of the population of Jerusalem from the city as a result of Apollonius' acts. He even speaks of "the wilderness in the sacred place," alluding to the abandonment of the Temple by the Jews; and we shall see below that this is no mere literary expression, but a statement of fact of great importance. II Macc. (5.27) relates the flight of Judah the Maccabee and his people from the city immediately after the actions of Apollonius, and before those of Antiochus; as II Macc. regards Judah as the initiator of the rising, it follows that its organization in effect began in the period preceding the Antiochan decree.

28 Those scholars who describe Antiochus as a Hellenizer or a "unifier" (see above, p. 178ff.), are forced to assume that his policy encountered severe opposition from the Jews even before the appearance of the Hasmoneans, and that the *Gezerot* came in response to this resistance. These scholars, however, in accordance with the sources and the prevailing view, see no need to lay special emphasis on this idea. Heinemann (p. 161ff.) is nearer than anybody to the correct solution when he seeks to explain the persecution by the Jews' disobedience to the royal order "for all to be one people" (above, n. 12). The other peoples of the realm saw no reason to refuse this order; but the Jews could not accept it "and no doubt there were very many Jews in Jerusalem who evinced resistance (to the order) and probably not only passive resistance" (p. 165). In answer to this resistance, the second order of Antiochus was promulgated (I Macc. 1.44), which contained the decrees against the Jewish religion.

29 On the Macedonians as a pseudo-ethnic group in the Hellenistic period, see M. Launey, *Recherches sur les armées héllenistiques*, 1950, 321, 330, 353, 360ff., etc

30 Bickermann, 111ff. As much as 70 years ago, Nestlé, in ZATW, 1884, 248, expressed the belief that "the abomination of desolation" (השקוץ המשומם) of Daniel, was "Baal Shamin," whose name had

HELLENISTIC CIVILIZATION AND THE JEWS

been purposely altered; he is followed by recent commentators (Montgomery, 388; Charles, 252). Baal Shamin was the chief Syrian deity whose cult was diffused from Phoenicia to Palmyra; see the articles of Seyrig in *Syria*, 14, 1933, 238ff.; 26, 1949, 29ff.; and of Eissfeldt in *ZATW*, 16, 1939, 1ff. Sometimes Baal Shamin was identified with Hadad (Avi-Yonah, in *Isr. Expl. Jl.*, II, 1952, 122), who himself was identified with Zeus (N. Glueck, *The Other Side of the Jordan*, 192ff.). Dushara was initially the desert god of the Arabs, and later became the wine-god and was identified with Dionysus. On him see J. Guttman's article in *The J. N. Epstein Jubilee Volume* (Heb.), 74. Athene is mentioned with Olympian Zeus as the goddess ruling on the Temple mount at Jerusalem by the Byzantine writer Malalas (Bickermann, 112); according to Bickermann she was identified with the Arab goddess Allat and also with the ancient Phoenician goddess Anat. On the identification of Athene with Allat see Wirshubski's article in *Eretz Yisrael* (Heb.), I, 90. The great Syrian goddess is generally known as Atargatis, and theoretically she ought to have been identified with "the Aphrodite of Heaven," and not with Athene. The Syrian troops at the Akra probably preferred to worship the goddess of war Allat or Anat, to the goddess of heaven, who was much more a goddess of women.

31 II Macc. 6.4. Cf. *Meg. Ta'anit* for the 23rd of Marḥeshvan: "On the twenty-third of Marḥeshvan the *Soreg* was broken up in the court. For the Gentiles built there a sacred place and placed prostitutes upon it, and when the head of the house of the Hasmoneans attacked it, they took it from them and hid it" (*Meg. Ta'an.*, ed. Lichtenstein, in *HUCA*, VIII-IX, 337; cf. 275).

32 The abandonment of the Temple by the Jews as a result of the domination of the "sinful people" over it, is explicitly alluded to in I Macc. 1.39: "The place of its holiness (*sc.* of Jerusalem) is desolate like the desert" (τὸ ἁγίασμα αὐτῆς ἠρημώθη ὡς ἔρημος). This is very important information, which testifies that the Temple was abandoned by the Jews not *after* the *Gezerot* of Antiochus but before them.

33 II Macc. (6.1) gives the date of the decree in vague language— "a short time afterwards," clearly not a precise indication. I Macc. (1.54, 59) puts the date of the decree on the 15th Kislev (the erection of the "abomination of desolation"), and on the 25th Kislev (the sacrificing of the first sacrifice on the profane altar) of the year 145 of the Seleucid era, namely, the month of December 167 B.C.E. (Bickermann, 158). As Antiochus' second visit to Jerusalem and the mission of Apollonius must be ascribed to the autumn of 168 (*ib.* 162), it follows that an interval of a year or more elapsed between the acts of Apollonius and the decree of Antiochus.

34 The envoy is called "an elder of Athens." In the Latin translation of II Macc., the envoy was not an Athenian but an "old man of Antioch," that is, on Motzo's interpretation (E. Motzo, *Saggi di Storia* *e Letteratura Giudeo-Ellenistica,* 123ff.) a member of the city-council of Antioch; cf. Momigliano, *Prime Linee di Storia della Tradizione Maccabaica,* 111, n. 2. This amendment is reasonable, since a member of the city-council of Antioch could have served as a high official in the Seleucid Empire, but this is difficult to assume concerning an Athenian elder who could only have been a visitor to the realm. Wilhelm (*Akad. d. Wiss. Wien, Anzeiger,* 74, 1937, 21) sees in *Geron* a personal name (on the basis of the existence of this name in Athenian inscriptions), being followed in this by Louis Robert (*REG,* 64, 1951, 130). But it is not the custom of II Macc. to introduce new people to the reader by name only, without indicating their positions (cf. for example 3.5; 3.7; 4.4; 4.28-29; 4.31; 5.24, etc.). "Geron the Athenian" leaves the reader no wiser, and if we are looking for personal names, it should not be forgotten that *Athenaios* can also be one. The passage is probably corrupt in the ms., and a word or two may have dropped out of the text.

35 On the High Priest Alcimus, see ch. 6.

36 I Macc. 2.42. It is worth remarking that this adherence took place immediately after Mattathias' decision to fight on the Sabbath. The decision, opposed to what had been accepted hitherto among the Jews, did not therefore deter the Ḥasidim from continuing their struggle against Antiochus forthwith under the standard of the Hasmoneans, showing that their loyalty to the ancestral faith was not so blind as to make them sacrifice all objectives of political and national value in their struggle.

37 Dan. 11.34: "And as they stumble, they shall be helped with a little help; but many shall join themselves unto them by the *ḥalaklakot.*" Commentators are agreed that the "little help" mentioned here refers to the Hasmoneans, and this is credible, although we lack decisive proofs for this supposition. By "unto them" in "join themselves unto them" the Ḥasidim are meant, and not the Hasmoneans, as Montgomery and Charles think: the grammatical subject has not changed from the beginning of the sentence. The interpretation of the last word (*ḥalaklakot*) is extremely difficult. Charles amends it from the Septuagint: "And many accompanied them (in the city and many) each in his holding," but this amendment itself requires interpretation. The word may have strayed into this passage from verse 32 ("and such as do wickedly against the Covenant shall be corrupted by blandishments"—*b'ḥalakot*), but it would be more correct to suppose that the word here refers to the difficulty of communications experienced by wayfarers, as in Psalms 35.6 ("let their way be dark and slippery") and Jerem. 23.12 ("wherefore their way shall be unto them as slippery places in the darkness"), the reference being to the indirect routes among the hills used by the freedom-fighters to reach the Hasmonean camp.

38 The opinion common to all the Christian scholars, including the theologians, is that the Jews of Palestine were on the point of complete Hellenization, and that their fate would probably have been no different from that of all the other oriental peoples who modified their original cultures under the influence of Hellenism, but for the hasty and foolish attempt of Antiochus to Hellenize the Jews by force. This attempt caused the Jews to realize the peril which threatened their religion and aroused them to a blind religious fanaticism, which caused the annihilation of Hellenism in Palestine and the revival of Judaism. See, for example, the well-known book of Schürer, I, 189ff. It is surprising that this view, which lacks all real basis, has become so deeply rooted in modern scholarship. Do scholars really believe that traditional Judaism was so frail a flower that the breeze of a superficial Hellenism could destroy it? It is strange that the Christian theologians, who place so high an evaluation on the monotheism of the Old Testament, are not aware of the contradiction implicit in their outlook. It should further be observed that no single oriental culture really surrendered its existence to Hellenism, but that all preserved their traditional heritages with great obstinacy. Why, then, should we assume that only Judaism faced complete intellectual liquidation? Scholars can, it is true, use the authority of I Macc., which says once or twice that the renegades from Judaism were "many" ($\pi o\lambda\lambda o\acute{\iota}$); cf. 1.11; *ib.* 43; *ib.* 52. But the word *polloi* means "many," and not necessarily "the majority"; I Macc. also uses the same word to denote the Jews who were devoted to the Law (cf. for example, 1.62; 2.29, etc.). This evidence is then no authority: it is clear that in the view of I Macc. the criminals and transgressors were "many," for had this not been so, the heroism of the Hasmoneans would not have been so very great.

39 The philosophers Anaxagoras and Protagoras were brought to trial because their philosophical views were opposed to the fundamentals of Greek religion; the educated Aspasia, mistress of Pericles, was accused of *asebeia*—lack of reverence for the gods. The most famous trial is that of Socrates, who was charged with bringing new gods into Athens and with corrupting the youth. Protagoras and Anaxagoras were forced to leave the city; Aspasia was rescued by Pericles with much difficulty from a heavy sentence; and the tragic fate of Socrates, who refused either to flee or to beg for mercy, is well known.

40 The religion of the Druids was prohibited to Roman citizens by Augustus; it was completely proscribed by Tiberius and later by Claudius. The Romans accused the Druids of human sacrifice and of general cruelty in their observances: Suetonius (*Vit. Claud.* 5, 25) speaks of the *dira immanitas* of the Druidic cult, and Tacitus (*Ann.* XIV, 30) of the *saeva superstitio* of their religious leaders. It should be remembered that the Druids were the leaders of the national movement in Gaul in the same way that the Zealots were in Palestine.

41 See Part II, ch. 3, end of the chapter.

42   The general opinion is that the decrees of Antiochus constituted a persecution of Judaism as a whole, wherever Jews were to be found. Bickermann however has stressed the fact that Judaism was prohibited only in Jerusalem and in Judaea. He supports his view by legal reasons: just as the declaration of Antiochus III on Jewish autonomy was made only for the Jews of Jerusalem and Judaea, so the rescinding of the declaration affected the same localities only (p. 122). However, the order of Antiochus Epiphanes proscribing Judaism was not intended to replace Antiochus III's edict, which had been long annulled and replaced by the new constitution of the *polis* of "Antioch." Had the administration of the *polis* published the order for the persecution of Judaism in the form of a municipal *psephisma* (resolution), Bickermann's juridical view would have been decidedly correct. But the persecution was decreed, not by the *polis*, but by a special order of the king, and could either relate to Jerusalem and Judaea alone, or equally possibly affect the Jewish population in other localities of the Seleucid empire, entirely according to the will and decision of the sovereign. According to I Macc. 1.44, the royal rescripts were sent "to Jerusalem and the cities of Judah," and the reason is obvious; the rising had spread only there, and only there was Judaism endangering the peace of the realm. As regards the fate of Judaism in various localities, everything depended on the initiative of the officials and the local population. The Samaritans hastened to address to the king a letter in which they emphasized that they were not identified with the Jews, despite the Law which both peoples possessed in common—showing that they too were threatened with persecution (*Ant.* XII, 257ff.). In the Hellenistic cities of Palestine a persecution of Judaism was also on the brink of breaking out on the initiative of the cities themselves (II Macc. 6.8). Had the Samaritans or the Jews living in the Hellenistic towns been actively supporting the Jewish rising in Jerusalem and Judaea, the royal letters would have been sent to those places as well.

43   Ed. Meyer, 137; Bickermann, 126ff.

44   We know several instances in history in which one people influenced another in the cultural sphere; thus, for example, the upper strata of society in Germany and Russia in the eighteenth century acquired French language and customs. These sympathies, however, possessed no political significance, and their "Frenchness" did not go beyond cultural influence and external changes in the conventional comportment of the high aristocracy.

NOTES   *part* **I**   *chapter* **6**

1   According to I Macc. 2.3, Simon was the second of the sons of Mattathias and Judah the third; but Josephus (*War* I, 37) says that Judah was the eldest brother, and this information accords better with the position he occupied in the family. It is not credible that Simon was the eldest, for after Judah's death not he but Jonathan occupied first place. During Judah's lifetime, as is well known, Simon fulfilled no special function; nevertheless, I Macc. saw need to put into the old Mattathias' mouth the words: "Here is Simon your brother; I know he is a man of counsel, so hearken to his voice all your days, and he will be a father unto you" (I Macc. 2.65). By contrast, Mattathias calls Judah solely a warrior and a captain (*ib.* 66).

2 B. Niese, *Kritik der beiden Makkabäerbücher*, 1900, p. 46.

3 Professor J. Klausner (*Hist. of the Sec. Common.* [Heb.], III, 14), believes that the Ḥasidic author of II Macc. did not wish to mention Mattathias, as the decision of the Hasmoneans to fight on the Sabbath was associated with his name (I Macc. 2.39ff.). But there was no need to erase Mattathias from history for this reason: it would have been sufficient to pass over this single fact in silence. Moreover, although the Hasmonean decision to fight on Sabbaths was linked with Mattathias' name, it is clear that Judah the Maccabee did not refrain from following him, yet II Macc. has no compunctions about relating the precise opposite, namely, that Judah was careful not to fight on the Sabbath (II Macc. 8.26ff.). This being so, what prevented the author reporting the same of Mattathias? It would be more correct to suppose that II Macc. had heard nothing at all about Mattathias or his role at the beginning of the rebellion; nor would this be surprising, for Jason of Cyrene, whose narrative is the basis of II Macc., was not an official historian of the Hasmoneans and did not know all the details of the family tradition created and preserved at the Hasmonean court. Cf. App. 1, §1, at end.

4 Cf. J. Klausner, *Hist.*, III, 37ff.; Schürer, *op. cit.*, I, 215; Wellhausen, *Pharisäer u. Sadduzäer*, 84; Kölbe, *Beiträge z. syrischen u. jüdischen Geschichte*, 1926, 162; E. Bevan, *Jerusalem under the High Priests*, 1904, 91ff.; L. Finkelstein, *The Pharisees*, 2, 595.

5 See above, p. 477f., n. 38.

6 In this connection it would be well to cite the view of Rostovtzeff, who places Judah the Maccabee in the broad setting of the Hellenistic world and evaluates his activity as one of the factors in the breakup of the Seleucid empire. After describing the pro-Hellenistic policy of Antiochus Epiphanes, Rostovtzeff continues in the following words: "It was not the fault of Epiphanes that, by pursuing this policy and by supporting the efforts of those who approved it among the higher classes of the population of Judaea, he encountered the fierce resistance of Judas and of his followers, who were ready to die for the old traditions and for their monotheistic religious seclusion. In fact Judah represented the ideals and the dreams of the large masses of the natives, a class neglected by the government and exploited by the city *bourgeoisie*. The revolt of Judas was directed more against the ruling classes than against the central government" (*SEHHW*, 2, 704ff. Cf. 709, 1105, 1107).

7 The best account is given by I Macc. which is followed by Jos. *Ant.* XII, 265ff. II Macc. also contains very important information, but its chronological order is frequently corrupt. The short narrative at the beginning of Josephus' *War* is full of errors and must be used with great caution.

8 This Apollonius was in charge of Samaria; Josephus calls him "*strategos* of Samaria" (*Ant.* XII, 287) and *meridarches* (*ib.* 264). Some scholars (R. Marcus, Abel) think that he was the same as Apollonius the "Mysarch" (cf. above, p. 188); but Apollonius was a very common name in the Hellenistic period and the identification is therefore not certain.

9 Seron is designated in I Macc. (3.13) as "commander of the forces of Coele-Syria." He was therefore senior in rank to Apollonius, then governing Samaria. Cf. on his position, Bengston, *Die Strategie*, II, 171.

10 On the military aspect of the Hasmonean battles (topographical and strategic questions and the like), cf. Avi-Yonah, "The Battles of the Books of the Maccabees," in the *Essays in memoriam Johannis Lewy* (Heb.), 13ff.

11 The text of I Macc. says δύναμις Συρίας, but according to Abel (commentary *ad loc.*) the Hebrew original had "Edom," hence the text should be amended to δύναμις Ἰδουμαίας.

12 I Macc. 3.41; II Macc. 8.11; 8.25; 8.34. In I Macc. 3.41, πέδας (chains) should be read, instead of παῖδας (slaves), to agree with *Ant.* XII, 299. Cf. Abel's commentary *ad loc.*; Bévenot's commentary, *ad loc.* The practice of taking fetters when the army marched out to war was usual and is mentioned, for instance, in Herodotus I, 66 (Sparta against Tegea).

13 II Macc. 2.6, 8. The invitation was sent on the initiative of the people of Ptolemais (II Macc. *ib.*). On hostile acts by the Syrians against the Jews, see p. 210.

14 At Narbatta, today En-Nirba, east of Tul Karem. The place is mentioned in the mss. of I Macc. 5.23, in corrupt form, as *en Arbaktois*, *Arbanois, Arbatnois*. On S. Klein's conjecture these should be amended as *en Narbattois*: Narbatta in Samaria being meant. See his book *Galiläa von der Makkabäerzeit bis 67*, 3. On Narbatta, see Avi-Yonah, *Hist. Geog.*, 117.

15 On the Jewish population in Transjordan in this period, see S. Klein, *Jewish Transjordan*, 1925 (Heb.), 1ff. On the Jews of the Land of Tov, see above, p. 430, n. 70.

16 II Macc. 8.25; *ib.* 30. II Macc. seeks to justify these actions by emphasizing the participation of the widows, orphans and old people in the sharing of the booty. Even if we assume that this was true, it does not alter the fact itself, but merely evidences that on occasion the entire rural population enjoyed the enemy's plunder.

17 I Macc. 6.24. The precise interpretation of *kleronomia* is "inheritance" or "ancestral estate." Since Judah looked upon the Hellenizers as social enemies (cf. above, p. 480, n. 6) it is to be assumed that their estates were sequestered for the benefit of the fighters of the war of liberation.

18 On the Akra as a Greek *polis* standing near Jerusalem and on the "symbiosis" between these two "towns" (Bickermann's view), see Appendix III. On the topography of the Akra scholars differ; see Schürer, *op. cit.*, I, 198, n. 37; Vincent, *RB*, 42, 1933, 83ff.; *ib.* 43, 1934, 220ff.; Johns, *QDAP*, 1950, 134ff.; J. Simons, *Jerusalem in the Old Test.*, 1952, 144ff.; Vincent and Steve, *Jérusalem de l'Anc. Test.*, 1954, 175ff.

19 See his article "Griechische Urkunden in der jüdischen-Hellenistischen Literatur," *Hist. Zeitschr.*, 136. On the question of the above-mentioned documents, cf. the present writer's article, "The Documents in the Second Book of the Maccabees," *Tarbitz*, I (Heb.), 1930, 31ff.

20 Thus also Bévenot in his commentary *ad loc.*, and Abel *ad loc.*

21 See Abel and Bévenot, comm. *ad loc.* According to Bévenot the name has been corrupted in the mss. and the month meant is the Macedonian Dystros, which preceded Xandikos. This date suits the order in which the documents were composed (cf. the next note).

22 Some scholars doubt that Lysias really fought the Jews twice. Cf., for example, Kolbe, *op. cit.*, 81. The present writer's opinion is that there are sufficient grounds for this view; see his above-mentioned article, p. 43. If we accept Bévenot's conjecture referred to in the previous note, Lysias' successive meetings with the Romans and the Jews took place in the month of Dystros, that is, about a month before the final discussion of the Jewish question at Antioch. This is highly probable.

23 Scholars entertain differing opinions on the question of which king it was who signed Document 3—Antiochus IV Epiphanes or his younger son Antiochus V Eupator. It seems to me that the latter is the only real possibility. According to information in the Babylonian Cuneiform Chronicle recently published (see Sachs and Wiseman, "A Babylonian King List of the Hellenistic Period," *Iraq*, 116, 1954, 202ff.; cf. Schaumberger, in *Biblica*, 36, 1955, 423ff.). The death of Antiochus Epiphanes should be dated Kislev (November-December) 164 and not 163 as had previously been thought. According to I Macc. 3.37, Antiochus left Antiocheia in autumn 166/5 (cf.

Schaumberger, 433), and we know from various sources that the activities of Antiochus in the east comprised Armenia, Babylonia, Elam and Persia and were also connected with widespread military operations (cf. Ed. Meyer, II, 216ff.; Niese, *GGMS*, III, 216ff.; Bevan, *CAH*, VIII, 513ff.). It is unthinkable that all these operations were carried out within the short period of approximately six months, and it is clear, therefore, that the dating of I Macc. is right. Antiochus V's extreme youth (he was about eight years old in 164) is no valid argument against the belief that the document was composed in his name; it was the practice in the Seleucid kingdom to give the heir to the throne a share of power and the title of king in his father's lifetime; nor, if he was a child, did his age prevent his theoretical conduct of the affairs of state. Cf. Bickermann, *Inst. des Sél.*, 21.

24 Those scholars who regard the Jews, with whom Lysias and the Romans conducted negotiations, as Judah the Maccabee and his party, rely *inter alia* on Lysias' form of address τῷ πλήθει τῶν Ἰουδαίων (I Macc. 11.16). In their opinion the term *plethos* denotes the unorganized mass, while the correct expression for "people" is *demos*. Cf. E. Meyer, *op. cit.*, II, 213; Bickermann, *Gott der Makk.*, 82. But the Romans addressing the same Jews call them *demos* (*ib.* 34), and they too were familiar with the legal terminology of the Hellenistic world. It is true that the accepted legal term applying to a people organized in a *polis* was *demos*, while *plethos* has a broader connotation, meaning the popular masses as a whole. But even in the classical period accuracy was not exercised in the choice of the word (the Athenian orator Lysias, for instance, regularly uses *plethos* when he is speaking of the organized Athenian people), and in the Hellenistic period the term *plethos* is sometimes used in official documents instead of *demos*. See C. B. Welles, *Royal Correspondence in the Hellenistic Period*, 1934, no. 15, 1.8; no. 22, 1.4; no. 52, 1.33; *OGIS*, no. 763, ll.33, 40. This lack of precision in terminology cannot therefore serve as a decisive argument against my own view, that the negotiations were conducted between Lysias and the Romans, on the one hand, and the city of Antioch-at-Jerusalem, on the other. E. Meyer (*op. cit.*, 214) regarded the third document, at least, as directed to the Hellenistic city ("the city of the Akra"), while Bickermann (*op. cit.*, 83) thinks that the *Gerousia* to which number 3 is addressed, represented the traditional Jewish community of Jerusalem (see App. III, at end). I find my own view expressed in M. B. Dagut's article in *JBL*, 72, 1953, 151; he, like myself, thinks that all these documents are directed to the Hellenists.

25 II Macc. 11.28: κατελθόντας ὑμᾶς γίνεσθαι πρὸς τοῖς ἰδίοις. The literal meaning of κατέρχεσθαι is "to go down," but Hellenistic-Roman offices used the word also for a wider conception—"to return home," the reference being generally to the return from an exile resulting from political disturbances and disorders to one's permanent abode.

In Egypt flight from the villages was known as *anachoresis*, strictly "ascent" (from the Nile valley to the hills), return home being expressed by various verbs, *epanerchesthai, katerchesthai*, etc. Cf. the amnesty proclamation of King Ptolemy VIII Euergetes II (*SP* 210, line 6), and the edict of the Roman governors of Egypt, Vibius Maximus (*ib.* no. 220, line 23ff.) and Sempronius Liberalis (*W. Chr.*, 19, line 9ff., 22).

26 II Macc. gives the names of the envoys: Joḥanan and Absalom (11.17). Is this Joḥanan identical with the one who obtained the φιλάνθρωπα βασιλικά from Antiochus III (*ib.* 4.11)? At first sight it is not easy to suppose that the Jewish statesman whose political work had been annulled by the Hellenizers sat as a member of the *gerousia* of Hellenistic "Antioch," but we have seen above that the *gerousia* opposed Menelaus, and we have stated that the Hellenistic reform was not in any sense bound up with the abolition of the Jewish religion. Apart from this, the delegates sent by the Hellenizers to Lysias in order to secure the annulment of Antiochus' decrees may have been intentionally selected from among those men who were sympathetic to ancestral tradition. In 164 Joḥanan would have been about seventy years old.

As to Absalom, I would like to draw attention, with all possible reservations, to the "House of Absalom" mentioned in the Habakkuk Commentary, v, 9. Cf. D. N. Freedman, *BASOR*, 114, April 1949, 11-12; K. E. Elliger, *Studien zum Habakuk-Kommentar*, 1953, p. 238ff. The name Absalom is also mentioned in I Macc. 11.70; 13.11. Clearly the identification of Absalom of II Macc. with one of the family of Absalom in the Habakkuk Commentary depends on the general question, as yet unresolved, of the date of the composition of the Dead Sea scrolls. Cf. Appendix I, 6.

27 See on this embassy, E. Meyer, *op. cit.*, II, 213.

28 On Ptolemy son of Makron see E. Meyer, *op. cit.*, II, 233. According to Bévenot's commentary *ad loc.*, he was identical with Ptolemy son of Dorimenes, a high Syrian commander, who more than once had occasion to handle Jewish matters (I Macc. 3.38; II Macc. 4.45; *ib.* 8.8). Cf. Bengston, *Die Strategie*, II, 164.

29 In these years the Macedonian month of Xandikos corresponded to Nisan—cf. *Ant.* XII, 321 and 412, where Josephus identifies Apellaios with Kislev and Dystros with Adar. As it is not to be assumed that the Jews would have left their abodes in Passover Week, only the short period of approximately a week was in effect allowed to those who desired to utilize the amnesty to return to their homes. Cf. Bévenot and Abel, commentaries *ad loc.*

30 Josephus writes that Judah was elected by the people as High Priest and served in the post three years (*Ant.* XII, 414, 419, 434).

But in other places (*Ant.* XII, 385; XX, 237) he calls Alcimus High Priest immediately after Menelaus without mentioning Judah at all, which is more in agreement with the account of events in the books of the Maccabees. It is not to be supposed that the Ḥasidim, who constituted the core of Judah the Maccabee's force, would have agreed to Judah's election as High Priest, as he did not belong to the traditional high priestly family.

31 The 25th Kislev was purposely chosen by Judah the Maccabee, because on that day three years previously the Temple had been profaned by the offering of a pagan sacrifice (I Macc. 59; *ib.* 4.44; II Macc. 10.5). We do not know why Antiochus had chosen the 25th Kislev to make the first sacrifice on the altar of the Temple; the conjecture that this was Antiochus' birthday (cf. Abel, *Comm.* on I Macc. 1.59) rests on no authority; in II Macc. 6.7 it is indeed stated that the Jews were compelled to make a monthly sacrifice in honor of the king's birthday, but it is not stated that this fell on the 25th of the month. Some think that the 25th Kislev was an ancient popular festival connected with the sun cult; cf. Ed. Meyer, II, 209, n. 5, who cites in authority Wellhausen; A. S. Rankin, *The Origins of the Festival of Hannukkah,* 1930.

The proofs, however, are very weak, nor are they supported by any source. Nevertheless, there may be a grain of truth in this supposition, for the very fact that both Antiochus and Judah chose the 25th Kislev for a great religious demonstration may justify the idea that an ancient popular festival was celebrated on that day, but nothing is known about it. At all events, the view is not tenable that the Festival of Hannukah developed from the Festival of Dionysus. Although it is true that during Antiochus' persecution the Jews were forced to celebrate this too (II Macc. 6.7), it is not stated that it fell on the 25th Kislev; as to the 25th December, thought to be the birthday of Dionysus according to the Roman calendar, this day does not necessarily correspond with 25th Kislev. (On the Dionysiac festival at Jerusalem during the *Gezerot* of Antiochus, see Otto Kern, in *Arch. f. Rel.,* 22, 1923-4, 198ff.; Willrich, *ib.* 24, 1926, 170ff.)

The decrees of Antiochus continued too short a time to enable the people to become accustomed to the Dionysiac festival or see it as a genuine popular holiday, nor is it to be assumed that Judah the Maccabee used a pronounced pagan festival on which to fix the day of the dedication of the Temple. The latter was apparently fixed to some extent in imitation of Tabernacles, which had not been properly celebrated during the persecutory decrees; see Abel, *Comm. to the Books of the Maccs.,* 416ff.; Höpfl, "Das Chanukafest," *Biblica,* 3, 1922, 165ff.; S. Zeitlin, *JQR,* 29, 1938-39, 1ff.

32 "On the 24th of Av they came to court." The "Scholion" comments: "In the days of the kingdom of Greece they judged according to the laws of the Gentiles, and when the hand of the House of the Hasmoneans prevailed and peace was made, they abolished these, returned to judging according to the laws of Israel, and the day that they abolished them they made a festival" (*Megillat Ta'anit,* ed. Lichtenstein, 278, 334).

33 According to Segal (in *Eretz Yisrael* (Heb.), I, 42), Judah began to collect the copies of the Bible immediately after the victory, the uniform and authoritative version of the Scripture being then determined. Cf. also his book *Introduction to the Bible* (Heb.), IV, 864ff.; Klausner, *Hist.,* III, 22.

34 The changes in the *Gerousia* may be inferred from II Macc. 14.37-38: Razis is called "one of the elders of Jerusalem" and is stated to have been especially devoted to Judaism and to have fought for it during the period of disturbances. Such men entered the *Gerousia* under Judah the Maccabee.

35 I Macc. 5; II Macc. 10.10ff.; 12.1ff.

36 Thus, for instance, at Ephron (I Macc. 5.51), Bosra (*ib.* 5.28), and Maspha (*ib.* 5.35).

37 Thus, for example, the slogans cited in II Macc.: θεοῦ βοηθείας (the help of God) and θεοῦ νίκην (God's victory)—(8.23; 8.15). If the scroll of "The War of the Sons of Light against the Sons of Darkness" reflects the Hasmonean struggle, as some scholars think (cf. Avi-Yonah, in *Isr. Explor. Journ.* 2, 1952, 1ff.), the number of slogans was much larger. See, however, on this scroll, Yigael Yadin *The Scroll of the War of the Sons of Light and the Sons of Darkness,* Jerusalem, 1955.

38 Professor M. Schwabe has drawn my attention to the fact that the passage 4.35 of I Macc. differs in style from what is normal in that book: what we have here is purely Hellenistic, not the biblical style characteristic of I Macc. The passage may therefore be a late interpolation and is not to be relied on as historically authentic.

39 On the question of the time of composition of Document 2, see the present writer's above-mentioned article in *Tarbitz* I.

40 Cf. for example, Antiochus III's letter to Ptolemy (above, p. 82). Other examples in Welles, *op. cit.,* nos. 9, 30, 36, 44, 47, 70.

41 τοῦ πατρὸς ἡμῶν εἰς θεοὺς μεταστάντος; this and similar expressions were frequently used in the Hellenistic period when the death of kings was mentioned; see *OGIS,* nos. 308, 338, 339. Cf. Welles, *op. cit.,* 348, s.v. μεταλλάσσω.

42 The revival of the previous laws is indicated explicitly in the sources: I Macc., 6.59; *Ant.* XII, 382.

43 According to II Macc. 14.3, Antiochus by this order broke the oath which had been sworn to the Jews before entering Jerusalem. However, the political outlook of the author of II Macc. crystallized in a period when the Hasmonean control of the fortresses was taken for granted. He regarded Antiochus' demand as an insult to Judah and "corrected" history according to his own taste.

44 *Ant.* XII, 385; II, 13, 4ff. The execution was carried out according to the cruel Persian practice; Bévenot points to the instance alluded to in Valerius Maximus IX, 2, 6.

45 The time of Alcimus' appointment as High Priest is not sufficiently clear in the sources. The books of the Maccabees first mention Alcimus only under King Demetrius, hence it was only then that he began to aspire to the High Priesthood (I Macc. 7.5). Josephus, on the other hand (*Ant.* XII, 387), stresses that Alcimus was appointed High Priest by Lysias immediately after the death of Menelaus, and he is termed "formerly High Priest" also in II Macc. 14.3. Josephus' chronology is apparently the correct one. It is hard to imagine that Lysias would have left Palestine without introducing political stability into the conduct of government in Judaea by appointing the High Priest who was responsible to the Syrian government as its supreme official in the country. Cf. Abel, comment. on I Macc. 7.5.

46 Klausner, *Hist.*, III, 40; cf. E. Meyer, *op. cit.*, II, 243; Schürer, *op. cit.*, I, 217; Oesterley, *op. cit.*, 1932, 239.

47 M. Peah II, 7. The Talmud relates that Yose ben Yoezer was the uncle of Yakim (Alcimus) and was executed by him, but the latter also died a violent death (*Gen. Rab.* 65, 22; *Mid. Psalms*, 11.7 (52). The story is full of imaginary features and cannot serve as a reliable historical source.

48 These negotiations between Nicanor and the Jews were the result of the activity of the Hellenizers: Nicanor, at any rate, had sent Jewish envoys to Judah (II Macc. 14.19—Theodotos and Mattathias); there were also Jewish troops serving in his army. If this was the case, this was the last attempt on the part of the Greeks to end the civil war with a compromise. However, Alcimus opposed compromise and frustrated the negotiations (*ib.* 14.26).

49 Thus, for example, the peasants of Judaea attacked the remnants of Nicanor's force after the latter had been defeated by Judah the Maccabee, and "mopped up" the enemy to the last man.

NOTES   *part* **I**   *chapter* **7**

1 In this short account only a précis of events is given, insofar as they concern our present subject. The reader will find a detailed narrative of the period in J. Klausner, *History*, III, 49ff.; Schürer, I, 223ff.; E. Meyer, *op. cit.*, II, 252ff.

2 *Syrische Territorien,* 55, n. 2.

3 *Meridarches*—the governor of a *meris,* or part. In Hellenistic Egypt Fayûm was divided into three *merides;* see Wilcken, *Grundzüge,* 11.

4 Bickermann, *Inst. des Séleucides,* 199; Bengston, *Die Strategie,* II, 26ff.; 170.

5 The name (סולמה של צור) is mentioned in Tosephta, Pesahim I, 28; in Greek it is κλῖμαξ Τύρου.

6 The reader will find a detailed account of the posts of the *strategoi* in the Hellenistic period in Bengston's above-mentioned work, *Die Strategie in der hellenistischen Zeit,* I-III (1937-1952).

7 Evidently the Gerar mentioned in Gen. 10.19, south of Gaza. Cf. Avi-Yonah, *Hist. Geog. of Eretz Yisrael,* 156.

8 Cf. Bengston, *op. cit.,* II, 176ff.

9 Cf. *Meg. Ta'anit,* for the 27th Iyyar: "On the twenty-seventh of the month they removed the *kelilah* from Jerusalem." The *kelilah* tax (Greek στέφανος) here connotes all the taxes paid to the king.

10 Cf. *Meg. Ta'anit* for the 23rd Iyyar: "on the twenty-third of the month the men of the Acra departed from Jerusalem."

11 Cf. *Meg. Ta'anit* for the 14th Siwan: "On the fourteenth of Siwan the capture of the tower of Zur." According to the "Scholion" of *Meg. Ta'anit,* Caesarea is meant, that is, Straton's Tower, and several modern scholars, following this suggestion, connect the information with the capture of Straton's Tower by Alexander Jannaeus. But the present author finds Lichtenstein's view (in his commentary *ad loc.*) more acceptable, which, following Graetz and others, connects this event with the taking of Bet Zur under Simon. Cf. I Macc. 14.33. In the same passage the fortification of the towns of Judaea (apart from Bet Zur) is referred to in a general sense.

12 The document is preserved in I Macc. 14.27ff. and it bears the date of "the 18th Ellul of the year 172 (of the Seleucid era), which is the third year of Simon the High Priest." Although the text of the document may have been worked over or corrected here and there, there are no grounds for doubting its general authenticity. Cf. Schürer, I, 250, n. 19; Abel, *Les Livres des Maccabées,* 254ff. S. Zeitlin,*The First Book of the Maccabees,* 1950, introd., 43f.

13 See, for example, E. Meyer, "(Dass) der Krieg . . . zur Entstehung eines unabhängigen jüdischen Staates führte, beruht nicht auf der inneren Kraft des jüdischen Volkes und der religiösen Bewegung, sondern auf der Gestaltung der politische Verhältnisse" (II, 252). Cf. Schürer, I, 222; Kolbe, *op. cit.,* 167; Bevan; *CAH,* VIII, 528ff.

14 Antiochus III's war with Xerxes: Polyb. VIII, 25; his war with Arsaces; *ib.* X, 28ff.; his peace treaty with Arsaces: Justin XLI, 7, 5;

his war with Euthydemos: Polyb. XI, 34. Cf. Niese, *GGMS*, II, 396ff.; Holleaux, *CAH*, VIII, 138ff.

15 Modern historians generally regard Rome as the power which destroyed the Hellenistic kingdoms; cf. for example, Rostovtzeff, *SEHHW*, I, 69ff., who describes Roman policy as "Machiavellian, often dishonest and always strictly egoistic" (71). But even he has to admit that Rome was not responsible for the internal decay of the Hellenistic kingdoms: he merely ascribes a "catastrophic" character to a process which would have developed in any case (*ib.* 72). A correct view is expressed by Launey in the following words: "C'est en lui-même qu'il (*sc.* le monde hellénistique) portait le germe de sa propre destruction et, même sans Rome, il aurait disparu; la conquête romaine, si elle anéantit politiquement, sauva en revanche ce qui pouvait encore être sauvé de la culture hellénique déjà sur son déclin" (II, 1094).

16 The capture of Yavneh is not mentioned in I Macc., but Josephus reckons the town, with Jaffa and Gezer, as one of the towns captured by Simon (*War* I, 50; *Ant.* XIII, 215). As Yavneh was in the hands of Kendebaios during his war with Simon (I Macc. 15.40), it may be supposed that Simon's sons took the city after Kendebaios had been forced to leave the country.

17 Charges against the Jews as foes and destroyers of culture were already being voiced in the ancient world; cf. Johanan Lewy's article in *MGWJ*, 77, 1933, 84ff. The hostility of the Hellenized Syrian of Palestine to the Hasmoneans is evidenced by a Greek inscription found in the excavations at Gezer: "May fire consume Simon's palace, says Pampras." This curse was incised on a block destined to be one of the stones of a building set up in Gezer, apparently by Simon's order. The author of the inscription was probably one of the building-laborers and a man of Gezer. Cf. Macalister, *The Excavations of Gezer*, 1, 210ff.; *CIJ* II, 1184.

18 Cf. for example E. Meyer, II, 280. The theologian's view has been most consistently expressed by E. Bevan in his book *Jerusalem under the High Priests*, and although the book was published as early as 1904, it is worth citing some extracts from it, as the approach of the theologians to the Hasmonean kingdom has not in principle altered since then. The author expresses the principle behind his outlook on the work of the Hasmoneans as follows: "It appears to me a question whether it was not at great spiritual cost that the Jewish people allowed itself to be launched by the sons of Hasmon upon a career of carnal strife. For the Jewish community could not be amenable to the same laws as ordinary nations; it was . . . more like a church; and the laws of a church's life were in that degree the true laws of its being" (98).

And this is his highly colored picture of the work of the Hasmoneans in Palestine: "Under the blast of the Jewish conquests, civilization in Palestine withered away.

Where there had been prosperous cities were heaps of ruins. Fields went back to brushwood, and roaming bands of marauders had free course in the land. Such a state of things marked the zenith of Hasmonean power" (128). How deep and contagious is the theological influence can be judged from the way Bickermann, neither a theologian nor a Christian, but a Jewish historian, ends his book *Der Gott der Makkabäer:* "Es liegt . . . ein tiefer Sinn in der historischen Ungerechtigkeit, die monotheistischen Religionen begingen, als sie zwar die Erinnerung an die Makkabäertage aufrecht erhielten, aber die Familie der Hasmonäer vergessen . . . Denn die Taten der Makkabäer sind nur darum ewig denkwürdig, weil sie die Rettung des Monotheismus bewirkten" (138f.).

19 Tyrants of this type were for example Zoilos of Dor and Straton's Tower (*Ant.* XIII, 324), Theodorus in Transjordan (*ib.* 356) and Zenon-Kotylas at Philadelpheia (*War* I, 60).

20 Head, *op. cit.,* p. 804.

21 Cf. Goodenough, *Yale Class. Stud.* I, p. 53ff.; Schubart, in *Arch. f. Pap., XII,* 1ff. It should be remarked that Augustus in his memoirs (*Res Gestae Divi Augusti,* 1) stressed that his aid to the Roman people was furnished *privato consilio et privata impensa.*

22 See Sukenik, in *Kedem,* I, 1941, 12ff.; Sellers, *The Citadel of Beth Zur,* 70; Hill, *QDAP* 6, 1938, 78ff.; Reifenberg, *ib.* 11, 1945, 33ff.; B. Kanael, in *Is. Expl. Jnl.,* 1, 1950-51, 170ff.

23 On the character of these petty Hellenistic kingdoms, see Rostovtzeff, *SEHHW,* II, 848ff.

24 See on the Hasmonean coins, G. F. Hill, *Catal. of the Greek Coins of Palestine,* 1914, 184ff.; S. Raphaeli, *Coins of the Jews* (Heb.), 1913, 91ff.; Narkiss, *Coins of the Jews* (Heb.), 95ff.; Reifenberg, *Ancient Jewish Coins,* 1947.

25 There is, indeed, some doubt that Aristobulus was the first king; this is what Josephus says (*Ant.* XIII, 301), but according to Strabo (XV, 762), Alexander Jannaeus was the first. Aptowitzer in his book *Parteipolitik der Hasmonäerzeit in Rabbinischen und Pseudepigraphischen Schriften,* 1927, 13ff., thinks that John Hyrcanus was the first to call himself king, and in this is followed by Oesterley (*A History of Israel,* II, 285ff.). However, their reasons do not appeal to the writer, nor is the fact mentioned in any historical source. Aristobulus appears on coins with his traditional title of High Priest, and this is an important proof of Strabo's statement. But it is possible that the Hasmoneans did not introduce the royal authority all at once, since it was apt to arouse much opposition among the people as a decidedly Hellenistic institution. Aristobulus therefore may have used the title "king" only to the outer world during negotiations with the Greeks, whereas Alexander Jannaeus may have been the first officially to add the title "king" to his traditional title of High Priest.

26 *Ant.* XIII, 318. Aristobulus was personally popular, as Strabo testifies, quoting the Greek historian Timagenes (*ib.* 329).

27 Weiss, *Dor Dor v'Dorshav*, I, 114ff.; Klausner, *History*, III, 107ff.; Schürer, II, 447ff.; E. Meyer, II, 282ff.; Wellhausen, *Pharisäer and Sadducäer*, 1874; Hölscher, *Der Sadduzäismus;* R. Travers Herford, *Pharisaism, its Aim and its Method*, 1912; *id., The Pharisees*, 1924; L. Baeck, "Die Pharisäer," in *Bericht der Hochsch. f. d. Wiss. d. Judentums*, 1927, 33-71; Lauterbach, "The Pharisees and their Teachings," in *HUCA* 6, 1929, 69-139; S. Zeitlin, *The Sadducees and the Pharisees*, 1937; L. Finkelstein, "The Pharisees: their Origin and their Philosophy," in *HTR*, 22, 1921, 185ff.; *id. The Pharisees*, I-II, 1946. It is to be remarked that in the great books of Herford and Finkelstein the treatment of the Pharisean sect is embedded in the general account of the development of the Mosaic Oral Law from the time of Ezra down to the conclusion of the Talmud, and for this reason the peculiar problems connected with the controversy between the Pharisees and the Sadducees under the Hasmoneans do not find their solutions.

28 *Ant.* XIII, 171ff.; 288ff.; *ib.* XVII; *ib.* XVIII, 41ff.; *War* II, 119, 162ff.

29 M. Erub. VI, 2; Hag. II, 7; Sota III, 4; Makkot, I, 6; Parah III, 7; Nidda IV, 2; Yadaim IV, 6-8.

30 The period of Jonathan, however, was such as to favor the appearance of new sects. It concluded the seven years of anarchy among the Jewish people during which the Jerusalem theocracy lacked a leader and the post of the High Priest remained vacant. The interpretation of the laws was in the hands of the Ḥasidim, but official authority was held by the Hellenizers, the Ḥasidic interpretations possessing no official validity. From the time of Jonathan, the scribes took over the conduct of affairs officially. Possibly, therefore, it was just at this time that their leaders reorganized themselves afresh as a sect separate from the others and took a new name, "Pharisees" instead of "Ḥasidim"; this new organization may have been essential, if it is assumed that in this period a split took place in the Ḥasidic sect, part of which, consisting of the extremists, organized itself as a distinct section, the "Essenes" (including perhaps the mysterious sect of Yaḥad newly discovered in the Dead Sea Scrolls). The reign of Jonathan was a period of crisis for the Sadducees also. The High Priesthood had passed to a new family, and members of the Jerusalem aristocracy, who regarded themselves as unjustly deprived of their rights by the rise of the *novi homines*, organized themselves as a conservative group under the slogan of the ancient theocratic authority. On this question cf. below, n. 40.

31 On the details of this story, cf. below, notes 33, 43.

32 Cf. above, p. 197ff.

33 This is not of course Josephus' private opinion, but the declared official view of the Hasmonean court. "And this was inquired into and not found (true)," says the Talmud; from this it is to be deduced that when rumors became current that John Hyrcanus' mother (not of course Alexander Jannaeus' mother, who could never have been a prisoner of the Greeks for good chronological reasons) had borne John when she was "a captive at Modiin" (during the persecution of Antiochus Epiphanes, at the latest at the beginning of Jonathan's reign) disqualifying John for the High Priesthood, the government had conducted an official inquiry into the matter, which failed to authenticate the allegation. "And the scholars of Israel were furious in their disagreement," that is, they would not acknowledge the conclusions of the official inquiry and continued to insist that John was disqualified for the High Priesthood. These are the conclusions to be drawn from the talmudic narrative, if we credit all its details. But as is well known, the Talmud's historical memories of the Hasmonean period were rather vague, as the substitution of Alexander Jannaeus for John Hyrcanus proves. Cf. on this question, Klausner, *History*, III, 138-139.

34 Cf. Aptowitzer, *Parteipolitik*, 15, 49.

35 *Ib.* 5ff. Cf. Klausner, *History*, III, 139.

36 Although we lack decisive proofs for the date of composition of the above-mentioned chapters of the *Book of Enoch*, their attribution to the time of Alexander Jannaeus is confirmed by several secondary features. The section was written in time of war, as is indicated by the great excitement and spirit of cruelty that bursts from it from time to time (*e.g.*, 98.12). This war is being waged between two Jewish parties, hence that between the Ḥasidim and the Hellenizers or between the Pharisees and the Sadducees may be considered. However, in 98.2 the pious author ascribes to his enemies the kingship, which excludes the Hellenizers, but is appropriate to Alexander Jannaeus. This war, indeed, also continued under Salomé Alexandra, but the Pharisees then had the upper hand, whereas from the *Book of Enoch* it is clear that the Pharisees are the side which is suffering. The period of Herod and the Roman procurators cannot be considered, especially for theological reasons: the questions of the resurrection of the dead, reward and punishment and the like, appears in the *Book of Enoch* (in the relevant portion) in the form of a new doctrine, which is not appropriate to the Herodian period, when questions of this sort had already assumed the form of permanent religious principles. The *Book of Enoch* has been preserved in the Ethiopian language, but the above-mentioned chapters have been found on a Greek papyrus. Cf. Campbell Bonner, *The Last Chapters of the Book of Enoch*, 1937.

37 It is doubtful if they could prove this. The Pentateuch, indeed, reports two sons of Aaron, Eleazar and Itamar, who were the ancestors of the priests (Num. 3.1ff.), and I Chron. 24.2ff. also relates that under David a third of all the priestly posts was kept for Itamar's descendants. However, in effect, tradition has strictly preserved the geneological tree only of the family of Eleazar, since Zaddok the High Priest in King David's time, was of this family (cf. I Chron. 5.27ff.). During the Babylonian exile the concept of "the sons of Zaddok" took the place of the wide concept of "the sons of Aaron" (Ezek. 44.15; cf. Num. 25.10ff.). It is to be supposed, therefore, that in the Hellenistic period all the priests were regarded as sons of Zaddok and an absolute identification was made between "the sons of Aaron" and "the sons of Zaddok." The Hasmoneans, of course, were not of the Oniad family, but in popular eyes they too were sons of Zaddok, just as they were sons of Aaron. If the Pharisees held that the Hasmoneans were not of Zaddok's family, they thereby in fact denied their membership of the priesthood altogether, and the basis of this strange slander could only be the doubtful origin of John, since his mother had been in captivity. It should be observed that the mysterious "Yaḥad" sect known to us from the *Book of the Damascus Covenant* and from the Qumran sectarian document, also identifies the sons of Zaddok with the priests; cf. *The Book of the Damascus Covenant*, VI, 1ff.; *Seraḥ ha-Yaḥad*, V, 2: *ib.* 9; Barthélemy and Milik, *Qumran Cave I*, 1955, p. 109ff. (Cal. I, 2, 24; Cal. II, 3; Cal. I, 16, 23; Cal. II, 13.)

38 See above, p. 155.

39 "Will mann von einer nationalen Partei reden so sind es die Sadducäer" (Wellhausen, *Phar. u. Sadd.*, 94-5).

40 Namely, priests called after Zaddok, the chief priest in King David's day (II Sam. 8.17; I Ki. i.8, etc.); cf. above, n. 37. This is the accepted opinion (Geiger, Wellhausen, Schürer, Klausner, Finkelstein and others). Another opinion is that the Sadducees were called after Zaddok, an unknown scholar who lived in the Hellenistic period and founded a new school opposed to the Pharisee doctrine (Graetz, E. Meyer). A third view holds that the word is derived from the Greek word *syndikos* which means "lawyer," "legal counsel," or the like (cf. T. W. Manson, in *Bull. of the John Rylands Library*, 22, 1938, 144ff.). None of these theories has convincing proofs to offer, but the first at least has the advantage that it connects the Sadducee sect with the priestly class, and such a close connection did exist from Herodian times on, there being grounds for the assumption of its prior existence.

41 According to Hölscher, for example, the Sadducees sought to introduce the principles of Roman law among the Jews; their attitude to the Jewish religion was not serious, and the disputes between them and the Pharisees reveal only the mockery which they heaped upon their opponents (Hölscher, *Der Sadduzäismus*, 26, 30).

42 The adherence to the written word on the part of the Sadducees is noticeable in the differences of opinion between the two sects preserved in the Mishnah; cf. Makk. I, 6; Menaḥot, X, 3; Peah III, 7. Their more austere application of legal principles is testified to by Josephus, *Ant.* XIII, 294; XX, 199.

43 The famous talmudic sentence: "And what will happen to the Torah?"—"It will be wrapped up and laid in a corner, and all who wish to come and study it, let them come and study" (above, n. 31)—sounds like a piece of clever mockery. In the Pharisee view, anarchy was the logical result of the Sadducee seizure of power.

44 This ideology, by the way, was of real advantage to the material situation of the priests: the Law of Moses granted the priestly class so many privileges that they might well prefer to content themselves with the Written Law rather than endanger their position by various interpretations, not all of which were invariably to their profit.

NOTES *part* **II** *chapter* **1**

1 Flacc. 45; cf. also *Vit. Mos.* II, 232.

2 If population pressure had been felt earlier, the Jews would first have settled in numbers in the towns of Palestine, whereas we have seen above (p. 209f.) that, as late as the time of Judah the Maccabee, the Jewish population was still weak. Relying on this fact, Willrich (*Juden und Griechen,* 170) thought that the Jewish dispersion in Egypt, Syria and the western countries was created only in the period of the Maccabean revolt. However, new information drawn from papyri and inscriptions contradicts this view.

3 On the Elephantine papyri, see Sachau, *Aramäische Papyrus u. Ostraka aus der Jüdischen Militärkolonie zu Elephantine,* I-II, 1911; Cowley, *Aramaic Papyri of the 5th century B.C.,* 1923; Kraeling, *The Brooklyn Museum Aramaic Papyri,* 1953; E. Meyer, *Der Papyrusfund von Elephantine,* 1912; Hoonacker, *Une communauté Judéo-Araméene à l'Éléphantine,* 1915; Vincent, *La religion des Judéo-Araméens d'Éléphantine,* 1937.

4 *Letter of Arist.,* 13. To what degree this information has been suspect in the eyes of scholars, can be seen from Wendland's sentence in a note to the German translation of the Aristeas letter: "Die Einwanderung mit den Persern beruht wohl auf Missverständnis einer Angabe des Hekataios. Die Jüdische Bundesgenossen des Psammetich ... sind sicher Fiktion" (Kautzch, *Apokr. und Pseudoep.* II, 6).

5 See the Greek inscription in Dittenberger, *Syll.,* I³, no. 1; cf. Schürer, III, 32. For the Semitic inscription, see *Corp. Inscr. Semit.* I, 1, no. 112 (p. 131-5).

6 On the evidence of Jeremiah (44.15ff.) the women readily took part in the cult of "the Queen of Heaven" (the goddess Isis?), and even the men supported them.

7 Arist. letter, 13:35. He is only mistaken when he says that the Persians brought these Jews from Jerusalem (35), since Jerusalem was not then a populous city, and these Jews were no doubt Babylonian Jews serving in the Persian royal army.

8 Josephus relates (*C. Ap.* II, 43) that Alexander settled the Jews in Alexandria "because he honored our people, as Hecataeus testifies" —and finds proof of his statement in what Hecataeus says about Samaria, namely, that Alexander (he alleges) gave it as a gift to the Jews (see above, p. 47).
It is clear therefore that Josephus did not find his information on the Jewish settlement in Alexandria in Hecataeus: had he done so, he would have cited it as proof of Alexander's respect for the Jews, without seeking other indications not directly connected with the subject of *Contra Apionem*.
In another passage (*ib.* I, 194) Josephus quotes the words of Hecataeus about the Jews brought to Babylon by the Persians (*sic*) and, immediately afterwards, about the Jews who, leaving Palestine, went to Egypt and Phoenicia "after Alexander's death." Hecataeus here passes in silence over Alexander's time, just as Aristeas does, showing that he had heard nothing at all about the contemporary Jewish migration to Egypt.

9 Juster, I, 204, n. 3; II, 8, n. 1.

10 On the inscription from the Ibrahimiye cemetery near Alexandria, see Breccia, *BSAA*, 9, 1907, 65; *id. BSAA*, 25, 1930, 108; *id.*, *Juifs et Chrétiens de l'ancienne Aléxandrie*, 1927, 6; Clermont-Ganneau, *RAO*, 8, 1924, 59ff.

11 Under Ptolemy II Philadelphus, indeed, a village called Samaria is mentioned in papyri, which evidences Samaritan settlement in Egypt in the middle of the third century; but this village was in Fayûm, not in the Thebais, and its existence in the middle of the third century does not oblige us to assume that the Samaritan colony had been founded in Egypt under Alexander.

12 It may be assumed, of course, that a small number of Jews came to Egypt in 312 with Hezekiah, but the large-scale immigration took place only in 302 with the arrival of the prisoners. On the dates, see above, p. 56ff.: it should again be mentioned that the fixing of the date is purely conjectural.

13 On the Jews as garrison-troops, see ch. 3.

14 Cf. above, p. 424, n. 45; *C. P. Jud.* I, p. 4, n. 10.

15 This has been pointed out by Niese (*GGMS*, III, 213, n. 3) and Schürer (III, 40). Willrich (*Juden u. Griechen*, 55) sought to

HELLENISTIC CIVILIZATION AND THE JEWS

prove that there was no anti-Semitism in Manetho's book, being followed in this by Laqueur and Heinemann, although for different reasons. On this question, see ch. 4.

16 Wilcken in *Arch. f. Pap.*, 12, 1937, 221ff.; Wilhelm, *ib.* 14, 1941, 30ff.

17 Although the date allowing for three days' notice is impossible, as Westermann rightly observed (see n. 19), the short period was no doubt an invention of the author of *The Letter of Aristeas*, in order to emphasize the speed with which the liberation of the Jews was carried out by the king (Westermann's view).

18 Philadelphus expresses the strange opinion that the enslavement of the Jews was carried out against his father's will and against his sense of justice, and he lays the responsibility upon the arbitrary will of the troops (τὴν στρατιωτικὴν προσπέτειαν). He thereby converts Ptolemy I's army into a troop of undisciplined ruffians, which is not to his father's credit; yet this credit he is supposedly concerned to defend. The passage on the Jews "who were already in the country, or were brought there afterwards" (εἴ τινες προῆσαν ἢ καὶ μετὰ ταῦτά εἰσιν εἰσηγμένοι) was absent in the original version of the order and was introduced into it by the explicit wish of the king, claims Aristeas (26).

We here leave the framework of Philadelphus' official order and enter the bounds of Aristeas' imaginary narrative (on the literary character of the Aristeas letter, see above, ch. 4). According to Westermann's correct supposition, this passage was not in the original version at the disposal of the author of the *Letter*, and it was he who interpolated it to show the king's generosity, in conformity with the general tendency of the book. The number of those set free is given in paragr. 19 as "a little more than 100,000," but if we make an exact calculation according to the redemption-money paid for them, we shall obtain the figure of 120,000 or even of 198,000 (cf. M. Hadas, *Aristeas to Philocrates*, 1951, 104, commentary *ad loc.*). The small sum of the redemption price (20 drachmae per slave) arouses justifiable suspicion among scholars; but the figure is supported by a papyrus of the period of Philadelphus (P. Gradew, 1; Plaumann, *Stzb. Heid. Ak. Ph.-Hist. Klas.* 5, 1914) and is therefore to be accepted as an authentic sum. It is also to be observed that had Aristeas sought to give a purely fictitious price which the king was prepared to pay for a Jewish slave, he would certainly have adopted a higher figure in order to emphasize the sympathy of Philadelphus for the Jews, in harmony with his book's general intention.

19 According to Westermann, *Amer. Jour. Philol.* 59, 1938, 1ff., the author of the Aristeas letter used the order of Ptolemy Philadelphus preserved in *SB* 8008 (see above, p. 60) as a model for his own.

Westermann rightly stressed those details of the order in Aristeas which bear the stamp of falsification, such as the brief space of three days, the special passage on those Jews "who were already in the country," and others; but in the present writer's opinion his conclusions go too far. Ptolemy Philadelphus' order in *SB* 8008 was certainly not the only one of this class of order (*prostagmata*) which dealt with slaves, public auctions, questions of administration in the conquered countries, etc., and it is hard to understand why the author of the Aristeas letter should have seen any need to adopt just this one as the model for the document which he was composing.

It should be mentioned, by the way, that the order *SB* 8008 does not refer to the Jews and it is therefore doubtful that a copy of it was preserved in some Jewish office (or in the book of some Jewish author) as late as Aristeas' time (more than a century later). The corresponding details in the order in Aristeas and *SB* 8008 are merely features common to the majority of documents of the period (*e.g.*, the designation of Southern Syria as "Syria and Phoenicia") and are not acceptable as proof of the direct influence of one document on the other.

20 Not, however, all of them, and the whole book is directed against those Jewish renegades. See ch. 2.

21 Some scholars entirely reject the historical value of the story. Thus, for example, Schürer, III, 489ff.; Bouché-Leclercq, I, 313ff.; Büchler (*Tobiaden u. Oniaden*, 172ff.) thought that the persecution of the Jews in the time of Philopator really took place, but not all over Egypt, or in Alexandria, but in Fayûm only. L. Fuchs also (*Die Juden Ägyptens*, 9ff., n. 7) inclined to this view. Willrich (in *Hermes*, 39, 1904, 244ff.) found the "historical germ" of the story in the persecution of the Jews under Ptolemy Lathyrus in 88 B.C.E. Latest research rejects the persecution under Philopator, but finds several historical features of the period preserved in *III Maccabees*.

22 See the present writer's article "The Third Book of the Maccabees as a Historical Source of the Augustan Period," in *Zion* (Heb.), X, 1ff. Cf. M. Hadas, *The Third and Fourth Books of the Maccabees*, 1953, 16ff.

23 *Juden u. Griechen*, 77ff.; 27ff.; *id.*, *Urkundenfälschung in der hellenistisch-jüdischen Literatur*, 1924.

24 Cf. Motzo, Esame storico-critico del III Libro dei Maccabei, in *Entaphia Pozzi*, 1913, 222f.; *id. Saggi*, etc., 185, n. 1.; Momigliano, *Prime linee di storia della tradizione Maccabaica*, 1931, 38f.; S. Zeitlin, *The History of the Second Jewish Commonwealth*, 28; Seeligmann, *The Septuagint Version of Isaiah*, 1948, 91ff.

25 See above, p. 172, also App. I.

26 Willrich cites two additional proofs for his conjecture: 1. In talmudic literature the founder of the "House of Onias" is called "Onias son of Simon" (Menaḥot, 109b; Jer. Yom. VI, 3), and this is Onias III. 2. Among the Jews there is no example of father and son possessing the same name. Against his first claim it may be remarked that the talmudic story on the quarrel of the two brothers and the flight of Onias to Egypt is nothing but an anecdote lacking all historical value. It is untrue in at least one detail (see next note) hence the rest of it is suspect.

As to Willrich's second contention, see Krauss, *Talmudische Archäologie*, II, 13, 440, n. 131, where the reader will find several examples contradicting Willrich's view. Cf. also *C. P. Jud.*, nos. 28, 29, 32, 77, 78, etc. Willrich could have found another reason to strengthen his theory had it existed in his time, namely, papyrus *U.P.Z.* 110 (= *C. P. Jud.* 132) dating from 164 B.C.E., which mentions a man named Onias, apparently a member of the court of Ptolemy Philometor and a high official (perhaps *strategos* of the Heliopolite nome). Were we to seek to identify this Onias with one of the Jerusalem priests known to us, we should have to select Onias III, for Onias IV left Judaea only after the murder of Menelaus, that is, after the year 162, and was therefore not in Egypt in 164. However, the above papyrus is not very reliable as only half the name "Onias" has been preserved, and was previously restored as [Θεω]νι: Wilcken, after additional examination of the papyrus in 1913, thought it possible to establish the reading 'Ονί[αι] "mit ziemlicher Sicherheit." With every respect for the great papyrologist's powers of deciphering (Wilcken has been justly regarded as "the father of modern papyrology"), far-reaching theories should not be erected on so doubtful a basis.

Nevertheless, even if we suppose that Wilcken's reading was correct, it is no proof that one of the priests of the Jerusalem Oniad family, just arrived from Palestine, was meant. The name Onias was fairly common in the Egyptian diaspora (cf. *C. P. Jud.*, nos. 137, 157, 451, 453). We may also express a certain doubt concerning Josephus' chronology: his knowledge of the pre-Maccabean era is very confused, and there is no guarantee that he was right in giving the date of the flight of Onias IV from Jerusalem as 162. I would rather doubt Josephus' chronological accuracy than question the information furnished by II Maccabees.

27 It is interesting that the talmudic legend has "corrected" history and transferred the House of Onias to Alexandria: "They sought to slay Onias; he fled from them and they pursued him. . . . He went to Alexandria of Egypt and there built an altar and sacrificed upon it to God," etc. (Men. 109b). In Zeitlin's opinion (*op. cit.*, 28), Onias chose the Heliopolite nome because, according to tradition, Jacob received that land as an inheritance from Pharaoh (*Ant.* II, 188). This tradition, however, cannot be relied upon, as we do not know when it originated, and the legend may have actually grown up by

reason of the developed Jewish population in Onias' territory and the
existence of a temple there.

28 In the *Sibylline Oracles,* V, 501, 507, some scholars have discovered an allusion to the House of Onias: cf. against this view,
Geffcken, *Komposition u. Entstehungszeit d. Oracula Sibyllina,* 1902,
26.

29 The author of the forged letters of Onias and Philometor put
into the king's mouth the following words: "It is to be doubted if God
wills that the Temple be built in a place that is contaminated and
full of sacred animals" (*Ant.* XIII, 70). These, of course, are the
doubts of the author himself, and simultaneously of Egyptian Jewry
as a whole.

30 Onias' letter to the king and queen (*Ant.* XIII, 65ff.), and of the
king and queen to Onias (*ib.* 70f.) are generally regarded as forgeries,
as is proved by their use of the citation from Isa. 19.19. But even a
forged document may contain a real historical detail, and it is credible
that the mention of the "war" alludes to a historical fact well known
to its readers. We do not know which war the author meant, for
many such took place in Philometor's period. He may have meant the
suppression of the Egyptian revolts, which frequently assumed the
character of real wars, or the prolonged war between Philometor and
Euergetes in Cyprus, or even the last campaign conducted by
Philometor in Coele-Syria.

31 *Notitia Dignitatum,* c. 25.

32 In four passages (*Ant.* XII, 388; XIII, 63; XX, 236; *War* I, 33)
Josephus stresses the similarity between the Temple of Onias and the
Temple of Jerusalem, and only in one (*War* VII, 427ff.) does he say
that the shrine itself was like a tower and therefore different from
the one at Jerusalem, although the altar was built after the model of
the altar in the latter. Whether we accept the first tradition or the
second, it is in any case clear that Onias built his temple wholly or
partly in intentional imitation of the Temple of Jerusalem. This is
proved by the excavations at Tel el-Yehudiyeh; cf. Flinders Petrie,
Egypt and Israel, New ed. (1923), 102ff. Priests and Levites also
served in Onias' shrine (*Ant.* XIII, 73).

33 On Philometor's Syrian war, see Bouché-Leclercq, II, 46ff.;
E. Bevan, *A History of Egypt under the Ptolemaic Dynasty,* 1927,
303ff.

34 Cf. W. Otto, "Zur Gesch. der Zeit d. 6 Ptolemäers," *Abh. Bayer.
Ak. Wiss.,* N. F., Heft 11, 1934, 96.

35 See the characterization of his reign in Bouché-Leclercq II, 55ff.;
Bevan, *op. cit.,* 306ff.; Cl. Préaux, *Actes du 5-me Congrès de Papyrol.,*
345ff.; W. Otto, "Zur Gesch. d. Niederganges des Ptolemäerreiches,"
Abh. Bayr. Ak., N. F., Heft 17, 1938.

36 Valerius Maximus IX, 2, 5.

37 Thus, for example, Schürer, III, 490: in his opinion Josephus preserves the old version of the story, while *III Macc.* has the late literary elaboration, but both the passages are simply fiction. Cf. Bludau, *Juden u. Judenvervolgungen in alten Alexandrien,* 62ff.

38 *SB* 5862, 7454.

39 This citation from Strabo is reproduced by Josephus, *Ant.* XIII, 287.

40 Josephus, *Ant.* XIII, 349, says that Helkias and Hananiah were the commanders of the entire Egyptian army; this, of course, is an exaggeration in Josephus' customary apologetic vein.

41 Helkias had meanwhile died in Coele-Syria, *Ant.* XIII, 351. On the inscribed stone of Helkias found in the territory of Onias see below, p. 521, n. 32.

42 In investigating the topographical question, we are aided by many documentary sources, such as inscriptions, papyri and ostraca. For the Egyptian inscriptions, see *CIJ* II, 1424-1539. On the papyri and ostraca, cf. the present writer's book *The Jews in Egypt* (Heb.), 24ff.

43 See above, p. 495, n. 12.

44 Flacc. 55. The five quarters of Alexandria were called after the first five letters of the Greek alphabet. The Jews resided in the fourth quarter, Delta (cf. *War* II, 495); the name of the other is unknown, but some scholars think it was Beta.

45 *OGIS*, 726.

46 See above, p. 270.

47 *Itin. Antonini,* c. 42.

48 *BGU* 1129 = *C. P. Jud.,* no. 145.

49 Athribis: *OGIS* 96; 101. Xenephyris and Nitriai: see above, n. 38.

50 P. Hamb. 2 = *C. P. Jud.* 417. There were numerous Syrian villages in Egypt. Cf. Henne, *Actes du 5ᵉ Congrès,* 151.

51 Aimé-Giron, *Textes araméens d'Egypte,* 1931, cf. Cowley, *op. cit.,* no. 37 and 42.

52 Cf. a full list of the Fayûm villages with Jewish populations in the author's *The Jews in Egypt,* p. 28ff.: cf. also the author's article "The History of the Jews of Fayûm in the Hellenistic Period," in *Magnes Jubilee Volume* (Heb.), 1938, 199ff.

53 *C. P. Jud.,* nos. 18, 24, 445. The Jews may also have dwelt in the nomes of Oxyrhynchus and Hermopolis Magna in the Hellenistic period; but the papyrological documents show evidence of Jewish settlement here only in the Roman and Byzantine periods.

54 *C. P. Jud.*, nos. 48-124.

55 The Jewish quarter at Edfu was discovered in the excavations of the joint Franco-Polish expedition of the years 1937-39: see *Tel Edfu*, I, 1937; II, 1938; III, 1939. For the ostraca of the Roman period: *C. P. Jud.*, nos. 160-408; of the Ptolemaic period, *ib.* nos. 111, 139, 140.

56 Diodorus (I, 31, 8) adopts a similar figure of seven million, apart from the population of Alexandria which numbered 300,000 (*ib.* XVII, 52, 6). In contrast to Philo's figures, these are highly credible and undoubtedly derive from official statistical sources.

57 It is to be assumed that the mountains of Judaea rather than those of Asia Minor are meant, as it is stated that the Jew came from Coele-Syria (*C. Ap.* I, 179).

58 Clearchus' information has encountered varying appreciations in learned literature. Schürer (III, 12) reported the information without any criticism and evidently believed it completely. Willrich (*Juden und Griechen*, 46) entirely rejects the trustworthiness of the story; so also H. Lewy ("Aristotle and the Jewish Sage, according to Clearchus of Soli," *HTR*, 31, 1938, 205ff.). Silberschlag (*JBL*, 52, 1933, 66ff.) admits the possibility of a meeting between Aristotle and the Jew, but does not see in it proof of the existence of Jewish communities in Asia Minor in the fourth century B.C.E.

59 The Jews of Ionia, who allegedly obtained citizen rights from "the Diadochi" are reported by Josephus (*C. Ap.* II, 39). He does not say who "the Diadochi" were, or whether he means the direct successors of Alexander the Great, or the kings of the Seleucid house as a whole; the conjecture that he here meant Antiochus II Theos is erroneous (see ch. 2).

60 Scholars of the last generation were divided in their estimate of the document: while Schürer (III, 12) and Eduard Meyer (II, 25, n. 2) acknowledged its trustworthiness, Willrich (*Juden u. Griechen*, 41ff.; *id., Urkundenfälschung*, 21ff.); Schubart (in *Arch. f. Pap.* VI, 343), and others attacked its authenticity. The document is now generally regarded as authentic; cf. Bickermann, in *Mélanges Isidore Lévy*, 1953, 17ff.

61 Josephus (*Ant.* XII, 147) indicates this, and it is probable also in view of the fact that the Jews sent to Asia Minor were Jews from Babylonia and Mesopotamia, not from Palestine. Antiochus III spent the years 212-204 in the eastern countries: see, on his activities there, Holleaux, *CAH*, VIII, 138ff.; Cary, *A History of the Greek World from 323 to 146 B.C.*, 69ff. Zeuxis, to whom Antiochus III addressed his letter, is mentioned several times by Polybius, once as governor of Babylonia (V, 45ff.) and once as governor of Lydia (*ib.* XVI, 1, 8-9; 24, 6; XXI, 13, 4)—assuming, of course, that the same man is meant in all the above passages. Zeuxis, at any rate, was a high official.

62 Rostovtzeff (*SEHHW*, I, 492; II, 646ff.) regards the settlement of Jewish troops in Lydia and Phrygia as a characteristic example of the colonization methods of the Seleucids in Asia Minor.

63 A *katoikia* in Phrygia was called *Judeni;* this may have been one of the colonies of Jewish troops of the time of Antiochus III. See Radet, *De Coloniis a Macedonibus in Asiam cis-Taurum deductis,* 1892, *s.v. Judeni.*

64 I Macc. 15.16ff. On the chronological question, see Schürer, I, 250ff.; Bickermann, in *Gnomon,* VI, 1930, 357ff.

65 Cicero, *Pro Flacco,* 28, 68.

66 Schürer gives a detailed list of the cities (III, 13f.), likewise Juster (I, 188ff.), who also cites sources for later periods. On the synagogue at Delos, see Plassart, *Mélanges Holleaux,* 201ff.; *RB* 1914, 523ff.

67 In the first century C.E. (or earlier) the Jews crossed the Black Sea, and a Jewish community is mentioned at Pantikapaion (Kerch) in C.E. 81 (Schürer, III, 23; *CIJ*, I, nos. 683-9).

68 In the Mishnah: Demai VI, 11; Shev. VI, 2; Maas. V, 5; Ḥalah IV, 7; IV, 11. In Tosephta: Dem. I, 4; Terum. II, 10f.

69 According to Thackeray (trans. of Josephus, in the Loeb Classical Library, Vol. III, 517), King Antiochus I Soter is meant, but the wording of sentences 43 and 44 is opposed to this assumption. In sentence 43 "the kings after Antiochus" are referred to, and 44 continues: "For Antiochus who was called Epiphanes destroyed Jerusalem and plundered the Temple, *whereas those who inherited the kingship after him,*" etc.; it is clear that in both sentences the same sovereigns are referred to. Nor is it probable that there would have been a large migration from Judaea to Syria as long as Palestine was under the rule of the Ptolemies.

70 See S. Krauss, *REJ,* 1902, 27ff.; Kraeling, *JBL* 51, 1932, 130ff.; Haddad, *Aspects of Social Life in Antioch,* 1949. According to a Christian tradition the "Maccabean martyrs" (that is, the aged Eleazar and the mother and her seven sons) were buried at Antioch in the Jewish quarter of Keration. The Byzantine chronographer Malalas says that this happened under King Demetrius, Demetrius I of Syria, who reigned from 162 to 150, being meant (Malalas VIII, 264). Cf. J. Guttman, *Commentationes in memor. Johan. Lewy* (Heb.), 36ff.; Dupont-Sommer, *Le quatrième livre des Maccabées,* 1939, 67ff.

71 War II, 479; M. Ḥallah IV, 11. The inscriptions date from a late period (the fourth century C.E.): see Schwabe's article in *Kedem* I, 1942, 87ff.; *CIJ*, II, 803-818.

72 The Book of the Damascus Covenant was first published in 1910 by Schechter from the Cairo Genizah (Schechter, *Documents of*

Jewish Sectaries, Vol. I, Fragments of a Zaddokite Work). Since the publication of the Dead Sea Scrolls, especially of the *Manual of Discipline,* we know that the "Damascus Covenant" is only part of a rich literature created by the mysterious sect. Although in a certain period of its history the sect concentrated round the Dead Sea, this is no proof that part of it did not at some period quit Judaea, on account of persecution, to find refuge in Damascus. I do not therefore think that J. Rabinowitz is right in his article on the subject in *JBL* 73, 1954, 11ff., when he interprets "Damascus" as a synonym for "exile," and thus entirely rejects the actual fact of the sect's flight to Syria. The flight is confirmed by the report in the *Megillat Ta'anit* on the flight of scholars to the Syrian city of Chalcis: "On the 17th of this month (= Adar) Gentiles rose against the refuge of scribes in Chalcis at Bet-Zebedee and there came release." The "Scholion" on *Megillat Ta'anit* interprets this that "When King Jannaeus sent to slay the scholars, they fled before him and went away to Syria and dwelt in the town of Chalcis, and the Gentiles of that place gathered and beset them to slay them . . . and they went away to the house of Zebedee and stayed there till darkness and fled from there . . ." (ed. Lichtenstein, 347ff.). If we accept this information in *Megillat Ta'anit* as a trustworthy record of historical evidence, we can fix the date of the flight of the sect to Syria (to Damascus and Chalcis) in the reign of Alexander Jannaeus, as several scholars have thought (see App. I, 7, p. 400ff.).

73 *Leg. ad Gaium,* 282; *Ant.* XV, 14; in *Ant.* XV, 39 the Jewish population of Babylonia is estimated at "not a few tens of thousands."

74 *Ant.* XVIII, 371f. Josephus calls Ctesiphon "a Greek city," which is incorrect. Strabo (XVI, 743) terms it a "village," showing that the Greeks did not regard it as a *polis.* The town stood opposite Seleuceia, separated from it only by the Euphrates; it served as one of the capitals of the Parthian kings.

75 Josephus (*Ant.* XVIII, 312) mentions a Jewish community at Nisibis; but he means not Nisibis in Mesopotamia, which was a Greek city in the Hellenistic period known as Antiocheia in Mygdonia, but Nisibia in Babylonia, on which we have no information. See Schürer, III, 9, n. 18. Nor was Nehardea, mentioned by Josephus (*ib.* 311ff.), a Greek town.

76 On the inscriptions at Cyrene, Apollonia, Ptolemais (Tolmeta), Teucheira-Arsinoë (Tocra) and Berenice (Benghazi), cf. S. Applebaum's article in *Zion,* XIX, 1954, 41ff. On the inscriptions at Teucheira see especially John Gray in Alan Rowe's *Cyrenaican Expedition of the Univ. of Manchester,* 1952, 43ff., and *SEG* IX, nos. 419-724. On the places called Ḥirbet el-Yahud, see Applebaum, *loc. cit.,* pp. 26, 43, 49.

77 On the rebellion in Cyrene, see S. Applebaum's articles, *JRS,*

HELLENISTIC CIVILIZATION AND THE JEWS

40, 1950, 87ff.; *Journ. Jew. Stud.*, II, 1951, 177ff.; *Zion*, XIX, 1954, 23ff.; cf. *C. P. Jud.*, vol. I, 86ff.

78 Schürer, III, 56; Juster, I, 187ff. For the inscriptions, see *CIJ* nos. 693-731. For the inscriptions at Delos, see Plassart, in *Mélanges Holleaux*, 1913, 210; Goodenough, *Jewish Symbols in the Greco-Roman Period*, vol. II, 1953, 71ff.

79 *CIJ*, 709/10. Cf. also *ib.* 711, where a certain *Ioudaios* (Judas?) is mentioned.

80 See Reifenberg's article in *JPOS*, 12, 1932, 213.

81 *Or. Sib.* III, 271.

82 Cited by Josephus, *Ant.* XIV, 115.

83 To be precise, 6,944,000. *Eodem tempore numerari iussit Claudius Judeos qui in regno ipsius essent, fuitque numerus ipsorum sexcenti nonaginta quattuor myriades et quattuor hominum millia.*

84 In the first (Hebrew) edition of this book, I expressed this view entirely as a theory. It has been accepted by J. Rosenthal in his article in the *American Jewish Yearbook*, X-XI, 1949, p. 320, but was rejected by Baron, *SRHJ*, I, 372. Rosenthal (in his article in *Jewish Social Studies*, XVI, 1954, 267ff.) produces striking proof of my supposition, pointing to Eusebius' citation of the above figure as the number of Roman citizens according to the Claudian census (Eus. *Chron.* ed. Schoene, 152-3: *Descriptione Romae facta sub Claudio inventa sunt civium Romanorum LXVIII centena et XLIIII millia*). Other figures of Eusebius in the Armenian translation of the *Chronica*, also in Synkellos and Jerome, are 6,941,000 or 6,943,000; cf. Momigliano, *Claudius*, 1934, 104, n. 8. It is therefore clear that Bar-Hebraeus (or his source) took the above figure from Eusebius' *Chronica* and applied it to the number of Jews in the Roman world. Eusebius' figure is approximately one million larger than that of the census of Roman citizens given by Tacitus (*Ann.* XI, 25), *viz.*, 5,984,072. The confusion in the census figures was perhaps introduced by the copyists (Tacitus' figure being correct: see Momigliano, *loc. cit.*).

85 Josephus tells, for example, of three million pilgrims at Jerusalem at the Passover festival (*War* II, 280; cf. *ib.* VI, 425), and of 1,100,000 who perished in the siege of Jerusalem (*ib.* VI, 420). There were in Galilee, according to Josephus (*Vita*, 45), 204 towns and villages in each of which the population was not less than 15,000 people (*War* III, 43). The calculation would indicate that in Galilee alone the population exceeded three million. These figures recall the imaginary figures given by Herodotus for Xerxes' host, namely, two and a half million troops, and with camp-followers, some five million people (Herod. VII, 184-6).

86 Rosenthal has collected the figures of various scholars in his above-mentioned article in the *American Jewish Yearbook*, 319ff.

504

Here are a few of them: Baron—eight million (three million in Palestine, and five million in the Diaspora); Beloch—six million (two million in Palestine, four million in the remaining countries of the Empire); Juster—seven million (five million in Palestine, two in the Diaspora); Harnack—more than four million, of whom about 700,000 in Palestine. On the basis of comparison with the population of Palestine in the British mandatory period, McCown (*JBL*, 66, 1947, 425ff.) estimates the total population of the country as less than a million souls, of whom 300,000 were Jews of Judaea and Galilee, numbering, with those of Transjordan and the Shephelah, less than half a million.

87 Manteufel has given the genealogies of the Jews of Edfu in his publication of the Edfu ostraca in the first volume of the Edfu excavation report (*Tell Edfu*, 1937, 147ff.). The material here, however, is not complete and the determination of the names is inaccurate. Full and corrected material on the Jewish families of Edfu will be furnished in the second volume of the *C. P. Jud.*, Section IX.

88 Cf., for instance, the numerous "Sambathions" in Egypt in the Roman period; these were Egyptians who observed the Sabbath and were not included among the Jews; see the present writer's article "The Sambathions," *Scripta Hierosolymitana* I, 1954, 78ff.

$$\text{NOTES} \quad part \ \textbf{II} \quad chapter \ \textbf{2}$$

1 Cf. Schürer, III, 71ff.; S. Krauss, *Synagogale Altertümer*, 1922; Oehler, "Epigr. Beiträge, z. Gesch. d. Judent.," *MGWJ*, 53, 1909, 528ff.; S. Baron, *The Jewish Community*, I-III, 1942.

2 This, for example, was the situation in Rome; see Schürer, III, 81ff.

3 *Ant.* XIV, 213: "The Jews in Delos"; the Ephesus inscription: "The Jews" (*CIJ* 745); inscriptions from various localities in Egypt: Athribis (*OGIS* 96), Schedia (*OGIS* 726), Xenephyris (*SB* 5862), Nitriai (*SB* 7454), Crocodilopolis-Arsinoë (*SB* 8939).

4 *CIG* 5361/2.

5 *CIJ* 775.

6 Various definitions have been offered of the term *politeuma* in learned literature: cf. Engers, in *Mnemosyne*, 54, 1926, 161; Ruppel, in *Philologus*, 82, 1927, 309; Preisigke, *Fachwörterbuch*, *s.v.* πολίτευμα. Cf. also the present writer's book, *The Jews in Egypt*, 130ff.

7 See Schürer, III, 72, n. 4; Oehler, *op. cit.*, 529.

8 The *politeumata* of the Idumaeans (*OGIS* 737), of the Phrygians (*OGIS* 658), the Cretans (P. Tebt., 32), the Lycians (*SB* 6025), the Cilicians (*SB* 7270) and the Boeotians (*SB* 6664).

9 The literature on the corporations is very rich. Cf. Ziebarth, *Das* *griechische Vereinswesen,* 1896; Poland, *Gesch. d. griech. Vereinswesen,* 1909; S. Nicolò, *Aegyptisches Vereinswesen zur Zeit d. Ptolemäer und Römer,* I-II, 1915; Roberts, Skeat and Nock, "The Gild of Zeus Hypsistos," *HTR,* 29, 1936, 39ff.

10 Even small ethnic groups were concentrated about the deities of their native lands: cf. the inscription of the Boeotian *politeuma* in Egypt: *SB* 6664. In the Roman period the communal organizations of the oriental peoples in Rome acted as important centers for the diffusion of the oriental cults: cf. F. Cumont, *Les religions orientales dans le paganisme romain,* 1929, 20ff.

11 Josephus does not cite the full text of Hecataeus, but selects what he regards as most important in it; the connection between the sentences is thus interrupted. Apart from this, there may be some errors in the text itself. Thus, for example, in the previous sentence it is related that Hezekiah gathered his people and read to them τὴν διαφορὰν πᾶσαν. The word *diaphora* is not sufficiently comprehensible. Hans Lewy in his article on Hecataeus (*ZNTW,* 31, 1932, 123) proposes to read διφθέρα, that is, "book"; this interpretation is bound up with his general conception of the sentence (see the following note), which does not command acceptance. The expression "the entire book" assumes that "the book" was previously referred to; but according to all the previous indications the subject was Ptolemy I and his attitude to the Jews, and not "the book." The word *diaphora* possesses *inter alia* the meaning of "distinction," and the author's intention may here have been to emphasize the way in which Ptolemy sought to confer favorable distinction upon the Jews who followed him. In that case the meaning of the word would be something like "benevolence" (*philanthropia*), which is required by the course of the narrative.

12 In harmony with his explanation of the word *diaphora* as "book," Lewy (*loc. cit.,* 123f.) thinks that the writing read by the High Priest to the Jews was the Pentateuch. Neither the expression *katoikesis* (settlement) nor *politeia* (political constitution) is appropriate to the Pentateuch. The word εἶχεν evidences that Hezekiah "had in his possession" some writing or other; but the Law of Moses was in the possession of many and Hezekiah could not have used it as an authority, as if it were a special document which belonged to him alone. Nor is it clear why the High Priest should have found it necessary to read the Torah to a group of Jews who were on their way to Egypt.

13 Cf. the present writer's book *The Jews in Egypt,* 132ff.; *C. P. Jud.* I, pp. 6ff.

14 The size of the Alexandrian codex with its many clauses can be judged from the collection of Alexandrian laws entitled *Dikaiomata* (*Pap. Hallens.* 1). When the Emperor Hadrian granted a constitution to the city of Antinoupolis founded by him, he wrote in a general fashion that he approved for the new town the existent constitution of the city of Naucratis, designated only the clause concerning permission to intermarry with the natives of the country, which he desired to alter. See Wilcken, *Chrestomathie*, no. 27. From the numerous examples of the royal letters collected by Welles, *Royal Correspondence in the Hellenistic Period*, 1934, it can be deduced that their rescripts were normally very brief and contained only the gist of the matters concerned.

15 See, for example, the refoundation of Lysimacheia in Thrace by Antiochus III: Appian, *Syr.* I. Cf. the present writer's book *Hell. Städtegr.* 197; Rostovtzeff, *SEHHW*, I, 492ff.

16 Cf. above, p. 438, n. 120.

17 Strabo, *ap.* Jos. *Ant.* XIV, 117.

18 On the date of the composition of the *Letter of Aristeas*, see ch. 4.

19 It is generally thought that he was speaking of "the elders" and "leaders," whence it is inferred that a council of elders (*Gerousia*) existed in the Alexandrian community as early as Aristeas' time. This view rests on the interpretation of a sentence in para. 310 in which Aristeas mentions the Jewish representatives present during the first solemn reading of the Pentateuch in Greek: "The priests and the elders of the translators and those of the *politeuma* who were the leaders of the people."

From this sentence it is to be deduced that the word "elders" relates only to "the translators" and not to "the leaders of the people": see on this question *C. P. Jud.* I, p. 9, n. 24. This does not of course mean that the Council of Elders may not have existed as early as Aristeas' time.

20 Philo (*loc. cit.*) relates that Augustus appointed the *Gerousia* after the death of the ethnarch (Philo writes *Genarch*, but this is merely a difference of terminology) and also officially informed Magius Maximus, the prefect of Egypt, of the fact. This information contradicts the words of the Emperor Claudius' edict given by Josephus, *Ant.* XIX, 283. However, this is not the only place in the above edict which is suspect of falsification. See on this question App. IV and cf. *C. P. Jud.* I, p. 57, n. 22.

21 Cf. S. B. Hoenig, *The Great Sanhedrin*, 1953, 71ff.

22 On the archons, see Schürer, III, 85ff.; Juster, I, 443ff.; Frey, *CIJ*, I, 82ff.; Baron, *The Jewish Community*, I, 95ff.; on the archontes in Rome, cf. N. Müller, *Die Inschriften der jüdischen Katakombe aus Monteverde*, 1919, 4. On the post of archon at Tlos, see the inscription *CIJ* 757. On the archons of the Jews of Thebes at Arsinoë in the Fayûm, see Wilcken, *Chrest.*, 193 (= *C. P. Jud.*, no. 432).

23 Cf. for example, Müller, *op. cit.*, no. 106 (a child of two years and ten months designated "future archon"); other examples in

HELLENISTIC CIVILIZATION AND THE JEWS

Schürer, III, 88, n. 45. The post of "chief of the synagogue" was also sometimes reserved for children: see Krauss, *Synag. Altertümer*, 118.

24 The sources concerning these posts have been collected by Juster, I, 438-456; cf. also Krauss, *op. cit.*, 112ff. In an inscription from the Jaffa cemetery, a Jew is designated "Alexandrian secretary," but it is hard to decide whether the Jewish community of Alexandria or the community of Alexandrian Jews at Jaffa, is meant. In an inscription at Xenephyris in Lower Egypt (*SB* 5862) two Jews are mentioned as "standing at the head" of the local community; Jewish "prostatin" (פרוסטטין) are mentioned in a Hebrew papyrus from Egypt in the Byzantine period (Cowley, "Notes on Hebrew Papyrus Fragments from Oxyrhinchus," in *JEA*, 2, 1915, 212).

25 A synagogue is on one occasion called εὐχεῖον, which also means "a place of prayer" (Wilcken, *Chrest.*, no. 193 = C. P. Jud., no. 432).

26 We know of synagogues in ten different places in Hellenistic and Roman Egypt: at Alexandria, Schedia, Xenephyris, Athribis, Nitriai, Crocodilopolis-Arsinoë, Alexandrou-Nesos and in three other localities whose names are not indicated in the sources. Cf. *C. P. Jud.* I, p. 8.

27 *OGIS* 129. On the Egyptian synagogues as places of refuge, cf. v. Woess, *Das Asylwesen Aegyptens in der Ptolemäerzeit*, 1923.

28 The usual text was: "To the welfare of King Ptolemy . . . (followed by his title) and Queen . . . the Jews at . . . built this synagogue." Cf. *OGIS* 96, 101, 726, 742; *SB* 5862, 6832, 7454, 8939.

29 This is the registry of the Alexandrian Jews alluded to by *BGU* 1151 (= *C. P. Jud.*, no. 143). The Greek word *archeion* has here been translated as "registry," "records office" or "archives," but its correct interpretation is "government office" or "notaries' office," and not a depository of obsolete papers. Cf. the talmudic terms ערכאות ערכי, ארכיון, which fit the meaning of the Greek word.

30 *CIJ* 775.

31 See the inscription from Pantikapaion of the year 81 B.C.E. (Schürer, III, 23f. = *CIJ* 683), in which a Jewish woman frees her slave, the scene of her act being the synagogue and the Jewish community acting as surety for its execution. Cf. also *CIJ* 684.

32 Alexandria: *Flacc.* 55; one of the two quarters was called "Delta" (the fourth quarter): *War* II, 495. At Edfu (Apollinopolis Magna) during the Roman period the Jews also lived in the fourth quarter, as many ostraca testify (cf. *C. P. Jud.*, nos. 194, 200, 202, 209, 213, etc.).

33 *Ant.* XIV, 258: The citizens of Halicarnassus permitted the Jews "to build the synagogues on the seashore, in accordance with their ancestral custom." The synagogue of Delos also stood by the seashore: cf. Plassart, "La synagogue juive de Délos," in *Mélanges Holleaux*, 1913, 210. On the custom of locating synagogues on the shore, see Krauss, *Synag. Altert.*, 281ff.; Sukenik, *Anc. Synags. in Palest. and Greece*, 1934, 49ff.

34 *Ant.* XIV, 260. The term θυσίαι here means "worship" in a general sense, not the offering of sacrifices, as I thought in the first edition of the present book; this was properly noted by Heinemann in *MGWJ*, 1934, 110, n. 2.

35 Josephus' allegation that it was the kings who allotted the Jews special quarters in which to settle, out of concern for their religion and customs, is simply a typical apologetic line: cf. below, especially n. 70.

36 A distinction must be made between Jewish rights and Jewish privileges. In their rights they did not differ in principle from the other peoples, including the Greeks, who enjoyed juridical and national autonomy. The rule of "living according to their ancestral laws" placed in the hands of the people itself the manner of implementing its desire to live its autonomous life. The government confirmed this rule and did not intervene in details (cf. above, p. 82ff.). Sometimes, however, intervention was necessary because the Jews in the Diaspora could not defend their rights by physical force and depended on the favor of their neighbors; their rights then became privileges.

In the ancient world, of course, the difference between "rights" and "privileges" was not noticed, and rightly so, since the difference lay, not in the thing itself, but in the reaction of the external world to Jewish autonomy. As may be learned from the documents, the Jews obtained their rights from the Hellenistic kings and the Roman governors, whereas the attack on them came from the Greek cities. The need of affording government protection of these rights converted them into privileges in the view of the Greeks.

37 Cf. Bickermann, in *Mélanges Isidore Lévy*, 1953, 15. This does not mean, indeed, that they have been preserved in good condition. In some places we find corruption of personal names, the confusion of two documents, and the like. As to the question of falsification, an exception must be made of Claudius' order in *Ant.* XIX, 280ff., which has, in my opinion, been reworked by a Jewish forger: see App. IV.

38 The reference is to the letter of the Roman governor of Syria, Petronius, to the citizens of Dor (*Ant.* XIX, 303f.). The document was written under the Emperor Claudius, a short time after Gaius had failed in his design to set up statues of the emperor in the synagogues— at a time when this very question had become immediately urgent and could not be glossed over even in an official document.

39 Laodiceia (*Ant.* XIV, 241ff.); Halicarnassus (*ib.* 258); Ephesus (*ib.* 263ff.).

40 Cf. *Ant.* XVI, 27.

41 *Ant.* XVI, 163; cf. *ib.*, 168.

42 *Ant.* XIV, 227: "And I also, like the governors before me, exempt them from military service."

43 "Jews who are Roman citizens" are mentioned in several documents (*Ant.* XIV, 228ff.) and it is to be supposed that in those passages which speak simply of "citizens," the word "Roman" has dropped out by accident.

44 The reason may be sought in the difficult contemporary conditions (the Roman civil war), in which the Roman commanders were recruiting people everywhere and drafting them forcibly into their contingents. A complete Jewish army (such as that of John Hyrcanus) could compel the commanders to consider Jewish demands not to desecrate the Sabbath, but individual Jews in the Roman army could not do this. They were forced to carry out the orders of their commanding officers without argument, otherwise they faced severe punishment. Hence the Jewish demand for general exemption from mobilization into the Roman army.

45 See the documents in *Ant.* XVI, 167ff.

46 *Ant.* XVI, 169/170; see above, ch. 4. Even Roman governors did not always resist the temptation to confiscate Jewish money; the classical instance was that of Flaccus, governor of Asia Minor, who in 59 B.C.E. confiscated the money of the Jews of that country. Cf. Cicero, *Pro Flacco*, 28, 67.

47 Schürer, III, 121ff.; Juster, II, 1ff.; De Sanctis, *Riv. di Filol.*, 52, 1924, 473ff.; Momigliano, *Claudius*, 1934, 96, n. 25.

48 Willrich, "Caligula," in *Klio* 3, 1903, 403ff.; Fuchs, *Die Juden Aegyptens*, 79ff.; Schubart, in *Arch. f. Pap.*, 5, 108ff.; Wilcken, *Zum Alexandr. Antisemitismus*, 786ff.; Engers, "Die staatsrechtliche Stellung der alexandrinischen juden," *Klio* 18, 1923, 79ff.; Jouguet, *La Vie municipale*, 18ff.; Bell, *Jews and Christians*, 12ff.

49 Cf. the present writer's article "Syntaxis and Laographia," in *Jnl. Jur. Pap.*, 4, 1950, 179ff.

50 The inhabitants of the *metropoleis*, or chief towns of districts (the "nomes"), who were of mixed Graeco-Egyptian origin, constituted a special problem. The Romans did not regard them as pure Greeks and therefore levied the poll-tax on them as they did on natives; but as they were Hellenized and had received a gymnasium education, they paid the tribute with certain reductions. See the present writer's article, *loc. cit.*, 196f.

51 I have treated in detail of the Jewish struggle for emancipation in my book *The Jews in Egypt*, 154ff.; cf. *C. P. Jud.* I, p. 60ff.

52 *BGU* 1140 = W. *Chrest.* 58 = *C. P. Jud.* 151. Cf. the present writer's book *op. cit.*, 98ff. A detailed commentary on the papyrus is given in the *C. P. Jud.*, no. 151.

53 *PSI* 1160 = *SB* 7448 = *C. P. Jud.* 150. Cf. also Musurillo, *The Acts of the Pagan Martyrs*, 1954, 1ff., 83ff. The papyrus is known among papyrologists as "the Papyrus of the Boulé."

54 The connection between the gymnasium education and entry into the ranks of the citizenry is confirmed by several documents. Cf. for example, the inscription from Egypt (apparently from Ptolemais, Upper Egypt), of the year 104 B.C.E.: a group of young men is accepted into a gymnasium by decision of the council and simultaneously its members are registered as citizens (*SB* 8031). On the confirmation of civil rights in Alexandria to the *epheboi* by the Emperor Claudius, see p. 314.

55 The reader will find a detailed account of the disturbances of the year 41 in the present writer's book *The Jews in Egypt*, 181ff., and in the commentary to the *C. P. Jud.*, nos. 153 and 156, where relevant literature is cited.

56 *P. Lon.* 1912 = *SP* 212 = *C. P. Jud.* 153. The literature on the letter is immense; see the introduction to *C.P. Jud.*, no. 153.

57 The accepted estimate of the Emperor Claudius as a ruler "sympathetic to the Jews" is based on his edict in favor of the Jews of Alexandria cited by Josephus, *Ant.* XIX, 280ff. However, this order is in part falsified and cannot be utilized in support of such a view: see App. IV, at the end of this book. Claudius' attitude to the Jews is to be determined from his letter to Alexandrians and not from the edict, and the conclusion to be drawn from the letter is that the Emperor, while restoring to the Jews the rights always enjoyed by them and unlawfully abolished by Gaius, did not extend their civic privileges and, further reprimanded them in very cavalier fashion. There is therefore no reason to regard him as a "philo-Semitic" ruler. Cf. *C. P. Jud.* I, 73f.

58 On the motive of these books, see the works of Goodenough, *The Politics of Philo Judaeus*, 1938; *An Introduction to Philo Judaeus*, 1940, 72ff.

59 For example, Schürer, III, 123, n. 13 (cf. n. 10).

60 *Politeia* meant a municipal constitution, a political organization, a social system, and several similar things. The constitution of a *politeuma* may also easily be denoted by this term. It may be observed that the "charter" obtained by the High Priest Hezekiah from Ptolemy I is called by Hecataeus a written *politeia* (see above, p. 300).

61 Juster, I, 222.

62 The name *Xenos* was applied by the Greeks to people who were to be found in the city for various chance reasons such as commerce and the like, but were not permanent residents there. Cf., for example, *The Letter of Aristeas*, 109-110 (according to which *Xenoi* were prohibited from staying in Alexandria more than twenty days). Villagers in Egypt were looked upon as *Xenoi* when they visited another village: cf., for example, P. Enteux. 83.

63 *Legat.*, 363.

64 In the Roman period free men might only be beaten with rods, while the use of the whip was reserved for slaves. Cf. Westermann, *RE*, Supp. VI, *s.v. Sklaverei*, col. 1052. Cf. the complaint of a weaver in his letter to Zenon (in the year 257 B.C.E. approximately): "Five Egyptians with whips . . . and I received blows to such an extent that my skin was lacerated . . ." (*PCZ* 59080).

65 As, for example, the desecration of synagogues by placing in them statues of the emperor. The expulsion of the Jews from their houses in the city and their confinement in the "Delta" quarter (that is, the creation of an artificial ghetto), carried out during the pogrom of 37, was an altogether arbitrary and unprecedented act, and it is quite comprehensible that the Emperor Claudius, on his accession, swiftly abolished these regulations, which had been illegally enacted against the Jews.

66 The Papyrus *BGU* 1211 = *SP* 208 bears witness to the king's special interest in the cult of Dionysus and his attempt to supervise the mysteries of the god in Egypt. The king's body, like those of other devotees of Dionysus, was marked with the god's symbol—the leaf of the *kissós*. See J. Tondriau, in *Aegyptus*, 30, 1950, 57ff.; *id*. in *Chron. d'Égypte*, 50, 1950, 293ff. Cf. the present writer's article "The Third Book of the Maccabees as a Historical Source of the Augustan Period," in *Zion* (Heb.), X, 3ff.

67 Cf. for example, Jouguet, *La Vie Municipale*, 21, 140.

68 *C. Ap.* II, 65; cf. ch. 4.

69 In *C. Ap.* I, 50, he himself confesses that he had utilized the assistance of specialists in Greek for his literary work. See, on these assistants, Thackeray, *Josephus the Man and the Historian*, 1929, 100ff.

70 It is generally thought that Josephus here used Hecataeus' book; but it has already been remarked above (p. 272) that Hecataeus did not know of Jewish settlements in Alexandria under Alexander the Great. Extracts from the Jewish story of the foundation of Alexandria have been preserved in the well known "Alexander Romance" ascribed to Callisthenes (the "Pseudo-Callisthenes"); see Pfister, "Eine jüdische Gründungsgeschichte Alexandrias," in *Stzb. Heidelb. Ak.*, 1914, 11, p. 22ff. It is here narrated that when the city was founded, Alexander decreed the worship of God in the city's Jewish quarter. In Pfister's

opinion the legend was composed in the first century of the present
era; and this is credible, for that period marks the flowering of the
apologetic literature.

71 Neither Josephus nor Philo troubles to hide his open hostility
to Egyptians. According to Josephus, the Egyptians were the Jews'
greatest enemies, guilty of the flourishing of anti-Semitism in Alexandria; they had always been a subject people who had never obtained
citizen-rights either from the kings or the emperors. Philo regards
the Egyptian religion as pointless and foolish, and in the philosophical
doctrine of Philo the Egyptian people symbolized the materialistic,
sensual and immoral element in life. Cf. *C. P. Jud.* I, p. 63, n. 33
(where references will be found).

72 Of the foundation of Alexandria, the sources report that Alexander indicated the spot where the town was to be built and approved
its building plan, but did not take part in the building itself. The
supervision of the building fell partly to the first governor of Egypt,
Cleomenes (cf. Justin, XIII, 4, 11: *Cleomenes qui Alexandriam
aedificaverit*), and it is to be assumed that in his time the first citizen
body of Alexandria was set up, chiefly from the town of Kanobos
(Curtius, IV, 8, 5; cf. Pseudo-Aristotle, *Oceon.*, II, 33); the Egyptian
inhabitants of the village of Rakotis also remained settled in the
Egyptian quarter of the new city. We hear nothing at all of Jewish
migration to Alexandria at this time, and even if we suppose that
isolated Jews happened to come to the new city, there is no proof that
they at once entered the Alexandrian citizen-body on an equal basis
with the Greeks. Jewish settlement at Alexandria at the time of its
foundation is a figment of the imagination of Jewish apologists: see
above, n. 70.

73 Schürer, III, 122, writes: "Alexander the Great gave them equal
constitutional rights with the Macedonians, who were citizens of
Alexandria possessing full rights" (*das sind eben die Alexandrinischen
Vollbürger*). Thus also Juster, II, 7: "They were citizens of Alexandria
possessing rights equal to those of the groups with the broadest
political privileges, *i.e.*, those known as Macedonians."

74 *Arch. f. Pap.* V, 111. Schubart is now followed by most scholars,
such as Engers (*Klio*, 18, 89), Fuchs, *op. cit.*, 88, etc. Cf. also
Wilcken, *Grundzüge*, 63.

75 *C. P. Jud.*, no. 143 (= *BGU* 1151, I).

76 *C. P. Jud.*, no. 142 (= *BGU* 1132).

77 On the Macedonians in Egypt, see M. Launey, *Recherches sur
les armées hellénistiques*, 1949-1950, I, 308ff. The overwhelming
majority of the Macedonians were organized in military colonies
(*cleruchies* or *katoikiai*), that is, in non-urban settlements; cf. *ib.*
331ff.

78 Macedonian garrisons in Greek cities were a typical phenomenon of the Hellenistic period; cf. Launey, *op. cit.*, II, 633. These troops were outside the citizen-body of the city and they were very rarely accepted into it, and then only by special decision of the municipal council; cf. *ib.* 652ff. Clearly no more did Macedonian troops stationed in Alexandria count as citizens.

79 See on this question in greater detail the writer's book *The Jews in Egypt*, 49ff.; cf. *C. P. Jud.*, I, p. 14.

80 His error is excusable, for the composition of the Alexandrian citizen-body was not homogeneous, at least two grades being distinguishable within it: those registered within the *phylai* and the *demes* (which apparently constituted the citizen aristocracy), and those called simply "Alexandrians" (the broad sections of the civic population). Those Jews who obtained citizenship belonged to the second group, as registration within the *phylai* and *demes* was probably associated with certain religious ceremonies (see Dessau, *Gesch. d. röm. Kaiserreichs*, II, 2, p. 669). As the "Alexandrians" composed the lower stratum of the citizenry, it may not have been difficult to penetrate among them in one way or another. Apart from this, every inhabitant of the city was an "Alexandrian" in popular parlance. Cf. *C. P. Jud.* I, p. 41, n. 102.

81 T. Reinach (*REJ*, 79, 1924, 123ff.) was the first to perceive Josephus' error in regard to the name of the Roman emperor inscribed on the monument. As the official name of Augustus till the year 27 B.C.E. was the same as that of his father, *viz.*, C. Julius Caesar, it was easy to make the mistake of believing that the "Caesar" mentioned on the monument was Julius Caesar. Julius Caesar, however, never ruled Egypt, and the Jewish status in Alexandria was not his concern. This function, on the other hand, fits Augustus very well, since he converted Egypt into a Roman province.

82 Augustus certainly granted the Jews of Alexandria the principal right of "living according to their ancestral laws." Cf. his edict concerning the rights of the Jews of Asia: "The Jews may utilize their own commandments according to the law of their fathers" (*Ant.* XVI, 163).

83 Josephus wrote his *Contra Apionem* circa 100, that is, some thirty years after he had visited Alexandria during the Great Rebellion. We do not know whether he had any opportunity of revisiting Alexandria in connection with his scholarly work.

84 From one of Pliny's letters to Trajan (*Ep. ad Traian.* 6) we learn that Alexandrian citizenship was a prerequisite for an Egyptian desiring to obtain Roman *civitas*. It is not to be deduced from this, of course, that this was the only way. An Egyptian slave freed by his Roman master became a Roman citizen, likewise a prisoner-of-war freed by a Roman victor. Hence it is not to be taken for granted that every Jew who was a Roman citizen in Egypt was also *ipso facto* an Alexandrian citizen.

85 This constitution was derived from Athens. Cf. *Dikaiomata* (*Pap. Hallensis*, 1); *P. Oxy.* 2177, frag. 1, col. 1.

86 This resemblance misled great scholars such as Schürer (III, 122ff.) and Dessau (*Gesch. d. röm. Kaiserreichs* II, 2, 727) to interpret the terms ἰσοπολιτεία, ἰσοτιμία, and ἰσομοιρία mentioned in Josephus (cf. ἴση πολιτεία in Claudius' edict cited by Josephus *Ant.* XIX, 281) as "equality of rights" between the Greek city and the Jewish community. The meaning of the term "isopoliteia" in Greek, however, was the granting of the citizenship of one city to all the citizens of another; thus, for instance, in 405 all the inhabitants of Samos received Athenian citizenship. Cf. Busolt-Swoboda, *Griechische Staatskunde*, 225f., 1245, 1510ff. Such instances were very rare, and I know no single instance of the granting of "isopoliteia" or "sympoliteia" by a Greek city to a "politeuma" of non-Greeks. The very fact that the internal organization of the Jewish community resembled the organization of the *polis* whose privileges were so great, proves, indeed, that it stood side by side with the *polis* as an independent political organization, requiring no citizen-rights within it. Only isolated Jews could aspire to equality of franchise with the Greeks, but not complete communities.

87 The granting of citizenship to a man who had deserved well of the city (being its *euergetés*) was characteristic of Greek cities everywhere; many resolutions of "the council and the people" have been preserved granting municipal rights to a man and sometimes also to his descendants. The Alexandrian privileges of the father of the Jew in *C. P. Jud.*, no. 151 mentioned above (p. 312) may have been derived from such a source and may not have passed to his son, having been given to the father personally.

88 As we know from Claudius' letter to the Alexandrians, the emperor ratified the reception of young men into the citizen-body of Alexandria. There is no doubt that in the previous period this right had been in the hands of the Ptolemaic kings. We read in Justin that Ptolemy VIII Euergetes II at the beginning of his reign introduced new citizens of non-Alexandrian origin into the Alexandrian citizen-body (*Just.* XXXVIII, 8, 7: *edicto peregrinos sollicitat*). We do not know whether there were Jews among these new citizens, but it may easily be imagined that under the previous king, Philometor, who had favored Jews, a number of them had obtained Alexandrian rights by royal decision. Cf. *C. P. Jud.* 1, p. 23, n. 58.

89 The existence of such "illegal" citizens is openly hinted at in the *Boulé* papyrus referred to above, p. 312f.

90 Cf. *C. P. Jud.*, no. 151, mentioned above (n. 87); an "Alexandrian" Jew, evidently a citizen of the city, is referred to in a document cited by Josephus (*Ant.* XIV, 236).

91 This information might be regarded as proof of the participation of the Jews of Antioch in the physical exercises at the gymnasium, which would be a fair indication of their being among the citizens of the town. However, the few Jews who took part in the games no doubt used the olive oil of the gentiles. Here, not these isolated Jews are meant, but the entire Jewish population which, of course, used olive oil like all oriental peoples, without any connection with athletics. The fact that the distribution of oil to the city's inhabitants was under the control of the gymnasiarch shows that he was the general lessee of the oil on behalf of the city; and necessarily so, since the municipal gymnasium was of course the largest consumer of all sorts of unguents.

92 The phrase "to them" applies, of course, to the Greeks, not to the Jews, as some scholars, including Schürer, have thought. Schürer, indeed, changed his mind in the second edition of his book (see III, 121, n. 14), but nevertheless retained his theory that the Jews also had obtained their rights from Antiochus Theos. He bases his view chiefly on the above-mentioned passage in *C. Ap.* II, 39, which says that the Jews of Ephesus and the towns of Ionia were called by the same names as those of the native citizens because the Diadochi had given them permission to do so. In place of "Diadochi" Schürer suggests that "Antiochus II" would be more accurate. Historical value is not, however, to be attributed to this report of Josephus, which is much the same as all his other stories of the attitude of the monarchs to the Jews, and bears the same Jewish apologetic stamp.

93 The word "citizens" in the resolution of the citizens of Sardis (*Ant.* XIV, 259) denotes the Jews who were Roman citizens and not citizens of Sardis. See above, n. 43

94 Cf. A. H. M. Jones, *The Cities of the Eastern Roman Provinces*, 1937, p. 361.

NOTES   *part* **II**   *chapter* **3**

1 Speck, *Handelsgeschichte des Altertums*, III, 2, p. 408.

2 Herzfeld, *Handelsgeschichte der Jüden des Altertums*, 2nd ed., 1894, 202f.

3 Cf. for example, Frey, *CIJ*, I, p. lxiv ("the western Diaspora was the offspring of the mercantile spirit"); Mahaffy, *Mélanges Nicole*, p. 661 (the Jews of Syene and Elephantine in the fifth century were "from a certain point of view" the bankers of Egypt); Fuchs, *Die Juden Aegyptens*, 4; Oehler, *MGWJ*, 53, 1909, 537; Bousset, *Die Religion d. Judentums*, 3d ed., 432 ("the Jewry of the Diaspora was compelled from the start to give up agriculture . . . here the Jew developed mainly as a trader"); Stähelin (*Der Antisemitismus des Altertums*, 1905) and Bludau (*Juden u. Judenvervolgungen in alten Alexandrien*, 1906) even attributed the development of ancient anti-Semitism to the commercial transactions and wealth of the Jews of the Diaspora.

4 On the literature on the Jews of Elephantine, see above, p. 494, n. 3. Cf. *Jews of Egypt*, 36ff.

5 See on the question of the Ptolemaic army in Egypt, Lesquier, *Les Institutions militaires de l'Egypte sous les Lagides*, 1916; Launey, *Recherches sur les armées hellénistiques*, I-II, 1949-50, *passim*.

6 Among the officers may be noted a Jewish *taktomisthos* of an infantry company (*C. P. Jud.*, no. 24); the *taktomisthoi* were apparently in charge of soldiers' pay; a "head of a company of cavalry" in Upper Egypt (*ib*. no. 27) and others. A Jewish *hegemon* is also mentioned in an inscription in the Fayûm (*SB* 27).

7 The regular servicemen are recorded as "Jews" without any additional adjective (*C. P. Jud.*, nos. 18, 22, 30), and the men of the reserves as "Jews of the *Epigoné*" (*ib*. nos. 19-21, 23, 24, 26).

8 The infantry soldiers generally appear in the documents without special designation. Only one of them, Agathokles son of Ptolemy, received a special identification as "Jew of the infantry battalion of Molossos (the name of the commanding officer) stationed in the Herakleopolite nome" (*ib*. no. 24). In the same papyrus appear two Jewish cavalrymen "of the first *hyparchy*." On the "head of a company of cavalry," see above, n. 6.

9 In the colony of Tobiah in Transjordan (see above, p. 64), one of the *cleruchs* is recorded by the name of "(. . . . .) son of Hananiah, a Persian" (*C. P. Jud.*, no. 1). As Hananiah is a Hebrew name, it is clear that this *cleruch* was not a Persian by race, but a Jew serving in a battalion of "Persians." "Jewish Persians of the *Epigoné*" are referred to in a papyrus of 59 C.E. (*ib*. no. 417), and several people with Hebrew names are designated as "Persians of the *Epigoné*" in the Roman period. In that period, however, "Persians of the *Epigoné*" had ceased to be soldiers. See below, p. 520, n. 30. On the Macedonian Jews, see above, p. 320.

10 Jews served in the Ptolemaic forces to the same extent as other peoples; this should be stressed to avoid creating the impression that the Hellenistic rulers resorted to the Jews more than others when they needed military personnel—an impression to be gained from the writings of Josephus. Although Josephus undoubtedly knew that members of other peoples also served as mercenaries under the Macedonian kings, he several times emphasizes that the latter resorted particularly to the Jews, because they were outstanding in their devotion to God and in their loyalty to rulers to whom they had sworn fealty. This is a typical apologetic approach without any historical value. The peoples with reputations as excellent mercenaries in the Hellenistic epoch were the Thracians, Thessalians, Moesians, Carians and Galatians, but not the Jews. Troops of Semitic derivation (including Jews) only became numerous in the second century, their number reaching its peak in the first century B.C.E., parallel with the steady decline of the Greek mercenaries. See on this question the interesting statistical material in Launey, *op. cit.*, I, 91ff.

11 Two of the Jewish members of the first *hyparchy* in *C. P. Jud.*, no. 24, belonged to "the owners of eighty *arourai*"; if we take into account that 100 *arourai* (about 68 acres) constituted the largest holdings given to servicemen in Egypt, it will be clear that these two Jews belonged to the high military "aristocracy" and were men of means. In a papyrus from Samareia (*C. P. Jud.*, no. 28) the military colony (apparently entirely composed of Jews, cf. the following note) is divided into three classes: the owners of 80 *arourai*, the owners of 30 *arourai* and "soldiers"; whence it is to be inferred that those who received 30 *arourai* and over were officers. On the question of the working of the land of the military settlers by Egyptian fellahin, see the present writer's book *The Jews of Egypt*, 62ff.

12 *C. P. Jud.*, no. 28. Among the settlers we encounter bearers of Hebrew names such as Shabbatai, Ḥaggai, Joḥanan, Jacob and Jonathan, and female names such as Sabbatis and Miriam (Marion), also Greek theophoric names typical of Jews, such as Dositheos and Theodotos, and a woman's name Theoxena.

13 See S. Applebaum's article in *Bull. of the Israel Expl. Society* (Heb.), XIX, 1955, 188ff. In Applebaum's opinion, Jews were settled on the Roman *ager publicus* in Cyrene, and an evidence of these agricultural settlements is preserved in the names of places called Ḥirbet el-Yahud down to our time. Cf. also Applebaum's article in *Zion*, XIX, p. 26ff.

14 See Lesquier, *op. cit.*, 224; cf. Wilcken, *Chrest.*, nos. 334/7.

15 See the ostraca *C. P. Jud.*, nos. 73-96. These are receipts of the state granary with the signature of the *Sitologos* (the official in charge of the collection of the land-tax levied in grain) according to a fixed formula: "so-and-so son of so-and-so has measured such and such a quantity of wheat to the granary of . . . (name of the place) for (his holding) in . . ." Cf. *C. P. Jud.*, p. 197ff. The variations in the amount of wheat "measured" at the granaries are large and range from one or two *artabai* to 90 *artabai* (cf. *Jews in Egypt*, 67). If each payment reflected the tax paid for a complete year, it would be possible to explain the variations by differences in the sizes of the holdings. But this is not the case, and several receipts (nos. 75, 78, 84, 96) indicate partial payments. Even if we assume that the partial payments are exceptional, we have to account for the variations, not only by the size of the estates, but also by the size of the harvest, which varied from year to year.

16 *BGU* 1129 = Mitteis, *Chrest.* 254 = *C. P. Jud.*, 145. As the "land of Helkias" is here mentioned as a place name and without any explanation, it may have been a large estate called after some well known man of wealth. It may be permissible to conjecture that it was the estate of the Jewish general Helkias who lived in the reign of Cleopatra III (above, p. 283; cf. below, n. 32). We know that high officials close to royalty received land "in gift" from the king (the best known instance being the estate of the finance minister Apollonius at Philadelpheia, extending over 10,000 *arourai* = 6,900 acres: see above, p. 60). As Helkias, together with his friend Ḥananiah, discharged an important military function in the state, it may easily be imagined that he received a present of this sort from the queen in reward for his loyal service.

17 Wilcken, *Chrest.*, no. 198 = *C. P. Jud.*, no. 36. Among the other names may be noted *Ḥazaros,* which may be Persian, but also Jewish; cf. the ordering of the Priests named Bene Ḥezir, I Chron. 24.15, and the inscription on the tomb of the Bene Ḥezir in the Valley of Jehoshaphat, *CIJ* II, 1394.

18 *C. P. Jud.*, nos. 14 and 15. The names of the vintners are Samuel and Alexander.

19 *C. P. Jud.*, nos. 9, 38, 39, 412, etc. As is to be inferred from the first two papyri, the shepherds also sold the wool to customers; cf. *P. Ent.* 1.

20 The family of potters: *C. P. Jud.*, no. 46; weavers: *ib.*, no. 95 (second century B.C.E., Upper Egypt), 405 (first or second century C.E., Edfu); flute-player, *ib.* 28 (second century B.C.E., Samaria in the Fayûm).

21 For this passage, see the commentary in Krauss, *Synag. Altert.*, 261ff., who gives parallel texts from Tosephta and the Jerusalem Talmud.

22 'Arakhin, 10b: "There was a bell in the Temple made of brass, with a sweet sound; but it became cracked, so they sent scholars and brought craftsmen from Alexandria of Egypt and they mended it . . . There was a mortar in the Temple, made of brass, from the days of Moses, in which they mixed the incenses; it became cracked, and they brought craftsmen from Alexandria of Egypt and they mended it . . ." Cf. Tosephta, Yom ha-Kippurim, II, 5-6.

Cf. also Yoma 38a (Jer. Yoma, 41a): Gates of the Temple brought to Jerusalem from Alexandria (see

HELLENISTIC CIVILIZATION AND THE JEWS

on this question the inscription *OGIS* 599 = *CIJ* 1256, mentioning "Nicanor of Alexandria who made the gates"; a controversy exists whether the "gates" mentioned in the inscription were gates of the Temple, in agreement with the passages of the Talmud cited above, or gates of the entrance to the tomb structure; see on this question, Roussel, *REG*, 37, 1924, 79ff.

23 On the trade of Alexandria, cf. Leider, *Der Handel von Alexandreia*, 1933. Its main commerce was in grain; Alexandrian grain was also known in Palestine: "Joshua ben Parhia says: Wheat coming from Alexandria is unclean on account of their baling machine" (besprinkling the wheat) (Tos., Makhshirin III, 4).

24 On the *emporos*, see Knorringa, *Emporos*, 1926. In a city such as Alexandria the *emporoi* also engaged chiefly in maritime trade. The "workshops" of the craftsmen of Alexandria are referred to by Philo, *Flacc.*, 56.

25 *OGIS* 74 = *CIJ* 1537: "Thanksgiving to the God! Theodotos son of Dorion the Jew who was saved from the sea." Another inscription from the same place (*OGIS* 73 = *CIJ* 1538: "Ptolemy son of Dionysius the Jew thanks the God") makes no mention of peril at sea, but the similarity of the text permits the assumption that the author of this inscription had also been saved from danger.

26 The post of Alabarch or Arabarch is found in various places at various periods: it is therefore to be supposed that it was not uniform in character, but changed its nature according to time and place. At any rate, it may be surmised that the Alabarchs were high fiscal officials and that in Egypt they were mainly charged with the collection of the customs revenue. Cf. Schürer, III, 132, n. 42; Dittenberger, *OGIS*, notes to 570; Rostovtzeff, *Yale Class. Stud.*, II, 49f.

27 *BGU* 1079 = *W. Chr.* 60 = *C. P. Jud.* 152.

28 ὡς ἅπαντες καὶ σὺ βλεπὲ σατὸν ἀπὸ τῶν Ἰουδαίων.

29 The first opinion is that of Wilcken, *Chrest.* 84: *Der Brief ist somit das älteste Zeugnis eines geschäftlichen Antisemitismus.* The second is that of Dessau (*Gesch. d. röm. Kaiserzeit*, II, 2, 667, Anm. 3).

30 The papyri from Alexandria of the time of Augustus were published in the fourth volume of *BGU*. Part of them originate from the Jewish quarter "Delta"; nevertheless, only a very few Jews are mentioned in them. (Allowance must of course be made for the fact that the assimilated Jews of Alexandria called themselves by Greek names, hence we cannot distinguish them unless their Jewishness is specifically indicated; cf. *C. P. Jud.*, nos. 142-9.)

The general impression is that the Jews appearing in these papyri are not of the comfortable class and earn their livings in straitened circumstances. Some owe money and are paying their debts in monthly installments, most of the sums advanced as dowries, loans or legacies, being very small indeed. In two documents (nos. 146-7) two Jewish wet-nurses are referred to who receive a monthly wage of eight drachmae; in another (no. 148) the subject is the "patron" of a Jewess who seems to have been a freedwoman. A section of the Jews are designated as "Persians of the *Epigoné*," which means that the person receiving the loan conceded in advance all flight to places of refuge (such as temples), and it is clear that only people who stood in dire need of loans would have signed contracts as "Persians of the *Epigoné*." See *C. P. Jud.* 1, p. 50ff. on the question of the Jews of Alexandria as they appear in *BGU;* on the "Persians of the *Epigoné*," *ib.* p. 51, n. 10.

31 Juvenal *Sat.* III, 14-16; Martial. *Epig.* XII, 57. Cf. the article of Hans (Johanan) Lewy "The Jewish Poor in Ancient Rome," in *Dinaburg Festschrift,* 104ff.

32 The ministers close to the crown were, of course, the well known Jewish generals Onias, Ḥananiah and Helkias. An inscription mentions Helkias (or his son) with the title of *Strategos,* and he may have been head of one of the Egyptian nomes; cf. Schürer, III, 132; Juster, II, 267. The Onias mentioned in *C. P. Jud.,* no. 132 (see above, p. 498) was a high official and member of the royal court. An assimilated Jew, Dositheos son of Drimylos, is referred to as priest of the (deified) kings in 222 B.C.E. (*C. P. Jud.,* no. 127; see above, ch. 4). Important in the Roman period is the brilliant career of Tiberius Julius Alexander, nephew of the philosopher Philo, who reached the highest position in Egypt—that of the Roman governor (*praefectus Aegypti*). On this man see *C. P. Jud.,* no. 418.

33 *C. P. Jud.,* no. 25.

34 Schürer (III, 43; cf. 132) writes cautiously: "He may only have been a friend of the Jews" (*Judenfreund*). This view cannot be refuted, even as it cannot be proved; but it is more natural to suppose that a man who built a synagogue to the God of Israel, jointly with the Jewish community, was himself a Jew. The fact that he does not include himself among the members of the Jewish community of Athribis only proves that he was not himself a resident of the town, but, as a government official, would have changed his place of residence with his duties.

35 "The Nile police" (*potamophylakía*) is alluded to in ostraca: *e.g., O. Theb.* 36, 93; *WO* 507; *O. Ashm.* 41; cf. Wilcken, *Ostraka,* I, 282ff.; *id., Grundz.* 392 and 396. Wilcken (*Ostr.* 283) thought that the Jews were not policemen in the exact sense of the term, but only performed a fiscal function as tax-collectors; this opinion, however, was based on the erroneous view that Jews could not be soldiers, and this has now been shown to be false. It may, however, be supposed that the Nile guard was associated with the levying of customs-dues on all the goods sent up or down the river (the customs station was at Schedia near Alexandria—see Strabo XVII, 800).

36 Schürer, III, 132.

37 Wilcken, *Ostr.*, I, 347ff.

38 On these ostraca, see *C. P. Jud.*, p. 194ff. (nos. 48-124). Wilcken was the first to discover the existence of the Jewish tax-collectors in Upper Egypt, but mistakenly believed that all the Jews mentioned in these ostraca were tax-collectors (*Ostr.* I, 523f.). In his article on anti-Semitism in Alexandria, which appeared in 1909 ("Zum alexandrinischen Antisemitismus," in *Abh. Sächs. Ges. Wiss., phil.-hist. Kl.*, 27, pp. 783-839), he changed his mind and admitted that part of the Jews appearing on the ostraca in Upper Egypt were farmers (cf. above, p. 336).

39 Cf. *The Jews of Egypt*, 54ff.

40 Cf. the description of tax-collectors as barbarians and destroyers of towns and villages, in Philo, *De spec. leg.* I, 143; II, 96; III, 162f.

41 On the gruelling conditions in which the tax-collectors worked in Ptolemaic Egypt, cf. Schubart, *Einführung in die Papyruskunde*, 1918, 253; Cl. Préaux, *L'économie royale des Lagides*, 1939, 454f.

42 *C. P. Jud.*, nos. 65, 69, 97, 100-103, 105. Cf. *Jews in Egypt*, 58ff.

43 *BGU* 715 = *C. P. Jud.* 428. Some of the *sitologoi* have Jewish names, such as Isaac, Shabbatai, Eleazar and Jose. The papyrus belongs to the year 101/102 C.E.

44 *BGU* 1730 = *SP* 209 = *C. P. Jud.* 137.

45 In the late Roman period (291 C.E.) a papyrus mentions Jewish slaves in Egypt (a mother and her two sons) who are redeemed from slavery by the Jewish community of Oxyrhynchos (*P. Oxy.* 1205 = *C. P. Jud.* 473).

46 See above, p. 291.

47 *CIJ*. 683/4. Cf. Juster II, 81, n. 2; Schürer III, 23.

48 On Antonius Rufus and his family, see *Jews in Egypt*, 202.

49 Individual priests are sometimes referred to in the sources; see for example, *C. P. Jud.*, nos. 120, 121, 139. On their function in the communities, see Baron, *The Jewish Community*, I, 97.

NOTES *part* II *chapter* 4

1 M. Friedländer, *Die Jüden in der vorchristlichen griechichen Welt*, 1897; *Geschichte der jüdischen Apologetik als Vorgeschichte des*

Christentums, 1903; *Die religiösen Bewegungen innerhalb des Jüdentums in Zeitalter Jesu,* 1905.

2 It is worthwhile to stress the difference of opinions between Friedländer and an outstanding scholar of our own time, Professor E. R. Goodenough (*Jewish Symbols in the Greco-Roman Period,* vols. I-IV, 1952-54).
The latter is anxious, as Friedländer was, to emphasize the Hellenization of the Jews; but in contrast to Friedländer, he does not consider Palestine a country outside the Hellenistic world. Recent studies in Palestinian life and culture have revealed that even "orthodox" Palestinian Judaism of the Roman-Byzantine period was not secure against the influence of Hellenism; cf. S. Lieberman, *Greek in Jewish Palestine,* 1942; *id., Hellenism in Jewish Palestine,* 1950.

3 The study of the Greek names of Jews in documents (inscriptions, papyri, ostraca) encounters numerous difficulties owing to the fact that we are unable to distinguish between Greeks and Jews with Greek names, unless the Jewish identity of the bearer is specifically indicated. Hence the scantiness of our knowledge, for example, of the Jews of Alexandria (cf. above, p. 520, n. 30). Only in a locality known to us as a Jewish quarter or colony are we permitted to regard all the people mentioned in the documents as Jews, and only here is a precise study of the non-Hebrew names possible. For this reason the inscriptions from the territory of Onias (below, n. 9) and the ostraca of the Roman period from Apollinopolis Magna (on these ostraca cf. *C. P. Jud.,* vol. II, Section 9) are especially important.

4 Among the Hebrew names which became special favorites among the Diaspora Jews in the Hellenistic period may be mentioned Shabbatai, Joseph, Joshua, Samuel and Judah. The names of the patriarchs (Abraham, Isaac and Jacob) become popular chiefly in the Roman period. Cf. *The Jews in Egypt,* 231ff.; *C. P. Jud.* 1, 29ff.

5 Among the theophoric names Dositheos takes first place. This name hardly appears in Greece before the end of the fourth century B.C.E., and in the Hellenistic period is found in use almost exclusively among the Jews. After it comes the name Theophilos (sometimes Theuphilos in documents) which was also popular chiefly among Jews. The theophoric names Theodoros, Dorotheos, Theodotos, etc. were not characteristic of Jews alone, although they were much used by them. In the Roman period Jews and Gentiles used theophoric names indiscriminately. Cf. *The Jews of Egypt,* 241ff. On the name Dositheos, cf. *C. P. Jud.,* no. 127, introd.

6 Cf. a series of double names among the Egyptian Jews in the Hellenistic-Roman period in the present writer's *Jews in Egypt,* 244. No definite rules can be set for the adaptation of the Hebrew to the Greek names. Sometimes the adaptation is based on the content of the name (*e.g.*, theophoric names corresponding to such names as Nathaniah, Mattathiah, Jonathan, etc.). Sometimes the Greek resembles the Hebrew name phonically (*e.g.*, Alcimus-Elyakim, Jason-Joshua); but generally complete anarchy prevails in the selection of the names. Cf. "Jose who is also Theophilos" or "Arsinoë who is also Sabbatis."

7 Besides the name Horus may be noted the names Pasis, Seos, Phaos, etc.; cf. *The Jews in Egypt*, 245ff. Cf. also the Egyptian names among the Jewish settlers in the territory of Onias: *CIJ*, II, 1480, 1484, 1486, 1489, 1493, 1496, 1520.

8 Among the military settlers at Fayûm only those can be regarded as Jews who are noted in the documents as such. Luckily their number is considerable, especially as in two documents each signed by six witnesses, all the latter are marked as "Jews" (*C. P. Jud.*, nos. 22 and 24). Hellenization had struck deep roots among these soldiers; only 25 per cent of the names mentioned among the Jewish servicemen at Fayûm are Hebrew, the rest being Greek. Cf. *ib.*, I, 27ff. As to the names of Jews known to us from the ostraca of Upper Egypt, cf. *C. P. Jud.* 1, 200ff. The number of Hebrew and Aramaic names here is large, but the explanation is simple: we do not know how many Jews there were among those who called themselves by Greek names. Cf. above, n. 3. Among the Greek names may be noted Aristobulus, Aristomenes, Straton, Pythangelos, Tryphon, and several of the theophoric group.

9 The inscriptions from Tel el-Yehudiyeh (the territory of Onias) have been collected in *CIJ* 1451-1530; cf. *ZNTW* 22, 1923, p. 280ff. Among the Greek names should be noted Alexander, Aristobulus, Agathokles, Glaukias, Theophilos, Theon, Nicanor, Nicomedes, Nicon, Tryphaina, Theodora, Nike, Irene, etc.

10 Cf. Schürer, III, 79, n. 20. The inscriptions of Teucheira (Toera) furnish us with abundant material concerning the names of Cyrenaican Jews. Some names are Hebrew (such as Judah, Simon, Shabtit, Sarra, Maria, Martha, Tubiah, etc.), or theophoric, but most are regular Greek names (Nicias, Nicon, Jason, Philocrates, etc.). It must be stressed that we have no means of identifying Jews in the inscriptions *SEG* 419-795, except when a Hebrew or a theophoric name points clearly to a Jew. An attempt to confront the Greek names in *SEG* 419ff. with those in the epitaphs from the Jewish cemetery of Teucheira published by John Gray (in A. Rowe, *Cyrenaican Expedition of the University of Manchester*, 1952, p. 43ff.) would certainly establish a series of Greek names especially favored by Jews and would enable us to recognize many more inscriptions in *SEG* 419ff. as Jewish epitaphs.

11 Cf. *C. P. Jud.* 1, 30, n. 76.

12 "The name in the Hebrew language is Penuel, but in our language . . ." (Philo, *de conf. linguar.*, 129). A few examples of Philo's curious etymology: Abraham knew that death (τελευτή) meant "the end" (*telos*) of life "as the name itself shows" (*de Abrah.* 230). God called the sky "heavens" (οὐρανός) "either because they are the limit of everything, or because they were created before visible things" (τὸν ὁρατόν) (*de opif. mundi*, 37). Other examples in C. Siegfried, *Philo*, 196. Josephus, unlike Philo, knew very well that a distinction must be made between Greek and Hebrew etymology: cf. *C. Ap.* I, 319.

13 Cf. Schürer, III, 426; H. B. Swete, *An Introduction to the Old Testament in Greek*, 2nd ed., 1914, 18ff.

14 According to the figures given by Frey (*CIJ*, I, p. lxv f.), 413 inscriptions (74 per cent) from Rome are Greek, and only 137 (24 per cent) are Latin.

15 Reinach, *Textes d'auteurs grecs et romains relatifs au judaïsme* 121. Cf. Lewy's article, in the *Dinaburg Festschrift*, 104ff.

16 *C. P. Jud.*, no. 107 ("Delous wrote (this) on request of Simon as he does not know how to write"); *ib.* no. 46 ("Chairemon son of Callicrates wrote (this) for them at their request as they said they did not know how to write"). In the first case the subject is a Jew, Simon ben Joezer, tax-collector in Thebais; in the second, two Jewish potters from the Syrian village in the Fayûm.

17 See *C. P. Jud.* 1, p. 101, 107ff.

18 As correctly remarked by Schürer, III, 90ff.

19 *C. P. Jud.*, no. 129: a petition to the king from the village of Alexandrou-nesos in the Fayûm of the year 218 B.C.E. *nákoros* is the Dorian form of *neokóros*. In an inscription from Apameia of the fourth century C.E. the term *hazzan* is translated into Greek as *diakonos*, servant: *CIJ*, 805; cf. Krauss, *Synag. Altert.*, 126ff.

20 Cowley, *JEA*, 2, 1915, 212.

21 Cf. for example the above-mentioned inscription from Berenice (above, n. 10).

22 The bestowal of a crown: the stone of Helkias (above, p. 32, n. 32); inscription from Phokaia (*CIJ* 738); in the last the *prohedria* is also bestowed, which among the Greeks meant permission to sit in the first rows of the amphitheater on days when the contests took place. Among the Jews the same permission was given in respect of places in the synagogue. For the erection of inscribed monuments in public places cf. the Berenice inscription already mentioned, ll. 25ff.: "and the archontes shall record the *psephisma* on a stele made of Parian stone and place it in a prominent place in the amphitheater."

23 *CIJ* 1440-1444, 1449; cf. *Jews in Egypt*, 137.

24 *C. P. Jud.*, nos. 18, 22, 23, 24.

25 *Ib.* nos. 23, 26.

26 In papyrus *C. P. Jud.,* no. 19, a case between a Jew and a Jewess is tried before a Greek court "according to the royal statutes and the city-laws," that is, according to the normal principles of Hellenistic law in Egypt. In no. 23 is mentioned the royal *diagramma* in accordance with which the matter is arbitrated between the two Jews.

27 The dispute between Dositheos, "a Jew of the *Epigoné*," and the Jewess Herakleia is the subject of arbitration before a Greek court (known as "the Court of Ten") at Arsinoë-Crocodilopolis, the chief town of the Fayûm.

28 *C. P. Jud.,* no. 144: the municipal office of Protarchos is mentioned in many documents from Alexandria (see *BGU* IV; cf. Schubart, *Arch.* 5, 57ff.). Matters involving Jews are dealt with in the same office; cf. *C. P. Jud.,* nos. 142-9.

29 On the position of the Jewish woman see Gulack, *Yéssodei hamishpat ha-wri* (Heb.), I, 36ff. On the function of the guardian in the life of the Greek woman, see Erdmann, *Die Ehe im alten Griechenland,* 1934, 33ff.; Egon Weiss, in *Arch.,* 4, 78. Cf. *Jews in Egypt,* 146ff.

30 *C. P. Jud.,* no. 20, 24. The interest mentioned in these documents is that normal in Hellenistic Egypt—24 per cent per annum (2 per cent per month). Cf. *Jews in Egypt,* 148f.

31 It should be particularly noted that all these examples are not cited in order to deny the fact of the existence of autonomous institutions belonging to the Jewish community—whose reality is undoubted—but merely to show the degree of assimilation among the Jews of Egypt. The available papyrological material is always fortuitous and every new discovery may alter our outlook considerably. Down to the present no traces have been found in Greek papyri of Hebrew law (apart from a vague allusion to a "political law of the Jews" in a very torn papyrus—*C. P. Jud.,* no. 128), but this is no proof that it may not some time be found. On the general question of Jewish and Hellenistic law, see *Jews in Egypt,* 128ff.; *C. P. Jud.* 1, 32ff.

32 Cf. Philo, *de spec. leg.,* II, 229ff.; *ib.* II, 246; *de opif. mundi,* 78; *de Joseph.* 81. Cf. the article of Ralph Marcus, in *Turoff Festschrift* (Heb.), 1938, 233ff.; Goodenough, *An Introduction to Philo Judaeus,* 8ff.

33 L. Robert, *REJ* v. 101 (1937), 73ff.; *id. Hellenica,* 3, 100.

34 *CIJ* 748.

35 *CIJ* 755. The inscription belongs to the second or third century C.E.

36 Bickermann (in his article *The Jews, their History, Culture and*

Religion, ed. L. Finkelstein, I, 100ff.) rightly emphasizes the fact that the translation of the Bible into Greek was a unique undertaking, as the ancient world was unacquainted with Greek translations from oriental languages. The modern literature devoted to the Septuagint is very rich. Most useful as an introduction to the various questions involved in its study is Swete, *An Introduction to the Old Testament in Greek,* 2nd ed., 1914.

37 Thus Philo the Poet aspired to be a sort of Jewish Homer and wrote a poem in hexameters *On Jerusalem;* Ezekiel wrote a tragedy on the Exodus in imitation of the Greek tragedies, more especially those of Euripides. The artistic value of these works is highly questionable. Cf. Schürer, III, 497ff. On Philo, cf. the article of Gutmann, "Philo the Epic Poet," in *Scripta Hierosolymitana,* I, 36ff.

38 It is usual to describe the entire Alexandrian literature as "apologetic," as if it were wholly a literature of defense and propaganda directed to the Greek reader. This is not the case, for Jewish Alexandrian literature appealed first to the Jewish reader in order to furnish him with the intellectual pabulum which he needed. This is the reason for its variety; it included epics, drama, history, historical "romances," learned works, supplements to the Bible stories, philosophy and other types of literature. The term "apologetics" should be reserved only for those works whose direct function was to defend the Jews from anti-Semitic attacks, such as Philo's *Apologia for the Jews* (which has not survived) or Josephus' *Contra Apionem.* Generally it may be said that the Jewish literature of the early Roman period was "apologetic" in the sense that several elements of Jewish defense are to be found in it; but the term should not be applied to the literature of the previous period. At any rate, care should be taken not to see it as an invariably propagandistic literature directed to the non-Jewish world. Cf. the present writer's article "Jewish Apologetic Literature Reconsidered," in *Eos,* 48, fasc. iii (Symbolae Taubenschlag, III), 1957, p. 169ff.

39 See the writer's article, "The Ideology of the Letter of Aristeas," *HTR* LI, 1958, 59-85. Cf. on the *Letter of Aristeas* generally, Moses Hadas' introduction to his English translation of the book (M. Hadas, *Aristeas to Philocrates,* 1951), with a rich bibliography, 84ff.

40 Scholars are divided on the date of the composition of the *Letter of Aristeas,* but the majority properly inclines to the belief that it was composed in the second half of the second century B.C.E. Cf. Hadas, *op. cit.,* 9ff.; Bickermann, *ZNTW,* 29 (1930), 280ff.

41 No peculiar proofs are required to demonstrate Philo's attitude, as his entire intellectual output constituted a synthesis between Judaism and Hellenism. On Philo generally, see Bréhier, *Les idées philosophiques et religieuses de Philon d'Alexandrie,* 1925; Heinemann, *Philos griechiche u. jüdische Bildung,* 1932; H. A. Wolfson, *Philo,* 1947.

42 Cf. Philo (ed. Loeb) VI, *De Vita Mosis,* II, 203 and n. *a* (pp. 550-1); VII, *De Specialibus Legibus,* I (§9), 53 and n. *c* (p. 129); cf. also Josephus (ed. Loeb) I, *C. Ap.,* II (§33), 237 (p. 389); IV, *Ant.,* IV, 207 and n. *c* (p. 575). Cf. further *C. P. Jud.,* 97-103.

43 See Freudenthal, *Alexander Polyhistor,* 143ff.; Schürer, III, 477ff.; M. Braun, *History and Romance in Graeco-Oriental Literature,* 1938, 26ff.

44 *CIJ* 749.

45 "Ptolemy son of Dionysius the Jew thanks the God": *CIJ* 1538 = *OGIS* 73.

46 See *C. P. Jud.,* no. 127.

47 He was Procurator in Palestine (in the forties of the first century C.E.), later Prefect of Egypt (at the time of Vespasian's accession); he also took part in the Roman war against the Jews in 70 as Titus' adviser (*War* VI, 237). His name is mentioned in several papyri—see *C. P. Jud.,* no. 418.

48 This occurred during the great war with Rome (*War* VII, 47ff.).

49 *Vita Mosis,* I, 31; *de Virtutibus,* 182.

50 *Vita Mosis,* I, 147.

51 *De Spec. leg.* III, 29; he especially stresses here the danger of these marriages to the younger generation ("to sons and daughters").

52 It were well to mention again that many Jews took Egyptian names; see above, p. 524, n. 7. On the Egyptian influence on the Greek population of the villages, see above, p. 21.

53 Philo speaks bitterly of those Jews who are so enchanted by "the frivolous spirit of life's success" that they alter their traditional mode of living and betray Judaism: *Vita Mosis* I, 30-31.

54 A papyrus from the Archives of Zenon (*PCZ* 59762 = *C. P. Jud.,* 10) may serve as a good example of the observance of the Sabbath on the Egyptian countryside. The papyrus contains a list of bricks received on the estate of Apollonius at Philadelpheia in the Fayûm; the foreman recorded daily the number of bricks received from the wagoners who brought the load. One day, instead of recording the number of bricks, he noted only one word: Sabbath. On that day either he or the wagoners who brought the bricks had not worked. It is to be noted that the building work on Apollonius' estate was proceeding at a forced pace and the chief overseer of the estate, Zenon, had no inclination to clemency or pity. To keep the Sabbath in such conditions would not have been easy.

55 A list of all the synagogues in Palestine and other countries is given by Krauss, *Synagogale Altertümer,* 199ff.

56 See the list in *C. P. Jud.* 1, 8; *Jews in Egypt,* 136.

57 Tos. Sukkah, IV, 6; Sukk. 51b; Jer. Sukk., V, 55a; cf. also above p. 284f.

58 *CIJ* 683-4.

59 Cf. for example, *Vita Mosis,* II, 216; *de Spec. leg.,* II, 62; *de Opif. mundi,* 128.

60 The traditional festivals are mentioned more than once in Philo and other sources; see, for example, the Berenice inscription, where the community's resolution was drafted "at the Assembly of the Festival of Tabernacles" (Schürer, III, 79, n. 20). "The Day of Mordecai" is referred to in II Macc. 15.37, as a day whose date was known to the readers (and the readers of the book were Jews of the Diaspora). On the festival of Purim, cf. also below, n. 62. On the Feast of Hannukah, see the following note.

61 II Macc. opens with a letter from the Jews of Palestine to their brethren in the Egyptian diaspora, dated in 124, which invites the Egyptian Jews to celebrate the festival of Hannukah; in the letter a second is referred to, sent to Egypt in 143-2 with the same purpose. See Bickermann's article in *ZNTW* 32 (1933), 233ff., where he has solved—in my opinion, most successfully—all the difficulties connected with the interpretation of this letter (II Macc. 1.1-9). On the Festival of Purim, see the following note.

62 At the end of the Book of Esther in its Greek translation (it would be more correct to call this translation a new version, as it contains many additions to the Hebrew text), two Jews are mentioned, Dositheus (designated as "a Priest and Levite") and his son Ptolemy, who introduced a "Purim Letter" into Egypt in the fourth year of "King Ptolemy and Cleopatra" (10.11). The Book of Esther, then, was deliberately sent from Palestine to stir the Jews of Egypt to celebrate the Feast of Purim. (On the chronological question, cf. *C. P. Jud.* 1, 46, n. 119.) The grandson of Sira, who translated his grandfather's book close to the end of the second century B.C.E. (cf. above, p. 462, n. 55), says that in his time "the Torah, the Prophets and the rest of the books" were translated into Greek; he means part of the Hagiographa, and it is to be assumed that books such as Judith, Tobit, etc., were also translated into Greek at this period. On these books, see R. H. Pfeiffer, *Hist. of New Testament Times,* 1949, 258ff.; 285ff.

63 The composition of *The Wisdom of Solomon* is normally attributed to the end of the Ptolemaic period; but the grounds for this attribution are not decisive; cf. *C. P. Jud.,* p. 75, n. 52. On the date of the composition of *III Macc.,* see the present writer's article "The

Third Book of the Maccabees as a Historical Source of the Augustan time" (Heb.), in *Zion*, X, 1ff.

64 Cf. above, p. 35f.

65 The populous Jewish community of Apollinopolis Magna was apparently destroyed at the time of the rebellion. Several decades later, under the Emperor M. Aurelius, we find in this town only one Jewish family. The father has a Graeco-Roman name (Achillas Rufus), but his three sons all have Egyptian names. Cf. *Tell Edfu*, I, 1937, nos. 168ff. (*C. P. Jud.*, no. 375ff.). Cf. *C. P. Jud.* 1, p. 94.

66 It is sufficient to mention that the citizens of Alexandria lacked the supreme institution of autonomous government, the Council (*boulé*), while at the head of the Jewish community of that city stood an Ethnarch "like the ruler of an independent state," and, subsequently, a Council of Elders of seventy-one men.

67 *C. Ap.* I, 176ff.; Reinach, *Textes,* no. 7.

68 Reinach, *Textes,* no. 8.

69 *Textes,* no. 5. Cf. on Theophrastus, the article of Y. Gutman, "Theophrastos on the Knowledge of Divinity in Israel," in *Tarbitz* (Heb.), XVIII, 157ff.

70 A typical "Utopia" (an ideal state on a remote island in the equatorial zone) was composed by Jamblichus; the contents of the book have been preserved in Diodorus II, 55ff. The famous book of Euhemerus, whose view of the nature of the gods had a great influence on the development of Greek religion in the Hellenistic period, was also written in the form of a Utopia. Cf. Diodor. VI, 2, 4ff.

71 Interest in questions of the philosophy of religion, especially strong at the beginning of the Hellenistic period, spurred the Greeks to seek religious (*e.g.,* monotheistic) ideas among various peoples; they sought ideas which could be conceived as parallels to the writings of the Greek philosophers. Cf. on this tendency, the article of W. Jaeger, "Greeks and Jews," in *Journ. of Relig.* 18, 1938, 127ff.; cf. also his book *Diokles von Karystos,* 1938, Excursus II, 134ff.

72 Diod. XL, 3; Reinach, *Textes,* no. 9. On Hecataeus, see Lewy's article, *ZNTW,* 31 (1932), 117ff. Cf. Jaeger's articles, already cited.

73 According to Hecataeus, Egypt was the land whence issued the wide movement of colonization which embraced almost the entire world. In the general view of the Greeks, the movement of emigration and colonization expanded according to a regular plan of successive migration, conquest, the foundation of towns, and the giving of laws. See Jaeger, in his above-named book on Diokles, p. 134ff., 147.

74 The story's importance for the study of the Hyksos question, which has attracted the special attention of scholars of the ancient east in our time, cannot be dealt with here.

75 *C. Ap.* I, 73ff. = Reinach, *Textes,* no. 10.

76 *C. Ap.* I, 228ff. = Reinach, *Textes,* no. 11.

77 In his article on Manetho, in *RE,* XXVII.

78 In his article on anti-Semitism in *RE, Supplementband.* V. Cf. M. Braun, *History and Romance,* 27.

79 This does not mean, of course, that they read the story in the Bible; in Manetho's time the Septuagint was not yet widely known, even if we assume that it was in existence. The story of the Exodus connected with the Festival of Passover was so widespread among the Jews that it would not have been hard for the Egyptian priests to learn of it from the Jews themselves. As is well known, Passover was celebrated by the Jews of Elephantine in the Persian period: cf. Cowley, *Aramaic Papyri of the fifth century B.C.,* no. 21; cf. nos. 30-31. Even as early as this period, the priests of Egypt revealed their hostility to the Jews, for the temple at Elephantine was destroyed by the priests of the Egyptian god Chnum. (Cf. Kraeling, *The Brooklyn Museum Aramaic Papyri,* 1953 111f.)

80 This is the same name, except for the substitution of the name Osiris for that of Yahwe.

81 *Pro Flacco,* 28, 67.

82 Strabo XVI, 760/1 = Reinach, *Textes,* no. 54 (p. 99). On Poseidonius and his attitude to the Jewish religion, see Heinemann's article, *MGWJ,* 1919, 113ff.

83 *C. Ap.* II, 112ff. = Reinach, *Textes,* no. 19.

84 Diod. XXXIV, 1, 3 = Reinach, *Textes,* no. 25.

85 Reinach, *Textes,* no. 60.

86 *C. Ap.* II, 80 = Reinach, *Textes,* no. 63.

87 Cf. G. Michaelides, in *Aegyptus,* 32, 1952, 45ff.; L. Vischer, *RHR,* 139 (1951), 14ff.

88 Plutarch, *On Isis and Osiris,* 31 = Reinach, *Textes,* no. 68.

89 E. Bickermann, "Ritualmord und Eselskult," in *MGWJ,* 1927, 255ff.

90 Reinach, *Textes,* no. 60.

91 See the above-cited article, p. 171ff. The practice of human sacrifice belongs, in Bickermann's opinion, to the story "style" of the Greek topical writers who wrote on the "conspiracy" (*Verschwörung*); examples are to be found in Plutarch (*Life of Publicola,* 4), Diodorus (XXII, 5), and Sallust (*The Conspiracy of Catilina,* XXII). Some features of the story (such as the fattening of the victim) belong to the type of story about "The Saturnalian King," which had world-wide currency. The Greek writer, therefore, lumped together the

HELLENISTIC CIVILIZATION AND THE JEWS

elements of two originally quite unconnected literary and religious phenomena (*ibid.*). Further research on the literary motifs of the blood-libel has been conducted by David Flusser in his article "The Ritual Murder Slander against the Jews in the Light of Outlooks in the Hellenistic Period" in *The Essays in Memoriam Joh. Lewy* (Heb.), 104ff.

92 Bickermann, *op. cit.*, 182ff. In this view Bickermann is following Josephus, who wrote of the anti-Semitic authors that they "are more concerned to defend the king from the charge of sacrilege than to relate what is just and true concerning us and our Temple" (*C. Ap.* II, 90).

93 Cf. the correct view of Dessau: "Die Umwandlung des jerusalemitischen Tempels in einen des olympischen Zeus war doch wahrlich keine Entweihung, die der König vor den Griechen zu rechtfertigen gehabt hätte" (Dessau, *Gesch. d. röm. Kaiserzeit*, II, 2, 723, Ann. 2).

94 Diod. XXXIV, 1, 1 = Reinach, *Textes*, no. 25.

95 *C. Ap.* II, 258 = Reinach, *Textes*, no. 27 (p. 64).

96 *C. Ap.* I, 309 = Reinach, *Textes*, no. 59. The accusation against the Jews of contempt of the gods is one of the recurring charges in anti-Semitic literature. Manetho speaks of the destruction of temples by "the men of Jerusalem," using in connection with them the expression *anosioi*, denoting lack of reverence, and sacrilege towards the gods (*C. Ap.* I, 248). It is worth noting that some 400 years after Manetho, during the rebellion of the Jews of Cyrene and Egypt against Rome, this term became a regular and accepted epithet for the Jews, and we find it even in official papers of the period; cf. *Jews of Egypt*, 225ff.; *C. P. Jud.*, nos. 157/8, 438, 443.

97 *C. Ap.* II, 121 = Reinach, *Textes*, no. 63 (p. 133).

98 Reinach, *Textes*, no. 96. To complete the note, the following Roman writers should also be consulted: Trogus Pompeius (Reinach, no. 138), Juvenal (*ib.* no. 172), Tacitus (*ib.* no. 180: *adversus omnes alios hostile odium*). Cf. the articles of Johanan Lewy, "Cicero and the Jews," in *Zion*, VII, 1942, 109ff.; "Tacitus on Jewish Antiquities and Character," in *Zion*, VIII, 1943, 1ff.

99 Tac. *Ann.*, XV, 44: *odium humani generis*. The blood-libel and the fable of ass-worship were also transferred, as is well known, to the Christians.

100 Reinach, *Textes*, Introd., p. xvi.

101 C. Ap. II, 148 = Reinach, *Textes*, no. 27.

102 C. Ap. I, 311 = Reinach, *Textes*, no. 59. Cf. above, n. 96.

103 C. Ap. II, 21 = Reinach, *Textes*, no. 63, p. 127.

104 E. Meyer, *Ursprung und Anfänge des Christ.*, II, 31ff.

105 See above, p. 516, n. 3.

106 "Merkwürdig bleibt, dass die Anklage des Wuchers oder der geschäftlichen Unredlichkeit von den Judenfeinden des Altertums nie gegen die Juden direkt erhoben worden ist" (Bludau, 33).

107 Two papyri have enjoyed special success with modern anti-Semites; one (*W. Chr.* 56 = P. Magd. 35 = P. Ent. 30 = *C. P. Jud.* 129) speaks of a Jew called Dorotheos who had stolen a lady's coat and fled with it to a synagogue; and the other (*W. Chrest.* 57 = P. Gren. I, 43 = *C. P. Jud.* 135) contains a letter from a Greek to his brother, in which he informs him that he is waiting to receive a horse (sent to him by his brother) "from a Jew whose name I do not know," but that the horse has not yet been handed over to him. As to the first instance, it is true that the coat had been stolen by a Jew, and if additional examples are required of the existence of thieves among the Jews, one may point to papyrus *C. P. Jud.* 21 which tells of three Jewish soldiers who had broken into a private vineyard, taken grapes from ten vines, beaten up the watchman and stolen a vinedresser's pruning hook. As regards the second instance, there are no proofs that the Jew who was to bring the horse was a horse-dealer who had cheated the purchaser, as Stähelin, Bludau and Wilcken think: dozens of reasons might be found why the Jew (who may not have been a trader at all, but a carter in the service of the letter-writer's brother) had not delivered the horse at the proper time. Cf. the commentaries on these papyri in *C. P. Jud.*, nos. 21, 129, 135.

108 Cf. P. Stengel, *Die griechischen Kultusaltertümer*, 1898, 138ff.; R. Herzog, "Aus dem Asklepieion von Kos," in *Arch. f. Religionswiss.*, 10 (1907), 400ff.

109 Diodor. I, 83, 8.

110 In the above-mentioned article on anti-Semitism, *loc. cit.*, p. 5f.

111 S. Lurié, *Anti-Semitism in the Ancient World*, 1923 (Russian).

112 On Alexandrian anti-Semitism, see Wilcken, *Zum alexandrinischen Antisemitismus*, 1909; H. I. Bell, "Anti-Semitism in Alexandria," *JRS* 31, 1941, 1ff.; id. "The Acts of the Alexandrines," in *Journ. Jur. Pap.*, 4, 1950, 19ff.; Segré, *Jew. Soc. Stud.*, 8, 127ff.

113 Cf. for example the position of metics in the classical world; see Glotz, *Histoire grecque*, II, 251ff.; Ed. Meyer, *Gesch. d. Altert.* IV, 11ff.; Busolt, *Griechische Staatskunde*, I, 292ff.

114 C. Ap. II, 65: *Quomodo ergo, si sunt cives, eosdem deos quos Alexandrini non colunt?*

NOTES *appendices*

1 Wellhausen, *Israel. u. jüd. Geschichte*, 3 Aufl., 1897, 242. In the last edition (the 7th, 1914) of the book, this sentence has been eliminated.

2 *Die Juden u. Greichen,* 67ff.

3 B. Niese, *Kritik der beiden Makkabäerbücher,* 1900. The book was previously printed in the form of an article in *Hermes,* 35.

4 R. Laqueur, *Kritische Untersuchungen z. II Makkabäerbuch,* 1904; W. Kölbe, *Beiträge z. Syrischen u. jüdischen Geschichte,* 1926; E. Meyer, *Ursprung u. Anfänge d. Christentums,* II, 454ff.; C. Gutberlet, *Das zweite Buch d. Makkabäer,* 1927; H. Bévenot, *Die beiden Makkabäerbücher,* 1931; E. Bickermann, *RE, s.v. Makkabäerbücher;* F.-M. Abel, *Les livres des Maccabées,* 1949.

5 The contention of S. Zeitlin (*The Second Book of the Maccabees,* 1954, 19) that this letter could not have been written by the Jews of Jerusalem, because in those days Judaea was an independent state and did not use the Seleucid dating in its documents, is not convincing, since the Seleucid date was accepted in many lands of the East and was used even after the end of the Seleucid dynasty; cf. Bickermann, *Inst. des Sél.,* 206. It may be noted that the author of I Macc., the official historian of the Hasmonean house, continued to date events by the Seleucid era even after Judaea had been declared an independent state. The declaration of independence itself bears a double date: Year 172 (of the Seleucid era) and Year 3 of the High Priesthood of Simon (I Macc. 14.27).

6 On the first ten verses of II Macc. and the two dates in line 7 (143/2 B.C.E.) and in line 10 (125/4 B.C.E.) many studies had been written and dozens of different conjectures expressed, till Bickermann solved the problem (I think) most successfully. We have here a letter of the Jews of Jerusalem to the Jews of Egypt, of the year 124, in which is cited an extract from a previous letter of 143/2. See his article in *ZNTW,* 32, 1933, 233ff. But the problem connected with Judah the Maccabee's long letter allegedly to "Aristobulus, tutor of King Ptolemy" (II Macc. 1.10-2.18) has not yet been solved. Everyone agrees that this letter is merely a literary creation quite unconnected with Judah the Maccabee, but opinions differ on the date of its composition.

There is no point in entering into this complicated question here, and I wish only to observe that it has no bearing on the dating of the composition of II Macc. It may be assumed that in the original edition of II Macc. the verse 2.19 came immediately after the beginning of 1.10. Or, on the other hand, the author of the book may have composed Judah's letter and inserted it into his work.

7 On the influence of Hasmonean Palestine on the Diaspora communities, see above, p. 283f.

8 Cf. for example, Abel, *op. cit.,* p. xxxiv. Against this view, cf. Gutberlet, *op. cit.,* 7.

9 Many scholars favor this date, *e.g.,* Niese (p. 25), E. Meyer (II, 455), Abel (p. xliii), J. C. Dancy, *A Commentary on I Maccabees,* 1954, 14, and others; others think of the first century B.C.E. The opinion of S. Zeitlin, *Commentary on II Macc.,* 27, who lowers the date of the Epitomator to the reign of Agrippa I (44-41 C.E.), approximates Willrich's opinion of sixty years ago (*Juden u. Griechen,* 76) and it is not to be supposed that it will find many followers today.

10 R. H. Pfeiffer, *History of New Testament Times,* 1949, 510, 519.

11 According to E. Meyer (*ib.* 457), Jason's book went down at least to the accession of Jonathan to the High Priesthood; but in that case it is clear that Jason, when he was writing his book, would have known at any rate the first steps of the Hasmonean dynasty, namely, the period of Jonathan and Simon; yet this is in contradiction to the whole spirit of the book: on this question, see below.

12 Cf. II Macc. 10.19ff.; 14.17. The brothers of Judah are referred to in 8.22-3 as captains under Judah's command.

13 Cf. above, p. 206f.

14 Abel, p. xli; cf. Keil, *Commentar über die Bücher der Makkabäer,* 1875, 275f.

15 *Der Gott der Makkabäer,* 33ff.

16 Polyb. 47, 6ff.

17 Cf. his article in the collection *The Jews, their History, Culture, Religion,* ed. by L. Finkelstein I, 1949, 108ff.; cf. *id., Die Makkabäer,* 1935, 72.

18 The writer has no desire to enter into theological questions and his intention is only to mention things here which are well known, namely, that the entire doctrine of reward and punishment in the Hebrew Bible rests on the assumption and principle that a man is free to choose between good and evil (Deut. 30.15ff.). A man could not "do evil in the sight of God" were he not free to decide to do as he wished.

The same outlook is found in the talmudical period: Despite the fact that "all is foreseen" by God, "freedom is given" to man to choose his way in life (*Avot,* 3.15). The reign of fate in a man's life, the predetermination of his steps from birth to death, and the agonies suffered by a man for offences of which he is not guilty are notions belonging to Greek religion.

19 *Der Gott der Makk.,* 18ff. The tradition in Polybius is not that of Seleucid historiography—*ib.* 168.

20 On Jason as the representative of "pathetic history-writing," cf. Bickermann, *Gott d. Makk.,* 147; Abel, *op. cit.,* p. xxxvi ff.; Pfeiffer, *op. cit.,* 518.

21 The work of abbreviation is most noticeable in section xiii, 22ff.

If one does not seek here a deliberate attempt to devise a completely new style (which would be curious, as this style would stand in opposition to the broad "pathetic" style in which the book was written) it may be thought that the Epitomator here used abrupt notes which he had made from Jason and had not managed to clothe in literary style. Zeitlin's opinion (*Comm. to II Macc.*, 22) that this laconic, jerky style is the original style of Jason, is not credible; no Hellenistic author would have permitted himself to write a long work in so poor a style, and had Jason thus written, he would have managed to relate in five books the events of so long a period that even the broad chronological limits set by Zeitlin to his work would have been too confined for him.

22   Kolbe, *op. cit.*, 124ff.; Abel, *op. cit.*, p. xxxix; Bickermann, *Gott der Makkabäer*, 147.

23   The scholars who proceed from the assumption that Jason's work corresponded chronologically to that of the Epitomator, divide the five chapters iii-vii between two books of Jason. Cf. Pfeiffer, *op. cit.*, 510. Clearly no dogmatic statement can be made on this question, and the whole history of the period preceding the appearance of Judah the Maccabee occupied only one book, serving as a sort of introduction to the actual narrative. Even in this case, however, the account of these events took up much space, perhaps no less than the entire II Macc.

24   See on *IV Macc.*, Dupont-Sommer, *Le quatrième livre des Maccabées*, 1939; Hadas, *The Third and Fourth Books of Maccabees*, 1953; Freudenthal, *Die Flavius Josephus beigelegte Schrift über die Herrschaft der Vernunft*, 1869. In the first (Hebrew) edition of the present book the author was also of this opinion, but renewed examination of *IV Macc.* has convinced him of his error.

25   Freudenthal, *Die Flavius Josephus beilegte Schrift über die Herrschaft der Vernunft*, 72ff.

26   Bickermann, "The Date of Fourth Maccabees," in *Louis Ginzberg Jubilee Volume*, 1945, 105ff.

27   See the present writer's article "War I, i, 1 as a historical source," in the collection *Madae ha-Yehadut* (Heb.) of the Hebrew University of Jerusalem, I, 1925, 179ff.

28   In the ms. "over the whole land of Syria" ($\pi\epsilon\rho\grave{\iota}$ ὅλης Συρίας), but this is a copyist's error, and here should be read $\pi\epsilon\rho\grave{\iota}$ κοίλης Συρίας (cf. Polyb. XXVIII, 1; *ib.* 15).

29   This idea was expressed—for the first time in my opinion—by Niese, *GGMS*, III, 230, n. 4.

30   Cf. above, p. 77ff. To the opinions there cited should be added that of Dalmann, who sees in the "sons of violence" Hyrcanus and his faction. Dalmann, "Die Tubiah-Inschrift von Arak el-Emir und Daniel XI, 14," *Paläst. Jahrb.* 1920, 33ff.

31 See above, p. 469, n. 40.

32 See on this question M. A. Beek, *Das Danielbuch,* 1935; Louis Ginzberg, *Studies in Daniel,* 1948. Without entering into the actual question, I should remark that at least three of the subsequent themes, the refusal of Daniel and his companions to taste the king's meat, the desecration of the Temple vessels by Belshazzar, and the promulgation of the anti-Jewish ordinance by King Darius are very appropriate to the atmosphere of the period of Antiochus.

33 The cave scrolls published down to 1951, including the "Damascus Covenant," have been assembled and published by Habermann, *Edah ve-Edut,* Jerusalem, 1951. Of the new publications should be mentioned E. L. Sukenik, *A Corpus of the Hidden Scrolls in Possession of the Hebrew University, Jerusalem,* 1954; D. Barthélemy and J. T. Milik, *Qumran Cave I,* 1955.

34 Cf. the short survey (chiefly relating to the date of composition of the scroll of the *Habakkuk Commentary*), made by Elliger, *Studien zum Habakkuk-Kommentar,* 1953, 238ff. The views of individual scholars who lower the time of composition of the scrolls to the middle ages, or think that they are forged, are not mentioned here.

35 For example, B. Reicke, *Studia Theologica,* 2, 1948, 45ff.; Avi-Yonah, in *Isr. Expl. Jnl.,* 2, 1952, 1ff.; Rabinowitz, *JBL* 72, 1952, 82.

36 For example, M. Z. Segal, "On the problem of the Cave-Scrolls," in the collection *Eretz Yisrael,* I, 1950, 39ff. Cf. his article in English in *JBL* 1951, 70, 131ff.

37 Dupont-Sommer places them at the beginning of the Roman period; he had defended his opinions in a long series of articles (*Aperçus préliminaires sur les manuscrits de la Mer Morte,* 1950; *Vetus Testam.,* 1, 1951, 200ff.; *Nouveaux Apercus* etc., 1953. Elliger attributes them to approximately the same period, in his above-mentioned book, 270ff. Cf. also Yigal Yadin, *The Scroll of the War of the Sons of Light and the Sons of Darkness,* 1955, 222ff., who on the basis of a detailed analysis of military problems and methods of combat, favors the period of Julius Caesar or Augustus.

38 By the "Khittaim" of the *Habakkuk Commentary,* III, 9ff. "who shall come from the islands of the sea to devour all the peoples like a vulture," the Romans are meant, in the view of most scholars, whereas "Katiei Ashur" and "Ha-katiim be-Mitzraim" of the Scroll of "The War of the Sons and Light and the Sons of Darkness" (I, 4, 2) are better suited to the Seleucids and the Ptolemies respectively (see, however, Y. Yadin, *op. cit.,* 21ff.).

39 "The house of Absalom" is mentioned in the *Habakkuk Commentary.*

40 On this question see Le Vaux, Binjamin-Minjamin, *RB*, 45, 1936, 400ff.

41 MS "L": *Simon autem quidam de tribu Balgea;* MS "B": *de Balgei cognatione.* In MS. "P" the two traditions are fused: *quidam Balgeus e tribu Benjamin.*

42 This is the ms. known as the Sinaiticus, in which II Macc. has not survived.

43 Bickermann in his book *Der Gott der Makkab.* 65, n. 1, admitted that Simon belonged to the Watch of Balgea. He changed his mind in his article on Heliodoros (*Annuaire de l'Institut de philol. et d'hist. orient.* VII, 1939-44, 8, n. 22) and explains the substitution of "Benjamin" for "Balgea" in the Latin text by the argument that the copyist was unable to understand how a High Priest could be other than of the seed of Aaron. However, it is difficult to suppose that the copyist was so familiar with the names of the priestly families, and if he was, why did he not change "Benjamin" to "Minjamin," which would have been a much easier thing to do? Bickermann's first opinion, therefore, seems to have been the correct one.

44 This is also Abel's opinion, *commentary ad loc.,* and that of Dancy, *Comm. I. Macc.,* 44.

45 "in eine öffentliche (und aufzustellende) Liste einzutragen."

46 *PCZ*, 59166.

47 *Annual of the British School of Athens,* 1905/6, 452 A.

48 It is clear that II Macc. means not the carrying out of the registration, but its general arrangement, and this was the task entrusted to the High Priest.

49 Bickermann himself writes: "Dadurch dass Jason die Befügnis erhält, die Liste der 'Antiochener' in Jerusalem aufzustellen, erfolgt die Bildung dieser Korporation." The "Antiochenes" did not exist in Jerusalem before Jason. Bickermann is unaware that in this sentence he himself has eliminated the proof based on his interpretation of the verb ἀναγράφειν with a simple accusative.

50 This supposition was expressed *inter alia* by E. Meyer (*op. cit.,* II, 145); cf. now Finkelstein, in *HTR*, 35, 1942, 319. It apparently rests on the assumption that there is a parallelism between the granting of the rights of a Greek city and the granting of Roman privileges. This parallelism does not in fact exist. Roman privileges were given generously to individuals and also to entire communities, which was not the case with Greek civic rights. Cases of συμπολιτεία, *i.e.,* the granting of the rights of one city to the citizens of another, were very rare. Cf. above, p. 515, n. 86.

51 The names of members of corporations normally terminated with

-stai or *-ioi*. For numerous examples, see Ziebarth, *Das griechiche Vereinwesen*, 1896, *passim*.

52 Cf., for example, *PCZ*, 59034; there is a conjecture that the "Hellenion" referred to in this papyrus belonged to the city of Gaza. Cf. Vincent in his article in *RB*, 1920, 169ff. A Greek quarter called "Hellenion" also existed at Arsinoë, the chief town of the Fayûm (*SP.*, nos. 319, 342).

53 The "Antiochenes from Jerusalem" are mentioned in one other place in II Macc.: Jason sends delegates to the athletic contests at Tyre ὡς ἀπὸ Ἱεροσολύμων Ἀντιοχέας (4.19). The text is corrupt and various mss. have retained different versions, *e.g.*, Ἀντιοχίας (A), Ἀντιοχεῖς ὄντας (V). The most reasonable translation is: Jason sent delegates "as Antiochenes from Jerusalem"; the official name of the delegates was "Antiochenes from Jerusalem." Bickermann finds in this passage additional support for his view that "the Antiochenes" were a corporation distinct from the city of Jerusalem.

However, it is clear that Jason's delegates could not be called simply "Antiochenes," as there were many such in the Seleucid state; the name "Jerusalem" had of necessity to appear in some connection or other with the name "Antiochenes" to indicate locality, nor can we conclude from the corrupt passage in II Macc. what exactly was the delegates' official title. On the analogy of "the Antiochenes in Ptolemais" (cf. above, p. 407), it may perhaps be deduced that the official name of the members of the city was Ἀντιοχεῖς οἱ ἐν Ἱεροσολύμοις.

54 Willrich, *Urkundenfälschung in der hellenistisch-jüdischen Literatur*, 1924.

55 In the following exposition Claudius' document in *Ant.* XIX, 280ff. will be called an "edict," and the document in Bell a "rescript."

56 Th. Reinach, "L'Empereur Claudius et les Juifs," *REJ* 79, 1924, 126.

57 Engers, "Der Brief d. Kaiser Claudius an die Alexandriner," *Klio*, 1926, 175.

58 See above, p. 314.

59 See above, p. 515, n. 86.

60 Cf. above, p. 302. Despite the change in the names of the governors, both sources are discussing one event; the governor Magius Maximus filled the post of governor of Egypt after Aquila (10/11-11/12 A.D. See A. Stein, *Die Präfekten von Aegypten*, 1950, 21f.). It is therefore reasonable to suppose that the last Jewish ethnarch died in the governorship of Aquila, and that Augustus' reform took place under Magius Maximus.

61 Bell, in his book *Jews and Christians*, 15.

62 Reinach rightly pointed out this contradiction in his above-mentioned article, 125ff.; he solves the difficulty by eliminating the suspect sentence on equality of rights, as we have seen above.

63 On the chronological question cf. *C. P. Jud.* 1, 69ff.

64 Line 8/87: ἅπερ καὶ ἐγὼ διακούσας ἀμφοτέρων ἐβεβαίωσα.

65 These were no doubt the two embassies of Philo and Apion respectively, which had previously met at the court of Gaius Caligula, and may well have spent a further period at Rome; cf. *C. P. Jud.* 1, p. 71.

BIBLIOGRAPHY

Abbott, F. and Johnson, A., *Municipal Administration in the Roman Empire*, 1926

Abel, Félix Marie, *Géographie de la Palestine*, 1933-38

————, *Histoire de la Palestine*, 1952

————, *Les livres des Maccabées*, 1949

Abrahams, Israel, *Campaigns in Palestine from Alexander the Great*, 1927

Actes du V⁰ Congrès International de Papyrologie, 1938

Aimé-Giron, Noel, *Textes araméens d'Egypte*, 1931

Albright, W. F., "The Excavations at Ascalon," *BASOR* 6 (May 1922), 11ff.

————, *From the Stone Age to Christianity*, 1940

————, "Two Cressets from Marisa and the Pillars of Jachin and Boaz," *BASOR* 85 (Feb. 1942), 18ff.

Andreades, M. A., *A History of Greek Public Finance*, 1933

Auerbach, E., *Wüste und Gelobtes Land*, 1936

Ausfeld, Adolf, *Der griechische Alexanderroman*, 1907

Avi-Yonah, M., "The Foundation of Tiberias," *Israel Exploration Journal* I (1950-1), 160ff.

————, *Historical Geography of Eretz Yisrael* (Heb.), 1950

————, "The City Boundaries of Roman Transjordan," *Bulletin of the Jewish Palestine Exploration Society* (Heb.), I-II (1943-4), 1ff.

Aymard, A., "Tutelle et usurpation dans les monarchies hellenistiques," *Aegyptus* 32 (1952), 85ff.

Babelon, E., *Les Perses Achéménides*, 1893

————, *Les rois de Syrie, d'Arménie et de Commagène*, 1890

Baeck, Leo, *Die Pharisäer*, 1927

Bar-Adon, Dorothy, "Archaeological Studies," *Eretz Israel* IV (Heb., 1956), 50ff.

Baramki, J., "Coin Hoards from Palestine," *QDAP* 11 (1944), 86ff.

Baron, Salo, *The Jewish Community*, 1942

————, *A Social and Religious History of the Jews*, 2d ed., 1952

Beek, M. A., *Das Danielbüch*, 1935

Bell, H. Idris, *Jews and Christians in Egypt*, 1924

————, "Philanthropia," in *Hommages à J. Bidez et à F. Cumont*, 1948

Beloch, K. J., *Griechische Geschichte*, 1922-25

Bengston, H., *Die Strategie in der hellenistischen Zeit*, 1937-52

Berve, H., *Das Alexanderreich auf prosopographischer Gründlage*, 1926

Bevan, E. R., *A History of Egypt Under the Ptolemaic Dynasty*, 1927

————, *The House of Seleucus*, 1902

————, *Jerusalem Under the High Priests*, 1904

HELLENISTIC CIVILIZATION AND THE JEWS

Bévenot, H., *Die beiden Makkabäerbücher*, 1931
Bickermann, Elias, "L'avènement de Ptolemy V Epiphane," *Chron. d'Egypte* 15 (1940), 124ff.
———, "La charte séleucide de Jérusalem," *REJ* 100 (1935), 4ff.
———, *Der Gott der Makkabäer*, 1937
———, "Héliodore au temple de Jérusalem," *Annuaire de l'Institut de Philologie et d'Histoire Orientale* VII (1939-44), 1ff.
———, *Les institutions des Séleucides*, 1938
———, "Recension of M. Ginsburg's book Rome et la Judée, 1928," *Gnomon* VI (1930), 357ff.
———, "Une proclamation séleucide relative au temple de Jérusalem," *Syria* 25 (1946/8), 67ff.
———, "Une question d'authenticité: les privileges juifs," in *Mélanges Isidore Levy*, 1953, 11ff.
Bludau, A., *Juden und Judenvervolgungen in alten Alexandrien*, 1906
Bonner, Campbell, *The Last Chapters of the Book of Enoch*, 1937
Bothmer, Dietrich von, "Greek Pottery from Tell en-Nasbeh," *BASOR* 83 (Oct. 1941), 25ff.
Bouché-Leclercq, A., *Histoire des Lagides*, 1903
———, *Histoire des Séleucides*, 1913
Bousset, Wilhelm, *Die Religion des Judentums*, 1906
Braun, M., *History and Romance in Graeco-Oriental Literature*, 1938
Breccia, E., "D'un édifice d'époque chrétienne à el-Dekhela," *BSAA* IX (1907), 3ff.
———, *Juifs et Chrétiens de l'ancienne Alexandrie*, 1927
Brehier, Emile, *Les ideès philosophiques et réligieuses de Philon d'Alexandrie*, 1925
Büchler, Adolf, *Die Tobiaden und Oniaden*, 1899
Busolt, G., *Griechische Stäatskunde* I, 1920
Butler, H. C., *The Princeton University Archaeological Expedition to Syria in 1904-1905*. Three divisions, 1907-16

Cary, M., *A History of the Greek World from 323 to 146 B.C.*, 1932
Charles, R. H., *Apocrypha and Pseudepigrapha*, 1913
———, *A Critical and Exegetical Commentary on the Book of Daniel*, 1929
Cowley, A. (ed.), *Aramaic Papyri of the 5th Century B.C.*, 1923
———, "Notes on Hebrew Papyrus Fragments from Oxyrrhinchus," *JEA* 2 (1915), 212ff.
Cumont, Franz, *Les réligions orientales dans le paganisme romain*, 1929
Cuq, E., "La condition juridique de la Coelé-Syrie au temps de Ptolémée V Epiphane," *Syria* 8 (1927), 143ff.

Dancy, J. S., *A Commentary on I Maccabees*, 1954
Dessau, Hermann, *Geschichte der römischen Kaiserzeit*, 1924

BIBLIOGRAPHY

Droysen, Joh., *Geschichte d. Hellenismus*, 1877
Dupont-Sommer, A., *Le quatrième livre des Maccabees*, 1939

Eisenstein, J., *Otzar Midrashim* (Heb.), 1915
Ellizer, K. E., *Studien zum Habakuk-Kommentar*, 1953
Engers, Maurits, "Der Brief d. Kaiser Claudius an die Alexandriner,"
  Klio 20 (1926), 175ff.
————, "Politeuma," *Mnemosyne* 54 (1926), 154ff.
————, "Die stäatsrechtichle Stellung der alexandrinischen juden,"
  Klio 18 (1923), 79-90
Erdmann, W., *Die Ehe im alten Griechenland*, 1934

Finkelstein, Louis (ed.), *The Jews, Their History, Culture, Religion*,
  1949
————, *The Pharisees and the Men of the Great Assembly*, 1941
————, *The Pharisees: The Sociological Background of Their Faith*,
  1946
————, "The Pharisees: Their Origin and Their Philosophy," *HTR*
  22 (1929), 186-261
Foerster, W., "Der Ursprung des Pharisäismus," *ZNTW* 34 (1935),
  35ff.
Freudenthal, J., *Die Flavius Josephus Beigelegte Schrift über die
  Herrschaft der Vernunft*, 1869
Friedlander, M., *Geschichte der Jüdischen Apologetik als Vorge-
  schichte des Christentums*, 1903
————, *Die Juden in der vorchristlichen griechichen Welt*, 1897
————, *Die religiosen Bewegungen innherhalb des Judentums im
  Zeitalter Jesu*, 1905
Fuchs, Leo, *Die Juden Agyptens in ptolemäischer und römischer Zeit*,
  1924

Galling, K., "Die syrisch-palästinische Küste nach der Beschreibung
  bei Pseudo-Scylax," *ZDPV* LXI (1938), 83ff.
Gaster, Moses, *The Samaritans*, 1925
Gauthier, H. and Sottas, H., "Un décrèt trilingue en honneur de
  Ptolemie IV," *Service des Antiquités de l'Egypte*, 1925
Geffcken, J., *Komposition u. Entstehungszeit d. Oracula Sibyllina*,
  1902
Ginsberg, H. Louis, *Studies in Daniel*, 1948
Glotz, G., *Histoire grecque*, 1936
Glueck, Nelson, *The Other Side of the Jordan*, 1940
————, "Ostraca from Elath," *BASOR* 80 (Dec. 1940), 3ff.
————, "Ostraca from Elath," *BASOR* 82 (April 1941), 3ff.
Goodenough, Erwin R., *An Introduction to Philo Judaeus*, 1940
————, *Jewish Symbols in the Greco-Roman Period*, vols. I-IV,
  1952-53
————, "The Political Philosophy of the Hellenistic Kingship," *Yale
  Classical Studies* I (1928), 53ff.

Goodenough, Erwin R., *The Politics of Philo Judaeus,* 1938

Graetz, Heinrich, *Geschichte der Juden,* 1853-76

Gray, John, "The Jewish Inscriptions in Greek and Hebrew at Tocra, Cyrene and Barce," in Rowe, Alan, *Cyrenaican Expedition of the University of Manchester,* 1952, 43-59

Gressmann, Hugo, "Die Ammonitischen Tobiaden," *Sitzungsberichte d. Preussischen Akademie d. Wissenschaften* XXXIX (1921), 128ff.

Gutberlet, C., *Das Zweite Buch. d. Makkabäer,* 1927

Gutman, Joshua, "Alexander of Macedonia in Palestine," *Tarbitz* XI (Heb., 1940), 271-294

——————, "The Canaanite God Shadrapa and His Nature," in *The Epstein Jubilee Volume* (Heb.), 68ff.

Gutmann, M., "Enslavement for Debt in Jewish Teaching," in *Dinaburg Anniversary Book* (Heb., 1949), 82-68

——————, "Philo, the Epic Poet," *Scripta Hierosolymitana* I (1954), 36ff.

Hadas, M., *Aristeas to Philocrates,* 1951

——————, *The Third and Fourth Books of Maccabees,* 1953

Haddad, George, *Aspects of Social Life in Antioch,* 1949

Harper, Jr., O. McLean, "A Study in the Commercial Relations between Egypt and Syria in the 3rd Century B.C.," *AJP* 49 (1928), 1ff.

Heinemann, Isaak, *Philons griechische u. jüdische Bildung,* 1932

Herford, R. Travers, *Pharisaism, its Aim and its Method,* 1912

Herzfeld, Levi, *Handelsgeschichte der Juden des Altertums,* 1894

Hildesheimer, H., *Beiträge zur Geographie Palästinas,* 1886

Hill, G. F., *Catalogue of the Greek Coins of Palestine,* 1914

Hoenig, S. B., *The Great Sanhedrin,* 1953

Hölscher, G., *Palästina in der persischen und hellenistischen Zeit,* 1903

Hoonacker, A. Van, *Une communauté judéo-araméene à l'Elephantine, en Egypte, aux VIᵉ siècle avant J.C.,* 1915

Iliffe, J. H., "Nabataean Pottery from the Negeb," *QDAP* VI (1936), 61ff.

Jacoby, Felix, *Die Fragmente der Griechischen Historiker,* B. no. 142, 1923

Jaeger, W., "Greeks and Jews," *Journal of Religion* 18 (1938), 127ff.

Janne, H., "La lettre de Claude aux Alexandrins et le Christianisme," in *Mélanges Franz Cumont,* 1936, 261ff.

Jansen, Ludin, *Die Politik Antiochos des IV,* 1943

Jeremias, J., *Jerusalem zur Zeit Jesu,* 1923-37

——————, "Die Einwohnerzahl Jerusalems zur Zeit Jesu," *ZDPV* 66 (1943), 24-31

Jones, Arnold Hugh Martin, *The Cities of the Eastern Roman Provinces,* 1937

Jouguet, Pierre, *L'impérialisme macédonien et l'hellenisation de l'Orient*, 1926
————, *La vie municipale dans l'Egypte romain*, 1911
Juster, Jean, *Les Juifs dans l'empire romain*, 1914

Kahrstedt, Ulrich, *Syrische Territorien in hellenistischer Zeit*, 1926
Kanael, B., "Notes on the Ancient Hebrew Script in the Judaean Scrolls," *Israel Exploration Journal* I (1950-51), 46-51
Kautzsch, Emil, *Apokryphen und Pseudepigraphen des Alten Testaments*, 1900
Keil, Carl F., *Commentär über die Bücher der Makkabäer*, 1875
Kittel, Rudolf, *Geschichte des Volkes Israel*, 1929
Klausner, J., *History of the Period of the Second Temple* (Heb.), 1949
————, *History of the Second Commonwealth* (Heb.), 1949-51
————, "Raphana, one of the ten cities," *Bulletin of the Jewish Palestine Exploration Society* II (Heb., 1937), 134ff.
Klein, Samuel, *Galiläa von der Makkabäerzeit*, 1928
————, *Das tannäitische Grenzverzeichnis Palästinas*, 1928
Kohler, A., *Urkunden und Untersuchungen z. Gesch. d. delisch-attischen Bundes*, 1869
Kolbe, W., *Beiträge z. griechischen und jüdischen Geschichte*, 1926
Kraeling, C. H., *Gerasa, City of the Decapolis*, 1938
Krauss, Samuel, *Griechische und lateinische Lehnwörter im Talmud, Midrasch und Targum*, 1898-99
————, *Synagogale Altertumer*, 1925
————, *Talmudische Archaologie* (Heb.), 3 vols., 1910-12
Kündig, W. et fils (eds.), *Mélanges Nicole*, 1905

Laqueur, R., *Kritische Untersuchungen z. II Makkabäerbuch*, 1904
Launey, M., *Recherches sur les armées hellenistiques*, 1949-50
Lauterbach, Jacob Z., "The Pharisees and Their Teachings," *HUCA* 6 (1929), 69ff.
Leider, E., *Der Handel von Alexandreia*, 1933
Lesquier, Jean, *Les militaires de l'Egypte sous les Lagides*, 1911
Lieberman, S., *Greek in Jewish Palestine*, 1942
————, *Hellenism in Jewish Palestine*, 1950
Lösch, S., *Epistula Claudiana*, 1930
Lurié, S., *Anti-Semitism in the Ancient World* (Russian), 1923

Macalister, R. A., *The Excavations of Gezer*, 1912
Mahaffy, J. P., "The Jews in Egypt," *Mélanges Nicole*, 1905, 659-662
Maisler, B., "The House of Tobiah," *Tarbitz* XII (Heb., 1941), 109-123
Manson, T. W., "Sadducee and Pharisee: The Origin and Significance of the Names," *Bulletin of the John Rylands Library* 22 (1938), 144-159

Marti, Karl, *Kurzer Hand-Commentar zum Alten Testament: Das Buch Daniel*, 1901

Mendelssohn, Isaac, "Guilds in Ancient Palestine," *BASOR* 80 (1940), 17ff.

—————, *Slavery in the Ancient Near East*, 1949

Meritt, B. D., Wade-Gery, H. T., and McGregor, M. F., *The Athenian Tribute Lists*, 1939

Meyer, Eduard, *Der Papyrusfund von Elephantine*, 1912

—————, *Ursprung und Anfänge des Christentums*, 1921

Michaelides, G., "Papyrus contenant un dessin du dieu Seth à tête d'ane," *Aegyptus* 32 (1952), 45ff.

Mittwoch, A., "Tribute and Land Tax in Seleucid Judaea," *Biblica* 36 (1955), 352ff.

Momigliano, A., *Claudius*, 1934

—————, "I Tobiadi nella prehistoria del moto maccabaico," *ARAST* 67 (1931/2), 176ff.

—————, *Prime linee di storia della tradizione maccabaica*, 1930

Montgomery, J. A., *A Critical and Exegetical Commentary on the Book of Daniel*, 1927

—————, *The Samaritans*, 1907

Moore, George F., *Judaism*, 1944

—————, "Simon the Righteous," in *Jewish Studies in Memory of Israel Abrahams*, 1927, 348ff.

Motzo, B., *Saggi di storia e letteratura Giudeo-Ellenistica*, 1925

Müller, C., *Geog. Graeci Minores*

Muller, N., *Die Inschriften der jüdische Katakombe aus Monteverde*, 1919

Musurillo, H. A. (ed.), *The Acts of the Pagan Martyrs*, 1954

Narkiss, Mordecai, *Coins of Eretz Yisrael* (Heb.), 1936

Niese, B., *Geschichte der griechischen und Makedonischen Stäaten seit der Schlacht bei Chaeronea*, 1892-1903

—————, *Kritik der beiden Makkabäerbücher*, 1900

Oehler, J., "Epigraphische Beiträge zur Geschichte des Judentums," *MGWJ* 53 (1909), 528ff.

Oesterley, W. O. E., *A History of Israel*, 1932

Olmstead, A. T., *History of Palestine and Syria to the Macedonian Conquest*, 1931

Otto, W., "Beiträge zur Seleukidengeschichte des III Jahrhunderts vor Christus," *Abh. Bayr. Ak.* 34 (1921), 1ff.

—————, "Zur Geschichte der Zeit des 6 Ptolemaers," *Abh. Bayr. Ak.* XI (1934)

————— and H. Bengston, "Zur Geschichte des Niederganges des Ptolemaerreiches," *Abh. Bayr. Ak.* XVII (1938)

Pauly, A. and Wissowa, G., *Real-Encyclopadie der classischen Altertumswissenschaft*, 1894

BIBLIOGRAPHY

Peters, J. P. and Thiersch, H., *The Painted Tombs of the Necropolis of Marissa*, 1905

Pfeiffer, R. H., *History of New Testament Times*, 1949

Pfister, F., "Eine jüdische Gründungsgeschichte Alexandrias," *Stzb. Heidelb. Akad.* 11 (1914), 23ff.

Plassart, A., "La synagogue juive de Délos," in *Mélanges Holleaux*, 1913

Poland, Franz, *Geschichte des griechischen Vereinswesens*, 1909

Préaux, Claire, *L'économie royale des Lagides*, 1939

————, *Les Grecs en Egypte d'après les archives de Zénon*, 1947

————, "La signification de l'époque d'Evergète II," in *Actes du V⁸ Congrès de Papyrologie*, 1938, 345-354

Preisigke, F., *Fachwörter des öffentlichen Verwaltungsdienstes Agyptens in den Griechischen Papyrusurkunden der ptolomäisch-römischen Zeit bearbeitet*, 1915

Press, Isaiah, "Topographical Researches," in A. M. Lunz (ed.), *Yerushalayim* (Heb.), 1928, 21-29

Pritchard, J. B., *Ancient Near Eastern Texts Relating to the Old Testament*, 1950

Radet, G., *Alexandre le grand*, 1931

————, *De Coloniis a Macedonibus in Asiam cis-Taurum Deductis*, 1892

Rankin, A. S., *The Origins of the Festival of Hannukkah*, 1930

Reicke, B., *Studia Theologica*, 1948

Reifenberg, A., *Jewish Coins* (Heb.), 1947

————, "Unpublished and Unusual Jewish Coins," *Israel Exploration Journal* I (1950-51), 176-78

Reinach, T., "L'empereur Claudius et les Juifs," *REJ* LXXIX (1924), 126ff.

————, *Textes d'auteurs grecs et romains rélatifs au Judaisme*, 1895

Renan, Ernest, *Histoire du peuple d'Israel*

Reuter, E., *Beiträge zur Beurteilung des Königs Antiochos Epiphanes*, 1938

Robert, Louis, *Hellenica, recueil d'épigraphie, de numismatique et d'antiquités grecques* VII, 1949

Roberts, C., Skeat, T., and Nock, A., "The Gild of Zeus Hypsistos," *HTR* 29 (1936), 39ff.

Rostovtzeff, M., *A Large Estate in Egypt in the Third Century, B.C.*, 1922

————, *Social and Economic History of the Hellenistic World*, 1941

————, *Studien z. Geschichte d. römischen Kolonates*, 1910

Rosenthal, J., "Bar Hebraeus and a Jewish Census under Claudius," *Jewish Social Studies* XVI (1944), 267ff.

Roussell, P., "Décrèt des Péliganes de Laodicée-sur-Mer," *Syria* 23 (1942-3), 21ff.

Rouvier, J., "Ptolemais-Acé, ses noms et ses ères sous les Séleucides et la domination romaine . . . (198 B.C.E.-54 C.E.)," *RB* 8 (1899), 393-404

Rowe, Alan, *Cyrenaican Expedition of the University of Manchester,* 1952

Ruppel, W., "Politeuma," *Philologus* 82 (1927), 269ff.

Saarisalo, A., "The Boundary between Issachar and Naphtali," *Ann. Acad. Sc. Fennicae* (1927/28)

Stahelin, F., *Der Antisemitismus des Altertums,* 1905

Stark, K. B., *Gaza und die philistäische Küste,* 1852

Stein, A., *Die Prafekten von Aegypten,* 1950

Stein, M., "The Pseudo-Hecateus, the Date and Purpose of His Book on the Jews and Their Country," *Zion* 6 (Heb., 1934), 1-11

Stengel, P., *Die griechischen Kultusaltertumer,* 1898

Sukenik, E. L., *Ancient Synagogues in Palestine and Greece,* 1934

————, *A Corpus of the Hidden Scrolls in Possession of the Hebrew University,* 1954

————, "A Jewish Tomb on the Slopes of Mount Scopus," *Journal of the Jewish Palestine Exploration Society* (1934), 62ff.

————, "Li-Kebiat Zemanam shel ha-Shekalim ha'Abim," *Kedem* I (Heb., 1941), 12ff.

————, "More About the Oldest Coins of Judaea," *JPOS* 15 (1935), 109ff.

Swete, H. B., *An Introduction to the Old Testament in Greek,* 2d ed., 1914

Tarn, W., *Hellenistic Civilization,* 1947

Taubler, E., "Jerusalem 201 to 199 B.C.E.," *JQR* 37 (1946/7), 1ff.

Tcherikover, V., "The Documents in the Second Book of the Maccabees," *Tarbitz* I (Heb., 1930), 31ff.

————, "Die hellenistischen Stadtegründungen von Alexander dem Grossen bis auf die Römerzeit," *Philol. Suppl.* XIX (1927), 182ff.

————, "The History of the Jews of Fayûm in the Hellenistic Period," *Magnes Jubilee Volume* (Heb.), 1938, 199ff.

————, "The Ideology of the Letter of Aristeas," *HTR* LI (1958), 59-85

————, "Palestine in the Light of the Zenon Papyri," *Tarbitz* IV (Heb., 1933), 226ff.

————, "Palestine under the Ptolemies," *Mizraim* IV-V (Heb., 1937), 9ff.

————, "The Sambathions," *Scripta Hierosolymitana* I (1954), 78ff.

————, "Syntaxis and Laographia," *J. Jur. Pap.* IV (1950), 183ff.

————, "The Third Book of the Maccabees as a Historical Source of the Augustan Period," *Zion* 10 (Heb., 1945), 1ff.

Thackeray, Henry, *Josephus the Man and the Historian,* 1929

Tolkovsky, S., *History of Jaffa* (Heb.), 1926

Tondriau, J., "Tatouage, lierre et syncrétismes," *Aegyptus* 30 (1950), 57ff.

―――――, "Un thiase dionysiaque à Péluse sous Ptolémée IV Philopator," *BSAA* 37 (1948), 1-11

Tramontano, R., *La lettera di Aristea e Filocrate*, 1931

Van Groningen, B. A., *Aristote, le second livre de l'économique*, 1933

Viereck, P., *Philadelpheia*, 1928

Vincent, Albert, *La réligion des Judéo-Araméens d'Elephantine*, 1937

Vincent, N., "Jérusalem d'après la lettre d'Aristée," *RB* V (1908), 520-532; VI (1909), 555-575

von Woess, F., *Das Asylwesen Aegyptens in der Ptolemäerzeit*, 1923

Watzinger, C., *Denkmaler Palästinas*, 1935

Watzinger, C. and Walzinger, K., *Damaskos, die antike Stadt*, 1921

Weiss, I. H., *Dor Dor v'Dorshav*, 1924

Welles, B., "Manumission and Adoption," *Mélanges de Vissher* II (1949), 507ff.

Welles, C. B., *Royal Correspondence in the Hellenistic Period*, 1934

Wellhausen, J., *Israelitische und jüdische Geschichte*, 3d ed., 1897

―――――, *Pharisäer u. Sadduzäer*, 1927

Westermann, W. L., "Enslaved Persons Who are Free," *Am. J. Philology* 59 (1938), 1ff.

Wilcken, U., *Zum Alexandrinischen Antisemitismus*, 1909

Wilhelm, A., "Zu dem Judenerlasse des Ptolemaios philadelphos," *Archiv. f. Papyrusforschung* XIV (1941), 30ff.

Willrich, Hugo, "Caligula," *Klio* 3 (1903), 397-470

―――――, *Juden und Griechen*, 1895

―――――, *Urkundenfälschung in der hellenistisch-jüdischen Literatur*, 1924

―――――, "Der Historische Kern des III Makkabäerbuches," *Hermes* 39 (1904), 244-58

Wolfson, H. A., *Philo*, 1947

Yadin, Yigal, *The Scroll of the War of the Sons of Light and the Sons of Darkness*, 1955

Yeivin, Samuel, *Kadmoniot Artzenu* (Heb.), 1956

Ziebarth, Erich, *Das griechische Vereinswesen*, 1896

Zeitlin, S., *The History of the Second Jewish Commonwealth*, 1933

―――――, "Simon the Just and the Great Assembly," *Ner Maaravi* II (Heb., 1925), 137-142

Baal Shamin, 181, 194-95, 200
Babylonia, 2, 4, 6, 10, 43
    Jews in, 271, 290
    Seleucids in, 17
Babylonian Exile, 296
Bacchides, 229, 231-32
Bactria, 6, 18, 242
Banias, see Paneas
Batanea, 61, 76
Beirut, 35, 63, 91
Beit Idis, 98
Belgea, 404
Benjamin, tribe of, 403-04
Ben Sira, 142-51
Berenice, 341
Beroea, 227
Bet-Anat, 67
Bet Shean, see Scythopolis
Bet Yeraḥ, 102; see also Philo-
    teria
Bet-Zur, 239
Bithynia, 18, 32, 288
Boeotia, 291
Bourgeoisie, Oriental, 33, 169
Bousiris, 285
Boutis, see Pella
Bubastis, 278
Byblos, 32

Caesar, Julius, 284, 321
Caesarea, see Straton's Tower
Caligula, 48
Cambyses, 270-71
Canatha, 97
Canwat, see Canatha
Cappadocia, 18
Caria, 288
Cassander, governor of Mace-
    don, 9
Chalkis, 289
Cilicia, 3, 251
Claudius, 313-14, 409-15
Cleopatra II, 278
Cleopatra III, 283
Cleopatra, daughter of Ptolemy
    V, 128
Cleopatra, daughter of Ptolemy
    VI, 236

Cnidus, 288
Coele-Syria, see Palestine
Colochoutos, 65-66
Commerce, 41
    in Diaspora, 333-34, 338-40
    in Palestine, 63, 67-69, 72, 108
Corinth, 291
Cos, 288
Council of Elders, see Gerousia
Courts, Jewish, 220
Ctesiphon, 290
Cultural fusion
    in Diaspora, 308-09, 344-56
    in Egypt, 7, 15-16, 20-21, 31,
        34, 270
    in Orient, 179, 207
    in Palestine, 70-71, 90-174,
        247, 249-53
    see also Oriental influence
Cyprus, 9, 283, 291
Cyrenaica, 10, 26, 290, 331, 339,
    372
Cyzikus, 178

Dagon, 113
Damascus, 32, 35, 41, 61
Daphne, 276, 289, 389-90
Darius, 3-4, 42
"Dead Sea Scrolls," 400-02
Decapolis, 106; see also under
    names of towns
Delos, 288
Delphi, 291
Demetrius I Soter, 232-33
Demetrius II Nicator, 236, 238-
    239
Demetrius III Eukairos, 252
Demetrius, son of Antigonus, 9,
    51
Diadochi, 8-11, 105; see also
    Ptolemy I, Seleucus I,
    Cassander, Lysimachus
Diaspora, characteristics of
    assimilation in, 309
    autonomy in, 298, 301, 304,
        326-27
    commerce in, 333
    communal life in, 356

Philip III Arrhidaeus, 102
Philip of Macedon, 1-2, 39
Philoteria, 73, 102, 105
Phocaia in Ionia, 288
Phoenicia, 32, 57
Phrygia, 9, 288
Pisidia, 251
Polis, 2, 21-36, 108
  in Egypt, 22, 31
    autonomy of, 22, 23, 72
    citizen rights in, 27, 31-32
    citizens of, 24, 31-32
    economy of, 33
    education in, 27
    fortification of, 23
    language in, 29
    location of, 29-31
    names of, 24, 32, 35
    political constitution of, 22, 26, 36
    relations with sovereign, 23
    religion in, 24
    rights of, 33
  in Palestine
    agriculture in, 108-09
    autonomy of, 107-08
    commerce in, 108-09
    founding of, 105-07, 109-110
    location of, 91-105, 112, 114
    names of, 107-10, 112
    political constitution of, 107-108, 168
    population of, 110-11, 113
    religion in, 113
Pompey, Cneius, 18, 102, 104
Pontus, 288
Priesthood, pagan, 15
Psamtik II, 270
Ptolemies
  attitude toward Judaism, 60, 65, 127, 303, 320
  attitude toward *poleis,* 25, 72
  as Hellenizers, 25, 71
  Jewish loyalty to, 65, 74, 76, 132, 187, 274
  political activity of, 71

Ptolemies—(*Continued*)
  and Seleucids, wars between, 14-15, 54, 59, 73-75, 96
Ptolemy I Soter, 15, 50, 321
  attitude toward Jews, 55-56
  conquest of Palestine, 52, 56
  empire of, 10
  war against Antigonus, 51, 52-53
Ptolemy II Philadelphus, 15, 16, 26, 60, 69
  city-building activity, 91, 102, 106
  emancipation of Jews, 273-74
Ptolemy III Euergetes, 59, 106, 127, 189
  and Joseph, 128-29
Ptolemy IV Philopator, 282, 339
  attitude toward Jews, 75, 274-275
  war against Antiochus III, 14-15, 54, 72-75, 96
Ptolemy V Epiphanes, 15, 75, 128
Ptolemy VI Philometor, 275-87
Ptolemy VII Neos Philopator, 278
Ptolemy VIII Euergetes II, 15, 32, 275, 282
Ptolemy IX Lathyrus, 283
Ptolemy XI Auletes, 284
Ptolemy son of Makron, 219, 224

Quintus Mummius, 215

Rabbat Ammon, 60-61, 70, 73, 100-01, 246
Ramatayim, 236
Raphana, 97-98
Raphia
  battle of, 14, 74, 96
  conquest of, 246
  history of, 96
Raphion, *see* Raphana
Red Sea, 341
Religion
  in Egypt, 4
  in Orient, 34, 88
  in *poleis,* 27-28

ABOUT THE AUTHOR
AND THE BOOK

Victor (Avigdor) Tcherikover was born in St. Petersburg in 1894. His education began with private instruction in Russian and Hebrew. At the age of sixteen he enrolled in the gymnasium, and, upon completing these secondary studies with distinction, matriculated at the University of Moscow, majoring in philosophy. He also did postgraduate work at that university, concentrating on the field of ancient history; but the year 1921 saw him in Germany, pursuing his study of ancient history at the University of Berlin under the supervision of Professors U. Wilcken and Eduard Meyer. In 1925, he was awarded a degree of Doctor of Philosophy for his work, *Die hellenistischen Städtegründungen von Alexander dem Grossen bis auf die Römerzeit*. The rest of his scholarly life was devoted to work in the same field, viz., the history of the Greek and Roman periods, about which he hoped some day to write a large work. His many published books and articles, however, revolved for the most part around the history of the Jews in the Hellenistic age. He was the first to make full use of a new type of source material for Jewish history in that period, namely, the Jewish papyri, thus inaugurating the specific branch of Jewish papyrology. A three-volume collection of Jewish papyri is even now (1959) in process of publication, only the first volume having thus far appeared (*Corpus Papyrorum Judaicarum*, vol. I, V. A. Tcherikover in collaboration with Alexander Fuks, Magnes Press and Harvard University Press, 1957).

Dr. Tcherikover went to Israel in 1925 and there became one of the founding faculty members at the Hebrew University in Jerusalem; he served as the first teacher of ancient history. He taught at the Hebrew University for thirty years, first as research fellow, then as lecturer, and after 1947 as full professor. In 1955, he was appointed head of the Departments of Classics and History. Professor Tcherikover died on 24 Tebet 5918 (January 16, 1958).

The first edition of Tcherikover's work on Hellenistic Jewry, called *Ha-Yehudim ve'ha-Yevanim*, was published in 1930. In 1954, Professor Tcherikover spent some time in the United States. The Jewish Publication Society took advantage of his visit to arrange for the appearance in English of the revised edition of the book which Dr. Tcherikover was then contemplating. Arrangements for the translation of the work were made through the kind cooperation of the Magnes Press of the Hebrew University.

During the intervening years, Dr. Tcherikover kept the JPS informed of the progress of the work. The last chapters of the translation were received from him only a few weeks before his death.

BRIEF CALCULUS

with Applications

FOURTH EDITION

ROLAND E. LARSON
The Pennsylvania State University
The Behrend College

ROBERT P. HOSTETLER
The Pennsylvania State University
The Behrend College

BRUCE H. EDWARDS
University of Florida

Case Studies Contributed by
James A. Kurre
Kenneth T. Louie
The Pennsylvania State University
The Behrend College

D. C. Heath and Company
Lexington, Massachusetts   Toronto

Address editorial correspondence to:

D. C. Heath and Company
125 Spring Street
Lexington, MA 02173

Acquisitions Editors: Ann Marie Jones, Charlie Hartford
Managing Editor: Cathy Cantin
Developmental Editor: Emily Keaton
Production Editor: Karen Carter
Marketing Manager: Christine Hoag
Designer: Jan Shapiro
Art Editor: Gary Crespo
Production Coordinator: Lisa Merrill
Photo Researchers: Melina Freedman, Donna Simons
Composition: Meridian Creative Group
Technical Art: Folium, Inc.
Cover: Tony Stone Images/Ed Honowitz

Preface

Brief Calculus with Applications, Fourth Edition, is designed for use in a beginning calculus course for students in business, management, economics, and the social and life sciences. In writing this edition, we were guided by two primary objectives. For students, our objective was to write in a precise and readable manner with the basic concepts, techniques, and applications of calculus clearly defined and demonstrated. For instructors, our objective was to create a comprehensive teaching instrument that uses proven pedagogical techniques, freeing instructors to make the most efficient use of classroom time.

Changes in the Fourth Edition

In the Fourth Edition, all textual elements were considered for revision, and many new examples, exercises, and applications were added to the text. The following are the major changes in the Fourth Edition.

Technology   Recognizing that graphing calculators and computer algebra systems are becoming increasingly available, we have provided the opportunity to incorporate their use throughout the Fourth Edition. Technology has been incorporated in the form of special notes in the expository text, technology-dedicated examples, and problems in the exercise sets that either require or can be solved with the use of technology. Technology is used as a means of discovery (see Discovery, page 26, and Exercises 37–40, Section 2.5), to reinforce concepts (see Technology Note, page 88, and Exercises 39 and 40, Section 3.5), and as an efficient problem-solving tool (see Technology Note, page 364, and Exercises 58 and 59, Section 2.2). In addition to addressing the benefits of technology, the text also points out the drawbacks of its use. For example, see the discussions given in the Technology Notes on pages 288 and 328.

Problem Solving   Helping students learn to be efficient and creative problem-solvers is the primary goal of any mathematics course. While the mechanics of calculus are stressed, the text has increased emphasis on the concepts of calculus. The range of exercises is much broader than in previous editions. Although the text still contains an abundance of exercises that are designed to develop skills, it now has many other types of exercises as well. Some exercises have multiple parts, leading students through mathematical exploration (Exercise 54, Section 2.6, and Exercises 33 and 34, Section 4.2); some exercises ask for interpretation (Exercise 60, Section 2.4, and Exercise 75, Section 7.4); and many exercises ask students to consider solving problems by combining numerical, analytical, and graphical methods (Exercises 51 and 52, Section 1.6, and Exercises 59 and 60, Section 2.1).

Real Applications and Real Data   In writing the Fourth Edition, we have included many new and interesting real-life applications and have tried, whenever possible, to use real rather than contrived data, as indicated by source lines. Applications are incorporated through the use of regular textual examples, through extended applications that introduce special topics, and in the exercise sets throughout the text. The applications come from a variety of fields, with an emphasis on applications in business, economics, and the life sciences. An index of applications follows the Table of Contents on page xxv.

Case Studies   To allow students the opportunity to use mathematics as a tool in decision making, case studies are included throughout the text. These feature a wide variety of real businesses and offer both consumer- and business-oriented decision-making opportunities. Each case study incorporates the mathematical skills presented in the chapter in an analysis of real data that was collected in a situation typical of the featured business. The case studies conclude with a set of questions that require the student to place him- or herself in a similar situation and to decide on a suitable course of action based on mathematical analysis.

Communicating Mathematics   In addition to problem solving, a way to reinforce students' understanding of calculus concepts is to give them the opportunity to communicate mathematical ideas to others; therefore, in the Fourth Edition, the development of communication skills has been emphasized. We have included many exercises that ask for descriptions, discussions, justifications, and conjectures. For example, see Exercise 59, Section 3.3, and Exercise 71, Section 5.1. Other opportunities for writing include essay questions (see Exercises 47 and 48, Section 5.5), discussion questions (see page 457), and case studies (see pages 360–361).

Improved Coverage   Many users of the Third Edition preferred to cover Exponential and Logarithmic Functions (previously Chapter 5) before covering Integration and Its Applications (previously Chapter 4). To accommodate this preference in topic order, these two chapters have been transposed and rewritten for the Fourth Edition. In addition, approaches to several topics have been enhanced. For instance, curve sketching in Section 3.7 now includes an expanded list of guidelines for sketching the graph of a function. New material on logistics growth has been added to Section 6.3. At the request of reviewers, L'Hôpital's Rule has been added as a new topic in the Trigonometry chapter.

Additional Appendices   Several new appendices in the Fourth Edition focus on utilizing technology to the best advantage. These include an introduction to the use of graphing utilities, translations of programs appearing in the text for additional graphing calculator models, and an introduction to the use of various computer algebra systems.

How to Study Calculus   Pages xxix and xxx of the front matter contain a summary of hints for how to study calculus effectively. Approaches to absorbing the material, checking homework, preparing for exams, and taking exams are discussed. This practice of presenting study strategies to students is carried throughout the text in the form of Study Tips for each chapter.

Accuracy   Throughout the entire revision process for the Fourth Edition, special care was given to creating a text that is accurate. We thank all of those who helped us improve the accuracy of the text.

Custom Publishing Option   Because topical coverage differs from school to school, we offer this edition with custom publication options. Any or all of the following chapters can be bound for your text: A Precalculus Review, Chapters 1–7, Probability and Calculus, Differential Equations, Series and Taylor Polynomials, and Trigonometric Functions.

Features of the Fourth Edition

The Fourth Edition has many new and improved design features that enhance the relevance of the text and make it an even more effective teaching and learning tool. These are shown on the following pages.

Features of the Fourth Edition

CHAPTER OPENERS

Each chapter opens with a portrait and brief discussion of a famous mathematician who is connected with or responsible for a key topic in that chapter. Also featured on the chapter openers are important formulas or notation presented within the chapter, as well as a list of section topics.

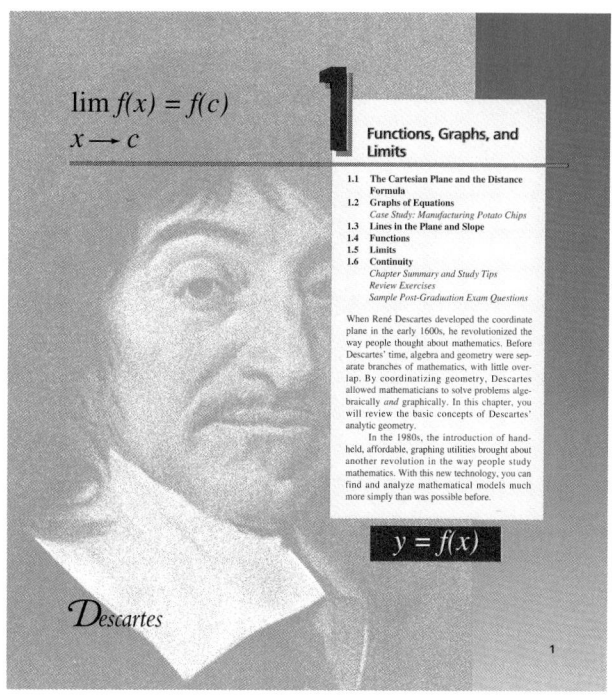

$$\lim_{x \to c} f(x) = f(c)$$

1

Functions, Graphs, and Limits

1.1 The Cartesian Plane and the Distance Formula
1.2 Graphs of Equations
   Case Study: Manufacturing Potato Chips
1.3 Lines in the Plane and Slope
1.4 Functions
1.5 Limits
1.6 Continuity
   Chapter Summary and Study Tips
   Review Exercises
   Sample Post-Graduation Exam Questions

When René Descartes developed the coordinate plane in the early 1600s, he revolutionized the way people thought about mathematics. Before Descartes' time, algebra and geometry were separate branches of mathematics, with little overlap. By coordinatizing geometry, Descartes allowed mathematicians to solve problems algebraically *and* graphically. In this chapter, you will review the basic concepts of Descartes' analytic geometry.

In the 1980s, the introduction of handheld, affordable, graphing utilities brought about another revolution in the way people study mathematics. With this new technology, you can find and analyze mathematical models much more simply than was possible before.

$$y = f(x)$$

Descartes

1

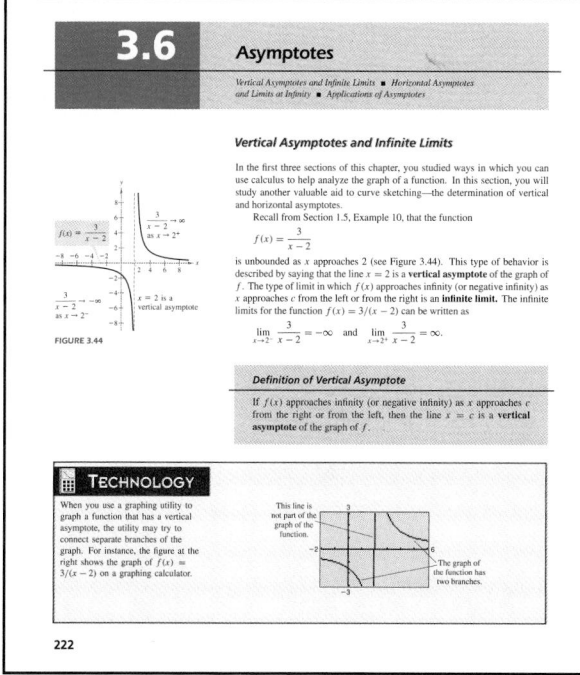

3.6 **Asymptotes**

Vertical Asymptotes and Infinite Limits ■ *Horizontal Asymptotes and Limits at Infinity* ■ *Applications of Asymptotes*

Vertical Asymptotes and Infinite Limits

In the first three sections of this chapter, you studied ways in which you can use calculus to help analyze the graph of a function. In this section, you will study another valuable aid to curve sketching—the determination of vertical and horizontal asymptotes.

Recall from Section 1.5, Example 10, that the function

$$f(x) = \frac{3}{x-2}$$

is unbounded as x approaches 2 (see Figure 3.44). This type of behavior is described by saying that the line $x = 2$ is a **vertical asymptote** of the graph of f. The type of limit in which $f(x)$ approaches infinity (or negative infinity) as x approaches c from the left or from the right is an **infinite limit.** The infinite limits for the function $f(x) = 3/(x - 2)$ can be written as

$$\lim_{x \to 2^-} \frac{3}{x-2} = -\infty \quad \text{and} \quad \lim_{x \to 2^+} \frac{3}{x-2} = \infty.$$

FIGURE 3.44

Definition of Vertical Asymptote

If $f(x)$ approaches infinity (or negative infinity) as x approaches c from the right or from the left, then the line $x = c$ is a **vertical asymptote** of the graph of f.

TECHNOLOGY

When you use a graphing utility to graph a function that has a vertical asymptote, the utility may try to connect separate branches of the graph. For instance, the figure at the right shows the graph of $f(x) = 3/(x - 2)$ on a graphing calculator.

222

SECTION OUTLINES

Each text section begins with a list of subsection topics. This outline can be used for easy reference and can help students study and synthesize the material in the section more efficiently.

TECHNOLOGY NOTES

Throughout the text, special notes teach students how to enhance their learning of calculus by utilizing technology. A graphing utility or a computer algebra system is used as a problem-solving tool to execute complicated computations, to visualize theoretical concepts, to discover approaches, and to verify the results of solution methods. Through technology notes, the text offers guidance on which tasks are best suited to the use of technology, indicates which commands and programs are to be used with certain utilities, and presents opportunities to develop an awareness of the possible misuses of technology.

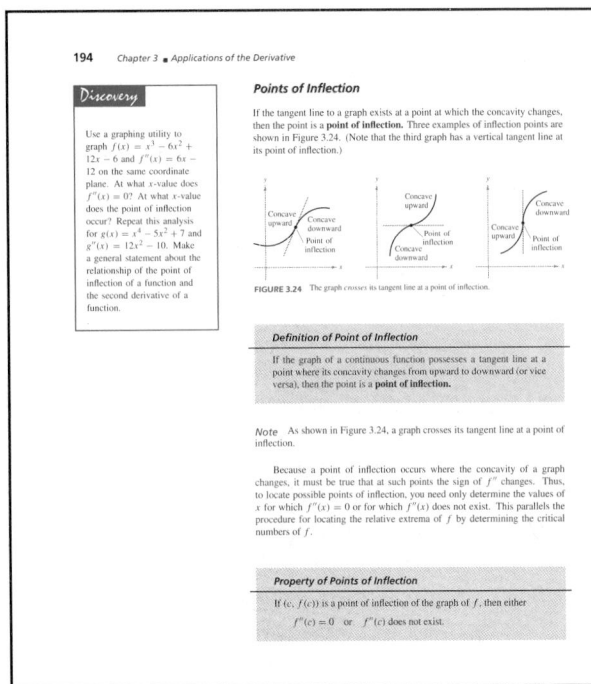

DISCOVERY

Students are encouraged to explore mathematical concepts and discover mathematical relationships through the use of these investigations. Carefully posed questions, often in conjunction with instructions for using a graphing utility, help students develop an intuitive understanding of theoretical topics.

DEFINITIONS AND THEOREMS

All definitions and theorems, as well as important results and formulas, are highlighted in blue for emphasis and easy reference.

EXAMPLES

To increase the usefulness of the text as a study tool, a wide variety of examples has been included to illustrate important mathematical concepts, problem-solving approaches, and computational techniques. An effort has been made to present not only theoretical examples but also those utilizing technology and those demonstrating real-life applications, often with actual data. Each example is titled for easy reference, and examples of real-life applications are labeled as such. Most examples in the Fourth Edition now include side comments in color that clarify the steps of the solution.

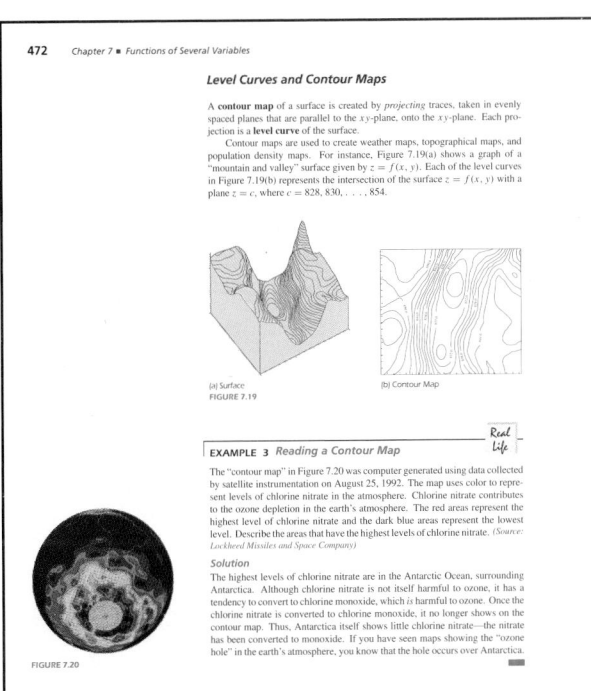

GRAPHICS

The Fourth Edition has over 1200 text and exercise figures and over 700 figures in the Answers to Odd-Numbered Exercises. Computer-generated for accuracy and designed with full color, this art program will help students interpret graphs and better visualize mathematical concepts. This is particularly true in the presentation of complex, three-dimensional material, for which the art was drawn in true perspective. Some figures were generated by the commercial software Mathematica.

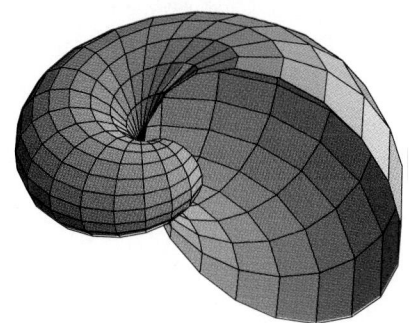

CONNECTIONS TO REAL LIFE

Color photographs help to reinforce the connection between calculus and its application to real-life situations.

DISCUSSION PROBLEMS

Each section in the text, except those in the Precalculus Review, closes with a discussion problem designed for use in class or assignment to small groups. These problems encourage thinking, reasoning, and writing about calculus and emphasize synthesis or further exploration of the concepts presented in the section.

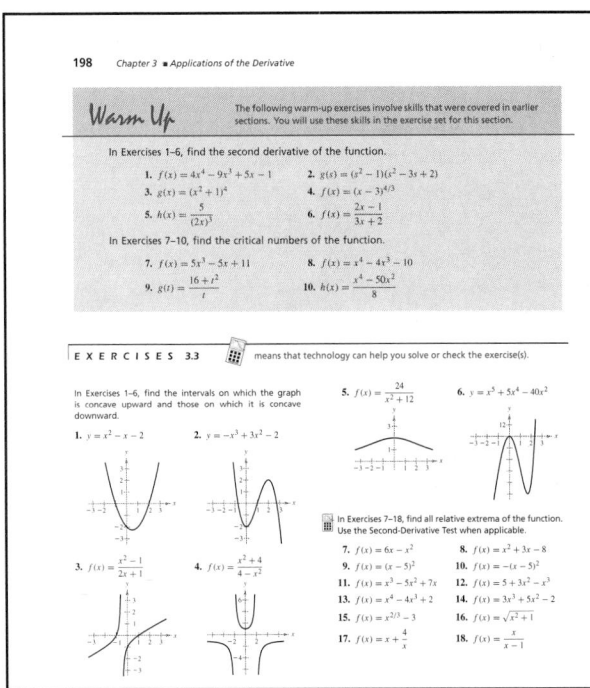

WARM-UP EXERCISES

Beginning with Chapter 1, the exercise set in each section is preceded by a set of ten warm-up exercises to help students review skills that are needed in the main exercise set. All warm-up exercises are answered in the back of the text.

RESEARCH PROJECTS

Appearing throughout the text are research projects that are keyed to business capsules. Using a library or other reference source, students are required first to collect real data or information about businesses similar to those described in the business capsules and then to analyze or synthesize this researched information to answer a posed question. Research projects are suitable for individual or group assignments.

BUSINESS CAPSULES

Nearly every chapter includes business capsules describing business situations that are connected to the mathematical concepts covered in the chapter.

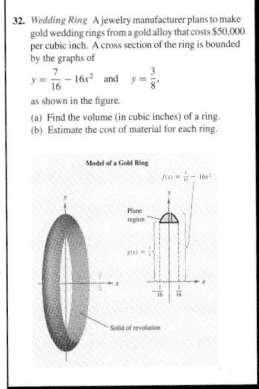

32. *Wedding Ring* A jewelry manufacturer plans to make gold wedding rings from a gold alloy that costs $50,000 per cubic inch. A cross section of the ring is bounded by the graphs of
$$y = \frac{7}{16} - 16x^2 \quad \text{and} \quad y = \frac{3}{8},$$
as shown in the figure.

(a) Find the volume (in cubic inches) of a ring.
(b) Estimate the cost of material for each ring.

Model of a Gold Ring

$f(x) = \frac{7}{16} - 16x^2$

Plane region

$g(x) = \frac{3}{8}$

Solid of revolution

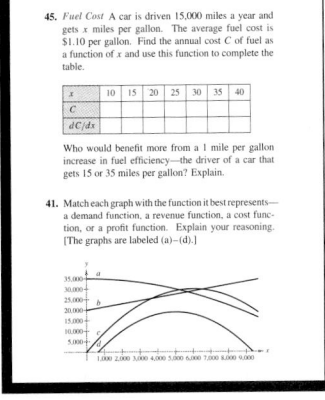

45. *Fuel Cost* A car is driven 15,000 miles a year and gets x miles per gallon. The average fuel cost is $1.10 per gallon. Find the annual cost C of fuel as a function of x and use this function to complete the table.

x	10	15	20	25	30	35	40
C							
dC/dx							

Who would benefit more from a 1 mile per gallon increase in fuel efficiency—the driver of a car that gets 15 or 35 miles per gallon? Explain.

41. Match each graph with the function it best represents—a demand function, a revenue function, a cost function, or a profit function. Explain your reasoning. [The graphs are labeled (a)–(d).]

True or False In Exercises 61–64, determine whether the statement is true or false. If it is false, explain why or give an example that shows the statement is false.

61. The slope of the graph of $y = x^2$ is different at every point on the graph of f.

62. If a function is continuous at a point, then it is differentiable at that point.

63. If a function is differentiable at a point, then it is continuous at that point.

64. A tangent line to a graph can intersect the graph at more than one point.

VARIETY OF PROBLEMS

The text offers a rich variety of problems to accommodate a wide range of teaching and learning styles: computational, conceptual, interpretational, matching (graphs to functions), true/false, essay, multipart, exploratory, and applied problems. An assortment of applications from a variety of disciplines is also included in the exercise sets. To emphasize the relevance of calculus to real-world situations, an effort has been made to incorporate real product and business names in addition to real data, as indicated by source lines. Problems are often labeled to indicate the subject of the application (as in "Fuel Cost" and "Wedding Ring") or to identify a special type of question (as in "True or False" and "Research Project") for easy reference.

EXERCISES

The approximately 5700 exercises in the Fourth Edition are designed to build competence, skill, and understanding. Each exercise set is carefully graded in difficulty to allow students to gain confidence as they progress. All odd-numbered exercises are solved in detail in the Student Solutions Guide, with answers appearing in the back of this text.

The symbol ▦ identifies all exercises in which technology can assist in solving or checking the exercise or in which students are specifically asked to use a graphing utility or computer algebra system.

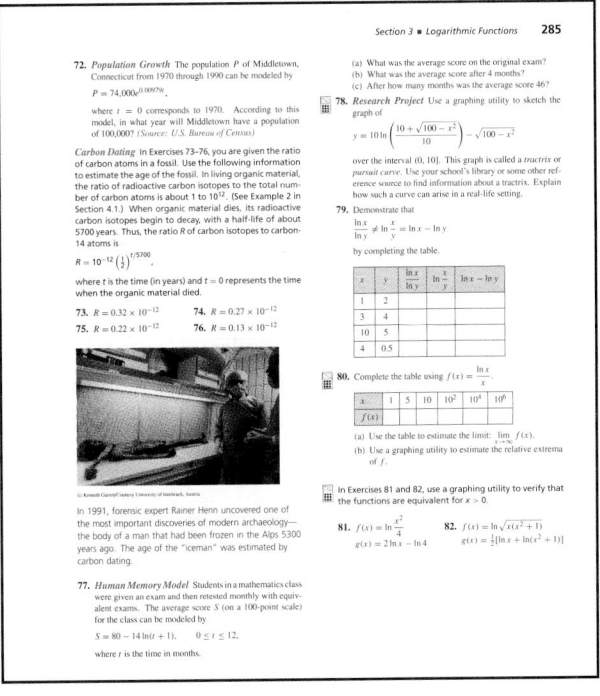

Section 3 ▪ Logarithmic Functions **285**

72. *Population Growth* The population P of Middletown, Connecticut from 1970 through 1990 can be modeled by
$$P = 74,000e^{0.0079t},$$
where $t = 0$ corresponds to 1970. According to this model, in what year will Middletown have a population of 100,000? (Source: U.S. Bureau of Census)

Carbon Dating In Exercises 73–76, you are given the ratio of carbon atoms in a fossil. Use the following information to estimate the age of the fossil. In living organic material, the ratio of radioactive carbon isotopes to the total number of carbon atoms is about 1 to 10^{12}. (See Example 2 in Section 4.1.) When organic material dies, its radioactive carbon isotopes begin to decay, with a half-life of about 5700 years. Thus, the ratio R of carbon isotopes to carbon-14 atoms is
$$R = 10^{-12}\left(\frac{1}{2}\right)^{t/5700},$$
where t is the time (in years) and $t = 0$ represents the time when the organic material died.

73. $R = 0.32 \times 10^{-12}$
74. $R = 0.27 \times 10^{-12}$
75. $R = 0.22 \times 10^{-12}$
76. $R = 0.13 \times 10^{-12}$

© Kenneth Garrett/Courtesy University of Innsbruck, Austria

In 1991, forensic expert Rainer Henn uncovered one of the most important discoveries of modern archaeology—the body of a man that had been frozen in the Alps 5300 years ago. The age of the "iceman" was estimated by carbon dating.

77. *Human Memory Model* Students in a mathematics class were given an exam and then retested monthly with equivalent exams. The average score S (on a 100-point scale) for the class can be modeled by
$$S = 80 - 14\ln(t + 1), \quad 0 \le t \le 12,$$
where t is the time in months.

(a) What was the average score on the original exam?
(b) What was the average score after 4 months?
(c) After how many months was the average score 46?

78. *Research Project* Use a graphing utility to sketch the graph of
$$y = 10\ln\left(\frac{10 + \sqrt{100 - x^2}}{10}\right) - \sqrt{100 - x^2}$$
over the interval (0, 10]. This graph is called a *tractrix* or *pursuit curve*. Use your school's library or some other reference source to find information about a tractrix. Explain how such a curve can arise in a real-life setting.

79. Demonstrate that
$$\frac{\ln x}{\ln y} \ne \ln \frac{x}{y} = \ln x - \ln y$$
by completing the table.

x	y	$\dfrac{\ln x}{\ln y}$	$\ln \dfrac{x}{y}$	$\ln x - \ln y$
1	2			
3	4			
10	5			
4	0.5			

80. Complete the table using $f(x) = \dfrac{\ln x}{x}$.

x	1	5	10	10^2	10^4	10^6
$f(x)$						

(a) Use the table to estimate the limit: $\lim_{x\to\infty} f(x)$.
(b) Use a graphing utility to estimate the relative extrema of f.

In Exercises 81 and 82, use a graphing utility to verify that the functions are equivalent for $x > 0$.

81. $f(x) = \ln \dfrac{x^2}{4}$
$g(x) = 2\ln x - \ln 4$

82. $f(x) = \ln \sqrt{x(x^2 + 1)}$
$g(x) = \frac{1}{2}[\ln x + \ln(x^2 + 1)]$

(Sample textbook pages 376–377 "Chapter Summary and Study Tips" shown as an illustration.)

CHAPTER SUMMARIES AND STUDY TIPS

Chapter summaries have been completely revised for the Fourth Edition to list the concepts taught in the chapter and point out the Review Exercises that test these concepts. Following each chapter summary is a short list of study hints for handling topics or situations specific to the chapter.

REVIEW EXERCISES

A set of Review Exercises at chapter's end gives students an opportunity for additional practice and review. Beginning in Chapter 1, the Review Exercises offer computational, conceptual, and applied problems covering a wide range of topics. Answers to the odd-numbered Review Exercises are given in the back of the text.

SAMPLE POST-GRADUATION EXAM QUESTIONS

Chapters 1–7 conclude with a full page of sample questions taken from certified public accountant exams, graduate management admissions tests, graduate records exams, actuarial exams, or college level academic skills tests to emphasize the variety of situations in which calculus problems arise. The answers to all Sample Post-Graduation Exam Questions are given in the back of the text.

CASE STUDIES

Chapters 1–7 include case studies that show how a real person or business uses mathematics to help make an informed consumer or business decision. Each case study gives a short profile of the featured business and concludes with a set of questions titled "What Would You Do?" which gives students the opportunity to make decisions based on mathematical reasoning. These case studies provide opportunities for individual or group work.

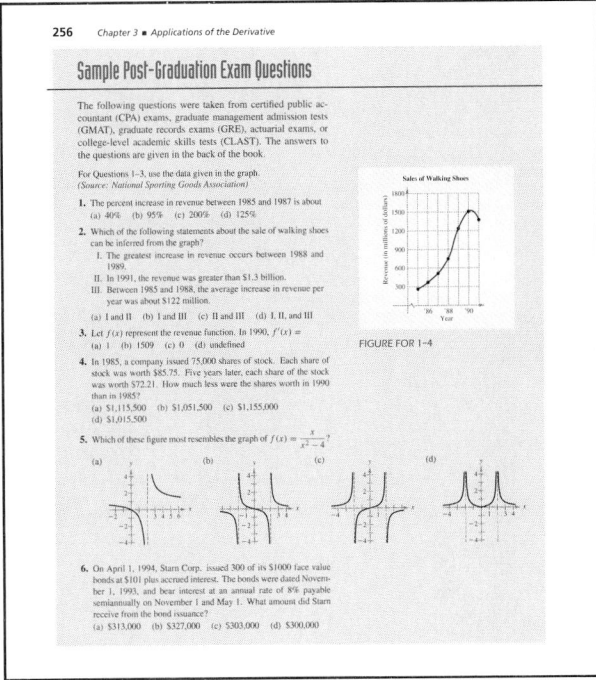

Supplements

A comprehensive supplements package with ancillaries for students, for instructors, and for classroom resources accompanies *Brief Calculus with Applications,* Fourth Edition, *Brief Calculus with Applications,* Alternate Fourth Edition, and all custom-published versions of these two texts by Larson, Hostetler, and Edwards. Most items are keyed directly to the texts.

PRINTED RESOURCES

For the student:

Student Solutions Guide by Dianna L. Zook, Indiana University and Purdue University at Fort Wayne, and Bruce H. Edwards, University of Florida
• Step-by-step solutions to all odd-numbered text exercises

The Algebra of Calculus by Eric J. Braude
• Review of algebra, trigonometry, and analytical geometry required for calculus
• Over 200 examples with solutions
• Pretests and exercises

Graphing Technology Keystroke Guide by Benjamin N. Levy
• Keystroke-level commands and instructions for use with the TI-81, TI-82, TI-85, Casio fx-7700 G, Sharp EL 9200-9300, and Hewlett Packard 48G-48GX
• Numerous screen displays
• Examples and technology tips

Study Guide and Workbook by Ronnie Khuri, University of Florida
• Numerous additional examples and exercises with answers
• Practice tests with answers

For the instructor:

Instructor's Guide
• Notes to the new teacher
• Chapter summaries
• Ready-made chapter tests, some of which require technology
• Answers to Discussion Problems, Warm-up Exercises, and Post-Graduation Exam Questions
• Teaching strategies

Solutions to Even-Numbered Exercises by Dianna L. Zook, Indiana University and Purdue University at Fort Wayne, and Bruce H. Edwards, University of Florida
- Step-by-step solutions to even-numbered text exercises

Test Item File
- Printed test bank
- Approximately 2000 test items
- Multiple-choice, open-ended, and writing questions coded by level of difficulty
- Technology-required test items coded for easy reference

Transparency Package
- Color transparencies

SOFTWARE RESOURCES

Brief Calculus TUTOR by Timothy R. Larson
- An IBM-PC-format "electronic study guide" for the text
- Examples with step-by-step solutions
- Additional exercises with diagnostic feedback
- An on-line glossary of key concepts
- Post-tests reviewing newly learned concepts

Computerized Testing
- Test-generating software for both IBM and Macintosh computers
- Approximately 2000 test items
- Also available as a printed test bank

Derive
- Symbolic algebra system
- Available to adopters at a discount

BestGrapher by George Best
- Function grapher for both IBM and Macintosh computers
- Simultaneous display of equation, graph, and table of values
- Zoom and print features

For information on ordering supplements, please call D. C. Heath's Customer Service toll free at 1-800-334-3284.

Acknowledgments

We would like to thank the many people who have helped us at various stages of this project during the past 14 years. Their encouragement, criticisms, and suggestions have been invaluable to us.

D.C. Heath would like to express our appreciation to the following people who offered their comments on pre-publication of the Fourth Edition: Yvonne Sandoval-Brown, Pima Community College; Mary Chabot, Mt. San Antonio College; Karen Hay, Mesa Community College; Arlene Jesky, Rose State College; Melvin Lax, California State University-Long Beach; Kevin McDonald, Mt. San Antonio College; Mike Nasab, Long Beach City College; Rita Richards, Scottsdale Community College; Jane Y. Smith, University of Florida; Carol G. Williams, Pepperdine University; Carlton Woods, Auburn University at Montgomery.

Fourth edition survey respondents: We would also like to thank the over 75 professors who took time to respond to the *Brief Calculus* Survey. We appreciate your comments.

Case Studies: Special thanks to James A. Kurre and Kenneth T. Louie, Professors of Economics, The Behrend College, The Pennsylvania State University, for creating the Case Studies.

Our thanks to David E. Heyd, The Behrend College, The Pennsylvania State University, for his contributions to this project.

Third Edition Reviewers: Carol Achs, Mesa Community College; John Chuchel, University of California, Davis; William Conway, University of Arizona; Ronnie Khuri, University of Florida; Peter J. Livorsi, Oakton Community College; Samuel A. Lynch, Southwest Missouri State University; Philip R. Montgomery, University of Kansas; Karla Neal, Louisiana State University; James Osterburg, University of Cincinnati; Jan E. Wynn, Brigham Young University.

First and Second Edition Reviewers: Miriam E. Connellan, Marquette University; Bruce H. Edwards, University of Florida; Roger A. Engle, Clarion University of Pennsylvania; William C. Huffman, Loyola University of Chicago; James A. Kurre, The Pennsylvania State University; Norbert Lerner, State University of New York at Cortland; Earl H. McKinney, Ball State University; Stephen B. Rodi, Austin Community College; DeWitt L. Sumners, Florida State University; Jonathan Wilkin, Northern Virginia Community College; Melvin R. Woodard, Indiana University of Pennsylvania; Robert A. Yawin, Springfield Technical Community College.

A special thanks to all the people at D. C. Heath and Company who worked with us in the development of the Fourth Edition, especially Ann Marie Jones and Charlie Hartford, Mathematics Acquisitions Editors; Cathy Cantin, Managing Editor; Emily Keaton, Developmental Editor; Karen Carter, Production Editor; Christine Hoag, Marketing Manager; Jan Shapiro, Designer; Gary Crespo, Art Editor; Carolyn Johnson, Editorial Associate; Lisa Merrill, Production Manager; and Melina Freedman and Donna Simons, Photo Researchers.

We would also like to thank the staff at Larson Texts, Inc., who assisted with proofreading the manuscript; preparing and proofreading the art package; and checking and typesetting the supplements.

On a personal level, we are grateful to our wives, Deanna Gilbert Larson, Eloise Hostetler, and Consuelo Edwards, for their love, patience, and support. Also, a special thanks goes to R. Scott O'Neil.

If you have suggestions for improving the text, please feel free to write to us. Over the past two decades we have received many useful comments from both instructors and students, and we value these comments very much.

Roland E. Larson
Robert P. Hostetler
Bruce H. Edwards

Contents

A Precalculus Review   *0–1*

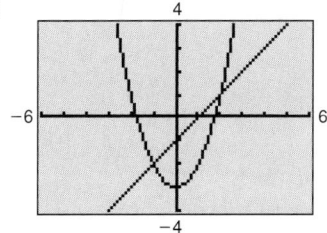

Functions, Graphs, and Limits   1

Differentiation   81

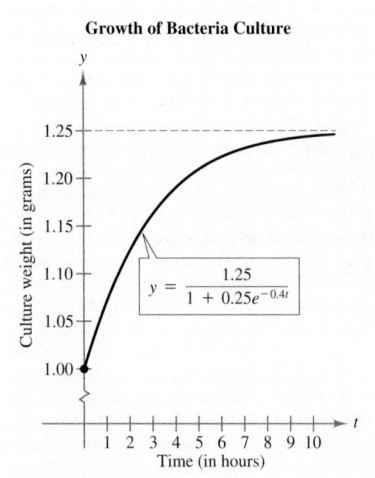

Maximum Revenue

$R = -x^3 + 450x^2 + 52,500x$

(350, 30,625,000)

(546, 0)

Revenue (in dollars)

Number of units

Applications of the Derivative   171

Growth of Bacteria Culture

$y = \dfrac{1.25}{1 + 0.25e^{-0.4t}}$

Culture weight (in grams)

Time (in hours)

Exponential and Logarithmic Functions   257

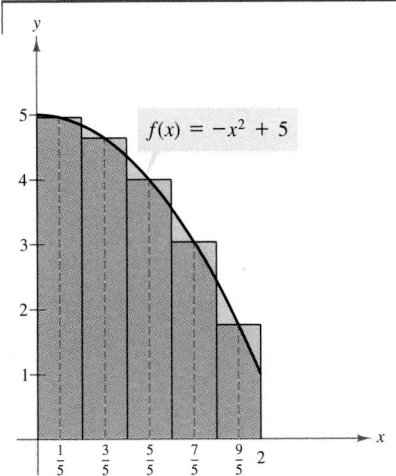

Integration and Its Applications   313

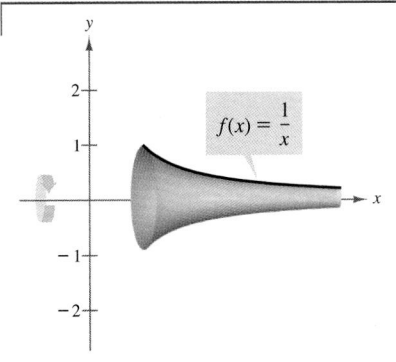

Techniques of Integration   383

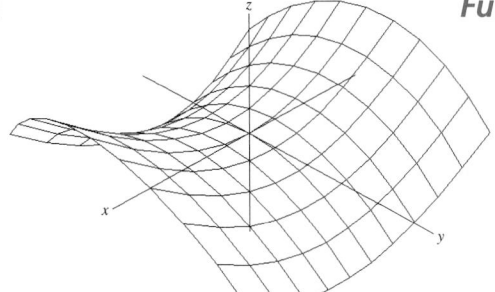

Functions of Several Variables   451

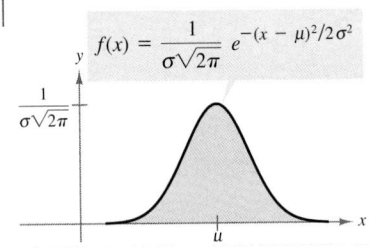

Probability and Calculus   *P-1*

Differential Equations   *D-1*

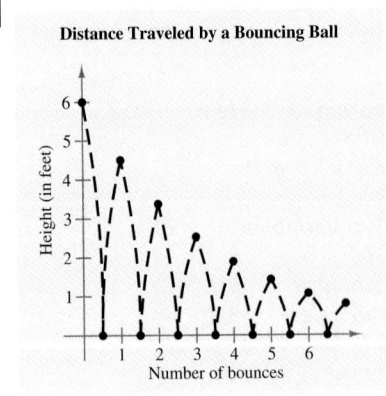

Series and Taylor Polynomials   *S-1*

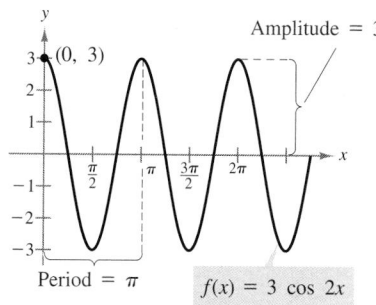

Amplitude = 3

Period = π

$f(x) = 3 \cos 2x$

Applications

Physical Sciences

How to Study Calculus

Studying Mathematics   When studying mathematics—and calculus—the material learned on one day is built upon material learned previously. It is necessary to keep up with course work day by day.

Making a Plan   Make your own course plan right now! Determine the number of hours per week you need to spend on calculus. A general guideline is to study two to four hours for every hour spent in class.

Absorbing the Material   The following practices will help you absorb the concepts of calculus:
a) Before attending class, read the portion of the text to be covered, paying special attention to boxed definitions, theorems, formulas, and summaries. Going to class prepared will enable you to benefit much more from your instructor's presentation.
b) Attend every class and arrive on time. If you have to miss a class, get the notes from another student or get help from your school's tutorial service. Learn the information that was taught in the missed class before attending the next class.
c) Take notes in class, focusing on the instructor's cues indicating important material. Then, as soon after class as possible, read through your notes, adding any explanations necessary to make your notes understandable to you.

Doing the Homework   Learning calculus is like acquiring any other skill. Practice, in the form of homework exercises, is essential to developing your understanding of calculus. Doing the homework while the concepts are still fresh in your mind increases your chances of retaining the information.

Finding a Study Partner   When you get stuck on a problem, it may help to try to work with someone else. Group work is an effective study technique. Even if you feel that you are giving more help than you are getting, you will find that teaching others is an excellent way to better understand calculus concepts.

Building a Math Library   Build a library of books that can help you with this course and future math courses. Consider using the Student Solutions Guide that accompanies this text. Also, after you finish this course, we suggest that you keep the text. It will be a valuable reference book in whatever discipline you are pursuing, not only for use in future classes but also for preparation for post-graduation examinations such as the Graduate Records Exam or the Graduate Management Admissions Test. Computer software and manuals on technology will also be valuable additions to your mathematics library.

Keeping Up with the Work   Don't let yourself fall behind in the course. If you think you are having trouble, seek help immediately. Ask your instructor or teaching assistant, attend your school's tutorial service, talk with your study partner, use additional study aids—do something. If you are having trouble with the material in one chapter of your calculus text, there is a good chance that you will also have trouble with subsequent chapters.

Getting Stuck   Anyone who has taken a math course has had the following experience: you are working on a problem and cannot solve it, or you have solved it but your answer does not agree with the answer given in the back of the text. One approach that often helps when you are stuck is to sketch a graph, either by hand or with a graphing utility. Not only will the sketch give you insight into whatever function you are facing, but it can also clarify such items as limits of integration or whether your answer should be positive or negative. Other approaches include asking for help, taking a break to clear your thoughts, sleeping on it, reworking the problem, comparing notes with a study partner, and rereading your notes or the section in the text. Don't get frustrated or spend too much time on a single problem.

Keeping Your Skills Sharp   Preceding each exercise set in the text is a short set of Warm-Up Exercises. These exercises will help you review skills that you learned in previous sections and retain them. These sets are designed to take only a few minutes to solve. We suggest that you work the entire warm-up set before you start the main exercise set. (All of the Warm-Up Exercises are answered at the end of the text.)

Checking Your Work   Learning to check your work is an important part of learning calculus and is especially useful in testing situations. One easy way to check your work is to ask yourself "Does my answer make sense?" or "Is this the answer I expected to get?" in the context of a specific problem. This simple step will help you determine whether or not your answer has the correct sign (positive or negative) or the correct magnitude. Other ways to check your work include studying in a group and then comparing answers and using technology or a different solution method to check your solution. Check the Study Tips at the ends of the chapters for more hints on checking problems specific to each chapter.

Preparing for Exams   If you have kept up with the work and followed the suggestions given here, you will be nearly ready for the exam. We have included several features that should help in your final preparation. Review the Chapter Summary, work the Review Exercises, and, if you have the Student Solutions Guide, take the practice tests offered there. These should point out areas in which you need more work. For additional practice in certain areas, you can always rework the assigned homework exercises or work the exercises not previously assigned. Analyze your work to locate possible test-taking errors.

Taking Exams   Most instructors suggest that you do not study right up to the minute you take a test. This practice tends to make people anxious. The best cure for anxiety during tests is good preparation. Once the test has begun, read the directions carefully and try to work at a steady pace. Rushing tends to cause people to make careless errors. Remember, there is no rule that says you must tackle the problems in the order given. You may solve them in whatever order with which you feel most comfortable. Often, approaching first the ones you feel are easiest will boost your confidence. If you finish early, take a few moments to check your work.

Learning from Mistakes   When you get an exam back, be sure to go over any errors that you have made. If you don't understand something that was marked as incorrect on your exam, be sure to ask your instructor about it or talk with a study partner. Understanding your errors will prevent you from repeating the same conceptual or systematic errors.

BRIEF CALCULUS

with Applications

FOURTH EDITION

$$x = \frac{-b \pm \sqrt{b^2 - 4ac}}{2a}$$

A Precalculus Review

0.1   **The Real Line and Order**
0.2   **Absolute Value and Distance on the Real Line**
0.3   **Exponents and Radicals**
0.4   **Factoring Polynomials**
0.5   **Fractions and Rationalization**

Mathematics evolved over the past few thousand years in many stages. All of the early stages were centered around the use of mathematics to answer questions about real life. This is much like the way we wrote *Brief Calculus with Applications*. We centered the concepts around the real-life use of mathematics.

The mathematics that you will study in this text is a combination of the work of literally thousands of people whose work took place independently in many different parts of the world: Africa, Asia, Europe, North America, and South America. For instance, the principles of geometry, as cataloged by Euclid (c. 365?–300 B.C.), and the principles of algebra, as developed in India and the Middle East, were known and used by many other civilizations throughout the world.

$$ax^2 + bx + c = 0$$

Euclid

The Bettmann Archive

0.1 The Real Line and Order

The Real Line ■ *Order and Intervals on the Real Line* ■
Solving Inequalities ■ *Applications*

The Real Line

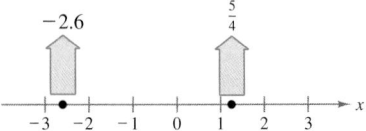

FIGURE 0.1   The Real Line

Real numbers can be represented with a coordinate system called the **real line** (or *x*-axis), as shown in Figure 0.1. The **positive direction** (to the right) is denoted by an arrowhead and indicates the direction of increasing values of *x*. The real number corresponding to a particular point on the real line is called the **coordinate** of the point. As shown in Figure 0.1, it is customary to label those points whose coordinates are integers.

The point on the real line corresponding to zero is called the **origin.** Numbers to the right of the origin are **positive,** and numbers to the left of the origin are **negative.** The term **nonnegative** describes a number that is either positive or zero.

The importance of the real line is that it provides you with a conceptually perfect picture of the real numbers. That is, each point on the real line corresponds to one and only one real number, and each real number corresponds to one and only one point on the real line. This type of relationship is called a **one-to-one correspondence** and is illustrated in Figure 0.2.

Each of the four points in Figure 0.2 corresponds to a real number that can be expressed as the ratio of two integers. (Note that $1.85 = \frac{37}{20}$ and $-2.6 = -\frac{13}{5}$.) Such numbers are called **rational.** Rational numbers have either terminating or infinitely repeating decimal representations.

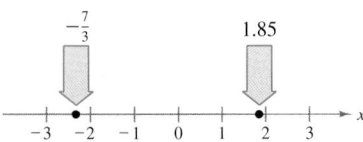

Every point on the real line corresponds to a real number.

Every real number corresponds to a point on the real line.

FIGURE 0.2

Terminating Decimals	*Infinitely Repeating Decimals*
$\dfrac{2}{5} = 0.4$	$\dfrac{1}{3} = 0.333\ldots = 0.\overline{3}$*
$\dfrac{7}{8} = 0.875$	$\dfrac{12}{7} = 1.714285714285\ldots = 1.\overline{714285}$

Real numbers that are not rational are called **irrational,** and they cannot be represented as the ratio of two integers (or as terminating or infinitely repeating decimals). To represent an irrational number, one usually resorts to a decimal approximation. Some irrational numbers occur so frequently in applications that mathematicians have invented special symbols to represent them. For example, the symbols $\sqrt{2}$, π, and e represent irrational numbers whose decimal approximations are as follows. (See Figure 0.3.)

$$\sqrt{2} \approx 1.4142135623$$

$$\pi \approx 3.1415926535$$

$$e \approx 2.7182818284$$

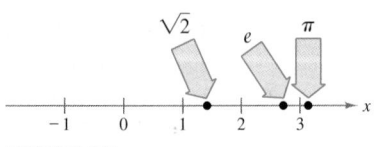

FIGURE 0.3

*The bar indicates which digit or digits repeat.

Order and Intervals on the Real Line

One important property of the real numbers is that they are **ordered:** 0 is less than 1, -3 is less than -2.5, π is less than $\frac{22}{7}$, and so on. You can visualize this property on the real line by observing that a is less than b if and only if a lies to the left of b. Symbolically, "a is less than b" is denoted by the inequality

$$a < b.$$

For example, the inequality $\frac{3}{4} < 1$ follows from the fact that $\frac{3}{4}$ lies to the left of 1 on the real line, as shown in Figure 0.4.

When three real numbers a, x, and b are ordered such that $a < x$ and $x < b$, we say that x is **between** a and b and write

$$a < x < b. \qquad\qquad \textit{x is between a and b.}$$

$\frac{3}{4}$ lies to the left of 1, so $\frac{3}{4} < 1$

FIGURE 0.4

The set of *all* real numbers between a and b is called the **open interval** between a and b and is denoted by (a, b). An interval of the form (a, b) does not contain the "endpoints" a and b. Intervals that include their endpoints are called **closed** and are denoted by $[a, b]$. Intervals of the form $[a, b)$ and $(a, b]$ are called **half-open intervals.** Figure 0.5 shows the nine types of intervals on the real line.

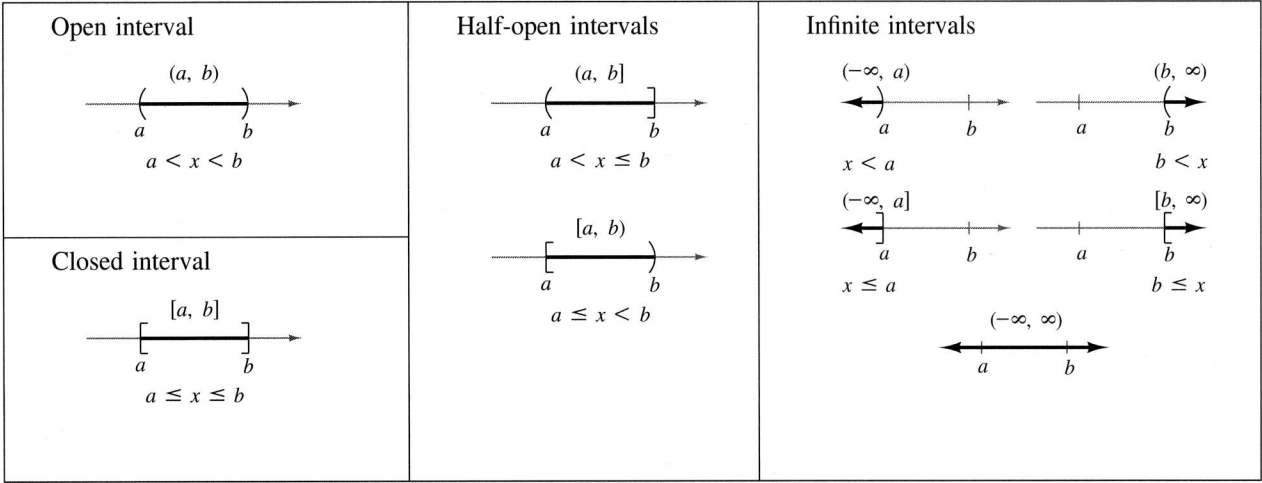

FIGURE 0.5   Intervals on the Real Line

Note   Note that a square bracket is used to denote "less than or equal to" ($\leq$). Furthermore, the symbols ∞ and $-\infty$ denote positive and negative infinity. These symbols do not denote real numbers; they merely let you describe unbounded conditions more concisely. For instance, the interval $[b, \infty)$ is unbounded to the right because it includes *all* real numbers that are greater than or equal to b.

Solving Inequalities

In calculus, you are frequently required to "solve inequalities" involving variable expressions such as $3x - 4 < 5$. The number a is a **solution** of an inequality if the inequality is true when a is substituted for x. The set of all values of x that satisfy an equality is called the **solution set** of the inequality. The following properties are useful for solving inequalities. (Similar properties are obtained if $<$ is replaced by $\leq$ and $>$ is replaced by $\geq$.)

Properties of Inequalities

1. Transitive property: $a < b$ and $b < c \Longrightarrow a < c$
2. Adding inequalities: $a < b$ and $c < d \Longrightarrow a + c < b + d$
3. Multiplying by a (positive) constant: $a < b \Longrightarrow ac < bc$, $c > 0$
4. Multiplying by a (negative) constant: $a < b \Longrightarrow ac > bc$, $c < 0$
5. Adding a constant: $a < b \Longrightarrow a + c < b + c$
6. Subtracting a constant: $a < b \Longrightarrow a - c < b - c$

Note Note that you *reverse the inequality* when you multiply by a negative number. For example, if $x < 3$, then $-4x > -12$. This principle also applies to division by a negative number. Thus, if $-2x > 4$, then $x < -2$.

EXAMPLE 1 *Solving an Inequality*

Find the solution set of the inequality $3x - 4 < 5$.

Solution

$$3x - 4 < 5 \qquad \textit{Original inequality}$$
$$3x - 4 + 4 < 5 + 4 \qquad \textit{Add 4 to each side.}$$
$$3x < 9 \qquad \textit{Simplify.}$$
$$\frac{1}{3}(3x) < \frac{1}{3}(9) \qquad \textit{Multiply each side by } \tfrac{1}{3}.$$
$$x < 3 \qquad \textit{Simplify.}$$

Thus, the solution set is the interval $(-\infty, 3)$, as shown in Figure 0.6. ■

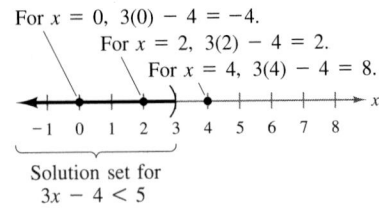

For $x = 0$, $3(0) - 4 = -4$.
For $x = 2$, $3(2) - 4 = 2$.
For $x = 4$, $3(4) - 4 = 8$.

Solution set for
$3x - 4 < 5$

FIGURE 0.6

Note In Example 1, all five inequalities listed as steps in the solution have the same solution set, and they are called **equivalent inequalities.**

Once you have solved an inequality, it is a good idea to check some x-values in your solution interval to see whether they satisfy the original inequality. You might also check some values outside your solution interval to verify that they do *not* satisfy the inequality. For example, Figure 0.6 shows that when $x = 0$ or $x = 2$ the inequality is satisfied, but when $x = 4$ the inequality is not satisfied.

The inequality in Example 1 involves a first-degree polynomial. To solve inequalities involving polynomials of higher degree, you can use the fact that a polynomial can change signs *only* at its real zeros (the real numbers that make the polynomial zero). Between two consecutive real zeros, a polynomial must be entirely positive or entirely negative. This means that when the real zeros of a polynomial are put in order, they divide the real line into **test intervals** in which the polynomial has no sign changes. That is, if a polynomial has the factored form

$$(x - r_1)(x - r_2), \ldots, (x - r_n), \qquad r_1 < r_2 < r_3 < \cdots < r_n,$$

then the test intervals are

$$(-\infty, r_1), \quad (r_1, r_2), \quad \ldots, \quad (r_{n-1}, r_n), \quad \text{and} \quad (r_n, \infty).$$

For example, the polynomial

$$x^2 - x - 6 = (x - 3)(x + 2)$$

can change signs only at $x = -2$ and $x = 3$. To determine the sign of the polynomial in the intervals $(-\infty, -2), (-2, 3)$, and $(3, \infty)$, you need to test only *one value* from each interval.

EXAMPLE 2 *Solving a Polynomial Inequality*

Find the solution set of the inequality $x^2 < x + 6$.

Solution

$$x^2 < x + 6 \qquad\qquad \textit{Original inequality}$$
$$x^2 - x - 6 < 0 \qquad\qquad \textit{Polynomial form}$$
$$(x - 3)(x + 2) < 0 \qquad\qquad \textit{Factor.}$$

Thus, the polynomial $x^2 - x - 6$ has $x = -2$ and $x = 3$ as its zeros. You can solve the inequality by testing the sign of the polynomial in each of the following intervals.

$$x < -2, \qquad -2 < x < 3, \qquad x > 3$$

To test an interval, choose a representative number in the interval and compute the sign of each factor. For example, for any $x < -2$, both of the factors $(x - 3)$ and $(x + 2)$ are negative. Consequently, the product (of two negative numbers) is positive, and the inequality is *not* satisfied in the interval

$$x < -2.$$

We suggest the testing format shown in Figure 0.7. Because the inequality is satisfied only by the center test interval, you conclude that the solution set is given by the interval

$$-2 < x < 3. \qquad\qquad \textit{Solution set}$$

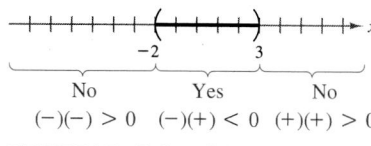

No   Yes   No

$(-)(-) > 0 \quad (-)(+) < 0 \quad (+)(+) > 0$

FIGURE 0.7 Is $(x - 3)(x + 2) < 0$?

Applications

Inequalities are frequently used to describe conditions that occur in business and science. For instance, the inequality

$$118 \le W \le 138$$

describes the recommended weight W for a woman whose height is 5 feet 6 inches. Example 3 shows how an inequality can be used to describe the production level of a manufacturing plant.

Real Life

EXAMPLE 3 *Production Levels*

In addition to fixed overhead costs of $500 per day, the cost of producing x units of a certain item is $2.50 per unit. During the month of August, the total cost of production varied from a high of $1325 to a low of $1200 per day. Find the high and low *production levels* during the month.

Solution

Because it costs $2.50 to produce one unit, it costs $2.5x$ to produce x units. Furthermore, because the fixed cost per day is $500, the total daily cost of producing x units is

$$C = 2.5x + 500.$$

Now, because the cost ranged from $1200 to $1325, you can write the following.

$$1200 \le \quad 2.5x + 500 \quad \le 1325$$
$$1200 - 500 \le 2.5x + 500 - 500 \le 1325 - 500$$
$$700 \le \quad 2.5x \quad \le 825$$
$$\frac{700}{2.5} \le \quad \frac{2.5x}{2.5} \quad \le \frac{825}{2.5}$$
$$280 \le \quad x \quad \le 330$$

Thus, the daily production levels during the month varied between a low of 280 units and a high of 330 units, as pictured in Figure 0.8.

FIGURE 0.8

EXERCISES 0.1

In Exercises 1–10, determine whether the real number is rational or irrational.

1. 0.7

2. -3678

3. $\dfrac{3\pi}{2}$

4. $3\sqrt{2} - 1$

5. $4.3451\overline{451}$

6. $\dfrac{22}{7}$

7. $\sqrt[3]{64}$

8. $0.8177\overline{8177}$

9. $\sqrt[3]{60}$

10. $2e$

In Exercises 11–14, determine whether the given value of x satisfies the inequality.

11. $5x - 12 > 0$

  (a) $x = 3$ (b) $x = -3$

  (c) $x = \frac{5}{2}$ (d) $x = \frac{3}{2}$

12. $x + 1 < \dfrac{2x}{3}$

  (a) $x = 0$ (b) $x = 4$

  (c) $x = -4$ (d) $x = -3$

13. $0 < \dfrac{x - 2}{4} < 2$

  (a) $x = 4$ (b) $x = 10$

  (c) $x = 0$ (d) $x = \frac{7}{2}$

14. $-1 < \dfrac{3 - x}{2} \le 1$

  (a) $x = 0$ (b) $x = \sqrt{5}$

  (c) $x = 1$ (d) $x = 5$

In Exercises 15–32, solve the inequality and sketch the graph of the solution on the real number line.

15. $x - 5 \ge 7$

16. $2x > 3$

17. $4x + 1 < 2x$

18. $2x + 7 < 3$

19. $2x - 1 \ge 0$

20. $3x + 1 \ge 2x + 2$

21. $4 - 2x < 3x - 1$

22. $x - 4 \le 2x + 1$

23. $-4 < 2x - 3 < 4$

24. $0 \le x + 3 < 5$

25. $\dfrac{3}{4} > x + 1 > \dfrac{1}{4}$

26. $-1 < -\dfrac{x}{3} < 1$

27. $\dfrac{x}{2} + \dfrac{x}{3} > 5$

28. $\dfrac{x}{2} - \dfrac{x}{3} > 5$

29. $x^2 \le 3 - 2x$

30. $x^2 - x \le 0$

31. $x^2 + x - 1 \le 5$

32. $2x^2 + 1 < 9x - 3$

33. *Simple Interest* P dollars is invested at a (simple) interest rate of r. After t years, the balance in the account is given by

$$A = P + Prt,$$

where the interest rate r is expressed in decimal form. In order for an investment of $1000 to grow to *more than* $1250 in 2 years, what must the interest rate be?

34. *Sales* A doughnut shop at a shopping mall sells a dozen doughnuts for $2.95. Beyond the fixed costs (for rent, utilities, and insurance) of $150 per day, it costs $1.45 for enough materials (flour, sugar, etc.) and labor to produce each dozen doughnuts. If the daily profit *varies between* $50 and $200, between what levels (in dozens) do the daily sales vary?

35. *Profit* The revenue for selling x units of a product is

$$R = 115.95x,$$

and the cost of producing x units is

$$C = 95x + 750.$$

In order to obtain a profit, the revenue must be *greater than* the cost. For what values of x will this product return a profit?

36. *Operating Cost* A utility company has a fleet of vans for which the annual operating cost per van is

$$C = 0.32m + 2300,$$

where m is the number of miles traveled by a van in a year. What number of miles will yield an annual operating cost per van that is *less than* $10,000?

37. *Area* A square region is to have an area of *at least* 500 square meters. What must the length of the sides of the region be?

38. *Area* An isosceles right triangle is to have an area of *at least* 32 square feet. What must the length of each side be?

In Exercises 39 and 40, determine whether each statement is true or false, given $a < b$.

39. (a) $-2a < -2b$ (b) $a + 2 < b + 2$

    (c) $6a < 6b$ (d) $\dfrac{1}{a} < \dfrac{1}{b}$

40. (a) $a - 4 < b - 4$ (b) $4 - a < 4 - b$

    (c) $-3b < -3a$ (d) $\dfrac{a}{4} < \dfrac{b}{4}$

Absolute Value and Distance on the Real Line

Absolute Value of a Real Number ■ *Distance on the Real Line* ■
Intervals Defined by Absolute Value ■ *Applications*

Absolute Value of a Real Number

Definition of Absolute Value

The **absolute value** of a real number a is

$$|a| = \begin{cases} a, & \text{if } a \geq 0 \\ -a, & \text{if } a < 0. \end{cases}$$

At first glance it may appear from this definition that the absolute value of a real number can be negative, but this is not possible. For example, let $a = -3$. Then, because $-3 < 0$, you have

$$|a| = |-3| = -(-3) = 3.$$

The following properties are useful for working with absolute values.

Properties of Absolute Value

1. Multiplication: $\quad |ab| = |a||b|$

2. Division: $\quad \left|\dfrac{a}{b}\right| = \dfrac{|a|}{|b|}, \quad b \neq 0$

3. Power: $\quad |a^n| = |a|^n$

4. Square root: $\quad \sqrt{a^2} = |a|$

Be sure you understand the fourth property in this list. A common error in algebra is to imagine that by squaring a number and then taking the square root, we come back to the original number. But this is true only if the original number is nonnegative. For instance, if $a = 2$, then

$$\sqrt{2^2} = \sqrt{4} = 2,$$

but if $a = -2$, then

$$\sqrt{(-2)^2} = \sqrt{4} = 2.$$

The reason for this is that (by definition) the square root symbol $\sqrt{}$ denotes only the nonnegative root.

Distance on the Real Line

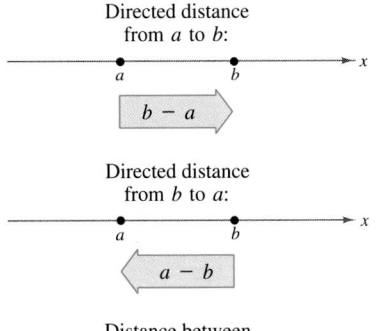

Directed distance from a to b:

$b - a$

Directed distance from b to a:

$a - b$

Distance between a and b:

$|a - b|$ or $|b - a|$

FIGURE 0.9

Consider two distinct points on the real line, as shown in Figure 0.9.

1. The **directed distance from a to b** is $b - a$.
2. The **directed distance from b to a** is $a - b$.
3. The **distance between a and b** is $|a - b|$ or $|b - a|$.

In Figure 0.9, note that because b is to the right of a, the directed distance from a to b (moving to the right) is positive. Moreover, because a is to the left of b, the directed distance from b to a (moving to the left) is negative. The distance *between* two points on the real line can never be negative.

Distance Between Two Points on the Real Line

The distance d between points x_1 and x_2 on the real line is given by

$$d = |x_2 - x_1| = \sqrt{(x_2 - x_1)^2}.$$

Note that the order of subtraction with x_1 and x_2 does not matter because

$$|x_2 - x_1| = |x_1 - x_2| \quad \text{and} \quad (x_2 - x_1)^2 = (x_1 - x_2)^2.$$

EXAMPLE 1 *Finding Distance on the Real Line*

Determine the distance between -3 and 4 on the real line. What is the directed distance from -3 to 4? From 4 to -3?

Solution
The distance between -3 and 4 is given by

$$|4 - (-3)| = |7| = 7 \quad \text{or} \quad |-3 - 4| = |-7| = 7.$$

The directed distance from -3 to 4 is

$$4 - (-3) = 7.$$

The directed distance from 4 to -3 is

$$-3 - 4 = -7.$$

(See Figure 0.10.)

Distance $= 7$

$$-4 \quad -3 \quad -2 \quad -1 \quad 0 \quad 1 \quad 2 \quad 3 \quad 4 \quad 5$$

FIGURE 0.10

Intervals Defined by Absolute Value

EXAMPLE 2 *Defining an Interval on the Real Line*

Find the interval on the real line that contains all numbers that lie no more than two units from 3.

Solution

Let x be any point in this interval. You need to find all x such that the distance between x and 3 is less than or equal to 2. This implies that

$$|x - 3| \leq 2.$$

Requiring the absolute value of $x - 3$ to be less than or equal to 2 means that $x - 3$ must lie between -2 and 2. Hence, you can write

$$-2 \leq x - 3 \leq 2.$$

Solving this pair of inequalities, you have

$$-2 + 3 \leq x - 3 + 3 \leq 2 + 3$$
$$1 \leq \quad x \quad \leq 5. \qquad \textit{Solution set}$$

Therefore, the interval is [1, 5], as shown in Figure 0.11.

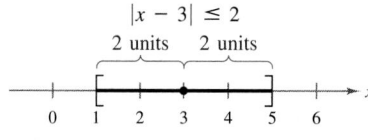

FIGURE 0.11

Two Basic Types of Inequalities Involving Absolute Value

Let a and d be real numbers, where $d > 0$.

$$|x - a| \leq d \text{ if and only if } a - d \leq x \leq a + d.$$
$$|x - a| \geq d \text{ if and only if } x \leq a - d \text{ or } a + d \leq x.$$

Inequality	Interpretation	Graph
$|x - a| \leq d$	All numbers x whose distance from a is less than or equal to d.	
$|x - a| \geq d$	All numbers x whose distance from a is greater than or equal to d.	

Note Be sure you see that inequalities of the form $|x - a| \geq d$ have solution sets consisting of two intervals. To describe the two intervals without using absolute values, we must use *two* separate inequalities, connected by an "or" to indicate union.

Applications

EXAMPLE 3 *Quality Control*

A large manufacturer hired a quality control firm to determine the reliability of a certain product. Using statistical methods, the firm determined that the manufacturer could expect $0.35\% \pm 0.17\%$ of the units to be defective. If the manufacturer offers a money-back guarantee on this product, how much should be budgeted to cover the refunds on 100,000 units? (Assume that the retail price is $8.95.)

Solution

Let r represent the percent of defective units (written in decimal form). You know that r will differ from 0.0035 by at most 0.0017.

$$0.0035 - 0.0017 \le r \le 0.0035 + 0.0017$$

$$0.0018 \le r \le 0.0052 \qquad \text{Figure 0.12(a)}$$

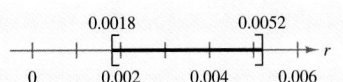

(a) Percent of defective units

Now, letting x be the number of defective units out of 100,000, it follows that $x = 100{,}000r$ and you have

$$0.0018(100{,}000) \le 100{,}000r \le 0.0052(100{,}000)$$

$$180 \le \quad x \quad \le 520. \qquad \text{Figure 0.12(b)}$$

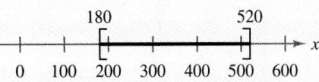

(b) Number of defective units

Finally, letting C be the cost of refunds, you have $C = 8.95x$. Thus, the total cost of refunds for 100,000 units should fall within the interval given by

$$180(8.95) \le 8.95x \le 520(8.95)$$

$$\$1611 \le \quad C \quad \le \$4654. \qquad \text{Figure 0.12(c)}$$ ■

(c) Cost of refunds

FIGURE 0.12

In Example 3, the manufacturer should expect to spend between \$1611 and \$4654 for refunds. Of course, the safer budget figure for refunds would be the higher of these estimates. However, from a statistical point of view, the most representative estimate would be the average of these two extremes. Graphically, the average of two numbers is the **midpoint** of the interval with the two numbers as endpoints, as shown in Figure 0.13.

FIGURE 0.13

Midpoint of an Interval

The **midpoint** of the interval with endpoints a and b is found by taking the average of the endpoints.

$$\text{Midpoint} = \frac{a + b}{2}$$

E X E R C I S E S   0.2

In Exercises 1–4, find (a) the directed distance from *a* to *b*, (b) the directed distance from *b* to *a*, and (c) the distance between *a* and *b*.

1. $a = 126, b = 75$ **2.** $a = -126, b = -75$

3. $a = 9.34, b = -5.65$ **4.** $a = \frac{16}{5}, b = \frac{112}{75}$

In Exercises 5–8, find the midpoint of the given interval.

5. $[7, 21]$ **6.** $[8.6, 11.4]$

7. $[-6.85, 9.35]$ **8.** $[-4.6, -1.3]$

In Exercises 9–22, solve the inequality and sketch the graph of the solution on the real line.

9. $|x| < 5$ **10.** $|2x| < 6$

11. $\left|\dfrac{x}{2}\right| > 3$ **12.** $|5x| > 10$

13. $|x + 2| < 5$ **14.** $|3x + 1| \geq 4$

15. $\left|\dfrac{x - 3}{2}\right| \geq 5$ **16.** $|2x + 1| < 5$

17. $|10 - x| > 4$ **18.** $|25 - x| \geq 20$

19. $|9 - 2x| < 1$ **20.** $\left|1 - \dfrac{2x}{3}\right| < 1$

21. $|x - a| \leq b$ **22.** $|2x - a| \geq b$

In Exercises 23–34, use absolute values to describe the given interval (or pair of intervals) on the real line.

23. $[-2, 2]$ **24.** $(-3, 3)$

25. $(-\infty, -2) \cup (2, \infty)$ **26.** $(-\infty, -3] \cup [3, \infty)$

27. $[2, 6]$ **28.** $(-7, -1)$

29. $(-\infty, 0) \cup (4, \infty)$ **30.** $(-\infty, 20) \cup (24, \infty)$

31. All numbers *less than* two units from 4.

32. All numbers *more than* six units from 3.

33. *y* is *at most* two units from *a*.

34. *y* is *less than* *h* units from *c*.

35. *Statistics* The heights *h* of two-thirds of the members of a certain population satisfy the inequality

$$\left|\frac{h - 68.5}{2.7}\right| \leq 1,$$

where *h* is measured in inches. Determine the interval on the real line in which these heights lie.

36. *Statistics* To determine whether a coin is fair, an experimenter tosses it 100 times and records the number of heads *x*. Statistical theory states that the coin should be declared unfair if

$$\left|\frac{x - 50}{5}\right| \geq 1.645.$$

For what values of *x* will the coin be declared unfair?

37. *Production* The estimated daily production *x* at a refinery is given by

$$|x - 200{,}000| \leq 125{,}000,$$

where *x* is measured in barrels of oil. Determine the high and low production levels.

38. *Stock Price* A stock market analyst predicts that over the next year the price *p* of a certain stock will not change from its current price of $\$33\frac{1}{8}$ by more than \$2. Use absolute values to write this prediction as an inequality.

Budget Variance In Exercises 39–42, (a) use absolute value notation to represent the two intervals in which expenses must lie if they are to be within \$500 and within 5% of the specified budget amount, and (b) using the more stringent constraint, determine whether the given expense is at variance with the budget restriction.

Item	Budget	Expense
39. Utilities	\$4,750.00	\$5,116.37
40. Insurance	\$15,000.00	\$14,695.00
41. Maintenance	\$20,000.00	\$22,718.35
42. Taxes	\$7,500.00	\$8,691.00

Exponents and Radicals

Expressions Involving Exponents or Radicals ■ *Operations with Exponents* ■ *Domain of an Algebraic Expression*

Expressions Involving Exponents or Radicals

Note If n is even, then the principal nth root is positive. For example, $\sqrt{4} = +2$ and $\sqrt[4]{81} = +3$.

Properties of Exponents

1. Whole number exponents: $\quad x^n = \underbrace{x \cdot x \cdot x \cdots x}_{n \text{ factors}}$

2. Zero exponent: $\quad x^0 = 1, \quad x \neq 0$

3. Negative exponents: $\quad x^{-n} = \dfrac{1}{x^n}, \quad x \neq 0$

4. Radicals (principal nth root): $\quad \sqrt[n]{x} = a \Longrightarrow x = a^n$

5. Rational exponents $(1/n)$: $\quad x^{1/n} = \sqrt[n]{x}$

6. Rational exponents (m/n): $\quad x^{m/n} = (x^{1/n})^m = \left(\sqrt[n]{x}\right)^m$

$$x^{m/n} = (x^m)^{1/n} = \sqrt[n]{x^m}$$

7. Special convention (square root): $\quad \sqrt[2]{x} = \sqrt{x}$

EXAMPLE 1 *Evaluating Expressions*

	Expression	x-Value	Substitution
a.	$y = -2x^2$	$x = 4$	$y = -2(4^2) = -2(16) = -32$
b.	$y = 3x^{-3}$	$x = -1$	$y = 3(-1)^{-3} = \dfrac{3}{(-1)^3} = \dfrac{3}{-1} = -3$
c.	$y = (-x)^2$	$x = \dfrac{1}{2}$	$y = \left(-\dfrac{1}{2}\right)^2 = \dfrac{1}{4}$
d.	$y = \dfrac{2}{x^{-2}}$	$x = 3$	$y = \dfrac{2}{3^{-2}} = 2(3^2) = 18$

EXAMPLE 2 *Evaluating Expressions*

	Expression	x-Value	Substitution
a.	$y = 2x^{1/2}$	$x = 4$	$y = 2\sqrt{4} = 2(2) = 4$
b.	$y = \sqrt[3]{x^2}$	$x = 8$	$y = 8^{2/3} = (8^{1/3})^2 = 2^2 = 4$

Operations with Exponents

Operations with Exponents

---

1. Multiplying like bases: $x^n x^m = x^{n+m}$ *Add exponents.*

2. Dividing like bases: $\dfrac{x^n}{x^m} = x^{n-m}$ *Subtract exponents.*

3. Removing parentheses: $(xy)^n = x^n y^n$

   $$\left(\dfrac{x}{y}\right)^n = \dfrac{x^n}{y^n}$$

   $$(x^n)^m = x^{nm}$$

4. Special conventions: $-x^n = -(x^n), \quad -x^n \neq (-x)^n$

   $$cx^n = c(x^n), \quad cx^n \neq (cx)^n$$

   $$x^{n^m} = x^{(n^m)}, \quad x^{n^m} \neq (x^n)^m$$

EXAMPLE 3 *Simplifying Expressions with Exponents*

Simplify the following expressions.

a. $2x^2(x^3)$ **b.** $(3x)^2 \sqrt[3]{x}$ **c.** $\dfrac{3x^2}{\left(\sqrt{x}\right)^3}$

d. $\dfrac{5x^4}{(x^2)^3}$ **e.** $x^{-1}(2x^2)$ **f.** $\dfrac{-\sqrt{x}}{5x^{-1}}$

Solution

a. $2x^2(x^3) = 2x^{2+3} = 2x^5$

b. $(3x)^2 \sqrt[3]{x} = 9x^2 x^{1/3} = 9x^{2+(1/3)} = 9x^{7/3}$

c. $\dfrac{3x^2}{\left(\sqrt{x}\right)^3} = \dfrac{3x^2}{(x^{1/2})^3} = 3\left(\dfrac{x^2}{x^{3/2}}\right) = 3x^{2-(3/2)} = 3x^{1/2}$

d. $\dfrac{5x^4}{(x^2)^3} = \dfrac{5x^4}{x^6} = \dfrac{5}{x^{6-4}} = \dfrac{5}{x^2}$

e. $x^{-1}(2x^2) = 2x^{-1}x^2 = 2x^{2-1} = 2x$

f. $\dfrac{-\sqrt{x}}{5x^{-1}} = -\dfrac{1}{5}\left(\dfrac{x^{1/2}}{x^{-1}}\right) = -\dfrac{1}{5}x^{(1/2)+1} = -\dfrac{1}{5}x^{3/2}$

Note in Example 3 that one characteristic of simplified expressions is the absence of negative exponents. Another characteristic of simplified expressions is that we usually prefer to write sums and differences in *factored form.* To do this, you can use the **distributive property.**

$$abx^n + acx^{n+m} = ax^n(b + cx^m)$$

Study the next example carefully to be sure that you understand the concepts involved in the factoring process.

EXAMPLE 4 *Simplifying by Factoring*

a. $2x^2 - x^3 = x^2(2 - x)$

b. $2x^3 + x^2 = x^2(2x + 1)$

c. $2x^{1/2} + 4x^{5/2} = 2x^{1/2}(1 + 2x^2)$

d. $2x^{-1/2} + 3x^{5/2} = x^{-1/2}(2 + 3x^3) = \dfrac{2 + 3x^3}{\sqrt{x}}$ ▬

Many algebraic expressions obtained in calculus occur in unsimplified form. For instance, the two expressions shown in the following example are the result of an operation in calculus called **differentiation.** [The first is the derivative of $2(x + 1)^{3/2}(2x - 3)^{5/2}$, and the second is the derivative of $2(x + 1)^{1/2}(2x - 3)^{5/2}$.]

EXAMPLE 5 *Simplifying by Factoring*

Simplify the following expressions by factoring.

a. $3(x + 1)^{1/2}(2x - 3)^{5/2} + 10(x + 1)^{3/2}(2x - 3)^{3/2}$

b. $(x + 1)^{-1/2}(2x - 3)^{5/2} + 10(x + 1)^{1/2}(2x - 3)^{3/2}$

Solution

a. $3(x + 1)^{1/2}(2x - 3)^{5/2} + 10(x + 1)^{3/2}(2x - 3)^{3/2}$

$$= (x + 1)^{1/2}(2x - 3)^{3/2}[3(2x - 3) + 10(x + 1)]$$
$$= (x + 1)^{1/2}(2x - 3)^{3/2}(6x - 9 + 10x + 10)$$
$$= (x + 1)^{1/2}(2x - 3)^{3/2}(16x + 1)$$

b. $(x + 1)^{-1/2}(2x - 3)^{5/2} + 10(x + 1)^{1/2}(2x - 3)^{3/2}$

$$= (x + 1)^{-1/2}(2x - 3)^{3/2}[(2x - 3) + 10(x + 1)]$$
$$= (x + 1)^{-1/2}(2x - 3)^{3/2}(2x - 3 + 10x + 10)$$
$$= (x + 1)^{-1/2}(2x - 3)^{3/2}(12x + 7)$$
$$= \dfrac{(2x - 3)^{3/2}(12x + 7)}{(x + 1)^{1/2}}$$ ▬

$\left(x + 1\right)^{-1/2} + 10\left(x + 1\right)^{1/2} =$

$\left(x + 1\right)^{-1/2}\left(10(x + 1)\right)$?

How does " 1 " factor out

from $-1/2$ & $+1/2$?

Example 6 shows some additional types of expressions that can occur in calculus. [The expression in part c is an antiderivative of $(x+1)^{2/3}(2x+3)$, and the expression in part d is the derivative of $(x+2)^3/(x-1)^3$.]

EXAMPLE 6 *Factors Involving Quotients*

Simplify the following expressions by factoring.

a. $\dfrac{3x^2 + x^4}{2x}$

b. $\dfrac{\sqrt{x} + x^{3/2}}{x}$

c. $\dfrac{3}{5}(x+1)^{5/3} + \dfrac{3}{4}(x+1)^{8/3}$

d. $\dfrac{3(x+2)^2(x-1)^3 - 3(x+2)^3(x-1)^2}{[(x-1)^3]^2}$

Solution

a. $\dfrac{3x^2 + x^4}{2x} = \dfrac{x^2(3+x^2)}{2x} = \dfrac{x^{2-1}(3+x^2)}{2} = \dfrac{x(3+x^2)}{2}$

b. $\dfrac{\sqrt{x} + x^{3/2}}{x} = \dfrac{x^{1/2}(1+x)}{x} = \dfrac{1+x}{x^{1-(1/2)}} = \dfrac{1+x}{\sqrt{x}}$

c. $\dfrac{3}{5}(x+1)^{5/3} + \dfrac{3}{4}(x+1)^{8/3} = \dfrac{12}{20}(x+1)^{5/3} + \dfrac{15}{20}(x+1)^{8/3}$

$\qquad\qquad = \dfrac{3}{20}(x+1)^{5/3}[4 + 5(x+1)]$

$\qquad\qquad = \dfrac{3}{20}(x+1)^{5/3}(4 + 5x + 5)$

$\qquad\qquad = \dfrac{3}{20}(x+1)^{5/3}(5x + 9)$

d. $\dfrac{3(x+2)^2(x-1)^3 - 3(x+2)^3(x-1)^2}{[(x-1)^3]^2}$

$\qquad = \dfrac{3(x+2)^2(x-1)^2[(x-1) - (x+2)]}{(x-1)^6}$

$\qquad = \dfrac{3(x+2)^2(x-1-x-2)}{(x-1)^{6-2}}$

$\qquad = \dfrac{-9(x+2)^2}{(x-1)^4}$

Domain of an Algebraic Expression

When working with algebraic expressions involving x, we face the potential difficulty of substituting a value of x for which the expression is not defined (does not produce a real number). For example, the expression $\sqrt{2x + 3}$ is *not defined* when $x = -2$ because $\sqrt{2(-2) + 3}$ is not a real number.

The set of all values for which an expression is defined is called its **domain.** Thus, the domain of $\sqrt{2x + 3}$ is the set of all values of x such that $\sqrt{2x + 3}$ is a real number. In order for $\sqrt{2x + 3}$ to represent a real number, it is necessary that $2x + 3 \geq 0$. In other words, $\sqrt{2x + 3}$ is defined only for those values of x that lie in the interval $\left[-\frac{3}{2}, \infty\right)$, as shown in Figure 0.14.

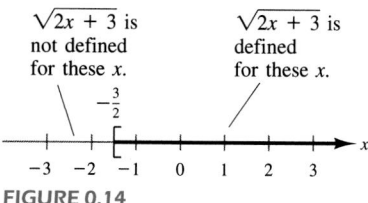

FIGURE 0.14

EXAMPLE 7 *Finding the Domain of an Expression*

Find the domain of each of the following expressions.

a. $\sqrt{3x - 2}$

b. $\dfrac{1}{\sqrt{3x - 2}}$

c. $\sqrt[3]{9x + 1}$

Solution

a. The domain of $\sqrt{3x - 2}$ consists of all x such that

$$3x - 2 \geq 0,$$

which implies that $x \geq \frac{2}{3}$. Therefore, the domain is $\left[\frac{2}{3}, \infty\right)$.

b. The domain of $1/\sqrt{3x - 2}$ is the same as the domain of $\sqrt{3x - 2}$, except that $1/\sqrt{3x - 2}$ is not defined when $3x - 2 = 0$. Because this occurs when $x = \frac{2}{3}$, we conclude that the domain is $\left(\frac{2}{3}, \infty\right)$.

c. Because $\sqrt[3]{9x + 1}$ is defined for *all* real numbers, we conclude that its domain is $(-\infty, \infty)$.

EXERCISES 0.3

In Exercises 1–20, evaluate the expression for the indicated value of x.

Expression	x-value	Expression	x-value
1. $-3x^3$	$x = 2$	2. $\dfrac{x^2}{2}$	$x = 6$
3. $4x^{-3}$	$x = 2$	4. $7x^{-2}$	$x = 4$
5. $\dfrac{1+x^{-1}}{x^{-1}}$	$x = 2$	6. $x - 4x^{-2}$	$x = 3$
7. $3x^2 - 4x^3$	$x = -2$	8. $5(-x)^3$	$x = 3$
9. $6x^0 - (6x)^0$	$x = 10$	10. $\dfrac{1}{(-x)^{-3}}$	$x = 4$
11. $\sqrt[3]{x^2}$	$x = 27$	12. $\sqrt{x^3}$	$x = \frac{1}{9}$
13. $x^{-1/2}$	$x = 4$	14. $x^{-3/4}$	$x = 16$
15. $x^{-2/5}$	$x = -32$	16. $(x^{2/3})^3$	$x = 10$
17. $500x^{60}$	$x = 1.01$	18. $\dfrac{10{,}000}{x^{120}}$	$x = 1.075$
19. $\sqrt[3]{x}$	$x = -154$	20. $\sqrt[6]{x}$	$x = 325$

In Exercises 21–34, simplify the expression.

21. $5x^4(x^2)$

22. $(8x^4)(2x^3)$

23. $6y^2(2y^4)^2$

24. $z^{-3}(3z^4)$

25. $10(x^2)^2$

26. $(4x^3)^2$

27. $\dfrac{7x^2}{x^{-3}}$

28. $\dfrac{r^4}{r^6}$

29. $\dfrac{12(x+y)^3}{9(x+y)}$

30. $\left(\dfrac{12s^2}{9s}\right)^3$

31. $\dfrac{3x\sqrt{x}}{x^{1/2}}$

32. $\left(\sqrt[3]{x^2}\right)^3$

33. $\left(\dfrac{\sqrt{2}\sqrt{x^3}}{\sqrt{x}}\right)^4$

34. $(2x^2yz^5)^0$

In Exercises 35–40, simplify by removing all possible factors from the radical.

35. (a) $\sqrt{8}$ (b) $\sqrt{18}$

36. (a) $\sqrt[3]{\frac{16}{27}}$ (b) $\sqrt[3]{\frac{24}{125}}$

37. (a) $\sqrt[3]{16x^5}$ (b) $\sqrt[4]{32x^4z^5}$

38. (a) $\sqrt[4]{(3x^2y^3)^4}$ (b) $\sqrt[3]{54x^7}$

39. (a) $\sqrt{75x^2y^{-4}}$ (b) $\sqrt{5(x-y)^3}$

40. (a) $\sqrt[5]{96b^6c^3}$ (b) $\sqrt{72(x+1)^4}$

In Exercises 41–50, find the domain of the given expression.

41. $\sqrt{x-1}$

42. $\sqrt{5-2x}$

43. $\sqrt{x^2+3}$

44. $\sqrt[5]{1-x}$

45. $\dfrac{1}{\sqrt[3]{x-1}}$

46. $\dfrac{1}{\sqrt{x+4}}$

47. $\dfrac{1}{\sqrt[4]{2x-6}}$

48. $\dfrac{\sqrt{x-1}}{x+1}$

49. $\sqrt{x-1}+\sqrt{5-x}$

50. $\dfrac{1}{\sqrt{2x+3}}+\sqrt{6-4x}$

Compound Interest In Exercises 51 and 52, a certificate of deposit has a principal of P and an annual percentage rate of r (expressed as a decimal) compounded n times per year. Use the compound interest formula

$$A = P\left(1+\frac{r}{n}\right)^N$$

to find the balance after N compoundings.

51. $P = \$10{,}000$, $r = 9.5\%$, $n = 12$, $N = 120$

52. $P = \$7000$, $r = 8\%$, $n = 365$, $N = 1000$

53. *Installment Loan* A 5-year auto loan for $P = \$7000$ with an annual percentage rate of $r = 0.14$ requires a monthly payment of $M = \$162.88$. Payments have been made on the loan for 2 years ($N = 24$ monthly payments). Determine the balance B due on the loan if that balance is given by the formula

$$B = \left(1+\frac{r}{12}\right)^N\left(P-\frac{12M}{r}\right)+\frac{12M}{r}.$$

54. *Annuity* A balance A, after n annual payments of P dollars have been made into an annuity earning an annual percentage rate of r compounded annually, is given by

$$A = P(1+r)+P(1+r)^2+\cdots+P(1+r)^n.$$

Rewrite this formula by completing the following factorization: $A = P(1+r)(\quad)$.

Factoring Polynomials

Factorization Techniques ■ *Factoring Polynomials of Degree Three or More* ■ *The Rational Zero Theorem*

Factorization Techniques

The Fundamental Theorem of Algebra states that every nth-degree polynomial

$$a_n x^n + a_{n-1} x^{n-1} + \cdots + a_1 x + a_0$$

has precisely n **zeros.** (The zeros may be repeated or imaginary.) The problem of finding the zeros of a polynomial is equivalent to the problem of factoring the polynomial into linear factors.

Special Products and Factorization Techniques

Quadratic Formula

$$ax^2 + bx + c = 0 \implies x = \frac{-b \pm \sqrt{b^2 - 4ac}}{2a}$$

Example

$$x^2 + 3x - 1 = 0 \implies x = \frac{-3 \pm \sqrt{13}}{2}$$

Special Products

$$x^2 - a^2 = (x - a)(x + a)$$
$$x^3 - a^3 = (x - a)(x^2 + ax + a^2)$$
$$x^3 + a^3 = (x + a)(x^2 - ax + a^2)$$
$$x^4 - a^4 = (x - a)(x + a)(x^2 + a^2)$$

Examples

$$x^2 - 9 = (x - 3)(x + 3)$$
$$x^3 - 8 = (x - 2)(x^2 + 2x + 4)$$
$$x^3 + 64 = (x + 4)(x^2 - 4x + 16)$$
$$x^4 - 16 = (x - 2)(x + 2)(x^2 + 4)$$

Binomial Theorem*

$$(x + a)^2 = x^2 + 2ax + a^2$$
$$(x - a)^2 = x^2 - 2ax + a^2$$
$$(x + a)^3 = x^3 + 3ax^2 + 3a^2x + a^3$$
$$(x - a)^3 = x^3 - 3ax^2 + 3a^2x - a^3$$
$$(x + a)^4 = x^4 + 4ax^3 + 6a^2x^2 + 4a^3x + a^4$$
$$(x - a)^4 = x^4 - 4ax^3 + 6a^2x^2 - 4a^3x + a^4$$

Examples

$$(x + 3)^2 = x^2 + 6x + 9$$
$$(x^2 - 5)^2 = x^4 - 10x^2 + 25$$
$$(x + 2)^3 = x^3 + 6x^2 + 12x + 8$$
$$(x - 1)^3 = x^3 - 3x^2 + 3x - 1$$
$$(x + 2)^4 = x^4 + 8x^3 + 24x^2 + 32x + 16$$
$$(x - 4)^4 = x^4 - 16x^3 + 96x^2 - 256x + 256$$

$$(x + a)^n = x^n + nax^{n-1} + \frac{n(n-1)}{2!} a^2 x^{n-2} + \frac{n(n-1)(n-2)}{3!} a^3 x^{n-3} + \cdots + na^{n-1}x + a^n$$

$$(x - a)^n = x^n - nax^{n-1} + \frac{n(n-1)}{2!} a^2 x^{n-2} - \frac{n(n-1)(n-2)}{3!} a^3 x^{n-3} + \cdots \pm na^{n-1}x \mp a^n$$

Factoring by Grouping

$$acx^3 + adx^2 + bcx + bd = ax^2(cx + d) + b(cx + d)$$
$$= (ax^2 + b)(cx + d)$$

Example

$$3x^3 - 2x^2 - 6x + 4 = x^2(3x - 2) - 2(3x - 2)$$
$$= (x^2 - 2)(3x - 2)$$

*The *factorial* symbol ! is defined as follows $0! = 1$, $1! = 1$, $2! = 2 \cdot 1 = 2$, $3! = 3 \cdot 2 \cdot 1 = 6$, $4! = 4 \cdot 3 \cdot 2 \cdot 1 = 24$, and so on.

EXAMPLE 1 *Applying the Quadratic Formula*

Use the Quadratic Formula to find all real zeros of the following polynomials.

a. $4x^2 + 6x + 1$ **b.** $x^2 + 6x + 9$ **c.** $2x^2 - 6x + 5$

Solution

a. Using $a = 4$, $b = 6$, and $c = 1$, you can write

$$x = \frac{-b \pm \sqrt{b^2 - 4ac}}{2a}$$

$$= \frac{-6 \pm \sqrt{36 - 16}}{8}$$

$$= \frac{-6 \pm \sqrt{20}}{8}$$

$$= \frac{-6 \pm 2\sqrt{5}}{8}$$

$$= \frac{2\left(-3 \pm \sqrt{5}\right)}{2(4)}$$

$$= \frac{-3 \pm \sqrt{5}}{4}.$$

Thus, there are two real zeros:

$$x = \frac{-3 - \sqrt{5}}{4} \approx -1.309 \quad \text{and} \quad x = \frac{-3 + \sqrt{5}}{4} \approx -0.191.$$

b. In this case, $a = 1$, $b = 6$, and $c = 9$, and the Quadratic Formula yields

$$x = \frac{-b \pm \sqrt{b^2 - 4ac}}{2a} = \frac{-6 \pm \sqrt{36 - 36}}{2} = -\frac{6}{2} = -3.$$

Thus, there is one (repeated) real zero: $x = -3$.

c. For this quadratic equation, $a = 2$, $b = -6$, and $c = 5$. Thus,

$$x = \frac{-b \pm \sqrt{b^2 - 4ac}}{2a} = \frac{6 \pm \sqrt{36 - 40}}{4} = \frac{6 \pm \sqrt{-4}}{4}.$$

Because $\sqrt{-4}$ is imaginary, there are no real zeros.

In Example 1, the zeros in part a are irrational, and the zeros in part c are imaginary. In both of these cases the quadratic is said to be **irreducible** because it cannot be factored into linear factors with rational coefficients. The next example shows how to find the zeros associated with *reducible* quadratics. In this example, factoring is used to find the zeros of each quadratic. Try using the Quadratic Formula to obtain the same zeros.

EXAMPLE 2 *Factoring Quadratics*

Find the zeros of the following quadratic polynomials.

a. $x^2 - 5x + 6$ **b.** $x^2 - 5x - 6$ **c.** $2x^2 + 5x - 3$

Solution

a. Because

$$x^2 - 5x + 6 = (x - 2)(x - 3),$$

the zeros are $x = 2$ and $x = 3$.

b. Because

$$x^2 - 5x - 6 = (x + 1)(x - 6),$$

the zeros are $x = -1$ and $x = 6$.

c. Because

$$2x^2 + 5x - 3 = (2x - 1)(x + 3),$$

the zeros are $x = \frac{1}{2}$ and $x = -3$.

EXAMPLE 3 *Finding the Domain of a Radical Expression*

Find the domain of $\sqrt{x^2 - 3x + 2}$.

Solution

Because

$$x^2 - 3x + 2 = (x - 1)(x - 2),$$

you know that the zeros of the quadratic are $x = 1$ and $x = 2$. Thus, you need to test the sign of the quadratic in the three intervals $(-\infty, 1)$, $(1, 2)$, and $(2, \infty)$, as shown in Figure 0.15. After testing each of these intervals, you can see that the quadratic is negative in the center interval and positive in the outer two intervals. Moreover, because the quadratic is zero when $x = 1$ and $x = 2$, you can conclude that the domain of $\sqrt{x^2 - 3x + 2}$ is

$$(-\infty, 1] \cup [2, \infty). \qquad \text{\textit{Domain}}$$

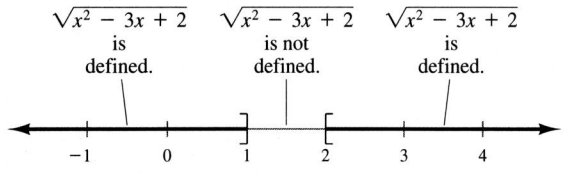

FIGURE 0.15

Factoring Polynomials of Degree Three or More

It can be difficult to find the zeros of polynomials of degree three or more. However, if one of the zeros of a polynomial is known, then you can use that zero to reduce the degree of the polynomial. For example, if you know that $x = 2$ is a zero of $x^3 - 4x^2 + 5x - 2$, then you know that $(x - 2)$ is a factor, and you can use long division to factor the polynomial as follows.

$$x^3 - 4x^2 + 5x - 2 = (x - 2)(x^2 - 2x + 1)$$
$$= (x - 2)(x - 1)(x - 1)$$

As an alternative to long division, many people prefer to use **synthetic division** to reduce the degree of a polynomial.

Synthetic Division for a Cubic Polynomial

Given: $x = x_1$ is a zero of $ax^3 + bx^2 + cx + d$.

Vertical pattern:
Add terms.

Diagonal pattern:
Multiply by x_1.

Coefficients for
quadratic factor

For example, performing synthetic division on the polynomial $x^3 - 4x^2 + 5x - 2$ using the given zero, $x = 2$, produces the following.

$$
\begin{array}{r|rrrr}
2 & 1 & -4 & 5 & -2 \\
  &   & 2 & -4 & 2 \\
\hline
  & 1 & -2 & 1 & 0
\end{array}
$$

$(x - 2)(x^2 - 2x + 1) = x^3 - 4x^2 + 5x - 2$

When you use synthetic division, remember to take *all* coefficients into account—*even if some of them are zero.* For instance, if you know that $x = -2$ is a zero of $x^3 + 3x + 14$, you can apply synthetic division as follows.

$$
\begin{array}{r|rrrr}
-2 & 1 & 0 & 3 & 14 \\
   &   & -2 & 4 & -14 \\
\hline
   & 1 & -2 & 7 & 0
\end{array}
$$

$(x + 2)(x^2 - 2x + 7) = x^3 + 3x + 14$

The Rational Zero Theorem

There is a systematic way to find the *rational* zeros of a polynomial. You can use the **Rational Zero Theorem** (also called the Rational Root Theorem).

Rational Zero Theorem

If a polynomial

$$a_n x^n + a_{n-1} x^{n-1} + \cdots + a_1 x + a_0$$

has integer coefficients, then every *rational* zero is of the form $x = p/q$, where p is a factor of a_0, and q is a factor of a_n.

EXAMPLE 4 *Using the Rational Zero Theorem*

Find all real zeros of $2x^3 + 3x^2 - 8x + 3$.

Solution

$$2x^3 + 3x^2 - 8x + 3$$

Factors of constant term: $\pm 1, \pm 3$

Factors of leading coefficient: $\pm 1, \pm 2$

The possible rational zeros are the factors of the constant term divided by the factors of the leading coefficient.

$$1, \ -1, \ 3, \ -3, \ \frac{1}{2}, \ -\frac{1}{2}, \ \frac{3}{2}, \ -\frac{3}{2}$$

By testing these possible zeros, you can see that $x = 1$ works.

$$2(1)^3 + 3(1)^2 - 8(1) + 3 = 2 + 3 - 8 + 3 = 0$$

Now, by synthetic division you have the following.

$$
\begin{array}{r|rrrr}
1 & 2 & 3 & -8 & 3 \\
  &   & 2 & 5 & -3 \\
\hline
  & 2 & 5 & -3 & 0
\end{array}
$$

$$(x - 1)(2x^2 + 5x - 3) = 2x^3 + 3x^2 - 8x + 3$$

Finally, by factoring the quadratic, $2x^2 + 5x - 3 = (2x - 1)(x + 3)$, you have

$$2x^3 + 3x^2 - 8x + 3 = (x - 1)(2x - 1)(x + 3)$$

and you can conclude that the zeros are $x = 1$, $x = \frac{1}{2}$, and $x = -3$. ■

E X E R C I S E S   0.4 means that technology can help you solve or check the exercise(s).

In Exercises 1–6, use the Quadratic Formula to find all real zeros of the second-degree polynomial.

1. $6x^2 - x - 1$ **2.** $8x^2 - 2x - 1$

3. $4x^2 - 12x + 9$ **4.** $9x^2 + 12x + 4$

5. $y^2 + 4y + 1$ **6.** $x^2 + 6x - 1$

In Exercises 7–16, write the second-degree polynomial as the product of two linear factors.

7. $x^2 - 4x + 4$ **8.** $x^2 + 10x + 25$

9. $4x^2 + 4x + 1$ **10.** $9x^2 - 12x + 4$

11. $x^2 + x - 2$ **12.** $2x^2 - x - 1$

13. $3x^2 - 5x + 2$ **14.** $x^2 - xy - 2y^2$

15. $x^2 - 4xy + 4y^2$ **16.** $a^2b^2 - 2abc + c^2$

In Exercises 17–30, completely factor the polynomial.

17. $81 - y^4$ **18.** $x^4 - 16$

19. $x^3 - 8$ **20.** $y^3 - 64$

21. $y^3 + 64$ **22.** $z^3 + 125$

23. $x^3 - 27$ **24.** $(x - a)^3 + b^3$

25. $x^3 - 4x^2 - x + 4$ **26.** $x^3 - x^2 - x + 1$

27. $2x^3 - 3x^2 + 4x - 6$ **28.** $x^3 - 5x^2 - 5x + 25$

29. $2x^3 - 4x^2 - x + 2$ **30.** $x^3 - 7x^2 - 4x + 28$

In Exercises 31–48, find all real solutions of the equation.

31. $x^2 - 5x = 0$ **32.** $2x^2 - 3x = 0$

33. $x^2 - 9 = 0$ **34.** $x^2 - 25 = 0$

35. $x^2 - 3 = 0$ **36.** $x^2 - 8 = 0$

37. $(x - 3)^2 - 9 = 0$ **38.** $(x + 1)^2 - 8 = 0$

39. $x^2 + x - 2 = 0$ **40.** $x^2 + 5x + 6 = 0$

41. $x^2 - 5x + 6 = 0$ **42.** $x^2 + x - 20 = 0$

43. $x^3 + 64 = 0$ **44.** $x^3 - 216 = 0$

45. $x^4 - 16 = 0$ **46.** $x^4 - 625 = 0$

47. $x^3 - x^2 - 4x + 4 = 0$ **48.** $2x^3 + x^2 + 6x + 3 = 0$

In Exercises 49–52, find the interval (or intervals) on which the given expression is defined.

49. $\sqrt{x^2 - 7x + 12}$ **50.** $\sqrt{x^2 - 4}$

51. $\sqrt{4 - x^2}$ **52.** $\sqrt{144 - 9x^2}$

In Exercises 53–56, use synthetic division to complete the indicated factorization.

53. $x^3 + 8 = (x + 2)(\quad)$

54. $x^3 - 2x^2 - x + 2 = (x + 1)(\quad)$

55. $2x^3 - x^2 - 2x + 1 = (x - 1)(\quad)$

56. $x^4 - 16x^3 + 96x^2 - 256x + 256 = (x - 4)(\quad)$

In Exercises 57–64, use the Rational Zero Theorem as an aid in finding all real solutions of the given equation.

57. $x^3 - x^2 - x + 1 = 0$

58. $x^3 - x^2 - 4x + 4 = 0$

59. $x^3 - 6x^2 + 11x - 6 = 0$

60. $x^3 + 2x^2 - 5x - 6 = 0$

61. $4x^3 - 4x^2 - x + 1 = 0$

62. $18x^3 - 9x^2 - 8x + 4 = 0$

63. $x^3 - 3x^2 - 3x - 4 = 0$

64. $4x^3 - 6x^2 + 2x + 3 = 0$

65. *Average Cost* The minimum average cost of producing x units of a certain product occurs when the production level is set at the (positive) solution of

$$0.0003x^2 - 1200 = 0.$$

Determine this production level.

66. *Profit* The profit P from sales is given by

$$P = -200x^2 + 2000x - 3800,$$

where x is the number of units sold per day (in hundreds). Determine the interval for x so that the profit will be greater than 1000.

0.5 Fractions and Rationalization

Operations with Fractions ■ *Expressions Involving Radicals* ■
Rationalization Techniques

Operations with Fractions

In the final section of this chapter we review operations involving fractional expressions such as

$$\frac{2}{x}, \quad \frac{x^2 + 2x - 4}{x + 6}, \quad \text{and} \quad \frac{1}{\sqrt{x^2 + 1}}.$$

The first two expressions have polynomials as both numerator and denominator and are called **rational expressions.** A rational expression is **proper** if the degree of the numerator is less than the degree of the denominator. For example, $x/(x^2 + 1)$ is proper. If the degree of the numerator is greater than or equal to the degree of the denominator, then the rational expression is improper. For example, $x^2/(x^2 + 1)$ is improper.

Operations with Fractions

---

1. Add fractions (find a common denominator):

$$\frac{a}{b} + \frac{c}{d} = \frac{a}{b}\left(\frac{d}{d}\right) + \frac{c}{d}\left(\frac{b}{b}\right) = \frac{ad}{bd} + \frac{bc}{bd} = \frac{ad + bc}{bd}$$

2. Subtract fractions (find a common denominator):

$$\frac{a}{b} - \frac{c}{d} = \frac{a}{b}\left(\frac{d}{d}\right) - \frac{c}{d}\left(\frac{b}{b}\right) = \frac{ad}{bd} - \frac{bc}{bd} = \frac{ad - bc}{bd}$$

3. Multiply fractions:

$$\left(\frac{a}{b}\right)\left(\frac{c}{d}\right) = \frac{ac}{bd}$$

4. Divide fractions (invert and multiply):

$$\frac{a/b}{c/d} = \left(\frac{a}{b}\right)\left(\frac{d}{c}\right) = \frac{ad}{bc}, \qquad \frac{a/b}{c} = \frac{a/b}{c/1} = \left(\frac{a}{b}\right)\left(\frac{1}{c}\right) = \frac{a}{bc}$$

5. Cancel:

$$\frac{\cancel{a}b}{\cancel{a}c} = \frac{b}{c}, \qquad \frac{ab + ac}{ad} = \frac{\cancel{a}(b + c)}{\cancel{a}d} = \frac{b + c}{d}$$

EXAMPLE 1 *Adding and Subtracting Rational Expressions*

Perform the indicated operations and simplify.

a. $x + \dfrac{1}{x}$ **b.** $\dfrac{1}{x+1} - \dfrac{2}{2x-1}$

Solution

a. $x + \dfrac{1}{x} = \dfrac{x^2}{x} + \dfrac{1}{x}$

$\qquad = \dfrac{x^2+1}{x}$

b. $\dfrac{1}{x+1} - \dfrac{2}{2x-1} = \dfrac{(2x-1)}{(x+1)(2x-1)} - \dfrac{2(x+1)}{(x+1)(2x-1)}$

$\qquad\qquad\qquad\quad = \dfrac{2x - 1 - 2x - 2}{2x^2 + x - 1}$

$\qquad\qquad\qquad\quad = \dfrac{-3}{2x^2 + x - 1}$

In adding (or subtracting) fractions whose denominators have no common factors, it is convenient to use the following pattern.

$$\frac{a}{b} + \frac{c}{d} = \frac{a \quad c}{b \quad d} = \frac{ad+bc}{bd}$$

For instance, in part b of Example 1, you could have used this pattern as follows.

$$\frac{1}{x+1} - \frac{2}{2x-1} = \frac{(2x-1) - 2(x+1)}{(x+1)(2x-1)}$$

$$= \frac{2x - 1 - 2x - 2}{(x+1)(2x-1)}$$

$$= \frac{-3}{2x^2 + x - 1}$$

In Example 1, the denominators of the rational expressions have no common factors. When the denominators do have common factors, it is best to find the least common denominator before adding or subtracting. For instance, when adding $1/x$ and $2/x^2$, you can recognize that the least common denominator is x^2 and write

$$\frac{1}{x} + \frac{2}{x^2} = \frac{x}{x^2} + \frac{2}{x^2}$$

$$= \frac{x+2}{x^2}.$$

This is further demonstrated in Example 2.

EXAMPLE 2 *Adding and Subtracting Rational Expressions*

Perform the indicated operations and simplify.

a. $\dfrac{x}{x^2 - 1} + \dfrac{3}{x + 1}$ **b.** $\dfrac{1}{2(x^2 + 2x)} - \dfrac{1}{4x}$

Solution

a. Because $x^2 - 1 = (x + 1)(x - 1)$, the least common denominator is $x^2 - 1$.

$$\frac{x}{x^2 - 1} + \frac{3}{x + 1} = \frac{x}{(x - 1)(x + 1)} + \frac{3}{x + 1}$$

$$= \frac{x}{(x - 1)(x + 1)} + \frac{3(x - 1)}{(x - 1)(x + 1)}$$

$$= \frac{x + 3x - 3}{(x - 1)(x + 1)}$$

$$= \frac{4x - 3}{x^2 - 1}$$

b. In this case, the least common denominator is $4x(x + 2)$.

$$\frac{1}{2(x^2 + 2x)} - \frac{1}{4x} = \frac{1}{2x(x + 2)} - \frac{1}{2(2x)}$$

$$= \frac{2}{2(2x)(x + 2)} - \frac{x + 2}{2(2x)(x + 2)}$$

$$= \frac{2 - x - 2}{4x(x + 2)}$$

$$= \frac{-\cancel{x}}{4\cancel{x}(x + 2)} \qquad \text{Cancel } x.$$

$$= \frac{-1}{4(x + 2)}$$

    To add more than two fractions you must find a denominator that is common to all the fractions. For instance, to add $\frac{1}{2}$, $\frac{1}{3}$, and $\frac{1}{5}$, use a (least) common denominator of 30 and write

$$\frac{1}{2} + \frac{1}{3} + \frac{1}{5} = \frac{15}{30} + \frac{10}{30} + \frac{6}{30}$$

$$= \frac{31}{30}.$$

To add more than two rational expressions, use a similar procedure, as demonstrated in Example 3. (Expressions such as those shown in this example are used in calculus to perform an integration technique called integration by partial fractions.)

EXAMPLE 3 *Adding More Than Two Rational Expressions*

Perform the indicated addition of rational expressions.

a. $\dfrac{A}{x+2} + \dfrac{B}{x-3} + \dfrac{C}{x+4}$

b. $\dfrac{A}{x+2} + \dfrac{B}{(x+2)^2} + \dfrac{C}{x-1}$

Solution

a. The least common denominator is $(x+2)(x-3)(x+4)$.

$$\frac{A}{x+2} + \frac{B}{x-3} + \frac{C}{x+4}$$

$$= \frac{A(x-3)(x+4) + B(x+2)(x+4) + C(x+2)(x-3)}{(x+2)(x-3)(x+4)}$$

$$= \frac{A(x^2+x-12) + B(x^2+6x+8) + C(x^2-x-6)}{(x+2)(x-3)(x+4)}$$

$$= \frac{Ax^2 + Bx^2 + Cx^2 + Ax + 6Bx - Cx - 12A + 8B - 6C}{(x+2)(x-3)(x+4)}$$

$$= \frac{(A+B+C)x^2 + (A+6B-C)x + (-12A+8B-6C)}{(x+2)(x-3)(x+4)}$$

b. Here the least common denominator is $(x+2)^2(x-1)$.

$$\frac{A}{x+2} + \frac{B}{(x+2)^2} + \frac{C}{x-1}$$

$$= \frac{A(x+2)(x-1) + B(x-1) + C(x+2)^2}{(x+2)^2(x-1)}$$

$$= \frac{A(x^2+x-2) + B(x-1) + C(x^2+4x+4)}{(x+2)^2(x-1)}$$

$$= \frac{Ax^2 + Cx^2 + Ax + Bx + 4Cx - 2A - B + 4C}{(x+2)^2(x-1)}$$

$$= \frac{(A+C)x^2 + (A+B+4C)x + (-2A-B+4C)}{(x+2)^2(x-1)}$$

Expressions Involving Radicals

In calculus, the operation of differentiation tends to produce "messy" expressions when applied to fractional expressions. This is especially true when the fractional expression involves radicals. When differentiation is used, it is important to be able to simplify these expressions so that you can obtain more manageable forms. All of the expressions in Examples 4 and 5 are the results of differentiation. In each case, note how much *simpler* the simplified form is than the original form.

EXAMPLE 4 *Simplifying an Expression with Radicals*

Simplify the following expressions.

a. $\dfrac{\sqrt{x+1} - \dfrac{x}{2\sqrt{x+1}}}{x+1}$

b. $\left(\dfrac{1}{x + \sqrt{x^2+1}}\right)\left(1 + \dfrac{2x}{2\sqrt{x^2+1}}\right)$

Solution

a.
$$\dfrac{\sqrt{x+1} - \dfrac{x}{2\sqrt{x+1}}}{x+1} = \dfrac{\dfrac{2(x+1)}{2\sqrt{x+1}} - \dfrac{x}{2\sqrt{x+1}}}{x+1}$$

$$= \dfrac{\dfrac{2x+2-x}{2\sqrt{x+1}}}{x+1}$$

$$= \dfrac{x+2}{2\sqrt{x+1}}\left(\dfrac{1}{x+1}\right)$$

$$= \dfrac{x+2}{2(x+1)^{3/2}}$$

b.
$$\left(\dfrac{1}{x + \sqrt{x^2+1}}\right)\left(1 + \dfrac{2x}{2\sqrt{x^2+1}}\right)$$

$$= \left(\dfrac{1}{x + \sqrt{x^2+1}}\right)\left(1 + \dfrac{x}{\sqrt{x^2+1}}\right)$$

$$= \left(\dfrac{1}{x + \sqrt{x^2+1}}\right)\left(\dfrac{\sqrt{x^2+1}}{\sqrt{x^2+1}} + \dfrac{x}{\sqrt{x^2+1}}\right)$$

$$= \left(\dfrac{1}{x + \sqrt{x^2+1}}\right)\left(\dfrac{x + \sqrt{x^2+1}}{\sqrt{x^2+1}}\right)$$

$$= \dfrac{1}{\sqrt{x^2+1}}$$

EXAMPLE 5 *Simplifying an Expression with Radicals*

Simplify the following expression.

$$\frac{-x\left(\dfrac{2x}{2\sqrt{x^2+1}}\right)+\sqrt{x^2+1}}{x^2}+\left(\frac{1}{x+\sqrt{x^2+1}}\right)\left(1+\frac{2x}{2\sqrt{x^2+1}}\right)$$

Solution

From part b of Example 4, you already know that the second part of this sum simplifies to $1/\sqrt{x^2+1}$. The first part simplifies as follows.

$$\frac{-x\left(\dfrac{2x}{2\sqrt{x^2+1}}\right)+\sqrt{x^2+1}}{x^2}=\frac{-x^2}{x^2\sqrt{x^2+1}}+\frac{\sqrt{x^2+1}}{x^2}$$

$$=\frac{-x^2}{x^2\sqrt{x^2+1}}+\frac{x^2+1}{x^2\sqrt{x^2+1}}$$

$$=\frac{-x^2+x^2+1}{x^2\sqrt{x^2+1}}$$

$$=\frac{1}{x^2\sqrt{x^2+1}}$$

Therefore, the sum is

$$\frac{-x\left(\dfrac{2x}{2\sqrt{x^2+1}}\right)+\sqrt{x^2+1}}{x^2}+\left(\frac{1}{x+\sqrt{x^2+1}}\right)\left(1+\frac{2x}{2\sqrt{x^2+1}}\right)$$

$$=\frac{1}{x^2\sqrt{x^2+1}}+\frac{1}{\sqrt{x^2+1}}$$

$$=\frac{1}{x^2\sqrt{x^2+1}}+\frac{x^2}{x^2\sqrt{x^2+1}}$$

$$=\frac{x^2+1}{x^2\sqrt{x^2+1}}$$

$$=\frac{\sqrt{x^2+1}}{x^2}.$$

Note To check that the simplified expression in Example 5 is equivalent to the original expression, try substituting values of x into each expression. For instance, when you substitute $x=1$ into each expression, you obtain $\sqrt{2}$.

Rationalization Techniques

In working with quotients involving radicals, it is often convenient to move the radical expression from the denominator to the numerator, or vice versa. For example, we can move $\sqrt{2}$ from the denominator to the numerator in the following quotient by multiplying by $\sqrt{2}/\sqrt{2}$.

Radical in Denominator	*Rationalize*	*Radical in Numerator*
$\dfrac{1}{\sqrt{2}}$	$\longrightarrow \quad \dfrac{1}{\sqrt{2}}\left(\dfrac{\sqrt{2}}{\sqrt{2}}\right) \longrightarrow$	$\dfrac{\sqrt{2}}{2}$

This process is called **rationalizing the denominator.** A similar process is used to **rationalize the numerator.**

Note The success of the second and third rationalizing techniques stems from the following.

$$\left(\sqrt{a} - \sqrt{b}\right)\left(\sqrt{a} + \sqrt{b}\right) = a - b$$

Rationalizing Techniques

1. If the denominator is $\sqrt{a}$, multiply by $\dfrac{\sqrt{a}}{\sqrt{a}}$.

2. If the denominator is $\sqrt{a} - \sqrt{b}$, multiply by $\dfrac{\sqrt{a} + \sqrt{b}}{\sqrt{a} + \sqrt{b}}$.

3. If the denominator is $\sqrt{a} + \sqrt{b}$, multiply by $\dfrac{\sqrt{a} - \sqrt{b}}{\sqrt{a} - \sqrt{b}}$.

The same guidelines apply to rationalizing numerators.

EXAMPLE 6 *Rationalizing Denominators and Numerators*

a. $\dfrac{3}{\sqrt{12}} = \dfrac{3}{2\sqrt{3}} = \dfrac{3}{2\sqrt{3}}\left(\dfrac{\sqrt{3}}{\sqrt{3}}\right) = \dfrac{3\sqrt{3}}{2(3)} = \dfrac{\sqrt{3}}{2}$

b. $\dfrac{\sqrt{x+1}}{2} = \dfrac{\sqrt{x+1}}{2}\left(\dfrac{\sqrt{x+1}}{\sqrt{x+1}}\right) = \dfrac{x+1}{2\sqrt{x+1}}$

c. $\dfrac{1}{\sqrt{5}+\sqrt{2}} = \dfrac{1}{\sqrt{5}+\sqrt{2}}\left(\dfrac{\sqrt{5}-\sqrt{2}}{\sqrt{5}-\sqrt{2}}\right) = \dfrac{\sqrt{5}-\sqrt{2}}{5-2} = \dfrac{\sqrt{5}-\sqrt{2}}{3}$

d. $\dfrac{1}{\sqrt{x}-\sqrt{x+1}} = \dfrac{1}{\sqrt{x}-\sqrt{x+1}}\left(\dfrac{\sqrt{x}+\sqrt{x+1}}{\sqrt{x}+\sqrt{x+1}}\right)$

$\qquad\qquad = \dfrac{\sqrt{x}+\sqrt{x+1}}{x-(x+1)} = -\sqrt{x}-\sqrt{x+1}$

E X E R C I S E S 0.5

In Exercises 1–28, perform the indicated operations and simplify your answer.

1. $\dfrac{5}{x-1} + \dfrac{x}{x-1}$

2. $\dfrac{2x-1}{x+3} + \dfrac{1-x}{x+3}$

3. $\dfrac{2x}{x^2+2} - \dfrac{1-3x}{x^2+2}$

4. $\dfrac{5x+10}{2x-1} - \dfrac{2x+10}{2x-1}$

5. $\dfrac{4}{x} - \dfrac{3}{x^2}$

6. $\dfrac{5}{x-1} + \dfrac{3}{x}$

7. $\dfrac{2}{x+2} - \dfrac{1}{x-2}$

8. $\dfrac{x}{x^2+x-2} - \dfrac{1}{x+2}$

9. $\dfrac{5}{x-3} + \dfrac{3}{3-x}$

10. $\dfrac{x}{2-x} + \dfrac{2}{x-2}$

11. $\dfrac{A}{x-6} + \dfrac{B}{x+3}$

12. $\dfrac{Ax+B}{x^2+2} + \dfrac{C}{x-4}$

13. $-\dfrac{1}{x} + \dfrac{2}{x^2+1}$

14. $\dfrac{2}{x+1} + \dfrac{1-x}{x^2-2x+3}$

15. $\dfrac{-x}{(x+1)^{3/2}} + \dfrac{2}{(x+1)^{1/2}}$

16. $2\sqrt{x}(x-2) + \dfrac{(x-2)^2}{2\sqrt{x}}$

17. $\dfrac{2-t}{2\sqrt{1+t}} - \sqrt{1+t}$

18. $-\dfrac{\sqrt{x^2+1}}{x^2} + \dfrac{1}{\sqrt{x^2+1}}$

19. $\dfrac{1}{x^2-x-2} - \dfrac{x}{x^2-5x+6}$

20. $\dfrac{x-1}{x^2+5x+4} + \dfrac{2}{x^2-x-2} + \dfrac{10}{x^2+2x-8}$

21. $\dfrac{A}{x+1} + \dfrac{B}{(x+1)^2} + \dfrac{C}{x-2}$

22. $\dfrac{A}{x-5} + \dfrac{B}{x+5} + \dfrac{C}{(x+5)^2}$

23. $\left(2x\sqrt{x^2+1} - \dfrac{x^3}{\sqrt{x^2+1}}\right) \div (x^2+1)$

24. $\left(\sqrt{x^3+1} - \dfrac{3x^3}{2\sqrt{x^3+1}}\right) \div (x^3+1)$

25. $\dfrac{(x^2+2)^{1/2} - x^2(x^2+2)^{-1/2}}{x^2}$

26. $\dfrac{x(x+1)^{-1/2} - (x+1)^{1/2}}{x^2}$

27. $\dfrac{\dfrac{\sqrt{x+1}}{\sqrt{x}} - \dfrac{\sqrt{x}}{\sqrt{x+1}}}{2(x+1)}$

28. $\dfrac{\dfrac{2x^2}{3(x^2-1)^{2/3}} - (x^2-1)^{1/3}}{x^2}$

In Exercises 29–48, rationalize the numerator or denominator and simplify.

29. $\dfrac{3}{\sqrt{27}}$

30. $\dfrac{5}{\sqrt{10}}$

31. $\dfrac{\sqrt{2}}{3}$

32. $\dfrac{\sqrt{26}}{2}$

33. $\dfrac{x}{\sqrt{x-4}}$

34. $\dfrac{4y}{\sqrt{y+8}}$

35. $\dfrac{\sqrt{y^3}}{6y}$

36. $\dfrac{x\sqrt{x^2+4}}{3}$

37. $\dfrac{49(x-3)}{\sqrt{x^2-9}}$

38. $\dfrac{10(x+2)}{\sqrt{x^2-x-6}}$

39. $\dfrac{5}{\sqrt{14}-2}$

40. $\dfrac{13}{6+\sqrt{10}}$

41. $\dfrac{2x}{5-\sqrt{3}}$

42. $\dfrac{x}{\sqrt{2}+\sqrt{3}}$

43. $\dfrac{1}{\sqrt{6}+\sqrt{5}}$

44. $\dfrac{\sqrt{15}+3}{12}$

45. $\dfrac{\sqrt{3}-\sqrt{2}}{x}$

46. $\dfrac{x-1}{\sqrt{x}+x}$

47. $\dfrac{2x-\sqrt{4x-1}}{2x-1}$

48. $\dfrac{10}{\sqrt{x}+\sqrt{x+5}}$

49. *Installment Loan* Determine the monthly payment M for an installment loan of $P = \$10{,}000$ at an annual percentage rate of 14% ($r = 0.14$) for 5 years ($N = 60$ monthly payments) given the formula

$$M = P\left[\dfrac{r/12}{1 - \left(\dfrac{1}{(r/12)+1}\right)^N}\right].$$

50. *Inventory* A retailer has determined that the cost C of ordering and storing x units of a product is

$$C = 6x + \dfrac{900{,}000}{x}.$$

(a) Write the expression for cost as a single fraction.
(b) Determine the cost for ordering and storing $x = 240$ units of this product.

$$\lim_{x \to c} f(x) = f(c)$$

1

Functions, Graphs, and Limits

When René Descartes developed the coordinate plane in the early 1600s, he revolutionized the way people thought about mathematics. Before Descartes' time, algebra and geometry were separate branches of mathematics, with little overlap. By coordinatizing geometry, Descartes allowed mathematicians to solve problems algebraically *and* graphically. In this chapter, you will review the basic concepts of Descartes' analytic geometry.

In the 1980s, the introduction of hand-held, affordable, graphing utilities brought about another revolution in the way people study mathematics. With this new technology, you can find and analyze mathematical models much more simply than was possible before.

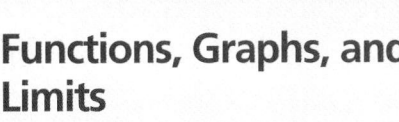

$$y = f(x)$$

Descartes

1.1 The Cartesian Plane and the Distance Formula

The Cartesian Plane ■ *The Distance Formula* ■ *The Midpoint Formula* ■ *Extended Application: Computer Graphics*

FIGURE 1.1   The Cartesian Plane

FIGURE 1.2

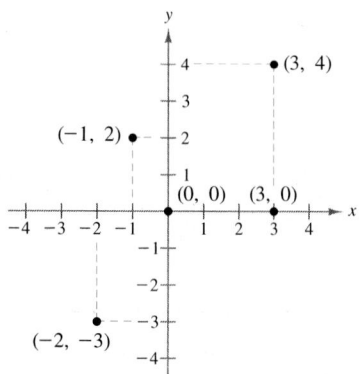

FIGURE 1.3

The Cartesian Plane

Just as you can represent real numbers by points on a real number line, you can represent ordered pairs of real numbers by points in a plane called the **rectangular coordinate system,** or the **Cartesian plane,** after the French mathematician René Descartes (1596–1650).

The Cartesian plane is formed by using two real lines intersecting at right angles, as shown in Figure 1.1. The horizontal real line is usually called the **x-axis,** and the vertical real line is usually called the **y-axis.** The point of intersection of these two axes is the **origin,** and the two axes divide the plane into four parts called **quadrants.**

Each point in the plane corresponds to an **ordered pair** (x, y) of real numbers x and y, called **coordinates** of the point. The **x-coordinate** represents the directed distance from the y-axis to the point, and the **y-coordinate** represents the directed distance from the x-axis to the point, as shown in Figure 1.2.

$$(x, y)$$

Directed distance from y-axis   Directed distance from x-axis

Note   The notation (x, y) denotes both a point in the plane and an open interval on the real line. The context will tell you which meaning is intended.

EXAMPLE 1   *Plotting Points in the Cartesian Plane*

Plot the points $(-1, 2)$, $(3, 4)$, $(0, 0)$, $(3, 0)$, and $(-2, -3)$.

Solution
To plot the point

$$(-1, 2),$$

x-coordinate   *y*-coordinate

imagine a vertical line through -1 on the x-axis and a horizontal line through 2 on the y-axis. The intersection of these two lines is the point $(-1, 2)$. The other four points can be plotted in a similar way, and are shown in Figure 1.3.

The beauty of a rectangular coordinate system is that it allows you to visualize relationships between two variables. It would be difficult to overestimate the importance of Descartes's introduction of coordinates to the plane. Today, his ideas are in common use in virtually every scientific and business-related field. In Example 2, notice how much your intuition is enhanced by the use of a graphical presentation.

Real Life

EXAMPLE 2 *Sketching a Scatter Plot*

From 1981 through 1990, the amount A (in millions of dollars) spent on water skis in the United States is given in Table 1.1, where t represents the year. Sketch a scatter plot of the data. *(Source: National Sporting Goods Association)*

TABLE 1.1

t	1981	1982	1983	1984	1985	1986	1987	1988	1989	1990
A	123	106	133	146	125	132	148	160	96	96

Solution

To sketch a *scatter plot* of the data given in the table, you simply represent each pair of values by an ordered pair (t, A), and plot the resulting points, as shown in Figure 1.4. For instance, the first pair of values is represented by the ordered pair $(1981, 123)$. Note that the break in the t-axis indicates that the numbers between 0 and 1981 have been omitted.

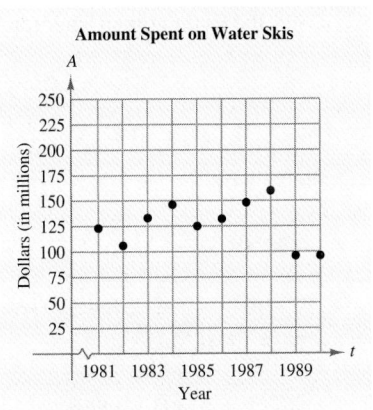

Amount Spent on Water Skis

FIGURE 1.4

TECHNOLOGY

The scatter plot in Example 2 is only one way to graphically represent the given data. Two other techniques are shown at right. The first is a *bar graph* and the second is a *line graph*. All three graphical representations were created with a computer. If you have access to computer graphing software, try using it to graphically represent the data given in Example 2.

Bar graph

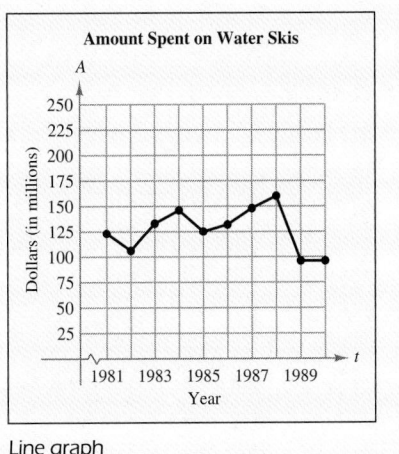

Line graph

Note   In Example 2, you could have let $t = 1$ represent the year 1981. In that case, the horizontal axis would not have been broken, and the tick marks would have been labeled 1 through 10 (instead of 1981 through 1990).

The Distance Formula

Recall from the Pythagorean Theorem that, for a right triangle with hypotenuse of length c and sides of lengths a and b, you have

$$a^2 + b^2 = c^2, \qquad \textit{Pythagorean Theorem}$$

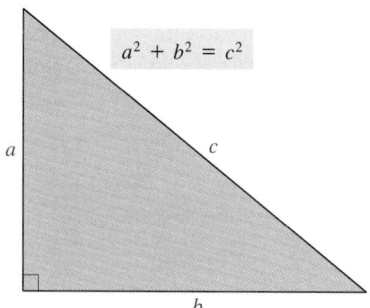

FIGURE 1.5   Pythagorean Theorem

as shown in Figure 1.5. (The converse is also true. That is, if $a^2 + b^2 = c^2$, then the triangle is a right triangle.)

Suppose you want to determine the distance d between two points (x_1, y_1) and (x_2, y_2) in the plane. With these two points, a right triangle can be formed, as shown in Figure 1.6. The length of the vertical side of the triangle is $|y_2 - y_1|$, and the length of the horizontal side is $|x_2 - x_1|$. By the Pythagorean Theorem, you can write

$$d^2 = |x_2 - x_1|^2 + |y_2 - y_1|^2$$
$$d = \sqrt{|x_2 - x_1|^2 + |y_2 - y_1|^2}$$
$$d = \sqrt{(x_2 - x_1)^2 + (y_2 - y_1)^2}.$$

This result is the **Distance Formula.**

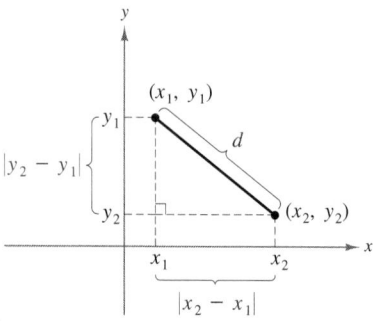

FIGURE 1.6   Distance Between Two Points

The Distance Formula

The distance d between the points (x_1, y_1) and (x_2, y_2) in the plane is

$$d = \sqrt{(x_2 - x_1)^2 + (y_2 - y_1)^2}.$$

EXAMPLE 3   *Finding a Distance*

Find the distance between the points $(-2, 1)$ and $(3, 4)$.

Solution

Let $(x_1, y_1) = (-2, 1)$ and $(x_2, y_2) = (3, 4)$. Then apply the Distance Formula as follows.

$$d = \sqrt{(x_2 - x_1)^2 + (y_2 - y_1)^2} \qquad \textit{Distance Formula}$$
$$= \sqrt{[3 - (-2)]^2 + (4 - 1)^2} \qquad \textit{Substitute for } x_1, y_1, x_2, \textit{ and } y_2.$$
$$= \sqrt{(5)^2 + (3)^2} \qquad \textit{Simplify.}$$
$$= \sqrt{34}$$
$$\approx 5.83 \qquad \textit{Use a calculator.}$$

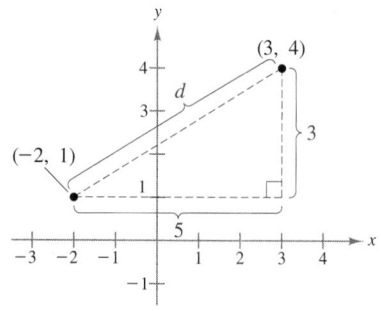

FIGURE 1.7

Note in Figure 1.7 that a distance of 5.83 looks about right. ▬

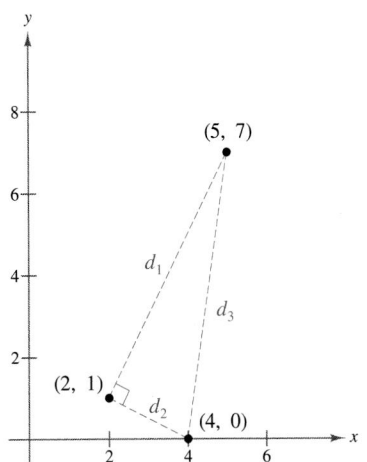

FIGURE 1.8

EXAMPLE 4 *Verifying a Right Triangle*

Use the Distance Formula to show that the points $(2, 1)$, $(4, 0)$, and $(5, 7)$ are vertices of a right triangle.

Solution

The three points are plotted in Figure 1.8. Using the Distance Formula, you can find the lengths of the three sides as follows.

$$d_1 = \sqrt{(5-2)^2 + (7-1)^2} = \sqrt{9+36} = \sqrt{45}$$
$$d_2 = \sqrt{(4-2)^2 + (0-1)^2} = \sqrt{4+1} = \sqrt{5}$$
$$d_3 = \sqrt{(5-4)^2 + (7-0)^2} = \sqrt{1+49} = \sqrt{50}$$

Because

$$d_1{}^2 + d_2{}^2 = 45 + 5 = 50 = d_3{}^2,$$

you can apply the converse of the Pythagorean Theorem to conclude that the triangle must be a right triangle.

The figures provided with Examples 3 and 4 were not really essential to the solution. *Nevertheless*, we strongly recommend that you develop the habit of including sketches with your solutions—even if they are not required.

Real Life

EXAMPLE 5 *Finding the Length of a Pass*

In a football game, a quarterback throws a pass from the 5-yard line, 20 yards from the sideline. The pass is caught by a wide receiver on the 45-yard line, 50 yards from the same sideline, as shown in Figure 1.9. How long was the pass?

Solution

You can find the length of the pass by finding the distance between the points $(20, 5)$ and $(50, 45)$.

$$d = \sqrt{(50-20)^2 + (45-5)^2} \qquad \textit{Distance Formula}$$
$$= \sqrt{900 + 1600}$$
$$= 50 \qquad\qquad\qquad\qquad \textit{Simplify.}$$

Thus, the pass was 50 yards long.

FIGURE 1.9

Note   In Example 5, the scale along the goal line does not normally appear on a football field. However, when you use coordinate geometry to solve real-life problems, you are free to place the coordinate system in any way that is convenient to the solution of the problem.

The Midpoint Formula

To find the **midpoint** of the line segment that joins two points in a coordinate plane, you can simply find the average values of the respective coordinates of the two endpoints.

The Midpoint Formula

The midpoint of the segment joining the points (x_1, y_1) and (x_2, y_2) is

$$\text{Midpoint} = \left(\frac{x_1 + x_2}{2}, \frac{y_1 + y_2}{2} \right).$$

EXAMPLE 6 *Finding a Segment's Midpoint*

Find the midpoint of the line segment joining the points $(-5, -3)$ and $(9, 3)$, as shown in Figure 1.10.

Solution

Let $(x_1, y_1) = (-5, -3)$ and $(x_2, y_2) = (9, 3)$.

$$\text{Midpoint} = \left(\frac{x_1 + x_2}{2}, \frac{y_1 + y_2}{2} \right) \qquad \textit{Midpoint Formula}$$

$$= \left(\frac{-5 + 9}{2}, \frac{-3 + 3}{2} \right) \qquad \textit{Substitute for } x_1, y_1, x_2, \textit{ and } y_2.$$

$$= (2, 0) \qquad \textit{Simplify.}$$

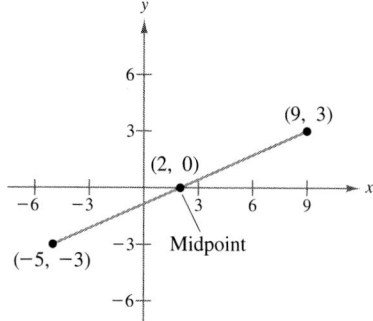

FIGURE 1.10

Real Life

EXAMPLE 7 *Estimating Annual Sales*

Eastman Kodak had annual sales of $17.0 billion in 1988 and $20.2 billion in 1992. Without knowing any additional information, what would you estimate the 1990 sales to have been? *(Source: Eastman Kodak Company)*

Solution

One solution to the problem is to assume that sales followed a linear pattern. With this assumption, you can estimate the 1990 sales by finding the midpoint of the segment connecting the points $(1988, 17.0)$ and $(1992, 20.2)$.

$$\text{Midpoint} = \left(\frac{1988 + 1992}{2}, \frac{17.0 + 20.2}{2} \right) = (1990, 18.6)$$

Hence, you would estimate the 1990 sales to have been about $18.6 billion, as shown in Figure 1.11. (The actual 1990 sales were $18.9 billion.)

FIGURE 1.11

Extended Application: Computer Graphics

The photo at the right shows a scene from *Terminator 2*. The pilot's expression is mirrored on the head of the computer-animated polyalloy robot, which takes on human form after pouring itself through a hole in the helicopter window. This movie was the first box-office success to use extensive computer graphics. Much of computer graphics consists of transformations of points in two- and three-dimensional space.

Shooting Star

EXAMPLE 8 *Translating Points in the Plane*

Figure 1.12 shows the vertices of a parallelogram. Find the vertices of the parallelogram after it has been translated two units down and four units to the right.

Solution

To translate each vertex two units down, subtract 2 from each y-coordinate. To translate each vertex four units to the right, add 4 to each x-coordinate.

Original Point	Translated Point
$(1, 0)$	$(1 + 4, 0 - 2) = (5, -2)$
$(3, 2)$	$(3 + 4, 2 - 2) = (7, 0)$
$(3, 6)$	$(3 + 4, 6 - 2) = (7, 4)$
$(1, 4)$	$(1 + 4, 4 - 2) = (5, 2)$

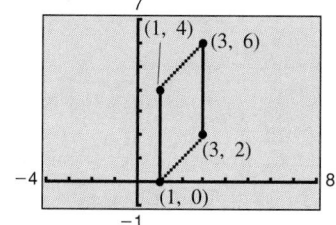

FIGURE 1.12

Discussion Problem   Extending the Example

Example 8 shows how to translate points in a coordinate plane. How are the following transformed points related to the original points?

Original Point	Transformed Point
(x, y)	$(-x, y)$
(x, y)	$(x, -y)$
(x, y)	$(-x, -y)$

Warm Up

The following warm-up exercises involve skills that were covered in earlier sections. You will use these skills in the exercise set for this section.

In Exercises 1–6, simplify the expression.

1. $\sqrt{(3-6)^2 + [1-(-5)]^2}$

2. $\sqrt{(-2-0)^2 + [-7-(-3)]^2}$

3. $\dfrac{5+(-4)}{2}$

4. $\dfrac{-3+(-1)}{2}$

5. $\sqrt{27} + \sqrt{12}$

6. $\sqrt{8} - \sqrt{18}$

In Exercises 7–10, solve for x or y.

7. $\sqrt{(3-x)^2 + (7-4)^2} = \sqrt{45}$

8. $\sqrt{(6-2)^2 + (-2-y)^2} = \sqrt{52}$

9. $\dfrac{x+(-5)}{2} = 7$

10. $\dfrac{-7+y}{2} = -3$

EXERCISES 1.1 means that technology can help you solve or check the exercise(s).

In Exercises 1–4, (a) find the length of each side of the right triangle, and (b) show that these lengths satisfy the Pythagorean Theorem.

*__1.__

__2.__

__3.__

__4.__

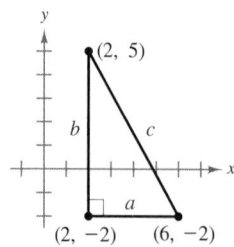

In Exercises 5–12, (a) plot the points, (b) find the distance between the points, and (c) find the midpoint of the line segment joining the points.

5. (3, 1), (5, 5)

6. (−3, 2), (3, −2)

7. $\left(\frac{1}{2}, 1\right), \left(-\frac{3}{2}, -5\right)$

8. $\left(\frac{2}{3}, -\frac{1}{3}\right), \left(\frac{5}{6}, 1\right)$

9. (2, 2), (4, 14)

10. (−3, 7), (1, −1)

11. $\left(1, \sqrt{3}\right), (-1, 1)$

12. $(-2, 0), \left(0, \sqrt{2}\right)$

In Exercises 13–16, show that the points form the vertices of the indicated figure. (A rhombus is a quadrilateral whose sides have the same length.)

Vertices	Figure
13. (0, 1), (3, 7), (4, −1)	Right triangle
14. (1, −3), (3, 2), (−2, 4)	Isosceles triangle
15. (0, 0), (1, 2), (2, 1), (3, 3)	Rhombus
16. (0, 1), (3, 7), (4, 4), (1, −2)	Parallelogram

*The *answers* to the odd-numbered exercises are given in the back of the text. *Worked-out solutions* to the odd-numbered exercises are given in the *Student Solutions Guide*.

In Exercises 17–20, use the Distance Formula to determine whether the points are collinear.

17. $(0, -4), (2, 0), (3, 2)$ **18.** $(0, 4), (7, -6), (-5, 11)$

19. $(-2, -6), (1, -3), (5, 2)$ **20.** $(-1, 1), (3, 3), (5, 5)$

In Exercises 21 and 22, find x so that the distance between the points is 5.

21. $(1, 0), (x, -4)$ **22.** $(2, -1), (x, 2)$

In Exercises 23 and 24, find y so that the distance between the points is 8.

23. $(0, 0), (3, y)$ **24.** $(5, 1), (5, y)$

25. Use the Midpoint Formula repeatedly to find the three points that divide the segment joining (x_1, y_1) and (x_2, y_2) into four equal parts.

26. Show that $\left(\frac{1}{3}[2x_1 + x_2], \frac{1}{3}[2y_1 + y_2]\right)$ is one of the points of trisection of the line segment joining (x_1, y_1) and (x_2, y_2). Then, find the second point of trisection by finding the midpoint of the segment joining

$$\left(\tfrac{1}{3}[2x_1 + x_2], \tfrac{1}{3}[2y_1 + y_2]\right) \text{ and } (x_2, y_2).$$

27. Use Exercise 25 to find the points that divide the line segment joining the given points into four equal parts.
(a) $(1, -2), (4, -1)$ (b) $(-2, -3), (0, 0)$

28. Use Exercise 26 to find the points of trisection of the line segment joining the given points.
(a) $(1, -2), (4, 1)$ (b) $(-2, -3), (0, 0)$

29. *Building Dimensions* The base and height of the trusses for the roof of a house are 32 feet and 5 feet, respectively (see figure).
(a) Find the distance from the eaves to the peak of the roof.
(b) The length of the house is 40 feet. Use the result of part (a) to find the number of square feet of roofing.

30. *Wire Length* A guy wire is stretched from a broadcasting tower at a point 200 feet above the ground to an anchor 125 feet from the base (see figure). How long is the wire?

In Exercises 31 and 32, use a scatter plot, a bar graph, or a line graph to represent the data. Describe any trends that appear.

31. *Cable TV* For 1983–1992, the number (in millions) of cable television subscribers in the United States is given in the table. *(Source: Television Bureau of Advertising, Inc.)*

Year	1983	1984	1985	1986	1987
Subscribers	25.0	37.3	39.9	42.2	44.9

Year	1988	1989	1990	1991	1992
Subscribers	48.6	52.6	54.9	55.8	57.2

32. *Magazine Purchases* From 1981 through 1990, the amount (in billions of dollars) spent on magazines, newspapers, and sheet music in the United States is given in the table. *(Source: U.S. Bureau of Economic Analysis)*

Year	1981	1982	1983	1984	1985
Amount	11.0	11.4	12.0	12.7	13.2

Year	1986	1987	1988	1989	1990
Amount	13.9	15.4	17.0	18.5	19.2

Dow Jones Average In Exercises 33 and 34, use the figure showing the Dow Jones Industrial Average for common stocks. *(Source: Dow Jones, Inc.)*

33. Estimate the Dow Jones Average for the following dates.
(a) August 1990   (b) November 1990
(c) December 1991   (d) March 1992

34. Estimate the percent increase or decrease in the Dow Jones Industrial Average (a) from August 1990 to November 1990 and (b) from December 1991 to June 1992.

FIGURE FOR 29

FIGURE FOR 30

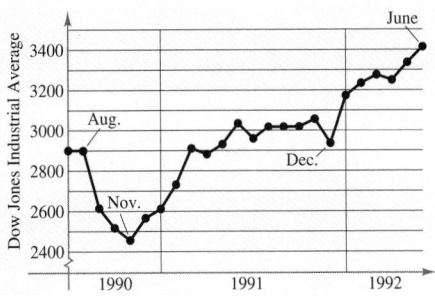

FIGURE FOR 33 AND 34

Housing Starts In Exercises 35 and 36, use the figure showing the number of housing starts (in millions) in the United States from 1990 through 1992. *(Source: U.S. Bureau of Census, Construction Reports)*

35. Estimate the number of housing starts for the following.
   (a) February 1990   (b) October 1990
   (c) January 1991   (d) April 1992

36. Estimate the percent increase or decrease in housing starts (a) from January 1990 to January 1991, and (b) from January 1991 to March 1992.

FIGURE FOR 35 AND 36

Research Project In Exercises 37 and 38, (a) use the Midpoint Formula to estimate the revenue and profit of the company in 1990. (b) Then use your school's library or some other reference source to find the actual revenue and profit for 1990. (c) Did the revenue and profit increase in a linear pattern from 1988 to 1992? Explain your reasoning. (d) What were the company's expenses during each of the given years? (e) How would you rate the company's growth from 1988 to 1992? *(Source: The Gillette Company and Helene Curtis)*

37. The Gillette Company

Year	1988	1990	1992
Revenue (millions of $)	3581.2	?	5162.8
Profit (millions of $)	268.5	?	513.4

38. Helene Curtis

Year	1988	1990	1992
Revenue (millions of $)	629.2	?	1167.8
Profit (millions of $)	14.4	?	22.1

Computer Graphics In Exercises 39 and 40, the red figure is translated to a new position in the plane to form the blue figure. (a) Find the vertices of the transformed figure. (b) Then use a graphing utility to draw both figures.

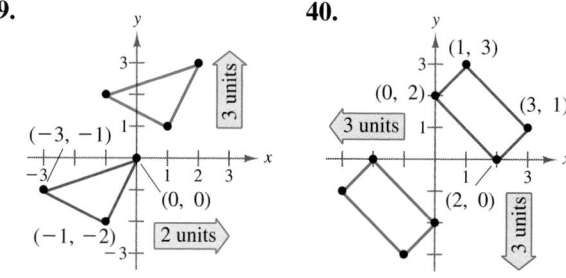

39.   **40.**

41. *Research Project* Use your school's library or some other reference source to collect data about a small business. Organize the data graphically. Then, interpret the data.

Graphs of Equations

The Graph of an Equation ■ *Intercepts of a Graph* ■ *Circles* ■
Points of Intersection ■ *Mathematical Models*

The Graph of an Equation

In Section 1.1, you used a coordinate system to graphically represent the relationship between two quantities. There, the graphical picture consisted of a collection of points in a coordinate plane (see Example 2 in Section 1.1).

Frequently, a relationship between two quantities is expressed as an equation. For instance, degrees on the Fahrenheit scale are related to degrees on the Celsius scale by the equation $F = \frac{9}{5}C + 32$. In this section, you will study some basic procedures for sketching the graph of such an equation. The **graph** of an equation is the set of all points that are solutions of the equation.

EXAMPLE 1 *Sketching the Graph of an Equation*

Sketch the graph of $y = 7 - 3x$.

Solution

The simplest way to sketch the graph of an equation is the *point-plotting method*. With this method, you construct a table of values that consists of several solution points of the equation, as shown in Table 1.2. For instance, when $x = 0$,

$$y = 7 - 3(0) = 7,$$

which implies that $(0, 7)$ is a solution point of the graph.

TABLE 1.2

x	0	1	2	3	4
$y = 7 - 3x$	7	4	1	−2	−5

From the table, it follows that $(0, 7)$, $(1, 4)$, $(2, 1)$, $(3, -2)$, and $(4, -5)$ are solution points of the equation. After plotting these points, you can see that they appear to lie on a line, as shown in Figure 1.13. The graph of the equation is the line that passes through the five plotted points.   ■

Note Even though we refer to the sketch shown in Figure 1.13 as the graph of $y = 7 - 3x$, it actually represents only a *portion* of the graph. The entire graph is a line that would extend off the page.

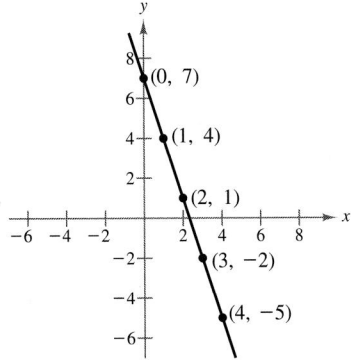

FIGURE 1.13   Solution Points for $y = 7 - 3x$

EXAMPLE 2 *Sketching the Graph of an Equation*

Sketch the graph of $y = x^2 - 2$.

Solution

Begin by constructing a table of values, as shown in Table 1.3.

TABLE 1.3

x	−2	−1	0	1	2	3
$y = x^2 - 2$	2	−1	−2	−1	2	7

Next, plot the points given in the table, as shown in Figure 1.14(a). Finally, connect the points by a smooth curve, as shown in Figure 1.14(b).

Note   The graph shown in Example 2 is a **parabola.** The graph of any second-degree equation of the form

$$y = ax^2 + bx + c, \qquad a \neq 0$$

has a similar shape. If $a > 0$, the parabola opens upward, as in Figure 1.14(b), and if $a < 0$, the parabola opens downward.

(a)

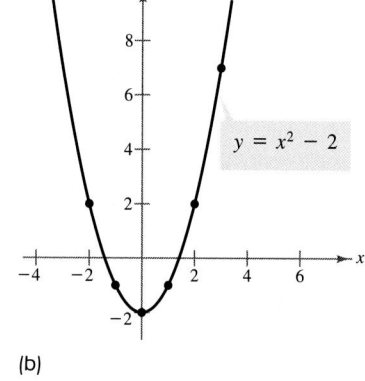

(b)

FIGURE 1.14

The point-plotting technique demonstrated in Examples 1 and 2 is easy to use, but it does have some shortcomings. With too few solution points, you can badly misrepresent the graph of a given equation. For instance, how would you connect the four points in Figure 1.15? Without further information, any one of the three graphs in Figure 1.16 would be reasonable.

FIGURE 1.15

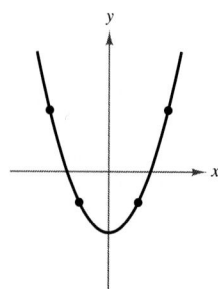

FIGURE 1.16

▦ TECHNOLOGY

Creating a Viewing Rectangle

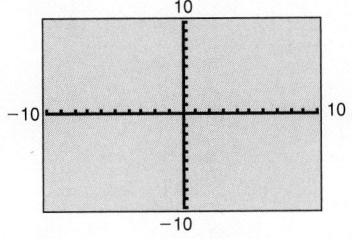

A **viewing rectangle** for a graph is a rectangular portion of the coordinate plane. A viewing rectangle is determined by six values: the minimum x-value, the maximum x-value, the x-scale, the minimum y-value, the maximum y-value, and the y-scale. When you enter these six values into a graphing utility, you are setting the **range** or **window.** Some graphing utilities have a standard viewing rectangle, as shown at the left.

By choosing different viewing rectangles for a graph, it is possible to obtain very different impressions of the graph's shape. For instance, below are four different viewing rectangles for the graph of

$$y = 0.1x^4 - x^3 + 2x^2.$$

Of these, the view shown in part (a) is the most complete.

(a)

(b)

(c)

(d)

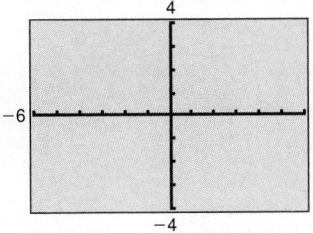

On most graphing utilities, the display screen is two-thirds as high as it is wide. On such screens, you can obtain a graph with a true geometric perspective by using a **square setting**—one in which

$$\frac{Y_{max} - Y_{min}}{X_{max} - X_{min}} = \frac{2}{3}.$$

One such setting is shown at the left. Notice that the x and y tick marks are equally spaced on a square setting, but not on a standard setting.

Intercepts of a Graph

It is often easy to determine the solution points that have zero as either the x-coordinate or the y-coordinate. These points are called **intercepts** because they are the points at which the graph intersects the x- or y-axis.

It is possible for a graph to have no intercepts or several intercepts, as shown in Figure 1.17.

No x-intercept
One y-intercept

Three x-intercepts
One y-intercept

One x-intercept
Two y-intercepts

No intercepts

FIGURE 1.17

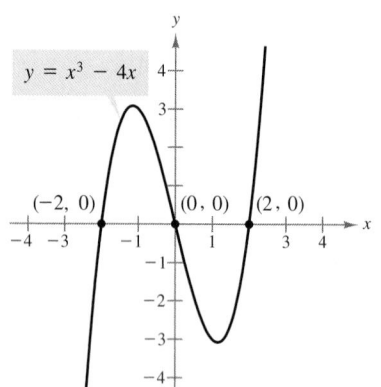

FIGURE 1.18

FIGURE 1.19

Finding Intercepts

1. To find x-intercepts, let y be zero and solve the equation for x.
2. To find y-intercepts, let x be zero and solve the equation for y.

EXAMPLE 3 *Finding x- and y-Intercepts*

Find the x- and y-intercepts for the graphs of the following equations.

a. $y = x^3 - 4x$

b. $y^2 - 3 = x$

Solution

a. Let $y = 0$. Then $0 = x(x^2 - 4)$ has solutions $x = 0$ and $x = \pm 2$.

x-intercepts: $(0, 0)$, $(2, 0)$, $(-2, 0)$

Let $x = 0$. Then $y = 0$.

y-intercept: $(0, 0)$ *(See Figure 1.18.)*

b. Let $y = 0$. Then $-3 = x$.

x-intercept: $(-3, 0)$

Let $x = 0$. Then $y^2 - 3 = 0$ has solutions $y = \pm\sqrt{3}$.

y-intercepts: $\left(0, \sqrt{3}\right)$, $\left(0, -\sqrt{3}\right)$ *(See Figure 1.19.)*

Zooming in to Find Intercepts

You can use the **zoom** feature of a graphing utility to approximate the x-intercepts of a graph. Suppose you want to approximate the x-intercept(s) of the graph of $y = 2x^3 - 3x + 2$. Begin by graphing the equation, as shown below in part (a). From the viewing rectangle shown, the graph appears to have only one x-intercept. This intercept lies between -2 and -1. By zooming in on the intercept, you can improve the approximation, as shown in part (b). To three decimal places, the solution is $x \approx -1.476$.

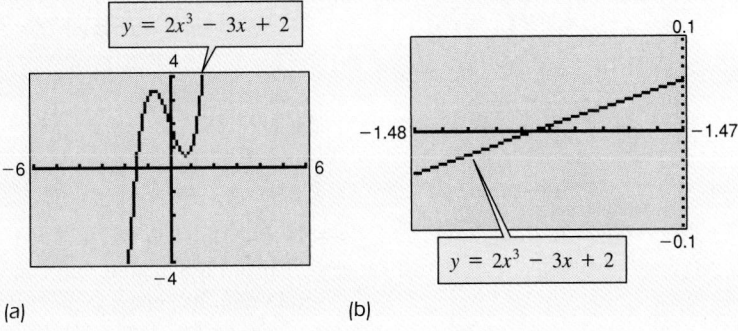

(a)   (b)

Here are some suggestions for using the zoom feature.

1. With each successive zoom-in, adjust the x-scale so that the viewing rectangle shows at least one tick mark on each side of the x-intercept.

2. The error in your approximation will be less than the distance between two scale marks.

3. The **trace** feature can usually be used to add one more decimal place of accuracy without changing the viewing rectangle.

Part (a) below shows the graph of $y = x^2 - 5x + 3$. Parts (b) and (c) show "zoom-in views" of the two intercepts. From these views, you can approximate the x-intercepts to be $x \approx 0.697$ and $x \approx 4.303$.

(a)

(b)

(c)

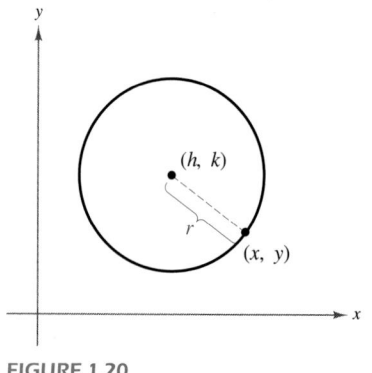

FIGURE 1.20

Circles

Throughout this course, you will learn to recognize several types of graphs from their equations. For instance, you should recognize that the graph of a second-degree equation of the form $y = ax^2 + bx + c$ is a parabola (see Example 2). Another easily recognized graph is that of a **circle.**

Consider the circle shown in Figure 1.20. A point (x, y) is on the circle if and only if its distance from the center (h, k) is r. By the Distance Formula,

$$\sqrt{(x - h)^2 + (y - k)^2} = r.$$

By squaring both sides of this equation, you obtain the **standard form of the equation of a circle.**

Standard Form of the Equation of a Circle

The point (x, y) lies on the circle of radius r and center (h, k) if and only if

$$(x - h)^2 + (y - k)^2 = r^2.$$

From this result, you can see that the standard form of the equation of a circle with its center at the origin, $(h, k) = (0, 0)$, is simply

$$x^2 + y^2 = r^2. \qquad \text{\textit{Circle with center at origin}}$$

EXAMPLE 4   *Finding the Equation of a Circle*

The point $(3, 4)$ lies on a circle whose center is at $(-1, 2)$, as shown in Figure 1.21. Find the standard form of the equation for this circle.

Solution

The radius of the circle is the distance between $(-1, 2)$ and $(3, 4)$.

$$r = \sqrt{[3 - (-1)]^2 + (4 - 2)^2} \qquad \text{\textit{Distance Formula}}$$
$$= \sqrt{16 + 4} \qquad \text{\textit{Simplify.}}$$
$$= \sqrt{20} \qquad \text{\textit{Radius}}$$

Using $(h, k) = (-1, 2)$, the standard form of the equation of the circle is

$$(x - h)^2 + (y - k)^2 = r^2$$
$$[x - (-1)]^2 + (y - 2)^2 = \left(\sqrt{20}\right)^2 \qquad \text{\textit{Substitute for h, k, and r.}}$$
$$(x + 1)^2 + (y - 2)^2 = 20. \qquad \text{\textit{Standard form}}$$

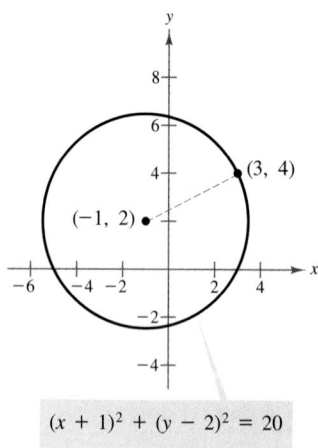

$$(x + 1)^2 + (y - 2)^2 = 20$$

FIGURE 1.21

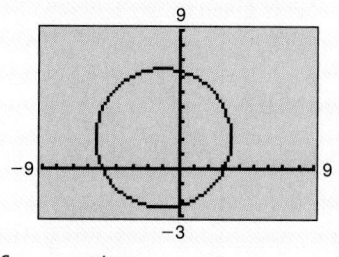
The general form of the equation of a circle is

$$Ax^2 + Ay^2 + Dx + Ey + F = 0, \qquad A \neq 0 \qquad \text{\textit{General form}}$$

To change from general form to standard form, you can use a process called **completing the square,** as demonstrated in Example 5.

EXAMPLE 5 *Completing the Square*

Sketch the graph of the circle whose general equation is

$$4x^2 + 4y^2 + 20x - 16y + 37 = 0.$$

Solution

First divide by 4 so that the coefficients of x^2 and y^2 are both 1.

$$4x^2 + 4y^2 + 20x - 16y + 37 = 0 \qquad \text{\textit{General form}}$$
$$x^2 + y^2 + 5x - 4y + \tfrac{37}{4} = 0 \qquad \text{\textit{Divide by 4.}}$$
$$(x^2 + 5x + \quad) + (y^2 - 4y + \quad) = -\tfrac{37}{4} \qquad \text{\textit{Group terms.}}$$
$$\left(x^2 + 5x + \tfrac{25}{4}\right) + (y^2 - 4y + 4) = -\tfrac{37}{4} + \tfrac{25}{4} + 4 \qquad \text{\textit{Complete the square.}}$$

(Half)^2 (Half)^2

$$\left(x + \tfrac{5}{2}\right)^2 + (y - 2)^2 = 1 \qquad \text{\textit{Standard form}}$$

From the standard form, you can see that the circle is centered at $\left(-\tfrac{5}{2}, 2\right)$ and has a radius of 1, as shown in Figure 1.22.

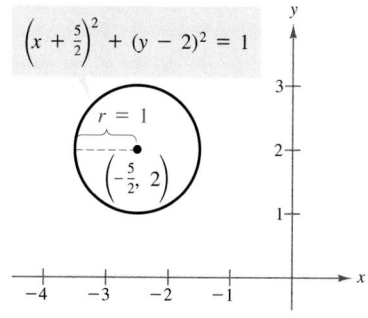

FIGURE 1.22

The general equation $Ax^2 + Ay^2 + Dx + Ey + F = 0$ may not always represent a circle. In fact, such an equation will have no solution points if the procedure of completing the square yields the impossible result

$$(x - h)^2 + (y - k)^2 = \text{negative number.} \qquad \text{\textit{No solution points}}$$

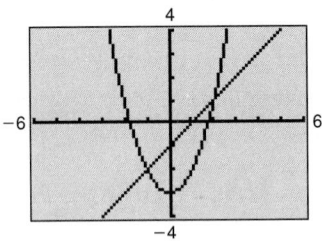

FIGURE 1.23

Points of Intersection

A **point of intersection** of two graphs is an ordered pair that is a solution point of both graphs. For instance, Figure 1.23 shows that the graphs of

$$y = x^2 - 3 \quad \text{and} \quad y = x - 1$$

have two points of intersection: $(2, 1)$ and $(-1, -2)$. To find the points analytically, set the two y-values equal to each other and solve the equation

$$x^2 - 3 = x - 1$$

for x.

A common business application that involves points of intersection is **break-even analysis.** The marketing of a new product typically requires an initial investment. When sufficient units have been sold so that the total revenue has offset the total cost, the sale of the product has reached the **break-even point.** The **total cost** of producing x units of a product is denoted by C, and the **total revenue** from the sale of x units of the product is denoted by R. Thus, you can find the break-even point by setting the cost C equal to the revenue R, and solving for x.

Real Life

EXAMPLE 6 *Finding a Break-Even Point*

A business manufactures a product at a cost of $0.65 per unit and sells the product for $1.20 per unit. The company's initial investment to produce the product was $10,000. How many units must the company sell to break even?

Solution

The total cost of producing x units of the product is given by

$$C = 0.65x + 10,000. \qquad \text{\textit{Cost equation}}$$

The total revenue from the sale of x units is given by

$$R = 1.2x. \qquad \text{\textit{Revenue equation}}$$

To find the break-even point, set the cost equal to the revenue and solve for x.

$$
\begin{aligned}
R &= C & &\text{\textit{Set revenue equal to cost.}} \\
1.2x &= 0.65x + 10,000 & &\text{\textit{Substitute for R and C.}} \\
0.55x &= 10,000 & &\text{\textit{Subtract 0.65x from both sides.}} \\
x &= \frac{10,000}{0.55} & &\text{\textit{Divide both sides by 0.55.}} \\
x &\approx 18,182 & &\text{\textit{Use a calculator.}}
\end{aligned}
$$

Thus the company must sell 18,182 units before it breaks even. This result is shown graphically in Figure 1.24.

Break-Even Analysis

Break-even point: 18,182 units

$C = 0.65x + 10,000$

Profit

Loss

$R = 1.2x$

Sales (in dollars)

Number of units

FIGURE 1.24

Mathematical Models

In this text, you will see many examples of the use of equations as **mathematical models** of real-life phenomena. In developing a mathematical model to represent actual data, you should strive for two (often conflicting) goals—accuracy and simplicity.

Real Life

EXAMPLE 7 *Using Mathematical Models*

Table 1.4 shows the annual sales, in millions of dollars, for K Mart Corporation and Wal-Mart Stores for 1985 through 1992.. In the summer of 1993, the publication of *Value Line* listed projected 1993 sales for the companies as $41,000 million and $68,470 million. How do you think these projections were obtained? *(Source: K Mart Corporation and Wal-Mart Stores)*

TABLE 1.4

Year	1985	1986	1987	1988	1989	1990	1991	1992
K Mart	22,420	23,812	25,627	27,301	29,533	32,070	34,580	37,725
Wal-Mart	8,452	11,909	15,959	20,649	25,811	32,602	43,887	55,550

Solution

The projections were obtained by using past revenues to predict future revenues. The past revenues were modeled by equations that were found by a statistical procedure called least-squares regression analysis.

$$R = 131.8t^2 - 67.9t + 19,494.6, \qquad 5 \le t \le 12 \qquad \text{\textit{K Mart}}$$
$$R = 28.72t^3 + 5263.8, \qquad 5 \le t \le 12 \qquad \text{\textit{Wal-Mart}}$$

Using $t = 13$ to represent 1993, you can predict the 1993 revenues to be

$$R = 131.8(13)^2 - 67.9(13) + 19,494.6 = \$40,886 \qquad \text{\textit{K Mart}}$$
$$R = 28.72(13)^3 + 5263.8 = \$68,362. \qquad \text{\textit{Wal-Mart}}$$

These two projections are close to those projected by *Value Line*. The graphs of the two models are shown in Figure 1.25. ■

To test the accuracy of a model, you can compare the actual data with the values given by the model. For instance, Table 1.5 compares the actual K Mart revenues with those given by the model.

TABLE 1.5

Year	1985	1986	1987	1988	1989	1990	1991	1992
Actual	22,420	23,812	25,627	27,301	29,533	32,070	34,580	37,725
Model	22,450	23,832	25,478	27,387	29,559	31,996	34,696	37,659

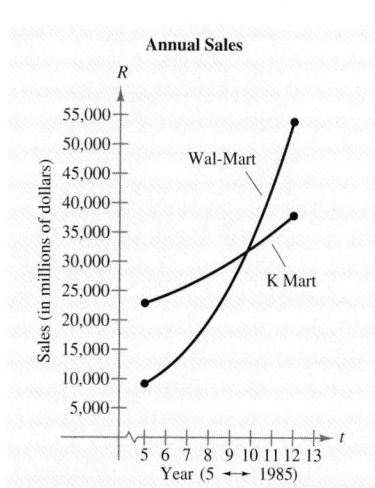

Annual Sales

Wal-Mart

K Mart

Sales (in millions of dollars)

Year (5 ↔ 1985)

FIGURE 1.25

Much of your study of calculus will center around the behavior of the graphs of mathematical models. Figure 1.26 shows the graphs of six basic algebraic equations. Familiarity with these graphs will help you in the creation and use of mathematical models.

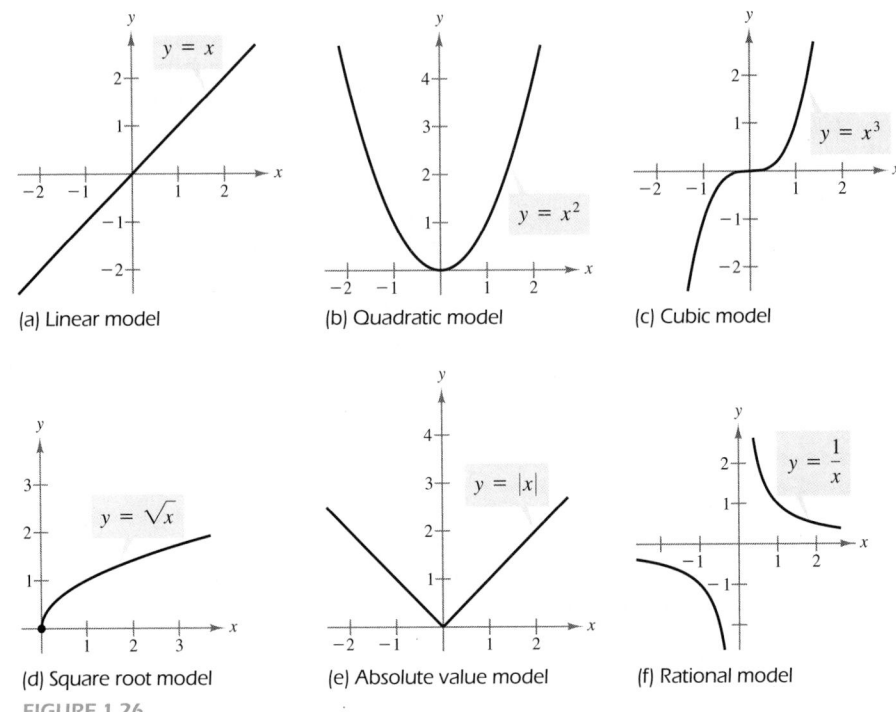

(a) Linear model

(b) Quadratic model

(c) Cubic model

(d) Square root model

(e) Absolute value model

(f) Rational model

FIGURE 1.26

Discussion Problem   Graphical, Numerical, and Analytical Solutions

Most problems in calculus can be solved in a variety of ways. Often, you can solve a problem graphically, numerically (using a table), and analytically. For instance, Example 6 compares a graphical and analytical approach to finding points of intersection.

In Example 7, suppose you were asked to find the time that Wal-Mart's revenues exceeded K Mart's revenues. Explain how to use *each* of the three approaches to answer the question. For this question, which approach do you think is best? Explain.

Suppose you answered the question and obtained $t = 9.66$. What date does this represent—August 1989 or August 1990? Explain.

Warm Up

The following warm-up exercises involve skills that were covered in earlier sections. You will use these skills in the exercise set for this section.

In Exercises 1–6, solve for y.

1. $5y - 12 = x$

2. $-y = 15 - x$

3. $x^3y + 2y = 1$

4. $x^2 + x - y^2 - 6 = 0$

5. $(x - 2)^2 + (y + 1)^2 = 9$

6. $(x + 6)^2 + (y - 5)^2 = 81$

In Exercises 7–10, factor the expression.

7. $x^2 - 3x + 2$

8. $x^2 + 5x + 6$

9. $y^2 - 3y + \frac{9}{4}$

10. $y^2 - 7y + \frac{49}{4}$

E X E R C I S E S   1.2   means that technology can help you solve or check the exercise(s).

In Exercises 1–4, determine whether the points are solution points of the given equation.

1. $2x - y - 3 = 0$

  (a) $(1, 2)$ (b) $(1, -1)$ (c) $(4, 5)$

2. $x^2 + y^2 = 4$

  (a) $(1, -\sqrt{3})$ (b) $\left(\frac{1}{2}, -1\right)$ (c) $\left(\frac{3}{2}, \frac{7}{2}\right)$

3. $x^2y + x^2 - 5y = 0$

  (a) $\left(0, \frac{1}{5}\right)$ (b) $(2, 4)$ (c) $(-2, -4)$

4. $x^2 - xy + 4y = 3$

  (a) $(0, 2)$ (b) $\left(-2, -\frac{1}{6}\right)$ (c) $(3, -6)$

 In Exercises 5–10, match the equation with its graph. Use a graphing utility, set with a square setting, to confirm your result. [The graphs are labeled (a)–(f).]

5. $y = x - 2$

6. $y = -\frac{1}{2}x + 2$

7. $y = x^2 + 2x$

8. $y = \sqrt{9 - x^2}$

9. $y = |x| - 2$

10. $y = x^3 - x$

(a)

(b)

(c)

(d)

(e)

(f)

In Exercises 11–20, find the intercepts of the graph of the given equation.

11. $2x - y - 3 = 0$

12. $y = (x - 1)(x - 3)$

13. $y = x^2 + x - 2$

14. $y^2 = x^3 - 4x$

15. $y = x^2\sqrt{9 - x^2}$

16. $xy = 4$

17. $y = \dfrac{x^2 - 4}{x - 2}$

18. $y = \dfrac{x^2 + 3x}{(3x + 1)^2}$

19. $x^2y - x^2 + 4y = 0$

20. $y = x^2 + 1$

In Exercises 21–38, sketch the graph of the equation and plot the intercepts.

21. $y = x$

22. $y = x + 3$

23. $y = -3x + 2$

24. $y = 2x - 3$

25. $y = -3 - x^2$

26. $y = x^2 + 3$

27. $y = x^3 + 2$

28. $y = 1 - x^3$

29. $y = (x + 2)^2$

30. $y = (x - 1)^2$

31. $y = \sqrt{x + 1}$

32. $y = -\sqrt[3]{x}$

33. $y = |x + 1|$

34. $y = -|x - 2|$

35. $y = \dfrac{1}{x - 3}$

36. $y = \dfrac{1}{x^2 + 1}$

37. $x = y^2 - 4$

38. $x = 4 - y^2$

In Exercises 39–46, write the general form of the equation of the circle.

39. Center: $(0, 0)$; radius: 3

40. Center: $(0, 0)$; radius: 5

41. Center: $(2, -1)$; radius: 4

42. Center: $(-4, 3)$; radius: $\frac{5}{8}$

43. Center: $(-1, 2)$; solution point: $(0, 0)$

44. Center: $(3, -2)$; solution point: $(-1, 1)$

45. Endpoints of a diameter: $(3, 3), (-3, 3)$

46. Endpoints of a diameter: $(-4, -1), (4, 1)$

In Exercises 47–54, complete the square to write the equation of the circle in standard form. Then use a graphing utility to graph the circle.

47. $x^2 + y^2 - 2x + 6y + 6 = 0$

48. $x^2 + y^2 - 2x + 6y - 15 = 0$

49. $x^2 + y^2 + 4x + 6y - 3 = 0$

50. $3x^2 + 3y^2 - 6y - 1 = 0$

51. $2x^2 + 2y^2 - 2x - 2y - 3 = 0$

52. $4x^2 + 4y^2 - 4x + 2y - 1 = 0$

53. $16x^2 + 16y^2 + 16x + 40y - 7 = 0$

54. $x^2 + y^2 - 4x + 2y + 3 = 0$

 In Exercises 55–64, find the points of intersection (if any) of the graphs of the equations. Use a graphing utility to check your results.

55. $x + y = 2, \ 2x - y = 1$

56. $2x - 3y = 13, \ 5x + 3y = 1$

57. $x + y = 7, \ 3x - 2y = 11$

58. $x^2 + y^2 = 25, \ 2x + y = 10$

59. $x^2 + y^2 = 5, \ x - y = 1$

60. $x^2 + y = 4, \ 2x - y = 1$

61. $y = x^3, \ y = 2x$

62. $y = \sqrt{x}, \ y = x$

63. $y = x^4 - 2x^2 + 1, \ y = 1 - x^2$

64. $y = x^3 - 2x^2 + x - 1, \ y = -x^2 + 3x - 1$

 65. *Break-Even Analysis* You are setting up a part-time business with an initial investment of $5000. The unit cost of the product is $11.80, and the selling price is $19.30.

   (a) Find equations for the total cost C and total revenue R for x units.

   (b) Find the break-even point by finding the point of intersection of the cost and revenue equations.

   (c) How many units would yield a profit of $100?

66. *Break-Even Analysis* A certain car model costs $14,500 with a gasoline engine and $15,450 with a diesel engine. The numbers of miles per gallon of fuel for cars with these two engines are 22 and 31, respectively. Assume that the price of each type of fuel is $1.389 per gallon.

   (a) Show that the cost C_g of driving the gasoline-powered car x miles is

$$C_g = 14,500 + \frac{1.389x}{22}$$

   and the cost C_d of driving the diesel model x miles is

$$C_d = 15,450 + \frac{1.389x}{31}.$$

   (b) Find the break-even point. That is, find the mileage at which the diesel-powered car becomes more economical than the gasoline-powered car.

Break-Even Analysis In Exercises 67–70, find the sales necessary to break even for the given cost and revenue equations. (Round your answer up to the nearest whole unit.)

67. $C = 0.85x + 35,000$, $R = 1.55x$

68. $C = 6x + 500,000$, $R = 35x$

69. $C = 8650x + 250,000$, $R = 9950x$

70. $C = 5.5\sqrt{x} + 10,000$, $R = 3.29x$

71. College Text Expenses The amount of money y (in millions of dollars) spent on college textbooks in the United States is given in the table. (*Source: Book Industry Study Group, Inc.*)

Year	1982	1985	1987	1988	1989	1990
Expense	1388	1575	1803	1998	2144	2319

A mathematical model for the data is

$$y = 10.40t^2 - 6.52t + 1355.74,$$

where t represents the year, with $t = 0$ corresponding to 1980.

(a) Compare the actual expenses with those given by the model. How good is the model? Explain your reasoning.

(b) Use the model to predict the expenses in 1995.

72. Farm Population The farm population in the United States, as a percent of the total population, is given in the table. (*Source: U.S. Department of Agriculture*)

Year	1950	1960	1970	1975	1980
Percent	15.3	8.7	4.8	4.2	2.8

Year	1986	1987	1988	1989	1990
Percent	2.2	2.1	2.1	2.0	1.9

A mathematical model for the data is

$$y = \frac{15.28 - 0.24t}{1 + 0.05t},$$

where y represents the percent and t represents the year, with $t = 0$ corresponding to 1950.

(a) Compare the actual percent with that given by the model. How good is the model? Explain your reasoning.

(b) Use the model to predict the farm population as a percent of the total population in 1996.

(c) Discuss the validity of your prediction in part (b).

73. Annual Salary A mathematical model for the average annual salary y of a person in finance, insurance, or real estate is

$$y = 15,848.32 + 1519.23t + 291.82\sqrt{t},$$

where t represents the year, with $t = 0$ corresponding to 1980. (*Source: U.S. Bureau of Economic Analysis*)

Year	1980	1985	1990	1991	1994
Salary					

(a) Use the model to complete the table.

(b) This model was created using actual data from 1980 through 1991. How accurate do you think the model is in predicting the 1994 average salary? Explain your reasoning.

(c) What does this model predict the average salary to be in the year 2000? How valid do you think this prediction is?

74. Define the break-even point for a business marketing a new product. Give examples of a linear cost equation and a linear revenue equation for which the break-even point is 10,000 units.

 In Exercises 75–80, find the point(s) of intersection of the graphs of the equations.

75. $y = 2x - 5$, $y = -x + 4$

76. $y = x + 6$, $y = 2x - 10$

77. $y = x + 2$, $y = -x^2 + 4$

78. $y = 2x - 3$, $y = x^2 - 3$

79. $y = x^2 + 1$, $y = -x^2 + 9$

80. $y = x^2$, $y = x^2 - 2x + 4$

 In Exercises 81–88, use a graphing utility to graph the equation. Use the graphing utility to approximate the intercepts of the graph.

81. $y = 0.24x^2 + 1.32x + 5.36$

82. $y = -0.56x^2 - 5.34x + 6.25$

83. $y = -0.1x^3 + 1.3x^2 - 4.3$

84. $y = 0.2x^3 - 2.4x^2 + 0.4x$

85. $y = \sqrt{0.3x^2 - 4.3x + 5.7}$

86. $y = \sqrt{-1.21x^2 + 2.34x + 5.6}$

87. $y = \dfrac{0.2x^2 + 1}{0.1x + 2.4}$ **88.** $y = \dfrac{0.4x - 5.3}{0.4x^2 + 5.3}$

Case Study: Manufacturing Potato Chips

Troyer Potato Products, Inc. makes a wide variety of snack foods, but potato chips are its mainstay. The profitability of the company depends, in part, on producing the product at the lowest possible cost. This in turn means getting the most chips possible from a potato.

But are all potatoes created equal? It is possible that one potato of a given weight will yield more chips than another *of the same weight.* If this is the case, the first potato will yield more output per pound of input, and thus result in more profit for the firm.

But how can two potatoes of the same weight yield a different amount (weight) of potato chips? The answer is that more of the weight in one potato may be due to water, which will disappear during cooking. One way to measure this is to consider the specific gravity of the potato, which gives the mass of the potato compared with the mass of a similar volume of water. A higher specific gravity means more potato per pound, and less water—and therefore more potato chips and greater profits. At least that's the theory.

Troyer tested this theory by comparing the specific gravities of 24 batches of potatoes with the amount of potato chips that each batch produced. The table shows the data. The method of least squares resulted in the following equation, which models the relationship:

$$OUTPUT = -35,219 + 38,535 \cdot \text{SPECGRAV}$$

or

$$Y = -35,219 + 38,535 \cdot X,$$

where OUTPUT (Y) is pounds of potato chips from each batch of potatoes, and SPECGRAV (X) is the specific gravity of the batch. Notice that the coefficient of SPECGRAV (X) is positive, indicating that a higher specific gravity means more output per batch, confirming the hypothesis.

Conclusion: The firm will be more profitable if it buys potatoes with a higher specific gravity, if all other aspects of the potatoes are the same. Farmers who supply chipping potatoes to Troyer are well aware of this relationship, and provide information on the specific gravity of their crop as part of their transaction.

Specific Gravity	Pounds of Potato Chips	Specific Gravity	Pounds of Potato Chips
1.069	6226	1.094	6991
1.098	6895	1.066	5910
1.073	5981	1.072	6138
1.070	5893	1.075	6024
1.089	7124	1.066	6003
1.096	6982	1.096	6884
1.069	6057	1.097	7056
1.088	7012	1.071	6084
1.074	6099	1.095	7019
1.073	5538	1.090	6895
1.070	6100	1.099	7129
1.098	7002	1.096	6998

The figure shows the scatter diagram of the 24 data points from the table, along with the graph of the equation. The graph reveals an interesting pattern in the data: there are two distinct clusters of potatoes, Atlantic and Monona. Atlantic potatoes tend to have a higher specific gravity than the Monona, and also yield a much higher amount (weight) of potato chips.

Courtesy of Troyer Farms

What Would You Do?

1. The table shows the data for all 24 batches of potatoes. Can you tell by looking at the table only that there are two varieties of potatoes included in this test? The graph presents the same data, but shows the pattern much more clearly. The equation presents the relationship in yet another form. List the pros and cons of each method. Which of these is most useful for getting an intuitive feel for the data? Which is most useful for predicting the amount of output that will result from a batch with a specific gravity of 1.083?

2. Given the information discussed above, could Troyer make good decisions about potato purchases even without the specific gravity of each batch of potatoes it buys?

3. Summarize other factors that could affect the profitability of potato chips.

1.3

Lines in the Plane and Slope

Using Slope ■ *Finding the Slope of a Line* ■ *Writing Linear Equations* ■
Parallel and Perpendicular Lines ■ *Extended Application: Linear Depreciation*

Using Slope

The simplest mathematical model for relating two variables is the **linear equation** $y = mx + b$. The equation is called *linear* because its graph is a line. (In this text, we use the term *line* to mean *straight line*.) By letting $x = 0$, you can see that the line crosses the y-axis at $y = b$, as shown in Figure 1.27. In other words, the y-intercept is $(0, b)$. The steepness or slope of the line is m.

$$y = mx + b$$

Slope ⌐   ⌐ y-Intercept

The **slope** of a line is the number of units the line rises (or falls) vertically for each unit of horizontal change from left to right, as shown in Figure 1.27.

Positive slope, line rises.

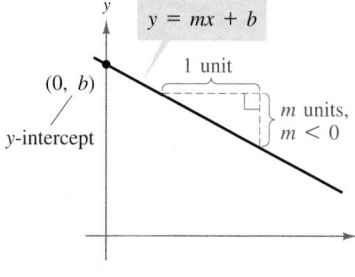

Negative slope, line falls.

FIGURE 1.27

A linear equation that is written in the form $y = mx + b$ is said to be written in **slope-intercept form.**

The Slope-Intercept Form of the Equation of a Line

The graph of the equation

$$y = mx + b$$

is a line whose slope is m and whose y-intercept is $(0, b)$.

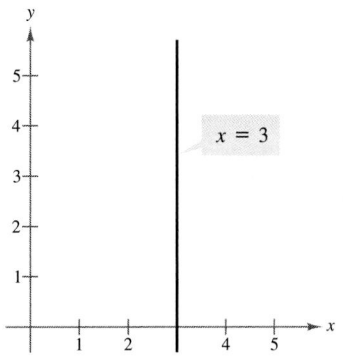

FIGURE 1.28   When the line is vertical, the slope is undefined.

Once you have determined the slope and the y-intercept of a line, it is a relatively simple matter to sketch its graph.

In the following example, note that none of the lines is vertical. A vertical line has an equation of the form

$$x = a. \qquad\qquad\qquad\qquad \textit{Vertical line}$$

Because such an equation cannot be written in the form $y = mx + b$, it follows that the slope of a vertical line is undefined, as indicated in Figure 1.28.

EXAMPLE 1 *Graphing a Linear Equation*

Sketch the graphs of the following linear equations.

a. $y = 2x + 1$ **b.** $y = 2$ **c.** $x + y = 2$

Solution

a. Because $b = 1$, the y-intercept is $(0, 1)$. Moreover, because the slope is $m = 2$, the line *rises* two units for each unit the line moves to the right, as shown in Figure 1.29(a).

b. By writing this equation in the form $y = (0)x + 2$, you can see that the y-intercept is $(0, 2)$ and the slope is zero. A zero slope implies that the line is horizontal—that is, it doesn't rise *or* fall, as shown in Figure 1.29(b).

c. By writing this equation in slope-intercept form

$$x + y = 2 \qquad\qquad\qquad \textit{Original equation}$$
$$y = -x + 2 \qquad\qquad\qquad \textit{Subtract x from both sides.}$$
$$y = (-1)x + 2 \qquad\qquad\qquad \textit{Slope-intercept form}$$

you can see that the y-intercept is $(0, 2)$. Moreover, because the slope is $m = -1$, this line *falls* one unit for each unit the line moves to the right, as shown in Figure 1.29(c).

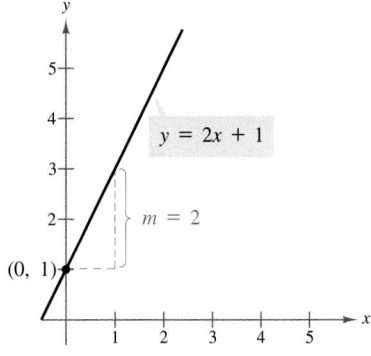

(a) When m is positive, the line rises.

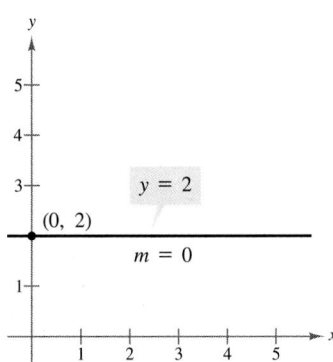

(b) When m is zero, the line is horizontal.

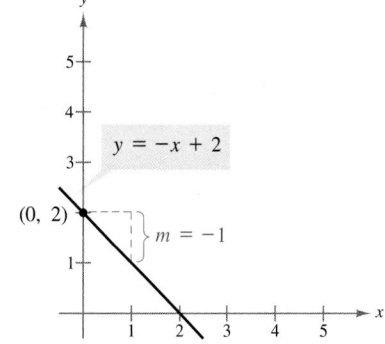

(c) When m is negative, the line falls.

FIGURE 1.29

In real-life problems, the slope of a line can be interpreted as either a *ratio* or a *rate*. If the *x*-axis and *y*-axis have the same unit of measure, then the slope has no units and is a **ratio.** If the *x*-axis and *y*-axis have different units of measure, then the slope is a **rate** or **rate of change.**

Real Life

EXAMPLE 2 *Using Slope as a Ratio*

The maximum recommended slope of a wheelchair ramp is $\frac{1}{12}$. A business is installing a wheelchair ramp that rises 22 inches over a horizontal length of 24 feet. Is the ramp steeper than recommended? *(Source: American Disabilities Act Handbook)*

Solution

The horizontal length of the ramp is 12(24) or 288 inches, as shown in Figure 1.30. Thus the slope of the ramp is

$$\text{Slope} = \frac{\text{vertical change}}{\text{horizontal change}} = \frac{22 \text{ in.}}{288 \text{ in.}} \approx 0.076.$$

Thus, the slope is not steeper than recommended.

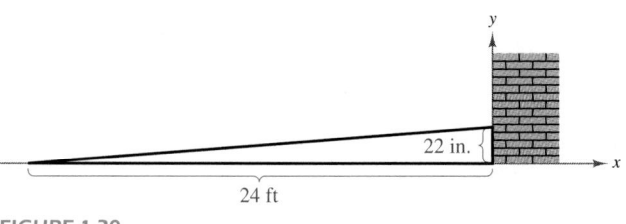

FIGURE 1.30

Real Life

EXAMPLE 3 *Using Slope as a Rate of Change*

A manufacturing company determines that the total cost in dollars of producing *x* units of a product is

$$C = 25x + 3500. \qquad \textit{Cost equation}$$

Describe the practical significance of the *y*-intercept and slope of the line given by this equation.

Solution

The *y*-intercept (0, 3500) tells you that the cost of producing zero units is $3500. This is the **fixed cost** of production—it includes costs that must be paid regardless of the number of units produced. The slope of $m = 25$ tells you that the cost of producing each unit is $25, as shown in Figure 1.31. Economists call the cost per unit the **marginal cost.** If the production increases by one unit, then the "margin" or extra amount of cost is $25.

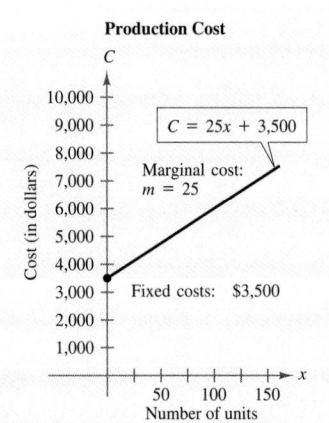

FIGURE 1.31

Finding the Slope of a Line

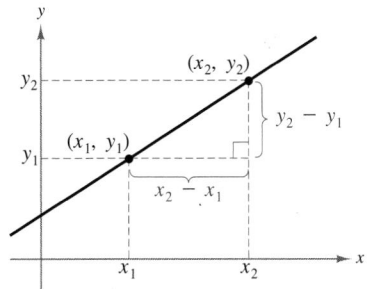

FIGURE 1.32

Given an equation of a line, you can find its slope by writing the equation in slope-intercept form. If you are not given an equation, you can still find the slope of a line. For instance, suppose you want to find the slope of the line passing through the points (x_1, y_1) and (x_2, y_2), as shown in Figure 1.32. As you move from left to right along this line, a change of $(y_2 - y_1)$ units in the vertical direction corresponds to a change of $(x_2 - x_1)$ units in the horizontal direction. These two changes are denoted by the symbols

$$\Delta y = y_2 - y_1 = \text{the change in } y$$

and

$$\Delta x = x_2 - x_1 = \text{the change in } x.$$

(Δ is the Greek capital letter delta, and the symbols Δy and Δx are read as "delta y" and "delta x.") The ratio of Δy to Δx represents the slope of the line that passes through the points (x_1, y_1) and (x_2, y_2).

$$\text{Slope} = \frac{\Delta y}{\Delta x} = \frac{y_2 - y_1}{x_2 - x_1}$$

Be sure you see that Δx represents a single number, not the product of two numbers (Δ and x). The same is true for Δy.

The Slope of a Line Passing Through Two Points

The **slope** m of the line passing through (x_1, y_1) and (x_2, y_2) is

$$m = \frac{\Delta y}{\Delta x} = \frac{y_2 - y_1}{x_2 - x_1}$$

where $x_1 \neq x_2$.

When this formula is used for slope, the *order of subtraction* is important. Given two points on a line, you are free to label either one of them as (x_1, y_1) and the other as (x_2, y_2). However, once you have done this, you must form the numerator and denominator using the same order of subtraction.

$$m = \frac{y_2 - y_1}{x_2 - x_1} \qquad m = \frac{y_1 - y_2}{x_1 - x_2} \qquad m = \frac{y_2 - y_1}{x_1 - x_2}$$

Correct   Correct   Incorrect

For instance, the slope of the line passing through the points $(3, 4)$ and $(5, 7)$ can be calculated as

$$m = \frac{7 - 4}{5 - 3} = \frac{3}{2} \quad \text{or} \quad m = \frac{4 - 7}{3 - 5} = \frac{-3}{-2} = \frac{3}{2}.$$

EXAMPLE 4 *Finding the Slope of a Line*

Find the slope of the line passing through the pairs of points.

a. $(-2, 0)$ and $(3, 1)$

b. $(-1, 2)$ and $(2, 2)$

c. $(0, 4)$ and $(1, -1)$

d. $(3, 4)$ and $(3, 1)$

Solution

a. Letting $(x_1, y_1) = (-2, 0)$ and $(x_2, y_2) = (3, 1)$, you obtain a slope of

$$m = \frac{y_2 - y_1}{x_2 - x_1} = \frac{1 - 0}{3 - (-2)} = \frac{1}{5}. \quad \leftarrow \text{Difference in } y\text{-values} \\ \leftarrow \text{Difference in } x\text{-values}$$

b. The slope of the line passing through $(-1, 2)$ and $(2, 2)$ is

$$m = \frac{2 - 2}{2 - (-1)} = \frac{0}{3} = 0.$$

c. The slope of the line passing through $(0, 4)$ and $(1, -1)$ is

$$m = \frac{-1 - 4}{1 - 0} = \frac{-5}{1} = -5.$$

d. The slope of the vertical line passing through $(3, 4)$ and $(3, 1)$ is not defined because division by zero is undefined. (See Figure 1.33.)

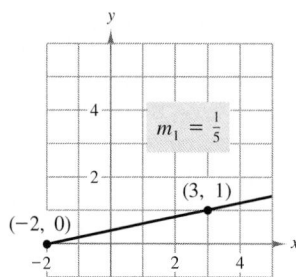

(a) Positive slope; line rises.

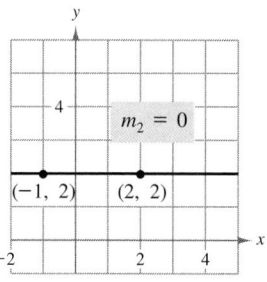

(b) Zero slope; line is horizontal.

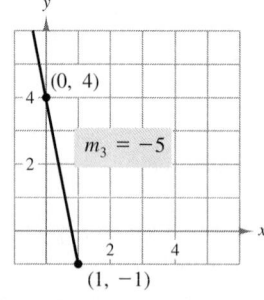

(c) Negative slope; line falls.

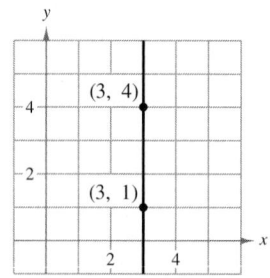

(d) Vertical line; undefined slope.

FIGURE 1.33

Writing Linear Equations

If (x_1, y_1) is a point lying on a line of slope m and (x, y) is *any other* point on the line, then

$$\frac{y - y_1}{x - x_1} = m.$$

This equation, involving the variables x and y, can be rewritten in the form $y - y_1 = m(x - x_1)$, which is the **point-slope form** of the equation of a line.

Point-Slope Form of the Equation of a Line

The equation of the line with slope m passing through the point (x_1, y_1) is

$$y - y_1 = m(x - x_1).$$

The point-slope form is most useful for *finding* the equation of a line. You should remember this formula—it is used repeatedly throughout the text.

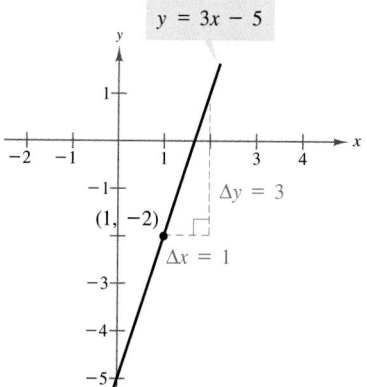

$y = 3x - 5$

FIGURE 1.34

EXAMPLE 5 *Using the Point-Slope Form*

Find the equation of the line that has a slope of 3 and passes through the point $(1, -2)$, as shown in Figure 1.34.

Solution

Use the point-slope form with $m = 3$ and $(x_1, y_1) = (1, -2)$.

$$y - y_1 = m(x - x_1) \qquad \text{\textit{Point-slope form}}$$
$$y - (-2) = 3(x - 1) \qquad \text{\textit{Substitute for } m, x_1, \text{ and } y_1.}$$
$$y + 2 = 3x - 3 \qquad \text{\textit{Simplify.}}$$
$$y = 3x - 5 \qquad \text{\textit{Slope-intercept form}}$$

The point-slope form can be used to find an equation of the line passing through points (x_1, y_1) and (x_2, y_2). To do this, first find the slope of the line

$$m = \frac{y_2 - y_1}{x_2 - x_1}, \qquad x_1 \neq x_2,$$

and then use the point-slope form to obtain the equation

$$y - y_1 = \frac{y_2 - y_1}{x_2 - x_1}(x - x_1). \qquad \text{\textit{Two-point form}}$$

This is sometimes called the **two-point form** of the equation of a line.

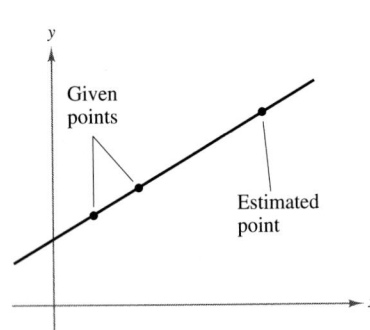

Bausch & Lomb, Inc. Cash Flow

(4, 4.06)
(3, 3.64)
(2, 3.22)
$y = 0.42t + 2.38$
(1, 2.80)
(0, 2.38)

Year (0 ↔ 1988)

FIGURE 1.35

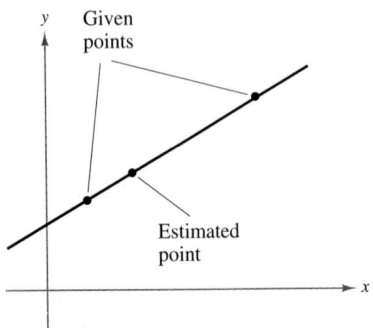

(a) Linear Extrapolation

(b) Linear Interpolation

FIGURE 1.36

EXAMPLE 6 *Predicting Cash Flow Per Share*

The cash flow per share for Bausch & Lomb, Inc. was $2.38 in 1988 and $2.80 in 1989. Using only this information, write a linear equation that gives the cash flow per share in terms of the year. *(Source: Bausch & Lomb, Inc.)*

Solution

Let $t = 0$ represent 1988. Then the two given values are represented by the ordered pairs $(0, 2.38)$ and $(1, 2.80)$. The slope of the line passing through these points is

$$m = \frac{2.80 - 2.38}{1 - 0} = 0.42.$$

Using the point-slope form, you can find the equation that relates the cash flow C and the year t to be

$$y = 0.42t + 2.38.$$

You can use this model to predict future cash flows. For instance, it predicts the cash flows in 1990, 1991, and 1992 to be $3.22, $3.64, and $4.06, as shown in Figure 1.35. (In this case, the predictions are quite good—the actual cash flows in 1990, 1991, and 1992 were $3.38, $3.65, and $4.16.) ▬

The prediction method illustrated in Example 6 is called **linear extrapolation.** Note in Figure 1.36(a) that an extrapolated point does not lie between the given points. When the estimated point lies between two given points, shown in Figure 1.36(b), the procedure is called **linear interpolation.**

Because the slope of a vertical line is not defined, its equation cannot written in slope-intercept form. However, every line has an equation that can be written in the **general form**

$$Ax + By + C = 0,\qquad \textit{General form}$$

where A and B are not both zero. For instance, the vertical line given by $x = a$ can be represented by the general form $x - a = 0$. The five most common forms of equations of lines are summarized below.

Equations of Lines

1. General form:	$Ax + By + C = 0$
2. Vertical line:	$x = a$
3. Horizontal line:	$y = b$
4. Slope-intercept form:	$y = mx + b$
5. Point-slope form:	$y - y_1 = m(x - x_1)$

Parallel and Perpendicular Lines

The slope of a line is a convenient tool for determining whether two lines are parallel or perpendicular.

Parallel and Perpendicular Lines

1. Two distinct nonvertical lines are **parallel** if and only if their slopes are equal. That is, $m_1 = m_2$.
2. Two nonvertical lines are **perpendicular** if and only if their slopes are negative reciprocals of each other. That is, $m_1 = -1/m_2$.

EXAMPLE 7 *Finding Parallel and Perpendicular Lines*

Find an equation of the line that passes through the point $(2, -1)$ and is

a. parallel to the line $2x - 3y = 5$
b. perpendicular to the line $2x - 3y = 5$.

Solution
By writing the given equation in slope-intercept form

$$2x - 3y = 5 \qquad \text{\textit{Given equation}}$$
$$-3y = -2x + 5 \qquad \text{\textit{Subtract 2x from both sides.}}$$
$$y = \tfrac{2}{3}x - \tfrac{5}{3} \qquad \text{\textit{Slope-intercept form}}$$

you can see that it has a slope of $m = \tfrac{2}{3}$, as shown in Figure 1.37.

a. Any line parallel to the given line must also have a slope of $\tfrac{2}{3}$. Thus, the line through $(2, -1)$ that is parallel to the given line has the following equation.

$$y - (-1) = \tfrac{2}{3}(x - 2) \qquad \text{\textit{Point-slope form}}$$
$$3(y + 1) = 2(x - 2) \qquad \text{\textit{Multiply both sides by 3.}}$$
$$3y + 3 = 2x - 4 \qquad \text{\textit{Distribute.}}$$
$$2x - 3y = 7 \qquad \text{\textit{Simplify.}}$$
$$y = \tfrac{2}{3}x - \tfrac{7}{3} \qquad \text{\textit{Slope-intercept form}}$$

b. Any line perpendicular to the given line must have a slope of $-1/(2/3)$ or $-\tfrac{3}{2}$. Therefore, the line through $(2, -1)$ that is perpendicular to the given line has the following equation.

$$y - (-1) = -\tfrac{3}{2}(x - 2) \qquad \text{\textit{Point-slope form}}$$
$$2(y + 1) = -3(x - 2) \qquad \text{\textit{Multiply both sides by 2.}}$$
$$3x + 2y = 4 \qquad \text{\textit{General form}}$$
$$y = -\tfrac{3}{2}x + 2 \qquad \text{\textit{Slope-intercept form}}$$

FIGURE 1.37

Extended Application: Linear Depreciation

Most business expenses can be deducted the same year they occur. One exception to this is the cost of property that has a useful life of more than one year, such as buildings, cars, or equipment. Such costs must be **depreciated** over the useful life of the property. If the *same amount* is depreciated each year, the procedure is called **linear depreciation.**

Real Life

EXAMPLE 8 *Depreciating Equipment*

Your company has purchased a $12,000 machine that has a useful life of 8 years. The salvage value at the end of 8 years is $2000. Write a linear equation that describes the *nondepreciated* value of the machine each year.

Solution

Let V represent the value of the machine at the end of year t. You can represent the initial value of the machine by the ordered pair $(0, 12,000)$ and the salvage value of the machine by the ordered pair $(8, 2000)$. The slope of the line is

$$m = \frac{2000 - 12,000}{8 - 0} = -\$1250,$$

which represents the annual depreciation in *dollars per year.* Using the point-slope form, you can write the equation of the line as follows.

$$V - 12,000 = -1250(t - 0) \qquad \textit{Point-slope form}$$
$$V = -1250t + 12,000 \qquad \textit{Slope-intercept form}$$

Table 1.6 shows the nondepreciated value of the machine at the end of each year.

TABLE 1.6

t	0	1	2	3	4	5	6	7	8
V	12,000	10,750	9500	8250	7000	5750	4500	3250	2000

The graph of this equation is shown in Figure 1.38.

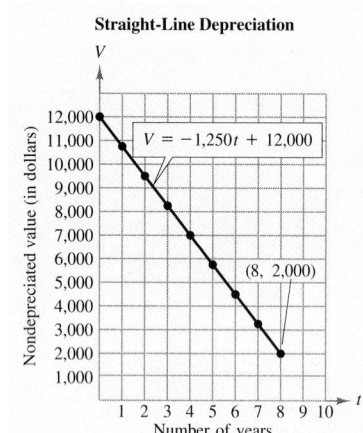

Straight-Line Depreciation

$V = -1,250t + 12,000$

(8, 2,000)

Number of years

FIGURE 1.38

Discussion Problem Comparing Different Types of Depreciation

The Internal Revenue Service allows businesses to choose different types of depreciation. Another type is

$$\textit{Uniform Declining Balances: } V = 12,000 \left(\frac{n - 1.605}{n}\right)^t, \qquad n = 8.$$

Construct a table that compares this type of depreciation with linear depreciation. What are the advantages of each type?

Warm Up

The following warm-up exercises involve skills that were covered in earlier sections. You will use these skills in the exercise set for this section.

In Exercises 1 and 2, simplify the expression.

1. $\dfrac{5 - (-2)}{-3 - 4}$

2. $\dfrac{-7 - (-0)}{4 - 1}$

3. Evaluate $-\dfrac{1}{m}$ when $m = -3$.

4. Evaluate $-\dfrac{1}{m}$ when $m = \dfrac{6}{7}$.

In Exercises 5–10, solve for y in terms of x.

5. $-4x + y = 7$

6. $3x - y = 7$

7. $y - 2 = 3(x - 4)$

8. $y - (-5) = -1[x - (-2)]$

9. $y - (-3) = \dfrac{4 - (-3)}{2 - 1}(x - 2)$

10. $y - 1 = \dfrac{-3 - 1}{-7 - (-1)}[x - (-1)]$

E X E R C I S E S   1.3   means that technology can help you solve or check the exercise(s).

In Exercises 1–6, estimate the slope of the line.

1.

2.

5.

6.

3.

4.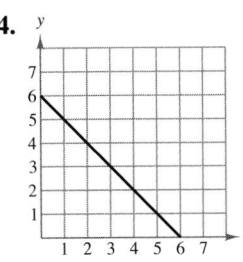

In Exercises 7–14, plot the points and find the slope of the line passing through the points.

7. $(3, -4), (5, 2)$

8. $(-2, 1), (4, -3)$

9. $\left(\dfrac{1}{2}, 2\right), (6, 2)$

10. $\left(-\dfrac{3}{2}, -5\right), \left(\dfrac{5}{6}, 4\right)$

11. $(-8, -3), (-8, -5)$

12. $(2, 1), (2, 5)$

13. $(1, 2), (-2, 2)$

14. $\left(\dfrac{7}{8}, \dfrac{3}{4}\right), \left(\dfrac{5}{4}, -\dfrac{1}{4}\right)$

In Exercises 15–22, use the point on the line and slope of the line to find three additional points on the line. (There are many correct solutions.)

Point	Slope		Point	Slope
15. $(2, 1)$	$m = 0$		**16.** $(-3, 4)$	m undefined
17. $(6, -4)$	$m = -2$		**18.** $(-2, -2)$	$m = 2$
19. $(1, 7)$	$m = -3$		**20.** $(10, -6)$	$m = -1$
21. $(-8, 1)$	m undefined		**22.** $(-3, -1)$	$m = 0$

In Exercises 23–28, find the slope and y-intercept (if possible) of the line.

23. $x + 5y = 20$
24. $2x + y = 40$
25. $7x - 5y = 15$
26. $6x - 5y = 15$
27. $x = 4$
28. $y = -1$

 In Exercises 29–36, write an equation of the line that passes through the points. Then use the equation to sketch the line.

29. $(4, 3), (0, -5)$
30. $(-3, -4), (1, 4)$
31. $(0, 0), (-1, 3)$
32. $(-3, 6), (1, 2)$
33. $(2, 3), (2, -2)$
34. $(6, 1), (10, 1)$
35. $(1, -2), (3, -2)$
36. $\left(\frac{7}{8}, \frac{3}{4}\right), \left(\frac{5}{4}, -\frac{1}{4}\right)$

 In Exercises 37–46, write an equation of the indicated line. Then use the equation to sketch the line.

Point	Slope		Point	Slope
37. $(0, 3)$	$m = \frac{3}{4}$		**38.** $(-1, 2)$	m undefined
39. $(0, 0)$	$m = \frac{2}{3}$		**40.** $(-1, -4)$	$m = \frac{1}{4}$
41. $(-2, 7)$	$m = -3$		**42.** $(-2, 4)$	$m = -\frac{3}{5}$
43. $(0, 2)$	$m = 4$		**44.** $\left(0, -\frac{2}{3}\right)$	$m = \frac{1}{6}$
45. $\left(0, \frac{2}{3}\right)$	$m = \frac{3}{4}$		**46.** $(0, 4)$	$m = 0$

In Exercises 47 and 48, explain how to use the concept of slope to determine whether the three points are collinear. Then explain how to use the Distance Formula to determine whether the points are collinear.

47. $(-2, 1), (-1, 0), (2, -2)$
48. $(0, 4), (7, -6), (-5, 11)$

49. Write an equation of the vertical line with x-intercept at 3.

50. Write an equation of the horizontal line through $(0, -5)$.

In Exercises 51–58, write an equation of the line through the given point (a) parallel to the given line and (b) perpendicular to the given line. Then graph all three equations on the same set of coordinate axes.

Point	Line		Point	Line
51. $(-3, 2)$	$x + y = 7$		**52.** $(2, 1)$	$4x - 2y = 3$
53. $(-6, 4)$	$3x + 4y = 7$		**54.** $\left(\frac{7}{8}, \frac{3}{4}\right)$	$5x + 3y = 0$
55. $(-1, 0)$	$y = -3$		**56.** $(2, 5)$	$x = 4$
57. $(1, 1)$	$-2x + 3y = -3$		**58.** $(12, -3)$	$x + 4y = 4$

In Exercises 59–66, sketch the graph of the equation.

59. $y = -2$
60. $x = 4$
61. $2x - y - 3 = 0$
62. $x + 2y + 6 = 0$
63. $y = -2x + 1$
64. $y - 1 = 3(x + 4)$
65. $y + 2 = -4(x + 1)$
66. $4x + 5y = 20$

67. *Temperature Conversion* Write a linear equation that expresses the relationship between the temperature in degrees Celsius, C, and degrees Fahrenheit, F. Use the fact that water freezes at $0°$ Celsius ($32°$ Fahrenheit) and boils at $100°$ Celsius ($212°$ Fahrenheit).

68. *Temperature Conversion* Use the result of Exercise 67 to complete the table.

C		$-10°$	$10°$			$177°$
F	$0°$			$68°$	$90°$	

69. *Reimbursed Expenses* A company reimburses its sales representatives $100 per day for lodging and meals, plus $0.25 per mile driven. Write a linear equation giving the daily cost C in terms of x, the number of miles driven.

70. *Union Negotiation* You are on a negotiating panel in a union hearing for a large corporation. The union is asking for a base pay of $8.75 per hour *plus* an additional piecework rate of $0.80 per unit produced. The corporation is offering a base pay of $6.35 per hour *plus* a piecework rate of $1.15.

(a) Write a linear equation for the hourly wages W in terms of x, the number of units produced per hour, for each pay schedule.

(b) Use a graphing utility to graph each linear equation and find the point of intersection.

(c) Interpret the meaning of the point of intersection of the graphs. How would you use this information to advise the corporation and the union?

71. Annual Salary Your annual salary was $26,300 in 1992 and $29,700 in 1994. Assume your salary can be modeled by a linear equation.

(a) Write a linear equation giving your salary S in terms of the year t where $t = 0$ corresponds to the year 1992.

(b) Use the linear model to predict your salary in 1997.

(c) Does a linear model assume that your salary increases by the same *amount* each year or the same *percent* each year? Explain.

(d) If you assume your salary can be modeled by the equation $S = 26,300(1.0627)^t$, would it be increasing by the same *amount* each year or the same *percent*? Would you prefer this model over the linear one? Explain.   *What is that %*

72. Linear Depreciation A company constructs a warehouse for $825,000. The warehouse has an estimated useful life of 25 years, after which its value is expected to be $75,000. Write a linear equation giving the value y of the warehouse during its 25 years of useful life. (Let t represent the time in years.)

 73. Linear Depreciation A small business purchases a piece of equipment for $1025. After 5 years the equipment will be outdated, having no value.

(a) Write a linear equation giving the value of the equipment in terms of the time t, $0 \le t \le 5$.

(b) Use a graphing utility to graph the equation.

(c) Move the cursor along the graph and estimate (to two decimal place accuracy) the value of the equipment when $t = 3$.

(d) Move the cursor along the graph and estimate (to two decimal place accuracy) the time when the value of the equipment will be $600.

74. Apartment Rental A real estate office handles an apartment complex with 50 units. When the rent is $380 per month, all 50 units are occupied. When the rent is $425, however, the average number of occupied units drops to 47. Assume that the relationship between the monthly rent p and the demand x is linear. (The term *demand* refers to the number of occupied units.)

(a) Write a linear equation expressing x in terms of p.

(b) *Linear Extrapolation* Predict the number of occupied units when the rent is set at $455.

(c) *Linear Interpolation* Predict the number of occupied units when the rent is set at $395.

 75. Profit You are a contractor and have purchased a piece of equipment for $26,500. The equipment costs an average of $5.25 per hour for fuel and maintenance, and the operator is paid $9.50 per hour.

(a) Write a linear equation giving the total cost C of operating the equipment for t hours.

(b) You charge your customers $25 per hour of machine use. Write an equation for the revenue R derived from t hours of use.

(c) Use the formula for profit, $P = R - C$, to write an equation for the profit derived from t hours of use.

(d) Find the number of hours you must operate the equipment before you break even.

76. Research Project Personal income (in billions of dollars) in the United States was 3380 in 1985 and 4834 in 1991. Assume that the relationship between the personal income Y and the time t (in years) is linear. Let $t = 0$ correspond to 1985. *(Source: U.S. Bureau of Economic Analysis)*

(a) Write a linear model for the data.

(b) *Linear Interpolation* Estimate the personal income in 1988.

(c) *Linear Extrapolation* Estimate the personal income in 1992.

(d) Use your school's library or some other reference source to find the actual personal income in 1988 and 1992. How close were your estimates?

 In Exercises 77–82, use a graphing utility to graph the cost function. Determine the maximum production level x, given that the cost C cannot exceed $100,000.

77. $C = 23,500 + 3100x$ **78.** $C = 30,000 + 575x$

79. $C = 18,375 + 1150x$ **80.** $C = 24,900 + 1785x$

81. $C = 75,500 + 89x$ **82.** $C = 83,620 + 67x$

 83. Sales Commission As a salesperson, you receive a monthly salary of $2000, plus a commission of 7% of sales. You are offered a new job at $2300 per month, plus a commission of 5% of sales.

(a) Write a linear equation for your current monthly wage W in terms of your monthly sales S.

(b) Write a linear equation for the monthly wage W of your job offer in terms of the monthly sales S.

(c) Use a graphing utility to graph both equations on the same viewing rectangle. Find the point of intersection. What does it signify?

(d) You think you can sell $20,000 per month. Should you change jobs? Explain.

Functions ■ *The Graph of a Function* ■ *Function Notation* ■
Combinations of Functions ■ *Inverse Functions*

Functions

In many common relationships between two variables, the value of one of the variables depends on the value of the other variable. For example, the sales tax on an item depends on its selling price, the distance an object moves in a given amount of time depends on its speed, the price of mailing a package with an overnight delivery service depends on the package's weight, and the area of a circle depends on its radius.

Consider the relationship between the area of a circle and its radius. This relationship can be expressed by the equation

$$A = \pi r^2.$$

In this equation, the value of A depends on the choice of r. Because of this, A is the **dependent variable** and r is the **independent variable.**

Most of the relationships that you will study in this course have the property that for a given value of the independent variable, there corresponds exactly one value of the dependent variable. Such a relationship is a **function.**

Definition of a Function

A **function** is a relationship between two variables such that to each value of the independent variable there corresponds exactly one value of the dependent variable.

The **domain** of the function is the set of all values of the independent variable for which the function is defined. The **range** of the function is the set of all values taken on by the dependent variable.

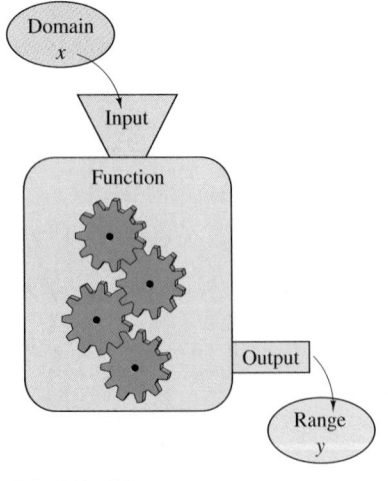

FIGURE 1.39

In Figure 1.39, notice that you can think of a function as a machine that inputs values of the independent variable and outputs values of the dependent variable.

Although functions can be described by various means such as tables, graphs, or diagrams, they are most often specified by formulas or equations. For instance, the equation $y = 4x^2 + 3$ describes y as a function of x. For this function, x is the independent variable and y is the dependent variable.

■ **TECHNOLOGY**

The procedure used in Example 1, isolating the dependent variable on the left side, is also useful for graphing equations with a graphing utility. In fact, the standard graphing program on most graphing utilities is a "function grapher." To graph equations in which y is not a function of x, such as a circle, you usually have to enter two or more equations into the graphing utility.

EXAMPLE 1 *Deciding Whether Relations Are Functions*

Which of the following equations define y as a function of x?

a. $x + y = 1$ **b.** $x^2 + y^2 = 1$
c. $x^2 + y = 1$ **d.** $x + y^2 = 1$

Solution

To decide whether an equation defines a function, it is helpful to isolate the dependent variable on the left side. For instance, to decide whether the equation $x + y = 1$ defines y as a function of x, write the equation in the form

$$y = 1 - x.$$

From this form, you can see that for any value of x, there is exactly one value of y. Thus, y is a function of x.

	Original Equation	*Rewritten Equation*	*Test: Is y a function of x?*
a.	$x + y = 1$	$y = 1 - x$	Yes, each value of x determines exactly one value of y.
b.	$x^2 + y^2 = 1$	$y = \pm\sqrt{1 - x^2}$	No, some values of x determine two values of y.
c.	$x^2 + y = 1$	$y = 1 - x^2$	Yes, each value of x determines exactly one value of y.
d.	$x + y^2 = 1$	$y = \pm\sqrt{1 - x}$	No, some values of x determine two values of y.

Note that the equations that assign two values ($\pm$) to the dependent variable for a given value of the independent variable do not define functions of x. For instance, in part b, when $x = 0$, the equation

$$y = \pm\sqrt{1 - x^2}$$

indicates that $y = +1$ or $y = -1$. Figure 1.40 shows the graphs of the four equations.

(a)

(b)

(c)

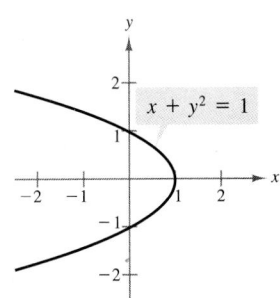

(d)

FIGURE 1.40

The Graph of a Function

When the graph of a function is sketched, the standard convention is to let the horizontal axis represent the independent variable. When this convention is used, the test described in Example 1 has a nice graphical interpretation called the **vertical line test.** This test states that if every vertical line intersects the graph of an equation at most once, then the equation defines y as a function of x. For instance, in Figure 1.40, the graphs in parts (a) and (c) pass the vertical line test, but those in parts (b) and (d) do not.

The domain of a function may be described explicitly, or it may be *implied* by an equation used to define the function. For example, the function given by $y = 1/(x^2 - 4)$ has an implied domain that consists of all real x except $x = \pm 2$. These two values are excluded from the domain because division by zero is undefined.

Another type of implied domain is that used to avoid even roots of negative numbers, as indicated in Example 2.

EXAMPLE 2 *Finding the Domain and Range of a Function*

Find the domain and range of the following functions.

a. $y = \sqrt{x - 1}$ **b.** $y = \begin{cases} 1 - x, & x < 1 \\ \sqrt{x - 1}, & x \geq 1 \end{cases}$

Solution

a. Because $\sqrt{x - 1}$ is not defined for $x - 1 < 0$ (that is, for $x < 1$), it follows that the domain of the function is the interval $x \geq 1$ or $[1, \infty)$. To find the range, observe that $\sqrt{x - 1}$ is never negative. Moreover, as x takes on the various values in the domain, y takes on all nonnegative values. Thus, the range is the interval $y \geq 0$ or $[0, \infty)$. The graph of the function, shown in Figure 1.41(a), confirms these results.

b. Because this **compound** function is defined for $x < 1$ *and* for $x \geq 1$, the domain is the entire set of real numbers. When $x \geq 1$, the function behaves as in part a. For $x < 1$, the value of $1 - x$ is positive, and therefore the range of the function is $y \geq 0$ or $[0, \infty)$, as shown in Figure 1.41(b). ▪

A function is **one-to-one** if to each value of the dependent variable in the range there corresponds exactly one value of the independent variable. For instance, the function in Example 2a is one-to-one, whereas the function in Example 2b is not one-to-one.

Geometrically, a function is one-to-one if every horizontal line intersects the graph of the function at most once. This geometrical interpretation is the **horizontal line test** for one-to-one functions. Thus, a graph that represents a one-to-one function must satisfy *both* the vertical line test and the horizontal line test.

(a)

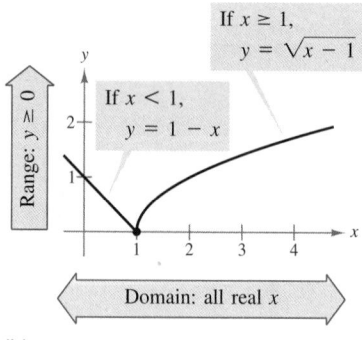

(b)

FIGURE 1.41

Function Notation

When using an equation to define a function, you generally isolate the dependent variable on the left. For instance, writing the equation $x + 2y = 1$ as

$$y = \frac{1 - x}{2}$$

indicates that y is the dependent variable. In **function notation,** this equation has the form

$$f(x) = \frac{1 - x}{2}. \qquad\qquad \textit{Function notation}$$

The independent variable is x, and the name of the function is "f." The symbol $f(x)$ is read as "f of x," and it denotes the value of the dependent variable. For instance, the value of f when $x = 3$ is

$$f(3) = \frac{1 - (3)}{2} = \frac{-2}{2} = -1.$$

The value $f(3)$ is called a **function value,** and it lies in the range of f. This means that the point $(3, f(3))$ lies on the graph of f. One of the advantages of function notation is that it allows you to be less wordy. For instance, instead of asking "What is the value of y when $x = 3$?" you can ask "What is $f(3)$?"

EXAMPLE 3 *Evaluating a Function*

Find the value of the function

$$f(x) = 2x^2 - 4x + 1$$

when x is $-1, 0$, and 2. Is f one-to-one?

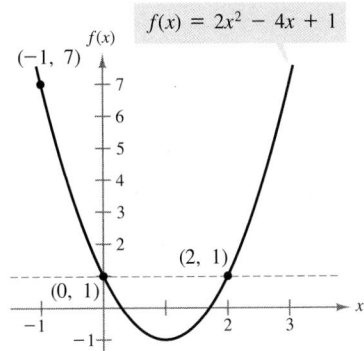

$f(x) = 2x^2 - 4x + 1$

FIGURE 1.42

Solution
When $x = -1$, the value of f is

$$f(-1) = 2(-1)^2 - 4(-1) + 1 = 2 + 4 + 1 = 7.$$

When $x = 0$, the value of f is

$$f(0) = 2(0)^2 - 4(0) + 1 = 0 - 0 + 1 = 1.$$

When $x = 2$, the value of f is

$$f(2) = 2(2)^2 - 4(2) + 1 = 8 - 8 + 1 = 1.$$

Because two different values of x yield the same value of $f(x)$, the function is *not* one-to-one, as shown in Figure 1.42. ▬

Note You can use the horizontal line test to determine whether the function in Example 3 is one-to-one. Because the line $y = 1$ intersects the graph of the function twice, the function is *not* one-to-one.

TECHNOLOGY

Most graphing utilities can be programmed to evaluate functions. The program depends on the calculator used. Here is a sample program for the *TI-81* or *TI-82*. See Appendix D for other calculator models.

```
Prgm: EVALUATE
:Lbl 1
:Disp ''ENTER X''
:Input X
:Disp Y₁
:Goto 1
```

To use this program, enter a function in Y_1. Then run the program—it will allow you to evaluate the function at several values of x.

Example 3 suggests that the role of the variable x in the equation

$$f(x) = 2x^2 - 4x + 1$$

is simply that of a placeholder. Informally, f could be defined by the equation

$$f(\ \ \ ) = 2(\ \ \ )^2 - 4(\ \ \ ) + 1.$$

To evaluate $f(-2)$, simply place -2 in each set of parentheses.

$$f(-2) = 2(-2)^2 - 4(-2) + 1 = 8 + 8 + 1 = 17$$

The ratio in part b of the next example is called a *difference quotient*. In Section 2.1, you will see that it has special significance in calculus.

EXAMPLE 4 *Evaluating a Function*

For the function $f(x) = x^2 - 4x + 7$, evaluate the following.

a. $f(x + \Delta x)$ **b.** $\dfrac{f(x + \Delta x) - f(x)}{\Delta x}$

Solution

a. To evaluate f at $x + \Delta x$, substitute $x + \Delta x$ into each set of parentheses, as follows.

$$f(x + \Delta x) = (x + \Delta x)^2 - 4(x + \Delta x) + 7$$
$$= x^2 + 2x\Delta x + (\Delta x)^2 - 4x - 4\Delta x + 7$$

b. Using the result of part a, you can write the following.

$$\frac{f(x + \Delta x) - f(x)}{\Delta x}$$
$$= \frac{[(x + \Delta x)^2 - 4(x + \Delta x) + 7] - [x^2 - 4x + 7]}{\Delta x}$$
$$= \frac{x^2 + 2x\Delta x + (\Delta x)^2 - 4x - 4\Delta x + 7 - x^2 + 4x - 7}{\Delta x}$$
$$= \frac{2x\Delta x + (\Delta x)^2 - 4\Delta x}{\Delta x}$$
$$= 2x + \Delta x - 4, \qquad \Delta x \neq 0$$

Although f is often used as a convenient function name and x as the independent variable, you can use other symbols. For instance, the following equations all define the same function.

$$f(x) = x^2 - 4x + 7$$
$$f(t) = t^2 - 4t + 7$$
$$g(s) = s^2 - 4s + 7$$

Combinations of Functions

Two functions can be combined in various ways to create new functions. For instance, if $f(x) = 2x - 3$ and $g(x) = x^2 + 1$, you can form the following functions.

$$f(x) + g(x) = (2x - 3) + (x^2 + 1) = x^2 + 2x - 2 \qquad \textit{Sum}$$

$$f(x) - g(x) = (2x - 3) - (x^2 + 1) = -x^2 + 2x - 4 \qquad \textit{Difference}$$

$$f(x)g(x) = (2x - 3)(x^2 + 1) = 2x^3 - 3x^2 + 2x - 3 \qquad \textit{Product}$$

$$\frac{f(x)}{g(x)} = \frac{2x - 3}{x^2 + 1} \qquad \textit{Quotient}$$

You can combine two functions in yet another way called the **composition**. The resulting function is a **composite function.**

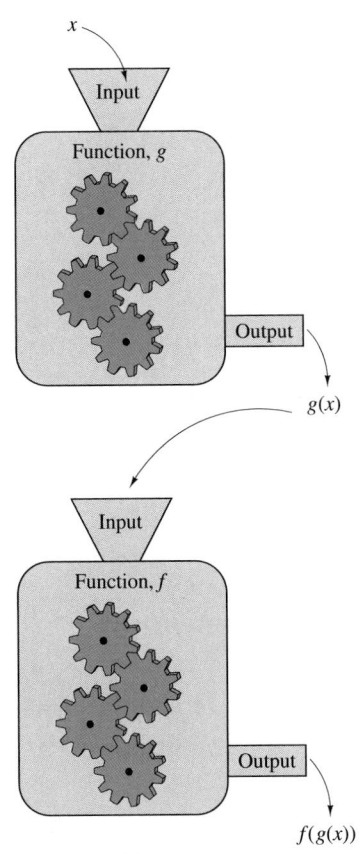

FIGURE 1.43

Definition of Composite Function

The function given by $(f \circ g)(x) = f(g(x))$ is the **composite** of f with g. The **domain** of $(f \circ g)$ is the set of all x in the domain of g such that $g(x)$ is in the domain of f, as indicated in Figure 1.43.

The composite of f with g may not be equal to the composite of g with f, as illustrated in the following example.

EXAMPLE 5 *Forming Composite Functions*

Given $f(x) = 2x - 3$ and $g(x) = x^2 + 1$, find the following.

a. $f(g(x))$ **b.** $g(f(x))$

Solution
a. The composite of f with g is given by

$$f(g(x)) = 2(g(x)) - 3 \qquad \textit{Evaluate } f \textit{ at } g(x).$$
$$= 2(x^2 + 1) - 3 \qquad \textit{Substitute } x^2 + 1 \textit{ for } g(x).$$
$$= 2x^2 - 1. \qquad \textit{Simplify.}$$

b. The composite of g with f is given by

$$g(f(x)) = (f(x))^2 + 1 \qquad \textit{Evaluate } g \textit{ at } f(x).$$
$$= (2x - 3)^2 + 1 \qquad \textit{Substitute } 2x - 3 \textit{ for } f(x).$$
$$= 4x^2 - 12x + 10. \qquad \textit{Simplify.}$$

Inverse Functions

Informally, the inverse of a function f is another function g that "undoes" what f has done.

$$x \xrightarrow{\;\;\;f\;\;\;} f(x) \xrightarrow{\;\;\;g\;\;\;} g(f(x)) = x$$

Definition of Inverse Function

Two functions, f and g, are **inverses** of each other if

$$f(g(x)) = x$$

for each x in the domain of g and

$$g(f(x)) = x$$

for each x in the domain of f. The function g is denoted by f^{-1}, which is read as "f inverse." For f and g to be inverses of each other, the range of g must be equal to the domain of f, and vice versa.

Note   Don't be confused by the "exponential notation" for inverse functions. Whenever we write $f^{-1}(x)$, we will *always* be referring to the inverse of the function f, not to the reciprocal of f.

EXAMPLE 6   *Finding Inverse Functions*

Several functions and their inverses are shown below. In each case, note that the inverse function "undoes" the original function. For instance, to undo multiplication by 2, you should divide by 2.

a. $f(x) = 2x$ $f^{-1}(x) = \frac{1}{2}x$

b. $f(x) = \frac{1}{3}x$ $f^{-1}(x) = 3x$

c. $f(x) = x + 4$ $f^{-1}(x) = x - 4$

d. $f(x) = 2x - 5$ $f^{-1}(x) = \frac{1}{2}(x + 5)$

e. $f(x) = x^3$ $f^{-1}(x) = \sqrt[3]{x}$

f. $f(x) = \dfrac{1}{x}$ $f^{-1}(x) = \dfrac{1}{x}$

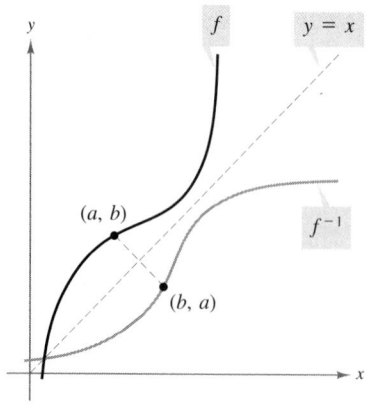

FIGURE 1.44   The graph of f^{-1} is a reflection of the graph of f in the line $y = x$.

The graphs of f and f^{-1} are mirror images of each other (with respect to the line $y = x$), as shown in Figure 1.44. Try using a graphing utility to confirm this for each of the functions given in Example 6.

The functions in Example 6 are simple enough so that their inverses can be found by inspection. The next example demonstrates a strategy for finding the inverses of more complicated functions.

EXAMPLE 7 *Finding the Inverse of a Function*

Find the inverse of the function $f(x) = \sqrt{2x - 3}$.

Solution

Begin by substituting y for $f(x)$. Then, interchange x and y and solve for y.

$$f(x) = \sqrt{2x - 3} \qquad\qquad \text{\textit{Original function}}$$
$$y = \sqrt{2x - 3} \qquad\qquad \text{\textit{Substitute } y \text{ for } f(x).}$$
$$x = \sqrt{2y - 3} \qquad\qquad \text{\textit{Interchange } x \text{ and } y.}$$
$$x^2 = 2y - 3 \qquad\qquad \text{\textit{Square both sides.}}$$
$$x^2 + 3 = 2y \qquad\qquad \text{\textit{Add 3 to both sides.}}$$
$$\frac{x^2 + 3}{2} = y \qquad\qquad \text{\textit{Divide both sides by 2.}}$$

Thus, the inverse function has the form

$$f^{-1}(\rule{0.5cm}{0.2cm}) = \frac{(\rule{0.5cm}{0.2cm})^2 + 3}{2}.$$

Using x as the independent variable, you can write

$$f^{-1}(x) = \frac{x^2 + 3}{2}, \qquad x \geq 0.$$

In Figure 1.45, note that the domain of f^{-1} coincides with the range of f. ▪

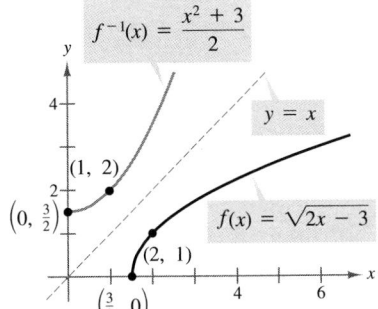

$f^{-1}(x) = \dfrac{x^2 + 3}{2}$

$y = x$

$(1, 2)$

$\left(0, \frac{3}{2}\right)$

$f(x) = \sqrt{2x - 3}$

$(2, 1)$

$\left(\frac{3}{2}, 0\right)$

FIGURE 1.45

After you have found the inverse of a function, you should check your results. You can check your results *graphically* by observing that the graphs of f and f^{-1} are reflections of each other in the line $y = x$. You can check your results *algebraically* by evaluating $f(f^{-1}(x))$ and $f^{-1}(f(x))$—both should be equal to x.

Check That $f(f^{-1}(x)) = x$

$$f(f^{-1}(x)) = f\left(\frac{x^2 + 3}{2}\right)$$
$$= \sqrt{2\left(\frac{x^2 + 3}{2}\right) - 3}$$
$$= \sqrt{x^2}$$
$$= x, \qquad x \geq 0$$

Check That $f^{-1}(f(x)) = x$

$$f^{-1}(f(x)) = f^{-1}\left(\sqrt{2x - 3}\right)$$
$$= \frac{(\sqrt{2x - 3})^2 + 3}{2}$$
$$= \frac{2x}{2}$$
$$= x, \qquad x \geq \frac{3}{2}$$

Not every function possesses an inverse. In fact, for a function to have an inverse, it must be one-to-one.

EXAMPLE 8 *A Function That Has No Inverse*

Show that the function

$$f(x) = x^2 - 1$$

has no inverse. (Assume that the domain of f is the set of all real numbers.)

Solution

Begin by sketching the graph of f, as shown in Figure 1.46. Note that

$$f(2) = (2)^2 - 1 = 3$$

and

$$f(-2) = (-2)^2 - 1 = 3.$$

Thus f does not pass the horizontal line test, which implies that it is not one-to-one, and therefore has no inverse. The same conclusion can by obtained by trying to find the inverse of f.

$f(x) = x^2 - 1$	*Original function*
$y = x^2 - 1$	*Substitute y for $f(x)$.*
$x = y^2 - 1$	*Interchange x and y.*
$x + 1 = y^2$	*Add 1 to both sides.*
$\pm\sqrt{x + 1} = y$	*Take square root of both sides.*

The last equation does not define y as a function of x, and thus f has no inverse.

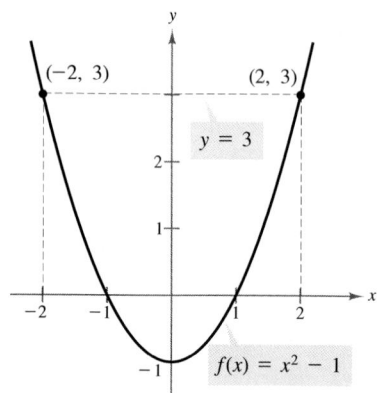

FIGURE 1.46 f is not one-to-one and has no inverse.

Discussion Problem   Comparing Composition Orders

You are buying an automobile whose price is $14,500. Which of the following options would you choose? Explain.

a. You are given a factory rebate of $2000, followed by a dealer discount of 10%.

b. You are given a dealer discount of 10%, followed by a factory rebate of $2000.

Let $f(x) = x - 2000$ and let $g(x) = 0.9x$. Which option is represented by the composite $f(g(x))$? Which is represented by the composite $g(f(x))$?

Warm Up

The following warm-up exercises involve skills that were covered in earlier sections. You will use these skills in the exercise set for this section.

In Exercises 1–6, simplify the expression.

1. $5(-1)^2 - 6(-1) + 9$

2. $(-2)^3 + 7(-2)^2 - 10$

3. $(x - 2)^2 + 5x - 10$

4. $(3 - x) + (x + 3)^3$

5. $\dfrac{1}{1 - (1 - x)}$

6. $1 + \dfrac{x - 1}{x}$

In Exercises 7–10, solve for y in terms of x.

7. $2x + y - 6 = 11$

8. $5y - 6x^2 - 1 = 0$

9. $(y - 3)^2 = 5 + (x + 1)^2$

10. $y^2 - 4x^2 = 2$

E X E R C I S E S   1.4   means that technology can help you solve or check the exercise(s).

In Exercises 1–6, evaluate the function at the specified values of the independent variable. Simplify the result.

1. $f(x) = 2x - 3$
  (a) $f(0)$ (b) $f(-3)$
  (c) $f(x - 1)$ (d) $f(1 + \Delta x)$

2. $f(x) = x^2 - 2x + 2$
  (a) $f\left(\frac{1}{2}\right)$ (b) $f(-1)$
  (c) $f(c)$ (d) $f(x + \Delta x)$

3. $g(x) = \frac{1}{2}x^2$
  (a) $g(-2)$ (b) $g(6)$
  (c) $g(c)$ (d) $g(x + \Delta x)$

4. $g(x) = \dfrac{1}{x}$
  (a) $g(2)$ (b) $g\left(\frac{1}{4}\right)$
  (c) $g(x + \Delta x)$ (d) $g(x + \Delta x) - g(x)$

5. $f(x) = \dfrac{|x|}{x}$
  (a) $f(2)$ (b) $f(-2)$
  (c) $f(x^2)$ (d) $f(x - 1)$

6. $f(x) = |x| + 4$
  (a) $f(2)$ (b) $f(-2)$
  (c) $f(x^2)$ (d) $f(x + \Delta x) - f(x)$

In Exercises 7–12, evaluate the difference quotient and simplify the result.

7. $f(x) = 3x - 1$
$$\dfrac{f(x + \Delta x) - f(x)}{\Delta x}$$

8. $f(x) = 5 - 4x$
$$\dfrac{f(x + \Delta x) - f(x)}{\Delta x}$$

9. $h(x) = x^2 - x + 1$
$$\dfrac{h(2 + \Delta x) - h(2)}{\Delta x}$$

10. $h(x) = x^3$
$$\dfrac{h(x + \Delta x) - h(x)}{\Delta x}$$

11. $f(x) = x^3 - x$
$$\dfrac{f(x + \Delta x) - f(x)}{\Delta x}$$

12. $f(x) = \dfrac{1}{\sqrt{x - 1}}$
$$\dfrac{f(x) - f(2)}{x - 2}$$

In Exercises 13–20, decide whether the equation defines y as a function of x.

13. $x^2 + y^2 = 4$

14. $3x - 2y + 5 = 0$

15. $\frac{1}{2}x - 6y = -3$

16. $x + y^2 = 4$

17. $x^2 + y = 4$

18. $x^2 + y^2 - 2x - 4y + 1 = 0$

19. $y^2 = x^2 - 1$

20. $x^2 y - x^2 + 4y = 0$

In Exercises 21–26, find the domain and range of the function. Use interval notation to write your result.

21. $f(x) = 4 - 2x$

22. $f(x) = x^3$

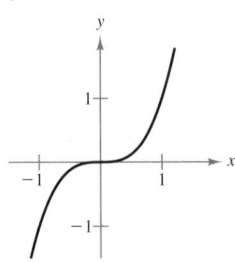

23. $f(x) = \sqrt{2x - 3}$

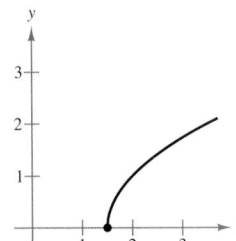

24. $f(x) = 4 - x^2$

25. $f(x) = \dfrac{1}{|x|}$

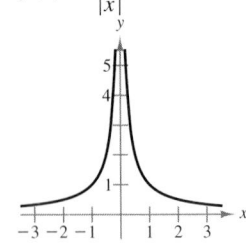

26. $f(x) = |x - 2|$

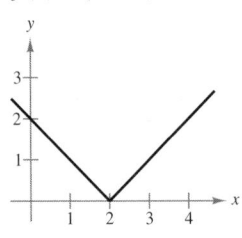

In Exercises 27–32, use a graphing utility to graph the function. Then determine the domain and range of the function.

27. $f(x) = \sqrt{9 - x^2}$

28. $f(x) = 5x^3 + 6x^2 - 1$

29. $f(x) = \dfrac{|x|}{x}$

30. $f(x) = \dfrac{1}{\sqrt{x}}$

31. $f(x) = \dfrac{x - 2}{x + 4}$

32. $f(x) = \dfrac{x^2}{1 - x}$

In Exercises 33–38, use the vertical line test to determine whether y is a function of x.

33. $y = x^2$

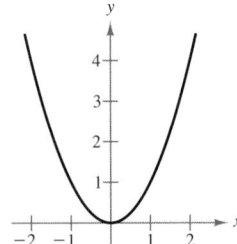

34. $y = x^3 - 1$

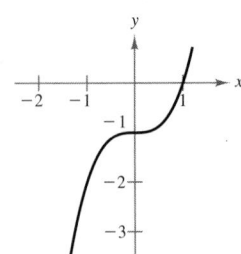

35. $x^2 + y^2 = 9$

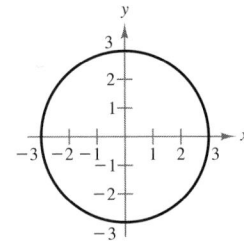

36. $x - xy + y + 1 = 0$

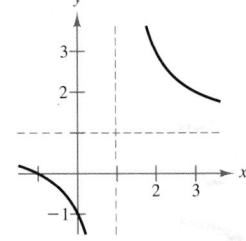

37. $x^2 = xy - 1$

38. $x = |y|$

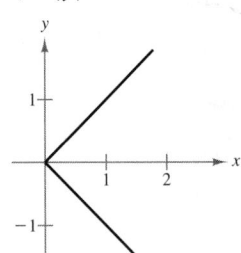

In Exercises 39–46, find (a) $f(x) + g(x)$, (b) $f(x) \cdot g(x)$, and (c) $f(x)/g(x)$. Also, find (d) $f(g(x))$ and (e) $g(f(x))$ if defined.

39. $f(x) = x + 1$ $g(x) = x - 1$

40. $f(x) = 2x - 5$ $g(x) = 1 - x$

41. $f(x) = 2x^2$ $g(x) = x^2 - 1$

42. $f(x) = 2x - 5$ $g(x) = 5$

43. $f(x) = x^2 + 5$ $g(x) = \sqrt{1 - x}$

44. $f(x) = \sqrt{x^2 - 4}$ $g(x) = \dfrac{x^2}{x^2 + 1}$

45. $f(x) = \dfrac{1}{x}$ $g(x) = \dfrac{1}{x^2}$

46. $f(x) = \dfrac{x}{x + 1}$ $g(x) = x^3$

In Exercises 47–52, show that f and g are inverse functions by showing that $f(g(x)) = x$ and $g(f(x)) = x$. Then sketch the graphs of f and g on the same coordinate axes.

47. $f(x) = x^3$ $g(x) = \sqrt[3]{x}$

48. $f(x) = \dfrac{1}{x}$ $g(x) = \dfrac{1}{x}$

49. $f(x) = 5x + 1$ $g(x) = \dfrac{x - 1}{5}$

50. $f(x) = 9 - x^2$, $x \geq 0$ $g(x) = \sqrt{9 - x}$, $x \leq 9$

51. $f(x) = \sqrt{x - 4}$ $g(x) = x^2 + 4$, $x \geq 0$

52. $f(x) = 1 - x^3$ $g(x) = \sqrt[3]{1 - x}$

In Exercises 53–60, find the inverse of f. Then sketch the graphs of f and f^{-1} on the same coordinate axes.

53. $f(x) = 2x - 3$ **54.** $f(x) = 6 - 3x$

55. $f(x) = x^5$ **56.** $f(x) = x^3 + 1$

57. $f(x) = \sqrt{9 - x^2}$, $0 \leq x \leq 3$

58. $f(x) = \sqrt{x^2 - 4}$, $x \geq 2$

59. $f(x) = x^{2/3}$, $x \geq 0$

60. $f(x) = x^{3/5}$

In Exercises 61–66, graph the function. Then use the horizontal line test to decide whether the function is one-to-one. If it is, find its inverse.

61. $f(x) = 3 - 7x$ **62.** $f(x) = \sqrt{x - 2}$

63. $f(x) = x^2$ **64.** $f(x) = x^4$

65. $f(x) = |x - 2|$ **66.** $f(x) = 3$

67. Given $f(x) = \sqrt{x}$ and $g(x) = x^2 - 1$, find the composite functions.
  (a) $f(g(1))$ (b) $g(f(1))$
  (c) $g(f(0))$ (d) $f(g(-4))$
  (e) $f(g(x))$ (f) $g(f(x))$

68. Given $f(x) = 1/x$ and $g(x) = x^2 - 1$, find the composite functions.
  (a) $f(g(2))$ (b) $g(f(2))$
  (c) $f\left(g\left(1/\sqrt{2}\right)\right)$ (d) $g\left(f\left(1/\sqrt{2}\right)\right)$
  (e) $f(g(x))$ (f) $g(f(x))$

In Exercises 69–72, select a function from (a) $f(x) = cx$, (b) $g(x) = cx^2$, (c) $h(x) = c\sqrt{|x|}$, or (d) $r(x) = c/x$ and determine the value of the constant c so that the function fits the data in the table.

69.

x	-4	-1	0	1	4
y	-32	-2	0	-2	-32

70.

x	-4	-1	0	1	4
y	-1	$-\frac{1}{4}$	0	$\frac{1}{4}$	1

71.

x	-4	-1	0	1	4
y	-8	-32	undef.	32	8

72.

x	-4	-1	0	1	4
y	6	3	0	3	6

73. Use the graph of $f(x) = \sqrt{x}$ below to sketch the graph of each function.
  (a) $y = \sqrt{x} + 2$
  (b) $y = -\sqrt{x}$
  (c) $y = \sqrt{x - 2}$
  (d) $y = \sqrt{x + 3}$
  (e) $y = \sqrt{x - 4}$
  (f) $y = 2\sqrt{x}$

74. Use the graph of $f(x) = x^2$ to find a formula for each of the functions whose graphs are shown.
  (a)   (b)

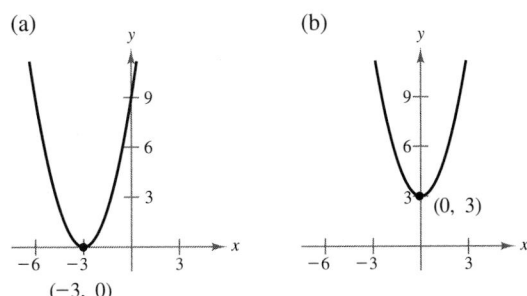

$(-3, 0)$ $(0, 3)$

75. *Real Estate* Express the value V of a real estate firm in terms of x, the number of acres of property owned. Each acre is valued at \$2500 and other company assets total \$750,000.

76. *Cost* The inventor of a new game believes that the variable cost for producing the game is $0.95 per unit. The fixed cost is $6000.
  (a) Express the total cost C as a function of x, the number of games sold.
  (b) Find a formula for the average cost per unit $\overline{C} = C/x$.
  (c) The selling price for each game is $1.69. How many units must be sold before the average cost per unit falls below the selling price?

77. *Demand* The demand function for a commodity is

$$p = \frac{14.75}{1 + 0.01x}, \qquad x \geq 0,$$

where p is the price per unit and x is the number of units sold.
  (a) Find x as a function of p.
  (b) Find the number of units sold when the price is $10.

78. *Cost* A power station is on one side of a river that is $\frac{1}{2}$ mile wide. A factory is 3 miles downstream on the other side of the river (see figure). It costs $10/ft to run the power lines on land and $15/ft to run them underwater. Express the cost C of running the line from the power station to the factory as a function of x.

79. *Market Equilibrium* The supply function for a product relates the number of units x that producers are willing to supply for a given price per unit p. The supply and demand functions for a market are

$$p = \tfrac{2}{5}x + 4 \qquad Supply$$
$$p = -\tfrac{16}{25}x + 30. \qquad Demand$$

  (a) Use a graphing utility to graph the supply and demand functions on the same viewing rectangle.
  (b) Use the trace feature of the graphing utility to find the *equilibrium point* for the market. That is, find the point of intersection of the two graphs.
  (c) For what values of x does the demand exceed the supply?
  (d) For what values of x does the supply exceed the demand?

80. *Profit* A radio manufacturer charges $90 per unit for units that cost $60 to produce. To encourage large orders from distributors, the manufacturer will reduce the price by $0.01 per unit for each unit in excess of 100 units. (For example, an order of 101 units would have a price of $89.99 per unit, and an order of 102 units would have a price of $89.98 per unit.) This price reduction is discontinued when the price per unit drops to $75.
  (a) Express the price per unit p as a function of the order size x.
  (b) Express the profit P as a function of the order size x.

81. *Cost, Revenue, and Profit* A company invests $98,000 for equipment to produce a new product. Each unit of the product costs $12.30 and is sold for $17.98. Let x be the number of units produced and sold.
  (a) Write the total cost C as a function of x.
  (b) Write the revenue R as a function of x.
  (c) Write the profit P as a function of x.

82. *Charter Bus Fares* For groups of 80 or more people, a charter bus company determines the rate r (in dollars per person) according to the formula

$$r = 8 - 0.05(n - 80), \qquad n \geq 80,$$

where n is the number of people.
  (a) Express the revenue R for the bus company as a function of n.
  (b) Complete the following table.

n	90	100	110	120	130	140	150
R							

  (c) Criticize the formula for the rate. Would you use this formula? Explain your reasoning.

In Exercises 83–88, use a graphing utility to graph the function. Then use the zoom and trace features to find the zeros of the function. Is the function one-to-one?

83. $f(x) = x\sqrt{9 - x^2}$

84. $f(x) = 2\left(3x^2 - \dfrac{6}{x}\right)$

85. $g(t) = \dfrac{t + 3}{1 - t}$

86. $h(x) = 6x^3 - 12x^2 + 4$

87. $f(x) = \dfrac{4 - x^2}{x}$

88. $g(x) = \left|\tfrac{1}{2}x^2 - 4\right|$

Limits

The Limit of a Function ■ *Properties of Limits* ■ *Techniques for Evaluating Limits* ■ *One-Sided Limits* ■ *Unbounded Behavior*

The Limit of a Function

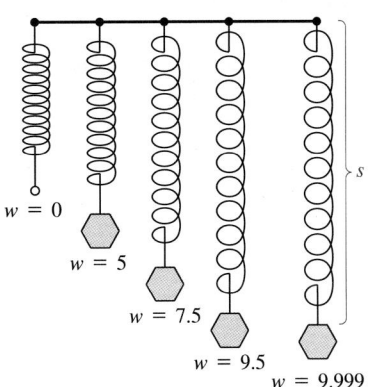

FIGURE 1.47 What is the limit of s as w approaches 10 lb?

In everyday language, we refer to a speed limit, a wrestler's weight limit, the limit of one's endurance, or stretching a spring to its limit. These phrases all suggest that a limit is a bound, which on some occasions may not be reached but on other occasions may be reached or exceeded.

Consider a spring that will break only if a weight of 10 or more pounds is attached. To determine how far the spring will stretch without breaking, you could attach increasingly heavier weights and measure the spring length s for each weight w, as shown in Figure 1.47. If the spring length approaches a value of L, then we say that "the limit of s as w approaches 10 is L." A mathematical limit is much like the limit of a spring. The notation for a limit is

$$\lim_{x \to c} f(x) = L,$$

which is read as "the limit of $f(x)$ as x approaches c is L."

EXAMPLE 1 *Finding a Limit*

Find the limit: $\lim_{x \to 1} (x^2 + 1)$.

Solution

Let $f(x) = x^2 + 1$. From the graph of f in Figure 1.48, it appears that $f(x)$ approaches 2 as x approaches 1 from either side, and you can write

$$\lim_{x \to 1} (x^2 + 1) = 2.$$

Table 1.7 yields the same conclusion. Notice that as x gets closer and closer to 1, $f(x)$ gets closer and closer to 2.

$\lim_{x \to 1} (x^2 + 1) = 2$

FIGURE 1.48

TABLE 1.7

	x approaches 1				x approaches 1		
x	0.900	0.990	0.999	1.000	1.001	1.010	1.100
$f(x)$	1.810	1.980	1.998	2.000	2.002	2.020	2.200
		$f(x)$ approaches 2			$f(x)$ approaches 1		

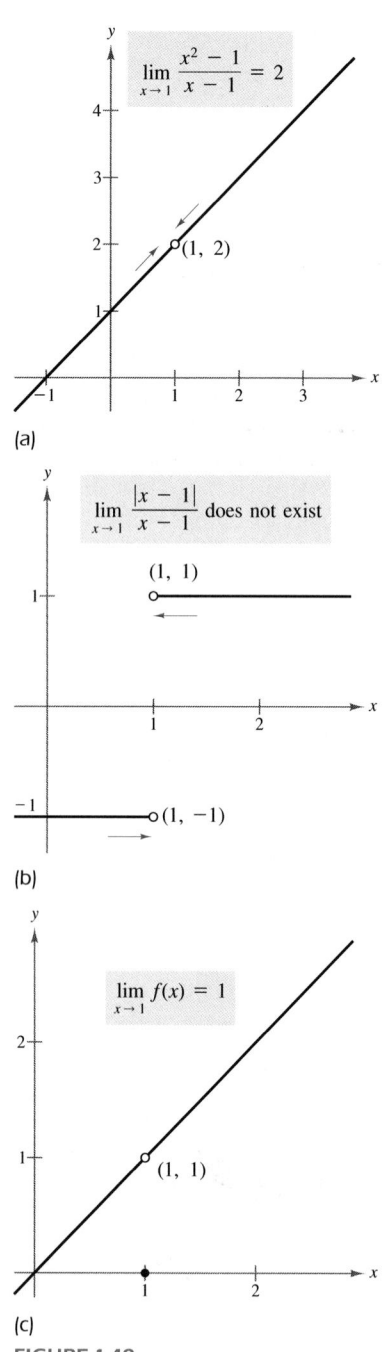

(a)

(b)

(c)

FIGURE 1.49

EXAMPLE 2 *Finding Limits Graphically and Numerically*

Find the limit: $\lim\limits_{x \to 1} f(x)$.

a. $f(x) = \dfrac{x^2 - 1}{x - 1}$ **b.** $f(x) = \dfrac{|x - 1|}{x - 1}$ **c.** $f(x) = \begin{cases} x, & x \neq 1 \\ 0, & x = 1 \end{cases}$

Solution

a. From the graph of f, in Figure 1.49(a), it appears that $f(x)$ approaches 2 as x approaches 1 from either side. This conclusion is reinforced by Table 1.8. Be sure you see that *it does not matter that $f(x)$ is undefined when $x = 1$*. The limit depends only on values of $f(x)$ near 1, not at 1.

TABLE 1.8

	x approaches 1				x approaches 1		
x	0.900	0.990	0.999	1.000	1.001	1.010	1.100
$f(x)$	1.900	1.990	1.999	?	2.001	2.010	2.100

            $f(x)$ approaches 2 $f(x)$ approaches 1

b. From the graph of f, in Figure 1.49(b), you can see that $f(x) = -1$ for all values to the left of $x = 1$ and $f(x) = 1$ for all values to the right of $x = 1$. Thus, $f(x)$ is approaching a different value from the left of $x = 1$ than it is from the right of $x = 1$. In such situations, we say that the *limit does not exist*. This conclusion is reinforced by Table 1.9.

TABLE 1.9

	x approaches 1				x approaches 1		
x	0.900	0.990	0.999	1.000	1.001	1.010	1.100
$f(x)$	-1.000	-1.000	-1.000	?	1.000	1.000	1.000

            $f(x)$ approaches -1 $f(x)$ approaches 1

c. From the graph of f, in Figure 1.49(c), it appears that $f(x)$ approaches 1 as x approaches 1 from either side. This conclusion is reinforced by Table 1.10. It does not matter that $f(1) = 0$. The limit depends only on values of $f(x)$ near 1, not at 1.

TABLE 1.10

	x approaches 1				x approaches 1		
x	0.900	0.990	0.999	1.000	1.001	1.010	1.100
$f(x)$	0.900	0.990	0.999	0.000	1.001	1.010	1.100

            $f(x)$ approaches 1 $f(x)$ approaches 1

TECHNOLOGY

Try using a graphing utility to determine the following limit.

$$\lim_{x \to 1} \frac{x^3 + 4x - 5}{x - 1}$$

You can do this by graphing

$$f(x) = \frac{x^3 + 4x - 5}{x - 1}$$

and zooming in near $x = 1$. From the graph, what does the limit appear to be?

There are three important ideas to learn from Examples 1 and 2.

1. Saying that the limit of $f(x)$ approaches L as x approaches c means that the value of $f(x)$ may be made *arbitrarily close* to the number L by choosing x closer and closer to c.

2. For a limit to exist, you must allow x to approach c from *either side* of c. If $f(x)$ approaches a different number as x approaches c from the left than it does when x approaches c from the right, then the limit *does not exist*. (See Example 2b.)

3. The value of $f(x)$ when $x = c$ has no bearing on the existence or nonexistence of the limit of $f(x)$ as x approaches c. For instance, in Example 2a, the limit of $f(x)$ exists as x approaches 1 even though the function f is not defined at $x = 1$.

Definition of the Limit of a Function

If $f(x)$ becomes arbitrarily close to a single number L as x approaches c from either side, then

$$\lim_{x \to c} f(x) = L$$

which is read as "the **limit** of $f(x)$ as x approaches c is L."

Properties of Limits

Many times the limit of $f(x)$ as x approaches c is simply $f(c)$, as illustrated in Example 1. Whenever the limit of $f(x)$ as x approaches c is

$$\lim_{x \to c} f(x) = f(c), \qquad \textit{Direct substitution}$$

we say that the limit can be evaluated by **direct substitution.** (In the next section, you will learn that a function that has this property is *continuous at c.*) It is important that you learn to recognize the types of functions that have this property. Some basic ones are given in the following list.

Properties of Limits

Let b and c be real numbers, and let n be a positive integer.

1. $\lim_{x \to c} b = b$ 2. $\lim_{x \to c} x = c$

3. $\lim_{x \to c} x^n = c^n$ 4. $\lim_{x \to c} \sqrt[n]{x} = \sqrt[n]{c}$

In Property 4, if n is even, then c must be positive.

By combining the properties of limits with the following rules for operating with limits, you can find limits for a wide variety of algebraic functions.

Operations with Limits

Let b and c be real numbers and let n be a positive integer. If the limits of $f(x)$ and $g(x)$ exist as x approaches c, then the following operations are valid.

1. Constant multiple: $\lim_{x \to c} [bf(x)] = b \left[\lim_{x \to c} f(x) \right]$

2. Addition: $\lim_{x \to c} [f(x) \pm g(x)] = \lim_{x \to c} f(x) \pm \lim_{x \to c} g(x)$

3. Multiplication: $\lim_{x \to c} [f(x) \cdot g(x)] = \left[\lim_{x \to c} f(x) \right]\left[\lim_{x \to c} g(x) \right]$

4. Division: $\lim_{x \to c} \dfrac{f(x)}{g(x)} = \dfrac{\lim_{x \to c} f(x)}{\lim_{x \to c} g(x)}$, $\quad \lim_{x \to c} g(x) \neq 0$

5. Power: $\lim_{x \to c} [f(x)]^n = \left[\lim_{x \to c} f(x) \right]^n$

6. Radical: $\lim_{x \to c} \sqrt[n]{f(x)} = \sqrt[n]{\lim_{x \to c} f(x)}$

In Property 6, if n is even and $\lim_{x \to c} f(x) = L$, then L must be positive.

EXAMPLE 3 *Evaluating the Limit of a Polynomial*

$$\lim_{x \to 2} (x^2 + 2x - 3) = \lim_{x \to 2} x^2 + \lim_{x \to 2} 2x - \lim_{x \to 2} 3 \quad \text{\textit{Addition Property}}$$
$$= 2^2 + 2(2) - 3 \quad \text{\textit{Direct substitution}}$$
$$= 4 + 4 - 3 \quad \text{\textit{Simplify.}}$$
$$= 5$$

Example 3 is an illustration of the following important result, which states that the limit of a polynomial can be evaluated by direct substitution.

The Limit of a Polynomial Function

If p is a polynomial function and c is any real number, then

$$\lim_{x \to c} p(x) = p(c).$$

Techniques for Evaluating Limits

Many techniques for evaluating limits are based on the following important theorem. Basically, the theorem states that if two functions agree at all but a single point c, then they have identical limit behavior at $x = c$.

The Replacement Theorem

Let c be a real number and $f(x) = g(x)$ for all $x \neq c$. If the limit of $g(x)$ exists as $x \to c$, then the limit of $f(x)$ also exists and

$$\lim_{x \to c} f(x) = \lim_{x \to c} g(x).$$

To apply the Replacement Theorem, you can use a result from algebra which states that for a polynomial function p, $p(c) = 0$ if and only if $(x - c)$ is a factor of $p(x)$. This concept is demonstrated in Example 4.

EXAMPLE 4 *Evaluating a Limit*

Evaluate the limit: $\displaystyle \lim_{x \to 1} \frac{x^3 - 1}{x - 1}$.

Solution

Note that the numerator and denominator are zero when $x = 1$. This implies that $(x - 1)$ is a factor of both, and you can cancel this common factor.

$$\frac{x^3 - 1}{x - 1} = \frac{(x - 1)(x^2 + x + 1)}{x - 1} \qquad \textit{Factor numerator.}$$

$$= \frac{(x - 1)(x^2 + x + 1)}{x - 1} \qquad \textit{Cancel common factor.}$$

$$= x^2 + x + 1, \qquad x \neq 1 \qquad \textit{Simplify.}$$

Thus, the rational function $(x^3 - 1)/(x - 1)$ and the polynomial function $x^2 + x + 1$ agree for all values of x other than $x = 1$, and you can apply the Replacement Theorem.

$$\lim_{x \to 1} \frac{x^3 - 1}{x - 1} = \lim_{x \to 1} (x^2 + x + 1) = 1^2 + 1 + 1 = 3$$

Figure 1.50 illustrates this result graphically. Note that the two graphs are identical except that the graph of g contains the point $(1, 3)$, whereas this point is missing on the graph of f. (In Figure 1.50, the missing point is denoted by an open dot.)

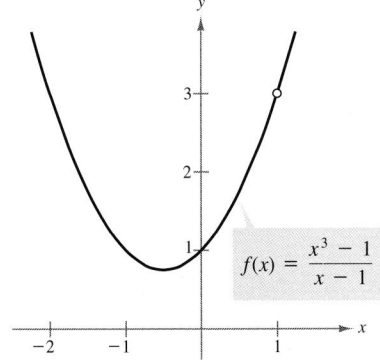

$$f(x) = \frac{x^3 - 1}{x - 1}$$

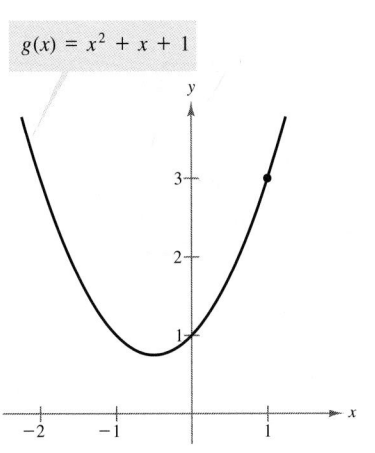

$$g(x) = x^2 + x + 1$$

FIGURE 1.50

The technique used to evaluate the limit in Example 4 is called the **cancellation technique.** This technique is further demonstrated in the next example.

EXAMPLE 5 *Using the Cancellation Technique*

Evaluate the limit: $\lim\limits_{x \to -3} \dfrac{x^2 + x - 6}{x + 3}$.

Solution

Direct substitution fails because both the numerator and the denominator are zero when $x = -3$.

$$\lim_{x \to -3} \dfrac{x^2 + x - 6}{x + 3} \qquad \begin{matrix} \longleftarrow & \lim\limits_{x \to -3} (x^2 + x - 6) = 0 \\ \longleftarrow & \lim\limits_{x \to -3} (x + 3) = 0 \end{matrix}$$

However, because the limits of both the numerator and denominator are zero, you know that they have a *common factor* of $(x + 3)$. Thus, for all $x \neq -3$, you can cancel this factor to obtain the following.

$$\lim_{x \to -3} \dfrac{x^2 + x - 6}{x + 3} = \lim_{x \to -3} \dfrac{(x - 2)(x + 3)}{x + 3} \qquad \textit{Factor numerator.}$$

$$= \lim_{x \to -3} \dfrac{(x - 2)\cancel{(x + 3)}}{\cancel{x + 3}} \qquad \textit{Cancel common factor.}$$

$$= \lim_{x \to -3} (x - 2) \qquad \textit{Simplify.}$$

$$= -5 \qquad \textit{Direct substitution}$$

This result is shown graphically in Figure 1.51. Note that the graph of f coincides with the graph of $g(x) = x - 2$, except that the graph of f has a hole at $(-3, -5)$. ▪

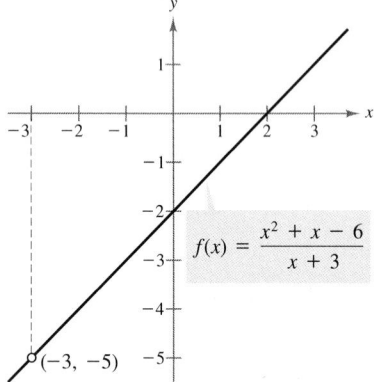

FIGURE 1.51 f is undefined when $x = -3$.

EXAMPLE 6 *Evaluating a Limit*

Evaluate the limit: $\lim\limits_{x \to -2} \dfrac{x^2 + x - 2}{x - 2}$.

Solution

Because the limit of the denominator is not zero, you can use the limit of a quotient (Property 4 of Operations with Limits) to obtain

$$\lim_{x \to -2} \dfrac{x^2 + x - 2}{x - 2} = \lim_{x \to -2} \dfrac{(-2)^2 - 2 - 2}{-2 - 2} \qquad \textit{Direct substitution}$$

$$= \dfrac{0}{-4} \qquad \textit{Simplify.}$$

$$= 0. \qquad \textit{The limit is 0.}$$ ▪

One-Sided Limits

In Example 2b, you saw that one way in which a limit can fail to exist is when a function approaches a different value from the left of c than it approaches from the right of c. This type of behavior can be described more concisely with the concept of a **one-sided limit.**

$$\lim_{x \to c^-} f(x) = L \qquad\qquad\qquad \textit{Limit from the left}$$

$$\lim_{x \to c^+} f(x) = L \qquad\qquad\qquad \textit{Limit from the right}$$

The first of these two limits is read as "the limit of $f(x)$ as x approaches c from the left is L." The second is read as "the limit of $f(x)$ as x approaches c from the right is L."

EXAMPLE 7 *Evaluating One-Sided Limits*

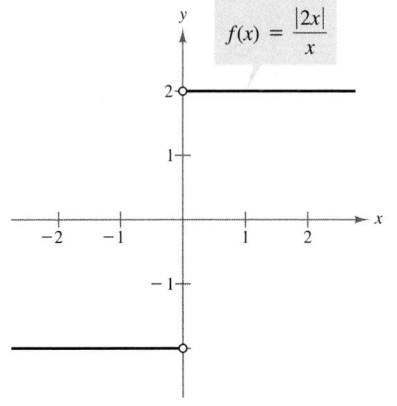

$f(x) = \dfrac{|2x|}{x}$

FIGURE 1.52

Find the limit as $x \to 0$ from the left and the limit as $x \to 0$ from the right for the function

$$f(x) = \frac{|2x|}{x}.$$

Solution
From the graph of f, shown in Figure 1.52, you can see that $f(x) = -2$ for all $x < 0$. Therefore, the limit from the left is

$$\lim_{x \to 0^-} \frac{|2x|}{x} = -2. \qquad\qquad \textit{Limit from the left}$$

Because $f(x) = 2$ for all $x > 0$, the limit from the right is

$$\lim_{x \to 0^+} \frac{|2x|}{x} = 2. \qquad\qquad \textit{Limit from the right}$$

In Example 7, note that the function approaches different limits from the left and from the right. In such cases, the limit of $f(x)$ as $x \to c$ does not exist. For the limit of a function to exist as $x \to c$, it must be true that *both* one-sided limits exist and are equal.

Existence of a Limit

If f is a function and c and L are real numbers, then

$$\lim_{x \to c} f(x) = L$$

if and only if both the left and right limits are equal to L.

EXAMPLE 8 *Evaluating One-Sided Limits*

Find the limit of $f(x)$ as x approaches 1.

$$f(x) = \begin{cases} 4 - x, & x < 1 \\ 4x - x^2, & x > 1 \end{cases}$$

Solution

Remember that you are concerned about the value of f near $x = 1$ rather than at $x = 1$. Thus, for $x < 1$, $f(x)$ is given by $4 - x$, and you can use direct substitution to obtain

$$\lim_{x \to 1^-} f(x) = \lim_{x \to 1^-} (4 - x) = 4 - 1 = 3.$$

For $x > 1$, $f(x)$ is given by $4x - x^2$, and you can use direct substitution to obtain

$$\lim_{x \to 1^+} f(x) = \lim_{x \to 1^+} (4x - x^2) = 4 - 1 = 3.$$

Because both one-sided limits exist and are equal to 3, it follows that

$$\lim_{x \to 1} f(x) = 3.$$

The graph in Figure 1.53 confirms this conclusion.

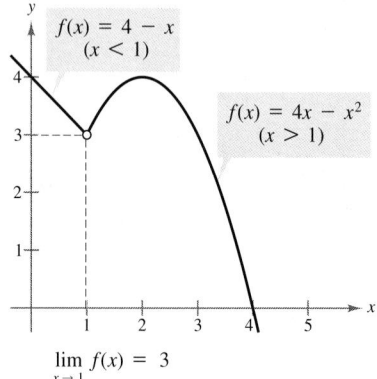

$f(x) = 4 - x$
$(x < 1)$

$f(x) = 4x - x^2$
$(x > 1)$

$$\lim_{x \to 1} f(x) = 3$$

FIGURE 1.53

Real Life

EXAMPLE 9 *Comparing One-Sided Limits*

An overnight delivery service charges $8 for the first pound and $2 for each additional pound. Let x represent the weight of a parcel and let $f(x)$ represent the shipping cost.

$$f(x) = \begin{cases} 8, & 0 < x \le 1 \\ 10, & 1 < x \le 2 \\ 12, & 2 < x \le 3 \end{cases}$$

Show that the limit of $f(x)$ as $x \to 2$ does not exist.

Solution

The graph of f is shown in Figure 1.54. The limit of $f(x)$ as x approaches 2 from the left is

$$\lim_{x \to 2^-} f(x) = 10,$$

whereas the limit of $f(x)$ as x approaches 2 from the right is

$$\lim_{x \to 2^+} f(x) = 12.$$

Because these one-sided limits are not equal, the limit of $f(x)$ as $x \to 2$ does not exist.

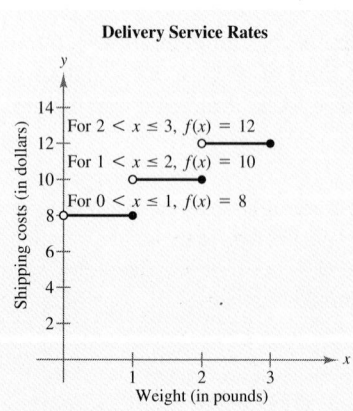

Delivery Service Rates

For $2 < x \le 3$, $f(x) = 12$
For $1 < x \le 2$, $f(x) = 10$
For $0 < x \le 1$, $f(x) = 8$

Shipping costs (in dollars)

Weight (in pounds)

FIGURE 1.54

Unbounded Behavior

Example 9 illustrates a limit that fails to exist because the limits from the left and right differ. Another important way in which a limit can fail to exist is when $f(x)$ increases or decreases without bound as x approaches c.

FIGURE 1.55

EXAMPLE 10 *An Unbounded Function*

Evaluate the limit (if possible): $\lim\limits_{x \to 2} \dfrac{3}{x-2}$.

Solution

From Figure 1.55, you can see that $f(x)$ decreases without bound as x approaches 2 from the left and $f(x)$ increases without bound as x approaches 2 from the right. Symbolically, you can write this as

$$\lim_{x \to 2^-} \frac{3}{x-2} = -\infty$$

and

$$\lim_{x \to 2^+} \frac{3}{x-2} = \infty.$$

Because f is unbounded as x approaches 2, the limit does not exist. ∎

Note   The equal sign in the statement

$$\lim_{x \to c^+} f(x) = \infty$$

does not mean that the limit exists! On the contrary, it tells you how the limit *fails to exist* by denoting the unbounded behavior of $f(x)$ as x approaches c.

Discussion Problem   Evaluating a Limit

Consider the following limit.

$$\lim_{x \to 0} \frac{\sqrt{x+1}-1}{x}$$

a. Approximate the limit graphically, using a graphing utility.
b. Approximate the limit numerically, by constructing a table.
c. Evaluate the limit analytically, using the following equation.

$$\frac{\sqrt{x+1}-1}{x} = \left(\frac{\sqrt{x+1}-1}{x}\right)\left(\frac{\sqrt{x+1}+1}{\sqrt{x+1}+1}\right) = \frac{1}{\sqrt{x+1}+1}$$

Which method do you prefer? Explain.

Warm Up

In Exercises 1–4, evaluate the expression and simplify.

1. $f(x) = x^2 - 3x + 3$ (a) $f(-1)$ (b) $f(c)$ (c) $f(x+h)$

2. $f(x) = \begin{cases} 2x - 2, & x < 1 \\ 3x + 1, & x \geq 1 \end{cases}$ (a) $f(-1)$ (b) $f(3)$ (c) $f(t^2 + 1)$

3. $f(x) = x^2 - 2x + 2$ $\dfrac{f(1+h) - f(1)}{h}$

4. $f(x) = 4x$ $\dfrac{f(2+h) - f(2)}{h}$

In Exercises 5–8, find the domain and range of the function and sketch its graph.

5. $h(x) = -\dfrac{5}{x}$ **6.** $g(x) = \sqrt{25 - x^2}$

7. $f(x) = |x - 3|$ **8.** $f(x) = \dfrac{|x|}{x}$

In Exercises 9 and 10, determine whether y is a function of x.

9. $9x^2 + 4y^2 = 49$ **10.** $2x^2y + 8x = 7y$

E X E R C I S E S 1.5   means that technology can help you solve or check the exercise(s).

In Exercises 1–8, complete the table and estimate the limit.

1. $\lim\limits_{x \to 2} (5x + 4)$

x	1.9	1.99	1.999	2	2.001	2.01	2.1
$f(x)$	?	?	?	?	?	?	?

2. $\lim\limits_{x \to 2} \dfrac{x - 2}{x^2 - x - 2}$

x	1.9	1.99	1.999	2	2.001	2.01	2.1
$f(x)$	?	?	?	?	?	?	?

3. $\lim\limits_{x \to 2} \dfrac{x - 2}{x^2 - 4}$

x	1.9	1.99	1.999	2	2.001	2.01	2.1
$f(x)$	?	?	?	?	?	?	?

4. $\lim\limits_{x \to 2} \dfrac{x^5 - 32}{x - 2}$

x	1.9	1.99	1.999	2	2.001	2.01	2.1
$f(x)$	?	?	?	?	?	?	?

5. $\lim\limits_{x \to 0} \dfrac{\sqrt{x + 3} - \sqrt{3}}{x}$

x	-0.1	-0.01	-0.001	0	0.001	0.01	0.1
$f(x)$	?	?	?	?	?	?	?

6. $\lim\limits_{x \to 0} \dfrac{\sqrt{x + 2} - \sqrt{2}}{x}$

x	-0.1	-0.01	-0.001	0	0.001	0.01	0.1
$f(x)$	?	?	?	?	?	?	?

7. $\lim\limits_{x \to 2^-} \dfrac{2-x}{\sqrt{4-x^2}}$

x	1.5	1.9	1.99	1.999	2
$f(x)$	?	?	?	?	?

8. $\lim\limits_{x \to 0^+} \dfrac{[1/(2+x)] - (1/2)}{2x}$

x	0.5	0.1	0.01	0.001	0
$f(x)$	?	?	?	?	?

In Exercises 9–12, use the graph to visually determine the limit.

9.

10.

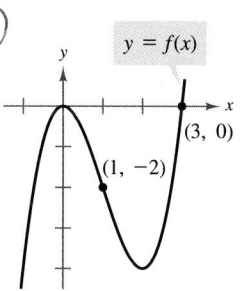

(a) $\lim\limits_{x \to 0} f(x)$

(b) $\lim\limits_{x \to -1} f(x)$

(a) $\lim\limits_{x \to 1} f(x)$

(b) $\lim\limits_{x \to 3} f(x)$

11.

12.

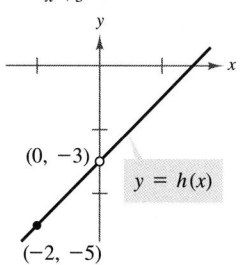

(a) $\lim\limits_{x \to 0} g(x)$

(b) $\lim\limits_{x \to -1} g(x)$

(a) $\lim\limits_{x \to -2} h(x)$

(b) $\lim\limits_{x \to 0} h(x)$

In Exercises 13 and 14, find the limit of (a) $f(x) + g(x)$, (b) $f(x)g(x)$, and (c) $f(x)/g(x)$ as x approaches c.

13. $\lim\limits_{x \to c} f(x) = 3$

$\lim\limits_{x \to c} g(x) = 9$

14. $\lim\limits_{x \to c} f(x) = \frac{3}{2}$

$\lim\limits_{x \to c} g(x) = \frac{1}{2}$

In Exercises 15–20, use the graph to visually determine the limit (if it exists).

(a) $\lim\limits_{x \to c^+} f(x)$ (b) $\lim\limits_{x \to c^-} f(x)$ (c) $\lim\limits_{x \to c} f(x)$

Right   *Left*   *either*

15.

16.

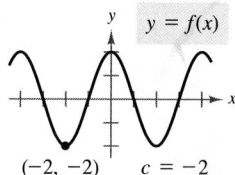

Why is the lim = 0? Ue am I confused?!?!

17.

18.

19.

20.

$x \to c^+$ $\varnothing$
$x \to c^-$ 2
$x \to c\varnothing$ $\varnothing$

In Exercises 21–32, find the limit.

21. $\lim\limits_{x \to 2} x^2$

22. $\lim\limits_{x \to -3} (3x + 2)$

23. $\lim\limits_{x \to 0} (2x - 3)$

24. $\lim\limits_{x \to 1} (1 - x^2)$

25. $\lim\limits_{x \to 2} (-x^2 + x - 2)$

26. $\lim\limits_{x \to 1} (3x^3 - 2x^2 + 4)$

27. $\lim\limits_{x \to 3} \sqrt{x + 1}$

28. $\lim\limits_{x \to 4} \sqrt[3]{x + 4}$

29. $\lim\limits_{x \to 2} -\dfrac{2}{x}$

30. $\lim\limits_{x \to -3} \dfrac{2}{x + 2}$

31. $\lim\limits_{x \to 3} \dfrac{3x - 5}{x + 3}$

32. $\lim\limits_{x \to -2} \dfrac{3x + 1}{2 - x}$

Factor & Simplify

In Exercises 33–54, find the limit (if it exists).

33. $\lim\limits_{x \to -1} \dfrac{x^2 - 1}{x + 1}$

34. $\lim\limits_{x \to -1} \dfrac{2x^2 - x - 3}{x + 1}$

35. $\lim\limits_{x \to 2} \dfrac{x - 2}{x^2 - 4x + 4}$

36. $\lim\limits_{x \to 2} \dfrac{2 - x}{x^2 - 4}$

37. $\lim\limits_{t \to 5} \dfrac{t - 5}{t^2 - 25}$

38. $\lim\limits_{t \to 1} \dfrac{t^2 + t - 2}{t^2 - 1}$

39. $\lim\limits_{x \to -2} \dfrac{x^3 + 8}{x + 2}$

40. $\lim\limits_{x \to 1} \dfrac{x^3 - 1}{x - 1}$

41. $\lim\limits_{x \to 0} \dfrac{|x|}{x}$

42. $\lim\limits_{x \to 2} \dfrac{|x - 2|}{x - 2}$

Piecewise functions

43. $\lim\limits_{x \to 3} f(x)$, where $f(x) = \begin{cases} \frac{1}{3}x - 2, & x \le 3 \\ -2x + 5, & x > 3 \end{cases}$

44. $\lim\limits_{s \to 1} f(s)$, where $f(s) = \begin{cases} s, & s \le 1 \\ 1 - s, & s > 1 \end{cases}$

45. $\lim\limits_{x \to 1} f(x)$, where $f(x) = \begin{cases} x^3 + 1, & x < 1 \\ x + 1, & x \ge 1 \end{cases}$

46. $\lim\limits_{x \to 2} f(x)$, where $f(x) = \begin{cases} x^2 - 4x + 6, & x < 2 \\ -x^2 + 4x - 2, & x \ge 2 \end{cases}$

47. $\lim\limits_{\Delta x \to 0} \dfrac{2(x + \Delta x) - 2x}{\Delta x}$

48. $\lim\limits_{\Delta x \to 0} \dfrac{(1 + \Delta x)^3 - 1}{\Delta x}$

49. $\lim\limits_{\Delta x \to 0} \dfrac{(x + \Delta x)^3 - x^3}{\Delta x}$

50. $\lim\limits_{\Delta x \to 0} \dfrac{\sqrt{x + \Delta x} - \sqrt{x}}{\Delta x}$

Chapt 2 Also

51. $\lim\limits_{\Delta t \to 0} \dfrac{(t + \Delta t)^2 - 5(t + \Delta t) - (t^2 - 5t)}{\Delta t}$

52. $\lim\limits_{\Delta x \to 0} \dfrac{(x + \Delta x)^2 - 2(x + \Delta x) + 1 - (x^2 - 2x + 1)}{\Delta x}$

53. $\lim\limits_{x \to 0} \dfrac{\sqrt{2 + x} - \sqrt{2}}{x}$

54. $\lim\limits_{x \to 4} \dfrac{\sqrt{x} - 2}{x - 4}$

In Exercises 55–60, find the one-sided limit (if it exists).

55. $\lim\limits_{x \to 1^-} \dfrac{2}{x^2 - 1}$

56. $\lim\limits_{x \to 1^+} \dfrac{5}{1 - x}$

57. $\lim\limits_{x \to -2^-} \dfrac{1}{x + 2}$

58. $\lim\limits_{x \to 0^-} \dfrac{x + 1}{x}$

59. $\lim\limits_{x \to 5^+} \dfrac{2}{(x - 5)^2}$

60. $\lim\limits_{x \to 3^+} \dfrac{x}{x^2 - 2x - 3}$

61. Find $\lim\limits_{x \to 0} f(x)$, given
$$4 - x^2 \le f(x) \le 4 + x^2, \quad \text{for all } x.$$

62. The limit of $f(x) = (1 + x)^{1/x}$ is a natural base for many business applications.
$$\lim\limits_{x \to 0} (1 + x)^{1/x} = e \approx 2.718$$

$= \lim (1 + \frac{1}{x})^x$, $x \to \infty$

(a) Show the reasonableness of this limit by completing the table.

x	-0.01	-0.001	-0.0001	0	0.0001	0.001	0.01
$f(x)$	?	?	?	?	?	?	?

(b) Use a graphing utility to graph f and to confirm the answer in part (a).

(c) Find the domain and range of the function.

In Exercises 63–66, use a graphing utility to estimate the limit (if it exists).

63. $\lim\limits_{x \to 2} \dfrac{x^2 - 5x + 6}{x^2 - 4x + 4}$

64. $\lim\limits_{x \to 1} \dfrac{x^2 + 6x - 7}{x^3 - x^2 + 2x - 2}$

65. $\lim\limits_{x \to -4} \dfrac{x^3 + 4x^2 + x + 4}{2x^2 + 7x - 4}$

66. $\lim\limits_{x \to -2} \dfrac{4x^3 + 7x^2 + x + 6}{3x^2 - x - 14}$

67. *Compound Interest* You deposit $1000 into an account that is compounded quarterly at an annual rate of r (in decimal form). The balance A after 10 years is
$$A = 1000 \left(1 + \frac{r}{4}\right)^{40}.$$
Does the limit of A exist as the interest rate approaches 6%? If so, what is the limit?

68. *Compound Interest* Consider a certificate of deposit that pays 10% (annual percentage rate) on an initial deposit of $500. The balance A after 10 years is
$$A = 500(1 + 0.1x)^{10/x},$$
where x is the length of the compounding period (in years).

(a) Use a graphing utility to graph A, where $0 \le x \le 1$.

(b) Use the zoom and trace features to estimate the balance for quarterly compounding and daily compounding.

(c) Use the zoom and trace features to estimate
$$\lim\limits_{x \to 0^+} A.$$
What do you think this limit represents? Explain your reasoning.

1.6 Continuity

Continuity ▪ *Continuity on a Closed Interval* ▪ *The Greatest Integer Function* ▪ *Extended Application: Compound Interest*

Continuity

In mathematics, the term "continuous" has much the same meaning as it does in everyday use. To say that a function is continuous at $x = c$ means that there is no interruption in the graph of f at c. The graph of f is unbroken at c, and there are no holes, jumps, or gaps. As simple as this concept may seem, its precise definition eluded mathematicians for many years. In fact, it was not until the early 1800s that a precise definition was finally developed.

Before looking at this definition, consider the function whose graph is shown in Figure 1.56. This figure identifies three values of x at which the function f is not continuous.

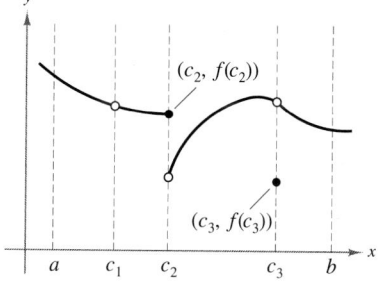

1. At $x = c_1$, $f(c_1)$ is not defined.

2. At $x = c_2$, $\lim\limits_{x \to c_2} f(x)$ does not exist.

3. At $x = c_3$, $f(c_3) \neq \lim\limits_{x \to c_3} f(x)$.

FIGURE 1.56 f is not continuous when $x = c_1, c_2, c_3$.

At all other points in the interval (a, b), the graph of f is uninterrupted, which implies that the function f is continuous at all other points in the interval (a, b).

Definition of Continuity

Let c be a number in the interval (a, b), and let f be a function whose domain contains the interval (a, b). The function f is **continuous at the point** c if the following conditions are true.

1. $f(c)$ is defined.

2. $\lim\limits_{x \to c} f(x)$ exists.

3. $\lim\limits_{x \to c} f(x) = f(c)$.

If f is continuous at every point in the interval (a, b), then it is **continuous on the interval** (a, b).

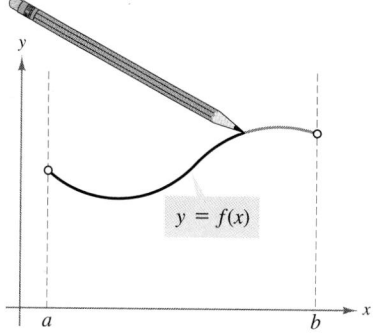

FIGURE 1.57 On the interval (a, b), the graph of f can be traced with a pencil.

Roughly, you can say that a function is continuous on an interval if its graph on the interval can be traced using a pencil and paper without lifting the pencil from the paper, as shown in Figure 1.57.

TECHNOLOGY

Most graphing utilities can draw graphs in two different modes: connected mode and dot mode. The connected mode works well as long as the function is continuous on the entire interval represented by the viewing rectangle. If, however, the function is not continuous at one or more x-values in the viewing rectangle, then the connected mode may try to "connect" parts of the graphs that should not be connected. For instance, try graphing the function $y_1 = (x + 3)/(x - 2)$ on the viewing rectangle $-9 \le x \le 9$ and $-6 \le y \le 6$. Do you notice any problems?

In Section 1.5, you studied several types of functions that meet the three conditions for continuity. Specifically, if *direct substitution* can be used to evaluate the limit of a function at c, then the function is continuous at c. Two types of functions that have this property are polynomial functions and rational functions.

Continuity of Polynomial and Rational Functions

1. A polynomial function is continuous at every real number.
2. A rational function is continuous at every number in its domain.

EXAMPLE 1 *Determining Continuity of a Function*

Discuss the continuity of the following functions.

a. $f(x) = x^2 - 2x + 3$ **b.** $f(x) = x^3 - x$

Solution

Each of these functions is a *polynomial function*. Therefore, each is continuous on the entire real line, as indicated in Figure 1.58.

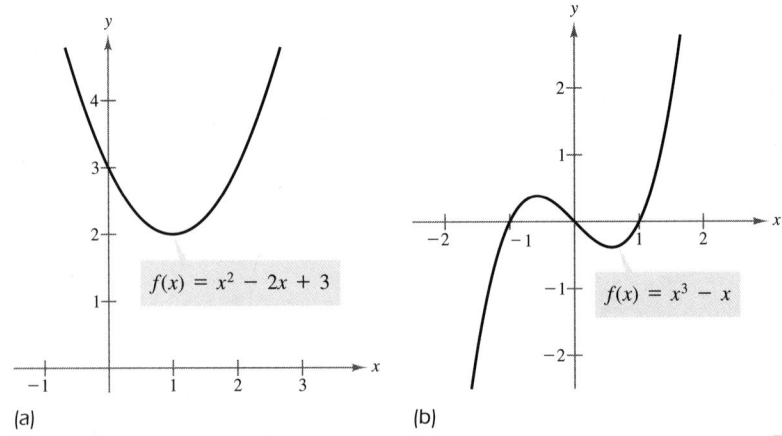

(a)   (b)

FIGURE 1.58 Both functions are continuous on $(-\infty, \infty)$.

Polynomial functions are one of the most important types of functions used in calculus. Be sure you see from Example 1 that the graph of a polynomial function is continuous on the entire real line, and therefore has no holes, jumps, or gaps. Rational functions, on the other hand, need not be continuous on the entire real line, as shown in Example 2.

EXAMPLE 2 *Determining Continuity of a Function*

Discuss the continuity of the following functions.

a. $f(x) = \dfrac{1}{x}$ **b.** $f(x) = \dfrac{x^2 - 1}{x - 1}$ **c.** $f(x) = \dfrac{1}{x^2 + 1}$

Solution

Each of these functions is a rational function and is therefore continuous at every number in its domain.

a. The domain of $f(x) = 1/x$ consists of all real numbers other than $x = 0$. Therefore, this function is continuous on the intervals $(-\infty, 0)$ and $(0, \infty)$. (See Figure 1.59a.)

b. The domain of $f(x) = (x^2 - 1)/(x - 1)$ consists of all real numbers other than $x = 1$. Therefore, this function is continuous on the intervals $(-\infty, 1)$ and $(1, \infty)$. (See Figure 1.59b.)

c. The domain of $f(x) = 1/(x^2 + 1)$ consists of all real numbers. Therefore, this function is continuous on the entire real line. (See Figure 1.59c.)

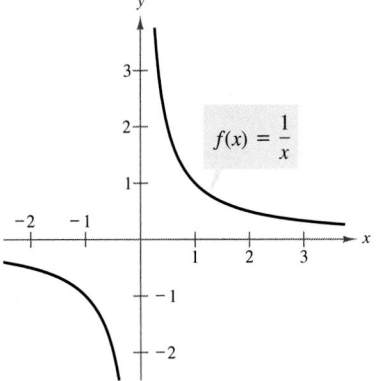

(a) Continuous on $(-\infty, 0)$ and $(0, \infty)$

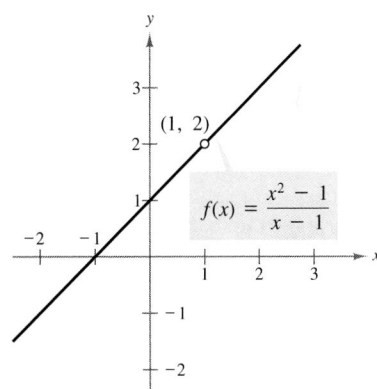

(b) Continuous on $(-\infty, 1)$ and $(1, \infty)$

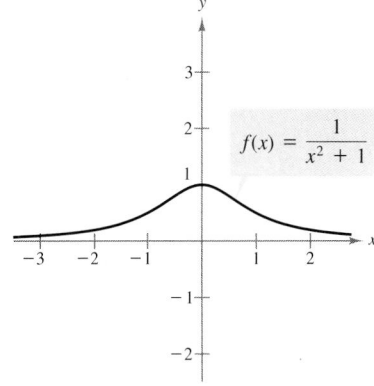

(c) Continuous on $(-\infty, \infty)$

FIGURE 1.59

If a function is continuous at every number in an open interval except c, then c is a **discontinuity** of the function. Discontinuities fall into two categories: removable and nonremovable. The number c is a **removable** discontinuity of f if the graph of f has a hole at the point (c, L) where L is the limit of $f(x)$ as x approaches c. For instance, the function in Example 2b has a removable discontinuity at $(1, 2)$. To remove the discontinuity, all you need to do is redefine the function so that $f(1) = 2$.

A discontinuity at $x = c$ is **nonremovable** if the function cannot be made continuous at $x = c$ by defining or redefining the function at $x = c$. For instance, the function in Example 2a has a nonremovable discontinuity at $x = 0$.

Continuity on a Closed Interval

The intervals discussed in Examples 1 and 2 are open. To discuss continuity on a closed interval, you can use the concept of one-sided limits, as defined in Section 1.5.

Definition of Continuity on a Closed Interval

Let f be defined on a closed interval $[a, b]$. If f is continuous on the open interval (a, b) and

$$\lim_{x \to a^+} f(x) = f(a) \quad \text{and} \quad \lim_{x \to b^-} f(x) = f(b),$$

then f is **continuous on the closed interval** $[a, b]$. Moreover, f is **continuous from the right** at a and **continuous from the left** at b.

Similar definitions can be made to cover continuity on half-open intervals of the form $(a, b]$ and $[a, b)$, or on infinite intervals. For example, the function

$$f(x) = \sqrt{x}$$

is continuous on the infinite interval $[0, \infty)$.

EXAMPLE 3 *Examining Continuity at an Endpoint*

Discuss the continuity of

$$f(x) = \sqrt{3 - x}.$$

Solution

Notice that the domain of f is the set $(-\infty, 3]$. Moreover, f is continuous from the left at $x = 3$ because

$$\lim_{x \to 3^-} f(x) = \lim_{x \to 3^-} \sqrt{3 - x}$$
$$= 0$$
$$= f(3).$$

For all $x < 3$, the function f satisfies the three conditions for continuity. Thus, you can conclude that f is continuous on the interval $(-\infty, 3]$, as shown in Figure 1.60. ■

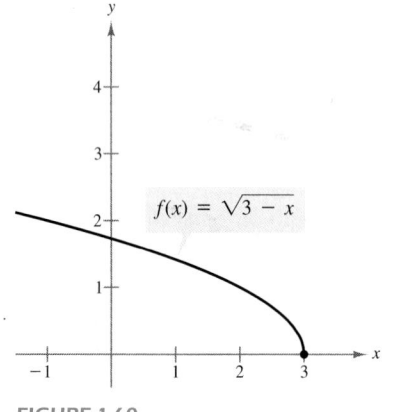

$f(x) = \sqrt{3 - x}$

FIGURE 1.60

Note When working with radical functions of the form $f(x) = \sqrt{g(x)}$, remember that the domain of f coincides with the solution of $g(x) \geq 0$.

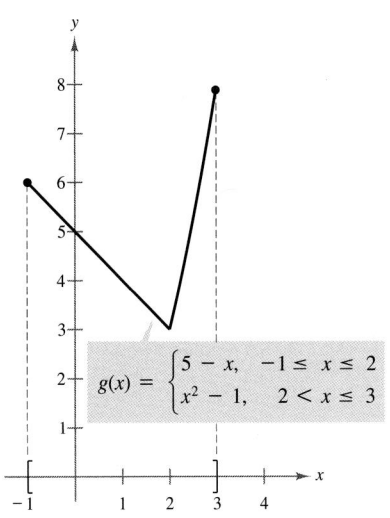

FIGURE 1.61

EXAMPLE 4 *Examining Continuity on a Closed Interval*

Discuss the continuity of

$$g(x) = \begin{cases} 5 - x, & -1 \leq x \leq 2 \\ x^2 - 1, & 2 < x \leq 3. \end{cases}$$

Solution

The polynomial functions $5 - x$ and $x^2 - 1$ are continuous on the intervals $[-1, 2)$ and $(2, 3]$, respectively. Thus, to conclude that g is continuous on the entire interval $[-1, 3]$, you need only check the behavior of g when $x = 2$. You can do this by taking the one-sided limits when $x = 2$.

$$\lim_{x \to 2^-} g(x) = \lim_{x \to 2^-} (5 - x) = 3 \qquad \text{\textit{Limit from the left}}$$

and

$$\lim_{x \to 2^+} g(x) = \lim_{x \to 2^+} (x^2 - 1) = 3 \qquad \text{\textit{Limit from the right}}$$

Because these two limits are equal,

$$\lim_{x \to 2} g(x) = g(2) = 3.$$

Thus, g is continuous at $x = 2$ and, consequently, it is continuous on the entire interval $[-1, 3]$. The graph of g is shown in Figure 1.61. ■

The Greatest Integer Function

Many functions that are used in business applications are **step functions.** For instance, the function in Example 9 in Section 1.5 is a step function. The **greatest integer function** is another example of a step function. This function is denoted by

$[\![x]\!]$ = greatest integer less than or equal to x.

For example,

$[\![-2.1]\!]$ = greatest integer less than or equal to $-2.1 = -3$

$[\![-2]\!]$ = greatest integer less than or equal to $-2 = -2$

$[\![1.5]\!]$ = greatest integer less than or equal to $1.5 = 1$.

Note that the graph of the greatest integer function (Figure 1.62) jumps up one unit at each integer. This implies that the function is not continuous at each integer.

In real-life applications, the domain of the greatest integer function is often restricted to nonnegative values of x. In such cases this function serves the purpose of **truncating** the decimal portion of x. For example, 1.345 is truncated to 1 and 3.57 is truncated to 3. That is,

$[\![1.345]\!] = 1 \quad$ and $\quad [\![3.57]\!] = 3$.

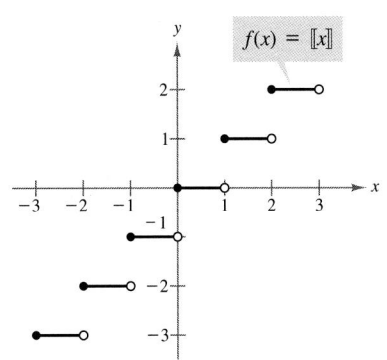

FIGURE 1.62 Greatest Integer Function

Ask about greatest integer functions!

EXAMPLE 5 *Modeling a Cost Function*

A bookbinding company produces 10,000 books in an 8-hour shift. The fixed costs *per shift* amount to $5000, and the unit cost *per book* is $3. Using the greatest integer function, you can write the cost of producing x books as

$$C = 5000 \left(1 + \left[\!\left[\frac{x - 1}{10,000}\right]\!\right]\right) + 3x.$$

Sketch the graph of this cost function.

Solution

Note that during the first 8-hour shift

$$\left[\!\left[\frac{x - 1}{10,000}\right]\!\right] = 0, \quad 1 \le x \le 10,000,$$

which implies

$$C = 5000 \left(1 + \left[\!\left[\frac{x - 1}{10,000}\right]\!\right]\right) + 3x = 5000 + 3x.$$

During the second 8-hour shift

$$\left[\!\left[\frac{x - 1}{10,000}\right]\!\right] = 1, \quad 10,001 \le x \le 20,000,$$

which implies

$$C = 5000 \left(1 + \left[\!\left[\frac{x - 1}{10,000}\right]\!\right]\right) + 3x = 10,000 + 3x.$$

The graph of C is shown in Figure 1.63. Note the graph's discontinuities.

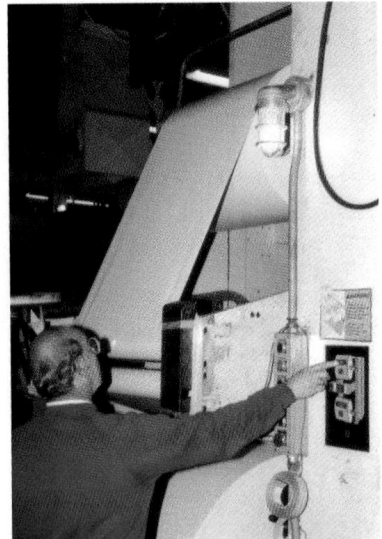

Courtesy of R. R. Donnelley

R. R. Donnelley & Sons Company is the world's largest commercial printer. It prints and binds a major share of the national publications in the United States, including Time, Newsweek, TV Guide, and this book. In 1993, printing and binding of books accounted for 11% of Donnelley's business. The other part of its business came from printing and binding of catalogs, magazines, directories, and other types of publications. In the photo, an employee is aligning a roll of paper on a printing press in one of Donnelley's plants.

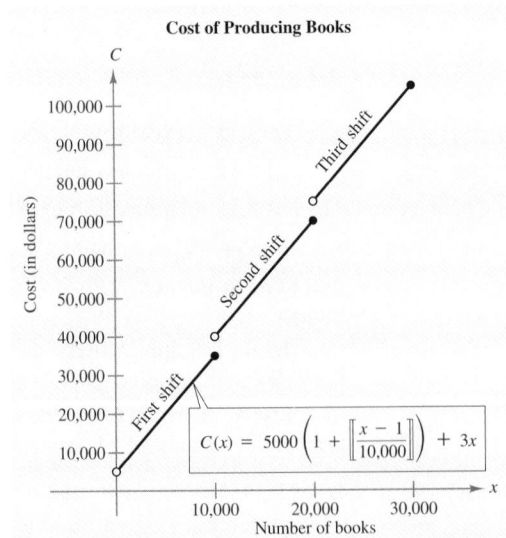

Cost of Producing Books

$$C(x) = 5000 \left(1 + \left[\!\left[\frac{x - 1}{10,000}\right]\!\right]\right) + 3x$$

FIGURE 1.63

▦ TECHNOLOGY

Step Functions and Compound Functions

To graph a step function or compound function with a graphing utility, you must be familiar with the utility's programming language. For instance, the *TI-81*, *TI-82*, and *TI-85* have two different "integer truncation" functions. One is IPart(x), and it yields the truncated integer part of x. For example, IPart(-1.2) $= -1$ and IPart(3.4) $= 3$. The other function is Int(x), which is the greatest integer function. The graphs of these two functions are shown below. When graphing a step function, you should set your graphing utility to dot mode.

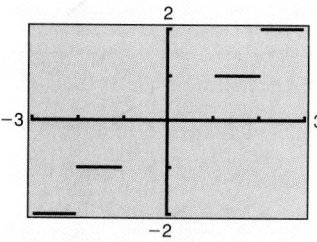

Graph of $f(x) = $ IPart(x)   Graph of $f(x) = $ Int(x)

On the *TI-81*, *TI-82*, or *TI-85*, you can graph a compound function such as

$$f(x) = \begin{cases} x^2 - 4, & x \le 2 \\ -x + 2, & 2 < x \end{cases}$$

by entering

$$Y_1 = (X^2 - 4)(X \le 2) + (-X + 2)(2 < X).$$

The graph of this function is shown below.

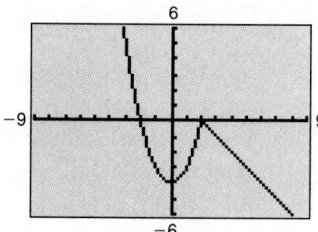

Extended Application: Compound Interest

Banks and other financial institutions differ on how interest is paid to an account. If the interest is added to the account so that future interest is paid on previously earned interest, then the interest is said to be **compounded.** Suppose, for example, that you deposited $10,000 in an account that pays 6% interest, compounded quarterly. Because the 6% is the annual interest rate, the quarterly rate is $\frac{1}{4}(0.06) = 0.015$ or 1.5%. The balances during the first five quarters are shown below.

Quarter	Balance
1st	$10,000.00
2nd	$10,000.00 + (0.015)(10,000.00) = \$10,150.00$
3rd	$10,150.00 + (0.015)(10,150.00) = \$10,302.25$
4th	$10,302.25 + (0.015)(10,302.25) = \$10,456.78$
5th	$10,456.78 + (0.015)(10,456.78) = \$10,613.63$

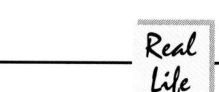

EXAMPLE 6 *Graphing Compound Interest*

Sketch the graph of the balance in the account described above.

Solution

Let A represent the balance in the account and let t represent the time, in years. You can use the greatest integer function to represent the balance, as follows.

$$A = 10,000(1 + 0.015)^{[\![4t]\!]}$$

From the graph shown in Figure 1.64, notice that the function has a discontinuity at each quarter. ■

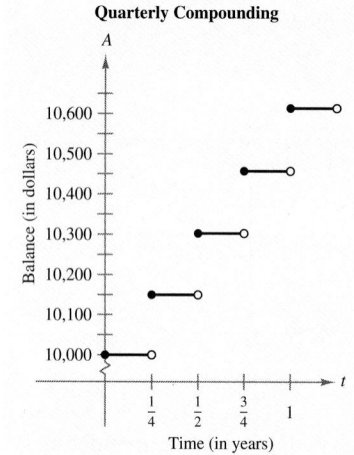

Quarterly Compounding

Balance (in dollars) — values: 10,600, 10,500, 10,400, 10,300, 10,200, 10,100, 10,000

Time (in years) — $\frac{1}{4}$, $\frac{1}{2}$, $\frac{3}{4}$, 1

FIGURE 1.64

Discussion Problem Compound Interest

If P dollars is deposited into an account, compounded n times per year, with an annual rate of r (in decimal form), then the balance A after t years is given by

$$A = P\left(1 + \frac{r}{n}\right)^{nt}.$$

Sketch the graph of each of the following. Which function is continuous? Describe the differences in policy between a bank that uses the first formula and a bank that uses the second formula.

a. $A = P\left(1 + \dfrac{r}{n}\right)^{nt}$ **b.** $A = P\left(1 + \dfrac{r}{n}\right)^{[\![nt]\!]}$

Warm Up

The following warm-up exercises involve skills that were covered in earlier sections. You will use these skills in the exercise set for this section.

In Exercises 1–4, simplify the expression.

1. $\dfrac{x^2 + 6x + 8}{x^2 - 6x - 16}$

2. $\dfrac{x^2 - 5x - 6}{x^2 - 9x + 18}$

3. $\dfrac{2x^2 - 2x - 12}{4x^2 - 24x + 36}$

4. $\dfrac{x^3 - 16x}{x^3 + 2x^2 - 8x}$

In Exercises 5–8, solve for x.

5. $x^2 + 7x = 0$

6. $x^2 + 4x - 5 = 0$

7. $3x^2 + 8x + 4 = 0$

8. $x^3 + 5x^2 - 24x = 0$

In Exercises 9 and 10, find the limit.

9. $\lim\limits_{x \to 3} (2x^2 - 3x + 4)$

10. $\lim\limits_{x \to -2} (3x^3 - 8x + 7)$

EXERCISES 1.6   means that technology can help you solve or check the exercise(s).

In Exercises 1–4, decide whether the function is continuous on the entire real line. Explain your reasoning.

1. $5x^3 - x^2 + 2$

2. $(x^2 - 1)^3$

3. $\dfrac{1}{x^2 - 4}$

4. $\dfrac{1}{4 + x^2}$

In Exercises 5–32, find the intervals on which the function is continuous.

5. $f(x) = -\dfrac{x^3}{2}$

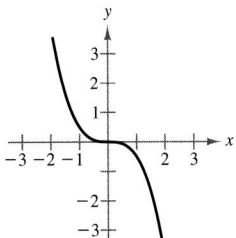

6. $f(x) = \dfrac{x^2 - 1}{x}$

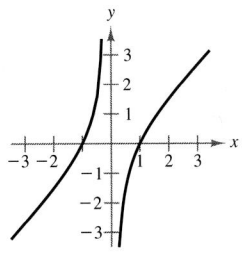

7. $f(x) = \dfrac{x^2 - 1}{x + 1}$

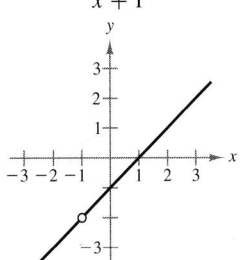

8. $f(x) = \dfrac{1}{x^2 - 4}$

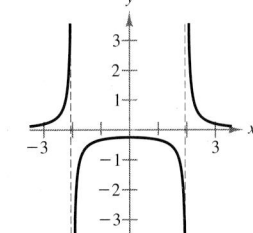

9. $f(x) = x^2 - 2x + 1$

10. $f(x) = \dfrac{1}{x^2 + 1}$

11. $f(x) = \dfrac{1}{x - 1}$

12. $f(x) = \dfrac{x}{x^2 - 1}$

13. $f(x) = \dfrac{x}{x^2 + 1}$

14. $f(x) = \dfrac{x - 3}{x^2 - 9}$

15. $f(x) = \dfrac{x - 5}{x^2 - 9x + 20}$

16. $f(x) = \dfrac{x - 1}{x^2 + x - 2}$

17. $f(x) = \begin{cases} -x, & x < 1 \\ 1, & x = 1 \\ x, & x > 1 \end{cases}$

18. $f(x) = \dfrac{[\![x]\!]}{2} + x$

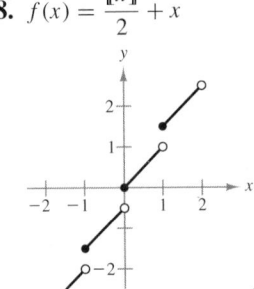

19. $f(x) = \begin{cases} x, & x \le 1 \\ x^2, & x > 1 \end{cases}$

20. $f(x) = \begin{cases} -2x + 3, & x < 1 \\ x^2, & x \ge 1 \end{cases}$

21. $f(x) = \begin{cases} \frac{1}{2}x + 1, & x \le 2 \\ 3 - x, & x > 2 \end{cases}$

22. $f(x) = \begin{cases} -2x, & x \le 2 \\ x^2 - 4x + 1, & x > 2 \end{cases}$

23. $f(x) = \begin{cases} 3 + x, & x \le 2 \\ x^2 + 1, & x > 2 \end{cases}$

24. $f(x) = \begin{cases} |x - 2| + 3, & x < 0 \\ x + 5, & x \ge 0 \end{cases}$

25. $f(x) = \dfrac{|x + 1|}{x + 1}$

26. $f(x) = \dfrac{|4 - x|}{4 - x}$

27. $f(x) = [\![x - 1]\!]$

28. $f(x) = x - [\![x]\!]$

29. $f(x) = [\![x]\!] - 2$

30. $f(x) = \frac{1}{2}[\![x]\!]$

31. $h(x) = f(g(x)), \ f(x) = \dfrac{1}{\sqrt{x}}, \ g(x) = x - 1, x > 1$

32. $h(x) = f(g(x)), \ f(x) = \dfrac{1}{x - 1}, \ g(x) = x^2 + 5$

In Exercises 33–36, discuss the continuity of the function on the closed interval. If there are any discontinuities, determine whether they are removable.

Function	Interval
33. $f(x) = x^2 - 4x - 5$	$[-1, 5]$
34. $f(x) = \dfrac{5}{x^2 + 1}$	$[-2, 2]$

Function	Interval
35. $f(x) = \dfrac{1}{x - 2}$	$[1, 4]$
36. $f(x) = \dfrac{x}{x^2 - 4x + 3}$	$[0, 4]$

In Exercises 37–42, sketch the graph of the function and describe the intervals on which the function is continuous.

37. $f(x) = \dfrac{x^2 - 16}{x - 4}$

38. $f(x) = \dfrac{2x^2 + x}{x}$

39. $f(x) = \dfrac{x^3 + x}{x}$

40. $f(x) = \dfrac{x^4 - 1}{x^2 - 1}$

41. $f(x) = \begin{cases} x^2 + 1, & x < 0 \\ x - 1, & x \ge 0 \end{cases}$

42. $f(x) = x - 2[\![x]\!]$

43. Determine the constant a so that the function is continuous on the entire real line.

$$f(x) = \begin{cases} x^3, & x \le 2 \\ ax^2, & x > 2 \end{cases}$$

44. Determine the constants a and b so that the function is continuous on the entire real line.

$$f(x) = \begin{cases} 2, & x \le -1 \\ ax + b, & -1 < x < 3 \\ -2, & x \ge 3 \end{cases}$$

In Exercises 45 and 46, use a graphing utility to graph the function. Then use the graph to determine any x-values at which the function is not continuous.

45. $h(x) = \dfrac{1}{x^2 - x - 2}$

46. $f(x) = \begin{cases} 2x - 4, & x \le 3 \\ x^2 - 2x, & x > 3 \end{cases}$

In Exercises 47–50, find the interval(s) on which the function is continuous.

47. $f(x) = \dfrac{x}{x^2 + 1}$

48. $f(x) = x\sqrt{x + 3}$

49. $f(x) = \frac{1}{2}[\![2x]\!]$

50. $f(x) = \frac{x+1}{\sqrt{x}}$

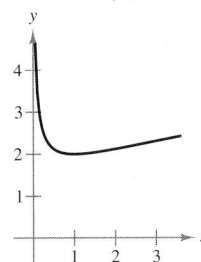

Essay In Exercises 51 and 52, use a graphing utility to graph the function on the interval $[-4, 4]$. Does the graph of the function appear continuous on this interval? *Is* the function continuous on $[-4, 4]$? Write a short paragraph about the importance of examining a function analytically as well as graphically.

51. $f(x) = \frac{x^2 + x}{x}$

52. $f(x) = \frac{x^3 - 8}{x - 2}$

53. *Compound Interest* A deposit of $7500 is made into an account that pays 6% compounded quarterly. The amount A in the account after t years is

$$A = 7500(1.015)^{[\![4t]\!]}, \qquad t \geq 0.$$

(a) Sketch the graph of A. Is the graph continuous? Explain.

(b) What is the balance after 7 years?

54. *Environmental Cost* The cost C (in millions of dollars) of removing x percent of the pollutants emitted from the smokestack of a factory can be modeled by

$$C = \frac{2x}{100 - x}.$$

(a) What is the implied domain of C? Explain.

(b) Graph the cost function. Is the function continuous on its domain? Explain.

(c) Find the cost of removing 75% of the pollutants from the smokestack.

55. *Telephone Rates* A dial-direct long distance call between two cities costs $1.04 for the first 2 minutes and $0.36 for each additional minute or fraction thereof.

(a) Use the greatest integer function to write the cost C of a call in terms of the time t (in minutes). Graph the cost function and discuss its continuity.

(b) Find the cost of a 9-minute call.

56. *Salary Contract* A union contract guarantees a 9% increase yearly for 5 years. For a current salary of $28,500, the salary for the next 5 years is given by

$$S = 28,500(1.09)^{[\![t]\!]},$$

where $t = 0$ represents the present year.

(a) Graph the salary function and discuss its continuity.

(b) Find the salary during the fifth year (when $t = 5$).

57. *Inventory Management* The number of units in inventory in a small company is

$$N = 25 \left(2 \left[\!\left[\frac{t + 2}{2} \right]\!\right] - t \right), \qquad 0 \leq t \leq 12,$$

where the real number t is the time in months.

(a) Graph this function and discuss its continuity.

(b) How often must the company replenish its inventory?

58. *Owning a Franchise* You have purchased a franchise similar to that described below. You have determined a linear model for your revenue as a function of time. Is the model a continuous function? Would your actual revenue be a continuous function of time? Explain.

— *Business Capsule* —

Dan Bryant for "5 Keys to Successful Franchise Ownership" by Ingrid Sturgis in *Black Enterprise* May 1993, Vol. 23, No. 10, pages 77-82.

Twins Rodney and Roger Wagner used an inheritance of $25,000 and a small business loan of $85,000 to purchase a franchise for "I Can't Believe It's Yogurt" in 1988. By 1993, they had expanded to three outlets in the Dallas, Texas area.

Chapter Summary and Study Tips

After studying this chapter, you should have acquired the following skills. The exercise numbers are keyed to the Review Exercises that begin on page 76. Answers to odd-numbered Review Exercises are given in the back of the text.

■ Plot points in a coordinate plane and read data presented graphically. (*Section 1.1*) — Review Exercises 1–4

■ Find the distance between two points in a coordinate plane. (*Section 1.1*) — Review Exercises 5–8

$$d = \sqrt{(x_2 - x_1)^2 + (y_2 - y_1)^2}$$

■ Find the midpoint of the segment connecting two points. (*Section 1.1*) — Review Exercises 9–12

$$\text{Midpoint} = \left(\frac{x_1 + x_2}{2}, \frac{y_1 + y_2}{2} \right)$$

■ Interpret real-life data that is presented graphically. (*Section 1.1*) — Review Exercises 13, 14

■ Translate points in a coordinate plane. (*Section 1.1*) — Review Exercises 15, 16

■ Sketch the graph of an equation by hand *and* using a graphing utility. (*Section 1.2*) — Review Exercises 17–24

■ Find the x- and y-intercepts of the graph of an equation algebraically *and* graphically using a graphing utility. (*Section 1.2*) — Review Exercises 25, 26

■ Write the standard equation of a circle, given the center and a point on the circle. (*Section 1.2*) — Review Exercises 27, 28

$$(x - h)^2 + (y - k)^2 = r^2$$

■ Convert an equation of a circle from general form to standard form by completing the square. (*Section 1.2*) — Review Exercises 29, 30

■ Find the points of intersection of two graphs algebraically *and* graphically using a graphing utility. (*Section 1.2*) — Review Exercises 31–34

■ Find the break-even point for a business. (*Section 1.2*) — Review Exercises 35, 36

The break-even point occurs when the revenue R is equal to the cost C.

■ Use the slope-intercept form of a linear equation to sketch its graph. (*Section 1.3*) — Review Exercises 37–42

$$y = mx + b$$

■ Find the slope of the line passing through two points. (*Section 1.3*) — Review Exercises 43–46

$$m = \frac{y_2 - y_1}{x_2 - x_1}$$

■ Use the point-slope form to write an equation of a line. (*Section 1.3*) — Review Exercises 47, 48

$$y - y_1 = m(x - x_1)$$

*Several student study aids are available with this text. The *Student Solutions Guide* includes detailed solutions to all odd-numbered exercises, as well as practice chapter tests with answers. The *Graphics Calculator Guide* offers instructions on the use of a variety of graphing calculators and computer graphing software. The *Brief Calculus TUTOR* includes additional examples for selected exercises in the text.

■ Find equations of parallel and perpendicular lines. (*Section 1.3*)	Review Exercises 49, 50

$$\text{Parallel lines: } m_1 = m_2 \qquad \text{Perpendicular lines: } m_1 = -\frac{1}{m_2}$$

■ Use linear equations to solve real-life problems such as predicting future sales or creating a linear depreciation schedule. (*Section 1.3*)	Review Exercises 51, 52
■ Use the vertical line test to decide whether an equation defines a function. (*Section 1.4*)	Review Exercises 53–56
■ Use function notation to evaluate functions. (*Section 1.4*)	Review Exercises 57, 58
■ Find the domain and range of a function. (*Section 1.4*)	Review Exercises 59–64
■ Combine functions to form other functions. (*Section 1.4*)	Review Exercises 65, 66
■ Use the horizontal line test to determine whether a function has an inverse. If it does, find the inverse. (*Section 1.4*)	Review Exercises 67–70
■ Determine whether a limit exists. If it does, approximate the limit graphically and numerically using a table. (*Section 1.5*)	Review Exercises 71–88
■ Evaluate limits analytically and evaluate one-sided limits. (*Section 1.5*)	Review Exercises 89–94
■ Determine whether a function is continuous at a point, in an open interval, and in a closed interval. (*Section 1.6*)	Review Exercises 95–104
■ Create mathematical models using the greatest integer function and other step functions. (*Section 1.6*)	Review Exercises 105, 106

On pages xxix–xxx of the preface, we included a feature called *How to Study Calculus*. If you have not already read this, we encourage you to do so now. Here are some other tips that can help you succeed in this course.

■ Use a Graphing Utility   A graphing calculator or graphing software for a computer can help you in this course in two important ways. As an *exploratory device*, a graphing utility allows you to learn concepts by allowing you to compare graphs of equations. For instance, sketching the graphs of $y = x^2$, $y = x^2 + 1$, and $y = x^2 - 1$ helps confirm that adding (or subtracting) a constant from a function shifts the graph of the function vertically. As a *problem-solving tool*, a graphing utility frees you of some of the drudgery of sketching complicated graphs by hand. The time that you save can be spent using mathematics to solve real-life problems.

■ Use the Warm-Up Exercises   Each exercise set in this text begins with a set of 10 warm-up exercises. We urge you to begin each homework session by quickly working all 10 warm-up exercises (all are answered in the back of the text). The "old" skills covered in the warm-up exercises are needed to master the "new" skills in the section-exercise set. The warm-up exercises remind you that mathematics is cumulative—to be successful in this course, you must retain "old" skills.

■ Use the Additional Study Aids   The additional study aids were prepared specifically to help you master the concepts discussed in the text. They are the *Student Solutions Guide*, the *Brief Calculus TUTOR*, and the *Graphics Calculator Guide*.

Review Exercises

 means that technology can help you solve or check the exercise(s).

In Exercises 1–4, match the data with the real-life situation that it represents. [Graphs are labeled (a)–(d).]

(a)

(b)

(c)

(d)

1. Population of Texas *a*   **2.** Population of California *c*

3. Number of U.S. Business Failures *b*   **4.** IBM Revenues *d*

In Exercises 5–8, find the distance between the two points.

5. $(0, 0)$, $(5, 2)$ **6.** $(1, 2)$, $(4, 3)$

7. $(-1, 3)$, $(-4, 6)$ **8.** $(6, 8)$, $(-3, 7)$
$x_1\ y_1\ x_2\ y_2$

In Exercises 9–12, find the midpoint of the segment connecting the two points.

9. $(5, 6)$, $(9, 2)$ **10.** $(0, 0)$, $(-4, 8)$

11. $(-10, 4)$, $(-6, 8)$ **12.** $(7, -9)$, $(-3, 5)$
$x_1\ y_1\ x_2\ y_2$

In Exercises 13 and 14, use the graph below, which gives the revenues, costs, and profits for *Kimberly-Clark Corporation* from 1987 through 1992. *(Source: Kimberly-Clark Corporation)*

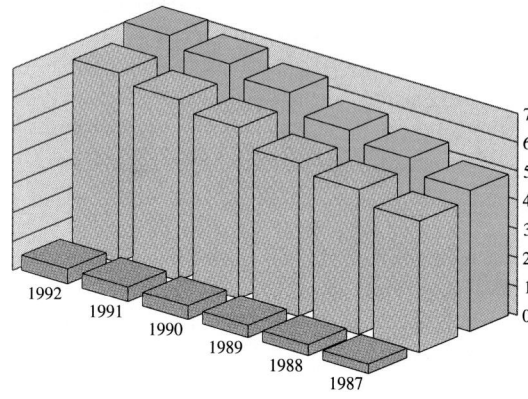

FIGURE FOR 13 AND 14

13. Which bars on the graph represent the revenues? Which represent the costs? Which represent the profits? Explain your reasoning. Write an equation that relates the revenue R, cost C, and profit P.

14. Estimate the revenue, cost, and profit for Kimberly-Clark Corporation in 1992. Do you think these numbers are in billions of dollars, millions of dollars, or thousands of dollars? Explain your reasoning. (Kimberly-Clark is the maker of *Kleenex, Huggies Disposable Diapers*, and other paper products.)

15. Translate the triangle whose vertices are $(1, 3)$, $(2, 4)$, and $(5, 6)$ three units to the right and four units up. Find the coordinates of the translated vertices.

16. Translate the quadrilateral whose vertices are $(-2, 4)$, $(5, 0)$, $(2, 6)$, and $(-1, 3)$ four units to the left and three units down. Find the coordinates of the translated vertices.

In Exercises 17–24, sketch the graph of the equation.

17. $y = 4x - 12$ **18.** $y = 4 - 3x$

19. $y = x^2 + 5$ **20.** $y = 1 - x^2$

21. $y = x^2 + 5x + 6$ **22.** $y = |2x - 3|$

23. $y = x^3 + 4$ **24.** $y = \sqrt{2x}$

In Exercises 25 and 26, find the intercepts of the graph of the equation algebraically. Check your results with a graphing utility.

25. $4x + y + 3 = 0$ **26.** $y = (x-1)^3 + 2(x-1)^2$

In Exercises 27 and 28, write the standard form of the circle.

27. Center: (0, 0); **28.** Center: (2, −1);
  Solution point: $\left(2, \sqrt{5}\right)$ Solution point: (−1, 7)

In Exercises 29 and 30, complete the square to write the equation of the circle in standard form. Determine the radius and center of the circle. Then sketch the circle.

29. $x^2 + y^2 - 6x + 8y = 0$
30. $x^2 + y^2 + 10x + 4y - 7 = 0$

 In Exercises 31–34, find the points of intersection of the graphs algebraically. Then use a graphing utility to check your results.

31. $x + y = 2$, $2x - y = 1$ **32.** $x^2 + y^2 = 5$, $x - y = 1$
33. $y = x^3$, $y = x$ **34.** $y = \sqrt{x}$, $y = x$

 35. *Break-Even Analysis* The student government association wants to raise money by having a T-shirt sale. Each shirt costs $8. The silk screening costs $200 for the design, plus $2 per shirt. Each shirt will sell for $14.

(a) Find equations for the total cost C and the total revenue R for selling x shirts.
(b) Find the break-even point.

 36. *Break-Even Analysis* You are starting a part-time business. You make an initial investment of $6000. The unit cost of the product is $6.50, and the selling price is $13.90.

(a) Find equations for the total cost C and the total revenue R for selling x units of the product.
(b) Find the break-even point.

 In Exercises 37–42, find the slope and y-intercept (if possible) of the linear equation. Then sketch the graph of the equation.

37. $3x + y = -2$ **38.** $-\frac{1}{3}x + \frac{5}{6}y = 1$
39. $y = -\frac{5}{3}$ **40.** $x = -3$
41. $-2x - 5y - 5 = 0$ **42.** $3.2x - 0.8y + 5.6 = 0$

In Exercises 43–46, find the slope of the line passing through the two points.

43. (0, 0), (7, 6)   **44.** (−1, 5), (−5, 7)
45. (10, 17), (−11, −3)   **46.** (−11, −3), (−1, −3)

 In Exercises 47 and 48, find an equation of the line that passes through the point and has the indicated slope. Then sketch the line.

47. Point: (3, −1); Slope: $m = -2$
48. Point: (−3, −3); Slope: $m = \frac{1}{2}$

In Exercises 49 and 50, find the general form of the equation of the line passing through the point and satisfying the given condition.

 49. Point: (−3, 6)
  (a) Slope is $\frac{7}{8}$.
  (b) Parallel to the line $4x + 2y = 7$.
  (c) Passes through the origin.
  (d) Perpendicular to the line $3x - 2y = 2$.

50. Point: (1, −3)
  (a) Parallel to the x-axis.
  (b) Perpendicular to the x-axis.
  (c) Parallel to the line $-4x + 5y = -3$.
  (d) Perpendicular to the line $5x - 2y = 3$.

 51. *Demand* When a wholesaler sold a product at $32 per unit, sales were 750 units per week. After a price increase of $5 per unit, however, the sales dropped to 700 units per week.

(a) Write the quantity demanded x as a linear function of the price p.
(b) *Linear Interpolation* Predict the number of units sold at a price of $34.50 per unit.
(c) *Linear Extrapolation* Predict the number of units sold at a price of $42.00 per unit.

 52. *Linear Depreciation* A small business purchases a type-setting system for $117,000. After 9 years, the system will be obsolete and have no value.

(a) Write a linear equation giving the value v of the system in terms of the time t.
(b) Use a graphing utility to graph the function.
(c) Use a graphing utility to estimate the value of the system after 4 years.
(d) Use a graphing utility to estimate the time when the system's value will be $84,000.

In Exercises 53–56, use the vertical line test to determine whether y is a function of x.

53. $y = -x^2 + 2$

54. $x^2 + y^2 = 4$

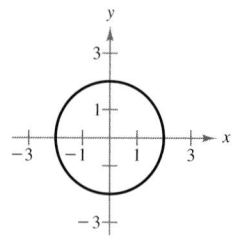

55. $y^2 - \frac{1}{4}x^2 = 4$

56. $y = |x + 4|$

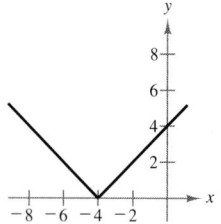

57. Given $f(x) = 3x + 4$, find the following.

   (a) $f(1)$ (b) $f(x + 1)$ (c) $f(2 + \Delta x)$

58. Given $f(x) = x^2 + 4x + 3$, find the following.

   (a) $f(0)$ (b) $f(x - 1)$ (c) $f(x + \Delta x) - f(x)$

In Exercises 59–64, use a graphing utility to graph the function. Then find the domain and range of the function.

59. $f(x) = x^2 + 3x + 2$ **60.** $f(x) = 2$

61. $f(x) = \sqrt{x + 1}$ **62.** $f(x) = \dfrac{x - 3}{x^2 + x - 12}$

63. $f(x) = -|x| + 3$ **64.** $f(x) = -\frac{12}{13}x - \frac{7}{8}$

In Exercises 65 and 66, use f and g to find the following.

(a) $f(x) + g(x)$ (b) $f(x) - g(x)$ (c) $f(x)g(x)$

(d) $\dfrac{f(x)}{g(x)}$ (e) $f(g(x))$ (f) $g(f(x))$

65. $f(x) = 1 + x^2,$ $g(x) = 2x - 1$

66. $f(x) = 2x - 3,$ $g(x) = \sqrt{x + 1}$

In Exercises 67–70, find the inverse of f (if it exists).

67. $f(x) = \frac{3}{2}x$

68. $f(x) = |x + 1|$

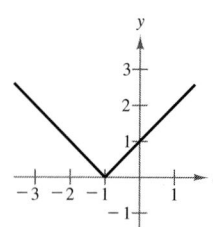

69. $f(x) = -x^2 + \frac{1}{2}$

70. $f(x) = x^3 - 1$

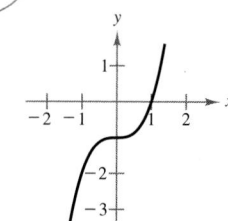

In Exercises 71–86, find the limit (if it exists).

71. $\lim\limits_{x \to 2} (5x - 3)$ **72.** $\lim\limits_{x \to 2} (2x + 9)$

73. $\lim\limits_{x \to 2} (5x - 3)(2x + 3)$ **74.** $\lim\limits_{x \to 2} \dfrac{5x - 3}{2x + 9}$

75. $\lim\limits_{t \to 3} \dfrac{t^2 + 1}{t}$ **76.** $\lim\limits_{t \to 1} \dfrac{t + 1}{t - 2}$

77. $\lim\limits_{t \to 0} \dfrac{t^2 + 1}{t}$ **78.** $\lim\limits_{t \to 2} \dfrac{t + 1}{t - 2}$

79. $\lim\limits_{x \to -2} \dfrac{x + 2}{x^2 - 4}$ **80.** $\lim\limits_{x \to 3^-} \dfrac{x^2 - 9}{x - 3}$

81. $\lim\limits_{x \to 0^+} \left(x - \dfrac{1}{x}\right)$ **82.** $\lim\limits_{x \to 1/2} \dfrac{2x - 1}{6x - 3}$

83. $\lim\limits_{x \to 0} \dfrac{[1/(x - 2)] - 1}{x}$ **84.** $\lim\limits_{s \to 0} \dfrac{(1/\sqrt{1 + s}) - 1}{s}$

85. $\lim\limits_{\Delta x \to 0} \dfrac{(x + \Delta x)^3 - (x + \Delta x) - (x^3 - x)}{\Delta x}$

86. $\lim\limits_{\Delta x \to 0} \dfrac{1 - (x + \Delta x)^2 - (1 - x^2)}{\Delta x}$

In Exercises 87 and 88, use a table to estimate the limit.

87. $\lim\limits_{x \to 1^+} \dfrac{\sqrt{2x + 1} - \sqrt{3}}{x - 1}$ **88.** $\lim\limits_{x \to 1^+} \dfrac{1 - \sqrt[3]{x}}{x - 1}$

In Exercises 89–94, determine whether the statement is true or false.

89. $\lim\limits_{x \to 0} \dfrac{|x|}{x} = 1$

90. $\lim\limits_{x \to 0} x^3 = 0$

91. $\lim\limits_{x \to 0} \sqrt{x} = 0$

92. $\lim\limits_{x \to 0} \sqrt[3]{x} = 0$

93. $\lim\limits_{x \to 2} f(x) = 3, \quad f(x) = \begin{cases} 3, & x \le 2 \\ 0, & x > 2 \end{cases}$

94. $\lim\limits_{x \to 3} f(x) = 1, \quad f(x) = \begin{cases} x - 2, & x \le 3 \\ -x^2 + 8x - 14, & x > 3 \end{cases}$

In Exercises 95–102, find the intervals on which the function is continuous.

95. $f(x) = \dfrac{1}{(x+4)^2}$

96. $f(x) = \dfrac{x+2}{x}$

97. $f(x) = \dfrac{3}{x+1}$

98. $f(x) = \dfrac{x+1}{2x+2}$

99. $f(x) = [\![x + 3]\!]$

100. $f(x) = \dfrac{3x^2 - x - 2}{x - 1}$

101. $f(x) = \begin{cases} x, & x \le 0 \\ x + 1, & x > 0 \end{cases}$

102. $f(x) = \begin{cases} x, & x \le 0 \\ x^2, & x > 0 \end{cases}$

In Exercises 103 and 104, find a so that f is continuous on $(-\infty, \infty)$.

103. $f(x) = \begin{cases} -x + 1, & x \le 3 \\ ax - 8, & x > 3 \end{cases}$

104. $f(x) = \begin{cases} x + 1, & x < 1 \\ 2x + a, & x \ge 1 \end{cases}$

105. *National Debt* The table lists the national debt D (in billions of dollars) for selected years. A mathematical model for the national debt is

$$D = 0.2t^3 + 2.74t^2 + 8.47t + 358.78,$$

where $t = 0$ represents 1970. *(Source: U.S. Office of Management and Budget)*

t	0	5	10	15	20	21
D	381	542	909	1817	3206	3599

(a) Use a graphing utility to graph the model.

(b) Create a table that compares the values given by the model with the actual data.

(c) Use the model to estimate the national debt in 1995.

106. *Recycling* A recycling center pays $0.25 for each pound of aluminum cans. Twenty-four aluminum cans weigh 1 pound. A mathematical model for the amount paid A by the recycling center is

$$A = \frac{1}{4}\left[\!\!\left[\frac{x}{24}\right]\!\!\right],$$

where x is the number of cans.

(a) Sketch the graph of the function and then discuss its continuity.

(b) How much does a recycling center pay out for 1500 cans?

Sample Post-Graduation Exam Questions

The following questions were taken from certified public accountant (CPA) exams, graduate management admission tests (GMAT), graduate records exams (GRE), actuarial exams, or college-level academic skills tests (CLAST). The answers to the questions are given in the back of the book.

In Questions 1–5, use the data given in the graph at the right. *(Source: U.S. Bureau of the Census)*

1. The total labor force in 1985 was about y million with y equal to
   (a) 65   (b) 81   (c) 100   (d) 108   (e) 115

2. In 1975, the percent of women in the labor force who were married was about
   (a) 19   (b) 32   (c) 45   (d) 60   (e) 82

3. What was the first year when more than 50 million women were in the labor force?
   (a) 1976   (b) 1984   (c) 1985   (d) 1988   (e) 1991

4. Between 1974 and 1991, the number of women in the labor force
   (a) increased by about 25%   (b) increased by about 50%
   (c) increased by about 100%   (d) increased by about 150%
   (e) increased by about 200%

5. Which of the following statements about the labor force can be inferred from the graphs?
   I. Between 1974 and 1991, there were no years when more than 15 million widowed, divorced, or separated women were in the labor force.
   II. In every year between 1974 and 1991, the number of single women in the labor force increased.
   III. In every year between 1975 and 1991, women made up at least $\frac{2}{5}$ of the total labor force.

   (a) I only   (b) II only   (c) I and II only   (d) I and III only
   (e) I, II, and III

6. What is the length of the line segment connecting $(1, 3)$ to $(-1, 5)$?
   (a) $\sqrt{3}$ (b) 2   (c) $2\sqrt{2}$ (d) 4   (e) 8

7. The interest charged on a loan is p dollars per $1000 for the first month and q dollars per $1000 for each month after the first month. How much interest will be charged during the first 3 months on a loan of $10,000?

   (a) $30p$ (b) $30q$ (c) $p+2q$ (d) $20p+10q$ (e) $10p+20q$

8. If $x + y > 5$ and $x - y > 3$, which of the following describes the x solutions?

   (a) $x > 3$ (b) $x > 4$ (c) $x > 5$ (d) $x < 5$ (e) $x < 3$

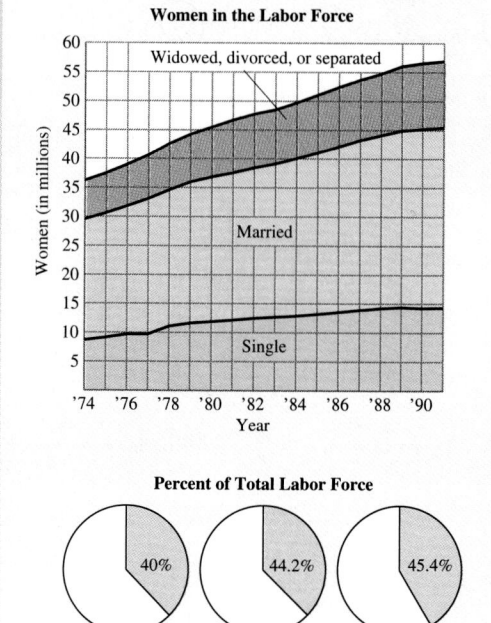

FIGURE FOR 1–5

$$\lim_{\Delta x \to 0} \frac{\Delta y}{\Delta x} = \frac{dy}{dx}$$

2 Differentiation

Calculus is the mathematics of change. When Isaac Newton and other 17th century mathematicians developed calculus, they were concerned with describing changes in moving objects, such as the planets. As their investigations deepened, their unresolved questions centered around four problems: the tangent line problem, the velocity and acceleration problem, the minimum-maximum problem, and the area problem.

In what turned out to be the most famous mathematical discovery in history, Newton realized that all four problems were intimately connected and could be solved by calculating *derivatives* and *antiderivatives*.

$$y' = f'(x)$$

Newton

2.1

The Derivative and the Slope of a Graph

Tangent Line to a Graph ■ *Slope of a Graph* ■ *Slope and the Limit Process* ■ *The Derivative of a Function* ■ *Differentiability and Continuity*

Tangent Line to a Graph

Calculus is a branch of mathematics that studies rates of change of functions. In this course, you will learn that rates of change have many applications in real life. In Section 1.3, you learned how the slope of a line indicates the rate at which a line rises or falls. For a line, this rate (or slope) is the same at every point on the line. For graphs other than lines, the rate at which the graph rises or falls changes from point to point. For instance, in Figure 2.1, the parabola is rising more quickly at the point (x_1, y_1) than it is at the point (x_2, y_2). At the vertex (x_3, y_3), the graph levels off, and at the point (x_4, y_4), the graph is falling.

To determine the rate at which a graph rises or falls at a *single point*, you can find the slope of the tangent line at the point. In simple terms, the **tangent line** to the graph of a function f at a point $P(x_1, y_1)$ is the line that best approximates the graph at that point, as shown in Figure 2.1. Figure 2.2 shows other examples of tangent lines.

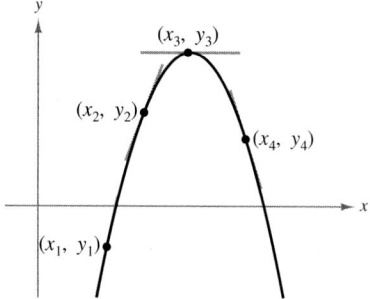

FIGURE 2.1 The slope of a graph changes from one point to another.

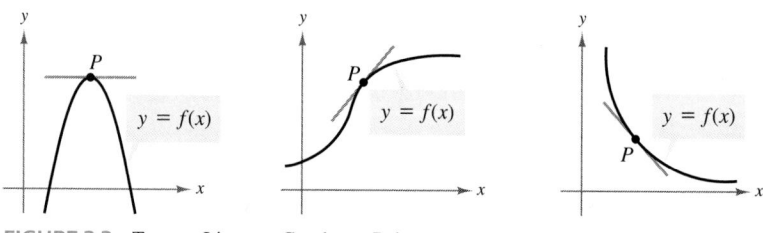

FIGURE 2.2 Tangent Line to a Graph at a Point

When Isaac Newton (1642–1727) was working on the "tangent line problem," he realized that it is difficult to define precisely what is meant by a tangent to a general curve. From geometry, you know that a line is tangent to a circle if the line intersects the circle at only one point, as shown in Figure 2.3. Tangent lines to noncircular graphs, however, can intersect the graph at more than one point. For instance, in the second graph in Figure 2.2, if the tangent line were extended, it would intersect the graph at a point other than the point of tangency. In this section, you will see how the notion of a limit can be used to define a general tangent line.

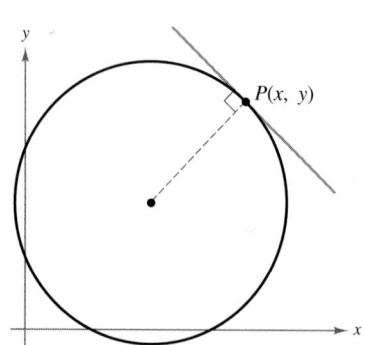

FIGURE 2.3 Tangent Line to a Circle

Slope of a Graph

Because a tangent line approximates the graph at a point, the problem of finding the slope of a graph at a point becomes one of finding the slope of the tangent line at the point.

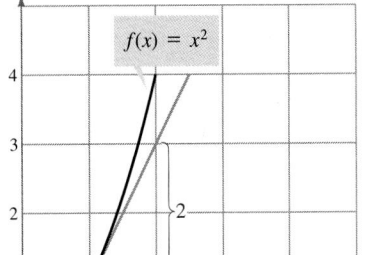

FIGURE 2.4

EXAMPLE 1 *Approximating the Slope of a Graph*

Use the graph in Figure 2.4 to approximate the slope of the graph of $f(x) = x^2$ at the point $(1, 1)$.

Solution
From the graph of $f(x) = x^2$, you can see that the tangent line at $(1, 1)$ rises approximately two units for each unit change in x. Thus, the slope of the tangent line at $(1, 1)$ is given by

$$\text{Slope} = \frac{\text{change in } y}{\text{change in } x} \approx \frac{2}{1} = 2.$$

Because the tangent line at the point $(1, 1)$ has a slope of about 2, you can conclude that the graph has a slope of about 2 at the point $(1, 1)$. ■

Note When visually approximating the slope of a graph, note that the scales on the horizontal and vertical axes may differ. When this happens (as it frequently does in applications), the slope of the tangent line is distorted, and you must be careful to account for the difference in scales.

Real Life

EXAMPLE 2 *Interpreting Slope*

Figure 2.5 graphically depicts the average daily temperature (in degrees Fahrenheit) in Duluth, Minnesota. Estimate the slope of this graph at the indicated point and give a physical interpretation of the result. *(Source: National Oceanic and Atmospheric Administration)*

Solution
From the graph, you can see that the tangent line at the given point falls approximately 27 units for each two-unit change in x. Thus, you can estimate the slope at the given point to be

$$\text{Slope} = \frac{\text{change in } y}{\text{change in } x} \approx \frac{-27}{2} = -13.5 \text{ degrees per month.}$$

This means that you can expect the average daily temperatures in November to be about 13.5 degrees *lower* than the corresponding temperatures in October. ■

FIGURE 2.5

Slope and the Limit Process

In Examples 1 and 2, you approximated the slope of a graph at a point by making a careful graph and then "eyeballing" the tangent line at the point of tangency. A more precise method of approximating tangent lines makes use of a **secant line** through the point of tangency and a second point on the graph, as shown in Figure 2.6. If $(x, f(x))$ is the point of tangency and $(x + \Delta x, f(x + \Delta x))$ is a second point on the graph of f, then the slope of the secant line through the two points is

$$m_{\sec} = \frac{f(x + \Delta x) - f(x)}{\Delta x} = \frac{\Delta y}{\Delta x}. \qquad \textit{Slope of secant line}$$

The right side of this equation is called the **difference quotient.** The denominator Δx is the **change in x**, and the numerator is the **change in y.** The beauty of this procedure is that you obtain better and better approximations of the slope of the tangent line by choosing the second point closer and closer to the point of tangency, as shown in Figure 2.7.

Using the limit process, you can find the *exact* slope of the tangent line at $(x, f(x))$.

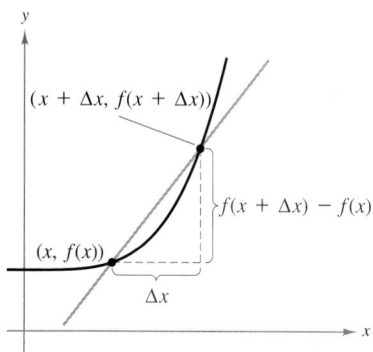

FIGURE 2.6 The Secant Line Through $(x, f(x))$ and $(x + \Delta x, f(x + \Delta x))$

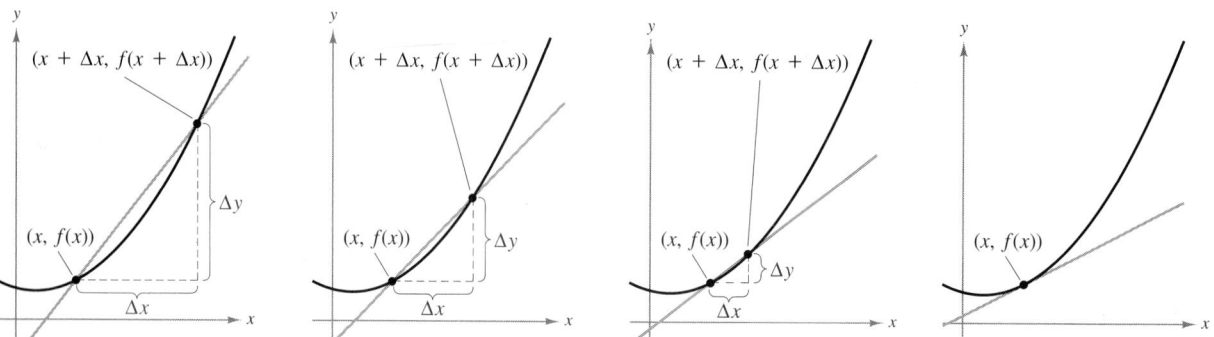

FIGURE 2.7 As Δx approaches 0, the secant lines approach the tangent line.

Note Δx is used as a variable to represent the change in x in the definition of the slope of a graph. Other variables may also be used. For instance, this definition is sometimes written as

$$m = \lim_{h \to 0} \frac{f(x + h) - f(x)}{h}.$$

Definition of the Slope of a Graph

The **slope** m of the graph of f at the point $(x, f(x))$ is equal to the slope of its tangent line at $(x, f(x))$, and is given by

$$m = \lim_{\Delta x \to 0} m_{\sec} = \lim_{\Delta x \to 0} \frac{f(x + \Delta x) - f(x)}{\Delta x}$$

provided this limit exists.

EXAMPLE 3 *Finding Slope by the Limit Process*

Find the slope of the graph of $f(x) = x^2$ at the point $(-2, 4)$.

Solution

Begin by finding an expression that represents the slope of a secant line at the point $(-2, 4)$.

$$m_{\sec} = \frac{f(-2 + \Delta x) - f(-2)}{\Delta x} \qquad \text{Set up difference quotient.}$$

$$= \frac{(-2 + \Delta x)^2 - (-2)^2}{\Delta x} \qquad \text{Use } f(x) = x^2.$$

$$= \frac{4 - 4\Delta x + (\Delta x)^2 - 4}{\Delta x} \qquad \text{Expand terms.}$$

$$= \frac{-4\Delta x + (\Delta x)^2}{\Delta x} \qquad \text{Simplify.}$$

$$= \frac{\Delta x(-4 + \Delta x)}{\Delta x} \qquad \text{Factor and cancel.}$$

$$= -4 + \Delta x, \qquad \Delta x \neq 0 \qquad \text{Simplify.}$$

Next, take the limit of $m_{\sec}$ as $\Delta x \to 0$.

$$m = \lim_{\Delta x \to 0} m_{\sec} = \lim_{\Delta x \to 0} (-4 + \Delta x) = -4$$

Thus, the graph of f has a slope of -4 at the point $(-2, 4)$, as shown in Figure 2.8.

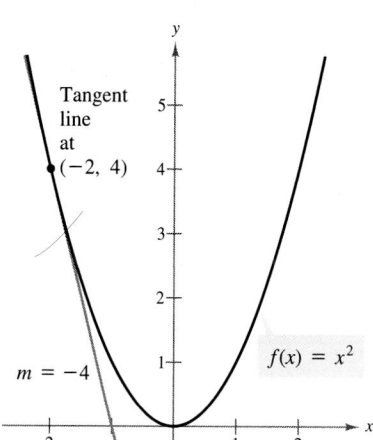

Tangent line at $(-2, 4)$

$m = -4$

$f(x) = x^2$

FIGURE 2.8

EXAMPLE 4 *Finding the Slope of a Graph*

Find the slope of $f(x) = -2x + 4$.

Solution

You know from your study of linear functions that the line given by $f(x) = -2x + 4$ has a slope of -2, as shown in Figure 2.9. This conclusion is consistent with the limit definition of slope.

$$m = \lim_{\Delta x \to 0} \frac{f(x + \Delta x) - f(x)}{\Delta x}$$

$$= \lim_{\Delta x \to 0} \frac{[-2(x + \Delta x) + 4] - [-2x + 4]}{\Delta x}$$

$$= \lim_{\Delta x \to 0} \frac{-2x - 2\Delta x + 4 + 2x - 4}{\Delta x}$$

$$= \lim_{\Delta x \to 0} \frac{-2\Delta x}{\Delta x}$$

$$= -2$$

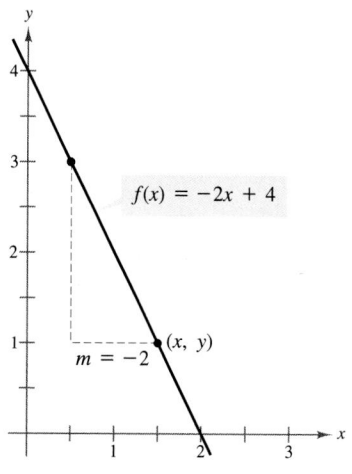

$f(x) = -2x + 4$

$m = -2$

(x, y)

FIGURE 2.9

It is important that you see the distinction between the ways the difference quotients were set up in Examples 3 and 4. In Example 3, you were finding the slope of a graph at a specific point $(c, f(c))$. To find the slope, you can use the following form of a difference quotient.

$$m = \lim_{\Delta x \to 0} \frac{f(c + \Delta x) - f(c)}{\Delta x} \qquad \text{Slope at specific point}$$

In Example 4, however, you were finding a formula for the slope at *any* point on the graph. In such cases, you should use x, rather than c, in the difference quotient.

$$m = \lim_{\Delta x \to 0} \frac{f(x + \Delta x) - f(x)}{\Delta x} \qquad \text{Formula for slope}$$

Except for linear functions, this form will always produce a function of x, which can then be evaluated to find the slope at any desired point.

EXAMPLE 5 *Finding a Formula for the Slope of a Graph*

Find a formula for the slope of the graph of $f(x) = x^2 + 1$. What is the slope at the points $(-1, 2)$ and $(2, 5)$?

Solution

$$\begin{aligned}
m_{\sec} &= \frac{f(x + \Delta x) - f(x)}{\Delta x} && \text{Set up difference quotient.} \\
&= \frac{[(x + \Delta x)^2 + 1] - [x^2 + 1]}{\Delta x} && \text{Use } f(x) = x^2 + 1. \\
&= \frac{x^2 + 2x\Delta x + (\Delta x)^2 + 1 - x^2 - 1}{\Delta x} && \text{Expand terms.} \\
&= \frac{2x\Delta x + (\Delta x)^2}{\Delta x} && \text{Simplify.} \\
&= \frac{\Delta x(2x + \Delta x)}{\Delta x} && \text{Factor and cancel.} \\
&= 2x + \Delta x, \qquad \Delta x \neq 0 && \text{Simplify.}
\end{aligned}$$

Next, take the limit of $m_{\sec}$ as $\Delta x \to 0$.

$$\begin{aligned}
m &= \lim_{\Delta x \to 0} m_{\sec} \\
&= \lim_{\Delta x \to 0} (2x + \Delta x) \\
&= 2x
\end{aligned}$$

Using the formula $m = 2x$, you can find the slope at the specified points. At $(-1, 2)$, the slope is $m = 2(-1) = -2$, and at $(2, 5)$, the slope is $m = 2(2) = 4$. The graph of f is shown in Figure 2.10.

$f(x) = x^2 + 1$

Tangent line at $(2, 5)$

Tangent line at $(-1, 2)$

FIGURE 2.10

The Derivative of a Function

In Example 5, you started with the function $f(x) = x^2 + 1$, and used the limit process to derive another function, $m = 2x$, that represents the slope of the graph of f at the point $(x, f(x))$. This derived function is called the **derivative** of f at x. It is denoted by $f'(x)$, which is read as "f prime of x."

Note The notation dy/dx is read "the derivative of y with respect to x," and using limit notation, you can write

$$\frac{dy}{dx} = \lim_{\Delta x \to 0} \frac{\Delta y}{\Delta x}$$
$$= \lim_{\Delta x \to 0} \frac{f(x + \Delta x) - f(x)}{\Delta x}$$
$$= f'(x).$$

Definition of the Derivative

The **derivative of f at x** is given by

$$f'(x) = \lim_{\Delta x \to 0} \frac{f(x + \Delta x) - f(x)}{\Delta x}$$

provided this limit exists. A function is **differentiable** at x if its derivative exists at x. The process of finding derivatives is called **differentiation.**

In addition to $f'(x)$, other notations can be used to denote the derivative of $y = f(x)$. The most common are

$$\frac{dy}{dx}, \quad y', \quad \frac{d}{dx}[f(x)], \quad \text{and} \quad D_x[y].$$

EXAMPLE 6 *Finding a Derivative*

Find the derivative of $f(x) = 3x^2 - 2x$.

Solution

$$f'(x) = \lim_{\Delta x \to 0} \frac{f(x + \Delta x) - f(x)}{\Delta x}$$
$$= \lim_{\Delta x \to 0} \frac{[3(x + \Delta x)^2 - 2(x + \Delta x)] - [3x^2 - 2x]}{\Delta x}$$
$$= \lim_{\Delta x \to 0} \frac{3x^2 + 6x\Delta x + 3(\Delta x)^2 - 2x - 2\Delta x - 3x^2 + 2x}{\Delta x}$$
$$= \lim_{\Delta x \to 0} \frac{6x\Delta x + 3(\Delta x)^2 - 2\Delta x}{\Delta x}$$
$$= \lim_{\Delta x \to 0} \frac{\Delta x(6x + 3\Delta x - 2)}{\Delta x}$$
$$= \lim_{\Delta x \to 0} (6x + 3\Delta x - 2)$$
$$= 6x - 2$$

Thus, the derivative of $f(x) = 3x^2 - 2x$ is $f'(x) = 6x - 2$.   ■

In many applications, it is convenient to use a variable other than x as the independent variable. Example 7 shows a function that uses t as the independent variable.

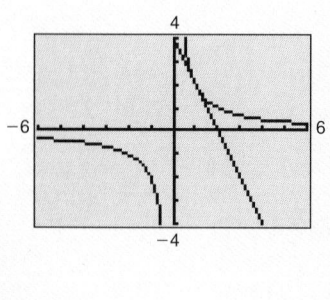
EXAMPLE 7   *Finding a Derivative*

Find the derivative of y with respect to t for the function

$$y = \frac{2}{t}.$$

Solution
Consider $y = f(t)$, and use the limit process as follows.

$$\frac{dy}{dt} = \lim_{\Delta t \to 0} \frac{f(t + \Delta t) - f(t)}{\Delta t} \qquad \textit{Set up difference quotient.}$$

$$= \lim_{\Delta t \to 0} \frac{\left(\dfrac{2}{t + \Delta t} - \dfrac{2}{t}\right)}{\Delta t} \qquad \textit{Use } f(t) = 2/t.$$

$$= \lim_{\Delta t \to 0} \frac{\left(\dfrac{2t - 2t - 2\Delta t}{t(t + \Delta t)}\right)}{\Delta t} \qquad \textit{Expand terms.}$$

$$= \lim_{\Delta t \to 0} \frac{-2\Delta t}{t(\Delta t)(t + \Delta t)} \qquad \textit{Factor and cancel.}$$

$$= \lim_{\Delta t \to 0} \frac{-2}{t(t + \Delta t)} \qquad \textit{Simplify.}$$

$$= -\frac{2}{t^2} \qquad \textit{Evaluate the limit.}$$

Thus, the derivative of y with respect to t is

$$\frac{dy}{dt} = -\frac{2}{t^2}.$$

Remember that the derivative of a function gives you a formula for finding the slope of the tangent at any point on the function's graph. For example, the slope of the tangent line to the graph of f at the point $(1, 2)$ is given by

$$f'(1) = -\frac{2}{1^2} = -2.$$

To find the slope of the graph at other points, substitute the x-coordinate of the point into the derivative, as shown below.

Point	x-Coordinate	Slope
$(2, 1)$	$x = 1$	$m = f'(2) = -\dfrac{2}{2^2} = -\dfrac{1}{2}$
$(-2, -1)$	$x = 1$	$m = f'(-2) = -\dfrac{2}{(-2)^2} = -\dfrac{1}{2}$

Differentiability and Continuity

Not every function is differentiable. Figure 2.11 shows some common situations in which a function will not be differentiable at a point—vertical tangent lines, discontinuities, and sharp turns in the graph. Each of the functions shown in Figure 2.11 is differentiable at every value of x *except* $x = 0$.

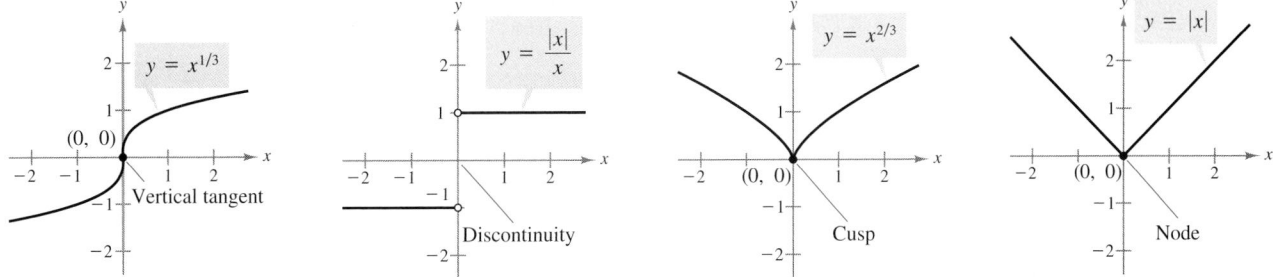

FIGURE 2.11   Functions That Are Not Differentiable at $(0, 0)$

From Figure 2.11, you can see that continuity is not a strong enough condition to guarantee differentiability. [All but one of the functions are continuous at $(0, 0)$, but none is differentiable there.] On the other hand, if a function is differentiable at a point, then it must be continuous. This important result is stated in the following theorem.

Differentiability Implies Continuity

If a function is differentiable at $x = c$, then it is continuous at $x = c$.

Discussion Problem   A Graphing Utility Experiment

Use a graphing utility to sketch the graph of $f(x) = x^3 - 3x$. On the same screen, graph the following lines. Which of the lines appear to be tangent lines to the graph of f? If the line appears to be tangent to the graph, state the point of tangency. (*Hint:* Use the zoom feature of your graphing utility.)

a. $y = 2$ **b.** $y = x - 3$ **c.** $y = -3x$ **d.** $y = -x + 1$

Explain how you can verify your conclusion analytically.

Warm Up

The following warm-up exercises involve skills that were covered in earlier sections. You will use these skills in the exercise set for this section.

In Exercises 1 and 2, find an equation of the line containing P and Q.

1. $P(2, 1)$, $Q(2, 4)$

2. $P(2, 2)$, $Q(-5, 2)$

In Exercises 3–6, evaluate the limit.

3. $\displaystyle\lim_{\Delta x \to 0} \frac{2x\Delta x + (\Delta x)^2}{\Delta x}$

4. $\displaystyle\lim_{\Delta x \to 0} \frac{3x^2\Delta x + 3x(\Delta x)^2 + (\Delta x)^3}{\Delta x}$

5. $\displaystyle\lim_{\Delta x \to 0} \frac{1}{x(x + \Delta x)}$

6. $\displaystyle\lim_{\Delta x \to 0} \frac{(x + \Delta x)^2 - x^2}{\Delta x}$

In Exercises 7–10, find the domain of the function.

7. $f(x) = \dfrac{1}{x - 1}$

8. $f(x) = \dfrac{1}{5}x^3 - 2x^2 + \dfrac{1}{3}x - 1$

9. $f(x) = \dfrac{6x}{x^3 + x}$

10. $f(x) = \dfrac{x^2 - 2x - 24}{x^2 + x - 12}$

E X E R C I S E S   2.1   means that technology can help you solve or check the exercise(s).

In Exercises 1–4, trace the graph and sketch the tangent lines at (x_1, y_1) and (x_2, y_2).

1.

2.

3.

4.

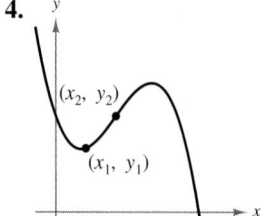

In Exercises 5–10, estimate the slope of the graph at the point (x, y). (Each square on the grid is 1 unit by 1 unit.)

5.

6.

7.

8.

9.

(x, y)

10.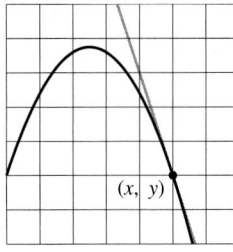

(x, y)

11. *Revenue* The graph represents the revenue R (in millions of dollars) for Dairy Queen from 1989 through 1993. Estimate the slope of the graph in 1990 and in 1992. *(Source: International Dairy Queen)*

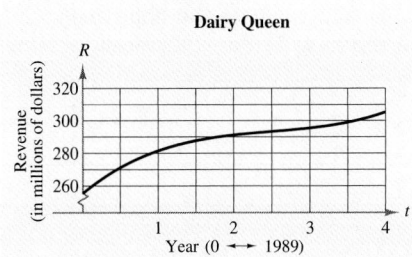

Dairy Queen

Revenue (in millions of dollars)
Year (0 ⟷ 1989)

12. *Revenue* The graph represents the revenue R (in billions of dollars) for Chrysler Corporation from 1989 through 1993. Estimate the slope of the graph in 1990 and in 1992. *(Source: Chrysler Corporation)*

Chrysler Corporation

Revenue (in billions of dollars)
Year (0 ⟷ 1989)

In Exercises 13–26, use the limit definition to find the derivative of the function.

13. $f(x) = 3$ **14.** $f(x) = -4$

15. $f(x) = -5x + 3$ **16.** $f(x) = \frac{1}{2}x$

17. $f(x) = x^2$ **18.** $f(x) = 1 - x^2$

19. $f(x) = 3x^2 - 5x - 2$ **20.** $f(x) = x - x^2$

21. $h(t) = \sqrt{t - 1}$ **22.** $f(x) = \sqrt{2x}$

23. $f(t) = t^3 - 12t$ **24.** $f(t) = t^3 + t^2$

25. $f(x) = \dfrac{1}{x^2}$ **26.** $g(s) = \dfrac{1}{s - 1}$

In Exercises 27–38, find the slope of the tangent line to the graph of f at the indicated point.

Function	*Point of Tangency*
27. $f(x) = 6 - 2x$	$(2, 2)$
28. $f(x) = 2x + 4$	$(1, 6)$
29. $f(x) = -x$	$(0, 0)$
30. $f(x) = 6$	$(-2, 6)$
31. $f(x) = x^2 - 2$	$(2, 2)$
32. $f(x) = x^2 + 2x + 1$	$(-3, 4)$
33. $f(x) = x^3$	$(2, 8)$
34. $f(x) = x^3 + 3$	$(-2, -5)$
35. $f(x) = \sqrt{x + 1}$	$(3, 2)$
36. $f(x) = \dfrac{1}{x + 1}$	$(0, 1)$
37. $f(x) = x^3 + 2x$	$(1, 3)$
38. $f(x) = \sqrt{2x - 2}$	$(9, 4)$

In Exercises 39–44, find an equation of the tangent line to the graph of f at the indicated point. Then verify your result by sketching the graph of f and the tangent line.

Function	*Point of Tangency*
39. $f(x) = \frac{1}{2}x^2$	$(2, 2)$
40. $f(x) = -x^2$	$(-1, -1)$
41. $f(x) = (x - 1)^2$	$(-2, 9)$
42. $f(x) = 2x^2 - 1$	$(0, -1)$
43. $f(x) = \sqrt{x} + 1$	$(4, 3)$
44. $f(x) = \dfrac{1}{x}$	$(1, 1)$

In Exercises 45–48, find an equation of the line that is tangent to the graph of f *and* parallel to the given line.

Function	*Line*
45. $f(x) = -\frac{1}{4}x^2$	$x + y = 0$
46. $f(x) = x^2 + 1$	$2x + y = 0$
47. $f(x) = -\frac{1}{2}x^3$	$6x + y + 4 = 0$
48. $f(x) = \dfrac{1}{\sqrt{x}}$	$x + 2y - 6 = 0$

In Exercises 49–58, describe the x-values at which the function is differentiable. Explain your reasoning.

49. $y = |x + 3|$

50. $y = |x^2 - 9|$

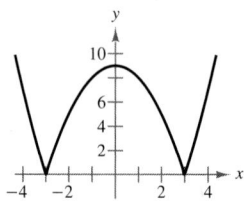

51. $y = \dfrac{1}{x + 1}$

52. $y = \dfrac{2x}{x - 1}$

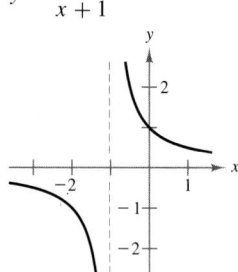

53. $y = (x - 3)^{2/3}$

54. $y = x^{2/5}$

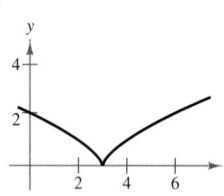

55. $y = \sqrt{x - 1}$

56. $y = \dfrac{x^2}{x^2 - 4}$

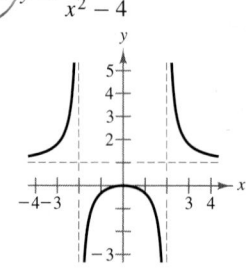

57. $y = \begin{cases} x^3 + 3, & x < 0 \\ x^3 - 3, & x \geq 0 \end{cases}$

58. $y = \begin{cases} x^2, & x \leq 1 \\ -x^2, & x > 1 \end{cases}$

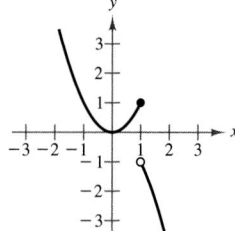

In Exercises 59 and 60, use a graphing utility to graph f over the interval [−2, 2]. Then complete the table by *graphically* estimating the slope of the graph at the indicated points. Finally, evaluate the slope *analytically* and compare your results with those graphically obtained.

x	-2	$-\frac{3}{2}$	-1	$-\frac{1}{2}$	0	$\frac{1}{2}$	1	$\frac{3}{2}$	2
$f(x)$									
$f'(x)$									

59. $f(x) = \frac{1}{4}x^3$

60. $f(x) = \frac{1}{2}x^2$

True or False In Exercises 61–64, determine whether the statement is true or false. If it is false, explain why or give an example that shows the statement is false.

61. The slope of the graph of $y = x^2$ is different at every point on the graph of f.

62. If a function is continuous at a point, then it is differentiable at that point.

63. If a function is differentiable at a point, then it is continuous at that point.

64. A tangent line to a graph can intersect the graph at more than one point.

In Exercises 65 and 66, find the derivative of the given function f. Then graph f and its derivative on the same set of coordinate axes. What does the x-intercept of the derivative indicate about the graph of f?

65. $f(x) = x^2 - 4x$

66. $f(x) = 2 + 6x - x^2$

Some Rules for Differentiation

The Constant Rule ■ *The Power Rule* ■ *The Constant Multiple Rule* ■
The Sum and Difference Rules ■ *Extended Application: Increasing Sales*

The Constant Rule

In Section 2.1, you found derivatives by the limit process. This process is tedious, even for simple functions, and fortunately there are rules that greatly simplify differentiation. These rules allow you to calculate derivatives without the *direct* use of limits.

The Constant Rule

The derivative of a constant function is zero. That is,

$$\frac{d}{dx}[c] = 0, \qquad c \text{ is a constant.}$$

Proof Let $f(x) = c$. Then, by the limit definition of the derivative, you can write

$$f'(x) = \lim_{\Delta x \to 0} \frac{f(x + \Delta x) - f(x)}{\Delta x} = \lim_{\Delta x \to 0} \frac{c - c}{\Delta x} = \lim_{\Delta x \to 0} 0 = 0.$$

Therefore,

$$\frac{d}{dx}[c] = 0.$$

Note Note in Figure 2.12 that the Constant Rule is equivalent to saying that the slope of a horizontal line is zero.

$f(x) = c$

The slope of a horizontal line is zero.

The derivative of a constant function is zero.

FIGURE 2.12

EXAMPLE 1 *Finding Derivatives of Constant Functions*

a. $\dfrac{d}{dx}[7] = 0$

b. If $f(x) = 0$, then $f'(x) = 0$.

c. If $y = 2$, then $\dfrac{dy}{dx} = 0$.

d. If $g(t) = -\dfrac{3}{2}$, then $g'(t) = 0$.

93

The Power Rule

The binomial expansion process is used to prove the Power Rule.

$$(x + \Delta x)^2 = x^2 + 2x\Delta x + (\Delta x)^2$$

$$(x + \Delta x)^3 = x^3 + 3x^2\Delta x + 3x(\Delta x)^2 + (\Delta x)^3$$

$$(x + \Delta x)^n = x^n + nx^{n-1}\Delta x + \frac{n(n-1)x^{n-2}}{2}(\Delta x)^2 + \cdots + (\Delta x)^n$$

$$\underbrace{\phantom{\frac{n(n-1)x^{n-2}}{2}(\Delta x)^2 + \cdots + (\Delta x)^n}}$$

$(\Delta x)^2$ is a factor of these terms.

The (Simple) Power Rule

$$\frac{d}{dx}[x^n] = nx^{n-1}, \qquad n \text{ is any real number.}$$

Proof   We prove only the case in which n is a positive integer. Let $f(x) = x^n$. Using the binomial expansion, you can write

$$f'(x) = \lim_{\Delta x \to 0} \frac{f(x + \Delta x) - f(x)}{\Delta x}$$

$$= \lim_{\Delta x \to 0} \frac{(x + \Delta x)^n - x^n}{\Delta x}$$

$$= \lim_{\Delta x \to 0} \frac{x^n + nx^{n-1}\Delta x + \dfrac{n(n-1)x^{n-2}}{2}(\Delta x)^2 + \cdots + (\Delta x)^n - x^n}{\Delta x}$$

$$= \lim_{\Delta x \to 0} \left[nx^{n-1} + \frac{n(n-1)x^{n-2}}{2}(\Delta x) + \cdots + (\Delta x)^{n-1} \right]$$

$$= nx^{n-1} + 0 + \cdots + 0$$

$$= nx^{n-1}. \qquad \blacksquare$$

For the Power Rule, the case in which $n = 1$ is worth remembering as a separate differentiation rule. That is,

$$\frac{d}{dx}[x] = 1. \qquad \textit{The derivative of } x \textit{ is } 1.$$

This rule is consistent with the fact that the slope of the line given by $y = x$ is 1, as shown in Figure 2.13.

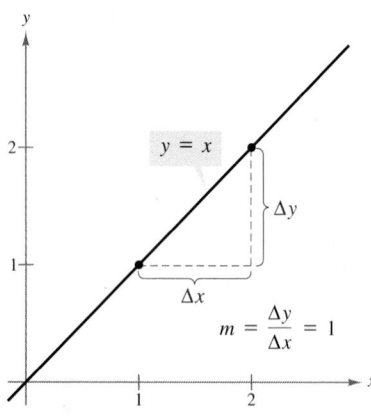

FIGURE 2.13   The slope of the line $y = x$ is 1.

EXAMPLE 2 *Applying the Power Rule*

Function	*Derivative*
a. $f(x) = x^3$	$f'(x) = 3x^2$
b. $y = \dfrac{1}{x^2} = x^{-2}$	$\dfrac{dy}{dx} = (-2)x^{-3} = -\dfrac{2}{x^3}$
c. $g(t) = t$	$g'(t) = 1$
d. $R = x^4$	$\dfrac{dR}{dx} = 4x^3$

In Example 2b, note that *before* differentiating, you should rewrite $1/x^2$ as x^{-2}. Rewriting is the first step in *many* differentiation problems.

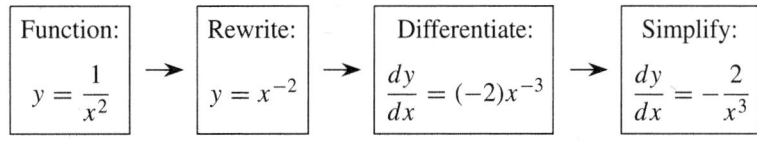

Function:	Rewrite:	Differentiate:	Simplify:
$y = \dfrac{1}{x^2}$	$y = x^{-2}$	$\dfrac{dy}{dx} = (-2)x^{-3}$	$\dfrac{dy}{dx} = -\dfrac{2}{x^3}$

Remember that the derivative of a function f is another function that gives the slope of the graph of f at any point at which f is differentiable. Thus, you can use the derivative to find slopes, as shown in Example 3.

EXAMPLE 3 *Finding the Slope of a Graph*

Find the slope of the graph of

$$f(x) = x^2 \qquad \text{\textit{Original function}}$$

when $x = -2, -1, 0, 1,$ and 2.

Solution

Begin by using the Power Rule to find the derivative of f.

$$f'(x) = 2x \qquad \text{\textit{Derivative}}$$

You can use the derivative to find the slope of the graph of f, as follows.

x-Value	*Slope of Graph of f*
$x = -2$	$m = f'(-2) = 2(-2) = -4$
$x = -1$	$m = f'(-1) = 2(-1) = -2$
$x = 0$	$m = f'(0) = 2(0) = 0$
$x = 1$	$m = f'(1) = 2(1) = 2$
$x = 2$	$m = f'(2) = 2(2) = 4$

The graph of f is shown in Figure 2.14.

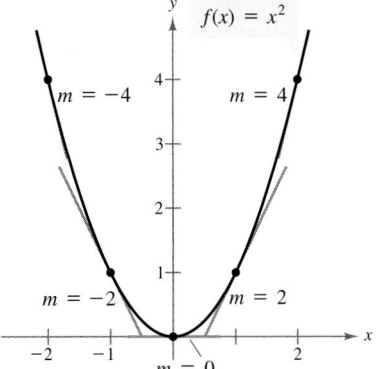

FIGURE 2.14

The Constant Multiple Rule

To prove the Constant Multiple Rule, the following property of limits is used.

$$\lim_{x \to a} cg(x) = c \left[\lim_{x \to a} g(x) \right]$$

The Constant Multiple Rule

If f is a differentiable function of x, and c is a real number, then

$$\frac{d}{dx}[cf(x)] = cf'(x), \qquad c \text{ is a constant.}$$

Proof Apply the definition of the derivative to produce

$$\frac{d}{dx}[cf(x)] = \lim_{\Delta x \to 0} \frac{cf(x + \Delta x) - cf(x)}{\Delta x}$$

$$= \lim_{\Delta x \to 0} c \left[\frac{f(x + \Delta x) - f(x)}{\Delta x} \right]$$

$$= c \left[\lim_{\Delta x \to 0} \frac{f(x + \Delta x) - f(x)}{\Delta x} \right]$$

$$= cf'(x).$$

Informally, the Constant Multiple Rule states that constants can be factored out of the differentiation process.

$$\frac{d}{dx}[cf(x)] = c\frac{d}{dx}[f(x)] = cf'(x)$$

The usefulness of this rule is often overlooked, especially when the constant appears in the denominator, as follows.

$$\frac{d}{dx}\left[\frac{f(x)}{c} \right] = \frac{d}{dx}\left[\frac{1}{c}f(x) \right] = \frac{1}{c}\left[\frac{d}{dx}[f(x)] \right] = \frac{1}{c}f'(x)$$

To use the Constant Multiple Rule efficiently, look for constants that can be factored out *before* differentiating. For example,

$$\frac{d}{dx}[5x^2] = 5\frac{d}{dx}[x^2] = 5(2x) = 10x$$

and

$$\frac{d}{dx}\left[\frac{x^2}{5} \right] = \frac{1}{5}\left[\frac{d}{dx}[x^2] \right] = \frac{1}{5}(2x) = \frac{2}{5}x.$$

EXAMPLE 4 *Using the Power and Constant Multiple Rules*

Differentiate the following functions.

a. $y = 2x^{1/2}$ **b.** $f(t) = \dfrac{4t^2}{5}$

Solution

a. Using the Constant Multiple Rule and the Power Rule, you can write

$$\frac{dy}{dx} = \frac{d}{dx}[2x^{1/2}] = 2\underbrace{\frac{d}{dx}[x^{1/2}]}_{\text{Constant Multiple Rule}} = 2\underbrace{\left(\frac{1}{2}x^{-1/2}\right)}_{\text{Power Rule}} = x^{-1/2} = \frac{1}{\sqrt{x}}.$$

b. Begin by rewriting $f(t)$ as

$$f(t) = \frac{4t^2}{5} = \frac{4}{5}t^2.$$

Then, use the Constant Multiple Rule and the Power Rule to obtain

$$f'(t) = \frac{d}{dt}\left[\frac{4}{5}t^2\right] = \frac{4}{5}\left[\frac{d}{dt}(t^2)\right] = \frac{4}{5}(2t) = \frac{8}{5}t. \qquad \blacksquare$$

You may find it helpful to combine the Constant Multiple Rule and the Power Rule into one combined rule.

$$\frac{d}{dx}[cx^n] = cnx^{n-1}, \qquad n \text{ is a real number, } c \text{ is a constant.}$$

For instance, in Example 4b, you can apply this combined rule to obtain

$$\frac{d}{dx}\left[\frac{4}{5}t^2\right] = \left(\frac{4}{5}\right)(2)(t) = \frac{8}{5}t.$$

The three functions in the next example are simple, yet errors are frequently made in differentiating functions involving a constant multiple of the first power of x. Keep in mind that

$$\frac{d}{dx}[cx] = c, \qquad c \text{ is a constant.}$$

EXAMPLE 5 *Applying the Constant Multiple Rule*

Original Function	*Derivative*
a. $y = -\dfrac{3x}{2}$	$y' = -\dfrac{3}{2}$
b. $y = 3\pi x$	$y' = 3\pi$
c. $y = -\dfrac{x}{2}$	$y' = -\dfrac{1}{2}$

$\blacksquare$

Parentheses can play an important role in the use of the Constant Multiple Rule and the Power Rule. In Example 6, be sure you understand the mathematical conventions involving the use of parentheses.

EXAMPLE 6 *Using Parentheses When Differentiating*

Find the derivative of each function.

a. $y = \dfrac{5}{2x^3}$ **b.** $y = \dfrac{5}{(2x)^3}$ **c.** $y = \dfrac{7}{3x^{-2}}$ **d.** $y = \dfrac{7}{(3x)^{-2}}$

Solution

Function	Rewrite	Differentiate	Simplify
a. $y = \dfrac{5}{2x^3}$	$y = \dfrac{5}{2}(x^{-3})$	$y' = \dfrac{5}{2}(-3x^{-4})$	$y' = -\dfrac{15}{2x^4}$
b. $y = \dfrac{5}{(2x)^3}$	$y = \dfrac{5}{8}(x^{-3})$	$y' = \dfrac{5}{8}(-3x^{-4})$	$y' = -\dfrac{15}{8x^4}$
c. $y = \dfrac{7}{3x^{-2}}$	$y = \dfrac{7}{3}(x^2)$	$y' = \dfrac{7}{3}(2x)$	$y' = \dfrac{14x}{3}$
d. $y = \dfrac{7}{(3x)^{-2}}$	$y = 63(x^2)$	$y' = 63(2x)$	$y' = 126x$ ▬

When differentiating functions involving radicals, you should rewrite the function with rational exponents. For instance, you should rewrite $y = \sqrt[3]{x}$ as $y = x^{1/3}$, and you should rewrite

$$y = \dfrac{1}{\sqrt[3]{x^4}} \quad \text{as} \quad y = x^{-4/3}.$$

EXAMPLE 7 *Differentiating Radical Functions*

Find the derivative of each function.

a. $y = \sqrt{x}$ **b.** $y = \dfrac{1}{2\sqrt[3]{x^2}}$ **c.** $y = \sqrt{2x}$

Solution

Function	Rewrite	Differentiate	Simplify
a. $y = \sqrt{x}$	$y = x^{1/2}$	$y' = \left(\dfrac{1}{2}\right)x^{-1/2}$	$y' = \dfrac{1}{2\sqrt{x}}$
b. $y = \dfrac{1}{2\sqrt[3]{x^2}}$	$y = \dfrac{1}{2}x^{-2/3}$	$y' = \dfrac{1}{2}\left(-\dfrac{2}{3}\right)x^{-5/3}$	$y' = -\dfrac{1}{3x^{5/3}}$
c. $y = \sqrt{2x}$	$y = \sqrt{2}(x^{1/2})$	$y' = \sqrt{2}\left(\dfrac{1}{2}\right)x^{-1/2}$	$y' = \dfrac{1}{\sqrt{2x}}$ ▬

The Sum and Difference Rules

The next two rules are ones that you might expect to be true, and you may have used them without thinking about it. For instance, if you were asked to differentiate $y = 3x + 2x^3$, you would probably write

$$y' = 3 + 6x^2$$

without questioning your answer. The validity of differentiating a sum term by term is given by the Sum and Difference Rules.

The Sum and Difference Rules

The derivative of the sum (or difference) of two differentiable functions is the sum (or difference) of their derivatives.

$$\frac{d}{dx}[f(x) + g(x)] = f'(x) + g'(x) \qquad \textit{Sum Rule}$$

$$\frac{d}{dx}[f(x) - g(x)] = f'(x) - g'(x) \qquad \textit{Difference Rule}$$

Proof Let $h(x) = f(x) + g(x)$. Then, you can prove the Sum Rule as follows.

$$
\begin{aligned}
h'(x) &= \lim_{\Delta x \to 0} \frac{h(x + \Delta x) - h(x)}{\Delta x} \\
&= \lim_{\Delta x \to 0} \frac{f(x + \Delta x) + g(x + \Delta x) - f(x) - g(x)}{\Delta x} \\
&= \lim_{\Delta x \to 0} \frac{f(x + \Delta x) - f(x) + g(x + \Delta x) - g(x)}{\Delta x} \\
&= \lim_{\Delta x \to 0} \left[\frac{f(x + \Delta x) - f(x)}{\Delta x} + \frac{g(x + \Delta x) - g(x)}{\Delta x} \right] \\
&= \lim_{\Delta x \to 0} \frac{f(x + \Delta x) - f(x)}{\Delta x} + \lim_{\Delta x \to 0} \frac{g(x + \Delta x) - g(x)}{\Delta x} \\
&= f'(x) + g'(x)
\end{aligned}
$$

Thus,

$$\frac{d}{dx}[f(x) + g(x)] = f'(x) + g'(x).$$

The Difference Rule can be proved in a similar manner. ■

The Sum and Difference Rules can be extended to the sum or difference of any finite number of functions. For instance, if $y = f(x) + g(x) + h(x)$, then $y' = f'(x) + g'(x) + h'(x)$.

With the four differentiation rules listed in this section, you can differentiate *any* polynomial function.

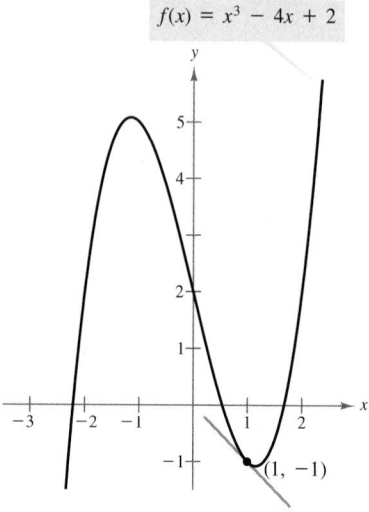

$f(x) = x^3 - 4x + 2$

Slope $= -1$

FIGURE 2.15

EXAMPLE 8 *Using the Sum and Difference Rules*

Find the slope of the graph of $f(x) = x^3 - 4x + 2$ at the point $(1, -1)$.

Solution
The derivative of $f(x)$ is

$$f'(x) = 3x^2 - 4.$$

Thus, the slope of the graph of f at $(1, -1)$ is

$$\text{Slope} = f'(1) = 3(1)^2 - 4 = -1,$$

as shown in Figure 2.15.

Example 8 illustrates the use of the derivative for determining the shape of a graph. A rough sketch of the graph of $f(x) = x^3 - 4x + 2$ might lead you to think that the point $(1, -1)$ is a minimum point of the graph. After finding the slope at this point to be -1, however, you can conclude that the minimum point (where the slope is 0) is farther to the right. (You will study techniques for finding minimum and maximum points in Section 3.2.)

EXAMPLE 9 *Using the Sum and Difference Rules*

Find an equation of the tangent line to the graph of

$$g(x) = -\tfrac{1}{2}x^4 + 3x^3 - 2x$$

at the point $\left(-1, -\tfrac{3}{2}\right)$.

Solution
The derivative of $g(x)$ is

$$g'(x) = -2x^3 + 9x^2 - 2$$

which implies that the slope of the graph at the point $\left(-1, -\tfrac{3}{2}\right)$ is

$$\begin{aligned}\text{Slope} = g'(-1) &= -2(-1)^3 + 9(-1)^2 - 2 \\ &= 2 + 9 - 2 \\ &= 9,\end{aligned}$$

as shown in Figure 2.16. Using the point-slope form, you can write the equation of the tangent line at $\left(-1, -\tfrac{3}{2}\right)$ as follows.

$$y - \left(-\tfrac{3}{2}\right) = 9[x - (-1)] \qquad \textit{Point-slope form}$$
$$y = 9x + \tfrac{15}{2} \qquad \textit{Equation of tangent line}$$

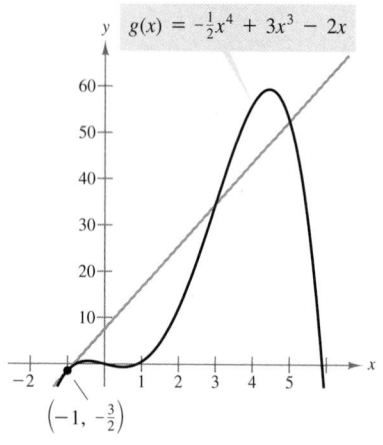

$g(x) = -\tfrac{1}{2}x^4 + 3x^3 - 2x$

$\left(-1, -\tfrac{3}{2}\right)$

FIGURE 2.16

Extended Application: Increasing Sales

Real Life

EXAMPLE 10 *Modeling Sales*

From 1983 through 1992, the revenue R (in millions of dollars) for Microsoft Corporation can be modeled by

$$R = 0.76t^4 - 16.77t^3 + 153.05t^2 - 571.84t + 789.84,$$

where $t = 3$ corresponds to 1983. At what rate was Microsoft's revenue changing in 1990? *(Source: Microsoft Corporation)*

Solution

One way to answer this question is to find the derivative of the revenue model with respect to time.

$$\frac{dR}{dt} = 3.04t^3 - 50.31t^2 + 306.1t - 571.84$$

In 1990 (when $t = 10$), the rate of change of the revenue with respect to the time is given by

$$\frac{dR}{dt} = 3.04(10)^3 - 50.31(10)^2 + 306.1(10) - 571.84$$
$$\approx 500.$$

Because R is measured in millions of dollars and t is measured in years, it follows that the derivative dR/dt is measured in millions of dollars per year. Thus, at the end of 1990, Microsoft's revenues were increasing at a rate of about $500 million per year, as shown in Figure 2.17. ■

Revenue for Microsoft

Revenue (in millions of dollars)

Year (3 ◀─▶ 1983)

Slope = 500

FIGURE 2.17

Discussion Problem   Units for Rates of Change

In Example 10, the units for R are millions of dollars and the units for dR/dt are millions of dollars per year. State the units for the derivatives of each of the following models.

a. A population model which gives the population P (in millions of people) of the United States in terms of the year, t. What are the units for dP/dt?

b. A position model which gives the height s (in feet) of an object in terms of the time t (in seconds). What are the units for ds/dt?

c. A demand model which gives the price per unit p (in dollars) of a product in terms of the number of units x sold. What are the units for dp/dx?

Warm Up   The following warm-up exercises involve skills that were covered in earlier sections. You will use these skills in the exercise set for this section.

In Exercises 1 and 2, evaluate each expression when $x = 2$.

1. (a) $2x^2$ (b) $(2x)^2$ (c) $2x^{-2}$ **2.** (a) $\dfrac{1}{(3x)^2}$ (b) $\dfrac{1}{4x^3}$ (c) $\dfrac{(2x)^{-3}}{4x^{-2}}$

In Exercises 3–6, simplify the expression.

3. $4(3)x^3 + 2(2)x$

4. $\frac{1}{2}(3)x^2 - \frac{3}{2}x^{1/2}$

5. $\left(\frac{1}{4}\right)x^{-3/4}$

6. $\frac{1}{3}(3)x^2 - 2\left(\frac{1}{2}\right)x^{-1/2} + \frac{1}{3}x^{-2/3}$

In Exercises 7–10, solve the equation.

7. $3x^2 + 2x = 0$

8. $x^3 - x = 0$

9. $x^2 + 8x - 20 = 0$

10. $x^2 - 10x - 24 = 0$

E X E R C I S E S   2.2   means that technology can help you solve or check the exercise(s).

In Exercises 1–4, find the slope of the tangent line to $y = x^n$ at the point $(1, 1)$.

1. (a) $y = x^2$ (b) $y = x^{1/2}$ **3.** (a) $y = x^{-1}$ (b) $y = x^{-1/3}$

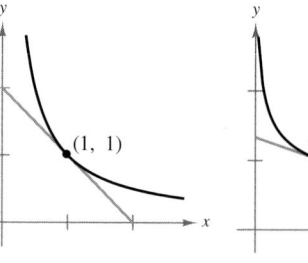

2. (a) $y = x^{3/2}$ (b) $y = x^3$ **4.** (a) $y = x^{-1/2}$ (b) $y = x^{-2}$

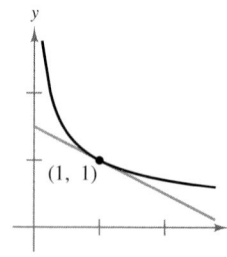

In Exercises 5–20, use the differentiation rules in this section to find the derivative of the function.

5. $y = 3$

6. $f(x) = -2$

7. $f(x) = x + 1$

8. $g(x) = 3x - 1$

9. $g(x) = x^2 + 4$

10. $y = t^2 + 2t - 3$

11. $f(t) = -3t^2 + 2t - 4$

12. $y = x^3 - 9$

13. $s(t) = t^3 - 2t + 4$

14. $y = 2x^3 - x^2 + 3x - 1$

15. $y = 4t^{4/3}$

16. $h(x) = x^{5/2}$

17. $f(x) = 4\sqrt{x}$

18. $g(x) = 4\sqrt[3]{x} + 2$

19. $y = 4x^{-2} + 2x^2$

20. $s(t) = 4t^{-1} + 1$

In Exercises 21–26, use Example 6 as a model to find the derivative.

Function	Rewrite	Derivative	Simplify
21. $y = \dfrac{1}{4x^3}$			
22. $y = \dfrac{2}{3x^2}$			
23. $y = \dfrac{1}{(4x)^3}$			
24. $y = \dfrac{\pi}{(3x)^2}$			
25. $y = \dfrac{\sqrt{x}}{x}$			
26. $y = \dfrac{4}{x^{-3}}$			

In Exercises 27–32, find the value of the derivative of the function at the indicated point.

Function	Point
27. $f(x) = \dfrac{1}{x}$	$(1, 1)$
28. $f(x) = -\frac{1}{2} + \frac{7}{5}x^3$	$\left(0, -\frac{1}{2}\right)$
29. $f(t) = 4 - \dfrac{4}{3t}$	$\left(\frac{1}{2}, \frac{4}{3}\right)$
30. $y = 3x\left(x^2 - \dfrac{2}{x}\right)$	$(2, 18)$
31. $y = (2x + 1)^2$	$(0, 1)$
32. $f(x) = 3(5 - x)^2$	$(5, 0)$

In Exercises 33–44, find $f'(x)$.

33. $f(x) = x^2 - \dfrac{4}{x}$

34. $f(x) = x^2 - 3x - 3x^{-2} + 5x^{-3}$

35. $f(x) = x^2 - 2x - \dfrac{2}{x^4}$

36. $f(x) = x^2 + 4x + \dfrac{1}{x}$

37. $f(x) = \dfrac{2x^3 - 4x^2 + 3}{x^2}$

38. $f(x) = \dfrac{2x^2 - 3x + 1}{x}$

39. $f(x) = x(x^2 + 1)$

40. $f(x) = (x^2 + 2x)(x + 1)$

41. $f(x) = x^{4/5}$

42. $f(x) = x^{1/3} - 1$

43. $f(x) = \sqrt[3]{x} + \sqrt[5]{x}$

44. $f(x) = \dfrac{1}{\sqrt[3]{x^2}}$

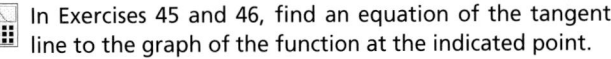 In Exercises 45 and 46, find an equation of the tangent line to the graph of the function at the indicated point.

Function	Point
45. $y = -2x^4 + 5x^2 - 3$	$(1, 0)$
46. $y = x^3 + x$	$(-1, -2)$

In Exercises 47–50, determine the point(s), if any, at which the graph of the function has a horizontal tangent line.

47. $y = -x^4 + 3x^2 - 1$

48. $y = \frac{1}{2}x^2 + 5x$

49. $y = x^3 + x$

50. $y = x^2 + 1$

 In Exercises 51 and 52, perform the following.

(a) Sketch the graphs of f, g, and h on the same set of coordinate axes.

(b) Find $f'(1)$, $g'(1)$, and $h'(1)$.

(c) Sketch the graph of the tangent lines to each graph when $x = 1$.

51. $f(x) = x^3$

$g(x) = x^3 + 3$

$h(x) = x^3 - 2$

52. $f(x) = \sqrt{x}$

$g(x) = \sqrt{x} + 4$

$h(x) = \sqrt{x} - 2$

53. Use the Constant Rule, the Constant Multiple Rule, and the Sum Rule to find $h'(1)$ given that $f'(1) = 3$.

(a) $h(x) = f(x) - 2$

(b) $h(x) = 2f(x)$

(1, −1)

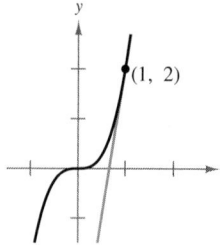
(1, 2)

(c) $h(x) = -f(x)$

(d) $h(x) = -1 + 2f(x)$

(1, −1)

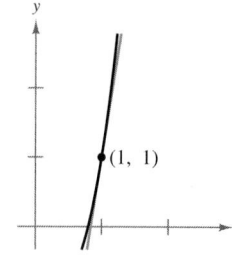
(1, 1)

54. *Revenue* The revenue R (in millions of dollars) for Dairy Queen from 1989 through 1993 can be modeled by

$$R = 1.83t^3 - 13.7t^2 + 37.97t + 255.4,$$

where $t = 0$ represents 1989. *(Source: International Dairy Queen)*

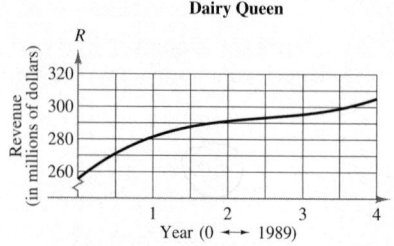

Dairy Queen

(a) Find the slope of the graph in 1990 ($t = 1$) and in 1992 ($t = 3$).

(b) Compare your results with those obtained in Exercise 11 in Section 2.1.

(c) What are the units for the slope of the graph? Interpret the slope of the graph in the context of the problem.

55. *Revenue* The revenue R (in billions of dollars) for Chrysler Corporation from 1989 through 1993 can be modeled by

$$R = -6.1t^3 + 23.6t^{5/2} - 22.6t^2 + 35.2,$$

where $t = 0$ represents 1989. *(Source: Chrysler Corp.)*

Chrysler Corporation

(a) Find the slope of the graph in 1990 ($t = 1$) and in 1992 ($t = 3$).

(b) Compare your results with those obtained in Exercise 12 in Section 2.1.

(c) What are the units for the slope of the graph? Interpret the slope of the graph in the context of the problem.

56. *Cost* The variable cost for manufacturing an electrical component is $7.75 per unit, and the fixed cost is $500. Write the cost C as a function of x, the number of units produced. Show that the derivative of this cost function is constant and equal to the variable cost.

57. *Cost* A college club raises funds by selling candy bars for $1.00 each. The club pays $0.60 for each candy bar and has annual fixed costs of $250. Write the profit P as a function of x, the number of candy bars sold. Show that the derivative of the profit function is a constant and that it is equal to the profit on each candy bar sold.

In Exercises 58 and 59, use a graphing utility to graph f and f' over the given interval. Determine any points at which the graph of f has horizontal tangents.

Function	*Interval*
58. $f(x) = 4.1x^3 - 12x^2 + 2.5x$	$[0, 3]$
59. $f(x) = x^3 - 1.4x^2 - 0.96x + 1.44$	$[-2, 2]$

2.3 Rates of Change: Velocity and Marginals

Average Rate of Change ■ *Instantaneous Rate of Change and Velocity* ■ *Rates of Change in Economics: Marginals*

Average Rate of Change

In Sections 2.1 and 2.2, you studied the two primary applications of derivatives.

1. **Slope** The derivative of f is a function that gives the slope of the graph of f at a point $(x, f(x))$.
2. **Rate of Change** The derivative of f is a function that gives the rate of change of $f(x)$ with respect to x at the point $(x, f(x))$.

In this section, you will see that there are many real-life applications of rates of change. A few are velocity, acceleration, population growth rates, unemployment rates, production rates, and water flow rates. Although rates of change often involve change with respect to time, you can investigate the rate of change of one variable with respect to any other related variable.

When determining the rate of change of one variable with respect to another, you must be careful to distinguish between *average* and *instantaneous* rates of change. The distinction between these two rates of change is comparable to the distinction between the slope of the secant line through two points on a graph and the slope of the tangent line at one point on the graph.

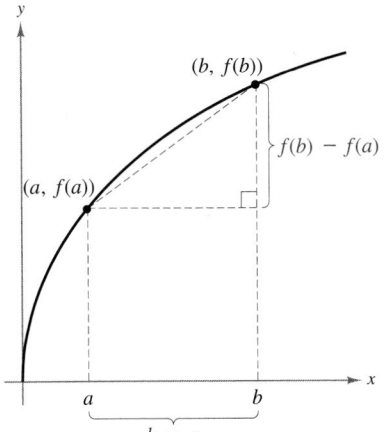

FIGURE 2.18

Definition of Average Rate of Change

If $y = f(x)$, then the **average rate of change** of y with respect to x on the interval $[a, b]$ is

$$\text{Average rate of change} = \frac{f(b) - f(a)}{b - a} = \frac{\Delta y}{\Delta x}.$$

Note that $f(a)$ is the value of the function at the *left* endpoint of the interval, $f(b)$ is the value of the function at the *right* endpoint of the interval, and $b - a$ is the width of the interval, as shown in Figure 2.18.

Note In real-life problems, it is important to list the units of measure for a rate of change. The units for $\Delta y/\Delta x$ are "y-units" per "x-units." For example, if y is measured in miles and x is measured in hours, then $\Delta y/\Delta x$ is measured in *miles per hour.*

Real
Life

EXAMPLE 1 *Drug Concentration*

The concentration C (in milligrams per milliliter) of a drug in a patient's blood-stream is monitored over 10-minute intervals for 2 hours, where t is measured in minutes, as shown in Table 2.1. Find the average rates of change over the following intervals.

a. [0, 10]   **b.** [0, 20]   **c.** [100, 110]

TABLE 2.1

t	0	10	20	30	40	50	60	70	80	90	100	110	120
C	0	2	17	37	55	73	89	103	111	113	113	103	68

Note In Example 1, the average rate of change is positive when the concentration increases and negative when the concentration decreases, as shown in Figure 2.19.

Solution

a. For the interval [0, 10], the average rate of change is

Value of C at Right Endpoint
Value of C at Left Endpoint

$$\frac{\Delta C}{\Delta t} = \frac{2 - 0}{10 - 0} = \frac{2}{10} = 0.2 \text{ mg per ml/min.}$$

Width of Interval

b. For the interval [0, 20], the average rate of change is

$$\frac{\Delta C}{\Delta t} = \frac{17 - 0}{20 - 0} = \frac{17}{20} = 0.85 \text{ mg per ml/min.}$$

c. For the interval [100, 110], the average rate of change is

$$\frac{\Delta C}{\Delta t} = \frac{103 - 113}{110 - 100} = \frac{-10}{10} = -1 \text{ mg per ml/min.}$$

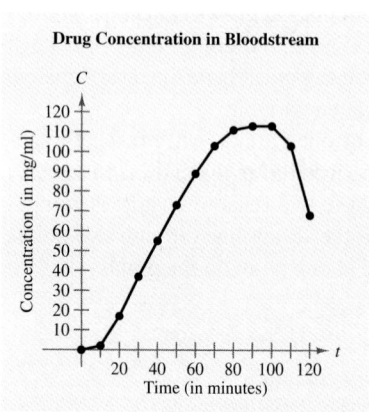

Drug Concentration in Bloodstream

FIGURE 2.19

The rates of change in Example 1 are in milligrams per milliliter per minute because the concentration is measured in milligrams per milliliter and the time is measured in minutes.

Concentration is measured in milligrams per milliliter.

Rate of change is measured in milligrams per milliliter per minute.

$$\frac{\Delta C}{\Delta t} = \frac{2 - 0}{10 - 0} = \frac{2}{10} = 0.2 \text{ mg per ml/min.}$$

Time is measured in minutes.

A common application of an average rate of change is to find the **average velocity** of an object that is moving in a straight line. That is,

$$\text{Average velocity} = \frac{\text{change in distance}}{\text{change in time}}.$$

This formula is demonstrated in Example 2.

Real Life

EXAMPLE 2 *Finding an Average Velocity*

If a free-falling object is dropped from a height of 100 feet, and *air resistance is neglected*, the height h (in feet) of the object at time t (in seconds) is given by

$$h = -16t^2 + 100,$$

as indicated in Figure 2.20. Find the average velocity of the object over the following intervals.

a. $[1, 2]$ **b.** $[1, 1.5]$ **c.** $[1, 1.1]$

Solution

You can use the position equation $h = -16t^2 + 100$ to determine the heights at $t = 1$, $t = 1.1$, $t = 1.5$, and $t = 2$, as shown in Table 2.2.

TABLE 2.2

t (in seconds)	0	1	1.1	1.5	2
h (in feet)	100	84	80.64	64	36

a. For the interval $[1, 2]$, the object falls from a height of 84 feet to a height of 36 feet. Thus, the average velocity is

$$\frac{\Delta h}{\Delta t} = \frac{36 - 84}{2 - 1} = \frac{-48}{1} = -48 \text{ ft/sec.}$$

b. For the interval $[1, 1.5]$, the average velocity is

$$\frac{\Delta h}{\Delta t} = \frac{64 - 84}{1.5 - 1} = \frac{-20}{0.5} = -40 \text{ ft/sec.}$$

c. For the interval $[1, 1.1]$, the average velocity is

$$\frac{\Delta h}{\Delta t} = \frac{80.64 - 84}{1.1 - 1} = \frac{-3.36}{0.1} = -33.6 \text{ ft/sec.}$$

Note In Example 2, the average velocities are negative because the object is moving downward.

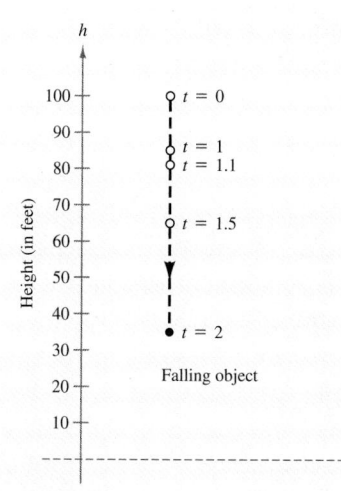

FIGURE 2.20
Some falling objects have considerable air resistance. Other falling objects have negligible air resistance. When modeling a falling-body problem, you must decide whether to account for air resistance or neglect it.

Instantaneous Rate of Change and Velocity

Suppose in Example 2 you wanted to find the rate of change of h at the instant $t = 1$ second. Such a rate is called an **instantaneous rate of change.** You can approximate the instantaneous rate of change at $t = 1$ by calculating the average rate of change over smaller and smaller intervals of the form $[1, 1 + \Delta t]$, as shown in Table 2.3. From the table, it seems reasonable to conclude that the instantaneous rate of change of the height when $t = 1$ is -32 feet per second.

TABLE 2.3

Δt approaches 0

Δt	1	0.5	0.1	0.01	0.001	0.0001	0
$\dfrac{\Delta h}{\Delta t}$	-48	-40	-33.6	-32.16	-32.016	-32.0016	-32

$\dfrac{\Delta h}{\Delta t}$ approaches -32

Note The limit in this definition is the same as the limit in the definition of the derivative of f at x. This is the second major interpretation of the derivative — as an *instantaneous rate of change in one variable with respect to another*. Recall that the first interpretation of the derivative is as the slope of the graph of f at x.

Definition of Instantaneous Rate of Change

The **instantaneous rate of change** (or simply **rate of change**) of $y = f(x)$ at x is the limit of the average rate of change on the interval $[x, x + \Delta x]$, as Δx approaches 0.

$$\lim_{\Delta x \to 0} \frac{\Delta y}{\Delta x} = \lim_{\Delta x \to 0} \frac{f(x + \Delta x) - f(x)}{\Delta x}$$

If y is a length and x is time, then the rate of change is a **velocity.**

Real Life

EXAMPLE 3 *Finding a Rate of Change*

Find the velocity of the object in Example 2 when $t = 1$.

Solution
From Example 2, you know that the height of the falling object is given by

$$h = -16t^2 + 100. \qquad \textit{Position function}$$

By taking the derivative of this position function, you obtain the velocity function.

$$h'(t) = -32t \qquad \textit{Velocity function}$$

The velocity function gives the velocity at *any* time. Thus, when $t = 1$, the velocity is $h'(1) = -32(1) = -32$ feet per second. ■

The general **position function** for a free-falling object, neglecting air resistance, is

$$h = -16t^2 + v_0t + h_0, \qquad \textit{Position function}$$

where h is the height (in feet), t is the time (in seconds), v_0 is the initial velocity (in feet per second), and h_0 is the initial height (in feet). Remember that the model assumes that positive velocities indicate upward motion and negative velocities indicate downward motion. The derivative $h' = -32t + v_0$ is the **velocity function.** The absolute value of the velocity is the **speed** of the object.

Real Life

EXAMPLE 4 *Finding the Velocity of a Diver*

At time $t = 0$, a diver jumps from a diving board that is 32 feet high, as shown in Figure 2.21. Because the diver's initial velocity is 16 feet per second, his position function is

$$h = -16t^2 + 16t + 32. \qquad \textit{Position function}$$

a. When does the diver hit the water?

b. What is the diver's velocity at impact?

Solution

a. To find the time at which the diver hits the water, let $h = 0$ and solve for t.

$$-16t^2 + 16t + 32 = 0 \qquad \textit{Set h equal to 0.}$$
$$-16(t^2 - t - 2) = 0 \qquad \textit{Factor out common factor.}$$
$$-16(t + 1)(t - 2) = 0 \qquad \textit{Factor trinomial.}$$
$$t = -1 \text{ or } t = 2 \qquad \textit{Solve for t.}$$

The solution $t = -1$ doesn't make sense in the problem, so you can conclude that the diver hits the water when $t = 2$ seconds.

b. The velocity at time t is given by the derivative

$$h' = -32t + 16. \qquad \textit{Velocity function}$$

The velocity at time $t = 2$ is $h' = -32(2) + 16 = -48$ feet per second.

In Example 4, note that the diver's initial velocity is $v_0 = 16$ feet per second (upward) and his initial height is $h_0 = 32$ feet.

Initial velocity is 16 feet per second.
Initial height is 32 feet.

$$h = -16t^2 + 16t + 32$$

Graph the polynomial function $h = -16t^2 + 16t + 32$ from Example 4 on the domain $0 \le t \le 2$. What is the maximum value of h? What is the derivative of h at this maximum point? In general, discuss how the derivative can be used to find the maximum or minimum values of a function.

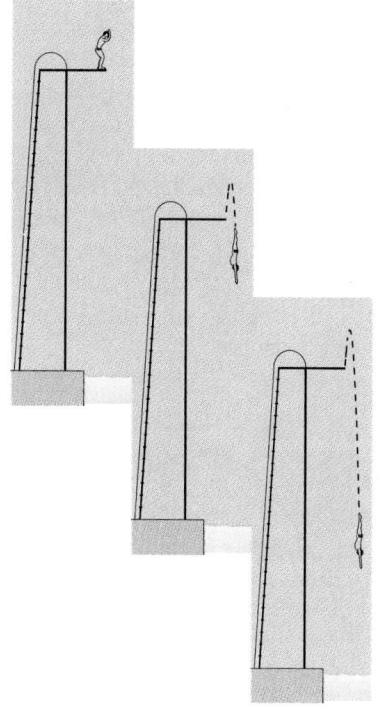

FIGURE 2.21

Rates of Change in Economics: Marginals

Another important use of rates of change is in the field of economics. Economists refer to *marginal profit*, *marginal revenue*, and *marginal cost* as the rates of change of the profit, revenue, and cost with respect to the number x of units produced or sold. An equation that relates these three quantities is

$$P = R - C,$$

where P, R, and C represent the following quantities.

$$P = \text{total profit}, \quad R = \text{total revenue}, \quad \text{and} \quad C = \text{total cost}$$

The derivatives of these quantities are called the **marginal profit, marginal revenue,** and **marginal cost,** respectively.

$$\frac{dP}{dx} = \text{marginal profit}$$

$$\frac{dR}{dx} = \text{marginal revenue}$$

$$\frac{dC}{dx} = \text{marginal cost}$$

In many business and economics problems, the number of units produced or sold is restricted to positive integer values, as indicated in Figure 2.22(a). (Of course, it could happen that a sale involves half or quarter units, but it is hard to conceive of a sale involving $\sqrt{2}$ units.) The variable that denotes such units is called a **discrete variable.** To analyze a function of a discrete variable x, you can temporarily assume that x is a **continuous variable** and is able to take on any real value in a given interval, as indicated in Figure 2.22(b). Then, you can use the methods of calculus to find the x-value that corresponds to the marginal revenue, maximum profit, minimum cost, or whatever is called for. Finally, you should round the solution to the nearest sensible x-value—cents, dollars, units, or days, depending on the context of the problem.

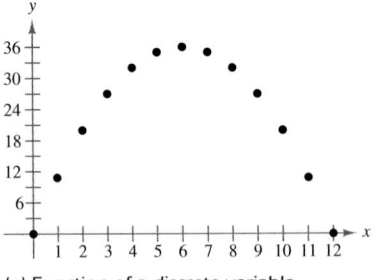

(a) Function of a discrete variable

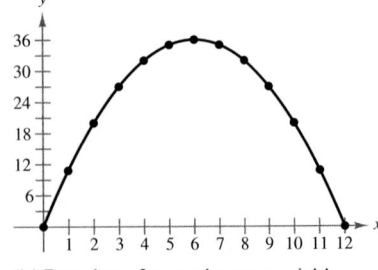

(b) Function of a continuous variable

FIGURE 2.22

Real
Life

EXAMPLE 5 *Finding the Marginal Profit*

The profit derived from selling x units of an item is given by

$$P = 0.0002x^3 + 10x.$$

a. Find the marginal profit for a production level of 50 units.

b. Compare this with the actual gain in profit obtained by increasing the production level from 50 to 51 units.

Solution

a. Because the profit is $P = 0.0002x^3 + 10x$, the marginal profit is given by the derivative

$$\frac{dP}{dx} = 0.0006x^2 + 10.$$

When $x = 50$, the marginal profit is

$$\frac{dP}{dx} = 0.0006(50)^2 + 10 \qquad \textit{Substitute 50 for } x.$$

$$= 1.5 + 10$$

$$= \$11.50 \text{ per unit.} \qquad \textit{Marginal profit for } x = 50$$

b. For $x = 50$, the actual profit is

$$P = (0.0002)(50)^3 + 10(50) \qquad \textit{Substitute 50 for } x.$$

$$= 25 + 500$$

$$= \$525.00, \qquad \textit{Actual profit for } x = 50$$

and for $x = 51$, the actual profit is

$$P = (0.0002)(51)^3 + 10(51) \qquad \textit{Substitute 51 for } x.$$

$$= 26.53 + 510$$

$$= \$536.53. \qquad \textit{Actual profit for } x = 51$$

Thus, the additional profit obtained by increasing the production level from 50 to 51 units is

$$536.53 - 525.00 = \$11.53. \qquad \textit{Extra profit for one unit}$$

Note that the actual profit increase of \$11.53 (when x increases from 50 to 51 units) can be approximated by the marginal profit of \$11.50 per unit (when $x = 50$), as shown in Figure 2.23. ■

Marginal Profit

FIGURE 2.23

Note The reason the marginal profit gives a good approximation of the actual change in profit is that the graph of P is nearly straight over the interval $50 \le x \le 51$. You will study more about the use of marginals to approximate actual changes in Section 3.8.

The profit function in Example 5 is unusual in that the profit continues to increase as long as the number of units sold increases. In practice, it is more common to encounter situations in which sales can be increased only by lowering the price per item. Such reductions in price will ultimately cause the profit to decline.

The number of units x that consumers are willing to purchase at a given price per unit p is given by the **demand function**

$$p = f(x). \qquad\qquad \textit{Demand function}$$

The total revenue R is then related to the price per unit and the quantity demanded (or sold) by the equation

$$R = xp. \qquad\qquad \textit{Revenue function}$$

Real Life

EXAMPLE 6 *Finding a Demand Function*

A business sells 2000 items per month at a price of $10 each. It is estimated that monthly sales will increase 250 units for each $0.25 reduction in price. Use this information to find the demand function and total revenue function.

Solution

From the given estimate, x increases 250 units each time p drops $0.25 from the original cost of $10. This is described by the equation

$$x = 2000 + 250\left(\frac{10 - p}{0.25}\right)$$

$$= 2000 + 10{,}000 - 1000p$$

$$= 12{,}000 - 1000p.$$

Solving for p in terms of x produces

$$p = 12 - \frac{x}{1000}. \qquad\qquad \textit{Demand function}$$

This, in turn, implies that the revenue function is

$$R = xp \qquad\qquad \textit{Formula for revenue}$$

$$= x\left(12 - \frac{x}{1000}\right)$$

$$= 12x - \frac{x^2}{1000}. \qquad\qquad \textit{Revenue function}$$

The graph of the demand function is shown in Figure 2.24. Notice that the price decreases as the quantity demanded increases.

Demand Function

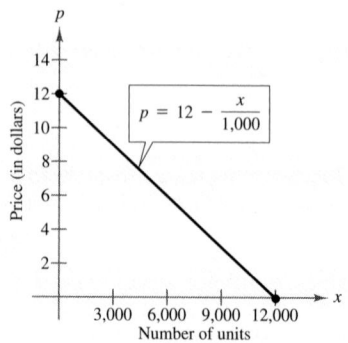

$$p = 12 - \frac{x}{1{,}000}$$

Price (in dollars)

Number of units

FIGURE 2.24

Modeling a Demand Function

To model a demand function, you need data that indicates how many units of a product will sell at a given price. As you might imagine, this type of data is not easy to obtain for a new product. After a product has been on the market awhile, however, its sales history can provide the necessary data.

As an example, consider the two bar graphs shown below. From these graphs, you can see that from 1981 through 1989, the price of prerecorded video cassettes dropped from an average price of about $65 to an average price of about $15. During that time, the number of units sold increased from about 1 million to about 89 million. *(Source: Paul Kagan Associates, Inc.)*

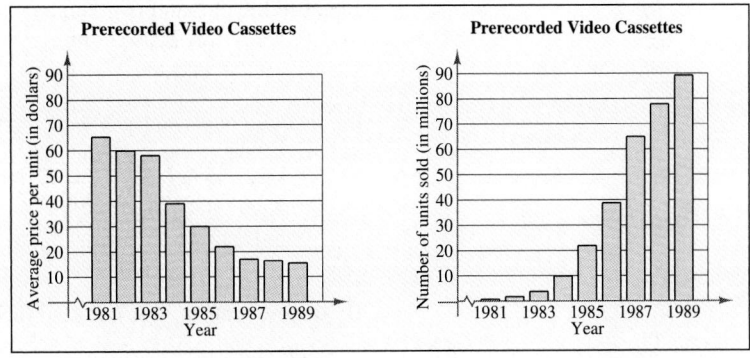

The information in the two bar graphs is combined in Table 2.4, where p represents the price (in dollars) and x represents the units sold (in millions).

TABLE 2.4

t	1981	1982	1983	1984	1985	1986	1987	1988	1989
x	0.72	1.72	3.76	9.80	21.94	38.78	64.90	77.90	89.20
p	65.28	59.88	57.98	38.98	29.99	22.00	17.00	16.34	15.36

By entering the ordered pairs (x, p) into a calculator or computer that has a linear regression program, you can find the following linear model for the demand for prerecorded video cassettes: $p = -0.52x + 53.70$. A graph of this demand function is shown at the left.

Demand Function

FIGURE 2.25   As the price decreases, more hamburgers are sold.

EXAMPLE 7 *Finding the Marginal Revenue*

A fast-food restaurant has determined that the monthly demand for their hamburgers is given by

$$p = \frac{60,000 - x}{20,000}.$$

Figure 2.25 shows that as the price decreases, the quantity demanded increases. Table 2.5 shows the demand for hamburgers at various prices.

TABLE 2.5

x	60,000	50,000	40,000	30,000	20,000	10,000	0
p	\$0.00	\$0.50	\$1.00	\$1.50	\$2.00	\$2.50	\$3.00

Find the increase in revenue per hamburger for monthly sales of 20,000 hamburgers. In other words, find the marginal revenue when $x = 20,000$.

Solution

Because the demand is given by

$$p = \frac{60,000 - x}{20,000},$$

the revenue is given by $R = xp$, and you have

$$R = xp = x \left(\frac{60,000 - x}{20,000} \right)$$

$$= \frac{1}{20,000} (60,000x - x^2).$$

By differentiating, you can find the marginal revenue to be

$$\frac{dR}{dx} = \frac{1}{20,000} (60,000 - 2x).$$

Thus, when $x = 20,000$, the marginal revenue is

$$\frac{dR}{dx} = \frac{1}{20,000} [60,000 - 2(20,000)]$$

$$= \frac{20,000}{20,000}$$

$$= \$1 \text{ per unit.}$$

Note   Writing a demand function in the form $p = f(x)$ is a convention used in economics. From a consumer's point of view, it might seem more reasonable to think that the quantity demanded is a function of the price. Mathematically, however, the two points of view are equivalent because a typical demand function is one-to-one and therefore possesses an inverse. For instance, in Example 7, you could write the demand function as $x = 60,000 - 20,000p$.

Real
Life

EXAMPLE 8 *Finding the Marginal Profit*

Suppose in Example 7 that the cost of producing x hamburgers is

$$C = 5000 + 0.56x, \qquad 0 \le x \le 50{,}000.$$

Find the profit and the marginal profit for the following production levels.

a. $x = 20{,}000$ **b.** $x = 24{,}400$ **c.** $x = 30{,}000$

Solution

From Example 7, you know that the total revenue from selling x units is

$$R = \frac{1}{20{,}000}(60{,}000x - x^2).$$

Because the total profit is given by $P = R - C$, you have

$$P = \frac{1}{20{,}000}(60{,}000x - x^2) - (5000 + 0.56x)$$

$$= 3x - \frac{x^2}{20{,}000} - 5000 - 0.56x$$

$$= 2.44x - \frac{x^2}{20{,}000} - 5000.$$

(See Figure 2.26.) Thus, the marginal profit is

$$\frac{dP}{dx} = 2.44 - \frac{x}{10{,}000}.$$

Using these formulas, you can compute the profit and marginal profit.

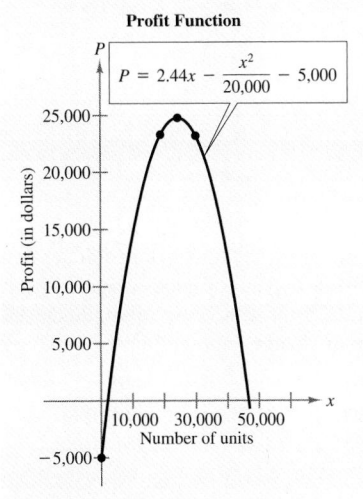

Profit Function

$$P = 2.44x - \frac{x^2}{20{,}000} - 5{,}000$$

Profit (in dollars)

Number of units

FIGURE 2.26

Production	*Profit*	*Marginal Profit*
a. $x = 20{,}000$	$P = \$23{,}800.00$	$\dfrac{dP}{dx} = \$0.44$ per unit
b. $x = 24{,}400$	$P = \$24{,}768.00$	$\dfrac{dP}{dx} = \$0.00$ per unit
c. $x = 30{,}000$	$P = \$23{,}200.00$	$\dfrac{dP}{dx} = -\$0.56$ per unit

Discussion Problem   *Interpreting Marginal Profit*

In Example 8 and Figure 2.26, notice that when 20,000 hamburgers are sold the marginal profit is positive, when 24,400 are sold, the marginal profit is zero, and when 30,000 are sold, the marginal profit is negative. What does this mean? If you owned this business, how much would you charge for hamburgers? Explain your reasoning.

Warm Up The following warm-up exercises involve skills that were covered in earlier sections. You will use these skills in the exercise set for this section.

In Exercises 1 and 2, evaluate the expression.

1. $\dfrac{-63 - (-105)}{21 - 7}$

2. $\dfrac{-37 - 54}{16 - 3}$

In Exercises 3–10, find the derivative of the function.

3. $y = 4x^2 - 2x + 7$

4. $y = -3t^3 + 2t^2 - 8$

5. $s = -16t^2 + 24t + 30$

6. $y = -16x^2 + 54x + 70$

7. $A = \frac{1}{10}(-2r^3 + 3r^2 + 5r)$

8. $y = \frac{1}{9}(6x^3 - 18x^2 + 63x - 15)$

9. $y = 12x - \dfrac{x^2}{5000}$

10. $y = 138 + 74x - \dfrac{x^3}{10,000}$

EXERCISES 2.3 means that technology can help you solve or check the exercise(s).

1. *Research and Development* The graph below shows the amount A (in billions of constant 1982 dollars) spent on research and development in the United States from 1960 through 1990. Approximate the average rate of change of A during the following periods. *(Source: National Science Foundation)*

(a) 1960–1968 (b) 1968–1975
(c) 1980–1985 (d) 1960–1990

2. *Trade Deficit* The graph below shows the value I (in billions of dollars) of goods imported to the United States and the value E (in billions of dollars) of goods exported from the United States from 1970 through 1991. Approximate the indicated average rate of change. *(Source: U.S. Bureau of Census)*

(a) Imports: 1970–1980 (b) Exports: 1970–1980
(c) Imports: 1981–1985 (d) Exports: 1981–1985

Research and Development

Trade Deficit

In Exercises 3–12, sketch the graph of the function and find its average rate of change on the interval. Compare this with the instantaneous rates of change at the endpoints of the interval.

Function	Interval
3. $f(t) = 2t + 7$	$[1, 2]$
4. $f(t) = 3t - 1$	$\left[0, \frac{1}{3}\right]$
5. $h(x) = 1 - x^2$	$[0, 1]$
6. $h(x) = x^2 - 4$	$[-2, 2]$
7. $f(t) = t^2 + 2$	$[1, 1.1]$
8. $f(x) = x^2 - 6x - 1$	$[-1, 3]$
9. $f(x) = \dfrac{1}{x}$	$[1, 4]$
10. $f(x) = x^{-1/2}$	$[1, 4]$
11. $g(x) = 4\sqrt{x}$	$[1, 9]$
12. $g(x) = x^3 - 1$	$[-1, 1]$

13. *Drug Effectiveness* The effectiveness E (on a scale from 0 to 1) of a pain-killing drug t hours after entering the bloodstream is given by

$$E = \tfrac{1}{27}(9t + 3t^2 - t^3), \qquad 0 \le t \le 4.5.$$

Find the average rate of change of E on the indicated intervals and compare this with the instantaneous rates of change at the endpoints of the intervals.

(a) $[0, 1]$ (b) $[1, 2]$ (c) $[2, 3]$ (d) $[3, 4]$

14. *Wind Chill* At $0°$ Celsius, the heat loss H (in kilocalories per square meter per hour) from a person's body can be modeled by

$$H = 33(10\sqrt{v} - v + 10.45),$$

where v is the wind speed (in meters per second). Find the rate of change of H when (a) $v = 2$ and (b) $v = 5$.

15. *Velocity* The height s (in feet) at time t (in seconds) of a silver dollar dropped from the top of the Washington Monument is

$$s = -16t^2 + 555.$$

(a) Find the average velocity on the interval $[2, 3]$.
(b) Find the instantaneous velocity when $t = 2$ and when $t = 3$.
(c) How long will it take the dollar to hit the ground?
(d) Find the velocity of the dollar when it hits the ground.

16. *Velocity* The height s (in feet) of an object fired straight up from ground level with an initial velocity of 200 feet per second is given by

$$s = -16t^2 + 200t,$$

where t is the time (in seconds).

(a) How fast is the object moving after one second?
(b) During which interval of time is the speed decreasing?
(c) During which interval of time is the speed increasing?

17. *Velocity* The position s (in feet) of an accelerating car is

$$s = 10t^{3/2}, \qquad 0 \le t \le 10,$$

where t is the time (in seconds). Find the velocity of the car at the following times.

(a) $t = 0$ (b) $t = 1$ (c) $t = 4$ (d) $t = 9$

18. *Velocity* Derive the equation for the velocity of an object whose position s (in meters) is $s(t) = t^2 + 2t$, where t is the time (in seconds).

Marginal Cost In Exercises 19–22, find the marginal cost for producing x units. (The cost is measured in dollars.)

19. $C = 4500 + 1.47x$

20. $C = 104{,}000 + 7200x$

21. $C = 55{,}000 + 470x - 0.25x^2, \quad 0 \le x \le 940$

22. $C = 100\left(9 + 3\sqrt{x}\right)$

Marginal Revenue In Exercises 23–26, find the marginal revenue for producing x units. (The revenue is measured in dollars.)

23. $R = 50x - 0.5x^2$

24. $R = 30x - x^2$

25. $R = -6x^3 + 8x^2 + 200x$

26. $R = 50(20x - x^{3/2})$

Marginal Profit In Exercises 27–30, find the marginal profit for producing x units. (The profit is measured in dollars.)

27. $P = -2x^2 + 72x - 145$

28. $P = -0.25x^2 + 2000x - 1{,}250{,}000$

29. $P = -0.00025x^2 + 12.2x - 25{,}000$

30. $P = -0.5x^3 + 30x^2 - 164.25x - 1000$

31. *Marginal Revenue* The revenue (in dollars) from producing x units of a product is

$$R = 125x - 0.002x^2.$$

(a) Find the additional revenue when production is increased from 15,000 units to 15,001 units.
(b) Find the marginal revenue when $x = 15,000$.
(c) Compare the results of parts (a) and (b).

32. *Marginal Revenue* The revenue (in dollars) from renting x apartments can be modeled by

$$R = 2x(900 + 32x - x^2).$$

(a) Find the additional revenue when the number of rentals is increased from 14 to 15.
(b) Find the marginal revenue when $x = 14$.
(c) Compare the results of parts (a) and (b).

33. *Marginal Cost* The cost (in dollars) of producing x units of a product is given by

$$C = 3.6\sqrt{x} + 500.$$

(a) Find the additional cost when the production increases from nine to ten units.
(b) Find the marginal cost when $x = 9$.
(c) Compare the results of parts (a) and (b).

34. *Marginal Profit* The profit (in dollars) from selling x units of a product is

$$P = -0.1x^2 + 2x - 100.$$

(a) Find the additional profit when the sales increase from seven to eight units.
(b) Find the marginal profit when $x = 7$.
(c) Compare the results of parts (a) and (b).

35. *Marginal Profit* The profit (in dollars) for selling x units of a product can be modeled by

$$P = 2400 - 403.4x + 32x^2 - 0.664x^3, \qquad 10 \le x \le 25.$$

Find the marginal profit for the following sales.

(a) $x = 10$ (b) $x = 20$ (c) $x = 23$ (d) $x = 25$

36. *Marginal Profit* The profit (in dollars) for selling x units of a product is given by

$$P = 36{,}000 + 2048\sqrt{x} - \frac{1}{8x^2}, \qquad 150 \le x \le 275.$$

Find the marginal profit for the following sales.

(a) $x = 150$ (b) $x = 175$ (c) $x = 200$
(d) $x = 225$ (e) $x = 250$ (f) $x = 275$

37. *Profit* The monthly demand function and cost function for x newspapers at a newsstand are

$$p = 5 - 0.001x \quad \text{and} \quad C = 35 + 1.5x.$$

(a) Find the monthly revenue as a function of x.
(b) Find the monthly profit as a function of x.
(c) Complete the table.

x	600	1200	1800	2400	3000
dR/dx					
dP/dx					
P					

38. *Profit* The demand function and cost function for x units of a product are

$$p = 25\left(20 - \sqrt{x}\right) \quad \text{and} \quad C = 42.50 + 1.25x.$$

(a) Find the revenue as a function of x.
(b) Find the profit as a function of x.
(c) Complete the table.

x	40	80	120	160	200
dR/dx					
dP/dx					
P					

39. *Marginal Profit* When the admission price to a baseball game was $6 per ticket, 36,000 tickets were sold. When the price was raised to $7, only 33,000 tickets were sold. Assume that the demand function is linear and that the variable and fixed costs for the ballpark owners are $0.20 and $85,000, respectively.

(a) Find the profit P as a function of x, the number of tickets sold.
(b) Find the marginal profit when 18,000 tickets are sold.

40. *Marginal Profit* In Exercise 39, suppose ticket sales decreased to 30,000 when the price increased to $7. How does this change the answers to Exercise 39?

41. *Marginal Cost* The cost C of producing x units is modeled by

$$C = v(x) + k,$$

where v represents the variable cost and k represents the fixed cost. Show that the marginal cost is independent of the fixed cost.

42. *Profit* The demand function for a product is

$$p = \frac{50}{\sqrt{x}}, \qquad 1 \le x \le 8000,$$

and the cost function is

$$C = 0.5x + 500, \qquad 0 \le x \le 8000.$$

Find the marginal profit for the following sales.

(a) $x = 900$ (b) $x = 1600$
(c) $x = 2500$ (d) $x = 3600$

If you were in charge of setting the price for this product, what price would you set? Explain your reasoning.

43. *Inventory Management* The annual inventory cost for a manufacturer is

$$C = \frac{1,008,000}{Q} + 6.3Q,$$

where Q is the order size when the inventory is replenished. Find the change in annual cost when Q is increased from 350 to 351, and compare this with the instantaneous rate of change when $Q = 350$.

44. *Center of Population* Since 1790, the center of population of the United States has been gradually moving westward. Use the figure below to estimate the rate (in miles per year) at which the center of population was moving *westward* during the given period. *(Source: U.S. Bureau of Census)*

(a) From 1790 to 1900
(b) From 1900 to 1990
(c) From 1790 to 1990

45. *Fuel Cost* A car is driven 15,000 miles a year and gets x miles per gallon. The average fuel cost is $1.10 per gallon. Find the annual cost C of fuel as a function of x and use this function to complete the table.

x	10	15	20	25	30	35	40
C							
dC/dx							

Who would benefit more from a 1 mile per gallon increase in fuel efficiency—the driver of a car that gets 15 or 35 miles per gallon? Explain.

46. Use a graphing utility to sketch the graph of f and f' for

$$f(x) = \frac{4}{x}, \qquad 0 < x \le 5.$$

(a) Complete the table.

x	$\frac{1}{8}$	$\frac{1}{4}$	$\frac{1}{2}$	1	2	3	4	5
$f(x)$								
$f'(x)$								

(b) Find the average rate of change of f over the intervals determined by consecutive x-values in the table.

In Exercises 47 and 48, use a graphing utility to sketch the graphs of f and f'. Then determine the points (if any) at which f has a horizontal tangent.

47. $f(x) = \frac{1}{4}x^3, \quad -2 \le x \le 2$

48. $f(x) = x^4 - 12x^3 + 52x^2 - 96x + 64, \quad 1 \le x \le 5$

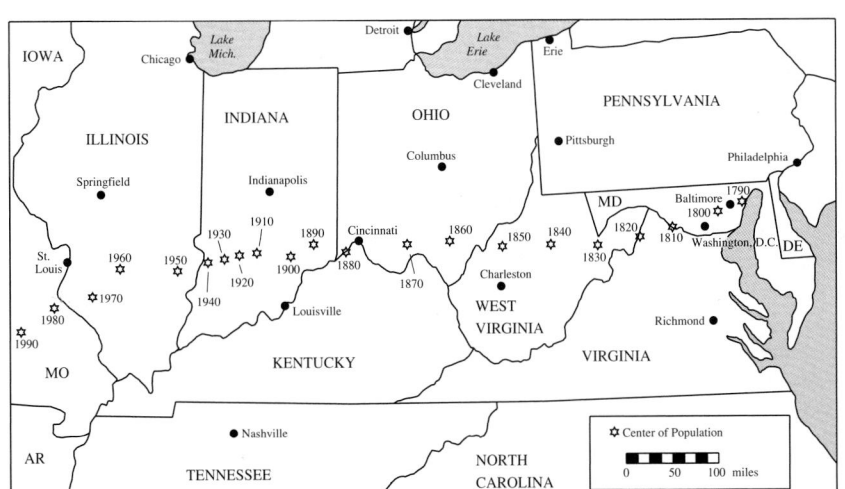

FIGURE FOR 44

Case Study: Shipping Costs to the Far East

Hosford International, Inc. of Erie, Pennsylvania is an international freight forwarding company that provides services to firms that export and import products worldwide. The company assists its clients in preparing documentation such as letters of credit, which spell out the terms of payment, as well as in arranging the scheduling and transportation of freight shipments using the most cost-efficient methods of shipment.

Actual shipping costs will, of course, vary according to such factors as the mode of transportation, the distance over which the cargo must be shipped, and the actual freight line chosen to transport the cargo. Approximately half of the overseas shipments of Hosford International's clients are transported by air, while the remainder is transported by ship.

In addition, some ocean freight lines base their shipping fees on how much space (out of a standard-sized full container) is taken up by the cargo. A full container's capacity is generally 1800 cubic feet, or in the language of the trade, 45 "measures," where one "measure" is equal to 40 cubic feet. One particular ocean freight shipping company, Maersk Line, has quoted the following costs as of March 1994 for shipping machinery from Baltimore to Hong Kong:

$332 per measure (i.e., 40 cubic feet) of cargo, or

$4690 for a full container of 45 measures (i.e., 1800 cubic feet).

A company with a small volume of machinery to ship might choose to pay the per-measure cost, but a company with a much larger freight volume could lower its average shipping costs per measure by renting a full container. For example, the average shipping cost per measure of cargo remains fixed at $332 up to the point where the cargo load is 14.13 measures ($4690/$332), but begins to decline thereafter, reaching a minimum of $104.22 per measure at a full load of 45 measures. Thus, for all cargo loads ranging from 14.13 measures up to a full load of 45 measures, the average shipping cost per measure of cargo is given by the equation

$$Y = 4690X^{-1},$$

where:

Y = average shipping cost (in dollars) per measure of cargo

X = volume of cargo (in number of measures).

Note: freight charges are also assessed on fractions of measures.

The diagram shows the graph of this function over the relevant domain. For all cargo volumes over 14.13 measures, up to a full load, average shipping costs decline, but at a diminishing rate. The *rate* at which average shipping costs decline as the volume of cargo increases is obtained by taking the derivative of the average cost function with respect to cargo volume:

$$\frac{dY}{dX} = -4690X^{-2}.$$

Such patterns in freight shipping costs may have practical implications for a company that is in the process of shipping a final product overseas. As illustrated in the graph, knowing the rate at which average shipping costs decline with cargo volume will help in making the right decisions.

What Would You Do?

1. If transportation costs were the only consideration in shipping your final product overseas, how would you decide whether to transport partial shipments of the product as it rolls off the assembly line or to wait until more of the product is produced in order to increase cargo volume? Summarize the issues relevant to such a decision.

2. Suppose you have more than enough cargo to fill one full load, but not enough to fill two loads. How would you use the cost functions discussed above to decide whether to make one shipment first or ship all of your goods at the same time?

3. Of course, transport costs must be considered in light of many other factors and constraints that a company faces. What other considerations do you think are important in deciding when and how much to ship?

4. Suppose that a shipping line charges the following rates for shipping freight from Baltimore to London, England:
   $261 per measure of cargo
   $5079 per full container of 45 measures
(a) Formulate a general guideline for when to choose the per-measure cost or the full measure cost, and justify with calculations.
(b) Construct a function that reflects the average shipping cost per measure for this situation, and sketch a graph of the function.
(c) At which shipment level is it more beneficial in terms of cost to increase the shipment size by one measure – at 25 measures or at 35 measures? Explain your reasoning.

The Product and Quotient Rules

The Product Rule ■ *The Quotient Rule* ■ *Simplifying Derivatives* ■
Extended Application: Blood Pressure

The Product Rule

In Section 2.2 you saw that the derivative of a sum or difference of two functions is simply the sum or difference of their derivatives. The rules for the derivative of a product or quotient of two functions are not as simple.

The Product Rule

The derivative of the product of two differentiable functions is equal to the first function times the derivative of the second plus the second function times the derivative of the first.

$$\frac{d}{dx}[f(x)g(x)] = f(x)g'(x) + g(x)f'(x)$$

Note Rather than trying to remember the formula for the Product Rule, we suggest that you remember its verbal statement: *the first function times the derivative of the second plus the second function times the derivative of the first.*

Proof Some mathematical proofs, such as the proof of the Sum Rule, are straightforward. Others involve clever steps that may appear unmotivated. The following proof involves such a step—adding and subtracting the same quantity. (This step is shown in color.) Let $F(x) = f(x)g(x)$.

$$F'(x) = \lim_{\Delta x \to 0} \frac{F(x + \Delta x) - F(x)}{\Delta x}$$

$$= \lim_{\Delta x \to 0} \frac{f(x + \Delta x)g(x + \Delta x) - f(x)g(x)}{\Delta x}$$

$$= \lim_{\Delta x \to 0} \frac{f(x + \Delta x)g(x + \Delta x) - f(x + \Delta x)g(x) + f(x + \Delta x)g(x) - f(x)g(x)}{\Delta x}$$

$$= \lim_{\Delta x \to 0} \left[f(x + \Delta x)\frac{g(x + \Delta x) - g(x)}{\Delta x} + g(x)\frac{f(x + \Delta x) - f(x)}{\Delta x} \right]$$

$$= \lim_{\Delta x \to 0} f(x + \Delta x)\frac{g(x + \Delta x) - g(x)}{\Delta x} + \lim_{\Delta x \to 0} g(x)\frac{f(x + \Delta x) - f(x)}{\Delta x}$$

$$= \left[\lim_{\Delta x \to 0} f(x + \Delta x) \right]\left[\lim_{\Delta x \to 0} \frac{g(x + \Delta x) - g(x)}{\Delta x} \right]$$

$$+ \left[\lim_{\Delta x \to 0} g(x) \right]\left[\lim_{\Delta x \to 0} \frac{f(x + \Delta x) - f(x)}{\Delta x} \right]$$

$$= f(x)g'(x) + g(x)f'(x)$$

EXAMPLE 1 Finding the Derivative of a Product

Find the derivative of $y = (3x - 2x^2)(5 + 4x)$.

Solution

Using the Product Rule, you can write

$$\frac{dy}{dx} = \overbrace{(3x - 2x^2)}^{\text{(First)}}\overbrace{\frac{d}{dx}[5 + 4x]}^{\binom{\text{Derivative}}{\text{of second}}} + \overbrace{(5 + 4x)}^{\text{(Second)}}\overbrace{\frac{d}{dx}[3x - 2x^2]}^{\binom{\text{Derivative}}{\text{of first}}}$$

$$= (3x - 2x^2)(4) + (5 + 4x)(3 - 4x)$$

$$= (12x - 8x^2) + (15 - 8x - 16x^2)$$

$$= 15 + 4x - 24x^2.$$

Note   In general, the derivative of the product of two functions is not equal to the product of the derivatives of the two functions. To see this, compare the product of the derivatives of $f(x) = 3x - 2x^2$ and $g(x) = 5 + 4x$ with the derivative found in Example 1.

In the next example, notice that the first step in differentiating is *rewriting the original function.*

EXAMPLE 2 Finding the Derivative of a Product

Find the derivative of

$$f(x) = \left(\frac{1}{x} + 1\right)(x - 1). \qquad \text{\textit{Original function}}$$

Solution

Rewrite the function. Then use the Product Rule to find the derivative.

$$f(x) = (x^{-1} + 1)(x - 1). \qquad \text{\textit{Rewrite function.}}$$

$$f'(x) = (x^{-1} + 1)\frac{d}{dx}[x - 1] + (x - 1)\frac{d}{dx}[x^{-1} + 1] \quad \text{\textit{Product Rule}}$$

$$= (x^{-1} + 1)(1) + (x - 1)(-x^{-2})$$

$$= \frac{1}{x} + 1 - \frac{x - 1}{x^2}$$

$$= \frac{x + x^2 - x + 1}{x^2}$$

$$= \frac{x^2 + 1}{x^2} \qquad \text{\textit{Simplify.}}$$

TECHNOLOGY

If you have access to a symbolic differentiation utility, such as *Derive, Maple,* or *Mathematica,* try using it to confirm several of the derivatives in this section. The form of the derivative can depend on how you use software. For instance, when we used *Derive* to differentiate the function in Example 2, we obtained the same form listed in the example. But when we used *Derive* to first expand the function, and then differentiate, we obtained

$$f'(x) = 1 + \frac{1}{x^2}.$$

You now have two differentiation rules that deal with products—the Constant Multiple Rule and the Product Rule. The difference between these two rules is that the Constant Multiple Rule deals with the product of a constant and a variable quantity,

Constant   Variable Quantity

$$F(x) = c\overbrace{f(x)}, \qquad\qquad \textit{Use Constant Multiple Rule.}$$

whereas the Product Rule deals with the product of two variable quantities,

Variable Quantity   Variable Quantity

$$F(x) = \overbrace{f(x)}\overbrace{g(x)}. \qquad\qquad \textit{Use Product Rule.}$$

The next example compares these two rules.

EXAMPLE 3 *Comparing Differentiation Rules*

Find the derivatives of the functions.

a. $y = 2x(x^2 + 3x)$

b. $y = 2(x^2 + 3x)$

Solution

a. By the Product Rule,

$$\frac{dy}{dx} = (2x)\frac{d}{dx}[x^2 + 3x] + (x^2 + 3x)\frac{d}{dx}[2x] \qquad \textit{Product Rule}$$

$$= (2x)(2x + 3) + (x^2 + 3x)(2)$$

$$= 4x^2 + 6x + 2x^2 + 6x$$

$$= 6x^2 + 12x.$$

b. By the Constant Multiple Rule,

$$\frac{dy}{dx} = 2\frac{d}{dx}[x^2 + 3x] \qquad\qquad\qquad \textit{Constant Multiple Rule}$$

$$= 2(2x + 3)$$

$$= 4x + 6. \qquad\qquad\qquad\qquad\qquad\qquad ■$$

The Product Rule can be extended to products that have more than two factors. For example, if f, g, and h, are differentiable functions of x, then

$$\frac{d}{dx}[f(x)g(x)h(x)] = f'(x)g(x)h(x) + f(x)g'(x)h(x) + f(x)g(x)h'(x).$$

The Quotient Rule

In Section 2.2, you saw that by using the Constant Rule, Power Rule, Constant Multiple Rule, and Sum and Difference Rules, you were able to differentiate *any* polynomial function. By combining these rules with the Quotient Rule, you can now differentiate *any* rational function.

Note From this differentiation rule, you can see that the derivative of a quotient is not, in general, the quotient of the derivatives. That is,

$$\frac{d}{dx}\left[\frac{f(x)}{g(x)}\right] \neq \frac{f'(x)}{g'(x)}.$$

The Quotient Rule

The derivative of the quotient of two differentiable functions is equal to the denominator times the derivative of the numerator minus the numerator times the derivative of the denominator, all divided by the square of the denominator.

$$\frac{d}{dx}\left[\frac{f(x)}{g(x)}\right] = \frac{g(x)f'(x) - f(x)g'(x)}{[g(x)]^2}, \qquad g(x) \neq 0$$

Proof Let $F(x) = f(x)/g(x)$. As in the proof of the Product Rule, a key step in this proof is adding and subtracting the same quantity.

$$F'(x) = \lim_{\Delta x \to 0} \frac{F(x + \Delta x) - F(x)}{\Delta x}$$

$$= \lim_{\Delta x \to 0} \frac{\dfrac{f(x + \Delta x)}{g(x + \Delta x)} - \dfrac{f(x)}{g(x)}}{\Delta x}$$

$$= \lim_{\Delta x \to 0} \frac{g(x)f(x + \Delta x) - f(x)g(x + \Delta x)}{\Delta x g(x)g(x + \Delta x)}$$

$$= \lim_{\Delta x \to 0} \frac{g(x)f(x + \Delta x) - f(x)g(x) + f(x)g(x) - f(x)g(x + \Delta x)}{\Delta x g(x)g(x + \Delta x)}$$

$$= \frac{\displaystyle\lim_{\Delta x \to 0} \frac{g(x)[f(x + \Delta x) - f(x)]}{\Delta x} - \lim_{\Delta x \to 0} \frac{f(x)[g(x + \Delta x) - g(x)]}{\Delta x}}{\displaystyle\lim_{\Delta x \to 0} [g(x)g(x + \Delta x)]}$$

$$= \frac{g(x)\left[\displaystyle\lim_{\Delta x \to 0} \frac{f(x + \Delta x) - f(x)}{\Delta x}\right] - f(x)\left[\displaystyle\lim_{\Delta x \to 0} \frac{g(x + \Delta x) - g(x)}{\Delta x}\right]}{\displaystyle\lim_{\Delta x \to 0} [g(x)g(x + \Delta x)]}$$

$$= \frac{g(x)f'(x) - f(x)g'(x)}{[g(x)]^2}.$$

Note As suggested for the Product Rule, we recommend that you remember the verbal statement of the Quotient Rule rather than trying to remember the formula for the rule.

EXAMPLE 4 *Finding the Derivative of a Quotient*

Find the derivative of

$$y = \frac{x-1}{2x+3}.$$

Solution
Apply the Quotient Rule, as follows.

$$\frac{dy}{dx} = \frac{(2x+3)\dfrac{d}{dx}[x-1] - (x-1)\dfrac{d}{dx}[2x+3]}{(2x+3)^2}$$

$$= \frac{(2x+3)(1) - (x-1)(2)}{(2x+3)^2}$$

$$= \frac{2x+3-2x+2}{(2x+3)^2}$$

$$= \frac{5}{(2x+3)^2}$$

EXAMPLE 5 *Finding the Derivative of a Quotient*

Find the derivative of

$$y = \frac{2x^2 - 4x + 3}{2 - 3x}.$$

Solution
Apply the Quotient Rule, as follows.

$$\frac{dy}{dx} = \frac{(2-3x)\dfrac{d}{dx}[2x^2-4x+3] - (2x^2-4x+3)\dfrac{d}{dx}[2-3x]}{(2-3x)^2}$$

$$= \frac{(2-3x)(4x-4) - (2x^2-4x+3)(-3)}{(2-3x)^2}$$

$$= \frac{-12x^2+20x-8 - (-6x^2+12x-9)}{(2-3x)^2}$$

$$= \frac{-12x^2+20x-8+6x^2-12x+9}{(2-3x)^2}$$

$$= \frac{-6x^2+8x+1}{(2-3x)^2}$$

Note When applying the Quotient Rule, we suggest that you enclose all factors and derivatives in parentheses. Also, pay special attention to the subtraction required in the numerator.

EXAMPLE 6 *Finding the Derivative of a Quotient*

Find the derivative of

$$y = \frac{3 - (1/x)}{x + 5}.$$

Solution

Begin by rewriting the original function. Then apply the Quotient Rule and simplify the result.

$$y = \frac{3 - (1/x)}{x + 5} \qquad \textit{Original function}$$

$$= \frac{3x - 1}{x(x + 5)} \qquad \textit{Multiply numerator and denominator by } x.$$

$$= \frac{3x - 1}{x^2 + 5x} \qquad \textit{Rewritten function}$$

$$\frac{dy}{dx} = \frac{(x^2 + 5x)(3) - (3x - 1)(2x + 5)}{(x^2 + 5x)^2} \qquad \textit{Apply Quotient Rule.}$$

$$= \frac{(3x^2 + 15x) - (6x^2 + 13x - 5)}{(x^2 + 5x)^2}$$

$$= \frac{-3x^2 + 2x + 5}{(x^2 + 5x)^2} \qquad \textit{Simplify.}$$

Not every quotient needs to be differentiated by the Quotient Rule. For instance, each of the quotients in the next example can be considered as the product of a constant and a function of x. In such cases, the Constant Multiple Rule is more efficient than the Quotient Rule.

EXAMPLE 7 *Rewriting Before Differentiating*

	Original Function	*Rewrite*	*Differentiate*	*Simplify*
a.	$y = \dfrac{x^2 + 3x}{6}$	$y = \dfrac{1}{6}(x^2 + 3x)$	$y' = \dfrac{1}{6}(2x + 3)$	$y' = \dfrac{1}{3}x + \dfrac{1}{2}$
b.	$y = \dfrac{5x^4}{8}$	$y = \dfrac{5}{8}x^4$	$y' = \dfrac{5}{8}(4x^3)$	$y' = \dfrac{5}{2}x^3$
c.	$y = \dfrac{-3(3x - 2x^2)}{7x}$	$y = -\dfrac{3}{7}(3 - 2x)$	$y' = -\dfrac{3}{7}(-2)$	$y' = \dfrac{6}{7}$
d.	$y = \dfrac{9}{5x^2}$	$y = \dfrac{9}{5}(x^{-2})$	$y' = \dfrac{9}{5}(-2x^{-3})$	$y' = -\dfrac{18}{5x^3}$

Note To see the efficiency of using the Constant Multiple Rule in Example 7, try using the Quotient Rule to find the derivatives of the four functions.

Simplifying Derivatives

EXAMPLE 8 *Combining the Product and Quotient Rules*

Find the derivative of

$$y = \frac{(1-2x)(3x+2)}{5x-4}.$$

Solution

This function contains a product within a quotient. You could first multiply the factors in the numerator and then apply the Quotient Rule. However, to gain practice in using the Product Rule within the Quotient Rule, try differentiating as follows.

$$
\begin{aligned}
y' &= \frac{(5x-4)\dfrac{d}{dx}[(1-2x)(3x+2)] - (1-2x)(3x+2)\dfrac{d}{dx}[5x-4]}{(5x-4)^2} \\[2mm]
&= \frac{(5x-4)[(1-2x)(3) + (3x+2)(-2)] - (1-2x)(3x+2)(5)}{(5x-4)^2} \\[2mm]
&= \frac{(5x-4)(-12x-1) - (1-2x)(15x+10)}{(5x-4)^2} \\[2mm]
&= \frac{(-60x^2+43x+4) - (-30x^2-5x+10)}{(5x-4)^2} \\[2mm]
&= \frac{-30x^2+48x-6}{(5x-4)^2}
\end{aligned}
$$

In the examples in this section, much of the work in obtaining the final form of the derivative occurs *after* the differentiation. As summarized in the following list, direct application of differentiation rules often yields results that are not in simplified form. Note that two characteristics of simplified form are the absence of negative exponents and the combining of like terms.

	f'(x) After Differentiating	*f'(x) After Simplifying*
Example 1	$(3x-2x^2)(4) + (5+4x)(3-4x)$	$15+4x-24x^2$
Example 2	$(x^{-1}+1)(1) + (x-1)(-x^{-2})$	$\dfrac{x^2+1}{x^2}$
Example 5	$\dfrac{(2-3x)(4x-4) - (2x^2-4x+3)(-3)}{(2-3x)^2}$	$\dfrac{-6x^2+8x+1}{(2-3x)^2}$
Example 8	$\dfrac{(5x-4)[(1-2x)(3)+(3x+2)(-2)] - (1-2x)(3x+2)(5)}{(5x-4)^2}$	$\dfrac{-30x^2+48x-6}{(5x-4)^2}$

Extended Application: Blood Pressure

Real Life

EXAMPLE 9 *Rate of Change of Blood Pressure*

As blood moves from the heart through the major arteries out to the capillaries and back through the veins, the systolic pressure continuously drops. (See Figure 2.27.) Consider a person whose blood pressure P (in millimeters of mercury) is given by

$$P = \frac{25t^2 + 125}{t^2 + 1}, \quad 0 \le t \le 10,$$

where t is measured in seconds. At what rate is the blood pressure changing 5 seconds after blood leaves the heart?

Solution
Begin by applying the Quotient Rule.

$$\frac{dP}{dt} = \frac{(t^2 + 1)(50t) - (25t^2 + 125)(2t)}{(t^2 + 1)^2} \qquad \textit{Quotient Rule}$$

$$= \frac{50t^3 + 50t - 50t^3 - 250t}{(t^2 + 1)^2}$$

$$= -\frac{200t}{(t^2 + 1)^2} \qquad \textit{Simplify.}$$

When $t = 5$, the rate of change is

$$\frac{dP}{dt} = -\frac{200(5)}{26^2}$$

$$\approx -1.48 \text{ mm/sec.}$$

Therefore, the pressure is *dropping* at a rate of 1.48 millimeters per second when $t = 5$ seconds.

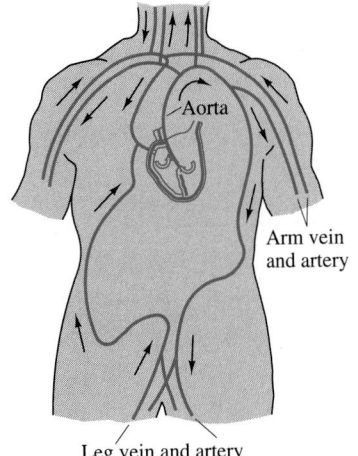

Aorta

Arm vein and artery

Leg vein and artery

FIGURE 2.27

Discussion Problem   **Testing Differentiation Rules**

What is wrong with the following differentiations?

$$f(x) = (x^3)(x^4)$$
$$f'(x) = (3x^2)(4x^3)$$

$$g(x) = \frac{x^3}{x^4}$$
$$g'(x) = \frac{3x^2}{4x^3}$$

If you were teaching a calculus class, how could you convince your class that these derivatives are incorrect?

Warm Up

The following warm-up exercises involve skills that were covered in earlier sections. You will use these skills in the exercise set for this section.

In Exercises 1–6, simplify the expression.

1. $(x^2 + 1)(2) + (2x + 7)(2x)$

2. $(2x - x^3)(8x) + (4x^2)(2 - 3x^2)$

3. $\dfrac{(2x + 7)(5) - (5x + 6)(2)}{(2x + 7)^2}$

4. $\dfrac{(x^2 - 4)(2x + 1) - (x^2 + x)(2x)}{(x^2 - 4)^2}$

5. $(x^{-1} + x)(2) + (2x - 3)(-x^{-2} + 1)$

6. $\dfrac{(1 - x^{-1})(1) - (x - 4)(x^{-2})}{(1 - x^{-1})^2}$

In Exercises 7–10, find $f'(2)$.

7. $f(x) = 3x^2 - x + 4$

8. $f(x) = -x^3 + x^2 + 8x$

9. $f(x) = \dfrac{1}{x}$

10. $f(x) = x^2 - \dfrac{1}{x^2}$

EXERCISES 2.4   means that technology can help you solve or check the exercise(s).

In Exercises 1–10, find the value of the derivative of the function at the indicated point.

Function	Point
1. $f(x) = x^2(3x^3 - 1)$	$(1, 2)$
2. $f(x) = (x^2 + 1)(2x + 5)$	$(-1, 6)$
3. $f(x) = \frac{1}{3}(2x^3 - 4)$	$\left(0, -\frac{4}{3}\right)$
4. $f(x) = \frac{1}{7}(5 - 6x^2)$	$\left(1, -\frac{1}{7}\right)$
5. $g(x) = (x^2 - 4x + 3)(x - 2)$	$(4, 6)$
6. $g(x) = (x^2 - 2x + 1)(x^3 - 1)$	$(1, 0)$
7. $h(x) = \dfrac{x}{x - 5}$	$(6, 6)$
8. $h(x) = \dfrac{x^2}{x + 3}$	$\left(-1, \frac{1}{2}\right)$
9. $f(t) = \dfrac{2t^2 - 3}{3t}$	$\left(2, \frac{5}{6}\right)$
10. $f(x) = \dfrac{x + 1}{x - 1}$	$(2, 3)$

In Exercises 11–18, find the derivative of the function. Use Example 7 as a model.

Function	Rewrite	Derivative	Simplify
11. $y = \dfrac{x^2 + 2x}{x}$			
12. $y = \dfrac{4x^{3/2}}{x}$			
13. $y = \dfrac{7}{3x^3}$			
14. $y = \dfrac{4}{5x^2}$			
15. $y = \dfrac{4x^2 - 3x}{8\sqrt{x}}$			
16. $y = \dfrac{x^2 - 4}{x + 2}$			
17. $y = \dfrac{x^2 - 4x + 3}{x - 1}$			
18. $y = \dfrac{3x^2 - 4x}{6x}$			

In Exercises 19–40, differentiate the function.

19. $f(x) = (x^3 - 3x)(2x^2 + 3x + 5)$

20. $f(x) = (x - 1)(x^2 - 3x + 2)$

21. $h(t) = (t^5 - 1)(4t^2 - 7t - 3)$

22. $g(t) = (2t^2 - 3)(4 - t^2 - t^4)$

23. $h(p) = (p^3 - 2)^2$ **24.** $h(x) = (x^2 - 1)^2$

25. $f(x) = \sqrt[3]{x}\left(\sqrt{x} + 3\right)$ **26.** $f(x) = \sqrt[3]{x}(x + 1)$

27. $f(x) = \dfrac{3x - 2}{2x - 3}$ **28.** $f(x) = \dfrac{x^3 + 3x + 2}{x^2 - 1}$

29. $f(x) = \dfrac{3 - 2x - x^2}{x^2 - 1}$ **30.** $f(x) = x^3\left(\dfrac{x - 2}{x + 1}\right)$

31. $f(x) = (x^5 - 3x)\left(\dfrac{1}{x^2}\right)$ **32.** $f(x) = x\left(1 - \dfrac{2}{x + 1}\right)$

33. $h(t) = \dfrac{t + 2}{t^2 + 5t + 6}$ **34.** $g(s) = \dfrac{5}{s^2 + 2s + 2}$

35. $f(x) = \dfrac{x + 1}{\sqrt{x}}$ **36.** $f(x) = \dfrac{\sqrt{x}}{x + 1}$

37. $g(x) = \left(\dfrac{x - 3}{x + 4}\right)(x^2 + 2x + 1)$

38. $f(x) = \left(\dfrac{x^2 - x - 3}{x^2 + 1}\right)(x^2 + x + 1)$

39. $f(x) = (3x^3 + 4x)(x - 5)(x + 1)$

40. $f(x) = (x^2 - x)(x^2 + 1)(x^2 + x + 1)$

In Exercises 41–44, find an equation of the tangent line to the graph of the function at the indicated point.

Function	*Point*
41. $f(x) = \dfrac{2x}{x + 2}$	$(2, 1)$
42. $f(x) = (x - 1)(x^2 - 2)$	$(0, 2)$
43. $f(x) = (x^3 - 3x + 1)(x + 2)$	$(1, -3)$
44. $f(x) = \dfrac{x - 1}{x + 1}$	$\left(2, \dfrac{1}{3}\right)$

In Exercises 45–48, find the point(s), if any, at which the graph of f has a horizontal tangent.

45. $f(x) = \dfrac{x^2}{x - 1}$ **46.** $f(x) = \dfrac{x^2}{x^2 + 1}$

47. $f(x) = \dfrac{x^4}{x^3 + 1}$ **48.** $f(x) = \dfrac{x^4 + 3}{x^2 + 1}$

In Exercises 49–52, use a graphing utility to graph f and f' on the interval $[-2, 2]$.

49. $f(x) = x(x + 1)$

50. $f(x) = x^2(x + 1)$

51. $f(x) = x(x + 1)(x - 1)$

52. $f(x) = x^2(x + 1)(x - 1)$

Demand In Exercises 53 and 54, use the demand function to find the rate of change in the demand x for the given price p.

53. $x = 275\left(1 - \dfrac{3p}{5p + 1}\right)$, $p = \$4$

54. $x = 300 - p - \dfrac{2p}{p + 1}$, $p = \$3$

55. *Oxygen Level* The model

$$f(t) = \frac{t^2 - t + 1}{t^2 + 1}$$

measures the percent of the normal level of oxygen in a pond, where t is the time (in weeks) after organic waste is dumped into the pond. Find the rate of change of f with respect to t when (a) $t = 0.5$, (b) $t = 2$, and (c) $t = 8$.

56. *Refrigeration* The temperature T of food placed in a refrigerator is modeled by

$$T = 10\left(\frac{4t^2 + 16t + 75}{t^2 + 4t + 10}\right),$$

where t is the time (in hours). What is the initial temperature of the food? Find the rate of change of T with respect to t when (a) $t = 1$, (b) $t = 3$, (c) $t = 5$, and (d) $t = 10$.

57. *Population Growth* A population of bacteria is introduced into a culture. The number of bacteria P can be modeled by

$$P = 500\left(1 + \frac{4t}{50 + t^2}\right),$$

where t is the time (in hours). Find the rate of change of the population when $t = 2$.

58. *Quality Control* The percent P of defective parts produced by a new employee t days after the employee starts work can be modeled by

$$P = \frac{t + 1750}{50(t + 2)}.$$

Find the rate of change of P when (a) $t = 1$ and (b) $t = 10$.

59. *Profit* The demand x for a product is inversely proportional to the square of the price for $x \geq 5$.

(a) The price is $1000, the demand is 16 units. Find the demand function.

(b) The product costs $250 per unit and the fixed cost is $10,000. Find the cost function.

(c) Find the profit function and graph it. From the graph, what price would you set for this product? Explain your reasoning.

 60. *Profit* You are managing a store and have been adjusting the price of an item. You have found that you make a profit of $50 when 10 units are sold, $60 when 12 units are sold, and $65 when 14 units are sold.

(a) Fit this data to the following quadratic model.
$$P = ax^2 + bx + c$$

(b) Use a graphing utility to graph P.

(c) Find the point on the graph at which the marginal profit is zero. Interpret this point in the context of the problem.

 61. *Demand Function* Given $f(x) = x^2 + 1$, which of the following would most likely represent a demand function?

(a) $p = f(x)$ (b) $p = xf(x)$

(c) $p = \dfrac{f(x)}{x}$ (d) $p = \dfrac{1}{f(x)}$

Explain your reasoning. Use a graph of each function as part of your explanation.

 62. *Cost* The cost of producing x units of a product is
$$C = x^3 - 15x^2 + 87x - 73, \quad 4 \leq x \leq 9.$$

(a) Use a graphing utility to graph the marginal cost function and the average cost function, C/x, on the same set of axes.

(b) Find the point of intersection of the graphs of dC/dx and C/x. What significance, if any, does this point have?

63. *Inventory Replenishment* The ordering and transportation cost C (in thousands of dollars) of the components used in manufacturing a product is
$$C = 100\left(\frac{200}{x^2} + \frac{x}{x+30}\right), \quad 1 \leq x,$$

where x is the order size (in hundreds). Find the rate of change of C with respect to x for the following order sizes.

(a) $x = 10$ (b) $x = 15$ (c) $x = 20$

What do these rates of change imply about increasing the size of an order?

Nardin.

64. *Sales Analysis* The monthly sale of memberships M at a newly built fitness center is modeled by
$$M(t) = \frac{300t}{t^2 + 1} + 8,$$

where t is the number of months that the center has been open.

(a) Find $M'(t)$.

(b) Find $M(3)$ and $M'(3)$ and interpret the results.

(c) Find $M(24)$ and $M'(24)$ and interpret the results.

65. *Research Project* Use your school's library or some other reference source to find information about a company that performs market research. Write a short paper about the company. (One such company is described below.)

— *Business Capsule* —

Hispanic Market Connections, Inc.

Isabel Valdes is the founder of Hispanic Market Connections Inc. The database compiled by her company was considered so useful that the company won an award from *American Demographics* magazine as one of America's "Best 100 Sources of Marketing Information." In 1993, Isabel Valdes, who has two Master's degrees from Stanford University, co-authored a 450-page book entitled *Handbook on Marketing to Hispanics*. Of her book, Valdes says that "it offers a lot more than the traditional demographic tables and statistics."

2.5 The Chain Rule

The Chain Rule ■ *The General Power Rule* ■ *Simplification Techniques* ■
Extended Application: Revenue Per Share ■ *Summary of Differentiation Rules*

The Chain Rule

In this section, you will study one of the most powerful rules of differential calculus—the **Chain Rule.** This differentiation rule deals with composite functions and adds versatility to the rules presented in Sections 2.2 and 2.4. For example, compare the following functions. Those on the left can be differentiated without the Chain Rule, whereas those on the right are best done with the Chain Rule.

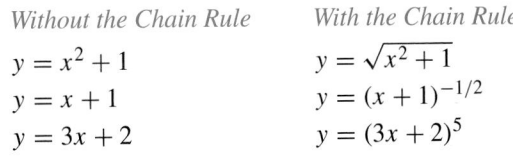

Without the Chain Rule

$y = x^2 + 1$

$y = x + 1$

$y = 3x + 2$

With the Chain Rule

$y = \sqrt{x^2 + 1}$

$y = (x + 1)^{-1/2}$

$y = (3x + 2)^5$

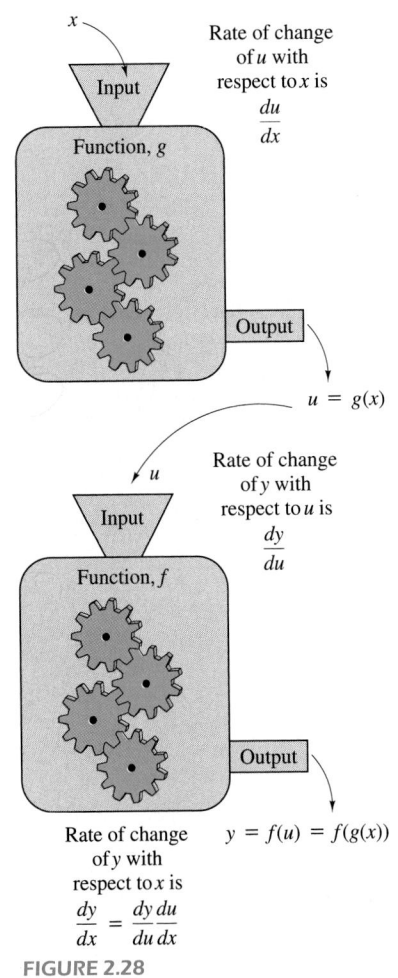

x

Input

Function, *g*

Rate of change of *u* with respect to *x* is $\dfrac{du}{dx}$

Output

$u = g(x)$

u

Input

Function, *f*

Rate of change of *y* with respect to *u* is $\dfrac{dy}{du}$

Output

$y = f(u) = f(g(x))$

Rate of change of *y* with respect to *x* is
$\dfrac{dy}{dx} = \dfrac{dy}{du}\dfrac{du}{dx}$

FIGURE 2.28

The Chain Rule

If $y = f(u)$ is a differentiable function of u, and $u = g(x)$ is a differentiable function of x, then $y = f(g(x))$ is a differentiable function of x, and

$$\frac{dy}{dx} = \frac{dy}{du}\frac{du}{dx}$$

or, equivalently,

$$\frac{d}{dx}[f(g(x))] = f'(g(x))g'(x).$$

Basically, the Chain Rule states that if y changes dy/du times as fast as u, and u changes du/dx times as fast as x, then y changes

$$\frac{dy}{du}\frac{du}{dx}$$

times as fast as x, as illustrated in Figure 2.28. One advantage of the dy/dx notation for derivatives is that it helps you remember differentiation rules, such as the Chain Rule. For instance, in the formula $dy/dx = (dy/du)(du/dx)$, you can imagine that the du's cancel.

When applying the Chain Rule, it helps to think of the composite function $y = f(g(x))$ or $y = f(u)$ as having two parts—an *inside* and an *outside*—as illustrated below.

Inside

$$y = f(g(x)) = f(u)$$

Outside

The Chain Rule tells you that the derivative of $y = f(u)$ is the derivative of the outer function (at the inner function u) *times* the derivative of the inner function. That is,

$$y' = f'(u) \cdot u'.$$

EXAMPLE 1 *Decomposing Composite Functions*

Write each function as the composition of two functions.

a. $y = \dfrac{1}{x+1}$ **b.** $y = \sqrt{3x^2 - x + 1}$

Solution

There is more than one correct way to decompose each function. One way for each is shown below.

$y = f(g(x))$	$u = g(x)$ *(inside)*	$y = f(u)$ *(outside)*
a. $y = \dfrac{1}{x+1}$	$u = x + 1$	$y = \dfrac{1}{u}$
b. $y = \sqrt{3x^2 - x + 1}$	$u = 3x^2 - x + 1$	$y = \sqrt{u}$

EXAMPLE 2 *Using the Chain Rule*

Note Try checking the result of Example 2 by expanding the function to obtain

$$y = x^6 + 3x^4 + 3x^2 + 1$$

and differentiating. Do you obtain the same answer?

Find the derivative of $y = (x^2 + 1)^3$.

Solution

To apply the Chain Rule, you need to identify the inside function u.

$$y = \overset{u}{\overbrace{(x^2 + 1)}}^3 = u^3$$

By the Chain Rule, you can write the derivative as follows.

$$\frac{dy}{dx} = \overset{\frac{dy}{du}}{\overbrace{3(x^2 + 1)^2}}\,\overset{\frac{du}{dx}}{\overbrace{(2x)}}$$

$$= 6x(x^2 + 1)^2$$

The General Power Rule

The function in Example 2 illustrates one of the most common types of composite functions—a power function of the form

$$y = [u(x)]^n.$$

The rule for differentiating such functions is called the **General Power Rule,** and it is a special case of the Chain Rule.

The General Power Rule

If $y = [u(x)]^n$, where u is a differentiable function of x and n is a real number, then

$$\frac{dy}{dx} = n[u(x)]^{n-1}\frac{du}{dx}$$

or, equivalently,

$$\frac{d}{dx}[u^n] = nu^{n-1}u'.$$

Proof Apply the Chain Rule and the Simple Power Rule as follows.

$$\frac{dy}{dx} = \frac{dy}{du}\frac{du}{dx}$$

$$= \frac{d}{du}[u^n]\frac{du}{dx}$$

$$= nu^{n-1}\frac{du}{dx}$$

■

EXAMPLE 3 *Using the General Power Rule*

Find the derivative of $f(x) = (3x - 2x^2)^3$.

Solution
The inside function is $u = 3x - 2x^2$. Thus, by the General Power Rule,

$$f'(x) = \overbrace{3}^{n}\overbrace{(3x - 2x^2)^2}^{u^{n-1}}\overbrace{\frac{d}{dx}[3x - 2x^2]}^{u'}$$

$$= 3(3x - 2x^2)^2(3 - 4x)$$

$$= (9 - 12x)(3x - 2x^2)^2.$$

■

EXAMPLE 4 *Rewriting Before Differentiating*

Find the derivative of

$$y = \sqrt[3]{(x^2 + 2)^2}. \qquad\qquad \textit{Original function}$$

Solution

Begin by rewriting the function in rational exponent form.

$$y = (x^2 + 2)^{2/3} \qquad\qquad \textit{Rewrite original function.}$$

Then, using the inside function, $u = x^2 + 2$, apply the General Power Rule.

$$\frac{dy}{dx} = \overbrace{\frac{2}{3}}^{n}\overbrace{(x^2 + 2)^{-1/3}}^{u^{n-1}}\overbrace{(2x)}^{u'} \qquad\qquad \textit{Apply General Power Rule.}$$

$$= \frac{4x(x^2 + 2)^{-1/3}}{3}$$

$$= \frac{4x}{3\sqrt[3]{x^2 + 2}} \qquad\qquad \textit{Simplify.}$$

The derivative of a quotient can sometimes be found more easily with the General Power Rule than with the Quotient Rule. This is especially true when the numerator is a constant, as illustrated in the next example.

EXAMPLE 5 *Finding the Derivative of a Quotient*

Find the derivative of the functions.

a. $y = \dfrac{3}{x^2 + 1}$ **b.** $y = \dfrac{3}{(x + 1)^2}$

Solution

a. Begin by rewriting the function as

$$y = 3(x^2 + 1)^{-1}. \qquad\qquad \textit{Rewrite original function.}$$

Then apply the General Power Rule to obtain

$$\frac{dy}{dx} = -3(x^2 + 1)^{-2}(2x) = -\frac{6x}{(x^2 + 1)^2}. \qquad \textit{Apply General Power Rule.}$$

b. Begin by rewriting the function as

$$y = 3(x + 1)^{-2}. \qquad\qquad \textit{Rewrite original function.}$$

Then apply the General Power Rule to obtain

$$\frac{dy}{dx} = -6(x + 1)^{-3}(1) = -\frac{6}{(x + 1)^3}. \qquad \textit{Apply General Power Rule.}$$

Simplification Techniques

Throughout this chapter we have emphasized writing derivatives in simplified form. The reason for this is that most applications of derivatives require a simplified form. The next two examples illustrate some useful simplification techniques.

EXAMPLE 6 Simplifying by Factoring Out Least Powers

$$y = x^2\sqrt{1-x^2} \qquad \text{\textit{Original function}}$$

$$= x^2(1-x^2)^{1/2} \qquad \text{\textit{Rewrite function.}}$$

$$y' = x^2 \frac{d}{dx}[(1-x^2)^{1/2}] + (1-x^2)^{1/2}\frac{d}{dx}[x^2] \qquad \text{\textit{Product Rule}}$$

$$= x^2\left[\frac{1}{2}(1-x^2)^{-1/2}(-2x)\right] + (1-x^2)^{1/2}(2x) \qquad \text{\textit{Power Rule}}$$

$$= -x^3(1-x^2)^{-1/2} + 2x(1-x^2)^{1/2}$$

$$= x(1-x^2)^{-1/2}[-x^2(1) + 2(1-x^2)] \qquad \text{\textit{Factor.}}$$

$$= x(1-x^2)^{-1/2}(2-3x^2)$$

$$= \frac{x(2-3x^2)}{\sqrt{1-x^2}} \qquad \text{\textit{Simplify.}}$$

Note In Example 6, note that you subtract exponents when factoring. That is, when $(1-x^2)^{-1/2}$ is factored out of $(1-x^2)^{1/2}$, the *remaining* factor has an exponent of $\frac{1}{2} - \left(-\frac{1}{2}\right)$ or 1. Thus,

$$(1-x^2)^{1/2} = (1-x^2)^{-1/2}(1-x^2)^1.$$

EXAMPLE 7 Differentiating a Quotient Raised to a Power

Find the derivative of

$$f(x) = \left(\frac{3x-1}{x^2+3}\right)^2.$$

Solution

$$f'(x) = 2\underbrace{\left(\frac{3x-1}{x^2+3}\right)}_{u^{n-1}}\overset{n}{}\underbrace{\frac{d}{dx}\left[\frac{3x-1}{x^2+3}\right]}_{u'}$$

$$= \left[\frac{2(3x-1)}{x^2+3}\right]\left[\frac{(x^2+3)(3) - (3x-1)(2x)}{(x^2+3)^2}\right]$$

$$= \frac{2(3x-1)(3x^2+9-6x^2+2x)}{(x^2+3)^3}$$

$$= \frac{2(3x-1)(-3x^2+2x+9)}{(x^2+3)^3}$$

Note In Example 7, try to find $f'(x)$ by applying the Quotient Rule to

$$f(x) = \frac{(3x-1)^2}{(x^2+3)^2}.$$

Which method do you prefer?

Extended Application: Revenue Per Share

Real Life

EXAMPLE 8 *Finding Rates of Change*

From 1979 through 1993, the revenue per share r (in dollars) for MCI can be modeled by

$$r = (0.288t + 0.909)^2, \qquad -1 \le t \le 13,$$

where $t = 0$ corresponds to 1980. Use the model to approximate the rate of change in the revenue per share in 1984, 1988, and 1992. If you had been an MCI stockholder from 1979 through 1993, would you have been satisfied with the performance of this stock? *(Source: MCI Communications Corporation)*

Solution

The rate of change in r is given by the derivative, dr/dt. You can use the General Power Rule to find the derivative.

$$\frac{dr}{dt} = 2(0.288t + 0.909)^1(0.288) = 0.576(0.288t + 0.909)$$

In 1984, the revenue per share was increasing at a rate of

$$\frac{dr}{dt} = 0.576[0.288(4) + 0.909] \approx \$1.19 \text{ per share per year.} \qquad 1984$$

In 1988, the revenue per share was increasing at a rate of

$$\frac{dr}{dt} = 0.576[0.288(8) + 0.909] \approx \$1.85 \text{ per share per year.} \qquad 1988$$

In 1992, the revenue per share was increasing at a rate of

$$\frac{dr}{dt} = 0.576[0.288(12) + 0.909] \approx \$2.51 \text{ per share per year.} \qquad 1992$$

The graph of the revenue per share function is shown in Figure 2.29. For most investors, the performance of MCI stock would be considered to be very good.

FIGURE 2.29

The Stock Market/© Ted Horowitz

After AT&T was required to split up its national telephone system, several new telecommunications companies started and prospered. The most successful of these new companies is MCI. In 1993, it had 2107 million circuit-miles of microwave and fiber optics in its network. The photo shows an example of fiber optics.

Note Example 8 deals with *revenues* per share, which is not the same as *dividends* per share.

Summary of Differentiation Rules

You now have all the rules you need to differentiate *any* algebraic function. For your convenience, they are summarized below.

Summary of Differentiation Rules

1. Constant Rule
$$\frac{d}{dx}[c] = 0, \quad c \text{ is a constant.}$$

2. Constant Multiple Rule
$$\frac{d}{dx}[cu] = c\frac{du}{dx}, \quad c \text{ is a constant.}$$

3. Sum and Difference Rules
$$\frac{d}{dx}[u \pm v] = \frac{du}{dx} \pm \frac{dv}{dx}$$

4. Product Rule
$$\frac{d}{dx}[uv] = u\frac{dv}{dx} + v\frac{du}{dx}$$

5. Quotient Rule
$$\frac{d}{dx}\left[\frac{u}{v}\right] = \frac{v\frac{du}{dx} - u\frac{dv}{dx}}{v^2}$$

6. Power Rules
$$\frac{d}{dx}[x^n] = nx^{n-1}$$

$$\frac{d}{dx}[u^n] = nu^{n-1}\frac{du}{dx}$$

7. Chain Rule
$$\frac{dy}{dx} = \frac{dy}{du}\frac{du}{dx}$$

Discussion Problem   Comparing Power Rules

You now have two power rules for differentiation.

$$\frac{d}{dx}[x^n] = nx^{n-1} \qquad \qquad \textit{Simple Power Rule}$$

$$\frac{d}{dx}[u^n] = nu^{n-1}\frac{du}{dx} \qquad \qquad \textit{General Power Rule}$$

Explain how you can tell which rule to use. Then state whether you would use the simple or general rule for each of the following.

a. $y = x^4$ **b.** $y = (x^2 + 1)$ **c.** $y = (x^2 + 1)^2$

d. $y = \dfrac{1}{x^4}$ **e.** $y = \dfrac{1}{x - 1}$ **f.** $y = \dfrac{1}{\sqrt{2x - 1}}$

Warm Up

The following warm-up exercises involve skills that were covered in earlier sections. You will use these skills in the exercise set for this section.

In Exercises 1–6, rewrite the expression with rational exponents.

1. $\sqrt[5]{(1-5x)^2}$

2. $\sqrt[4]{(2x-1)^3}$

3. $\dfrac{1}{\sqrt{4x^2+1}}$

4. $\dfrac{1}{\sqrt[3]{x-6}}$

5. $\dfrac{\sqrt{x}}{\sqrt[3]{1-2x}}$

6. $\dfrac{\sqrt{(3-7x)^3}}{2x}$

In Exercises 7–10, factor the expression.

7. $3x^3 - 6x^2 + 5x - 10$

8. $5x\sqrt{x} - x - 5\sqrt{x} + 1$

9. $4(x^2+1)^2 - x(x^2+1)^3$

10. $-x^5 + 3x^3 + x^2 - 3$

EXERCISES 2.5 means that technology can help you solve or check the exercise(s).

In Exercises 1–8, identify the inside function, $u = g(x)$, and the outside function, $y = f(u)$.

$y = f(g(x))$	$u = g(x)$	$y = f(u)$
1. $y = (6x-5)^4$		
2. $y = (x^2 - 2x + 3)^3$		
3. $y = (4 - x^2)^{-1}$		
4. $y = (x^2 + 1)^{4/3}$		
5. $y = \sqrt{5x - 2}$		
6. $y = \sqrt{9 - x^2}$		
7. $y = (3x + 1)^{-1}$		
8. $y = (x + 1)^{-1/2}$		

In Exercises 9–12, match the function with the rule that you would use to *most efficiently* find the derivative.

(a) Simple Power Rule (b) Constant Rule

(c) General Power Rule (d) Quotient Rule

9. $f(x) = \dfrac{2}{1 - x^3}$

10. $f(x) = \dfrac{2x}{1 - x^3}$

11. $f(x) = \sqrt[3]{8^2}$

12. $f(x) = \sqrt[3]{x^2}$

In Exercises 13–34, use the General Power Rule to find the derivative of the function.

13. $y = (2x - 7)^3$

14. $y = (3x^2 + 1)^4$

15. $f(x) = 2(x^2 - 1)^3$

16. $g(x) = 3(9x - 4)^4$

17. $g(x) = (4 - 2x)^3$

18. $h(t) = (1 - t^2)^4$

19. $h(x) = (6x - x^3)^2$

20. $f(x) = (4x - x^2)^3$

21. $f(x) = (x^2 - 9)^{2/3}$

22. $f(t) = (9t + 2)^{2/3}$

23. $f(t) = \sqrt{t + 1}$

24. $g(x) = \sqrt{2x + 3}$

25. $s(t) = \sqrt{2t^2 + 5t + 2}$

26. $y = \sqrt[3]{3x^3 + 4x}$

27. $y = \sqrt[3]{9x^2 + 4}$

28. $g(x) = \sqrt{x^2 - 2x + 1}$

29. $y = 2\sqrt{4 - x^2}$

30. $f(x) = -3\sqrt[4]{2 - 9x}$

31. $f(x) = (25 + x^2)^{-1/2}$

32. $g(x) = (6 + 3x^2)^{-2/3}$

33. $h(x) = (4 - x^3)^{-4/3}$

34. $f(x) = (4 - 3x)^{-5/2}$

In Exercises 35 and 36, find an equation of the tangent line to the graph of f at the point $(2, f(2))$.

35. $f(x) = \sqrt{4x^2 - 7}$

36. $f(x) = x\sqrt{x^2 + 5}$

In Exercises 37–40, use a symbolic differentiation utility to find the derivative of the function. Graph the function and its derivative on the same viewing rectangle. Describe the behavior of the function when the derivative is zero.

37. $f(x) = \dfrac{\sqrt{x}+1}{x^2+1}$

38. $f(x) = \sqrt{\dfrac{2x}{x+1}}$

39. $f(x) = \sqrt{\dfrac{x+1}{x}}$

40. $f(x) = \sqrt{x}(2-x^2)$

In Exercises 41–66, find the derivative of the function.

41. $y = \dfrac{1}{x-2}$

42. $s(t) = \dfrac{1}{t^2+3t-1}$

43. $f(t) = \left(\dfrac{6}{3-t}\right)^2$

44. $y = -\dfrac{4}{(t+2)^2}$

45. $f(x) = \dfrac{3}{x^3-4}$

46. $f(x) = \dfrac{1}{(x^2-3x)^2}$

47. $y = \dfrac{1}{\sqrt{x+2}}$

48. $g(t) = \dfrac{1}{t^2-2}$

49. $g(x) = \dfrac{3}{\sqrt[3]{x^3-1}}$

50. $s(x) = \dfrac{1}{\sqrt{x^2-3x+4}}$

51. $y = x\sqrt{2x+3}$

52. $y = t\sqrt{t+1}$

53. $y = t^2\sqrt{t-2}$

54. $y = \dfrac{x}{\sqrt{25+x^2}}$

55. $f(x) = x^3(x-4)^2$

56. $f(x) = x(3x-9)^3$

57. $f(t) = (t^2-9)\sqrt{t+2}$

58. $y = \sqrt{x}(x-2)^2$

59. $f(x) = \sqrt{\dfrac{3-2x}{4x}}$

60. $y = \sqrt{\dfrac{2x}{x+1}}$

61. $g(t) = \dfrac{3t^2}{\sqrt{t^2+2t-1}}$

62. $f(x) = \dfrac{x+1}{2x-3}$

63. $f(x) = \dfrac{\sqrt[3]{x^3+1}}{x}$

64. $y = \sqrt{x-1}+\sqrt{x+1}$

65. $y = \left(\dfrac{6-5x}{x^2-1}\right)^2$

66. $y = \left(\dfrac{4x^2}{3-x}\right)^3$

67. *Compound Interest* You deposit $1000 in an account with an annual rate of r (in decimal form) compounded monthly. At the end of 5 years, the balance is

$$A = 1000\left(1+\dfrac{r}{12}\right)^{60}.$$

Find the rate of change of A with respect to r when (a) $r = 0.08$, (b) $r = 0.10$, and (c) $r = 0.12$.

68. *Cost* An assembly plant purchases electric motors to install in one of its products. Management estimates that the cost per motor over the next 5 years is

$$C = 9(1.68t + 12)^{4/3},$$

where t is the time in years. Complete the following table. What can you conclude?

t	1	2	3	4	5
dC/dt					

69. *Population Growth* The number N of bacteria in a culture after t days is modeled by

$$N = 400\left[1 - \dfrac{3}{(t^2+2)^2}\right].\quad N' = \dfrac{4800\,t}{(t^2+2)^3}$$

Complete the following table. What can you conclude?

t	0	1	2	3	4
dN/dt	0	122.8	44.4	10.8	

70. *Depreciation* The value V of a machine t years after it is purchased is inversely proportional to the square root of $t + 1$. The initial value of the machine is $10,000.

(a) Write V as a function of t.
(b) Find the rate of depreciation when $t = 1$.
(c) Find the rate of depreciation when $t = 3$.

71. *Depreciation* Repeat Exercise 70 given that the value of the machine t years after it is purchased is inversely proportional to the cube root of $t + 1$.

72. *Credit-Card Rate* The average annual rate r (in percent form) for commercial bank credit cards from 1980 through 1991 can be modeled by

$$r = \dfrac{-0.05t^5 + 1.43t^4 - 12.55t^3 + 32.5t^2 + 31.2t + 1730}{100},$$

where $t = 0$ represents 1980. (*Source: Federal Reserve Bulletin*)

(a) Find the derivative of this model. Which differentiation rules did you use?
(b) Use a graphing utility to graph the derivative. Use the interval $0 \le t \le 11$.
(c) Use the trace feature to find the years during which the finance rate was changing the most.
(d) Use the trace feature to find the years during which the finance rate was changing the least.

2.6 Higher-Order Derivatives

Second, Third, and Higher-Order Derivatives ■
Acceleration

Second, Third, and Higher-Order Derivatives

The derivative of f' is the **second derivative** of f and is denoted by f''.

$$\frac{d}{dx}[f'(x)] = f''(x) \qquad \text{\textit{Second derivative}}$$

The derivative of f'' is the **third derivative** of f and is denoted by f'''.

$$\frac{d}{dx}[f''(x)] = f'''(x) \qquad \text{\textit{Third derivative}}$$

By continuing this process, you obtain **higher-order derivatives** of f.

Note In the context of higher-order derivatives, the "standard" derivative f' is often called the **first derivative** of f.

EXAMPLE 1 *Finding Higher-Order Derivatives*

$f(x) = 2x^4 - 3x^2$	*Original function*
$f'(x) = 8x^3 - 6x$	*First derivative*
$f''(x) = 24x^2 - 6$	*Second derivative*
$f'''(x) = 48x$	*Third derivative*
$f^{(4)}(x) = 48$	*Fourth derivative*
$f^{(5)}(x) = 0$	*Fifth derivative*

Notation for Higher-Order Derivatives

1. 1st derivative:	y',	$f'(x)$,	$\dfrac{dy}{dx}$,	$\dfrac{d}{dx}[f(x)]$,	$D_x[y]$
2. 2nd derivative:	y'',	$f''(x)$,	$\dfrac{d^2y}{dx^2}$,	$\dfrac{d^2}{dx^2}[f(x)]$,	$D_x^2[y]$
3. 3rd derivative:	y''',	$f'''(x)$,	$\dfrac{d^3y}{dx^3}$,	$\dfrac{d^3}{dx^3}[f(x)]$,	$D_x^3[y]$
4. 4th derivative:	$y^{(4)}$,	$f^{(4)}(x)$,	$\dfrac{d^4y}{dx^4}$,	$\dfrac{d^4}{dx^4}[f(x)]$,	$D_x^4[y]$
5. nth derivative:	$y^{(n)}$,	$f^{(n)}(x)$,	$\dfrac{d^ny}{dx^n}$,	$\dfrac{d^n}{dx^n}[f(x)]$,	$D_x^n[y]$

EXAMPLE 2 *Finding Higher-Order Derivatives*

Find the value of $g'''(2)$ for the function

$$g(t) = -t^4 + 2t^3 + t + 4. \qquad \textit{Original function}$$

Solution

Begin by differentiating three times.

$$g'(t) = -4t^3 + 6t^2 + 1 \qquad \textit{First derivative}$$

$$g''(t) = -12t^2 + 12t \qquad \textit{Second derivative}$$

$$g'''(t) = -24t + 12 \qquad \textit{Third derivative}$$

Then, evaluate the third derivative of g at $t = 2$.

$$g'''(2) = -24(2) + 12 = -36 \qquad \textit{Value of third derivative}$$

Examples 1 and 2 show how to find higher-order derivatives of *polynomial* functions. Note that with each successive differentiation, the degree of the polynomial drops by one. Eventually, higher-order derivatives of polynomial functions degenerate to a constant function. Specifically, the nth-order derivative of an nth-degree polynomial function

$$f(x) = a_n x^n + a_{n-1} x^{n-1} + \cdots + a_1 x + a_0$$

is the constant function

$$f^{(n)}(x) = n! a_n,$$

where $n! = 1 \cdot 2 \cdot 3 \cdots n$. Each derivative of order higher than n is the zero function. Polynomial functions are the *only* functions with this characteristic. For other functions, successive differentiation never produces a constant function.

TECHNOLOGY

Higher-order derivatives of nonpolynomial functions can be difficult to find by hand. If you have access to a symbolic differentiation utility such as *Derive*, *Maple*, or *Mathematica*, try using it to find higher-order derivatives. For instance, if you use *Derive* to find the third derivative of $y = 1/(x^2 + 1)$, you will obtain the following.

1: $\dfrac{1}{x^2 + 1}$

2: $\left[\dfrac{d}{dx} \right]^3 \dfrac{1}{x^2 + 3}$

3: $\dfrac{24x(1 - x^2)}{(x^2 + 1)^2}$

EXAMPLE 3 *Finding Higher-Order Derivatives*

$$y = x^{-1} = \frac{1}{x} \qquad \textit{Original function}$$

$$y' = (-1)x^{-2} = -\frac{1}{x^2} \qquad \textit{First derivative}$$

$$y'' = (-1)(-2)x^{-3} = \frac{2}{x^3} \qquad \textit{Second derivative}$$

$$y''' = (-1)(-2)(-3)x^{-4} = -\frac{6}{x^4} \qquad \textit{Third derivative}$$

$$y^{(4)} = (-1)(-2)(-3)(-4)x^{-5} = \frac{24}{x^5} \qquad \textit{Fourth derivative}$$

Acceleration

In Section 2.3, you saw that the velocity of an object moving in a straight path is given by the derivative of its position function. In other words, the rate of change of the position with respect to time is defined to be the velocity. In a similar way, the rate of change of the velocity with respect to time is defined to be the **acceleration** of the object.

Note Acceleration is measured in units of length per unit of time squared. For instance, if the velocity is measured in feet per second, then the acceleration is measured in "feet per second squared," or more formally as "feet per second per second."

$$s = f(t) \qquad \text{\textit{Position function}}$$

$$\frac{ds}{dt} = f'(t) \qquad \text{\textit{Velocity function}}$$

$$\frac{d^2s}{dt^2} = f''(t) \qquad \text{\textit{Acceleration function}}$$

To find the position, velocity, or acceleration at a particular time t, substitute the given value of t into the appropriate function, as illustrated in Example 4.

EXAMPLE 4 *Finding Acceleration*

Real Life

A ball is thrown into the air from the top of a 160-foot cliff, as shown in Figure 2.30. The initial velocity of the ball is 48 feet per second, which implies that the position function is

$$s = -16t^2 + 48t + 160,$$

where the time t is measured in seconds. Find the height, the velocity, and the acceleration of the ball when $t = 3$.

Solution

Begin by differentiating to find the velocity and acceleration functions.

$$s = -16t^2 + 48t + 160 \qquad \text{\textit{Position function}}$$

$$\frac{ds}{dt} = -32t + 48 \qquad \text{\textit{Velocity function}}$$

$$\frac{d^2s}{dt^2} = -32 \qquad \text{\textit{Acceleration function}}$$

To find the height, velocity, and acceleration when $t = 3$, substitute $t = 3$ into each of the above functions.

$$s = -16(3)^2 + 48(3) + 160 = 160 \text{ ft} \qquad \text{\textit{Position when } } t = 3$$

$$\frac{ds}{dt} = -32(3) + 48 = -48 \text{ ft/sec} \qquad \text{\textit{Velocity when } } t = 3$$

$$\frac{d^2s}{dt^2} = -32 \text{ ft/sec}^2 \qquad \text{\textit{Acceleration when } } t = 3$$

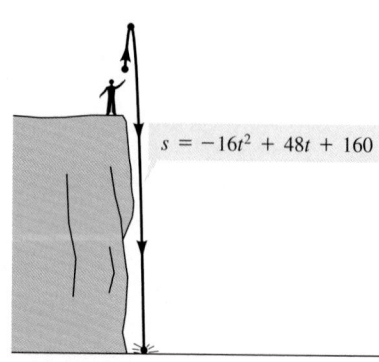

$$s = -16t^2 + 48t + 160$$

FIGURE 2.30

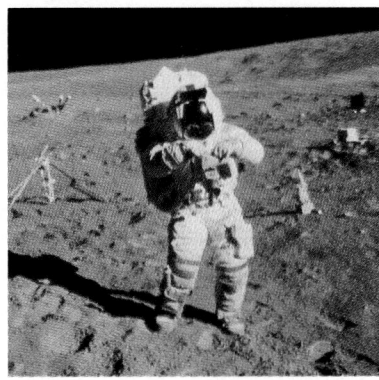

The acceleration due to gravity on the surface of the moon is only about one-sixth that exerted by the earth. Thus, if you were on the moon and threw an object into the air, it would rise to a greater height than it would on the earth's surface.

In Example 4, notice that the acceleration of the ball is -32 ft/sec² at any time t. This constant acceleration is due to the gravitational force of the earth and is called the **acceleration due to gravity.** Note that the negative value indicates that the ball is being pulled *down*—toward the earth.

Although the acceleration exerted on a falling object is relatively constant near the earth's surface, it varies greatly throughout our solar system. Large planets exert a much greater gravitational pull than do small planets or moons. The next example describes the motion of a free-falling object on the moon.

Real Life

EXAMPLE 5 *Finding Acceleration on the Moon*

An astronaut standing on the surface of the moon throws a rock into the air. The height s (in feet) of the rock is given by

$$s = -\frac{27}{10}t^2 + 27t + 6,$$

where t is measured in seconds. How does the acceleration due to gravity on the moon compare to that on the earth?

Solution

$$s = -\frac{27}{10}t^2 + 27t + 6 \qquad \textit{Position function}$$

$$\frac{ds}{dt} = -\frac{27}{5}t + 27 \qquad \textit{Velocity function}$$

$$\frac{d^2s}{dt^2} = -\frac{27}{5} \qquad \textit{Acceleration function}$$

Thus, the acceleration at any time is $-\frac{27}{5} = -5.4$ ft/sec²—about one-sixth of the acceleration due to gravity on the earth. ∎

The position function described in Example 5 neglects air resistance, which is appropriate because the moon has no atmosphere—and *no air resistance*. This means that the position function for any free-falling object on the moon is given by

$$s = -\frac{27}{10}t^2 + v_0 t + h_0,$$

where s is the height (in feet), t is the time (in seconds), v_0 is the initial velocity, and h_0 is the initial height. For instance, the rock in Example 5 was thrown upward with an initial velocity of 27 feet per second and had an initial height of 6 feet. This position function is valid for all objects—heavy ones such as hammers and light ones such as feathers.

In 1971, astronaut David R. Scott demonstrated the lack of atmosphere on the moon by dropping a hammer and feather from the same height. Both took exactly the same time to fall to the ground. If they were dropped from a height of 6 feet, how long did each take to hit the ground?

This drawing depicts the first moon landing on July 20, 1969. The event was witnessed live by millions of observers on the earth via satellite television. Can you see what is wrong with the drawing?

Real
Life

EXAMPLE 6 *Finding Velocity and Acceleration*

The velocity v (in feet per second) of a certain automobile starting from rest is

$$v = \frac{80t}{t+5},$$ *Velocity function*

where t is the time (in seconds). The position of the automobile is shown in Figure 2.31. Find the velocity and acceleration of the automobile at 10-second intervals from $t = 0$ to $t = 60$.

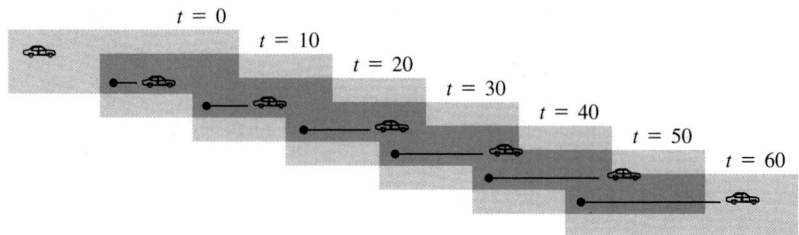

FIGURE 2.31

Solution

To find the acceleration function, differentiate the velocity function.

$$\frac{dv}{dt} = \frac{(t+5)(80) - (80t)(1)}{(t+5)^2} = \frac{400}{(t+5)^2}$$ *Acceleration function*

TABLE 2.6

t (seconds)	0	10	20	30	40	50	60
v (ft/sec)	0	53.3	64.0	68.6	71.1	72.7	73.8
$\frac{dv}{dt}$ (ft/sec^2)	16	1.78	0.64	0.33	0.20	0.13	0.09

In Table 2.6, note that the acceleration approaches zero as the velocity levels off. This observation should agree with your experience—when riding in an accelerating automobile, you do not feel the velocity, but you do feel the acceleration. In other words, you feel changes in velocity. ■

Discussion Problem   Acceleration Due to Gravity

Newton's law of universal gravitation states that the gravitational attraction of two objects is directly proportional to their masses and inversely proportional to the square of the distance between their centers. The earth has a mass of 5.979×10^{24} kilograms and a radius of 6371 kilometers. The moon has a mass of 7.354×10^{22} kilograms and a radius of 1738 kilometers. Find the ratio of the earth's gravity to the moon's gravity.

Warm Up

The following warm-up exercises involve skills that were covered in earlier sections. You will use these skills in the exercise set for this section.

In Exercises 1–4, solve the equation.

1. $-16t^2 + 24t = 0$

2. $-16t^2 + 80t + 224 = 0$

3. $-16t^2 + 128t + 320 = 0$

4. $-16t^2 + 9t + 1440 = 0$

In Exercises 5–8, find dy/dx.

5. $y = x^2(2x + 7)$

6. $y = (x^2 + 3x)(2x^2 - 5)$

7. $y = \dfrac{x^2}{2x + 7}$

8. $y = \dfrac{x^2 + 3x}{2x^2 - 5}$

In Exercises 9 and 10, find the domain and range of f.

9. $f(x) = x^2 - 4$

10. $f(x) = \sqrt{x - 7}$

EXERCISES 2.6   means that technology can help you solve or check the exercise(s).

In Exercises 1–16, find the second derivative of the function.

1. $f(x) = 5 - 4x$

2. $f(x) = 3x - 1$

3. $f(x) = x^2 + 7x - 4$

4. $f(x) = 3x^2 + 4x$

5. $g(t) = \frac{1}{3}t^3 - 4t^2 + 2t$

6. $g(t) = 5t^4 + 10t^2 + 3$

7. $g(t) = t^{-1/3}$

8. $f(t) = \dfrac{3}{4t^2}$

9. $f(x) = 4(x^2 - 1)^2$

10. $f(x) = 3(2 - x^2)^3$

11. $f(x) = x\sqrt[3]{x}$

12. $f(x) = \sqrt{9 - x^2}$

13. $f(x) = \dfrac{x + 1}{x - 1}$

14. $g(t) = -\dfrac{4}{(t + 2)^2}$

15. $y = x^2(x^2 + 4x + 8)$

16. $h(s) = s^3(s^2 - 2s + 1)$

In Exercises 17–24, find the third derivative of the function.

17. $f(x) = x^5 - 3x^4$

18. $f(x) = x^4 - 2x^3$

19. $f(x) = 5x(x + 4)^3$

20. $f(x) = (x - 1)^2$

21. $f(x) = \dfrac{3}{(4x)^2}$

22. $f(x) = \dfrac{1}{x}$

23. $f(x) = \sqrt{4 - x}$

24. $f(t) = \sqrt{2t + 3}$

In Exercises 25–30, find the indicated derivative.

Given	Derivative
25. $f'(x) = 2x^2$	$f''(x)$
26. $f''(x) = 20x^3 - 36x^2$	$f'''(x)$
27. $f''(x) = \dfrac{2x - 2}{x}$	$f'''(x)$
28. $f'''(x) = 2\sqrt{x - 1}$	$f^{(4)}(x)$
29. $f^{(4)}(x) = (x + 1)^2$	$f^{(6)}(x)$
30. $f(x) = x^3 - 2x$	$f''(x)$

In Exercises 31–38, find the second derivative and solve the equation $f''(x) = 0$.

31. $f(x) = x^3 - 9x^2 + 27x - 27$

32. $f(x) = 3x^3 - 9x + 1$

33. $f(x) = (x + 3)(x - 4)(x + 5)$

34. $f(x) = x^4 - 8x^3 + 18x^2 - 16x + 2$

35. $f(x) = 3x^4 - 18x^2$

36. $f(x) = x\sqrt{4 - x^2}$

37. $f(x) = \dfrac{x}{x^2 + 3}$

38. $f(x) = \dfrac{x}{x^2 + 1}$

39. *Velocity and Acceleration* A ball is propelled straight up from ground level with an initial velocity of 144 feet per second.

(a) Write the position function of the ball.

(b) Write the velocity and acceleration functions.

(c) When is the ball at its highest point? How high is this point?

(d) How fast is the ball traveling when it hits the ground? How is this speed related to its initial velocity?

40. *Velocity and Acceleration* A brick becomes dislodged from the top of the Empire State Building (at a height of 1250 feet) and falls to the sidewalk below.

(a) Write the position function of the brick.

(b) Write the velocity and acceleration functions.

(c) How long does it take the brick to hit the sidewalk?

(d) How fast is the brick traveling when it hits the side-walk?

41. *Velocity and Acceleration* The velocity (in feet per second) of an automobile starting from rest is modeled by

$$\frac{ds}{dt} = \frac{90t}{t + 10}.$$

Complete the table showing the velocity and acceleration at 10-second intervals during the first minute of travel. What can you conclude?

t	0	10	20	30	40	50	60
$\dfrac{ds}{dt}$							
$\dfrac{d^2s}{dt^2}$							

42. *Stopping Distance* A car is traveling at a rate of 66 feet per second (45 miles per hour) when the brakes are applied. The position function for the car is

$$s = -8.25t^2 + 66t, \quad S'=\text{Velocity} \quad S''=\text{Acceleration}$$

where s is measured in feet and t is measured in seconds. Complete the table showing the position, velocity, and acceleration for the given values of t. What can you conclude?

t	0	1	2	3	4	5
$s(t)$						
$v(t)$						
$a(t)$						

In Exercises 43 and 44, use a graphing utility to graph f, f', and f'' on the same viewing rectangle. What is the relationship between the degree of f and the degrees of its successive derivatives? In general, what is the relationship between the degree of a polynomial function and the degrees of its successive derivatives?

43. $f(x) = x^2 - 6x + 6$ **44.** $f(x) = 3x^3 - 9x$

In Exercises 45 and 46, the graphs of f, f', and f'' are shown together. Which is which? Explain your reasoning.

45.   **46.**

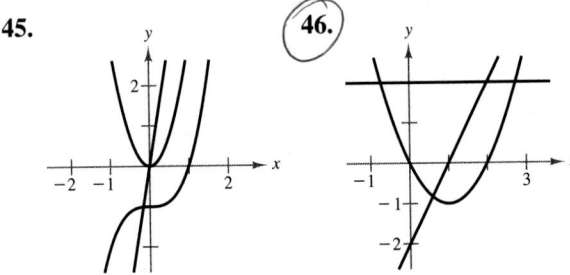

True or False In Exercises 47–53, determine whether the statement is true or false. Explain your reasoning.

47. If $y = f(x)g(x)$, then $y' = f'(x)g'(x)$.

48. If $y = (x + 1)(x + 2)(x + 3)(x + 4)$, then $y^{(5)} = 0$.

49. If $f'(c)$ and $g'(c)$ are zero and $h(x) = f(x)g(x)$, then $h'(c) = 0$.

50. If $f(x)$ is an nth-degree polynomial, then $f^{(n+1)}(x) = 0$.

51. The second derivative represents the rate of change of the first derivative.

52. If the velocity of an object is constant, then its acceleration is zero.

53. If $f'(x) = g'(x)$, then $f(x) = g(x)$.

54. *Projectile Motion* An object is thrown upward from the top of a 64-foot building with an initial velocity of 48 feet per second.

(a) Write the position function of the object.

(b) Write the velocity and acceleration functions.

(c) When will the object hit the ground?

(d) When is the velocity of the object zero?

(e) How high does the object go?

Implicit Differentiation

Implicit and Explicit Functions ■ *Implicit Differentiation* ■
Extended Application: Demand Function

Implicit and Explicit Functions

So far in the text, functions involving two variables have generally been expressed in the **explicit form** $y = f(x)$. That is, one of the two variables has been explicitly given in terms of the other. For example,

$$y = 3x - 5, \quad s = -16t^2 + 20t, \quad \text{and} \quad u = 3w - w^2$$

are each written in explicit form, and we say that y, s, and u are functions of x, t, and w, explicitly. Many functions, however, are not given explicitly and are only implied by a given equation, as illustrated in Example 1.

EXAMPLE 1 *Finding a Derivative Explicitly*

Find dy/dx for the equation $xy = 1$.

Solution
In this equation, y is **implicitly** defined as a function of x. One way to find dy/dx is to first solve the equation for y, then differentiate as usual.

$$xy = 1 \qquad\qquad\qquad \textit{Implicit form}$$

$$y = \frac{1}{x} \qquad\qquad\qquad \textit{Solve for y.}$$

$$= x^{-1} \qquad\qquad\qquad \textit{Rewrite.}$$

$$\frac{dy}{dx} = -x^{-2} \qquad\qquad\qquad \textit{Differentiate with respect to x.}$$

$$= -\frac{1}{x^2} \qquad\qquad\qquad \textit{Simplify.}$$

The procedure shown in Example 1 works well whenever you can easily write the given function explicitly. You cannot, however, use this procedure when you are unable to solve for y as a function of x. For instance, how would you find dy/dx in the equation

$$x^2 - 2y^3 + 4y = 2,$$

where it is very difficult to express y as a function of x explicitly? To do this, you can use a procedure called **implicit differentiation.**

Implicit Differentiation

To understand how to find dy/dx implicitly, you must realize that the differentiation is taking place *with respect to x*. This means that when you differentiate terms involving x alone, you can differentiate as usual. *But* when you differentiate terms involving y, you must apply the Chain Rule because you are assuming that y is defined implicitly as a function of x. Study the next example carefully. Note in particular how the Chain Rule is used to introduce the dy/dx factors in parts b and d.

EXAMPLE 2 *Applying the Chain Rule*

Differentiate the following with respect to x.

a. $3x^2$ **b.** $2y^3$ **c.** $x + 3y$ **d.** xy^2

Solution

a. The only variable in this expression is x. Thus, to differentiate with respect to x, you can use the Simple Power Rule and the Constant Multiple Rule to obtain

$$\frac{d}{dx}[3x^2] = 6x.$$

b. This case is different. The variable in the expression is y, and yet you are asked to differentiate with respect to x. To do this, assume that y is a differentiable function of x and use the Chain Rule.

$$\frac{d}{dx}[2y^3] = \overbrace{2}^{cu^n}\ \overbrace{(3)}^{c}\ \overbrace{y^2}^{n\ \ u^{n-1}}\ \overbrace{\frac{dy}{dx}}^{u'} \qquad \text{\textit{Chain Rule}}$$

$$= 6y^2\frac{dy}{dx}$$

c. This expression involves both x and y. By the Sum Rule and the Constant Multiple Rule, you can write

$$\frac{d}{dx}[x + 3y] = 1 + 3\frac{dy}{dx}.$$

d. By the Product Rule and the Chain Rule, you can write

$$\frac{d}{dx}[xy^2] = x\frac{d}{dy}[y^2] + y^2\frac{d}{dx}[x] \qquad \text{\textit{Product Rule}}$$

$$= x\left(2y\frac{dy}{dx}\right) + y^2(1) \qquad \text{\textit{Chain Rule}}$$

$$= 2xy\frac{dy}{dx} + y^2.$$

Implicit Differentiation

Consider an equation involving x and y in which y is a differentiable function of x. You can use the following steps to find dy/dx.

1. Differentiate both sides of the equation *with respect to x*.
2. Write the result so that all terms involving dy/dx are on the left side of the equation and all other terms are on the right side of the equation.
3. Factor dy/dx out of the terms on the left side of the equation.
4. Solve for dy/dx by dividing both sides of the equation by the left-hand factor that does not contain dy/dx.

In Example 3, note that implicit differentiation can produce an expression for dy/dx that contains both x and y.

EXAMPLE 3 *Finding the Slope of a Graph Implicitly*

Find the slope of the tangent line to the ellipse given by $x^2 + 4y^2 = 4$ at the point $\left(\sqrt{2}, -1/\sqrt{2}\right)$, as shown in Figure 2.32.

Solution

$$x^2 + 4y^2 = 4 \qquad\qquad \textit{Original equation}$$

$$\frac{d}{dx}[x^2 + 4y^2] = \frac{d}{dx}[4] \qquad\qquad \textit{Differentiate with respect to x.}$$

$$2x + 8y\left(\frac{dy}{dx}\right) = 0 \qquad\qquad \textit{Implicit differentiation}$$

$$8y\left(\frac{dy}{dx}\right) = -2x \qquad\qquad \textit{Subtract 2x from both sides.}$$

$$\frac{dy}{dx} = \frac{-2x}{8y} \qquad\qquad \textit{Divide both sides by 8y.}$$

$$\frac{dy}{dx} = -\frac{x}{4y} \qquad\qquad \textit{Simplify.}$$

To find the slope at the given point, substitute $x = \sqrt{2}$ and $y = -1/\sqrt{2}$ into the derivative.

$$\frac{dy}{dx} = -\frac{x}{4y} \qquad\qquad \textit{Derivative}$$

$$= -\frac{\sqrt{2}}{4\left(-1/\sqrt{2}\right)} \qquad\qquad \textit{Substitute for x and y.}$$

$$= \frac{1}{2} \qquad\qquad \textit{Simplify.}$$

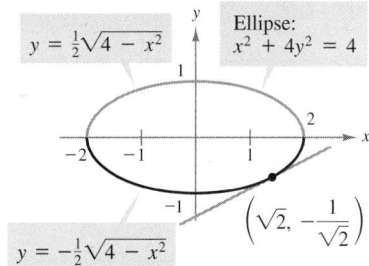

Ellipse:
$x^2 + 4y^2 = 4$

$y = \frac{1}{2}\sqrt{4 - x^2}$

$y = -\frac{1}{2}\sqrt{4 - x^2}$

$\left(\sqrt{2}, -\frac{1}{\sqrt{2}}\right)$

FIGURE 2.32 Slope of tangent line is $\frac{1}{2}$

Note To see the benefit of implicit differentiation, try reworking Example 3 using the explicit function

$$y = -\frac{1}{2}\sqrt{4 - x^2}.$$

The graph of this function is the lower half of the ellipse.

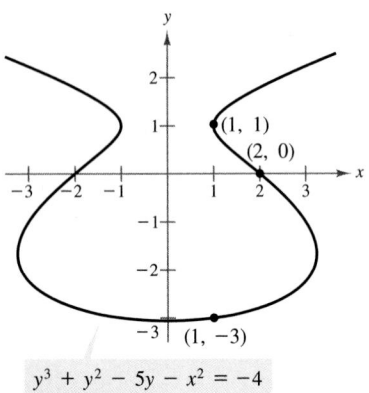

$$y^3 + y^2 - 5y - x^2 = -4$$

FIGURE 2.33

EXAMPLE 4 *Using Implicit Differentiation*

Find dy/dx for the equation $y^3 + y^2 - 5y - x^2 = -4$.

Solution

$$y^3 + y^2 - 5y - x^2 = -4 \qquad \text{Original equation}$$

$$\frac{d}{dx}[y^3 + y^2 - 5y - x^2] = \frac{d}{dx}[-4] \qquad \begin{array}{l}\text{Differentiate}\\ \text{both sides.}\end{array}$$

$$3y^2\frac{dy}{dx} + 2y\frac{dy}{dx} - 5\frac{dy}{dx} - 2x = 0 \qquad \begin{array}{l}\text{Implicit}\\ \text{differentiation}\end{array}$$

$$3y^2\frac{dy}{dx} + 2y\frac{dy}{dx} - 5\frac{dy}{dx} = 2x \qquad \begin{array}{l}\text{Collect}\\ dy/dx \text{ terms.}\end{array}$$

$$\frac{dy}{dx}(3y^2 + 2y - 5) = 2x \qquad \text{Factor.}$$

$$\frac{dy}{dx} = \frac{2x}{3y^2 + 2y - 5}$$

The graph of the original equation is shown in Figure 2.33. What is the slope of the graph at the points $(1, -3)$, $(2, 0)$, and $(1, 1)$?

EXAMPLE 5 *Finding the Slope of a Graph Implicitly*

Find the slope of the graph of $3(x^2 + y^2)^2 = 100xy$ at the point $(3, 1)$.

Solution

$$3(x^2 + y^2)^2 = 100xy$$

$$\frac{d}{dx}[3(x^2 + y^2)^2] = \frac{d}{dx}[100xy]$$

$$3(2)(x^2 + y^2)\left(2x + 2y\frac{dy}{dx}\right) = 100\left[x\frac{dy}{dx} + y(1)\right]$$

$$12y(x^2 + y^2)\frac{dy}{dx} - 100x\frac{dy}{dx} = 100y - 12x(x^2 + y^2)$$

$$[12y(x^2 + y^2) - 100x]\frac{dy}{dx} = 100y - 12x(x^2 + y^2)$$

$$\frac{dy}{dx} = \frac{100y - 12x(x^2 + y^2)}{12y(x^2 + y^2) - 100x}$$

$$\frac{dy}{dx} = \frac{25y - 3x(x^2 + y^2)}{-25x + 3y(x^2 + y^2)}$$

At the point $(3, 1)$, the slope of the graph is

$$\frac{dy}{dx} = \frac{25(1) - 3(3)(3^2 + 1^2)}{-25(3) + 3(1)(3^2 + 1^2)} = \frac{25 - 90}{-75 + 30} = \frac{-65}{-45} = \frac{13}{9},$$

as shown in Figure 2.34. The graph is called a **lemniscate.**

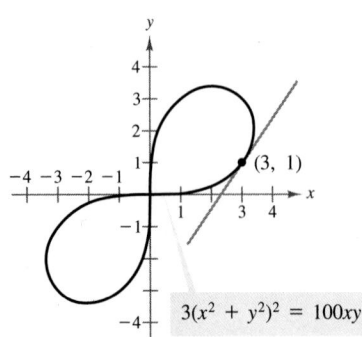

$$3(x^2 + y^2)^2 = 100xy$$

FIGURE 2.34 Lemniscate

Extended Application: Demand Function

Real Life

EXAMPLE 6 *Using a Demand Function*

The demand function for a product is modeled by

$$p = \frac{3}{0.000001x^3 + 0.01x + 1},$$

where p is measured in dollars and x is measured in thousands of units, as shown in Figure 2.35. Find the rate of change of the demand x with respect to the price p when $x = 100$.

Solution

To simplify the differentiation, begin by rewriting the function. Then, differentiate *with respect to p*.

$$p = \frac{3}{0.000001x^3 + 0.01x + 1}$$

$$0.000001x^3 + 0.01x + 1 = \frac{3}{p}$$

$$0.000003x^2 \frac{dx}{dp} + 0.01 \frac{dx}{dp} = -\frac{3}{p^2}$$

$$(0.000003x^2 + 0.01) \frac{dx}{dp} = -\frac{3}{p^2}$$

$$\frac{dx}{dp} = -\frac{3}{p^2(0.000003x^2 + 0.01)}$$

When $x = 100$, the price is

$$p = \frac{3}{0.000001(100)^3 + 0.01(100) + 1} = \$1.$$

Thus, when $x = 100$ and $p = 1$, the rate of change of the demand with respect to the price is

$$\frac{dx}{dp} = -\frac{3}{(1)^2[0.000003(100)^2 + 0.01]} = -75.$$

This means that when $x = 100$, the demand is dropping at the rate of 75 thousand units for each dollar increase in price.   ■

Demand Function

(0, 3)

(100, 1)

Price (in dollars)

50   100   150   200   250
Demand (in thousands of units)

FIGURE 2.35

Discussion Problem   **Comparing Derivatives**

In Example 6, the derivative dx/dp does not represent the slope of the graph of the demand function. Because the demand function is given by $p = f(x)$, the slope of the graph is given by dp/dx. Find dp/dx and show that the two derivatives are related by $dx/dp = 1/(dp/dx)$.

Warm Up

The following warm-up exercises involve skills that were covered in earlier sections. You will use these skills in the exercise set for this section.

In Exercises 1–6, solve the equation for y.

1. $x - \dfrac{y}{x} = 2$

2. $\dfrac{4}{x-3} = \dfrac{1}{y}$

3. $xy - x + 6y = 6$

4. $12 + 3y = 4x^2 + x^2y$

5. $x^2 + y^2 = 5$

6. $x = \pm\sqrt{6 - y^2}$

In Exercises 7–10, evaluate the expression at the indicated point.

7. $\dfrac{3x^2 - 4}{3y^2}$, $(2, 1)$

8. $\dfrac{x^2 - 2}{1 - y}$, $(0, -3)$

9. $\dfrac{5x}{3y^2 - 12y + 5}$, $(-1, 2)$

10. $\dfrac{1}{y^2 - 2xy + x^2}$, $(4, 3)$

EXERCISES 2.7   means that technology can help you solve or check the exercise(s).

In Exercises 1–6, find dy/dx.

1. $5xy = 1$

2. $\frac{1}{2}x^2 - y = 6x$

3. $y^2 = 1 - x^2$, $0 \le x \le 1$

4. $4x^2y - \dfrac{3}{y} = 0$

5. $\dfrac{2 - x}{y - 3} = 5$

6. $\dfrac{xy - y^2}{y - x} = 1$

In Exercises 7–22, find dy/dx by implicit differentiation and evaluate the derivative at the indicated point.

Equation	*Point*
7. $x^2 + y^2 = 49$	$(0, 7)$
8. $x^2 - y^2 = 16$	$(4, 0)$
9. $y + xy = 4$	$(-5, -1)$
10. $4xy + x^2 = 5$	$(1, 1)$
11. $x^2 - y^3 = 3$	$(2, 1)$
12. $x^3 + y^3 = 8$	$(0, 2)$
13. $x^3 - xy + y^2 = 4$	$(0, -2)$
14. $x^2y + y^2x = -2$	$(2, -1)$
15. $x^3y^3 - y = x$	$(0, 0)$

Equation	*Point*
16. $x^3 + y^3 = 2xy$	$(1, 1)$
17. $x^{1/2} + y^{1/2} = 9$	$(16, 25)$
18. $\sqrt{xy} = x - 2y$	$(4, 1)$
19. $x^{2/3} + y^{2/3} = 5$	$(8, 1)$
20. $(x + y)^3 = x^3 + y^3$	$(-1, 1)$
21. $x^3 - 3x^2y + 3xy^2 = 26$	$(2, 3)$
22. $y^2(x^2 + 9) = x^2 - 9$	$(3, 0)$

In Exercises 23–26, find the slope of the graph at the indicated point.

23. $3x^2 - 2y + 5 = 0$

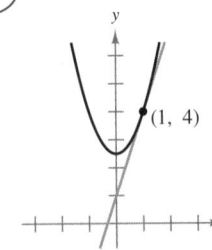

24. $x^2 + y^2 = 4$

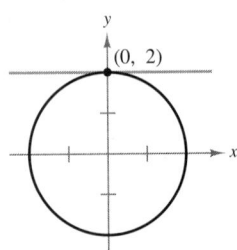

25. $4x^2 + 9y^2 = 36$

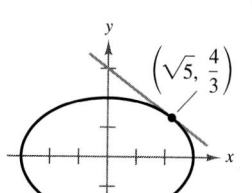

26. $x^2 - y^3 = 0$

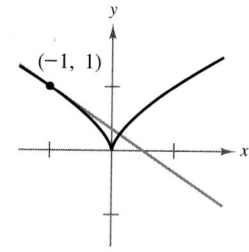

In Exercises 27–30, find dy/dx implicitly and explicitly (the explicit functions are shown on the graph) and show that the results are equivalent. Use the graph to estimate the slope of the tangent line at the labeled point. Then verify your result analytically by evaluating dy/dx at the point.

27. $x^2 + y^2 = 25$

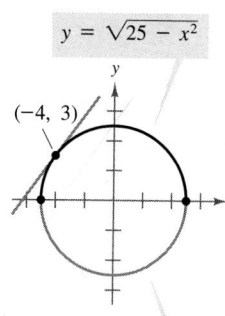

28. $x - y^2 - 1 = 0$

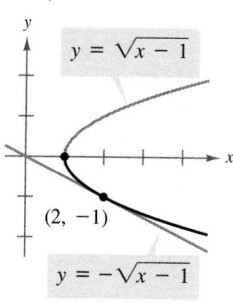

29. $9x^2 + 16y^2 = 144$

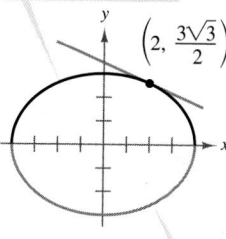

30. $4y^2 - x^2 = 7$

 In Exercises 31–34, find equations of the tangent lines to the graph at the given points. Graph the equation and the tangent lines on the same viewing rectangle.

Equation	Points
31. $x^2 + y^2 = 169$	$(5, 12)$ and $(-12, 5)$
32. $x^2 + y^2 = 9$	$(0, 3)$ and $\left(2, \sqrt{5}\right)$
33. $y^2 = 5x^3$	$\left(1, \sqrt{5}\right)$ and $\left(1, -\sqrt{5}\right)$
34. $y^2 = \dfrac{x^3}{4 - x}$	$(2, 2)$ and $(2, -2)$

Demand In Exercises 35–38, find the rate of change of x with respect to p.

35. $p = 0.006x^4 + 0.02x^2 + 10, \quad x \geq 0$

36. $p = \dfrac{725}{0.02x}$

37. $p = \dfrac{200 - x}{2x}, \quad 0 < x \leq 200$

38. $p = \sqrt{\dfrac{500 - x}{2x}}, \quad 0 < x \leq 500$

 39. **Production** Let x represent the units of labor and y the capital invested in a manufacturing process. When 135,540 units are produced, the relationship between labor and capital can be modeled by

$$100x^{0.75}y^{0.25} = 135,540.$$

(a) Find the rate of change of y with respect to x when $x = 1500$ and $y = 1000$.

(b) The model used in the problem is called the *Cobb-Douglas production function*. Graph the model and describe the relationship between labor and capital.

40. **AIDS Epidemic** The number of cases y of AIDS reported in the United States from 1984 to 1991 can be modeled by

$$y = \frac{115.01t^2 + 25.84t + 5.92}{0.01t^2 - 0.18t + 1}, \quad 4 \leq t \leq 11,$$

where $t = 4$ represents 1984.

(a) Graph the model and describe the results.

(b) Use the graph to determine the year during which the number of reported cases increased most rapidly.

(c) Complete the table to confirm your estimate.

t	4	5	6	7	8	9	10	11
y								
y'								

2.8

Related Rates

Related Variables ■ *Solving Related-Rate Problems*

Related Variables

In this section you will study problems involving variables that are changing with respect to time. If two (or more) such variables are related to each other, then their rates of change with respect to time are also related.

For instance, suppose that x and y are related by the equation $y = 2x$. If both variables are changing with respect to time, then their rates of change will also be related.

x and y The rates of change of
are related. x and y are related.

$$y = 2x \quad \longrightarrow \quad \frac{dy}{dt} = 2\frac{dx}{dt}$$

In this simple example, you can see that because y always has twice the value of x, it follows that the rate of change of y with respect to time is always twice the rate of change of x with respect to time.

EXAMPLE 1 *Examining Two Rates That Are Related*

The variables x and y are differentiable functions of t and are related by the equation $y = x^2 + 3$. When $x = 1$, $dx/dt = 2$. Find dy/dt when $x = 1$.

Solution
Use the Chain Rule to differentiate both sides of the equation *with respect to t*.

$$y = x^2 + 3 \qquad\qquad \textit{Original equation}$$

$$\frac{d}{dt}[y] = \frac{d}{dt}[x^2 + 3] \qquad\qquad \textit{Differentiate with respect to t.}$$

$$\frac{dy}{dt} = 2x\frac{dx}{dt} \qquad\qquad \textit{Chain Rule}$$

When $x = 1$ and $dx/dt = 2$, you have

$$\frac{dy}{dt} = 2x\frac{dx}{dt} = 2(1)(2) = 4.$$

■

156

Solving Related-Rate Problems

In Example 1, you are *given* the mathematical model.

Given equation: $y = x^2 + 3$

Given rate: $\dfrac{dx}{dt} = 2$ when $x = 1$

Find: $\dfrac{dy}{dt}$ when $x = 1$

In the next example, you are asked to *create* a similar mathematical model.

EXAMPLE 2 *Changing Area*

Real Life

A pebble is dropped into a calm pool of water, causing ripples in the form of concentric circles, as shown in Figure 2.36. The radius r of the outer ripple is increasing at a constant rate of 1 foot per second. When the radius is 4 feet, at what rate is the total area A of the disturbed water changing?

Solution

The variables r and A are related by the equation for the area of a circle, $A = \pi r^2$. To solve this problem, use the fact that the rate of change of the radius is given by dr/dt.

Equation: $A = \pi r^2$

Given rate: $\dfrac{dr}{dt} = 1$ when $r = 4$

Find: $\dfrac{dA}{dt}$ when $r = 4$

Using this model, you can proceed as in Example 1.

$$A = \pi r^2 \qquad \textit{Equation}$$

$$\frac{d}{dt}[A] = \frac{d}{dt}[\pi r^2] \qquad \textit{Differentiate with respect to t.}$$

$$\frac{dA}{dt} = 2\pi r \frac{dr}{dt} \qquad \textit{Chain Rule}$$

When $r = 4$ and $dr/dt = 1$, you have

$$\frac{dA}{dt} = 2\pi r \frac{dr}{dt} = 2\pi(4)(1) = 8\pi \ \text{ft}^2/\text{sec}.$$

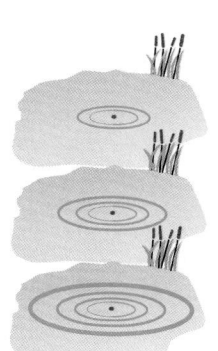

FIGURE 2.36

Note   In Example 2, note that the radius changes at a *constant* rate ($dr/dt = 1$ for all t), but the area changes at a *nonconstant* rate.

When $r = 1$ ft	When $r = 2$ ft	When $r = 3$ ft	When $r = 4$ ft
$\dfrac{dA}{dt} = 2\pi$ ft^2/sec	$\dfrac{dA}{dt} = 4\pi$ ft^2/sec	$\dfrac{dA}{dt} = 6\pi$ ft^2/sec	$\dfrac{dA}{dt} = 8\pi$ ft^2/sec

The solution shown in Example 2 illustrates the steps for solving a related-rate problem.

Guidelines for Solving a Related-Rate Problem

1. Assign symbols to all *given* quantities and all quantities *to be determined*. Make a sketch and label the quantities if feasible.
2. Write an equation that relates all variables whose rates of change are either given or to be determined.
3. Use the Chain Rule to differentiate both sides of the equation *with respect to time*.
4. Substitute into the resulting equation all known values of the variables and their rates of change. Then solve for the required rate of change.

Note   Be sure you notice the order of Steps 3 and 4 in the guidelines. You do not substitute the known values for the variables until after you have differentiated.

In Step 2 of the guidelines, note that you must write an equation that relates the given variables. To help you with this step we have included, in the back of the book, reference tables that summarize many common formulas. For instance, the volume of a sphere of radius r is given by the formula

$$V = \frac{4}{3}\pi r^3,$$

as listed in the Appendix in Reference Table 15.

The following table shows the mathematical models for some common rates of change which can be used in the first step of the solution of a related-rate problem.

Verbal Statement	Mathematical Model
The velocity of a car after traveling 1 hour is 50 miles per hour.	$x =$ distance traveled $\frac{dx}{dt} = 50$ when $t = 1$
Water is being pumped into a swimming pool at the rate of 10 cubic feet per minute.	$V =$ volume of water in pool $\frac{dV}{dt} = 10$ ft³/min
A population of bacteria is increasing at the rate of 2000 per hour.	$x =$ number in population $\frac{dx}{dt} = 2000$ bacteria per hour
Revenue is increasing at the rate of $4000 per month.	$R =$ revenue $\frac{dR}{dt} = 4000$ dollars per month

Real
Life

EXAMPLE 3 *Inflating a Balloon*

Air is being pumped into a spherical balloon at the rate of 4.5 cubic inches per minute, as indicated in Figure 2.37. Find the rate of change of the radius when the radius is 2 inches.

Solution

Let V represent the volume of the balloon and let r represent the radius. Because the volume is increasing at the rate of 4.5 cubic inches per minute, you know that $dV/dt = 4.5$. An equation that relates V and r is $V = \frac{4}{3}\pi r^3$. Thus, the problem can be represented by the following model.

$$\text{Equation: } V = \frac{4}{3}\pi r^3$$

$$\text{Given rate: } \frac{dV}{dt} = 4.5$$

$$\text{Find: } \frac{dr}{dt} \text{ when } r = 2$$

By differentiating the equation, you obtain

$$V = \frac{4}{3}\pi r^3 \qquad\qquad \textit{Equation}$$

$$\frac{d}{dt}[V] = \frac{d}{dt}\left[\frac{4}{3}\pi r^3\right] \qquad \textit{Differentiate with respect to t.}$$

$$\frac{dV}{dt} = \frac{4}{3}\pi (3r^2)\frac{dr}{dt} \qquad \textit{Chain Rule}$$

$$\frac{1}{4\pi r^2}\frac{dV}{dt} = \frac{dr}{dt}. \qquad \textit{Solve for dr/dt.}$$

When $r = 2$ and $dV/dt = 4.5$, the rate of change of the radius is

$$\frac{dr}{dt} = \frac{1}{4\pi r^2}\frac{dV}{dt} = \frac{1}{4\pi (2^2)}(4.5) \approx 0.09 \text{ in./min.}$$

In Example 3, note that the volume is increasing at a *constant* rate but the radius is increasing at a *variable* rate. In this particular example, the radius is increasing more and more slowly as t increases. This is illustrated in Figure 2.37 and Table 2.7.

TABLE 2.7

t	1	3	5	7	9	11
$V = 4.5t$	4.5	13.5	22.5	31.5	40.5	49.5
$r = \sqrt[3]{\dfrac{3V}{4\pi}}$	1.02	1.48	1.75	1.96	2.13	2.28
$\dfrac{dr}{dt}$	0.34	0.16	0.12	0.09	0.08	0.07

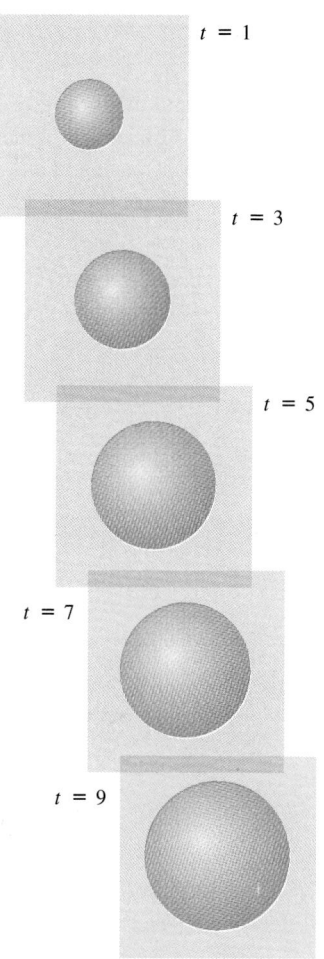

$t = 1$

$t = 3$

$t = 5$

$t = 7$

$t = 9$

FIGURE 2.37 Expanding Balloon

Real Life

EXAMPLE 4 *Tracking an Airplane by Radar*

An airplane is flying at an altitude of 6 miles on a flight path that will take it directly over a radar tracking station. Let s represent the distance (in miles) between the radar station and the plane. The distance s is decreasing at a rate of 400 miles per hour when s is 10 miles. What is the velocity of the plane?

Solution

Begin by drawing a figure and labeling the distances, as shown in Figure 2.38. The Pythagorean Theorem can be used to write an equation that relates x and s.

$$\text{Equation:} \quad x^2 + 6^2 = s^2$$

$$\text{Given rate:} \quad \frac{ds}{dt} = -400 \text{ when } s = 10$$

$$\text{Find:} \quad \frac{dx}{dt} \text{ when } s = 10$$

By differentiating the equation, you obtain

$$x^2 + 6^2 = s^2 \qquad \text{\textit{Equation}}$$

$$\frac{d}{dt}[x^2 + 6^2] = \frac{d}{dt}[s^2] \qquad \text{\textit{Differentiate with respect to t.}}$$

$$2x\frac{dx}{dt} = 2s\frac{ds}{dt} \qquad \text{\textit{Chain Rule}}$$

$$\frac{dx}{dt} = \frac{s}{x}\left(\frac{ds}{dt}\right). \qquad \text{\textit{Solve for dx/dt.}}$$

To find dx/dt, you must first find x when $s = 10$.

$$x^2 + 6^2 = s^2 \qquad \text{\textit{Equation}}$$

$$x^2 = s^2 - 36 \qquad \text{\textit{Subtract 36 from both sides.}}$$

$$x = \sqrt{s^2 - 36} \qquad \text{\textit{Take square root of both sides.}}$$

$$x = \sqrt{10^2 - 36} \qquad \text{\textit{Substitute 10 for s.}}$$

$$x = \sqrt{64}$$

$$x = 8 \qquad \text{\textit{Solve for x.}}$$

Using $s = 10$, $ds/dt = -400$, and $x = 8$, you can find dx/dt as follows.

$$\frac{dx}{dt} = \frac{s}{x}\left(\frac{ds}{dt}\right) = \frac{10}{8}(-400) = -500 \text{ mi/hr}$$

Because the velocity of the airplane is -500 miles per hour, it follows that its *speed* is 500 miles per hour. ■

Note In Example 4, note that the rate of change of the distance x is negative because x is decreasing.

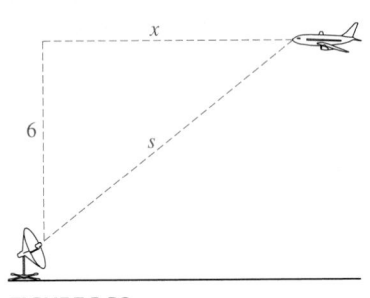

FIGURE 2.38

Real Life

EXAMPLE 5 *Increasing Production*

A company is increasing the production of a product at the rate of 200 units per week. The weekly demand function is modeled by

$$p = 100 - 0.001x,$$

where p is the price per unit and x is the number of units produced in a week. Find the rate of change of the revenue with respect to time when the weekly production is 2000 units.

Solution

$$\text{Equation: } R = xp = x(100 - 0.001x) = 100x - 0.001x^2$$

$$\text{Given rate: } \frac{dx}{dt} = 200$$

$$\text{Find: } \frac{dR}{dt} \text{ when } x = 2000$$

By differentiating the equation, you obtain

$$R = 100x - 0.001x^2 \qquad \textit{Equation}$$

$$\frac{d}{dt}[R] = \frac{d}{dt}[100x - 0.001x^2] \qquad \textit{Differentiate with respect to } t.$$

$$\frac{dR}{dt} = (100 - 0.002x)\frac{dx}{dt}. \qquad \textit{Chain Rule}$$

Using $x = 2000$ and $dx/dt = 200$, you have

$$\frac{dR}{dt} = (100 - 0.002x)\frac{dx}{dt}$$

$$= [100 - 0.002(2000)](200)$$

$$= \$19{,}200 \text{ per week.}$$

Discussion Problem Extending the Example

In Example 5, the company is increasing its revenue for the product by decreasing the price. The number of units produced and the price per unit during the first 10 weeks are shown in Table 2.8.

TABLE 2.8

t	1	2	3	4	5	6	7	8	9	10
x	200	400	600	800	1000	1200	1400	1600	1800	2000
p	$99.8	$99.6	$99.4	$99.2	$99.0	$98.8	$98.6	$98.4	$98.2	$98.0

Is the revenue increasing during this 10-week period? For how many weeks can the company continue to drop the price before the revenue begins to decline?

Warm Up

The following warm-up exercises involve skills that were covered in earlier sections. You will use these skills in the exercise set for this section.

In Exercises 1–6, write a formula for the given quantity.

1. Area of a circle πr^2

2. Volume of a sphere

3. Surface area of a cube

4. Volume of a cube

5. Volume of a cone $\dfrac{\pi r^2 h}{3}$

6. Area of a triangle

In Exercises 7–10, find dy/dx by implicit differentiation.

7. $x^2 + y^2 = 9$

8. $3xy - x^2 = 6$

9. $x^2 + 2y + xy = 12$

10. $x + xy^2 - y^2 = xy$

EXERCISES 2.8

In Exercises 1–4, find the indicated values of dy/dt and dx/dt.

Equation		Find	Given
1. $y = x^2 - \sqrt{x}$	(a)	$\dfrac{dy}{dt}$	$x = 4,\ \dfrac{dx}{dt} = 8$
	(b)	$\dfrac{dx}{dt}$	$x = 16,\ \dfrac{dy}{dt} = 12$
2. $y = x^2 - 3x$	(a)	$\dfrac{dy}{dt}$	$x = 3,\ \dfrac{dx}{dt} = 2$
	(b)	$\dfrac{dx}{dt}$	$x = 1,\ \dfrac{dy}{dt} = 5$
3. $xy = 4$	(a)	$\dfrac{dy}{dt}$	$x = 8,\ \dfrac{dx}{dt} = 10$
	(b)	$\dfrac{dx}{dt}$	$x = 1,\ \dfrac{dy}{dt} = -6$
4. $x^2 + y^2 = 25$	(a)	$\dfrac{dy}{dt}$	$x = 3,\ y = 4,\ \dfrac{dx}{dt} = 8$
	(b)	$\dfrac{dx}{dt}$	$x = 4,\ y = 3,\ \dfrac{dy}{dt} = -2$

5. *Area* The radius r of a circle is increasing at a rate of 2 inches per minute. Find the rate of change of the area when (a) $r = 6$ inches and (b) $r = 24$ inches.

6. *Volume* The radius r of a sphere is increasing at a rate of 2 inches per minute. Find the rate of change of the volume when (a) $r = 6$ inches and (b) $r = 24$ inches.

7. *Area* Let A be the area of a circle of radius r that is changing with respect to time. If dr/dt is constant, is dA/dt constant? Explain your reasoning.

8. *Volume* Let V be the volume of a sphere of radius r that is changing with respect to time. If dr/dt is constant, is dV/dt constant? Explain your reasoning.

9. *Inflating Balloon* A spherical balloon is inflated with gas at the rate of 20 cubic feet per minute. How fast is the radius of the balloon changing at the instant the radius is (a) 1 foot and (b) 2 feet?

10. *Volume of Cone* The radius r of a right circular cone is increasing at a rate of 2 inches per minute. The height h of the cone is related to the radius by $h = 3r$. Find the rate of change of the volume when (a) $r = 6$ inches and (b) $r = 24$ inches.

11. *Falling Sand* Sand is falling off a conveyer and is forming a conical pile at the rate of 20 cubic feet per minute. The diameter of the base of the cone is approximately three times the height of the cone. At what rate is the height of the pile changing when the pile is 10 feet high?

12. *Water Tank* A conical tank (with vertex down) is 10 feet across the top and 12 feet deep. Water is flowing into the tank at a rate of 10 cubic feet per minute. Find the rate of change of the water depth when the depth is 8 feet.

13. *Expanding Cube* All edges of a cube are expanding at a rate of 3 centimeters per second. How fast is the volume changing when each edge is (a) 1 centimeter and (b) 10 centimeters?

14. *Expanding Cube* All edges of a cube are expanding at a rate of 3 centimeters per second. How fast is the surface area changing when each edge is (a) 1 centimeter and (b) 10 centimeters?

15. *Moving Point* A point is moving along the graph of $y = x^2$ so that dx/dt is 2 centimeters per minute. Find dy/dt for the following.
   (a) $x = -3$ (b) $x = 0$ (c) $x = 1$ (d) $x = 3$

16. *Moving Point* A point is moving along the graph of $y = 1/(1 + x^2)$ so that dx/dt is 2 centimeters per minute. Find dy/dt for the following.
   (a) $x = -2$ (b) $x = 2$ (c) $x = 0$ (d) $x = 10$

17. *Sliding Ladder* A 25-foot ladder is leaning against a house (see figure). The base of the ladder is pulled away from the house at a rate of 2 feet per second. How fast is the top of the ladder moving down the wall when the base is (a) 7 feet, (b) 15 feet, and (c) 24 feet from the house?

FIGURE FOR 17   FIGURE FOR 18

18. *Boat Speed* A boat is pulled by a winch on a dock, and the winch is 12 feet above the deck of the boat (see figure). The winch pulls the rope at a rate of 4 feet per second. Find the speed of the boat when 13 feet of rope is out. What happens to the speed of the boat as it gets closer and closer to the dock?

19. *Air Traffic Control* An air traffic controller spots two airplanes at the same altitude converging to a point as they fly at right angles to each other. One airplane is 150 miles from the point and has a speed of 450 miles per hour. The other is 200 miles from the point and has a speed of 600 miles per hour.
   (a) At what rate is the distance between the planes changing?
   (b) How much time does the controller have to get one of the airplanes on a different flight path?

20. *Airplane Speed* An airplane flying at an altitude of 6 miles passes directly over a radar antenna (see figure). When the airplane is 10 miles away ($s = 10$), the radar detects that the distance s is changing at a rate of 240 miles per hour. What is the speed of the airplane?

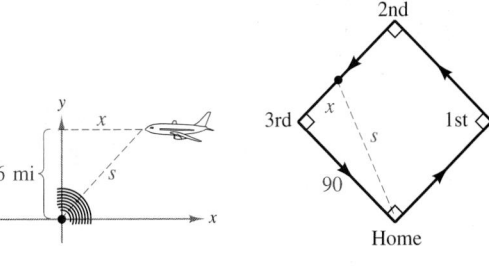

FIGURE FOR 20   FIGURE FOR 21

21. *Baseball* A (square) baseball diamond has sides that are 90 feet long (see figure). A player 26 feet from third base is running at a speed of 30 feet per second. At what rate is the player's distance from home plate changing?

22. *Environment* An accident at an oil drilling platform is causing a circular oil slick. Engineers determine that the slick is 0.08 feet thick, and when the radius is 750 feet, the slick is increasing at the rate of 0.5 feet per minute. At what rate (in cubic feet per minute) is oil flowing from the site of the accident?

23. *Profit* A company is increasing the production of a product at the rate of 25 units per week. The demand and cost functions for the product are
$$p = 50 - 0.01x \quad \text{and} \quad C = 4000 + 40x - 0.02x^2.$$
Find the rate of change of the profit with respect to time when the weekly sales are $x = 800$ units.

24. *Sales* The profit for a product is increasing at a rate of $6384 per week. The demand and cost functions for the product are
$$p = 6000 - 0.4x^2 \quad \text{and} \quad C = 2400x + 5200.$$
Find the rate of change of sales with respect to time when the weekly sales are $x = 44$ units.

25. *Drug Costs* The annual cost (in millions of dollars) for a government agency to seize $p\%$ of an illegal drug is
$$C = \frac{528p}{100 - p}, \qquad 0 \le p < 100.$$
The agency's goal is to increase p by 5% per year. Find the rate of change of the cost when (a) $p = 30\%$ and (b) $p = 60\%$.

Chapter Summary and Study Tips

After studying this chapter, you should have acquired the following skills. The exercise numbers are keyed to the Review Exercises that begin on page 166. Answers to odd-numbered Review Exercises are given in the back of the text. Worked-out solutions are listed in the *Student Study Guide*.

■ Approximate the slope of the tangent line to a graph at a point. (*Section 2.1*)   Review Exercises 1–4

■ Interpret the slope of a graph in a real-life setting. (*Section 2.1*)   Review Exercises 5, 6

■ Use the limit definition to find the slope of a graph at a point. (*Section 2.1*)   Review Exercises 7–10

■ Use the limit definition to find the derivative of a function. (*Section 2.1*)   Review Exercises 11–14

$$f'(x) = \lim_{\Delta x \to 0} \frac{f(x + \Delta x) - f(x)}{\Delta x}$$

■ Use the derivative to find the slope of a graph at a point. (*Section 2.1*)   Review Exercises 15–18

■ Use the derivative to find an equation of a tangent line to a graph at a point. (*Section 2.1*)   Review Exercises 19, 20

$$y - y_1 = m(x - x_1)$$

■ Use the graph of a function to recognize points at which the function is not differentiable. (*Section 2.1*)   Review Exercises 21–24

■ Use the Constant Rule for differentiation. (*Section 2.2*)   Review Exercises 25, 26

$$\frac{d}{dx}[c] = 0$$

■ Use the Simple Power Rule for differentiation. (*Section 2.2*)   Review Exercises 27–30

$$\frac{d}{dx}[x^n] = nx^{n-1}$$

■ Use the Constant Multiple Rule for differentiation. (*Section 2.2*)   Review Exercises 31–34

$$\frac{d}{dx}[cf(x)] = cf'(x)$$

■ Use the Sum and Difference Rules for differentiation. (*Section 2.2*)   Review Exercises 35–38

$$\frac{d}{dx}[f(x) \pm g(x)] = f'(x) \pm g'(x)$$

■ Find the average rate of change of a function over an interval and the instantaneous rate of change at a point. (*Section 2.3*)   Review Exercises 39, 40

$$\text{Average rate of change} = \frac{f(b) - f(a)}{b - a}$$

$$\text{Instantaneous rate of change} = \lim_{\Delta x \to 0} \frac{f(x + \Delta x) - f(x)}{\Delta x}$$

■ Find the average and instantaneous rates of change of a quantity in a real-life problem. (*Section 2.3*)   Review Exercises 41, 42

*Several student study aids are available with this text. The *Student Solutions Guide* includes detailed solutions to all odd-numbered exercises, as well as practice chapter tests with answers. The *Graphics Calculator Guide* offers instructions on the use of a variety of graphing calculators and computer graphing software. The *Brief Calculus TUTOR* includes additional examples for selected exercises in the text.

- Find the velocity of an object that is moving in a straight line. (*Section 2.3*)   Review Exercises 43, 44
- Create mathematical models for the revenue, cost, and profit for a product.   Review Exercises 45, 46
(*Section 2.3*)

$$P = R - C, \qquad R = xp$$

- Find the marginal revenue, marginal cost, and marginal profit for a product. (*Section 2.3*)   Review Exercises 47–52

- Use the Product Rule for differentiation. (*Section 2.4*)   Review Exercises 53–56

$$\frac{d}{dx}[f(x)g(x)] = f(x)g'(x) + g(x)f'(x)$$

- Use the Quotient Rule for differentiation. (*Section 2.4*)   Review Exercises 57–60

$$\frac{d}{dx}\left[\frac{f(x)}{g(x)}\right] = \frac{g(x)f'(x) - f(x)g'(x)}{[g(x)]^2}$$

- Use the General Power Rule for differentiation. (*Section 2.5*)   Review Exercises 61–64

$$\frac{d}{dx}[u^n] = nu^{n-1}u'$$

- Use differentiation rules efficiently to find the derivative of any algebraic function. Then simplify the result. (*Section 2.5*)   Review Exercises 65–76

- Use derivatives to answer questions about real-life situations. (*Sections 2.1–2.5*)   Review Exercises 77, 78
- Find higher-order derivatives. (*Section 2.6*)   Review Exercises 79–86
- Find and use the position function to determine the velocity and acceleration of a moving object. (*Section 2.6*)   Review Exercises 87, 88
- Find derivatives implicitly. (*Section 2.7*)   Review Exercises 89–96
- Solve related rate problems. (*Section 2.8*)   Review Exercises 97, 98

- Simplify Your Derivatives   Often our students ask if they have to simplify their derivatives. Our answer is "Yes, if you expect to use them!" In the next chapter, you will see that almost all applications of derivatives require that the derivatives be written in simplified form. It is not difficult to see the advantage of a derivative in simplified form. Consider, for instance, the derivative of $f(x) = x/\sqrt{x^2 + 1}$. The "raw form" produced by the Quotient and Chain Rules

$$f'(x) = \frac{(x^2 + 1)^{1/2}(1) - (x)\left(\frac{1}{2}\right)(x^2 + 1)^{-1/2}(2x)}{(\sqrt{x^2 + 1})^2}$$

is obviously much more difficult to use than the simplified form

$$f'(x) = \frac{1}{(x^2 + 1)^{3/2}}.$$

- List Units of Measure in Applied Problems   When using derivatives in real-life applications, be sure to list the units of measure for each variable. For instance, if R is measured in dollars and t is measured in years, then the derivative dR/dt is measured in dollars per year.

Review Exercises

means that technology can help you solve or check the exercise(s).

In Exercises 1–4, approximate the slope of the tangent line to the graph at (x, y).

1.

2.

3.

4.

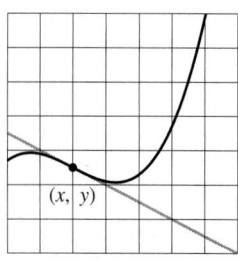

5. *Revenue* The graph below approximates the annual revenue (in millions of dollars) of Bethlehem Steel Corporation for the years 1985–1992, with $t = 0$ corresponding to 1980. Estimate the slope of the graph when $t = 7$ and $t = 10$. Interpret each slope in the context of the problem. *(Source: Bethlehem Steel Corporation)*

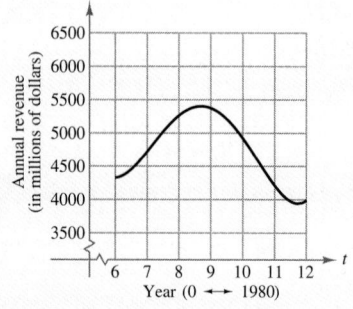

6. *Cellular Telephones* The graph below approximates the number of subscribers (in thousands) of cellular telephones for the years 1984–1991, with $t = 0$ corresponding to 1980. Estimate the slope of the graph when $t = 6$ and $t = 10$. Interpret each slope in the context of the problem. *(Source: Cellular Telecommunications Industry Association)*

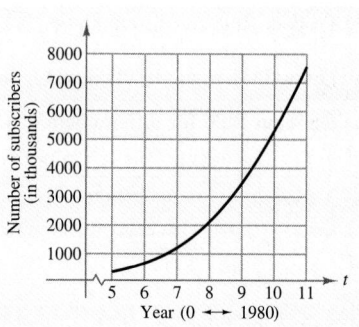

In Exercises 7–10, use the limit definition to find the slope of the tangent line to the graph of f at the indicated point.

7. $f(x) = -3x - 5;$ $(-2, 1)$

8. $f(x) = x^2 + 10;$ $(2, 14)$

9. $f(x) = \sqrt{x + 9};$ $(-5, 2)$

10. $f(x) = \dfrac{x + 1}{x};$ $(1, 2)$

In Exercises 11–14, use the limit definition to find the derivative of the function.

11. $f(x) = 7x + 3$

12. $f(x) = x^2 - 7x - 8$

13. $f(x) = \dfrac{1}{x - 5}$

14. $f(x) = \sqrt{x - 5}$

In Exercises 15–18, find the slope of the graph of f at the indicated point.

15. $f(x) = 8 - 5x;$ $(3, -7)$

16. $f(x) = -\frac{1}{2}x^2 + 2x;$ $(2, 2)$ $m = 2$oo : ASK

17. $f(x) = \sqrt{x} + 2;$ $(9, 5)$

18. $f(x) = \dfrac{5}{x};$ $(1, 5)$

In Exercises 19 and 20, use the derivative to find an equation of the tangent line to the graph of *f* at the indicated point.

19. $f(x) = \dfrac{x^2 + 3}{x}$; $(1, 4)$

20. $f(x) = -x^2 - 4x - 4$; $(-4, -4)$

In Exercises 21–24, determine the *x*-value at which the function is not differentiable.

21. $y = \dfrac{x + 1}{x - 1}$

22. $y = -|x| + 3$

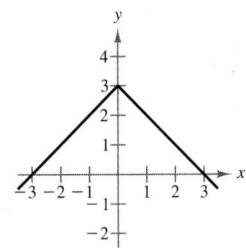

23. $y = \begin{cases} -x - 2, & x \le 0 \\ x^3 + 2, & x > 0 \end{cases}$

24. $y = (x + 1)^{2/3}$

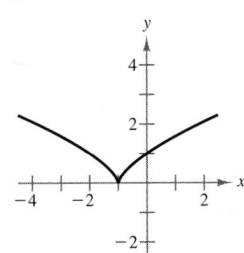

In Exercises 25–38, find the derivative of the function.

25. $f(x) = \sqrt{5}$

26. $f(x) = -10^2$

27. $y = x^5$

28. $g(x) = -\dfrac{1}{x^3}$

29. $y = \sqrt{x}$

30. $h(t) = \dfrac{1}{\sqrt{t}}$

31. $f(x) = 3x^4$

32. $f(x) = \dfrac{4}{x^4}$

33. $g(t) = \dfrac{2}{3t^2}$

34. $h(x) = \dfrac{2}{(3x)^2}$

35. $y = 11x^4 - 5x^2 + 1$

36. $y = x^3 - 5 + \dfrac{3}{x^3}$

37. $f(x) = \sqrt{x} - \dfrac{1}{\sqrt{x}}$

38. $f(x) = 2x^{-3} + 4 - \sqrt{x}$

In Exercises 39 and 40, find the average rate of change of the function over the indicated interval. Then compare the average rate of change with the instantaneous rates of change at the endpoints of the interval.

39. $f(x) = x^2 + 3x - 4$; $[0, 1]$

40. $f(x) = x^3 + x$; $[-2, 2]$

41. *Revenue* The annual revenue *R* (in millions of dollars) of Bethlehem Steel Corporation for the years 1984–1992 can be modeled by

$$R = 18.45t^4 - 650.94t^3 + 8292.83t^2 - 45,165.42t + 93,432.28,$$

where $t = 0$ corresponds to 1980. *(Source: Bethlehem Steel Corporation)*

(a) Find the average rate of change for the interval from 1986 to 1990.

(b) Find the instantaneous rate of change of the model in 1986 and 1990.

(c) Interpret the results of parts (a) and (b) in the context of the problem.

42. *Cellular Telephones* The number of subscribers *S* (in thousands) for cellular telephones for the years 1984–1991 can be modeled by

$$S = -2.3t^4 + 82.23t^3 - 865.34t^2 + 3890.15t + 6301.7,$$

where $t = 0$ corresponds to 1980. *(Source: Cellular Telecommunications Industry Association)*

(a) Find the average rate of change for the interval from 1986 to 1990.

(b) Find the instantaneous rate of change of the model in 1986 and 1990.

(c) Interpret the results of parts (a) and (b) in the context of the problem.

43. *Velocity* A rock is dropped from a tower on the Brooklyn Bridge, 276 feet above the East River. Let t represent the time in seconds.

(a) Write a model for the position function (assume that air resistance is negligible).
(b) Find the average velocity during the first 2 seconds.
(c) Find the instantaneous velocity when $t = 2$ and $t = 3$.
(d) How long will it take for the rock to hit the water?
(e) When it hits the water, what is the rock's speed?

44. *Velocity* The straight-line distance s (in feet) traveled by an accelerating bicyclist can be modeled by

$$s = 2t^{3/2}, \qquad 0 \le t \le 8,$$

where t is the time (in seconds). Complete the table showing the velocity of the bicyclist at 2-second intervals.

Time, t	0	2	4	6	8
Velocity					

45. *Revenue, Cost, and Profit* The fixed cost of operating a small flower shop is \$2500 per month. The average cost of a floral arrangement is \$15 and the average price is \$27.50. Write the monthly revenue, cost, and profit functions for the floral shop in terms of x, the number of arrangements sold.

46. *Profit* The weekly demand and cost functions for a product are

$$p = 1.89 - 0.0083x \quad \text{and} \quad C = 21 + 0.65x.$$

Write the profit function for this product.

Marginal Cost In Exercises 47 and 48, find the marginal cost function.

47. $C = 2500 + 320x$ **48.** $C = 475 + 5.25x^{2/3}$

Marginal Revenue In Exercises 49 and 50, find the marginal revenue function.

49. $R = \dfrac{35x}{\sqrt{x-2}}, \quad x \ge 6$ **50.** $R = x\left(5 + \dfrac{10}{\sqrt{x}}\right)$

Marginal Profit In Exercises 51 and 52, find the marginal profit function.

51. $P = -0.0002x^3 + 6x^2 - x - 2000$

52. $P = -\frac{1}{15}x^3 + 4000x^2 - 120x - 144{,}000$

In Exercises 53–76, find the derivative of the function. Simplify your result.

53. $f(x) = x^3(5 - 3x^2)$ **54.** $y = (3x^2 + 7)(x^2 - 2x)$

55. $y = (4x - 3)(x^3 - 2x^2)$ **56.** $s = \left(4 - \dfrac{1}{t^2}\right)(t^2 - 3t)$

57. $f(x) = \dfrac{6x - 5}{x^2 + 1}$ **58.** $f(x) = \dfrac{x^2 + x - 1}{x^2 - 1}$

59. $g(t) = \dfrac{(1/t) - 2t}{t^3 - 1}$ **60.** $h(x) = \dfrac{4x^2 + \sqrt{x}}{3x^2 - 2}$

61. $f(x) = (5x^2 + 2)^3$ **62.** $f(x) = \sqrt[3]{x^2 - 1}$

63. $h(x) = \dfrac{2}{\sqrt{x + 1}}$ **64.** $g(x) = \sqrt{x^6 - 12x^3 + 9}$

65. $g(x) = x\sqrt{x^2 + 1}$ **66.** $g(t) = \dfrac{t}{(1 - t)^3}$

67. $f(t) = (t + 1)\sqrt{t^2 + 1}$ **68.** $y = 3x(x + 2)^3$

69. $f(x) = -2(1 - 4x^2)^2$ **70.** $f(x) = \left(x^2 + \dfrac{1}{x}\right)^5$

71. $h(x) = [x^2(2x + 3)]^3$

72. $f(x) = [(x - 2)(x + 4)]^2$

73. $f(x) = x^2(x - 1)^5$ **74.** $f(s) = s^3(s^2 - 1)^{5/2}$

75. $h(t) = \dfrac{\sqrt{3t + 1}}{(1 - 3t)^2}$ **76.** $g(x) = \dfrac{(3x + 1)^2}{(x^2 + 1)^2}$

77. *Refrigeration* The temperature T (in degrees Fahrenheit) of food placed in a freezer can be modeled by

$$T = \dfrac{1300}{t^2 + 2t + 25},$$

where t is the time (in hours).

(a) Find the rate of change of T when $t = 1$, $t = 3$, $t = 5$, and $t = 10$.

(b) Graph the model and describe the rate at which the temperature is changing.

78. *Forestry* According to the *Doyle Log Rule*, the volume V (in board feet) of a log of length L (feet) and diameter D (inches) at the small end is

$$V = \left(\dfrac{D - 4}{4}\right)^2 L.$$

Find the rate at which the volume is changing for a 12-foot-long log whose smallest diameter is (a) 8 inches, (b) 16 inches, (c) 24 inches, and (d) 36 inches.

In Exercises 79–86, find the indicated derivative.

79. Given $f(x) = 3x^2 + 7x + 1$, find $f''(x)$.

80. Given $f'(x) = 5x^4 - 6x^2 + 2x$, find $f'''(x)$.

81. Given $f'''(x) = -\dfrac{6}{x^4}$, find $f^{(5)}(x)$.

82. Given $f(x) = \sqrt{x}$, find $f^{(4)}(x)$.

83. Given $f'(x) = 7x^{5/2}$, find $f''(x)$.

84. Given $f(x) = x^2 + \dfrac{3}{x}$, find $f''(x)$.

85. Given $f''(x) = 6\sqrt[3]{x}$, find $f'''(x)$.

86. Given $f'''(x) = 20x^4 - \dfrac{2}{x^3}$, find $f^{(5)}(x)$.

87. *Diver* A person dives from a 30-foot platform with an initial velocity of 5 feet per second (upward).
   (a) Find the position function of the diver.
   (b) How long will it take for the diver to hit the water?
   (c) What is the diver's velocity at impact?
   (d) What is the diver's acceleration at impact?

88. *Velocity and Acceleration* The position function of a particle is given by
$$s = \frac{1}{t^2 + 2t + 1},$$
where s is the height (in feet) and t is the time (in seconds). Find the velocity and acceleration functions.

In Exercises 89–96, use implicit differentiation to find dy/dx.

89. $x^2 + 3xy + y^3 = 10$

90. $x^2 + 9y^2 - 4x + 3y - 7 = 0$

91. $y^2 - x^2 = 49$

92. $y^2 + x^2 - 6y - 2x - 5 = 0$

93. $y^2 = (x - y)(x^2 + y)$

94. $y^2 - 3 = 2\sqrt{xy}$

95. $2\sqrt[3]{x} + 3\sqrt{y} = 10$

96. $y^3 - 2x^2y + 3xy^2 = -1$

97. *Water Level* A swimming pool is 40 feet long, 20 feet wide, 4 feet deep at the shallow end, and 9 feet deep at the deep end (see figure). Water is being pumped into the pool at the rate of 10 cubic feet per minute. How fast is the water level rising when there is 4 feet of water in the deep end?

98. *Profit* The demand and cost functions for a product can be modeled by
$$p = 211 - 0.002x$$
and
$$C = 30x + 1,500,000,$$
where x is the number of units produced.
   (a) Write the profit function for this product.
   (b) Find the marginal profit when 80,000 units are produced.
   (c) Graph the profit function and use the graph to determine the price you would charge for the product. Explain your reasoning.

Sample Post-Graduation Exam Questions

The following questions were taken from certified public accountant (CPA) exams, graduate management admission tests (GMAT), graduate records exams (GRE), actuarial exams, or college-level academic skills tests (CLAST). The answers to the questions are given in the back of the book.

1. What is the length of the line segment that connects A to B (see graph)?

    (a) 2   (b) 4   (c) $2\sqrt{2}$ (d) 6   (e) $\sqrt{3}$

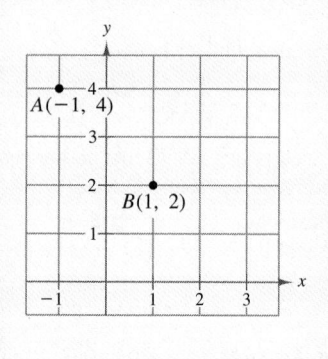

FIGURE FOR 1

For Questions 2–4, refer to the following table.

Participation in National Elections (millions of persons)

Characteristic	1984 Persons of voting age	1984 Percent voted	1988 Persons of voting age	1988 Percent voted	1992 Persons of voting age	1992 Percent voted
Total	170.0	59.9	178.1	57.4	185.7	61.3
Male	80.3	59.0	84.5	56.4	88.6	60.2
Female	89.6	60.8	93.6	58.3	97.1	62.3
Age 18 to 20	11.2	36.7	10.7	33.2	9.7	38.5
21 to 24	16.7	43.5	14.8	38.3	14.6	45.7
25 to 34	40.3	54.5	42.7	48.0	41.6	53.2
35 to 44	30.7	63.5	35.2	61.3	39.7	63.6
45 to 64	44.3	69.8	45.9	67.9	49.1	70.0
65 years and over	26.7	67.7	28.8	68.8	30.8	70.1

2. Which of the following groups had the highest percent of voters in 1992?

    (a) male   (b) age 35 to 44   (c) age 25 to 34
    (d) age 18 to 20   (e) female

3. In 1984, what percent (to the nearest percent) of persons of voting age were female?

    (a) 47   (b) 53   (c) 55   (d) 57   (e) 52

4. In 1988, how many males of voting age voted?

    (a) 47,658,000   (b) 48,503,000   (c) 102,229,400
    (d) 47,377,000   (e) 54,568,800

For Questions 5 and 6, refer to the following example.

Suppose the position s at time t of an accelerating object is given by $s(t) = t(t^2 - 2)^2$.

5. The acceleration function is

    (a) $5t^4 - 12t^2 + 4$ (b) $5t^4 - 8t$ (c) $20t^3 - 24t$
    (d) $20t^3 - 8$ (e) $t^5 - 4t^2 + 4$

6. The velocity of the object at time $t = 3$ is

    (a) 301   (b) 381   (c) 147   (d) 532   (e) 468

$$\frac{d^2y}{dx^2} < 0$$

3

Applications of the Derivative

Calculus, like most other branches of mathematics, was created as a language for modeling real life. All of the early work in calculus dealt with real-life problems such as finding the maximum distance between the earth and the sun. The applied nature of calculus was evident in one of the first comprehensive texts on the subject, published in 1748 by the Italian mathematician Maria Gaetana Agnesi (1718–1799).

Today, calculus, combined with technology, is still an important tool for solving optimization problems, such as finding the minimum cost, the maximum profit, or the minimum distance.

$$f'(x) = 0$$

Agnesi

e Bettmann Archive

Increasing and Decreasing Functions

Increasing and Decreasing Functions ■ *Critical Numbers and Their Use* ■ *Extended Application: Profit, Revenue, and Cost*

Increasing and Decreasing Functions

A function is **increasing** if its graph moves up as x moves to the right and **decreasing** if its graph moves down as x moves to the right. The following definition states this more formally.

Definition of Increasing and Decreasing Functions

A function f is **increasing** on an interval if for any x_1 and x_2 in the interval

$$x_2 > x_1 \quad \text{implies} \quad f(x_2) > f(x_1).$$

A function f is **decreasing** on an interval if for any x_1 and x_2 in the interval

$$x_2 > x_1 \quad \text{implies} \quad f(x_2) < f(x_1).$$

The function in Figure 3.1 is decreasing on the interval $(-\infty, a)$, constant on the interval (a, b), and increasing on the interval (b, ∞). Actually, from the definition of increasing and decreasing functions, the function shown in Figure 3.1 is decreasing on the interval $(-\infty, a]$ and increasing on the interval $[b, \infty)$. In this text, however, we restrict the discussion to finding *open* intervals on which a function is increasing or decreasing.

The derivative of a function can be used to determine whether the function is increasing or decreasing on an interval.

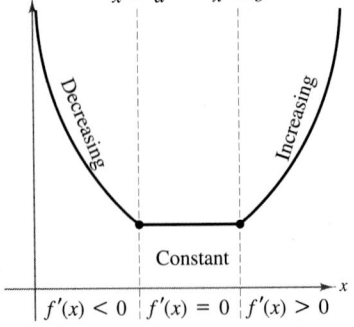

FIGURE 3.1

Test for Increasing or Decreasing Functions

Let f be differentiable on the interval (a, b).

1. If $f'(x) > 0$ for all x in (a, b), then f is increasing on (a, b).
2. If $f'(x) < 0$ for all x in (a, b), then f is decreasing on (a, b).
3. If $f'(x) = 0$ for all x in (a, b), then f is constant on (a, b).

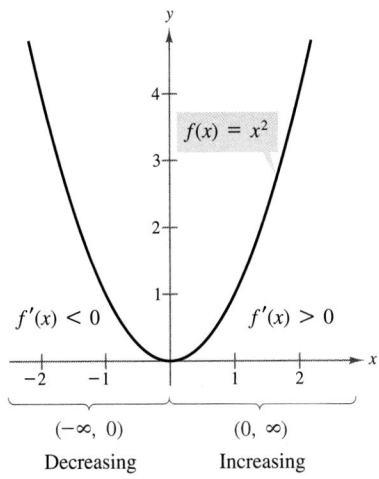

$f(x) = x^2$

$f'(x) < 0$ $f'(x) > 0$

$\underbrace{}_{\substack{(-\infty,\ 0)\\ \text{Decreasing}}}$ $\underbrace{}_{\substack{(0,\ \infty)\\ \text{Increasing}}}$

FIGURE 3.2

Discovery

Use a graphing utility to graph $f(x) = 2 - x^2$ and $f'(x) = -2x$ on the same coordinate plane. On what interval is f increasing? On what interval is f' positive? Describe how the first derivative can be used to determine where a function is increasing and decreasing. Repeat this analysis for $g(x) = x^3 - x$ and $g'(x) = 3x^2 - 1$.

EXAMPLE 1 *Testing for Increasing and Decreasing Functions*

Show that the function

$$f(x) = x^2$$

is decreasing on the open interval $(-\infty, 0)$ and increasing on the open interval $(0, \infty)$.

Solution
The derivative of f is

$$f'(x) = 2x.$$

On the open interval $(-\infty, 0)$, the fact that x is negative implies that $f'(x) = 2x$ is also negative. Hence, by the test for a decreasing function, you can conclude that f is *decreasing* on this interval. Similarly, on the open interval $(0, \infty)$, the fact that x is positive implies that $f'(x) = 2x$ is also positive. Hence, it follows that f is *increasing* on this interval, as shown in Figure 3.2.   ■

Real Life

EXAMPLE 2 *Modeling Poultry Consumption*

From 1970 through 1990, the consumption C of poultry (in boneless pounds per person per year) can be modeled by

$$C = 33.5 + 0.074t^2, \qquad 0 \le t \le 20,$$

where $t = 0$ represents 1970 (see Figure 3.3). Show that the consumption of poultry was increasing from 1970 through 1990. *(Source: U.S. Department of Agriculture)*

Solution
The derivative of this model is $dC/dt = 0.148t$. As long as t is positive, the derivative is positive. Therefore, the function is increasing, which implies that the consumption of poultry was increasing from 1970 through 1990.

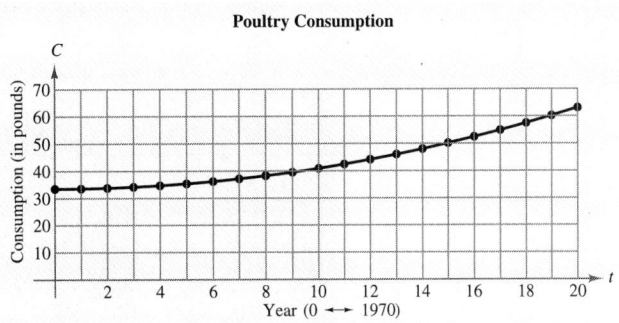

FIGURE 3.3   ■

Critical Numbers and Their Use

In Example 1, you were given two intervals—one on which the function is decreasing and one on which it is increasing. Suppose you had been asked to determine these intervals. To do this, you could have used the fact that for a continuous function, $f'(x)$ can change signs only at x-values where $f'(x) = 0$ or at x-values where $f'(x)$ is undefined, as shown in Figure 3.4. These two types of numbers are called the **critical numbers** of f.

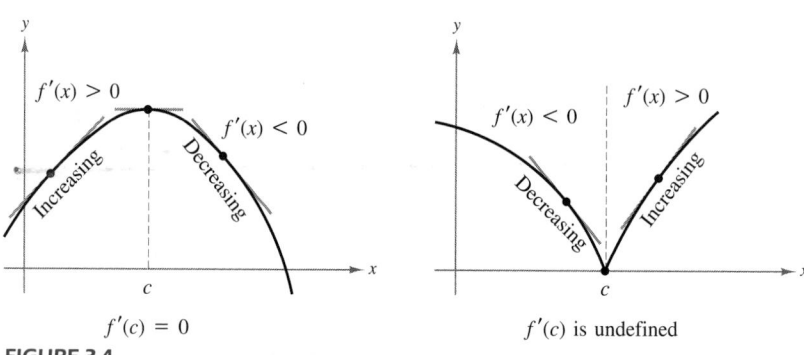

FIGURE 3.4

Note This definition requires that a critical number be in the domain of the function.

Definition of a Critical Number

If f is defined at c, then c is a critical number of f if $f'(c) = 0$ or if f' is undefined at c.

To determine the intervals on which a continuous function is increasing or decreasing, you can use the following guidelines.

Guidelines for Applying Increasing/Decreasing Test

1. Find the derivative of f.
2. Locate the critical numbers of f and use these numbers to determine test intervals. That is, find all x for which $f'(x) = 0$ or $f'(x)$ is undefined.
3. Test the sign of $f'(x)$ at an arbitrary number in each of the test intervals.
4. Use the test for increasing or decreasing functions to decide whether f is increasing or decreasing on each interval.

EXAMPLE 3 *Finding Increasing and Decreasing Intervals*

Find the open intervals on which the function

$$f(x) = x^3 - \tfrac{3}{2}x^2$$

is increasing or decreasing.

Solution

Begin by finding the derivative of f. Then set the derivative equal to zero and solve for the critical numbers.

$$f'(x) = 3x^2 - 3x \qquad \text{\textit{Differentiate original function.}}$$
$$3x^2 - 3x = 0 \qquad \text{\textit{Set derivative equal to 0.}}$$
$$3(x)(x - 1) = 0 \qquad \text{\textit{Factor.}}$$
$$x = 0, \ x = 1 \qquad \text{\textit{Critical numbers}}$$

Because there are no x-values for which f' is undefined, it follows that $x = 0$ and $x = 1$ are the *only* critical numbers. Thus, the intervals that need to be tested are $(-\infty, 0)$, $(0, 1)$, and $(1, \infty)$. Table 3.1 summarizes the testing of these three intervals.

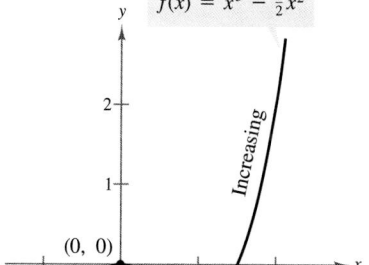

$f(x) = x^3 - \tfrac{3}{2}x^2$

(0, 0)

Increasing

Decreasing $\left(1, -\tfrac{1}{2}\right)$

Increasing

Increasing

FIGURE 3.5

TABLE 3.1

Interval	$-\infty < x < 0$	$0 < x < 1$	$1 < x < \infty$
Test value	$x = -1$	$x = \tfrac{1}{2}$	$x = 2$
Sign of $f'(x)$	$f'(-1) = 6 > 0$	$f'\left(\tfrac{1}{2}\right) = -\tfrac{3}{4} < 0$	$f'(2) = 6 > 0$
Conclusion	Increasing	Decreasing	Increasing

The graph of f is shown in Figure 3.5. Note that the test values in the intervals were chosen for convenience—other x-values could have been used. ■

▣ TECHNOLOGY

You can use the trace feature of a graphing utility to confirm the result of Example 3. Begin by graphing the function, as shown at the right. Then activate the trace feature and move the cursor from left to right. In intervals in which the function is increasing, note that the y-values increase as the x-values increase, whereas in intervals in which the function is decreasing, the y-values decrease as the x-values increase.

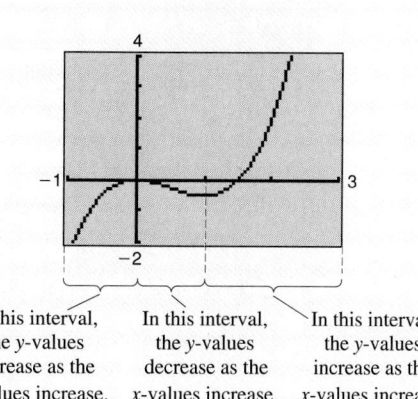

In this interval, the y-values increase as the x-values increase.

In this interval, the y-values decrease as the x-values increase.

In this interval, the y-values increase as the x-values increase.

Not only is the function in Example 3 continuous on the entire real line, it is also differentiable there. For such functions, the only critical numbers are those for which $f'(x) = 0$. The next example considers a continuous function that has *both* types of critical numbers—those for which $f'(x) = 0$ and those for which f' is undefined.

EXAMPLE 4 *Finding Increasing and Decreasing Intervals*

Find the open intervals on which the function

$$f(x) = (x^2 - 4)^{2/3}$$

is increasing or decreasing.

Solution
Begin by finding the derivative of the function.

$$f'(x) = \frac{2}{3}(x^2 - 4)^{-1/3}(2x) \qquad\qquad \textit{Differentiate.}$$

$$= \frac{4x}{3(x^2 - 4)^{1/3}} \qquad\qquad \textit{Simplify.}$$

From this, you can see that the derivative is zero when $x = 0$ and the derivative is undefined when $x = \pm 2$. Thus, the critical numbers are

$$x = -2, \quad x = 0, \quad \text{and} \quad x = 2. \qquad \textit{Critical numbers}$$

This implies that the test intervals are

$$(-\infty, -2), \quad (-2, 0), \quad (0, 2), \quad \text{and} \quad (2, \infty). \quad \textit{Test intervals}$$

Table 3.2 summarizes the testing of these four intervals, and the graph of the function is shown in Figure 3.6.

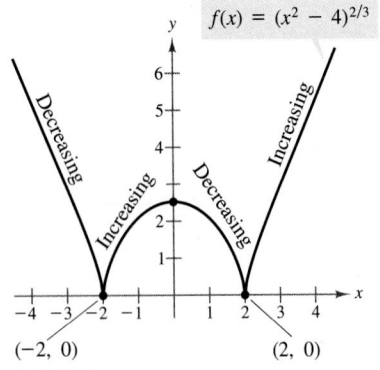

$f(x) = (x^2 - 4)^{2/3}$

Decreasing · Increasing · Decreasing · Increasing

$(-2, 0)$ $(2, 0)$

FIGURE 3.6

TABLE 3.2

Interval	$-\infty < x < -2$	$-2 < x < 0$	$0 < x < 2$	$2 < x < \infty$
Test value	$x = -3$	$x = -1$	$x = 1$	$x = 3$
Sign of $f'(x)$	$f'(-3) < 0$	$f'(-1) > 0$	$f'(1) < 0$	$f'(3) > 0$
Conclusion	Decreasing	Increasing	Decreasing	Increasing

Note In Table 3.2, it is not necessary to *evaluate* $f'(x)$ at the test values— you need only to determine its sign. For example, you can determine the sign of $f'(-3)$ as follows.

$$f'(-3) = \frac{4(-3)}{3(9 - 4)^{1/3}} = \frac{\text{negative}}{\text{positive}} = \text{negative}$$

The functions in Examples 1–4 are continuous on the entire real line. If there are isolated x-values at which a function is not continuous, then these x-values should be used along with the critical numbers to determine the test intervals. For example, the function

$$f(x) = \frac{x^4 + 1}{x^2}$$

is not continuous when $x = 0$. Because the derivative of f,

$$f'(x) = \frac{2(x^4 - 1)}{x^3},$$

is zero when $x = \pm 1$, you should use the following numbers to determine the test intervals.

$$x = -1, \ x = 1 \qquad\qquad \textit{Critical numbers}$$
$$x = 0 \qquad\qquad\qquad \textit{Discontinuity}$$

After testing $f'(x)$, you can determine that the function is decreasing on the intervals $(-\infty, -1)$ and $(0, 1)$, and increasing on the intervals $(-1, 0)$ and $(1, \infty)$, as shown in Figure 3.7.

The converse of the test for increasing and decreasing functions is *not* true. For instance, it is possible for a function to be increasing on an interval even though its derivative is not positive at every point in the interval.

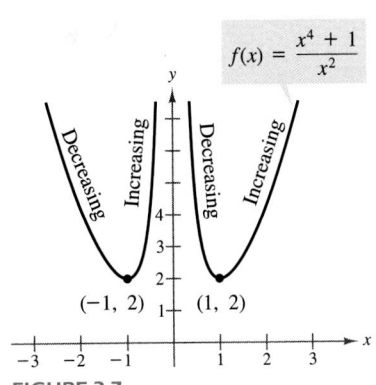

FIGURE 3.7

EXAMPLE 5 *Testing an Increasing Function*

Show that $f(x) = x^3 - 3x^2 + 3x$ is increasing on the entire real line.

Solution

From the derivative of f,

$$f'(x) = 3x^2 - 6x + 3 = 3(x - 1)^2,$$

you can see that the only critical number is $x = 1$. Thus, the test intervals are $(-\infty, 1)$ and $(1, \infty)$. Table 3.3 summarizes the testing of these two intervals. From Figure 3.8, you can see that f is increasing on the entire real line—even though $f'(1) = 0$. To convince yourself of this, look back at the definition of an increasing function.

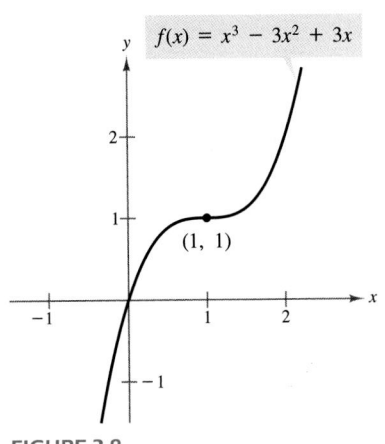

FIGURE 3.8

TABLE 3.3

Interval	$-\infty < x < 1$	$1 < x < \infty$
Test value	$x = 0$	$x = 2$
Sign of $f'(x)$	$f'(0) = 3(-1)^2 > 0$	$f'(2) = 3(2)^2 > 0$
Conclusion	Increasing	Increasing

Extended Application: Profit, Revenue, and Cost

Real Life

EXAMPLE 6 *Profit Analysis*

A national toy distributor determines the following cost and revenue models for one of its games.

$$C = 2.4x - 0.0002x^2, \qquad 0 \le x \le 6000$$
$$R = 7.2x - 0.001x^2, \qquad 0 \le x \le 6000$$

Determine the interval on which the profit function is increasing.

Solution

The profit for producing x units is

$$P = R - C$$
$$= (7.2x - 0.001x^2) - (2.4x - 0.0002x^2)$$
$$= 4.8x - 0.0008x^2.$$

To find the interval on which the profit is increasing, set the marginal profit P' equal to zero and solve for x.

$$P' = 4.8 - 0.0016x \qquad \text{\textit{Differentiate profit function.}}$$
$$4.8 - 0.0016x = 0 \qquad \text{\textit{Set } P' \text{ \textit{equal to} 0.}}$$
$$-0.0016x = -4.8 \qquad \text{\textit{Subtract 4.8 from both sides.}}$$
$$x = \frac{-4.8}{-0.0016} \qquad \text{\textit{Divide both sides by} } -0.0016.$$
$$x = 3000 \text{ units} \qquad \text{\textit{Simplify.}}$$

In the interval $(0, 3000)$, P' is positive and the profit is *increasing*. In the interval $(3000, 6000)$, P' is negative and the profit is *decreasing*. The graphs of the cost, revenue, and profit functions are shown in Figure 3.9.

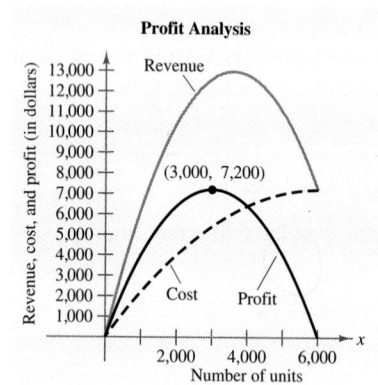

Profit Analysis

Revenue, cost, and profit (in dollars)

(3,000, 7,200)

Revenue

Cost   Profit

Number of units

FIGURE 3.9

Discussion Problem Comparing Cost, Revenue, and Profit

Use the models given in Example 6 to answer the following questions.

1. What is the demand function for the product described in the example?
2. What price would you set to obtain a maximum profit?
3. What price would you set to obtain a maximum revenue?
4. Why doesn't the maximum revenue occur at the same x-value as the maximum profit?

Warm Up

The following warm-up exercises involve skills that were covered in earlier sections. You will use these skills in the exercise set for this section.

In Exercises 1–4, solve the equation.

1. $x^2 = 8x$ **2.** $15x = \dfrac{5}{8}x^2$ **3.** $\dfrac{x^2 - 25}{x^3} = 0$ **4.** $\dfrac{2x}{\sqrt{1 - x^2}} = 0$

In Exercises 5–8, find the domain of the expression.

5. $\dfrac{x + 3}{x - 3}$ **6.** $\dfrac{2}{\sqrt{1 - x}}$ **7.** $\dfrac{2x + 1}{x^2 - 3x - 10}$ **8.** $\dfrac{3x}{\sqrt{9 - 3x^2}}$

In Exercises 9 and 10, evaluate the expression when $x = -2$, 0, and 2.

9. $\dfrac{4}{3}x^3 - 6x^2 + \dfrac{1}{3}$ **10.** $\dfrac{2x - 3}{x^2 - 3x - 1}$

EXERCISES 3.1

means that technology can help you solve or check the exercise(s).

In Exercises 1–4, evaluate the derivative of the function at the indicated points on the graph.

1. $f(x) = \dfrac{x^2}{x^2 + 4}$

2. $f(x) = x + \dfrac{32}{x^2}$

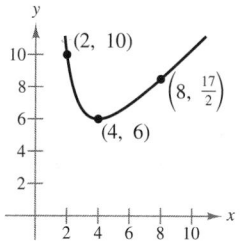

3. $f(x) = (x + 2)^{2/3}$

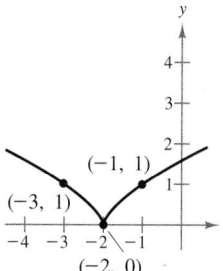

4. $f(x) = -3x\sqrt{x + 1}$

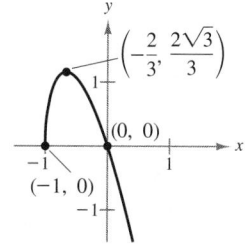

In Exercises 5–8, identify the open intervals on which the function is increasing or decreasing.

5. $f(x) = -(x + 1)^2$

6. $f(x) = \dfrac{x^3}{4} - 3x$

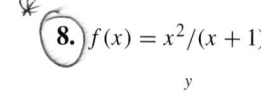

7. $f(x) = x^4 - 2x^2$

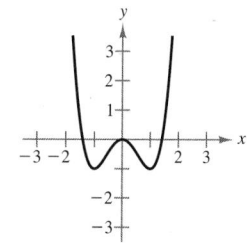

8. $f(x) = x^2/(x + 1)$

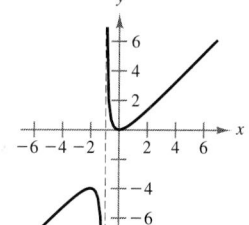

In Exercises 9–18, find the critical numbers and the open intervals on which the function is increasing or decreasing. Sketch the graph of the function.

9. $f(x) = 2x - 3$

10. $f(x) = 5 - 3x$

11. $g(x) = -(x-1)^2$

12. $g(x) = (x+2)^2$

13. $y = x^2 - 5x$

14. $y = -(x^2 - 2x)$

15. $y = x^3 - 6x^2$

16. $y = (x-2)^3$

17. $f(x) = -(x+1)^3$

18. $f(x) = \sqrt{4 - x^2}$

In Exercises 19–30, find the critical numbers and the open intervals on which the function is increasing or decreasing.

19. $f(x) = -2x^2 + 4x + 3$

20. $f(x) = x^2 + 8x + 10$

21. $y = 3x^3 + 12x^2 + 15x$

22. $y = (x-1)^2(x+2)$

23. $h(x) = x^{2/3}$

24. $h(x) = \sqrt[3]{x-1}$

25. $f(x) = x^4 - 2x^3$

26. $f(x) = x\sqrt{x+1}$

27. $f(x) = 2x\sqrt{3-x}$

28. $f(x) = 2(x+2)\sqrt{1-x}$

29. $f(x) = \dfrac{x}{x^2+4}$

30. $f(x) = \dfrac{x^2}{x^2+4}$

In Exercises 31–36, find the critical numbers and the open intervals on which the function is increasing or decreasing. (*Hint:* Check for discontinuities.)

31. $f(x) = x + \dfrac{1}{x}$

32. $f(x) = \dfrac{x}{x+1}$

33. $f(x) = \dfrac{2x}{16 - x^2}$

34. $y = \begin{cases} 2x+1, & x \le -1 \\ x^2 - 2, & x > -1 \end{cases}$

35. $y = \begin{cases} 4 - x^2, & x \le 0 \\ -2x, & x > 0 \end{cases}$

36. $y = \begin{cases} -x^3 + 1, & x \le 0 \\ -x^2 + 2x, & x > 0 \end{cases}$

37. *Ordering and Transportation Cost* The ordering and transportation cost C (in hundreds of dollars) for an automobile dealership is

$$C = 10\left(\dfrac{1}{x} + \dfrac{x}{x+3}\right), \qquad 1 \le x,$$

where x is the number of automobiles ordered.

(a) Find the intervals on which C is increasing or decreasing.

(b) Use a graphing utility to graph the cost function.

(c) Use the trace feature to determine the order sizes for which the cost is $900. Assuming that the revenue function is increasing for $x \ge 0$, which order size would you use? Explain your reasoning.

38. *Drug Concentration* A drug is administered to a patient. A model giving the drug concentration C (in milligrams per milliliter) in the patient's bloodstream over a 2-hour period is

$$C = 0.29483t + 0.04253t^2 - 0.00035t^3, \qquad 0 \le t \le 120,$$

where t is the time (in minutes).

(a) Find the intervals on which C is increasing or decreasing.

(b) Use a graphing utility to graph the function.

(c) Explain how to use the test for increasing and decreasing functions to determine that the concentration will never reach 120 milligrams.

Position Function In Exercises 39 and 40, the position function gives the height s (in feet) of a ball, where the time t is measured in seconds. Find the time interval in which the ball is rising and the interval in which it is falling.

39. $s = 96t - 16t^2, \qquad 0 \le t \le 6$

40. $s = -16t^2 + 64t, \qquad 0 \le t \le 4$

41. *Bankers* The number y (in thousands) of people employed in banking and financing can be modeled by

$$y = -1.27t^3 + 6.63t^{5/2} + 1706.88, \qquad 0 \le t \le 21,$$

where $t = 0$ corresponds to 1970. (*Source: U.S. Bureau of Labor Statistics*)

(a) Use a graphing utility to graph the model. Then graphically estimate the years during which the model is increasing and the years during which it is decreasing.

(b) Use the test for increasing and decreasing functions to verify the result of part (a).

42. *Profit* The profit P made by a cinema for selling x bags of popcorn can be modeled by

$$P = 2.36x - \dfrac{x^2}{25,000} - 3500, \qquad 0 \le x \le 50,000.$$

(a) Find the intervals on which P is increasing or decreasing.

(b) If you owned the cinema, what price would you charge to obtain a maximum profit for popcorn? Explain.

In Exercises 43 and 44, use a graphing utility to (a) sketch the graphs of f and f' on the same viewing rectangle, (b) find the critical numbers of f, and (c) find the intervals on which f' is positive and on which it is negative. Describe the behavior of f relative to the sign of f'.

Function	Interval
43. $f(x) = 2x\sqrt{9 - x^2}$	$[-3, 3]$
44. $f(x) = 10\left(5 - \sqrt{x^2 - 3x + 16}\right)$	$[0, 5]$

Extrema and the First-Derivative Test

Relative Extrema ■ *The First-Derivative Test* ■ *Absolute Extrema* ■ *Applications of Extrema*

Relative Extrema

In the preceding section, you used the derivative to determine the intervals on which a function is increasing or decreasing. In this section, you will examine the points at which a function changes from increasing to decreasing, or vice versa. At such a point, the function has a **relative extremum.** (The plural of extremum is *extrema.*) The **relative extrema** of a function include the **relative minima** and **relative maxima** of the function. For instance, the function shown in Figure 3.10 has two relative extrema—the left point is a relative maximum and the right point is a relative minimum.

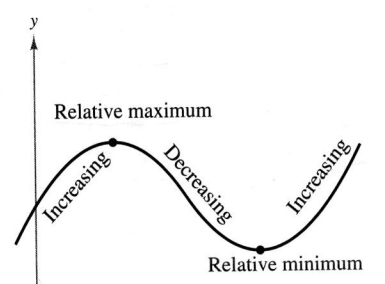

FIGURE 3.10

Definition of Relative Extrema

Let f be a function defined at c.

1. $f(c)$ is a **relative maximum** of f if there exists an interval (a, b) containing c such that $f(x) \le f(c)$ for all x in (a, b).
2. $f(c)$ is a **relative minimum** of f if there exists an interval (a, b) containing c such that $f(x) \ge f(c)$ for all x in (a, b).

If $f(c)$ is a relative extremum of f, then the relative extremum is said to *occur* at $x = c$.

For a continuous function, the relative extrema must occur at critical numbers of the function, as shown in Figure 3.11.

Occurrence of Relative Extrema

If f has a relative minimum or relative maximum when $x = c$, then c is a critical number of f. That is, either

$$f'(c) = 0 \quad \text{or} \quad f'(c) \text{ is undefined.}$$

FIGURE 3.11

The First-Derivative Test

The result on the previous page implies that in your search for relative extrema of a continuous function, you need only test the critical numbers of the function. Once you have determined that c is a critical number of a function f, the **First-Derivative Test** for relative extrema enables you to classify $f(c)$ as a relative minimum, a relative maximum, or neither.

First-Derivative Test for Relative Extrema

Let f be continuous on the interval (a, b) in which c is the only critical number. If f is differentiable on the interval (except possibly at c), then $f(c)$ can be classified as a relative minimum, a relative maximum, or neither, as follows.

1. In the interval (a, b), if $f'(x)$ is negative to the left of $x = c$ and positive to the right of $x = c$, then $f(c)$ is a relative minimum.
2. In the interval (a, b), if $f'(x)$ is positive to the left of $x = c$ and negative to the right of $x = c$, then $f(c)$ is a relative maximum.
3. In the interval (a, b), if $f'(x)$ has the same sign to the left and right of $x = c$, then $f(c)$ is not a relative extremum of f.

A graphical interpretation of the First-Derivative Test is shown below in Figure 3.12.

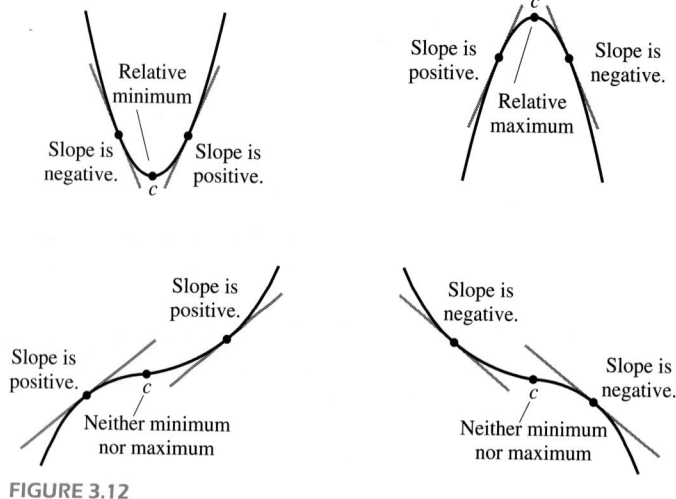

FIGURE 3.12

EXAMPLE 1   *Finding Relative Extrema*

Find all relative extrema of the function

$$f(x) = 2x^3 - 3x^2 - 36x + 14.$$

Solution

Begin by finding the critical numbers of f.

$$f'(x) = 6x^2 - 6x - 36 \qquad \text{\textit{Find derivative of } f.}$$
$$6x^2 - 6x - 36 = 0 \qquad \text{\textit{Set derivative equal to} 0.}$$
$$6(x^2 - x - 6) = 0 \qquad \text{\textit{Factor out common factor.}}$$
$$6(x - 3)(x + 2) = 0 \qquad \text{\textit{Factor.}}$$
$$x = -2, \ 3 \qquad \text{\textit{Critical numbers}}$$

Because $f'(x)$ is defined for all x, the only critical numbers of f are $x = -2$ and $x = 3$. Using these numbers, you can form the three test intervals $(-\infty, -2)$, $(-2, 3)$, and $(3, \infty)$. The testing of the three intervals is shown in Table 3.4.

TABLE 3.4

Interval	$-\infty < x < -2$	$-2 < x < 3$	$3 < x < \infty$
Test value	$x = -3$	$x = 0$	$x = 4$
Sign of $f'(x)$	$f'(-3) = 36 > 0$	$f'(0) = -36 < 0$	$f'(4) = 36 > 0$
Conclusion	Increasing	Decreasing	Increasing

Using the First-Derivative Test, you can conclude that the critical number -2 yields a relative maximum [$f'(x)$ changes sign from positive to negative], and the critical number 3 yields a relative minimum [$f'(x)$ changes sign from negative to positive].

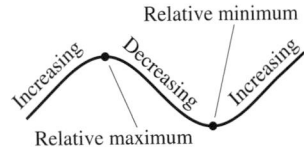

The graph of f is shown in Figure 3.13. To find the y-coordinates of the relative extrema, substitute the x-coordinates into the function. For instance, the relative maximum is $f(-2) = 58$ and the relative minimum is $f(3) = -67$.

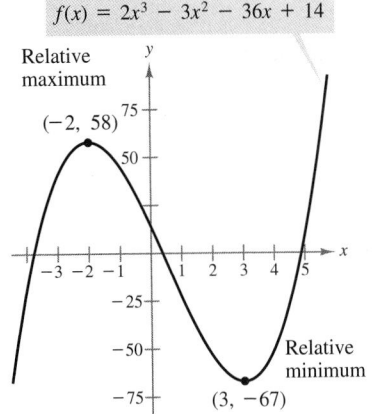

$f(x) = 2x^3 - 3x^2 - 36x + 14$

Relative maximum

$(-2, 58)$

Relative minimum

$(3, -67)$

FIGURE 3.13

Note   In Section 2.2, Example 8, you examined the graph of the function $f(x) = x^3 - 4x + 2$ and discovered that it does *not* have a relative minimum at the point $(1, -1)$. Try using the First-Derivative Test to find the point at which the graph *does* have a relative minimum.

In Example 1, both critical numbers yielded relative extrema. In the next example, only one of the two critical numbers yields a relative extremum.

EXAMPLE 2 *Finding Relative Extrema*

Find all relative extrema of the function

$$f(x) = x^4 - x^3.$$

Solution

From the derivative of the function,

$$f'(x) = 4x^3 - 3x^2 = x^2(4x - 3),$$

you can see that the function has only two critical numbers: $x = 0$ and $x = \frac{3}{4}$. These numbers produce the test intervals $(-\infty, 0)$, $\left(0, \frac{3}{4}\right)$, and $\left(\frac{3}{4}, \infty\right)$, which are tested in Table 3.5.

TABLE 3.5

Interval	$-\infty < x < 0$	$0 < x < \frac{3}{4}$	$\frac{3}{4} < x < \infty$
Test value	$x = -1$	$x = \frac{1}{2}$	$x = 1$
Sign of $f'(x)$	$f'(-1) = -7 < 0$	$f'\left(\frac{1}{2}\right) = -\frac{1}{4} < 0$	$f'(1) = 1 > 0$
Conclusion	Decreasing	Decreasing	Increasing

By the First-Derivative Test, it follows that f has a relative minimum when $x = \frac{3}{4}$, as shown in Figure 3.14. Note that the critical number $x = 0$ does not yield a relative extremum.

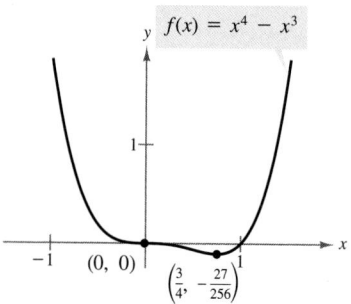

$f(x) = x^4 - x^3$

$(0, 0)$

$\left(\frac{3}{4}, -\frac{27}{256}\right)$

Relative minimum

FIGURE 3.14

EXAMPLE 3 *Finding Relative Extrema*

Find all relative extrema of the function

$$f(x) = 2x - 3x^{2/3}.$$

Solution

From the derivative of the function,

$$f'(x) = 2 - \frac{2}{x^{1/3}} = \frac{2(x^{1/3} - 1)}{x^{1/3}},$$

you can see that $f'(1) = 0$ and f' is undefined at $x = 0$. Therefore, the function has two critical numbers: $x = 1$ and $x = 0$. These numbers produce the test intervals

$$(-\infty, 0), \quad (0, 1), \quad \text{and} \quad (1, \infty).$$

By testing these intervals, you can conclude that f has a relative maximum at $(0, 0)$ and a relative minimum at $(1, -1)$, as shown in Figure 3.15.

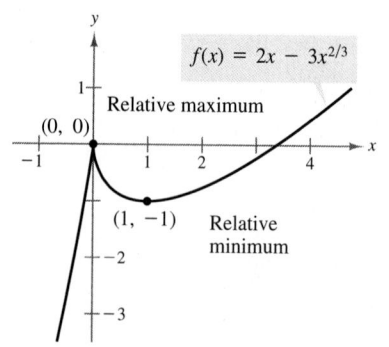

$f(x) = 2x - 3x^{2/3}$

Relative maximum

$(0, 0)$

$(1, -1)$ Relative minimum

FIGURE 3.15

TECHNOLOGY

Finding Relative Extrema

There are several ways to use technology to find relative extrema of a function. One way is to use a graphing utility to graph the function, and then use the zoom and trace features to find the relative minimum and relative maximum points. For instance, consider the graph of $f(x) = 3.1x^3 - 7.3x^2 + 1.2x + 2.5$, as shown at the left. From the graph, you can see that the function has one relative maximum and one relative minimum. You can approximate the coordinates of these points by zooming in and using the trace feature, as shown below.

A second way to use technology to find relative extrema is to perform the First-Derivative Test with a symbolic differentiation utility. For instance, you can use *Derive* to differentiate the function, set the derivative equal to zero, and solve the resulting equation. After obtaining the critical numbers, 0.087015 and 1.482878, you can graph the function and observe that the first yields a relative maximum and the second yields a relative minimum.

1: $3.1x^3 - 7.3x^2 + 1.2x + 2.5$		*Author.*
2: $\dfrac{d}{dx}(3.1x^3 - 7.3x^2 + 1.2x + 2.5)$		*Differentiate.*
3: $\dfrac{93x^2}{10} - \dfrac{73x}{5} + \dfrac{6}{5}$		*Simplify.*
4: $x = \dfrac{73}{93} - \dfrac{\sqrt{4213}}{93}$		*Solve(1st solution).*
5: $x = \dfrac{\sqrt{4213}}{93} + \dfrac{73}{93}$		*Solve(2nd solution).*
6: $x = 0.0870148$		*Approximate(1st solution).*
7: $x = 1.48287$		*Approximate(2nd solution).*

Absolute Extrema

The terms *relative minimum* and *relative maximum* describe the *local* behavior of a function. To describe the *global* behavior of the function on an entire interval, you can use the terms **absolute maximum** and **absolute minimum.**

Definition of Absolute Extrema

Let f be defined on an interval I containing c.

1. $f(c)$ is an **absolute minimum of** f on I if $f(c) \le f(x)$ for every x in I.
2. $f(c)$ is an **absolute maximum of** f on I if $f(c) \ge f(x)$ for every x in I.

The absolute minimum and absolute maximum values of a function on an interval are sometimes simply called the **minimum** and **maximum** of f on I.

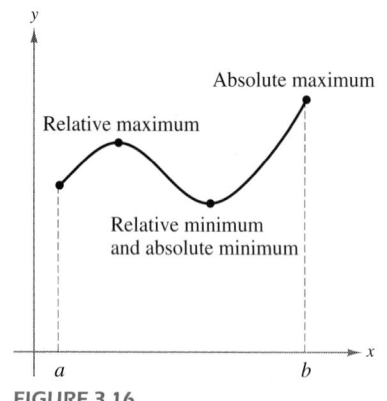

FIGURE 3.16

Be sure that you understand the distinction between relative extrema and absolute extrema. For instance, in Figure 3.16, the function has a relative minimum that also happens to be an absolute minimum on the interval $[a, b]$. The relative maximum of f, however, is not the absolute maximum on the interval $[a, b]$. The next theorem points out that if a continuous function has a closed interval as its domain, then it *must* have both an absolute minimum and an absolute maximum on the interval. From Figure 3.16, note that these can occur at an endpoint of the interval.

Extreme Value Theorem

If f is continuous on $[a, b]$, then f takes on both a minimum value and a maximum value on $[a, b]$.

Although a continuous function has just one minimum and one maximum value on a closed interval, either of these values can occur for more than one x-value. For instance, on the interval $[-3, 3]$, the function

$$f(x) = 9 - x^2$$

has a minimum value of zero when $x = -3$ *and* when $x = 3$, as shown in Figure 3.17.

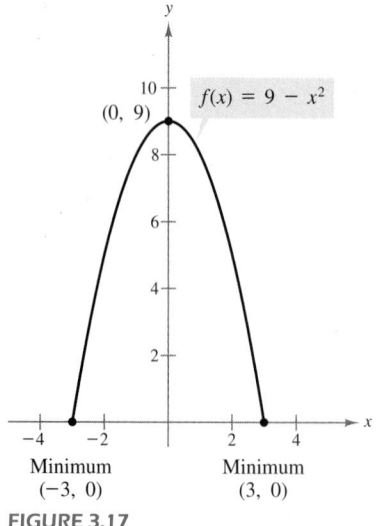

FIGURE 3.17

When looking for the extreme values of a function on a *closed* interval, remember that you must consider the values of the function at the endpoints as well as at the critical numbers of the function. You can use the following guidelines to find extrema on a closed interval.

Guidelines for Finding Extrema on a Closed Interval

To find the extrema of a continuous function f on a closed interval $[a, b]$, use the following steps.

1. Evaluate f at each of its critical numbers in (a, b).
2. Evaluate f at each endpoint, a and b.
3. The least of these values is the minimum, and the greatest is the maximum.

EXAMPLE 4   *Finding Extrema on a Closed Interval*

Find the minimum and maximum values of

$$f(x) = x^2 - 6x + 2$$

on the interval $[0, 5]$.

Solution

Begin by finding the critical numbers of the function.

$f'(x) = 2x - 6$	*Find derivative of f.*
$2x - 6 = 0$	*Set derivative equal to 0.*
$2x = 6$	*Add 6 to both sides.*
$x = 3$	*Solve for x.*

From this, you can see that the only critical number of f is $x = 3$. Because this number lies in the interval under question, you should test the values of $f(x)$ at this number *and* at the endpoints of the interval, as shown in Table 3.6.

TABLE 3.6

x-value	Endpoint: $x = 0$	Critical number: $x = 3$	Endpoint: $x = 5$
$f(x)$	$f(0) = 2$	$f(3) = -7$	$f(5) = -3$
Conclusion	Maximum	Minimum	

From the table, you can see that the minimum of f on the interval $[0, 5]$ is $f(3) = -7$. Moreover, the maximum of f on the interval $[0, 5]$ is $f(0) = 2$. This is confirmed by the graph of f, as shown in Figure 3.18. ■

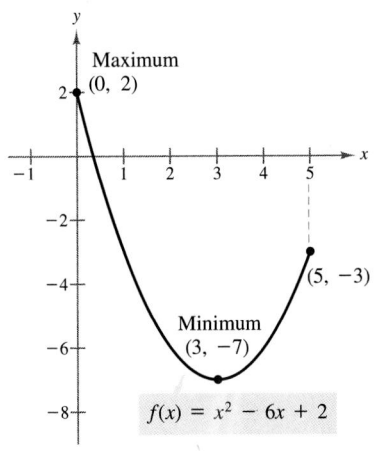

FIGURE 3.18

Applications of Extrema

Finding the minimum and maximum values of a function is one of the most common applications of calculus.

Real Life

EXAMPLE 5 *Finding the Maximum Profit*

In Examples 7 and 8 in Section 2.3, we discussed a fast-food restaurant whose profit function for hamburgers is

$$P = 2.44x - \frac{x^2}{20,000} - 5000, \qquad 0 \le x \le 50,000.$$

Find the production level that produces a maximum profit.

Solution

Begin by setting the marginal profit equal to zero and solving for x.

$$P' = 2.44 - \frac{x}{10,000} \qquad \text{\textit{Find marginal profit.}}$$

$$2.44 - \frac{x}{10,000} = 0 \qquad \text{\textit{Set marginal profit equal to 0.}}$$

$$-\frac{x}{10,000} = -2.44 \qquad \text{\textit{Subtract 2.44 from both sides.}}$$

$$x = 24,400 \text{ units} \qquad \text{\textit{Critical number}}$$

From Figure 3.19, you can see that the critical number $x = 24,400$ corresponds to the production level that produces a maximum profit. To find the maximum profit, substitute $x = 24,400$ into the profit function.

$$P = 2.44x - \frac{x^2}{20,000} - 5000$$

$$= 2.44(24,400) - \frac{(24,400)^2}{20,000} - 5000$$

$$= \$24,768$$

Maximum Profit

$P = 2.44x - \dfrac{x^2}{20,000} - 5,000$

Profit (in dollars)

Number of units

FIGURE 3.19

Discussion Problem **Setting the Price of a Product**

In Example 5, we discovered that a production level of 24,400 units corresponds to a maximum profit. Remember that this model assumes that the quantity demanded and the price per unit are related by a demand function. Thus, the only way to sell more hamburgers is to lower the price, and consequently lower the profit. What is the demand function for Example 5? What is the price per unit that produces a maximum profit?

$\mathcal{W}arm\ \mathcal{U}p$

The following warm-up exercises involve skills that were covered in earlier sections. You will use these skills in the exercise set for this section.

In Exercises 1–4, solve the equation $f'(x) = 0$.

1. $f(x) = 4x^4 - 2x^2 + 1$

2. $f(x) = \frac{1}{3}x^3 - \frac{3}{2}x^2 - 10x$

3. $f(x) = 5x^{4/5} - 4x$

4. $f(x) = \frac{1}{2}x^2 - 3x^{5/3}$

In Exercises 5–8, use $g(x) = -x^5 - 2x^4 + 4x^3 + 2x - 1$ to determine the sign of the derivative.

5. $g'(-4)$

6. $g'(0)$

7. $g'(1)$

8. $g'(3)$

In Exercises 9 and 10, decide whether the function is increasing or decreasing on the given interval.

9. $f(x) = 2x^2 - 11x - 6$, $(3, 6)$

10. $f(x) = x^3 + 2x^2 - 4x - 8$, $(-2, 0)$

EXERCISES 3.2   means that technology can help you solve or check the exercise(s).

In Exercises 1–4, use a table similar to that in Example 1 to find all relative extrema of the function.

1. $f(x) = -2x^2 + 4x + 3$

2. $f(x) = x^2 + 8x + 10$

3. $f(x) = x^2 - 6x$

4. $f(x) = (x-1)^2(x+2)$

In Exercises 5–20, find all relative extrema of the function.

5. $g(x) = 6x^3 - 15x^2 + 12x$

6. $g(x) = \frac{1}{5}(x^5 - 5x)$

7. $h(x) = -(x+4)^3$

8. $h(x) = (x-3)^3$

9. $f(x) = x^3 - 6x^2 + 15$

10. $f(x) = x^4 - 1$

11. $f(x) = x^4 - 2x^3$

12. $f(x) = x^4 - 32x + 4$

13. $f(x) = x^{1/5} + 2$

14. $f(t) = (t-1)^{1/3}$

15. $g(t) = t^{2/3}$

16. $h(t) = (t-1)^{2/3}$

17. $f(x) = x + \frac{1}{x}$

18. $f(x) = \frac{x}{x+1}$

19. $h(x) = \frac{4}{x^2+1}$

20. $g(x) = 4\left(1 + \frac{1}{x} + \frac{1}{x^2}\right)$

In Exercises 21–30, find the absolute extrema of the function on the closed interval.

Function	Interval
21. $f(x) = 2(3 - x)$	$[-1, 2]$
22. $f(x) = \frac{1}{3}(2x + 5)$	$[0, 5]$
23. $f(x) = 5 - 2x^2$	$[0, 3]$
24. $f(x) = x^2 + 2x - 4$	$[-1, 1]$
25. $f(x) = x^3 - 3x^2$	$[-1, 3]$
26. $f(x) = x^3 - 12x$	$[0, 4]$
27. $f(x) = 3x^{2/3} - 2x$	$[-1, 2]$
28. $g(t) = \frac{t^2}{t^2 + 3}$	$[-1, 1]$
29. $h(s) = \frac{1}{3 - s}$	$[0, 2]$
30. $h(t) = \frac{t}{t - 2}$	$[3, 5]$

In Exercises 31–34, use a graphing utility to graphically find the absolute extrema of the function on the closed interval.

Function	Interval
31. $f(x) = 0.4x^3 - 1.8x^2 + x - 3$	$[0, 5]$
32. $f(x) = \frac{4}{3}x\sqrt{3-x}$	$[0, 3]$
33. $f(x) = 3.2x^5 + 5x^3 - 3.5x$	$[0, 1]$
34. $f(x) = 4\sqrt{x} - 2x + 1$	$[0, 6]$

In Exercises 35–38, find the absolute extrema of the function on the interval $[0, \infty)$.

35. $f(x) = \dfrac{4x}{x^2 + 1}$

36. $f(x) = \dfrac{8}{x+1}$

37. $f(x) = 3 - \dfrac{2}{x^2 - 4x + 5}$ *How would I know if it was A min or A max?!*

38. $f(x) = \dfrac{4}{(x-1)^2 + 1}$

In Exercises 39 and 40, find the maximum value of $|f''(x)|$ on the closed interval. (You will use this skill in Section 6.5 to estimate the error in the Trapezoidal Rule.)

Function	Interval
39. $f(x) = x^3(3x^2 - 10)$	$[0, 1]$
40. $f(x) = \dfrac{1}{x^2 + 1}$	$[0, 3]$

In Exercises 41 and 42, find the maximum value of $|f^{(4)}(x)|$ on the closed interval. (You will use this skill in Section 6.5 to estimate the error in Simpson's Rule.)

Function	Interval
41. $f(x) = 15x^4 - \left(\dfrac{2x-1}{2}\right)^6$	$[0, 1]$
42. $f(x) = \dfrac{1}{x^2}$	$[1, 2]$

43. *Cost* A retailer has determined the cost C for ordering and storing x units of a product to be

$$C = 3x + \frac{20{,}000}{x}, \qquad 0 < x \le 200.$$

The delivery truck can bring at most 200 units per order. Find the order size that will minimize the cost.

44. *Profit* The quantity demanded x for a product is inversely proportional to the cube of the price p for $p > 1$. When the price is $10 per unit, the quantity demanded is eight units. The initial cost is $100 and the cost per unit is $4. What price will yield a maximum profit?

45. *Profit* When soft drinks sold for $0.80 per can at football games, approximately 6000 cans were sold. When the price was raised to $1.00 per can, the quantity demanded dropped to 5600. The initial cost is $5000 and the cost per unit is $0.40. Assuming that the demand function is linear, what price will yield a maximum profit?

46. *Trachea Contraction* Coughing forces the trachea (windpipe) to contract, which in turn affects the velocity of the air through the trachea. The velocity of the air during coughing can be modeled by

$$v = k(R - r)r^2, \qquad 0 \le r < R,$$

where k is a constant, R is the normal radius of the trachea, and r is the radius during coughing. What radius r will produce the maximum air velocity?

47. *Demographics* From 1940 to 1991, the number r of males to 100 females in the United States can be modeled by

$$r = 0.000045t^3 - 0.2295t + 100.84,$$

where $t = 0$ corresponds to 1940. *(Source: U.S. Bureau of the Census)* Determine the year in which the number r was a minimum. In that year, were there more females or more males in the population? Explain.

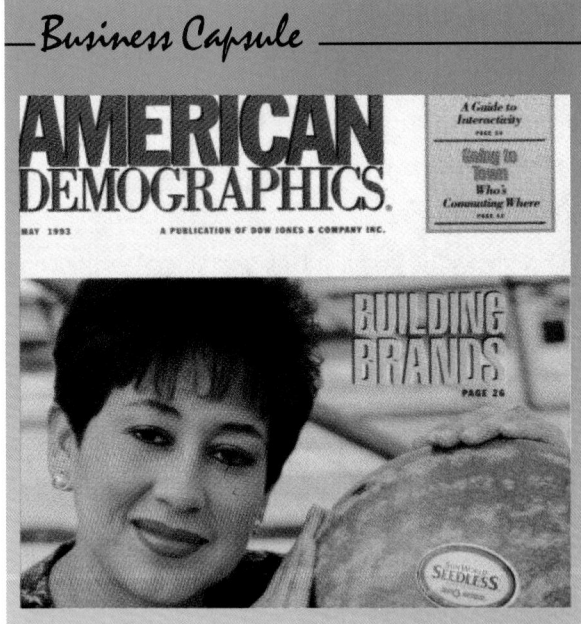

— *Business Capsule* —

Courtesy of *American Demographics*

American Demographics magazine is a monthly publication that analyzes population attitudes and characteristics in the United States.

Critical points for §3

Concavity ■ *Points of Inflection* ■ *The Second-Derivative Test* ■ *Extended Application: Diminishing Returns*

Concavity

You already know that locating the intervals in which a function f increases or decreases is helpful in determining its graph. In this section, you will see that locating the intervals in which f' increases or decreases, can determine where the graph of f is curving upward or curving downward. This notion of curving upward or downward is defined formally as the **concavity** of the graph of the function.

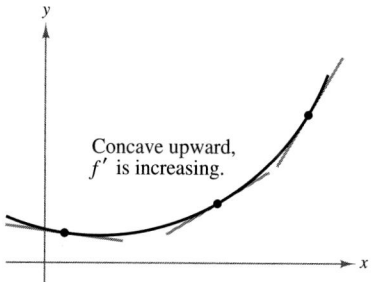

Concave upward, f' is increasing.

Definition of Concavity

Let f be differentiable on an open interval I. The graph of f is

1. **concave upward** on I if f' is increasing on the interval.
2. **concave downward** on I if f' is decreasing on the interval.

From Figure 3.20, you can observe the following graphical interpretation of concavity.

1. A curve that is concave upward lies *above* its tangent line.
2. A curve that is concave downward lies *below* its tangent line.

This visual test for concavity is useful when the graph of a function is given. To determine concavity without seeing a graph, you need an analytic test. It turns out that you can use the second derivative to determine these intervals in much the same way that you used the first derivative to determine the intervals in which f is increasing or decreasing.

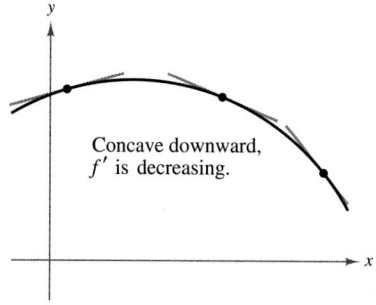

Concave downward, f' is decreasing.

FIGURE 3.20

Test for Concavity

Let f be a function whose second derivative exists on an open interval I.

1. If $f''(x) > 0$ for all x in I, then f is concave upward on I.
2. If $f''(x) < 0$ for all x in I, then f is concave downward on I.

Discovery

Use a graphing utility to graph the function $f(x) = x^3 - x$ and its second derivative $f''(x) = 6x$ on the same coordinate plane. On what interval is f concave upward? On what interval is f'' positive? Describe how the second derivative can be used to determine where a function is concave upward and concave downward. Repeat this analysis for the functions $g(x) = x^4 - 6x^2$ and $g''(x) = 12x^2 - 12$.

For a *continuous* function f, you can find the intervals on which the graph of f is concave upward and concave downward as follows. [For a function that is not continuous, the test intervals should be formed using points of discontinuity, along with the points at which $f''(x)$ is zero or undefined.]

Guidelines for Applying Concavity Test

1. Locate the x-values at which $f''(x) = 0$ or $f''(x)$ is undefined.
2. Use these x-values to determine the test intervals.
3. Test the sign of $f''(x)$ in each test interval.

EXAMPLE 1 *Applying the Test for Concavity*

a. The graph of the function

$$f(x) = x^2 \qquad\qquad \textit{Function}$$

is concave upward on the entire real line because its second derivative

$$f''(x) = 2 \qquad\qquad \textit{Second derivative}$$

is positive for all x. (See Figure 3.21.)

b. The graph of the function

$$f(x) = \sqrt{x} \qquad\qquad \textit{Function}$$

is concave downward for $x > 0$, because its second derivative

$$f''(x) = -\frac{1}{4}x^{-3/2} \qquad\qquad \textit{Second derivative}$$

is negative for all $x > 0$. (See Figure 3.22.)

FIGURE 3.21   Concave Upward

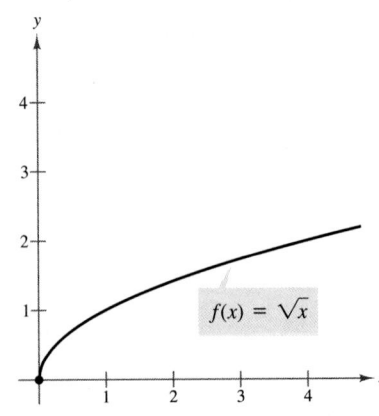

FIGURE 3.22   Concave Downward

EXAMPLE 2 *Determining Concavity*

Determine the intervals in which the graph of the function is concave upward or concave downward.

$$f(x) = \frac{6}{x^2 + 3}$$

Solution

Begin by finding the second derivative of f.

$$f(x) = 6(x^2 + 3)^{-1} \qquad \text{\textit{Original function}}$$

$$f'(x) = (-6)(2x)(x^2 + 3)^{-2} \qquad \text{\textit{Chain Rule}}$$

$$= \frac{-12x}{(x^2 + 3)^2} \qquad \text{\textit{Simplify.}}$$

$$f''(x) = \frac{(x^2 + 3)^2(-12) - (-12x)(2)(2x)(x^2 + 3)}{(x^2 + 3)^4} \quad \text{\textit{Quotient Rule}}$$

$$= \frac{-12(x^2 + 3) + (48x^2)}{(x^2 + 3)^3} \qquad \text{\textit{Simplify.}}$$

$$= \frac{36(x^2 - 1)}{(x^2 + 3)^3} \qquad \text{\textit{Simplify.}}$$

From this, you can see that $f''(x)$ is defined for all real numbers and $f''(x) = 0$ when $x = \pm 1$. Thus, you can test the concavity of f by testing the intervals $(-\infty, -1)$, $(-1, 1)$, and $(1, \infty)$, as shown in Table 3.7. The graph of f is shown in Figure 3.23.

TABLE 3.7

Interval	$-\infty < x < -1$	$-1 < x < 1$	$1 < x < \infty$
Test value	$x = -2$	$x = 0$	$x = 2$
Sign of $f''(x)$	$f''(-2) > 0$	$f''(0) < 0$	$f''(2) > 0$
Conclusion	Concave upward	Concave downward	Concave upward

Note In Example 2, f' is increasing on the interval $(1, \infty)$ even though f is decreasing there. Be sure you see that the increasing or decreasing of f' does not necessarily correspond to the increasing or decreasing of f.

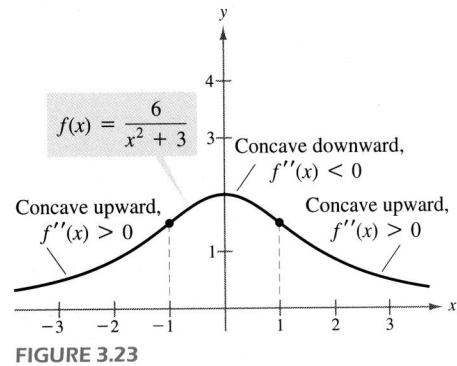

FIGURE 3.23

Discovery

Use a graphing utility to graph $f(x) = x^3 - 6x^2 + 12x - 6$ and $f''(x) = 6x - 12$ on the same coordinate plane. At what x-value does $f''(x) = 0$? At what x-value does the point of inflection occur? Repeat this analysis for $g(x) = x^4 - 5x^2 + 7$ and $g''(x) = 12x^2 - 10$. Make a general statement about the relationship of the point of inflection of a function and the second derivative of a function.

Points of Inflection

If the tangent line to a graph exists at a point at which the concavity changes, then the point is a **point of inflection.** Three examples of inflection points are shown in Figure 3.24. (Note that the third graph has a vertical tangent line at its point of inflection.)

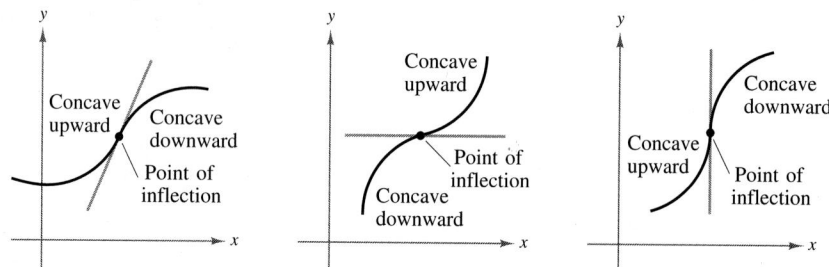

FIGURE 3.24   The graph *crosses* its tangent line at a point of inflection.

Definition of Point of Inflection

If the graph of a continuous function possesses a tangent line at a point where its concavity changes from upward to downward (or vice versa), then the point is a **point of inflection.**

Note   As shown in Figure 3.24, a graph crosses its tangent line at a point of inflection.

Because a point of inflection occurs where the concavity of a graph changes, it must be true that at such points the sign of f'' changes. Thus, to locate possible points of inflection, you need only determine the values of x for which $f''(x) = 0$ or for which $f''(x)$ does not exist. This parallels the procedure for locating the relative extrema of f by determining the critical numbers of f.

Property of Points of Inflection

If $(c, f(c))$ is a point of inflection of the graph of f, then either

$$f''(c) = 0 \quad \text{or} \quad f''(c) \text{ does not exist.}$$

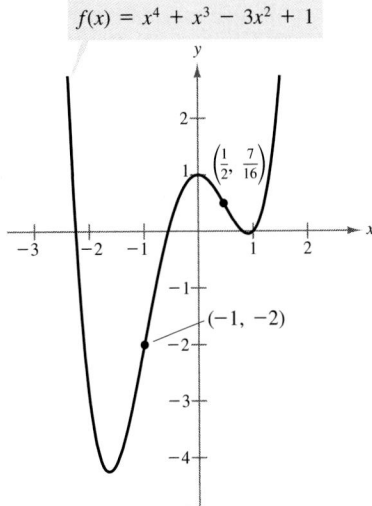

$$f(x) = x^4 + x^3 - 3x^2 + 1$$

FIGURE 3.25 Two Points of Inflection

EXAMPLE 3 *Finding Points of Inflection*

Discuss the concavity of the graph of f and find its points of inflection.

$$f(x) = x^4 + x^3 - 3x^2 + 1$$

Solution

Begin by finding the second derivative of f.

$$f'(x) = 4x^3 + 3x^2 - 6x \qquad \textit{Find first derivative.}$$
$$f''(x) = 12x^2 + 6x - 6 \qquad \textit{Find second derivative.}$$
$$= 6(2x - 1)(x + 1) \qquad \textit{Factor.}$$

From this, you can see that the possible points of inflection occur at $x = \frac{1}{2}$ and $x = -1$. After testing the intervals

$$(-\infty, -1), \quad \left(-1, \frac{1}{2}\right), \quad \text{and} \quad \left(\frac{1}{2}, \infty\right),$$

you can determine that the graph is concave upward in $(-\infty, -1)$, concave downward in $\left(-1, \frac{1}{2}\right)$, and concave upward in $\left(\frac{1}{2}, \infty\right)$. Because the concavity changes at $x = -1$ and $x = \frac{1}{2}$, you can conclude that the graph has points of inflection at these x-values, as shown in Figure 3.25.

It is possible for the second derivative to be zero at a point that is *not* a point of inflection. For example, compare the graphs of $f(x) = x^3$ and $g(x) = x^4$, as shown in Figure 3.26. Both second derivatives are zero when $x = 0$, but only the graph of f has a point of inflection at $x = 0$. This shows that before concluding that a point of inflection exists at a value of x for which $f''(x) = 0$, you must test to be certain that the concavity actually changes at the point.

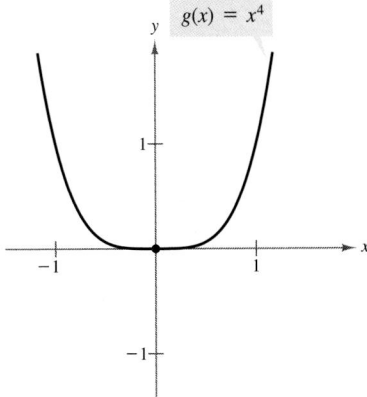

$f''(0) = 0$, and $(0, 0)$ is a point of inflection.

$g''(0) = 0$, but $(0, 0)$ is not a point of inflection.

FIGURE 3.26

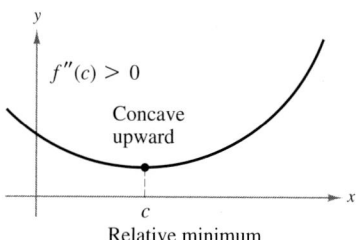

FIGURE 3.27

The Second-Derivative Test

The second derivative can be used to perform a simple test for relative minima and relative maxima. If f is a function such that $f'(c) = 0$ and the graph of f is concave upward at $x = c$, then $f(c)$ is a relative minimum of f. Similarly, if f is a function such that $f'(c) = 0$, and the graph of f is concave downward at $x = c$, then $f(c)$ is a relative maximum of f, as shown in Figure 3.27.

Second-Derivative Test

Let $f'(c) = 0$, and let f'' exist on an open interval containing c.
1. If $f''(c) > 0$, then $f(c)$ is a relative minimum.
2. If $f''(c) < 0$, then $f(c)$ is a relative maximum.
3. If $f''(c) = 0$, then the test fails. In such cases, you can use the First-Derivative Test to determine whether $f(c)$ is a relative minimum or relative maximum.

EXAMPLE 4 Using the Second-Derivative Test

Find the relative extrema of

$$f(x) = -3x^5 + 5x^3.$$

Solution
Begin by finding the first derivative of f.

$$f'(x) = -15x^4 + 15x^2 = 15x^2(1 - x^2)$$

From this derivative, you can see that $x = 0$, $x = -1$, and $x = 1$ are the only critical numbers of f. Using the second derivative,

$$f''(x) = -60x^3 + 30x,$$

you can apply the Second-Derivative Test, as follows.

Point	Sign of $f''(x)$	Conclusion
$(-1, -2)$	$f''(-1) = 30 > 0$	Relative minimum
$(0, 0)$	$f''(0) = 0$	Test fails.
$(1, 2)$	$f''(1) = -30 < 0$	Relative maximum

Because the test fails at $(0, 0)$, you can apply the First-Derivative Test to conclude that the point $(0, 0)$ is neither a relative minimum nor a relative maximum—a test for concavity would show that this point is a point of inflection. The graph of f is shown in Figure 3.28. ▬

FIGURE 3.28

Extended Application: *Diminishing Returns*

In economics, the notion of concavity is related to the concept of **diminishing returns.** Consider a function

Output ─┐   ┌─ Input

$$y = f(x),$$

where x measures the input (in dollars) and y measures the output (in dollars). In Figure 3.29, notice that the graph of this input-output function is concave upward in the interval (a, c) and is concave downward in the interval (c, b). In the interval (a, c), each additional dollar of input returns more than the previous input dollar. By contrast, in the interval (c, b), each additional dollar of input returns less than the previous input dollar. The point $(c, f(c))$ is called the **point of diminishing returns.** An increased investment beyond this point is usually considered a poor use of capital.

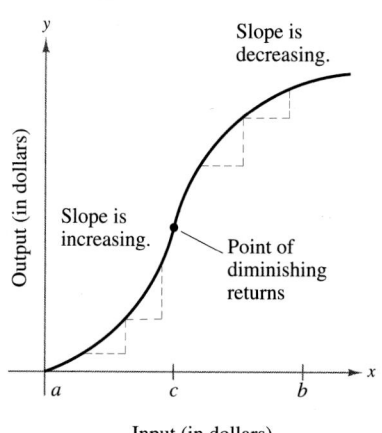

FIGURE 3.29

EXAMPLE 5 *Exploring Diminishing Returns*

Real Life

By increasing its advertising cost x (in thousands of dollars) for a product, a company discovers that it can increase the sales y (in thousands of dollars) according to the model

$$y = \frac{1}{10,000}(300x^2 - x^3), \qquad 0 \le x \le 200.$$

Find the point of diminishing returns for this product.

Solution
Begin by finding the first and second derivatives.

$$y' = \frac{1}{10,000}(600x - 3x^2) \qquad \textit{First derivative}$$

$$y'' = \frac{1}{10,000}(600 - 6x) \qquad \textit{Second derivative}$$

The second derivative is zero only when $x = 100$. By testing the intervals $(0, 100)$ and $(100, 200)$, you can conclude that the graph has a point of diminishing returns when $x = 100$, as shown in Figure 3.30. ▬

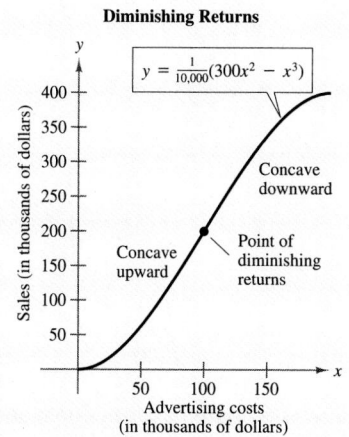

FIGURE 3.30

Discussion Problem Diminishing Returns

Use the function in Example 5 to verify that additional dollars of input return more than the previous input dollars in the interval $(0, 100)$, and less than the previous input dollars in the interval $(100, 200)$.

Warm Up   The following warm-up exercises involve skills that were covered in earlier sections. You will use these skills in the exercise set for this section.

In Exercises 1–6, find the second derivative of the function.

1. $f(x) = 4x^4 - 9x^3 + 5x - 1$

2. $g(s) = (s^2 - 1)(s^2 - 3s + 2)$

3. $g(x) = (x^2 + 1)^4$

4. $f(x) = (x - 3)^{4/3}$

5. $h(x) = \dfrac{5}{(2x)^3}$

6. $f(x) = \dfrac{2x - 1}{3x + 2}$

In Exercises 7–10, find the critical numbers of the function.

7. $f(x) = 5x^3 - 5x + 11$

8. $f(x) = x^4 - 4x^3 - 10$

9. $g(t) = \dfrac{16 + t^2}{t}$

10. $h(x) = \dfrac{x^4 - 50x^2}{8}$

E X E R C I S E S   3.3   means that technology can help you solve or check the exercise(s).

In Exercises 1–6, find the intervals on which the graph is concave upward and those on which it is concave downward.

1. $y = x^2 - x - 2$

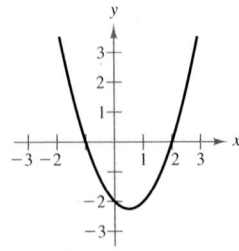

2. $y = -x^3 + 3x^2 - 2$

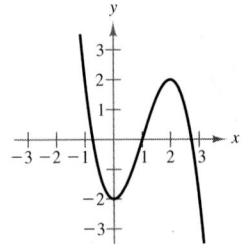

3. $f(x) = \dfrac{x^2 - 1}{2x + 1}$

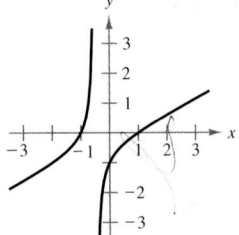

4. $f(x) = \dfrac{x^2 + 4}{4 - x^2}$

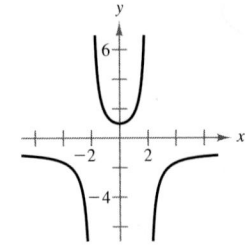

5. $f(x) = \dfrac{24}{x^2 + 12}$

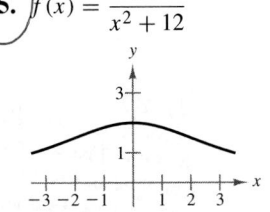

6. $y = x^5 + 5x^4 - 40x^2$

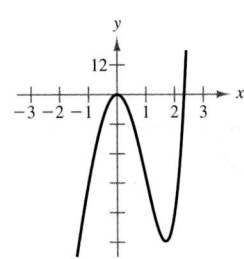

In Exercises 7–18, find all relative extrema of the function. Use the Second-Derivative Test when applicable.

7. $f(x) = 6x - x^2$

8. $f(x) = x^2 + 3x - 8$

9. $f(x) = (x - 5)^2$

10. $f(x) = -(x - 5)^2$

11. $f(x) = x^3 - 5x^2 + 7x$

12. $f(x) = 5 + 3x^2 - x^3$

13. $f(x) = x^4 - 4x^3 + 2$

14. $f(x) = 3x^3 + 5x^2 - 2$

15. $f(x) = x^{2/3} - 3$

16. $f(x) = \sqrt{x^2 + 1}$

17. $f(x) = x + \dfrac{4}{x}$

18. $f(x) = \dfrac{x}{x - 1}$

In Exercises 19–22, state the sign of $f'(x)$ and $f''(x)$ in the interval $(0, 2)$.

19.

20.

21.

22.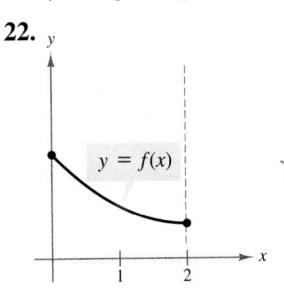

In Exercises 43 and 44, sketch a graph of a function f having the given characteristics.

Function	First Derivative	Second Derivative
43. $f(2) = 0$ $f(4) = 0$	$f'(x) < 0,\ x < 3$ $f'(3) = 0$ $f'(x) > 0,\ x > 3$	$f''(x) > 0$
44. $f(2) = 0$ $f(4) = 0$	$f'(x) > 0,\ x < 3$ $f'(3)$ is undefined $f'(x) < 0,\ x > 3$	$f''(x) > 0,\ x \neq 3$

In Exercises 45 and 46, use the graph to sketch the graph of f'. Find the intervals on which (a) $f'(x)$ is positive, (b) $f'(x)$ is negative, (c) f' is increasing, and (d) f' is decreasing. For each of these intervals, describe the corresponding behavior of f.

45.

46.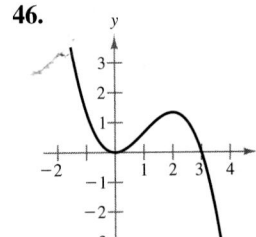

In Exercises 23–30, find the points of inflection of the graph.

23. $f(x) = x^3 - 9x^2 + 24x - 18$

24. $f(x) = x(6 - x)^2$

25. $f(x) = (x - 1)^3(x - 5)$

26. $f(x) = x^4 - 18x^2 + 5$

27. $g(x) = 2x^4 - 8x^3 + 12x^2 + 12x$

28. $f(x) = -4x^3 - 8x^2 + 32$

29. $h(x) = (x - 2)^3(x - 1)$

30. $f(t) = (1 - t)(t - 4)(t^2 - 4)$

In Exercises 31–42, sketch the graph of the function and identify all relative extrema and points of inflection.

31. $f(x) = x^3 - 12x$

32. $f(x) = x^3 + 1$

33. $f(x) = x^3 - 6x^2 + 12x$

34. $f(x) = x^3 - \frac{3}{2}x^2 - 6x$

35. $f(x) = \frac{1}{4}x^4 - 2x^2$

36. $f(x) = 2x^4 - 8x + 3$

37. $g(x) = (x - 2)(x + 1)^2$

38. $g(x) = (x - 6)(x + 2)^3$

39. $g(x) = x\sqrt{x + 3}$

40. $g(x) = \frac{x^3}{16}(x + 4)$

41. $f(x) = \frac{4}{1 + x^2}$

42. $f(x) = x - 4\sqrt{x + 1}$

Point of Diminishing Returns In Exercises 47–50, identify the point of diminishing returns for the input-output function. For each function, R is the revenue and x is the amount spent on advertising.

47. $R = \frac{1}{50,000}(600x^2 - x^3),\quad 0 \le x \le 400$

48. $R = -\frac{4}{27}(x^3 - 33x^2 + 120x - 845),\quad 0 \le x \le 20$

49. $R = -\frac{4}{9}(x^3 - 9x^2 - 27),\quad 0 \le x \le 5$

50. $R = \frac{200x^2}{100 + x^2},\quad 0 \le x \le 50$

Average Cost In Exercises 51–54, you are given the total cost of producing x units. Find the production level that minimizes the average cost per unit.

51. $C = 0.5x^2 + 15x + 5000$

52. $C = 0.16x^2 + 10x + 256$

53. $C = 0.002x^3 + 20x + 500$

54. $C = 0.001x^3 + 0.10x + 750$

Productivity In Exercises 55 and 56, consider a college student who works from 7 P.M. to 11 P.M. assembling mechanical components. The number N of components assembled after t hours is given by the function. At what time is the student assembling components at the greatest rate?

55. $N = -0.12t^3 + 0.54t^2 + 8.22t$, $0 \le t \le 4$

56. $N = \dfrac{20t^2}{4 + t^2}$, $0 \le t \le 4$

Sales Growth In Exercises 57 and 58, find the time t in years when the annual sales x of a new product are increasing at the greatest rate.

57. $x = \dfrac{10,000t^2}{9 + t^2}$

58. $x = \dfrac{500,000t^2}{36 + t^2}$

59. *Sales* A company introduces a new product line. The annual sales of the product increase over time, as shown in the graph. Visually locate the point of inflection of the graph. Describe its significance.

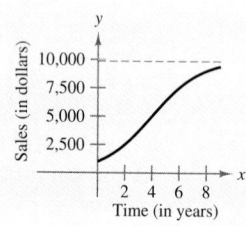

60. Show that the point of inflection of the graph of $f(x) = x(x - 6)^2$ lies midway between the relative extrema of f.

In Exercises 61–64, use a graphing utility to graph f, f', and f'' on the same viewing rectangle. Graphically locate the relative extrema and points of inflection of the graph.

Function	*Interval*
61. $f(x) = \dfrac{2x}{x^2 - x + 1}$	$[-2, 2]$
62. $f(x) = \dfrac{4x^2}{x^2 + 2}$	$[-3, 3]$
63. $f(x) = \frac{1}{2}x^3 - x^2 + 3x - 5$	$[0, 3]$
64. $f(x) = -\frac{1}{20}x^5 - \frac{1}{12}x^2 - \frac{1}{3}x + 1$	$[-2, 2]$

65. *Millionaires* The number N (in thousands) of millionaires having a net worth of x dollars (in millions) in 1986 can be modeled by

$$N = -\frac{4211.02}{x^2} + \frac{5897.24}{x^{3/2}} - 135.91.$$

Use a graphing utility to graph the function. *(Source: Internal Revenue Service)*

66. *Research Project* Use your school's library or some other reference source to research the financial history of a business person. Gather the data on the person's net worth over a period of time, and use a graphing utility to graph a scatter plot of the data. Fit a model to the data. Does the model appear to be concave up or down? Does it appear to be increasing or decreasing? Discuss the implications of your answers.

— *Business Capsule* —

©1993 Kathleen King

Bill Gates, president of Microsoft Corporation, was the wealthiest person in America in 1992. He wrote his first computer program at age 13, and scored a perfect 800 in math on his SAT test. In 1992, his net worth was $6.3 billion.

Optimization Problems

Solving Optimization Problems

Solving Optimization Problems

One of the most common applications of calculus is the determination of optimum (minimum or maximum) values. Before outlining a general method for solving optimization problems, we present an example.

Real Life

EXAMPLE 1 *Finding the Maximum Volume*

A manufacturer wants to design an open box that has a square base and a surface area of 108 square inches, as shown in Figure 3.31. What dimensions will produce a box with a maximum volume?

Solution

Because the base of the box is square, the volume is

$$V = x^2h. \qquad \text{\textit{Primary equation}}$$

This equation is called the **primary equation** because it gives a formula for the quantity to be optimized. The surface area of the box is

$$S = \text{(area of base)} + \text{(area of four sides)}$$

$$108 = x^2 + 4xh. \qquad \text{\textit{Secondary equation}}$$

Because V is to be optimized, it helps to express V as a function of just one variable. To do this, solve the secondary equation for h in terms of x to obtain $h = (108 - x^2)/4x$ and substitute into the primary equation.

$$V = x^2h = x^2\left(\frac{108 - x^2}{4x}\right) = 27x - \frac{1}{4}x^3 \qquad \text{\textit{Function of one variable}}$$

Before finding which x-value yields a maximum value of V, you need to determine the **feasible domain** of the function. That is, what values of x make sense in the problem? Because x must be nonnegative and the area of the base $(A = x^2)$ is at most 108, you can conclude that the feasible domain is

$$0 \leq x \leq \sqrt{108}. \qquad \text{\textit{Feasible domain}}$$

Using the techniques described in the first three sections of this chapter, you can determine that (in the interval $0 \leq x \leq \sqrt{108}$) this function has an absolute maximum when $x = 6$ inches and $h = 3$ inches. ∎

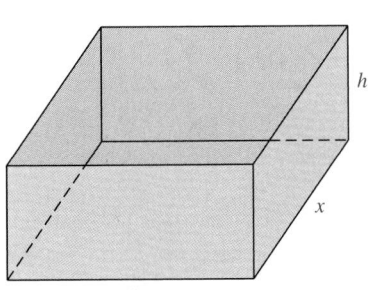

FIGURE 3.31 Open Box with Square Base
$S = x^2 + 4xh = 108$

In studying Example 1, be sure that you understand the basic question that it asks. Some students have trouble with optimization problems because they are too eager to start solving the problem by using a pat formula. For instance, in Example 1, you should realize that there are infinitely many open boxes having 108 square inches of surface area. You might begin to solve this problem by asking yourself which basic shape would seem to yield a maximum volume. Should the box be tall, cubical, or squat? You might even try calculating a few volumes, as shown in Figure 3.32, to see if you can get a good feeling for what the optimum dimensions should be.

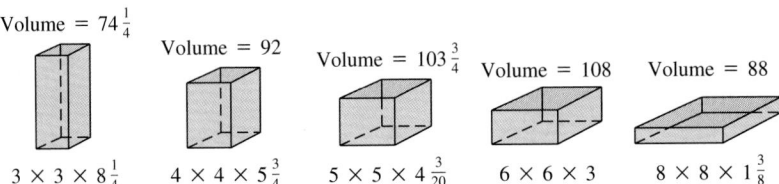

Volume $= 74\frac{1}{4}$ Volume $= 92$ Volume $= 103\frac{3}{4}$ Volume $= 108$ Volume $= 88$

$3 \times 3 \times 8\frac{1}{4}$ $4 \times 4 \times 5\frac{3}{4}$ $5 \times 5 \times 4\frac{3}{20}$ $6 \times 6 \times 3$ $8 \times 8 \times 1\frac{3}{8}$

FIGURE 3.32 Which size box has the maximum volume?

Remember that you are not ready to begin solving an optimization problem until you have clearly identified what the problem is. Once you are sure you understand what is being asked, you are ready to begin considering a method for solving the problem.

There are several steps in the solution of Example 1. The first step is to sketch a diagram and assign symbols to all *known* quantities and to all quantities *to be determined*. The second step is to write a primary equation for the quantity to be optimized. Then, a secondary equation is used to rewrite the primary equation as a function of one variable. Finally, calculus is used to determine the optimum value. These steps are summarized below.

Note When performing Step 5, remember that to determine the maximum or minimum value of a continuous function f on a closed interval, you need to compare the values of f at its critical numbers with the values of f at the endpoints of the interval. The largest of these values is the desired maximum and the smallest is the desired minimum.

Guidelines for Solving Optimization Problems

1. Assign symbols to all given quantities and to all quantities to be determined. When feasible, sketch a diagram.
2. Write a **primary equation** for the quantity to be maximized or minimized. (A summary of several common formulas is given in Appendix B.)
3. Reduce the primary equation to one having a single independent variable: this may involve the use of a **secondary equation** that relates the independent variables of the primary equation.
4. Determine the **feasible domain** of the primary equation. That is, determine the values for which the stated problem makes sense.
5. Use calculus to find the desired maximum or minimum value.

EXAMPLE 2 *Finding a Maximum Sum*

The product of two positive numbers is 288. Minimize the sum of the second number and twice the first number.

Solution

1. Let x be the first number, y the second, and S the sum to be minimized.
2. Because you want to minimize S, the primary equation is

$$S = 2x + y. \qquad \text{\textit{Primary equation}}$$

3. Because the product of the two numbers is 288, you can write the following secondary equation.

$$xy = 288 \qquad \text{\textit{Secondary equation}}$$

$$y = \frac{288}{x}$$

Using this result, you can rewrite the primary equation as a function of one variable.

$$S = 2x + \frac{288}{x} \qquad \text{\textit{Function of one variable}}$$

4. Because the numbers are nonnegative, the feasible domain is

$$0 < x. \qquad \text{\textit{Feasible domain}}$$

5. To find the maximum value of S, begin by finding its critical numbers.

$$\frac{dS}{dx} = 2 - \frac{288}{x^2} \qquad \text{\textit{Find derivative of S.}}$$

$$0 = 2 - \frac{288}{x^2} \qquad \text{\textit{Set derivative equal to 0.}}$$

$$x^2 = 144 \qquad \text{\textit{Simplify.}}$$

$$x = \pm 12 \qquad \text{\textit{Critical numbers}}$$

Choosing the positive x-value, you can use the First-Derivative Test to conclude that S is decreasing in the interval $(0, 12)$ and increasing in the interval $(12, \infty)$, as shown in Table 3.8. Therefore, $x = 12$ yields a minimum and the two numbers are

$$x = 12 \quad \text{and} \quad y = \frac{288}{12} = 24.$$

TABLE 3.8

Interval	$0 < x < 12$	$12 < x < \infty$
Test value	$x = 1$	$x = 13$
Sign of $\dfrac{dS}{dx}$	$\dfrac{dS}{dx} < 0$	$\dfrac{dS}{dx} > 0$
Conclusion	S is decreasing	S is increasing

TECHNOLOGY

After you have written the primary equation as a function of a single variable, you can estimate the optimum value by graphing the function. For instance, the graph of

$$S = 2x + \frac{288}{x},$$

shown below, indicates that the minimum value of S occurs when x is about 12.

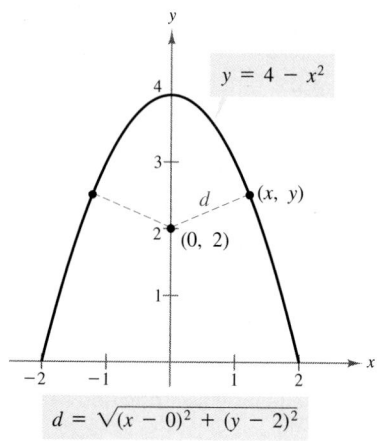

$d = \sqrt{(x-0)^2 + (y-2)^2}$

FIGURE 3.33

EXAMPLE 3 *Finding a Minimum Distance*

Find the points on the graph of $y = 4 - x^2$ that are closest to $(0, 2)$.

Solution

1. Figure 3.33 indicates that there are two points at a minimum distance from the point $(0, 2)$.

2. You are asked to minimize the distance d. Hence, you can use the Distance Formula to obtain a primary equation.

$$d = \sqrt{(x-0)^2 + (y-2)^2}. \qquad \textit{Primary equation}$$

3. Using the secondary equation $y = 4 - x^2$, you can rewrite the primary equation as a function of a single variable.

$$d = \sqrt{x^2 + (4 - x^2 - 2)^2} \qquad \textit{Substitute } 4 - x^2 \textit{ for } y.$$
$$= \sqrt{x^4 - 3x^2 + 4} \qquad \textit{Simplify.}$$

Because d is smallest when the expression under the radical is smallest, you simplify the problem by finding the minimum value of

$$f(x) = x^4 - 3x^2 + 4.$$

4. The domain of f is the entire real line.

5. To find the minimum value of $f(x)$, first find the critical numbers of f.

$$f'(x) = 4x^3 - 6x \qquad \textit{Find derivative of } f.$$
$$0 = 4x^3 - 6x \qquad \textit{Set derivative equal to 0.}$$
$$0 = 2x(2x^2 - 3) \qquad \textit{Factor.}$$
$$x = 0, \ \sqrt{\tfrac{3}{2}}, \ -\sqrt{\tfrac{3}{2}} \qquad \textit{Critical numbers}$$

By the First-Derivative Test, you can conclude that $x = 0$ yields a relative maximum, whereas both $\sqrt{3/2}$ and $-\sqrt{3/2}$ yield a minimum. Hence, on the graph of $y = 4 - x^2$, the points that are closest to the point $(0, 2)$ are

$$\left(\sqrt{\tfrac{3}{2}}, \tfrac{5}{2}\right) \quad \text{and} \quad \left(-\sqrt{\tfrac{3}{2}}, \tfrac{5}{2}\right).$$

Note To confirm the result in Example 3, try computing the distance between several points on the graph of $y = 4 - x^2$ and the point $(0, 2)$. For instance, the distance between $(1, 3)$ and $(0, 2)$ is

$$d = \sqrt{(0-1)^2 + (2-3)^2} = \sqrt{2} \approx 1.414.$$

Note that this is greater than the distance between $\left(\sqrt{3/2}, 5/2\right)$ and $(0, 2)$, which is

$$d = \sqrt{\left(0 - \sqrt{\tfrac{3}{2}}\right)^2 + \left(2 - \tfrac{5}{2}\right)^2} = \sqrt{\tfrac{7}{4}} \approx 1.323.$$

Real
Life

EXAMPLE 4 *Finding a Minimum Area*

A rectangular page is to contain 24 square inches of print. The margins at the top and bottom of the page are $1\frac{1}{2}$ inches wide. The margins on each side are 1 inch. What should the dimensions of the page be so that the least amount of paper is used?

Solution
1. A diagram of the page is shown in Figure 3.34.
2. Letting A be the area to be minimized, the primary equation is

$$A = (x+3)(y+2).$$ *Primary equation*

3. The printed area inside the margins is given by

$$24 = xy.$$ *Secondary equation*

Solving this equation for y produces

$$y = \frac{24}{x}.$$

By substituting this into the primary equation, you obtain

$$A = (x+3)\left(\frac{24}{x}+2\right)$$ *Function of one variable*

$$= (x+3)\left(\frac{24+2x}{x}\right)$$

$$= \frac{2x^2+30x+72}{x}$$

$$= 30 + 2x + \frac{72}{x}.$$ *Simplify.*

4. Because x must be positive, the feasible domain is $x > 0$.
5. To find the minimum area, begin by finding the critical numbers of A.

$$\frac{dA}{dx} = 2 - \frac{72}{x^2}$$ *Find derivative of A.*

$$0 = 2 - \frac{72}{x^2}$$ *Set derivative equal to 0.*

$$x^2 = 36$$

$$x = \pm 6$$ *Critical numbers*

Because $x = -6$ is not in the feasible domain, you need only consider the critical number $x = 6$. Using the First-Derivative Test, it follows that A is a minimum when $x = 6$. Thus, the dimensions of the page should be

$$x + 3 = 6 + 3 = 9 \text{ inches}$$

by

$$y + 2 = \frac{24}{6} + 2 = 6 \text{ inches.}$$

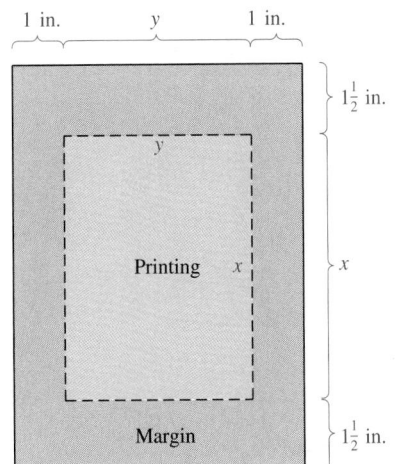

1 in. y 1 in.

$1\frac{1}{2}$ in.

y

Printing x x

Margin $1\frac{1}{2}$ in.

$A = (x+3)(y+2)$

FIGURE 3.34

As applications go, the four examples described in this section are fairly simple, and yet the resulting primary equations are quite complicated. Real-life applications often involve equations that are at least as complex as these four, and you should expect this. Remember that one of the main goals of this course is to enable you to use the power of calculus to analyze equations that at first glance seem formidable.

Also remember that once you have found the primary equation, you can use the graph of the equation as an aid to solving the optimization problem. For instance, the graphs of the primary equations in Examples 1 through 4 are shown in Figure 3.35.

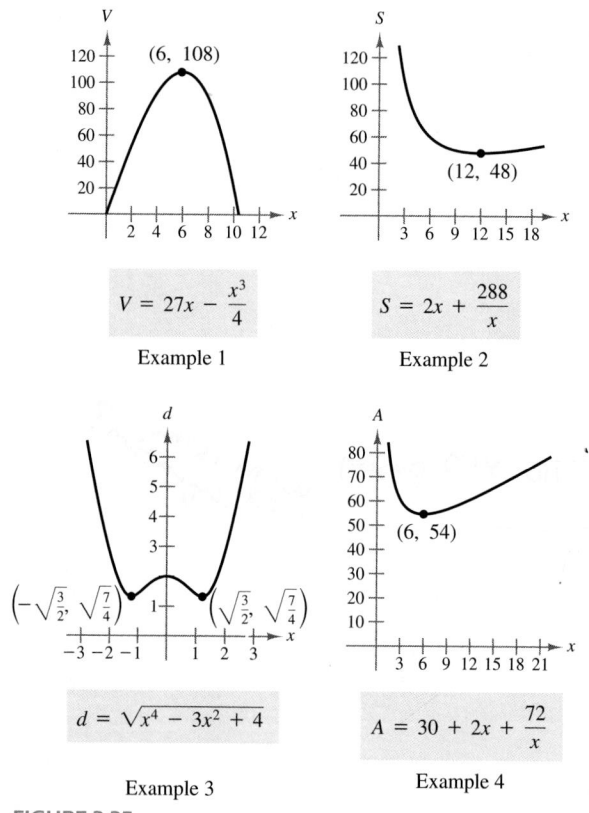

$$V = 27x - \frac{x^3}{4}$$

Example 1

$$S = 2x + \frac{288}{x}$$

Example 2

$$d = \sqrt{x^4 - 3x^2 + 4}$$

Example 3

$$A = 30 + 2x + \frac{72}{x}$$

Example 4

FIGURE 3.35

Discussion Problem *Using Technology*

Use a graphing utility to reproduce the graphs shown above. Then, use the zoom and trace features to approximate the optimum values.

Warm Up

The following warm-up exercises involve skills that were covered in earlier sections. You will use these skills in the exercise set for this section.

In Exercises 1–4, write a formula for the written statement.

1. The sum of one number and half a second number is 12.

2. The product of one number and twice another is 24.

3. The area of a rectangle is 24 square units.

4. The distance between two points is 10 units.

In Exercises 5–10, find the critical numbers of the function.

5. $y = x^2 + 6x - 9$

6. $y = 2x^3 - x^2 - 4x$

7. $y = 5x + \dfrac{125}{x}$

8. $y = 3x + \dfrac{96}{x^2}$

9. $y = \dfrac{x^2 + 1}{x}$

10. $y = \dfrac{x}{x^2 + 9}$

E X E R C I S E S   3.4   means that technology can help you solve or check the exercise(s).

In Exercises 1–6, find two positive numbers satisfying the given requirements.

(handwritten: 110 = x+y   p=xy)

1. The sum is 110 and the product is a maximum. *(handwritten: what is the 2nd equation?)*

2. The sum is S and the product is a maximum.

3. The sum of the first and twice the second is 36 and the product is a maximum.

4. The sum of the first and twice the second is 100 and the product is a maximum.

5. The product is 192 and the sum is a minimum.

6. The product is 192 and the sum of the first plus three times the second is a minimum.

7. What positive number x minimizes the sum of x and its reciprocal?

8. The difference of two numbers is 50. Find the two numbers so that their product is a minimum.

9. Verify that each rectangular solid has a surface area of 150 square inches (see figure). Find the volume of each.

10. Verify that each right circular cylinder has a surface area of 24π (see figure). Find the volume of each.

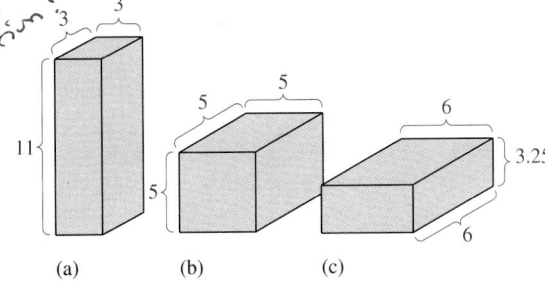

(a) (b) (c)

FIGURE FOR 9

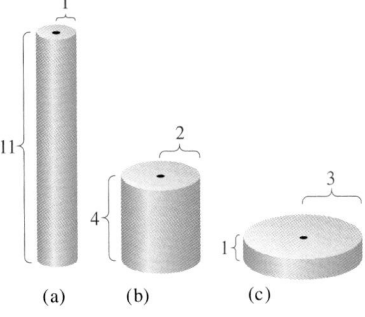

(a) (b) (c)

FIGURE FOR 10

In Exercises 11 and 12, find the length and width of the specified rectangle.

11. Maximum area; Perimeter: 100 feet

12. Minimum perimeter; Area: 64 square feet

13. *Area* A rancher has 200 feet of fencing to enclose two adjacent rectangular corrals (see figure). What dimensions should be used so that the enclosed area will be a maximum?

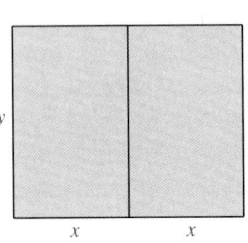

FIGURE FOR 13   FIGURE FOR 15

14. *Fence Length* A dairy farmer plans to enclose a rectangular pasture adjacent to a river. To provide enough grass for the herd, the pasture must contain 180,000 square meters. No fencing is required along the river. What dimensions use the least amount of fencing?

15. *Volume* An open box is to be made from a 6-inch by 6-inch square piece of material by cutting equal squares from each corner and turning up the sides (see figure). Find the volume of the largest box that can be made in this manner.

16. *Volume* An open box is to be made from a 2-foot by 3-foot rectangular piece of material by cutting equal squares from each corner and turning up the sides. Find the volume of the largest box that can be made in this manner.

17. *Surface Area* A net enclosure for golf practice is open at one end (see figure). The volume of the enclosure is $83\frac{1}{3}$ cubic meters. Find the dimensions that require the least amount of netting.

FIGURE FOR 17

FIGURE FOR 21

18. *Volume* For the golf practice enclosure in Exercise 17, assume that 192 square feet of netting is available. What dimensions will maximize the volume?

19. *Area* An indoor physical fitness room consists of a rectangular region with a semicircle on each end. The perimeter of the room is to be a 200-meter running track. Find the dimensions that will make the area of the rectangular region as large as possible.

20. *Area* A page is to contain 30 square inches of print. The margins at the top and bottom of the page are each 2 inches wide. The margins on each side are only 1 inch wide. What dimensions will minimize the amount of paper used?

21. *Area* A rectangle is bounded by the x- and y-axes and the graph of $y = (6-x)/2$ (see figure). What length and width should the rectangle have so that its area is a maximum?

22. *Area* A right triangle is formed in the first quadrant by the x- and y-axes and a line through the point $(2, 3)$. Find the vertices of the triangle so that its area is a minimum.

23. *Area* A rectangle is bounded by the x-axis and the semicircle $y = \sqrt{25 - x^2}$ (see figure). What length and width should the rectangle have so that its area is a maximum?

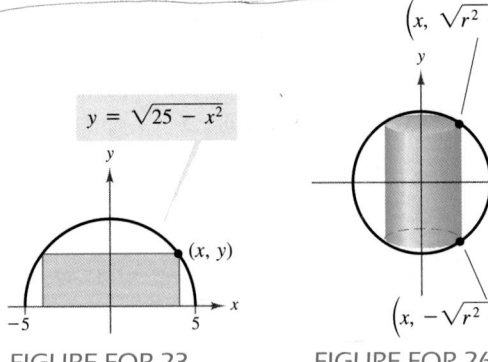

FIGURE FOR 23   FIGURE FOR 26

24. *Area* Find the dimensions of the largest rectangle that can be inscribed in a semicircle of radius r. (See Exercise 23.)

25. *Volume* You are designing a soft drink container that has the shape of a right circular cylinder. The container is to hold 12 fluid ounces (1 fluid ounce is approximately 1.80469 cubic inches). Find the dimensions that will use a minimum amount of construction material.

26. *Volume* Find the volume of the largest right circular cylinder that can be inscribed in a sphere of radius r (see figure).

27. *Closest Point* Find the point on the graph of $y = x^2 + 1$ that is closest to the point $(0, 4)$.

28. *Closest Point* Find the point on the graph of $y = x^2$ that is closest to the point $\left(2, \frac{1}{2}\right)$.

29. *Volume* A rectangular package to be sent by a postal service can have a maximum combined length and girth of 108 inches. Find the dimensions of the package with maximum volume. As shown in the figure, assume the package's dimensions are x by x by y.

FIGURE FOR 29   FIGURE FOR 33

30. *Surface Area* A container is formed by adjoining two hemispheres to each end of a right circular cylinder. The total volume of the container is 12 cubic inches. Find the radius of the cylinder that produces the minimum surface area.

31. *Area* The combined perimeter of a circle and a square is 16. Find the dimensions of the circle and square that produce a minimum total area.

32. *Area* The combined perimeter of an equilateral triangle and a square is 10. Find the dimensions of the triangle and square that produce a minimum total area.

33. *Time* You are in a boat 2 miles from the nearest point on the coast. You are to go to point Q, 3 miles down the coast and 1 mile inland (see figure). You can row at a rate of 2 miles per hour and can walk at a rate of 4 miles per hour. Toward which point on the coast should you row in order to reach point Q in the least time?

34. *Time* The conditions are the same as in Exercise 33, except that you can row at a rate of 4 miles per hour. How does this change the solution?

35. *Strength of a Beam* A wooden beam has a rectangular cross section of height h and width w (see figure). The strength S of the beam is directly proportional to its width and the square of its height. What are the dimensions of the strongest beam that can be cut from a round log of diameter 24 inches? (*Hint:* $S = kh^2w$, where k is the proportionality constant.)

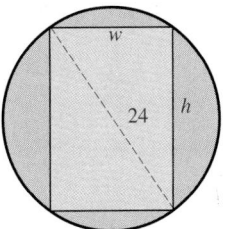

FIGURE FOR 35

36. *Surface Area* A right circular cylinder of radius r and height h has a volume of 25 cubic inches. The surface area of the cylinder is given by

$$S = 2\pi r \left(r + \frac{25}{\pi r^2} \right).$$

Use a graphing utility to graph S and S' and find the value of r that yields the minimum surface area.

37. *Area* Use a graphing utility to graph the primary equation and its first derivative to find the dimensions of the rectangle of maximum area that can be inscribed in a semicircle of radius 10.

38. *Area* Four feet of wire is to be used to form a square and a circle.

(a) Express the sum of the areas of the square and the circle as a function $A(x)$ of the side of the square x.

(b) What is the domain of $A(x)$?

(c) Use a graphing utility to graph A on its domain.

(d) How much wire should be used for the square and how much for the circle in order to enclose the least amount of total area?

(e) How much wire should be used for the square and how much for the circle in order to enclose the most amount of total area?

3.5 Business and Economics Applications

Optimization in Business and Economics ■ *Price Elasticity of Demand* ■ *Business Terms and Formulas*

Optimization in Business and Economics

The problems in this section are primarily optimization problems. Hence, the five-step procedure used in Section 3.4 is an appropriate strategy to follow.

Real Life

EXAMPLE 1 *Finding the Maximum Revenue*

A company has determined that its total revenue (in dollars) for a product can be modeled by

$$R = -x^3 + 450x^2 + 52,500x,$$

where x is the number of units produced (and sold). What production level will yield a maximum revenue?

Solution

1. A sketch of the revenue function is given in Figure 3.36.
2. The primary equation is the given revenue function.

$$R = -x^3 + 450x^2 + 52,500x \qquad \text{\textit{Primary equation}}$$

3. Because R is already given as a function of one variable, you do not need a secondary equation.
4. The feasible domain of the primary equation is

$$0 \le x \le 546. \qquad \text{\textit{Feasible domain}}$$

This is determined by finding the x-intercepts of the revenue function, as shown in Figure 3.36.
5. To maximize the revenue, find the critical numbers.

$$\frac{dR}{dx} = -3x^2 + 900x + 52,500 = 0 \qquad \text{\textit{Set derivative equal to 0.}}$$

$$-3(x - 350)(x + 50) = 0 \qquad \text{\textit{Factor.}}$$

$$x = 350,\ -50 \qquad \text{\textit{Critical numbers}}$$

The only critical number in the feasible domain is $x = 350$. From the graph of the function, you can see that a production level of 350 units corresponds to a maximum revenue. ■

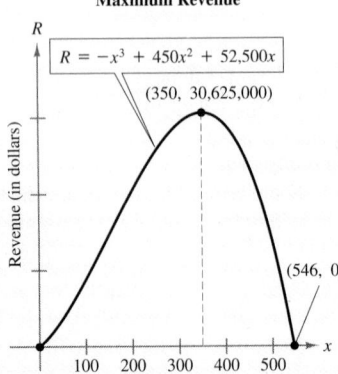

Maximum Revenue

$R = -x^3 + 450x^2 + 52,500x$

(350, 30,625,000)

(546, 0)

Revenue (in dollars)

100   200   300   400   500
Number of units

FIGURE 3.36 Maximum revenue occurs when $dR/dx = 0$.

To study the effects of production levels on cost, economists use the **average cost function** $\overline{C}$, which is defined as

$$\overline{C} = \frac{C}{x},$$

Average cost function

where $C = f(x)$ is the total cost function and x is the number of units produced.

EXAMPLE 2 *Finding the Minimum Average Cost* **Real Life**

A company estimates that the cost (in dollars) of producing x units of a product can be modeled by

$$C = 800 + 0.04x + 0.0002x^2.$$

Find the production level that minimizes the average cost per unit.

Solution

1. C represents the total cost, x represents the number of units produced, and $\overline{C}$ represents the average cost per unit.

2. The primary equation is

$$\overline{C} = \frac{C}{x}.$$

Primary equation

3. Substituting the given equation for C produces

$$\overline{C} = \frac{800 + 0.04x + 0.0002x^2}{x}$$

Substitute for C.

$$= \frac{800}{x} + 0.04 + 0.0002x.$$

Function of one variable

4. The feasible domain for this function is

$$0 < x.$$

Feasible domain

5. You can find the critical numbers as follows.

$$\frac{d\overline{C}}{dx} = -\frac{800}{x^2} + 0.0002 = 0$$

Set derivative equal to 0.

$$0.0002 = \frac{800}{x^2}$$

$$x^2 = \frac{800}{0.0002}$$

$$x^2 = 4{,}000{,}000$$

$$x = \pm 2000$$

Critical numbers

By choosing the positive value of x and sketching the graph of $\overline{C}$, as shown in Figure 3.37, you can see that a production level of $x = 2000$ minimizes the average cost per unit. ■

Minimum Average Cost

$$\overline{C} = \frac{800}{x} + 0.04 + 0.0002x$$

Average cost (in dollars)

Number of units

FIGURE 3.37 Minimum average cost when $d\overline{C}/dx = 0$.

Note To see that $x = 2000$ corresponds to a minimum average cost in Example 2, try evaluating $\overline{C}$ for several values of x. For instance, when $x = 400$, the average cost per unit is $\overline{C} = \$2.12$, but when $x = 2000$, the average cost per unit is $\overline{C} = \$0.84$.

Real Life

EXAMPLE 3 *Finding the Maximum Revenue*

A business sells 2000 units per month at a price of $10 each. It can sell 250 more items per month for each $0.25 reduction in price. What price per unit will maximize the monthly revenue?

Solution

1. Let x represent the number of units sold in a month, let p represent the price per unit, and let R represent the monthly revenue.
2. Because the revenue is to be maximized, the primary equation is

$$R = xp. \qquad \text{\textit{Primary equation}}$$

3. A price of $p = \$10$ corresponds to $x = 2000$ and a price of $p = \$9.75$ corresponds to $x = 2250$. Using this information, you can use the point-slope form to create the demand equation.

$$p - 10 = \frac{10 - 9.75}{2000 - 2250}(x - 2000) \qquad \text{\textit{Point-slope form}}$$

$$p - 10 = -0.001(x - 2000) \qquad \text{\textit{Simplify.}}$$

$$p = -0.001x + 12 \qquad \text{\textit{Secondary equation}}$$

Substituting this value into the revenue equation produces

$$R = x(-0.001x + 12) \qquad \text{\textit{Substitute for } p.}$$

$$= -0.001x^2 + 12x. \qquad \text{\textit{Function of one variable}}$$

4. The feasible domain of the revenue function is

$$0 \le x \le 12{,}000. \qquad \text{\textit{Feasible domain}}$$

5. To maximize the revenue, find the critical numbers.

$$\frac{dR}{dx} = 12 - 0.002x = 0 \qquad \text{\textit{Set derivative equal to } 0.}$$

$$-0.002x = -12$$

$$x = 6000 \qquad \text{\textit{Critical number}}$$

From the graph of R in Figure 3.38, you can see that this production level yields a maximum revenue. The price that corresponds to this production level is

$$p = 12 - 0.001(x) \qquad \text{\textit{Demand function}}$$

$$= 12 - 0.001(6000) \qquad \text{\textit{Substitute 6000 for } x.}$$

$$= \$6. \qquad \text{\textit{Price per unit}} \qquad \blacksquare$$

Note In Example 3, the revenue function was written as a function of x. It could also have been written as a function of p. That is, $R = 1000(12p - p^2)$. By finding the critical numbers of this function, you can determine that the maximum revenue occurs when $p = 6$.

Maximum Revenue

$R = 12x - 0.001x^2$

(6000, 36,000)

Revenue (in dollars)

Number of units

FIGURE 3.38

Real
Life

EXAMPLE 4 *Finding the Maximum Profit*

The marketing department for a business has determined that the demand for a product can be modeled by

$$p = \frac{50}{\sqrt{x}}.$$

The cost of producing x units is given by $C = 0.5x + 500$. What price will yield a maximum profit?

Solution

1. Let R represent the revenue, P the profit, p the price per unit, x the number of units, and C the total cost of producing x units.
2. Because you are maximizing the profit, the primary equation is

$$P = R - C. \qquad\qquad \textit{Primary equation}$$

3. Because the revenue is $R = xp$, you can write the profit function as

$$
\begin{aligned}
P &= R - C \\
&= xp - (0.5x + 500) && \textit{Substitute for C.} \\
&= x\left(\frac{50}{\sqrt{x}}\right) - 0.5x - 500 && \textit{Substitute for p.} \\
&= 50\sqrt{x} - 0.5x - 500. && \textit{Function of one variable}
\end{aligned}
$$

4. The feasible domain of the function is $0 < x \le 7872$. (When x is greater than 7872, the profit is negative.)
5. To maximize the profit, find the critical numbers.

$$\frac{dP}{dx} = \frac{25}{\sqrt{x}} - 0.5 = 0 \qquad\qquad \textit{Set derivative equal to 0.}$$

$$\sqrt{x} = 50$$

$$x = 2500 \qquad\qquad \textit{Critical number}$$

From the graph of the profit function shown in Figure 3.39, you can see that $x = 2500$ corresponds to a maximum profit. The price that corresponds to $x = 2500$ is

$$p = \frac{50}{\sqrt{x}} = \frac{50}{\sqrt{2500}} = \frac{50}{50} = \$1.00. \qquad \textit{Price per unit}$$

Note To find the maximum profit in Example 4, we differentiated the equation $P = R - C$ and set dP/dx equal to zero. From the equation

$$\frac{dP}{dx} = \frac{dR}{dx} - \frac{dC}{dx} = 0,$$

it follows that the maximum profit occurs when the marginal revenue is equal to the marginal cost, as shown in Figure 3.40.

Maximum Profit

$$P = 50\sqrt{x} - 0.5x - 500$$

(2500, 750)

Profit (in dollars)

Number of units

FIGURE 3.39

Marginal Revenue and Marginal Cost

$$R = 50\sqrt{x}$$

Maximum profit:
$$\frac{dR}{dx} = \frac{dC}{dx}$$

$$C = 0.5x + 500$$

Number of units

FIGURE 3.40

Price Elasticity of Demand

One way economists measure the responsiveness of consumers to a change in the price of a product is with **price elasticity of demand.** For example, a drop in the price of vegetables might result in a much greater demand for vegetables—such a demand is called **elastic.** On the other hand, items such as milk and water are relatively unresponsive to changes in price—the demand for such items is called **inelastic**.

More formally, the elasticity of demand is the percent change of a quantity demanded x, divided by the percent change in its price p. You can develop a formula for price elasticity of demand using the approximation

$$\frac{\Delta p}{\Delta x} \approx \frac{dp}{dx},$$

which is based on the definition of the derivative. Using this approximation, you can write

$$\text{Price elasticity of demand} = \frac{\text{rate of change in demand}}{\text{rate of change in price}}$$

$$= \frac{\Delta x / x}{\Delta p / p}$$

$$= \frac{p/x}{\Delta p / \Delta x}$$

$$\approx \frac{p/x}{dp/dx}.$$

Note The following list shows some estimates of elasticities of demand for common products.
(Source: Principles of Economics *by James Kearl)*

Item	Absolute Value of Elasticity
Cottonseed oil	6.92
Tomatoes	4.60
Restaurant meals	1.63
Automobiles	1.35
Cable TV	1.20
Beer	1.13
Housing	1.00
Movies	0.87
Clothing	0.60
Cigarettes	0.51
Coffee	0.25
Gasoline	0.15
Newspapers	0.10
Mail	0.05

Which of these items are elastic? Which are inelastic?

Definition of Price Elasticity of Demand

If $p = f(x)$ is a differentiable function, then the **price elasticity of demand** is given by

$$\eta = \frac{p/x}{dp/dx},$$

where η is the lowercase Greek letter eta. For a given price, the demand is **elastic** if $|\eta| > 1$, the demand is **inelastic** if $|\eta| < 1$, and the demand has **unit elasticity** if $|\eta| = 1$.

Price elasticity of demand is related to the total revenue function, as indicated in Figure 3.41 and the following list.

1. If the demand is *elastic*, then a decrease in price is accompanied by a sufficient increase in unit sales to increase the total revenue.
2. If the demand is *inelastic*, then a decrease in price is not accompanied by a sufficient increase in unit sales to increase the total revenue.

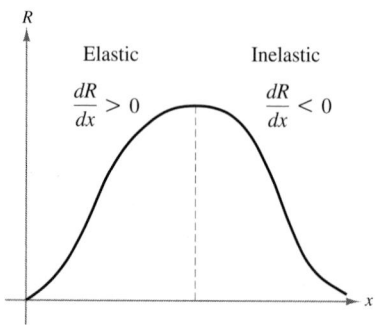

FIGURE 3.41 Revenue Curve

Real
Life

EXAMPLE 5 *Comparing Elasticity and Revenue*

The demand function for a product is modeled by

$$p = \sqrt{450 - x}, \qquad 0 \le x \le 450.$$

a. Find the intervals on which the demand is elastic, inelastic, and of unit elasticity.

b. Use the result of part a to describe the behavior of the revenue function.

Solution

a. The price elasticity of demand is given by

$$\eta = \frac{p/x}{dp/dx}$$

$$= \frac{\left(\dfrac{\sqrt{450 - x}}{x}\right)}{\left(\dfrac{-1}{2\sqrt{450 - x}}\right)}$$

$$= \frac{-900 + 2x}{x}$$

$$= -\frac{900}{x} + 2.$$

The demand is of unit elasticity when $|\eta| = 1$. In the interval $[0, 450]$, the only solution of the equation

$$|\eta| = \left| -\frac{900}{x} + 2 \right| = 1 \qquad\qquad\qquad \textit{Unit elasticity}$$

is $x = 300$. Thus, the demand is of unit elasticity when $x = 300$. For x-values in the interval $(0, 300)$,

$$|\eta| = \left| -\frac{900}{x} + 2 \right| > 1, \qquad 0 < x < 300, \qquad\qquad \textit{Elastic}$$

which implies that the demand is elastic when $0 < x < 300$. For x-values in the interval $(300, 450)$,

$$|\eta| = \left| -\frac{900}{x} + 2 \right| < 1, \qquad 300 < x < 450, \qquad\qquad \textit{Inelastic}$$

which implies that the demand is inelastic when $300 < x < 450$.

b. From part a, you can conclude that the revenue function R is increasing on the open interval $(0, 300)$, is decreasing on the open interval $(300, 450)$, and has a maximum when $x = 300$, as indicated in Figure 3.42. ■

(a)

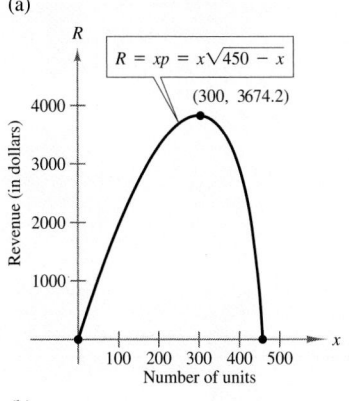

(b)

FIGURE 3.42

Note In our discussion of price elasticity of demand, the price is assumed to decrease as the quantity demanded increases. Thus, the demand function $p = f(x)$ is decreasing and dp/dx is negative.

Business Terms and Formulas

We conclude with a summary of the basic business terms and formulas used in this section.

Summary of Business Terms and Formulas

x = number of units produced (or sold)

p = price per unit

R = total revenue from selling x units = xp

C = total cost of producing x units

P = total profit from selling x units = $R - C$

$\overline{C}$ = average cost per unit = $\dfrac{C}{x}$

η = price elasticity of demand = $\dfrac{p/x}{dp/dx}$

dR/dx = marginal revenue

dC/dx = marginal cost

dP/dx = marginal profit

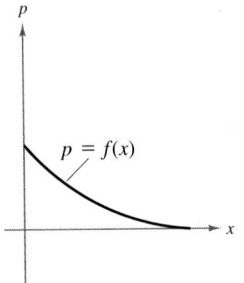

Demand function

Quantity demanded increases as price decreases.

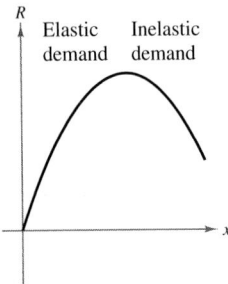

Revenue function

The low prices required to sell more units eventually result in a decreasing revenue.

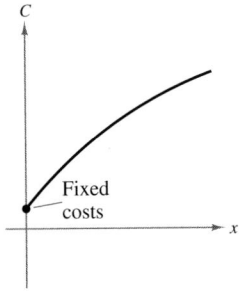

Cost function

As x increases, the average cost per unit decreases.

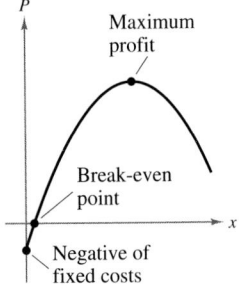

Profit function

The break-even point occurs when R = C.

FIGURE 3.43

Discussion Problem Demand Function

Throughout this text, we assume that demand functions are decreasing. Can you think of a product that has an increasing demand function? That is, can you think of a product that becomes more in demand as its price increases?

Warm Up

In Exercises 1–4, evaluate the expression with $x = 150$.

1. $\left| -\dfrac{300}{x} + 3 \right|$

2. $\left| -\dfrac{600}{5x} + 2 \right|$

3. $\left| \dfrac{(20x^{-1/2})/x}{-10x^{-3/2}} \right|$

4. $\left| \dfrac{(4000/x^2)/x}{-8000x^{-3}} \right|$

In Exercises 5–10, find the marginal revenue, cost, or profit.

5. $C = 650 + 1.2x + 0.003x^2$

6. $P = 0.01x^2 + 11x$

7. $R = 14x - \dfrac{x^2}{2000}$

8. $R = 3.4x - \dfrac{x^2}{1500}$

9. $P = -0.7x^2 + 7x - 50$

10. $C = 1700 + 4.2x + 0.001x^3$

EXERCISES 3.5

means that technology can help you solve or check the exercise(s).

In Exercises 1–4, find the number of units x that produces a maximum revenue R.

1. $R = 800x - 0.2x^2$

2. $R = 48x^2 - 0.02x^3$

3. $R = 400x - x^2$

4. $R = 30x^{2/3} - 2x$

In Exercises 5–8, find the number of units x that produces the minimum average cost per unit $\overline{C}$.

5. $C = 1.25x^2 + 25x + 8000$

6. $C = 0.001x^3 - 5x + 250$

7. $C = 3000x - x^2\sqrt{300 - x}$

8. $C = (2x^3 - x^2 + 5000x)/(x^2 + 2500)$

In Exercises 9–12, find the price per unit p that produces the maximum profit P.

Cost Function	*Demand Function*
9. $C = 100 + 30x$	$p = 90 - x$
10. $C = 2400x + 5200$	$p = 6000 - 0.4x^2$
11. $C = 8000 + 50x + 0.03x^2$	$p = 70 - 0.001x$
12. $C = 35x + 500$	$p = 50 - 0.1\sqrt{x}$

Average Cost In Exercises 13 and 14, use the cost function to find the production level for which the average cost is a minimum. For this production level, show that the marginal cost and average cost are equal.

13. $C = 2x^2 + 5x + 18$

14. $C = x^3 - 6x^2 + 13x$

15. *Profit* A commodity has a demand function modeled by $p = 100 - 0.5x^2$ and a total cost function modeled by $C = 40x + 37.5$.

(a) What price yields a maximum profit?

(b) When the profit is maximized, what is the average cost per unit?

16. *Profit* How would the answer to Exercise 15 change if the marginal cost rose from \$40 per unit to \$50 per unit? In other words, rework Exercise 15 using the cost function $C = 50x + 37.5$.

Profit In Exercises 17 and 18, find the amount s of advertising that maximizes the profit P. (s and P are measured in thousands of dollars.) Find the point of diminishing returns.

17. $P = -2s^3 + 35s^2 - 100s + 200$

18. $P = -0.1s^3 + 6s^2 + 400$

19. *Profit* The cost per unit in the production of a type of radio is $60. The manufacturer charges $90 per unit for orders of 100 or less. To encourage large orders, however, the manufacturer reduces the charge by $0.10 per radio for each order in excess of 100 units. For instance, an order of 101 radios would be $89.90 per radio, an order of 102 radios would be $89.80 per radio, and so on. Find the largest order the manufacturer should allow to obtain a maximum profit.

20. *Profit* A real estate office handles 50 apartment units. When the rent is $540 per month, all units are occupied. For each $30 increase in rent, however, an average of one unit becomes vacant. Each occupied unit requires an average of $36 per month for service and repairs. What rent should be charged to obtain a maximum profit?

21. *Revenue* When a wholesaler sold a certain product at $40 per unit, sales were 300 units each week. After a price increase of $5, however, the average number of units sold dropped to 275 each week. Assuming that the demand function is linear, what price per unit will yield a maximum total revenue?

22. *Profit* Assume that the amount of money deposited in a bank is proportional to the square of the interest rate the bank pays on the money. Furthermore, the bank can reinvest the money at 12% simple interest. Find the interest rate the bank should pay to maximize its profit.

23. *Cost* A power station is on one side of a river that is 0.5 mile wide, and a factory is 6 miles downstream on the other side of the river (see figure). It costs $6 per foot to run power lines overland and $8 per foot to run them underwater. Find the most economical path for the power line from the power station to the factory.

24. *Cost* An offshore oil well is 1 mile off the coast. The refinery is 2 miles down the coast. Laying pipe in the ocean is twice as expensive as laying it on land. Find the most economical path for the pipe from the well to the refinery.

25. *Cost* A small business uses a minivan to make deliveries. The cost per hour for fuel for the van is $C = v^2/600$, where v is the speed of the minivan (in miles per hour). The driver of the minivan is paid $10 per hour. Find the speed that minimizes the cost of a 110-mile trip. (Assume there are no costs other than fuel and wages.)

26. *Cost* Repeat Exercise 25 for a fuel cost per hour of

$$C = \frac{v^2 + 360}{720}$$

and a wage of $8 per hour.

Elasticity In Exercises 27–32, find the price elasticity of demand for the demand function at the indicated *x*-value. Is the demand elastic, inelastic, or of unit elasticity at the indicated *x*-value?

Demand Function	Quantity Demanded
27. $p = 400 - 3x$	$x = 20$
28. $p = 5 - 0.03x$	$x = 100$
29. $p = 300 - 0.2x^2$	$x = 30$
30. $p = \dfrac{500}{x+2}$	$x = 23$
31. $p = \dfrac{100}{x^2} + 2$	$x = 10$
32. $p = 100 - \sqrt{0.2x}$	$x = 125$

33. *Elasticity* The demand function for a product is

$$x = 20 - 2p^2.$$

(a) Consider a price of $2. If the price increases by 5%, what is the corresponding percent change in the quantity demanded?

(b) Average elasticity of demand is defined to be the percent change in quantity divided by the percent change in price. Use the percent of part (a) to find the average elasticity over the interval [2, 2.1].

(c) Find the elasticity for a price of $2 and compare the result with that of part (b).

(d) Find an expression for the total revenue and find the values of x and p that maximize the total revenue.

34. *Elasticity* The demand function for a product is

$$p^3 + x^3 = 9.$$

(a) Find the price elasticity of demand when $x = 2$.

(b) Find the values of x and p that maximize the total revenue.

(c) For the value of x found in part (b), show that the price elasticity of demand has unit elasticity.

35. *Elasticity* The demand function for a product is

$$p = (16 - x)^{1/2}, \qquad 0 < x < 16.$$

(a) Find the price elasticity of demand when $x = 9$.
(b) Find the values of x and p that maximize the total revenue.
(c) For the value of x found in part (b), show that the price elasticity of demand has unit elasticity.

Know this ↗

36. *Revenue* The demand for a car wash is

$$x = 600 - 50p,$$

where the current price is $5.00. Can revenue be increased by lowering the price and thus attracting more customers? Use price elasticity of demand to determine your answer.

37. *Revenue* Repeat Exercise 36 with a demand function of

$$x = 800 - 40p.$$

38. A demand function is modeled by $x = a/p^m$, where a is a constant and $m > 1$. Show that $\eta = -m$. In other words, show that a 1% increase in price results in an $m\%$ decrease in the quantity demanded.

39. *Railroad Revenues* The annual revenue (in millions of dollars) for Union Pacific for the years 1985–1994 can be modeled by

$$R = 4.7t^4 - 193.5t^3 + 2941.7t^2 - 19{,}294.7t + 52{,}012,$$

where $t = 0$ corresponds to 1980. *(Source: Union Pacific Corporation)*

(a) During which year, between 1985 and 1994, was Union Pacific's revenue the least?
(b) During which year was the revenue the greatest?
(c) Find the revenue for each year in parts (a) and (b).
(d) Use a graphing utility to graph the revenue function. Then use the zoom and trace features to confirm the results in parts (a), (b), and (c).

40. *Banana Sales* The annual net profit (in millions of dollars) for Chiquita Brands for the years 1983–1991 can be modeled by

$$P = 0.33t^4 - 9.35t^3 + 94.88t^2 - 399.98t + 616.62,$$

where $t = 0$ corresponds to 1980. *(Source: Chiquita Brands International, Inc.)*

(a) During which year, between 1983 and 1991, was Chiquita's profit the least?
(b) During which year was the profit the greatest?
(c) Find the profit for each year in parts (a) and (b).
(d) Use a graphing utility to graph the profit function. Then use the zoom and trace features to confirm the results in parts (a), (b), and (c).

41. Match each graph with the function it best represents—a demand function, a revenue function, a cost function, or a profit function. Explain your reasoning. [The graphs are labeled (a)–(d).]

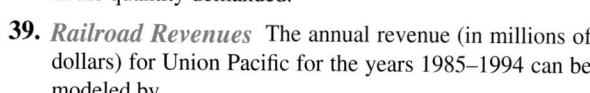

42. *Research Project* Choose an innovative product like the one describe below. Use your school's library or some other reference source to research the history of the product. Collect data about the revenue that product has generated, and find a mathematical model for the data. Summarize your findings.

— *Business Capsule* —

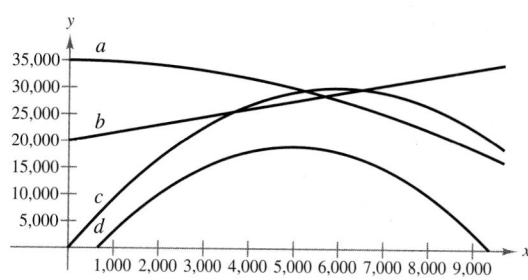

Courtesy of the University of Michigan Economics Club, Flint Michigan

The economics club at the University of Michigan at Flint marketed "Economist Greats" trading cards, featuring statistics on 29 famous economists, such as Milton Friedman. Profits from the cards were used to finance trips to the Chicago Federal Reserve Bank. Pictured are: (left to right, kneeling) Thomas Lowell, vice president; Michael Kidder, president; Bryan Klawuhir, secretary; Bonnie Kincaid, treasurer; and (left to right standing) Vikac Kapur; Professor Dale Matcheck, club advisor; and Michael Wickerham.

Case Study: Consumer Response to Price Changes

PROFILE

COMPANY
Central and South West Services, Inc.
■
LOCATION
Dallas, TX
■
TYPE OF BUSINESS
A holding company that owns four electric utilities
■

Economists and business managers are often interested in how consumers respond to a change in the price of a product or service. Knowledge of the precise magnitude of the response or *price elasticity of demand* for its product is often useful in helping a firm formulate its pricing strategy.

Central and South West (C & SW), Inc. is a public utility holding company in Dallas, Texas that currently owns four electric utilities. Among its many customers are a large number of commercial and industrial purchasers of electricity. Analysts at Central and South West Services, a subsidiary of C & SW, are sometimes called upon to construct models of the demand for electricity by commercial and industrial users. Such models, in turn, can be used to generate price elasticities of demand for electrical usage.

The quantity of electricity demanded is likely to be a function of many variables in addition to the price. To estimate commercial and industrial electricity demand in the state of Texas, C & SW Services constructed a model including the price of electricity and several other "explanatory" variables. In order to hold constant all of the other variables so that the focus is solely on the effects of *price* changes on electricity demand, the values of the explanatory variables for the second quarter of 1993 were plugged into the model to yield the following, more compact electricity demand equation:

$$Y = 429937.843 - 7.4363X.$$

where:
 Y = Total quarterly sales of electricity to commercial and industrial users (kilowatt hours, KWH)
 X = Price of electricity ($/KWH), obtained from typical bills of commercial and industrial electricity users

This equation describes how the quantity of electricity demanded by commercial and industrial users (Y) varies with the price (X), *given the economic conditions that prevailed in the second quarter of 1993.* Moreover, taking the derivative of electricity demand with respect to price yields

$$dY/dX = -7.4363.$$

Applying the definition of price elasticity of demand (η) yields the elasticity coefficient:

$$\eta = (dY/dX) \cdot (X/Y)$$
$$= -7.4363 \cdot (X/Y)$$

This equation can be used to compute the price elasticity of demand at each price (X) and the corresponding quantity of electricity demanded (Y). The table below shows these calculations over a sample range of electricity prices. Note that the elasticity coefficient is negative, indicating an inverse relation between price and quantity of electricity demanded. Also, note that $|\eta| < 1$, indicating that electricity demand is *inelastic* over this range. For example, at a price of 3645.73, the quantity of electricity demanded falls by about 0.07 percent for a 1 percent increase in price.

Price ($/KWH) (X)	Commercial and Industrial Electricity Sales (KWH) (Y)	Price Elasticity of Demand (η)
3645.73	402,827.101	−0.067
3745.73	402,083.471	−0.069
3845.73	401,339.841	−0.071
3945.73	400,596.211	−0.073
4045.73	399,852.581	−0.075
4145.73	399,108.951	−0.077
4245.73	398,365.321	−0.079
4345.73	397,621.691	−0.081
4445.73	396,878.061	−0.083
4545.73	396,134.431	−0.085
4645.73	395,390.801	−0.087
4745.73	394,647.171	−0.089
4845.73	393,903.541	−0.091
4945.73	393,159.911	−0.094
5045.73	392,416.281	−0.096
5145.73	391,672.651	−0.098
5245.73	390,929.021	−0.100
5345.73	390,185.391	−0.102
5445.73	389,441.761	−0.104
5545.73	388,698.131	−0.106

Courtesy of CSW, Inc.

Dr. Enrique Mejorada is a Senior Strategic Planning Consultant for Central and South West Services, Inc. ■

What Would You Do?

1. Plot the data on the quantity of electricity sales at various prices to show that the commercial and industrial demand curve for electricity is *linear*. Why does the price elasticity of demand change along a linear demand curve? What implications might this have on the pricing decisions of an electric utility?

2. Why do you think the demand for electricity by commercial and industrial users is *inelastic* with respect to price?

3. Given that the demand for electricity is inelastic, what would you expect to happen to an electric utility's total revenue as it sold more electricity by lowering its price? Show this using some of the price and sales figures presented in the table.

3.6 | Asymptotes

Vertical Asymptotes and Infinite Limits ■ *Horizontal Asymptotes and Limits at Infinity* ■ *Applications of Asymptotes*

Vertical Asymptotes and Infinite Limits

In the first three sections of this chapter, you studied ways in which you can use calculus to help analyze the graph of a function. In this section, you will study another valuable aid to curve sketching—the determination of vertical and horizontal asymptotes.

Recall from Section 1.5, Example 10, that the function

$$f(x) = \frac{3}{x-2}$$

is unbounded as x approaches 2 (see Figure 3.44). This type of behavior is described by saying that the line $x = 2$ is a **vertical asymptote** of the graph of f. The type of limit in which $f(x)$ approaches infinity (or negative infinity) as x approaches c from the left or from the right is an **infinite limit.** The infinite limits for the function $f(x) = 3/(x-2)$ can be written as

$$\lim_{x \to 2^-} \frac{3}{x-2} = -\infty \quad \text{and} \quad \lim_{x \to 2^+} \frac{3}{x-2} = \infty.$$

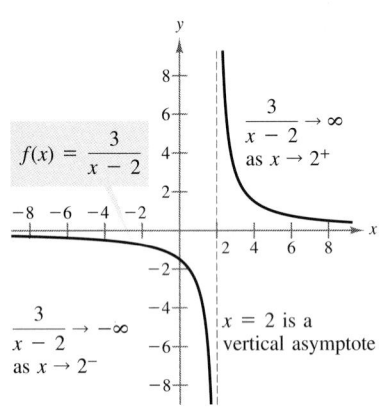

$$f(x) = \frac{3}{x-2}$$

$\dfrac{3}{x-2} \to \infty$ as $x \to 2^+$

$\dfrac{3}{x-2} \to -\infty$ as $x \to 2^-$

$x = 2$ is a vertical asymptote

FIGURE 3.44

Definition of Vertical Asymptote

If $f(x)$ approaches infinity (or negative infinity) as x approaches c from the right or from the left, then the line $x = c$ is a **vertical asymptote** of the graph of f.

▦ TECHNOLOGY

When you use a graphing utility to graph a function that has a vertical asymptote, the utility may try to connect separate branches of the graph. For instance, the figure at the right shows the graph of $f(x) = 3/(x-2)$ on a graphing calculator.

This line is not part of the graph of the function.

The graph of the function has two branches.

One of the most common instances of a vertical asymptote is the graph of a *rational function*—that is, a function of the form $f(x) = p(x)/q(x)$, where $p(x)$ and $q(x)$ are polynomials. If c is a real number such that $q(c) = 0$ and $p(c) \neq 0$, then the graph of f has a vertical asymptote at $x = c$. Example 1 shows four typical cases.

EXAMPLE 1 *Finding Infinite Limits*

Limit from the Left	*Limit from the Right*	
a. $\displaystyle\lim_{x \to 1^-} \frac{1}{x - 1} = -\infty$	$\displaystyle\lim_{x \to 1^+} \frac{1}{x - 1} = \infty$	(See Figure 3.45a.)
b. $\displaystyle\lim_{x \to 1^-} \frac{-1}{x - 1} = \infty$	$\displaystyle\lim_{x \to 1^+} \frac{-1}{x - 1} = -\infty$	(See Figure 3.45b.)
c. $\displaystyle\lim_{x \to 1^-} \frac{-1}{(x - 1)^2} = -\infty$	$\displaystyle\lim_{x \to 1^+} \frac{-1}{(x - 1)^2} = -\infty$	(See Figure 3.45c.)
d. $\displaystyle\lim_{x \to 1^-} \frac{1}{(x - 1)^2} = \infty$	$\displaystyle\lim_{x \to 1^+} \frac{1}{(x - 1)^2} = \infty$	(See Figure 3.45d.)

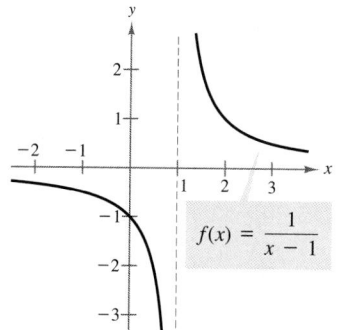

$f(x) = \dfrac{1}{x - 1}$

$\displaystyle\lim_{x \to 1^-} \frac{1}{x - 1} = -\infty \qquad \lim_{x \to 1^+} \frac{1}{x - 1} = \infty$

(a)

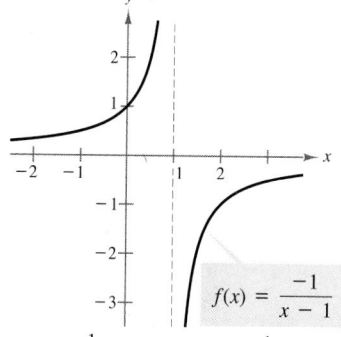

$f(x) = \dfrac{-1}{x - 1}$

$\displaystyle\lim_{x \to 1^-} \frac{-1}{x - 1} = \infty \qquad \lim_{x \to 1^+} \frac{-1}{x - 1} = -\infty$

(b)

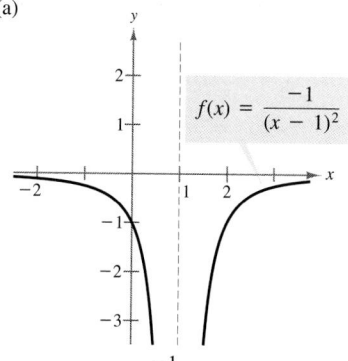

$f(x) = \dfrac{-1}{(x - 1)^2}$

$\displaystyle\lim_{x \to 1} \frac{-1}{(x - 1)^2} = -\infty$

(c)

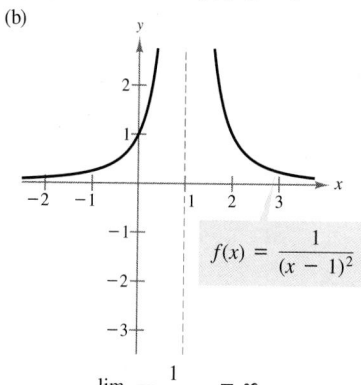

$f(x) = \dfrac{1}{(x - 1)^2}$

$\displaystyle\lim_{x \to 1} \frac{1}{(x - 1)^2} = \infty$

(d)

FIGURE 3.45

Each of the graphs in Example 1 has only one vertical asymptote. As shown in the next example, the graph of a rational function can have more than one vertical asymptote.

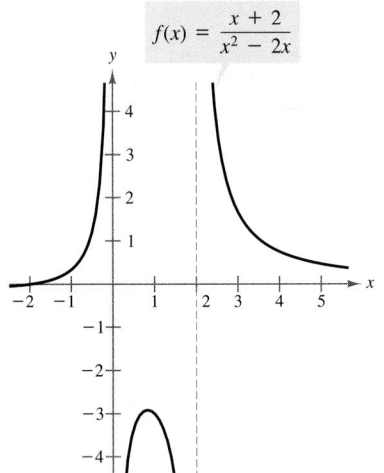

$$f(x) = \frac{x + 2}{x^2 - 2x}$$

FIGURE 3.46   Vertical Asymptotes at $x = 0$ and $x = 2$

EXAMPLE 2 *Finding Vertical Asymptotes*

Determine the vertical asymptotes of the graph of

$$f(x) = \frac{x + 2}{x^2 - 2x}.$$

Solution

The possible vertical asymptotes correspond to the x-values for which the denominator is zero.

$x^2 - 2x = 0$	*Set denominator equal to 0.*
$x(x - 2) = 0$	*Factor.*
$x = 0, \ 2$	*Zeros of denominator*

Because the numerator of $f(x)$ is not zero at either of these x-values, you can conclude that the graph of f has two vertical asymptotes—one at $x = 0$ and one at $x = 2$, as shown in Figure 3.46.   ▪

EXAMPLE 3 *Finding a Vertical Asymptote*

Determine the vertical asymptotes of the graph of

$$f(x) = \frac{x^2 + 2x - 8}{x^2 - 4}.$$

Solution

First factor the numerator and denominator. Then cancel common factors.

$f(x) = \dfrac{x^2 + 2x - 8}{x^2 - 4}$	*Original function*
$= \dfrac{(x + 4)(x - 2)}{(x + 2)(x - 2)}$	*Factor numerator and denominator.*
$= \dfrac{(x + 4)\cancel{(x - 2)}}{(x + 2)\cancel{(x - 2)}}$	*Cancel common factors.*
$= \dfrac{x + 4}{x + 2}, \qquad x \neq 2$	*Simplify.*

For all values of x other than $x = 2$, the graph of this simplified function is the same as the graph of f. Thus, you can conclude that the graph of f has only one vertical asymptote. This occurs at $x = -2$, as shown in Figure 3.47.   ▪

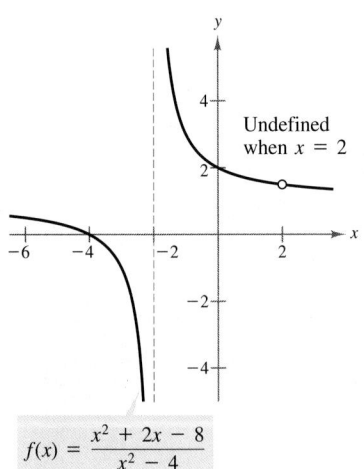

Undefined when $x = 2$

$$f(x) = \frac{x^2 + 2x - 8}{x^2 - 4}$$

FIGURE 3.47   Vertical Asymptote at $x = -2$

From Example 3, you know that the graph of

$$f(x) = \frac{x^2 + 2x - 8}{x^2 - 4}$$

has a vertical asymptote at $x = -2$. This implies that the limit of $f(x)$ as $x \to -2$ from the right (or from the left) is either ∞ or $-\infty$. But without looking at the graph, how can you determine that the limit from the left is *negative* infinity and the limit from the right is *positive* infinity? That is, why is

$$\lim_{x \to 2^-} \frac{x^2 + 2x - 8}{x^2 - 4} = -\infty \qquad \textit{Limit from the left}$$

and

$$\lim_{x \to 2^+} \frac{x^2 + 2x - 8}{x^2 - 4} = \infty ? \qquad \textit{Limit from the right}$$

It is cumbersome to determine these limits analytically, and you may find the graphical method shown in Example 4 to be more efficient.

EXAMPLE 4 *Determining Infinite Limits*

Find the limits.

$$\lim_{x \to 1^-} \frac{x^2 - 3x}{x - 1} \quad \text{and} \quad \lim_{x \to 1^+} \frac{x^2 - 3x}{x - 1}$$

Solution

Begin by considering the function

$$f(x) = \frac{x^2 - 3x}{x - 1}.$$

Because the denominator is zero when $x = 1$ and the numerator is not zero when $x = 1$, it follows that the graph of the function has a vertical asymptote at $x = 1$. This implies that each of the given limits is either ∞ or $-\infty$. To determine which, use a graphing utility to graph the function, as shown in Figure 3.48. From the graph, you can see that the limit from the left is positive infinity and the limit from the right is negative infinity. That is,

$$\lim_{x \to 1^-} \frac{x^2 - 3x}{x - 1} = \infty \qquad \textit{Limit from the left}$$

and

$$\lim_{x \to 1^+} \frac{x^2 - 3x}{x - 1} = -\infty. \qquad \textit{Limit from the right}$$

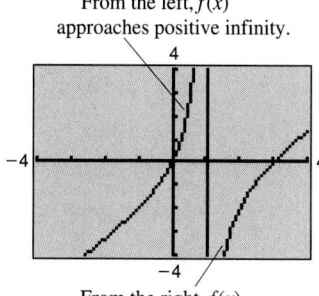

From the left, $f(x)$
approaches positive infinity.

From the right, $f(x)$
approaches negative infinity.

FIGURE 3.48

Note In Example 4, try evaluating $f(x)$ at x-values that are just barely to the left of 1. You will find that you can make the values of $f(x)$ arbitrarily large by choosing x sufficiently close to 1. For instance, $f(0.99999) = 199,999$.

Horizontal Asymptotes and Limits at Infinity

Another type of limit, called a **limit at infinity,** specifies a finite value approached by a function as x increases (or decreases) without bound.

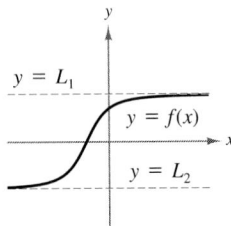

Definition of Horizontal Asymptote

If f is a function and L_1 and L_2 are real numbers, the statements

$$\lim_{x \to \infty} f(x) = L_1 \quad \text{and} \quad \lim_{x \to -\infty} f(x) = L_2$$

denote **limits at infinity.** The lines $y = L_1$ and $y = L_2$ are **horizontal asymptotes** of the graph of f.

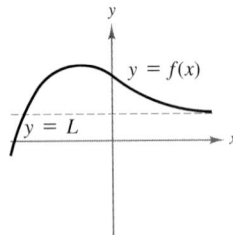

FIGURE 3.49

Figure 3.49 shows two ways in which the graph of a function can approach one or more horizontal asymptotes. Note that it is possible for the graph of a function to cross its horizontal asymptote.

Limits at infinity share many of the properties of limits discussed in Section 1.5. When finding horizontal asymptotes, you can use the property that

$$\lim_{x \to \infty} \frac{1}{x^r} = 0, \quad r > 0 \qquad \text{and} \qquad \lim_{x \to -\infty} \frac{1}{x^r} = 0, \quad r > 0.$$

(The second limit assumes that x^r is defined when $x < 0$.)

EXAMPLE 5 *Finding Limits at Infinity*

Find the limit: $\displaystyle \lim_{x \to \infty} \left(5 - \frac{2}{x^2} \right)$.

Solution

$$\lim_{x \to \infty} \left(5 - \frac{2}{x^2} \right) = \lim_{x \to \infty} 5 - \lim_{x \to \infty} \frac{2}{x^2}$$

$$= \lim_{x \to \infty} 5 - 2 \left(\lim_{x \to \infty} \frac{1}{x^2} \right)$$

$$= 5 - 2(0)$$

$$= 5$$

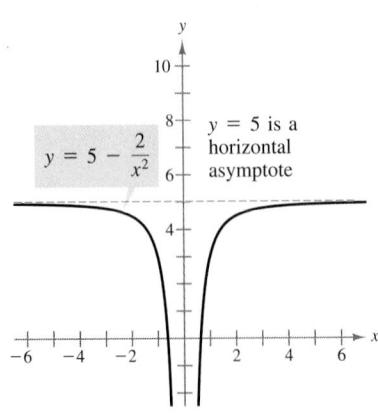

$y = 5 - \dfrac{2}{x^2}$ $y = 5$ is a horizontal asymptote

FIGURE 3.50

You can verify this limit by sketching the graph of

$$f(x) = 5 - \frac{2}{x^2},$$

as shown in Figure 3.50. Note that the graph has $y = 5$ as a horizontal asymptote to the right. By evaluating the limit of $f(x)$ as $x \to -\infty$, you can show that this line is also a horizontal asymptote to the left. ■

Some functions have two horizontal asymptotes: one to the right and one to the left. For instance, try sketching the graph of

$$f(x) = \frac{x}{\sqrt{x^2 + 1}}.$$

What horizontal asymptotes does the function appear to have?

There is an easy way to determine whether the graph of a *rational* function has a horizontal asymptote. This shortcut is based on a comparison of the degrees of the numerator and denominator of the rational function.

Horizontal Asymptotes of Rational Functions

Let $f(x) = p(x)/q(x)$ be a rational function.

1. If the degree of the numerator is less than the degree of the denominator, then $y = 0$ is a horizontal asymptote of the graph of f (to the left and to the right).
2. If the degree of the numerator is equal to the degree of the denominator, then $y = a/b$ is a horizontal asymptote of the graph of f (to the left and to the right), where a and b are the leading coefficients of $p(x)$ and $q(x)$, respectively.
3. If the degree of the numerator is greater than the degree of the denominator, then the graph of f has no horizontal asymptote.

EXAMPLE 6 *Finding Horizontal Asymptotes*

Find the horizontal asymptotes of the graphs of the functions.

a. $y = \dfrac{-2x + 3}{3x^2 + 1}$ **b.** $y = \dfrac{-2x^2 + 3}{3x^2 + 1}$ **c.** $y = \dfrac{-2x^3 + 3}{3x^2 + 1}$

Solution

a. Because the degree of the numerator is less than the degree of the denominator horizontal asymptote. (See Figure 3.51a.)
b. Because the degree of the numerator is equal to the degree of the denominator, the line $y = -\frac{2}{3}$ is a horizontal asymptote. (See Figure 3.51b.)
c. Because the degree of the numerator is greater than the degree of the denominator, the graph has no horizontal asymptote. (See Figure 3.51c.)

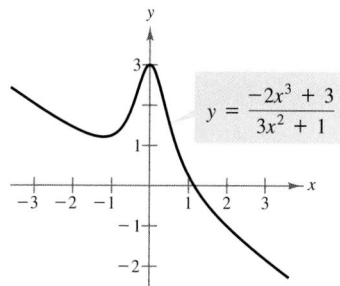

(a) $y = 0$ is a horizontal asymptote.

(b) $y = -\frac{2}{3}$ is a horizontal asymptote.

(c) No horizontal asymptote.

FIGURE 3.51

Applications of Asymptotes

There are many examples of asymptotic behavior in real life. For instance, Example 7 describes the asymptotic behavior of an average cost function.

Real Life

EXAMPLE 7 *Modeling Average Cost*

A small business invests $5000 in a new product. In addition to this initial investment, the product will cost $0.50 per unit to produce. Find the average cost per unit if 1000 units are produced, if 10,000 units are produced, and if 100,000 units are produced. What is the limit of the average cost as the number of units produced increases?

Solution

From the given information, you can model the total cost C (in dollars) by

$$C = 0.5x + 5000, \qquad \text{\textit{Total cost function}}$$

where x is the number of units produced. This implies that the average cost function is

$$\overline{C} = \frac{C}{x} = 0.5 + \frac{5000}{x}. \qquad \text{\textit{Average cost function}}$$

If only 1000 units are produced, then the average cost per unit is

$$\overline{C} = 0.5 + \frac{5000}{1000} = \$5.50. \qquad \text{\textit{Average cost for 1000 units}}$$

If 10,000 units are produced, then the average cost per unit is

$$\overline{C} = 0.5 + \frac{5000}{10,000} = \$1.00. \qquad \text{\textit{Average cost for 10,000 units}}$$

If 100,000 units are produced, then the average cost per unit is

$$\overline{C} = 0.5 + \frac{5000}{100,000} = \$0.55. \qquad \text{\textit{Average cost for 100,000 units}}$$

As x approaches infinity, the limiting average cost per unit is

$$\lim_{x \to \infty} \left(0.5 + \frac{5000}{x} \right) = \$0.50.$$

As shown in Figure 3.52, this example points out one of the major problems of small businesses. That is, it is difficult to have competitively low prices when the production level is low. ■

FIGURE 3.52 As $x \longrightarrow \infty$, the average cost per unit approaches $0.50.

Note In Example 7, suppose that the small business had made an initial investment of $50,000. How would this change the answers to the questions? Would it change the average cost of producing x units? Would it change the limiting average cost per unit?

Real
Life

EXAMPLE 8 *Modeling Smokestack Emission*

During the 1980s, industries in the United States spent billions of dollars to reduce air pollution. For instance, the estimated cost of air pollution control in 1989 was 1.8 billion dollars. *(Source: U.S. Bureau of the Census, Current Industrial Reports)*

A manufacturing plant has determined that the cost C (in dollars) of removing $p\%$ of the smokestack pollutants of its main smokestack is modeled by

$$C = \frac{80,000p}{100 - p}.$$

What is the vertical asymptote of this function? What does the vertical asymptote mean to the plant owners?

Solution

The graph of the cost function is shown in Figure 3.53. From the graph, you can see that $p = 100$ is the vertical asymptote. This means that as the plant attempts to remove higher and higher percents of the pollutants, the cost increases dramatically. For instance, the cost of removing 85% of the pollutants is

$$C = \frac{80,000(85)}{100 - 85} \approx \$453,333 \qquad \textit{Cost for 85\% removal}$$

but the cost of removing 90% is

$$C = \frac{80,000(90)}{100 - 90} \approx \$720,000. \qquad \textit{Cost for 90\% removal}$$

Smokestack Emission

FIGURE 3.53

Discussion Problem   *Indirect Costs*

In Example 8, the given cost model considers only the direct cost for the manufacturing plant. Describe the possible indirect costs incurred by society as the plant attempts to remove more and more of the pollutants from its smokestack emission.

Warm Up

The following warm-up exercises involve skills that were covered in earlier sections. You will use these skills in the exercise set for this section.

In Exercises 1–6, find the limit.

1. $\lim_{x \to 2} (x + 1)$

2. $\lim_{x \to -1} (3x + 4)$

3. $\lim_{x \to -3} \dfrac{2x^2 + x - 15}{x + 3}$

4. $\lim_{x \to 2} \dfrac{3x^2 - 8x + 4}{x - 2}$

5. $\lim_{x \to 0^+} \sqrt{x}$

6. $\lim_{x \to 1^+} \left(x + \sqrt{x - 1}\right)$

In Exercises 7–10, find the average cost and the marginal cost.

7. $C = 150 + 3x$

8. $C = 1900 + 1.7x + 0.002x^2$

9. $C = 0.005x^2 + 0.5x + 1375$

10. $C = 760 + 0.05x$

E X E R C I S E S   3.6

 means that technology can help you solve or check the exercise(s).

In Exercises 1–8, find the vertical and horizontal asymptotes.

1. $f(x) = \dfrac{x^2 + 1}{x^2}$

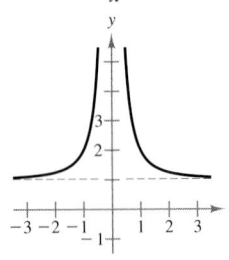

2. $f(x) = \dfrac{4}{(x - 2)^3}$

5. $f(x) = \dfrac{x^3}{x^2 - 1}$

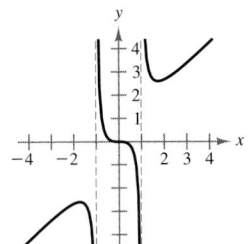

6. $f(x) = \dfrac{-4x}{x^2 + 4}$

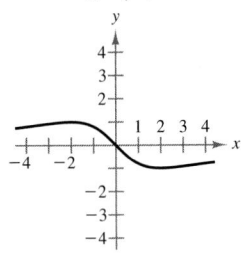

3. $f(x) = \dfrac{x^2 - 2}{x^2 - x - 2}$

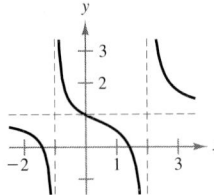

4. $f(x) = \dfrac{2 + x}{1 - x}$

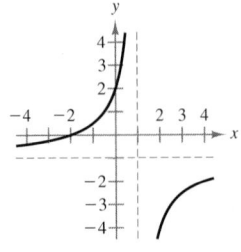

7. $f(x) = \dfrac{x^2 - 1}{2x^2 - 8}$

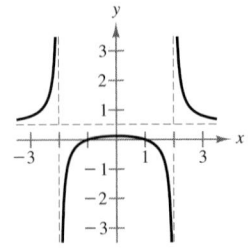

8. $f(x) = \dfrac{x^2 + 1}{x^3 - 8}$

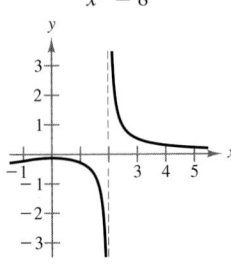

In Exercises 9–14, match the function with its graph. Use horizontal asymptotes as an aid. [The graphs are labeled (a)–(f).]

9. $f(x) = \dfrac{3x^2}{x^2 + 2}$

10. $f(x) = \dfrac{2x}{\sqrt{x^2 + 2}}$

11. $f(x) = \dfrac{x}{x^2 + 2}$

12. $f(x) = 2 + \dfrac{x^2}{x^4 + 1}$

13. $f(x) = 5 - \dfrac{1}{x^2 + 1}$

14. $f(x) = \dfrac{2x^2 - 3x + 5}{x^2 + 1}$

(a)

(b)

(c)

(d)

(e)

(f)
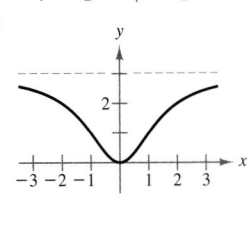

In Exercises 15–22, find the limit.

15. $\displaystyle\lim_{x \to -2^-} \dfrac{1}{(x + 2)^2}$

16. $\displaystyle\lim_{x \to -2^-} \dfrac{1}{x + 2}$

17. $\displaystyle\lim_{x \to 3^+} \dfrac{x - 4}{x - 3}$

18. $\displaystyle\lim_{x \to 1^+} \dfrac{2 + x}{1 - x}$

19. $\displaystyle\lim_{x \to 4^-} \dfrac{x^2}{x^2 - 16}$

20. $\displaystyle\lim_{x \to 4} \dfrac{x^2}{x^2 + 16}$

21. $\displaystyle\lim_{x \to 0^-} \left(1 + \dfrac{1}{x}\right)$

22. $\displaystyle\lim_{x \to 0^-} \left(x^2 - \dfrac{1}{x}\right)$

In Exercises 23–32, find the limit.

23. $\displaystyle\lim_{x \to \infty} \dfrac{2x - 1}{3x + 2}$

24. $\displaystyle\lim_{x \to \infty} \dfrac{5x^3 + 1}{10x^3 - 3x^2 + 7}$

25. $\displaystyle\lim_{x \to \infty} \dfrac{3x}{4x^2 - 1}$

26. $\displaystyle\lim_{x \to \infty} \dfrac{2x^{10} - 1}{10x^{11} - 3}$

27. $\displaystyle\lim_{x \to -\infty} \dfrac{5x^2}{x + 3}$

28. $\displaystyle\lim_{x \to \infty} \dfrac{x^3 - 2x^2 + 3x + 1}{x^2 - 3x + 2}$

29. $\displaystyle\lim_{x \to \infty} (2x - x^{-2})$

30. $\displaystyle\lim_{x \to \infty} (x + 3)^{-2}$

31. $\displaystyle\lim_{x \to -\infty} \left(\dfrac{2x}{x - 1} + \dfrac{3x}{x + 1}\right)$

32. $\displaystyle\lim_{x \to \infty} \left(\dfrac{2x^2}{x - 1} + \dfrac{3x}{x + 1}\right)$

In Exercises 33 and 34, complete the table. Then use the result to estimate the limit of $f(x)$ as x approaches infinity.

33. $f(x) = \dfrac{x + 1}{x\sqrt{x}}$

x	10^0	10^1	10^2	10^3	10^4	10^5	10^6
$f(x)$							

34. $f(x) = x^2 - x\sqrt{x(x - 1)}$

x	10^0	10^1	10^2	10^3	10^4	10^5	10^6
$f(x)$							

In Exercises 35 and 36, complete the table and use the result to estimate the limit of $f(x)$ as x approaches infinity and as x approaches negative infinity.

35. $f(x) = \dfrac{2x}{\sqrt{x^2 + 4}}$

x	-10^6	-10^4	-10^2	10^0	10^2	10^4	10^6
$f(x)$							

36. $f(x) = x - \sqrt{x(x - 1)}$

x	-10^6	-10^4	-10^2	10^0	10^2	10^4	10^6
$f(x)$							

In Exercises 37–54, sketch the graph of the equation. Use intercepts, extrema, and asymptotes as sketching aids.

37. $y = \dfrac{2+x}{1-x}$

38. $y = \dfrac{x-3}{x-2}$

39. $f(x) = \dfrac{x^2}{x^2+9}$

40. $f(x) = \dfrac{x^2}{x^2-9}$

41. $g(x) = \dfrac{x^2}{x^2-16}$

42. $g(x) = \dfrac{x}{x^2-4}$

43. $xy^2 = 4$

44. $x^2y = 4$

45. $y = \dfrac{2x}{1-x}$

46. $y = \dfrac{2x}{1-x^2}$

47. $y = 3(1-x^{-2})$

48. $y = 1 + x^{-1}$

49. $f(x) = \dfrac{1}{x^2-x-2}$

50. $f(x) = \dfrac{x-2}{x^2-4x+3}$

51. $g(x) = \dfrac{x^2-x-2}{x-2}$

52. $g(x) = \dfrac{x^2-9}{x+3}$

53. $y = \dfrac{2x^2-6}{(x-1)^2}$

54. $y = \dfrac{x}{(x+1)^2}$

55. *Cost* The cost C (in dollars) of producing x units of a product is $C = 1.35x + 4570$.
  (a) Find $\overline{C}$ when $x = 100$ and when $x = 1000$.
  (b) What is the limit of $\overline{C}$ as x approaches infinity?

56. *Average Cost* A business has a cost (in dollars) of $C = 0.5x + 500$ for producing x units. Find the limit of the average cost per unit as x approaches infinity.

57. *Cost* The cost C (in millions of dollars) for the federal government to seize $p\%$ of a type of illegal drug as it enters the country is modeled by
$$C = \frac{528p}{100 - p}, \qquad 0 \le p < 100.$$
  (a) Find the cost of seizing 25%.
  (b) Find the cost of seizing 50%.
  (c) Find the cost of seizing 75%.
  (d) Find the limit of C as $p \to 100^-$.

58. *Cost* The cost C (in dollars) of removing $p\%$ of the air pollutants in the stack emission of a utility company that burns coal is modeled by
$$C = \frac{80,000p}{100 - p}, \qquad 0 \le p < 100.$$
  (a) Find the cost of removing 15%.
  (b) Find the cost of removing 50%.
  (c) Find the cost of removing 90%.
  (d) Find the limit of C as $p \to 100^-$.

59. *Learning Curve* Psychologists have developed mathematical models to predict performance P (the percent of correct responses) as a function of n, the number of times a task is performed. One such model is
$$P = \frac{b + \theta a(n-1)}{1 + \theta(n-1)},$$
where a, b, and θ are constants that depend on the actual learning situation. Find the limit of P as n approaches infinity.

 60. *Learning Curve* Consider the learning curve given by
$$P = \frac{0.5 + 0.9(n-1)}{1 + 0.9(n-1)}, \qquad 0 < n.$$
  (a) Complete the table for the model.

n	1	2	3	4	5	6	7	8	9	10
P										

  (b) Find the limit as n approaches infinity.
  (c) Graph this learning curve, and interpret the graph in the context of the problem.

61. *Wildlife Management* The state game commission introduces 30 elk into a new state park. The population N of the herd is modeled by
$$N = \frac{10(3 + 4t)}{1 + 0.1t},$$
where t is the time in years.
  (a) Find the size of the herd after 5, 10, and 25 years.
  (b) According to this model, what is the limiting size of the herd as time progresses?

62. *Average Profit* The cost and revenue functions for a product are
$$C = 34.5x + 15{,}000 \quad \text{and} \quad R = 69.9x.$$
  (a) Find the average profit function
$$\overline{P} = \frac{R - C}{x}.$$
  (b) Find the average profit when x is 1000, 10,000, and 100,000.
  (c) What is the limit of the average profit function as x approaches infinity?

 63. Use a graphing utility to graph
$$f(x) = \frac{3x}{\sqrt{4x^2 + 1}}$$
and locate any horizontal asymptotes.

Curve Sketching: A Summary

Summary of Curve Sketching Techniques ■ *Summary of Simple Polynomial Graphs*

Summary of Curve Sketching Techniques

It would be difficult to overstate the importance of using graphs in mathematics. Descartes's introduction of analytic geometry contributed significantly to the rapid advances of calculus that began during the mid-seventeenth century.

So far, you have studied several concepts that are useful in analyzing the graph of a function.

■ x-intercepts and y-intercepts	(Section 1.2)
■ Domain and range	(Section 1.4)
■ Continuity	(Section 1.6)
■ Differentiability	(Section 2.1)
■ Relative extrema	(Section 3.2)
■ Concavity	(Section 3.3)
■ Points of inflection	(Section 3.3)
■ Vertical asymptotes	(Section 3.6)
■ Horizontal asymptotes	(Section 3.6)

When you are sketching the graph of a function, either by hand or with a graphing utility, remember that you cannot normally show the *entire* graph. The decision as to which part of the graph to show is crucial. For instance, which of the viewing rectangles in Figure 3.54 better represents the graph of

$$f(x) = x^3 - 25x^2 + 74x - 20?$$

The lower viewing rectangle gives a more complete view of the graph, but the context of the problem might indicate that the upper view is better. Here are some guidelines for analyzing the graph of a function.

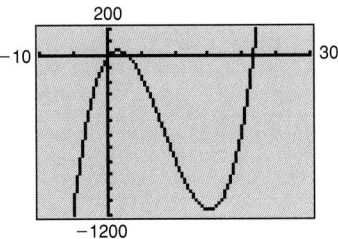

FIGURE 3.54

Guidelines for Analyzing the Graph of a Function

1. Determine the domain and range of the function. If the function models a real-life situation, consider the context.

2. Determine the intercepts and asymptotes of the graph.

3. Locate the x-values where $f'(x)$ and $f''(x)$ are zero or undefined. Use the results to determine the relative extrema and points of inflection.

EXAMPLE 1 *Analyzing a Graph*

Analyze the graph of

$$f(x) = x^3 + 3x^2 - 9x + 5.$$ *Original function*

Solution

Begin by finding the intercepts of the graph. This function factors as

$$f(x) = (x - 1)^2(x + 5).$$ *Factored form*

Thus, the x-intercepts occur when $x = 1$ and $x = -5$. The derivative is

$$f'(x) = 3x^2 + 6x - 9$$ *First derivative*
$$= 3(x - 1)(x + 3).$$ *Factored form*

Thus, the critical numbers of f are $x = 1$ and $x = -3$. The second derivative of f is

$$f''(x) = 6x + 6$$ *Second derivative*
$$= 6(x + 1),$$ *Factored form*

which implies that the second derivative is zero when $x = -1$. Testing the values of $f'(x)$ and $f''(x)$, as shown in Table 3.9, you can see that f has one relative minimum, one relative maximum, and one point of inflection. The graph of f is shown in Figure 3.55.

TABLE 3.9

	$f(x)$	$f'(x)$	$f''(x)$	Shape of graph
x in $(-\infty, -3)$		+	−	Increasing, concave downward
$x = -3$	32	0	−	Relative maximum
x in $(-3, -1)$		−	−	Decreasing, concave downward
$x = -1$	16	−	0	Point of inflection
x in $(-1, 1)$		−	+	Decreasing, concave upward
$x = 1$	0	0	+	Relative minimum
x in $(1, \infty)$		+	+	Increasing, concave upward

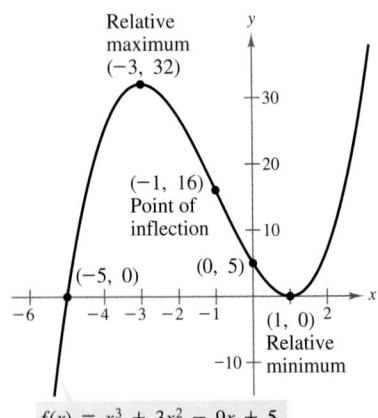

Relative maximum $(-3, 32)$
$(-1, 16)$ Point of inflection
$(-5, 0)$
$(0, 5)$
$(1, 0)$ Relative minimum

$$f(x) = x^3 + 3x^2 - 9x + 5$$

FIGURE 3.55

Note In Example 1, you are able to find the zeros of f, f', and f'' algebraically (by factoring). When this is not feasible, you can use a graphing utility to find the zeros. For instance, the function

$$g(x) = x^3 + 3x^2 - 9x + 6$$

is similar to the function in the example, but it doesn't factor with integer coefficients. Using a graphing utility, you can determine that the function has only one x-intercept, $x \approx -5.0275$.

EXAMPLE 2 *Analyzing a Graph*

Analyze the graph of

$$f(x) = x^4 - 12x^3 + 48x^2 - 64x. \qquad \text{\textit{Original function}}$$

Solution

Begin by finding the intercepts of the graph. This function factors as

$$f(x) = x(x^3 - 12x^2 + 48x - 64)$$
$$= x(x-4)^3. \qquad \text{\textit{Factored form}}$$

Thus, the x-intercepts occur when $x = 0$ and $x = 4$. The derivative is

$$f'(x) = 4x^3 - 36x^2 + 96x - 64 \qquad \text{\textit{First derivative}}$$
$$= 4(x-1)(x-4)^2. \qquad \text{\textit{Factored form}}$$

Thus, the critical numbers of f are $x = 1$ and $x = 4$. The second derivative of f is

$$f''(x) = 12x^2 - 72x + 96 \qquad \text{\textit{Second derivative}}$$
$$= 12(x-4)(x-2), \qquad \text{\textit{Factored form}}$$

which implies that the second derivative is zero when $x = 2$ and $x = 4$. Testing the values of $f'(x)$ and $f''(x)$, as shown in Table 3.10, you can see that f has a minimum and two points of inflection. The graph is shown in Figure 3.56.

TABLE 3.10

	$f(x)$	$f'(x)$	$f''(x)$	Shape of graph
x in $(-\infty, 1)$		$-$	$+$	Decreasing, concave upward
$x = 1$	-27	0	$+$	Minimum
x in $(1, 2)$		$+$	$+$	Increasing, concave upward
$x = 2$	-16	$+$	0	Point of inflection
x in $(2, 4)$		$+$	$-$	Increasing, concave downward
$x = 4$	0	0	0	Point of inflection
x in $(4, \infty)$		$+$	$+$	Increasing, concave upward

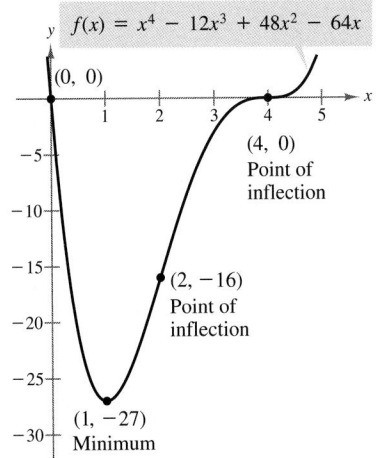

$f(x) = x^4 - 12x^3 + 48x^2 - 64x$

(0, 0)

(4, 0)
Point of inflection

(2, −16)
Point of inflection

(1, −27)
Minimum

FIGURE 3.56

Note A polynomial function of degree n can have at most $n - 1$ relative extrema and at most $n - 2$ points of inflection. For instance, the third-degree polynomial in Example 1 has two relative extrema and one point of inflection. Similarly, the fourth-degree polynomial function in Example 2 has one relative extremum and two points of inflection. Is it possible for a third-degree function to have no relative extrema? Is it possible for a fourth-degree function to have no relative extrema?

Discovery

Show that the function in Example 3 can be rewritten as

$$f(x) = \frac{x^2 - 2x + 4}{x - 2}$$

$$= x + \frac{4}{x - 2}.$$

Use a graphing utility to graph f together with the line $y = x$. How do the two graphs compare as you zoom out? Describe what is meant by a "slant asymptote." Find the slant asymptote of the function $g(x) = \dfrac{x^2 - x - 1}{x - 1}$.

EXAMPLE 3 *Analyzing a Graph*

Analyze the graph of

$$f(x) = \frac{x^2 - 2x + 4}{x - 2}.$$ *Original function*

Solution

The y-intercept occurs at $(0, -2)$. Using the Quadratic Formula on the numerator, you can see that there are no x-intercepts. Because the denominator is zero when $x = 2$ (and the numerator is not zero when $x = 2$), it follows that $x = 2$ is a vertical asymptote of the graph. There are no horizontal asymptotes because the degree of the numerator is greater than the degree of the denominator. The derivative is

$$f'(x) = \frac{(x - 2)(2x - 2) - (x^2 - 2x + 4)}{(x - 2)^2}$$ *First derivative*

$$= \frac{x(x - 4)}{(x - 2)^2}.$$ *Factored form*

Thus, the critical numbers of f are $x = 0$ and $x = 4$. The second derivative is

$$f''(x) = \frac{(x - 2)^2(2x - 4) - (x^2 - 4x)(2)(x - 2)}{(x - 2)^4}$$ *Second derivative*

$$= \frac{(x - 2)(2x^2 - 8x + 8 - 2x^2 + 8x)}{(x - 2)^4}$$

$$= \frac{8}{(x - 2)^3}.$$ *Factored form*

Because the second derivative has no zeros and because $x = 2$ is not in the domain of the function, you can conclude that the graph has no points of inflection. Testing the values of $f'(x)$ and $f''(x)$, as shown in Table 3.11, you can see that f has one relative minimum and one relative maximum. The graph of f is shown in Figure 3.57.

TABLE 3.11

	$f(x)$	$f'(x)$	$f''(x)$	Shape of graph
x in $(-\infty, 0)$		$+$	$-$	Increasing, concave downward
$x = 0$	-2	0	$-$	Relative maximum
x in $(0, 2)$		$-$	$-$	Decreasing, concave downward
$x = 2$	Undef.	Undef.	Undef.	Vertical asymptote
x in $(2, 4)$		$-$	$+$	Decreasing, concave upward
$x = 4$	6	0	$+$	Relative minimum
x in $(4, \infty)$		$+$	$+$	Increasing, concave upward

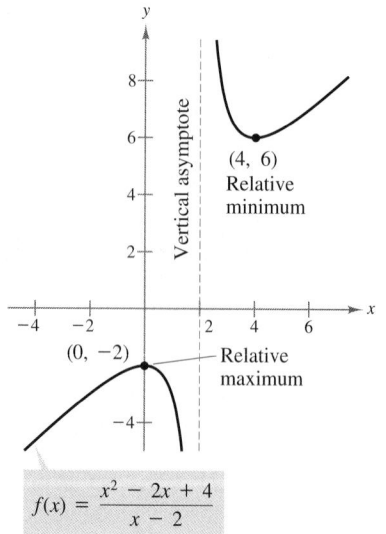

$$f(x) = \frac{x^2 - 2x + 4}{x - 2}$$

FIGURE 3.57

EXAMPLE 4 *Analyzing a Graph*

Analyze the graph of

$$f(x) = \frac{2(x^2 - 9)}{x^2 - 4}.$$ *Original function*

Solution

Begin by writing the function in factored form.

$$f(x) = \frac{2(x - 3)(x + 3)}{(x - 2)(x + 2)}$$ *Factored form*

The y-intercept is $\left(0, \frac{9}{2}\right)$, and the x-intercepts are $(-3, 0)$ and $(3, 0)$. There are vertical asymptotes at $x = \pm 2$ and a horizontal asymptote at $y = 2$. The first derivative is

$$f'(x) = \frac{2[(x^2 - 4)(2x) - (x^2 - 9)(2x)]}{(x^2 - 4)^2}$$ *First derivative*

$$= \frac{20x}{(x^2 - 4)^2}.$$ *Factored form*

Thus, the critical number of f is $x = 0$. The second derivative of f is

$$f''(x) = \frac{(x^2 - 4)^2(20) - (20x)(2)(2x)(x^2 - 4)}{(x^2 - 4)^4}$$ *Second derivative*

$$= \frac{20(x^2 - 4)(x^2 - 4 - 4x^2)}{(x^2 - 4)^4}$$

$$= -\frac{20(3x^2 + 4)}{(x^2 - 4)^3}.$$ *Factored form*

Because the second derivative has no zeros and $x = \pm 2$ is not in the domain of the function, you can conclude that the graph has no points of inflection. Testing the values of $f'(x)$ and $f''(x)$, as shown in Table 3.12, you can see that f has one relative minimum. The graph of f is shown in Figure 3.58.

TABLE 3.12

	$f(x)$	$f'(x)$	$f''(x)$	Shape of graph
x in $(-\infty, -2)$		$-$	$-$	Decreasing, concave downward
$x = -2$	Undef.	Undef.	Undef.	Vertical asymptote
x in $(-2, 0)$		$-$	$+$	Decreasing, concave upward
$x = 0$	$\frac{9}{2}$	0	$+$	Relative minimum
x in $(0, 2)$		$+$	$+$	Increasing, concave upward
$x = 2$	Undef.	Undef.	Undef.	Vertical asymptote
x in $(2, \infty)$		$+$	$-$	Increasing, concave downward

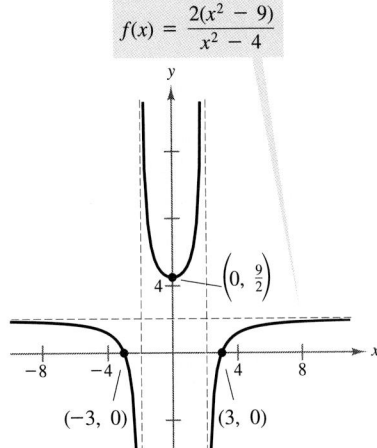

$$f(x) = \frac{2(x^2 - 9)}{x^2 - 4}$$

FIGURE 3.58

EXAMPLE 5 *Analyzing a Graph*

Analyze the graph of

$$f(x) = 2x^{5/3} - 5x^{4/3}.$$ *Original function*

Solution

Begin by writing the function in factored form.

$$f(x) = x^{4/3}(2x^{1/3} - 5)$$ *Factored form*

One of the intercepts is $(0, 0)$. A second x-intercept occurs when $2x^{1/3} = 5$.

$$2x^{1/3} = 5$$
$$x^{1/3} = \tfrac{5}{2}$$
$$x = \left(\tfrac{5}{2}\right)^3$$
$$x = \tfrac{125}{8}$$

The first derivative is

$$f'(x) = \tfrac{10}{3}x^{2/3} - \tfrac{20}{3}x^{1/3}$$ *First derivative*
$$= \tfrac{10}{3}x^{1/3}(x^{1/3} - 2).$$ *Factored form*

Thus, the critical numbers of f are $x = 0$ and $x = 8$. The second derivative is

$$f''(x) = \tfrac{20}{9}x^{-1/3} - \tfrac{20}{9}x^{-2/3}$$ *Second derivative*
$$= \tfrac{20}{9}x^{-2/3}(x^{1/3} - 1)$$
$$= \frac{20(x^{1/3} - 1)}{9x^{2/3}}.$$ *Factored form*

Thus, possible points of inflection occur when $x = 1$ and when $x = 0$. Testing the values of $f'(x)$ and $f''(x)$, as shown in Table 3.13, you can see that f has one relative maximum, one relative minimum, and one point of inflection. The graph of f is shown in Figure 3.59.

TABLE 3.13

	$f(x)$	$f'(x)$	$f''(x)$	Shape of graph
x in $(-\infty, 0)$		$+$	$-$	Increasing, concave downward
$x = 0$	0	0	Undef.	Relative maximum
x in $(0, 1)$		$-$	$-$	Decreasing, concave downward
$x = 1$	-3	$-$	0	Point of inflection
x in $(1, 8)$		$-$	$+$	Decreasing, concave upward
$x = 8$	-16	0	$+$	Relative minimum
x in $(8, \infty)$		$+$	$+$	Increasing, concave upward

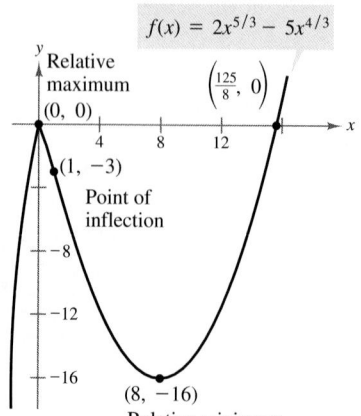

$$f(x) = 2x^{5/3} - 5x^{4/3}$$

FIGURE 3.59

Summary of Simple Polynomial Graphs

A summary of the graphs of polynomial functions of degrees 0, 1, 2, and 3 is shown in Figure 3.60. Because of their simplicity, lower-degree polynomial functions are commonly used as mathematical models.

Constant function (degree 0):

$$y = a$$

Horizontal line

Linear function (degree 1):

$$y = ax + b$$

Line of slope a

$a < 0 \qquad a > 0$

Quadratic function (degree 2):

$$y = ax^2 + bx + c$$

Parabola

$a < 0 \qquad a > 0$

Cubic function (degree 3):

$$y = ax^3 + bx^2 + cx + d$$

Cubic curve

$a < 0 \qquad a > 0$

FIGURE 3.60

Note   The graph of any cubic polynomial has one point of inflection. The slope of the graph at the point of inflection may be zero or nonzero.

Discussion Problem   **Graphs of Fourth-Degree Polynomial Functions**

In the summary shown above, the graphs of cubic functions have been classified as four basic types. How many basic types of graphs are possible with fourth-degree polynomial functions? Make a rough sketch of each type. Then use a graphing utility to classify each of the following. (In each case, use a viewing rectangle that shows all the basic characteristics of the graph.)

a. $y = x^4$

b. $y = -x^4 + 5x^2$

c. $y = x^4 - x^3 + x$

d. $y = -x^4 - 4x^3 - 3x^2 + x$

e. $y = -x^4 + 2x^2$

f. $y = -x^4 + x^3$

g. $y = x^4 - 5x$

h. $y = x^4 - 8x^3 + 8x^2$

Warm Up

The following warm-up exercises involve skills that were covered in earlier sections. You will use these skills in the exercise set for this section.

In Exercises 1–4, find the vertical and horizontal asymptotes of the graph.

1. $f(x) = \dfrac{1}{x^2}$

2. $f(x) = \dfrac{8}{(x-2)^2}$

3. $f(x) = \dfrac{40x}{x+3}$

4. $f(x) = \dfrac{x^2 - 3}{x^2 - 4x + 3}$

In Exercises 5–10, determine the open intervals on which the function is increasing or decreasing.

5. $f(x) = x^2 + 4x + 2$

6. $f(x) = -x^2 - 8x + 1$

7. $f(x) = x^3 - 3x + 1$

8. $f(x) = \dfrac{-x^3 + x^2 - 1}{x^2}$

9. $f(x) = \dfrac{x-2}{x-1}$

10. $f(x) = -x^3 - 4x^2 + 3x + 2$

EXERCISES 3.7   means that technology can help you solve or check the exercise(s).

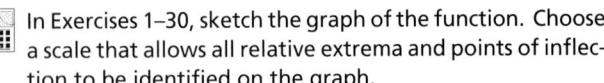 In Exercises 1–30, sketch the graph of the function. Choose a scale that allows all relative extrema and points of inflection to be identified on the graph.

1. $y = -x^2 - 2x + 3$

2. $y = 2x^2 - 4x + 1$

3. $y = x^3 - 4x^2 + 6$

4. $y = -\frac{1}{3}(x^3 - 3x + 2)$

5. $y = 2 - x - x^3$

6. $y = x^3 + 3x^2 + 3x + 2$

7. $y = 3x^3 - 9x + 1$

8. $y = \frac{1}{3}(x-1)^2 + 2$

9. $y = 3x^4 + 4x^3$

10. $y = 3x^4 - 6x^2$

11. $y = (x+1)(x-2)(x-5)$

12. $y = -x^3 + 3x^2 + 9x - 2$

13. $y = x^4 - 8x^3 + 18x^2 - 16x + 5$

14. $y = x^4 - 4x^3 + 16x - 16$

15. $y = x^4 - 4x^3 + 16x$

16. $y = x^5 + 1$

17. $y = x^5 - 5x$

18. $y = (x-1)^5$

19. $y = |2x - 3|$

20. $y = |x^2 - 6x + 5|$

21. $y = \dfrac{x^2 + 2}{x^2 + 1}$

22. $y = \dfrac{x}{x^2 + 1}$

23. $y = 3x^{2/3} - 2x$

24. $y = 3x^{2/3} - x^2$

25. $y = 1 - x^{2/3}$

26. $y = (1 - x)^{2/3}$

27. $y = x^{1/3} + 1$

28. $y = x^{-1/3}$

29. $y = x^{5/3} - 5x^{2/3}$

30. $y = x^{4/3}$

In Exercises 31–40, sketch the graph of the function. Label the intercepts, relative extrema, points of inflection, and asymptotes. Then state the domain of the function.

31. $y = \dfrac{1}{x-2} - 3$

32. $y = \dfrac{x^2 + 1}{x^2 - 2}$

33. $y = \dfrac{2x}{x^2 - 1}$

34. $y = \dfrac{x^2 - 6x + 12}{x - 4}$

35. $y = x\sqrt{4 - x}$

36. $y = x\sqrt{4 - x^2}$

37. $y = \dfrac{x - 3}{x}$

38. $y = x + \dfrac{32}{x^2}$

39. $y = \dfrac{x^3}{x^3 - 1}$

40. $y = \dfrac{x^4}{x^4 - 1}$

In Exercises 41–44, find values of *a, b, c,* and *d* so that the graph of

$$f(x) = ax^3 + bx^2 + cx + d$$

will resemble the given graph. Then use a graphing utility to confirm your result. (There are many correct answers.)

41.

42.

43.

44.

In Exercises 45–48, use the graph of f' or f'' to sketch the graph of *f*. (There are many correct answers.)

45.

46.

47.

48.
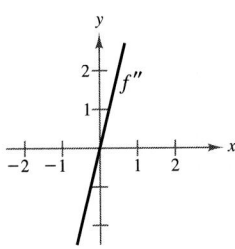

In Exercises 49 and 50, sketch a graph of a function *f* having the given characteristics. (There are many correct answers.)

Function	First Derivative
49. $f(-2)=0$	$f'(x) > 0, \; -\infty < x < -1$
$f(0)=0$	$f'(-1)=0$
$f(2)=0$	$f'(x) < 0, \; -1 < x < 0$
	$f'(0)=0$
	$f'(x) > 0, \; 0 < x < 1$
	$f'(1)=0$
	$f'(x) < 0, \; 1 < x < \infty$

Function	Second Derivative
50. $f(4)=2$	$f''(x) > 0, \; x \neq 4$

51. *Cost* An employee of a delivery company earns \$9 per hour driving a delivery van in an area where gasoline costs \$1.20 per gallon. When the van is driven at a constant speed *s* (in miles per hour with $40 \le s \le 65$), the van gets $500/s$ miles per gallon.

(a) Find the cost *C* as a function of *s* for a 100-mile trip on an interstate highway.

(b) Sketch the graph of the function found in part (a) and determine the most economical speed.

52. *Cost* Repeat Exercise 51 with a gasoline cost of \$1.50 per gallon.

53. *Consumer Preference* Use a graphing utility to graph the consumer indifference curve

$$5 = \frac{xy}{x+y}, \qquad x > 5, \; y > 5,$$

where *x* and *y* are measures of preference of two products.

54. *Profit* The management of a company is considering three possible models to predict the company's profit from 1995 through 2000. Model I gives the expected annual profit if the current trends continue. Models II and III give the expected annual profit for various combinations of increased labor and energy costs. In each model, *P* is the profit (in billions of dollars) and $t = 0$ corresponds to 1995.

Model I: $P = 0.03t^2 - 0.01t + 3.39$
Model II: $P = 0.08t + 3.36$
Model III: $P = -0.07t^2 + 0.05t + 3.38$

(a) Use a graphing utility to graph all three models on the same viewing rectangle.

(b) For which models are profits increasing during the interval from 1995 through 2000?

(c) Which model is the most optimistic? Which is the most pessimistic?

3.8 Differentials and Marginal Analysis

Differentials ■ Marginal Analysis ■ Formulas for Differentials ■ Error Propagation

Differentials

When the derivative was defined in Section 2.1 as the limit of the ratio $\Delta y/\Delta x$, it seemed natural to retain the quotient symbolism for the limit itself. Thus, the derivative of y with respect to x was denoted by

$$\frac{dy}{dx} = \lim_{\Delta x \to 0} \frac{\Delta y}{\Delta x}$$

even though we did not interpret dy/dx as the quotient of two separate quantities. In this section, you will see that the quantities dy and dx can be assigned meanings in such a way that their quotient, when $dx \neq 0$, is equal to the derivative of y with respect to x.

Definition of Differentials

Let $y = f(x)$ represent a differentiable function. The **differential of x** (denoted by dx) is any nonzero real number. The **differential of y** (denoted by dy) is

$$dy = f'(x)\,dx.$$

Note In this definition, dx can have any nonzero value. In most applications, however, dx is chosen to be small and this choice is denoted by $dx = \Delta x$.

One use of differentials is in approximating the change in $f(x)$ that corresponds to a change in x, as shown in Figure 3.61. This change is denoted by

$$\Delta y = f(x + \Delta x) - f(x). \qquad \text{Change in } y$$

In Figure 3.61, notice that as Δx gets smaller and smaller, the values of dy and Δy get closer and closer. That is, when Δx is small,

$$dy \approx \Delta y.$$

This approximation is the basis for most applications of differentials.

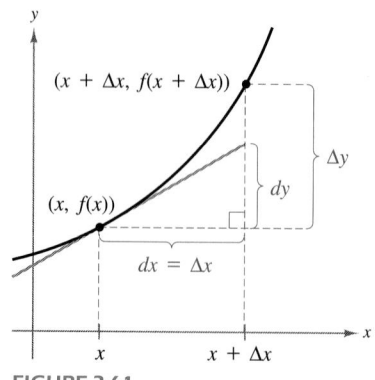

FIGURE 3.61

EXAMPLE 1 *Interpreting Differentials Graphically*

Consider the function

$$f(x) = x^2. \qquad \text{\textit{Original function}}$$

Find the value of dy when $x = 1$ and $dx = 0.01$. Compare this with the value of Δy when $x = 1$ and $\Delta x = 0.01$. Interpret the results graphically.

Solution

Begin by finding the derivative of f.

$$f'(x) = 2x \qquad \text{\textit{Derivative of }} f$$

When $x = 1$ and $dx = 0.01$, the value of the differential dy is

$$
\begin{aligned}
dy &= f'(x)\,dx & &\text{\textit{Differential of }} y \\
&= f'(1)(0.01) & &\text{\textit{Substitute 1 for }} x \text{ \textit{and 0.01 for }} dx. \\
&= 2(1)(0.01) & &\text{\textit{Use }} f'(x) = 2x. \\
&= 0.02. & &\text{\textit{Simplify.}}
\end{aligned}
$$

When $x = 1$ and $\Delta x = 0.01$, the value of Δy is

$$
\begin{aligned}
\Delta y &= f(x + \Delta x) - f(x) & &\text{\textit{Change in }} y \\
&= f(1.01) - f(1) & &\text{\textit{Substitute 1 for }} x \text{ \textit{and 0.01 for }} \Delta x. \\
&= (1.01)^2 - (1)^2 & & \\
&= 0.0201. & &\text{\textit{Simplify.}}
\end{aligned}
$$

Note that $dy \approx \Delta y$, as shown in Figure 3.62. ▬

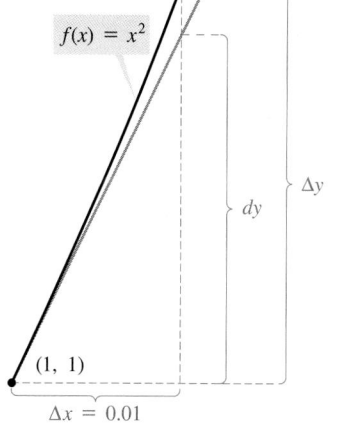

$y = 2x - 1$

$f(x) = x^2$

Δy

dy

$(1, 1)$

$\Delta x = 0.01$

FIGURE 3.62

The validity of the approximation

$$dy \approx \Delta y, \qquad dx \neq 0$$

stems from the definition of the derivative. That is, the existence of the limit

$$f'(x) = \lim_{\Delta x \to 0} \frac{f(x + \Delta x) - f(x)}{\Delta x}$$

implies that when Δx is close to zero, then $f'(x)$ is close to the difference quotient. Thus, you can write

$$
\begin{aligned}
\frac{f(x + \Delta x) - f(x)}{\Delta x} &\approx f'(x) \\
f(x + \Delta x) - f(x) &\approx f'(x)\,\Delta x \\
\Delta y &\approx f'(x)\,\Delta x.
\end{aligned}
$$

Substituting dx for Δx and dy for $f'(x)\,dx$ produces

$$\Delta y \approx dy.$$

Marginal Analysis

Differentials are used in economics to approximate changes in revenue, cost, and profit. Suppose that $R = f(x)$ is the total revenue for selling x units of a product. When the number of units increases by 1, the change in x is $\Delta x = 1$, and the change in R is

$$\Delta R = f(x + \Delta x) - f(x) \approx dR = \frac{dR}{dx}\, dx.$$

In other words, you can use the differential dR to approximate the change in the revenue that accompanies the sale of one additional unit. Similarly, the differentials dC and dP can be used to approximate the change in cost or profit that accompanies the sale (or production) of one additional unit.

Real Life

EXAMPLE 2 *Using Marginal Analysis*

The demand function for a product is modeled by

$$p = \sqrt{400 - x}.$$

Use differentials to approximate the change in revenue as sales increase from 256 units to 257 units. Compare this with the actual change in revenue.

Solution

Begin by finding the marginal revenue, dR/dx.

$$R = xp \qquad\qquad\qquad\qquad\qquad\qquad \textit{Formula for revenue}$$

$$= x\sqrt{400 - x} \qquad\qquad\qquad\qquad \textit{Use } p = \sqrt{400 - x}.$$

$$\frac{dR}{dx} = x\left(\frac{1}{2}\right)(400 - x)^{-1/2}(-1) + (400 - x)^{1/2}(1) \quad \textit{Product Rule}$$

$$= \frac{800 - 3x}{2\sqrt{400 - x}} \qquad\qquad\qquad\qquad \textit{Simplify.}$$

When $x = 256$ and $dx = \Delta x = 1$, you can approximate the change in the revenue to be

$$dR = \frac{dR}{dx}\, dx$$

$$= \frac{800 - 3(256)}{2\sqrt{400 - 256}}(1)$$

$$\approx \$1.33.$$

When x increases from 256 to 257, the actual change in revenue is

$$\Delta R = 257\sqrt{400 - 257} - 256\sqrt{400 - 256}$$

$$= 3073.27 - 3072.00$$

$$\approx \$1.27.$$

Real Life

EXAMPLE 3 *Using Marginal Analysis*

The profit derived from selling x units of an item is modeled by

$$P = 0.0002x^3 + 10x.$$

Use the differential dP to approximate the change in profit when the production level changes from 50 to 51 units. Compare this with the actual gain in profit obtained by increasing the production level from 50 to 51 units.

Solution

The marginal profit is

$$\frac{dP}{dx} = 0.0006x^2 + 10.$$

When $x = 50$ and $dx = 1$, the differential dP is

$$\begin{aligned} dP &= \frac{dP}{dx} \, dx \\ &= [0.0006(50)^2 + 10](1) \\ &= \$11.50. \end{aligned}$$

When x changes from 50 to 51 units, the actual change in profit is

$$\begin{aligned} \Delta P &= [(0.0002)(51)^3 + 10(51)] - [(0.0002)(50)^3 + 10(50)] \\ &\approx 536.53 - 525.00 \\ &= \$11.53. \end{aligned}$$

These values are shown graphically in Figure 3.63.

Note Example 3 uses differentials to solve the same problem that was solved in Example 5 in Section 2.3. Look back at that solution. Which approach do you prefer?

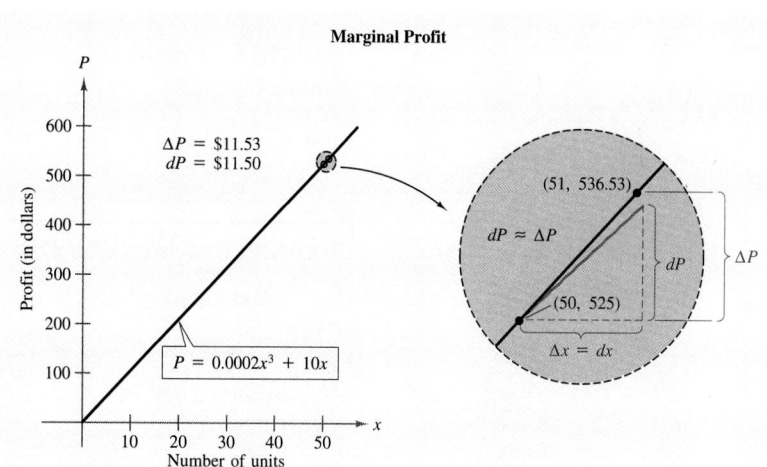

Marginal Profit

$\Delta P = \$11.53$
$dP = \$11.50$

$P = 0.0002x^3 + 10x$

Profit (in dollars)

Number of units

$(51,\ 536.53)$
$dP \approx \Delta P$
$(50,\ 525)$
$\Delta x = dx$
dP
ΔP

FIGURE 3.63

Formulas for Differentials

You can use the definition of differentials to rewrite each differentiation rule in **differential form.** For example, if u and v are differentiable functions of x, then $du = u' \, dx$ and $dv = v' \, dx$, which implies that you can write the Product Rule in the following differential form.

$$
\begin{aligned}
d[uv] &= \frac{d}{dx}[uv] \, dx && \textit{Differential of uv} \\
&= [uv' + vu'] \, dx && \textit{Product Rule} \\
&= uv' \, dx + vu' \, dx \\
&= u \, dv + v \, du && \textit{Differential form of Product Rule}
\end{aligned}
$$

The following summary gives the differential forms of the differentiation rules presented so far in the text.

Differential Forms of Differentiation Rules

Constant Multiple Rule:	$d[cu] = c \, du$
Sum or Difference Rule:	$d[u \pm v] = du \pm dv$
Product Rule:	$d[uv] = u \, dv + v \, du$
Quotient Rule:	$d\left[\dfrac{u}{v}\right] = \dfrac{v \, du - u \, dv}{v^2}$
Constant Rule:	$d[c] = 0$
Power Rule:	$d[x^n] = nx^{n-1} \, dx$
	$d[x] = 1$

The next example compares the derivatives and differentials of several simple functions.

EXAMPLE 4 *Finding Differentials*

	Function	*Derivative*	*Differential*
a.	$y = x^2$	$\dfrac{dy}{dx} = 2x$	$dy = 2x \, dx$
b.	$y = \dfrac{3x + 2}{5}$	$\dfrac{dy}{dx} = \dfrac{3}{5}$	$dy = \dfrac{3}{5} \, dx$
c.	$y = 2x^2 - 3x$	$\dfrac{dy}{dx} = 4x - 3$	$dy = (4x - 3) \, dx$
d.	$y = \dfrac{1}{x}$	$\dfrac{dy}{dx} = -\dfrac{1}{x^2}$	$dy = -\dfrac{1}{x^2} \, dx$

Error Propagation

A common use of differentials is the estimation of errors that are propagated by physical measuring devices. This is illustrated in Example 5.

Real Life

EXAMPLE 5 *Estimating Measurement Errors*

The radius of a ball bearing is measured to be 0.7 inch, as shown in Figure 3.64. This implies that the volume of the ball bearing is $\frac{4}{3}\pi(0.7)^3 \approx 1.4368$ cubic inches. You are told that the measurement of the radius is correct to within 0.01 inch. How far off could the calculation of the volume be?

Solution
Because the value of r can be off by 0.01 inch, it follows that

$$-0.01 \leq \Delta r \leq 0.01. \qquad \textit{Possible error in measuring}$$

Using $\Delta r = dr$, you can estimate the possible error in the volume.

$$V = \tfrac{4}{3}\pi r^3 \qquad\qquad \textit{Formula for volume}$$
$$dV = \frac{dV}{dr}\,dr \qquad\qquad \textit{Formula for differential of V}$$
$$= 4\pi r^2\,dr$$
$$= 4\pi(0.7)^2(\pm 0.01) \qquad \textit{Substitute for r and dr.}$$
$$\approx \pm 0.0616 \text{ cubic inch} \qquad \textit{Possible error}$$

Thus, the volume of the ball bearing could range between $(1.4368 - 0.0616) = 1.3752$ cubic inches and $(1.4368 + 0.0616) = 1.4984$ cubic inches.

FIGURE 3.64

0.7 in.

In Example 5, the **relative error** in the volume is defined to be the ratio of dV to V. This ratio is

$$\frac{dV}{V} \approx \frac{\pm 0.0616}{1.4368} \approx \pm 0.0429.$$

This corresponds to a **percentage error** of 4.29%.

Discussion Problem   **Finding Propagated Errors**

a. In Example 5, if the radius of the ball bearing were measured to be 1.5 inches, correct to within 0.01 inch, would the percentage error of the volume be greater or smaller than in the example?

b. In Example 5, if the radius of the ball bearing were measured to be 0.7 inches, correct to within 0.02 inch, would the percentage error of the volume be greater or smaller than in the example?

Warm Up

The following warm-up exercises involve skills that were covered in earlier sections. You will use these skills in the exercise set for this section.

In Exercises 1–6, find the derivative.

1. $C = 44 + 0.09x^2$

2. $R = x(1.25 + 0.02\sqrt{x})$

3. $P = -0.03x^{1/3} + 1.4x - 2250$

4. $A = \frac{1}{4}\sqrt{3}x^2$

5. $C = 2\pi r$

6. $S = 4\pi r^2$

In Exercises 7–10, write a formula for the quantity.

7. Area A of a circle of radius r

8. Area A of a square of side x

9. Volume V of a cube of edge x

10. Volume V of a sphere of radius r

E X E R C I S E S   3.8   means that technology can help you solve or check the exercise(s).

In Exercises 1–10, find the differential *dy*.

1. $y = 3x^2 - 4$

2. $y = 2x^{3/2}$

3. $y = (4x - 1)^3$

4. $y = (1 - 2x^2)^{-2}$

5. $y = \sqrt{x^2 + 1}$

6. $y = \sqrt[3]{6x^2}$

7. $y = x\sqrt{1 - x^2}$

8. $y = -4x^{-1}$

9. $y = \dfrac{x - 3}{1 - 3x}$

10. $y = \dfrac{x}{x^2 + 1}$

In Exercises 11–14, let $x = 1$ and $\Delta x = 0.01$. Find Δy.

11. $f(x) = 5x^2 - 1$

12. $f(x) = \sqrt{3x}$

13. $f(x) = \dfrac{4}{\sqrt[3]{x}}$

14. $f(x) = \dfrac{x}{x^2 + 1}$

In Exercises 15–18, compare the values of *dy* and Δy.

15. $y = x^3$ $x = 1$ $\Delta x = dx = 0.1$

16. $y = 1 - 2x^2$ $x = 0$ $\Delta x = dx = -0.1$

17. $y = x^4 + 1$ $x = -1$ $\Delta x = dx = 0.01$

18. $y = 2x + 1$ $x = 2$ $\Delta x = dx = 0.01$

In Exercises 19–22, let $x = 2$ and complete the table for the function.

$dx = \Delta x$	dy	Δy	$\Delta y - dy$	$dy/\Delta y$
1.000				
0.500				
0.100				
0.010				
0.001				

19. $y = x^2$

20. $y = \dfrac{1}{x^2}$

21. $y = x^5$

22. $y = \sqrt{x}$

23. *Demand* The demand function for a product is modeled by

$$p = 75 - 0.25x.$$

(a) If x changes from 7 to 8, what is the corresponding change in p? Compare the values of Δp and dp.

(b) Repeat part (a) when x changes from 70 to 71 units.

24. *Wildlife Management* A state game commission introduces 50 deer into newly acquired state game lands. The population N of the herd can be modeled by

$$N = \frac{10(5 + 3t)}{1 + 0.04t},$$

where t is the time in years. Use differentials to approximate the change in the herd size from $t = 5$ to $t = 6$.

Marginal Analysis In Exercises 25–28, use differentials to approximate the change in cost, revenue, or profit corresponding to an increase in sales of *one unit*. For instance, in Exercise 25, approximate the change in cost as x increases from 12 units to 13 units.

Function	x-Value
25. $C = 0.05x^2 + 4x + 10$	$x = 12$
26. $R = 30x - 0.15x^2$	$x = 75$
27. $P = -0.5x^3 + 2500x - 6000$	$x = 50$
28. $P = -x^2 + 60x - 100$	$x = 25$

29. *Marginal Analysis* A retailer has determined that the monthly sales x of a watch is 150 units when the price is \$50, but decreases to 120 units when the price is \$60. Assume that the demand is a linear function of the price. Find the revenue R as a function of x and approximate the change in revenue for a one-unit increase in sales when $x = 141$. Make a sketch showing dR and ΔR.

30. *Marginal Analysis* A manufacturer determines that the demand x for a product is inversely proportional to the square of the price p. When the price is \$10, the demand is 2500. Find the revenue R as a function of x and approximate the change in revenue for a one-unit increase in sales when $x = 3000$. Make a sketch showing dR and ΔR.

31. *Marginal Analysis* The demand x for a radio is 30,000 units per week when the price is \$25 and 40,000 units when the price is \$20. The initial investment is \$275,000 and the cost per unit is \$17. Assume that the demand is a linear function of the price. Find the profit P as a function of x and approximate the change in profit for a one-unit increase in sales when $x = 28,000$. Make a sketch showing dP and ΔP.

32. *Marginal Analysis* The variable cost for the production of a calculator is \$14.25 and the initial investment is \$110,000. Find the total cost C as a function of x, the number of units produced. Then use differentials to approximate the change in the cost for a one-unit increase in production when $x = 50,000$. Make a sketch showing dC and ΔC. Explain why $dC = \Delta C$ in this problem.

33. The area A of a square of side x is $A = x^2$.
(a) Compute dA and ΔA in terms of x and Δx.
(b) In the figure, identify the region whose area is dA.
(c) In the figure, identify the region whose area is $\Delta A - dA$.

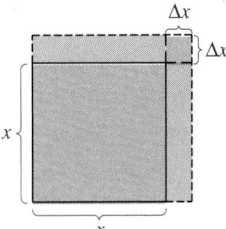

34. *Area* The side of a square is measured to be 12 inches, with a possible error of $\frac{1}{64}$ inch. Use differentials to approximate the possible error and the relative error in computing the area of the square.

35. *Area* The radius of a circle is measured to be 10 inches, with a possible error of $\frac{1}{8}$ inch. Use differentials to approximate the possible error and the relative error in computing the area of the circle.

36. *Volume and Surface Area* The edge of a cube is measured to be 12 inches, with a possible error of 0.03 inch. Use differentials to approximate the possible error and the relative error in computing (a) the volume of the cube, and (b) the surface area of the cube.

37. *Volume* The radius of a sphere is measured to be 6 inches, with a possible error of 0.02 inch. Use differentials to approximate the possible error and the relative error in computing the volume of the sphere.

38. *Drug Concentration* The concentration C (in milligrams per milliliter) in a patient's bloodstream t hours after injection into muscle tissue is modeled by

$$C = \frac{3t}{27 + t^3}.$$

Use differentials to approximate the change in the concentration when t changes from $t = 1$ to $t = 1.5$.

39. *Profit* The profit P for a company selling x units of a product is modeled by

$$P = R - C = (500x - x^2) - (0.5x^2 - 77x + 3000).$$

Approximate the change in the profit as the production changes from $x = 115$ to $x = 120$.

Chapter Summary and Study Tips

After studying this chapter, you should have acquired the following skills. The exercise numbers are keyed to the Review Exercises that begin on page 252. Answers to odd-numbered Review Exercises are given in the back of the text.

- Find the critical numbers of a function. (*Section 3.1*)   Review Exercises 1–4
  c is a critical number of f if $f'(c) = 0$ or $f'(c)$ is undefined.

- Find the open intervals on which a function is increasing or decreasing. (*Section 3.1*)   Review Exercises 5–8
  Increasing if $f'(x) > 0$
  Decreasing if $f'(x) < 0$

- Find intervals on which a real-life model is increasing or decreasing, and interpret the results in context. (*Section 3.1*)   Review Exercises 9, 10

- Use the First-Derivative Test to find the relative extrema of a function. (*Section 3.2*)   Review Exercises 11–20

- Find the absolute extrema of a continuous function on a closed interval. (*Section 3.2*)   Review Exercises 21–28

- Find minimum and maximum values of a real-life model and interpret the results in context. (*Section 3.2*)   Review Exercises 29, 30

- Find the open intervals on which the graph of a function is concave upward or concave downward. (*Section 3.3*)   Review Exercises 31–34
  Concave upward if $f''(x) > 0$
  Concave downward if $f''(x) < 0$

- Find the points of inflection of the graph of a function. (*Section 3.3*)   Review Exercises 35–38

- Use the Second-Derivative Test to find the relative extrema of a function. (*Section 3.3*)   Review Exercises 39–42

- Find the point of diminishing returns of an input-output model. (*Section 3.3*)   Review Exercises 43, 44

- Solve real-life optimization problems. (*Section 3.4*)   Review Exercises 45–48

- Solve business and economics optimization problems. (*Section 3.5*)   Review Exercises 49–54

- Find the price elasticity of demand for a demand function. (*Section 3.5*)   Review Exercises 55, 56

- Find the vertical and horizontal asymptotes of a rational function and sketch its graph. (*Section 3.6*)   Review Exercises 57–62

- Find infinite limits and limits at infinity. (*Section 3.6*)   Review Exercises 63–68

- Use asymptotes to answer questions about real life. (*Section 3.6*)   Review Exercises 69, 70

- Analyze the graph of a function. (*Section 3.7*)   Review Exercises 71–80

- Find the differential of a function. (*Section 3.8*)   Review Exercises 81–84

- Use differentials to approximate changes in a function. (*Section 3.8*)   Review Exercises 85–88

- Use differentials to approximate changes in real-life models. (*Section 3.8*)   Review Exercises 89, 90

*Several student study aids are available with this text. The *Student Solutions Guide* includes detailed solutions to all odd-numbered exercises, as well as practice chapter tests with answers. The *Graphics Calculator Guide* offers instructions on the use of a variety of graphing calculators and computer graphing software. The *Brief Calculus TUTOR* includes additional examples for selected exercises in the text.

■ Solve Problems Graphically, Analytically, and Numerically   When analyzing the graph of a function, use a variety of problem-solving strategies. For instance, if you were asked to analyze the graph of $f(x) = x^3 - 4x^2 + 5x - 4$, you could begin *graphically*. That is, you could use a graphing utility to find a viewing rectangle that appears to show the important characteristics of the graph. From the graph shown below, the function appears to have one relative minimum, one relative maximum, and one point of inflection.

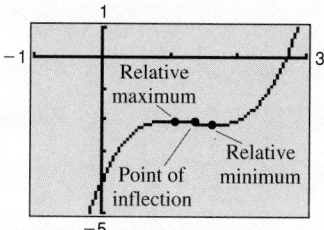

Next, you could use calculus to *analyze* the graph. Because the derivative of f is $f'(x) = 3x^2 - 8x + 5 = (3x - 5)(x - 1)$, the critical numbers of f are $x = \frac{5}{3}$ and $x = 1$. By the First-Derivative Test, you can conclude that $x = \frac{5}{3}$ yields a relative minimum and $x = 1$ yields a relative maximum. Because $f''(x) = 6x - 8$, you can conclude that $x = \frac{4}{3}$ yields a point of inflection. Finally, you could analyze the graph *numerically*. For instance, you could construct a table of values and observe that f is increasing in the interval $(-\infty, 1)$, decreasing in the interval $(1, \frac{5}{3})$, and increasing in the interval $(\frac{5}{3}, \infty)$.

■ Problem-Solving Strategies   If you get stuck when trying to solve an optimization problem, consider the following strategies.

1. *Draw a Diagram.* If feasible, draw a diagram that represents the problem. Label all known values and unknown values on the diagram.
2. *Solve a Simpler Problem.* Simplify the problem, or write several simple examples of the problem. For instance, if you are asked to find the dimensions that will produce a maximum area, try calculating the area of several examples.
3. *Rewrite the Problem in Your Own Words.* Rewriting a problem can help you understand it better.
4. *Guess and Check.* Try guessing the answer, then check your guess in the statement of the original problem. By refining your guesses, you may be able to think of a general strategy for solving the problem.

Review Exercises

 means that technology can help you solve or check the exercise(s).

In Exercises 1–4, find the critical numbers of the function.

1. $f(x) = -x^2 + 2x + 4$

2. $g(x) = (x - 1)^2(x - 3)$

3. $h(x) = \sqrt{x}(x - 3)$

4. $f(x) = (x + 1)^3$

 In Exercises 5–8, determine the open intervals on which the function is increasing or decreasing. Solve the problem analytically and graphically.

5. $f(x) = x^2 + x - 2$

6. $g(x) = -x^2 + 7x - 12$

7. $h(x) = \dfrac{x^2 - 3x - 4}{x - 3}$

8. $f(x) = -x^3 + 6x^2 - 2$

 9. *Temperature* The daily maximum temperature T (in degrees Fahrenheit) for New York City can be modeled by

$$T = 0.036t^4 - 0.909t^3 + 5.874t^2 - 2.599t + 37.789,$$

where $0 \le t \le 12$ and $t = 0$ corresponds to January 1. *(Source: National Oceanic and Atmospheric Administration)*

(a) Find the intervals in which the model is increasing.
(b) Find the intervals in which the model is decreasing.
(c) Interpret the results of parts (a) and (b).
(d) Sketch a graph of the model.

10. *Newspaper Publishers* The number N of morning newspaper publishers in the United States from 1940 through 1990 can be modeled by

$$N = 0.0063t^3 - 0.0281t^{5/2} - 14.968t^{1/2} + 375.018,$$

where $0 \le t \le 50$ and $t = 0$ corresponds to 1940. *(Source: American Newspaper Publishers Association)*

(a) Find the intervals in which the model is increasing.
(b) Find the intervals in which the model is decreasing.
(c) Interpret the results of parts (a) and (b).
(d) Sketch a graph of the model.

 In Exercises 11–20, use the First-Derivative Test to find the relative extrema of the function. Then use a graphing utility to confirm your result.

11. $f(x) = 4x^3 - 6x^2 - 2$

12. $f(x) = \frac{1}{4}x^4 - 8x$

13. $g(x) = x^2 - 16x + 12$

14. $h(x) = 4 + 10x - x^2$

15. $h(x) = 2x^2 - x^4$

16. $s(x) = x^4 - 8x^2 + 3$

17. $f(x) = \dfrac{6}{x^2 + 1}$

18. $f(x) = \dfrac{2}{x^2 - 1}$

19. $h(x) = \dfrac{x^2}{x - 2}$

20. $g(x) = x - 6\sqrt{x}$, $x > 0$

 In Exercises 21–28, find the absolute extrema of the function on the indicated interval. Then use a graphing utility to confirm your result.

21. $f(x) = x^2 + 5x + 6$; $[-3, 0]$

22. $f(x) = x^4 - 2x^3$; $[0, 2]$

23. $f(x) = x^3 - 12x + 1$; $[-4, 4]$

24. $f(x) = \dfrac{8}{x} + x$; $[1, 4]$

25. $f(x) = 3x^4 - 6x^2 + 2$; $[0, 2]$

26. $f(x) = -x^4 + x^2 + 2$; $[0, 2]$

27. $f(x) = \dfrac{2x}{x^2 + 1}$; $[-1, 2]$

28. $f(x) = 4\sqrt{x} - x^2$; $[0, 3]$

 29. *Diamond Prices* During the 1980s, the average price p (in dollars) on the Antwerp Index of a 1-carat diamond can be modeled by

$$p = -0.7t^3 + 16.25t^2 - 106t + 388,$$

where $2 \le t \le 10$ and $t = 2$ corresponds to 1982. *(Source: Diamond High Council)*

(a) Estimate the maximum average price between 1982 and 1990. When did this price occur?
(b) Estimate the minimum average price between 1982 and 1990. When did this price occur?

30. *Waste Oxidation* When organic waste is dumped into a pond, the decomposition of the waste consumes oxygen. A model for the oxygen level O (where 1 is the normal level) of a pond as waste material oxidizes is

$$O = \dfrac{t^2 - t + 1}{t^2 + 1}, \qquad 0 \le t,$$

where t is the time in weeks.

(a) When is the oxygen level lowest? What is this level?
(b) When is the oxygen level highest? What is this level?
(c) Describe the oxygen level as t increases.

In Exercises 31–34, determine the open intervals on which the graph of the function is concave upward or concave downward. Then use a graphing utility to confirm your result.

31. $f(x) = (x - 2)^3$

32. $h(x) = x^5 - 10x^2$

33. $g(x) = \frac{1}{4}(-x^4 + 8x^2 - 12)$

34. $h(x) = x^3 - 6x$

In Exercises 35–38, find the points of inflection of the graph of the function.

35. $f(x) = \frac{1}{2}x^4 - 4x^3$

36. $f(x) = (x + 2)^2(x - 4)$

37. $f(x) = x^3(x - 3)^2$

38. $f(x) = \frac{1}{4}x^4 - 2x^2 - x$

In Exercises 39–42, use the Second-Derivative Test to find the relative extrema of the function.

39. $f(x) = x^5 - 5x^3$

40. $f(x) = x(x^2 - 3x - 9)$

41. $f(x) = (x - 1)^3(x + 4)^2$

42. $f(x) = \dfrac{(x - 2)^2}{4 - x}$

In Exercises 43 and 44, identify the point of diminishing returns for the input-output function. For each function, R is the revenue (in thousands of dollars) and x is the amount spent on advertising (in thousands of dollars).

43. $R = \frac{1}{1500}(150x^2 - x^3)$, $\quad 0 \le x \le 100$

44. $R = -\frac{2}{3}(x^3 - 12x^2 - 6)$, $\quad 0 \le x \le 8$

45. *Minimum Sum* Find two positive numbers whose product is 169 and whose sum is a minimum. Solve the problem analytically *and* graphically.

46. *Length* The wall of a building is to be braced by a beam that must pass over a 5-foot fence that is parallel to the building and 4 feet from the building. Find the length of the shortest beam that can be used.

47. *Charitable Contributions* The percent P of income that Americans give to charities can be modeled by

$$P = 0.0014x^2 - 0.1529x + 5.855, \qquad 5 \le x \le 100,$$

where x is the annual income in thousands of dollars. (*Source: Independent Sector*)

(a) What income level corresponds to the least percent of charitable contributions?

(b) What income level corresponds to the greatest percent of charitable contributions?

48. *Construction Costs* A fence is to be built to enclose a rectangular region of 4800 square feet. The fencing material along three sides costs $3 per foot. The fencing material along the fourth side cost $4 per foot.

(a) Find the most economical dimensions of the region.

(b) How would the result of part (a) change if the fencing material costs for all sides increased by $1 per foot?

49. *Profit* The demand and cost functions for a product are

$$p = 36 - 4x \quad \text{and} \quad C = 2x^2 + 6.$$

(a) What level of production will produce a maximum profit?

(b) What level of production will produce a minimum average cost per unit?

50. *Profit* The demand and cost functions for a product are

$$p = 75 - x \quad \text{and} \quad C = 0.5x^2 + 62x + 125.$$

(a) What level of production will produce a maximum profit?

(b) What level of production will produce a minimum average cost per unit?

51. *Revenue* For groups of 20 or more, a theater determines the ticket price p according to the formula

$$p = 15 - 0.1(n - 20), \qquad 20 \le n \le N,$$

where n is the number in the group. What should the value of N be? Explain your reasoning.

52. *Cost* The cost of fuel to run a locomotive is proportional to the $\frac{3}{2}$ power of the speed. At a speed of 25 miles per hour, the cost of fuel is $50 per hour. Other costs amount to $100 per hour. Find the speed that will minimize the cost per mile.

53. *Inventory Cost* The cost C of inventory depends on ordering and storage costs,

$$C = \left(\frac{Q}{x}\right)s + \left(\frac{x}{2}\right)r,$$

where Q is the number of units sold per year, r is the cost of storing one unit for 1 year, s is the cost of placing an order, and x is the number of units in the order. Determine the order size that will minimize the cost when $Q = 10{,}000$, $s = 4.5$, and $r = 5.76$.

54. *Profit* The demand and cost functions for a product are

$$p = 600 - 3x \quad \text{and} \quad C = 0.3x^2 + 6x + 600,$$

where p is the price per unit, x is the number of units, and C is the total cost. The profit for producing x units is

$$P = xp - C - xt,$$

where t is the excise tax per unit. Find the maximum profit for excise taxes of $t = \$5$, $t = \$10$, and $t = \$20$.

In Exercises 55 and 56, find the intervals on which the demand is elastic, inelastic, and of unit elasticity.

55. $p = \dfrac{36}{\sqrt[3]{x}}, \qquad x > 0$

56. $p = \sqrt{1900 - x}, \qquad 0 \le x \le 1900$

In Exercises 57–62, find the vertical and horizontal asymptotes of the graph. Then sketch the graph.

57. $h(x) = \dfrac{2x + 3}{x - 4}$

58. $g(x) = \dfrac{5x^2}{x^2 + 2}$

59. $f(x) = \dfrac{1 - 3x}{x}$

60. $h(x) = \dfrac{3x}{\sqrt{x^2 + 2}}$

61. $f(x) = \dfrac{3}{x^2 - 5x + 4}$

62. $h(x) = \dfrac{2x^2 + 3x - 5}{x - 1}$

In Exercises 63–68, find the limit, if it exists.

63. $\displaystyle \lim_{x \to 0^+} \left(x - \dfrac{1}{x^3} \right)$

64. $\displaystyle \lim_{x \to -1^+} \dfrac{x^2 - 2x + 1}{x + 1}$

65. $\displaystyle \lim_{x \to \infty} \dfrac{5x^2 + 3}{2x^2 - x + 1}$

66. $\displaystyle \lim_{x \to \infty} \dfrac{3x^2 - 2x + 3}{x + 1}$

67. $\displaystyle \lim_{x \to -\infty} \dfrac{3x^2}{x + 2}$

68. $\displaystyle \lim_{x \to -\infty} \left(\dfrac{x}{x - 2} + \dfrac{2x}{x + 2} \right)$

69. *Ultraviolet Radiation* For a person with sensitive skin, the amount T (in hours) of exposure to the sun can be modeled by

$$T = \dfrac{0.37s + 23.8}{s}, \qquad 0 < s \le 120,$$

where s is the Sunsor Scale reading. *(Source: Sunsor, Inc.)*

(a) Use a graphing utility to graph the model. Compare your result with the graph below.

(b) Describe the value of T as s increases.

70. *Average Cost and Profit* The cost and revenue functions for a product are

$$C = 10{,}000 + 48.9x \quad \text{and} \quad R = 68.5x.$$

(a) Find the average cost function.

(b) What is the limit of the average cost as x approaches infinity?

(c) Find the average profit when x is 1 million, 2 million, and 10 million.

(d) What is the limit of the average profit as x increases without bound?

In Exercises 71–80, sketch the graph of the function. Label the intercepts, relative extrema, points of inflection, and asymptotes. State the domain of the function.

71. $f(x) = 4x - x^2$

72. $f(x) = 4x^3 - x^4$

73. $f(x) = x\sqrt{16 - x^2}$

74. $f(x) = x + \dfrac{4}{x^2}$

75. $f(x) = \dfrac{x + 1}{x - 1}$

76. $f(x) = x^2 + \dfrac{2}{x}$

77. $f(x) = x^3(x + 1)$

78. $f(x) = \dfrac{2x}{1 + x^2}$

79. $f(x) = x^{4/5}$

80. $f(x) = x^3 + \dfrac{243}{x}$

In Exercises 81–84, find the differential dy.

81. $y = 6x^2 - 5$

82. $y = (3x^2 - 2)^3$

83. $y = -\dfrac{5}{\sqrt[3]{x}}$

84. $y = \dfrac{2 - x}{x + 5}$

In Exercises 85–88, use differentials to approximate the change in cost, revenue, or profit corresponding to an increase in sales of one unit.

85. $C = 40x^2 + 1225, \quad x = 10$

86. $C = 1.5\sqrt[3]{x} + 500, \quad x = 125$

87. $R = 6.25x + 0.4x^{3/2}, \quad x = 225$

88. $P = 0.003x^2 + 0.019x - 1200, \quad x = 750$

89. *Surface Area and Volume* The diameter of a sphere is measured to be 18 inches with a possible error of 0.05 inch. Use differentials to approximate the possible error in the surface area and the volume of the sphere.

90. *Demand* A company finds that the demand for its product is modeled by $p = 85 - 0.125x$. If x changes from 7 to 8, what is the corresponding change in p? Compare the values of Δp and dp.

Sample Post-Graduation Exam Questions

The following questions were taken from certified public accountant (CPA) exams, graduate management admission tests (GMAT), graduate records exams (GRE), actuarial exams, or college-level academic skills tests (CLAST). The answers to the questions are given in the back of the book.

For Questions 1–3, use the data given in the graph.
(Source: National Sporting Goods Association)

1. The percent increase in revenue between 1985 and 1987 is about
   (a) 40%   (b) 95%   (c) 200%   (d) 125%

2. Which of the following statements about the sale of walking shoes can be inferred from the graph?
   I. The greatest increase in revenue occurs between 1988 and 1989.
   II. In 1991, the revenue was greater than $1.3 billion.
   III. Between 1985 and 1988, the average increase in revenue per year was about $122 million.

   (a) I and II   (b) I and III   (c) II and III   (d) I, II, and III

3. Let $f(x)$ represent the revenue function. In 1990, $f'(x) =$
   (a) 1   (b) 1509   (c) 0   (d) undefined

4. In 1985, a company issued 75,000 shares of stock. Each share of stock was worth $85.75. Five years later, each share of the stock was worth $72.21. How much less were the shares worth in 1990 than in 1985?
   (a) $1,115,500   (b) $1,051,500   (c) $1,155,000
   (d) $1,015,500

Sales of Walking Shoes

FIGURE FOR 1–4

5. Which of these figure most resembles the graph of $f(x) = \dfrac{x}{x^2 - 4}$?

(a)   (b)   (c)   (d)

6. On April 1, 1994, Starn Corp. issued 300 of its $1000 face value bonds at $101 plus accrued interest. The bonds were dated November 1, 1993, and bear interest at an annual rate of 8% payable semiannually on November 1 and May 1. What amount did Starn receive from the bond issuance?
   (a) $313,000   (b) $327,000   (c) $303,000   (d) $300,000

$$\frac{d}{dx}[\ln x] = \frac{1}{x}$$

4
Exponential and Logarithmic Functions

During the past 300 years, as calculus was developing into its modern-day form, three categories of functions have proved most useful for modeling real life. These are algebraic functions (polynomial functions, rational functions, and radical functions), exponential and logarithmic functions, and trigonometric functions.

Algebraic functions are the oldest. In fact, records of polynomial functions date back to Babylonian times. Nonalgebraic functions, such as exponential and logarithmic functions, are much newer. Many mathematicians, including the Swiss mathematician Leonhard Euler (1707–1783) and the Indian mathematician Srinivasa Ramanujan (1887–1920), have contributed to the representation of nonalgebraic functions.

$$e \approx 2.71828$$

Ramanujan

Exponential Functions

Exponential Functions ■ *Natural Exponential Functions* ■
Extended Application: Compound Interest

Exponential Functions

You are already familiar with the behavior of algebraic functions such as

$$f(x) = x^2, \quad g(x) = \sqrt{x} = x^{1/2}, \quad \text{and} \quad h(x) = \frac{1}{x} = x^{-1},$$

which involve a variable raised to a constant power. By interchanging roles and raising a constant to a variable power, you obtain another important class of functions called **exponential functions.** Some simple examples are

$$f(x) = 2^x, \quad g(x) = \left(\frac{1}{10}\right)^x = \frac{1}{10^x}, \quad \text{and} \quad h(x) = 3^{2x} = 9^x.$$

In general, you can use any positive base $a \neq 1$ as the base of an exponential function.

Definition of Exponential Function

If $a > 0$ and $a \neq 1$, then the **exponential function** with base a is given by

$$f(x) = a^x.$$

For working with exponential functions, the following properties of exponents are useful.

Properties of Exponents

Let a and b be positive numbers.

1. $a^0 = 1$ **2.** $a^x a^y = a^{x+y}$ **3.** $\dfrac{a^x}{a^y} = a^{x-y}$

4. $(a^x)^y = a^{xy}$ **5.** $(ab)^x = a^x b^x$ **6.** $\left(\dfrac{a}{b}\right)^x = \dfrac{a^x}{b^x}$

7. $a^{-x} = \dfrac{1}{a^x}$

EXAMPLE 1 *Applying Properties of Exponents*

a. $(2^2)(2^3) = 2^{2+3} = 2^5 = 32$ *Property 2*

b. $(2^2)(2^{-3}) = 2^{2-3} = 2^{-1} = \frac{1}{2}$ *Properties 2 and 7*

c. $(3^2)^3 = 3^{2(3)} = 3^6 = 729$ *Property 4*

d. $\left(\frac{1}{3}\right)^{-2} = \frac{1}{(1/3)^2} = \left(\frac{1}{1/3}\right)^2 = 3^2 = 9$ *Properties 6 and 7*

e. $\frac{3^2}{3^3} = 3^{2-3} = 3^{-1} = \frac{1}{3}$ *Properties 3 and 7*

f. $(2^{1/2})(3^{1/2}) = [(2)(3)]^{1/2} = 6^{1/2} = \sqrt{6}$ *Property 5*   ▬

Although Example 1 demonstrates the properties of exponents with integer and rational exponents, it is important to realize that the properties hold for *all* real exponents. With a calculator, you can obtain approximations of a^x for any base a and any real exponent x. Here are some examples.

$$2^{-0.6} \approx 0.660, \qquad \pi^{0.75} \approx 2.360, \qquad (1.56)^{\sqrt{2}} \approx 1.876$$

Real Life

EXAMPLE 2 *Dating Organic Material*

In living organic material, the ratio of radioactive carbon isotopes to the total number of carbon atoms is about 1 to 10^{12}. When organic material dies, its radioactive carbon isotopes begin to decay, with a half-life of about 5700 years. This means that after 5700 years, the ratio of isotopes to atoms will have decreased to one-half the original ratio, after a second 5700 years the ratio will have decreased to one-fourth of the original, and so on. Figure 4.1 shows this decreasing ratio. The formula for the ratio R of carbon isotopes to carbon atoms is

$$R = \left(\frac{1}{10^{12}}\right)\left(\frac{1}{2}\right)^{t/5700},$$

where t is the time (in years). Find the value of R for the following times.

a. 10,000 years   b. 20,000 years   c. 25,000 years

Solution

a. $R = \left(\frac{1}{10^{12}}\right)\left(\frac{1}{2}\right)^{10,000/5700} \approx 2.964 \times 10^{-13}$ *Ratio for 10,000 years*

b. $R = \left(\frac{1}{10^{12}}\right)\left(\frac{1}{2}\right)^{20,000/5700} \approx 8.785 \times 10^{-14}$ *Ratio for 20,000 years*

c. $R = \left(\frac{1}{10^{12}}\right)\left(\frac{1}{2}\right)^{25,000/5700} \approx 4.783 \times 10^{-14}$ *Ratio for 25,000 years*   ▬

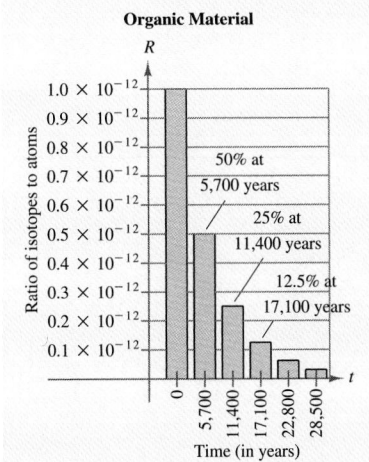

Organic Material

R

Ratio of isotopes to atoms

50% at 5,700 years

25% at 11,400 years

12.5% at 17,100 years

Time (in years)

FIGURE 4.1

EXAMPLE 3 *Graphing Exponential Functions*

Sketch the graphs of the following exponential functions.

a. $f(x) = 2^x$ **b.** $g(x) = \left(\frac{1}{2}\right)^x = 2^{-x}$ **c.** $h(x) = 3^x$

Solution

To sketch these functions by hand, you can begin by constructing a table of values, as shown in Table 4.1.

TABLE 4.1

x	-3	-2	-1	0	1	2	3	4
$f(x) = 2^x$	$\frac{1}{8}$	$\frac{1}{4}$	$\frac{1}{2}$	1	2	4	8	16
$g(x) = 2^{-x}$	8	4	2	1	$\frac{1}{2}$	$\frac{1}{4}$	$\frac{1}{8}$	$\frac{1}{16}$
$h(x) = 3^x$	$\frac{1}{27}$	$\frac{1}{9}$	$\frac{1}{3}$	1	3	9	27	81

The graphs of the three functions are shown in Figure 4.2. Note that the graphs of $f(x) = 2^x$ and $h(x) = 3^x$ are increasing, whereas the graph of $g(x) = 2^{-x}$ is decreasing.

(a)

(b)

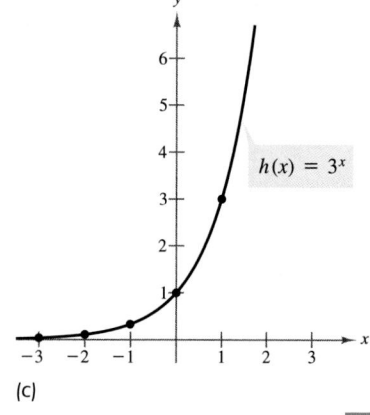

(c)

FIGURE 4.2

▦ TECHNOLOGY

Try graphing the functions $f(x) = 2^x$ and $h(x) = 3^x$ on the same viewing rectangle, as shown at the right.
From the display, you can see that the graph of h is increasing more rapidly than the graph of f.

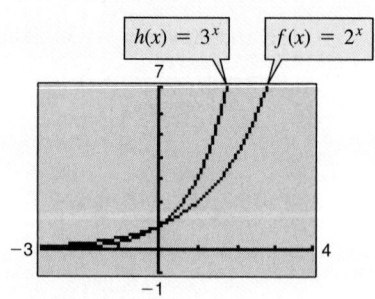

The forms of the graphs in Figure 4.2 are typical of the graphs of the exponential functions $y = a^{-x}$ and $y = a^x$, where $a > 1$. The basic characteristics of such graphs are summarized in Figure 4.3.

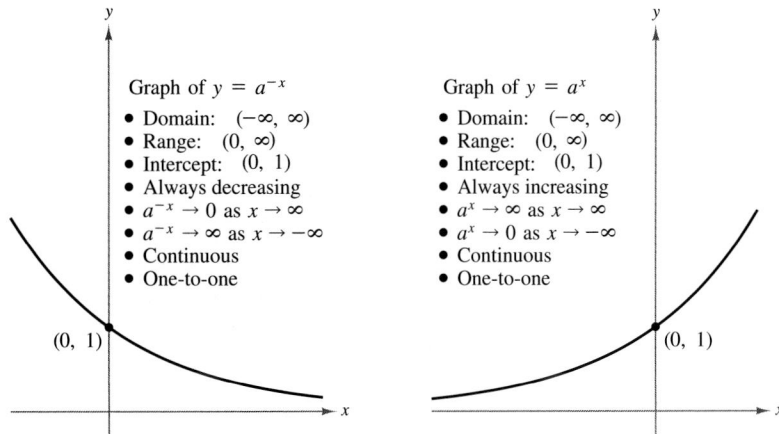

Graph of $y = a^{-x}$
- Domain: $(-\infty, \infty)$
- Range: $(0, \infty)$
- Intercept: $(0, 1)$
- Always decreasing
- $a^{-x} \to 0$ as $x \to \infty$
- $a^{-x} \to \infty$ as $x \to -\infty$
- Continuous
- One-to-one

Graph of $y = a^x$
- Domain: $(-\infty, \infty)$
- Range: $(0, \infty)$
- Intercept: $(0, 1)$
- Always increasing
- $a^x \to \infty$ as $x \to \infty$
- $a^x \to 0$ as $x \to -\infty$
- Continuous
- One-to-one

FIGURE 4.3   Characteristics of the Exponential Functions a^{-x} and $a^x (a > 1)$

EXAMPLE 4 *Graphing an Exponential Function*

Sketch the graph of

$$f(x) = 3^{-x} - 1.$$

Solution

Begin by creating a table of values, as shown in Table 4.2.

TABLE 4.2

x	-2	-1	0	1	2
$f(x)$	$3^2 - 1 = 8$	$3^1 - 1 = 2$	$3^0 - 1 = 0$	$3^{-1} - 1 = -\frac{2}{3}$	$3^{-2} - 1 = -\frac{8}{9}$

From the limit

$$\lim_{x \to \infty} (3^{-x} - 1) = \lim_{x \to \infty} 3^{-x} - \lim_{x \to \infty} 1$$
$$= \lim_{x \to \infty} \frac{1}{3^x} - \lim_{x \to \infty} 1$$
$$= 0 - 1$$
$$= -1,$$

you can see that $y = -1$ is a horizontal asymptote of the graph. The graph is shown in Figure 4.4. ▬

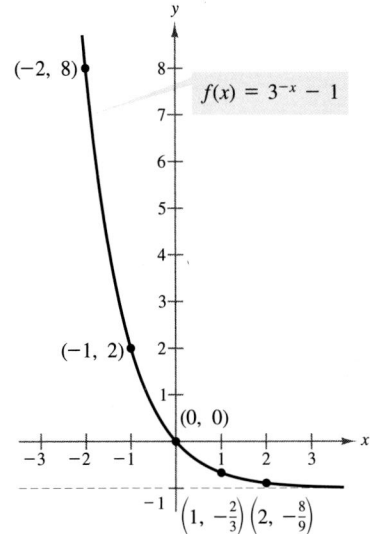

$f(x) = 3^{-x} - 1$

$(-2, 8)$
$(-1, 2)$
$(0, 0)$
$\left(1, -\frac{2}{3}\right) \left(2, -\frac{8}{9}\right)$

FIGURE 4.4

Natural Exponential Functions

At the beginning of this section, exponential functions were introduced using an unspecified base a. In calculus, the most convenient (or natural) choice for a base is the irrational number e, whose decimal approximation is

$$e \approx 2.71828182846.$$

Although this choice of base may seem unusual, its convenience will become apparent as the rules for differentiating exponential functions are developed in Section 4.2. In that development, you will encounter the limit used in the following definition of e.

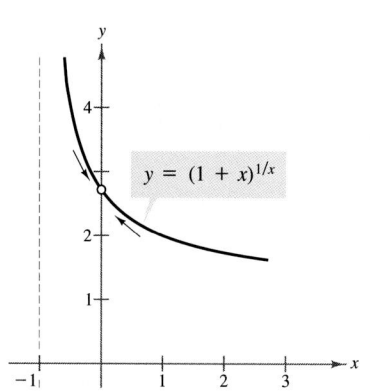

$$\lim_{x \to 0}(1+x)^{1/x} \approx 2.71828$$

FIGURE 4.5

Limit Definition of e

The irrational number e is defined to be the limit of $(1+x)^{1/x}$ as $x \to 0$. That is,

$$\lim_{x \to 0}(1+x)^{1/x} = e.$$

The graph of $y = (1+x)^{1/x}$ is shown in Figure 4.5. Try reproducing this graph with a graphing utility. Then, use the zoom and trace features to find values of y near $x = 0$. You will find that the y-values get closer and closer to the number $e \approx 2.71828$.

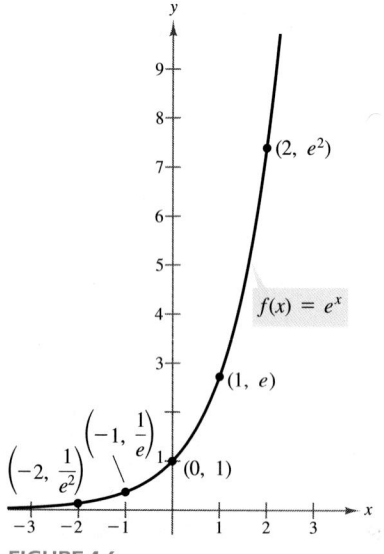

FIGURE 4.6

EXAMPLE 5 *Graphing the Natural Exponential Function*

Sketch the graph of

$$f(x) = e^x.$$

Solution

Begin by evaluating the function for several values of x, as shown in Table 4.3.

TABLE 4.3

x	-2	-1	0	1	2
$f(x)$	$e^{-2} \approx 0.135$	$e^{-1} \approx 0.368$	$e^0 = 1$	$e^1 \approx 2.718$	$e^2 \approx 7.389$

The graph of $f(x) = e^x$ is shown in Figure 4.6. Note that e^x is positive for all values of x. Moreover, the graph has the x-axis as a horizontal asymptote to the left. That is,

$$\lim_{x \to -\infty} e^x = 0.$$

FPG International/© Telegraph Colour Library

When a culture is grown in a dish, the size of the dish and the available food limit the culture's growth.

Exponential functions are often used to model the growth of a quantity or a population. When the quantity's growth is *not* restricted, an exponential model is often used. When the quantity's growth *is* restricted, the best model is often a **logistics growth function** of the form

$$f(t) = \frac{a}{1 + be^{-kt}}.$$

Graphs of both types of population growth models are shown in Figure 4.7.

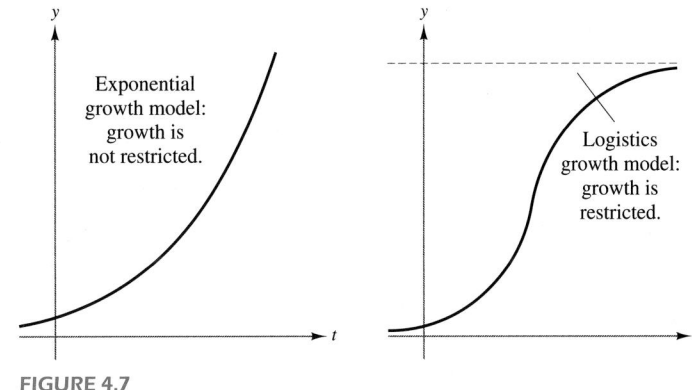

FIGURE 4.7

Real Life

EXAMPLE 6 *Modeling a Population*

A bacterial culture is growing according to the *logistics growth model*

$$y = \frac{1.25}{1 + 0.25e^{-0.4t}}, \qquad 0 \le t,$$

where y is the culture weight (in grams) and t is the time (in hours). Find the weight of the culture after 0 hours, 1 hour, and 10 hours. What is the limit of the model as t increases without bound?

Solution

$$y = \frac{1.25}{1 + 0.25e^{-0.4(0)}} = 1 \text{ gram} \qquad \textit{Weight when } t = 0$$

$$y = \frac{1.25}{1 + 0.25e^{-0.4(1)}} \approx 1.071 \text{ grams} \qquad \textit{Weight when } t = 1$$

$$y = \frac{1.25}{1 + 0.25e^{-0.4(10)}} \approx 1.244 \text{ grams} \qquad \textit{Weight when } t = 10$$

As t approaches infinity, the limit of y is

$$\lim_{t \to \infty} \frac{1.25}{1 + 0.25e^{-0.4t}} = \lim_{t \to \infty} \frac{1.25}{1 + (0.25/e^{0.4t})} = \frac{1.25}{1 + 0} = 1.25.$$

Thus, as t increases without bound, the weight of the culture approaches 1.25 grams. The graph of the model is shown in Figure 4.8.

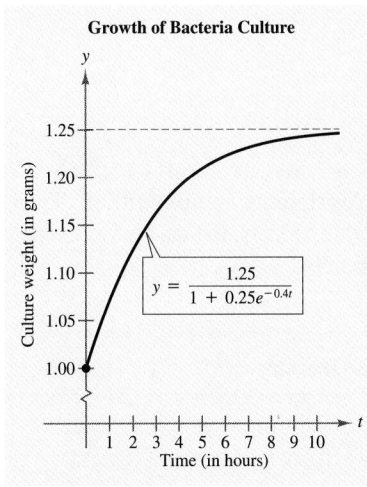

Growth of Bacteria Culture

$$y = \frac{1.25}{1 + 0.25e^{-0.4t}}$$

Culture weight (in grams)

Time (in hours)

FIGURE 4.8

Extended Application: Compound Interest

If P dollars is deposited in an account at an annual interest rate of r (in decimal form), what is the balance after 1 year? The answer depends on the number of times the interest is compounded, according to the formula

$$A = P\left(1 + \frac{r}{n}\right)^{n},$$

where n is the number of compoundings per year. The balances for a deposit of $1000 at 8%, at various compounding periods, are shown in Table 4.4.

TABLE 4.4

Number of times compounded per year, n	Balance (in dollars), A
Annually, $n = 1$	$A = P\left(1 + \frac{0.08}{1}\right)^{1} = \$1080.00$
Semiannually, $n = 2$	$A = P\left(1 + \frac{0.08}{2}\right)^{2} = \$1081.60$
Quarterly, $n = 4$	$A = P\left(1 + \frac{0.08}{4}\right)^{4} = \$1082.43$
Monthly, $n = 12$	$A = P\left(1 + \frac{0.08}{12}\right)^{12} = \$1083.00$
Daily, $n = 365$	$A = P\left(1 + \frac{0.08}{365}\right)^{365} = \$1083.28$

It may surprise you to discover that as n increases, the balance A approaches a limit, as indicated in the following development. In this development, let $x = r/n$. Then $x \to 0$ as $n \to \infty$, and you have

$$
\begin{aligned}
A &= \lim_{n\to\infty} P\left(1 + \frac{r}{n}\right)^{n} \\
&= P \lim_{n\to\infty} \left[\left(1 + \frac{r}{n}\right)^{n/r}\right]^{r} \\
&= P \left[\lim_{x\to 0} (1 + x)^{1/x}\right]^{r} \qquad \text{\textit{Substitute x for r/n.}} \\
&= Pe^{r}.
\end{aligned}
$$

This limit is the balance after one year of **continuous compounding.** Thus, for a deposit of $1000 at 8%, compounded continuously, the balance at the end of the year would be $A = 1000e^{0.08} \approx \$1083.29$.

Summary of Compound Interest Formulas

Let P be the amount deposited, t be the number of years, A be the balance, and r be the annual interest rate (in decimal form).

1. Compounded n times per year: $A = P\left[1 + (r/n)\right]^{nt}$

2. Compounded continuously: $A = Pe^{rt}$

The average interest rates paid by banks for savings accounts have varied greatly during the past 30 years. At times, savings accounts have earned as much as 12% annual interest and at times they have earned as little as 3%. The next example shows how the annual interest rate can affect the balance of an account.

Real Life

EXAMPLE 7 *Finding Account Balances*

You are creating a trust fund for your newborn nephew. You deposit $25,000 in an account, with instructions that the account will be turned over to your nephew on his 25th birthday. Compare the balances in the account for the following.

a. 6%, compounded continuously   **b.** 6%, compounded quarterly

c. 10%, compounded continuously   **d.** 10%, compounded quarterly

Solution

a. $25{,}000e^{0.06(25)} = \$112{,}042.23$ *6%, compounded continuously*

b. $25{,}000\left(1 + \dfrac{0.06}{4}\right)^{4(25)} = \$110{,}801.14$ *6%, compounded quarterly*

c. $25{,}000e^{0.1(25)} = \$304{,}562.35$ *10%, compounded continuously*

d. $25{,}000\left(1 + \dfrac{0.1}{4}\right)^{4(25)} = \$295{,}342.91$ *10%, compounded quarterly*

The growth of the account for parts a and c is shown in Figure 4.9. Notice the dramatic difference between the balances at 6% and at 10%.   ▬

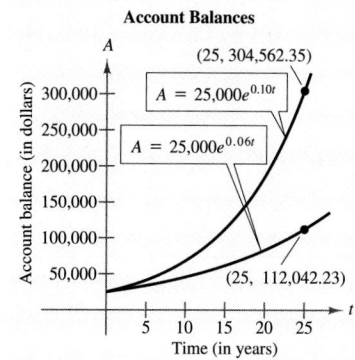

Account Balances

$A = 25{,}000e^{0.10t}$ — (25, 304,562.35)

$A = 25{,}000e^{0.06t}$ — (25, 112,042.23)

Account balance (in dollars)

Time (in years)

FIGURE 4.9

Discussion Problem   **Compound Interest**

You want to invest $5000 in a certificate of deposit for 10 years. You are given the following options. Which would you choose?

a. You can buy a 10-year certificate of deposit that earns 7%, compounded continuously. You are guaranteed a 7% rate for the entire 10 years, but you cannot withdraw the money early without paying a substantial penalty.

b. You can buy a 5-year certificate of deposit that earns 6%, compounded continuously. After 5 years, you can reinvest your money at whatever the current interest rate is at that time.

c. You can buy a 2-year certificate of deposit that earns 5%, compounded continuously. After 2 years, you can reinvest your money at whatever the current interest rate is at that time.

Warm Up

The following warm-up exercises involve skills that were covered in earlier sections. You will use these skills in the exercise set for this section.

In Exercises 1 and 2, discuss the continuity of the function.

1. $f(x) = \dfrac{3x^2 + 2x + 1}{x^2 + 1}$

2. $g(x) = \dfrac{x^2 - 9x + 20}{x - 4}$

In Exercises 3–10, find the limit.

3. $\displaystyle\lim_{x\to\infty} \frac{25}{1 + 4x}$

4. $\displaystyle\lim_{x\to\infty} \frac{16x}{3 + x^2}$

5. $\displaystyle\lim_{x\to\infty} \frac{8x^3 + 2}{2x^3 + x}$

6. $\displaystyle\lim_{x\to\infty} \frac{x}{2x}$

7. $\displaystyle\lim_{x\to\infty} \frac{3}{2 + (1/x)}$

8. $\displaystyle\lim_{x\to\infty} \frac{6}{1 + x^{-2}}$

9. $\displaystyle\lim_{x\to\infty} 2^{-x}$

10. $\displaystyle\lim_{x\to\infty} \frac{7}{1 + 5x}$

E X E R C I S E S   4.1   means that technology can help you solve or check the exercise(s).

In Exercises 1 and 2, evaluate each expression.

1. (a) $5(5^3)$ (b) $27^{2/3}$
    (c) $64^{3/4}$ (d) $81^{1/2}$
    (e) $25^{3/2}$ (f) $32^{2/5}$

2. (a) $\left(\frac{1}{5}\right)^3$ (b) $\left(\frac{1}{8}\right)^{1/3}$
    (c) $64^{2/3}$ (d) $\left(\frac{5}{8}\right)^2$
    (e) $100^{3/2}$ (f) $4^{5/2}$

In Exercises 3–8, use the properties of exponents to simplify the expression.

3. (a) $(5^2)(5^3)$ (b) $(5^2)(5^{-3})$
    (c) $(5^2)^2$ (d) 5^{-3}

4. (a) $\dfrac{5^3}{5^6}$ (b) $\left(\frac{1}{5}\right)^{-2}$
    (c) $(8^{1/2})(2^{1/2})$ (d) $(32^{3/2})\left(\frac{1}{2}\right)^{3/2}$

5. (a) $\dfrac{5^3}{25^2}$ (b) $(9^{2/3})(3)(3^{2/3})$
    (c) $[(25^{1/2})(5^2)]^{1/3}$ (d) $(8^2)(4^3)$

6. (a) $(4^3)(4^2)$ (b) $\left(\frac{1}{4}\right)^2 (4^2)$
    (c) $(4^6)^{1/2}$ (d) $[(8^{-1})(8^{2/3})]^3$

7. (a) $(e^3)(e^4)$ (b) $(e^3)^4$
    (c) $(e^3)^{-2}$ (d) e^0

8. (a) $\left(\frac{1}{e}\right)^{-2}$ (b) $\left(\frac{e^5}{e^2}\right)^{-1}$
    (c) $\dfrac{e^5}{e^3}$ (d) $\dfrac{1}{e^{-3}}$

In Exercises 9–22, solve the equation for x.

9. $3^x = 81$ **10.** $5^{x+1} = 125$

11. $\left(\frac{1}{3}\right)^{x-1} = 27$ **12.** $\left(\frac{1}{5}\right)^{2x} = 625$

13. $4^3 = (x + 2)^3$ **14.** $4^2 = (x + 2)^2$

15. $x^{3/4} = 8$ **16.** $(x + 3)^{4/3} = 16$

17. $e^{-3x} = e$ **18.** $e^x = 1$

19. $e^{\sqrt{x}} = e^3$ **20.** $e^{-1/x} = \sqrt{e}$

21. $x^{2/3} = \sqrt[3]{e^2}$ **22.** $\dfrac{x^2}{2} = e^2$

In Exercises 23–28, match the function with its graph. [The graphs are labeled (a)–(f).]

23. $f(x) = 3^x$

24. $f(x) = 3^{-x/2}$

25. $f(x) = -3^x$

26. $f(x) = 3^{x-2}$

27. $f(x) = 3^{-x} - 1$

28. $f(x) = 3^x + 2$

(a)

(b)

(c)

(d)

(e)

(f)

 In Exercises 29–44, sketch the graph of the function.

29. $f(x) = 6^x$

30. $f(x) = 4^x$

31. $f(x) = \left(\frac{1}{5}\right)^x = 5^{-x}$

32. $f(x) = \left(\frac{1}{4}\right)^x = 4^{-x}$

33. $y = 3^{-x^2}$

34. $y = 2^{-x^2}$

35. $y = 3^{-|x|}$

36. $y = 3^{|x|}$

37. $s(t) = \frac{1}{4}(3^{-t})$

38. $s(t) = 2^{-t} + 3$

39. $h(x) = e^{x-2}$

40. $f(x) = e^{2x}$

41. $N(t) = 500e^{-0.2t}$

42. $A(t) = 500e^{0.15t}$

43. $g(x) = \dfrac{2}{1 + e^{x^2}}$

44. $g(x) = \dfrac{10}{1 + e^{-x}}$

Compound Interest In Exercises 45–48, complete the table to determine the balance A for P dollars invested at rate r for t years, compounded n times per year.

n	1	2	4	12	365	Continuous compounding
A						

45. $P = \$1000, r = 3\%, t = 10$ years

46. $P = \$2500, r = 5\%, t = 20$ years

47. $P = \$1000, r = 3\%, t = 40$ years

48. $P = \$2500, r = 5\%, t = 40$ years

Compound Interest In Exercises 49–52, complete the table to determine the amount of money P that should be invested at rate r to produce a final balance of $\$100,000$ in t years.

t	1	10	20	30	40	50
P						

49. $r = 4\%$, compounded continuously

50. $r = 3\%$, compounded continuously

51. $r = 5\%$, compounded monthly

52. $r = 6\%$, compounded daily

53. *Demand* The demand function for a product is modeled by

$$p = 5000\left(1 - \frac{4}{4 + e^{-0.002x}}\right),$$

as shown in the figure. Find the price of the product if the quantity demanded is (a) $x = 100$ units and (b) $x = 500$ units. What is the limit of the price as x increases without bound?

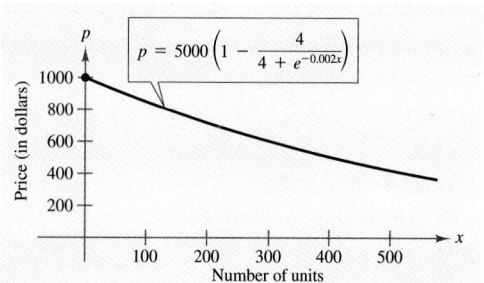

54. *Demand* The demand function for a product is modeled by $p = 500 - 0.5e^{0.004x}$, as shown in the figure. Find the price of the product if the quantity demanded is (a) $x = 1000$ units and (b) $x = 1500$ units.

55. *Probability* The average time between incoming calls at a switchboard is 3 minutes. If a call has just come in, the probability that the next call will come within the next t minutes is $P(t) = 1 - e^{-t/3}$. Find the probability of the following.

(a) A call comes in within $\frac{1}{2}$ minute.
(b) A call comes in within 2 minutes.
(c) A call comes in within 5 minutes.

56. *Fuel Efficiency* An automobile gets 28 miles per gallon at speeds of up to 50 miles per hour. At speeds of 50 miles per hour or greater, the number of miles per gallon drops at the rate of 12% for each 10 miles per hour. If s is the speed (in miles per hour) and y is the miles per gallon, then

$$y = 28e^{0.6 - 0.012s}, \qquad s \geq 50.$$

Use this information to complete the table. What can you conclude?

Speed (s)	50	55	60	65	70
Miles per gallon (y)					

57. *Population Growth* The population y of a bacterial culture is modeled by the logistics function

$$y = \frac{925}{1 + e^{-0.3t}},$$

where t is the time in days.

(a) Sketch the graph of the model.
(b) Does the population have a limit as t increases without bound? Explain your answer.

58. *Forestry* The yield V (in millions of cubic feet per acre) of a forest at age t years is modeled by

$$V = 6.7e^{-48/t}.$$

(a) Find the yield after 20 years and after 50 years.
(b) Sketch the graph of the model.
(c) Does the yield have a limit as t increases without bound? Explain your answer.

59. *Learning Theory* In a learning theory project, the proportion P of correct responses after n trials can be modeled by

$$P = \frac{0.83}{1 + e^{-0.2n}}.$$

(a) Use a graphing utility to estimate the proportion of correct responses after ten trials. Check your result analytically.
(b) Use a graphing utility to estimate the number of trials required to have a proportion of correct responses of 0.75.
(c) Does the proportion of correct responses have a limit as n increases without bound? Explain your answer.

60. *Learning Theory* In a typing class, the average number N of words per minute typed after t weeks of lessons can be modeled by

$$N = \frac{95}{1 + 8.5e^{-0.12t}}.$$

(a) Use a graphing utility to estimate the average number of words per minute typed after 10 weeks. Check your result analytically.
(b) Use a graphing utility to estimate the number of weeks required to produce an average of 70 words per minute.
(c) Does the number of words per minute have a limit as t increases without bound? Explain your answer.

In Exercises 61–64, use a graphing utility to graph the function. Determine whether the function has any horizontal asymptotes and discuss the continuity of the function.

61. $f(x) = \dfrac{e^x + e^{-x}}{2}$

62. $f(x) = \dfrac{e^x - e^{-x}}{2}$

63. $f(x) = \dfrac{2}{1 + e^{1/x}}$

64. $f(x) = \dfrac{2}{1 + 2e^{-0.2x}}$

4.2 Derivatives of Exponential Functions

Derivatives of Exponential Functions ■ *Applications* ■
The Normal Probability Density Function

Derivatives of Exponential Functions

In Section 4.1, we stated that the most convenient base for exponential functions is the irrational number e. The convenience of this base stems primarily from the fact that the function $f(x) = e^x$ *is its own derivative.* You will see that this is not true of other exponential functions of the form $y = a^x$ where $a \neq e$. To verify that $f(x) = e^x$ is its own derivative, notice that the limit

$$\lim_{\Delta x \to 0} (1 + \Delta x)^{1/\Delta x} = e$$

implies that for small values of Δx, $e \approx (1 + \Delta x)^{1/\Delta x}$, or $e^{\Delta x} \approx 1 + \Delta x$. This approximation is used in the following derivation.

$$f'(x) = \lim_{\Delta x \to 0} \frac{f(x + \Delta x) - f(x)}{\Delta x} \qquad \text{\textit{Definition of derivative}}$$

$$= \lim_{\Delta x \to 0} \frac{e^{x+\Delta x} - e^x}{\Delta x} \qquad \text{\textit{Use } } f(x) = e^x.$$

$$= \lim_{\Delta x \to 0} \frac{e^x(e^{\Delta x} - 1)}{\Delta x} \qquad \text{\textit{Factor numerator.}}$$

$$= \lim_{\Delta x \to 0} \frac{e^x[(1 + \Delta x) - 1]}{\Delta x} \qquad \text{\textit{Substitute } } 1 + \Delta x \text{ \textit{for } } e^{\Delta x}.$$

$$= \lim_{\Delta x \to 0} \frac{e^x(\Delta x)}{\Delta x} \qquad \text{\textit{Cancel common factor.}}$$

$$= \lim_{\Delta x \to 0} e^x \qquad \text{\textit{Simplify.}}$$

$$= e^x \qquad \text{\textit{Evaluate limit.}}$$

By applying the Chain Rule, you can obtain the derivative of e^u with respect to x. Both formulas are summarized as follows.

Derivatives of Exponential Functions

Let u be a differentiable function of x.

1. $\dfrac{d}{dx}[e^x] = e^x$ **2.** $\dfrac{d}{dx}[e^u] = e^u u'$

EXAMPLE 1 *Interpreting Derivatives Graphically*

Find the slope of the tangent line of

$$f(x) = e^x \qquad\qquad Original\ function$$

at the points $(0, 1)$ and $(1, e)$. What conclusion can you make?

Solution

Because the derivative of f is

$$f'(x) = e^x, \qquad\qquad Derivative$$

it follows that the slope of the tangent line to the graph of f is

$$f'(0) = e^0 = 1 \qquad\qquad Slope\ at\ point\ (0, 1)$$

at the point $(0, 1)$, and the slope of the tangent line to the graph of f is

$$f'(1) = e^1 = e \qquad\qquad Slope\ at\ point\ (1, e)$$

at the point $(1, e)$, as shown in Figure 4.10. From this pattern, you can see that the slope of the tangent line to the graph of $f(x) = e^x$ at any point (x, e^x) is equal to the y-coordinate of the point. ■

At the point $(1, e)$ the slope is $e \approx 2.72$.

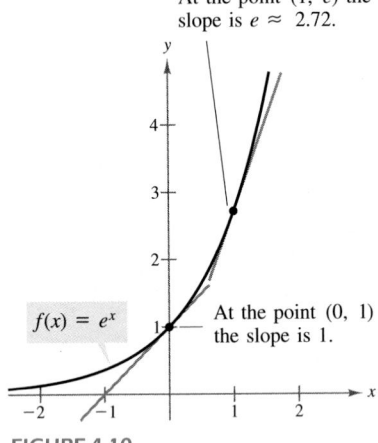

$f(x) = e^x$

At the point $(0, 1)$ the slope is 1.

FIGURE 4.10

EXAMPLE 2 *Differentiating Exponential Functions*

Differentiate the following functions.

a. $f(x) = e^{2x}$ **b.** $f(x) = e^{-3x^2}$

c. $f(x) = 6e^{x^3}$ **d.** $f(x) = e^{-x}$

Solution

a. Let $u = 2x$. Then $u' = 2$, and you can apply the Chain Rule.

$$f'(x) = e^u u' = e^{2x}(2) = 2e^{2x}$$

b. Let $u = -3x^2$. Then $u' = -6x$, and you can apply the Chain Rule.

$$f'(x) = e^u u' = e^{-3x^2}(-6x) = -6xe^{-3x^2}$$

c. Let $u = x^3$. Then $u' = 3x^2$, and you can apply the Chain Rule.

$$f'(x) = 6e^u u' = 6e^{x^3}(3x^2) = 18x^2 e^{x^3}$$

d. Let $u = -x$. Then $u' = -1$, and you can apply the Chain Rule.

$$f'(x) = e^u u' = e^{-x}(-1) = -e^{-x} \qquad ■$$

Note In Example 2, notice that when you differentiate an exponential function, the exponent does not change. For instance, the derivative of $y = e^{3x}$ is $y' = 3e^{3x}$. In both the function and its derivative, the exponent is $3x$.

The differentiation rules that you studied in Chapter 2 can be used with exponential functions, as illustrated in Example 3.

EXAMPLE 3 *Differentiating Exponential Functions*

Differentiate the following functions.

a. $f(x) = xe^x$ 　　　　　　 **b.** $f(x) = \dfrac{e^x - e^{-x}}{2}$

c. $f(x) = \dfrac{e^x}{x}$ 　　　　　　 **d.** $f(x) = xe^x - e^x$

Solution

a. $f(x) = xe^x$ 　　　　　　　　　　　*Original function*

　　$f'(x) = xe^x + e^x(1)$ 　　　　　　　*Product Rule*

　　　　$= xe^x + e^x$ 　　　　　　　　　*Simplify.*

b. $f(x) = \dfrac{e^x - e^{-x}}{2}$ 　　　　　　*Original function*

　　　　$= \frac{1}{2}(e^x - e^{-x})$ 　　　　　　*Rewrite.*

　　$f'(x) = \frac{1}{2}(e^x + e^{-x})$ 　　　　　　*Constant Multiple Rule*

c. $f(x) = \dfrac{e^x}{x}$ 　　　　　　　　　*Original function*

　　$f'(x) = \dfrac{xe^x - e^x(1)}{x^2}$ 　　　　　*Quotient Rule*

　　　　$= \dfrac{e^x(x - 1)}{x^2}$ 　　　　　　*Simplify.*

d. $f(x) = xe^x - e^x$ 　　　　　　　*Original function*

　　$f'(x) = [xe^x + e^x(1)] - e^x$ 　　　*Product and Difference Rules*

　　　　$= xe^x + e^x - e^x$

　　　　$= xe^x$ 　　　　　　　　　　　*Simplify.*

▦ TECHNOLOGY

If you have access to a symbolic differentiation utility such as *Derive*, *Maple*, or *Mathematica*, try using it to find the derivatives of the functions in Example 3. For example, the display at the right shows how *Derive* can be used to find the derivative of $f(x) = xe^x - e^x$.

　1: 　x EXP (x) - EXP (x) 　　　　　　　*Author.*

　2: 　$\dfrac{d}{dx}$ (x EXP (x) - EXP (x)) 　　*Differentiate.*

　3: 　x ê^x 　　　　　　　　　　　　　*Simplify.*

Utility wires strung between poles have the shape of a catenary.

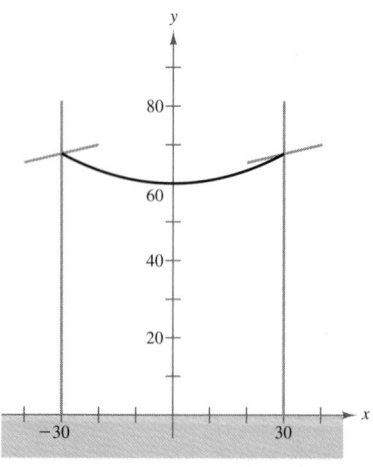

FIGURE 4.11

Applications

In Chapter 3, you learned how to use derivatives to analyze the graph of a function. The next example applies these techniques to a function composed of exponential functions. In the example, notice that $e^a = e^b$ implies that $a = b$.

Real Life

EXAMPLE 4 *Analyzing a Catenary*

When a telephone wire is hung between two poles, the wire forms a U-shaped curve called a **catenary.** For instance, the function

$$y = 30(e^{x/60} + e^{-x/60}), \qquad -30 \le x \le 30$$

models the shape of a telephone wire that is strung between two poles that are 60 feet apart (x and y are measured in feet). Show that the lowest point on the wire is midway between the two poles. How much does the wire sag between the two poles?

Solution
The derivative of the function is

$$y' = 30\left[e^{x/60}\left(\tfrac{1}{60}\right) + e^{-x/60}\left(-\tfrac{1}{60}\right)\right] = \tfrac{1}{2}(e^{x/60} - e^{-x/60}).$$

To find the critical numbers, set the derivative equal to zero.

$\tfrac{1}{2}(e^{x/60} - e^{-x/60}) = 0$	*Set derivative equal to 0.*
$e^{x/60} - e^{-x/60} = 0$	*Multiply both sides by 2.*
$e^{x/60} = e^{-x/60}$	*Add $e^{-x/60}$ to both sides.*
$\dfrac{x}{60} = -\dfrac{x}{60}$	*If $e^a = e^b$, then $a = b$.*
$x = -x$	*Multiply both sides by 60.*
$2x = 0$	*Add x to both sides.*
$x = 0$	*Divide both sides by 2.*

Using the First-Derivative Test, you can determine that the critical number $x = 0$ yields a relative minimum of the function. From the graph in Figure 4.11, you can see that this relative minimum is actually a minimum on the interval $[-30, 30]$. To find how much the wire sags between the two poles, you can compare its height at each pole with the height at the midpoint.

$y = 30(e^{-30/60} + e^{-(-30)/60}) \approx 67.7$ feet	*Height at left pole*
$y = 30(e^{0/60} + e^{-(0)/60}) = 60$ feet	*Height at midpoint*
$y = 30(e^{30/60} + e^{-(30)/60}) \approx 67.7$ feet	*Height at right pole*

From this, you can see that the wire sags about 7.7 feet. ∎

EXAMPLE 5 *Finding a Maximum Revenue*

The demand function for a product is modeled by

$$p = 56e^{-0.000012x}, \qquad \textit{Demand function}$$

where p is the price per unit (in dollars) and x is the number of units. What price will yield a maximum revenue?

Solution

The revenue function is

$$R = xp = 56xe^{-0.000012x}. \qquad \textit{Revenue function}$$

To find the maximum revenue *analytically*, you would set the marginal revenue, dR/dx, equal to zero and solve for x. In this problem, it is easier to use a *graphical* approach. After experimenting to find a reasonable viewing rectangle, you can obtain a graph of R that is similar to that shown in Figure 4.12. Using the zoom and trace features, you can conclude that the maximum revenue occurs when x is about 83,300 units. To find the price that corresponds to this production level, substitute $x \approx 83,300$ into the demand function.

$$p \approx 56e^{-0.000012(83,300)}$$
$$\approx \$20.61.$$

Thus, a price of about \$20.61 will yield a maximum revenue.

FIGURE 4.12   Use the zoom and trace features to approximate the x-value that corresponds to the maximum revenue.

Note   Try solving the problem in Example 5 analytically. When you do this, you obtain

$$\frac{dR}{dx} = 56xe^{-0.000012x}(-0.000012) + e^{-0.000012x}(56) = 0.$$

Explain how you would solve this equation. What is the solution?

The Normal Probability Density Function

If you take a course in statistics or quantitative business analysis, you will spend quite a bit of time studying the characteristics and use of the **normal probability density function** given by

$$f(x) = \frac{1}{\sigma\sqrt{2\pi}} e^{-(x-\mu)^2/2\sigma^2},$$

where σ is the lowercase Greek letter sigma, and μ is the lowercase Greek letter mu. In this formula, σ represents the standard deviation of the probability distribution, and μ represents the mean of the probability distribution.

EXAMPLE 6   *Exploring a Probability Density Function*

Show that the graph of the normal probability density function

$$f(x) = \frac{1}{\sqrt{2\pi}} e^{-x^2/2} \qquad\qquad \textit{Original function}$$

has points of inflection at $x = \pm 1$.

Solution
Begin by finding the second derivative of the function.

$$f'(x) = \frac{1}{\sqrt{2\pi}}(-x)e^{-x^2/2} \qquad\qquad \textit{First derivative}$$

$$f''(x) = \frac{1}{\sqrt{2\pi}}[(-x)(-x)e^{-x^2/2} + (-1)e^{-x^2/2}] \quad \textit{Second derivative}$$

$$= \frac{1}{\sqrt{2\pi}}(e^{-x^2/2})(x^2 - 1) \qquad\qquad \textit{Simplify.}$$

By setting the second derivative equal to zero, you can determine that $x = \pm 1$. By testing the concavity of the graph, you can then conclude that these x-values yield points of inflection, as shown in Figure 4.13. ▬

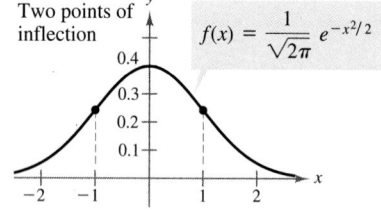

Two points of inflection

$$f(x) = \frac{1}{\sqrt{2\pi}} e^{-x^2/2}$$

FIGURE 4.13 The graph of the normal probability density function is bell-shaped.

Discussion Problem   The Normal Probability Density Function

Use Example 6 as a model to show that the graph of the normal probability density function with $\mu = 0$,

$$f(x) = \frac{1}{\sigma\sqrt{2\pi}} e^{-x^2/2\sigma^2},$$

has points of inflection at $x = \pm\sigma$. What is the maximum of the function?

Warm Up

The following warm-up exercises involve skills that were covered in earlier sections. You will use these skills in the exercise set for this section.

In Exercises 1–4, factor the expression.

1. $x^2 e^x - \frac{1}{2} e^x$

2. $(xe^{-x})^{-1} + e^x$

3. $xe^x - e^{2x}$

4. $e^x - xe^{-x}$

In Exercises 5–8, find the derivative of the function.

5. $f(x) = \dfrac{3}{7x^2}$

6. $g(x) = 3x^2 - \dfrac{x}{6}$

7. $f(x) = (4x - 3)(x^2 + 9)$

8. $f(t) = \dfrac{t - 2}{\sqrt{t}}$

In Exercises 9 and 10, find the relative extrema of the function.

9. $f(x) = \frac{1}{8}x^3 - 2x$

10. $f(x) = x^4 - 2x^2 + 5$

EXERCISES 4.2

 means that technology can help you solve or check the exercise(s).

In Exercises 1–4, find the slope of the tangent line to the exponential function at the point (0, 1).

1. $y = e^{3x}$

2. $y = e^{2x}$

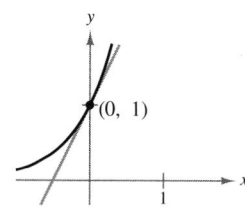

3. $y = e^{-x}$

4. $y = e^{-2x}$

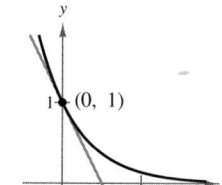

In Exercises 5–20, find the derivative of the function.

5. $y = e^{4x}$

6. $y = e^{1-x}$

7. $y = e^{-2x+x^2}$

8. $y = e^{-x^2}$

9. $f(x) = e^{1/x}$

10. $f(x) = e^{-1/x^2}$

11. $g(x) = e^{\sqrt{x}}$

12. $g(x) = e^{x^3}$

13. $f(x) = (x^2 + 1)e^{4x}$

14. $y = x^2 e^{-x}$

15. $y = (e^{-x} + e^x)^3$

16. $y = (10e^{-x})^2$

17. $f(x) = \dfrac{2}{e^x + e^{-x}}$

18. $f(x) = \dfrac{e^x + e^{-x}}{2}$

Sign So[**19.** $y = xe^x - 4e^{-x}$]

20. $y = x^2 e^x - 2xe^x + 2e^x$

In Exercises 21 and 22, find dy/dx implicitly.

21. $xe^x + 2ye^x = 0$

22. $e^{xy} + x^2 - y^2 = 10$

In Exercises 23–26, find the second derivative.

23. $f(x) = 2e^{3x} + 3e^{-2x}$

24. $f(x) = (1 + 2x)e^{4x}$

25. $f(x) = 5e^{-x} - 2e^{-5x}$

26. $f(x) = (3 + 2x)e^{-3x}$

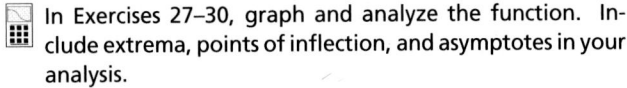

In Exercises 27–30, graph and analyze the function. Include extrema, points of inflection, and asymptotes in your analysis.

27. $f(x) = \dfrac{1}{2 - e^{-x}}$

28. $f(x) = \dfrac{e^x - e^{-x}}{2}$

29. $f(x) = x^2 e^{-x}$

30. $f(x) = xe^{-x}$

In Exercises 31 and 32, use a graphing utility to graph the function. Determine any asymptotes of the graph.

31. $f(x) = \dfrac{8}{1 + e^{-0.5x}}$

32. $g(x) = \dfrac{8}{1 + e^{-0.5/x}}$

Depreciation In Exercises 33 and 34, the value V (in dollars) of an item is a function of the time t (in years).

(a) Graph the function over the interval [0, 10].
(b) Find the rate of change of V when $t = 1$.
(c) Find the rate of change of V when $t = 5$.
(d) Compare this depreciation model with a linear model. What are the advantages of each?

33. $V = 15,000e^{-0.6286t}$ **34.** $V = 500,000e^{-0.2231t}$

35. *Forest Defoliation* To estimate the defoliation p (in percent of foliage) caused by gypsy moths during a year, a forester counts the number x (in thousands) of egg masses on $\frac{1}{40}$ of an acre the preceding fall. The defoliation is modeled by

$$p = \dfrac{300}{3 + 17e^{-1.57x}}.$$

(Source: National Forest Service)

(a) Use a graphing utility to graph the model.
(b) Estimate the percent of defoliation if 2000 egg masses are counted.
(c) Estimate the number of egg masses for which the amount of defoliation is increasing most rapidly.

36. *Learning Theory* The average typing speed N (in words per minute) after t weeks of lessons is modeled by

$$N = \dfrac{95}{1 + 8.5e^{-0.12t}}.$$

Find the rate at which the typing speed is changing when (a) $t = 5$ weeks, (b) $t = 10$ weeks, and (c) $t = 30$ weeks.

37. *Compound Interest* The balance A (in dollars) in a savings account is given by $A = 5000e^{0.08t}$, where t is measured in years. Find the rate at which the balance is changing when (a) $t = 1$ year, (b) $t = 10$ years, and (c) $t = 50$ years.

38. *Ebbinghaus Model* The *Ebbinghaus Model* for human memory is

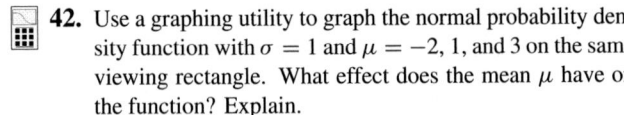

$$p = (100 - a)e^{-bt} + a,$$

where p is the percent retained after t weeks. (The constants a and b vary from one person to another.) If $a = 20$ and $b = 0.5$, at what rate is information being retained after 1 week? After 3 weeks?

39. *Orchard Yield* The yield V (in pounds per acre) for an orchard at age t (in years) is modeled by

$$V = 7955.6e^{-0.0458/t}.$$

At what rate is the yield changing when $t = 5$ years? When $t = 10$ years? When $t = 25$ years?

40. *Self-Employed Workers* From 1980 to 1991, the number y (in thousands) of self-employed workers in the United States can be modeled by

$$y = 6787.05 + 1851.06e^{0.06t},$$

where $t = 0$ corresponds to 1980. *(Source: U.S. Bureau of Labor Statistics)*

(a) Use a graphing utility to graph the model.
(b) Use the graph to estimate the rate of change in the number of self-employed people in 1980 and in 1990.
(c) Confirm the result of part (b) analytically.

41. Use a graphing utility to graph the normal probability density function with $\mu = 0$ and $\sigma = 2, 3,$ and 4 on the same viewing rectangle. What effect does the standard deviation σ have on the function? Explain.

42. Use a graphing utility to graph the normal probability density function with $\sigma = 1$ and $\mu = -2, 1,$ and 3 on the same viewing rectangle. What effect does the mean μ have on the function? Explain.

Logarithmic Functions

The Natural Logarithmic Function ■ *Properties of Logarithmic Functions* ■ *Solving Exponential and Logarithmic Equations* ■ *Applications*

The Natural Logarithmic Function

From your previous algebra courses, you should be somewhat familiar with logarithms. For instance, the **common logarithm** $\log_{10} x$ is defined as

$$\log_{10} x = b \quad \text{if and only if} \quad 10^b = x.$$

The base of common logarithms is 10. In calculus, the most useful base for logarithms is the number e.

Definition of the Natural Logarithmic Function

The **natural logarithmic function**, denoted by $\ln x$, is defined as

$$\ln x = b \quad \text{if and only if} \quad e^b = x.$$

$\ln x$ is read as "el-en of x" or as "the natural log of x."

This definition implies that the natural logarithmic function and the natural exponential function are inverses of each other. Thus, every logarithmic equation can be written in an equivalent exponential form and every exponential equation can be written in logarithmic form. Here are some examples.

Logarithmic form $\ln 1 = 0 \quad \ln e = 1 \quad \ln \dfrac{1}{e} = -1 \quad \ln 2 \approx 0.693$

Exponential form $e^0 = 1 \quad\quad e^1 = e \quad\quad e^{-1} = \dfrac{1}{e} \quad\quad e^{0.693} \approx 2$

Because the functions $f(x) = e^x$ and $g(x) = \ln x$ are inverses of each other, their graphs are reflections of each other in the line $y = x$. This reflective property is illustrated in Figure 4.14. The figure also contains a summary of several properties of the graph of the natural logarithmic function.

Notice that the domain of the natural logarithmic function is the set of *positive real numbers*—be sure you see that $\ln x$ is not defined for zero or for negative numbers. You can test this on your calculator. If you try evaluating $\ln(-1)$ or $\ln 0$, your calculator should indicate that the value is not a real number.

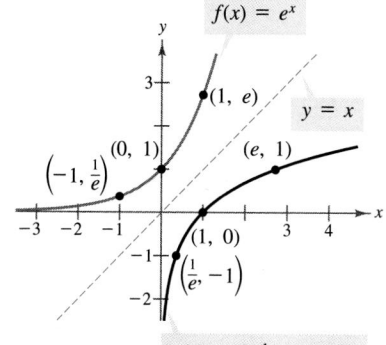

$g(x) = \ln x$

- Domain: $(0, \infty)$
- Range: $(-\infty, \infty)$
- Intercept: $(1, 0)$
- Always increasing
- $\ln x \to \infty$ as $x \to \infty$
- $\ln x \to -\infty$ as $x \to 0^+$
- Continuous
- One-to-one

FIGURE 4.14

EXAMPLE 1 *Graphing Logarithmic Functions*

Sketch the graphs of the following functions.

a. $f(x) = \ln(x + 1)$ **b.** $f(x) = 2\ln(x - 2)$

Solution

a. Because the natural logarithmic function is defined only for positive values, the domain of the function is $0 < x + 1$, or

$$-1 < x. \qquad\qquad Domain$$

To sketch the graph, begin by constructing a table of values, as shown in Table 4.5. Then, plot the points in the table and connect them with a smooth curve, as shown in Figure 4.15(a).

TABLE 4.5

x	−0.5	0	0.5	1	1.5	2
$\ln(x + 1)$	−0.693	0	0.405	0.693	0.916	1.099

b. The domain of this function is $0 < x - 2$, or

$$2 < x. \qquad\qquad Domain$$

Table 4.6 shows a table of values for the function, and its graph is shown in Figure 4.15(b).

TABLE 4.6

x	2.5	3	3.5	4	4.5	5
$2\ln(x - 2)$	−1.386	0	0.811	1.386	1.833	2.197

(a)

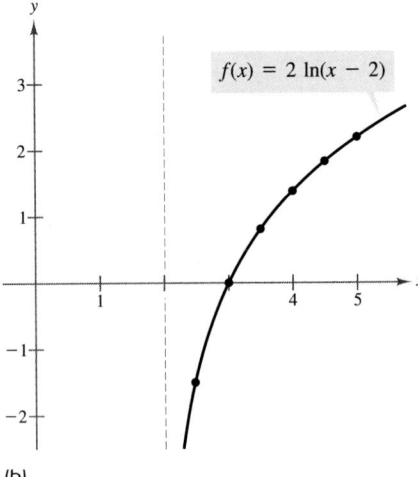

(b)

FIGURE 4.15

Properties of Logarithmic Functions

Recall from Section 1.4 that inverse functions possess the property that

$$f(f^{-1}(x)) = x \quad \text{and} \quad f^{-1}(f(x)) = x.$$

The properties listed below follow from the fact that the natural logarithmic function and natural exponential function are inverses of each other.

Inverse Properties of Logarithms and Exponents

1. $\ln e^x = x$ **2.** $e^{\ln x} = x$

EXAMPLE 2 *Applying Inverse Properties*

Simplify the following expressions.

a. $\ln e^{\sqrt{2}}$ **b.** $e^{\ln 3x}$

Solution

a. Because $\ln e^x = x$, it follows that

$$\ln e^{\sqrt{2}} = \sqrt{2}.$$

b. Because $e^{\ln x} = x$, it follows that

$$e^{\ln 3x} = 3x.$$

Most of the properties of exponential functions can be rewritten in terms of logarithmic functions. For instance, the property

$$e^x e^y = e^{x+y}$$

states that you can multiply two exponential expressions by adding their exponents. In terms of logarithms, this property becomes

$$\ln xy = \ln x + \ln y.$$

This property and two other properties of logarithms are summarized below.

Properties of Logarithms

1. $\ln xy = \ln x + \ln y$ **2.** $\ln \dfrac{x}{y} = \ln x - \ln y$

3. $\ln x^n = n \ln x$

Rewriting a logarithm of a single quantity as the sum, difference, or multiple of logarithms is called *expanding* the logarithmic expression. The reverse procedure is called *condensing* a logarithmic expression.

EXAMPLE 3 *Expanding Logarithmic Expressions*

Use the properties of logarithms to write each expression as a sum, difference, or multiple of logarithms. (Assume $x > 0$ and $y > 0$.)

a. $\ln \dfrac{10}{9}$ **b.** $\ln \sqrt{x^2 + 1}$ **c.** $\ln \dfrac{xy}{5}$ **d.** $\ln \dfrac{x^2}{6y^3}$

Solution

a. $\ln \dfrac{10}{9} = \ln 10 - \ln 9$ *Property 2*

b. $\ln \sqrt{x^2 + 1} = \ln(x^2 + 1)^{1/2}$ *Write with rational exponents.*

               $= \tfrac{1}{2} \ln(x^2 + 1)$ *Property 3*

c. $\ln \dfrac{xy}{5} = \ln(xy) - \ln 5$ *Property 2*

         $= \ln x + \ln y - \ln 5$ *Property 1*

d. $\ln \dfrac{x^2}{6y^3} = \ln x^2 - \ln 6y^3$ *Property 2*

         $= \ln x^2 - (\ln 6 + \ln y^3)$ *Property 1*

         $= \ln x^2 - \ln 6 - \ln y^3$ *Simplify.*

         $= 2 \ln x - \ln 6 - 3 \ln y$ *Property 3*   ▬

TECHNOLOGY

Try using a graphing utility to verify the results of Example 3b. That is, try graphing the functions

$$y = \ln \sqrt{x^2 + 1}$$

and

$$y = \frac{1}{2} \ln(x^2 + 1).$$

Because these two functions are equivalent, their graphs should coincide.

EXAMPLE 4 *Condensing Logarithmic Expressions*

Use the properties of logarithms to rewrite each expression as the logarithm of a single quantity. (Assume $x > 0$ and $y > 0$.)

a. $\ln x + 2 \ln y$ **b.** $\ln(x + 1) + \ln(x + 2) - 3 \ln x$

Solution

a. $\ln x + 2 \ln y = \ln x + \ln y^2$ *Property 3*

         $= \ln xy^2$ *Property 1*

b. $\ln(x + 1) + \ln(x + 2) - 3 \ln x = \ln(x + 1)(x + 2) - 3 \ln x$

                       $= \ln(x^2 + 3x + 2) - \ln x^3$

                       $= \ln \dfrac{x^2 + 3x + 2}{x^3}$ ▬

Solving Exponential and Logarithmic Equations

The inverse properties of logarithms and exponents can be used to solve exponential and logarithmic equations, as illustrated in the next two examples.

EXAMPLE 5 *Solving Exponential Equations*

Solve the following equations.

a. $e^x = 5$ **b.** $10 + 3e^{0.1t} = 14$

Solution

a.

$e^x = 5$	*Original equation*
$\ln e^x = \ln 5$	*Take log of both sides.*
$x = \ln 5$	*Inverse property:* $\ln e^x = x$

Note In the examples on this page, note that the key step to solving an exponential equation is to "take the log of both sides," and the key step to solving a logarithmic equation is to "exponentiate both sides."

b.

$10 + 3e^{0.1t} = 14$	*Original equation*
$3e^{0.1t} = 4$	*Subtract 10 from both sides.*
$e^{0.1t} = \frac{4}{3}$	*Divide both sides by 3.*
$\ln e^{0.1t} = \ln \frac{4}{3}$	*Take log of both sides.*
$0.1t = \ln \frac{4}{3}$	*Inverse property:* $\ln e^{0.1t} = 0.1t$
$t = 10 \ln \frac{4}{3}$	*Multiply both sides by 10.*

EXAMPLE 6 *Solving Logarithmic Equations*

Solve the following equations.

a. $\ln x = 5$ **b.** $3 + 2 \ln x^2 = 7$

Solution

a.

$\ln x = 5$	*Original equation*
$e^{\ln x} = e^5$	*Exponentiate both sides.*
$x = e^5$	*Inverse property:* $e^{\ln x} = x$

b.

$3 + 2 \ln x^2 = 7$	*Original equation*
$2 \ln x^2 = 4$	*Subtract 3 from both sides.*
$\ln x^2 = 2$	*Divide both sides by 2.*
$e^{\ln x^2} = e^2$	*Exponentiate both sides.*
$x^2 = e^2$	*Inverse property:* $e^{\ln x^2} = x^2$
$x = \pm e$	*Solve for x.*

Applications

Real Life

EXAMPLE 7 *Finding Doubling Time*

You deposit P dollars in an account whose annual interest rate is r, compounded continuously. How long will it take for your balance to double?

Solution

The balance in the account after t years is

$$A = Pe^{rt}.$$

Thus, the balance will have doubled when $Pe^{rt} = 2P$. To find the "doubling time," solve this equation for t.

$Pe^{rt} = 2P$	*Balance in account has doubled.*
$e^{rt} = 2$	*Divide both sides by P.*
$\ln e^{rt} = \ln 2$	*Take log of both sides.*
$rt = \ln 2$	*Inverse property:* $\ln e^{rt} = rt$
$t = \dfrac{1}{r} \ln 2$	*Divide both sides by r.*

From this result, you can see that the time it takes for the balance to double is inversely proportional to the interest rate r. Table 4.7 shows the doubling times for several interest rates. Notice that the doubling time decreases as the rate increases. The relationship between doubling time and the interest rate is shown graphically in Figure 4.16.

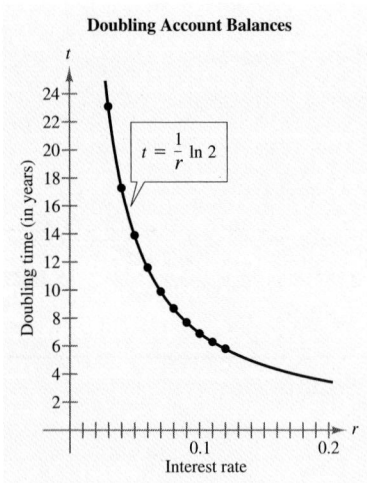

Doubling Account Balances

$t = \dfrac{1}{r} \ln 2$

Doubling time (in years)

Interest rate

FIGURE 4.16

TABLE 4.7

r	3%	4%	5%	6%	7%	8%	9%	10%	11%	12%
t	23.1	17.3	13.9	11.6	9.9	8.7	7.7	6.9	6.3	5.8

Discussion Problem   Tripling Time

You deposit P dollars in an account whose annual interest rate is r, compounded continuously. Use Example 7 as a model to determine how long it will take for your balance to triple. Complete the following table and use a graph to illustrate your answer.

Rate, r	3%	4%	5%	6%	7%	8%	9%	10%	11%	12%
Tripling time, t										

The following warm-up exercises involve skills that were covered in earlier sections. You will use these skills in the exercise set for this section.

In Exercises 1–4, use the properties of exponents to simplify the expression.

1. $(4^2)(4^{-3})$

2. $(2^3)^2$

3. e^0

4. $(3e)^4$

In Exercises 5–8, solve for *x*.

5. $0 < x + 4$

6. $0 < x^2 + 1$

7. $0 < \sqrt{x^2 - 1}$

8. $0 < x - 5$

In Exercises 9 and 10, find the balance in the account after 10 years.

9. $P = \$1900$, $r = 6\%$, compounded continuously

10. $P = \$2500$, $r = 3\%$, compounded continuously

E X E R C I S E S   4.3   means that technology can help you solve or check the exercise(s).

In Exercises 1–8, write the logarithmic equation as an exponential equation, or vice versa.

1. $\ln 2 = 0.6931 \ldots$

2. $\ln 8.4 = 2.1282 \ldots$

3. $\ln 0.2 = -1.6094 \ldots$

4. $\ln 0.056 = -2.8824 \ldots$

5. $e^0 = 1$

6. $e^2 = 7.3891 \ldots$

7. $e^{-3} = 0.0498 \ldots$

8. $e^{0.25} = 1.2840 \ldots$

 In Exercises 9–12, match the function with its graph. [The graphs are labeled (a)–(d).]

9. $f(x) = 2 + \ln x$

10. $f(x) = -\ln x$

11. $f(x) = \ln(x + 2)$

12. $f(x) = -\ln(x - 1)$

(a)

(b)

(c)

(d)
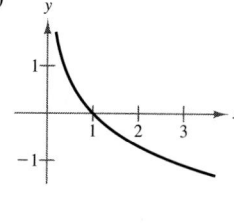

In Exercises 13–18, sketch the graph of the function.

13. $y = \ln(x - 1)$

14. $y = \ln |x|$

15. $y = \ln 2x$

16. $y = 5 + \ln x$

17. $y = 3 \ln x$

18. $y = \frac{1}{4} \ln x$

In Exercises 19–22, show, analytically *and* graphically, that the functions are inverses of each other.

19. $f(x) = e^{2x}$
$g(x) = \ln \sqrt{x}$

20. $f(x) = e^x - 1$
$g(x) = \ln(x + 1)$

21. $f(x) = e^{2x-1}$
$g(x) = \frac{1}{2} + \ln \sqrt{x}$

22. $f(x) = e^{x/3}$
$g(x) = \ln x^3$

In Exercises 23–28, apply the inverse properties of logarithmic and exponential functions to simplify the expression.

23. $\ln e^{x^2}$

24. $\ln e^{2x-1}$

25. $e^{\ln(5x+2)}$

26. $-1 + \ln e^{2x}$

27. $e^{\ln\sqrt{x}}$

28. $-8 + e^{\ln x^3}$

In Exercises 29 and 30, use the properties of logarithms and the fact that $\ln 2 \approx 0.6931$ and $\ln 3 \approx 1.0986$ to approximate the logarithm. Then use a calculator to confirm your approximation.

29. (a) $\ln 6$ (b) $\ln\frac{3}{2}$
   (c) $\ln 81$ (d) $\ln\sqrt{3}$

30. (a) $\ln 0.25$ (b) $\ln 24$
   (c) $\ln\sqrt[3]{12}$ (d) $\ln\frac{1}{72}$

In Exercises 31–40, use the properties of logarithms to write the expression as a sum, difference, or multiple of logarithms.

31. $\ln\frac{2}{3}$

32. $\ln\frac{1}{5}$

33. $\ln xyz$

34. $\ln\frac{xy}{z}$

35. $\ln\sqrt{x^2+1}$

36. $\ln\sqrt{2^3}$

37. $\ln\frac{2x}{\sqrt{x^2-1}}$

38. $\ln\frac{1}{e}$

39. $\ln\frac{3x(x+1)}{(2x+1)^2}$

40. $\ln z(z-1)^2$

In Exercises 41–50, write the expression as the logarithm of a single quantity.

41. $\ln(x-2) - \ln(x+2)$

42. $\ln(2x+1) + \ln(2x-1)$

43. $3\ln x + 2\ln y - 4\ln z$

44. $\frac{1}{3}[2\ln(x+3) + \ln x - \ln(x^2-1)]$

45. $3[\ln x + \ln(x+3) - \ln(x+4)]$

46. $2\ln 3 - \frac{1}{2}\ln(x^2+1)$

47. $\frac{3}{2}[\ln x(x^2+1) - \ln(x+1)]$

48. $2\ln x + \frac{1}{2}\ln(x+1)$

49. $2[\ln x - \ln(x+1)] - 3[\ln x - \ln(x-1)]$

50. $\frac{1}{2}\ln(x-2) + \frac{3}{2}\ln(x+2)$

In Exercises 51–66, solve for x or t.

51. $e^{\ln x} = 4$

52. $e^{\ln x^2} - 9 = 0$

53. $\ln x = 0$

54. $2\ln x = 4$

55. $e^{x+1} = 4$

56. $e^{-0.5x} = 0.075$

57. $300e^{-0.2t} = 700$

58. $e^{-0.0174t} = 0.5$

59. $5^{2x} = 15$

60. $2^{1-x} = 6$

61. $500(1.07)^t = 1000$

62. $400(1.06)^t = 1300$

63. $1000\left(1+\frac{0.07}{12}\right)^{12t} = 3000$

64. $1000\left(1+\frac{0.06}{12}\right)^{12t} = 3000$

65. $\frac{36}{1+e^{-t}} = 20$

66. $\frac{45}{1+e^{-2t}} = 24$

67. *Compound Interest* A deposit of $1000 is made into an account that earns interest at an annual rate of 5%. How long will it take for the balance to double if the interest is compounded (a) annually, (b) monthly, (c) daily, and (d) continuously?

68. *Compound Interest* A deposit of $1000 is made into an account that earns interest at an annual rate of 4.5%. How long will it take for the balance to triple if the interest is compounded (a) annually, (b) monthly, (c) daily, and (d) continuously?

69. *Compound Interest* Complete the table showing the time t necessary for P dollars to triple if the interest is compounded continuously at the rate of r.

r	2%	4%	6%	8%	10%	12%	14%
t							

70. *Demand* The demand function for a product is
$$p = 250 - 0.8e^{0.005x},$$
where p is the price per unit and x is the number of units sold. Find the number of units sold for a price of (a) $p = \$200$ and (b) $p = \$125$.

71. *Population Growth* The population P of Pensacola, Florida from 1970 through 1990 can be modeled by
$$P = 243{,}000e^{0.01737t},$$
where $t = 0$ corresponds to 1970. According to this model, in what year will Pensacola have a population of 400,000?
(Source: U.S. Bureau of Census)

72. *Population Growth* The population P of Middletown, Connecticut from 1970 through 1990 can be modeled by

$$P = 74{,}000e^{0.00979t},$$

where $t = 0$ corresponds to 1970. According to this model, in what year will Middletown have a population of 100,000? *(Source: U.S. Bureau of Census)*

Carbon Dating In Exercises 73–76, you are given the ratio of carbon atoms in a fossil. Use the following information to estimate the age of the fossil. In living organic material, the ratio of radioactive carbon isotopes to the total number of carbon atoms is about 1 to 10^{12}. (See Example 2 in Section 4.1.) When organic material dies, its radioactive carbon isotopes begin to decay, with a half-life of about 5700 years. Thus, the ratio R of carbon isotopes to carbon-14 atoms is

$$R = 10^{-12}\left(\tfrac{1}{2}\right)^{t/5700},$$

where t is the time (in years) and $t = 0$ represents the time when the organic material died.

73. $R = 0.32 \times 10^{-12}$ **74.** $R = 0.27 \times 10^{-12}$

75. $R = 0.22 \times 10^{-12}$ **76.** $R = 0.13 \times 10^{-12}$

In 1991, forensic expert Rainer Henn uncovered one of the most important discoveries of modern archaeology—the body of a man that had been frozen in the Alps 5300 years ago. The age of the "iceman" was estimated by carbon dating.

77. *Human Memory Model* Students in a mathematics class were given an exam and then retested monthly with equivalent exams. The average score S (on a 100-point scale) for the class can be modeled by

$$S = 80 - 14\ln(t+1), \qquad 0 \le t \le 12,$$

where t is the time in months.

(a) What was the average score on the original exam?
(b) What was the average score after 4 months?
(c) After how many months was the average score 46?

78. *Research Project* Use a graphing utility to sketch the graph of

$$y = 10\ln\left(\frac{10 + \sqrt{100 - x^2}}{10}\right) - \sqrt{100 - x^2}$$

over the interval $(0, 10]$. This graph is called a *tractrix* or *pursuit curve*. Use your school's library or some other reference source to find information about a tractrix. Explain how such a curve can arise in a real-life setting.

79. Demonstrate that

$$\frac{\ln x}{\ln y} \ne \ln\frac{x}{y} = \ln x - \ln y$$

by completing the table.

x	y	$\dfrac{\ln x}{\ln y}$	$\ln\dfrac{x}{y}$	$\ln x - \ln y$
1	2			
3	4			
10	5			
4	0.5			

80. Complete the table using $f(x) = \dfrac{\ln x}{x}$.

x	1	5	10	10^2	10^4	10^6
$f(x)$						

(a) Use the table to estimate the limit: $\displaystyle\lim_{x\to\infty} f(x)$.
(b) Use a graphing utility to estimate the relative extrema of f.

In Exercises 81 and 82, use a graphing utility to verify that the functions are equivalent for $x > 0$.

81. $f(x) = \ln\dfrac{x^2}{4}$

   $g(x) = 2\ln x - \ln 4$

82. $f(x) = \ln\sqrt{x(x^2+1)}$

   $g(x) = \frac{1}{2}[\ln x + \ln(x^2+1)]$

4.4 Derivatives of Logarithmic Functions

Derivatives of Logarithmic Functions ■ *Applications* ■
Other Bases

Derivatives of Logarithmic Functions

Implicit differentiation can be used to develop the derivative of the natural logarithmic function.

$$y = \ln x \qquad\qquad \textit{Natural logarithmic function}$$

$$e^y = x \qquad\qquad \textit{Write in exponential form.}$$

$$\frac{d}{dx}[e^y] = \frac{d}{dx}[x] \qquad\qquad \textit{Differentiate with respect to } x.$$

$$e^y \frac{dy}{dx} = 1 \qquad\qquad \textit{Chain Rule}$$

$$\frac{dy}{dx} = \frac{1}{e^y} \qquad\qquad \textit{Divide both sides by } e^y.$$

$$\frac{dy}{dx} = \frac{1}{x} \qquad\qquad \textit{Substitute } x \textit{ for } e^y.$$

This result and its Chain Rule version are summarized below.

Derivative of the Natural Logarithmic Function

Let u be a differentiable function of x.

1. $\dfrac{d}{dx}[\ln x] = \dfrac{1}{x}$ **2.** $\dfrac{d}{dx}[\ln u] = \dfrac{1}{u}u'$

EXAMPLE 1 *Differentiating a Logarithmic Function*

Find the derivative of

$$f(x) = \ln 2x.$$

Solution
Let $u = 2x$. Then $u' = 2$, and you can apply the Chain Rule as follows.

$$f'(x) = \frac{1}{u}u' = \frac{1}{2x}(2) = \frac{1}{x}$$

EXAMPLE 2 *Differentiating Logarithmic Functions*

Find the derivatives of the functions.

a. $f(x) = \ln(2x^2 + 4)$　　　　**b.** $f(x) = x \ln x$

Solution

a. Let $u = 2x^2 + 4$. Then $u' = 4x$, and you can apply the Chain Rule.

$$f'(x) = \frac{1}{u}u' \qquad\qquad \textit{Chain Rule}$$

$$= \frac{1}{2x^2 + 4}(4x)$$

$$= \frac{2x}{x^2 + 2} \qquad\qquad \textit{Simplify.}$$

b. Using the Product Rule, you can find the derivative.

$$f'(x) = x\frac{d}{dx}[\ln x] + (\ln x)\frac{d}{dx}[x] \qquad \textit{Product Rule}$$

$$= x\left(\frac{1}{x}\right) + (\ln x)(1) \qquad\qquad \textit{Derivative of } \ln x$$

$$= 1 + \ln x \qquad\qquad\qquad \textit{Simplify.}$$

When differentiating logarithmic functions, it is often helpful to use the properties of logarithms to rewrite the function *before* differentiating, as shown in the next example.

Discovery

What is the domain of the function $f(x) = \ln\sqrt{x+1}$ in Example 3? What is the domain of the function $f'(x) = 1/[2(x+1)]$? In general, you must be careful to understand the domains of functions involving logarithms. For example, are the domains of the functions $y_1 = \ln x^2$ and $y_2 = 2\ln x$ the same? Try graphing them on your graphing utility.

EXAMPLE 3 *Rewriting Before Differentiating*

Find the derivative of $f(x) = \ln\sqrt{x+1}$.

Solution

$$f(x) = \ln\sqrt{x+1} \qquad\qquad \textit{Original function}$$

$$= \ln(x+1)^{1/2} \qquad\qquad \textit{Rewrite with rational exponent.}$$

$$= \frac{1}{2}\ln(x+1) \qquad\qquad \textit{Property of logarithms}$$

$$f'(x) = \frac{1}{2}\left(\frac{1}{x+1}\right) \qquad\qquad \textit{Differentiate.}$$

$$= \frac{1}{2(x+1)} \qquad\qquad \textit{Simplify.}$$

Note　To see the advantage of rewriting before differentiating, try using the Chain Rule to differentiate $f(x) = \ln\sqrt{x+1}$ and compare your work with that shown in Example 3.

The next example is an even more dramatic illustration of the benefit of rewriting a function before differentiating.

EXAMPLE 4 *Rewriting Before Differentiating*

Find the derivative of

$$f(x) = \ln \frac{x(x^2 + 1)^2}{\sqrt{2x^3 + 1}}.$$

Solution

$$f(x) = \ln \frac{x(x^2 + 1)^2}{\sqrt{2x^3 + 1}} \qquad \textit{Original function}$$

$$= \ln x(x^2 + 1)^2 - \ln(2x^3 + 1)^{1/2} \qquad \textit{Logarithmic properties}$$

$$= \ln x + ln(x^2 + 1)^2 - \ln(2x^3 + 1)^{1/2} \qquad \textit{Logarithmic properties}$$

$$= \ln x + 2\ln(x^2 + 1) - \frac{1}{2}\ln(2x^3 + 1) \qquad \textit{Logarithmic properties}$$

$$f'(x) = \frac{1}{x} + 2\left(\frac{2x}{x^2 + 1}\right) - \frac{1}{2}\left(\frac{6x^2}{2x^3 + 1}\right) \qquad \textit{Differentiate.}$$

$$= \frac{1}{x} + \frac{4x}{x^2 + 1} - \frac{3x^2}{2x^3 + 1} \qquad \textit{Simplify.}$$

Note Finding the derivative of the function in Example 4 without first rewriting would be a formidable task.

$$f'(x) = \frac{1}{x(x^2 + 1)^2/\sqrt{2x^3 + 1}} \frac{d}{dx}\left[\frac{x(x^2 + 1)^2}{\sqrt{2x^3 + 1}}\right]$$

You might try showing that this yields the same result obtained in Example 4, but be careful—the algebra is messy.

⊞ TECHNOLOGY

If you use a symbolic differentiation utility to differentiate logarithmic functions, you should be aware that it will not generally list the derivative in the form given in Example 4. For instance, the result listed by *Derive* is shown at the right. To show that the two forms are equivalent, you could rewrite the answer given in Example 4 as a single fraction.

1: $\ \text{LN}\left[\dfrac{x(x^2 + 1)^2}{\sqrt{(2x^3 - 1)}}\right]$ *Author.*

2: $\ \dfrac{d}{dx}\text{LN}\left[\dfrac{x(x^2 + 1)^2}{\sqrt{(2x^3 - 1)}}\right]$ *Differentiate.*

3: $\ \dfrac{7x^5 - x^3 - 5x^2 - 1}{x(2x^3 - 1)(x^2 + 1)}$ *Simplify.*

Applications

EXAMPLE 5 *Analyzing a Graph*

Analyze the graph of the function $f(x) = x^2 - \ln x$.

Solution

From Figure 4.17, it appears that the function has a minimum just to the left of $x = 1$. To find the minimum analytically, find the critical numbers by setting the derivative of f equal to zero and solving for x.

$$f(x) = x^2 - \ln x \qquad \qquad \textit{Original function}$$

$$f'(x) = 2x - \frac{1}{x} \qquad \qquad \textit{Differentiate.}$$

$$2x - \frac{1}{x} = 0 \qquad \qquad \textit{Set derivative equal to 0.}$$

$$2x = \frac{1}{x} \qquad \qquad \textit{Add } 1/x \textit{ to both sides.}$$

$$2x^2 = 1 \qquad \qquad \textit{Multiply both sides by x.}$$

$$x^2 = \tfrac{1}{2} \qquad \qquad \textit{Divide both sides by 2.}$$

$$x = \pm\sqrt{\tfrac{1}{2}} \qquad \qquad \textit{Take square root of both sides.}$$

Of these two possible critical numbers, only the positive one lies in the domain of f. By applying the First-Derivative Test, you can confirm that the function has a relative minimum when $x = 1/\sqrt{2} \approx 0.707$.

FIGURE 4.17

EXAMPLE 6 *Finding a Rate of Change*

Real Life

A group of 200 college students were tested every 6 months over a 4-year period. The group was composed of students who took French during the fall semester of their freshman year and did not take subsequent French courses. The average test score p (in percent) is modeled by

$$p = 91.6 - 15.6 \ln(t + 1), \qquad 0 \le t \le 48,$$

where t is the time in months, as shown in Figure 4.18. At what rate was the average score changing after 1 year?

Solution

The rate of change is

$$\frac{dp}{dt} = -\frac{15.6}{t+1}.$$

When $t = 12$, $dp/dt = -1.2$, which means that the average score was decreasing at the rate of 1.2% per month.

Human Memory Model

FIGURE 4.18

Other Bases

This chapter began with a definition of a general exponential function

$$f(x) = a^x,$$

where a is a positive number such that $a \neq 1$. The corresponding **logarithm to the base a** is defined by

$$\log_a x = b \quad \text{if and only if} \quad a^b = x.$$

As with the natural logarithmic function, the domain of the logarithmic function to the base a is the set of positive numbers.

EXAMPLE 7   *Evaluating Logarithms*

a. $\log_2 8 = 3$ This is true because $2^3 = 8$.

b. $\log_{10} 100 = 2$ This is true because $10^2 = 100$.

c. $\log_{10} \frac{1}{10} = -1$ This is true because $10^{-1} = \frac{1}{10}$.

d. $\log_3 81 = 4$ This is true because $3^4 = 81$.

e. $\log_{10} 4 \approx 0.602$ This is true because $10^{0.602} \approx 4$.   ▬

    Logarithms to the base 10 are called **common logarithms.** Most calculators have only two logarithm keys—a natural logarithm key denoted by $\boxed{\text{LN}}$ and a common logarithm key denoted by $\boxed{\text{LOG}}$. Logarithms to other bases can be evaluated with the following change of base formula.

$$\log_a x = \frac{\ln x}{\ln a} \qquad\qquad \textit{Change of base formula}$$

EXAMPLE 8   *Evaluating Logarithms*

Evaluate the following logarithms.

a. $\log_2 3$ **b.** $\log_3 6$ **c.** $\log_2(-1)$

Solution

In each case, use the change of base formula and a calculator.

a. $\log_2 3 = \dfrac{\ln 3}{\ln 2} \approx 1.585$

b. $\log_3 6 = \dfrac{\ln 6}{\ln 3} \approx 1.631$

c. $\log_2(-1)$ is not defined.   ▬

To find derivatives of exponential or logarithmic functions to bases other than e, you can either convert to base e using the formulas

$$a^x = e^{(\ln a)x} \quad \text{and} \quad \log_a x = \left(\frac{1}{\ln a}\right)\ln x$$

or use the following differentiation rules.

Other Bases and Differentiation

Let u be a differentiable function of x.

1. $\dfrac{d}{dx}[a^x] = (\ln a)a^x$ **2.** $\dfrac{d}{dx}[a^u] = (\ln a)a^u u'$

3. $\dfrac{d}{dx}[\log_a x] = \left(\dfrac{1}{\ln a}\right)\dfrac{1}{x}$ **4.** $\dfrac{d}{dx}[\log_a u] = \left(\dfrac{1}{\ln a}\right)\dfrac{u'}{u}$

Real Life

EXAMPLE 9 *Finding a Rate of Change*

Radioactive carbon isotopes have a half-life of 5700 years. If 1 gram of the isotopes is present in an object now, the amount A (in grams) that will be present after t years is

$$A = \left(\frac{1}{2}\right)^{t/5700}.$$

At what rate is the amount changing when $t = 10{,}000$ years?

Solution

The derivative of A with respect to t is

$$\frac{dA}{dt} = \left(\ln\frac{1}{2}\right)\left(\frac{1}{2}\right)^{t/5700}\left(\frac{1}{5700}\right).$$

When $t = 10{,}000$, the value of the derivative is

$$\frac{dA}{dt} = \left(\ln\frac{1}{2}\right)\left(\frac{1}{2}\right)^{10{,}000/5700}\left(\frac{1}{5700}\right) \approx -0.000036,$$

which implies that the amount of isotopes in the object is decreasing at the rate of 0.000036 gram per year.   ■

Discussion Problem   *Deriving Differentiation Rules*

Explain how to use the change of base formulas listed at the top of this page to derive the formulas for the derivatives of $f(x) = a^x$ and $f(x) = \log_a x$.

Warm Up

The following warm-up exercises involve skills that were covered in earlier sections. You will use these skills in the exercise set for this section.

In Exercises 1–6, expand the logarithmic expression.

1. $\ln(x+1)^2$ **2.** $\ln x(x+1)$ **3.** $\ln \dfrac{x}{x+1}$

4. $\ln\left(\dfrac{x}{x-3}\right)^3$ **5.** $\ln \dfrac{4x(x-7)}{x^2}$ **6.** $\ln \dfrac{x^3(x+1)}{\sqrt{x-2}}$

In Exercises 7 and 8, find dy/dx implicitly.

7. $y^x + xy = 7$ **8.** $x^2y - xy^2 = 3x$

In Exercises 9 and 10, find the second derivative of f.

9. $f(x) = x^2(x+1) - 3x^3$ **10.** $f(x) = -\dfrac{1}{x^2}$

E X E R C I S E S   4.4 means that technology can help you solve or check the exercise(s).

In Exercises 1–6, find the slope of the tangent line to the graph of the function at the point $(1, 0)$.

1. $y = \ln x^3$

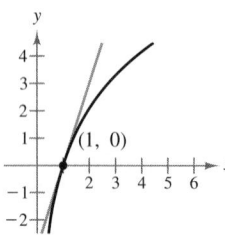

2. $y = \ln x^{5/2}$

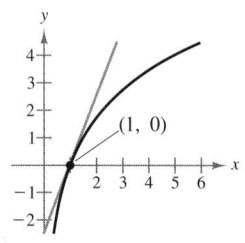

3. $y = \ln x^2$

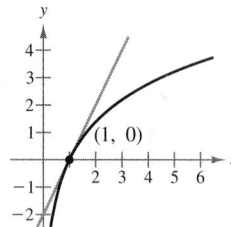

4. $y = \ln x^{1/2}$

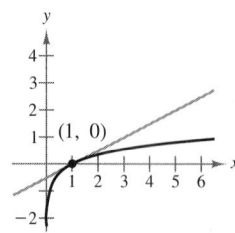

5. $y = \ln x^{3/2}$

6. $y = \ln x$

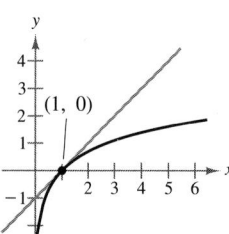

In Exercises 7–34, find the derivative of the function.

7. $y = \ln x^2$ **8.** $y = \ln(x^2 + 3)$

9. $f(x) = \ln 2x$ **10.** $f(x) = \ln(1 - x^2)$

11. $y = \ln \sqrt{x^4 - 4x}$ **12.** $y = \ln(1 - x)^{3/2}$

13. $y = \frac{1}{2}(\ln x)^6$ **14.** $y = (\ln x^2)^2$

15. $y = x \ln x$ **16.** $f(x) = x^2 \ln x$

17. $y = \ln(x\sqrt{x^2 - 1})$ **18.** $y = \ln[x^2(x+1)^3]$

19. $y = \ln \dfrac{x}{x^2 + 1}$ **20.** $y = \ln \dfrac{x}{x+1}$

21. $y = \ln \dfrac{x+1}{x-1}$

22. $y = \ln \dfrac{x-1}{x+1}$

23. $y = \ln \sqrt{\dfrac{x+1}{x-1}}$

24. $y = \ln \sqrt[3]{\dfrac{x-1}{x+1}}$

25. $y = \dfrac{\ln x}{x^2}$

26. $y = \dfrac{\ln x}{x}$

27. $y = \ln \dfrac{\sqrt{4+x^2}}{x}$

28. $y = \ln(x + \sqrt{4+x^2})$

29. $y = \ln \sqrt{2x^2 - 3}$

30. $y = \dfrac{-\sqrt{x^2+1}}{x} + \ln(x + \sqrt{x^2+1})$

in notes

31. $g(x) = e^{-x} \ln x$

32. $g(x) = \ln \dfrac{e^x + e^{-x}}{2}$

33. $f(x) = \ln e^{x^2}$

34. $f(x) = \ln \dfrac{1 + e^x}{1 - e^x}$

In Exercises 35–38, write the expression with base e.

in notes.

35. 2^x

36. 3^x

37. $\log_4 x$

38. $\log_3 x$

In Exercises 39–44, evaluate the logarithm.

39. $\log_2 4$

40. $\log_5 12$

41. $\log_3 \frac{1}{2}$

42. $\log_7 343$

43. $\log_{10} 31$

44. $\log_9 3$

In Exercises 45–56, find the derivative of the function.

45. $y = 3^x$

46. $y = \left(\frac{1}{4}\right)^x$

47. $f(x) = \log_2 x$

48. $g(x) = \log_5 x$

49. $h(x) = 4^{2x-3}$

50. $y = 6^{5x}$

51. $y = \log_3(3x + 7)$

52. $y = \log_{10}(x^2 + 6x)$

53. $f(x) = 10^{x^2}$

54. $g(x) = 25^{2x^2}$

55. $y = x2^x$

56. $y = 3x3^x$

In Exercises 57–60, find dy/dx implicitly.

57. $x^2 - 3\ln y + y^2 = 10$

58. $\ln xy + 5x = 30$

59. $4x^3 + \ln y^2 + 2y = 2x$

60. $4xy + \ln(x^2 y) = 7$

In Exercises 61–64, find the second derivative of the function.

61. $f(x) = x \ln \sqrt{x} + 2x$

62. $f(x) = 3 + 2\ln x$

63. $f(x) = 5^x$

64. $f(x) = \log_{10} x$

In Exercises 65–70, find the slope of the graph at the indicated point. Then write an equation of the tangent line at the point.

65. $f(x) = 1 + 2x \ln x$

66. $f(x) = 2 \ln x^3$

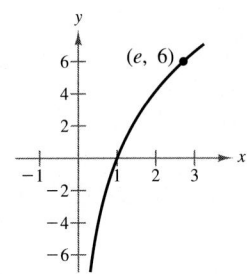

67. $f(x) = \ln \dfrac{5(x+2)}{x}$

68. $f(x) = \ln(x\sqrt{x+3})$

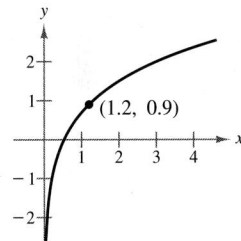

69. $f(x) = \log_2 x$

70. $f(x) = x^2 \log_3 x^2$

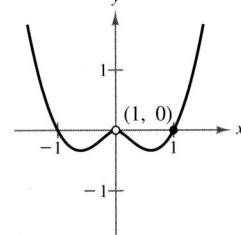

In Exercises 71–76, graph and analyze the function. Include any relative extrema and points of inflection in your analysis.

71. $y = x - \ln x$

72. $y = \frac{1}{2}x^2 - \ln x$

73. $y = \dfrac{\ln x}{x}$

74. $y = x \ln x$

75. $y = x^2 \ln x$

76. $y = (\ln x)^2$

In Exercises 77–80, find dx/dp for the demand function. Interpret this rate of change when the price is $10.

77. $x = \ln \dfrac{1000}{p}$

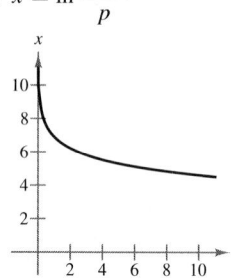

78. $x = 1000 - p \ln p$

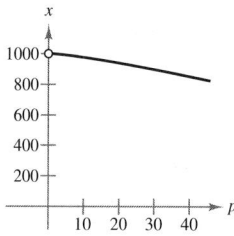

79. $x = \dfrac{500}{\ln(p^2 + 1)}$

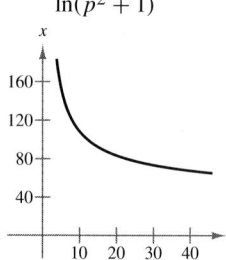

80. $x = 300 - 50 \ln(\ln p)$

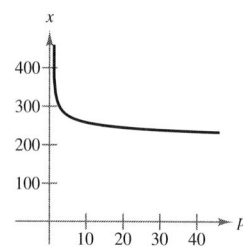

81. Solve the demand function in Exercise 77 for p. Use the result to find dp/dx. Then find the value of dp/dx when $p = \$10$. What is the relationship between this derivative and dx/dp?

82. Solve the demand function in Exercise 79 for p. Use the result to find dp/dx. Then find the value of dp/dx when $p = \$10$. What is the relationship between this derivative and dx/dp?

 83. *Minimum Average Cost* The cost of producing x units of a product is

$$C = 500 + 300x - 300 \ln x, \qquad x \geq 1.$$

Use a graphing utility to find the minimum average cost. Then confirm your result analytically.

84. *Chemistry* Radioactive Einsteinium isotopes have a half-life of 276 days. If 1 gram of the isotopes is present in an object now, the amount A (in grams) present after t days is

$$A = \left(\frac{1}{2}\right)^{t/276}.$$

At what rate is the amount changing when $t = 500$ days?

85. *Nonprofit Organizations* The number T (in thousands) of income tax returns filed by nonprofit organizations from 1984 to 1992 can be modeled by

$$T = -\frac{682.83 \ln t}{t} + 0.025t^3 - 15.19t + 317.92,$$

where $t = 4$ corresponds to 1984. *(Source: Internal Revenue Service)*

(a) Use a graphing utility to graph T over the interval $[4, 12]$.

(b) Estimate the number of returns filed by nonprofit organizations in 1991.

(c) At what rate was the number of filed returns changing in 1991?

86. *Research Project* Use your school's library or some other reference source to research information about a nonprofit organization, such as that mentioned below. Collect data about the organization (revenue or membership over a 20-year period, for example) and find a mathematical model to represent the data.

Courtesy of Edward Santalone

— *Business Capsule* —

In 1993, James A. Cunningham was the senior vice president for finance and administration of the National Audubon Society, in New York City. Founded in 1905, the National Audubon Society is one of the oldest and largest national conservation organizations in the world. In 1992, the society received revenue of more than $43 million.

Exponential Growth and Decay

Exponential Growth and Decay ■ *Applications*

Exponential Growth and Decay

In this section you will learn to create models of *exponential growth and decay*. Real-life situations that involve exponential growth and decay deal with a substance or population whose *rate of change at any time t is proportional to the amount of the substance present at that time.* For example, the rate of decomposition of a radioactive substance is proportional to the amount of radioactive substance at a given instant. In its simplest form, this relationship is described by the following equation.

Rate of change of y ⌐ is ⌐ proportional to y.

$$\frac{dy}{dt} = ky$$

In this equation, k is a constant and y is a function of t. The solution of this equation is given below.

Note In the model $y = Ce^{kt}$, C is called the "initial value" because when $t = 0$,

$$y = Ce^{k(0)} = C(1) = C.$$

Discovery

Use a graphing utility to graph $y = Ce^{2t}$ for $C = 1, 2$, and 5. How does the value of C affect the shape of the graph? Now graph $y = 2e^{kt}$ for $k = -2, -1, 0, 1$, and 2. How does the value of k affect the shape of the graph? Which function grows faster, $y = e^x$ or $y = x^{10}$?

Law of Exponential Growth and Decay

If y is a positive quantity whose rate of change with respect to time is proportional to the quantity present at any time t, then y is of the form

$$y = Ce^{kt},$$

where C is the **initial value** and k is the **constant of proportionality. Exponential growth** is indicated by $k > 0$ and **exponential decay** by $k < 0$.

Proof Because the rate of change of y is proportional to y, you can write

$$\frac{dy}{dt} = ky.$$

You can see that $y = Ce^{kt}$ is a solution of this equation by differentiating to obtain $dy/dt = kCe^{kt}$ and substituting

$$\frac{dy}{dt} = kCe^{kt} = k(Ce^{kt}) = ky.$$

Applications

Radioactive decay is measured in terms of **half-life,** the number of years required for half of the atoms in a sample of radioactive material to decay. The half-lives of some common radioactive isotopes are as follows.

Uranium (U^{238})   4,510,000,000   years
Plutonium (Pu^{239})   24,360   years
Carbon (C^{14})   5,730   years
Radium (Ra^{226})   1,620   years
Einsteinium (Es^{254})   270   days
Nobelium (No^{257})   23   seconds

Real Life

EXAMPLE 1   *Modeling Radioactive Decay*

Much of the cost of nuclear energy is the cost of disposing of radioactive waste. Because of the long half-life of the waste, it must be stored in containers that will remain undisturbed for thousands of years.

A sample contains 1 gram of radium. How much radium will remain after 1000 years?

Solution

Let y represent the mass (in grams) of the radium in the sample. Because the rate of decay is proportional to y, you can apply the Law of Exponential Decay to conclude that y is of the form $y = Ce^{kt}$, where t is measured in years. From the given information, you know that $y = 1$ when $t = 0$. Substituting these values into the model produces

$$1 = Ce^{k(0)}, \qquad\qquad \textit{Substitute 1 for y and 0 for t.}$$

which implies that $C = 1$. Because radium has a half-life of 1620 years, you know that $y = \frac{1}{2}$ when $t = 1620$. Substituting these values into the model allows to you solve for k.

$y = e^{kt}$	*Exponential decay model*
$\frac{1}{2} = e^{k(1620)}$	*Substitute $\frac{1}{2}$ for y and 1620 for t.*
$\ln \frac{1}{2} = 1620k$	*Take log of both sides.*
$\frac{1}{1620} \ln \frac{1}{2} = k$	*Divide both sides by 1620.*

Thus, $k \approx -0.0004279$, and the exponential decay model is

$$y = e^{-0.0004279t}.$$

To find the amount of radium remaining in the sample after 1000 years, substitute $t = 1000$ into the model. This produces

$$y = e^{-0.0004279(1000)} \approx 0.652 \text{ grams}.$$

The graph of the model is shown in Figure 4.19.

Radioactive Half-life of 1620 Years

FIGURE 4.19

The steps used in Example 1 are summarized below.

Guidelines for Modeling Exponential Growth and Decay

1. Use the given information to write *two* sets of conditions involving y and t.
2. Substitute the given conditions into the model $y = Ce^{kt}$ and use the results to solve for the constants C and k. (If one of the conditions involves $t = 0$, substitute that value first to solve for C.)
3. Use the model $y = Ce^{kt}$ to answer the question.

Real Life

EXAMPLE 2 *Modeling Population Growth*

In a research experiment, a population of fruit flies is increasing according to the law of exponential growth. After 2 days, there are 100 flies, and after 4 days, there are 300 flies. How many flies will there be after 5 days?

Solution

Let y be the number of flies at time t. From the given information, you know that $y = 100$ when $t = 2$ and $y = 300$ when $t = 4$. Substituting this information into the model $y = Ce^{kt}$ produces

$$100 = Ce^{2k} \quad \text{and} \quad 300 = Ce^{4k}.$$

To solve for k, solve for C in the first equation and substitute into the second equation.

$$300 = Ce^{4k} \qquad \qquad \textit{Second equation}$$

$$300 = \left(\frac{100}{e^{2k}}\right)e^{4k} \qquad \textit{Substitute } 100/e^{2k} \textit{ for } C.$$

$$\frac{300}{100} = e^{2k} \qquad \qquad \textit{Divide both sides by 100.}$$

$$\ln 3 = 2k \qquad \qquad \textit{Take log of both sides.}$$

$$\frac{1}{2}\ln 3 = k \qquad \qquad \textit{Solve for k.}$$

Using $k = \frac{1}{2}\ln 3 \approx 0.5493$, you can determine that $C \approx 100/e^{2(0.5493)} \approx 33$. Thus, the exponential growth model is

$$y = 33e^{0.5493t},$$

as shown in Figure 4.20. This implies that, after 5 days, the population is

$$y = 33e^{0.5493(5)} \approx 514 \text{ flies.}$$

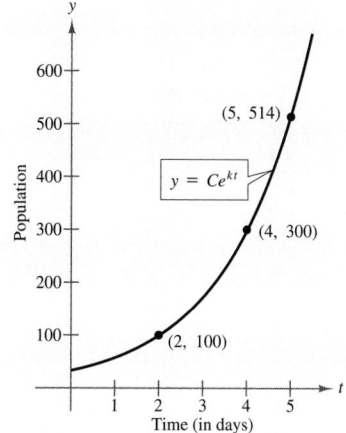

Population Growth of Fruit Flies

(5, 514)

$y = Ce^{kt}$

(4, 300)

(2, 100)

Time (in days)

FIGURE 4.20

Real Life

EXAMPLE 3 *Modeling Compound Interest*

Money is deposited in an account for which the interest is compounded continuously. The balance in the account doubles in 6 years. What is the annual interest rate?

Solution

The balance A in an account with continuously compounded interest is given by the exponential growth model

$$A = Pe^{rt}, \qquad\qquad \textit{Exponential growth model}$$

where P is the original deposit, r is the annual interest rate (in decimal form), and t is the time (in years). From the given information, you know that $A = 2P$ when $t = 6$, as shown in Figure 4.21. Use this information to solve for r.

$$
\begin{aligned}
A &= Pe^{rt} &&\textit{Exponential growth model} \\
2P &= Pe^{r(6)} &&\textit{Substitute } 2P \textit{ for } A \textit{ and } 6 \textit{ for } t. \\
2 &= e^{6r} &&\textit{Divide both sides by } P. \\
\ln 2 &= 6r &&\textit{Take log of both sides.} \\
\frac{1}{6}\ln 2 &= r &&\textit{Divide both sides by 6.}
\end{aligned}
$$

Thus, the annual interest rate is $r = \frac{1}{6}\ln 2 \approx 0.1155$ or about 11.55%. ■

Continuously Compounded Interest

Balance

- $4P$ — (12, 4P)
- $3P$
- $A = Pe^{rt}$
- $2P$ — (6, 2P)
- P — (0, P)

2   4   6   8   10   12 t
Time (in years)

FIGURE 4.21

Each of the examples in this section uses the exponential growth model in which the base is e. Exponential growth, however, can be modeled with *any* base. That is, the model

$$y = Ca^{bt}$$

also represents exponential growth. (To see this, note that the model can be written in the form $y = Ce^{(\ln a)bt}$.) In some real-life settings, bases other than e are more convenient. For instance, in Example 1, knowing that the half-life of radium is 1620 years, you can immediately write the exponential decay model as

$$y = \left(\frac{1}{2}\right)^{t/1620}.$$

Using this model, the amount of radium left in the sample after 1000 years is

$$y = \left(\frac{1}{2}\right)^{1000/1620} \approx 0.652 \text{ grams,}$$

which is the same answer obtained in Example 1.

Note Can you see why you can immediately write the model $y = \left(\frac{1}{2}\right)^{t/1620}$ for the radioactive decay described in Example 1? Notice that when $t = 1620$, the value of y is $\frac{1}{2}$, when $t = 3240$, the value of y is $\frac{1}{4}$, and so on.

⊞ TECHNOLOGY

Fitting an Exponential Model to Data

Most graphing utilities have programs that allow you to find the *least-squares regression exponential model* for data. Depending on the type of graphing utility, the program may fit the data to a model of the form

$$y = ab^x, \qquad \text{\textit{Exponential model with base b}}$$

or it may fit the data to a model of the form

$$y = ae^{bx}. \qquad \text{\textit{Exponential model with base e}}$$

To see how to use such a program, consider the following.

The total amount y (in billions of dollars) of life insurance in the United States from 1950 through 1990 is listed in Table 4.8. *(Source: American Council of Life Insurance)*

TABLE 4.8

Year	1950	1955	1960	1965	1970	1975	1980	1985	1990
Amount	234	372	586	901	1402	2140	3541	6053	9393

To fit an exponential model to this data, let $x = 0$ represent 1950. Then enter the following coordinates into the statistical data bank of the graphing utility.

$$(0, 234), (5, 372), (10, 586), (15, 901), (20, 1402)$$

$$(25, 2140), (30, 3541), (35, 6053), (40, 9393)$$

After running the exponential regression program with a graphing utility that uses the model $y = ab^x$, the display should read $a \approx 229.8$ and $b \approx 1.0964$. (The correlation of $r \approx 0.9996$ tells you that the fit is very good.) Thus, a model for the data is

$$y = 229.8(1.0964)^x. \qquad \text{\textit{Exponential model with base b}}$$

The graph of the model is shown at the left. Notice that one way to interpret the model is that the total amount of life insurance in the United States increased by about 9.64% each year from 1950 through 1990.

If you use a graphing utility that uses the model $y = ae^{bx}$, then the display should read $a \approx 229.8$ and $b \approx 0.0920$. The corresponding model is

$$y = 229.8e^{0.0920x}. \qquad \text{\textit{Exponential model with base e}}$$

You can use either model to predict the total amount of life insurance in future years. For instance, in 1995 $(x = 45)$, the amount is predicted to be

$$y = 229.8(1.0964)^{45} \approx \$14{,}450 \text{ billion.}$$

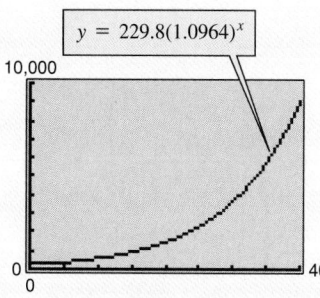

$y = 229.8(1.0964)^x$

10,000

0

0   40

Real
Life

EXAMPLE 4 *Modeling Sales*

Four months after discontinuing advertising on national television, a manufacturer notices that sales have dropped from 100,000 units per month to 80,000 units. If the sales follow an exponential pattern of decline, what will they be after another 4 months?

Solution

Let y represent the number of units, let t represent the time (in months), and consider the exponential growth model

$$y = Ce^{kt}.$$ *Exponential growth model*

From the given information, you know that $y = 100{,}000$ when $t = 0$. Using this information, you have

$$100{,}000 = Ce^{0},$$

which implies that $C = 100{,}000$. To solve for k, use the fact that $y = 80{,}000$ when $t = 4$.

$$y = 100{,}000e^{kt}$$ *Exponential decay model*

$$80{,}000 = 100{,}000e^{k(4)}$$ *Substitute* 80,000 *for y and* 4 *for t.*

$$0.8 = e^{4k}$$ *Divide both sides by* 100,000.

$$\ln 0.8 = 4k$$ *Take log of both sides.*

$$\frac{1}{4}\ln 0.8 = k$$ *Divide both sides by* 4.

Thus, $k = \frac{1}{4}\ln 0.8 \approx -0.0558$, which means that the model is

$$y = 100{,}000e^{-0.0558t}.$$

After 4 more months $(t = 8)$, you can expect sales to drop to

$$y = 100{,}000e^{-0.0558(8)} \approx 64{,}000 \text{ units},$$

as shown in Figure 4.22.

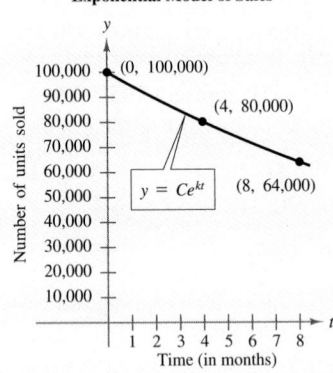

Exponential Model of Sales

y

100,000 (0, 100,000)
90,000
80,000   (4, 80,000)
70,000
60,000
50,000 $y = Ce^{kt}$ (8, 64,000)
40,000
30,000
20,000
10,000

1 2 3 4 5 6 7 8 → t
Time (in months)

Number of units sold

FIGURE 4.22

Discussion Problem   **Comparing Exponential and Linear Models**

In Example 4, it was assumed that the sales were following an exponential pattern of decline. This implies that the sales were dropping by the same *percent* each month. Suppose instead that the sales were following a linear pattern of decline (dropping by the same *amount* each month). How would this affect the answer to the question given in Example 4? Which of the two models do you think might be more realistic? Explain your reasoning.

In Exercises 1–4, solve the equation for k.

1. $12 = 24e^{4k}$

2. $10 = 3e^{5k}$

3. $25 = 16e^{3k}$

4. $22 = 32e^{20k}$

In Exercises 5–8, find the derivative of the function.

5. $y = 32e^{0.23t}$

6. $y = 24e^{-1.4t}$

7. $y = 18e^{0.072t}$

8. $y = 25e^{-0.001t}$

In Exercises 9 and 10, simplify the expression.

9. $e^{\ln 4}$

10. $4e^{\ln 3}$

E X E R C I S E S   4.5   means that technology can help you solve or check the exercise(s).

In Exercises 1–6, find the exponential function $y = Ce^{kt}$ that passes through the two given points.

1. $y = Ce^{kt}$

2. $y = Ce^{kt}$

5. $y = Ce^{kt}$

6. $y = Ce^{kt}$

3. $y = Ce^{kt}$

4. $y = Ce^{kt}$

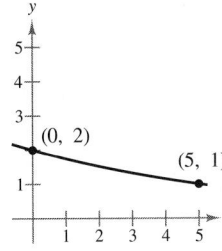

In Exercises 7–10, use the given information to write an equation for y. Confirm your result analytically by showing that the function satisfies the equation $dy/dt = Cy$. Does the function represent exponential growth or decay?

7. $\dfrac{dy}{dt} = 2y, \quad y = 10$ when $t = 0$

8. $\dfrac{dy}{dt} = -\dfrac{2}{3}y, \quad y = 20$ when $t = 0$

9. $\dfrac{dy}{dt} = -4y, \quad y = 30$ when $t = 0$

10. $\dfrac{dy}{dt} = 5.2y, \quad y = 18$ when $t = 0$

Radioactive Decay In Exercises 11–16, complete the table for the given radioactive isotope.

Isotope	Half-Life (in Years)	Initial Quantity	Amount After 1,000 Years	Amount After 10,000 Years
11. Ra^{226}	1,620	10 grams		
12. Ra^{226}	1,620		1.5 grams	
13. C^{14}	5,730			2 grams
14. C^{14}	5,730	3 grams		
15. Pu^{239}	24,360		2.1 grams	
16. Pu^{239}	24,360			0.4 grams

17. *Radioactive Decay* What percent of a present amount of radioactive radium (Ra^{226}) will remain after 900 years?

18. *Radioactive Decay* Find the half-life of a radioactive material if after 1 year 99.57% of the initial amount remains.

19. *Carbon Dating* C^{14} dating assumes that the carbon dioxide on the earth today has the same radioactive content as it did centuries ago. If this is true, then the amount of C^{14} absorbed by a tree that grew several centuries ago should be the same as the amount of C^{14} absorbed by a similar tree today. A piece of ancient charcoal contains only 15% as much of the radioactive carbon as a piece of modern charcoal. How long ago was the tree burned to make the ancient charcoal? (The half-life of C^{14} is 5730 years.)

20. *Carbon Dating* Repeat Exercise 19 for a piece of charcoal that contains 30% as much radioactive carbon as a modern piece.

21. *Population Growth* The number of a certain type of bacteria increases continuously at a rate proportional to the number present. There are 150 present at a given time and 450 present 5 hours later.

(a) How many will there be 10 hours after the initial time?

(b) How long will it take for the population to double?

(c) Does the answer to part (b) depend on the starting time? Explain.

22. *School Expenditures* In 1980, the total amount spent on schools in the United States was $270.9 billion. By 1988, the total amount had risen to $343.1 billion. Assume the total amount spent can be modeled by exponential growth. *(Source: U.S. National Center for Education Statistics)*

(a) Estimate the total amount spent in 1985.

(b) How many years would it take for the amount to double?

(c) By what percent is the amount increasing each year?

Compound Interest In Exercises 23–28, complete the table for an account in which interest is compounded continuously.

Initial Investment	Annual Rate	Time to Double	Amount After 10 Years	Amount After 25 Years
23. $1,000	12%			
24. $20,000	$10\frac{1}{2}\%$			
25. $750		$7\frac{3}{4}$ years		
26. $10,000		5 years		
27. $500			$1,292.85	
28. $2,000				$6,008.33

29. *Effective Yield* The effective yield is the annual rate i that will produce the same interest per year as the nominal rate r compounded n times per year.

(a) For a rate r that is compounded n times per year, show that the effective yield is

$$i = \left(1 + \frac{r}{n}\right)^n - 1.$$

(b) Find the effective yield for a nominal rate of 6%, compounded monthly.

30. *Effective Yield* The effective yield is the annual rate i that will produce the same interest per year as the nominal rate r.

(a) For a rate r that is compounded continuously, show that the effective yield is

$$i = e^r - 1.$$

(b) Find the effective yield for a nominal rate of 6%, compounded continuously.

Effective Yield In Exercises 31 and 32, use the results of Exercises 29 and 30 to complete the table showing the effective yield for a nominal rate of r.

Number of compoundings per year	4	12	365	Continuous
Effective yield				

31. $r = 5\%$ **32.** $r = 7\frac{1}{2}\%$

33. *Rule of 70* Verify that the time necessary for an investment to double its value is approximately $70/r$, where r is the annual interest rate. (This formula requires that r be entered as a percent, not a decimal.)

34. *Rule of 70* Use the Rule of 70 given in Exercise 33 to approximate the time necessary for an investment to double in value if (a) $r = 10\%$ and (b) $r = 7\%$.

35. *Revenue* The revenue for La-Z-Boy Chair Company was $254.9 million in 1983 and $684.1 million in 1992. *(Source: La-Z-Boy Chair Company)*

(a) Use an exponential growth model to predict the 1996 revenue.

(b) Use a linear model to predict the 1996 revenue.

36. *Net Worth* The net worth for American Greetings Corporation was $365.5 million in 1983 and $952.5 million in 1992. *(Source: American Greetings Corporation)*

(a) Use an exponential growth model to predict the 1996 net worth.

(b) Use a linear model to predict the 1996 net worth.

37. *Sales* The cumulative sales S (in thousands of units) of a new product after it has been on the market for t years is modeled by

$$S = Ce^{k/t}.$$

During the first year, 5000 units were sold. The saturation point for the market is 30,000 units. That is, the limit of S as $t \to \infty$ is 30,000.

(a) Solve for C and k in the model.

(b) How many units will be sold after 5 years?

(c) Sketch the graph of the sales function.

38. *Sales* The cumulative sales S (in thousands of units) of a new product after it has been on the market for t years is modeled by

$$S = 30(1 - 3^{kt}).$$

During the first year, 5000 units were sold.

(a) Solve for k in the model.

(b) What is the saturation point for this product?

(c) How many units will be sold after 5 years?

(d) Sketch the graph of the sales function.

39. *Learning Curve* The management of a factory finds that the maximum number of units a worker can produce in a day is 30. The learning curve for the number of units N produced per day after a new employee has worked t days is modeled by

$$N = 30(1 - e^{kt}).$$

After 20 days on the job, a worker is producing 19 units in a day. How many days should pass before this worker is producing 25 units per day?

40. *Learning Curve* The management in Exercise 39 requires that a new employee be producing at least 20 units per day after 30 days on the job.

(a) Find a learning curve model that describes this minimum requirement.

(b) Find the number of days before a minimal achiever is producing 25 units per day.

41. *Revenue* A small business assumes that the demand function for one of its products can be modeled by

$$p = Ce^{kx}.$$

When $p = \$45$, $x = 1000$ units, and when $p = \$40$, $x = 1200$ units.

(a) Solve for C and k.

(b) Find the values of x and p that will maximize the revenue for this product.

42. *Revenue* Repeat Exercise 41 given that when $p = \$5$, $x = 300$ units, and when $p = \$4$, $x = 400$ units.

43. *Forestry* The value V (in dollars) of a tract of timber can be modeled by

$$V = 100{,}000e^{0.75\sqrt{t}},$$

where $t = 0$ corresponds to 1990. If money earns interest at a rate of 4%, compounded continuously, then the present value A of the timber at any time t is

$$A = Ve^{-0.04t}.$$

Find the year in which the timber should be harvested to maximize the present value.

44. *Forestry* Repeat Exercise 43 using the model

$$V = 100{,}000e^{0.6\sqrt{t}}.$$

45. *Earthquake Intensity* On the Richter Scale, the magnitude R of an earthquake of intensity I is given by

$$R = \frac{\ln I - \ln I_0}{\ln 10},$$

where I_0 is the minimum intensity used for comparison. Assume $I_0 = 1$.

(a) Find the intensity of the 1906 San Francisco earthquake in which $R = 8.3$.

(b) Find the factor by which the intensity is increased when the value of R is doubled.

(c) Find dR/dI.

Case Study: Investing for Retirement

Many workers today are faced with decisions about how to invest for retirement, as companies offer them more choices and discretion in managing their pension funds. Because workers are often unfamiliar with these kinds of decisions, they frequently opt for safety—investing in assets such as U.S. Government bonds that virtually guarantee that none of their money will be lost.

However, safety has its cost. Investments typically offer a tradeoff between safety and rate of return. Companies that are safer—those that have consistently paid dividends on their stock and have always paid the interest and principal on their bonds—can typically pay a lower rate of return and still acquire all the funds they need. Companies that are riskier— perhaps because it is not clear that they will have profits to share with stockholders, or even enough income to pay their creditors on time—typically have to pay a higher rate of return to get the investment capital that they need.

In choosing their retirement investments, workers opting for safety without taking account of the cost, may be unknowingly choosing a much lower standard of living in retirement than they would otherwise enjoy. Owing to the effects of compounding, small differences in the rate of return on different investments can make major differences in the value of a retirement savings fund over the worklife of an employee.

Towers Perrin, a management consulting firm with a branch office in Valhalla, New York, offers such a retirement savings plan to its employees. The board of directors was concerned that employees had chosen to invest approximately 50 percent of their profit-sharing funds in fixed-income, low-return investments. It was suspected that some employees made their choices without a full understanding of the investment alternatives and risk-return relationships associated with them. As a result, Towers Perrin set up a task force to develop options and explain them to the employees. Five different investment portfolios, embodying different combinations of risk and return, were developed (see table and graph).

	Portfolios				
	Mix A	Mix B	Mix C	Mix D	Mix E
No. of	6.6%	7.8%	9.0%	10.2%	11.0%
Years	0.066	0.078	0.09	0.102	0.11
1	1,066	1,078	1,090	1,102	1,110
2	1,136	1,162	1,188	1,214	1,232
3	1,211	1,253	1,295	1,338	1,368
4	1,291	1,350	1,412	1,475	1,518
5	1,377	1,456	1,539	1,625	1,685
6	1,467	1,569	1,677	1,791	1,870
7	1,564	1,692	1,828	1,974	2,076
8	1,667	1,824	1,993	2,175	2,305
9	1,778	1,966	2,172	2,397	2,558
10	1,895	2,119	2,367	2,641	2,839
15	2,608	3,085	3,642	4,293	4,785
20	3,590	4,491	5,604	6,976	8,062
25	4,942	6,538	8,623	11,338	13,585
30	6,803	9,518	13,268	18,427	22,892

The most conservative investment portfolio, called "Mix A," has 80% of its funds invested in conservative securities, such as bonds and fixed-income investments. This portfolio has a very small chance of losing money in any given year, but it is expected to return only 6.6% per year on average in the future. At the other end of the spectrum is "Mix E," with a high proportion of small-company and international stocks, which are much riskier in the short run. In any given year, this portfolio is much more likely to drop in value, but it is also expected to average 11.0% annually over the long term. Mixes B, C, and D represent intermediate positions between these extremes.

You might think that the Mix A portfolio would provide about 60% (6.6% / 11.0%) of the income of Mix E over the years. But, owing to the effects of compounding, the difference is significantly greater than this. The accompanying table and graph show the value of $1000 invested in each of the five portfolios, after various amounts of time. This $1000 will grow to $6803 after 30 years at 6.6%, but it will grow to $22,892 after the same number of years at 11.0%—more than three times as much!

After they were educated about the tradeoff between risk and return and the impact of compounding, only 5% of active Towers Perrin employees chose to invest 100% of their money in fixed-income investments. This contrasts with 24% before the education program.

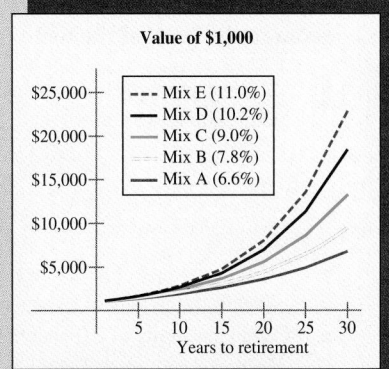

What Would You Do?

1. Which one of the five portfolios would you choose if you were a Towers Perrin employee, and why? Suppose you could also choose to divide your retirement savings among any combination of the five portfolios. Compare the following options. Which would you prefer? List your assumptions. Explain your reasoning and calculations.

(a) 20% of your retirement savings invested in Mix A, 20% in B, 20% in C, 20% in D, and 20% in E.

(b) 0% in A, 30% in B, 40% in C, 20% in D, and 10% in E

(c) 10% in A, 20% in B, 20% in C, 25% in D, and 25% in E

2. What are your own feelings about risk? Are you willing to take a greater risk of seeing your savings plummet in value in some years, in return for a higher rate of growth on average? Or would your blood pressure rise with every drop in the stock market?

3. Would your risk/return decision be different if you were two years away from retirement? . . . if you were a 25-year-old just starting with the company? Why?

4. Many people put off saving for retirement until a higher interest rate comes along or until they feel financially able to put aside a larger sum of money. Compare the following options using the portfolio chart. Which is better and why? Make a generalization on retirement savings strategy based on your findings.

(a) Putting aside $2000 (lump sum) at 6.6% 30 years before retirement.

(b) Putting aside $5000 (lump sum) at 10.2% 10 years before retirement.

(c) Putting aside $3000 (lump sum) at 7.8% 20 years before retirement.

Chapter Summary and Study Tips

After studying this chapter, you should have acquired the following skills. The exercise numbers are keyed to the Review Exercises that begin on page 308. Answers to odd-numbered Review Exercises are given in the back of the text.

■ Use the properties of exponents to evaluate and simplify exponential expressions. (*Section 4.1*)

Review Exercises 1–12

$$a^0 = 1, \quad a^x a^y = a^{x+y}, \quad \frac{a^x}{a^y} = a^{x-y}, \quad (a^x)^y = a^{xy}$$

$$(ab)^x = a^x b^x, \quad \left(\frac{a}{b}\right)^x = \frac{a^x}{b^x}, \quad a^{-x} = \frac{1}{a^x}$$

■ Use properties of exponents to answer questions about real life. (*Section 4.1*) — Review Exercises 13, 14

■ Sketch the graphs of exponential functions. (*Section 4.1*) — Review Exercises 15–18

■ Evaluate limits of exponential functions in real life. (*Section 4.1*) — Review Exercises 19, 20

■ Evaluate and graph functions involving the natural exponential function. (*Section 4.1*) — Review Exercises 21–24

$$\lim_{x \to 0} (1 + x)^{1/x} = e \approx 2.71828$$

■ Sketch the graphs of logistics growth functions. (*Section 4.1*) — Review Exercises 25, 26

■ Solve compound interest problems. (*Section 4.1*) — Review Exercises 27–30

$$A = P\left(1 + \frac{r}{n}\right)^{nt}, \quad A = Pe^{rt}$$

■ Answer questions involving the natural exponential function as a real-life model. (*Section 4.1*) — Review Exercises 31, 32

■ Find the derivatives of natural exponential functions. (*Section 4.2*) — Review Exercises 33–40

$$\frac{d}{dx}[e^x] = e^x, \quad \frac{d}{dx}[e^u] = e^u u'$$

■ Use calculus to analyze the graphs of functions that involve the natural exponential function. (*Section 4.2*) — Review Exercises 41–44

■ Use the definition of the natural logarithmic function to write exponential equations in logarithmic form, and vice versa. (*Section 4.3*) — Review Exercises 45–48

$$\ln x = b \quad \text{if and only if} \quad e^b = x.$$

■ Sketch the graphs of natural logarithmic functions. (*Section 4.3*) — Review Exercises 49–52

■ Use properties of logarithms to expand and condense logarithmic expressions. (*Section 4.3*) — Review Exercises 53–56

$$\ln xy = \ln x + \ln y, \quad \ln \frac{x}{y} = \ln x - \ln y, \quad \ln x^n = n \ln x$$

■ Use inverse properties of exponential and logarithmic functions to solve exponential and logarithmic equations. (*Section 4.3*) — Review Exercises 57–64

$$\ln e^x = x, \quad e^{\ln x} = x$$

*Several student study aids are available with this text. The *Student Solutions Guide* includes detailed solutions to all odd-numbered exercises, as well as practice chapter tests with answers. The *Graphics Calculator Guide* offers instructions on the use of a variety of graphing calculators and computer graphing software. The *Brief Calculus TUTOR* includes additional examples for selected exercises in the text.

■ Use properties of natural logarithms to answer questions about real life. (*Section 4.3*)

■ Find the derivatives of natural logarithmic functions. (*Section 4.4*)

$$\frac{d}{dx}[\ln x] = \frac{1}{x}, \qquad \frac{d}{dx}[\ln u] = \frac{1}{u}u'$$

■ Use calculus to analyze the graphs of functions that involve the natural logarithmic function. (*Section 4.4*)

■ Use the definition of logarithms to evaluate logarithmic expressions involving other bases. (*Section 4.4*)

$$\log_a x = b \quad \text{if and only if} \quad a^b = x$$

■ Use the change of base formula to evaluate logarithmic expressions involving other bases. (*Section 4.4*)

$$\log_a x = \frac{\ln x}{\ln a}$$

■ Find the derivatives of exponential and logarithmic functions involving other bases. (*Section 4.4*)

$$\frac{d}{dx}[a^x] = (\ln a)a^x, \qquad \frac{d}{dx}[a^u] = (\ln a)a^u u'$$

$$\frac{d}{dx}[\log_a x] = \left(\frac{1}{\ln a}\right)\frac{1}{x}, \qquad \frac{d}{dx}[\log_a u] = \left(\frac{1}{\ln a}\right)\frac{u'}{u}$$

■ Use calculus to answer questions about real-life rates of change. (*Section 4.4*)

■ Use exponential growth and decay to model real-life situations. (*Section 4.5*)

■ Classifying Differentiation Rules   Differentiation rules fall into two basic classes: (1) general rules that apply to all differentiable functions and (2) specific rules that apply to special types of functions. At this point in the course, you have studied six general rules: the Constant Rule, the Constant Multiple Rule, the Sum Rule, the Difference Rule, the Product Rule, and the Quotient Rule. Although these rules were introduced in the context of algebraic functions, remember that they can also be used with exponential and logarithmic functions. You have also studied three specific rules: the Power Rule, the Exponential Rule, and the Log Rule. Each of these rules comes in two forms: the "simple" version, such as $D_x[e^x] = e^x$, and the Chain Rule version, such as $D_x[e^u] = e^u u'$.

■ To Memorize or Not to Memorize?   When studying mathematics, you need to memorize some formulas and rules. Much of this will come from practice—the formulas that you use most often will be committed to memory. Some formulas, however, are used only infrequently. With these, it is helpful to be able to *derive* the formula from a *known* formula. For instance, knowing the Log Rule for differentiation and change of base formula, $\log_a x = (\ln x)/(\ln a)$, allows you to derive the formula for the derivative of a logarithmic function to base a.

Review Exercises

 means that technology can help you solve or check the exercise(s).

In Exercises 1–4, evaluate the expression.

1. $4(4^4)$

2. $16^{3/2}$

3. $\left(\frac{1}{5}\right)^4$

4. $\left(\frac{27}{8}\right)^{-1/3}$

In Exercises 5–8, use the properties of exponents to simplify the expression.

5. $\left(\frac{25}{4}\right)^0$

6. $(9^{1/3})(3^{1/3})$

7. $\dfrac{6^3}{36^2}$

8. $\dfrac{1}{4}\left(\dfrac{1}{2}\right)^{-3}$

In Exercises 9–12, solve the equation for x.

9. $5^x = 625$

10. $x^{3/4} = 8$

11. $e^{-1/2} = e^{x-1}$

12. $\dfrac{x^3}{3} = e^3$

13. *New York Stock Exchange* The total number y (in millions) of shares of stocks listed on the New York Stock Exchange between 1940 and 1990 can be modeled by

$$y = 29.619(1.0927)^t, \qquad 40 \le t \le 90,$$

where $t = 40$ corresponds to 1940. Use this model to estimate the total number of shares listed in 1950, 1970, and 1990. *(Source: New York Stock Exchange)*

14. *Recycling* Between 1960 and 1988, the percent p of materials in municipal waste that was recycled can be modeled by

$$p = 4.92 + 1.29(1.097)^t, \qquad 0 \le t \le 28,$$

where $t = 0$ corresponds to 1960. Use the model to estimate the percent of recycled materials in 1960, 1970, and 1988. *(Source: Franklin Associates, Ltd.)*

 In Exercises 15–18, sketch the graph of the function.

15. $f(x) = 9^{x/2}$

16. $f(t) = \left(\frac{1}{6}\right)^t$

17. $f(x) = \left(\frac{1}{2}\right)^{2x} + 4$

18. $g(x) = \frac{1}{4}(2)^{-3x}$

19. *Demand* The demand function for a product is

$$p = 12{,}500 - \frac{10{,}000}{2 + e^{-0.001x}},$$

where p is the price per unit and x is the number of units produced (see figure). What is the limit of the price as x increases without bound? Explain what this means in the context of the problem.

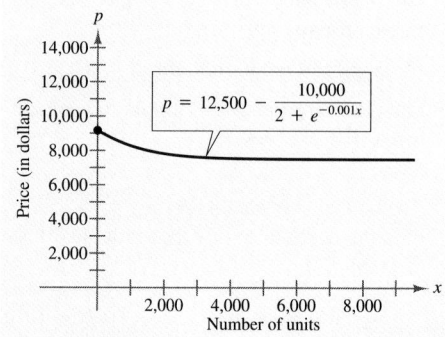

20. *Endangered Species* Biologists consider a species of a plant or animal to be endangered if it is expected to become extinct in less than 20 years. The population y of a certain species is modeled by

$$y = 1096e^{-0.39t}$$

(see figure). Is this species endangered? Explain your reasoning.

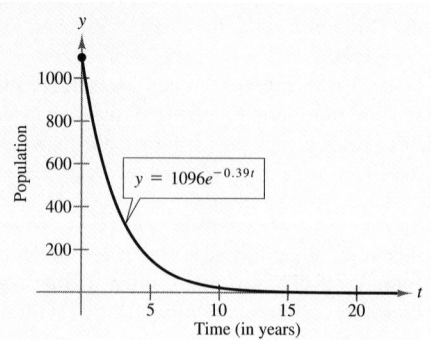

In Exercises 21–24, evaluate the function at the indicated value. Then sketch its graph.

21. $f(x) = 2e^{x-1}$, $x = 2$

22. $f(t) = e^{4t} - 1$, $t = 0$

23. $g(t) = 12e^{-0.2t}$, $t = 17$

24. $g(x) = \dfrac{24}{1 + e^{-0.3x}}$, $x = 300$

25. *Stocking a Lake with Fish* A lake is stocked with 500 fish and the fish population P begins to increase according to the logistics model

$$P = \frac{10,000}{1 + 19e^{-t/5}}, \qquad 0 \le t,$$

where t is measured in months.

(a) Use a graphing utility to graph the function.
(b) Estimate the number of fish in the lake after 4 months.
(c) Does the population have a limit as t increases without bound? Explain your reasoning.
(d) After how many months is the population increasing most rapidly? Explain your reasoning.

26. *Spread of a Virus* On a college campus of 5000 students, the spread of a flu virus through the student body is modeled by

$$P = \frac{5000}{1 + 4999e^{-0.8t}}, \qquad 0 \le t,$$

where P is the total number of infected people and t is the time, measured in days.

(a) Use a graphing utility to graph the function.
(b) How many students will be infected after 5 days?
(c) According to this model, will all the students on campus become infected with the flu? Explain your reasoning.

In Exercises 27 and 28, complete the table to determine the balance A when P dollars is invested at an annual rate of r for t years, compounded n times per year.

n	1	2	4	12	365	Continuous compounding
A						

27. $P = \$1000$, $r = 4\%$, $t = 5$ years

28. $P = \$5000$, $r = 6\%$, $t = 20$ years

In Exercises 29 and 30, \$2000 is deposited in an account. Decide which account, (a) or (b), will have the greater balance after 10 years.

29. (a) 5%, compounded continuously
     (b) 6%, compounded quarterly

30. (a) $6\frac{1}{2}\%$, compounded monthly
     (b) $6\frac{1}{4}\%$, compounded continuously

31. *Age at First Marriage* The average age A of an American man at his first marriage from 1970 to 1990 can be modeled by

$$A = 22.38 + \frac{1}{0.1513 + 9.6155e^{-0.3708t}}, \qquad 0 \le t \le 20,$$

where $t = 0$ corresponds to 1970. Use this model to estimate the average age of an American man at his first marriage in 1970, 1980, and 1990. *(Source: U.S. Center for Health Statistics)*

32. *Profit* The profit P (in millions of dollars) for Blockbuster Video from 1986 to 1993 can be modeled by

$$P = 1.96e^{0.3696t} - 17.24,$$

where $t = 6$ corresponds to 1986. Use this model to estimate the profit for Blockbuster Video in 1986, 1990, and 1993. *(Source: Blockbuster Entertainment Corporation)*

In Exercises 33–40, find the derivative of the function.

33. $y = 4e^{x^2}$

34. $y = x^2 e^x$

35. $y = \dfrac{x}{e^{2x}}$

36. $y = \dfrac{x-1}{e^x + 2x^2}$

37. $y = \sqrt{4e^{4x}}$

38. $y = \sqrt[3]{xe^{3x}}$

39. $y = \dfrac{5}{1 + e^{2x}}$

40. $y = \dfrac{e^x}{1 - xe^x}$

In Exercises 41–44, graph and analyze the function. Include any relative extrema, points of inflection, and asymptotes in your analysis.

41. $f(x) = 4e^{-x}$

42. $f(x) = x^3 e^x$

43. $f(x) = \dfrac{e^x}{x^2}$

44. $f(x) = \dfrac{1}{xe^x}$

In Exercises 45 and 46, write the logarithmic equation as an exponential equation.

45. $\ln 12 \approx 2.4849$

46. $\ln 0.6 \approx -0.5108$

In Exercises 47 and 48, write the exponential equation as a logarithmic equation.

47. $e^{1.5} \approx 4.4817$ **48.** $e^{-4} \approx 0.0183$

 In Exercises 49–52, sketch the graph of the function.

49. $y = \ln(4 - x)$ **50.** $y = 5 + \ln x$

51. $y = \ln \dfrac{x}{3}$ **52.** $y = -\dfrac{5}{6} \ln x$

In Exercises 53–56, use the properties of logarithms to write the expression as a sum, difference, or multiple of logarithms.

53. $\ln \sqrt{x^2(x - 1)}$ **54.** $\ln \dfrac{x^2}{(x + 1)^3}$

55. $\ln \left(\dfrac{1 - x}{3x} \right)^3$ **56.** $\ln \dfrac{e^4}{5x}$

In Exercises 57–64, solve the equation for x.

57. $e^{\ln x} = 3$ **58.** $\ln x = 3e^{-1}$

59. $\ln 2x - \ln(3x - 1) = 0$ **60.** $e^{2x - 1} - 6 = 0$

61. $\ln x + \ln(x - 3) = 0$ **62.** $e^{-1.386x} = 0.25$

63. $9^{6x} - 27 = 0$ **64.** $100(1.21)^x = 110$

 65. *Home Mortgage* The monthly payment M for a home mortgage of P dollars for t years at an annual interest rate of $r\%$ is given by

$$M = P \left(\dfrac{\dfrac{r}{12}}{1 - \left(\dfrac{1}{(r/12) + 1} \right)^{12t}} \right).$$

(a) Use a graphing utility to graph the model when $P = \$100,000$ and $r = 8\%$.
(b) You are given a choice of a 20-year term or a 30-year term. Which would you choose? Explain.

 66. *Hourly Wages* The average hourly wage w in the United States from 1970 to 1991 can be modeled by

$$w = 50.92 - 47.7e^{-0.0077t},$$

where $t = 0$ corresponds to 1970. (*Source: U.S. Bureau of Labor Statistics*)

(a) Use a graphing utility to graph the model.
(b) Use the model to determine the year in which the average hourly wage was $10.
(c) For how many years past 1991 do you think this equation might be a good model for the average hourly wage? Explain your reasoning.

In Exercises 67–74, find the derivative of the function.

67. $f(x) = \ln 3x^2$ **68.** $y = \ln \dfrac{x(x - 1)}{x - 2}$

69. $y = x\sqrt{\ln x}$ **70.** $f(x) = \ln \sqrt{4x}$

71. $y = \dfrac{\ln x}{x^3}$ **72.** $y = \ln(x^2 - 2)^{2/3}$

73. $f(x) = \ln e^{-x^2}$ **74.** $y = \ln \dfrac{e^x}{1 + e^x}$

In Exercises 75–78, graph and analyze the function. Include any relative extrema and points of inflection in your analysis.

75. $y = \ln(x + 3)$ **76.** $y = \dfrac{8 \ln x}{x^2}$

77. $y = \ln \dfrac{10}{x + 2}$ **78.** $y = \ln \dfrac{x^2}{9 - x^2}$

In Exercises 79–82, evaluate the logarithm.

79. $\log_7 49$ **80.** $\log_2 32$

81. $\log_{10} 1$ **82.** $\log_4 \frac{1}{64}$

In Exercises 83–86, use the change of base formula to evaluate the logarithm. Round the result to four decimal places.

83. $\log_5 10$ **84.** $\log_4 12$

85. $\log_{16} 64$ **86.** $\log_{10} 125$

In Exercises 87–90, find the derivative of the function.

87. $y = \log_3(2x - 1)$ **88.** $y = \log_{10} \dfrac{3}{x}$

89. $y = \log_2 \dfrac{1}{x^2}$ **90.** $y = \log_{16}(x^2 - 3x)$

91. *Depreciation* After t years, the value V of a car purchased for $20,000 is

$$V = 20,000(0.75)^t.$$

(a) Sketch a graph of the function and determine the value of the car 2 years after it was purchased.
(b) Find the rate of change of V with respect to t when $t = 1$ and when $t = 4$.
(c) After how many years will the car be worth $5000?

92. *Inflation* If the annual rate of inflation averages 5% over the next 10 years, then the approximate cost of goods or services C during any year in that decade is

$$C = P(1.05)^t,$$

where t is the time in years and P is the present cost.

(a) The price of an oil change is presently $24.95. Estimate the price of an oil change 10 years from now.

(b) Find the rate of change of C with respect to t when $t = 1$.

93. *Drug Decomposition* A medical solution contains 500 milligrams of a drug per milliliter when the solution is prepared. After 40 days, it contains only 300 milligrams per milliliter. Assuming that the rate of decomposition is proportional to the concentration present, find an equation giving the concentration A after t days.

94. *Population Growth* A population is growing continuously at the rate of $2\frac{1}{2}\%$ per year. Find the time necessary for the population to (a) double in size and (b) triple in size.

95. *Half-Life* A sample of radioactive waste is taken from a nuclear plant. The sample contains 50 grams of strontium-90 at time $t = 0$ years and 42.031 grams after 7 years. What is the half-life of strontium-90?

96. *Half-Life* The half-life of cobalt-60 is 5.2 years. Find the time it would take for a sample of 0.5 grams of cobalt-60 to decay to 0.1 grams.

97. *Profit* The profit for Wendy's was $3.5 million in 1987 and $64.7 million in 1992 (see figure). Use an exponential growth model to predict the 1996 profit. *(Source: Wendy's International, Inc.)*

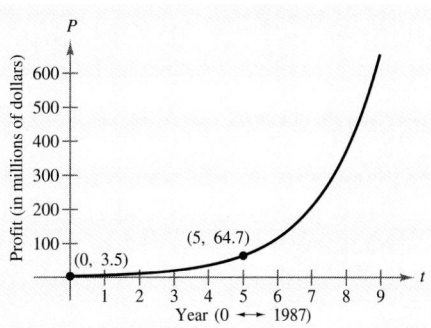

FIGURE FOR 97

98. *Net Worth* The net worth of Toys'R'Us was $459.7 million in 1983 and $2889.0 million in 1992 (see figure). Use an exponential growth model to predict the 1996 net worth. *(Source: Toys'R'Us)*

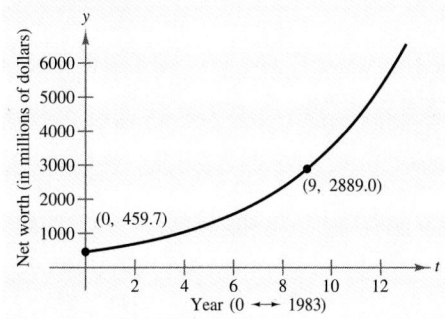

Sample Post-Graduation Exam Questions

The following questions were taken from certified public accountant (CPA) exams, graduate management admission tests (GMAT), graduate records exams (GRE), actuarial exams, or college-level academic skills tests (CLAST). The answers to the questions are given in the back of the book.

1. The rate of decay of a radioactive substance is proportional to the amount of the substance present. Three years ago there were 6 grams of substance. Now there are 5 grams. How many grams will there be 3 years from now?

    (a) 4   (b) $\frac{25}{6}$ (c) $\frac{125}{36}$ (d) $\frac{75}{36}$

2. In a certain town, 45% of the people have brown hair, 30% have brown eyes, and 15% have both brown hair and brown eyes. What percent of the people in the town have neither brown hair nor brown eyes?

    (a) 25%   (b) 35%   (c) 40%   (d) 50%

3. You have $900 and deposit it in a savings account that is compounded continuously at 4.76%. After 16 years the amount in the account will be

    (a) $1927.53   (b) $1077.81   (c) $943.88   (d) $2827.53

4. A bookstore orders 75 books. Each book costs the bookstore $29 and is sold for $42. The bookstore must pay a $4 service charge for each unsold book returned. If the bookstore returns seven books, how much profit will the bookstore make?

    (a) $975   (b) $947   (c) $653   (d) $681

For Questions 5–7, use the data given in the graph.

5. In how many of the years was spending larger than in the preceding year?

    (a) 2   (b) 4   (c) 1   (d) 3

6. In which year was the profit the greatest?

    (a) 1988   (b) 1991   (c) 1987   (d) 1989

7. In 1990, profits decreased by x percent from 1989 with x equal to

    (a) 60%   (b) 140%   (c) 340%   (d) 40%

FIGURE FOR 5–7

$$\int_a^b f'(x)\, dx = f(b) - f(a)$$

5 Integration and Its Applications

Calculus involves two basic operations: differentiation and integration (or antidifferentiation). Because these operations are inverses of each other, some applications of integration are straightforward. For instance, integrating an acceleration function produces a velocity function. Other applications are surprisingly unrelated to derivatives and rates of change. For instance, integration can be used to find the area of a region, the average value of a function, and the volume of a solid.

Although integration was used by the early developers of calculus (such as Newton), its rigorous development is usually associated with the German mathematician Georg Friedrich Riemann (1826–1866).

$$\int f'(x)\, dx = f(x) + C$$

Riemann

Antiderivatives and Indefinite Integrals

Antiderivatives ▪ *Notation for Antiderivatives and Indefinite Integrals* ▪
Finding Antiderivatives ▪ *Particular Solutions* ▪ *Applications*

Antiderivatives

Up to this point in the text, you have been concerned primarily with this problem: given a function, find its derivative. Many important applications of calculus involve the inverse problem: given the derivative of a function, find the function. For example, suppose you are given

$$f'(x) = 2, \quad g'(x) = 3x^2, \quad \text{and} \quad s'(t) = 4t.$$

Your goal is to determine the functions f, g, and s. By making educated guesses, you might come up with the following.

$$f(x) = 2x \quad \text{because} \quad \frac{d}{dx}[2x] = 2$$

$$g(x) = x^3 \quad \text{because} \quad \frac{d}{dx}[x^3] = 3x^2$$

$$s(t) = 2t^2 \quad \text{because} \quad \frac{d}{dt}[2t^2] = 4t$$

This operation of determining the original function from its derivative is the inverse operation of differentiation. It is called **antidifferentiation.**

Definition of Antiderivative

A function F is an **antiderivative** of a function f if for every x in the domain of f, it follows that $F'(x) = f(x)$.

If $F(x)$ is an antiderivative of $f(x)$, then $F(x) + C$, where C is any constant, is also an antiderivative of $f(x)$. For example,

$$F(x) = x^3, \quad G(x) = x^3 - 5, \quad \text{and} \quad H(x) = x^3 + 0.3$$

are antiderivatives of $3x^2$ because the derivative of each is $3x^2$. As it turns out, *all* antiderivatives of $3x^2$ are of the form $x^3 + C$. Thus, the process of antidifferentiation does not determine a single function, but rather a *family* of functions, each differing from the others by a constant.

Notation for Antiderivatives and Indefinite Integrals

The antidifferentiation process is also called **integration** and is denoted by the symbol

$$\int,$$
Integral sign

called an **integral sign.** The symbol

$$\int f(x)\,dx$$
Indefinite integral

is the **indefinite integral** of $f(x)$, and it denotes the family of antiderivatives of $f(x)$. That is, if $F'(x) = f(x)$ for all x, then you can write

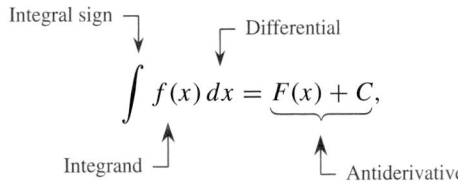

where $f(x)$ is the **integrand** and C is the **constant of integration.** The differential dx in the indefinite integral identifies the variable of integration. That is, the symbol $\int f(x)\,dx$ denotes the "antiderivative of f *with respect to* x" just as the symbol dy/dx denotes the "derivative of y *with respect to* x."

Integral Notation of Antiderivatives

The notation

$$\int f(x)\,dx = F(x) + C,$$

where C is an arbitrary constant, means that F is an antiderivative of f. That is, $F'(x) = f(x)$ for all x in the domain of f.

EXAMPLE 1 *Notation for Antiderivatives*

Using integral notation, you can write the three antiderivatives given at the beginning of this section as follows.

a. $\displaystyle\int 2\,dx = 2x + C$ **b.** $\displaystyle\int 3x^2\,dx = x^3 + C$ **c.** $\displaystyle\int 4t\,dt = 2t^2 + C$

Finding Antiderivatives

The inverse relationship between the operations of integration and differentiation can be shown symbolically, as follows.

$$\frac{d}{dx}\left[\int f(x)\,dx\right] = f(x)$$ *Differentiation is the inverse of integration.*

$$\int f'(x)\,dx = f(x) + C$$ *Integration is the inverse of differentiation.*

This inverse relationship between integration and differentiation allows you to obtain integration formulas directly from differentiation formulas. The following summary lists the integration formulas that correspond to some of the differentiation formulas you have studied.

Basic Integration Rules

1. $\displaystyle\int k\,dx = kx + C, \quad k$ is a constant   *Constant Rule*

2. $\displaystyle\int kf(x)\,dx = k\int f(x)\,dx$ *Constant Multiple Rule*

3. $\displaystyle\int [f(x) + g(x)]\,dx = \int f(x)\,dx + \int g(x)\,dx$ *Sum Rule*

4. $\displaystyle\int [f(x) - g(x)]\,dx = \int f(x)\,dx - \int g(x)\,dx$ *Difference Rule*

5. $\displaystyle\int x^n\,dx = \frac{x^{n+1}}{n+1} + C, \quad n \neq -1$ *Simple Power Rule*

Note You will study the General Power Rule for integration in Section 5.2 and the Exponential and Log Rules in Section 5.3.

Be sure you see that the Simple Power Rule has the restriction that n cannot be -1. Thus, you *cannot* use the Simple Power Rule to evaluate the integral

$$\int \frac{1}{x}\,dx.$$

To evaluate this integral, you need the Log Rule (Section 5.3).

Note In Example 2b, the integral $\int 1\,dx$ is usually shortened to the form $\int dx$.

EXAMPLE 2 *Finding Indefinite Integrals*

a. $\displaystyle\int 2\,dx = 2x + C$ **b.** $\displaystyle\int 1\,dx = x + C$ **c.** $\displaystyle\int -5\,dt = -5t + C$

EXAMPLE 3 *Finding an Indefinite Integral*

Find the indefinite integral $\int 3x\,dx$.

Solution

$$\int 3x\,dx = 3\int x\,dx \qquad\qquad \textit{Constant Multiple Rule}$$

$$= 3\int x^1\,dx \qquad\qquad \textit{Rewrite x as } x^1.$$

$$= 3\left(\frac{x^2}{2}\right) + C \qquad\qquad \textit{Power Rule with } n = 1$$

$$= \frac{3}{2}x^2 + C \qquad\qquad \textit{Simplify.}$$

In finding indefinite integrals, a strict application of the basic integration rules tends to produce cumbersome constants of integration. For instance, in Example 3, you could have written

$$\int 3x\,dx = 3\int x\,dx = 3\left(\frac{x^2}{2} + C\right) = \frac{3}{2}x^2 + 3C.$$

However, because C represents *any* constant, it is unnecessary to write $3C$ as the constant of integration. You can simply write $\frac{3}{2}x^2 + C$.

In Example 3, note that the general pattern of integration is similar to that of differentiation.

Given:	Rewrite:	Integrate:	Simplify:
$\int 3x\,dx$	$3\int x^1\,dx$	$3\left(\dfrac{x^2}{2}\right) + C$	$\dfrac{3}{2}x^2 + C$

EXAMPLE 4 *Rewriting Before Integrating*

Given Integral	*Rewrite*	*Integrate*	*Simplify*
a. $\int \dfrac{1}{x^3}\,dx$	$\int x^{-3}\,dx$	$\dfrac{x^{-2}}{-2} + C$	$-\dfrac{1}{2x^2} + C$
b. $\int \sqrt{x}\,dx$	$\int x^{1/2}\,dx$	$\dfrac{x^{3/2}}{3/2} + C$	$\dfrac{2}{3}x^{3/2} + C$

Note   Remember that you can check your answer to an antidifferentiation problem by differentiating. For instance, in Example 4b, you can check that $\frac{2}{3}x^{3/2}$ is the correct antiderivative by differentiating to obtain

$$\frac{d}{dx}\left[\frac{2}{3}x^{3/2}\right] = \left(\frac{2}{3}\right)\left(\frac{3}{2}\right)x^{1/2} = \sqrt{x}.$$

With the five basic integration rules, you can integrate *any* polynomial function, as demonstrated in the next example.

EXAMPLE 5 *Integrating Polynomial Functions*

Find the following indefinite integrals.

a. $\displaystyle\int (x+2)\,dx$ **b.** $\displaystyle\int (3x^4 - 5x^2 + x)\,dx$

Solution

a. Use the Sum Rule to integrate each part separately.

$$\int (x+2)\,dx = \int x\,dx + \int 2\,dx$$

$$= \frac{x^2}{2} + 2x + C$$

b. Try to identify each basic integration rule used to evaluate this integral.

$$\int (3x^4 - 5x^2 + x)\,dx = 3\left(\frac{x^5}{5}\right) - 5\left(\frac{x^3}{3}\right) + \frac{x^2}{2} + C$$

$$= \frac{3}{5}x^5 - \frac{5}{3}x^3 + \frac{1}{2}x^2 + C$$

EXAMPLE 6 *Rewriting Before Integrating*

Find the indefinite integral

$$\int \frac{x+1}{\sqrt{x}}\,dx.$$

Solution

Begin by rewriting the quotient in the integrand as a sum. Then rewrite each term using rational exponents.

$$\int \frac{x+1}{\sqrt{x}}\,dx = \int \left(\frac{x}{\sqrt{x}} + \frac{1}{\sqrt{x}}\right)dx \qquad \textit{Rewrite as a sum.}$$

$$= \int \left(x^{1/2} + x^{-1/2}\right)dx \qquad \textit{Use rational exponents.}$$

$$= \frac{x^{3/2}}{3/2} + \frac{x^{1/2}}{1/2} + C \qquad \textit{Apply Power Rule.}$$

$$= \frac{2}{3}x^{3/2} + 2x^{1/2} + C \qquad \textit{Simplify.}$$

Note When integrating quotients, don't make the mistake of integrating the numerator and denominator separately. For instance, in Example 6, be sure you see that

$$\int \frac{x+1}{\sqrt{x}}\,dx \neq \frac{\int (x+1)\,dx}{\int \sqrt{x}\,dx}.$$

If you have access to a symbolic integration program, try using it for this example. When we tried it, the program listed the antiderivative as $2\sqrt{x}(x + 3)/3$, which is equivalent to the result listed above.

Particular Solutions

You have already seen that the equation $y = \int f(x)\, dx$ has many solutions, each differing from the others by a constant. This means that the graphs of any two antiderivatives of f are vertical translations of each other. For instance, Figure 5.1 shows the graphs of several antiderivatives of the form

$$y = F(x) = \int (3x^2 - 1)\, dx = x^3 - x + C.$$

Each of these antiderivatives is a solution of $dy/dx = 3x^2 - 1$.

In many applications of integration, you are given enough information to determine a **particular solution.** To do this, you need only know the value of $F(x)$ for one value of x. (This information is called an **initial condition.**) For example, in Figure 5.1, there is only one curve that passes through the point $(2, 4)$. To find this curve, use the following information.

$$F(x) = x^3 - x + C \qquad\qquad \textit{General solution}$$
$$F(2) = 4 \qquad\qquad \textit{Initial condition}$$

By using the initial condition in the general solution, you can determine that $F(2) = 2^3 - 2 + C = 4$, which implies that $C = -2$. Thus, the particular solution is

$$F(x) = x^3 - x - 2. \qquad\qquad \textit{Particular solution}$$

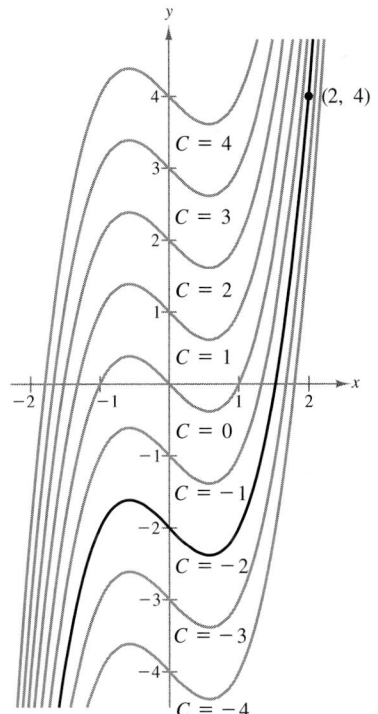

$F(x) = x^3 - x + C$

FIGURE 5.1

$C = 4$

$C = 3$

$C = 2$

$C = 1$

$C = 0$

$C = -1$

$C = -2$

$C = -3$

$C = -4$

$(2,\ 4)$

EXAMPLE 7 *Finding a Particular Solution*

Find the general solution of $F'(x) = 2x - 2$, and find the particular solution that satisfies the initial condition $F(1) = 2$.

Solution

Begin by integrating to find the general solution.

$$F(x) = \int (2x - 2)\, dx \qquad\qquad \textit{Integrate } F'(x) \textit{ to obtain } F(x).$$

$$= x^2 - 2x + C \qquad\qquad \textit{General solution}$$

Using the initial condition $F(1) = 2$, you can write

$$F(1) = 1^2 - 2(1) + C = 2,$$

which implies that $C = 3$. Thus, the particular solution is

$$F(x) = x^2 - 2x + 3. \qquad\qquad \textit{Particular solution}$$

This solution is shown graphically in Figure 5.2. Note that each of the gray curves represents a solution of the equation $F'(x) = 2x - 2$. The black curve, however, is the only solution that passes through the point $(1, 2)$, which means that $F(x) = x^2 - 2x + 3$ is the only solution that satisfies the initial condition.

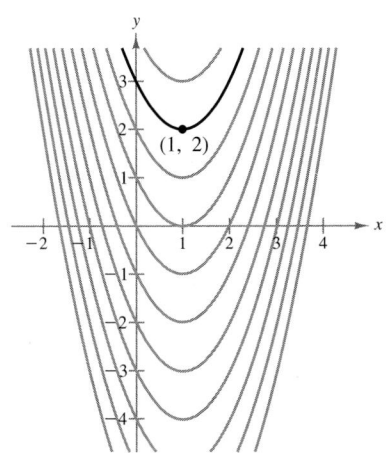

$(1,\ 2)$

FIGURE 5.2

Applications

In Chapter 2, you used the general position function for a falling object, $s(t) = -16t^2 + v_0 t + s_0$, where $s(t)$ is the height (in feet) and t is the time (in seconds). In the next example, integration is used to *derive* this function.

Real Life

EXAMPLE 8 *Deriving a Position Function*

A ball is thrown upward with an initial velocity of 64 feet per second from an initial height of 80 feet, as shown in Figure 5.3. Derive the position function giving the height s (in feet) as a function of the time t (in seconds). When does the ball hit the ground?

Solution

Let $t = 0$ represent the initial time. Then the two given conditions can be written as follows.

$$s(0) = 80 \qquad\qquad \text{\textit{Initial height is 80 feet.}}$$
$$s'(0) = 64 \qquad\qquad \text{\textit{Initial velocity is 64 feet per second.}}$$

Because the acceleration due to gravity is -32 feet per second per second, you have the following.

$$s''(t) = -32 \qquad\qquad \text{\textit{Acceleration due to gravity}}$$
$$s'(t) = \int -32\, dt \qquad\qquad \text{\textit{Integrate } } s''(t) \text{ \textit{to obtain} } s'(t).$$
$$= -32t + C_1 \qquad\qquad \text{\textit{Velocity function}}$$

Using the initial velocity, you can conclude that $C_1 = 64$.

$$s'(t) = -32t + 64 \qquad\qquad \text{\textit{Velocity function}}$$
$$s(t) = \int (-32t + 64)\, dt \qquad\qquad \text{\textit{Integrate } } s'(t) \text{ \textit{to obtain} } s(t).$$
$$= -16t^2 + 64t + C_2 \qquad\qquad \text{\textit{Position function}}$$

Using the initial height, it follows that $C_2 = 80$. Thus, the position function is

$$s(t) = -16t^2 + 64t + 80. \qquad\qquad \text{\textit{Position function}}$$

To find the time when the ball hits the ground, set the position function equal to zero and solve for t.

$$-16t^2 + 64t + 80 = 0 \qquad\qquad \text{\textit{Set } } s(t) \text{ \textit{equal to zero.}}$$
$$-16(t + 1)(t - 5) = 0 \qquad\qquad \text{\textit{Factor.}}$$
$$t = -1,\ t = 5 \qquad\qquad \text{\textit{Solve for } } t.$$

Because the time must be positive, you can conclude that the ball hits the ground 5 seconds after it is thrown.   ▬

FIGURE 5.3

Real
Life

EXAMPLE 9 *Finding a Cost Function*

The marginal cost for producing x units of a product is modeled by

$$\frac{dC}{dx} = 32 - 0.04x. \qquad\qquad \textit{Marginal cost}$$

It costs \$50 to produce one unit. Find the total cost of producing 200 units.

Solution

To find the cost function, integrate the marginal cost function.

$$C = \int (32 - 0.04x)\,dx \qquad\qquad \textit{Integrate } dC/dx \textit{ to obtain } C.$$

$$= 32x - 0.04\left(\frac{x^2}{2}\right) + K$$

$$= 32x - 0.02x^2 + K \qquad\qquad \textit{Cost function}$$

To solve for K, use the initial condition that $C = 50$ when $x = 1$.

$$50 = 32(1) - 0.02(1)^2 + K \qquad\qquad \textit{Substitute 50 for C and 1 for x.}$$

$$18.02 = K \qquad\qquad \textit{Solve for K.}$$

Thus, the total cost function is

$$C = 32x - 0.02x^2 + 18.02, \qquad\qquad \textit{Cost function}$$

which implies that the cost of producing 200 units is

$$C = 32(200) - 0.02(200)^2 + 18.02$$

$$= \$5618.02.$$

Discussion Problem **Investigating Marginal Cost**

In Example 9, you were given a marginal cost function of

$$\frac{dC}{dx} = 32 - 0.04x.$$

This means that the cost of making each additional unit decreases by about \$0.04. You can confirm this by finding the cost of making different amounts of the product.

x	1	2	3	4	5	6
C	\$50.00	\$81.94	\$113.84	\$145.70	\$177.52	\$209.30

From this, you can see that the first unit cost \$50, the second cost \$31.94, the third cost \$31.90, the fourth cost \$31.86, the fifth cost \$31.82, and so on. At what production level would this costing scheme cease to make sense? Explain your reasoning.

Warm Up

The following warm-up exercises involve skills that were covered in earlier sections. You will use these skills in the exercise set for this section.

In Exercises 1–6, rewrite the expression using rational exponents.

1. $\dfrac{\sqrt{x}}{x}$

2. $\sqrt[3]{2x}\,(2x)$

3. $\sqrt{5x^3} + \sqrt{x^5}$

4. $\dfrac{1}{\sqrt{x}} + \dfrac{1}{\sqrt[3]{x^2}}$

5. $\dfrac{(x+1)^3}{\sqrt{x+1}}$

6. $\dfrac{\sqrt{x}}{\sqrt[3]{x}}$

In Exercises 7–10, let $(x, y) = (2, 2)$, and solve the equation for C.

7. $y = x^2 + 5x + C$

8. $y = 3x^3 - 6x + C$

9. $y = -16x^2 + 26x + C$

10. $y = -\frac{1}{4}x^4 - 2x^2 + C$

E X E R C I S E S   5.1

 means that technology can help you solve or check the exercise(s).

In Exercises 1–8, verify the statement by showing that the derivative of the right side is equal to the integrand of the left side.

1. $\displaystyle\int \left(-\frac{9}{x^4}\right) dx = \frac{3}{x^3} + C$

2. $\displaystyle\int \frac{4}{\sqrt{x}}\, dx = 8\sqrt{x} + C$

3. $\displaystyle\int \left(4x^3 - \frac{1}{x^2}\right) dx = x^4 + \frac{1}{x} + C$

4. $\displaystyle\int \left(1 - \frac{1}{\sqrt[3]{x^2}}\right) dx = x - 3\sqrt[3]{x} + C$

5. $\displaystyle\int 2x^3 \sqrt{x}\, dx = \frac{4}{9}x^{9/2} + C$

6. $\displaystyle\int (x - 2)(x + 2)\, dx = \frac{x^3}{3} - 4x + C$

7. $\displaystyle\int \frac{x^2 - 1}{x^{3/2}}\, dx = \frac{2(x^2 + 3)}{3\sqrt{x}} + C$

8. $\displaystyle\int \frac{2x - 1}{x^{4/3}}\, dx = \frac{3(x + 1)}{\sqrt[3]{x}} + C$

In Exercises 9–18, find the indefinite integral and check your result by differentiation.

9. $\displaystyle\int 6\, dx$

10. $\displaystyle\int -4\, dx$

11. $\displaystyle\int 3t^2\, dt$

12. $\displaystyle\int t^4\, dt$

13. $\displaystyle\int 5x^{-3}\, dx$

14. $\displaystyle\int 4y^{-3}\, dy$

15. $\displaystyle\int du$

16. $\displaystyle\int e\, dt$

17. $\displaystyle\int x^{3/2}\, dx$

18. $\displaystyle\int v^{-1/2}\, dv$

In Exercises 19–24, complete a table using Example 4 as a model.

19. $\displaystyle\int \sqrt[3]{x}\, dx$

20. $\displaystyle\int \frac{1}{x^2}\, dx$

21. $\displaystyle\int \frac{1}{x\sqrt{x}}\, dx$

22. $\displaystyle\int x(x^2 + 3)\, dx$

23. $\displaystyle\int \frac{1}{2x^3}\, dx$

24. $\displaystyle\int \frac{1}{(2x)^3}\, dx$

In Exercises 25 and 26, find two functions that have the given derivative, and sketch the graph of each. (There is more than one correct answer.)

25.

26.

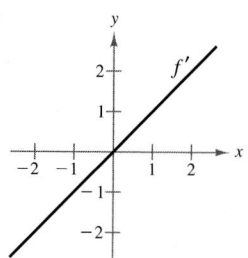

In Exercises 27–44, find the indefinite integral and check your result by differentiation.

27. $\int (x^3 + 2)\, dx$

28. $\int (x^2 - 2x + 3)\, dx$

29. $\int (2x^{4/3} + 3x - 1)\, dx$

30. $\int \left(\sqrt{x} + \dfrac{1}{2\sqrt{x}}\right) dx$

31. $\int \sqrt[3]{x^2}\, dx$

32. $\int (\sqrt[4]{x^3} + 1)\, dx$

33. $\int \dfrac{1}{x^3}\, dx$

34. $\int \dfrac{1}{x^4}\, dx$

35. $\int \dfrac{1}{4x^2}\, dx$

36. $\int (2x + x^{-1/2})\, dx$

37. $\int \dfrac{t^2 + 2}{t^2}\, dt$

38. $\int \dfrac{x^2 + 1}{x^2}\, dx$

39. $\int u(3u^2 + 1)\, du$

40. $\int \sqrt{x}(x + 1)\, dx$

41. $\int (x - 1)(6x - 5)\, dx$

42. $\int (2t^2 - 1)^2\, dt$

43. $\int y^2 \sqrt{y}\, dy$

44. $\int (1 + 3t)t^2\, dt$

In Exercises 45–50, find the particular solution $y = f(x)$ that satisfies the differential equation and initial condition.

45. $f'(x) = 3\sqrt{x} + 3$, $f(1) = 4$

46. $f'(x) = \frac{1}{5}x - 2$, $f(10) = -10$

47. $f'(x) = 6x(x - 1)$, $f(1) = -1$

48. $f'(x) = (2x - 3)(2x + 3)$, $f(3) = 0$

49. $f'(x) = \dfrac{2 - x}{x^3}$, $x > 0$, $f(2) = \dfrac{3}{4}$

50. $f'(x) = -\dfrac{5}{(x - 2)^2}$, $x \neq 2$, $f(7) = 1$

 In Exercises 51 and 52, you are shown a family of graphs, each of which is a solution of the given differential equation. Find the equation of the particular solution that passes through the indicated point.

51. $\dfrac{dy}{dx} = -5x - 2$

52. $\dfrac{dy}{dx} = 2(x - 1)$

(0, 2)

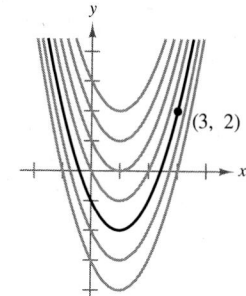

(3, 2)

In Exercises 53 and 54, find the equation of the function f whose graph passes through the point.

	Derivative	*Point*
53.	$f'(x) = 6\sqrt{x} - 10$	(4, 2)
54.	$f'(x) = \dfrac{6}{x^2}$	(2, 5)

In Exercises 55–58, find a function f that satisfies the given conditions.

55. $f''(x) = 2$, $f'(2) = 5$, $f(2) = 10$

56. $f''(x) = x^2$, $f'(0) = 6$, $f(0) = 3$

57. $f''(x) = x^{-2/3}$, $f'(8) = 6$, $f(0) = 0$

58. $f''(x) = x^{-3/2}$, $f'(1) = 2$, $f(9) = -4$

Cost In Exercises 59–62, find the cost function for the marginal cost and fixed cost.

	Marginal Cost	*Fixed Cost* ($x = 0$)
59.	$\dfrac{dC}{dx} = 85$	\$5500
60.	$\dfrac{dC}{dx} = \dfrac{1}{50}x + 10$	\$1000
61.	$\dfrac{dC}{dx} = \dfrac{1}{20\sqrt{x}} + 4$	\$750
62.	$\dfrac{dC}{dx} = \dfrac{\sqrt[4]{x}}{10} + 10$	\$2300

Demand Function In Exercises 63 and 64, find the revenue and demand functions for the given marginal revenue. (Use the fact that $R = 0$ when $x = 0$.)

63. $\dfrac{dR}{dx} = 225 - 3x$

64. $\dfrac{dR}{dx} = 100 - 6x - 2x^2$

Profit In Exercises 65 and 66, find the profit function for the given marginal profit and initial condition.

Marginal Profit	*Initial Condition*

65. $\dfrac{dP}{dx} = -18x + 1650$ $P(15) = \$22{,}725$

66. $\dfrac{dP}{dx} = -40x + 250$ $P(5) = \$650$

Vertical Motion In Exercises 67–70, use $a(t) = -32$ feet per second^2 as the acceleration due to gravity. (Neglect air resistance.)

67. A ball is thrown vertically upward with an initial velocity of 60 feet per second. How high will the ball go?

68. *Grand Canyon* The Grand Canyon is 6000 feet deep at the deepest part. A rock is dropped from this height. Express the height of the rock as a function of the time t (in seconds). How long will it take the rock to hit the canyon floor?

69. With what initial velocity must an object be thrown upward from the ground to reach the height of the Washington Monument (550 feet)?

70. A balloon, rising vertically with a velocity of 16 feet per second, releases a sandbag at an instant when the balloon is 64 feet above the ground.

(a) How many seconds after its release will the bag strike the ground?

(b) With what velocity will the bag strike the ground?

71. *Cost* A company produces a product for which the marginal cost of producing x units is

$$\frac{dC}{dx} = 2x - 12$$

and the fixed costs are $\$125$.

(a) Find the total cost function and the average cost function.

(b) Find the total cost of producing 50 units.

(c) In part (b), how much of the total cost is fixed? How much is variable? Give examples of fixed costs associated with the manufacturing of a product. Give examples of variable costs.

72. *Population Growth* The growth rate of a city's population is modeled by

$$\frac{dP}{dt} = 500t^{1.06},$$

where t is the time in years. The city's population is now 50,000. What will the population be in 10 years?

73. *Natural Gas Consumption* The consumption S (in quadrillion Btu's) of natural gas in the United States increased steadily between 1986 and 1992. The rate of increase can be modeled by

$$\frac{dS}{dt} = -0.175t^2 + 0.4t + 0.81, \qquad 0 \le t \le 6,$$

where $t = 0$ represents 1986. In 1986, the consumption was 16.7 quadrillion Btu's. Find a model for the consumption from 1986 through 1992 and determine the consumption in 1992. *(Source: U.S. Energy Information Administration)*

74. *Research Project* Use your school's library or some other reference source to research a company that markets a natural resource. Find data on the revenue of the company and on the consumption of the resource. Then find a model for each. Is the company's revenue related to the consumption of the resource? Explain.

The General Power Rule

The General Power Rule ■ *Substitution* ■
Extended Application: Propensity to Consume

The General Power Rule

In Section 5.1, you used the Simple Power Rule

$$\int x^n \, dx = \frac{x^{n+1}}{n+1} + C, \qquad n \neq -1$$

to find antiderivatives of functions expressed as powers of x alone. In this section, you will study a technique for finding antiderivatives of more complicated functions.

To begin, consider how you might find the antiderivative of $2x(x^2 + 1)^3$. Because you are hunting for a function whose derivative is $2x(x^2 + 1)^3$, you might discover the following.

$$\frac{d}{dx}[(x^2 + 1)^4] = 4(x^2 + 1)^3(2x) \qquad \textit{Use Chain Rule.}$$

$$\frac{d}{dx}\left[\frac{(x^2 + 1)^4}{4}\right] = (x^2 + 1)^3(2x) \qquad \textit{Divide both sides by 4.}$$

$$\frac{(x^2 + 1)^4}{4} + C = \int 2x(x^2 + 1)^3 \, dx \qquad \textit{Write in integral form.}$$

The key to this solution is the presence of the factor $2x$ in the integrand. In other words, this solution works because $2x$ is precisely the derivative of $(x^2 + 1)$. Letting $u = x^2 + 1$, you can write

$$\int \underbrace{2x}\overbrace{(x^2 + 1)^3} \, dx = \int u^3 \frac{du}{dx} \, dx = \frac{u^4}{4} + C.$$

This is an example of the **General Power Rule** for integration.

General Power Rule for Integration

If u is a differentiable function of x, then

$$\int u^n \frac{du}{dx} \, dx = \frac{u^{n+1}}{n+1} + C, \qquad n \neq -1.$$

When using the General Power Rule, you must first identify a factor u of the integrand that is raised to a power. Then, you must show that its derivative du/dx is also a factor of the integrand. This is demonstrated in Example 1.

EXAMPLE 1 *Applying the General Power Rule*

Find the following indefinite integrals.

a. $\displaystyle\int 3(3x-1)^4\,dx$ **b.** $\displaystyle\int (2x+1)(x^2+x)\,dx$

c. $\displaystyle\int 3x^2\sqrt{x^3-2}\,dx$ **d.** $\displaystyle\int \frac{-4x}{(1-2x^2)^2}\,dx$

Solution

a. $\displaystyle\int 3(3x-1)^4\,dx = \int \overbrace{(3x-1)^4}^{u^n}\overbrace{(3)}^{\frac{du}{dx}}\,dx$ *Let $u = 3x - 1$.*

$\displaystyle\qquad\qquad\qquad = \frac{(3x-1)^5}{5} + C$ *General Power Rule*

Note Example 1b illustrates a case of the General Power Rule that is sometimes overlooked— when the power is $n = 1$. In this case, the rule takes the form

$$\int u\frac{du}{dx}\,dx = \frac{u^2}{2} + C.$$

b. $\displaystyle\int (2x+1)(x^2+x)\,dx = \int \overbrace{(x^2+x)}^{u^n}\overbrace{(2x+1)}^{\frac{du}{dx}}\,dx$ *Let $u = x^2 + x$.*

$\displaystyle\qquad\qquad\qquad\qquad = \frac{(x^2+x)^2}{2} + C$ *General Power Rule*

c. $\displaystyle\int 3x^2\sqrt{x^3-2}\,dx = \int \overbrace{(x^3-2)^{1/2}}^{u^n}\overbrace{(3x^2)}^{\frac{du}{dx}}\,dx$ *Let $u = x^3 - 2$.*

$\displaystyle\qquad\qquad\qquad = \frac{(x^3-2)^{3/2}}{3/2} + C$ *General Power Rule*

$\displaystyle\qquad\qquad\qquad = \frac{2}{3}(x^3-2)^{3/2} + C$ *Simplify.*

d. $\displaystyle\int \frac{-4x}{(1-2x^2)^2}\,dx = \int \overbrace{(1-2x^2)^{-2}}^{u^n}\overbrace{(-4x)}^{\frac{du}{dx}}\,dx$ *Let $u = 1 - 2x^2$.*

$\displaystyle\qquad\qquad\qquad = \frac{(1-2x^2)^{-1}}{-1} + C$ *General Power Rule*

$\displaystyle\qquad\qquad\qquad = -\frac{1}{1-2x^2} + C$ *Simplify.*

Peace

Many times, part of the derivative du/dx is missing from the integrand, and in *some* cases you can make the necessary adjustments to apply the General Power Rule.

EXAMPLE 2 *Multiplying and Dividing by a Constant*

Find the indefinite integral $\displaystyle\int x(3 - 4x^2)^2 \, dx$.

Solution

Let $u = 3 - 4x^2$. To apply the General Power Rule, you need to create $du/dx = -8x$ as a factor of the integrand. You can accomplish this by multiplying and dividing by the constant -8.

$$\int x(3 - 4x^2)^2 \, dx = \int \left(-\frac{1}{8}\right) \overbrace{(3 - 4x^2)^2}^{u^n}\overbrace{(-8x)}^{\frac{du}{dx}} \, dx \qquad \text{Multiply and divide by } -8.$$

$$= -\frac{1}{8}\int (3 - 4x^2)^2(-8x) \, dx \qquad \text{Factor } -\tfrac{1}{8} \text{ out of integrand.}$$

$$= \left(-\frac{1}{8}\right)\frac{(3 - 4x^2)^3}{3} + C \qquad \text{General Power Rule}$$

$$= -\frac{(3 - 4x^2)^3}{24} + C \qquad \text{Simplify.}$$

Note   Try using the Chain Rule to check the result of Example 2. After differentiating $-\frac{1}{24}(3 - 4x^2)^3$ and simplifying, you should obtain the original integrand.

EXAMPLE 3 *A Failure of the General Power Rule*

Find the indefinite integral $\displaystyle\int -8(3 - 4x^2)^2 \, dx$.

Solution

Let $u = 3 - 4x^2$. As in Example 2, to apply the General Power Rule you must create $du/dx = -8x$ as a factor of the integrand. In Example 2, you could do this by multiplying and dividing by a constant, and then factoring that constant out of the integrand. This strategy doesn't work with variables. That is,

$$\int -8(3 - 4x^2)^2 \, dx \neq \frac{1}{x}\int (3 - 4x^2)^2(-8x) \, dx.$$

To find this indefinite integral, you can expand the integrand and use the Simple Power Rule.

$$\int -8(3 - 4x^2)^2 \, dx = \int (-72 + 192x^2 - 128x^4) \, dx$$

$$= -72x + 64x^3 - \frac{128}{5}x^5 + C$$

Note   In Example 3, be sure you see that you cannot factor variable quantities outside the integral sign. After all, if this were permissible, then you could move the entire integrand outside the integral sign and eliminate the need for all integration rules except the rule $\int dx = x + C$.

When an integrand contains an extra constant factor that is not needed as part of u', you can simply move the factor outside the integral sign, as illustrated in the next example.

EXAMPLE 4 *Applying the General Power Rule*

Find the indefinite integral $\int 7x^2 \sqrt{x^3 + 1}\, dx$.

Solution

Let $u = x^3 + 1$. Then you need to create $u' = 3x^2$ by multiplying and dividing by 3. The constant factor $\frac{7}{3}$ is not needed as part of u', and can be moved outside the integral sign.

$$\int 7x^2 \sqrt{x^3 + 1}\, dx = \int 7x^2 (x^3 + 1)^{1/2}\, dx \qquad \text{\textit{Write with rational exponents.}}$$

$$= \int \frac{7}{3}(x^3 + 1)^{1/2}(3x^2)\, dx \qquad \text{\textit{Multiply and divide by 3.}}$$

$$= \frac{7}{3} \int (x^3 + 1)^{1/2}(3x^2)\, dx \qquad \text{\textit{Factor } \frac{7}{3} \text{ outside integral.}}$$

$$= \frac{7}{3} \frac{(x^3 + 1)^{3/2}}{3/2} + C \qquad \text{\textit{General Power Rule}}$$

$$= \frac{14}{9}(x^3 + 1)^{3/2} \qquad \text{\textit{Simplify.}}$$

1: $\sqrt{(x^3 + 1)}$ *Author.*

2: $\int \sqrt{(x^3 + 1)}\ dx$ *Integrate.*

3: $\dfrac{3\int \dfrac{1}{\sqrt{(x^3 + 1)}}\ dx}{5} + \dfrac{2x\sqrt{(x^3 + 1)}}{5}$ *Simplify.*

1: $\sqrt{(x^2 + 1)}$ *Author.*

2: $\int \sqrt{(x^2 + 1)}\ dx$ *Integrate.*

3: $\dfrac{\text{LN}(\sqrt{(x^2 + 1)} + x)}{2} + \dfrac{x\sqrt{(x^2 + 1)}}{2}$ *Simplify.*

Substitution

The integration technique used in Examples 1, 2, and 4 depends on your ability to recognize or create an integrand of the form $u^n u'$. With more complicated integrands, it is difficult to recognize the steps needed to fit the integrand to a basic integration formula. When this occurs, an alternative procedure called **substitution** or **change of variables** can be helpful. With this procedure, you completely rewrite the integral in terms of u and du. That is, if $u = f(x)$, then $du = f'(x)\,dx$, and the General Power Rule takes the form

$$\int u^n \frac{du}{dx}\,dx = \int u^n\,du.$$ *General Power Rule*

EXAMPLE 5 *Integrating by Substitution*

Find the indefinite integral $\displaystyle\int \sqrt{1 - 3x}\,dx$.

Solution
Begin by letting $u = 1 - 3x$. Then, $u' = -3$ and $du = -3\,dx$. This implies that $dx = -\frac{1}{3}\,du$, and you can find the indefinite integral as follows.

$$\int \sqrt{1 - 3x}\,dx = \int (1 - 3x)^{1/2}\,dx \qquad \text{\textit{Write with rational exponent.}}$$

$$= \int u^{1/2}\left(-\frac{1}{3}\,du\right) \qquad \text{\textit{Substitute } u \text{ and } du.}$$

$$= -\frac{1}{3}\int u^{1/2}\,du \qquad \text{\textit{Factor} } -\tfrac{1}{3} \text{ \textit{out of integrand.}}$$

$$= -\frac{1}{3}\frac{u^{3/2}}{3/2} + C \qquad \text{\textit{Apply Power Rule.}}$$

$$= -\frac{2}{9}u^{3/2} + C \qquad \text{\textit{Simplify.}}$$

$$= -\frac{2}{9}(1 - 3x)^{3/2} + C \qquad \text{\textit{Substitute } 1 - 3x \text{ for } u.}$$

To become efficient at integration, you should learn to use *both* techniques discussed in this section. For simpler integrals, you should use pattern recognition and create du/dx by multiplying and dividing by an appropriate constant. For more complicated integrals, you should use a formal change of variables, as illustrated in Example 5. (You will learn more about this technique in Chapter 6.) For the integrals in this section's exercise set, try working several of the problems twice—once with pattern recognition and once using formal substitution.

Extended Application: Propensity to Consume

In 1990, the U. S. poverty level for a family of four was about $13,400. Families at or below the poverty level tend to consume 100% of their income—that is, they use all their income to purchase necessities such as food, clothing, and shelter. As income level increases, the average consumption tends to drop below 100%. For instance, a family earning $15,000 may be able to save $318 and thus consume only $14,682 (97.9%) of their income. As the income increases, the ratio of consumption to savings tends to decrease. The rate of change of consumption with respect to income is called the **marginal propensity to consume.** *(Source: U.S. Bureau of Census)*

EXAMPLE 6 *Analyzing Consumption*

Real Life

For a family of four in 1990, the marginal propensity to consume income x can be modeled by

$$\frac{dQ}{dx} = \frac{0.97}{(x - 13,399)^{0.03}}, \qquad x \geq 13,400,$$

where Q represents the income consumed. Use the model to estimate the amount consumed by a family of four whose 1990 income was $26,000.

Solution

Begin by integrating dQ/dx to find a model for the consumption Q. Use the initial condition that $Q = 13,400$ when $x = 13,400$.

$$\frac{dQ}{dx} = \frac{0.97}{(x - 13,399)^{0.03}} \qquad \textit{Marginal propensity to consume}$$

$$Q = \int \frac{0.97}{(x - 13,399)^{0.03}}\, dx \qquad \textit{Integrate to obtain Q.}$$

$$= \int 0.97(x - 13,399)^{-0.03}\, dx \quad \textit{Rewrite.}$$

$$= (x - 13,399)^{0.97} + C \qquad \textit{General Power Rule}$$

$$= (x - 13,399)^{0.97} + 13,399 \qquad \textit{Use initial condition to find C.}$$

Using this model, you can estimate that a family of four with an income of $x = 26,000$ consumed about $22,892. The graph of Q is shown in Figure 5.4.

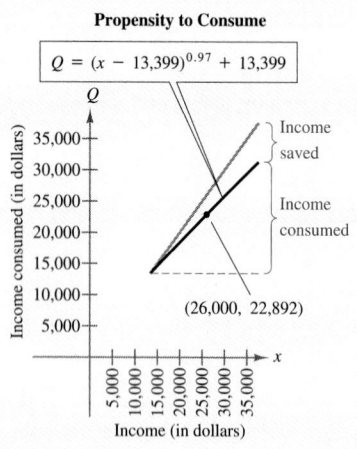

Propensity to Consume

$Q = (x - 13,399)^{0.97} + 13,399$

Income saved

Income consumed

(26,000, 22,892)

Income consumed (in dollars): 5,000 / 10,000 / 15,000 / 20,000 / 25,000 / 30,000 / 35,000

Income (in dollars): 5,000 / 10,000 / 15,000 / 20,000 / 25,000 / 30,000 / 35,000

FIGURE 5.4

Discussion Problem   Extending the Example

According to the model in Example 6, at what income level would a family of four consume $30,000?

Warm Up

The following warm-up exercises involve skills that were covered in earlier sections. You will use these skills in the exercise set for this section.

In Exercises 1–6, find the indefinite integral.

1. $\displaystyle\int (2x^3 + 1)\,dx$ **2.** $\displaystyle\int (x^{1/2} + 3x - 4)\,dx$

3. $\displaystyle\int \frac{1}{x^2}\,dx$ **4.** $\displaystyle\int \frac{1}{3t^3}\,dt$

5. $\displaystyle\int (1 + 2t)t^{3/2}\,dt$ **6.** $\displaystyle\int \sqrt{x}(2x - 1)\,dx$

In Exercises 7–10, simplify the expression.

7. $\displaystyle\left(-\frac{5}{4}\right)\frac{(x-2)^4}{4}$ **8.** $\displaystyle\left(\frac{1}{6}\right)\frac{(x-1)^{-2}}{-2}$

9. $\displaystyle (6)\frac{(x^2+3)^{2/3}}{2/3}$ **10.** $\displaystyle\left(\frac{5}{2}\right)\frac{(1-x^3)^{-1/2}}{-1/2}$

EXERCISES 5.2

means that technology can help you solve or check the exercise(s).

In Exercises 1–6, identify u and du/dx for the integral $\int u^n (du/dx)\,dx$.

1. $\displaystyle\int (5x^2 + 1)^2(10x)\,dx$ **2.** $\displaystyle\int (3 - 4x^2)^3(-8x)\,dx$

3. $\displaystyle\int \sqrt{1 - x^2}(-2x)\,dx$ **4.** $\displaystyle\int 3x^2\sqrt{x^3 + 1}\,dx$

5. $\displaystyle\int \left(4 + \frac{1}{x^2}\right)\left(\frac{-2}{x^3}\right)\,dx$ **6.** $\displaystyle\int \frac{1}{(1 + 2x)^2}(2)\,dx$

In Exercises 7–32, find the indefinite integral and check the result by differentiation.

7. $\displaystyle\int (1 + 2x)^4(2)\,dx$ **8.** $\displaystyle\int (x^2 - 1)^3(2x)\,dx$

9. $\displaystyle\int \sqrt{5x^2 - 4}(10x)\,dx$ **10.** $\displaystyle\int \sqrt{3 - x^3}(3x^2)\,dx$

11. $\displaystyle\int (x - 1)^4\,dx$ **12.** $\displaystyle\int (x - 3)^{5/2}\,dx$

13. $\displaystyle\int x(x^2 - 1)^7\,dx$ **14.** $\displaystyle\int x(1 - 2x^2)^3\,dx$

15. $\displaystyle\int \frac{x^2}{(1 + x^3)^2}\,dx$ **16.** $\displaystyle\int \frac{x^2}{(x^3 - 1)^2}\,dx$

17. $\displaystyle\int \frac{x + 1}{(x^2 + 2x - 3)^2}\,dx$ **18.** $\displaystyle\int \frac{6x}{(1 + x^2)^3}\,dx$

19. $\displaystyle\int \frac{x - 2}{\sqrt{x^2 - 4x + 3}}\,dx$ **20.** $\displaystyle\int \frac{4x + 6}{(x^2 + 3x + 7)^3}\,dx$

21. $\displaystyle\int 5x\sqrt[3]{1 - x^2}\,dx$ **22.** $\displaystyle\int u^3\sqrt{u^4 + 2}\,du$

23. $\displaystyle\int \frac{4x}{\sqrt{1 + x^2}}\,dx$ **24.** $\displaystyle\int \frac{x^2}{\sqrt{1 - x^3}}\,dx$

25. $\displaystyle\int \frac{-3}{\sqrt{2x + 3}}\,dx$ **26.** $\displaystyle\int \frac{t + 2t^2}{\sqrt{t}}\,dt$

27. $\displaystyle\int \frac{x^3}{\sqrt{1 - x^4}}\,dx$ **28.** $\displaystyle\int \left(1 + \frac{1}{t}\right)^3\left(\frac{1}{t^2}\right)\,dt$

Help **29.** $\displaystyle\int \frac{1}{\sqrt{2x}}\,dx$ **30.** $\displaystyle\int \frac{1}{3x^2}\,dx$

31. $\displaystyle\int (x^3 + 3x)(x^2 + 1)\,dx$

32. $\displaystyle\int (3 - 2x - 4x^2)(1 + 4x)\,dx$

In Exercises 33–40, use formal substitution (as illustrated in Example 5) to find the indefinite integral.

33. $\int x(6x^2 - 1)^3 \, dx$

34. $\int x^2(1 - x^3)^2 \, dx$

35. $\int x^2(2 - 3x^3)^{3/2} \, dx$

36. $\int t\sqrt{t^2 + 1} \, dt$

37. $\int \dfrac{x}{\sqrt{x^2 + 25}} \, dx$

38. $\int \dfrac{3}{\sqrt{2x + 1}} \, dx$

39. $\int \dfrac{x^2 + 1}{\sqrt{x^3 + 3x + 4}} \, dx$

40. $\int \sqrt{x}(4 - x^{3/2})^2 \, dx$

In Exercises 41–44, perform the integration in two ways: once using the Simple Power Rule and once using the General Power Rule. Explain the difference in the results.

41. $\int (2x - 1)^2 \, dx$

42. $\int (3 - 2x)^2 \, dx$

43. $\int x(x^2 - 1)^2 \, dx$

44. $\int x(2x^2 + 1)^2 \, dx$

45. Find the equation of the function f whose graph passes through the point $(0, \frac{4}{3})$ and whose derivative is

$$f'(x) = x\sqrt{1 - x^2}.$$

46. Find the equation of the function f whose graph passes through the point $(0, \frac{7}{3})$ and whose derivative is

$$f'(x) = x\sqrt{1 - x^2}.$$

47. *Cost* The marginal cost of a product is modeled by

$$\frac{dC}{dx} = \frac{4}{\sqrt{x + 1}}.$$

When $x = 15$, $C = 50$.

(a) Find the cost function.

(b) Graph dC/dx and C on the same set of axes.

48. *Cost* The marginal cost of a product is modeled by

$$\frac{dC}{dx} = \frac{12}{\sqrt[3]{12x + 1}}.$$

When $x = 13$, $C = 100$.

(a) Find the cost function.

(b) Graph dC/dx and C on the same set of axes.

Supply Function In Exercises 49 and 50, find the supply function $x = f(p)$ that satisfies the given conditions.

49. $\dfrac{dx}{dp} = p\sqrt{p^2 - 25}$, $\quad x = 600$ when $p = \$13$

50. $\dfrac{dx}{dp} = \dfrac{10}{\sqrt{p - 3}}$, $\quad x = 100$ when $p = \$3$

Demand Function In Exercises 51 and 52, find the demand function $x = f(p)$ that satisfies the given conditions.

51. $\dfrac{dx}{dp} = -\dfrac{6000p}{(p^2 - 16)^{3/2}}$, $\quad x = 5000$ when $p = \$5$

52. $\dfrac{dx}{dp} = -\dfrac{400}{(0.02p - 1)^3}$, $\quad x = 10,000$ when $p = \$100$

53. *Depreciation* The rate of depreciation dV/dt of a machine is inversely proportional to the square of $t + 1$, where V is the value of the machine t years after it is purchased. The initial value of the machine is \$500,000. By the end of the first year, the value of the machine decreases \$100,000. Estimate its value after 4 years.

54. *Cash Flow* The rate of disbursement dQ/dt of a \$2 million federal grant is proportional to the square of $100 - t$, where t is the time (in days, $0 \le t \le 100$) and Q is the amount that remains to be disbursed. Find the amount that remains to be disbursed after 50 days. Assume that the entire grant will be disbursed after 100 days.

In Exercises 55 and 56, (a) use the marginal propensity to consume, dQ/dx, to write Q as a function of x, where x is the income and Q is the income consumed. Assume that 100% of the income is consumed for families that have an annual income of \$20,000 or less. (b) Use the result of part (a) to complete the table showing the income consumed and the income saved, $x - Q$, for various incomes. (c) Graphically represent the income consumed and saved.

x	20,000	50,000	100,000	150,000
Q				
$x - Q$				

55. $\dfrac{dQ}{dx} = \dfrac{0.95}{(x - 19,999)^{0.05}}$, $\quad 20,000 \le x$

56. $\dfrac{dQ}{dx} = \dfrac{0.93}{(x - 19,999)^{0.07}}$, $\quad 20,000 \le x$

In Exercises 57 and 58, use a symbolic integration utility to find the indefinite integral. Verify the result by differentiating.

57. $\int \dfrac{1}{\sqrt{x} + \sqrt{x + 1}} \, dx$

58. $\int \dfrac{x}{\sqrt{3x + 2}} \, dx$

Exponential and Logarithmic Integrals

Using the Exponential Rule ■ *Using the Log Rule*

Using the Exponential Rule

Each of the differentiation rules for exponential functions has its corresponding integration rule.

Integrals of Exponential Functions

Let u be a differentiable function of x.

$$\int e^x \, dx = e^x + C \qquad \text{\textit{Simple Exponential Rule}}$$

$$\int e^u \frac{du}{dx} \, dx = \int e^u \, du = e^u + C \qquad \text{\textit{General Exponential Rule}}$$

EXAMPLE 1 *Integrating Exponential Functions*

a. $\displaystyle\int 2e^x \, dx = 2 \int e^x \, dx$ *Constant Multiple Rule*

$\qquad\qquad = 2e^x + C$ *Simple Exponential Rule*

b. $\displaystyle\int 2e^{2x} \, dx = \int e^{2x}(2) \, dx$ *Let $u = 2x$, then $u' = 2$.*

$\qquad\qquad = \int e^u u' \, dx$

$\qquad\qquad = e^{2x} + C$ *General Exponential Rule*

c. $\displaystyle\int (e^x + x) \, dx = \int e^x \, dx + \int x \, dx$ *Sum Rule*

$\qquad\qquad\qquad = e^x + \dfrac{x^2}{2} + C$ *Simple Exponential and Power Rules*

You can check each of these results by differentiating. ▬

EXAMPLE 2 *Integrating an Exponential Function*

Find the indefinite integral $\displaystyle\int e^{3x+1}\, dx$.

Solution

Let $u = 3x + 1$, then $du/dx = 3$. You can introduce the missing factor of 3 in the integrand by multiplying and dividing by 3.

$$\int e^{3x+1}\, dx = \frac{1}{3}\int e^{3x+1}(3)\, dx \qquad \text{\textit{Multiply and divide by 3.}}$$

$$= \frac{1}{3}\int e^{u}\frac{du}{dx}\, dx \qquad \text{\textit{Substitute u and du/dx.}}$$

$$= \frac{1}{3}e^{u} + C \qquad \text{\textit{General Exponential Rule}}$$

$$= \frac{1}{3}e^{3x+1} + C \qquad \text{\textit{Substitute for u.}}$$

EXAMPLE 3 *Integrating an Exponential Function*

Find the indefinite integral $\displaystyle\int 5xe^{-x^2}\, dx$.

Solution

Let $u = -x^2$, then $du/dx = -2x$. You can create the factor of $(-2x)$ in the integrand by multiplying and dividing by -2.

$$\int 5xe^{-x^2}\, dx = \int \left(-\frac{5}{2}\right)e^{-x^2}(-2x)\, dx \qquad \text{\textit{Multiply and divide by }} -2.$$

$$= -\frac{5}{2}\int e^{-x^2}(-2x)\, dx \qquad \begin{array}{l}\textit{Factor the constant } -\frac{5}{2}\\ \textit{out of the integrand.}\end{array}$$

$$= -\frac{5}{2}\int e^{u}\frac{du}{dx}\, dx \qquad \text{\textit{Substitute u and du/dx.}}$$

$$= -\frac{5}{2}e^{u} + C \qquad \text{\textit{General Exponential Rule}}$$

$$= -\frac{5}{2}e^{-x^2} + C \qquad \text{\textit{Substitute for u.}}$$

Note Remember that you cannot introduce a missing *variable* in the integrand. For instance, you cannot find $\int e^{x^2}\, dx$ by multiplying and dividing by $2x$ and then factoring $1/(2x)$ out of the integral. That is,

$$\int e^{x^2}\, dx \neq \frac{1}{2x}\int e^{x^2}(2x)\, dx.$$

▦ **TECHNOLOGY**

If you use a symbolic integration utility to find antiderivatives of exponential or logarithmic functions, you can easily obtain results that are beyond the scope of this course. For instance, the following antiderivative of e^{x^2} involves the imaginary unit i and the probability function called "ERF." In this course, you are not expected to interpret or use such results. You can simply state that the function cannot be integrated using elementary functions.

1: `EXP (x²)`

2: $\displaystyle\int$ `EXP (x²) dx`

3: $-\dfrac{\hat{i}\sqrt{\pi}\ \text{ERF }(\hat{i}x)}{2}$

Using the Log Rule

When the Power Rules for integration were introduced in Sections 5.1 and 5.2, you saw that they work for powers other than $n = -1$.

$$\int x^n \, dx = \frac{x^{n+1}}{n+1} + C, \qquad n \neq -1 \qquad \textit{Simple Power Rule}$$

$$\int u^n \frac{du}{dx} \, dx = \frac{u^{n+1}}{n+1} + C, \qquad n \neq -1 \qquad \textit{General Power Rule}$$

The Log Rules for integration allow you to integrate functions of the form $\int x^{-1} \, dx$ and $\int u^{-1} \, du$.

Note Notice the absolute values in the Log Rules. For those special cases in which u or x cannot be negative, you can omit the absolute value. For instance, in Example 4b, it is not necessary to write the antiderivative as $\ln|x^2| + C$ because x^2 cannot be negative.

Integrals of Logarithmic Functions

Let u be a differentiable function of x.

$$\int \frac{1}{x} \, dx = \ln|x| + C \qquad \textit{Simple Logarithmic Rule}$$

$$\int \frac{u'}{u} \, dx = \int \frac{1}{u} \, du = \ln|u| + C \qquad \textit{General Logarithmic Rule}$$

You can verify each of these rules by differentiating. For instance, to verify that $d/dx[\ln|x|] = 1/x$, notice that

$$\frac{d}{dx}[\ln x] = \frac{1}{x} \quad \text{and} \quad \frac{d}{dx}[\ln(-x)] = \frac{-1}{-x} = \frac{1}{x}.$$

EXAMPLE 4 *Integrating Logarithmic Functions*

a. $\displaystyle \int \frac{4}{x} \, dx = 4 \int \frac{1}{x} \, dx$ *Constant Multiple Rule*

$\displaystyle \qquad\qquad = 4 \ln|x| + C$ *Simple Logarithmic Rule*

b. $\displaystyle \int \frac{2x}{x^2} \, dx = \int \frac{u'}{u} \, dx$ *Let $u = x^2$, then $u' = 2x$.*

$\displaystyle \qquad\qquad = \ln|u| + C$ *General Logarithmic Rule*

$\displaystyle \qquad\qquad = \ln x^2 + C$ *Substitute for u.*

c. $\displaystyle \int \frac{3}{3x+1} \, dx = \int \frac{u'}{u} \, dx$ *Let $u = 3x + 1$, then $u' = 3$.*

$\displaystyle \qquad\qquad = \ln|u| + C$ *General Logarithmic Rule*

$\displaystyle \qquad\qquad = \ln|3x+1| + C$ *Substitute for u.*

EXAMPLE 5 *Using the Log Rule*

Find the indefinite integral $\displaystyle \int \frac{1}{2x-1}\,dx$.

Solution

Let $u = 2x - 1$, then $du/dx = 2$. You can create the necessary factor of 2 in the integrand by multiplying and dividing by 2.

$$
\begin{aligned}
\int \frac{1}{2x-1}\,dx &= \frac{1}{2}\int \frac{2}{2x-1}\,dx && \textit{Multiply and divide by 2.} \\
&= \frac{1}{2}\int \frac{u'}{u}\,dx && \textit{Substitute } u \textit{ and } u'. \\
&= \frac{1}{2}\ln|u| + C && \textit{General Log Rule} \\
&= \frac{1}{2}\ln|2x-1| + C && \textit{Substitute for } u.
\end{aligned}
$$

EXAMPLE 6 *Using the Log Rule*

Find the indefinite integral $\displaystyle \int \frac{6x}{x^2+1}\,dx$.

Solution

Let $u = x^2 + 1$, then $du/dx = 2x$. You can create the necessary factor of $2x$ in the integrand by factoring a 3 out of the integrand.

$$
\begin{aligned}
\int \frac{6x}{x^2+1}\,dx &= 3\int \frac{2x}{x^2+1}\,dx && \textit{Factor 3 out of integrand.} \\
&= 3\int \frac{u'}{u}\,dx && \textit{Substitute } u \textit{ and } u'. \\
&= 3\ln|u| + C && \textit{General Log Rule} \\
&= 3\ln(x^2+1) + C && \textit{Substitute for } u.
\end{aligned}
$$

Integrals to which the Log Rule can be applied are often given in disguised form. For instance, if a rational function has a numerator of degree greater than or equal to that of the denominator, you should use long division to rewrite the integrand. Here is an example.

$$
\begin{aligned}
\int \frac{x^2 + 6x + 1}{x^2+1}\,dx &= \int \left(1 + \frac{6x}{x^2+1}\right)dx \\
&= x + 3\ln(x^2+1) + C.
\end{aligned}
$$

The next example summarizes some additional situations in which it is helpful to rewrite the integrand in order to recognize the antiderivative.

EXAMPLE 7 *Rewriting Before Integrating*

Find the following indefinite integrals.

a. $\displaystyle\int \frac{3x^2 + 2x - 1}{x^2}\,dx$ **b.** $\displaystyle\int \frac{1}{1 + e^{-x}}\,dx$ **c.** $\displaystyle\int \frac{x^2 + x + 1}{x - 1}\,dx$

Solution

a. Begin by rewriting the integrand as the sum of three fractions.

$$\int \frac{3x^2 + 2x - 1}{x^2}\,dx = \int \left(\frac{3x^2}{x^2} + \frac{2x}{x^2} - \frac{1}{x^2} \right) dx$$

$$= \int \left(3 + \frac{2}{x} - \frac{1}{x^2} \right) dx$$

$$= 3x + 2\ln|x| + \frac{1}{x} + C$$

b. Begin by rewriting the integrand by multiplying and dividing by e^x.

$$\int \frac{1}{1 + e^{-x}}\,dx = \int \left(\frac{e^x}{e^x} \right) \frac{1}{1 + e^{-x}}\,dx$$

$$= \int \frac{e^x}{e^x + 1}\,dx$$

$$= \ln(e^x + 1) + C$$

c. Begin by dividing the numerator by the denominator.

$$\int \frac{x^2 + x + 1}{x - 1}\,dx = \int \left(x + 2 + \frac{3}{x - 1} \right) dx$$

$$= \frac{x^2}{2} + 2x + 3\ln|x - 1| + C$$

Discussion Problem   **Using the General Log Rule**

One of the most common applications of the Log Rule is to find indefinite integrals of the form

$$\int \frac{a}{bx + c}\,dx.$$

Describe a quick way to find this indefinite integral. Then apply your technique to the following.

a. $\displaystyle\int \frac{1}{2x - 5}\,dx$ **b.** $\displaystyle\int \frac{4}{3x + 2}\,dx$ **c.** $\displaystyle\int \frac{7}{8x - 3}\,dx$

Warm Up

The following warm-up exercises involve skills that were covered in earlier sections. You will use these skills in the exercise set for this section.

In Exercises 1 and 2, find the domain of the function.

1. $y = \ln(2x - 5)$

2. $y = \ln(x^2 - 5x + 6)$

In Exercises 3–6, use long division to rewrite the quotient.

3. $\dfrac{x^2 + 4x + 2}{x + 2}$

4. $\dfrac{x^2 - 6x + 9}{x - 4}$

5. $\dfrac{x^3 + 4x^2 - 30x - 4}{x^2 - 4x}$

6. $\dfrac{x^4 - x^3 + x^2 + 15x + 2}{x^2 + 5}$

In Exercises 7–10, evaluate the integral.

7. $\displaystyle \int \left(x^3 + \dfrac{1}{x^2} \right) dx$

8. $\displaystyle \int \dfrac{x^2 + 2x}{x} \, dx$

9. $\displaystyle \int \dfrac{x^3 + 4}{x^2} \, dx$

10. $\displaystyle \int \dfrac{x + 3}{x^3} \, dx$

E X E R C I S E S   5.3   means that technology can help you solve or check the exercise(s).

In Exercises 1–16, use the Exponential Rule to find the indefinite integral.

1. $\displaystyle \int 2e^{2x} \, dx$

2. $\displaystyle \int -3e^{-3x} \, dx$

3. $\displaystyle \int e^{4x} \, dx$

4. $\displaystyle \int e^{-0.25x} \, dx$

5. $\displaystyle \int 9xe^{-x^2} \, dx$

6. $\displaystyle \int 3xe^{0.5x^2} \, dx$

7. $\displaystyle \int 5x^2 e^{x^3} \, dx$

8. $\displaystyle \int (2x + 1)e^{x^2 + x} \, dx$

9. $\displaystyle \int (x^2 + 2x)e^{x^3 + 3x^2 - 1} \, dx$

10. $\displaystyle \int 3(x - 4)e^{x^2 - 8x} \, dx$

11. $\displaystyle \int 5e^{2-x} \, dx$

12. $\displaystyle \int 3e^{-(x+1)/2} \, dx$

13. $\displaystyle \int \dfrac{1}{x^2} e^{2/x} \, dx$

14. $\displaystyle \int \dfrac{1}{x^3} e^{1/4x^2} \, dx$

15. $\displaystyle \int \dfrac{1}{\sqrt{x}} e^{\sqrt{x}} \, dx$

16. $\displaystyle \int (e^x - e^{-x})^2 \, dx$

In Exercises 17–32, use the Log Rule to find the indefinite integral.

17. $\displaystyle \int \dfrac{1}{x + 1} \, dx$

18. $\displaystyle \int \dfrac{1}{x - 5} \, dx$

19. $\displaystyle \int \dfrac{1}{3 - 2x} \, dx$

20. $\displaystyle \int \dfrac{1}{6x - 5} \, dx$

21. $\displaystyle \int \dfrac{x}{x^2 + 1} \, dx$

22. $\displaystyle \int \dfrac{x^2}{3 - x^3} \, dx$

23. $\displaystyle \int \dfrac{x^2}{x^3 + 1} \, dx$

24. $\displaystyle \int \dfrac{x}{x^2 + 4} \, dx$

25. $\displaystyle \int \dfrac{x + 3}{x^2 + 6x + 7} \, dx$

26. $\displaystyle \int \dfrac{x^2 + 2x + 3}{x^3 + 3x^2 + 9x + 1} \, dx$

27. $\displaystyle \int \dfrac{1}{x \ln x} \, dx$

28. $\displaystyle \int \dfrac{e^x}{1 + e^x} \, dx$

29. $\displaystyle \int \dfrac{e^{-x}}{1 + e^{-x}} \, dx$

30. $\displaystyle \int \dfrac{3e^x}{2 + e^x} \, dx$

31. $\displaystyle \int \dfrac{4e^{2x}}{5 - e^{2x}} \, dx$

32. $\displaystyle \int \dfrac{-e^{3x}}{2 - e^{3x}} \, dx$

In Exercises 33–50, use any basic integration formula or formulas to find the indefinite integral.

33. $\int \dfrac{e^{2x} + 2e^x + 1}{e^x} \, dx$

34. $\int (6x + e^x)\sqrt{3x^2 + e^x} \, dx$

35. $\int e^x \sqrt{1 - e^x} \, dx$

36. $\int \dfrac{2(e^x - e^{-x})}{(e^x + e^{-x})^2} \, dx$

37. $\int \dfrac{1}{(x - 1)^2} \, dx$

38. $\int \dfrac{1}{\sqrt{x + 1}} \, dx$

39. $\int \dfrac{x^2 - 4}{x} \, dx$

40. $\int \dfrac{x + 5}{x} \, dx$

41. $\int \dfrac{x^3 - 8x}{2x^2} \, dx$

42. $\int \dfrac{x - 1}{4x} \, dx$

43. $\int \dfrac{2}{1 + e^{-x}} \, dx$

44. $\int \dfrac{3}{1 + e^{-3x}} \, dx$

45. $\int \dfrac{x^2 + 2x + 5}{x - 1} \, dx$

46. $\int \dfrac{x - 3}{x + 3} \, dx$

47. $\int \dfrac{x^3 + 4x^2 + 3x}{x^2 - x} \, dx$

48. $\int \dfrac{x^4 - x^3 + x^2 + 2}{x + 5} \, dx$

49. $\int \dfrac{1 + e^{-x}}{1 + xe^{-x}} \, dx$

50. $\int \dfrac{5}{e^{-5x} + 7} \, dx$

51. Bacteria Growth A population of bacteria is growing at the rate of

$$\frac{dP}{dt} = \frac{3000}{1 + 0.25t},$$

where t is the time in days. When $t = 0$, the population is 1000.

(a) Write an equation that models the population P in terms of the time t.

(b) What is the population after 3 days?

(c) After how many days will the population be 12,000?

52. Population Decline Because of an insufficient oxygen supply, the trout population in a lake is dying. The population's rate of change can be modeled by

$$\frac{dP}{dt} = -125e^{-t/20},$$

where t is the time in days. When $t = 0$, the population is 2500.

(a) Write an equation that models the population P in terms of the time t.

(b) What is the population after 15 days?

(c) According to this model, how long will it take for the entire trout population to die?

53. Demand The marginal price for the demand of a product can be modeled by

$$\frac{dp}{dx} = 0.1e^{-x/500},$$

where x is the quantity demanded. When the demand is 600 units, the price is $30.

(a) Find the demand function, $p = f(x)$.

(b) Use a graphing utility to graph the demand function. Does the price increase or decrease as the demand increases?

(c) Use the zoom and trace features of the graphing utility to find the quantity demanded when the price is $22.

54. Revenue The marginal revenue for the sale of a product can be modeled by

$$\frac{dR}{dx} = 50 - 0.02x + \frac{100}{x + 1},$$

where x is the quantity demanded.

(a) Find the revenue function.

(b) Use a graphing utility to graph the revenue function.

(c) Find the revenue when 1500 units are sold.

(d) Use the zoom and trace features of the graphing utility to find the number of units sold when the revenue is $60,230.

55. ATM Transactions From 1986 through 1992, the number of automatic teller machine (ATM) transactions T (in millions) in the United States changed at the rate of

$$\frac{dT}{dt} = 23.23t^{3/2} - 7.89t^2 + 44.71e^{-t},$$

where $t = 0$ corresponds to 1986. In 1992, there were 600 million transactions. (Source: Bank Network News)

(a) Write a model that gives the total number of ATM transactions per year.

(b) Use the model to find the number of ATM transactions in 1987.

56. Revenue The rate of change in revenue for Lotus Development Corporation from 1983 through 1993 can be modeled by

$$\frac{dR}{dt} = \frac{2358.96}{t} - \frac{12{,}756.78}{t^2} + 15{,}456.42e^{-t},$$

where R is the revenue (in millions) and $t = 3$ corresponds to 1983. In 1989, the revenue for Lotus was $556 million. (Source: Lotus Development Corporation.)

(a) Find a model for Lotus's revenue from 1983 through 1993.

(b) Find Lotus's revenue in 1991.

5.4 Area and the Fundamental Theorem of Calculus

Area and Definite Integrals ■ *The Fundamental Theorem of Calculus* ■
Marginal Analysis ■ *Average Value* ■ *Even and Odd Functions*

Area and Definite Integrals

From your study of geometry, you know that area is a number that suggests the size of a bounded region. For simple regions, such as rectangles, triangles, and circles, area can be found using a geometric formula.

In this section, you will learn how to use calculus to find the area of nonstandard regions, such as the region R shown in Figure 5.5.

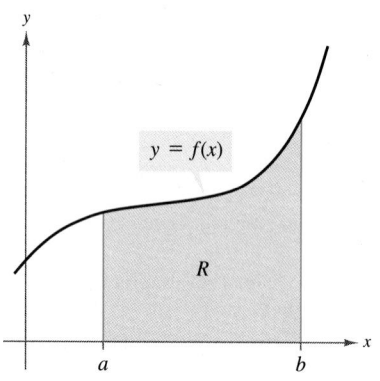

FIGURE 5.5 $\int_a^b f(x)\,dx = \text{Area}$

Definition of a Definite Integral

Let f be nonnegative and continuous on the closed interval $[a, b]$. The area of the region bounded by the graph of f, the x-axis, and the lines $x = a$ and $x = b$ is denoted by

$$\text{Area} = \int_a^b f(x)\,dx.$$

The expression $\int_a^b f(x)\,dx$ is called the **definite integral** from a to b, where a is the **lower limit of integration** and b is the **upper limit of integration.**

EXAMPLE 1 *Evaluating a Definite Integral*

Evaluate the definite integral $\int_0^2 2x\,dx$.

Solution
This definite integral represents the area of the region bounded by the graph of $f(x) = 2x$, the x-axis, and the line $x = 2$, as shown in Figure 5.6. The region is triangular, with a height of four units and a base of two units.

$$\int_0^2 2x\,dx = \frac{1}{2}(\text{base})(\text{height}) \qquad \textit{Formula for area of triangle}$$

$$= \frac{1}{2}(2)(4)$$

$$= 4 \qquad \textit{Simplify.}$$

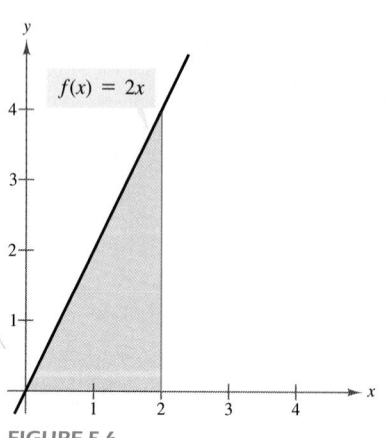

FIGURE 5.6

The Fundamental Theorem of Calculus

Consider the function $A(x)$, which denotes the area of the region shown in Figure 5.7. To discover the relationship between $A(x)$ and $f(x)$, let x increase by an amount Δx. This increases the area by ΔA. Let $f(m)$ and $f(M)$ denote the minimum and maximum values of f on the interval $[x, x + \Delta x]$.

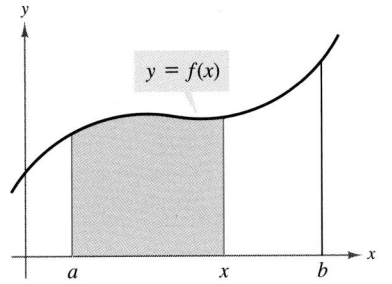

FIGURE 5.7 $A(x) = $ Area from a to x

  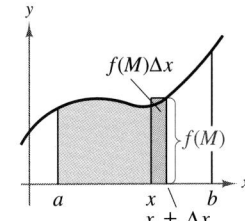

FIGURE 5.8

As indicated in Figure 5.8, you can write the following inequality.

$$f(m)\,\Delta x \le \quad \Delta A \quad \le f(M)\,\Delta x \qquad \text{See Figure 5.8.}$$

$$f(m) \le \quad \frac{\Delta A}{\Delta x} \quad \le f(M) \qquad \text{Divide each term by } \Delta x.$$

$$\lim_{\Delta x \to 0} f(m) \le \lim_{\Delta x \to 0} \frac{\Delta A}{\Delta x} \le \lim_{\Delta x \to 0} f(M) \qquad \text{Take limit of each term.}$$

$$f(x) \le \quad A'(x) \quad \le f(x) \qquad \text{Definition of derivative of } A(x)$$

Thus, $f(x) = A'(x)$, and $A(x) = F(x) + C$, where $F'(x) = f(x)$. Because $A(a) = 0$, it follows that $C = -F(a)$. Thus, $A(x) = F(x) - F(a)$, which implies that

$$A(b) = \int_a^b f(x)\,dx = F(b) - F(a).$$

This equation tells you that *if you can find an antiderivative for* f, then you can use the antiderivative to evaluate the definite integral $\int_a^b f(x)\,dx$. This result is called the **Fundamental Theorem of Calculus.**

The Fundamental Theorem of Calculus

If f is nonnegative and continuous on the closed interval $[a, b]$, then

$$\int_a^b f(x)\,dx = F(b) - F(a),$$

where F is any function such that $F'(x) = f(x)$ for all x in $[a, b]$.

Three comments about the Fundamental Theorem of Calculus are in order.

1. The Fundamental Theorem of Calculus describes a way of *evaluating* a definite integral, not a procedure for finding antiderivatives.
2. In applying the Fundamental Theorem, it is helpful to use the notation

$$\int_a^b f(x)\,dx = F(x)\Big]_a^b = F(b) - F(a).$$

3. The constant of integration C can be dropped because

$$\int_a^b f(x)\,dx = \Big[F(x) + C\Big]_a^b$$
$$= [F(b) + C] - [F(a) + C]$$
$$= F(b) - F(a) + C - C$$
$$= F(b) - F(a).$$

In the development of the Fundamental Theorem of Calculus, f was assumed to be nonnegative on the closed interval $[a, b]$. As such, the definite integral was defined as an area. Now, with the Fundamental Theorem, the definition can be extended to include functions that are negative on all or part of the closed interval $[a, b]$. Specifically, if f is *any* function that is continuous on a closed interval $[a, b]$, then the **definite integral** of $f(x)$ from a to b is defined to be

$$\int_a^b f(x)\,dx = F(b) - F(a),$$

where F is an antiderivative of f. Remember that definite integrals do not necessarily represent areas and can be negative, zero, or positive.

Note Be sure you see the distinction between indefinite and definite integrals. The *indefinite integral*

$$\int f(x)\,dx$$

denotes a family of *functions*, each of which is an antiderivative of f, whereas the *definite integral*

$$\int_a^b f(x)\,dx$$

is a *number*.

Properties of Definite Integrals

Let f and g be continuous on the closed interval $[a, b]$.

1. $\int_a^b kf(x)\,dx = k\int_a^b f(x)\,dx,\quad k$ is a constant.

2. $\int_a^b [f(x) \pm g(x)]\,dx = \int_a^b f(x)\,dx \pm \int_a^b g(x)\,dx$

3. $\int_a^b f(x)\,dx = \int_a^c f(x)\,dx + \int_c^b f(x)\,dx,\quad a < c < b$

4. $\int_a^a f(x)\,dx = 0$

5. $\int_a^b f(x)\,dx = -\int_b^a f(x)\,dx$

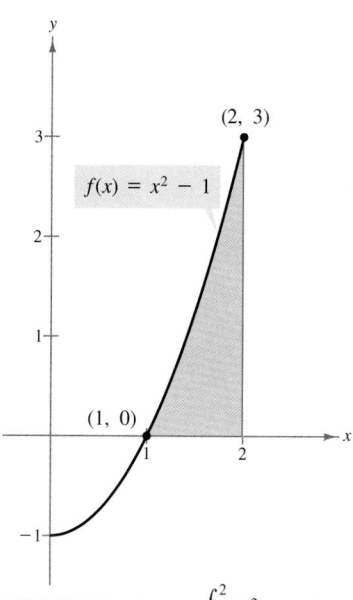

FIGURE 5.9   Area $= \int_{1}^{2} (x^2 - 1)\,dx$

EXAMPLE 2 *Finding Area by the Fundamental Theorem*

Find the area of the region bounded by the x-axis and the graph of

$$f(x) = x^2 - 1, \qquad 1 \le x \le 2.$$

Solution

Note that $f(x) \ge 0$ on the interval $1 \le x \le 2$, as shown in Figure 5.9. There-fore, you can represent the area of the region by a definite integral. To find the area, use the Fundamental Theorem of Calculus.

$$\text{Area} = \int_{1}^{2} (x^2 - 1)\,dx \qquad \textit{Definition of definite integral}$$

$$= \left[\frac{x^3}{3} - x\right]_{1}^{2} \qquad \textit{Find antiderivative.}$$

$$= \left(\frac{(2)^3}{3} - 2\right) - \left(\frac{(1)^3}{3} - 1\right) \qquad \textit{Apply Fundamental Theorem.}$$

$$= \frac{4}{3} \qquad \textit{Simplify.}$$

Thus, the area of the region is $\frac{4}{3}$ square units.

Note   It is easy to make errors in signs when evaluating definite integrals. To avoid such errors, enclose the values of the antiderivative at the upper and lower limits of integration in separate sets of parentheses, as shown above.

EXAMPLE 3 *Evaluating a Definite Integral*

Evaluate the definite integral

$$\int_{0}^{1} (4t + 1)^2\,dt,$$

and sketch the region whose area is represented by the integral.

Solution

$$\int_{0}^{1} (4t + 1)^2\,dt = \frac{1}{4}\int_{0}^{1} (4t + 1)^2 (4)\,dt \qquad \textit{Multiply and divide by 4.}$$

$$= \frac{1}{4}\left[\frac{(4t + 1)^3}{3}\right]_{0}^{1} \qquad \textit{Find antiderivative.}$$

$$= \frac{1}{4}\left[\left(\frac{5^3}{3}\right) - \left(\frac{1}{3}\right)\right] \qquad \textit{Apply Fundamental Theorem.}$$

$$= \frac{31}{3}. \qquad \textit{Simplify.}$$

The region is shown in Figure 5.10.

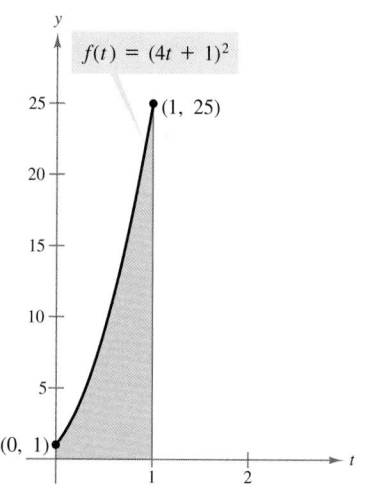

FIGURE 5.10

EXAMPLE 4 *Evaluating Definite Integrals*

a. $\displaystyle \int_0^3 e^{2x}\, dx = \frac{1}{2} e^{2x} \Big]_0^3 = \frac{1}{2}(e^6 - e^0) \approx 201.21$

b. $\displaystyle \int_1^2 \frac{1}{x}\, dx = \ln x \Big]_1^2 = \ln 2 - \ln 1 = \ln 2 \approx 0.69$

c. $\displaystyle \int_1^4 -3\sqrt{x}\, dx = -3 \int_1^4 x^{1/2}\, dx$ *Write with rational exponent.*

$$= -3 \left[\frac{x^{3/2}}{3/2} \right]_1^4 \qquad \textit{Find antiderivative.}$$

$$= -2x^{3/2} \Big]_1^4$$

$$= -2(4^{3/2} - 1^{3/2}) \qquad \textit{Apply Fundamental Theorem.}$$

$$= -2(8 - 1)$$

$$= -14 \qquad\qquad \textit{Simplify.}$$

Note In Example 4c, note that the value of a definite integral can be negative.

EXAMPLE 5 *Interpreting Absolute Value*

Evaluate the definite integral $\displaystyle \int_0^2 |2x - 1|\, dx$.

Solution

The region represented by the definite integral is shown in Figure 5.11. From the definition of absolute value, you can write

$$|2x - 1| = \begin{cases} -(2x - 1), & x < \frac{1}{2} \\ 2x - 1, & x \geq \frac{1}{2}. \end{cases}$$

Using Property 3 of definite integrals, you can rewrite the integral as two definite integrals.

$$\int_0^2 |2x - 1|\, dx = \int_0^{1/2} -(2x - 1)\, dx + \int_{1/2}^2 (2x - 1)\, dx$$

$$= \left[-x^2 + x \right]_0^{1/2} + \left[x^2 - x \right]_{1/2}^2$$

$$= \left(-\frac{1}{4} + \frac{1}{2} \right) - (0 + 0) + (4 - 2) - \left(\frac{1}{4} - \frac{1}{2} \right)$$

$$= \frac{5}{2}$$

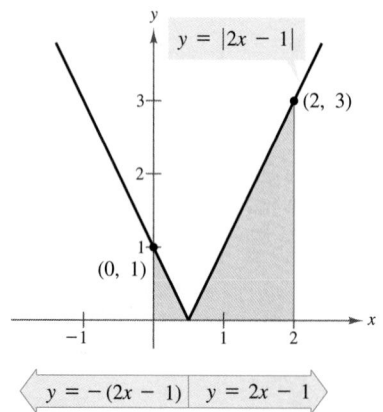

$y = -(2x - 1) \quad y = 2x - 1$

FIGURE 5.11

Marginal Analysis

You have already studied *marginal analysis* in the context of derivatives and differentials (Sections 2.3 and 3.8). There, you were given a cost, revenue, or profit function, and you used the derivative to approximate the additional cost, revenue, or profit obtained by selling one additional unit. In this section, you will examine the reverse process. That is, you will be given the marginal cost, marginal revenue, or marginal profit and will be asked to use a definite integral to find the exact increase or decrease in cost, revenue, or profit obtained by selling one or several additional units.

For instance, suppose you wanted to find the additional revenue obtained by increasing sales from x_1 to x_2 units. If you knew the revenue function $R(x)$, you could simply subtract $R(x_1)$ from $R(x_2)$. If you didn't know the revenue function, but did know the marginal revenue function, you could still find the additional revenue by using a definite integral, as follows.

$$\int_{x_1}^{x_2} \frac{dR}{dx}\, dx = R(x_2) - R(x_1)$$

Real
Life

EXAMPLE 6 *Analyzing a Profit Function*

The marginal profit for a product is modeled by

$$\frac{dP}{dx} = -0.0005x + 12.2.$$

a. Find the change in profit when sales increase from 100 to 101 units.
b. Find the change in profit when sales increase from 100 to 110 units.

Solution
a. The change in profit obtained by increasing sales from 100 to 101 units is

$$\int_{100}^{101} \frac{dP}{dx}\, dx = \int_{100}^{101} (-0.0005x + 12.2)\, dx$$

$$= \left[-0.00025x^2 + 12.2x \right]_{100}^{101}$$

$$\approx \$12.15.$$

b. The change in profit obtained by increasing sales from 100 to 110 units is

$$\int_{100}^{110} \frac{dP}{dx}\, dx = \int_{100}^{110} (-0.0005x + 12.2)\, dx$$

$$= \left[-0.00025x^2 + 12.2x \right]_{100}^{110}$$

$$\approx \$121.48.$$

■ TECHNOLOGY

Symbolic integration programs, such as *Derive*, *Maple*, and *Mathematica*, can be used to evaluate definite integrals as well as indefinite integrals. If you have access to such a program, try using it to evaluate several of the definite integrals in this section.

Average Value

The *average value* of a function on a closed interval is defined as follows.

Definition of the Average Value of a Function

If f is continuous on $[a, b]$, then the **average value** of f on $[a, b]$ is

$$\text{Average value of } f \text{ on } [a, b] = \frac{1}{b-a}\int_a^b f(x)\,dx.$$

Real Life

EXAMPLE 7 *Finding the Average Cost*

The cost per unit c of producing a product over a 2-year period is modeled by

$$c = 0.005t^2 + 0.01t + 13.15, \qquad 0 \le t \le 24,$$

where t is the time in months. Approximate the average cost per unit over the 2-year period.

Solution

The average cost can be found by integrating c over the interval $[0, 24]$.

$$\text{Average cost per unit} = \frac{1}{24}\int_0^{24} (0.005t^2 + 0.01t + 13.15)\,dt$$

$$= \frac{1}{24}\left[\frac{0.005t^3}{3} + \frac{0.01t^2}{2} + 13.15t\right]_0^{24}$$

$$= \frac{1}{24}(341.52)$$

$$= \$14.23$$

To check the reasonableness of the average value found in Example 7, assume that one unit is produced each month, beginning with $t = 0$ and ending with $t = 24$. When $t = 0$, the cost is

$$c = 0.005(0)^2 + 0.01(0) + 13.15 = \$13.15.$$

Similarly, when $t = 1$, the cost is

$$c = 0.005(1)^2 + 0.01(1) + 13.15 \approx \$13.17.$$

Each month, the cost increases, and the average of the 25 costs is

$$\frac{13.15 + 13.17 + 13.19 + 13.23 + \cdots + 16.27}{25} \approx \$14.25.$$

Even and Odd Functions

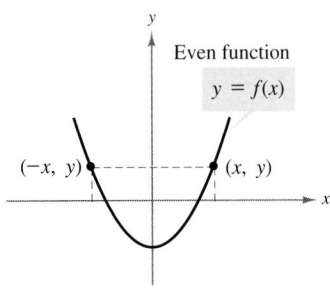

Even function
$y = f(x)$

$(-x, y)$ (x, y)

(a) y-Axis symmetry

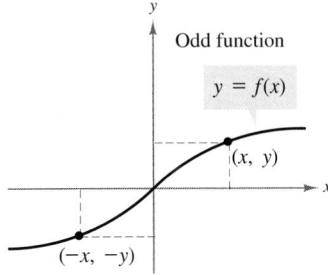

Odd function
$y = f(x)$

(x, y)

$(-x, -y)$

(b) Origin symmetry

FIGURE 5.12

Several common functions have graphs that are symmetric to the y-axis or the origin, as shown in Figure 5.12. If the graph of f is symmetric to the y-axis, as in Figure 5.12(a), then

$$f(-x) = f(x), \qquad \text{\textit{Even function}}$$

and f is called an **even** function. If the graph of f is symmetric to the origin, as in Figure 5.12(b), then

$$f(-x) = -f(x), \qquad \text{\textit{Odd function}}$$

and f is called an **odd** function.

Integration of Even and Odd Functions

1. If f is an *even* function, then $\displaystyle\int_{-a}^{a} f(x)\,dx = 2\int_{0}^{a} f(x)\,dx.$

2. If f is an *odd* function, then $\displaystyle\int_{-a}^{a} f(x)\,dx = 0.$

EXAMPLE 8 *Integrating Even and Odd Functions*

a. Because $f(x) = x^2$ is even,

$$\int_{-2}^{2} x^2\,dx = 2\int_{0}^{2} x^2\,dx = 2\left[\frac{x^3}{3}\right]_{0}^{2} = 2\left(\frac{8}{3} - 0\right) = \frac{16}{3}.$$

b. Because $f(x) = x^3$ is odd,

$$\int_{-2}^{2} x^3\,dx = 0.$$

Discussion Problem   Using Geometry to Evaluate Definite Integrals

When using the Fundamental Theorem of Calculus to evaluate $\int_{a}^{b} f(x)\,dx$, remember that you must first be able to find an antiderivative of $f(x)$. If you are unable to find an antiderivative, you cannot use the Fundamental Theorem. In some cases, you can still evaluate the definite integral. For instance, explain how you can use geometry to evaluate

$$\int_{-2}^{2} \sqrt{4 - x^2}\,dx.$$

Warm Up

The following warm-up exercises involve skills that were covered in earlier sections. You will use these skills in the exercise set for this section.

In Exercises 1–4, find the indefinite integral.

1. $\displaystyle\int (3x+7)\,dx$

2. $\displaystyle\int (x^{3/2} + 2\sqrt{x})\,dx$

3. $\displaystyle\int \frac{1}{5x}\,dx$

4. $\displaystyle\int e^{-6x}\,dx$

In Exercises 5 and 6, evaluate the expression when $a = 5$ and $b = 3$.

5. $\left(\dfrac{a}{5} - a\right) - \left(\dfrac{b}{5} - b\right)$

6. $\left(6a - \dfrac{a^3}{3}\right) - \left(6b - \dfrac{b^3}{3}\right)$

In Exercises 7–10, integrate the marginal function.

7. $\dfrac{dC}{dx} = 0.02x^{3/2} + 29{,}500$

8. $\dfrac{dR}{dx} = 9000 + 2x$

9. $\dfrac{dP}{dx} = 25{,}000 - 0.01x$

10. $\dfrac{dC}{dx} = 0.03x^2 + 4600$

E X E R C I S E S   5.4   means that technology can help you solve or check the exercise(s).

In Exercises 1–4, sketch the region whose area is represented by the definite integral. Then use a geometric formula to evaluate the integral.

1. $\displaystyle\int_{0}^{2} 3\,dx$

2. $\displaystyle\int_{0}^{3} 2x\,dx$

3. $\displaystyle\int_{0}^{5} (x+1)\,dx$

4. $\displaystyle\int_{-3}^{3} \sqrt{9-x^2}\,dx$

In Exercises 5–10, find the area of the region.

5. $y = x - x^2$

6. $y = \dfrac{1}{x^2}$

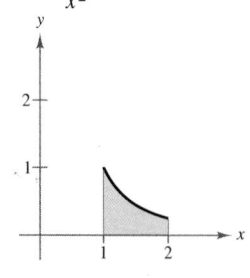

7. $y = 1 - x^4$

8. $y = 3e^{-x/2}$

9. $y = \sqrt[3]{2x}$

10. $y = \dfrac{x^2 + 4}{x}$

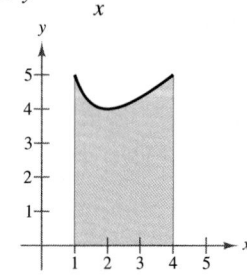

In Exercises 11–38, evaluate the definite integral.

11. $\int_0^1 2x \, dx$

12. $\int_2^7 3 \, dv$

13. $\int_{-1}^0 (2x + 1) \, dx$

14. $\int_2^5 (-3x + 4) \, dx$

15. $\int_{-1}^1 (2t - 1)^2 \, dt$

16. $\int_0^3 (3x^2 + x - 2) \, dx$

17. $\int_0^1 (2t - 1)^2 \, dt$

18. $\int_2^2 (x - 3)^4 \, dx$

19. $\int_{-1}^1 (\sqrt[3]{t} - 2) \, dt$

20. $\int_1^4 \sqrt{\dfrac{2}{x}} \, dx$

21. $\int_1^4 \dfrac{2u - 1}{\sqrt{u}} \, du$

22. $\int_0^1 \dfrac{x - \sqrt{x}}{3} \, dx$

23. $\int_{-1}^0 (t^{1/3} - t^{2/3}) \, dt$

24. $\int_0^4 (x^{1/2} + x^{1/4}) \, dx$

25. $\int_0^4 \dfrac{1}{\sqrt{2x + 1}} \, dx$

26. $\int_0^2 \dfrac{x}{\sqrt{1 + 2x^2}} \, dx$

27. $\int_0^1 e^{-2x} \, dx$

28. $\int_1^2 e^{1-x} \, dx$

29. $\int_1^3 \dfrac{e^{3/x}}{x^2} \, dx$

30. $\int_{-1}^1 (e^x - e^{-x}) \, dx$

31. $\int_{-1}^1 |4x| \, dx$

32. $\int_0^3 |2x - 3| \, dx$

33. $\int_0^4 (2 - |x - 2|) \, dx$

34. $\int_{-4}^4 (4 - |x|) \, dx$

35. $\int_{-1}^2 \dfrac{x}{x^2 - 9} \, dx$

36. $\int_2^3 \dfrac{x + 1}{x^2 + 2x - 3} \, dx$

37. $\int_0^3 \dfrac{2e^x}{2 + e^x} \, dx$

38. $\int_1^2 \dfrac{(2 + \ln x)^3}{x} \, dx$

In Exercises 39–44, evaluate the definite integral. Then sketch the region whose area is represented by the integral.

39. $\int_1^3 (4x - 3) \, dx$

40. $\int_0^2 (x + 4) \, dx$

41. $\int_0^1 (x - x^3) \, dx$

42. $\int_0^1 \sqrt{x}(1 - x) \, dx$

43. $\int_2^4 \dfrac{3x^2}{x^3 - 1} \, dx$

44. $\int_0^{\ln 6} \dfrac{e^x}{2} \, dx$

45. Find the area of the region bounded by the graphs of $y = 3x^2 + 1$, $y = 0$, $x = 0$, and $x = 2$.

46. Find the area of the region bounded by the graphs of $y = 1 + \sqrt{x}$, $y = 0$, $x = 0$, and $x = 4$.

47. Find the area of the region bounded by the graphs of $y = (x + 5)/x$, $y = 0$, $x = 1$, and $x = 5$.

48. Find the area of the region bounded by the graphs of $y = 3e^x$, $y = 0$, $x = -2$, and $x = 1$.

In Exercises 49 and 50, use the values $\int_0^5 f(x) \, dx = 8$ and $\int_0^5 g(x) \, dx = 3$ to evaluate the definite integral.

49. (a) $\int_0^5 [f(x) + g(x)] \, dx$ (b) $\int_0^5 [f(x) - g(x)] \, dx$

(c) $\int_0^5 -4f(x) \, dx$ (d) $\int_0^5 [f(x) - 3g(x)] \, dx$

50. (a) $\int_0^5 2g(x) \, dx$ (b) $\int_5^0 f(x) \, dx$

(c) $\int_5^5 f(x) \, dx$ (d) $\int_0^5 [f(x) - f(x)] \, dx$

In Exercises 51–56, sketch the graph of the function over the interval. Find the average value of the function over the interval. Then find all x-values in the interval for which the function is equal to its average value.

Function	Interval
51. $f(x) = 6 - x^2$	$[-2, 2]$
52. $f(x) = 5e^{0.2(x-10)}$	$[0, 10]$
53. $f(x) = x\sqrt{4 - x^2}$	$[0, 2]$
54. $f(x) = \dfrac{5x}{x^2 + 1}$	$[0, 7]$
55. $f(x) = x - 2\sqrt{x}$	$[0, 4]$
56. $f(x) = \dfrac{1}{(x - 3)^2}$	$[0, 2]$

In Exercises 57–60, state whether the function is even, odd, or neither.

57. $f(x) = 3x^4$

58. $g(x) = x^3 - 2x$

59. $g(t) = 2t^5 - 3t^2$

60. $f(t) = 5t^4 + 1$

61. Use the value $\int_0^2 x^2 \, dx = \frac{8}{3}$ to evaluate the definite integral. Explain your reasoning.

(a) $\int_{-2}^0 x^2 \, dx$ (b) $\int_{-2}^2 x^2 \, dx$ (c) $\int_0^2 -x^2 \, dx$

62. Use the value $\int_0^2 x^3 \, dx = 4$ to evaluate the definite integral. Explain your reasoning.

(a) $\int_{-2}^0 x^3 \, dx$ (b) $\int_{-2}^2 x^3 \, dx$ (c) $\int_0^2 3x^3 \, dx$

Marginal Analysis In Exercises 63–68, find the change in cost C, revenue R, or profit P, for the given marginal. In each case, assume the number of units x increases by 3 from the specified value of x.

Marginal	Number of Units, x
63. $\dfrac{dC}{dx} = 2.25$	$x = 100$
64. $\dfrac{dC}{dx} = \dfrac{20{,}000}{x^2}$	$x = 10$
65. $\dfrac{dR}{dx} = 48 - 3x$	$x = 12$
66. $\dfrac{dR}{dx} = 75\left(20 + \dfrac{900}{x}\right)$	$x = 500$
67. $\dfrac{dP}{dx} = \dfrac{400 - x}{150}$	$x = 200$
68. $\dfrac{dP}{dx} = 12.5(40 - 3\sqrt{x})$	$x = 125$

Capital Accumulation In Exercises 69–72, you are given the rate of investment dI/dt. Find the capital accumulation over a 5-year period by evaluating the definite integral

$$\text{Capital accumulation} = \int_0^5 \frac{dI}{dt}\, dt,$$

where t is the time in years.

69. $\dfrac{dI}{dt} = 500$ **70.** $\dfrac{dI}{dt} = 500\sqrt{t + 1}$

71. $\dfrac{dI}{dt} = 100t$ **72.** $\dfrac{dI}{dt} = \dfrac{12{,}000t}{(t^2 + 2)^2}$

73. *Cost* The total cost of purchasing and maintaining a piece of equipment for x years can be modeled by

$$C = 5000\left(25 + 3\int_0^x t^{1/4}\, dt\right).$$

Find the total cost after (a) 1 year, (b) 5 years, and (c) 10 years.

74. *Depreciation* A company purchases a new machine for which the rate of depreciation can be modeled by

$$\frac{dV}{dt} = 10{,}000(t - 6), \qquad 0 \le t \le 5,$$

where V is the value of the machine after t years. Set up and evaluate the definite integral that yields the total loss of value of the machine over the first 3 years.

75. *Compound Interest* A deposit of $2250 is made in a savings account at an annual rate of 12%, compounded continuously. Find the average balance in the account during the first 5 years.

76. *Blood Flow* The velocity v of blood at a distance r from the center of an artery of radius R can be modeled by

$$v = k(R^2 - r^2),$$

where k is a constant. Find the average velocity along a radius of the artery. (Use 0 and R as the limits of integration.)

77. *Computer Industry* The rate of change in revenue for the computer and data processing industry in the United States from 1985 through 1990 can be modeled by

$$\frac{dR}{dt} = 6.972\sqrt{t} - 0.40t^2, \qquad 0 \le t \le 5,$$

where R is the revenue (in billions of dollars) and $t = 0$ represents 1985. In 1985, the revenue was $45.2 billion. *(Source: U.S. Bureau of Census)*

(a) Write a model for the revenue as a function of t.

(b) What was the average revenue for 1985 through 1990?

78. *Death Rate* In the United States, the annual death rate R (in deaths per 1000 people x years old) can be modeled by

$$R = 0.036x^2 - 2.8x + 58.14, \qquad 40 \le x \le 60$$

(see figure). Find the average death rate for people between (a) 40 and 50 years of age, and (b) 50 and 60 years of age.

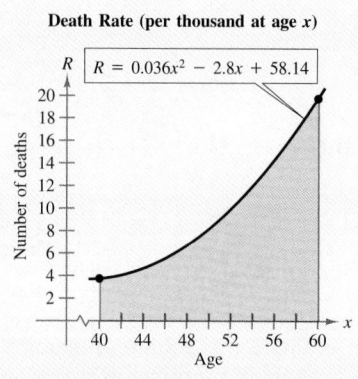

Death Rate (per thousand at age x)

$R = 0.036x^2 - 2.8x + 58.14$

In Exercises 79–82, use a symbolic integration utility to evaluate the definite integral.

79. $\displaystyle \int_3^6 \frac{x}{3\sqrt{x^2 - 8}}\, dx$ **80.** $\displaystyle \int_{1/2}^1 (x + 1)\sqrt{1 - x}\, dx$

81. $\displaystyle \int_2^5 \left(\frac{1}{x^2} - \frac{1}{x^3}\right) dx$ **82.** $\displaystyle \int_0^1 x^3(x^3 + 1)^3\, dx$

5.5 The Area of a Region Bounded by Two Graphs

Area of a Region Bounded by Two Graphs ■
Consumer and Producer Surplus ■ *Applications*

Area of a Region Bounded by Two Graphs

With a few modifications, you can extend the use of definite integrals from finding the area of a region *under a graph* to finding the area of a region *bounded by two graphs*. To see how this is done, consider the region bounded by the graphs of f, g, $x = a$, and $x = b$, as shown in Figure 5.13. If the graphs of both f and g lie above the x-axis, then you can interpret the area of the region between the graphs as the area of the region under the graph of g subtracted from the area of the region under the graph of f, as shown in Figure 5.13.

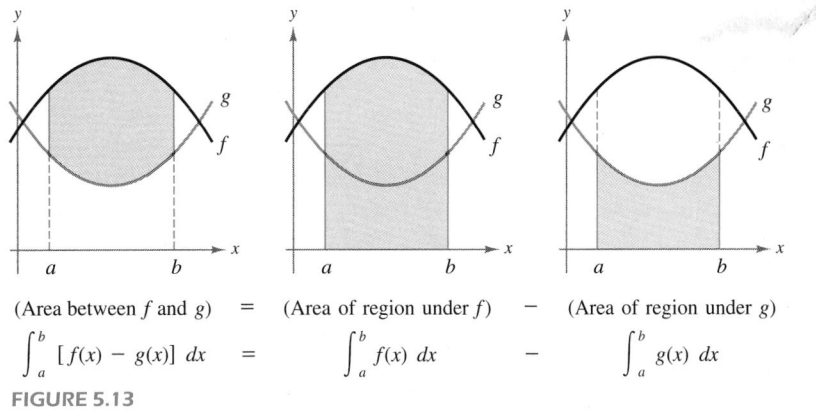

(Area between f and g)	=	(Area of region under f)	−	(Area of region under g)
$\int_a^b [f(x) - g(x)]\,dx$	=	$\int_a^b f(x)\,dx$	−	$\int_a^b g(x)\,dx$

FIGURE 5.13

Although Figure 5.13 depicts the graphs of f and g lying above the x-axis, this is not necessary, and the same integrand $[f(x) - g(x)]$ can be used as long as both functions are continuous and $g(x) \le f(x)$ on the interval $[a, b]$.

Area of a Region Bounded by Two Graphs

If f and g are continuous on $[a, b]$ and $g(x) \le f(x)$ for all x in the interval, then the area of the region bounded by the graphs of f, g, $x = a$, and $x = b$ is given by

$$A = \int_a^b [f(x) - g(x)]\,dx.$$

EXAMPLE 1 *Finding the Area Bounded by Two Graphs*

Find the area of the region bounded by the graphs of $y = x^2 + 2$ and $y = x$, for $0 \le x \le 1$.

Solution

Begin by sketching the graphs of both functions, as shown in Figure 5.14. From the figure, you can see that $x \le x^2 + 2$ for all x in $[0, 1]$. Thus, you can let $f(x) = x^2 + 2$ and $g(x) = x$. Then compute the area as follows.

$$
\begin{aligned}
\text{Area} &= \int_a^b [f(x) - g(x)]\,dx && \textit{Area between } f \textit{ and } g \\[2mm]
&= \int_0^1 [(x^2 + 2) - (x)]\,dx && \textit{Substitute for } f \textit{ and } g. \\[2mm]
&= \int_0^1 (x^2 - x + 2)\,dx && \\[2mm]
&= \left[\frac{x^3}{3} - \frac{x^2}{2} + 2x \right]_0^1 && \textit{Find antiderivative.} \\[2mm]
&= \frac{11}{6} \text{ square units} && \textit{Apply Fundamental Theorem.}
\end{aligned}
$$

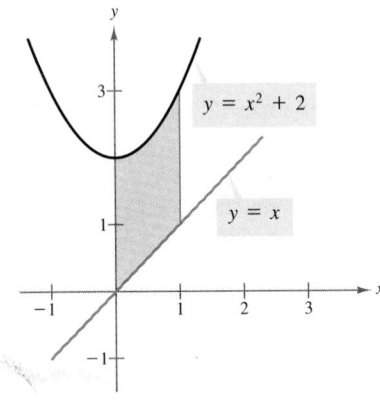

FIGURE 5.14

EXAMPLE 2 *Finding Area Between Intersecting Graphs*

Find the area of the region bounded by the graphs of $y = 2 - x^2$ and $y = x$.

Solution

In this problem, the values of a and b are not given and you must compute them by finding the points of intersection of the two graphs. To do this, equate the two functions and solve for x. When you do this, you will obtain $x = -2$ and $x = 1$. From Figure 5.15, you can see that the graph of $f(x) = 2 - x^2$ lies above the graph of $g(x) = x$ for all x in the interval $[-2, 1]$.

$$
\begin{aligned}
\text{Area} &= \int_a^b [f(x) - g(x)]\,dx && \textit{Area between } f \textit{ and } g \\[2mm]
&= \int_{-2}^1 [(2 - x^2) - (x)]\,dx && \textit{Substitute for } f \textit{ and } g. \\[2mm]
&= \int_{-2}^1 (-x^2 - x + 2)\,dx && \\[2mm]
&= \left[-\frac{x^3}{3} - \frac{x^2}{2} + 2x \right]_{-2}^1 && \textit{Find antiderivative.} \\[2mm]
&= \frac{9}{2} \text{ square units} && \textit{Apply Fundamental Theorem.}
\end{aligned}
$$

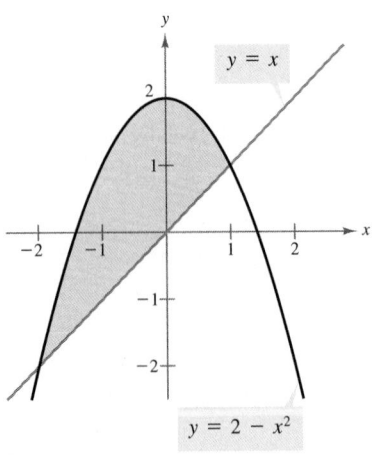

FIGURE 5.15

EXAMPLE 3 *Finding Area Below the x-Axis*

Find the area of the region bounded by the graph of $y = x^2 - 3x - 4$ and the x-axis.

Solution

Begin by finding the intercepts of the graph. To do this, set the function equal to zero and solve for x.

$$x^2 - 3x - 4 = 0 \qquad\qquad \text{\textit{Set function equal to 0.}}$$
$$(x - 4)(x + 1) = 0 \qquad\qquad \text{\textit{Factor.}}$$
$$x = 4, \ -1 \qquad\qquad \text{\textit{Solve for x.}}$$

From Figure 5.16, you can see that $x^2 - 3x - 4 \leq 0$ for all x in the interval $[-1, 4]$. Therefore, you can let $f(x) = 0$ and $g(x) = x^2 - 3x - 4$, and compute the area as follows.

$$
\begin{aligned}
\text{Area} &= \int_a^b [f(x) - g(x)]\,dx & \text{\textit{Area between f and g}} \\
&= \int_{-1}^4 [(0) - (x^2 - 3x - 4)]\,dx & \text{\textit{Substitute for f and g.}} \\
&= \int_{-1}^4 (-x^2 + 3x + 4)\,dx & \\
&= \left[-\frac{x^3}{3} + \frac{3x^2}{2} + 4x \right]_{-1}^4 & \text{\textit{Find antiderivative.}} \\
&= \frac{125}{6} & \text{\textit{Apply Fundamental Theorem.}}
\end{aligned}
$$

Therefore, the area of the region is $\frac{125}{6}$ square units.

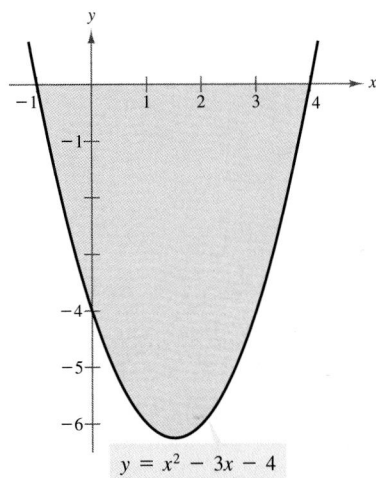

$$y = x^2 - 3x - 4$$

FIGURE 5.16

TECHNOLOGY

Most graphing utilities can display regions that are bounded by two graphs. For instance, to graph the region in Example 3 on a *TI-81* or *TI-82*, set the viewing rectangle to $-1 \leq x \leq 4$ and $-7 \leq y \leq 1$. Then enter

Shade(X² − 3X − 4, 0)

and press ENTER. You should obtain the graph shown at the right.

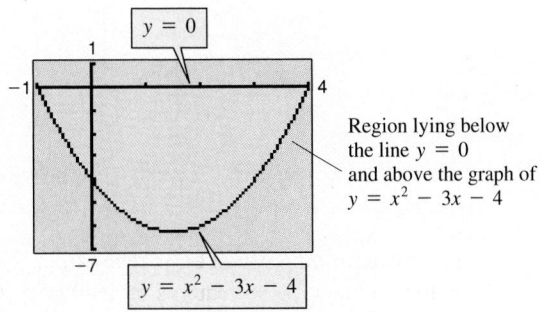

$y = 0$

Region lying below the line $y = 0$ and above the graph of $y = x^2 - 3x - 4$

$y = x^2 - 3x - 4$

Sometimes two graphs intersect at more than two points. To determine the area of the region bounded by two such graphs, you must find *all* points of intersection and check to see which graph is above the other in each interval determined by the points.

EXAMPLE 4 *Using Multiple Points of Intersection*

Find the area of the region bounded by the graphs of

$$f(x) = 3x^3 - x^2 - 10x \quad \text{and} \quad g(x) = -x^2 + 2x.$$

Solution

To find the points of intersection of the two graphs, set the functions equal to each other and solve for x.

$f(x) = g(x)$	*Set $f(x)$ equal to $g(x)$.*
$3x^3 - x^2 - 10x = -x^2 + 2x$	*Substitute for $f(x)$ and $g(x)$.*
$3x^3 - 12x = 0$	*Write in standard form.*
$3x(x^2 - 4) = 0$	
$3x(x - 2)(x + 2) = 0$	*Factor.*
$x = 0, \ 2, \ -2$	*Solve for x.*

These three points of intersection determine two intervals of integration: $[-2, 0]$ and $[0, 2]$. In Figure 5.17, you can see that $g(x) \leq f(x)$ in the interval $[-2, 0]$, and that $f(x) \leq g(x)$ in the interval $[0, 2]$. Therefore, you must use two integrals to determine the area of the region bounded by the graphs of f and g—one for the interval $[-2, 0]$ and one for the interval $[0, 2]$.

$$\text{Area} = \int_{-2}^{0} [f(x) - g(x)]\, dx + \int_{0}^{2} [g(x) - f(x)]\, dx$$

$$= \int_{-2}^{0} (3x^3 - 12x)\, dx + \int_{0}^{2} (-3x^3 + 12x)\, dx$$

$$= \left[\frac{3x^4}{4} - 6x^2 \right]_{-2}^{0} + \left[-\frac{3x^4}{4} + 6x^2 \right]_{0}^{2}$$

$$= (0 - 0) - (12 - 24) + (-12 + 24) - (0 + 0)$$

$$= 24$$

Thus, the region has an area of 24 square units. ▬

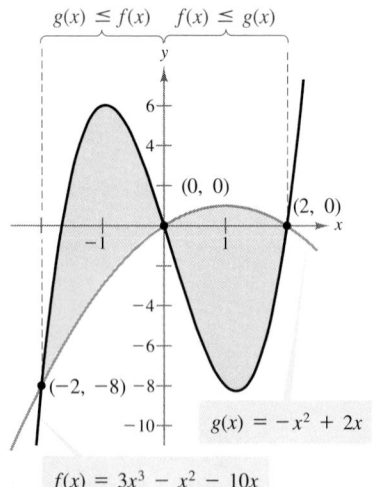

$g(x) \leq f(x) \quad f(x) \leq g(x)$

(0, 0)

(2, 0)

(−2, −8)

$g(x) = -x^2 + 2x$

$f(x) = 3x^3 - x^2 - 10x$

FIGURE 5.17

Note   It is easy to make an error when calculating areas such as that in Example 4. To give yourself some idea about the reasonableness of your solution, you could make a careful sketch of the region on graph paper and then use the grid on the graph paper to approximate the area. Try doing this with the graph shown in Figure 5.17. Is your approximation close to 24 square units?

Consumer and Producer Surplus

FIGURE 5.18

You already know that a demand function relates the price of a product to the consumer demand. A **supply function** relates the price of a product to producers' willingness to supply the product. Whereas a typical demand function is decreasing, a typical supply function is increasing. That is, as the price increases, more and more producers become willing to supply the product. The point (x_0, p_0) at which a demand function $p = D(x)$ and a supply function $p = S(x)$ intersect is called the **point of equilibrium.**

Economists call the area of the region bounded by the graph of the demand function, the horizontal line $p = p_0$, and the vertical line $x = 0$ the **consumer surplus.** Similarly, the area of the region bounded by the graph of the supply function, the horizontal line $p = p_0$, and the vertical line $x = 0$ is called the **producer surplus,** as shown in Figure 5.18.

Real Life

EXAMPLE 5 *Finding Surplus*

The demand and supply functions for a product are modeled by

$$\text{Demand: } p = -0.36x + 9 \quad \text{and} \quad \text{Supply: } p = 0.14x + 2,$$

where x is the number of units (in millions). Find the consumer and producer surplus for this product.

Solution
By equating the demand and supply functions, you can determine that the point of equilibrium occurs when $x = 14$ (million) and the price is \$3.96 per unit. The consumer surplus and producer surplus are shown in Figure 5.19.

$$\text{Consumer surplus} = \int_0^{14} (\text{demand function} - \text{price})\, dx$$
$$= \int_0^{14} [(-0.36x + 9) - 3.96]\, dx$$
$$= \left[-0.18x^2 + 5.04x \right]_0^{14}$$
$$= 35.28$$

$$\text{Producer surplus} = \int_0^{14} (\text{price} - \text{supply function})\, dx$$
$$= \int_0^{14} [3.96 - (0.14x + 2)]\, dx$$
$$= \left[-0.07x^2 + 1.96x \right]_0^{14}$$
$$= 13.72$$

FIGURE 5.19

Tony Stone Images/Martin Rogers

In 1992, the United States imported more than 9 million barrels of oil per day. This accounted for about half of the daily U.S. oil consumption.

U.S. Fuel Consumption

f: Pre-1979 consumption rate
g: Post-1979 consumption rate

FIGURE 5.20

Applications

In addition to consumer and producer surplus, there are many other types of applications involving the area of a region bounded by two graphs. Example 6 illustrates one of these applications.

Real Life

EXAMPLE 6 *Finding Fuel Consumption*

The total U. S. consumption (in billions of barrels per year) of petroleum fuel for transportation from 1950 to 1979 can be modeled by

$$f(t) = 0.000433t^2 + 0.0962t + 2.76, \qquad -20 \le t \le 9,$$

where $t = 0$ represents January 1, 1970. When crude oil prices increased dramatically in the late 1970s, fuel consumption changed and began following the model

$$g(t) = -0.00831t^2 + 0.152t + 2.81, \qquad 9 \le t \le 16,$$

as shown in Figure 5.20. Find the total amount of fuel saved from 1979 to 1986 as a result of fuel being consumed at the post-1979 rate rather than at the pre-1979 rate. *(Source: U.S. Department of Energy)*

Solution

Because the graph of the pre-1979 model f lies above the graph of the post-1979 model g on the interval [9, 16], the amount of fuel saved can be approximated by the following integral.

$$\text{Fuel saved} = \int_9^{16} [f(t) - g(t)]\, dt$$

$$= \int_9^{16} (0.008743t^2 - 0.0558t - 0.05)\, dt$$

$$= \left[\frac{0.008743t^3}{3} - \frac{0.0558t^2}{2} - 0.05t \right]_9^{16}$$

$$= 4.58 \text{ billion barrels}$$

Thus, about 4.58 billion barrels of fuel were saved. (At 42 gallons per barrel, that is a savings of almost 200 billion gallons!) ▄

Discussion Problem   **Finding Units for Area**

In Example 6, the vertical axis is measured in billions of barrels per year and the horizontal axis is measured in years. Explain why the area of the region shown in Figure 5.20 is measured in billions of barrels.

Warm Up

The following warm-up exercises involve skills that were covered in earlier sections. You will use these skills in the exercise set for this section.

In Exercises 1–4, simplify the expression.

1. $(-x^2 + 4x + 3) - (x + 1)$ **2.** $(-2x^2 + 3x + 9) - (-x + 5)$

3. $(-x^3 + 3x^2 - 1) - (x^2 - 4x + 4)$ **4.** $(3x + 1) - (-x^3 + 9x + 2)$

In Exercises 5–10, find the points of intersection of the graphs.

5. $f(x) = x^2 - 4x + 4$, $g(x) = 4$ **6.** $f(x) = -3x^2$, $g(x) = 6 - 9x$

7. $f(x) = x^2$, $g(x) = -x + 6$ **8.** $f(x) = \frac{1}{2}x^3$, $g(x) = 2x$

9. $f(x) = x^2 - 3x$, $g(x) = 3x - 5$ **10.** $f(x) = e^x$, $g(x) = e$

E X E R C I S E S   5.5   means that technology can help you solve or check the exercise(s).

In Exercises 1–8, find the area of the region.

1. $f(x) = x^2 - 6x$
$g(x) = 0$

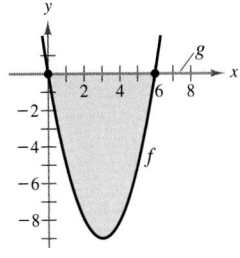

2. $f(x) = x^2 + 2x + 1$
$g(x) = 2x + 5$

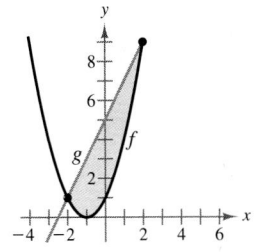

5. $f(x) = 3(x^3 - x)$
$g(x) = 0$

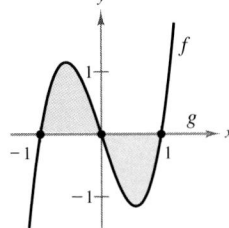

6. $f(x) = (x - 1)^3$
$g(x) = x - 1$

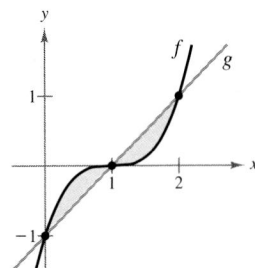

3. $f(x) = x^2 - 4x + 3$
$g(x) = -x^2 + 2x + 3$

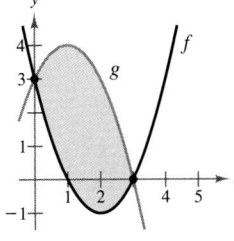

4. $f(x) = x^2$
$g(x) = x^3$

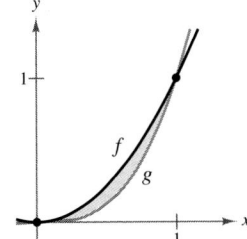

7. $f(x) = e^x - 1$
$g(x) = 0$

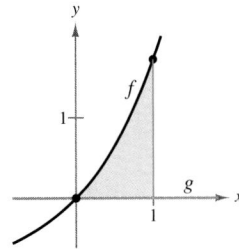

8. $f(x) = -x + 3$
$g(x) = 2x^{-1}$

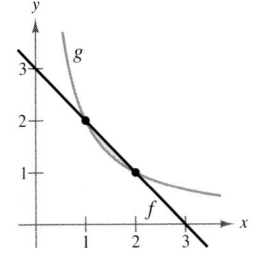

In Exercises 9 and 10, sketch the region whose area is represented by the definite integral.

9. $\int_0^4 [(x+1) - \frac{1}{2}x]\,dx$

10. $\int_{-1}^1 [(1-x^2) - (x^2-1)]\,dx$

In Exercises 11–34, sketch the region bounded by the graphs of the functions and find the area of the region.

11. $f(x) = x^2 - 4x, \; g(x) = 0$

12. $f(x) = 3 - 2x - x^2, \; g(x) = 0$

13. $f(x) = x^2 + 2x + 1, \; g(x) = x + 1$

14. $f(x) = -x^2 + 4x + 2, \; g(x) = x + 2$

15. $y = 2x, \; y = 4 - 2x, \; y = 0$

16. $y = \frac{1}{x^2}, \; y = 0, \; x = 1, \; x = 5$

17. $f(x) = x^2 - x, \; g(x) = 2(x+2)$

18. $f(x) = x(x^2 - 3x + 3), \; g(x) = x^2$

19. $y = x^3 - 2x + 1, \; y = -2x, \; x = 1$

20. $f(x) = \sqrt[3]{x}, \; g(x) = x$

21. $f(x) = \sqrt{3x} + 1, \; g(x) = x + 1$

22. $f(x) = x^2 + 5x - 6, \; g(x) = 6x - 6$

23. $y = x^2 - 4x + 3, \; y = 3 + 4x - x^2$

24. $y = x^4 - 2x^2, \; y = 2x^2$

25. $f(y) = y^2, \; g(y) = y + 2$

26. $f(y) = y(2 - y), \; g(y) = -y$

27. $x = y^2 + 2, \; x = 0, \; y = -1, \; y = 2$

28. $f(y) = \sqrt{y}, \; y = 9, \; x = 0$

29. $f(x) = e^{0.5x}, \; g(x) = -\frac{1}{x}, \; x = 1, \; x = 2$

30. $f(x) = \frac{1}{x}, \; g(x) = -e^x, \; x = \frac{1}{2}, \; x = 1$

31. $y = \frac{4}{x}, \; y = x, \; x = 1, \; x = 4$

32. $y = \frac{8}{x}, \; y = x^2, \; x = 1, \; x = 4$

33. $y = xe^{-x^2}, \; y = 0, \; x = 0, \; x = 1$

34. $y = \frac{e^{1/x}}{x^2}, \; y = 0, \; x = 1, \; x = 3$

In Exercises 35 and 36, use integration to find the area of the triangular region having the given vertices.

35. $(0,0), (4,0), (4,4)$ **36.** $(0,0), (4,0), (6,4)$

Consumer and Producer Surplus In Exercises 37–46, find the consumer and producer surplus.

	Demand Function	Supply Function
37.	$p_1(x) = 50 - 0.5x$	$p_2(x) = 0.125x$
38.	$p_1(x) = 60 - x$	$p_2(x) = 10 + \frac{7}{3}x$
39.	$p_1(x) = 300 - x$	$p_2(x) = 100 + x$
40.	$p_1(x) = -0.05x + 100$	$p_2(x) = 0.1x + 25$
41.	$p_1(x) = 200 - 0.02x^2$	$p_2(x) = 100 + x$
42.	$p_1(x) = 1000 - 0.4x^2$	$p_2(x) = 42x$
43.	$p_1(x) = -0.125x + 50$	$p_2(x) = 10 + 0.025x$
44.	$p_1(x) = 10 - 0.00001x^2$	$p_2(x) = 5 + 0.005x$
45.	$p_1(x) = \dfrac{10{,}000}{\sqrt{x + 100}}$	$p_2(x) = 100\sqrt{0.05x + 10}$
46.	$p_1(x) = \sqrt{25 - 0.1x}$	$p_2(x) = \sqrt{9 + 0.1x} - 2$

47. *Essay* Describe the characteristics of typical demand and supply functions.

48. *Essay* Suppose that the demand and supply functions for a product did not intersect. What could you conclude?

Revenue In Exercises 49 and 50, two models, R_1 and R_2, are given for revenue (in billions of dollars) for a large corporation. Both models are estimates of revenues for 1996–2000, with $t = 6$ representing 1996. Which model is projecting the greater revenue? How much more total revenue does that model project over the 4-year period?

49. $R_1 = 7.21 + 0.58t, \; R_2 = 7.21 + 0.45t$

50. $R_1 = 7.21 + 0.26t + 0.02t^2, \; R_2 = 7.21 + 0.1t + 0.01t^2$

51. *Fuel Cost* The projected fuel cost C (in millions of dollars) for an airline company from 1995 through 2005 is

$$C_1 = 568.5 + 7.15t,$$

where $t = 5$ represents 1995. If the company purchases more efficient airplane engines, fuel costs are expected to decrease and follow the model

$$C_2 = 525.6 + 6.43t.$$

How much can the company save on the more efficient engines? Explain your reasoning.

52. *Decreasing Profits* The profit (in millions of dollars) for Federal Express from 1985 through 1988 can be modeled by

$$P = 461.43 - 0.076t^3 - 1879.35t^{-1}, \qquad 5 \le t \le 8,$$

where $t = 5$ represents 1985. From 1989 through 1992, the company's profit can be modeled by

$$P = 603.45 - 59.34t + 0.122t^3 - 0.00023e^t, \ 8 < t \le 12.$$

How much more or less profit would Federal Express have made if the first model had continued to be valid from 1989 through 1992? *(Source: Federal Express)*

53. *Consumer and Producer Surplus* Factory orders for an air conditioner are about 6000 units per week when the price is \$331 and about 8000 units per week when the price is \$303. The supply function is given by $p = 0.0275x$. Find the consumer and producer surplus. (Assume the demand function is linear.)

54. *Consumer and Producer Surplus* Repeat Exercise 53 with a demand of about 6000 units per week when the price is \$325 and about 8000 units per week when the price is \$300. Find the consumer and producer surplus. (Assume the demand function is linear.)

55. *Profit* The revenue from a manufacturing process (in millions of dollars) is projected to follow the model $R = 100$ for 10 years. Over the same period of time, the cost (in millions of dollars) is projected to follow the model $C = 60 + 0.2t^2$, where t is the time (in years). Approximate the profit over the 10-year period.

56. *Profit* Repeat Exercise 55 for revenue and cost models given by $R = 100 + 0.08t$ and $C = 60 + 0.2t^2$.

57. *Lorenz Curve* Economists use *Lorenz curves* to illustrate the distribution of income in a country. Letting x represent the percent of families in a country and y represent the percent of total income, the model $y = x$ would represent a country in which each family has the same income. The Lorenz curve, $y = f(x)$, represents the actual income distribution. The area between these two models, for $0 \le x \le 100$, indicates the "income inequality" of a country. In 1990, the Lorenz curve for the United States could be modeled by

$$y = 0.344x + 0.0658x^{3/2}, \qquad 0 \le x \le 100,$$

where x is measured from the poorest to the wealthiest families. Find the income inequality for the United States in 1990. *(Source: U.S. Bureau of Census)*

58. *Income Distribution* Use the Lorenz curve given in Exercise 57 to complete the table, which lists the percent of total income earned by each quintile in the United States in 1990.

Quintile	Lowest	2nd	3rd	4th	Highest
Percent					

59. *Research Project* Use your school's library or some other reference source to research a small company similar to that described below. Describe the costs, market conditions, and competition that affect the company's success.

Business Capsule

Pacific Drifters, Inc.

In July of 1987, accountant Doug Stavoe invested \$25,000 to start Pacific Drifters, Inc. in Newport Beach, California. Pacific Drifters does sky-writing and banner-pulling for business and personal messages including birthdays, marriage proposals, and anniversaries. Between 1987 and 1993, Stavoe's sales increased by about 20% per year.

Case Study: Airline Passenger Demand

With over 2500 domestic flight legs daily, one major task faced by Delta Air Lines is deciding, in light of cost and other constraints, how to assign its fleet of over 500 aircraft along its daily routes so as to match the number of available seats to the expected number of passengers on any given flight. With the help of mathematical programming algorithms, experts at Delta have developed a solution to the fleet assignment problem that is expected to save Delta millions of dollars over the next few years.

Although the overall process of cost minimization is very complex to analyze because it has so many facets, an important element is the attempt to minimize costs due to "spill"— i.e., the number of passengers that cannot be accommodated because of insufficient aircraft capacity resulting from incorrect fleet assignments. While some of these spilled passengers may be "recaptured" on other Delta flights, those passengers who are lost to competing airlines represent opportunity costs in the form of forgone revenues for Delta. Of course, assigning too *large* an aircraft for a particular flight could create the opposite problem—losses due to empty seats and higher operating costs. An important objective is therefore to estimate the expected size of the spill for any given size of aircraft.

Making the assumption that passenger demand (x) is normally distributed (a common airline-industry assumption) with a given mean and standard deviation, spill is represented diagrammatically as the truncation of the passenger demand function at the point of an aircraft's capacity. In this case, standard deviation is a measure of the amount of variation in passenger demand. In the figure on page 361, where passenger demand is assumed to have a mean of 120 passengers and a standard deviation of 25 passengers, the probability that there will be spill for a Boeing 727 (which has a capacity of 148) is given by the shaded area under the normally distributed demand function to the right of 148 passengers. We can use calculus to determine the size of this area. Converting the given normally distributed demand function $f(x)$ into a *standard* normal function $f(z)$ with a mean of zero and a standard deviation of 1, we have:

$$P(148 < x) = P(1.12 < z) = \int_{1.12}^{\infty} \frac{1}{\sqrt{2\pi}} e^{-z^2/2}\, dz = 0.1314.$$

Thus, with the given passenger demand distribution, there is a 13 percent chance that there will be more passengers than can be accommodated by a Boeing 727. The definite integral above cannot actually be evaluated by finding an antiderivative, so the probability must be obtained using a statistical table such as the one found in Reference Table 24 of Appendix B. This probability can then be used to estimate the expected *number* of spilled passengers for a Boeing 727. If the distribution of passenger demand is known, this procedure can yield the expected spill for any given size of aircraft.

Multiplying the expected number of spilled passengers by the percent that is expected to be lost to competitors (i.e., not "recaptured" on other Delta flights) gives the estimated total number of lost spilled passengers. Finally, when the number of lost spilled passengers is multiplied by the average revenue per spilled passenger, the result is an estimate of spill cost to Delta.

Source: The Operations Research Society of America and The Institute of Management Sciences, 290 Westminster Street, Providence, RI 02903.

What Would You Do?

1. With a given passenger demand function for a particular scheduled flight, explain what happens to the expected spill as larger-sized aircraft are assigned to that flight.

2. Explain what would happen to the expected size of spill for a given size of aircraft if the *variation* in passenger demand were to increase. Describe factors that might affect the variations in passenger demand.

3. For a hypothetical aircraft, construct an estimate of spill cost. Invent and justify your own figures required to use the process given in the last paragraph. How could you improve this situation?

The Midpoint Rule

In Section 5.4, you learned that you cannot use the Fundamental Theorem of Calculus to evaluate a definite integral unless you can find an antiderivative of the integrand. In cases when this cannot be done, you can approximate the value of the integral using an approximation technique. One such technique is called the **Midpoint Rule.** (Two other techniques are discussed in Section 6.5.)

EXAMPLE 1 *Approximating the Area of a Plane Region*

Use the five rectangles in Figure 5.21 to approximate the area of the region bounded by the graph of $f(x) = -x^2 + 5$, the x-axis, and the lines $x = 0$ and $x = 2$.

Solution

You can find the heights of the five rectangles by evaluating f at the midpoint of each of the following intervals.

$$\left[0, \frac{2}{5}\right], \qquad \left[\frac{2}{5}, \frac{4}{5}\right], \qquad \left[\frac{4}{5}, \frac{6}{5}\right], \qquad \left[\frac{6}{5}, \frac{8}{5}\right], \qquad \left[\frac{8}{5}, \frac{10}{5}\right]$$

Evaluate $f(x)$ at the midpoints of these intervals.

The width of each rectangle is $\frac{2}{5}$. Hence, the sum of the five areas is

$$\text{Area} \approx \frac{2}{5} f\left(\frac{1}{5}\right) + \frac{2}{5} f\left(\frac{3}{5}\right) + \frac{2}{5} f\left(\frac{5}{5}\right) + \frac{2}{5} f\left(\frac{7}{5}\right) + \frac{2}{5} f\left(\frac{9}{5}\right)$$

$$= \frac{2}{5}\left[f\left(\frac{1}{5}\right) + f\left(\frac{3}{5}\right) + f\left(\frac{5}{5}\right) + f\left(\frac{7}{5}\right) + f\left(\frac{9}{5}\right)\right]$$

$$= \frac{2}{5}\left(\frac{124}{25} + \frac{116}{25} + \frac{100}{25} + \frac{76}{25} + \frac{44}{25}\right)$$

$$= \frac{920}{125}$$

$$= 7.36.$$

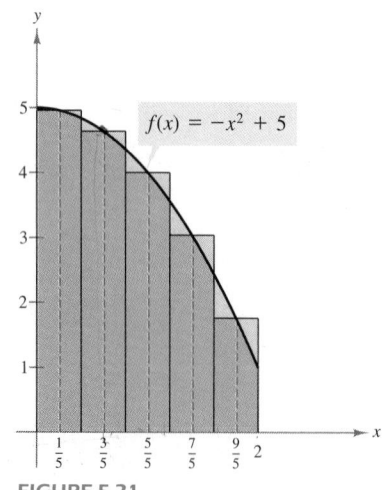

$f(x) = -x^2 + 5$

FIGURE 5.21

For the region in Example 1, you can find the exact area with a definite integral. That is,

$$\text{Area} = \int_0^2 (-x^2 + 5)\, dx$$

$$= \frac{22}{3}$$

$$\approx 7.33.$$

The approximation procedure used in Example 1 is the **Midpoint Rule.** You can use the Midpoint Rule to approximate *any* definite integral—not just those representing area. The basic steps are summarized below.

Guidelines for Using the Midpoint Rule

To approximate the definite integral $\int_a^b f(x)\, dx$ with the Midpoint Rule, use the following steps.

1. Divide the interval $[a, b]$ into n subintervals, each of width

$$\Delta x = \frac{b - a}{n}.$$

2. Find the midpoint of each subinterval.

$$\text{Midpoints} = \{x_1, x_2, x_3, \ldots, x_n\}$$

3. Evaluate f at each midpoint and form the following sum.

$$\int_a^b f(x)\, dx \approx \frac{b - a}{n}[f(x_1) + f(x_2) + f(x_3) + \cdots + f(x_n)]$$

Note In Example 1, the Midpoint Rule is used to approximate an integral whose exact value can be found with the Fundamental Theorem of Calculus. This was done to illustrate the accuracy of the rule. In practice, of course, you would use the Midpoint Rule to approximate the values of definite integrals for which you cannot find an antiderivative. Examples 2 and 3 illustrate such integrals.

An important characteristic of the Midpoint Rule is that the approximation tends to improve as n increases. Table 5.1 shows the approximations for the area of the region described in Example 1 for various values of n. For example, for $n = 10$, the Midpoint Rule yields

$$\int_0^2 (-x^2 + 5)\, dx = \frac{2}{10}\left[f\left(\frac{1}{10}\right) + f\left(\frac{3}{10}\right) + \cdots + f\left(\frac{19}{10}\right)\right]$$

$$\approx 7.3400.$$

TABLE 5.1

n	5	10	15	20	25	30
Approximation	7.3600	7.3400	7.3363	7.3350	7.3344	7.3341

Note that as n increases, the approximation gets closer and closer to the exact value of the integral, which was found to be $\frac{22}{3} \approx 7.3333$.

TECHNOLOGY

Programming the Midpoint Rule

The easiest way to use the Midpoint Rule to approximate the definite integral $\int_a^b f(x)\,dx$ is to program it into a computer or programmable calculator. For instance, the following program will evaluate the Midpoint Rule on a *TI-81* or *TI-82* calculator. See Appendix D for other models.

```
Prgm1:MIDPOINT
:Disp ''LOWER LIMIT''        Prompt for value of a.
:Input A                     Input value of a.
:Disp ''UPPER LIMIT''        Prompt for value of b.
:Input B                     Input value of b.
:Disp ''N DIVISIONS''        Prompt for value of n.
:Input N                     Input value of n.
:0→S                         Initialize sum of areas.
:(B−A)/N→W                   Calculate width of subinterval.
:1→J                         Initialize counter.
:Lbl 1                       Begin loop.
:A+(J−1)W→L                  Calculate left endpoint.
:A+JW→R                      Calculate right endpoint.
:(L+R)/2→X                   Calculate midpoint of subinterval.
:S+WY₁ →S                    Add area to sum.
:IS>(J,N)                    Test counter.
:Goto 1                      End loop.
:Disp ''APPROXIMATION''
:Disp S                      Display approximation.
```

Before executing the program, enter the function as Y_1. When the program is executed, you will be prompted to enter the lower and upper limits of integration, and the number of subintervals you want to use.

With most integrals, you can determine the accuracy of the approximation by using increasingly larger values of n. For example, if you use the program to approximate the value of $\int_0^2 \sqrt{x^3 + 1}\,dx$, you will obtain the following approximations.

n	10	20	30	40	50	60	70
Approximation	3.238	3.240	3.241	3.241	3.241	3.241	3.241

Thus, it seems clear that the approximation of 3.241 is accurate to three decimal places.

EXAMPLE 2 *Using the Midpoint Rule*

Use the Midpoint Rule with $n = 5$ to approximate

$$\int_0^1 \frac{1}{x^2 + 1} \, dx.$$

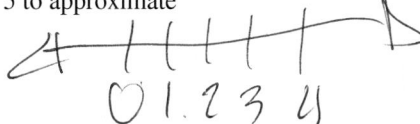

Solution

With $n = 5$, the interval $[0, 1]$ is divided into five subintervals.

$$\left[0, \frac{1}{5}\right], \quad \left[\frac{1}{5}, \frac{2}{5}\right], \quad \left[\frac{2}{5}, \frac{3}{5}\right], \quad \left[\frac{3}{5}, \frac{4}{5}\right], \quad \left[\frac{4}{5}, 1\right]$$

The midpoints of these intervals are $\frac{1}{10}, \frac{3}{10}, \frac{5}{10}, \frac{7}{10},$ and $\frac{9}{10}$. Because each subinterval has a width of $\Delta x = (1 - 0)/5 = \frac{1}{5}$, you can approximate the value of the definite integral as follows.

$$\int_0^1 \frac{1}{x^2 + 1} \, dx = \frac{1}{5} \left(\frac{1}{1.01} + \frac{1}{1.09} + \frac{1}{1.25} + \frac{1}{1.49} + \frac{1}{1.81} \right)$$
$$\approx 0.786$$

The region whose area is represented by the definite integral is shown in Figure 5.22. The actual area of this region is $\pi/4 \approx 0.785$. Thus, the approximation is off by only 0.001. ■

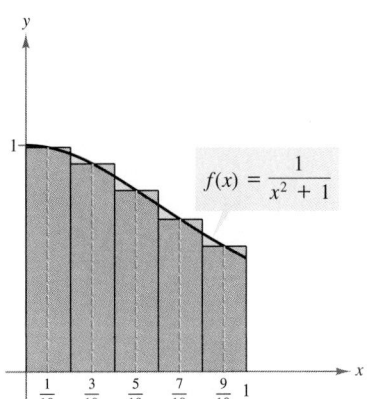

$$f(x) = \frac{1}{x^2 + 1}$$

FIGURE 5.22

EXAMPLE 3 *Using the Midpoint Rule*

Use the Midpoint Rule with $n = 10$ to approximate $\displaystyle\int_1^3 \sqrt{x^2 + 1} \, dx$.

Solution

Begin by dividing the interval $[1, 3]$ into ten subintervals. The midpoints of these intervals are

$$\frac{11}{10}, \quad \frac{13}{10}, \quad \frac{3}{2}, \quad \frac{17}{10}, \quad \frac{19}{10}, \quad \frac{21}{10}, \quad \frac{23}{10}, \quad \frac{5}{2}, \quad \frac{27}{10}, \quad \text{and} \quad \frac{29}{10}.$$

Because each subinterval has a width of $\Delta x = (3 - 1)/10 = \frac{1}{5}$, you can approximate the value of the definite integral as follows.

$$\int_1^3 \sqrt{x^2 + 1} \, dx = \frac{1}{5} \left[\sqrt{(1.1)^2 + 1} + \sqrt{(1.3)^2 + 1} + \cdots + \sqrt{(2.9)^2 + 1} \right]$$
$$\approx 4.504$$

The region whose area is represented by the definite integral is shown in Figure 5.23. Using techniques that are not within the scope of this course, it can be shown that the actual area is

$$\frac{1}{2} \left[3\sqrt{10} + \ln\left(3 + \sqrt{10}\right) - \sqrt{2} - \ln\left(1 + \sqrt{2}\right) \right] \approx 4.505.$$

Thus, the approximation is off by only 0.001. ■

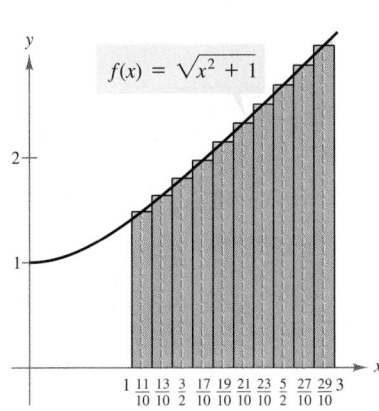

$$f(x) = \sqrt{x^2 + 1}$$

FIGURE 5.23

The Definite Integral as the Limit of a Sum

Consider the closed interval $[a, b]$, divided into n subintervals whose midpoints are x_i and whose widths are $\Delta x = (b - a)/n$. In this section you have seen that the midpoint approximation

$$\int_a^b f(x)\,dx \approx f(x_1)\Delta x + f(x_2)\Delta x + f(x_3)\Delta x + \cdots + f(x_n)\Delta x$$

$$= [f(x_1) + f(x_2) + f(x_3) + \cdots + f(x_n)]\Delta x$$

becomes better and better as n increases. In fact, the limit of this sum as n approaches infinity is exactly equal to the definite integral. That is,

$$\int_a^b f(x)\,dx = \lim_{n \to \infty} [f(x_1) + f(x_2) + f(x_3) + \cdots + f(x_n)]\Delta x.$$

It can be shown that this limit is valid as long as x_i is *any* point in the ith interval.

EXAMPLE 4 *Approximating a Definite Integral*

Use a computer or programmable calculator to approximate the definite integral

$$\int_0^1 e^{-x^2}\,dx.$$

Solution

Using the program on page 364, with $n = 10, 20, 30, 40$, and 50, it appears that the value of the integral is approximately 0.7468. If you have access to a computer or calculator with a built-in program to approximate definite integrals, try using it to approximate this integral. When we used *Derive* to approximate the integral, we obtained 0.746824. ■

Discussion Problem A Failure of the Midpoint Rule

Suppose you use the Midpoint Rule to approximate the definite integral

$$\int_0^1 \frac{1}{x^2}\,dx.$$

The table shows the approximations that are obtained with $n = 10, 20, 30, 40, 50$, and 60.

n	10	20	30	40	50	60
Approximation	48.3	97.7	147.0	196.4	245.7	295.1

Why are the approximations getting larger and larger? Why isn't the Midpoint Rule working?

Warm Up

In Exercises 1–6, find the midpoint of the interval.

1. $[0, \frac{1}{3}]$

2. $[\frac{1}{10}, \frac{2}{10}]$

3. $[\frac{3}{20}, \frac{4}{20}]$

4. $[1, \frac{7}{6}]$

5. $[2, \frac{31}{15}]$

6. $[\frac{26}{9}, 3]$

In Exercises 7–10, find the limit.

7. $\lim\limits_{x \to \infty} \dfrac{2x^2 + 4x - 1}{3x^2 - 2x}$

8. $\lim\limits_{x \to \infty} \dfrac{4x + 5}{7x - 5}$

9. $\lim\limits_{x \to \infty} \dfrac{x - 7}{x^2 + 1}$

10. $\lim\limits_{x \to \infty} \dfrac{5x^3 + 1}{x^3 + x^2 + 4}$

EXERCISES 5.6

 means that technology can help you solve or check the exercise(s).

In Exercises 1–4, use the Midpoint Rule with $n = 4$ to approximate the area of the region. Compare your result with the exact area obtained with a definite integral.

1. $f(x) = -2x + 3$, $[0, 1]$

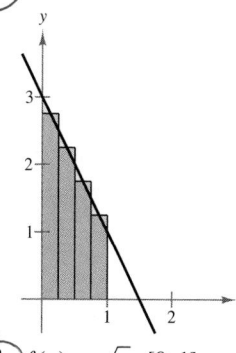

2. $f(x) = \sqrt{x} + 1$, $[0, 2]$

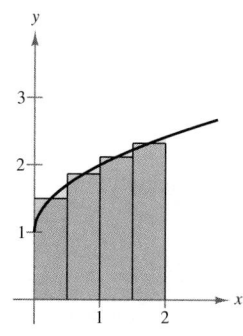

3. $f(x) = \sqrt{x}$, $[0, 1]$

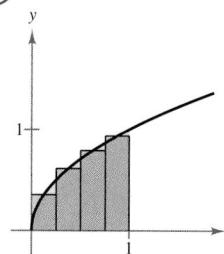

4. $f(x) = 1 - x^2$, $[-1, 1]$

 In Exercises 5–14, use the Midpoint Rule with $n = 4$ to approximate the area of the region bounded by the graph of f and the x-axis over the interval. Compare your result with the exact area. Sketch the region.

Function	Interval
5. $f(x) = x^2 + 2$	$[-1, 1]$
6. $f(x) = 3x - 4$	$[2, 5]$
7. $f(x) = 2x^2$	$[1, 3]$
8. $f(x) = 2x - x^3$	$[0, 1]$
9. $f(x) = x^3 - 1$	$[1, 2]$
10. $f(x) = x^2 - x^3$	$[0, 1]$
11. $f(x) = x^2 - x^3$	$[-1, 0]$
12. $f(x) = 2x^2 - x + 1$	$[0, 2]$
13. $f(x) = x(1 - x)^2$	$[0, 1]$
14. $f(x) = x^2(3 - x)$	$[0, 3]$

 In Exercises 15 and 16, use a program similar to that on page 364 to approximate the area of the region. How large must n be to obtain an approximation that is correct to within 0.01?

15. $\displaystyle\int_0^4 (2x^2 + 3)\, dx$

16. $\displaystyle\int_0^4 (2x^3 + 3)\, dx$

In Exercises 17 and 18, use the Midpoint Rule with $n = 4$ to approximate the area of the region. Compare your result with the exact area obtained with a definite integral.

17. $f(y) = \frac{1}{4}y$, $[2, 4]$ **18.** $f(y) = 4y - y^2$, $[0, 4]$

 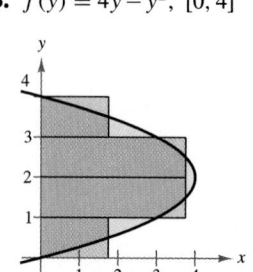

In Exercises 19–22, use the Midpoint Rule to complete the table.

Number of subintervals	2	4	6	8	10
Approximation	?	?	?	?	?

19. $\int_0^4 \sqrt{16 - x^2}\, dx$ **20.** $\int_{-1}^1 (3-x)\sqrt{1-x^2}\, dx$

21. $\int_0^2 \sqrt{1 + x^3}\, dx$ **22.** $\int_0^2 x\sqrt{1 + x^3}\, dx$

Trapezoidal Rule In Exercises 23 and 24, use the Trapezoidal Rule with $n = 8$ to approximate the definite integral. Compare the result with the exact value and the approximation obtained with $n = 8$ and the Midpoint Rule. Which approximation technique appears to be better? Let f be continuous on $[a, b]$ and let n be the number of equal subintervals (see figure). Then the Trapezoidal Rule for approximating $\int_a^b f(x)\, dx$ is

$$\frac{b-a}{2n}[f(x_0) + 2f(x_1) + \cdots + 2f(x_{n-1}) + f(x_n)].$$

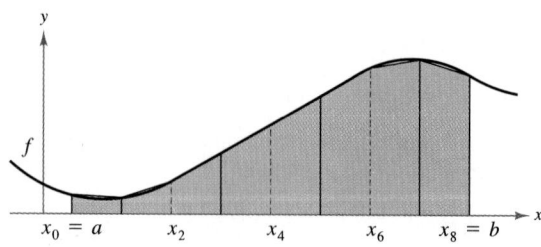

FIGURE FOR 23 AND 24

23. $\int_0^2 x^3\, dx$ **24.** $\int_1^3 \frac{1}{x^2}\, dx$

In Exercises 25–28, use the Trapezoidal Rule to approximate the definite integral with $n = 4$.

25. $\int_0^2 \frac{1}{x+1}\, dx$ **26.** $\int_0^4 \sqrt{1 + x^2}\, dx$

27. $\int_{-1}^1 \frac{1}{x^2 + 1}\, dx$ **28.** $\int_1^5 \frac{\sqrt{x-1}}{x}\, dx$

In Exercises 29 and 30, use a computer or programmable calculator to complete the table.

n	Midpoint rule	Trapezoidal rule
4		
8		
12		
16		
20		

29. $\int_0^4 \sqrt{2 + 3x^2}\, dx$ **30.** $\int_0^2 \frac{5}{x^3 + 1}\, dx$

In Exercises 31 and 32, use the Trapezoidal Rule with $n = 10$ to approximate the area of the region bounded by the graphs of the equations.

31. $y = \sqrt{\frac{x^3}{4-x}}$, $y = 0$, $x = 3$

32. $y = x\sqrt{\frac{4-x}{4+x}}$, $y = 0$, $x = 4$

33. *Velocity and Acceleration* The table lists the velocity v (in feet per second) of an accelerating car over a 20-second interval. Use the Trapezoidal Rule to approximate the distance in feet that the car travels during the 20 seconds. (The distance is given by $s = \int_0^{20} v\, dt$.)

Time, t	0	5	10	15	20
Velocity, v	0.0	29.3	51.3	66.0	73.3

Volumes of Solids of Revolution

The Disc Method ▪ *The Washer Method* ▪ *Applications*

The Disc Method

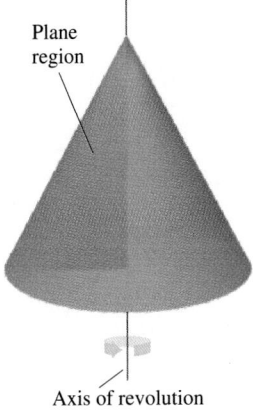

Plane region

Axis of revolution

FIGURE 5.24

As shown in Figure 5.24, a **solid of revolution** is formed by revolving a plane region about a line. The line is called the **axis of revolution.**

To develop a formula for finding the volume of a solid of revolution, consider a continuous function f that is nonnegative on the interval $[a, b]$. Suppose that the area of the region is approximated by n rectangles, each of width Δx, as shown in Figure 5.25. By revolving the rectangles about the x-axis, you obtain n circular discs, each with a volume of $\pi[f(x_i)]^2\Delta x$. The volume of the solid formed by revolving the region about the x-axis is approximately equal to the sum of the volumes of the n discs. Moreover, by taking the limit as n approaches infinity, you can see that the exact volume is given by a definite integral. This result is called the **Disc Method.**

The Disc Method

The volume of the solid formed by revolving the region bounded by the graph of f and the x-axis ($a \le x \le b$) about the x-axis is

$$\text{Volume} = \pi \int_a^b [f(x)]^2\, dx.$$

Approximation by *n* rectangles

Approximation by *n* discs

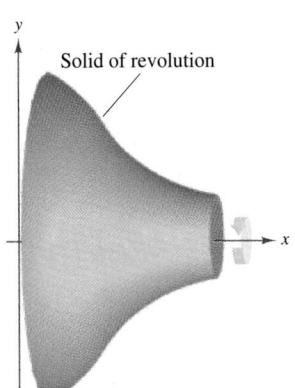

FIGURE 5.25

EXAMPLE 1 *Finding the Volume of a Solid of Revolution*

Find the volume of the solid formed by revolving the region bounded by the graph of $f(x) = -x^2 + x$ and the x-axis about the x-axis.

Solution

Begin by sketching the region bounded by the graph of f and the x-axis. As shown in Figure 5.26(a), sketch a representative rectangle whose height is $f(x)$ and whose width is Δx. From this rectangle, you can see that the radius of the solid is

$$\text{Radius} = f(x) = -x^2 + x.$$

Using the Disc Method, you can find the volume of the solid of revolution.

$$\begin{aligned}
\text{Volume} &= \pi \int_0^1 [f(x)]^2 \, dx && \textit{Disc Method} \\
&= \pi \int_0^1 (-x^2 + x)^2 \, dx && \textit{Substitute for } f(x). \\
&= \pi \int_0^1 (x^4 - 2x^3 + x^2) \, dx && \textit{Expand integrand.} \\
&= \pi \left[\frac{x^5}{5} - \frac{x^4}{2} + \frac{x^3}{3} \right]_0^1 && \textit{Find antiderivative.} \\
&= \frac{\pi}{30} && \textit{Apply Fundamental Theorem.} \\
&\approx 0.105 && \textit{Round to three decimal places.}
\end{aligned}$$

Thus, the volume of the solid is about 0.105 cubic units.

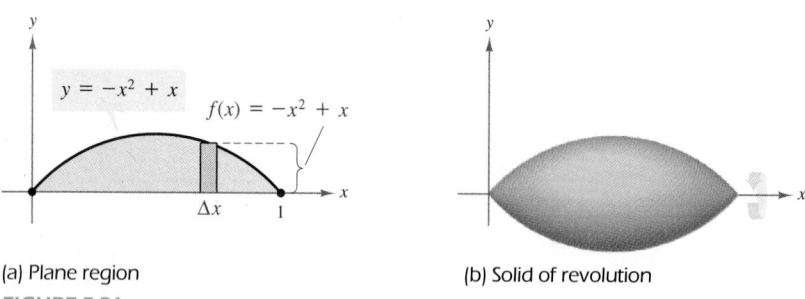

(a) Plane region   (b) Solid of revolution

FIGURE 5.26

Note   In Example 1, the entire problem was solved *without* referring to the three-dimensional sketch given in Figure 5.26(b). In general, to set up the integral for calculating the volume of a solid of revolution, a sketch of the plane region is more useful than a sketch of the solid, because the radius is more readily visualized in the plane region.

The Washer Method

You can extend the Disc Method to find the volume of a solid of revolution with a *hole*. Consider a region that is bounded by the graphs of f and g, as shown in Figure 5.27(a). If the region is revolved about the x-axis, then the volume of the resulting solid can be found by applying the Disc Method to f and g and subtracting the results.

$$\text{Volume} = \pi \int_a^b [f(x)]^2 \, dx - \pi \int_a^b [g(x)]^2 \, dx$$

Writing this as a single integral produces the **Washer Method.**

The Washer Method

Let f and g be continuous and nonnegative on the closed interval $[a, b]$, as shown in Figure 5.27(a). If $g(x) \leq f(x)$ for all x in the interval, then the volume of the solid formed by revolving the region bounded by the graphs of f and g ($a \leq x \leq b$) about the x-axis is

$$\text{Volume} = \pi \int_a^b ([f(x)]^2 - [g(x)]^2) \, dx.$$

$f(x)$ is the **outer radius** and $g(x)$ is the **inner radius.**

In Figure 5.27(b), note that the solid of revolution has a hole. Moreover, the radius of the hole is $g(x)$, the inner radius.

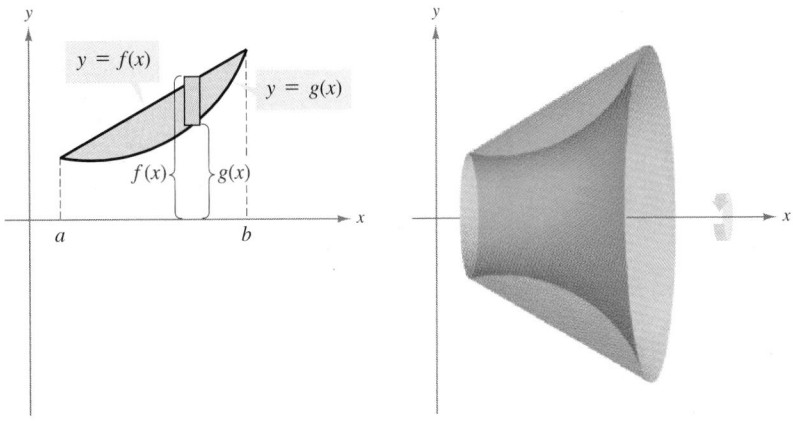

(a) Plane region

(b) Solid of revolution with hole

FIGURE 5.27

EXAMPLE 2 *Using the Washer Method*

Find the volume of the solid formed by revolving the region bounded by the graphs of $f(x) = \sqrt{25 - x^2}$ and $g(x) = 3$ about the x-axis (see Figure 5.28).

Solution

First find the points of intersection of f and g by setting $f(x)$ equal to $g(x)$ and solving for x.

$$f(x) = g(x) \qquad \textit{Set } f(x) \textit{ equal to } g(x).$$

$$\sqrt{25 - x^2} = 3 \qquad \textit{Substitute for } f(x) \textit{ and } g(x).$$

$$25 - x^2 = 9 \qquad \textit{Square both sides.}$$

$$16 = x^2$$

$$\pm 4 = x \qquad \textit{Solve for } x.$$

Using $f(x)$ as the outer radius and $g(x)$ as the inner radius, you can find the volume of the solid as follows.

$$\text{Volume} = \pi \int_{-4}^{4} ([f(x)]^2 - [g(x)]^2)\,dx \qquad \textit{Washer Method}$$

$$= \pi \int_{-4}^{4} \left[\left(\sqrt{25 - x^2} \right)^2 - (3)^2 \right] dx \quad \textit{Substitute for } f(x) \textit{ and } g(x).$$

$$= \pi \int_{-4}^{4} (16 - x^2)\,dx \qquad \textit{Simplify.}$$

$$= \pi \left[16x - \frac{x^3}{3} \right]_{-4}^{4} \qquad \textit{Find antiderivative.}$$

$$= \frac{256\pi}{3} \qquad \textit{Apply Fundamental Theorem.}$$

$$\approx 268.08 \qquad \textit{Round to two decimal places.}$$

Thus, the volume of the solid is about 268.08 cubic inches.

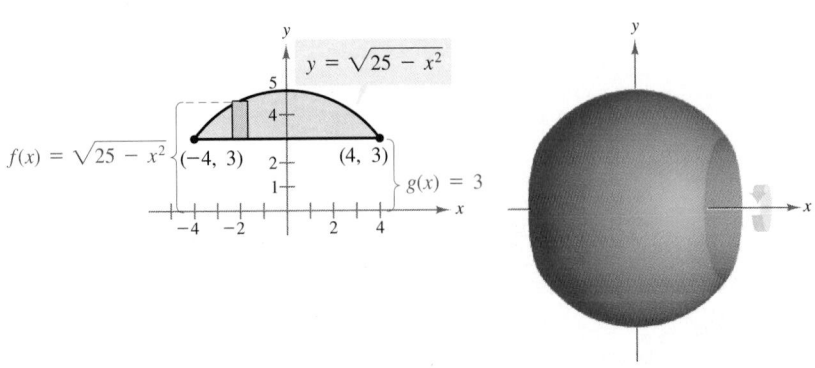

(a) Plane region

(b) Solid of revolution

FIGURE 5.28

Applications

American football, in its modern form, is a twentieth-century invention. In the 1800s a rough, soccer-like game was played with a "round football." In 1905, at the request of President Theodore Roosevelt, the Intercollegiate Athletic Association (which became the NCAA in 1910) was formed. With the introduction of the forward pass in 1906, the shape of the ball was altered to make it easier to grip.

Real Life

EXAMPLE 3 *Finding a Football's Volume*

A regulation-size football can be modeled as a solid of revolution formed by revolving the graph of

$$f(x) = -0.0944x^2 + 3.4, \qquad -5.5 \le x \le 5.5$$

about the x-axis, as shown in Figure 5.29. Use this model to find the volume of a football. (In the model, x and y are measured in inches.)

Solution

To find the volume of the solid of revolution, use the Disc Method.

$$\text{Volume} = \pi \int_{-5.5}^{5.5} [f(x)]^2 \, dx \qquad \textit{Disc Method}$$

$$= \pi \int_{-5.5}^{5.5} (-0.0944x^2 + 3.4)^2 \, dx \quad \textit{Substitute for } f(x).$$

$$\approx 232 \text{ cubic inches} \qquad \textit{Volume}$$

Thus, the volume of the football is about 232 cubic inches.

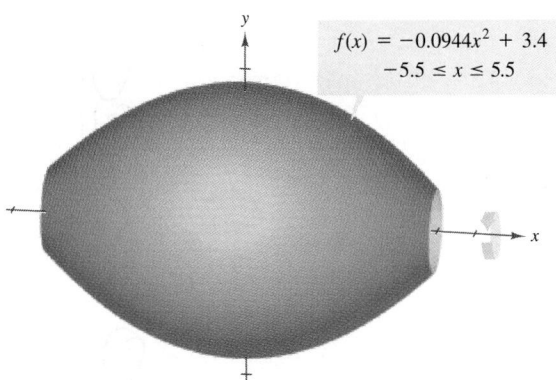

$$f(x) = -0.0944x^2 + 3.4$$
$$-5.5 \le x \le 5.5$$

FIGURE 5.29   A football-shaped solid is formed by revolving a parabolic segment about the x-axis.

Discussion Problem   *Testing the Reasonableness of an Answer*

A football is about 11 inches long and has a diameter of about 7 inches. In Example 3, the volume of a football was approximated to be 232 cubic inches. Explain how you can determine whether this answer is reasonable.

Warm Up

The following warm-up exercises involve skills that were covered in earlier sections. You will use these skills in the exercise set for this section.

In Exercises 1–6, solve for x.

1. $x^2 = 2x$

2. $-x^2 + 4x = x^2$

3. $x = -x^3 + 5x$

4. $x^2 + 1 = x + 3$

5. $-x + 4 = \sqrt{4x - x^2}$

6. $\sqrt{x - 1} = \frac{1}{2}(x - 1)$

In Exercises 7–10, evaluate the integral.

7. $\int_0^2 2e^{2x}\, dx$

8. $\int_{-1}^3 \frac{2x + 1}{x^2 + x + 2}\, dx$

9. $\int_0^2 x\sqrt{x^2 + 1}\, dx$

10. $\int_1^5 \frac{(\ln x)^2}{x}\, dx$

E X E R C I S E S   5.7   means that technology can help you solve or check the exercise(s).

In Exercises 1–16, find the volume of the solid formed by revolving the region bounded by the graph(s) of the equation(s) about the *x*-axis.

1. $y = \sqrt{4 - x^2}$

2. $y = x^2$

3. $y = \sqrt{x}$

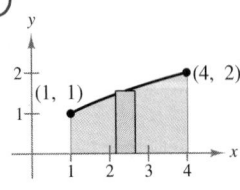

4. $y = \sqrt{4 - x^2}$

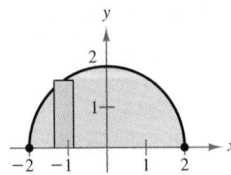

5. $y = 4 - x^2$, $y = 0$

6. $y = x$, $y = 0$, $x = 4$

7. $y = 1 - \frac{1}{4}x^2$, $y = 0$

8. $y = x^2 + 1$, $y = 5$

9. $y = -x + 1$, $y = 0$, $x = 0$

10. $y = x$, $y = e^{x-1}$, $x = 0$

11. $y = \frac{1}{x} - \frac{1}{2}$, $y = -\frac{1}{2}x + 1$

12. $y = \sqrt{x}$, $y = 0$, $x = 4$

13. $y = 2x^2$, $y = 0$, $x = 2$

14. $y = \frac{1}{x}$, $y = 0$, $x = 1$, $x = 3$

15. $y = e^x$, $y = 0$, $x = 0$, $x = 1$

16. $y = x^2$, $y = 4x - x^2$

In Exercises 17–24, find the volume of the solid formed by revolving the region bounded by the graph(s) of the equation(s) about the *y*-axis.

17. $y = x^2$, $y = 4$, $0 \le x \le 2$

18. $y = \sqrt{16 - x^2}$, $y = 0$, $0 \le x \le 4$

19. $x = 1 - \frac{1}{2}y$, $x = 0$, $y = 0$

20. $x = y(y - 1)$, $x = 0$

21. $y = x^{2/3}$

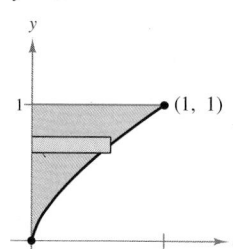

(1, 1)

22. $x = -y^2 + 4y$

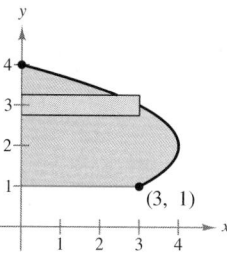

(3, 1)

23. $y = \sqrt{4 - x}$, $y = 0$, $x = 0$

24. $y = 4$, $y = 0$, $x = 2$, $x = 0$

25. The line segment from $(0, 0)$ to $(6, 3)$ is revolved about the x-axis to form a cone. What is the volume of the cone?

26. Use the Disc Method to verify that the volume of a right circular cone is $\frac{1}{3}\pi r^2 h$, where r is the radius of the base and h is the height.

27. Use the Disc Method to verify that the volume of a sphere of radius r is $\frac{4}{3}\pi r^3$.

28. The right half of the ellipse $9x^2 + 25y^2 = 225$ is revolved about the y-axis to form an oblate spheroid (shaped like an M&M candy). Find the volume of the spheroid.

29. The upper half of the ellipse $9x^2 + 16y^2 = 144$ is revolved about the x-axis to form a prolate spheroid (shaped like a football). Find the volume of the spheroid.

30. *Fuel Tank* A tank on the wing of a jet is modeled by revolving the region bounded by the graph of $y = \frac{1}{8}x^2\sqrt{2 - x}$ and the x-axis about the x-axis, where x and y are measured in meters (see figure). Find the volume of the tank.

Jet Wing Tank

$y = \frac{1}{8}x^2\sqrt{2 - x}$

Distance (in meters)

Distance (in meters)

31. *Fish Population* A pond is to be stocked with a species of fish. The food supply in 500 cubic feet of pond water can adequately support one fish. The pond is nearly circular, is 20 feet deep at its center, and has a radius of 200 feet. The bottom of the pond can be modeled by

$$y = 20[(0.005x)^2 - 1].$$

(a) How much water is in the pond?
(b) Estimate the maximum number of fish the pond can support.

32. *Wedding Ring* A jewelry manufacturer plans to make gold wedding rings from a gold alloy that costs \$50,000 per cubic inch. A cross section of the ring is bounded by the graphs of

$$y = \frac{7}{16} - 16x^2 \quad \text{and} \quad y = \frac{3}{8},$$

as shown in the figure.

(a) Find the volume (in cubic inches) of a ring.
(b) Estimate the cost of material for each ring.

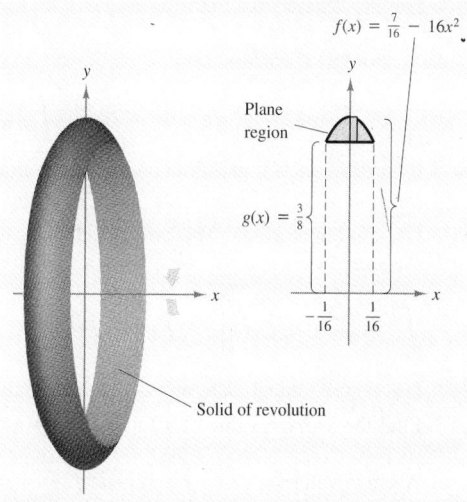

Model of a Gold Ring

$f(x) = \frac{7}{16} - 16x^2$

Plane region

$g(x) = \frac{3}{8}$

$-\frac{1}{16}$ $\frac{1}{16}$

Solid of revolution

In Exercises 33 and 34, use the Midpoint Rule with $n = 4$ to approximate the volume of the solid generated by revolving the region bounded by the graphs of the equations about the x-axis.

33. $y = \sqrt[3]{x + 1}$, $y = 0$, $x = 0$, $x = 7$

34. $y = \dfrac{10}{x^2 + 1}$, $y = 0$, $x = 0$, $x = 3$

Chapter Summary and Study Tips

After studying this chapter, you should have acquired the following skills. The exercise numbers are keyed to the Review Exercises that begin on page 378. Answers to odd-numbered Review Exercises are given in the back of the text.

▪ Use basic integration formulas to find antiderivatives. (*Section 5.1*)   Review Exercises 1–8

$$\int k\,dx = kx + C \qquad\qquad \int [f(x) - g(x)]\,dx = \int f(x)\,dx - \int g(x)\,dx$$

$$\int kf(x)\,dx = k\int f(x)\,dx \qquad\qquad \int x^n\,dx = \frac{x^{n+1}}{n+1} + C, \qquad n \neq -1$$

$$\int [f(x) + g(x)]\,dx = \int f(x)\,dx + \int g(x)\,dx$$

▪ Use initial conditions to find particular solutions of indefinite integrals. (*Section 5.1*)   Review Exercises 9–12
▪ Use antiderivatives to solve real-life problems. (*Section 5.1*)   Review Exercises 13, 14
▪ Use the General Power Rule to find antiderivatives. (*Section 5.2*)   Review Exercises 15–22

$$\int u^n \frac{du}{dx}\,dx = \frac{u^{n+1}}{n+1} + C, \qquad n \neq -1$$

▪ Use the General Power Rule to solve real-life problems. (*Section 5.2*)   Review Exercises 23, 24
▪ Use the Exponential and Log Rules to find antiderivatives. (*Section 5.3*)   Review Exercises 25–32

$$\int e^x\,dx = e^x + C \qquad\qquad \int \frac{1}{x}\,dx = \ln|x| + C$$

$$\int e^u \frac{du}{dx}\,dx = \int e^u\,du = e^u + C \qquad \int \frac{u'}{u}\,dx = \int \frac{1}{u}\,du = \ln|u| + C$$

▪ Find the area of a region bounded by the graph of a function and the *x*-axis. (*Section 5.4*)   Review Exercises 33–38
▪ Use the Fundamental Theorem of Calculus to evaluate a definite integral. (*Section 5.4*)   Review Exercises 39–50

$$\int_a^b f(x)\,dx = F(x)\Big]_a^b = F(b) - F(a), \qquad \text{where } F'(x) = f(x)$$

▪ Use definite integrals to solve marginal analysis problems. (*Section 5.4*)   Review Exercises 51, 52
▪ Find the average value of a function over a closed interval. (*Section 5.4*)   Review Exercises 53–56

$$\text{Average value} = \frac{1}{b-a}\int_a^b f(x)\,dx$$

▪ Use average values to solve real-life problems. (*Section 5.4*)   Review Exercises 57, 58

* Several student study aids are available with this text. The *Student Solutions Guide* includes detailed solutions to all odd-numbered exercises, as well as practice chapter tests with answers. The *Graphics Calculator Guide* offers instructions on the use of a variety of graphing calculators and computer graphing software. The *Brief Calculus TUTOR* includes additional examples for selected exercises in the text.

■ Use properties of even and odd functions to help evaluate definite integrals. (*Section 5.4*)

Review Exercises 59–62

Even function: $f(-x) = f(x)$ Odd function: $f(-x) = -f(x)$

■ Find the area of a region bounded by two graphs. (*Section 5.5*)

Review Exercises 63–70

$$A = \int_a^b [f(x) - g(x)]\, dx$$

■ Find consumer and producer surplus. (*Section 5.5*)

Review Exercises 71, 72

■ Use the area of a region bounded by two graphs to solve real-life problems. (*Section 5.5*)

Review Exercises 73, 74

■ Use the Midpoint Rule to approximate the value of a definite integral. (*Section 5.6*)

Review Exercises 75–78

$$\int_a^b f(x)\, dx \approx \frac{b - a}{n}[f(x_1) + f(x_2) + f(x_3) + \cdots + f(x_n)]$$

■ Use the Disc Method to find the volume of a solid of revolution. (*Section 5.7*)

Review Exercises 79–82

$$\text{Volume} = \pi \int_a^b [f(x)]^2\, dx$$

■ Use the Washer Method to find the volume of a solid of revolution with a hole. (*Section 5.7*)

Review Exercises 83–86

$$\text{Volume} = \pi \int_a^b ([f(x)]^2 - [g(x)]^2)\, dx$$

■ Use solids of revolution to solve real-life problems. (*Section 5.7*)

Review Exercises 87, 88

■ Indefinite and Definite Integrals   When evaluating integrals, remember that an indefinite integral is a *family of antiderivatives*, each differing by a constant C, whereas a definite integral is a number.

■ Check Antiderivatives by Differentiating   When finding an antiderivative, remember that you can check your result by differentiating. For example, you can check that the antiderivative

$$\int (3x^3 - 4x)\, dx = \frac{3}{4}x^4 - 2x^2 + C$$

is correct by differentiating to obtain

$$\frac{d}{dx}\left[\frac{3}{4}x^4 - 2x^2 + C\right] = 3x^3 - 4x.$$

Because the derivative is equal to the original integrand, you know that the antiderivative is correct.

■ Grouping Symbols and the Fundamental Theorem   When using the Fundamental Theorem of Calculus to evaluate a definite integral, you can avoid sign errors by using grouping symbols. Here is an example.

$$\int_1^3 (x^3 - 9x)\, dx = \left[\frac{x^4}{4} - \frac{9x^2}{2}\right]_1^3 = \left[\frac{3^4}{4} - \frac{9(3^2)}{2}\right] - \left[\frac{1^4}{4} - \frac{9(1^2)}{2}\right] = \frac{81}{4} - \frac{81}{2} - \frac{1}{4} + \frac{9}{2} = -16$$

Review Exercises

 means that technology can help you solve or check the exercise(s).

In Exercises 1–8, find the indefinite integral.

1. $\int 16\,dx$

2. $\int \frac{3}{5}x\,dx$

3. $\int (2x^2 + 5x)\,dx$

4. $\int (5 - 6x^2)\,dx$

5. $\int \frac{2}{3\sqrt[3]{x}}\,dx$

6. $\int 6x^2\sqrt{x}\,dx$

7. $\int (\sqrt[3]{x^4} + 3x)\,dx$

8. $\int \left(\frac{4}{\sqrt{x}} + \sqrt{x}\right)\,dx$

In Exercises 9–12, find the particular solution, $y = f(x)$, that satisfies the given conditions.

9. $f'(x) = 3x + 1$, $f(2) = 6$

10. $f'(x) = x^{-1/3} - 1$, $f(8) = 4$

11. $f''(x) = 2x^2$, $f'(3) = 10$, $f(3) = 6$

12. $f''(x) = \frac{6}{\sqrt{x}} + 3$, $f'(1) = 12$, $f(4) = 56$

13. *Vertical Motion* An object is projected upward from the ground with an initial velocity of 80 feet per second.

(a) How long does it take the object to rise to its maximum height?

(b) What is the maximum height?

(c) When is the velocity of the object half of its initial velocity?

(d) What is the height of the object when its velocity is one-half the initial velocity?

14. *Forecasting* The weekly revenue for a new product has been increasing. The rate of change of the revenue can be modeled by

$$\frac{dR}{dt} = 0.675t^{3/2}, \qquad 0 \le t \le 225,$$

where t is the time (in weeks). When $t = 0$, $R = 0$.

(a) Find a model for the revenue function.

(b) When will the weekly revenue be $27,000?

In Exercises 15–22, find the indefinite integral.

15. $\int (1 + 5x)^2\,dx$

16. $\int (x - 6)^{4/3}\,dx$

17. $\int \frac{1}{\sqrt{5x - 1}}\,dx$

18. $\int \frac{4x}{\sqrt{1 - 3x^2}}\,dx$

19. $\int x(1 - 4x^2)\,dx$

20. $\int \frac{x^2}{(x^3 - 4)^2}\,dx$

21. $\int (x^4 - 2x)(2x^3 - 1)\,dx$

22. $\int \frac{\sqrt{x}}{(1 - x^{3/2})^3}\,dx$

23. *Production* The output P (in board feet) of a small sawmill changes according to the model

$$\frac{dP}{dt} = 2t(0.001t^2 + 0.5)^{1/4}, \qquad 0 \le t \le 40,$$

where t is measured in hours. Find the number of board feet produced in (a) 6 hours and (b) 12 hours.

24. *Cost* The marginal cost for a catering service to cater to x people can be modeled by

$$\frac{dC}{dx} = \frac{5x}{\sqrt{x^2 + 1000}}.$$

When $x = 225$, the cost is $1136.06. Find the cost of catering for (a) 500 people and (b) 1000 people.

In Exercises 25–32, find the indefinite integral.

25. $\int 3e^{-3x}\,dx$

26. $\int (2t - 1)e^{t^2 - t}\,dt$

27. $\int (x - 1)e^{x^2 - 2x}\,dx$

28. $\int \frac{4}{6x - 1}\,dx$

29. $\int \frac{x^2}{1 - x^3}\,dx$

30. $\int \frac{x - 4}{x^2 - 8x}\,dx$

31. $\int \frac{(\sqrt{x} + 1)^2}{\sqrt{x}}\,dx$

32. $\int \frac{e^{5x}}{5 + e^{5x}}\,dx$

In Exercises 33–38, find the area of the region.

33. $f(x) = 4 - 2x$

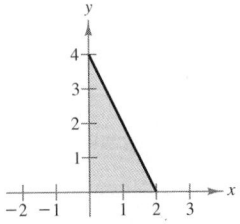

34. $f(x) = 4 - x^2$

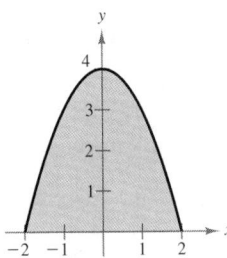

35. $f(y) = (y - 2)^2$

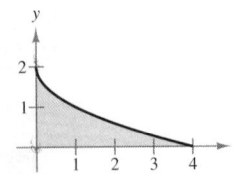

36. $f(x) = \sqrt{9 - x^2}$

37. $f(x) = \dfrac{2}{x+1}$

38. $f(x) = 2xe^{x^2-4}$

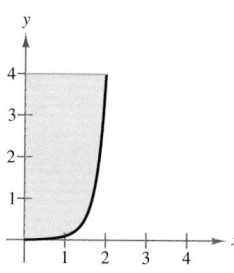

In Exercises 39–50, use the Fundamental Theorem of Calculus to evaluate the definite integral.

39. $\displaystyle\int_{0}^{4} (2+x)\,dx$

40. $\displaystyle\int_{-1}^{1} (t^2+2)\,dt$

41. $\displaystyle\int_{-1}^{1} (4t^3 - 2t)\,dt$

42. $\displaystyle\int_{1}^{4} 2x\sqrt{x}\,dx$

43. $\displaystyle\int_{0}^{3} \dfrac{1}{\sqrt{1+x}}\,dx$

44. $\displaystyle\int_{3}^{6} \dfrac{x}{3\sqrt{x^2-8}}\,dx$

45. $\displaystyle\int_{1}^{2} \left(\dfrac{1}{x^2} - \dfrac{1}{x^3}\right)dx$

46. $\displaystyle\int_{0}^{1} x^2(x^3+1)^3\,dx$

47. $\displaystyle\int_{1}^{3} \dfrac{(3+\ln x)}{x}\,dx$

48. $\displaystyle\int_{0}^{\ln 5} e^{x/5}\,dx$

49. $\displaystyle\int_{-1}^{1} 3xe^{x^2-1}\,dx$

50. $\displaystyle\int_{1}^{3} \dfrac{1}{x(\ln x + 2)^2}\,dx$

51. *Cost* The marginal cost for a typical additional client at a law firm can be modeled by

$$\dfrac{dC}{dx} = 675 + 0.5x,$$

where x is the number of clients. How does the cost C change when x increases from 50 to 51 clients?

52. *Profit* The marginal profit obtained by selling x dollars of automobile insurance can be modeled by

$$\dfrac{dP}{dx} = 0.4\left(1 - \dfrac{5000}{x}\right), \qquad x \geq 5000.$$

Find the change in the profit when x increases from \$75,000 to \$100,000.

In Exercises 53–56, find the average value of the function on the closed interval. Then find the values of x in the interval where the function assumes its average value.

53. $f(x) = \dfrac{4}{\sqrt{x-1}}$, [5, 10]

54. $f(x) = \dfrac{20\ln x}{x}$, [2, 10]

55. $f(x) = e^{5-x}$, [2, 5]

56. $f(x) = x^3$, [0, 2]

57. *Checking Account* An interest-bearing checking account yields 4% interest compounded continuously. If you deposit \$500 into such an account, and never write checks, what will the average value of the account be over a period of 2 years? Explain your reasoning.

58. *Fuel Cost* Suppose that the price p of gasoline can be modeled by

$$p = 1.00 + 0.1t + 0.02t^2,$$

where $t = 0$ represents January 1, 1990. Find the cost of driving an automobile that is driven 15,000 miles per year and gets 33 miles per gallon from 1990 through 1994.

In Exercises 59–62, explain how the given value can be used to evaluate the second integral.

59. $\displaystyle\int_{0}^{2} 6x^5\,dx = 64$, $\displaystyle\int_{-2}^{2} 6x^5\,dx$

60. $\displaystyle\int_{0}^{3} (x^4+x^2)\,dx = 57.6$, $\displaystyle\int_{-3}^{3} (x^4+x^2)\,dx$

61. $\displaystyle\int_{1}^{2} \dfrac{4}{x^2}\,dx = 2$, $\displaystyle\int_{-2}^{-1} \dfrac{4}{x^2}\,dx$

62. $\displaystyle\int_{0}^{1} (x^3-x)\,dx = -\dfrac{1}{4}$, $\displaystyle\int_{-1}^{0} (x^3-x)\,dx$

In Exercises 63–70, sketch the region bounded by the graphs of the equations. Then find the area of the region.

63. $y = \dfrac{1}{x^2}$, $y = 4$, $x = 3$

64. $y = x$, $y = 2 - x^2$

65. $y = 1 - \dfrac{1}{2}x$, $y = x - 2$, $y = 1$

66. $y = \dfrac{4}{\sqrt{x+1}}$, $y = 0$, $x = 0$, $x = 8$

67. $y = \sqrt{x}(x-1)$, $y = 0$

68. $y = x$, $y = x^5$

69. $y = (x-3)^2$, $y = 8 - (x-3)^2$

70. $y = 4 - x$, $y = x^2 - 5x + 8$, $x = 0$

Consumer and Producer Surplus In Exercises 71 and 72, find the consumer surplus and producer surplus for the demand and supply functions.

71. Supply function: $p_2(x) = 500 - x$

Demand function: $p_1(x) = 1.25x + 162.5$

72. Supply function: $p_2(x) = \sqrt{100{,}000 - 0.15x^2}$

Demand function: $p_1(x) = \sqrt{0.01x^2 + 36{,}000}$

73. *Ice Cream Consumption* The per capita consumption y (in pounds) of ice cream in the United States from 1981 through 1987 can be modeled by

$$y = 18.94 - \frac{5.175}{t} + \frac{3.632}{t^{3/2}}, \qquad 1 \le t \le 7,$$

where $t = 1$ represents December 31, 1981. The consumption from 1988 through 1990 can be modeled by

$$y = 0.019t^3 - 0.294t^2 + 26.465, \qquad 7 < t \le 10.$$

If the consumption had continued to follow the first model from 1988 through 1990, how much more or less ice cream would have been consumed? *(Source: U.S. Department of Agriculture)*

74. *Credit Card Sales* The annual sales s (in millions of dollars) for VISA, Mastercard, and American Express from 1983 through 1992 can be modeled by

$s = 15.969t - 6.318$ *VISA*

$s = 8.581t + 6.965$ *Mastercard*

$s = 6.214t + 10.345$ *American Express*

where $3 \le t \le 12$ represents the 10-year period from 1983 through 1992. *(Source: Credit Card News)*

(a) From 1983 through 1992, how much more were VISA's sales than Mastercard's sales?

(b) From 1983 through 1992, how much more were VISA's sales than American Express's sales?

In Exercises 75–78, use the Midpoint Rule with $n = 4$ to approximate the definite integral. Then use a programmable calculator or computer with $n = 20$. Compare the two approximations.

75. $\displaystyle \int_0^2 (x^2 + 1)^2 \, dx$

76. $\displaystyle \int_{-1}^1 \sqrt{1 - x^2} \, dx$

77. $\displaystyle \int_0^1 \frac{1}{x^2 + 1} \, dx$

78. $\displaystyle \int_{-1}^1 e^{3 - x^2} \, dx$

In Exercises 79–82, use the Disc Method to find the volume of the solid of revolution formed by revolving the region about the x-axis.

79. $y = \dfrac{1}{\sqrt{x}}$

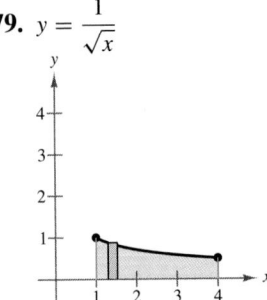

80. $y = \sqrt{16 - x}$

81. $y = e^{1-x}$

82. $y = \dfrac{1}{x}$

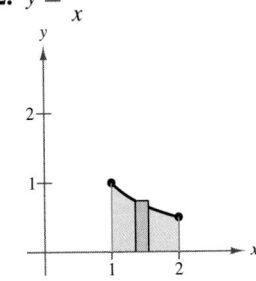

In Exercises 83–86, use the Washer Method to find the volume of the solid of revolution formed by revolving the region about the x-axis.

83. $y = 2x + 1, \; y = 1$

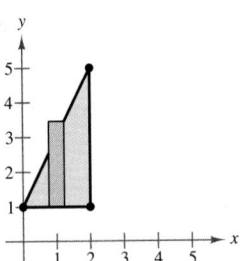

84. $y = \sqrt{x}, \; y = 2$

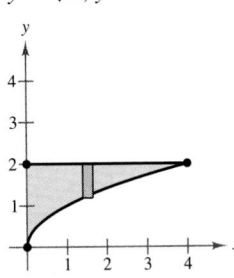

85. $y = x^2, \; y = x^3$

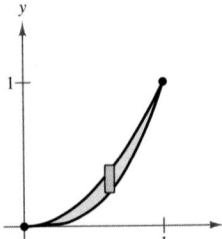

86. $y = 4 - \tfrac{1}{2}x^2, \; y = 2$

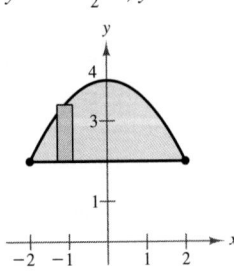

87. *Manufacturing* To create a part for an engine, a manufacturer drills a hole through the center of a metal sphere whose radius is 1 inch. The hole has a radius of 0.25 inch. What is the volume of the resulting ring?

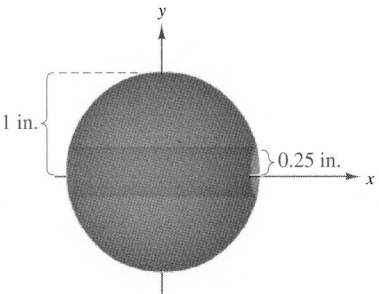

88. *Design* To create a computer design for a funnel, an engineer revolves the region bounded by the lines $y = 3 - x$, $y = 0$, and $x = 0$ about the y-axis, where x and y are measured in feet. Find the volume of the funnel.

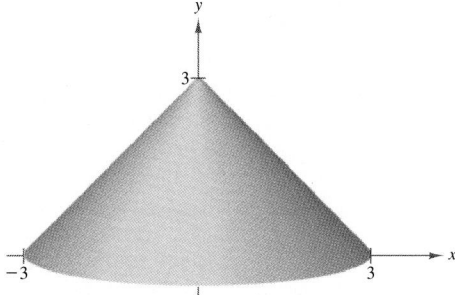

Sample Post-Graduation Exam Questions

The following questions were taken from certified public accountant (CPA) exams, graduate management admission tests (GMAT), graduate records exams (GRE), actuarial exams, or college-level academic skills tests (CLAST). The answers to the questions are given in the back of the book.

For Questions 1–3, use the data given in the table.

Number of Students	Number of Correct Answers
12	45 to 50
11	40 to 44
14	35 to 39
10	30 to 34
7	0 to 29

1. To pass the exam, a student must correctly answer 75% of the questions. What is the maximum number of students that could have passed the exam?

(a) 23   (b) 47   (c) 30   (d) 37

2. What percent of the class answered 40 or more questions correctly?

(a) 69%   (b) 43%   (c) 22%   (d) 31%

3. The number of students who answered 35 to 39 questions correctly is y times the number who answered 29 or fewer correctly, where y is

(a) $\frac{1}{2}$ (b) 1   (c) 2   (d) $\frac{7}{5}$

4. For which of the following statements is $x = -2$ a solution?

   I. $x^2 + 4x + 4 \leq 0$

   II. $|3x + 6| = 0$

   III. $x^2 + 7x + 10 > 0$

(a) I, II, and III   (b) I and II   (c) II and III   (d) I and III

5. The area of the shaded region in the graph is A square units, with A equal to

(a) $\frac{50}{3}$ (b) $\frac{25}{3}$ (c) 50   (d) $\frac{4}{3}$

For Questions 6–8, use the following data.
56, 58, 54, 54, 59, 56, 55, 57, 56, 62

6. The mean of the data is

(a) 55.5   (b) 56.7   (c) 56.5   (d) 56

7. The median of the data is

(a) 55.5   (b) 56.7   (c) 56.5   (d) 56

8. The mode of the data is

(a) 55.5   (b) 56.7   (c) 56.5   (d) 56

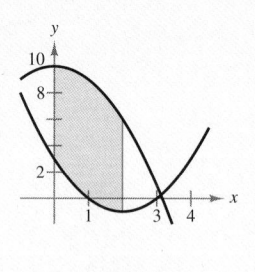

FIGURE FOR 5

$$\int_{-\infty}^{\infty} \frac{1}{\sigma\sqrt{2\pi}}\, e^{-x^2/2\sigma^2}\, dx = 1$$

6 Techniques of Integration

All algebraic, exponential, and logarithmic functions have derivatives that are algebraic, exponential, or logarithmic. This is not true with antiderivatives. For instance, an algebraic function can have an antiderivative that is an inverse trigonometric function. What is even more diabolical is that the antiderivatives of some algebraic, exponential, and logarithmic functions are not elementary functions.

Mathematicians, such as the Russian Sonya Kovalevsky (1850–1891), have devised ingenious techniques for *finding* antiderivatives of those functions that possess elementary antiderivatives, and for *approximating* definite integrals of functions that do not possess elementary antiderivatives.

$$\int u\, dv = uv - \int v\, du$$

Kovalevsky

e Bettmann Archive

6.1 Integration by Substitution

Review of Basic Integration Formulas ■ *Integration by Substitution* ■ *Substitution and Definite Integrals* ■ *Applications*

Review of Basic Integration Formulas

Each of the basic integration rules you studied in Chapter 5 was derived from a corresponding differentiation rule. It may surprise you to learn that, although you now have all the necessary tools for *differentiating* algebraic, exponential, and logarithmic functions, your set of tools for *integrating* these functions is by no means complete! The primary objective of this chapter is to develop several techniques that greatly expand the set of integrals to which the basic integration formulas can be applied.

Basic Integration Formulas

1. **Constant Rule:**

$$\int k\, dx = kx + C$$

2. **Simple Power Rule** $(n \neq -1)$:

$$\int x^n\, dx = \frac{x^{n+1}}{n+1} + C$$

3. **General Power Rule** $(n \neq -1)$:

$$\int u^n u'\, dx = \int u^n\, du = \frac{u^{n+1}}{n+1} + C$$

4. **Simple Exponential Rule:**

$$\int e^x\, dx = e^x + C$$

5. **General Exponential Rule:**

$$\int e^u u'\, dx = \int e^u\, du = e^u + C$$

6. **Simple Log Rule:**

$$\int \frac{1}{x}\, dx = \ln|x| + C$$

7. **General Log Rule:**

$$\int \frac{u'}{u}\, dx = \int \frac{1}{u}\, du = \ln|u| + C$$

You don't have to work many integration problems before you realize that integration is not nearly as straightforward as differentiation. A major part of any integration problem is determining which basic integration formula (or formulas) to use to solve the problem. This requires remembering the basic formulas, familiarity with various procedures for rewriting integrands in the basic forms, and lots of practice.

Integration by Substitution

There are several techniques for rewriting an integral so that it fits one or more of the basic formulas. One of the most powerful techniques is **integration by substitution.** With this technique, you choose part of the integrand to be u and then rewrite the entire integral in terms of u.

EXAMPLE 1 *Integration by Substitution*

Use the substitution $u = x + 1$ to find the indefinite integral

$$\int \frac{x}{(x+1)^2}\,dx.$$

Solution

From the substitution $u = x + 1$,

$$x = u - 1, \quad u' = 1, \quad \text{and} \quad dx = du.$$

Replacing *all* instances of x and dx with the appropriate u-variable forms produces the following.

$$\int \frac{x}{(x+1)^2}\,dx = \int \frac{u-1}{u^2}\,du \qquad \text{\textit{Substitute for } x \text{ \textit{and} } dx.}$$

$$= \int \left(\frac{u}{u^2} - \frac{1}{u^2}\right) du \qquad \text{\textit{Write as separate fractions.}}$$

$$= \int \left(\frac{1}{u} - \frac{1}{u^2}\right) du \qquad \text{\textit{Simplify.}}$$

$$= \ln|u| + \frac{1}{u} + C \qquad \text{\textit{Find antiderivative.}}$$

$$= \ln|x+1| + \frac{1}{x+1} + C \qquad \text{\textit{Substitute for } u.}$$

The basic steps for integration by substitution are outlined in the following guidelines.

Guidelines for Integration by Substitution

1. Let u be a function of x (usually part of the integrand).
2. Solve for x and dx in terms of u and du.
3. Convert the entire integral to u-variable form and try to fit it to one or more of the basic integration formulas. If none fits, try a different substitution.
4. After integrating, rewrite the antiderivative as a function of x.

EXAMPLE 2 *Integration by Substitution*

Find the indefinite integral

$$\int x\sqrt{x^2 - 1}\, dx.$$

Solution
Consider the substitution $u = x^2 - 1$, which produces $du = 2x\, dx$. To create $2x\, dx$ as part of the integral, multiply and divide by 2.

$$\int x\sqrt{x^2 - 1}\, dx = \frac{1}{2}\int \overbrace{(x^2 - 1)^{1/2}}^{u^{1/2}}\overbrace{2x\, dx}^{du} \qquad \textit{Multiply and divide by 2.}$$

$$= \frac{1}{2}\int u^{1/2}\, du \qquad \textit{Substitute for x and dx.}$$

$$= \frac{1}{2}\frac{u^{3/2}}{3/2} + C \qquad \textit{Power Rule}$$

$$= \frac{1}{3}u^{3/2} + C \qquad \textit{Simplify.}$$

$$= \frac{1}{3}(x^2 - 1)^{3/2} + C \qquad \textit{Substitute for u.}$$

You can check this result by differentiating. ▬

EXAMPLE 3 *Integration by Substitution*

Find the indefinite integral

$$\int \frac{e^{3x}}{1 + e^{3x}}\, dx.$$

Solution
Consider the substitution $u = 1 + e^{3x}$, which produces $du = 3e^{3x}\, dx$. To create $3e^{3x}\, dx$ as part of the integral, multiply and divide by 3.

$$\int \frac{e^{3x}}{1 + e^{3x}}\, dx = \frac{1}{3}\int \overbrace{\frac{1}{1 + e^{3x}}}^{1/u}\overbrace{3e^{3x}\, dx}^{du} \qquad \textit{Multiply and divide by 3.}$$

$$= \frac{1}{3}\int \frac{1}{u}\, du \qquad \textit{Substitute for x and dx.}$$

$$= \frac{1}{3}\ln|u| + C \qquad \textit{Log Rule}$$

$$= \frac{1}{3}\ln(1 + e^{3x}) + C \qquad \textit{Substitute for u.}$$

Note that the absolute value is not necessary in the final answer because the quantity $(1 + e^{3x})$ is positive for all values of x. ▬

EXAMPLE 4 *Integration by Substitution*

Find the indefinite integral

$$\int x\sqrt{x-1}\,dx.$$

Solution

Consider the substitution $u = x - 1$, which produces $du = dx$ and $x = u + 1$.

$$\int x\sqrt{x-1}\,dx = \int (u+1)(u^{1/2})\,du \qquad \text{\textit{Substitute for x}}$$
$$\textit{and dx.}$$

$$= \int (u^{3/2} + u^{1/2})\,du$$

$$= \frac{u^{5/2}}{5/2} + \frac{u^{3/2}}{3/2} + C \qquad \textit{Power Rule}$$

$$= \frac{2}{5}(x-1)^{5/2} + \frac{2}{3}(x-1)^{3/2} + C \qquad \textit{Substitute for u.}$$

This form of the antiderivative can be further simplified.

$$\frac{2}{5}(x-1)^{5/2} + \frac{2}{3}(x-1)^{3/2} + C = \frac{6}{15}(x-1)^{5/2} + \frac{10}{15}(x-1)^{3/2} + C$$

$$= \frac{2}{15}(x-1)^{3/2}[3(x-1)+5] + C$$

$$= \frac{2}{15}(x-1)^{3/2}(3x+2) + C$$

You can check this answer by differentiating. ▬

Example 4 demonstrates one of the characteristics of integration by substitution. That is, the form of the antiderivative as it exists immediately after resubstitution into x-variable form can often be simplified. Thus, when working the exercises in this section, don't assume that your answer is incorrect just because it doesn't look exactly like the answer given in the back of the text. You may be able to reconcile the two answers by algebraic simplification.

▦ TECHNOLOGY

If you have access to a symbolic integration utility such as *Derive*, *Maple*, or *Mathematica*, try using it to solve several of the exercises in this section. For instance, the display at the right shows how *Derive* can be used to find the indefinite integral in Example 4.

1: $x\sqrt{(x - 1)}$ *Author.*

2: $\int x\sqrt{(x - 1)}\ dx$ *Integrate.*

3: $\dfrac{2(x - 1)^{3/2}(3x + 2)}{15}$ *Simplify.*

Substitution and Definite Integrals

The fourth step outlined in the guidelines for integration by substitution suggests that you convert back to the variable x. To evaluate *definite* integrals, however, it is often more convenient to determine the limits of integration for the variable u. This is often easier than converting back to the variable x and evaluating the antiderivative at the original limits.

EXAMPLE 5 *Using Substitution with a Definite Integral*

Evaluate the definite integral $\displaystyle\int_1^5 \frac{x}{\sqrt{2x-1}}\,dx$.

Solution

Use the substitution $u = \sqrt{2x-1}$, which implies that $u^2 = 2x-1$, $x = \frac{1}{2}(u^2+1)$, and $dx = u\,du$. Before substituting, determine the new upper and lower limits of integration.

Lower limit: When $x = 1$, $u = \sqrt{2(1)-1} = 1$.
Upper limit: When $x = 5$, $u = \sqrt{2(5)-1} = 3$.

Now, substitute and integrate, as follows.

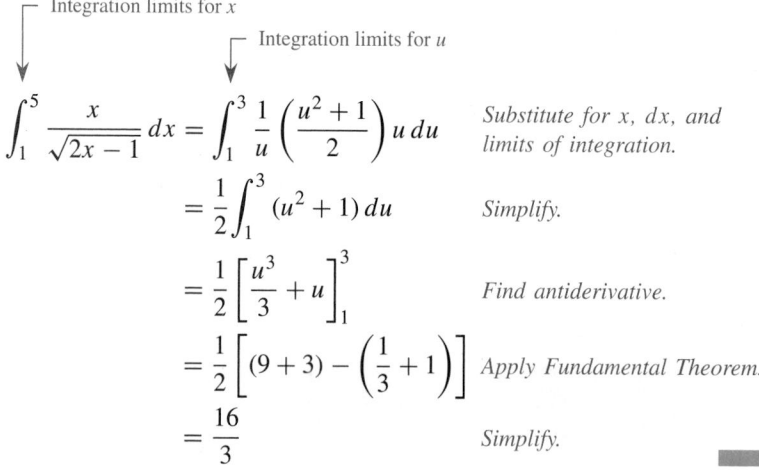

$$\underbrace{\int_1^5}\frac{x}{\sqrt{2x-1}}\,dx = \int_1^3 \frac{1}{u}\left(\frac{u^2+1}{2}\right)u\,du \qquad \text{Substitute for } x, dx, \text{ and limits of integration.}$$

$$= \frac{1}{2}\int_1^3 (u^2+1)\,du \qquad \text{Simplify.}$$

$$= \frac{1}{2}\left[\frac{u^3}{3}+u\right]_1^3 \qquad \text{Find antiderivative.}$$

$$= \frac{1}{2}\left[(9+3)-\left(\frac{1}{3}+1\right)\right] \qquad \text{Apply Fundamental Theorem.}$$

$$= \frac{16}{3} \qquad \text{Simplify.}$$

Integration limits for x
Integration limits for u

Note In Example 5, you can interpret the equation

$$\int_1^5 \frac{x}{\sqrt{2x-1}}\,dx = \int_1^3 \frac{1}{u}\left(\frac{u^2+1}{2}\right)u\,du$$

graphically to mean that the two different regions shown in Figures 6.1 and 6.2 have the same area.

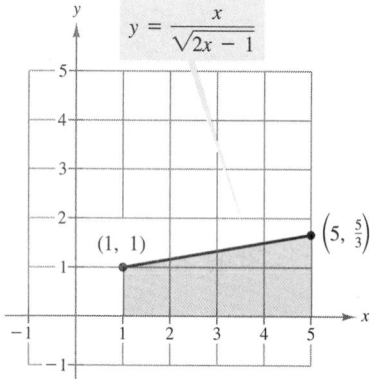

$$y = \frac{x}{\sqrt{2x-1}}$$

$(1, 1)$
$\left(5, \frac{5}{3}\right)$

FIGURE 6.1 Region Before Substitution

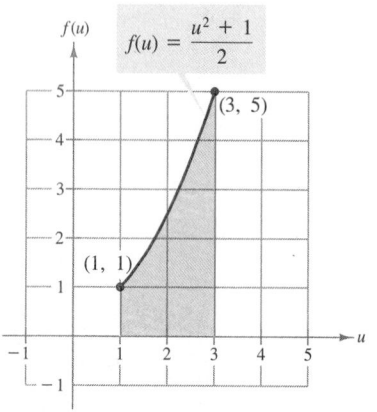

$$f(u) = \frac{u^2+1}{2}$$

$(3, 5)$
$(1, 1)$

FIGURE 6.2 Region After Substitution

Applications

Psychologists use definite integrals to represent the probability that an event will occur. For instance, a probability of 0.5 means that the event will occur about 50% of the time.

Integration can be used to find the probability that an event will occur. In such an application, the real-life situation is modeled by a *probability density function* f, and the probability that x will lie between a and b is represented by

$$P(a \le x \le b) = \int_a^b f(x)\,dx.$$

The probability $P(a \le x \le b)$ must be a number between 0 and 1.

Real Life

EXAMPLE 6 *Finding a Probability*

A psychologist finds that the probability that a participant in a memory experiment will recall between a and b percent (in decimal form) of the material is

$$P(a \le x \le b) = \int_a^b \frac{28}{9} x \sqrt[3]{1 - x}\,dx, \qquad 0 \le a \le b \le 1.$$

Find the probability that a randomly chosen participant will recall between 0% and 87.5% of the material.

Solution

Let $u = \sqrt[3]{1 - x}$. Then $u^3 = 1 - x$, $x = 1 - u^3$, and $dx = -3u^2\,du$.

   Lower limit: When $x = 0$, $u = \sqrt[3]{1 - 0} = 1$.
   Upper limit: When $x = 0.875$, $u = \sqrt[3]{1 - 0.875} = 0.5$.

To find the probability, substitute and integrate, as follows.

$$\int_0^{0.875} \frac{28}{9} x \sqrt[3]{1 - x}\,dx = \int_1^{1/2} \left[\frac{28}{9}(1 - u^3)(u)(-3u^2) \right] du$$

$$= 3\left(\frac{28}{9}\right) \int_1^{1/2} (u^6 - u^3)\,du$$

$$= \frac{28}{3} \left[\frac{u^7}{7} - \frac{u^4}{4} \right]_1^{1/2}$$

$$\approx 0.865$$

Thus, the probability is about 86.5%, as indicated in Figure 6.3.

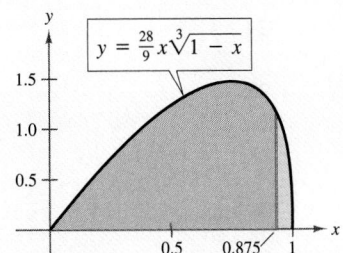

$y = \frac{28}{9} x \sqrt[3]{1 - x}$

FIGURE 6.3

Discussion Problem   *Extending the Example*

In Example 6, explain how you could find a value of b such that $P(0 \le x \le b) = 0.5$.

Warm Up

The following warm-up exercises involve skills that were covered in earlier sections. You will use these skills in the exercise set for this section.

In Exercises 1–6, evaluate the indefinite integral.

1. $\int 5\,dx$

2. $\int x^{3/2}\,dx$

3. $\int 2x(x^2+1)^3\,dx$

4. $\int 6e^{6x}\,dx$

5. $\int \dfrac{2}{2x+1}\,dx$

6. $\int 2xe^{-x^2}\,dx$

In Exercises 7–10, simplify the expression.

7. $2x(x-1)^2 + x(x-1)$

8. $6x(x+4)^3 - 3x^2(x+4)^2$

9. $3(x+7)^{1/2} - 2x(x+7)^{-1/2}$

10. $(x+5)^{1/3} - 5(x+5)^{-2/3}$

E X E R C I S E S   6.1   means that technology can help you solve or check the exercise(s).

In Exercises 1–40, evaluate the indefinite integral.

1. $\int (x-2)^4\,dx$

2. $\int (x+5)^{3/2}\,dx$

3. $\int \dfrac{2}{(t-9)^2}\,dt$

4. $\int \dfrac{2t-1}{t^2-t+2}\,dt$

5. $\int \sqrt{1+x}\,dx$

6. $\int (3+x)^5\,dx$

7. $\int \dfrac{12x+2}{3x^2+x}\,dx$

8. $\int \dfrac{6x^2+2}{x^3+x}\,dx$

9. $\int \dfrac{1}{(5x+1)^3}\,dx$

10. $\int \dfrac{1}{(3x+1)^2}\,dx$

11. $\int \dfrac{1}{\sqrt{x+1}}\,dx$

12. $\int \dfrac{1}{\sqrt{5x+1}}\,dx$

13. $\int \dfrac{e^{3x}}{1-e^{3x}}\,dx$

14. $\int 2xe^{3x^2}\,dx$

15. $\int \dfrac{x^2}{x-1}\,dx$

16. $\int \dfrac{2x}{x-4}\,dx$

17. $\int x\sqrt{x^2+4}\,dx$

18. $\int \dfrac{t}{\sqrt{1-t^2}}\,dt$

19. $\int e^{5x}\,dx$

20. $\int \dfrac{e^x}{1+e^x}\,dx$

21. $\int \dfrac{x}{(x+1)^4}\,dx$

22. $\int \dfrac{x^2}{(x+1)^3}\,dx$

23. $\int \dfrac{x}{(3x-1)^2}\,dx$

24. $\int \dfrac{5x}{(x-4)^3}\,dx$

25. $\int x(1-x)^4\,dx$

26. $\int x^2(1-x)^3\,dx$

27. $\int \dfrac{x-1}{x^2-2x}\,dx$

28. $\int \dfrac{x}{(x^2-1)^2}\,dx$

29. $\int x\sqrt{x-3}\,dx$

30. $\int x\sqrt{2x+1}\,dx$

31. $\int x^2\sqrt{1-x}\,dx$

32. $\int x^3\sqrt{x+2}\,dx$

33. $\int \dfrac{x^2-1}{\sqrt{2x-1}}\,dx$

34. $\int \dfrac{2x-1}{\sqrt{x+3}}\,dx$

35. $\int t\sqrt[3]{t+1}\,dt$

36. $\int x\sqrt[3]{x-2}\,dx$

37. $\int \dfrac{1}{\sqrt{t}-1}\,dt$

38. $\int \dfrac{1}{\sqrt{x}+1}\,dx$

39. $\int \dfrac{2\sqrt{t}+1}{t}\,dt$

40. $\int \dfrac{6x+\sqrt{2x}}{x}\,dx$

In Exercises 41–52, evaluate the definite integral.

41. $\int_0^4 \sqrt{2x + 1}\, dx$

42. $\int_2^4 \sqrt{4x + 1}\, dx$

43. $\int_0^1 3xe^{x^2}\, dx$

44. $\int_0^2 e^{-2x}\, dx$

45. $\int_0^4 \frac{x}{(x + 4)^2}\, dx$

46. $\int_0^1 x(x + 5)^4\, dx$

47. $\int_0^{0.5} x(1 - x)^3\, dx$

48. $\int_0^{0.5} x^2(1 - x)^3\, dx$

49. $\int_3^7 x\sqrt{x - 3}\, dx$

50. $\int_0^4 \frac{x}{\sqrt{2x + 1}}\, dx$

51. $\int_0^7 x\sqrt[3]{x + 1}\, dx$

52. $\int_1^2 (x - 1)\sqrt{2 - x}\, dx$

In Exercises 53–56, find the area of the region bounded by the graphs of the equations.

53. $y = -x\sqrt{x + 2}$, $y = 0$

54. $y = x\sqrt[3]{1 - x}$, $y = 0$

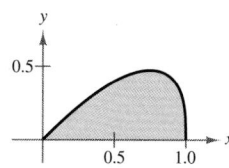

55. $y^2 = x^2(1 - x^2)$

(*Hint:* Find the area of the region bounded by $y = x\sqrt{1 - x^2}$ and $y = 0$. Then multiply by 4.)

56. $y = 1/\left(1 + \sqrt{x}\right)$, $y = 0$, $x = 0$, $x = 4$

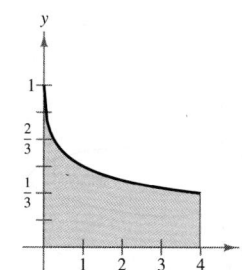

In Exercises 57 and 58, find the volume of the solid generated by revolving the region bounded by the graphs of the equations about the *x*-axis.

57. $y = x\sqrt{1 - x^2}$

58. $y = \sqrt{x}(1 - x)^2$, $y = 0$

In Exercises 59 and 60, find the average amount by which the function *f* exceeds the function *g* on the interval.

59. $f(x) = \frac{1}{x + 1}$, $g(x) = \frac{x}{(x + 1)^2}$, $[0, 1]$

60. $f(x) = x\sqrt{4x + 1}$, $g(x) = 2\sqrt{x^3}$, $[0, 2]$

61. *Probability* The probability of recall in an experiment is modeled by

$$P(a \le x \le b) = \int_a^b \frac{15}{4} x\sqrt{1 - x}\, dx,$$

where *x* is the percent of recall (see figure).

(a) What is the probability of recalling between 40% and 80%?

(b) What is the median percent recall? That is, for what value of *b* is $P(0 \le x \le b) = 0.5$?

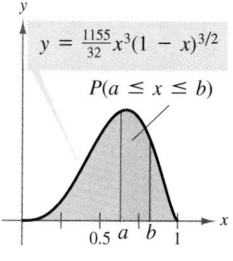

FIGURE FOR 61   FIGURE FOR 62

62. *Probability* The probability of finding between *a* and *b* percent of iron in ore samples is modeled by

$$P(a \le x \le b) = \int_a^b \frac{1155}{32} x^3(1 - x)^{3/2}\, dx$$

(see figure). Find the probability that a sample will contain between (a) 0% and 25%, and (b) 50% and 100% of iron.

63. *Revenue* A company sells a seasonal product that has a daily revenue modeled by

$$R = 0.06t^2(365 - t)^{1/2} + 1250, \qquad 0 \le t \le 365.$$

Find the average daily revenue over the period of 1 year.

64. *Revenue* Describe a product whose seasonal sales pattern resembles the model in Exercise 63. Explain your reasoning.

In Exercises 65 and 66, use the Midpoint Rule with $n = 10$ to approximate the area of the region bounded by the graph(s) of the equation(s).

65. $y = \sqrt[3]{x}\sqrt{4 - x}$, $y = 0$

66. $y^2 = x^2(1 - x^2)$

Integration by Parts

In this section, you will study an integration technique called **integration by parts.** This technique is particularly useful for integrands involving the products of algebraic and exponential or logarithmic functions, such as $\int x^2 e^x \, dx$ and $\int x \ln x \, dx$. Integration by parts is based on the Product Rule.

$$\frac{d}{dx}[uv] = uv' + vu' \qquad\qquad \textit{Product Rule}$$

$$uv = \int uv' \, dx + \int vu' \, dx \qquad \textit{Integrate both sides.}$$

$$uv = \int u \, dv + \int v \, du \qquad \textit{Write in differential form.}$$

$$\int u \, dv = uv - \int v \, du \qquad \textit{Rewrite.}$$

Note When using integration by parts, note that you can first choose dv or first choose u. After you do, however, the choice of the other factor is determined—it must be the remaining portion of the integrand. Also note that dv *must* contain the differential dx of the original integral.

Integration by Parts

Let u and v be differentiable functions of x.

$$\int u \, dv = uv - \int v \, du$$

Note that the formula for integration by parts expresses the original integral in terms of another integral. Depending on the choices for u and dv, it may be easier to evaluate the second integral than the original one.

Guidelines for Integration by Parts

1. Let dv be the most complicated portion of the integrand that fits a basic integration formula. Let u be the remaining factor.
2. Let u be the portion of the integrand whose derivative is a simpler function than u itself. Let dv be the remaining factor.

EXAMPLE 1 *Integration by Parts*

Find the indefinite integral $\int xe^x \, dx$.

Solution

To apply integration by parts, you must rewrite the original integral in the form $\int u \, dv$. That is, you must break $xe^x \, dx$ into two factors—one "part" representing u and the other "part" representing dv. There are several ways to do this.

$$\underbrace{\int (x)}_{u}\underbrace{(e^x \, dx)}_{dv} \quad \underbrace{\int (e^x)}_{u}\underbrace{(x \, dx)}_{dv} \quad \underbrace{\int (1)}_{u}\underbrace{(xe^x \, dx)}_{dv} \quad \underbrace{\int (xe^x)}_{u}\underbrace{(dx)}_{dv}$$

Following the guidelines, you should choose the first option because $dv = e^x \, dx$ is the most complicated portion of the integrand that fits a basic integration formula *and* because the derivative of $u = x$ is simpler than x.

$$dv = e^x \, dx \quad \longrightarrow \quad v = \int dv = \int e^x \, dx = e^x$$

$$u = x \quad \longrightarrow \quad du = dx$$

With these substitutions, you can apply the integration by parts formula as follows.

$$\int xe^x \, dx = xe^x - \int e^x \, dx \qquad \text{\textit{$\int u \, dv = uv - \int v \, du$}}$$

$$= xe^x - e^x + C \qquad \text{\textit{Integrate $\int e^x \, dx$.}} \qquad \blacksquare$$

Note In Example 1, notice that you do not need to include a constant of integration when solving $v = \int e^x \, dx = e^x$. To see why this is true, try replacing e^x by $e^x + C_1$ in the solution.

$$\int xe^x \, dx = x(e^x + C_1) - \int (e^x + C_1) \, dx$$

After integrating, you can see that the terms involving C_1 cancel.

1: x ê^x	*Author.*
2: $\int$ x ê^x dx	*Integrate.*
3: ê^x(x − 1)	*Simplify.*

Note To remember the integration by parts formula, you might like to use the following "Z" pattern. The top row represents the original integral, the diagonal row represents uv, and the bottom row represents the new integral.

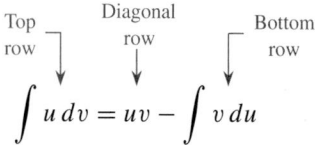

$$\int u \, dv = uv - \int v \, du$$

EXAMPLE 2 Integration by Parts

Find the indefinite integral $\int x^2 \ln x \, dx$.

Solution
For this integral, x^2 is more easily integrated than $\ln x$. Furthermore, the derivative of $\ln x$ is simpler than $\ln x$. Therefore, you should choose $dv = x^2 \, dx$.

$$dv = x^2 \, dx \quad \longrightarrow \quad v = \int dv = \int x^2 \, dx = \frac{x^3}{3}$$

$$u = \ln x \quad \longrightarrow \quad du = \frac{1}{x} \, dx$$

Using these substitutions, apply the integration by parts formula as follows.

$$\int x^2 \ln x \, dx = \frac{x^3}{3} \ln x - \int \left(\frac{x^3}{3} \right) \left(\frac{1}{x} \right) dx \qquad \int u \, dv = uv - \int v \, du$$

$$= \frac{x^3}{3} \ln x - \frac{1}{3} \int x^2 \, dx \qquad \textit{Simplify.}$$

$$= \frac{x^3}{3} \ln x - \frac{x^3}{9} + C \qquad \textit{Integrate.}$$

EXAMPLE 3 Integrating by Parts with a Single Factor

Find the indefinite integral $\int \ln x \, dx$.

Solution
This integral is unusual because it has only one factor. In such cases, you should choose $dv = dx$ and choose u to be the single factor.

$$dv = dx \quad \longrightarrow \quad v = \int dv = \int dx = x$$

$$u = \ln x \quad \longrightarrow \quad du = \frac{1}{x} \, dx$$

Using these substitutions, apply the integration by parts formula as follows.

$$\int \ln x \, dx = x \ln x - \int \left(\frac{1}{x} \right) (x) \, dx \qquad \int u \, dv = uv - \int v \, du$$

$$= x \ln x - \int dx \qquad \textit{Simplify.}$$

$$= x \ln x - x + C \qquad \textit{Integrate.}$$

EXAMPLE 4 *Using Integration by Parts Repeatedly*

Find the indefinite integral $\int x^2 e^x \, dx$.

Solution
Using the guidelines, notice that the derivative of x^2 becomes simpler, whereas the derivative of e^x does not. Therefore, you should let $u = x^2$ and let $dv = e^x \, dx$.

$$dv = e^x \, dx \quad \longrightarrow \quad v = \int dv = \int e^x \, dx = e^x$$

$$u = x^2 \quad \longrightarrow \quad du = 2x \, dx$$

Using these substitutions, apply the integration by parts formula as follows.

$$\int x^2 e^x \, dx = x^2 e^x - \int 2x e^x \, dx \qquad \begin{array}{l}\textit{First application of}\\ \textit{integration by parts}\end{array}$$

To evaluate the new integral on the right, apply integration by parts a second time, using the following substitutions.

$$dv = e^x \, dx \quad \longrightarrow \quad v = \int dv = \int e^x \, dx = e^x$$

$$u = 2x \quad \longrightarrow \quad du = 2 \, dx$$

Using these substitutions, apply the integration by parts formula as follows.

$$\int x^2 e^x \, dx = x^2 e^x - \int 2x e^x \, dx \qquad \begin{array}{l}\textit{First application of}\\ \textit{integration by parts}\end{array}$$

$$= x^2 e^x - \left(2x e^x - \int 2e^x \, dx\right) \qquad \begin{array}{l}\textit{Second application of}\\ \textit{integration by parts}\end{array}$$

$$= x^2 e^x - 2x e^x + 2e^x + C \qquad \textit{Integrate.}$$

$$= e^x (x^2 - 2x + 2) + C \qquad \textit{Simplify.}$$

You can confirm this result by differentiating.   ■

Note Remember that you can check an indefinite integral by differentiating. For instance, in Example 4, try differentiating the antiderivative

$$e^x (x^2 - 2x + 2) + C$$

to check that you obtain the original integrand, $x^2 e^x$.

When making repeated applications of integration by parts, be careful not to interchange the substitutions in successive applications. For instance, in Example 4, the first substitutions were $dv = e^x \, dx$ and $u = x^2$. If in the second application you had switched to $dv = 2x \, dx$ and $u = e^x$, you would have reversed the previous integration and returned to the *original* integral.

$$\int x^2 e^x \, dx = x^2 e^x - \left(x^2 e^x - \int x^2 e^x \, dx\right)$$

$$= \int x^2 e^x \, dx$$

EXAMPLE 5 *Evaluating a Definite Integral*

Evaluate the definite integral

$$\int_1^e \ln x \, dx.$$

Solution

Integration by parts was used to find the antiderivative of $\ln x$ in Example 3. Using this result, you can evaluate the definite integral as follows.

$$\int_1^e \ln x \, dx = \left[x \ln x - x \right]_1^e \qquad \textit{Use result of Example 3.}$$

$$= (e \ln e - e) - (1 \ln 1 - 1) \qquad \textit{Apply Fundamental Theorem.}$$

$$= (e - e) - (0 - 1)$$

$$= 1 \qquad \textit{Simplify.}$$

The area represented by this definite integral is shown in Figure 6.4. ▬

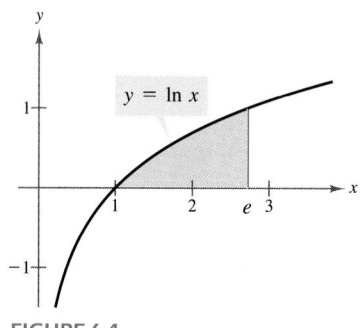

y = ln x

FIGURE 6.4

Before starting the exercises in this section, remember that it is not enough to know *how* to use the various integration techniques. You also must know *when* to use them. Integration is first and foremost a problem of recognition— recognizing which formula or technique to apply to obtain an antiderivative. Often, a slight alteration of an integrand will necessitate the use of a different integration technique. Here are some examples.

Integral	*Technique*	*Antiderivative*
$\int x \ln x \, dx$	Integration by parts	$\dfrac{x^2}{2} \ln x - \dfrac{x^2}{4} + C$
$\int \dfrac{\ln x}{x} \, dx$	Power Rule: $\int u^n \dfrac{du}{dx} \, dx$	$\dfrac{(\ln x)^2}{2} + C$
$\int \dfrac{1}{x \ln x} \, dx$	Log Rule: $\int \dfrac{1}{u} \dfrac{du}{dx} \, dx$	$\ln |\ln x| + C$

As you gain experience with integration by parts, your skill in determining u and dv will improve. The summary below gives suggestions for choosing u and dv.

Summary of Common Uses of Integration by Parts

1. $\int x^n e^{ax} \, dx$ Let $u = x^n$ and $dv = e^{ax} \, dx$. (Examples 1 and 4)

2. $\int x^n \ln x \, dx$ Let $u = \ln x$ and $dv = x^n \, dx$. (Examples 2 and 3)

Present Value

In some business applications, the future income for a business is known. For instance, the annual income might be given by $c(t)$. During a period of t_1 years, the total income would then be given by integrating $c(t)$ between $t = 0$ and $t = t_1$. To assign a **present value** to this income, you must use an exponential *damping factor* that takes into account future inflation. If the annual inflation rate is assumed to be r, then the damping factor is e^{-rt}.

Present Value

If $c(t)$ represents an income function over time and the annual rate of inflation is r, then the actual total income over t_1 years is

$$\text{Actual income over } t_1 \text{ years} = \int_0^{t_1} c(t)\,dt$$

and its **present value** is

$$\text{Present value} = \int_0^{t_1} c(t)e^{-rt}\,dt.$$

EXAMPLE 6 *Finding Present Value*

You have just won a state lottery for $1,000,000. You will be paid $50,000 a year for 20 years. Assuming an annual inflation rate of 6%, what is the present value of this income?

Solution

The income function for your winnings is $c(t) = 50{,}000$. Thus, your actual income is

$$\text{Actual income} = \int_0^{20} 50{,}000\,dt = \left[50{,}000t \right]_0^{20} = \$1{,}000{,}000.$$

Because you do not receive this entire amount now, its present value is less than $1,000,000, and is

$$\text{Present value} = \int_0^{20} 50{,}000e^{-0.06t}\,dt = \left[\frac{50{,}000}{-0.06}e^{-0.06t} \right]_0^{20} \approx \$582{,}338.$$

This present value represents the amount that the state must deposit now to cover your payments over the next 20 years. This shows why state lotteries are so profitable—for the states!

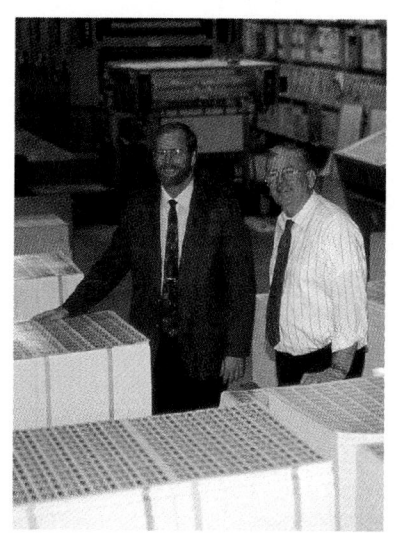

© Kent Sievers

In 1990, 32 states had state lotteries, and they totaled about $19 billion in revenue. Of this, 54% was paid out in prizes and 6% was used to cover the state lotteries' administration costs. These costs include the cost of making the lottery tickets. Chris and Chuck Harter, who own American Games, Inc., sell more than $15 million worth of lottery tickets and bingo cards to states and charitable organizations.

Present Value of Expected Income

FIGURE 6.5

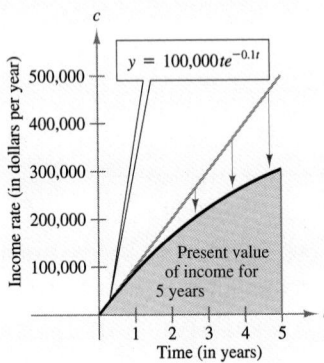

EXAMPLE 7 *Finding Present Value*

A company expects its income during the next 5 years to be given by

$$c(t) = 100,000t.$$

Assuming an annual inflation rate of 10%, what is the present value of this income?

Solution

The present value is

$$\text{Present value} = \int_0^5 100,000te^{-0.1t}\, dt = 100,000\int_0^5 te^{-0.1t}\, dt.$$

Using integration by parts, let $dv = e^{-0.1t}\, dt$ and obtain the following.

$$dv = e^{-0.1t}\, dt \quad \longrightarrow \quad v = \int dv = \int e^{-0.1t}\, dt = -10e^{-0.1t}$$
$$u = t \quad \longrightarrow \quad du = dt$$

This implies that

$$\int te^{-0.1t}\, dt = -10te^{-0.1t} + 10\int e^{-0.1t}\, dt$$
$$= -10te^{-01.t} - 100e^{-0.1t}$$
$$= -10e^{-0.1t}(t + 10).$$

Therefore, the present value is

$$\text{Present value} = 100,000\int_0^5 te^{-0.1t}\, dt$$
$$= 100,000\left[-10e^{-0.1t}(t + 10)\right]_0^5$$
$$\approx \$902,040.$$

Discussion Problem   Present Value

As shown in Figure 6.5, the actual income for the business in Example 7, over the next 5 years, is

$$\text{Actual income} = \int_0^5 100,000t\, dt = \$1,250,000.$$

If you were selling this company for its present value over a 5-year period, would it be to your advantage to argue that the inflation rate was lower than 10%? Explain your reasoning.

Warm Up

The following warm-up exercises involve skills that were covered in earlier sections. You will use these skills in the exercise set for this section.

In Exercises 1–6, find $f'(x)$.

1. $f(x) = 3x^4 + 2x - 1$

2. $f(x) = \frac{1}{4}x^2 + \frac{1}{8}x + 4$

3. $f(x) = \ln(x^4 + x^2)$

4. $f(x) = e^{x^3}$

5. $f(x) = x^2 e^x$

6. $f(x) = \dfrac{x + 1}{x - 3}$

In Exercises 7–10, find the area between the graphs of f and g.

7. $f(x) = -x^2 + 4$, $g(x) = x^2 - 4$

8. $f(x) = -x^2 + 2$, $g(x) = 1$

9. $f(x) = 4x$, $g(x) = x^2$

10. $f(x) = x^3 - 3x^2 + 2$, $g(x) = x - 1$

EXERCISES 6.2   means that technology can help you solve or check the exercise(s).

In Exercises 1–6, use integration by parts to find the indefinite integral.

1. $\displaystyle \int xe^{3x}\, dx$

2. $\displaystyle \int xe^{-x}\, dx$

3. $\displaystyle \int x^2 e^{-x}\, dx$

4. $\displaystyle \int x^2 e^{2x}\, dx$

5. $\displaystyle \int \ln 2x\, dx$

6. $\displaystyle \int \ln x^2\, dx$

In Exercises 7–30, find the indefinite integral. (*Hint:* Integration by parts is not required for all the integrals.)

7. $\displaystyle \int e^{4x}\, dx$

8. $\displaystyle \int e^{-2x}\, dx$

9. $\displaystyle \int xe^{4x}\, dx$

10. $\displaystyle \int xe^{-2x}\, dx$

11. $\displaystyle \int xe^{x^2}\, dx$ *do - awesome.*

12. $\displaystyle \int x^2 e^{x^3}\, dx$

13. $\displaystyle \int x^2 e^x\, dx$

14. $\displaystyle \int \dfrac{x}{e^x}\, dx$

15. $\displaystyle \int x^3 e^x\, dx$

16. $\displaystyle \int \dfrac{e^{1/t}}{t^2}\, dt$

17. $\displaystyle \int x^3 \ln x\, dx$

18. $\displaystyle \int x^2 \ln x\, dx$

19. $\displaystyle \int t \ln(t + 1)\, dt$

20. $\displaystyle \int \dfrac{1}{x(\ln x)^3}\, dx$

21. $\displaystyle \int x(\ln x)^2\, dx$

22. $\displaystyle \int \ln 3x\, dx$

23. $\displaystyle \int \dfrac{(\ln x)^2}{x}\, dx$

24. $\displaystyle \int \dfrac{\ln x}{x^2}\, dx$

25. $\displaystyle \int x\sqrt{x - 1}\, dx$

26. $\displaystyle \int x(x + 1)^2\, dx$

27. $\displaystyle \int (x^2 - 1)e^x\, dx$

28. $\displaystyle \int \dfrac{x}{\sqrt{2 + 3x}}\, dx$

 do this one 4REVIEW

29. $\displaystyle \int \dfrac{xe^{2x}}{(2x + 1)^2}\, dx$

30. $\displaystyle \int \dfrac{x^3 e^{x^2}}{(x^2 + 1)^2}\, dx$

In Exercises 31–34, evaluate the definite integral.

31. $\displaystyle \int_0^1 x^2 e^x\, dx$

32. $\displaystyle \int_0^2 \dfrac{x^2}{e^x}\, dx$

33. $\displaystyle \int_1^e x^5 \ln x\, dx$

34. $\displaystyle \int_0^1 \ln(1 + 2x)\, dx$

In Exercises 35–38, find the indefinite integral using the specified method.

35. $\int 2x\sqrt{2x-3}\,dx$

(a) By parts, letting $dv = \sqrt{2x-3}\,dx$

(b) By substitution, letting $u = \sqrt{2x-3}$

36. $\int x\sqrt{4+x}\,dx$

(a) By parts, letting $dv = \sqrt{4+x}\,dx$

(b) By substitution, letting $u = \sqrt{4+x}$

37. $\int \dfrac{x}{\sqrt{4+5x}}\,dx$

(a) By parts, letting $dv = \dfrac{1}{\sqrt{4+5x}}\,dx$

(b) By substitution, letting $u = \sqrt{4+5x}$

38. $\int x\sqrt{4-x}\,dx$

(a) By parts, letting $dv = \sqrt{4-x}\,dx$

(b) By substitution, letting $u = \sqrt{4-x}$

In Exercises 39 and 40, use integration by parts to verify the formula.

39. $\int x^n \ln x\,dx = \dfrac{x^{n+1}}{(n+1)^2}[-1+(n+1)\ln x]+C,$

$n \neq -1$

40. $\int x^n e^{ax}\,dx = \dfrac{x^n e^{ax}}{a} - \dfrac{n}{a}\int x^{n-1} e^{ax}\,dx$

In Exercises 41–44, use the results of Exercises 39 and 40 to find the indefinite integral.

41. $\int x^2 e^{5x}\,dx$

42. $\int xe^{-3x}\,dx$

43. $\int x^{-2}\ln x\,dx$

44. $\int x^{1/2}\ln x\,dx$

In Exercises 45 and 46, find the area of the region bounded by the graphs of the given equations.

45. $y = xe^{-x},\ y = 0,\ x = 4$

46. $y = \frac{1}{9}xe^{-x/3},\ y = 0,\ x = 0,\ x = 3$

47. Given the region bounded by the graphs of $y = 2\ln x$, $y = 0$, and $x = e$, find

(a) the area of the region.

(b) the volume of the solid generated by revolving the region about the x-axis.

48. Find the volume of the solid generated by revolving the region bounded by the graphs of $y = xe^x$, $y = 0$, $x = 0$, and $x = 1$ about the x-axis (see figure).

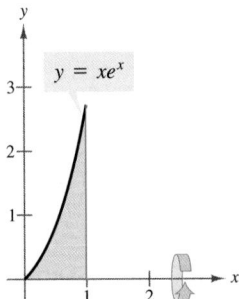

In Exercises 49–52, use a symbolic integrator to evaluate the integral.

49. $\int_0^2 t^3 e^{-4t}\,dt$

50. $\int_1^4 \ln x(x^2+4)\,dx$

51. $\int_0^5 x^4(25-x^2)^{3/2}\,dx$

52. $\int_1^e x^9 \ln x\,dx$

53. *Product Demand* A manufacturing company forecasts that the demand x (in units) for its product over the next 10 years can be modeled by

$$x = 500(20 + te^{-0.1t}), \qquad 0 \le t \le 10,$$

where t is the time in years.

(a) Is the company forecasting an increase or decrease in demand over the decade?

(b) According to the model, what is the total demand over the next 10 years?

(c) Find the average annual demand during the 10-year period.

54. *Capital Campaign* The board of trustees of a college is planning a 5-year capital gifts campaign to raise money for the college. The goal is to have an annual gift income I that is modeled by

$$I = 2000(375 + 68te^{-0.2t}), \qquad 0 \le t \le 5,$$

where t is the time in years.

(a) Does the board of trustees expect the gift income to increase or decrease over the 5-year period?

(b) Find the expected total gift income over the 5-year period.

(c) Determine the average annual gift income over the 5-year period. Compare the result with the income given when $t = 3$.

55. *Learning Theory*   A model for the ability M of a child to memorize, measured on a scale from 0 to 10, is

$$M = 1 + 1.6t \ln t, \qquad 0 < t \leq 4,$$

where t is the child's age in years. Find the average value of this model between

(a) the child's first and second birthdays.
(b) the child's third and fourth birthdays.

56. *Revenue*   A company sells a seasonal product. The revenue from the product can be modeled by

$$R = 410.5t^2 e^{-t/30} + 25{,}000, \qquad 0 \leq t \leq 365,$$

where t is the time in days.

(a) Find the average daily receipts during the first quarter, which is given by $0 \leq t \leq 91$.
(b) Find the average daily receipts during the fourth quarter, which is given by $274 \leq t \leq 365$.
(c) Find the total daily receipts during the year.

Present Value   In Exercises 57–62, find the present value of the income c (measured in dollars) over t_1 years at the given annual inflation rate r.

57. $c = 5000$, $r = 5\%$, $t_1 = 4$ years

58. $c = 450$, $r = 4\%$, $t_1 = 10$ years

59. $c = 150{,}000 + 2500t$, $r = 4\%$, $t_1 = 10$ years

60. $c = 30{,}000 + 500t$, $r = 7\%$, $t_1 = 6$ years

61. $c = 1000 + 50e^{t/2}$, $r = 6\%$, $t_1 = 4$ years

62. $c = 5000 + 25te^{t/10}$, $r = 6\%$, $t_1 = 10$ years

63. *Present Value*   A company expects its income c during the next 4 years to be modeled by

$$c = 150{,}000 + 75{,}000t.$$

(a) Find the actual income for the business over the 4 years.
(b) Assuming an annual inflation rate of 4%, what is the present value of this income?

64. *Contract Value*   A professional athlete signs a 3-year contract in which the earnings can be modeled by

$$c = 300{,}000 + 125{,}000t.$$

(a) Find the actual value of the athlete's contract.
(b) Assuming an annual inflation rate of 5%, what is the present value of the contract?

65. Use the Midpoint Rule with $n = 10$ to approximate

$$\int_1^4 \frac{4}{\sqrt{x} + \sqrt[3]{x}} \, dx.$$

66. Use the Midpoint Rule with $n = 12$ to approximate the volume of the solid generated by revolving the region bounded by the graphs of

$$y = \frac{10}{\sqrt{xe^x}}, \, y = 0, \, x = 1, \text{ and } x = 4$$

about the x-axis.

Future Value   In Exercises 67 and 68, find the future value of the income (in dollars) given by $f(t)$ over t_1 years at the annual interest rate of r. If f represents an investment function over a period of t_1 years that is continuously invested at an annual interest rate of r (compounded continuously), then the **future value** of the investment is given by

$$\text{Future value} = e^{rt_1} \int_0^{t_1} f(t)e^{-rt} \, dt.$$

67. $f(t) = 3000$, $r = 8\%$, $t_1 = 10$ years

68. $f(t) = 3000e^{0.05t}$, $r = 10\%$, $t_1 = 5$ years

69. *College Expenses*   In 1993, the total cost to attend Notre Dame University for 1 year was estimated to be \$19,937. If your grandparents had continuously invested in a college fund according to the model

$$f(t) = 250t$$

for 18 years, at an annual interest rate of 10%, would the fund have grown enough to allow you to cover 4 years of expenses at Notre Dame?

Case Study: Saving for a Child's College Education

We are often interested in determining the present value of a stream of income flows in the future. For example, an investor might wish to compute the present value of her accumulated savings over 20 years if she saves a fixed dollar amount every year. But Kay Johnson, a certified financial planner with Provident Wealth Management, Inc., explains that it is quite common for individuals seeking financial security to pose the question in reverse: In order to achieve a desired level of accumulated savings after, say, 20 years, how much needs to be saved every time period?

One typical scenario is that faced by parents who want to make sure that enough money will be saved for their newborn child's education. Suppose, for example, it is anticipated that $100,000 will be necessary for college expenses when the child turns 18. Generally, the following two options are available:

Option #1

The new parents could set aside one lump-sum amount today, investing it to earn the prevailing market interest rate so that, with the compounding of interest, the desired level of income would be achieved after 18 years. The concept of *present value* enables us to compute the lump-sum amount that needs to be invested today.

From Chapter 6, we know that if P is the amount deposited today and r is the annual interest rate (in decimal form), then the balance will grow to A after t years, if interest is compounded continuously, according to the following equation: $A = Pe^{rt}$. A is called the future value of P. But this equation can be rearranged to find the amount P that must be deposited today to achieve a specified level of A after t years: $P = Ae^{-rt}$. P is called the *present value* of A. So, for the new parents who want to accumulate $100,000 after 18 years, assuming an interest rate of 8 percent compounded continuously, the lump-sum deposit they must make today is: $P = (100,000)e^{-(0.08)(18)} = \$23,692.80$.

Option #2

Many young parents, however, are unable to set aside such a large lump-sum deposit all at once, despite the benefits from compound interest. For them, it might be more feasible to set aside a fixed dollar amount each year, over the course of 18 years. For these families, the question becomes: How much must be saved each year, if interest is compounded continuously, to accumulate $100,000 after 18 years? We know that the present value of a continuous income stream lasting for t_1 years at a constant rate of K dollars per year and an interest rate of r (in decimal form), compounded continuously, is:

$$\text{Present value} = \int_0^{t_1} Ke^{-rt}\, dt$$
$$= K \int_0^{t_1} e^{-rt}\, dt$$
$$= K \left[(-1/r)(e^{-rt})\right]_0^{t_1}$$
$$= \left[(-K/r)(e^{-rt_1})\right]_{t=0}^{t=t_1}$$
$$= \left[(-K/r)(e^{-rt_1} - 1)\right]$$
$$= (K/r)(1 - e^{-rt_1})$$

In option #1, we determined that it would be necessary to deposit $23,692.80 *today* to achieve the desired $100,000 18 years later. Using $23,692.80 as the present value in the equation just derived, we may solve for the constant deposit of K dollars per year that will lead to the desired present value of $23,692.80, and equivalently the desired future value of $100,000:

$$\$23{,}692.80 = (K/0.08)(1 - e^{-(0.08)(18)})$$

$$K = \$2483.94$$

Of course, if interest compounding and annual deposits are not continuous, but rather occur at discrete intervals, the amount of K will vary accordingly.

The following table summarizes and compares the two options:

Option	Total Accumulated Savings After 18 Years	Actual Savings	Interest Earned
#1	$100,000	$23,692.80	$76,307.20
#2	$100,000	$44,710.92 ($2483.94/year) · 18 years	$55,289.08

Edward D. Saloum

Donald L. Smith, Robin Smith, baby Alex, and Kay N. Johnson of the Provident Wealth Management Company ■

Assuming that option #2 is chosen, the actual dollar amount needed to be invested annually will still depend on both the interest rate and the desired level of total accumulated savings after 18 years. The table shows the required deposits per year for various levels of desired accumulated savings at different interest rates. Note that for any given interest rate, the amount of annual deposit will vary in direct proportion to the desired total accumulated savings.

Total Accumulated Savings After 18 Years	Annual Deposits Necessary at Various Interest Rates				
	$r = 6\%$	$r = 7\%$	$r = 8\%$	$r = 9\%$	$r = 10\%$
$100,000	3,085.35	2,771.82	2,483.94	2,220.53	1,980.34
$200,000	6,170.69	5,543.64	4,967.88	4,441.06	3,960.68
$300,000	9,256.03	8,315.46	7,451.82	6,661.59	5,941.02
$400,000	12,341.40	11,087.28	9,935.76	8,882.12	7,921.36

What Would You Do?

1. What effect would inflation have on the new parents' decisions concerning their saving for the education of their child? Recommend a strategy for overcoming inflation.

2. What would happen to the annual deposits under option #2 if the parents were able to deposit an increasing rather than a constant amount each year? Give examples.

3. Explore other circumstances to which the above analysis could be applicable.

Partial Fractions

In Sections 6.1 and 6.2, you studied integration by substitution and by parts. In this section you will study a third technique called **partial fractions.** This technique involves the decomposition of a rational function into the sum of two or more simple rational functions. For instance, suppose you know that

$$\frac{x+7}{x^2 - x - 6} = \frac{2}{x-3} - \frac{1}{x+2}.$$

Knowing the "partial fractions" on the right side would allow you to integrate the left side as follows.

$$\int \frac{x+7}{x^2 - x - 6}\, dx = \int \left(\frac{2}{x-3} - \frac{1}{x+2} \right) dx$$

$$= 2 \int \frac{1}{x-3}\, dx - \int \frac{1}{x+2}\, dx$$

$$= 2 \ln |x - 3| - \ln |x + 2| + C$$

To use this method, you must be able to factor the denominator of the original rational function *and* find the partial fraction decomposition of the function.

Note   A rational function $p(x)/q(x)$ is *proper* if the degree of the numerator is less than the degree of the denominator.

Partial Fractions

To find the partial fraction decomposition of the *proper* rational function $p(x)/q(x)$, factor $q(x)$ and write an equation that has the form

$$\frac{p(x)}{q(x)} = \text{(sum of partial fractions)}.$$

For each *distinct* linear factor $(ax + b)$, the right side should include a term of the form

$$\frac{A}{ax + b}.$$

For each *repeated* linear factor $(ax + b)^n$, the right side should include n terms of the form

$$\frac{A_1}{ax + b} + \frac{A_2}{(ax + b)^2} + \cdots + \frac{A_n}{(ax + b)^n}.$$

EXAMPLE 1 *Finding a Partial Fraction Decomposition*

Write the partial fraction decomposition for

$$\frac{x+7}{x^2-x-6}.$$

Solution

Begin by factoring the denominator as $x^2 - x - 6 = (x-3)(x+2)$. Then, write the partial fraction decomposition as

$$\frac{x+7}{x^2-x-6} = \frac{A}{x-3} + \frac{B}{x+2}.$$

To solve this equation for A and B, multiply both sides of the equation by the least common denominator $(x-3)(x+2)$. This produces the following **basic equation.**

$$x + 7 = A(x+2) + B(x-3) \qquad \textit{Basic equation}$$

Because this equation is true for all x, you can substitute any convenient values of x into the equation. The x-values that are especially convenient are the ones that make a factor of the least common denominator zero: $x = -2$ and $x = 3$.

Substitute $x = -2$:

$x + 7 = A(x+2) + B(x-3)$	*Basic equation*
$-2 + 7 = A(-2+2) + B(-2-3)$	*Substitute -2 for x.*
$5 = A(0) + B(-5)$	*Simplify.*
$-1 = B$	*Solve for B.*

Substitute $x = 3$:

$x + 7 = A(x+2) + B(x-3)$	*Basic equation*
$3 + 7 = A(3+2) + B(3-3)$	*Substitute 3 for x.*
$10 = A(5) + B(0)$	*Simplify.*
$2 = A$	*Solve for A.*

Now that you have solved the basic equation for A and B, you can write the partial fraction decomposition as

$$\frac{x+7}{x^2-x-6} = \frac{2}{x-3} - \frac{1}{x+2},$$

as indicated at the beginning of this section.

Note   Be sure you see that the substitutions for x in Example 1 are chosen for their convenience in solving for A and B. The value $x = -2$ is chosen because it eliminates the term $A(x+2)$, and the value $x = 3$ is chosen because it eliminates the term $B(x-3)$.

EXAMPLE 2 *Integrating with Repeated Factors*

Find the indefinite integral $\int \dfrac{5x^2 + 20x + 6}{x^3 + 2x^2 + x}\, dx$.

Solution
Begin by factoring the denominator as $x(x+1)^2$. Then, write the partial fraction decomposition as

$$\frac{5x^2 + 20x + 6}{x(x+1)^2} = \frac{A}{x} + \frac{B}{x+1} + \frac{C}{(x+1)^2}.$$

To solve this equation for A, B, and C, multiply both sides of the equation by the least common denominator $x(x+1)^2$.

$$5x^2 + 20x + 6 = A(x+1)^2 + Bx(x+1) + Cx \qquad \textit{Basic equation}$$

Now, solve for A and C by substituting $x = -1$ and $x = 0$ into the basic equation.

Substitute $x = -1$:
$$5(-1)^2 + 20(-1) + 6 = A(-1+1)^2 + B(-1)(-1+1) + C(-1)$$
$$-9 = A(0) + B(0) - C$$
$$9 = C \qquad \textit{Solve for C.}$$

Substitute $x = 0$:
$$5(0)^2 + 20(0) + 6 = A(0+1)^2 + B(0)(0+1) + C(0)$$
$$6 = A(1) + B(0) + C(0)$$
$$6 = A \qquad \textit{Solve for A.}$$

At this point, you have exhausted the convenient choices for x and have yet to solve for B. When this happens, you can use *any* other x-value along with the known values of A and C.

Substitute $x = 1$, $A = 6$, and $C = 9$:
$$5(1)^2 + 20(1) + 6 = (6)(1+1)^2 + B(1)(1+1) + (9)(1)$$
$$31 = 6(4) + B(2) + 9(1)$$
$$-1 = B \qquad \textit{Solve for B.}$$

Now that you have solved for A, B, and C, you can use the partial fraction decomposition to integrate.

$$\int \frac{5x^2 + 20x + 6}{x^3 + 2x^2 + x}\, dx = \int \left(\frac{6}{x} - \frac{1}{x+1} + \frac{9}{(x+1)^2} \right) dx$$
$$= 6\ln|x| - \ln|x+1| + 9\frac{(x+1)^{-1}}{-1} + C$$
$$= \ln \left| \frac{x^6}{x+1} \right| - \frac{9}{x+1} + C$$

TECHNOLOGY

The use of partial fractions depends on the ability to factor the denominator. If this cannot be easily done, then partial fractions should not be used. For instance, consider the integral

$$\int \frac{5x^2 + 20x + 6}{x^3 + 2x^2 + x + 1}\, dx.$$

This integral is only slightly different from that in Example 2, yet it is immensely more difficult to solve. When we tried using a symbolic integration utility on this integral, it was unable to solve it. Of course, if the integral had been a definite integral (as is true in many applied problems), then you can use an approximation technique such as the Midpoint Rule.

You can use the partial fraction decomposition technique outlined in Examples 1 and 2 only with a *proper* rational function—that is, a rational function whose numerator is of lower degree than its denominator. If the numerator is of equal or greater degree, you must divide first. For instance, the rational function

$$\frac{x^3}{x^2 + 1}$$

is improper because the degree of the numerator is greater than the degree of the denominator. Before applying partial fractions to this function, you should divide the denominator into the numerator to obtain

$$\frac{x^3}{x^2 + 1} = x - \frac{x}{x^2 + 1}.$$

EXAMPLE 3 *Integrating an Improper Rational Function*

Find the indefinite integral $\displaystyle\int \frac{x^5 + x - 1}{x^4 - x^3}\, dx$.

Solution

This rational function is improper—its numerator has a degree greater than that of its denominator. Thus, you should begin by dividing the denominator into the numerator to obtain

$$\frac{x^5 + x - 1}{x^4 - x^3} = x + 1 + \frac{x^3 + x - 1}{x^4 - x^3}.$$

Now, applying partial fraction decomposition produces

$$\frac{x^3 + x - 1}{x^3(x - 1)} = \frac{A}{x} + \frac{B}{x^2} + \frac{C}{x^3} + \frac{D}{x - 1}.$$

Multiplying both sides by the least common denominator $x^3(x - 1)$ produces the basic equation.

$$x^3 + x - 1 = Ax^2(x - 1) + Bx(x - 1) + C(x - 1) + Dx^3 \quad \begin{array}{l}\textit{Basic}\\ \textit{equation}\end{array}$$

Using techniques similar to those in the first two examples, you can solve for A, B, C, and D to obtain

$$A = 0, \quad B = 0, \quad C = 1, \quad \text{and} \quad D = 1.$$

Thus, you can integrate as follows.

$$\int \frac{x^5 + x - 1}{x^4 - x^3}\, dx = \int \left(x + 1 + \frac{x^3 + x - 1}{x^4 - x^3}\right) dx$$

$$= \int \left(x + 1 + \frac{1}{x^3} + \frac{1}{x - 1}\right) dx$$

$$= \frac{x^2}{2} + x - \frac{1}{2x^2} + \ln|x - 1| + C$$

(handwritten margin note) How did that they get that decomposition.

It often happens that you must use more than one integration technique to solve an integral. For instance, the next example uses both substitution and partial fractions.

EXAMPLE 4 *Using Substitution with Partial Fractions*

Find the indefinite integral $\displaystyle\int \frac{1}{e^x + 1}\, dx$.

Solution

Begin with the substitution $u = e^x$. Then, $du = e^x\, dx$. By multiplying and dividing by e^x *inside* the integral, you obtain the following.

$$\int \frac{1}{e^x + 1}\, dx = \int \frac{1}{e^x(e^x + 1)} e^x\, dx \qquad \text{\textit{Multiply and divide by } } e^x.$$

$$= \int \frac{1}{u(u + 1)}\, du \qquad \text{\textit{Substitute u and du.}}$$

To solve this integral, you can use a partial fraction decomposition to write

$$\frac{1}{u(u + 1)} = \frac{1}{u} - \frac{1}{u + 1}.$$

Thus, you can complete the integration as follows.

$$\int \frac{1}{e^x + 1}\, dx = \int \frac{1}{u(u + 1)}\, du \qquad \text{\textit{Substitution}}$$

$$= \int \left(\frac{1}{u} - \frac{1}{u + 1} \right) du \qquad \text{\textit{Partial fractions}}$$

$$= \ln |u| - \ln |u + 1| + C \qquad \text{\textit{Find antiderivative.}}$$

$$= \ln |e^x| - \ln |e^x + 1| + C \qquad \text{\textit{Substitute for u.}}$$

$$= x - \ln |e^x + 1| + C \qquad \text{\textit{Simplify.}}$$

Try checking this result by differentiating.

When integrating rational functions, remember that some can be integrated *without* using partial fractions. Here are three examples.

1. $\displaystyle\int \frac{x}{x^2 - 1}\, dx = \frac{1}{2}\int \frac{2x}{x^2 - 1}\, dx = \frac{1}{2} \ln |x^2 - 1| + C$

2. $\displaystyle\int \frac{x}{x(x - 1)^2}\, dx = \int \frac{1}{(x - 1)^2}\, dx = -\frac{1}{x - 1} + C$

3. $\displaystyle\int \frac{x^2 + 2x}{x^3 + 3x^2 - 4}\, dx = \frac{1}{3}\int \frac{3x^2 + 6x}{x^3 + 3x^2 - 4}\, dx = \frac{1}{3} \ln |x^3 + 3x^2 - 4| + C$

In the second example, note that it is generally a good idea to reduce a rational function as a first step to integration.

Logistics Growth Function

In Section 4.5, you saw that exponential growth occurs in situations for which the rate of growth is proportional to the quantity present at any given time. That is, if y is the quantity at time t, then

$$\frac{dy}{dt} = ky \qquad\qquad \frac{dy}{dt} \text{ is proportional to } y.$$

$$y = Ce^{kt}. \qquad\qquad \textit{Exponential growth function}$$

Exponential growth is unlimited. As long as C and k are positive, the value of Ce^{kt} can be made arbitrarily large by choosing sufficiently large values of t.

In many real-life situations, however, the growth of a quantity is limited and cannot increase beyond a certain size L, as shown in Figure 6.6. The **logistics growth** model assumes that the rate of growth is proportional to both the quantity y and the difference between the quantity and the limit L. That is,

$$\frac{dy}{dt} = ky(L - y). \qquad\qquad \frac{dy}{dt} \text{ is proportional to } y \text{ and } (L - y).$$

The solution of this *differential equation* is given in Example 5.

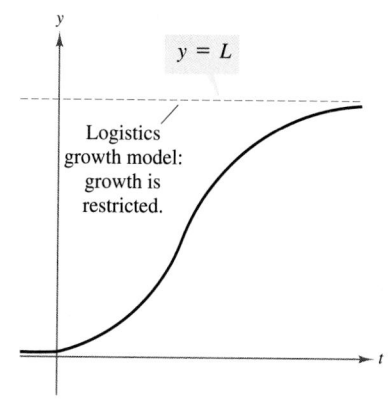

Logistics growth model: growth is restricted.

FIGURE 6.6

EXAMPLE 5 *Deriving the Logistics Growth Function*

Solve the equation $\dfrac{dy}{dt} = ky(1 - y)$. (Assume $y > 0$ and $1 - y > 0$.)

Solution

$$\frac{dy}{dt} = ky(1 - y) \qquad \textit{Differential equation}$$

$$\frac{1}{y(1 - y)}\,dy = k\,dt \qquad \textit{Write in differential form.}$$

$$\int \frac{1}{y(1 - y)}\,dy = \int k\,dt \qquad \textit{Integrate both sides.}$$

$$\int \left(\frac{1}{y} + \frac{1}{1 - y}\right) dy = \int k\,dt \qquad \textit{Rewrite using partial fractions.}$$

$$\ln y - \ln(1 - y) = kt + C_1 \qquad \textit{Find antiderivative.}$$

$$\ln \frac{y}{1 - y} = kt + C_1 \qquad \textit{Simplify.}$$

$$\frac{y}{1 - y} = Ce^{kt} \qquad \textit{Exponentiate and let } e^{C_1} = C.$$

Solving this equation for y produces

$$y = \frac{1}{1 + be^{-kt}}, \qquad\qquad \textit{Logistics growth function}$$

where $b = 1/C$.

Note The logistics growth model in Example 5 was simplified by assuming that the limit of the quantity y is 1. If the limit had been L, then the solution would have been

$$y = \frac{L}{1 + be^{-kt}}.$$

In the fourth step of the solution, notice that partial fractions were used to integrate the left side of the equation.

In the United States, the National Park System has more than 330 protected areas for wildlife, and the National Wildlife Refuge System includes more than 400 refuges. The deer shown in this photo is a white-tailed buck.

Real Life

EXAMPLE 6 *Modeling a Population*

The state game commission releases 100 deer into a game refuge. During the first 5 years, the population increases to 432 deer. The commission believes that the population can be modeled by logistics growth with a limit of 2000 deer. Write the logistics growth model for this population. Then use the model to create a table showing the size of the deer population over the next 30 years.

Solution

Let y represent the number of deer in year t. Assuming a logistics growth model means that the rate of change in the population is proportional to both y and $(2000 - y)$. That is

$$\frac{dy}{dt} = ky(2000 - y).$$

The solution of this equation is

$$y = \frac{2000}{1 + be^{-kt}}.$$

Using the fact that $y = 100$ when $t = 0$, you can solve for b.

$$100 = \frac{2000}{1 + be^{-k(0)}} \longrightarrow b = 19$$

Then, using the fact that $y = 432$ when $t = 5$, you can solve for k.

$$432 = \frac{2000}{1 + 19e^{-k(5)}} \longrightarrow k \approx 0.33106$$

Thus, the logistics growth model for the population is

$$y = \frac{2000}{1 + 19e^{-0.33106t}}. \qquad \textit{Logistics growth model}$$

The population, in 5-year intervals, is shown in Table 6.1.

TABLE 6.1

Time, t	0	5	10	15	20	25	30
Population, y	100	432	1181	1766	1951	1990	1998

Discussion Problem   Logistics Growth

Analyze the graph of the logistics growth function in Example 6. During which years is the *rate of growth* of the herd increasing? During which years is the *rate of growth* of the herd decreasing? How would these answers change if, instead of a limit of 2000 deer, the game refuge could contain a limit of 3000 deer?

Warm Up

The following warm-up exercises involve skills that were covered in earlier sections. You will use these skills in the exercise set for this section.

In Exercises 1–6, factor the expression.

1. $x^2 - x - 12$

2. $x^2 - 25$

3. $x^3 - x^2 - 2x$

4. $x^3 - 4x^2 + 4x$

5. $x^3 - 4x^2 + 5x - 2$

6. $x^3 - 5x^2 + 7x - 3$

In Exercises 7–10, rewrite the improper rational function as the sum of a proper rational function and a polynomial.

7. $\dfrac{x^2 - 2x + 1}{x - 2}$

8. $\dfrac{2x^2 - 4x + 1}{x - 1}$

9. $\dfrac{x^3 - 3x^2 + 2}{x - 2}$

10. $\dfrac{x^3 + 4x^2 + 5x + 2}{x^2 - 1}$

EXERCISES 6.3

 means that technology can help you solve or check the exercise(s).

In Exercises 1–12, write the expression as a sum of partial fractions.

1. $\dfrac{2(x + 20)}{x^2 - 25}$

2. $\dfrac{10x + 3}{x^2 + x}$

3. $\dfrac{8x + 3}{x^2 - 3x}$

4. $\dfrac{3x + 11}{x^2 - 2x - 3}$

5. $\dfrac{4x - 13}{x^2 - 3x - 10}$

6. $\dfrac{7x + 5}{6(2x^2 + 3x + 1)}$

7. $\dfrac{3x^2 - 2x - 5}{x^3 + x^2}$

8. $\dfrac{3x^2 - x + 1}{x(x + 1)^2}$

9. $\dfrac{x + 1}{3(x - 2)^2}$

10. $\dfrac{3x - 4}{(x - 5)^2}$

11. $\dfrac{8x^2 + 15x + 9}{(x + 1)^3}$

12. $\dfrac{6x^2 - 5x}{x^3 + 6x^2 + 12x + 8}$

In Exercises 13–32, find the indefinite integral.

13. $\displaystyle\int \dfrac{1}{x^2 - 1}\, dx$

14. $\displaystyle\int \dfrac{9}{x^2 - 9}\, dx$

15. $\displaystyle\int \dfrac{-2}{x^2 - 16}\, dx$

16. $\displaystyle\int \dfrac{-4}{x^2 - 4}\, dx$

17. $\displaystyle\int \dfrac{1}{3x^2 - x}\, dx$

18. $\displaystyle\int \dfrac{3}{x^2 - 3x}\, dx$

19. $\displaystyle\int \dfrac{1}{2x^2 + x}\, dx$

20. $\displaystyle\int \dfrac{5}{x^2 + x - 6}\, dx$

21. $\displaystyle\int \dfrac{3}{x^2 + x - 2}\, dx$

22. $\displaystyle\int \dfrac{1}{4x^2 - 9}\, dx$

23. $\displaystyle\int \dfrac{5 - x}{2x^2 + x - 1}\, dx$

24. $\displaystyle\int \dfrac{x + 1}{x^2 + 4x + 3}\, dx$

25. $\displaystyle\int \dfrac{x^2 + 12x + 12}{x^3 - 4x}\, dx$

26. $\displaystyle\int \dfrac{3x^2 - 7x - 2}{x^3 - x}\, dx$

27. $\displaystyle\int \dfrac{x + 2}{x^2 - 4x}\, dx$

28. $\displaystyle\int \dfrac{4x^2 + 2x - 1}{x^3 + x^2}\, dx$

29. $\displaystyle\int \dfrac{4 - 3x}{(x - 1)^2}\, dx$

30. $\displaystyle\int \dfrac{x^4}{(x - 1)^3}\, dx$

31. $\displaystyle\int \dfrac{4x^2 - 1}{2x(x^2 + 2x + 1)}\, dx$

32. $\displaystyle\int \dfrac{3x}{x^2 - 6x + 9}\, dx$

In Exercises 33–40, evaluate the definite integral.

33. $\displaystyle\int_4^5 \dfrac{1}{9 - x^2}\, dx$

34. $\displaystyle\int_0^1 \dfrac{3}{2x^2 + 5x + 2}\, dx$

35. $\displaystyle\int_1^5 \dfrac{x - 1}{x^2(x + 1)}\, dx$

36. $\displaystyle\int_0^1 \dfrac{x^2 - x}{x^2 + x + 1}\, dx$

37. $\int_0^1 \frac{x^3}{x^2 - 2} \, dx$

38. $\int_0^1 \frac{x^3 - 1}{x^2 - 4} \, dx$

39. $\int_1^2 \frac{x^3 - 2x^2 + 1}{x^2 - 3x} \, dx$

40. $\int_2^4 \frac{x^4 - 4}{x^2 - 1} \, dx$

In Exercises 41–46, find the indefinite integral using the indicated substitution.

	Integral	*Substitution*
41.	$\int \frac{e^x}{(e^x - 1)(e^x + 4)} \, dx$	$u = e^x$
42.	$\int \frac{e^x}{(e^{2x} - 1)(e^x + 1)} \, dx$	$u = e^x$
43.	$\int \frac{1}{x\sqrt{4 + x^2}} \, dx$	$u = \sqrt{4 + x^2}$
44.	$\int \frac{1}{x\sqrt{4 + x}} \, dx$	$u = \sqrt{4 + x}$
45.	$\int \frac{1}{\sqrt{3x}\left(\sqrt{3x} + 2\right)^2} \, dx$	$u = \sqrt{3x}$
46.	$\int \frac{1}{x\left[1 - (\ln x)^2\right]^2} \, dx$	$u = \ln x$

In Exercises 47–50, find the area of the shaded region.

47. $y = \dfrac{14}{16 - x^2}$

48. $y = \dfrac{-4}{(x + 2)(x - 3)}$

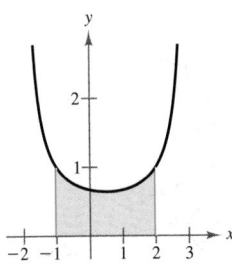

49. $y = \dfrac{x + 1}{x^2 - x}$

50. $y = \dfrac{x^2 + 2x - 1}{x^2 - 4}$

 In Exercises 51–54, write the partial fraction decomposition for the rational expression. Check your result algebraically. Then assign a value to the constant *a* to check the result graphically.

51. $\dfrac{1}{a^2 - x^2}$

52. $\dfrac{1}{x(x + a)}$

53. $\dfrac{1}{x(a - x)}$

54. $\dfrac{1}{(x + 1)(a - x)}$

In Exercises 55–58, find the volume of the solid generated by revolving the region bounded by the graphs of the given equations about the *x*-axis.

55. $y = \dfrac{10}{x(x + 10)}$, $y = 0$, $x = 1$, $x = 5$

56. $y = \dfrac{-4}{(x + 1)(x - 4)}$, $y = 0$, $x = 0$, $x = 3$

57. $y = \dfrac{2x}{x^3 - 4x}$, $x = 1$, $x = -1$, $y = 0$

58. $y = \dfrac{25x}{x^2 + x - 6}$, $x = -2$, $x = 0$, $y = 0$

59. *Population Growth* A conservation organization releases 100 animals of an endangered species into a game preserve. The organization believes that the preserve has a capacity of 1000 animals and that the growth of the herd will be logistic. That is, the size *y* of the herd will follow the equation

$$\int \frac{1}{y(1000 - y)} \, dy = \int k \, dt,$$

where *t* is measured in years. Find this logistic curve. (To solve for the constant of integration *C* and the proportionality constant *k*, assume that $y = 100$ when $t = 0$ and $y = 134$ when $t = 2$.) Sketch the graph of your solution.

60. *Epidemic Model* A single infected individual enters a community of 500 individuals susceptible to the disease. The disease spreads at a rate proportional to the product of the total number infected and the number of susceptible individuals not yet infected. A model for the time it takes for the disease to spread to *x* individuals is

$$t = 5010 \int \frac{1}{(x + 1)(500 - x)} \, dx,$$

where *t* is the time in hours.

(a) Find the time it takes for 75% of the population to become infected (when $t = 0$, $x = 1$).

(b) Find the number of people who are infected after 100 hours.

61. *Marketing* After test-marketing a new menu item, a fast-food restaurant predicts that sales of the new item will grow according to the model

$$\frac{dS}{dt} = \frac{2t}{(t+4)^2},$$

where t is the time in weeks and S is the sales in thousands of dollars. Find the sales of the menu item at 10 weeks.

62. *Population Growth* One gram of a bacterial culture is present at time $t = 0$, and 10 grams is the upper limit of the culture's weight. The time required for the culture to grow to y grams is modeled by

$$kt = \int \frac{1}{y(10-y)} dy,$$

where y is the weight of the culture in grams and t is the time in hours.

(a) Verify that the weight of the culture at time t is modeled by

$$y = \frac{10}{1 + 9e^{-10kt}}.$$

Use the fact that $y = 1$ when $t = 0$.

(b) Use the graph below to determine the constant k.

Weight (in grams) vs. Time (in hours). Point $(2, 2)$ marked.

63. *GMAT* The number of people who took the Graduate Management Admission Test (GMAT) each year between 1982 and 1992 can be modeled by

$$N = \frac{242t^2 - 17{,}922t - 18{,}164}{4t^2 - 96t - 100},$$

where t is the time in years, with $t = 0$ corresponding to the year beginning September 1, 1982, and N is the number of test-takers in thousands. Find the total number of people who took the test between September 1, 1983 and August 31, 1990. *(Source: Graduate Management Admission Council)*

64. *Research Project* Use your school's library or some other reference source to research the opportunity cost of attending graduate school for 2 years to receive a Masters of Business Administration (MBA) degree rather than working for 2 years with a bachelor's degree. Write a short paper describing these costs.

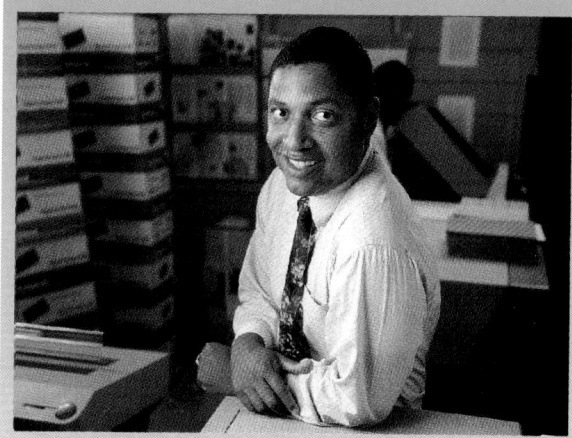

— *Business Capsule* —

© Voldi Tanner from *Black Enterprise* Nov. 1993, Vol. 24, No. 3, page 34.

Right after receiving his undergraduate degree in history and economics from Stanford University in 1988, Greg Crossfield opened Field Copy and Printing, Inc. Crossfield launched the photocopy business by charging $300 on his VISA card for marketing. By the end of the first year in business, revenues reached $30,000, and in 1992 the company grossed $210,000.

Integration Tables ■ *Reduction Formulas* ■ *Completing the Square*

Integration Tables

So far in this chapter, you have studied three integration techniques to be used along with the basic integration formulas. Certainly these do not cover every possible method for finding an antiderivative, but they do cover most of the important ones.

In this section, you will expand the list of integration formulas to form a table of integrals. As you add new integration formulas to the basic list, two things occur. On one hand, it becomes increasingly difficult to memorize, or even become familiar with, the entire list of formulas. On the other hand, with a longer list you need fewer techniques for fitting an integral to one of the formulas on the list. The procedure of integrating by means of a long list of formulas is called **integration by tables.** (The tables in this section have only a partial listing of integration formulas. Much longer lists exist, some having several hundred formulas.)

Integration by tables should not be considered a trivial taŝk. It requires considerable thought and insight, and it often requires substitution. Many people find a table of integrals to be a valuable supplement to the integration techniques discussed in the first three sections of this chapter. We encourage you to gain competence in the use of integration tables, as well as to continue to improve in the use of the various integration techniques. In doing so, you should find that a combination of techniques and tables is the most versatile approach to integration.

Each integration formula in the table on the following three pages can be developed using one or more of the techniques you have studied. You should try to verify several of the formulas. For instance, Formula 4

$$\int \frac{u}{(a + bu)^2} \, du = \frac{1}{b^2} \left(\frac{a}{a + bu} + \ln |a + bu| \right) + C \qquad \text{Formula 4}$$

can be verified using partial fractions, Formula 17

$$\int \frac{\sqrt{a + bu}}{u} \, du = 2\sqrt{a + bu} + a \int \frac{1}{u\sqrt{a + bu}} \, du \qquad \text{Formula 17}$$

can be verified using integration by parts, and Formula 37

$$\int \frac{1}{1 + e^u} \, du = u - \ln(1 + e^u) + C \qquad \text{Formula 37}$$

can be verified using substitution and partial fractions.

Note A symbolic integration utility, such as *Derive*, *Maple*, or *Mathematica*, consists, in part, of a database of integration tables. The primary difference between using a symbolic integrator and using a table of integrals is that with a symbolic integrator the computer searches through the database to find a fit. With a table of integrals, *you* must do the searching.

In the following table of integrals, the formulas have been grouped into eight different types according to the form of the integrand.

Forms involving u^n Forms involving $a + bu$

Forms involving $\sqrt{a + bu}$ Forms involving $\sqrt{u^2 \pm a^2}$

Forms involving $u^2 - a^2$ Forms involving $\sqrt{a^2 - u^2}$

Forms involving e^u Forms involving $\ln u$

Table of Integrals

Forms involving u^n

1. $\displaystyle \int u^n \, du = \frac{u^{n+1}}{n+1} + C, \quad n \neq -1$

2. $\displaystyle \int \frac{1}{u} \, du = \ln |u| + C$

Forms involving $a + bu$

3. $\displaystyle \int \frac{u}{a + bu} \, du = \frac{1}{b^2}(bu - a \ln |a + bu|) + C$

4. $\displaystyle \int \frac{u}{(a + bu)^2} \, du = \frac{1}{b^2}\left(\frac{a}{a + bu} + \ln |a + bu| \right) + C$

5. $\displaystyle \int \frac{u}{(a + bu)^n} \, du = \frac{1}{b^2}\left[\frac{-1}{(n-2)(a+bu)^{n-2}} + \frac{a}{(n-1)(a+bu)^{n-1}} \right] + C, \quad n \neq 1, 2$

6. $\displaystyle \int \frac{u^2}{a + bu} \, du = \frac{1}{b^3}\left[-\frac{bu}{2}(2a - bu) + a^2 \ln |a + bu| \right] + C$

7. $\displaystyle \int \frac{u^2}{(a + bu)^2} \, du = \frac{1}{b^3}\left(bu - \frac{a^2}{a + bu} - 2a \ln |a + bu| \right) + C$

8. $\displaystyle \int \frac{u^2}{(a + bu)^3} \, du = \frac{1}{b^3}\left[\frac{2a}{a + bu} - \frac{a^2}{2(a + bu)^2} + \ln |a + bu| \right] + C$

9. $\displaystyle \int \frac{u^2}{(a + bu)^n} \, du = \frac{1}{b^3}\left[\frac{-1}{(n-3)(a+bu)^{n-3}} + \frac{2a}{(n-2)(a+bu)^{n-2}} - \frac{a^2}{(n-1)(a+bu)^{n-1}} \right] + C, \quad n \neq 1, 2, 3$

10. $\displaystyle \int \frac{1}{u(a + bu)} \, du = \frac{1}{a} \ln \left| \frac{u}{a + bu} \right| + C$

11. $\displaystyle \int \frac{1}{u(a + bu)^2} \, du = \frac{1}{a}\left(\frac{1}{a + bu} + \frac{1}{a} \ln \left| \frac{u}{a + bu} \right| \right) + C$

12. $\displaystyle \int \frac{1}{u^2(a + bu)} \, du = -\frac{1}{a}\left(\frac{1}{u} + \frac{b}{a} \ln \left| \frac{u}{a + bu} \right| \right) + C$

13. $\displaystyle \int \frac{1}{u^2(a + bu)^2} \, du = -\frac{1}{a^2}\left[\frac{a + 2bu}{u(a + bu)} + \frac{2b}{a} \ln \left| \frac{u}{a + bu} \right| \right] + C$

Table of Integrals *(continued)*

Forms involving $\sqrt{a + bu}$

14. $\displaystyle \int u^n \sqrt{a + bu}\, du = \frac{2}{b(2n + 3)}\left[u^n(a + bu)^{3/2} - na \int u^{n-1}\sqrt{a + bu}\, du \right]$

15. $\displaystyle \int \frac{1}{u\sqrt{a + bu}}\, du = \frac{1}{\sqrt{a}} \ln\left| \frac{\sqrt{a + bu} - \sqrt{a}}{\sqrt{a + bu} + \sqrt{a}} \right| + C, \quad 0 < a$

16. $\displaystyle \int \frac{1}{u^n \sqrt{a + bu}}\, du = \frac{-1}{a(n - 1)}\left[\frac{\sqrt{a + bu}}{u^{n-1}} + \frac{(2n - 3)b}{2} \int \frac{1}{u^{n-1}\sqrt{a + bu}}\, du \right], \quad n \neq 1$

17. $\displaystyle \int \frac{\sqrt{a + bu}}{u}\, du = 2\sqrt{a + bu} + a \int \frac{1}{u\sqrt{a + bu}}\, du$

18. $\displaystyle \int \frac{\sqrt{a + bu}}{u^n}\, du = \frac{-1}{a(n - 1)}\left[\frac{(a + bu)^{3/2}}{u^{n-1}} + \frac{(2n - 5)b}{2} \int \frac{\sqrt{a + bu}}{u^{n-1}}\, du \right], \quad n \neq 1$

19. $\displaystyle \int \frac{u}{\sqrt{a + bu}}\, du = -\frac{2(2a - bu)}{3b^2}\sqrt{a + bu} + C$

20. $\displaystyle \int \frac{u^n}{\sqrt{a + bu}}\, du = \frac{2}{(2n + 1)b}\left(u^n\sqrt{a + bu} - na \int \frac{u^{n-1}}{\sqrt{a + bu}}\, du \right)$

Forms involving $\sqrt{u^2 \pm a^2},\ 0 < a$

21. $\displaystyle \int \sqrt{u^2 \pm a^2}\, du = \frac{1}{2}\left(u\sqrt{u^2 \pm a^2} \pm a^2 \ln|u + \sqrt{u^2 \pm a^2}| \right) + C$

22. $\displaystyle \int u^2\sqrt{u^2 \pm a^2}\, du = \frac{1}{8}\left[u(2u^2 \pm a^2)\sqrt{u^2 \pm a^2} - a^4 \ln|u + \sqrt{u^2 \pm a^2}| \right] + C$

23. $\displaystyle \int \frac{\sqrt{u^2 + a^2}}{u}\, du = \sqrt{u^2 + a^2} - a \ln\left| \frac{a + \sqrt{u^2 + a^2}}{u} \right| + C$

24. $\displaystyle \int \frac{\sqrt{u^2 \pm a^2}}{u^2}\, du = \frac{-\sqrt{u^2 \pm a^2}}{u} + \ln|u + \sqrt{u^2 \pm a^2}| + C$

25. $\displaystyle \int \frac{1}{\sqrt{u^2 \pm a^2}}\, du = \ln|u + \sqrt{u^2 \pm a^2}| + C$

26. $\displaystyle \int \frac{1}{u\sqrt{u^2 + a^2}}\, du = -\frac{1}{a} \ln\left| \frac{a + \sqrt{u^2 + a^2}}{u} \right| + C$

27. $\displaystyle \int \frac{u^2}{\sqrt{u^2 \pm a^2}}\, du = \frac{1}{2}\left(u\sqrt{u^2 \pm a^2} \mp a^2 \ln|u + \sqrt{u^2 \pm a^2}| \right) + C$

28. $\displaystyle \int \frac{1}{u^2\sqrt{u^2 \pm a^2}}\, du = \mp\frac{\sqrt{u^2 \pm a^2}}{a^2 u} + C$

(handwritten margin note, left side, rotated): Reduction formulas!! etc. Repeated Integrals. (no "+c").

Table of Integrals (continued)

Forms involving $u^2 - a^2$, $\ 0 < a$

29. $\displaystyle \int \frac{1}{u^2 - a^2}\, du = -\int \frac{1}{a^2 - u^2}\, du = \frac{1}{2a} \ln\left|\frac{u - a}{u + a}\right| + C$

30. $\displaystyle \int \frac{1}{(u^2 - a^2)^n}\, du = \frac{-1}{2a^2(n - 1)}\left[\frac{u}{(u^2 - a^2)^{n-1}} + (2n - 3)\int \frac{1}{(u^2 - a^2)^{n-1}}\, du\right], \quad n \neq 1$

Forms involving $\sqrt{a^2 - u^2}$, $0 < a$

31. $\displaystyle \int \frac{\sqrt{a^2 - u^2}}{u}\, du = \sqrt{a^2 - u^2} - a \ln\left|\frac{a + \sqrt{a^2 - u^2}}{u}\right| + C$

32. $\displaystyle \int \frac{1}{u\sqrt{a^2 - u^2}}\, du = -\frac{1}{a} \ln\left|\frac{a + \sqrt{a^2 - u^2}}{u}\right| + C$

33. $\displaystyle \int \frac{1}{u^2\sqrt{a^2 - u^2}}\, du = \frac{-\sqrt{a^2 - u^2}}{a^2 u} + C$

Forms involving e^u

34. $\displaystyle \int e^u\, du = e^u + C$

35. $\displaystyle \int u e^u\, du = (u - 1)e^u + C$

36. $\displaystyle \int u^n e^u\, du = u^n e^u - n\int u^{n-1} e^u\, du$

37. $\displaystyle \int \frac{1}{1 + e^u}\, du = u - \ln(1 + e^u) + C$

38. $\displaystyle \int \frac{1}{1 + e^{nu}}\, du = u - \frac{1}{n}\ln(1 + e^{nu}) + C$

Forms involving $\ln u$

39. $\displaystyle \int \ln u\, du = u(-1 + \ln u) + C$

40. $\displaystyle \int u \ln u\, du = \frac{u^2}{4}(-1 + 2\ln u) + C$

41. $\displaystyle \int u^n \ln u\, du = \frac{u^{n+1}}{(n + 1)^2}[-1 + (n + 1)\ln u] + C, \quad n \neq -1$

42. $\displaystyle \int (\ln u)^2\, du = u[2 - 2\ln u + (\ln u)^2] + C$

43. $\displaystyle \int (\ln u)^n\, du = u(\ln u)^n - n\int (\ln u)^{n-1}\, du$

EXAMPLE 1 *Using Integration Tables*

Find the indefinite integral

$$\int \frac{x}{\sqrt{x-1}}\, dx.$$

Solution

Because the expression inside the radical is linear, you should consider forms involving $\sqrt{a + bu}$, as in Formula 19.

$$\int \frac{u}{\sqrt{a + bu}}\, du = -\frac{2(2a - bu)}{3b^2}\sqrt{a + bu} + C \qquad \text{Formula 19}$$

Using this formula, let $a = -1$, $b = 1$, and $u = x$. Then $du = dx$, and you obtain the following.

$$\int \frac{x}{\sqrt{x-1}}\, dx = -\frac{2(-2 - x)}{3}\sqrt{x - 1} + C \qquad \text{\textit{Substitute values of} } a, b, \text{ \textit{and} } u.$$

$$= \frac{2}{3}(2 + x)\sqrt{x - 1} + C \qquad \text{\textit{Simplify.}}$$

TECHNOLOGY

Throughout this section, remember that a symbolic integration utility, such as *Derive*, *Mathematica*, or *Maple*, can be used instead of integration tables. If you have access to such a utility, try using it to find the indefinite integrals in Examples 1 and 2.

EXAMPLE 2 *Using Integration Tables*

Find the indefinite integral

$$\int x\sqrt{x^4 - 9}\, dx.$$

Solution

Because it is not clear which formula to use, you can begin by letting $u = x^2$ and $du = 2x\, dx$. With this substitution, you can write the integral as follows.

$$\int x\sqrt{x^4 - 9}\, dx = \frac{1}{2}\int \sqrt{(x^2)^2 - 9}(2x)\, dx \qquad \text{\textit{Multiply and divide by 2.}}$$

$$= \frac{1}{2}\int \sqrt{u^2 - 9}\, du \qquad \text{\textit{Substitute } u \text{ and } du.}$$

Now, it appears that you can use Formula 21.

$$\int \sqrt{u^2 - a^2}\, du = \frac{1}{2}\left(u\sqrt{u^2 - a^2} - a^2 \ln|u + \sqrt{u^2 - a^2}|\right) + C.$$

Letting $a = 3$, you obtain

$$\int x\sqrt{x^4 - 9}\, dx = \frac{1}{2}\int \sqrt{u^2 - a^2}\, du$$

$$= \frac{1}{2}\left[\frac{1}{2}\left(u\sqrt{u^2 - a^2} - a^2 \ln|u + \sqrt{u^2 - a^2}|\right)\right] + C$$

$$= \frac{1}{4}\left(x^2\sqrt{x^4 - 9} - 9\ln|x^2 + \sqrt{x^4 - 9}|\right) + C.$$

EXAMPLE 3 *Using Integration Tables*

Find the indefinite integral

$$\int \frac{1}{x\sqrt{x+1}}\, dx.$$

Solution

Considering forms involving $\sqrt{a+bu}$, where $a=1$, $b=1$, and $u=x$, you can use Formula 15.

$$\int \frac{1}{u\sqrt{a+bu}}\, du = \frac{1}{\sqrt{a}} \ln \left| \frac{\sqrt{a+bu}-\sqrt{a}}{\sqrt{a+bu}+\sqrt{a}} \right| + C, \qquad 0 < a.$$

Therefore,

$$\int \frac{1}{x\sqrt{x+1}}\, dx = \int \frac{1}{u\sqrt{a+bu}}\, du$$

$$= \frac{1}{\sqrt{a}} \ln \left| \frac{\sqrt{a+bu}-\sqrt{a}}{\sqrt{a+bu}+\sqrt{a}} \right| + C$$

$$= \ln \left| \frac{\sqrt{x+1}-1}{\sqrt{x+1}+1} \right| + C.$$

EXAMPLE 4 *Using Integration Tables*

Find the indefinite integral

$$\int \frac{x}{1+e^{-x^2}}\, dx.$$

Solution

Of the forms involving e^u, Formula 37

$$\int \frac{1}{1+e^u}\, du = u - \ln(1+e^u) + C$$

seems most appropriate. To use this formula, let $u = -x^2$ and $du = -2x\, dx$.

$$\int \frac{x}{1+e^{-x^2}}\, dx = -\frac{1}{2}\int \frac{1}{1+e^{-x^2}}(-2x)\, dx$$

$$= -\frac{1}{2}\int \frac{1}{1+e^u}\, du$$

$$= -\frac{1}{2}[u - \ln(1+e^u)] + C$$

$$= -\frac{1}{2}[-x^2 - \ln(1+e^{-x^2})] + C$$

$$= \frac{1}{2}[x^2 + \ln(1+e^{-x^2})] + C$$

Reduction Formulas

Several of the formulas in the integration table have the form

$$\int f(x)\,dx = g(x) + \int h(x)\,dx,$$

where the right side contains an integral. Such integration formulas are called **reduction formulas** because they reduce the original integral to the sum of a function and a simpler integral.

EXAMPLE 5   *Using a Reduction Formula*

Find the indefinite integral $\int x^2 e^x\,dx$.

Solution
Using Formula 36,

$$\int u^n e^u\,du = u^n e^u - n \int u^{n-1} e^u\,du,$$

you can let $u = x$ and $n = 2$. Then $du = dx$, and you can write

$$\int x^2 e^x\,dx = x^2 e^x - 2 \int x e^x\,dx.$$

Then, using Formula 35,

$$\int u e^u\,du = (u - 1)e^u + C,$$

you can write

$$\int x^2 e^x\,dx = x^2 e^x - 2 \int x e^x\,dx$$
$$= x^2 e^x - 2(x - 1)e^x + C$$
$$= x^2 e^x - 2x e^x + 2e^x + C$$
$$= e^x(x^2 - 2x + 2) + C.$$

⊞ TECHNOLOGY

You have now studied two ways to find the indefinite integral in Example 5. Example 5 uses an integration table, and Example 4 in Section 6.2 uses integration by parts. A third way would be to use a symbolic integrator. For instance, the screen at the right shows how to use *Derive* to solve the integral.

1:	$x^2 \hat{e}^x$	*Author.*
2:	$\int x^2 \hat{e}^x dx$	*Integrate.*
3:	$\hat{e}^x(x^2 - 2x + 2)$	*Simplify.*

Completing the Square

Many integration formulas involve the sum or difference of two squares. You can extend the use of these formulas by an algebraic procedure called **completing the square.** This procedure is demonstrated in Example 6.

EXAMPLE 6 *Completing the Square*

Find the indefinite integral

$$\int \frac{1}{x^2 - 4x + 1} \, dx.$$

Solution

Begin by writing the denominator as the difference of two squares.

$$x^2 - 4x + 1 = (x^2 - 4x + 4) - 4 + 1 = (x - 2)^2 - 3.$$

Therefore, you can rewrite the original integral as

$$\int \frac{1}{x^2 - 4x + 1} \, dx = \int \frac{1}{(x - 2)^2 - 3} \, dx.$$

Considering $u = x - 2$ and $a = \sqrt{3}$, you can apply Formula 29

$$\int \frac{1}{u^2 - a^2} \, du = \frac{1}{2a} \ln \left| \frac{u - a}{u + a} \right| + C$$

to conclude that

$$\int \frac{1}{x^2 - 4x + 1} \, dx = \int \frac{1}{(x - 2)^2 - 3} \, dx$$

$$= \int \frac{1}{u^2 - a^2} \, du$$

$$= \frac{1}{2a} \ln \left| \frac{u - a}{u + a} \right| + C$$

$$= \frac{1}{2\sqrt{3}} \ln \left| \frac{x - 2 - \sqrt{3}}{x - 2 + \sqrt{3}} \right| + C.$$

Discussion Problem **Using Integration Tables**

Which integration formulas on pages 415–417 would you use to integrate the following? Explain your choice of u for each integral.

a. $\displaystyle\int \frac{e^x}{e^x + 1} \, dx$ b. $\displaystyle\int \frac{1}{e^x + 1} \, dx$ c. $\displaystyle\int \frac{1}{e^{2x} + 1} \, dx$

Warm Up

The following warm-up exercises involve skills that were covered in earlier sections. You will use these skills in the exercise set for this section.

In Exercises 1–4, expand the expression.

1. $(x + 4)^2$

2. $\left(x + \frac{1}{2}\right)^2$

3. $(x - 1)^2$

4. $\left(x - \frac{1}{3}\right)^2$

In Exercises 5–8, write the partial fraction decomposition for the function.

5. $\dfrac{4}{x(x + 2)}$

6. $\dfrac{3}{x(x - 4)}$

7. $\dfrac{x + 4}{x^2(x - 2)}$

8. $\dfrac{3x^2 + 4x - 8}{x(x - 2)(x + 1)}$

In Exercises 9 and 10, use integration by parts to find the indefinite integral.

9. $\displaystyle\int 2xe^x\, dx$

10. $\displaystyle\int 3x^2 \ln x\, dx$

E X E R C I S E S   6.4

means that technology can help you solve or check the exercise(s).

In Exercises 1–10, use the indicated formula from the table of integrals in this section to find the indefinite integral.

1. $\displaystyle\int \dfrac{x}{(2 + 3x)^2}\, dx$, Formula 4

2. $\displaystyle\int \dfrac{1}{x(2 + 3x)^2}\, dx$, Formula 11

3. $\displaystyle\int \dfrac{x}{\sqrt{2 + 3x}}\, dx$, Formula 19

4. $\displaystyle\int \dfrac{4}{x^2 - 9}\, dx$, Formula 29

5. $\displaystyle\int \dfrac{2x}{\sqrt{x^4 - 9}}\, dx$, Formula 25

6. $\displaystyle\int x^2\sqrt{x^2 + 9}\, dx$, Formula 22

7. $\displaystyle\int x^3 e^{x^2}\, dx$, Formula 35

8. $\displaystyle\int \dfrac{x}{1 + e^{x^2}}\, dx$, Formula 37

9. $\displaystyle\int x \ln(x^2 + 1)\, dx$, Formula 39

10. $\displaystyle\int x^3 \ln x\, dx$, Formula 41

In Exercises 11–40, use the table of integrals in this section to find the indefinite integral.

11. $\displaystyle\int \dfrac{1}{x(1 + x)}\, dx$

12. $\displaystyle\int \dfrac{1}{x(1 + x)^2}\, dx$

13. $\displaystyle\int \dfrac{1}{x\sqrt{x^2 + 9}}\, dx$

14. $\displaystyle\int \dfrac{1}{\sqrt{x^2 - 1}}\, dx$

15. $\displaystyle\int \dfrac{1}{x\sqrt{4 - x^2}}\, dx$

16. $\displaystyle\int \dfrac{\sqrt{x^2 - 9}}{x^2}\, dx$

17. $\displaystyle\int x \ln x\, dx$

18. $\displaystyle\int x^2(\ln x^3)^2\, dx$

19. $\displaystyle\int \dfrac{6x}{1 + e^{3x^2}}\, dx$

20. $\displaystyle\int \dfrac{1}{1 + e^x}\, dx$

21. $\displaystyle\int x\sqrt{x^4 - 4}\, dx$

22. $\displaystyle\int \dfrac{x}{x^4 - 9}\, dx$

23. $\int \dfrac{t^2}{(2+3t)^3}\,dt$

24. $\int \dfrac{\sqrt{3+4t}}{t}\,dt$

25. $\int \dfrac{s}{s^2\sqrt{3+s}}\,ds$

26. $\int \sqrt{3+x^2}\,dx$

27. $\int \dfrac{x^2}{(3+2x)^5}\,dx$

28. $\int \dfrac{1}{x^2\sqrt{x^2-4}}\,dx$

29. $\int \dfrac{1}{x^2\sqrt{1-x^2}}\,dx$

30. $\int \dfrac{2x}{(1-3x)^2}\,dx$

31. $\int x^2 \ln x\,dx$

32. $\int xe^{x^2}\,dx$

33. $\int \dfrac{x^2}{(3x-5)^2}\,dx$

34. $\int \dfrac{1}{2x^2(2x-1)^2}\,dx$

35. $\int x^2\sqrt{x^2+4}\,dx$

36. $\int \dfrac{1}{\sqrt{x}(1+2\sqrt{x})}\,dx$

37. $\int \dfrac{2}{1+e^{4x}}\,dx$

38. $\int \dfrac{e^x}{(1-e^{2x})}\,dx$

39. $\int \dfrac{\ln x}{x(4+3\ln x)}\,dx$

40. $\int (\ln x)^3\,dx$

In Exercises 41–44, evaluate the definite integral.

41. $\int_0^5 \dfrac{x}{\sqrt{5+2x}}\,dx$

42. $\int_0^5 \dfrac{x}{(4+x)^2}\,dx$

43. $\int_0^4 \dfrac{6}{1+e^{0.5x}}\,dx$

44. $\int_1^4 x\ln x\,dx$

In Exercises 45–48, find the indefinite integral (a) using integration tables and (b) using the specified method.

Integral	*Method*
45. $\int x^2 e^x\,dx$	Integration by parts
46. $\int x^4 \ln x\,dx$	Integration by parts
47. $\int \dfrac{1}{x^2(x+1)}\,dx$	Partial fractions
48. $\int \dfrac{1}{x^2-75}\,dx$	Partial fractions

In Exercises 49 and 50, complete the square to express each polynomial as the sum or difference of squares.

49. (a) x^2+6x (b) x^2-8x+9
     (c) x^4+2x^2-5 (d) $3-2x-x^2$

50. (a) $2x^2+12x+14$ (b) $3x^2-12x-9$
     (c) x^2-2x (d) $9+8x-x^2$

In Exercises 51–58, complete the square and then use integration tables to find the indefinite integral.

51. $\int \dfrac{1}{x^2+6x-8}\,dx$

52. $\int \dfrac{1}{(x^2+4x-5)}\,dx$

53. $\int \dfrac{1}{(x-1)\sqrt{x^2-2x+2}}\,dx$

54. $\int \sqrt{x^2-6x}\,dx$

55. $\int \dfrac{1}{2x^2-4x-6}\,dx$

56. $\int \dfrac{\sqrt{7-6x-x^2}}{x+3}\,dx$

57. $\int \dfrac{x}{\sqrt{x^4+2x^2+2}}\,dx$

58. $\int \dfrac{x\sqrt{x^4+4x^2+5}}{x^2+2}\,dx$

In Exercises 59 and 60, find the area of the region bounded by the graphs of the equations.

59. $y = \dfrac{x}{\sqrt{x+1}}$, $y=0$, $x=8$

60. $y = \dfrac{x}{1+e^{x^2}}$, $y=0$, $x=2$

Population Growth In Exercises 61 and 62, find the average value of the growth function over the interval, where N is the size of a population and t is the time in days.

61. $N = \dfrac{50}{1+e^{4.8-1.9t}}$, [3, 4]

62. $N = \dfrac{375}{1+e^{4.20-0.25t}}$, [21, 28]

63. *Revenue* The marginal revenue (in dollars per year) for a new product is modeled by

$$\dfrac{dR}{dt} = 10{,}000\left[1 - \dfrac{1}{(1+0.1t^2)^{1/2}}\right],$$

where t is the time in years. Estimate the total revenue from sales of the product over its first 2 years on the market.

64. *Consumer and Producer Surplus* Find the consumer surplus and the producer surplus for a product with the given demand and supply functions.

Demand: $p = \dfrac{60}{\sqrt{x^2+81}}$,   Supply: $p = \dfrac{x}{3}$

(*Hint:* For a definition of consumer and producer surplus, see Section 5.5.)

Numerical Integration

Trapezoidal Rule ▪ *Simpson's Rule* ▪ *Error Analysis*

Trapezoidal Rule

In Section 5.6, you studied one technique for approximating the value of a *definite* integral—the Midpoint Rule. In this section, you will study two other approximation techniques: the **Trapezoidal Rule** and **Simpson's Rule.**

To develop the Trapezoidal Rule, consider a function f that is nonnegative and continuous on the closed interval $[a, b]$. To approximate the area represented by $\int_a^b f(x)\,dx$, partition the interval into n subintervals, each of width

$$\Delta x = \frac{b - a}{n}. \qquad \textit{Width of each subinterval}$$

Next, form n trapezoids, as shown in Figure 6.7. As you can see in Figure 6.8, the area of the first trapezoid is

$$\text{Area of first trapezoid} = \frac{b - a}{n}\left[\frac{f(x_0) + f(x_1)}{2}\right].$$

The areas of the other trapezoids follow a similar pattern, and the sum of the n areas is

$$\frac{b - a}{n}\left[\frac{f(x_0) + f(x_1)}{2} + \frac{f(x_1) + f(x_2)}{2} + \cdots + \frac{f(x_{n-1}) + f(x_n)}{2}\right]$$

$$= \frac{b - a}{2n}[f(x_0) + f(x_1) + f(x_1) + f(x_2) + \cdots + f(x_{n-1}) + f(x_n)]$$

$$= \frac{b - a}{2n}[f(x_0) + 2f(x_1) + 2f(x_2) + \cdots + 2f(x_{n-1}) + f(x_n)].$$

Although this development assumes f to be continuous *and* nonnegative on $[a, b]$, the resulting formula is valid as long as f is continuous on $[a, b]$.

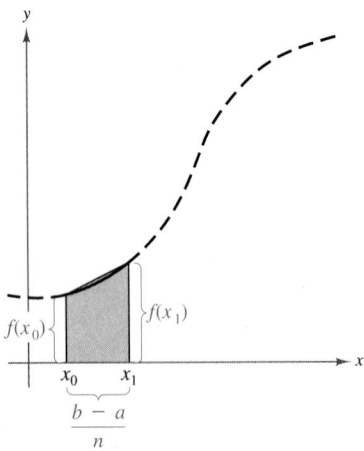

FIGURE 6.7

FIGURE 6.8

The Trapezoidal Rule

If f is continuous on $[a, b]$, then

$$\int_a^b f(x)\,dx \approx \frac{b - a}{2n}[f(x_0) + 2f(x_1) + \cdots + 2f(x_{n-1}) + f(x_n)].$$

EXAMPLE 1 Using the Trapezoidal Rule

Use the Trapezoidal Rule to approximate the definite integral

$$\int_0^1 e^x \, dx.$$

Compare the results for $n = 4$ and $n = 8$.

Solution

When $n = 4$, the width of each subinterval is $(1-0)/4 = \frac{1}{4}$ and the endpoints of the subintervals are

$$x_0 = 0, \quad x_1 = \frac{1}{4}, \quad x_2 = \frac{1}{2}, \quad x_3 = \frac{3}{4}, \quad \text{and} \quad x_4 = 1,$$

as indicated in Figure 6.9. Therefore, by the Trapezoidal Rule,

$$\int_0^1 e^x \, dx = \frac{1}{8}(e^0 + 2e^{0.25} + 2e^{0.5} + 2e^{0.75} + e^1)$$

$$\approx 1.7272. \qquad \qquad \textit{Approximation using } n = 4$$

When $n = 8$, the width of each subinterval is $(1-0)/8 = \frac{1}{8}$ and the endpoints of the subintervals are

$$x_0 = 0, \quad x_1 = \frac{1}{8}, \quad x_2 = \frac{1}{4}, \quad x_3 = \frac{3}{8}, \quad x_4 = \frac{1}{2}$$

$$x_5 = \frac{5}{8}, \quad x_6 = \frac{3}{4}, \quad x_7 = \frac{7}{8}, \quad \text{and} \quad x_8 = 1,$$

as indicated in Figure 6.10. Therefore, by the Trapezoidal Rule,

$$\int_0^1 e^x \, dx = \frac{1}{16}(e^0 + 2e^{0.125} + 2e^{0.25} + \cdots + 2e^{0.875} + e^1)$$

$$\approx 1.7205. \qquad \qquad \textit{Approximation using } n = 8$$

Of course, for *this particular* integral, you could have found an antiderivative and used the Fundamental Theorem to find the exact value of the definite integral. The exact value is

$$\int_0^1 e^x \, dx = e - 1 \approx 1.7183. \qquad \qquad \textit{Exact value}$$

■

There are two important points that should be made concerning the Trapezoidal Rule. First, the approximation tends to become more accurate as n increases. For instance, in Example 1, if $n = 16$, the Trapezoidal Rule yields an approximation of 1.7188. Second, although you could have used the Fundamental Theorem of Calculus to evaluate the integral in Example 1, this theorem cannot be used to evaluate an integral as simple as $\int_0^1 e^{x^2} \, dx$, because e^{x^2} has no elementary function as an antiderivative. Yet, the Trapezoidal Rule can be easily applied to this integral.

FIGURE 6.9 Four Subintervals

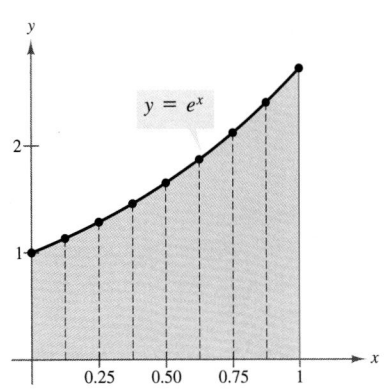

FIGURE 6.10 Eight Subintervals

Simpson's Rule

One way to view the Trapezoidal Rule is to say that on each subinterval, f is approximated by a first-degree polynomial. In Simpson's Rule, f is approximated by a second-degree polynomial on each subinterval.

To develop Simpson's Rule, partition the interval $[a, b]$ into an *even number n* of subintervals, each of width $(b - a)/n$. On the subinterval $[x_0, x_2]$, approximate the function f by the second-degree polynomial $p(x)$ that passes through the points

$$(x_0, f(x_0)), \quad (x_1, f(x_1)), \quad \text{and} \quad (x_2, f(x_2)),$$

as shown in Figure 6.11. The Fundamental Theorem of Calculus can be used to show that

$$\int_{x_0}^{x_2} f(x)\, dx \approx \int_{x_0}^{x_2} p(x)\, dx$$

$$= \frac{x_2 - x_0}{6} \left[p(x_0) + 4p\left(\frac{x_0 + x_2}{2}\right) + p(x_2) \right]$$

$$= \frac{2[(b - a)/n]}{6} [p(x_0) + 4p(x_1) + p(x_2)]$$

$$= \frac{b - a}{3n} [f(x_0) + 4f(x_1) + f(x_2)].$$

Repeating this process on the subintervals $[x_{i-2}, x_i]$ produces

$$\int_a^b f(x)\, dx \approx \frac{b - a}{3n} \big[f(x_0) + 4f(x_1) + f(x_2) + f(x_2) + 4f(x_3)$$

$$+ f(x_4) + \cdots + f(x_{n-2}) + 4f(x_{n-1}) + f(x_n) \big].$$

By grouping like terms, you can obtain the following approximation, which is known as Simpson's Rule. This rule is named after the English mathematician Thomas Simpson (1710–1761).

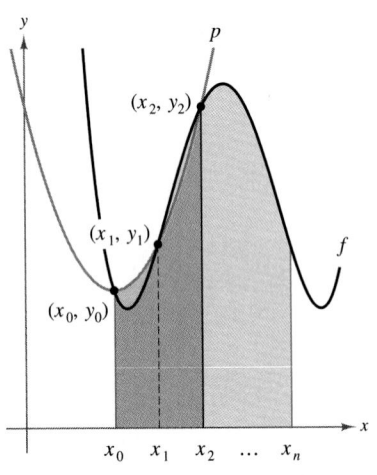

$$\int_{x_0}^{x_2} p(x)\, dx \approx \int_{x_0}^{x_2} f(x)\, dx$$

FIGURE 6.11

Simpson's Rule (n is Even)

If f is continuous on $[a, b]$, then

$$\int_a^b f(x)\, dx \approx \frac{b - a}{3n} [f(x_0) + 4f(x_1) + 2f(x_2) + 4f(x_3) +$$

$$\cdots + 4f(x_{n-1}) + f(x_n)].$$

Note   The coefficients in Simpson's Rule have the pattern

$$1 \quad 4 \quad 2 \quad 4 \quad 2 \quad 4 \quad \cdots \quad 4 \quad 2 \quad 4 \quad 1.$$

In Example 1, the Trapezoidal Rule was used to estimate the value of

$$\int_0^1 e^x \, dx.$$

The next example uses Simpson's Rule to approximate the same integral.

EXAMPLE 2 *Using Simpson's Rule*

Use Simpson's Rule to approximate the definite integral

$$\int_0^1 e^x \, dx.$$

Compare the results for $n = 4$ and $n = 8$.

Solution
When $n = 4$, the width of each subinterval is $(1 - 0)/4 = \frac{1}{4}$ and the endpoints of the subintervals are

$$x_0 = 0, \quad x_1 = \frac{1}{4}, \quad x_2 = \frac{1}{2}, \quad x_3 = \frac{3}{4}, \quad \text{and} \quad x_4 = 1.$$

Therefore, by Simpson's Rule,

$$\int_0^1 e^x \, dx = \frac{1}{12}(e^0 + 4e^{0.25} + 2e^{0.5} + 4e^{0.75} + e^1)$$

$$\approx 1.718319. \qquad \textit{Approximation using } n = 4$$

When $n = 8$, the width of each subinterval is $(1 - 0)/8 = \frac{1}{8}$ and the endpoints of the subintervals are

$$x_0 = 0, \quad x_1 = \frac{1}{8}, \quad x_2 = \frac{1}{4}, \quad x_3 = \frac{3}{8}, \quad x_4 = \frac{1}{2}$$

$$x_5 = \frac{5}{8}, \quad x_6 = \frac{3}{4}, \quad x_7 = \frac{7}{8}, \quad \text{and} \quad x_8 = 1.$$

Therefore, by Simpson's Rule,

$$\int_0^1 e^x \, dx = \frac{1}{24}(e^0 + 4e^{0.125} + 2e^{0.25} + \cdots + 4e^{0.875} + e^1)$$

$$\approx 1.718284. \qquad \textit{Approximation using } n = 8$$

Recall that the exact value of this integral is

$$\int_0^1 e^x \, dx = e - 1 \approx 1.718282.$$

Thus, with only eight subintervals, you obtained an approximation that is correct to the nearest 0.00002—an impressive result!

Note Comparing the results of Examples 1 and 2, you can see that for a given value of n, Simpson's Rule tends to be more accurate than the Trapezoidal Rule.

Programming Simpson's Rule

In Section 5.6, you saw how to program the Midpoint Rule into a computer or programmable calculator. The program below will evaluate Simpson's Rule on a *TI-81* or *TI-82* calculator. See Appendix D for other models.

```
Prgm1:SIMPSONS
:Disp ''LOWER LIMIT''        Prompt for value of a.
:Input A                     Input value of a.
:Disp ''UPPER LIMIT''        Prompt for value of b.
:Input B                     Input value of b.
:Disp ''N/2 DIVISIONS''      Prompt for value of n/2.
:Input D                     Input value of n/2.
:0→S                         Initialize sum of areas.
:(B−A)/(2D)→W                Calculate width of subinterval.
:1→J                         Initialize counter.
:Lbl 1                       Begin loop.
:A+2(J−1)W→L                 Calculate left endpoint.
:A+2JW→R                     Calculate right endpoint.
:(L+R)/2→M                   Calculate midpoint of subinterval.
:L→X
:Y₁→L                        Evaluate f(x) at left endpoint.
:M→X
:Y₁→M                        Evaluate f(x) at midpoint.
:R→X
:Y₁→R                        Evaluate f(x) at right endpoint.
:W(L+4M+R)/3+S→S             Simpson's Rule
:IS>(J,D)                    Check value of index, J.
:Goto 1                      End loop.
:Disp ''APPROXIMATION''
:Disp S                      Display approximation.
```

Before executing the program, enter the function as Y_1. When the program is executed, you will be prompted to enter the lower and upper limits of integration, and *half* the number of subintervals you want to use.

To check your steps, try running the program with the integral in Example 2. When $n = 8$ (input 4), you should obtain an approximation of

$$\int_0^1 e^x \, dx \approx 1.718284155.$$

Error Analysis

In Examples 1 and 2, you were able to calculate the exact value of the integral and compare that value with the approximations to see how good they were. In practice, you need to have a different way of telling how good an approximation is: such a way is provided in the next result.

Error in Trapezoidal and Simpson's Rules

The error E in approximating $\int_a^b f(x)\,dx$ is as follows.

Trapezoidal Rule: $|E| \leq \dfrac{(b-a)^3}{12n^2}\left[\max|f''(x)|\right], \qquad a \leq x \leq b$

Simpson's Rule: $|E| \leq \dfrac{(b-a)^5}{180n^4}\left[\max|f^{(4)}(x)|\right], \qquad a \leq x \leq b$

This result indicates that the errors generated by the Trapezoidal Rule and Simpson's Rule have upper bounds dependent on the extreme values of $f''(x)$ and $f^{(4)}(x)$ in the interval $[a, b]$. Furthermore, the bounds for the errors can be made arbitrarily small by *increasing n*. To determine what value of n to choose, consider the following steps.

Trapezoidal Rule

1. Find $f''(x)$.
2. Find the maximum of $|f''(x)|$ on the interval $[a, b]$.
3. Set up the inequality $|E| \leq \dfrac{(b-a)^3}{12n^2}\left[\max|f''(x)|\right].$
4. For an error less than ϵ, solve for n in the inequality

$$\frac{(b-a)^3}{12n^2}\left[\max|f''(x)|\right] < \epsilon.$$

5. Partition $[a, b]$ into n subintervals and apply the Trapezoidal Rule.

Simpson's Rule

1. Find $f^{(4)}(x)$.
2. Find the maximum of $|f^{(4)}(x)|$ on the interval $[a, b]$.
3. Set up the inequality $|E| \leq \dfrac{(b-a)^5}{180n^4}\left[\max|f^{(4)}(x)|\right].$
4. For an error less than ϵ, solve for n in the inequality

$$\frac{(b-a)^5}{180n^4}\left[\max|f^{(4)}(x)|\right] < \epsilon.$$

5. Partition $[a, b]$ into n subintervals and apply Simpson's Rule.

Discovery

How does the error in the Trapezoidal Rule decrease as you increase n, the number of subintervals? In Example 1 on page 425, you approximated the integral $\int_0^1 e^x\,dx$ using the Trapezoidal Rule with four and eight subintervals. Because the exact value of this integral is known to be $e - 1$, the errors are

$n = 4$ error: 0.008918

and

$n = 8$ error: 0.002218.

Notice that the error diminishes by a factor of approximately 4 when the number of subintervals is doubled. Explain how this is consistent with the formula for the Trapezoidal Rule error. What do you think the error would be if you used 16 subintervals in Example 1? (The actual error is 0.0005593, which is approximately 0.002218/4.) How does the error in Simpson's Rule diminish as you increase the number of subintervals?

EXAMPLE 3 *Using the Trapezoidal Rule*

Use the Trapezoidal Rule to estimate the value of the integral

$$\int_0^1 e^{-x^2} \, dx$$

so that the approximation error is less than 0.01.

Solution

1. Begin by finding the second derivative of $f(x) = e^{-x^2}$.

$$f(x) = e^{-x^2}$$

$$f'(x) = -2xe^{-x^2}$$

$$f''(x) = 4x^2 e^{-x^2} - 2e^{-x^2} = 2e^{-x^2}(2x^2 - 1)$$

2. Using calculus, you can determine that f'' has only one critical number in the interval $[0, 1]$ and that the maximum value of $|f''(x)|$ on this interval is $|f''(0)| = 2$.

3. The error E using the Trapezoidal Rule is bounded by

$$|E| \le \frac{(b-a)^3}{12n^2}(2) = \frac{1}{12n^2}(2) = \frac{1}{6n^2}.$$

4. To ensure that the approximation has an error of less than 0.01, you should choose n so that

$$\frac{1}{6n^2} < 0.01.$$

Solving for n, you can determine that n must be 5 or more.

5. Partition $[0, 1]$ into five subintervals, as shown in Figure 6.12. Then apply the Trapezoidal Rule to obtain

$$\int_0^1 e^{-x^2} \, dx = \frac{1}{10}\left(\frac{1}{e^0} + \frac{2}{e^{0.04}} + \frac{2}{e^{0.16}} + \frac{2}{e^{0.36}} + \frac{2}{e^{0.64}} + \frac{1}{e^1} \right)$$

$$\approx 0.744.$$

Therefore, with an error of less than 0.01, you know that

$$0.734 \le \int_0^1 e^{-x^2} \, dx \le 0.754.$$

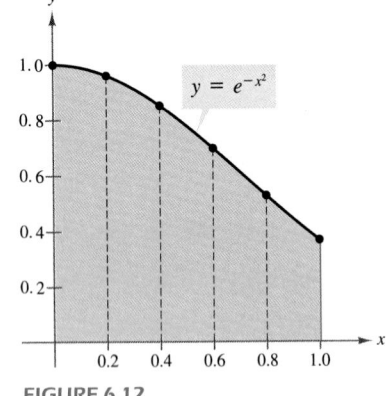

$y = e^{-x^2}$

FIGURE 6.12

Discussion Problem   **Simpson's Rule Error**

Rework Example 3 using Simpson's Rule instead of the Trapezoidal Rule.

Warm Up

The following warm-up exercises involve skills that were covered in earlier sections. You will use these skills in the exercise set for this section.

In Exercises 1–6, find the indicated derivative.

1. $f(x) = \dfrac{1}{x}$, $f''(x)$

2. $f(x) = \ln(2x + 1)$, $f^{(4)}(x)$

3. $f(x) = 2\ln x$, $f^{(4)}(x)$

4. $f(x) = x^3 - 2x^2 + 7x - 12$, $f''(x)$

5. $f(x) = e^{2x}$, $f^{(4)}(x)$

6. $f(x) = e^{x^2}$, $f''(x)$

In Exercises 7 and 8, find the absolute maximum of f on the interval.

7. $f(x) = -x^2 + 6x + 9$, $[0, 4]$

8. $f(x) = \dfrac{8}{x^3}$, $[1, 2]$

In Exercises 9 and 10, solve for n.

9. $\dfrac{1}{4n^2} < 0.001$

10. $\dfrac{1}{16n^4} < 0.0001$

E X E R C I S E S   6.5

 means that technology can help you solve or check the exercise(s).

In Exercises 1–10, use the Trapezoidal Rule and Simpson's Rule to approximate the value of the definite integral for the indicated value of *n*. Compare these results with the exact value of the definite integral. Round your answers to four decimal places.

1. $\displaystyle\int_0^2 x^2\,dx$, $n = 4$

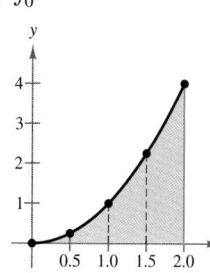

2. $\displaystyle\int_0^1 \left(\dfrac{x^2}{2} + 1\right) dx$, $n = 4$

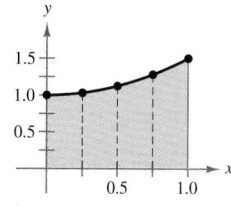

3. $\displaystyle\int_0^2 (x^4 + 1)\,dx$, $n = 4$

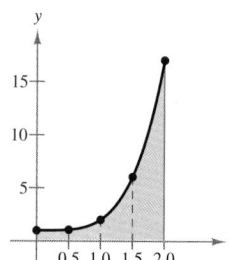

4. $\displaystyle\int_1^2 \dfrac{1}{x}\,dx$, $n = 4$

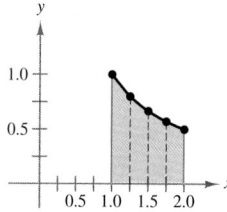

5. $\displaystyle\int_0^2 x^3\,dx$, $n = 8$

6. $\displaystyle\int_1^2 \dfrac{1}{x}\,dx$, $n = 8$

7. $\displaystyle\int_1^2 \dfrac{1}{x^2}\,dx$, $n = 4$

8. $\displaystyle\int_0^4 \sqrt{x}\,dx$, $n = 8$

9. $\displaystyle\int_0^1 \dfrac{1}{1+x}\,dx$, $n = 4$

10. $\displaystyle\int_0^2 x\sqrt{x^2 + 1}\,dx$, $n = 4$

In Exercises 11–20, approximate the integral using (a) the Trapezoidal Rule and (b) Simpson's Rule. (Round your answers to three significant digits.)

Definite Integral	Subdivisions
11. $\displaystyle\int_0^2 (1 + x^3)\, dx$	$n = 4$
12. $\displaystyle\int_0^2 \frac{1}{\sqrt{1 + x^3}}\, dx$	$n = 4$
13. $\displaystyle\int_0^1 \sqrt{x}\,\sqrt{1 - x}\, dx$	$n = 4$
14. $\displaystyle\int_0^1 \frac{1}{1 + x^2}\, dx$	$n = 4$
15. $\displaystyle\int_0^1 \sqrt{1 - x^2}\, dx$	$n = 4$
16. $\displaystyle\int_0^2 e^{-x^2}\, dx$	$n = 2$
17. $\displaystyle\int_0^1 \sqrt{1 - x^2}\, dx$	$n = 8$
18. $\displaystyle\int_0^2 e^{-x^2}\, dx$	$n = 4$
19. $\displaystyle\int_0^3 \frac{1}{2 - 2x + x^2}\, dx$	$n = 6$
20. $\displaystyle\int_0^3 \frac{x}{2 + x + x^2}\, dx$	$n = 6$

 Present Value In Exercises 21 and 22, use Simpson's Rule (with $n = 8$) to approximate the present value of the income $c(t)$ over t_1 years at the given annual interest rate r. (Present value is defined in Section 6.2.)

21. $c(t) = 6000 + 200\sqrt{t},\ r = 7\%,\ t_1 = 4$

22. $c(t) = 200{,}000 + 15{,}000\sqrt[3]{t},\ r = 10\%,\ t_1 = 8$

Marginal Analysis In Exercises 23 and 24, use Simpson's Rule (with $n = 4$) to approximate the change in revenue from the marginal revenue function dR/dx. In each case, assume that the number of units sold x increases from 14 to 16.

23. $\dfrac{dR}{dx} = 5\sqrt{8000 - x^3}$ **24.** $\dfrac{dR}{dx} = 50\sqrt{x}\,\sqrt{20 - x}$

Probability In Exercises 25 and 26, use Simpson's Rule (with $n = 6$) to approximate the indicated normal probability. The standard normal probability density function is

$$f(x) = \frac{1}{\sqrt{2\pi}}\, e^{-x^2/2}.$$

If x is chosen at random from a population with this density, then the probability that x lies in the interval $[a, b]$ is $P(a \le x \le b) = \int_a^b f(x)\, dx$.

25. $P(0 \le x \le 1)$ **26.** $P(0 \le x \le 2)$

 Surveying In Exercises 27 and 28, use Simpson's Rule to estimate the number of square feet of land in the lot where x and y are measured in feet, as shown in the accompanying figures. In each case the land is bounded by a stream and two straight roads.

27.

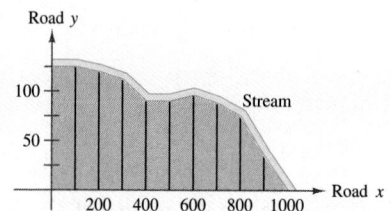

x	0	100	200	300	400	500
y	125	125	120	112	90	90

x	600	700	800	900	1000
y	95	88	75	35	0

28.

x	0	10	20	30	40	50	60
y	75	81	84	76	67	68	69

x	70	80	90	100	110	120
y	72	68	56	42	23	0

In Exercises 29–32, use the error formula to find bounds for the error in approximating the integral using (a) the Trapezoidal Rule and (b) Simpson's Rule. (Let $n = 4$.)

29. $\displaystyle\int_0^2 x^4\,dx$

30. $\displaystyle\int_0^1 \frac{1}{x+1}\,dx$

31. $\displaystyle\int_0^1 e^{x^3}\,dx$

32. $\displaystyle\int_0^1 e^{-x^2}\,dx$

In Exercises 33–36, use the error formula to find n so that the error in the approximation of the definite integral is less than 0.0001 using (a) the Trapezoidal Rule and (b) Simpson's Rule.

33. $\displaystyle\int_0^1 x^4\,dx$

34. $\displaystyle\int_1^3 \frac{1}{x}\,dx$

35. $\displaystyle\int_1^3 e^{2x}\,dx$

36. $\displaystyle\int_3^5 \ln x\,dx$

In Exercises 37–40, use the program for Simpson's Rule given on page 428 to approximate the integral.

37. $\displaystyle\int_1^4 x\sqrt{x+4}\,dx$

38. $\displaystyle\int_1^4 x^2\sqrt{x+4}\,dx$

39. $\displaystyle\int_2^5 10xe^{-x}\,dx$

40. $\displaystyle\int_2^5 10x^2 e^{-x}\,dx$

41. Prove that Simpson's Rule is exact when used to approximate the integral of a cubic polynomial function, and demonstrate the result for

$$\int_0^1 x^3\,dx, \qquad n = 2.$$

42. Use Simpson's Rule (with $n = 4$) to find the volume of the solid generated by revolving the region bounded by the graphs of

$$y = x\sqrt[3]{x+4}, \quad y = 0, \quad \text{and} \quad x = 4$$

about the x-axis.

In Exercises 43 and 44, use the following definite integral to find the required arc length. If f has a continuous derivative, then the arc length of f between the points $(a, f(a))$ and $(b, f(b))$ is

$$\int_a^b \sqrt{1 + [f'(x)]^2}\,dx.$$

43. *Arc Length* The suspension cable on a bridge that is 400 feet long is in the shape of a parabola whose equation is $y = x^2/800$ (see figure). Use Simpson's Rule (with $n = 12$) to approximate the length of the cable. Compare this result with the length obtained by using the table in Section 6.4 to perform the integration.

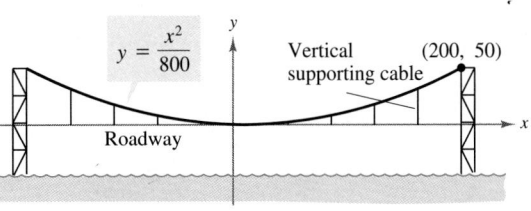

FIGURE FOR 43

44. *Arc Length* A fleeing object leaves the origin and moves up the y-axis (see figure). At the same time, a pursuer leaves the point $(1, 0)$ and always moves toward the fleeing object. If the pursuer's speed is twice that of the fleeing object, the equation of the pursuer's path is

$$y = \frac{1}{3}(x^{3/2} - 3x^{1/2} + 2).$$

Find the distance traveled by the pursuer by integrating over the interval $[0, 1]$.

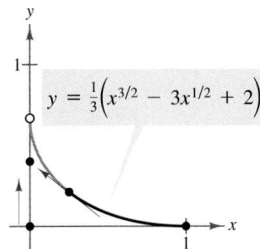

45. *Medicine* A body assimilates a 12-hour cold tablet at a rate modeled by

$$\frac{dC}{dt} = 8 - \ln(t^2 - 2t + 4), \qquad 0 \le t \le 12,$$

where dC/dt is measured in grams per hour and t is the time (in hours). Find the total amount of the drug absorbed into the body during the 12 hours.

46. *Medicine* The concentration M (in grams per liter) of a 6-hour allergy medicine in a body is modeled by

$$M = 12 - 4\ln(t^2 - 4t + 6), \qquad 0 \le t \le 6,$$

where t is the time in hours since the allergy medication was taken. Find the average level of concentration in the body over the 6-hour period.

47. *Magazine Subscribers* The rate of change S of subscribers to a newly introduced magazine is modeled by

$$\frac{dS}{dt} = 1000t^2 e^{-t}, \qquad 0 \le t \le 6,$$

where t is the time in years. Find the total increase in the number of subscribers during the first 6 years.

Improper Integrals

Improper Integrals ■ *Integrals with Infinite Limits of Integration* ■
Integrals with Infinite Integrands ■ *Applications*

Improper Integrals

The definition of the definite integral

$$\int_a^b f(x)\,dx$$

includes the requirements that the interval $[a, b]$ be finite and that f be bounded on $[a, b]$. In this section, you will study integrals that do not satisfy these requirements because of one of the following.

1. One or both of the limits of integration are infinite.
2. f has an infinite discontinuity on the interval $[a, b]$.

Integrals possessing either of these characteristics are called **improper integrals.** For instance, the integrals

$$\int_0^\infty e^{-x}\,dx \quad \text{and} \quad \int_{-\infty}^\infty \frac{1}{x^2+1}\,dx$$

are improper because one or both limits of integration are infinite, as indicated in Figure 6.13. Similarly, the integrals

$$\int_1^5 \frac{1}{\sqrt{x-1}}\,dx \quad \text{and} \quad \int_{-2}^2 \frac{1}{(x+1)^2}\,dx$$

are improper because their integrands approach infinity somewhere in the interval of integration, as indicated in Figure 6.14.

FIGURE 6.13

FIGURE 6.14

Integrals with Infinite Limits of Integration

To see how to evaluate an improper integral, consider the integral shown in Figure 6.15. As long as b is a real number that is greater than 1 (no matter how large), this is a definite integral whose value is

$$\int_1^b \frac{1}{x^2}\,dx = \left[-\frac{1}{x}\right]_1^b = -\frac{1}{b} + 1 = 1 - \frac{1}{b}.$$

Table 6.2 shows the values of this integral for several values of b.

TABLE 6.2

b	2	5	10	100	1000	10,000
$\int_1^b \dfrac{1}{x^2}\,dx = 1 - \dfrac{1}{b}$	0.5000	0.8000	0.9000	0.9900	0.9990	0.9999

From this table, it appears that the value of the integral is approaching a limit as b increases without bound. This limit is denoted by the following *improper integral.*

$$\int_1^\infty \frac{1}{x^2}\,dx = \lim_{b \to \infty} \int_1^b \frac{1}{x^2}\,dx$$

$$= \lim_{b \to \infty} \left(1 - \frac{1}{b}\right)$$

$$= 1$$

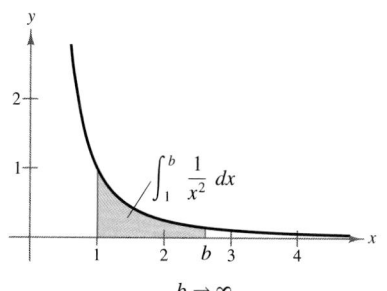

FIGURE 6.15

Improper Integrals (Infinite Limits of Integration)

1. If f is continuous on the interval $[a, \infty)$, then

$$\int_a^\infty f(x)\,dx = \lim_{b \to \infty} \int_a^b f(x)\,dx.$$

2. If f is continuous on the interval $(-\infty, b]$, then

$$\int_{-\infty}^b f(x)\,dx = \lim_{a \to -\infty} \int_a^b f(x)\,dx.$$

3. If f is continuous on the interval $(-\infty, \infty)$, then

$$\int_{-\infty}^\infty f(x)\,dx = \int_{-\infty}^c f(x)\,dx + \int_c^\infty f(x)\,dx,$$

where c is any real number.

In each case, if the limit exists, then the improper integral **converges;** otherwise the improper integral **diverges.** Thus, in the third case, the integral will diverge if either one of the integrals on the right diverges.

EXAMPLE 1 *Evaluating an Improper Integral*

Determine the convergence or divergence of the improper integral

$$\int_1^\infty \frac{1}{x}\,dx.$$

Solution

Begin by applying the definition of an improper integral.

$$\int_1^\infty \frac{1}{x}\,dx = \lim_{b\to\infty}\int_1^b \frac{1}{x}\,dx \qquad \textit{Definition of improper integral}$$

$$= \lim_{b\to\infty}\left[\ln x\right]_1^b \qquad \textit{Find antiderivative.}$$

$$= \lim_{b\to\infty}(\ln b - 0) \qquad \textit{Apply Fundamental Theorem.}$$

$$= \infty \qquad \textit{Evaluate limit.}$$

Because the limit is infinite, the improper integral diverges.

As you begin to work with improper integrals, you will find that integrals that appear to be similar can have very different values. For instance, consider the two improper integrals

$$\int_1^\infty \frac{1}{x}\,dx = \infty \qquad \textit{Divergent integral}$$

and

$$\int_1^\infty \frac{1}{x^2}\,dx = 1. \qquad \textit{Convergent integral}$$

The first integral diverges and the second converges to 1. Graphically, this means that the areas shown in Figure 6.16 are very different. The region lying between the graph of $y = 1/x$ and the x-axis (for $x \geq 1$) has an *infinite* area, and the region lying between the graph of $y = 1/x^2$ and the x-axis (for $x \geq 1$) has a *finite* area.

Diverges (infinite area)

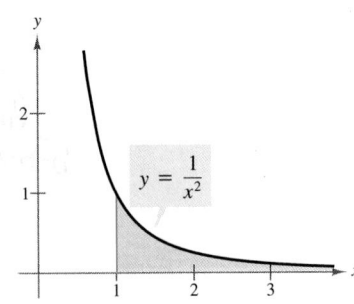

Converges (finite area)

FIGURE 6.16

EXAMPLE 2 *Evaluating an Improper Integral*

Evaluate the improper integral

$$\int_{-\infty}^{0} \frac{1}{(1-2x)^{3/2}}\, dx.$$

Solution

Begin by applying the definition of an improper integral.

$$\int_{-\infty}^{0} \frac{1}{(1-2x)^{3/2}}\, dx = \lim_{a\to -\infty} \int_{a}^{0} \frac{1}{(1-2x)^{3/2}}\, dx \qquad \text{\textit{Definition of improper integral}}$$

$$= \lim_{a\to -\infty} \left[\frac{1}{\sqrt{1-2x}}\right]_{a}^{0} \qquad \text{\textit{Find antiderivative.}}$$

$$= \lim_{a\to -\infty} \left(1 - \left(\frac{1}{\sqrt{1-2a}}\right)\right) \qquad \text{\textit{Apply Fundamental Theorem.}}$$

$$= 1 - 0 \qquad \text{\textit{Evaluate limit.}}$$

$$= 1 \qquad \text{\textit{Simplify.}}$$

Thus, the improper integral converges to 1. As shown in Figure 6.17, this implies that the region lying between the graph of $y = 1/(1-2x)^{3/2}$ and the x-axis (for $x \le 0$) has an area of 1.

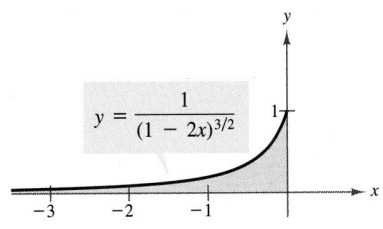

$$y = \frac{1}{(1-2x)^{3/2}}$$

FIGURE 6.17

EXAMPLE 3 *Evaluating an Improper Integral*

Evaluate the improper integral

$$\int_{0}^{\infty} 2xe^{-x^2}\, dx.$$

Solution

Begin by applying the definition of an improper integral.

$$\int_{0}^{\infty} 2xe^{-x^2}\, dx = \lim_{b\to\infty} \int_{0}^{b} 2xe^{-x^2}\, dx \qquad \text{\textit{Definition of improper integral}}$$

$$= \lim_{b\to\infty} \left[-e^{-x^2}\right]_{0}^{b} \qquad \text{\textit{Find antiderivative.}}$$

$$= \lim_{b\to\infty} \left(-e^{-b^2}+1\right) \qquad \text{\textit{Apply Fundamental Theorem.}}$$

$$= 0 + 1 \qquad \text{\textit{Evaluate limit.}}$$

$$= 1 \qquad \text{\textit{Simplify.}}$$

Thus, the improper integral converges to 1. As shown in Figure 6.18, this implies that the region lying between the graph of $y = 2xe^{-x^2}$ and the x-axis (for $x \ge 0$) has an area of 1.

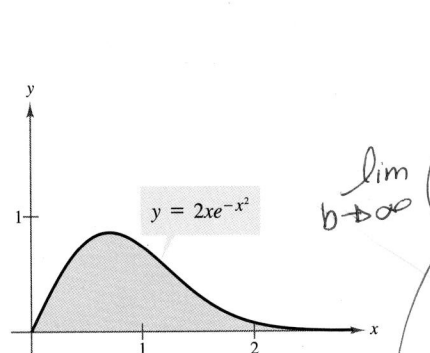

$$y = 2xe^{-x^2}$$

FIGURE 6.18

[handwritten annotations:]

Why is this +1 ?

$$\lim_{b\to\infty}\left(-e^{-b^2}+1\right)$$

oops!

because $\left[e^{-b^2}\right] - \left[e^{-0^2}\right] = \left[-e^{-b^2}\right] - \left[-1\right]$

$$= \left(-e^{-b^2}+1\right)$$

Integrals with Infinite Integrands

Improper Integrals (Infinite Integrands)

1. If f is continuous on the interval $[a, b)$ and approaches infinity at b, then

$$\int_a^b f(x)\, dx = \lim_{c \to b^-} \int_a^c f(x)\, dx.$$ *top.*

2. If f is continuous on the interval $(a, b]$ and approaches infinity at a, then

$$\int_a^b f(x)\, dx = \lim_{c \to a^+} \int_c^b f(x)\, dx.$$ *bottom*

3. If f is continuous on the interval $[a, b]$, except for some c in (a, b) at which f approaches infinity, then

$$\int_a^b f(x)\, dx = \int_a^c f(x)\, dx + \int_c^b f(x)\, dx.$$

In each case, if the limit exists, then the improper integral **converges;** otherwise the improper integral **diverges.**

(handwritten note:) Don't understand why this isn't $\lim_{b \to 1^+} \left(-2(t-1)^{-1/2} \right)$

EXAMPLE 4 *Evaluating an Improper Integral*

Evaluate the improper integral

$$\int_1^2 \frac{1}{\sqrt[3]{x-1}}\, dx.$$

(handwritten note:) $(x-1)^{-1/3}$

Solution

$$\int_1^2 \frac{1}{\sqrt[3]{x-1}}\, dx = \lim_{b \to 1^+} \int_b^2 \frac{1}{\sqrt[3]{x-1}}\, dx \qquad \text{\textit{Definition of improper integral}}$$

$$= \lim_{b \to 1^+} \left[\frac{3}{2}(x-1)^{2/3} \right]_b^2 \qquad \text{\textit{Find antiderivative.}}$$

$$= \lim_{b \to 1^+} \left[\frac{3}{2} - \frac{3}{2}(b-1)^{2/3} \right] \qquad \text{\textit{Apply Fundamental Theorem.}}$$

$$= \frac{3}{2} - 0 \qquad \text{\textit{Evaluate limit.}}$$

$$= \frac{3}{2} \qquad \text{\textit{Simplify.}}$$

Thus, the integral converges to $\frac{3}{2}$. This implies that the region shown in Figure 6.19 has an area of $\frac{3}{2}$.

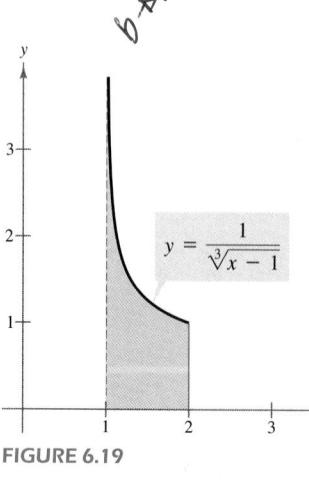

$$y = \frac{1}{\sqrt[3]{x-1}}$$

FIGURE 6.19

EXAMPLE 5 *Evaluating an Improper Integral*

Evaluate the improper integral

$$\int_1^2 \frac{2}{x^2 - 2x}\, dx.$$

Solution

$$\int_1^2 \frac{2}{x^2 - 2x}\, dx = \int_1^2 \left(\frac{1}{x-2} - \frac{1}{x}\right) dx \qquad \textit{Use partial fractions.}$$

$$= \lim_{b \to 2^-} \int_1^b \left(\frac{1}{x-2} - \frac{1}{x}\right) dx \qquad \begin{array}{l}\textit{Definition of}\\\textit{improper integral}\end{array}$$

$$= \lim_{b \to 2^-} \left[\ln|x-2| - \ln|x|\right]_1^b \qquad \textit{Find antiderivative.}$$

$$= -\infty \qquad \textit{Evaluate limit.}$$

Thus, you can conclude that the integral diverges. This implies that the region shown in Figure 6.20 has an infinite area.

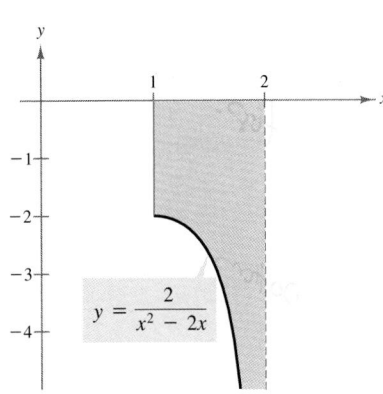

$$y = \frac{2}{x^2 - 2x}$$

FIGURE 6.20

EXAMPLE 6 *Evaluating an Improper Integral*

Evaluate the improper integral

$$\int_{-1}^2 \frac{1}{x^3}\, dx.$$

Solution

This integral is improper because the integrand has an infinite discontinuity at the interior value $x = 0$, as shown in Figure 6.21. Thus, you can write

$$\int_{-1}^2 \frac{1}{x^3}\, dx = \int_{-1}^0 \frac{1}{x^3}\, dx + \int_0^2 \frac{1}{x^3}\, dx.$$

By applying the definition of an improper integral, you can show that each of these integrals diverges. Therefore, the original improper integral also diverges.

Note   Had you not recognized that the integral in Example 6 was improper, you would have obtained the incorrect result

$$\int_{-1}^2 \frac{1}{x^3}\, dx = \left[-\frac{1}{2x^2}\right]_{-1}^2 = -\frac{1}{8} + \frac{1}{2} = \frac{3}{8}. \qquad \textit{Incorrect}$$

Improper integrals in which the integrand has an infinite discontinuity *between* the limits of integration are often overlooked, so keep alert for such possibilities. Even symbolic integrators can have trouble with this type of integral—when we used *Derive* to evaluate this integral, it gave us the same incorrect result.

$$y = \frac{1}{x^3}$$

FIGURE 6.21

Applications

In Section 4.2, you studied the graph of the *normal probability density function*

$$f(x) = \frac{1}{\sigma\sqrt{2\pi}}e^{-(x-\mu)^2/2\sigma^2}.$$

This function is used in statistics to represent a population that is normally distributed with a mean of μ and a standard deviation of σ. Specifically, if an outcome x is chosen at random from the population, the probability that x will have a value between a and b is

$$P(a \le x \le b) = \int_a^b \frac{1}{\sigma\sqrt{2\pi}}e^{-(x-\mu)^2/2\sigma^2}\,dx.$$

As shown in Figure 6.22, the probability $P(-\infty < x < \infty)$ is

$$P(-\infty < x < \infty) = \int_{-\infty}^{\infty} \frac{1}{\sigma\sqrt{2\pi}}e^{-(x-\mu)^2/2\sigma^2}\,dx = 1.$$

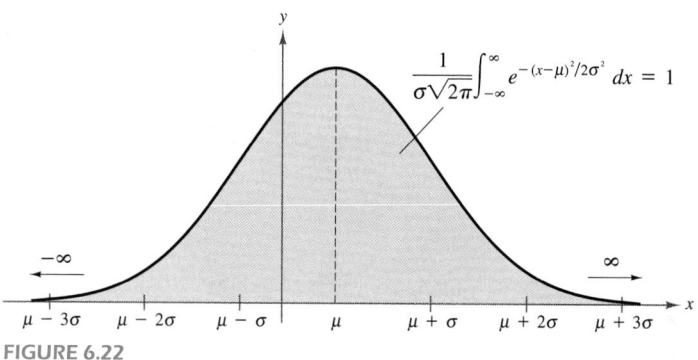

$$\frac{1}{\sigma\sqrt{2\pi}}\int_{-\infty}^{\infty} e^{-(x-\mu)^2/2\sigma^2}\,dx = 1$$

FIGURE 6.22

Real Life

EXAMPLE 7 *Finding a Probability*

In 1992, the mean height of American men (between 18 and 24 years old) was 70 inches, and the standard deviation was 3 inches. If an 18- to 24-year-old man was chosen at random from the population, what is the probability that he was 6 feet tall or taller? *(Source: National Center for Health Statistics)*

Solution

Using a mean of $\mu = 70$ and a standard deviation of $\sigma = 3$, the probability $P(72 \le x < \infty)$ is given by the improper integral

$$P(72 \le x < \infty) = \int_{72}^{\infty} \frac{1}{3\sqrt{2\pi}}e^{-(x-70)^2/18}\,dx.$$

Using a symbolic integrator, you can approximate the value of this integral to be 0.252. Thus, the probability that the man was 6 feet tall or taller is about 25.2%. ▬

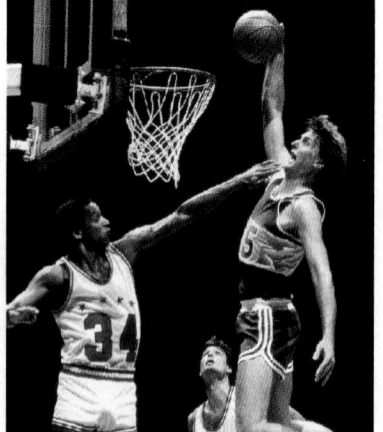

Many professional basketball players are over $6\frac{1}{2}$ feet tall. If a man is chosen at random from the population, the probability that he is $6\frac{1}{2}$ feet tall or taller is less than half of one percent.

Discovery

Example 8 shows that the volume of Gabriel's horn is finite. What is the *area* under the curve $f(x) = 1/x$ and above the x-axis for $x \geq 1$? It can be shown that the surface area of Gabriel's horn is given by the integral

$$2\pi \int_1^\infty \frac{1}{x}\sqrt{1 + \frac{1}{x^4}}\, dx.$$

Use a symbolic integration utility to show that this improper integral diverges. Hence, Gabriel's horn has finite volume but infinite surface area! How could you paint Gabriel's horn?

EXAMPLE 8 *Finding Volume*

The solid formed by revolving the graph of

$$f(x) = \frac{1}{x}, \qquad 1 \leq x < \infty$$

about the x-axis is called **Gabriel's horn.** (See Figure 6.23.) Find the volume of Gabriel's horn.

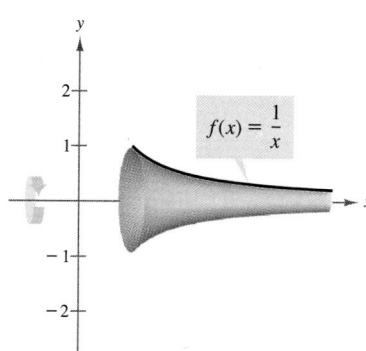

$f(x) = \dfrac{1}{x}$

FIGURE 6.23

Solution

You can find the volume of the horn using the Disc Method (see Section 5.7).

$$
\begin{aligned}
\text{Volume} &= \int_1^\infty \pi \left(\frac{1}{x}\right)^2 dx & &\text{Disc Method}\\
&= \lim_{b\to\infty} \int_1^b \frac{\pi}{x^2}\, dx & &\text{Definition of improper integral}\\
&= \lim_{b\to\infty} \left[-\frac{\pi}{x}\right]_1^b & &\text{Find antiderivative.}\\
&= \lim_{b\to\infty} \left(\pi - \frac{\pi}{b}\right) & &\text{Apply Fundamental Theorem.}\\
&= \pi & &\text{Evaluate limit.}
\end{aligned}
$$

Thus, Gabriel's horn has a volume of π cubic units.

Discussion Problem   Finite or Infinite?

Which of the following improper integrals converge? What can you conclude?

a. $\displaystyle\int_1^\infty \frac{1}{x^{0.9}}\, dx$ **b.** $\displaystyle\int_1^\infty \frac{1}{x^{1.0}}\, dx$ **c.** $\displaystyle\int_1^\infty \frac{1}{x^{1.1}}\, dx$

Warm Up

The following warm-up exercises involve skills that were covered in earlier sections. You will use these skills in the exercise set for this section.

In Exercises 1–6, find the limit.

1. $\lim\limits_{x \to 2} (2x + 5)$

2. $\lim\limits_{x \to 1} \left(\dfrac{1}{x} + 2x^2 \right)$

3. $\lim\limits_{x \to -4} \dfrac{x + 4}{x^2 - 16}$

4. $\lim\limits_{x \to 0} \dfrac{x^2 - 2x}{x^3 + 3x^2}$

5. $\lim\limits_{x \to 1} \dfrac{1}{\sqrt{x - 1}}$

6. $\lim\limits_{x \to -3} \dfrac{x^2 + 2x - 3}{x + 3}$

In Exercises 7–10, evaluate the expression when $x = b$ and when $x = 0$.

7. $\dfrac{4}{3}(2x - 1)^3$

8. $\dfrac{1}{x - 5} + \dfrac{3}{(x - 2)^2}$

9. $\ln(5 - 3x^2) - \ln(x + 1)$

10. $e^{3x^2} + e^{-3x^2}$

EXERCISES 6.6

In Exercises 1–14, determine whether the improper integral converges. If it does, evaluate the integral.

1. $\displaystyle\int_0^\infty e^{-x}\, dx$

2. $\displaystyle\int_{-\infty}^0 e^{2x}\, dx$

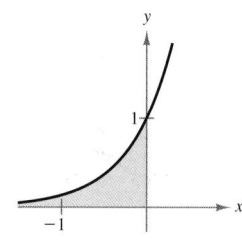

3. $\displaystyle\int_1^\infty \dfrac{1}{x^2}\, dx$

4. $\displaystyle\int_1^\infty \dfrac{1}{\sqrt{x}}\, dx$

5. $\displaystyle\int_0^\infty e^{x/3}\, dx$

6. $\displaystyle\int_0^\infty \dfrac{5}{e^{2x}}\, dx$

7. $\displaystyle\int_5^\infty \dfrac{x}{\sqrt{x^2 - 16}}\, dx$

8. $\displaystyle\int_{1/2}^\infty \dfrac{1}{\sqrt{2x - 1}}\, dx$

9. $\displaystyle\int_{-\infty}^0 e^{-x}\, dx$

10. $\displaystyle\int_{-\infty}^{-1} \dfrac{1}{x^2}\, dx$

11. $\displaystyle\int_{-\infty}^\infty e^{|x|}\, dx$

12. $\displaystyle\int_{-\infty}^\infty \dfrac{|x|}{x^2 + 1}\, dx$

13. $\displaystyle\int_{-\infty}^\infty 2xe^{-3x^2}\, dx$

14. $\displaystyle\int_{-\infty}^\infty x^2 e^{-x^3}\, dx$

In Exercises 15–18, determine the divergence or convergence of the given improper integral. Evaluate the integral if it converges.

15. $\displaystyle\int_0^4 \dfrac{1}{\sqrt{x}}\, dx$

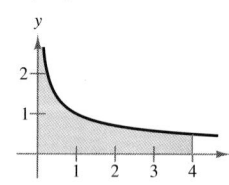

16. $\displaystyle\int_3^4 \dfrac{1}{\sqrt{x - 3}}\, dx$

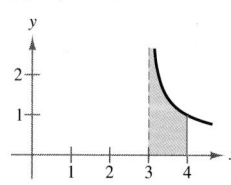

17. $\int_0^2 \frac{1}{(x-1)^{2/3}} \, dx$ **18.** $\int_0^2 \frac{1}{(x-1)^2} \, dx$

 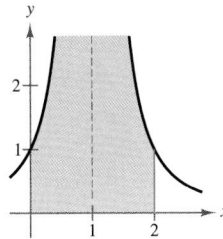

In Exercises 19–28, evaluate the improper integral.

19. $\int_0^1 \frac{1}{1-x} \, dx$ **20.** $\int_0^{27} \frac{5}{\sqrt[3]{x}} \, dx$

21. $\int_0^9 \frac{1}{\sqrt{9-x}} \, dx$ **22.** $\int_0^2 \frac{x}{\sqrt{4-x^2}} \, dx$

23. $\int_0^1 \frac{1}{x^2} \, dx$ **24.** $\int_0^1 \frac{1}{x} \, dx$

25. $\int_0^2 \frac{1}{\sqrt[3]{x-1}} \, dx$ **26.** $\int_0^2 \frac{1}{(x-1)^{4/3}} \, dx$

27. $\int_3^4 \frac{1}{\sqrt{x^2-9}} \, dx$ **28.** $\int_3^5 \frac{1}{x^2\sqrt{x^2-9}} \, dx$

In Exercises 29–32, complete the table for the specified values of a and n to demonstrate that

$$\lim_{x \to \infty} x^n e^{-ax} = 0, \quad a > 0, \ n > 0.$$

x	1	10	25	50
$x^n e^{-ax}$				

29. $a = 1, \ n = 1$ **30.** $a = 2, \ n = 4$

31. $a = \frac{1}{2}, \ n = 2$ **32.** $a = \frac{1}{2}, \ n = 5$

In Exercises 33–36, use the results of Exercises 29–32 to evaluate the improper integral.

33. $\int_0^\infty x^2 e^{-x} \, dx$ **34.** $\int_0^\infty (x-1)e^{-x} \, dx$

35. $\int_0^\infty xe^{-2x} \, dx$ **36.** $\int_0^\infty xe^{-x} \, dx$

37. *Present Value* You are asked to calculate the pay for a business that is forecast to yield a continuous flow of profit at the rate of $500,000 per year. If money will earn interest at the nominal rate of 9% per year compounded continuously, what is the present value of the business (a) for 20 years and (b) forever?

38. *Present Value* Repeat Exercise 37 for a farm that is expected to produce a profit of $75,000 per year. Assume that money will earn interest at the nominal rate of 8% compounded continuously.

Capitalized Cost In Exercises 39 and 40, find the capitalized cost C of an asset (a) for $n = 5$ years, (b) for $n = 10$ years, and (c) forever. The **capitalized cost** is given by

$$C = C_0 + \int_0^n c(t)e^{-rt} \, dt,$$

where C_0 is the original investment, t is the time in years, r is the annual interest rate compounded continuously, and $c(t)$ is the annual cost of maintenance. [*Hint:* For part (c), see Exercises 29–32.]

39. $C_0 = \$650{,}000, \ c(t) = \$25{,}000, \ r = 10\%$

40. $C_0 = \$650{,}000, \ c(t) = \$25{,}000(1 + 0.08t), \ r = 12\%$

In Exercises 41 and 42, (a) find the area of the region bounded by the graphs of the given equations and (b) find the volume of the solid generated by revolving the region about the x-axis.

41. $y = \frac{1}{x^2}, \ y = 0, \ x \geq 1$

42. $y = e^{-x}, \ y = 0, \ x \geq 0$

43. *Household Size* In 1991, the number of people per household in the United States was normally distributed with a mean of 3.07 and a standard deviation of 1.65. Find the probability that a person chosen at random lives

(a) alone.
(b) with 2 people.
(c) with 6 people.

(Source: U.S. Bureau of the Census)

44. *Quality Control* A company manufactures wooden yardsticks. The lengths of the yardsticks are normally distributed, with a mean of 36 inches and a standard deviation of 0.2 inch. Find the probability that a yardstick is (a) longer than 35.5 inches and (b) longer than 35.9 inches.

Chapter Summary and Study Tips

After studying this chapter, you should have acquired the following skills. The exercise numbers are keyed to the Review Exercises that begin on page 446. Answers to odd-numbered Review Exercises are given in the back of the text.

▪ Use the basic integration formulas to find antiderivatives. (*Section 6.1*)   Review Exercises 1–12

Constant Rule: $\int k\, dx = kx + C$

Power Rules: $\int x^n\, dx = \dfrac{x^{n+1}}{n+1} + C,$ $\int u^n u'\, dx = \dfrac{u^{n+1}}{n+1} + C,\ n \neq -1$

Exponential Rules: $\int e^x\, dx = e^x + C,$ $\int e^u u'\, dx = \int e^u\, du = e^u + C$

Log Rules: $\int \dfrac{1}{x}\, dx = \ln|x| + C,$ $\int \dfrac{u'}{u}\, dx = \int \dfrac{1}{u}\, du = \ln|u| + C$

▪ Use substitution to find antiderivatives. (*Section 6.1*)   Review Exercises 13–20

▪ Use substitution to evaluate definite integrals. (*Section 6.1*)   Review Exercises 21–24

▪ Use integration to solve real-life problems. (*Section 6.1*)   Review Exercises 25, 26

▪ Use integration by parts to find antiderivatives. (*Section 6.2*)   Review Exercises 27–30

$$\int u\, dv = uv - \int v\, du$$

▪ Use integration by parts repeatedly to find antiderivatives. (*Section 6.2*)   Review Exercises 31, 32

▪ Find the present value of future income. (*Section 6.2*)   Review Exercises 33–36

▪ Use partial fractions to find antiderivatives. (*Section 6.3*)   Review Exercises 37–42

▪ Use logistics growth functions to model real-life situations. (*Section 6.3*)   Review Exercises 43, 44

▪ Use integration tables to find antiderivatives. (*Section 6.4*)   Review Exercises 45–50

▪ Use reduction formulas to find antiderivatives. (*Section 6.4*)   Review Exercises 51–54

▪ Use completing the square to find antiderivatives. (*Section 6.4*)   Review Exercises 55–58

▪ Use the Trapezoidal Rule to approximate definite integrals. (*Section 6.5*)   Review Exercises 59–62

$$\int_a^b f(x)\, dx \approx \frac{b-a}{2n}[f(x_0) + 2f(x_1) + \cdots + 2f(x_{n-1}) + f(x_n)]$$

▪ Use Simpson's Rule to approximate definite integrals. (*Section 6.5*)   Review Exercises 63–66

$$\int_a^b f(x)\, dx \approx \frac{b-a}{3n}[f(x_0) + 4f(x_1) + 2f(x_2) + 4f(x_3) + \cdots + 4f(x_{n-1}) + f(x_n)]$$

▪ Analyze the sizes of the errors when approximating definite integrals with the Trapezoidal Rule. (*Section 6.5*)   Review Exercises 67, 68

$$|E| \leq \frac{(b-a)^3}{12n^2}\left[\max|f''(x)|\right], \qquad a \leq x \leq b$$

* Several student study aids are available with this text. The *Student Solutions Guide* includes detailed solutions to all odd-numbered exercises, as well as practice chapter tests with answers. The *Graphics Calculator Guide* offers instructions on the use of a variety of graphing calculators and computer graphing software. The *Brief Calculus TUTOR* includes additional examples for selected exercises in the text.

■ Analyze the sizes of the errors when approximating definite integrals with Simpson's Rule. (*Section 6.5*)

Review Exercises 69, 70

$$|E| \le \frac{(b-a)^5}{180n^4} \left[\max |f^{(4)}(x)| \right], \qquad a \le x \le b$$

■ Evaluate improper integrals with infinite limits of integration. (*Section 6.6*)

Review Exercises 71–74

$$\int_a^\infty f(x)\,dx = \lim_{b \to \infty} \int_a^b f(x)\,dx, \qquad \int_{-\infty}^b f(x)\,dx = \lim_{a \to -\infty} \int_a^b f(x)\,dx.$$

■ Evaluate improper integrals with infinite integrands. (*Section 6.6*)

Review Exercises 75–78

$$\int_a^b f(x)\,dx = \lim_{c \to b^-} \int_a^c f(x)\,dx, \qquad \int_a^b f(x)\,dx = \lim_{c \to a^+} \int_c^b f(x)\,dx$$

■ Use improper integrals to solve real-life problems. (*Section 6.6*)

Review Exercises 79–82

■ Use a Variety of Approaches   To be efficient at finding antiderivatives, you need to use a variety of approaches.

1. Check to see whether the integral fits one of the basic integration formulas—you should have these formulas memorized.
2. Try an integration technique such as substitution, integration by parts, partial fractions, or completing the square to rewrite the integral in a form that fits one of the basic integration formulas.
3. Use a table of integrals.
4. Use a symbolic integration utility such as *Derive*, *Maple*, or *Mathematica*.

■ Use Numerical Integration   When solving a definite integral, remember that you cannot apply the Fundamental Theorem of Calculus unless you can find an antiderivative of the integrand. This is not always possible—even with a symbolic integration utility. In such cases, you can use a numerical technique such as the Midpoint Rule, the Trapezoidal Rule, or Simpson's Rule to approximate the value of the integral.

■ Improper Integrals   When solving integration problems, remember that the symbols used to denote definite integrals are the same as those used to denote improper integrals. Evaluating an improper integral as a definite integral can lead to an incorrect value. For instance, if you evaluated the integral

$$\int_{-2}^1 \frac{1}{x^2}\,dx$$

as though it were a definite integral, you would obtain a value of $-\frac{3}{2}$. This is not, however, correct. This integral is actually a divergent improper integral. If you have access to a symbolic integration utility, try using it to evaluate this integral— it will probably make the same mistake.

do # 43 Sec 6.1 pg 391.

Review Exercises

do # 29 Sec. 6.2 pg # 399.

In Exercises 1–12, use a basic integration formula to find the indefinite integral.

1. $\int dt$

2. $\int (x^2 + 2x - 1)\,dx$

3. $\int (x + 5)^3\,dx$

4. $\int \dfrac{2}{(x-1)^2}\,dx$

5. $\int e^{10x}\,dx$

6. $\int 3xe^{-x^2}\,dx$

7. $\int \dfrac{1}{5x}\,dx$

8. $\int \dfrac{2x^3 - x}{x^4 - x^2 + 1}\,dx$

9. $\int x\sqrt{x^2 + 4}\,dx$

10. $\int \dfrac{1}{\sqrt{2x - 9}}\,dx$

11. $\int \dfrac{2e^x}{3 + e^x}\,dx$

12. $\int (x^2 - 1)e^{x^3 - 3x}\,dx$

In Exercises 13–20, use substitution to find the indefinite integral.

13. $\int x(x - 2)^3\,dx$

14. $\int x(1 - x)^2\,dx$

15. $\int x\sqrt{x + 1}\,dx$

16. $\int x^2\sqrt{x + 1}\,dx$

17. $\int 2x\sqrt{x - 3}\,dx$

18. $\int \dfrac{\sqrt{x}}{1 + \sqrt{x}}\,dx$

19. $\int (x + 1)\sqrt{1 - x}\,dx$

20. $\int \dfrac{x}{x - 1}\,dx$

In Exercises 21–24, use substitution to evaluate the definite integral.

21. $\int_2^3 x\sqrt{x - 2}\,dx$

22. $\int_2^3 x^2\sqrt{x - 2}\,dx$

23. $\int_1^3 x^2(x - 1)^3\,dx$

24. $\int_{-3}^0 x(x + 3)^4\,dx$

25. _Probability_ The probability of recall in an experiment is found to be

$$P(a \le x \le b) = \int_a^b \frac{105}{16}x^2\sqrt{1 - x}\,dx,$$

where x represents the percent of recall (see figure).

(a) Find the probability that a randomly chosen individual will recall 80% of the material.

(b) What is the median percent recall? That is, for what value of b is it true that $P(0 \le x \le b) = 0.5$?

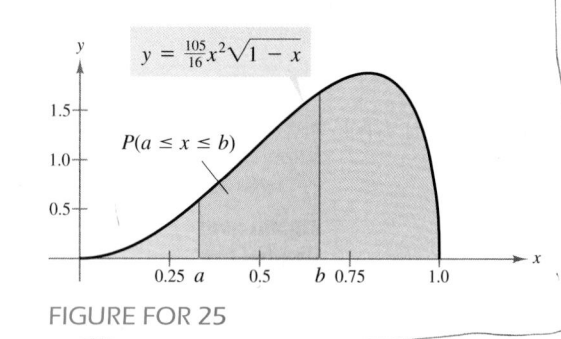

$y = \frac{105}{16}x^2\sqrt{1 - x}$

$P(a \le x \le b)$

FIGURE FOR 25

26. _Probability_ The probability of locating between a and b percent of oil and gas deposits in a region is

$$P(a \le x \le b) = \int_a^b \frac{140}{27}x^2(1 - x)^{1/3}\,dx$$

(see figure).

(a) Find the probability that between 40% and 60% of the deposits will be found.

(b) Find the probability that between 0% and 50% of the deposits will be found.

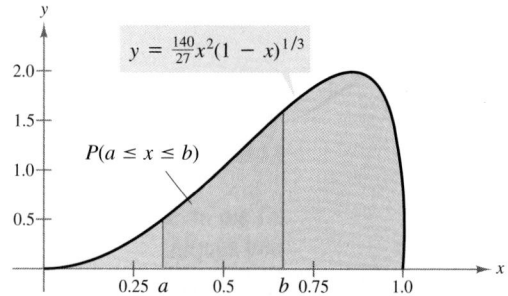

$y = \frac{140}{27}x^2(1 - x)^{1/3}$

$P(a \le x \le b)$

In Exercises 27–30, use integration by parts to find the indefinite integral.

27. $\int \dfrac{\ln x}{\sqrt{x}}\,dx$

28. $\int \sqrt{x}\ln x\,dx$

29. $\int (x - 1)e^x\,dx$

30. $\int \ln\left(\dfrac{x}{x + 1}\right)\,dx$

In Exercises 31 and 32, use integration by parts repeatedly to find the indefinite integral.

31. $\int 2x^2 e^{2x}\,dx$

32. $\int (\ln x)^3\,dx$

In Exercises 33–36, find the present value of the income given by $c(t)$ (measured in dollars) over t_1 years at the given annual inflation rate.

33. $c(t) = 10,000, \ r = 4\%, \ t_1 = 5$ years

34. $c(t) = 20,000 + 1500t, \ r = 6\%, \ t_1 = 10$ years

35. $c(t) = 12,000t, \ r = 5\%, \ t_1 = 10$ years

36. $c(t) = 10,000 + 100e^{t/2}, \ r = 5\%, \ t_1 = 5$ years

In Exercises 37–42, use partial fractions to find the indefinite integral.

37. $\displaystyle \int \frac{1}{x(x+5)} \, dx$

38. $\displaystyle \int \frac{4x-2}{3(x-1)^2} \, dx$

39. $\displaystyle \int \frac{4x-13}{x^2-3x-10} \, dx$

40. $\displaystyle \int \frac{4x^2-x-5}{x^2(x+5)} \, dx$

41. $\displaystyle \int \frac{x^2}{x^2+2x-15} \, dx$

42. $\displaystyle \int \frac{x^2+2x-12}{x(x+3)} \, dx$

43. *Sales Growth* When it is introduced to the market, a new product initially sells 1250 units per week. After 6 months, the number of sales increases to 6500. The sales can be modeled by logistics growth with a limit of 10,000 units per week.

(a) Find a logistics growth model for the number of units.

(b) Use the model to complete the table.

Time, t	0	3	6	12	24
Sales, y					

(c) Use the graph below to approximate the time t that sales will be 7500.

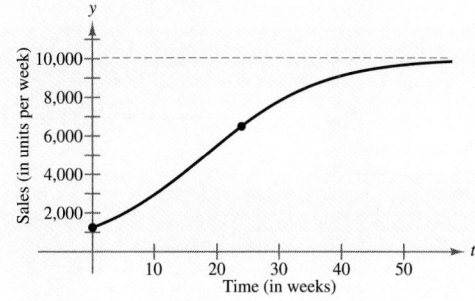

44. *Population Growth* A conservation society has introduced a population of 300 ring-neck pheasants into a new area. After 5 years the population has increased to 966. The population can be modeled by logistics growth with a limit of 2700 pheasants.

(a) Find a logistics growth model for the population of ring-neck pheasants.

(b) How many pheasants were present after 4 years?

(c) How long will it take to establish a population of 1750 pheasants?

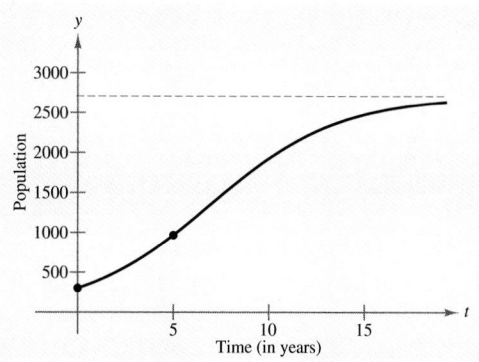

FIGURE FOR 44

In Exercises 45–50, use the table of integrals in Section 6.4 to evaluate the integral.

45. $\displaystyle \int \frac{\sqrt{x^2+25}}{x} \, dx$

46. $\displaystyle \int \frac{1}{x(4+3x)} \, dx$

47. $\displaystyle \int \frac{1}{(x^2-4)} \, dx$

48. $\displaystyle \int x(\ln x^2)^2 \, dx$

49. $\displaystyle \int_0^3 \frac{x}{\sqrt{1+x}} \, dx$

50. $\displaystyle \int_1^3 \frac{1}{x^2\sqrt{16-x^2}} \, dx$

In Exercises 51–54, use a reduction formula from the table of integrals in Section 6.4 to find the indefinite integral.

51. $\displaystyle \int \frac{\sqrt{1+x}}{x} \, dx$

52. $\displaystyle \int \frac{1}{(x^2-9)^2} \, dx$

53. $\displaystyle \int (x-5)^3 e^{x-5} \, dx$

54. $\displaystyle \int (\ln x)^4 \, dx$

In Exercises 55–58, complete the square and then use the table of integrals given in Section 6.4 to find the indefinite integral.

55. $\displaystyle \int \frac{1}{x^2+4x-21} \, dx$

56. $\displaystyle \int \frac{1}{x^2-8x-52} \, dx$

57. $\displaystyle \int \sqrt{x^2-10x} \, dx$

58. $\displaystyle \int \frac{x}{\sqrt{x^4+6x^2+10}} \, dx$

In Exercises 59–62, use the Trapezoidal Rule to approximate the definite integral.

59. $\int_1^3 \frac{1}{x^2} \, dx, \ n = 4$

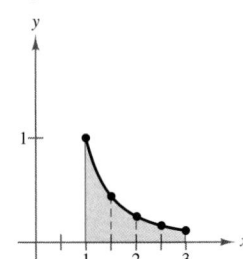

60. $\int_0^2 (x^2 + 1) \, dx, \ n = 4$

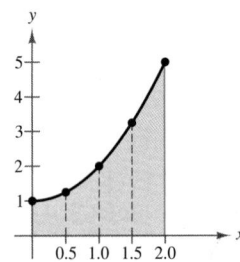

61. $\int_1^2 \frac{1}{1 + \ln x} \, dx, \ n = 4$

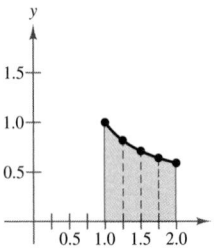

62. $\int_0^2 \frac{1}{\sqrt{1 + x^3}} \, dx, \ n = 8$

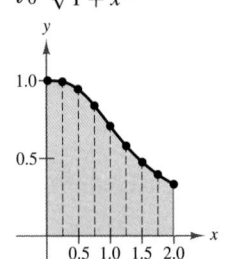

In Exercises 63–66, use Simpson's Rule to approximate the definite integral.

63. $\int_1^2 \frac{1}{x^3} \, dx, \ n = 4$

64. $\int_1^2 x^3 \, dx, \ n = 4$

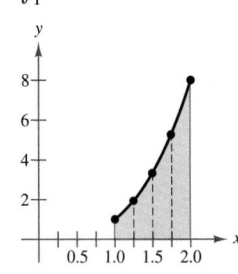

65. $\int_0^1 \frac{x^{3/2}}{2 - x^2} \, dx, \ n = 4$

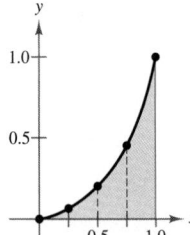

66. $\int_0^1 e^{x^2} \, dx, \ n = 6$

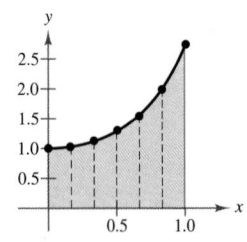

In Exercises 67 and 68, use the error formula to find bounds for the error in approximating the integral using the Trapezoidal Rule.

67. $\int_0^2 e^{2x} \, dx, \ n = 4$

68. $\int_0^2 e^{2x} \, dx, \ n = 8$

In Exercises 69 and 70, use the error formula to find bounds for the error in approximating the integral using Simpson's Rule.

69. $\int_2^4 \frac{1}{x - 1} \, dx, \ n = 4$

70. $\int_2^4 \frac{1}{x - 1} \, dx, \ n = 8$

In Exercises 71–78, evaluate the improper integral.

71. $\int_0^\infty 4xe^{-2x^2} \, dx$

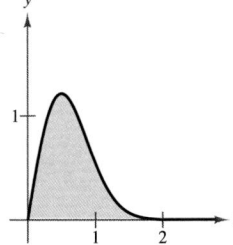

72. $\int_{-\infty}^0 \frac{3}{(1 - 3x)^{2/3}} \, dx$

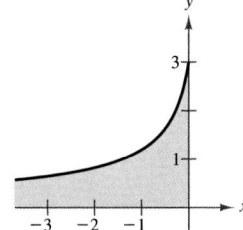

73. $\int_{-\infty}^0 \frac{1}{3x^2} \, dx$

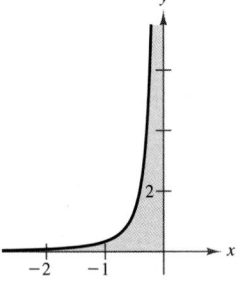

74. $\int_0^\infty 2x^2 e^{-x^3} \, dx$

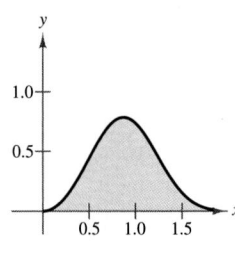

75. $\int_0^4 \frac{1}{\sqrt{4x}} \, dx$

76. $\int_1^2 \frac{x}{16(x - 1)^2} \, dx$

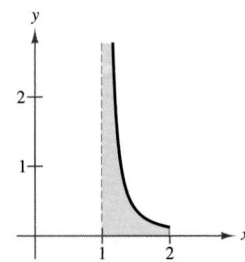

77. $\int_{2}^{3} \frac{1}{\sqrt{x-2}} \, dx$

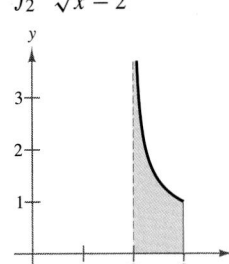

78. $\int_{0}^{2} \frac{x+2}{(x-1)^2} \, dx$

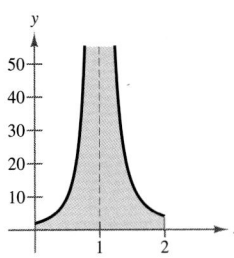

79. *Present Value* You are considering buying a franchise that yields a continuous income stream of $50,000 per year. Find the present value of the franchise (a) for 15 years and (b) forever. Assume that money earns 6% interest per year, compounded continuously.

80. *Capitalized Cost* A company invests $1.5 million in a new manufacturing plant that will cost $50,000 per year in maintenance. Find the capitalized cost for (a) 20 years and (b) forever. Assume that money earns 6% interest, compounded continuously.

81. *Per Capita Income* In 1991, the per capita income per state was approximately normally distributed with a mean of $18,188.38 and a standard deviation of $2736.16 (see figure). Find the probability that a state has a per capita income of (a) $20,000 or greater and (b) $30,000 or greater. *(Source: U.S. Bureau of Economic Analysis)*

$$y = \frac{1}{2736.16\sqrt{2\pi}} e^{-(x-18,188.38)^2/2(2736.16)^2}$$

82. *Eastern Warblers* The average length (from beak to tail) of different species of warblers in the eastern United States is approximately normally distributed with a mean of 12.9 centimeters and a standard deviation of 0.95 centimeters (see figure). Find the probability that a species of warbler has a length that is (a) 13 centimeters or greater and (b) 15 centimeters or greater. *(Source: Peterson Field Guide: Eastern Birds)*

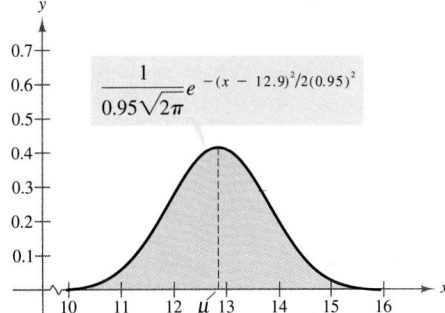

$$\frac{1}{0.95\sqrt{2\pi}} e^{-(x-12.9)^2/2(0.95)^2}$$

Sample Post-Graduation Exam Questions

The following questions were taken from certified public accountant (CPA) exams, graduate management admission tests (GMAT), graduate records exams (GRE), actuarial exams, or college-level academic skills tests (CLAST). The answers to the questions are given in the back of the book.

For Questions 1–4, the total 1988 population was 12,335,000; the total 1992 population was 13,488,000. Also use the data given in the graphs. *(Source: U.S. Bureau of the Census)*

1. Find the number of people aged 75 and over for the year 1992.
   (a) 986,800   (b) 944,160   (c) 1,079,840   (d) 863,450

2. Find the increase in population of 35 to 54 year olds from 1988 to 1992.
   (a) 411,600   (b) 18,490   (c) 153,370   (d) 288,250

3. In 1988, how many people were 54 years old or younger?
   (a) 8,881,200   (b) 8,757,850   (c) 9,576,480   (d) 11,471,550

4. In what age group did the population and the population percent decrease between 1988 and 1992?
   (a) 0–17   (b) 75 and over   (c) 18–34   (d) 55–74

5. $\displaystyle\int_1^6 \frac{x}{\sqrt{x+3}} =$

   (a) $\frac{10}{3}$ (b) $-\frac{20}{3}$ (c) -4 (d) $\frac{20}{3}$

6. $\displaystyle\lim_{x\to\infty} \frac{2x^2 + 5x - 16}{5x^2 - 15x + 48} =$

   (a) 0 (b) $\frac{2}{5}$ (c) ∞ (d) $\frac{1}{3}$

7. The city council is planning to construct a new street as shown in the figure. Construction costs of the new street are $110 per linear foot. What is the projected cost for constructing the new street?
   (a) $2,904,000   (b) $4,065,600   (c) $1,904,000
   (d) $3,864,000

8. The following information pertains to Varn Co.:
   Sales $1,000,000,   Variable Costs $200,000,
   Fixed Costs $50,000

   What is Varn's break-even point in sales dollars?
   (a) $40,000   (b) $250,000   (c) $62,500   (d) $200,000

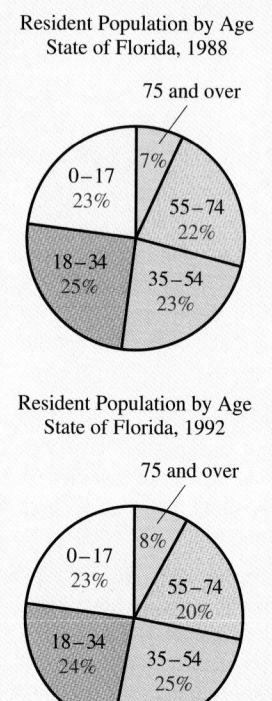

Resident Population by Age
State of Florida, 1988

Resident Population by Age
State of Florida, 1992

FIGURE FOR 1–4

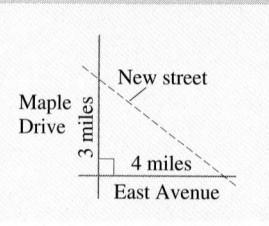

FIGURE FOR 7

$$\frac{\partial z}{\partial x} = \lim_{\Delta x \to 0} \frac{f(x + \Delta x, y) - f(x, y)}{\Delta x}$$

7 Functions of Several Variables

Calculus was originally developed to study functions of a single variable. It was later discovered that the two basic operations of calculus—differentiation and integration—can be meaningfully extended to functions of two or more variables.

Graphs of functions of *one* variable can be represented by curves in the plane. Graphs of functions of *two* variables can be represented by surfaces in space. A technique for computer generation of such "three-dimensional" graphs was developed by the African-American mathematician David Hedgley, Jr. (1937–).

$$\frac{\partial z}{\partial x} = f_x(x, y)$$

Hedgley

Courtesy of NASA

The Three-Dimensional Coordinate System ■ *The Distance and Midpoint Formulas* ■ *The Equation of a Sphere* ■ *Traces of Surfaces*

The Three-Dimensional Coordinate System

Recall that the Cartesian plane is determined by two perpendicular number lines called the x-axis and the y-axis. These axes together with their point of intersection (the origin) allow you to develop a two-dimensional coordinate system for identifying points in a plane. To identify a point in space, you must introduce a third dimension to the model. The geometry of this three-dimensional model is called **solid analytic geometry.**

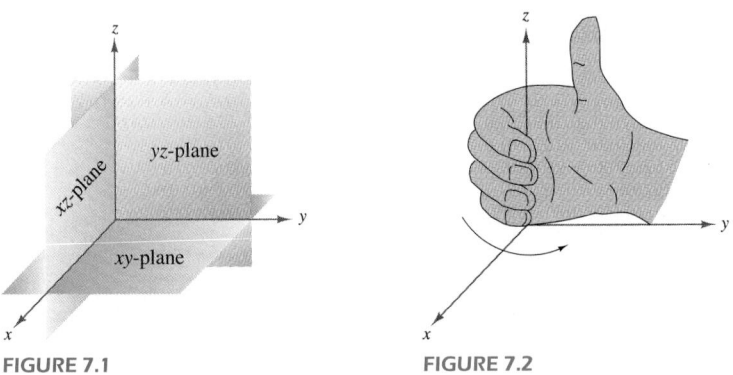

FIGURE 7.1   FIGURE 7.2

You can construct a **three-dimensional coordinate system** by passing a z-axis perpendicular to both the x- and y-axes at the origin. Figure 7.1 shows the positive portion of each coordinate axis. Taken as pairs, the axes determine three **coordinate planes:** the **xy-plane,** the **xz-plane,** and the **yz-plane.** These three coordinate planes separate the three-dimensional coordinate system into eight **octants.** The first octant is the one for which all three coordinates are positive. In this three-dimensional system, a point P in space is determined by an ordered triple (x, y, z), where x, y, and z are as follows.

$x =$ directed distance from yz-plane to P

$y =$ directed distance from xz-plane to P

$z =$ directed distance from xy-plane to P

A three-dimensional coordinate system can have either a **left-handed** or a **right-handed** orientation. In this text, we work exclusively with right-handed systems, as shown in Figure 7.2.

EXAMPLE 1 *Plotting Points in Space*

Plot the following points in space.

a. $(2, -3, 3)$ **b.** $(-2, 6, 2)$ **c.** $(1, 4, 0)$ **d.** $(2, 2, -3)$

Solution

To plot the point $(2, -3, 3)$, notice that $x = 2$, $y = -3$, and $z = 3$. To help visualize the point (see Figure 7.3), locate the point $(2, -3)$ in the xy-plane (denoted by a cross). The point $(2, -3, 3)$ lies three units above the cross. The other three points are also shown in the figure.

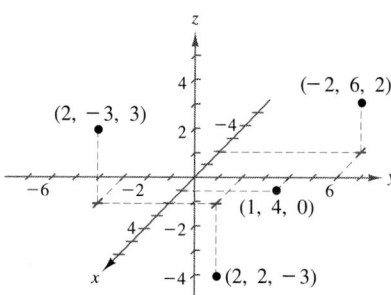

FIGURE 7.3

The Distance and Midpoint Formulas

Many of the formulas established for the two-dimensional coordinate system can be extended to three dimensions. For example, to find the distance between two points in space, you can use the Pythagorean Theorem twice, as shown in Figure 7.4. By doing this, you will obtain the formula for the distance between two points in space.

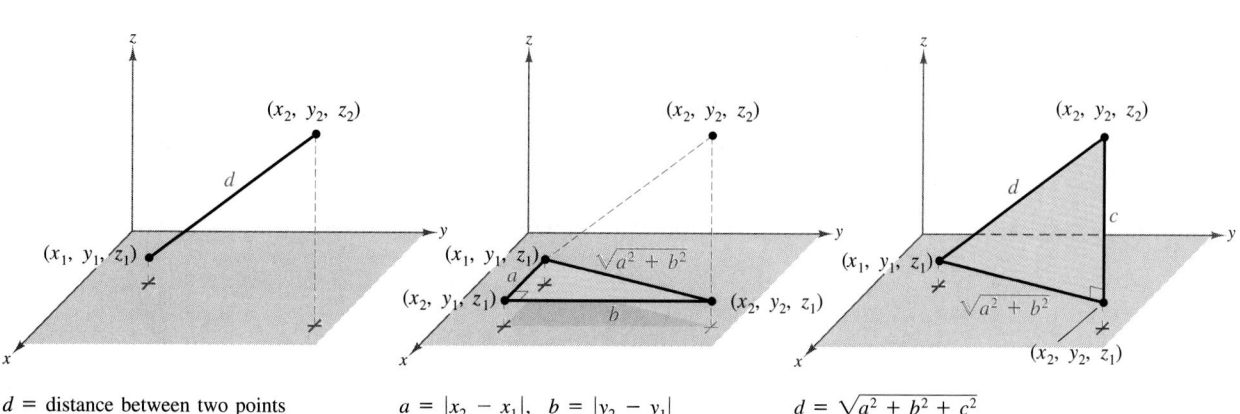

d = distance between two points

$a = |x_2 - x_1|$, $b = |y_2 - y_1|$

$d = \sqrt{a^2 + b^2 + c^2}$
$= \sqrt{(x_2 - x_1)^2 + (y_2 - y_1)^2 + (z_2 - z_1)^2}$

FIGURE 7.4

Distance Formula in Space

The distance between the points (x_1, y_1, z_1) and (x_2, y_2, z_2) is

$$d = \sqrt{(x_2 - x_1)^2 + (y_2 - y_1)^2 + (z_2 - z_1)^2}.$$

EXAMPLE 2 *Finding the Distance Between Two Points*

Find the distance between $(1, 0, 2)$ and $(2, 4, -3)$.

Solution

$$
\begin{aligned}
d &= \sqrt{(x_2 - x_1)^2 + (y_2 - y_1)^2 + (z_2 - z_1)^2} && \textit{Distance Formula} \\
&= \sqrt{(2 - 1)^2 + (4 - 0)^2 + (-3 - 2)^2} && \textit{Substitute.} \\
&= \sqrt{1 + 16 + 25} && \textit{Simplify.} \\
&= \sqrt{42}. && \textit{Simplify.}
\end{aligned}
$$

Notice the similarity between the Distance Formula in the plane and the Distance Formula in space. The Midpoint Formulas in the plane and in space are also similar.

Midpoint Formula in Space

The midpoint of the line segment joining the points (x_1, y_1, z_1) and (x_2, y_2, z_2) is

$$\text{Midpoint} = \left(\frac{x_1 + x_2}{2}, \frac{y_1 + y_2}{2}, \frac{z_1 + z_2}{2} \right).$$

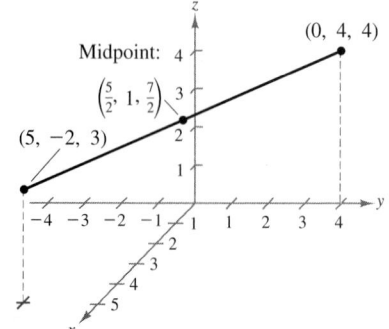

FIGURE 7.5

EXAMPLE 3 *Using the Midpoint Formula*

Find the midpoint of the line segment joining $(5, -2, 3)$ and $(0, 4, 4)$.

Solution

Using the Midpoint Formula, the midpoint is

$$\left(\frac{5 + 0}{2}, \frac{-2 + 4}{2}, \frac{3 + 4}{2} \right) = \left(\frac{5}{2}, 1, \frac{7}{2} \right),$$

as shown in Figure 7.5.

The Equation of a Sphere

A **sphere** with center at (h, k, l) and radius r is defined to be the set of all points (x, y, z) such that the distance between (x, y, z) and (h, k, l) is r, as shown in Figure 7.6. Using the Distance Formula, this condition can be written as

$$\sqrt{(x - h)^2 + (y - k)^2 + (z - l)^2} = r.$$

By squaring both sides of this equation, you obtain the standard equation of a sphere.

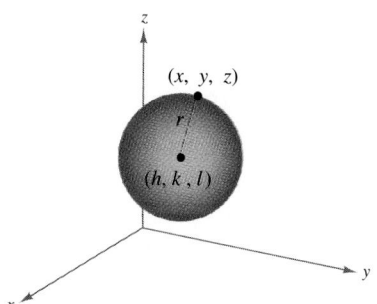

FIGURE 7.6   Sphere: Radius r, Center (h, k, l)

Standard Equation of a Sphere

The **standard equation of a sphere** whose center is (h, k, l) and whose radius is r is

$$(x - h)^2 + (y - k)^2 + (z - l)^2 = r^2.$$

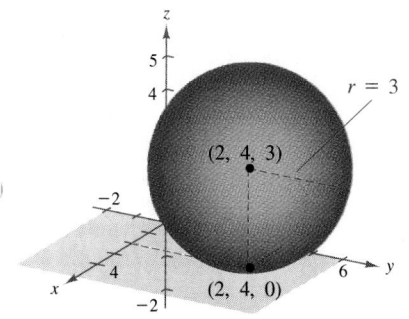

FIGURE 7.7

EXAMPLE 4   Finding the Equation of a Sphere

Find the standard equation for the sphere whose center is $(2, 4, 3)$ and whose radius is 3. Does this sphere intersect the xy-plane?

Solution

$$(x - h)^2 + (y - k)^2 + (z - l)^2 = r^2 \qquad \textit{Standard equation}$$
$$(x - 2)^2 + (y - 4)^2 + (z - 3)^2 = 3^2 \qquad \textit{Substitute.}$$

From the graph shown in Figure 7.7, you can see that the center of the sphere lies three units above the xy-plane. Because the sphere has a radius of 3, you can conclude that it does intersect the xy-plane—at the point $(2, 4, 0)$.   ■

EXAMPLE 5 *Finding the Equation of a Sphere*

Find the equation of the sphere that has the points $(3, -2, 6)$ and $(-1, 4, 2)$ as endpoints of a diameter.

Solution

By the Midpoint Formula, the center of the sphere is

$$(h, k, l) = \left(\frac{3-1}{2}, \frac{-2+4}{2}, \frac{6+2}{2} \right) \qquad \textit{Midpoint Formula}$$

$$= (1, 1, 4). \qquad \textit{Simplify.}$$

By the Distance Formula, the radius is

$$r = \sqrt{(3-1)^2 + (-2-1)^2 + (6-4)^2} \qquad \textit{Distance Formula}$$

$$= \sqrt{17}. \qquad \textit{Simplify.}$$

Therefore, the standard equation of the sphere is

$$(x-h)^2 + (y-k)^2 + (z-l)^2 = r^2 \qquad \textit{Formula for a sphere}$$

$$(x-1)^2 + (y-1)^2 + (z-4)^2 = 17. \qquad \textit{Substitute.} \qquad \blacksquare$$

EXAMPLE 6 *Finding the Center and Radius of a Sphere*

Find the center and radius of the sphere whose equation is

$$x^2 + y^2 + z^2 - 2x + 4y - 6z + 8 = 0.$$

Solution

You can obtain the standard equation of the sphere by completing the square. To do this, begin by grouping terms with the same variable. Then add "the square of half the coefficient of each linear term" to both sides of the equation. For instance, to complete the square of $(x^2 - 2x)$, add $[\frac{1}{2}(-2)]^2 = 1$ to both sides.

$$x^2 + y^2 + z^2 - 2x + 4y - 6z + 8 = 0$$

$$(x^2 - 2x + \underline{\quad}) + (y^2 + 4y + \underline{\quad}) + (z^2 - 6z + \underline{\quad}) = -8$$

$$(x^2 - 2x + 1) + (y^2 + 4y + 4) + (z^2 - 6z + 9) = -8 + 1 + 4 + 9$$

$$(x - 1)^2 + (y + 2)^2 + (z - 3)^2 = 6$$

Therefore, the center of the sphere is $(1, -2, 3)$, and its radius is $\sqrt{6}$, as shown in Figure 7.8. $\blacksquare$

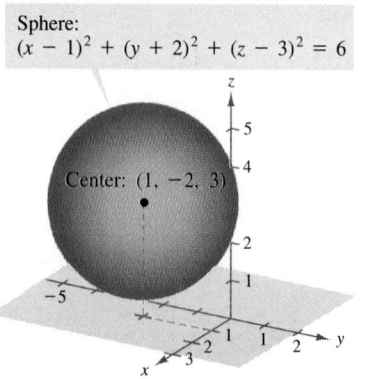

Sphere:
$(x - 1)^2 + (y + 2)^2 + (z - 3)^2 = 6$

Center: $(1, -2, 3)$

FIGURE 7.8

Note in Example 6 that the points satisfying the equation of the sphere are "surface points," not "interior points." In general, the collection of points satisfying an equation involving x, y, and z is called a **surface in space.**

Traces of Surfaces

Finding the intersection of a surface with one of the three coordinate planes (or with a plane parallel to one of the three coordinate planes) helps visualize the surface. Such an intersection is called a **trace** of the surface. For example, the xy-trace of a surface consists of all points that are common to both the surface *and* the xy-plane. Similarly, the xz-trace of a surface consists of all points that are common to both the surface and the xz-plane.

EXAMPLE 7 *Finding a Trace of a Surface*

Sketch the xy-trace of the sphere whose equation is

$$(x - 3)^2 + (y - 2)^2 + (z + 4)^2 = 5^2.$$

Solution

To find the xy-trace of this surface, use the fact that every point in the xy-plane has a z-coordinate of zero. This means that if you substitute $z = 0$ into the given equation, the resulting equation will represent the intersection of the surface with the xy-plane.

$$(x - 3)^2 + (y - 2)^2 + (z + 4)^2 = 5^2 \qquad \textit{Equation of sphere}$$
$$(x - 3)^2 + (y - 2)^2 + (0 + 4)^2 = 25 \qquad \textit{Let } z = 0 \textit{ to find } xy\textit{-trace.}$$
$$(x - 3)^2 + (y - 2)^2 + 16 = 25$$
$$(x - 3)^2 + (y - 2)^2 = 9$$
$$(x - 3)^2 + (y - 2)^2 = 3^2 \qquad \textit{Equation of circle}$$

From this equation, you can see that the xy-trace is a circle of radius 3, as shown in Figure 7.9. ■

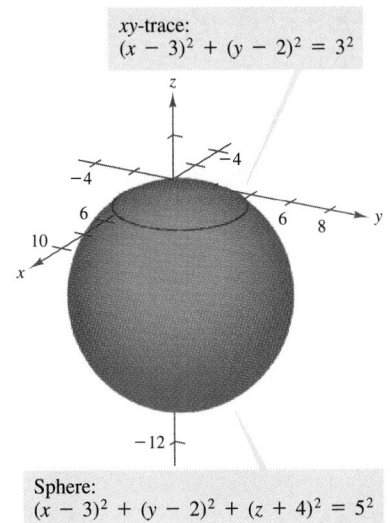

xy-trace:
$(x - 3)^2 + (y - 2)^2 = 3^2$

Sphere:
$(x - 3)^2 + (y - 2)^2 + (z + 4)^2 = 5^2$

FIGURE 7.9

Discussion Problem Comparing Two and Three Dimensions

In this section, you saw similarities between formulas in two-dimensional coordinate geometry and three-dimensional coordinate geometry. In two-dimensional coordinate geometry, the graph of the equation

$$ax + by + c = 0$$

is a line. In three-dimensional coordinate geometry, what is the graph of the equation

$$ax + by + c = 0?$$

Is it a line? Explain your reasoning.

Warm Up

The following warm-up exercises involve skills that were covered in earlier sections. You will use these skills in the exercise set for this section.

In Exercises 1–4, find the distance between the points.

1. $(5, 1), (3, 5)$ **2.** $(2, 3), (-1, -1)$

3. $(-5, 4), (-5, -4)$ **4.** $(-3, 6), (-3, -2)$

In Exercises 5–8, find the midpoint of the line segment connecting the points.

5. $(2, 5), (6, 9)$ **6.** $(-1, -2), (3, 2)$

7. $(-6, 0), (6, 6)$ **8.** $(-4, 3), (2, -1)$

In Exercises 9 and 10, write the standard equation of the circle.

9. Center: $(2, 3)$; Radius: 2   **10.** Diameter endpoints: $(4, 0), (-2, 8)$

E X E R C I S E S 7.1   means that technology can help you solve or check the exercise(s).

In Exercises 1–4, plot the points on the same three-dimensional coordinate system.

1. (a) $(2, 1, 3)$
    (b) $(-1, 2, 1)$

2. (a) $(3, -2, 5)$
    (b) $\left(\frac{3}{2}, 4, -2\right)$

3. (a) $(5, -2, 2)$
    (b) $(5, -2, -2)$

4. (a) $(0, 4, -5)$
    (b) $(4, 0, 5)$

In Exercises 5–8, find the distance between the two points.

5. $(4, 1, 5), (8, 2, 6)$

6. $(-4, -1, 1), (2, -1, 5)$

7. $(-1, -5, 7), (-3, 4, -4)$

8. $(8, -2, 2), (8, -2, 4)$

In Exercises 9–12, find the coordinates of the midpoint of the line segment joining the given points.

9. $(6, -9, 1), (-2, -1, 5)$

10. $(4, 0, -6), (8, 8, 20)$

11. $(-5, -2, 5), (6, 3, -7)$

12. $(0, -2, 5), (4, 2, 7)$

In Exercises 13–16, find (x, y, z).

13.

14.

15.

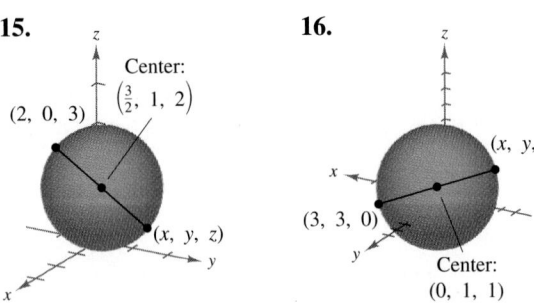

16.

In Exercises 17–20, find the lengths of the sides of the triangle with the indicated vertices, and determine whether the triangle is a right triangle, an isosceles triangle, or neither of these.

17. $(0, 0, 0)$, $(2, 2, 1)$, $(2, -4, 4)$

18. $(5, 3, 4)$, $(7, 1, 3)$, $(3, 5, 3)$

19. $(-2, 2, 4)$, $(-2, 2, 6)$, $(-2, 4, 8)$

20. $(5, 0, 0)$, $(0, 2, 0)$, $(0, 0, -3)$

In Exercises 21–28, find the standard form of the equation of the sphere.

21.

22.

23.

24.

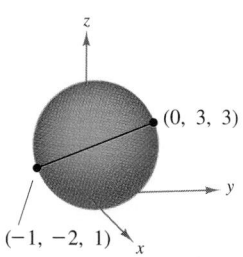

25. Center: $(1, 1, 5)$; Radius: 3

26. Center: $(4, -1, 1)$; Radius: 5

27. Diameter endpoints: $(2, 0, 0)$, $(0, 6, 0)$

28. Center: $(-2, 1, 1)$; Tangent to the xy-coordinate plane

In Exercises 29–36, find the sphere's center and radius.

29. $x^2 + y^2 + z^2 - 2x + 6y + 8z + 1 = 0$

30. $x^2 + y^2 + z^2 - 5x = 0$

31. $x^2 + y^2 + z^2 - 8y = 0$

32. $x^2 + y^2 + z^2 - 4y + 6z + 4 = 0$

33. $2x^2 + 2y^2 + 2z^2 - 4x - 12y - 8z + 3 = 0$

34. $x^2 + y^2 + z^2 = 36$

35. $9x^2 + 9y^2 + 9z^2 - 6x + 18y + 1 = 0$

36. $4x^2 + 4y^2 + 4z^2 - 4x - 32y + 8z + 33 = 0$

In Exercises 37 and 38, sketch the xy-trace of the sphere.

37. $(x - 1)^2 + (y - 3)^2 + (z - 2)^2 = 25$

38. $x^2 + y^2 + z^2 - 6x - 10y + 6z + 30 = 0$

In Exercises 39 and 40, sketch the yz-trace of the sphere.

39. $x^2 + y^2 + z^2 - 4x - 4y - 6z - 12 = 0$

40. $x^2 + y^2 + z^2 - 6x - 10y + 6z + 30 = 0$

In Exercises 41–44, sketch the trace of the intersection of each plane with the given sphere.

41. $x^2 + y^2 + z^2 = 25$; (a) $z = 3$, (b) $x = 4$

42. $x^2 + y^2 + z^2 = 169$; (a) $x = 5$, (b) $y = 12$

43. $x^2 + y^2 + z^2 - 4x - 6y + 9 = 0$; (a) $x = 2$, (b) $y = 3$

44. $x^2 + y^2 + z^2 - 8x - 6z + 16 = 0$; (a) $x = 4$, (b) $z = 3$

45. *Crystals* Crystals are classified according to their symmetry. Crystals shaped like cubes are classified as isometric. Suppose you have mapped the vertices of a crystal onto a three-dimensional coordinate system. Determine (x, y, z) if the crystal is isometric.

© Breck P. Kent

Halite crystals (rock salt) are classified as isometric.

7.2 Surfaces in Space

Equations of Planes in Space ■ *Drawing Planes in Space* ■
Quadric Surfaces

Equations of Planes in Space

In Section 7.1, you studied one type of surface in space—a sphere. In this section, you will study a second type—a plane in space. The **general equation of a plane** in space is

$$ax + by + cz = d. \qquad \textit{General equation of a plane}$$

Note the similarity of this equation to the general equation of a line in the plane. In fact, if you intersect the plane represented by this equation with each of the three coordinate planes, you will obtain traces that are lines, as shown in Figure 7.10.

In Figure 7.10, the points where the plane intersects the three coordinate axes are the x-, y-, and z-intercepts of the plane. By connecting these three points, you can form a triangular region, which helps you visualize the plane in space.

xz-trace: $ax + cz = d$

Plane: $ax + by + cz = d$

yz-trace: $by + cz = d$

xy-trace: $ax + by = d$

FIGURE 7.10

EXAMPLE 1 *Sketching a Plane in Space*

Find the x-, y-, and z-intercepts of the plane given by

$$3x + 2y + 4z = 12.$$

Then sketch the plane.

Solution
To find the x-intercept, let both y and z be zero.

$$3x + 2(0) + 4(0) = 12 \qquad \textit{Substitute 0 for y and z.}$$
$$3x = 12 \qquad \textit{Simplify.}$$
$$x = 4 \qquad \textit{Solve for x.}$$

Thus, the x-intercept is $(4, 0, 0)$. To find the y-intercept, let x and z be zero and conclude that $y = 6$. Thus, the y-intercept is $(0, 6, 0)$. Similarly, by letting x and y be zero, you can determine that $z = 3$ and that the z-intercept is $(0, 0, 3)$. Figure 7.11 shows the triangular portion of the plane formed by connecting the three intercepts.

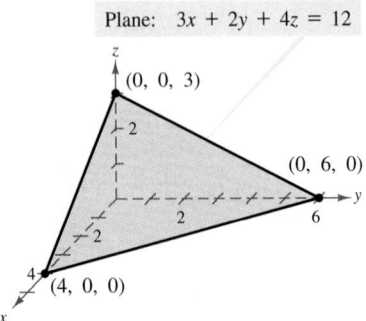

Plane: $3x + 2y + 4z = 12$

$(0, 0, 3)$

$(0, 6, 0)$

$(4, 0, 0)$

FIGURE 7.11 Sketch made by connecting intercepts: $(4, 0, 0)$, $(0, 6, 0)$, $(0, 0, 3)$

Drawing Planes in Space

The planes shown in Figures 7.10 and 7.11 each have three intercepts. When this occurs, we suggest that you draw the plane by sketching the triangular region formed by connecting the three intercepts.

It is possible for a plane in space to have fewer than three intercepts. This occurs when one or more of the coefficients in the equation $ax + by + cz = d$ is zero. Figure 7.12 shows some planes in space that have only one intercept, and Figure 7.13 shows some that have only two intercepts. In each figure, note the use of dashed lines and shading to give the illusion of three dimensions.

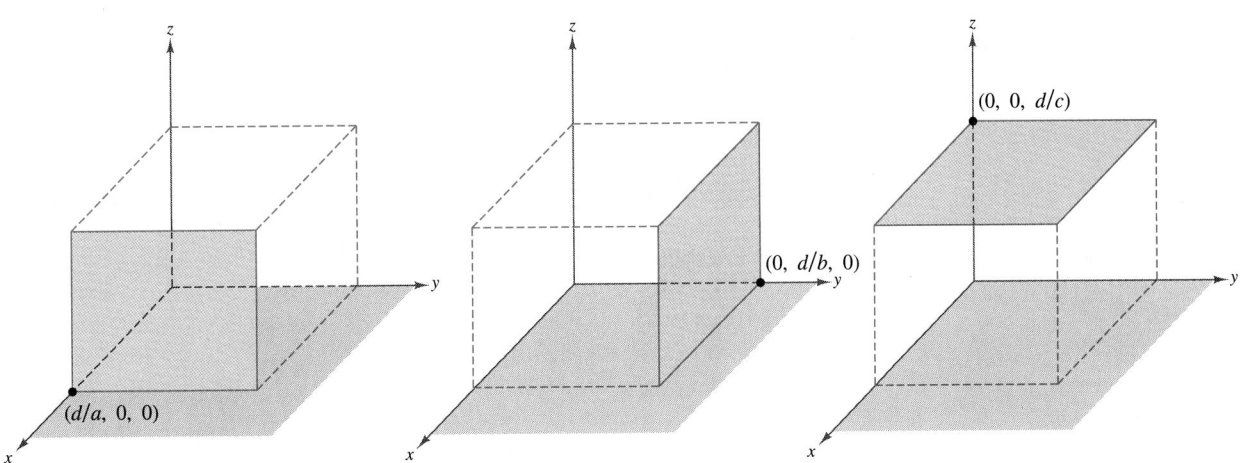

Plane $ax = d$ is parallel to yz-plane.   Plane $by = d$ is parallel to xz-plane.   Plane $cz = d$ is parallel to xy-plane.

FIGURE 7.12 Planes Parallel to Coordinate Planes

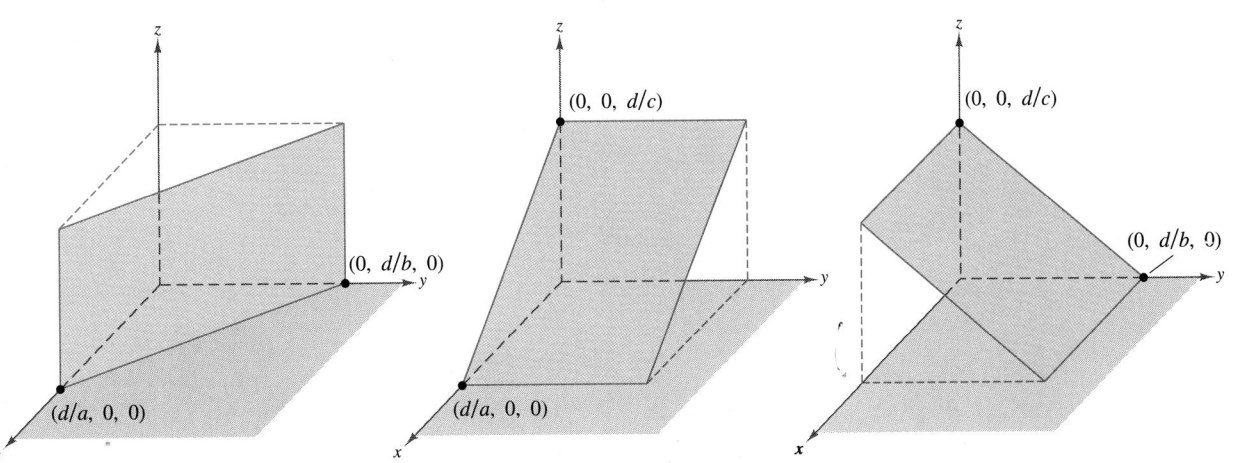

Plane $ax + by = d$ is parallel to z-axis.   Plane $ax + cz = d$ is parallel to y-axis.   Plane $by + cz = d$ is parallel to x-axis.

FIGURE 7.13 Planes Parallel to Coordinate Axes

Quadric Surfaces

A third common surface is a **quadric surface.** Every quadric surface has an equation of the form

$$Ax^2 + By^2 + Cz^2 + Dx + Ey + Fz + G = 0.$$

2nd-degree equation

There are six basic quadric surfaces.

1. Elliptic cone   **2.** Elliptic paraboloid

3. Hyperbolic paraboloid   **4.** Ellipsoid

5. Hyperboloid of one sheet   **6.** Hyperboloid of two sheets

The six types are summarized on pages 464 and 465. Notice that each surface is pictured with two types of three-dimensional sketches. The computer-generated sketches use traces with hidden lines to give the illusion of three dimensions. The artist-rendered sketches use shading to create the same illusion.

All of the quadric surfaces on pages 464 and 465 are centered at the origin and have axes along the coordinate axes. Moreover, only one of several possible orientations of each surface is shown. If the surface has a different center or is oriented along a different axis, then its standard equation will change accordingly. For instance, the ellipsoid

$$\frac{x^2}{1^2} + \frac{y^2}{3^2} + \frac{z^2}{2^2} = 1$$

has $(0, 0, 0)$ as its center, but the ellipsoid

$$\frac{(x - 2)^2}{1^2} + \frac{(y + 1)^2}{3^2} + \frac{(z - 4)^2}{2^2} = 1$$

has $(2, -1, 4)$ as its center. A computer-generated graph of the first ellipsoid is shown in Figure 7.14.

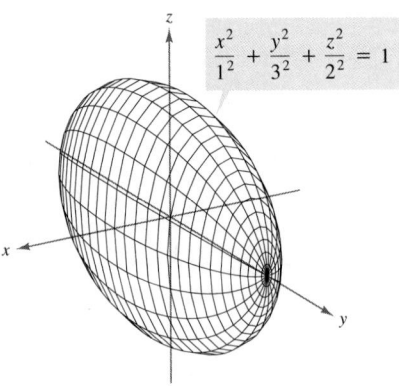

$$\frac{x^2}{1^2} + \frac{y^2}{3^2} + \frac{z^2}{2^2} = 1$$

FIGURE 7.14

▦ TECHNOLOGY

Using a Three-Dimensional Graphing Utility

Most three-dimensional graphing utilities represent surfaces by sketching several traces of the surface. The traces are usually taken in equally spaced parallel planes. Depending on the graphing utility, the sketch can be made with one set, two sets, or three sets of traces. For instance, the two sketches shown below use two sets of traces: in one set the traces are parallel to the xz-plane and in the other set the traces are parallel to the yz-plane.

To sketch the graph of an equation involving x, y, and z with a three-dimensional "function grapher," you must first solve the equation for z. After entering the equation, you need to specify a rectangular viewing box (the three-dimensional analog of a viewing rectangle).

The two sketches shown below were generated by *Derive*. If you have access to a three-dimensional graphing utility, try using it to duplicate these graphs.

Equation: $z = (x^2 + y^2)e^{1-x^2-y^2}$

Grid: 20 traces by 20 traces

Viewing Box: $-5 \le x \le 5$
$-5 \le y \le 5$
$-5 \le z \le 5$

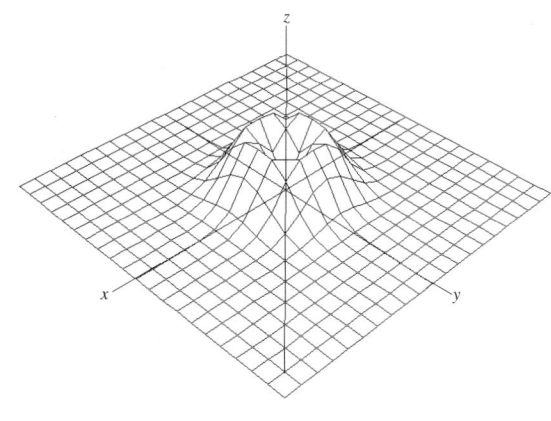

Generated by Derive

Equation: $z = \frac{1}{4}x^2 - \frac{1}{4}y^2$

Grid: 10 traces by 10 traces

Viewing Box: $-4 \le x \le 4$
$-4 \le y \le 4$
$-4 \le z \le 4$

Generated by Derive

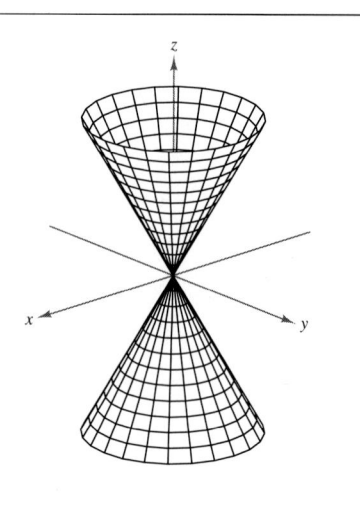

Elliptic Cone

$$\frac{x^2}{a^2} + \frac{y^2}{b^2} - \frac{z^2}{c^2} = 0$$

Trace	*Plane*
Ellipse	Parallel to xy-plane
Hyperbola	Parallel to xz-plane
Hyperbola	Parallel to yz-plane

The axis of the cone corresponds to the variable whose coefficient is negative. The traces in the coordinate planes parallel to this axis are intersecting lines.

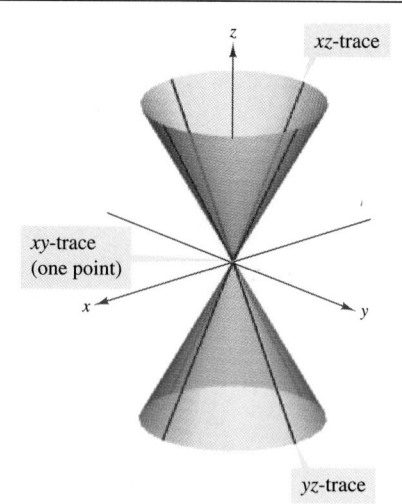

Elliptic Paraboloid

$$z = \frac{x^2}{a^2} + \frac{y^2}{b^2}$$

Trace	*Plane*
Ellipse	Parallel to xy-plane
Parabola	Parallel to xz-plane
Parabola	Parallel to yz-plane

The axis of the paraboloid corresponds to the variable raised to the first power.

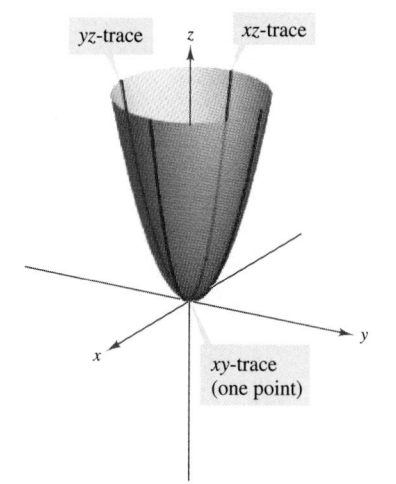

Hyperbolic Paraboloid

$$z = \frac{y^2}{b^2} - \frac{x^2}{a^2}$$

Trace	*Plane*
Hyperbola	Parallel to xy-plane
Parabola	Parallel to xz-plane
Parabola	Parallel to yz-plane

The axis of the paraboloid corresponds to the variable raised to the first power.

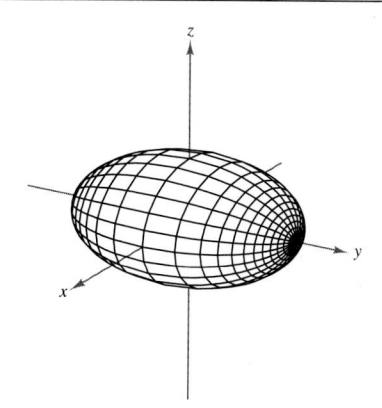

Ellipsoid

$$\frac{x^2}{a^2} + \frac{y^2}{b^2} + \frac{z^2}{c^2} = 1$$

Trace	Plane
Ellipse	Parallel to xy-plane
Ellipse	Parallel to xz-plane
Ellipse	Parallel to yz-plane

The surface is a sphere if the coefficients a, b, and c are equal and nonzero.

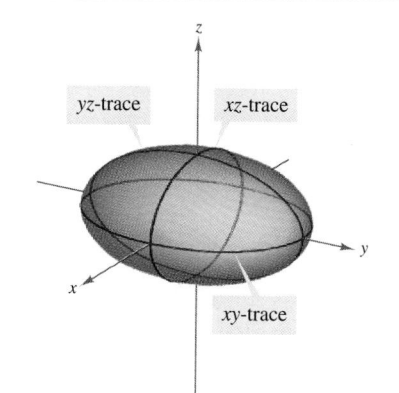

Hyperboloid of One Sheet

$$\frac{x^2}{a^2} + \frac{y^2}{b^2} - \frac{z^2}{c^2} = 1$$

Trace	Plane
Ellipse	Parallel to xy-plane
Hyperbola	Parallel to xz-plane
Hyperbola	Parallel to yz-plane

The axis of the hyperboloid corresponds to the variable whose coefficient is negative.

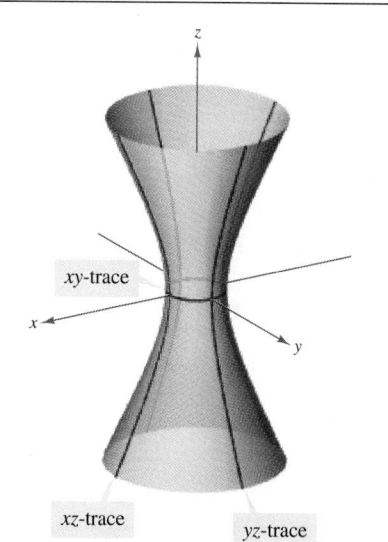

Hyperboloid of Two Sheets

$$\frac{z^2}{c^2} - \frac{x^2}{a^2} - \frac{y^2}{b^2} = 1$$

Trace	Plane
Ellipse	Parallel to xy-plane
Hyperbola	Parallel to xz-plane
Hyperbola	Parallel to yz-plane

The axis of the hyperboloid corresponds to the variable whose coefficient is positive. There is no trace in the coordinate plane perpendicular to this axis.

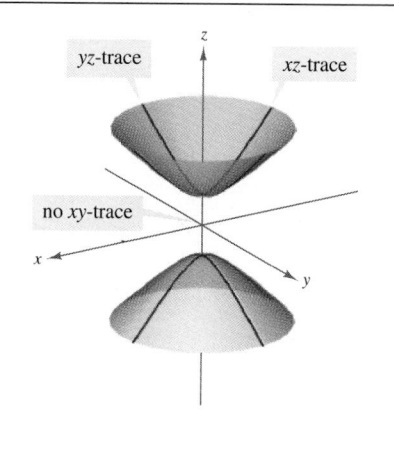

The And Trout fisherman was here 1248

When classifying quadric surfaces, note that the two types of paraboloids have one variable raised to the first power. The other four types of quadric surfaces have equations that are of second degree in *all* three variables.

EXAMPLE 2 *Classifying a Quadric Surface*

Classify the surface given by

$$x - y^2 - z^2 = 0.$$

Describe the traces of the surface in the xy-plane, the xz-plane, and the plane given by $x = 1$.

Solution

Because x is raised only to the first power, the surface is a paraboloid whose axis is the x-axis, as shown in Figure 7.15. In standard form, the equation is

$$x = y^2 + z^2.$$

The traces in the xy-plane, the xz-plane, and the plane given by $x = 1$ are as follows.

Trace in xy-plane ($z = 0$):	$x = y^2$	*Parabola*
Trace in xz-plane ($y = 0$):	$x = z^2$	*Parabola*
Trace in plane $x = 1$:	$y^2 + z^2 = 1$	*Circle*

These three traces are shown in Figure 7.16. From the traces, you can see that the surface is an elliptic (or circular) paraboloid. If you have access to a three-dimensional graphing utility, try using it to graph this surface. If you do this, you will discover that sketching surfaces in space is not a simple task—even with a graphing utility.

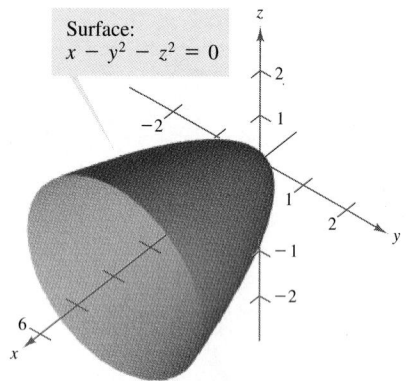

Surface:
$x - y^2 - z^2 = 0$

FIGURE 7.15 Elliptic Paraboloid

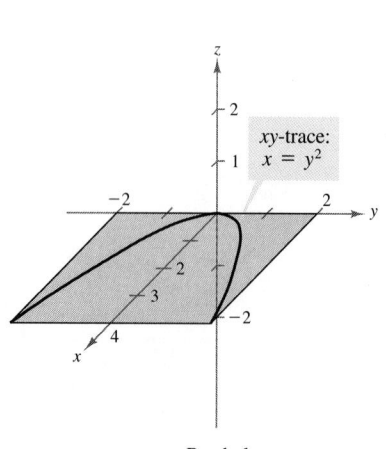

xy-trace:
$x = y^2$

Parabola

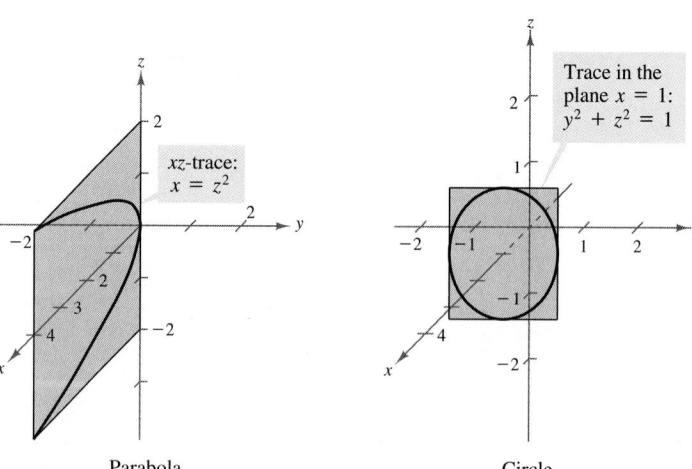

xz-trace:
$x = z^2$

Parabola

Trace in the plane $x = 1$:
$y^2 + z^2 = 1$

Circle

FIGURE 7.16

EXAMPLE 3 *Classifying Quadric Surfaces*

a. The equation

$$x^2 - 4y^2 - 4z^2 - 4 = 0 \qquad \text{\textit{Original equation}}$$

can be written in standard form as

$$\frac{x^2}{4} - y^2 - z^2 = 1. \qquad \text{\textit{Standard form}}$$

From the standard form, you can see that the graph is a hyperboloid of two sheets, with the x-axis as its axis, as shown in Figure 7.17(a).

b. The equation

$$x^2 + 4y^2 + z^2 - 4 = 0 \qquad \text{\textit{Original equation}}$$

can be written in standard form as

$$\frac{x^2}{4} + y^2 + \frac{z^2}{4} = 1. \qquad \text{\textit{Standard form}}$$

From the standard form, you can see that the graph is an ellipsoid, as shown in Figure 7.17(b).

Surface:
$x^2 - 4y^2 - 4z^2 - 4 = 0$

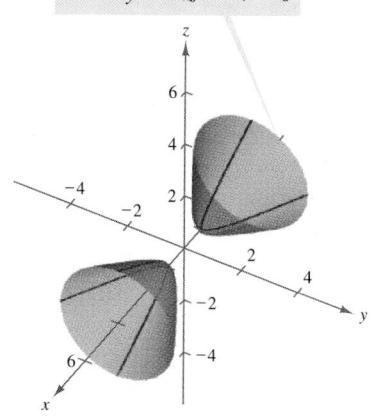

(a)

Surface:
$x^2 + 4y^2 + z^2 - 4 = 0$

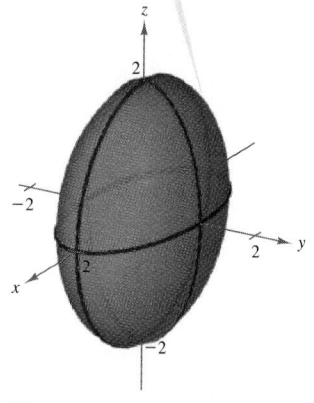

(b)

FIGURE 7.17

Discussion Problem   **Classifying Quadric Surfaces**

Classify the following quadric surfaces.

a. $\dfrac{x^2}{2^2} - \dfrac{y^2}{4^2} + \dfrac{z^2}{3^2} = 0$ **b.** $\dfrac{x^2}{2^2} + \dfrac{y^2}{4^2} + \dfrac{z^2}{3^2} = 1$ **c.** $\dfrac{x^2}{2^2} - \dfrac{y^2}{4^2} + \dfrac{z^2}{3^2} = 1$

Warm Up

The following warm-up exercises involve skills that were covered in earlier sections. You will use these skills in the exercise set for this section.

In Exercises 1–4, find the *x*- and *y*-intercepts of the function.

1. $3x + 4y = 12$ **2.** $6x + y = -8$ **3.** $-2x + y = -2$ **4.** $-x - y = 5$

In Exercises 5–8, rewrite the expression by completing the square.

5. $x^2 + y^2 + z^2 - 2x - 4y - 6z + 15 = 0$ **6.** $x^2 + y^2 - z^2 - 8x + 4y - 6z + 11 = 0$
7. $z - 2 = x^2 + y^2 + 2x - 2y$ **8.** $x^2 + y^2 + z^2 - 6x + 10y + 26z = -202$

In Exercises 9 and 10, write the expression in standard form.

9. $16x^2 - 16y^2 + 16z^2 = 4$ **10.** $9x^2 - 9y^2 + 9z^2 = 36$

E X E R C I S E S   7.2

 means that technology can help you solve or check the exercise(s).

In Exercises 1–16, find the intercepts and sketch the graph of the plane.

1. $4x + 2y + 6z = 12$ **2.** $3x + 6y + 2z = 6$

3. $3x + 3y + 5z = 15$ **4.** $x + y + z = 3$

5. $2x - y + 3z = 8$ **6.** $2x - y + z = 4$

7. $z = 3$ **8.** $y = -4$

9. $y + z = 5$ **10.** $x + 2y = 8$

11. $x + y - z = 0$ **12.** $x - 3z = 3$

13. $-x + 5y - 3z = 10$ **14.** $2y + 4z = 1$

15. $2y - 5z = 5$ **16.** $-x - y = 6$

In Exercises 17–24, determine whether the planes $a_1x + b_1y + c_1z = d_1$ and $a_2x + b_2y + c_2z = d_2$ are parallel, perpendicular, or neither. The planes are parallel if there exists a nonzero constant k such that $a_1 = ka_2$, $b_1 = kb_2$, $c_1 = kc_2$, and perpendicular if $a_1a_2 + b_1b_2 + c_1c_2 = 0$.

17. $5x - 3y + z = 4, x + 4y + 7z = 1$

18. $3x + y - 4z = 3, -9x - 3y + 12z = 4$

19. $x - 5y - z = 1, 5x - 25y - 5z = -3$

20. $x = 6, y = -1$

21. $x + 2y = 3, 4x + 8y = 5$

22. $x + 3y + z = 7, x - 5z = 0$

23. $2x + y = 3, 3x - 5z = 0$

24. $2x - z = 1, 4x + y + 8z = 10$

In Exercises 25–28, find the distance between the point and the plane (see figure). The distance D between a point (x_0, y_0, z_0) and the plane $ax + by + cz + d = 0$ is

$$D = \frac{|ax_0 + by_0 + cz_0 + d|}{\sqrt{a^2 + b^2 + c^2}}.$$

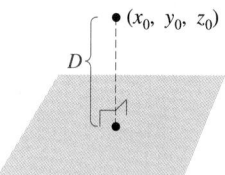

Plane:
$ax + by + cz + d = 0$

FIGURE FOR 25–28

25. $(0, 0, 0), 2x + 3y + z = 12$

26. $(1, 5, -4), 3x - y + 2z = 6$

27. $(1, 2, 3), 2x - y + z = 4$

28. $(10, 0, 0), x - 3y + 4z = 6$

In Exercises 29–36, match the given equation with the correct graph. [The graphs are labeled (a)–(h).]

29. $\dfrac{x^2}{9} + \dfrac{y^2}{16} + \dfrac{z^2}{9} = 1$

30. $x^2 - \dfrac{4y^2}{15} + z^2 = -\dfrac{4}{15}$

31. $4x^2 + 4y^2 - z^2 = 4$

32. $y^2 = 4x^2 + 9z^2$

33. $4x^2 - 4y + z^2 = 0$

34. $12z = -3y^2 + 4x^2$

35. $4x^2 - y^2 + 4z = 0$

36. $x^2 + y^2 + z^2 = 9$

In Exercises 37–40, describe the trace of the surface in the indicated planes.

Surface	*Planes*
37. $x^2 - y - z^2 = 0$	xy-plane, $y = 1$, yz-plane
38. $y = x^2 + z^2$	xy-plane, $y = 1$, yz-plane
39. $\dfrac{x^2}{4} + y^2 + z^2 = 1$	xy-plane, xz-plane, yz-plane
40. $y^2 + z^2 - x^2 = 1$	xy-plane, xz-plane, yz-plane

In Exercises 41–56, identify the quadric surface.

41. $x^2 + \dfrac{y^2}{4} + z^2 = 1$

42. $\dfrac{x^2}{9} + \dfrac{y^2}{16} + \dfrac{z^2}{16} = 1$

43. $25x^2 + 25y^2 - z^2 = 5$

44. $9x^2 + 4y^2 - 8z^2 = 72$

45. $x^2 - y + z^2 = 0$

46. $z = 4x^2 + y^2$

47. $x^2 - y^2 + z = 0$

48. $z^2 - x^2 - \dfrac{y^2}{4} = 1$

49. $4x^2 - y^2 + 4z^2 = -16$

50. $z^2 = x^2 + \dfrac{y^2}{4}$

51. $z^2 = 9x^2 + y^2$

52. $4y = x^2 + z^2$

53. $3z = -y^2 + x^2$

54. $z^2 = 2x^2 + 2y^2$

55. $2x^2 + 2y^2 + 2z^2 - 3x + 4z = 10$

56. $4x^2 + y^2 - 4z^2 - 16x - 6y - 16z + 9 = 0$

In Exercises 57–60, use a three-dimensional graphing utility to graph the function.

57. $z = y^2 - x^2 + 1$

58. $z = x^2 + y^2 + 1$

59. $z = \dfrac{x^2}{2} + \dfrac{y^2}{4}$

60. $z = \tfrac{1}{12}\sqrt{144 - 16x^2 - 9y^2}$

(a) (b)

(c) (d)

(e) (f)

(g) (h)

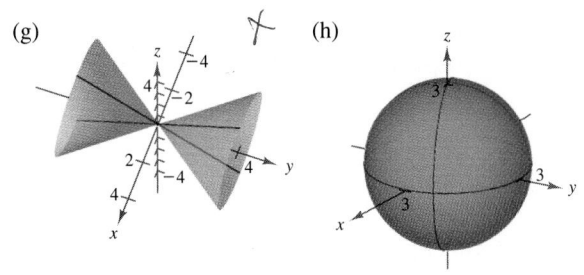

7.3 Functions of Several Variables

Functions of Several Variables ■ *The Graph of a Function of Two Variables* ■ *Level Curves and Contour Maps* ■ *Applications*

Functions of Several Variables

In the first six chapters of this text, you studied functions of a single independent variable. Many quantities in science, business, and technology, however, are functions not of one, but of two or more variables. For instance, the demand function for a product is often dependent on the price *and* the advertising, rather than on the price alone.

The notation for functions of two or more variables is similar to that used for functions of a single variable. For example,

$$f(\underbrace{x, y}_{\text{2 variables}}) = x^2 + xy \quad \text{and} \quad g(\underbrace{x, y}_{\text{2 variables}}) = e^{x+y}$$

are functions of two variables, and

$$f(\underbrace{x, y, z}_{\text{3 variables}}) = x + 2y - 3z$$

is a function of three variables.

Definition of a Function of Two Variables

If to each ordered pair (x, y) in some set D there corresponds a unique real number $z = f(x, y)$, then f is called a **function of x and y.** The set D is the **domain** of f, and the corresponding set of z-values is the **range** of f. Functions of three, four, or more variables are defined similarly.

EXAMPLE 1 *Evaluating Functions of Several Variables*

a. For $f(x, y) = 2x^2 - y^2$, you can evaluate $f(2, 3)$ as follows.

$$f(2, 3) = 2(2)^2 - (3)^2 = 8 - 9 = -1$$

b. For $f(x, y, z) = e^x(y + z)$, you can evaluate $f(0, -1, 4)$ as follows.

$$f(0, -1, 4) = e^0(-1 + 4) = (1)(3) = 3$$

The Graph of a Function of Two Variables

A function of two variables can be represented graphically as a surface in space by letting $z = f(x, y)$. When sketching the graph of a function of x and y, remember that even though the graph is three-dimensional, the domain of the function is two-dimensional—it consists of the points in the xy-plane for which the function is defined. As with functions of a single variable, unless specifically restricted, the domain of a function of two variables is assumed to be the set of all points (x, y) for which the defining equation has meaning.

EXAMPLE 2 *Finding the Domain and Range of a Function*

Find the domain and range of the function

$$f(x, y) = \sqrt{64 - x^2 - y^2}.$$

Solution

Because no restrictions are given, the domain is assumed to be the set of all points for which the defining equation makes sense.

$$64 - x^2 - y^2 \geq 0 \qquad \text{\textit{Quantity inside radical must be nonnegative.}}$$

$$x^2 + y^2 \leq 64 \qquad \text{\textit{Domain of the function}}$$

Thus, the domain is the set of all points that lie on or inside the circle given by $x^2 + y^2 = 8^2$. The range of f is the set

$$0 \leq z \leq 8. \qquad \text{\textit{Range of the function}}$$

As shown in Figure 7.18, the graph of the function is a hemisphere.

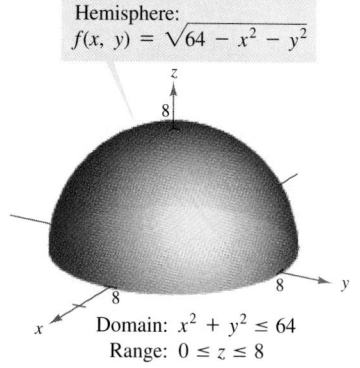

Hemisphere:
$f(x, y) = \sqrt{64 - x^2 - y^2}$

Domain: $x^2 + y^2 \leq 64$
Range: $0 \leq z \leq 8$

FIGURE 7.18

▦ TECHNOLOGY

Some three-dimensional graphing utilities can graph equations in x, y, and z. Others are programmed to graph only functions of x and y. A surface in space represents the graph of a function of x and y only if each vertical line intersects the surface at most once. For instance, the surface shown in Figure 7.18 does pass this vertical line test, but the surface at the right (drawn by *Mathematica*) does not represent the graph of a function of x and y.

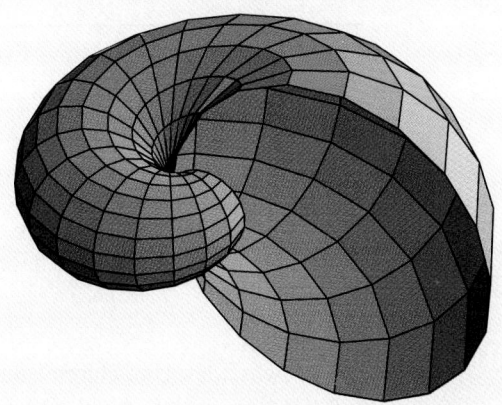

Some vertical lines intersect this surface more than once. Thus, the surface does not pass the vertical line test and is not a function of x and y.

Level Curves and Contour Maps

A **contour map** of a surface is created by *projecting* traces, taken in evenly spaced planes that are parallel to the xy-plane, onto the xy-plane. Each projection is a **level curve** of the surface.

Contour maps are used to create weather maps, topographical maps, and population density maps. For instance, Figure 7.19(a) shows a graph of a "mountain and valley" surface given by $z = f(x, y)$. Each of the level curves in Figure 7.19(b) represents the intersection of the surface $z = f(x, y)$ with a plane $z = c$, where $c = 828, 830, \ldots, 854$.

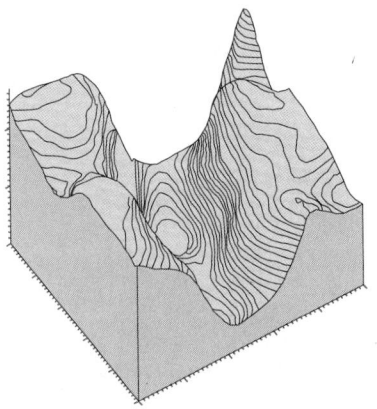

(a) Surface

(b) Contour Map

FIGURE 7.19

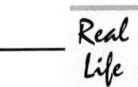

EXAMPLE 3 *Reading a Contour Map*

The "contour map" in Figure 7.20 was computer generated using data collected by satellite instrumentation on August 25, 1992. The map uses color to represent levels of chlorine nitrate in the atmosphere. Chlorine nitrate contributes to the ozone depletion in the earth's atmosphere. The red areas represent the highest level of chlorine nitrate and the dark blue areas represent the lowest level. Describe the areas that have the highest levels of chlorine nitrate. *(Source: Lockheed Missiles and Space Company)*

Solution

The highest levels of chlorine nitrate are in the Antarctic Ocean, surrounding Antarctica. Although chlorine nitrate is not itself harmful to ozone, it has a tendency to convert to chlorine monoxide, which *is* harmful to ozone. Once the chlorine nitrate is converted to chlorine monoxide, it no longer shows on the contour map. Thus, Antarctica itself shows little chlorine nitrate—the nitrate has been converted to monoxide. If you have seen maps showing the "ozone hole" in the earth's atmosphere, you know that the hole occurs over Antarctica.

FIGURE 7.20

Real Life

EXAMPLE 4 *Reading a Contour Map*

The contour map shown in Figure 7.21 represents the population density of the United States in 1990. Discuss the use of color to represent the level curves.

(Source: U.S. Bureau of Census)

Solution

You can see from the key that the light colored regions have population densities of less than 10 people per square mile. As the color darkens, the population density increases, so that the brown regions have population densities of more than 500 people per square mile. The most densely populated regions are urban areas and are represented by three different types of dots.

One advantage of such a map is that it allows you to "see" the population density of the country at a glance. From the map, it is clear that the Rocky Mountain region of the country has a population density that is much less than the region between Chicago and New York City.

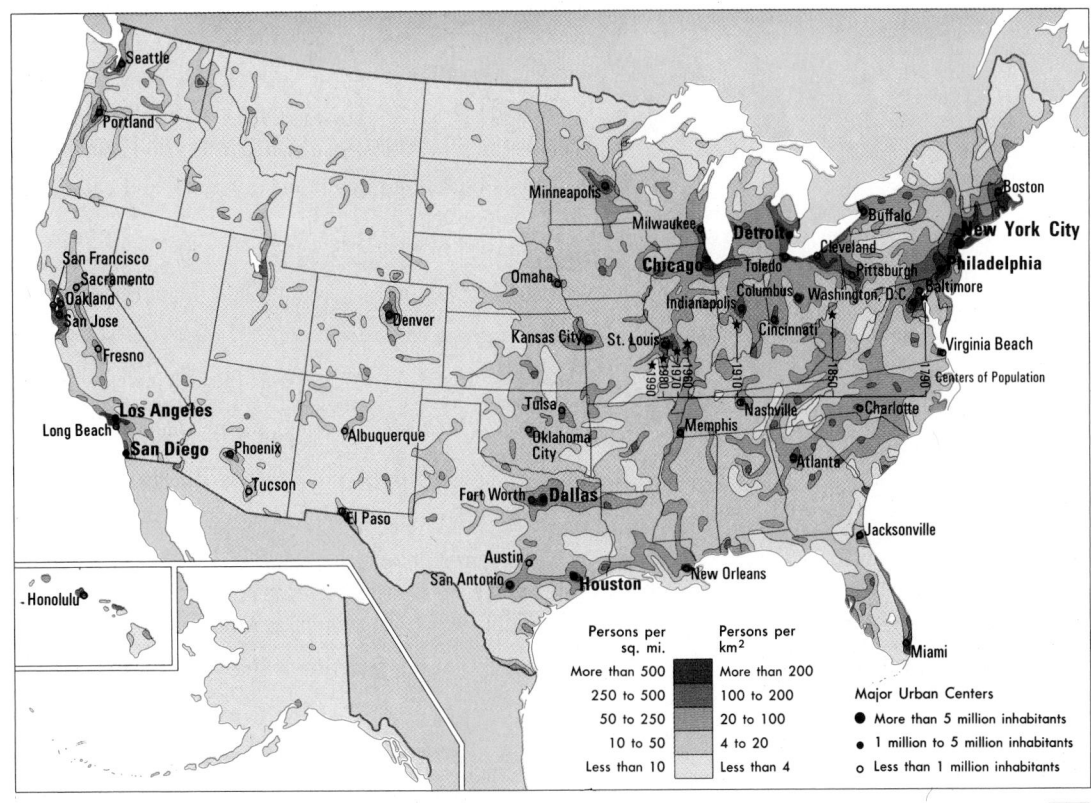

Persons per sq. mi.	Persons per km²
More than 500	More than 200
250 to 500	100 to 200
50 to 250	20 to 100
10 to 50	4 to 20
Less than 10	Less than 4

Major Urban Centers
● More than 5 million inhabitants
• 1 million to 5 million inhabitants
○ Less than 1 million inhabitants

FIGURE 7.21   From *The World Book Encyclopedia.* © World Book, Inc. By permission of the publisher.

Note   In Figure 7.21, the level curves do not correspond to equally spaced population density levels. If, for example, you wanted to represent population density levels of 0–50, 50–100, . . . , and 450–500, how would the map change? Do you think that the change would better illustrate the population density levels in the United States?

Applications

The **Cobb-Douglas production function** is used in economics to represent the number of units produced by varying amounts of labor and capital. Let x represent the number of units of labor and let y represent the number of units of capital. Then, the number of units produced is modeled by

$$f(x, y) = Cx^a y^{1-a},$$

where C is a constant and $0 < a < 1$.

EXAMPLE 5 *Using a Production Function*

Real Life

A manufacturer estimates that its production (measured in units of a product) can be modeled by

$$f(x, y) = 100x^{0.6} y^{0.4},$$

where the labor x is measured in person-hours and the capital y is measured in thousands of dollars.

a. What is the production level when $x = 1000$ and $y = 500$?

b. What is the production level when $x = 2000$ and $y = 1000$?

c. How does doubling the amounts of labor and capital from part a to part b affect the production?

Solution

a. When $x = 1000$ and $y = 500$, the production level is

$$f(1000, 500) = 100(1000)^{0.6}(500)^{0.4}$$
$$\approx 75{,}786 \text{ units.}$$

b. When $x = 2000$ and $y = 1000$, the production level is

$$f(2000, 1000) = 100(2000)^{0.6}(1000)^{0.4}$$
$$\approx 151{,}572 \text{ units.}$$

c. When the amounts of labor and capital are doubled, the production level also doubles. In Exercise 42, you are asked to show that this is characteristic of the Cobb-Douglas production function.

A contour graph of this function is shown in Figure 7.22.   ▬

Note   In Figure 7.22, note that the level curves of the function

$$f(x, y) = 100x^{0.6} y^{0.4}$$

occur at increments of 10,000.

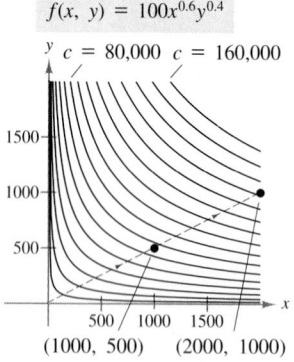

$f(x, y) = 100x^{0.6}y^{0.4}$

$c = 80{,}000$ $c = 160{,}000$

(1000, 500)   (2000, 1000)

FIGURE 7.22   Level Curves (at increments of 10,000)

Real
Life

EXAMPLE 6 *Finding Monthly Payments*

For many Americans, buying a house is the largest single purchase they will ever make. During the 1970s, 1980s, and 1990s, the annual interest rate on home mortgages varied drastically. It was as high as 18% and as low as 5%. Such variations can change monthly payments by hundreds of dollars.

The monthly payment M for an installment loan of P dollars taken out over t years at an annual rate of r is

$$M = f(P, r, t) = \frac{\dfrac{Pr}{12}}{1 - \left[\dfrac{1}{1 + (r/12)}\right]^{12t}}.$$

a. Find the monthly payment for a home mortgage of $95,000 taken out for 30 years at an annual interest rate of 9%.

b. Find the monthly payment for a car loan of $14,000 taken out for 5 years at an annual interest rate of 11%.

Solution

a. If $P = \$95{,}000$, $r = 0.09$, and $t = 30$, then the monthly payment is

$$M = f(95{,}000, 0.09, 30)$$

$$= \frac{\dfrac{(95{,}000)(0.09)}{12}}{1 - \left[\dfrac{1}{1 + (0.09/12)}\right]^{12(30)}}$$

$$= \$764.39.$$

b. If $P = \$14{,}000$, $r = 0.11$, and $t = 5$, then the monthly payment is

$$M = f(14{,}000, 0.11, 5)$$

$$= \frac{\dfrac{(14{,}000)(0.11)}{12}}{1 - \left[\dfrac{1}{1 + (0.11/12)}\right]^{12(5)}}$$

$$= \$304.39.$$

Discussion Problem Monthly Payments

You are taking out a home mortgage for $100,000, and you are given the following options. Which option would you choose? Explain your reasoning.

a. A fixed annual rate of 10%, over a term of 20 years.

b. A fixed annual rate of 9%, over a term of 30 years.

c. An adjustable annual rate of 9%, over a term of 20 years. The annual rate can fluctuate—each year it is set at 1% above the prime rate.

d. A fixed annual rate of 9%, over a term of 15 years.

Warm Up

The following warm-up exercises involve skills that were covered in earlier sections. You will use these skills in the exercise set for this section.

In Exercises 1–4, evaluate the function when $x = -3$.

1. $f(x) = 5 - 2x$

2. $f(x) = -x^2 + 4x + 5$

3. $y = \sqrt{4x^2 - 3x + 4}$

4. $y = \sqrt[3]{34 - 4x + 2x^2}$

In Exercises 5–8, find the domain of the function.

5. $f(x) = 5x^2 + 3x - 2$

6. $g(x) = \dfrac{1}{2x} - \dfrac{2}{x + 3}$

7. $h(y) = \sqrt{y - 5}$

8. $f(y) = \sqrt{y^2 - 5}$

In Exercises 9 and 10, evaluate the expression.

9. $(476)^{0.65}$

10. $(251)^{0.35}$

E X E R C I S E S   7.3   means that technology can help you solve or check the exercise(s).

In Exercises 1–14, find the function values.

1. $f(x, y) = \dfrac{x}{y}$

  (a) $f(3, 2)$ (b) $f(-1, 4)$ (c) $f(30, 5)$

  (d) $f(5, y)$ (e) $f(x, 2)$ (f) $f(5, t)$

2. $f(x, y) = 4 - x^2 - 4y^2$ ·

  (a) $f(0, 0)$ (b) $f(0, 1)$ (c) $f(2, 3)$

  (d) $f(1, y)$ (e) $f(x, 0)$ (f) $f(t, 1)$

3. $f(x, y) = xe^y$

  (a) $f(5, 0)$ (b) $f(3, 2)$ (c) $f(2, -1)$

  (d) $f(5, y)$ (e) $f(x, 2)$ (f) $f(t, t)$

4. $g(x, y) = \ln |x + y|$

  (a) $g(2, 3)$ (b) $g(5, 6)$ (c) $g(e, 0)$

  (d) $g(0, 1)$ (e) $g(2, -3)$ (f) $g(e, e)$

5. $h(x, y, z) = \dfrac{xy}{z}$

  (a) $h(2, 3, 9)$ (b) $h(1, 0, 1)$

6. $f(x, y, z) = \sqrt{x + y + z}$

  (a) $f(0, 5, 4)$ (b) $f(6, 8, -3)$

7. $V(r, h) = \pi r^2 h$

  (a) $V(3, 10)$ (b) $V(5, 2)$

8. $F(r, N) = 500 \left[1 + \dfrac{r}{12} \right]^N$

  (a) $F(0.09, 60)$ (b) $F(0.14, 240)$

9. $A(P, r, t) = P \left[\left(1 + \dfrac{r}{12} \right)^{12t} - 1 \right] \left(1 + \dfrac{12}{r} \right)$

  P   R   t

  (a) $A(100, 0.10, 10)$ (b) $A(275, 0.0925, 40)$

                                      P   R   t

10. $A(P, r, t) = Pe^{rt}$

  (a) $A(500, 0.10, 5)$ (b) $A(1500, 0.12, 20)$

11. $f(x, y) = \displaystyle\int_x^y (2t - 3)\,dt$

  (a) $f(1, 2)$ (b) $f(1, 4)$

12. $g(x, y) = \displaystyle\int_x^y \dfrac{1}{t}\,dt$

  (a) $g(4, 1)$ (b) $g(6, 3)$

13. $f(x, y) = x^2 - 2y$

  (a) $f(x + \Delta x, y)$ (b) $\dfrac{f(x, y + \Delta y) - f(x, y)}{\Delta y}$

14. $f(x, y) = 3xy + y^2$

  (a) $f(x + \Delta x, y)$ (b) $\dfrac{f(x, y + \Delta y) - f(x, y)}{\Delta y}$

In Exercises 15–18, describe the region *R* in the *xy*-coordinate plane that corresponds to the domain of the function, and find the range of the function.

15. $f(x, y) = \sqrt{16 - x^2 - y^2}$

16. $f(x, y) = x^2 + y^2 - 1$

17. $f(x, y) = e^{x/y}$

18. $f(x, y) = \ln(x + y)$

In Exercises 19–28, describe the region *R* in the *xy*-coordinate plane that corresponds to the domain of the function.

19. $f(x, y) = \sqrt{9 - 9x^2 - y^2}$

20. $f(x, y) = \sqrt{x^2 + y^2 - 1}$

21. $f(x, y) = \dfrac{x}{y}$

22. $f(x, y) = \dfrac{4y}{x - 1}$

23. $f(x, y) = \dfrac{1}{xy}$

24. $g(x, y) = \dfrac{1}{x - y}$

25. $h(x, y) = x\sqrt{y}$

26. $f(x, y) = \sqrt{xy}$

27. $g(x, y) = \ln(4 - x - y)$

28. $f(x, y) = ye^{1/x}$

In Exercises 29–32, match the graph of the surface with one of the contour maps. [The contour maps are labeled (a)–(d).]

29. $f(x, y) = x^2 + \dfrac{y^2}{4}$

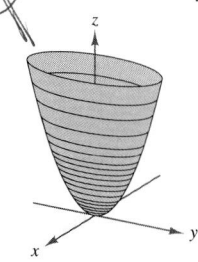

30. $f(x, y) = e^{1-x^2+y^2}$

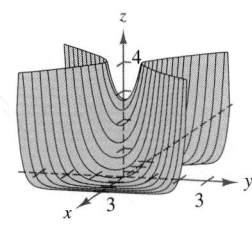

31. $f(x, y) = e^{1-x^2-y^2}$

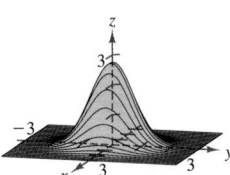

32. $f(x, y) = \ln|y - x^2|$

(a)

(b)

(c)

(d)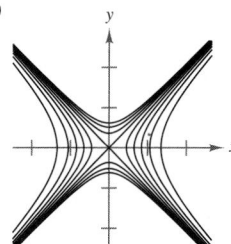

In Exercises 33–40, describe the level curves of the function. Sketch the level curves for the given *c*-values.

Function	*c*-Values
33. $z = x + y$	$c = -1, 0, 2, 4$
34. $z = 6 - 2x - 3y$	$c = 0, 2, 4, 6, 8, 10$
35. $z = \sqrt{16 - x^2 - y^2}$	$c = 0, 1, 2, 3, 4$
36. $f(x, y) = x^2 + y^2$	$c = 0, 2, 4, 6, 8$
37. $f(x, y) = xy$	$c = \pm 1, \pm 2, \ldots, \pm 6$
38. $z = e^{xy}$	$c = 1, 2, 3, 4, \frac{1}{2}, \frac{1}{3}, \frac{1}{4}$
39. $f(x, y) = \dfrac{x}{x^2 + y^2}$	$c = \pm\frac{1}{2}, \pm 1, \pm\frac{3}{2}, \pm 2$
40. $f(x, y) = \ln(x - y)$	$c = 0, \pm\frac{1}{2}, \pm 1, \pm\frac{3}{2}, \pm 2$

41. *Cobb-Douglas Production Function* A manufacturer estimates the Cobb-Douglas production function to be

$$f(x, y) = 100x^{0.75}y^{0.25}.$$

Estimate the production level when $x = 1500$ and $y = 1000$.

42. *Cobb-Douglas Production Function* Use the Cobb-Douglas production function (Example 5) to show that if both the number of units of labor and the number of units of capital are doubled, the production level is also doubled.

43. *Cost* A company manufactures two types of woodburning stoves: a free-standing model and a fireplace-insert model. The cost function for producing *x* freestanding stoves and *y* fireplace-insert stoves is

$$C(x, y) = 27\sqrt{xy} + 195x + 215y + 980.$$

Find the cost when $x = 80$ and $y = 20$.

44. *Forestry* The **Doyle Log Rule** is one of several methods used to determine the lumber yield of a log in board feet in terms of its diameter d in inches and its length L in feet. The number of board feet is given by

$$N(d, L) = \left(\frac{d - 4}{4}\right)^2 L.$$

(a) Find the number of board feet of lumber in a log with a diameter of 22 inches and a length of 12 feet.

(b) Find $N(30, 12)$.

45. *Profit* A corporation manufactures a product at two locations. The costs of producing x_1 units at location 1 and x_2 units at location 2 are

$$C_1(x_1) = 0.02x_1^2 + 4x_1 + 500$$

and

$$C_2(x_2) = 0.05x_2^2 + 4x_2 + 275,$$

respectively. If the product sells for $15 per unit, then the profit function for the product is

$$P(x_1, x_2) = 15(x_1 + x_2) - C_1(x_1) - C_2(x_2).$$

Find (a) $P(250, 150)$, and (b) $P(300, 200)$.

46. *Queuing Model* The average amount of time that a customer waits in line for service is given by

$$W(x, y) = \frac{1}{x - y}, \qquad y < x,$$

where y is the average arrival rate and x is the average service rate (x and y are measured in the number of customers per hour). Evaluate W at the following points.

(a) $(15, 10)$ (b) $(12, 9)$ (c) $(12, 6)$ (d) $(4, 2)$

47. *Investment* In 1994, an investment of $1000 was made in a bond earning 10% compounded annually. The investor pays tax at rate R and the annual rate of inflation is I. In the year 2004, the value V of the bond in constant 1994 dollars is

$$V(I, R) = 1000\left[\frac{1 + 0.10(1 - R)}{1 + I}\right]^{10}.$$

Use this function of two variables to complete the table.

	Inflation Rate, I		
Tax Rate, R	0.00	0.03	0.05
0.00			
0.28			
0.35			

48. *Investment* The sum of $1000 is deposited in a savings account earning r percent interest compounded continuously. The amount $A(r, t)$ after t years is given by

$$A(r, t) = 1000e^{rt}.$$

Use this function of two variables to complete the table.

	Number of Years, t			
Rate, r	5	10	15	20
0.06				
0.08				
0.10				

49. *Equity* The equity per share for Phillips Petroleum Company from 1986 through 1991 can be modeled by

$$z = 1.085x + 0.779y - 10.778,$$

where x is the total revenue (in billions of dollars) and y is the total assets (in billions of dollars). *(Source: Phillips Petroleum Company, 1992 Annual Report)*

(a) Find the equity per share when $x = 15$ and $y = 10$.

(b) Which of the two variables in this model has the greater influence on the equity per share of common stock? Explain your reasoning.

50. *A Contour Map* The contour map shown below represents the estimated annual hours of air conditioner use for an average household in 1991. *(Source: Association of Home Appliance Manufacturers)*

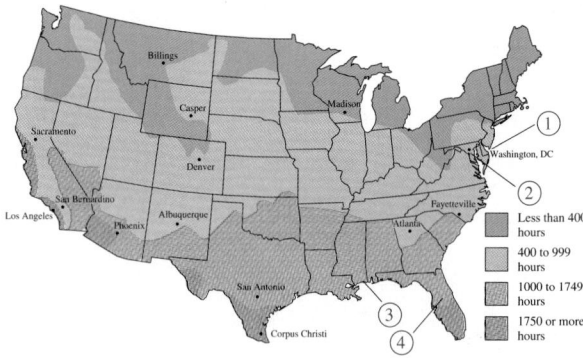

(a) Discuss the use of color to represent the level curves.

(b) Do the level curves correspond to equally spaced annual usage hours? Explain.

(c) Describe how to obtain a more detailed contour map.

Partial Derivatives

Functions of Two Variables ■ *Graphical Interpretation of Partial Derivatives* ■ *Functions of Three Variables* ■ *Higher-Order Partial Derivatives*

Functions of Two Variables

Real-life applications of functions of several variables are often concerned with how changes in one of the variables will affect the values of the functions. For instance, an economist who wants to determine the effect of a tax increase on the economy might make calculations using different tax rates while holding all other variables, such as unemployment, constant.

You can follow a similar procedure to find the rate of change of a function f with respect to one of its independent variables. That is, you find the derivative of f with respect to one independent variable, while holding the other variables constant. This process is called **partial differentiation**, and each derivative is called a **partial derivative.** A function of several variables has as many partial derivatives as it has independent variables.

Note Note that this definition indicates that partial derivatives of a function of two variables are determined by temporarily considering one variable to be fixed. For instance, if $z = f(x, y)$, then to find $\partial z/\partial x$, you consider y to be constant and differentiate with respect to x. Similarly, to find $\partial z/\partial y$, you consider x to be constant and differentiate with respect to y.

Partial Derivatives of a Function of Two Variables

If $z = f(x, y)$, then the **first partial derivatives of f with respect to x and y** are the functions $\partial z/\partial x$ and $\partial z/\partial y$, defined as follows.

$$\frac{\partial z}{\partial x} = \lim_{\Delta x \to 0} \frac{f(x + \Delta x, y) - f(x, y)}{\Delta x} \qquad \textit{y is held constant.}$$

$$\frac{\partial z}{\partial y} = \lim_{\Delta y \to 0} \frac{f(x, y + \Delta y) - f(x, y)}{\Delta y} \qquad \textit{x is held constant.}$$

EXAMPLE 1 *Finding Partial Derivatives*

Find $\partial z/\partial x$ and $\partial z/\partial y$ for the function $z = 3x - x^2y^2 + 2x^3y$.

Solution

$$\frac{\partial z}{\partial x} = 3 - 2xy^2 + 6x^2y \qquad \textit{Hold y constant and differentiate with respect to x.}$$

$$\frac{\partial z}{\partial y} = -2x^2y + 2x^3 \qquad \textit{Hold x constant and differentiate with respect to y.}$$

Notation for First Partial Derivatives

The first partial derivatives of $z = f(x, y)$ are denoted by

$$\frac{\partial z}{\partial x} = f_x(x, y) = z_x = \frac{\partial}{\partial x}[f(x, y)]$$

and

$$\frac{\partial z}{\partial y} = f_y(x, y) = z_y = \frac{\partial}{\partial y}[f(x, y)].$$

The values of the first partial derivatives at the point (a, b) are denoted by

$$\left. \frac{\partial z}{\partial x} \right|_{(a,b)} = f_x(a, b) \quad \text{and} \quad \left. \frac{\partial z}{\partial y} \right|_{(a,b)} = f_y(a, b).$$

TECHNOLOGY

Symbolic differentiation utilities, such as *Derive*, *Maple*, and *Mathematica*, can be used to find partial derivatives of a function of two variables. For instance, when *Derive* is used to find $f_x(x, y)$ for the function in Example 2, you obtain the following.

1: $x\hat{e}^{x^2 y}$

2: $\dfrac{d}{dx}\left[x\hat{e}^{x^2 y}\right]$

3: $\hat{e}^{x^2 y}(2x^2 y + 1)$

EXAMPLE 2 *Finding and Evaluating Partial Derivatives*

Find the first partial derivatives of $f(x, y) = xe^{x^2 y}$ and evaluate each at the point $(1, \ln 2)$.

Solution
To find the first partial derivative with respect to x, hold y constant and differentiate using the Product Rule.

$$f_x(x, y) = x\frac{\partial}{\partial x}[e^{x^2 y}] + e^{x^2 y}\frac{\partial}{\partial x}[x] \qquad \textit{Product Rule}$$

$$= x(2xy)e^{x^2 y} + e^{x^2 y} \qquad \textit{y is held constant.}$$

$$= e^{x^2 y}(2x^2 y + 1) \qquad \textit{Simplify.}$$

At the point $(1, \ln 2)$, the value of this derivative is

$$f_x(1, \ln 2) = e^{(1)^2 (\ln 2)}[2(1)^2(\ln 2) + 1] \qquad \textit{Substitute for x and y.}$$

$$= 2(2 \ln 2 + 1) \qquad \textit{Simplify.}$$

$$\approx 4.773. \qquad \textit{Use a calculator.}$$

To find the first partial derivative with respect to y, hold x constant and differentiate to obtain

$$f_y(x, y) = x(x^2)e^{x^2 y} \qquad \textit{Constant Multiple Rule}$$

$$= x^3 e^{x^2 y}. \qquad \textit{Simplify.}$$

At the point $(1, \ln 2)$, the value of this derivative is

$$f_y(1, \ln 2) = (1)^3 e^{(1)^2 (\ln 2)} \qquad \textit{Substitute for x and y.}$$

$$= 2 \qquad \textit{Simplify.}$$

Graphical Interpretation of Partial Derivatives

At the beginning of this course, you spent a lot of time studying graphical interpretations of the derivative of a function of a single variable. There, you found that $f'(x_0)$ represents the slope of the tangent line to the graph of $y = f(x)$ at the point (x_0, y_0). The partial derivatives of a function of two variables also have useful graphical interpretations. Consider the function

$$z = f(x, y). \qquad \text{\textit{Function of two variables}}$$

As shown in Figure 7.23(a), the graph of this function is a surface in space. If the variable y is fixed, say $y = y_0$, then

$$z = f(x, y_0) \qquad \text{\textit{Function of one variable}}$$

is a function of one variable. The graph of this function is the curve that is the intersection of the plane $y = y_0$ and the surface $z = f(x, y)$. On this curve, the partial derivative

$$f_x(x, y_0) \qquad \text{\textit{Slope in x-direction}}$$

represents the slope in the plane $y = y_0$, as shown in Figure 7.23(a). In a similar way, if the variable x is fixed, say $x = x_0$, then

$$z = f(x_0, y) \qquad \text{\textit{Function of one variable}}$$

is a function of one variable. Its graph is the intersection of the plane $x = x_0$ and the surface $z = f(x, y)$. On this curve, the partial derivative

$$f_y(x_0, y) \qquad \text{\textit{Slope in y-direction}}$$

represents the slope in the plane $x = x_0$, as shown in Figure 7.23(b).

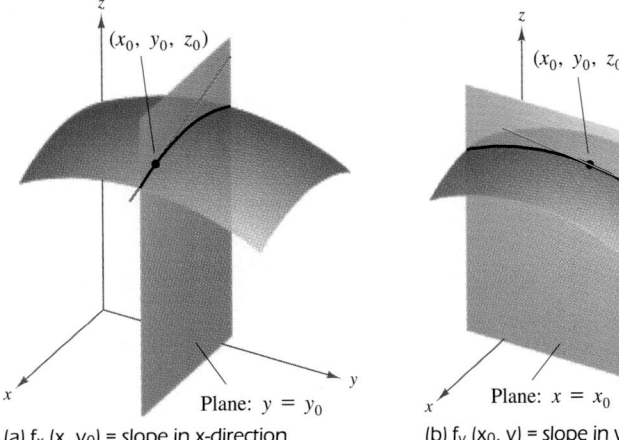

(a) $f_x(x, y_0)$ = slope in x-direction

(b) $f_y(x_0, y)$ = slope in y-direction

FIGURE 7.23

EXAMPLE 3 *Finding Slopes in the x- and y-Directions*

Find the slope of the surface given by

$$f(x, y) = -\frac{x^2}{2} - y^2 + \frac{25}{8}$$

at the point $\left(\frac{1}{2}, 1, 2\right)$ in (a) the x-direction and (b) the y-direction.

Solution

a. To find the slope in the x-direction, hold y constant and differentiate with respect to x to obtain

$$f_x(x, y) = -x.$$ *Partial derivative with respect to x*

At the point $\left(\frac{1}{2}, 1, 2\right)$, the slope in the x-direction is

$$f_x\left(\frac{1}{2}, 1\right) = -\frac{1}{2},$$ *Slope in x-direction*

as shown in Figure 7.24(a).

b. To find the slope in the y-direction, hold x constant and differentiate with respect to y to obtain

$$f_y(x, y) = -2y.$$ *Partial derivative with respect to y*

At the point $\left(\frac{1}{2}, 1, 2\right)$, the slope in the y-direction is

$$f_y\left(\frac{1}{2}, 1\right) = -2,$$ *Slope in y-direction*

as shown in Figure 7.24(b).

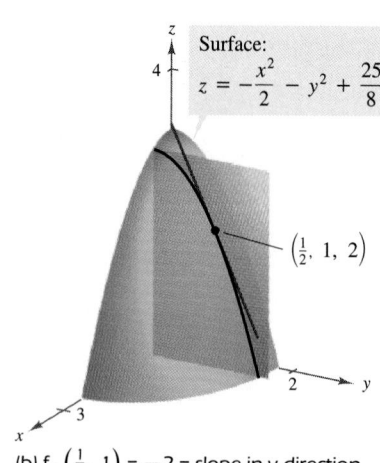

(a) $f_x\left(\frac{1}{2}, 1\right) = -\frac{1}{2}$ = slope in x-direction   (b) $f_y\left(\frac{1}{2}, 1\right) = -2$ = slope in y-direction

FIGURE 7.24

Consumer products in the same or related markets can be classified as **complementary** or **substitute products.** If two products have a complementary relationship, an increase in the sale of one product will be accompanied by an increase in the sale of the other product. For instance, videocassette recorders and videocassettes have a complementary relationship.

If two products have a substitute relationship, an increase in the sale of one product will be accompanied by a decrease in the sale of the other product. For instance, videocassette recorders and videodisc recorders both compete in the same home entertainment market and you would expect a drop in the price of one to be a deterrent to the sale of the other.

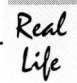

Real Life

EXAMPLE 4 *Examining a Demand Function*

The demand functions for two products are represented by

$$x_1 = f(p_1, p_2) \quad \text{and} \quad x_2 = g(p_1, p_2),$$

where p_1 and p_2 are the prices per unit for the two products, and x_1 and x_2 are the numbers of units sold. The graphs of two different demand functions for x_1 are shown below. Use the graphs to classify the products as complementary or substitute.

In 1993, Subway was chosen as the number one franchise by *Entrepreneur* magazine. At that time, Subway was opening more than 100 new stores each month. What type of product is complementary to a Subway sandwich? What type of product is a substitute?

(a)

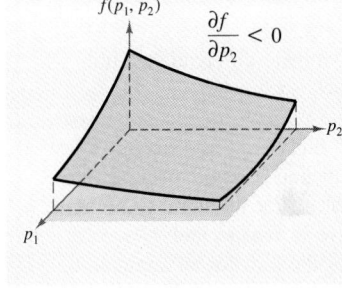

(b)

Solution

a. Notice that graph (a) represents the demand for the *first product*. From the graph of this function, you can see that for a fixed price p_1, an increase in p_2 results in an increase in the demand for the first product. This means that $\partial f/\partial p_2 > 0$ and the two products have a substitute relationship.

b. Notice that graph (b) represents a different demand for the *first product*. From the graph of this function, you can see that for a fixed price p_1, an increase in p_2 results in a decrease in the demand for the first product. This means that $\partial f/\partial p_2 < 0$ and the two products have a complementary relationship.

Functions of Three Variables

The concept of a partial derivative can be extended in a natural way to functions of three or more variables. For instance, the function $w = f(x, y, z)$ has three partial derivatives, each of which is formed by considering two of the variables to be constant. That is, to define the partial derivative of w with respect to x, consider y *and* z to be constant and write

$$\frac{\partial w}{\partial x} = f_x(x, y, z) = \lim_{\Delta x \to 0} \frac{f(x + \Delta x, y, z) - f(x, y, z)}{\Delta x}.$$

To define the partial derivative of w with respect to y, consider x *and* z to be constant and write

$$\frac{\partial w}{\partial y} = f_y(x, y, z) = \lim_{\Delta y \to 0} \frac{f(x, y + \Delta y, z) - f(x, y, z)}{\Delta y}.$$

To define the partial derivative of w with respect to z, consider x *and* y to be constant and write

$$\frac{\partial w}{\partial z} = f_z(x, y, z) = \lim_{\Delta z \to 0} \frac{f(x, y, z + \Delta z) - f(x, y, z)}{\Delta z}.$$

TECHNOLOGY

Symbolic differentiation utilities, such as *Derive*, *Maple*, and *Mathematica*, can be used to find partial derivatives of a function of three or more variables. For instance, when *Derive* is used to find $f_x(x, y, z)$ for the function in Example 5, you obtain the following.

1: $x\hat{e}^{xy+2z}$

2: $\dfrac{d}{dx}[x\hat{e}^{xy+2z}]$

3: $\hat{e}^{xy+2z}(xy + 1)$

EXAMPLE 5 *Finding Partial Derivatives of a Function*

Find the three partial derivatives of the function

$$w = xe^{xy+2z}.$$

Solution

Holding y and z constant, you obtain

$$\frac{\partial w}{\partial x} = x\frac{\partial}{\partial x}[e^{xy+2z}] + e^{xy+2z}\frac{\partial}{\partial x}[x] \qquad \textit{Product Rule}$$

$$= x(ye^{xy+2z}) + e^{xy+2z}(1) \qquad \textit{Hold y and z constant.}$$

$$= (xy + 1)e^{xy+2z}. \qquad \textit{Simplify.}$$

Holding x and z constant, you obtain

$$\frac{\partial w}{\partial y} = x(x)e^{xy+2z} \qquad \textit{Hold x and z constant.}$$

$$= x^2 e^{xy+2z}. \qquad \textit{Simplify.}$$

Holding x and y constant, you obtain

$$\frac{\partial w}{\partial z} = x(2)e^{xy+2z} \qquad \textit{Hold x and y constant.}$$

$$= 2xe^{xy+2z}. \qquad \textit{Simplify.}$$

Note that the Product Rule was used only when finding the partial derivative with respect to x. Can you see why? ▬

Higher-Order Partial Derivatives

As with ordinary derivatives, it is possible to find partial derivatives of second, third, or higher order. For instance, there are four different ways to find a second partial derivative of $z = f(x, y)$.

$$\frac{\partial}{\partial x}\left(\frac{\partial f}{\partial x}\right) = \frac{\partial^2 f}{\partial x^2} = f_{xx} \qquad \textit{Differentiate twice with respect to x.}$$

$$\frac{\partial}{\partial y}\left(\frac{\partial f}{\partial y}\right) = \frac{\partial^2 f}{\partial y^2} = f_{yy} \qquad \textit{Differentiate twice with respect to y.}$$

$$\frac{\partial}{\partial y}\left(\frac{\partial f}{\partial x}\right) = \frac{\partial^2 f}{\partial y \partial x} = f_{xy} \qquad \textit{Differentiate first with respect to x and then with respect to y.}$$

$$\frac{\partial}{\partial x}\left(\frac{\partial f}{\partial y}\right) = \frac{\partial^2 f}{\partial x \partial y} = f_{yx} \qquad \textit{Differentiate first with respect to y and then with respect to x.}$$

The third and fourth cases are *mixed* partial derivatives. Notice that with the two types of notation for mixed partials, different conventions are used for indicating the order of differentiation. For instance, the partial derivative

$$\frac{\partial}{\partial y}\left(\frac{\partial f}{\partial x}\right) = \frac{\partial^2 f}{\partial y \partial x} \qquad \textit{Right-to-left order}$$

indicates differentiation with respect to x first, but the partial

$$(f_y)_x = f_{yx} \qquad \textit{Left-to-right order}$$

indicates differentiation with respect to y first. To remember this, note that in each case you differentiate first with respect to the variable "nearest" f.

EXAMPLE 6 *Finding Second Partial Derivatives*

Find the second partial derivatives of

$$f(x, y) = 3xy^2 - 2y + 5x^2 y^2$$

and determine the value of $f_{xy}(-1, 2)$.

Solution

Begin by finding the first partial derivatives

$$f_x(x, y) = 3y^2 + 10xy^2 \quad \text{and} \quad f_y(x, y) = 6xy - 2 + 10x^2 y.$$

Then, differentiating with respect to x and y produces

$$f_{xx}(x, y) = 10y^2, \qquad\qquad f_{yy}(x, y) = 6x + 10x^2$$
$$f_{xy}(x, y) = 6y + 20xy, \qquad f_{yx}(x, y) = 6y + 20xy.$$

Finally, the value of $f_{xy}(x, y)$ at the point $(-1, 2)$ is

$$f_{xy}(-1, 2) = 6(2) + 20(-1)(2) = 12 - 40 = -28.$$

Note Notice in Example 6 that the two mixed partials are equal. This is often the case. In fact, it can be shown that if a function has continuous second partial derivatives, then the order in which the partial derivatives are taken is irrelevant.

A function of two variables has two first partial derivatives and four second partial derivatives. For a function of three variables, there are three first partials,

$$f_x, f_y, \text{ and } f_z$$

and nine second partials,

$$f_{xx}, f_{xy}, f_{xz}, f_{yx}, f_{yy}, f_{yz}, f_{zx}, f_{zy}, \text{ and } f_{zz},$$

six of which are mixed partials. To find partial derivatives of order three and higher, follow the same pattern used to find second partial derivatives. For instance, if $z = f(x, y)$, then

$$z_{xxx} = \frac{\partial}{\partial x}\left(\frac{\partial^2 f}{\partial x^2}\right) = \frac{\partial^3 f}{\partial x^3} \quad \text{and} \quad z_{xxy} = \frac{\partial}{\partial y}\left(\frac{\partial^2 f}{\partial x^2}\right) = \frac{\partial^3 f}{\partial y \partial x^2}.$$

EXAMPLE 7 *Finding Second Partial Derivatives*

Find the second partial derivatives of

$$f(x, y, z) = ye^x + x \ln z.$$

Solution
Begin by finding the first partial derivatives.

$$f_x(x, y, z) = ye^x + \ln z, \qquad f_y(x, y, z) = e^x, \qquad f_z(x, y, z) = \frac{x}{z}$$

Then, differentiate with respect to x, y, and z to find the nine second partial derivatives.

$$f_{xx}(x, y, z) = ye^x, \qquad f_{xy}(x, y, z) = e^x, \qquad f_{xz}(x, y, z) = \frac{1}{z}$$

$$f_{yx}(x, y, z) = e^x, \qquad f_{yy}(x, y, z) = 0, \qquad f_{yz}(x, y, z) = 0$$

$$f_{zx}(x, y, z) = \frac{1}{z}, \qquad f_{zy}(x, y, z) = 0, \qquad f_{zz}(x, y, z) = -\frac{x}{z^2}$$

Discussion Problem **Finding Partial Derivatives**

Find the indicated partial derivatives.

Function	Partial Derivative
a. $f(x, y) = 2x^2 + 3y^2$	$f_x(x, y)$
b. $g(r, t) = e^{rt^2}$	$g_t(r, t)$
c. $h(x, y, z) = 3xy^2 + 4yz^2$	$h_y(x, y, z)$
d. $f(x, y) = 4xy^2 + 2x^2 y$	$f_{xy}(x, y)$

Warm Up

The following warm-up exercises involve skills that were covered in earlier sections. You will use these skills in the exercise set for this section.

In Exercises 1–8, find the derivative of the function.

1. $f(x) = \sqrt{x^2 + 3}$

2. $g(x) = (3 - x^2)^3$

3. $g(t) = te^{2t+1}$

4. $f(x) = e^{2x}\sqrt{1 - e^{2x}}$

5. $f(x) = \ln(3 - 2x)$

6. $u(t) = \ln\sqrt{t^3 - 6t}$

7. $g(x) = \dfrac{5x^2}{(4x - 1)^2}$

8. $f(x) = \dfrac{(x + 2)^3}{(x^2 - 9)^2}$

In Exercises 9 and 10, evaluate the derivative at the point $(2, 6)$.

9. $f(x) = x^2 e^{x-2}$

10. $g(x) = x\sqrt{x^2 - x + 2}$

E X E R C I S E S   7.4   means that technology can help you solve or check the exercise(s).

In Exercises 1–18, find the first partial derivatives with respect to x and with respect to y.

1. $f(x, y) = 2x - 3y + 5$

2. $f(x, y) = x^2 - 3y^2 + 7$

3. $f(x, y) = 5\sqrt{x} - 6y^2$

4. $f(x, y) = x^{-1/2} + 4y^{3/2}$

5. $f(x, y) = xy$

6. $f(x, y) = \dfrac{x}{y}$

7. $z = x\sqrt{y}$

8. $z = x^2 - 3xy + y^2$

9. $f(x, y) = \sqrt{x^2 + y^2}$

10. $f(x, y) = \dfrac{xy}{x^2 + y^2}$

11. $z = x^2 e^{2y}$

12. $z = xe^{x+y}$

13. $h(x, y) = e^{-(x^2+y^2)}$

14. $g(x, y) = e^{x/y}$

15. $z = \ln(x^2 + y^2)$

16. $z = \ln\sqrt{xy}$

17. $z = \ln\dfrac{x - y}{(x + y)^2}$

18. $g(x, y) = \ln\sqrt{x^2 + y^2}$

In Exercises 19–24, let $f(x, y) = 3x^2 y e^{x-y}$ and $g(x, y) = 3xy^2 e^{y-x}$. Find each of the following.

19. $f_x(x, y)$

20. $f_y(x, y)$

21. $g_x(x, y)$

22. $g_y(x, y)$

23. $f_x(1, 1)$

24. $g_x(-2, -2)$

In Exercises 25–28, evaluate f_x and f_y at the point.

Function	Point
25. $f(x, y) = 3x^2 + xy - y^2$	$(2, 1)$
26. $f(x, y) = e^{3xy}$	$(0, 4)$
27. $f(x, y) = \dfrac{xy}{x - y}$	$(2, -2)$
28. $f(x, y) = \dfrac{4xy}{\sqrt{x^2 + y^2}}$	$(1, 0)$

In Exercises 29–36, evaluate w_x, w_y, and w_z at the point.

Function	Point
29. $w = \sqrt{x^2 + y^2 + z^2}$	$(2, -1, 2)$
30. $w = \dfrac{xy}{x + y + z}$	$(1, 2, 0)$
31. $w = \ln\sqrt{x^2 + y^2 + z^2}$	$(3, 0, 4)$
32. $w = \dfrac{1}{\sqrt{1 - x^2 - y^2 - z^2}}$	$(0, 0, 0)$
33. $w = 2xz^2 + 3xyz - 6y^2 z$	$(1, -1, 2)$
34. $w = xye^{z^2}$	$(2, 1, 0)$
35. $w = \dfrac{x + 2z}{(x + y + z)^2}$	$(2, 1, 2)$
36. $w = \dfrac{x + y + z}{(xyz + 1)^2}$	$(1, 1, 1)$

In Exercises 37–40, find values of x and y such that $f_x(x, y) = 0$ and $f_y(x, y) = 0$ simultaneously.

37. $f(x, y) = x^2 + 4xy + y^2 - 4x + 16y + 3$

38. $f(x, y) = 3x^3 - 12xy + y^3$

39. $f(x, y) = \dfrac{1}{x} + \dfrac{1}{y} + xy$

40. $f(x, y) = \ln(x^2 + y^2 + 1)$

In Exercises 41–48, find the slope of the surface at the indicated point in (a) the x-direction and (b) the y-direction.

Function	*Point*
41. $z = 2x - 3y + 5$	$(2, 1, 6)$
42. $z = xy$	$(1, 2, 2)$
43. $z = x^2 - 9y^2$	$(3, 1, 0)$
44. $z = x^2 + 4y^2$	$(2, 1, 8)$
45. $z = \sqrt{25 - x^2 - y^2}$	$(3, 0, 4)$
46. $z = \dfrac{x}{y}$	$(3, 1, 3)$
47. $z = 4 - x^2 - y^2$	$(1, 1, 2)$

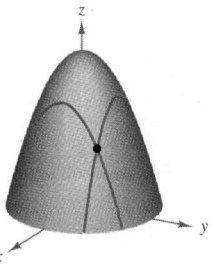

48. $z = x^2 - y^2$ $(-2, 1, 3)$

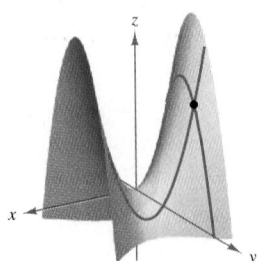

In Exercises 49–52, show that $\partial^2 z/\partial x\partial y = \partial^2 z/\partial y\partial x$.

49. $z = x^2 - 2xy + 3y^2$ **50.** $z = x^4 - 3x^2 y^2 + y^4$

51. $z = \dfrac{e^{2xy}}{4x}$ **52.** $z = \dfrac{x^2 - y^2}{2xy}$

In Exercises 53–64, find the second partial derivatives

$$\frac{\partial^2 z}{\partial x^2}, \quad \frac{\partial^2 z}{\partial y^2}, \quad \frac{\partial^2 z}{\partial y\partial x}, \quad \text{and} \quad \frac{\partial^2 z}{\partial x\partial y}.$$

53. $z = x^3 - 4y^2$

54. $z = 3x^2 - xy + 2y^3$

55. $z = 4x^3 + 3xy^2 - 4y^3$

56. $z = x^4 - 3x^2 y^2 + y^4$

57. $z = 9 + 4x - 6y - x^2 - y^2$

58. $z = \sqrt{9 - x^2 - y^2}$

59. $z = \dfrac{xy}{x - y}$ **60.** $z = \dfrac{x}{x + y}$

61. $z = \sqrt{x^2 + y^2}$ **62.** $z = \ln(x - y)$

63. $z = xe^{-y^2}$ **64.** $z = xe^y + ye^x$

In Exercises 65–68, find the first partial derivatives with respect to $x, y,$ and z.

65. $w = 3x^2 y - 5xyz + 10yz^2$

66. $w = \sqrt{x^2 + y^2 + z^2}$

67. $w = \dfrac{xy}{x + y + z}$

68. $w = \dfrac{1}{\sqrt{1 - x^2 - y^2 - z^2}}$

69. *Marginal Cost* A company manufactures two models of bicycles: a mountain bike and a racing bike. The cost function for producing x mountain bikes and y racing bikes is

$$C = 10\sqrt{xy} + 149x + 189y + 675.$$

Find the marginal costs ($\partial C/\partial x$ and $\partial C/\partial y$) when $x = 120$ and $y = 160$.

70. *Marginal Revenue* A corporation has two plants that produce the same product. If x_1 and x_2 are the numbers of units produced at plant 1 and plant 2, respectively, then the total revenue for the product is given by

$$R = 200x_1 + 200x_2 - 4x_1^2 - 8x_1 x_2 - 4x_2^2.$$

If $x_1 = 4$ and $x_2 = 12$, find the following.

(a) The marginal revenue for plant 1, $\partial R/\partial x_1$

(b) The marginal revenue for plant 2, $\partial R/\partial x_2$

71. *Marginal Productivity* Let $x = 1000$ and $y = 500$ in the Cobb-Douglas production function

$$f(x, y) = 100x^{0.6}y^{0.4}.$$

(a) Find the marginal productivity of labor, $\partial f / \partial x$.
(b) Find the marginal productivity of capital, $\partial f / \partial y$.

72. *Marginal Productivity* Repeat Exercise 71 for the production function

$$f(x, y) = 100x^{0.75}y^{0.25}.$$

73. *Complementary and Substitute Products* Using the notation of Example 4 for this section, we let x_1 and x_2 be the demands for products 1 and 2, respectively, and p_1 and p_2 the prices of products 1 and 2, respectively. Determine if the following demand functions describe complementary or substitute product relationships.

(a) $x_1 = 150 - 2p_1 - \frac{5}{2}p_2,$ $x_2 = 350 - \frac{3}{2}p_1 - 3p_2$

(b) $x_1 = 150 - 2p_1 + 1.8p_2,$ $x_2 = 350 + \frac{3}{4}p_1 - 1.9p_2$

(c) $x_1 = \dfrac{1000}{\sqrt{p_1 p_2}},$ $x_2 = \dfrac{750}{p_2\sqrt{p_1}}$

74. *Investment* The value of an investment of $1000 earning 10% compounded annually is given by

$$V(I, R) = 1000 \left[\frac{1 + 0.10(1 - R)}{1 + I} \right]^{10},$$

where I is the annual rate of inflation and R is the tax rate for the person making the investment. Calculate $V_I(0.03, 0.28)$ and $V_R(0.03, 0.28)$ and determine whether the tax rate or rate of inflation is the greater negative factor in the growth of the investment.

75. *University Admissions* Let N be the number of applicants to a university, p the charge for food and housing at the university, and t the tuition. Suppose that N is a function of p and t such that $\partial N / \partial p < 0$ and $\partial N / \partial t < 0$. How would you interpret the fact that both partials are negative?

76. *Apparent Temperature* A measure of what hot weather feels like to two average persons is the Apparent Temperature index. A model for this index is

$$A = 0.885t - 78.7h + 1.20th + 2.70,$$

where A is the apparent temperature, t is the air temperature, and h is the relative humidity in decimal form. (*Source: The UMAP Journal*)

(a) Find $\partial A / \partial t$ and $\partial A / \partial h$ when $t = 90°C$ and $h = 0.80$.
(b) Which has a greater effect on A, air temperature or humidity? Explain.

77. *Marginal Utility* The utility function $U = f(x, y)$ is a measure of the utility (or satisfaction) derived by a person from the consumption of two goods x and y. Suppose the utility function is

$$U = -5x^2 + xy - 3y^2.$$

(a) Determine the marginal utility of good x.
(b) Determine the marginal utility of good y.
(c) When $x = 2$ and $y = 3$, should a person consume one more unit of good x or one more unit of good y? Explain your reasoning.
(d) Use a three-dimensional graphing utility to graph the function. Interpret the marginal utilities of goods x and y graphically.

78. *Research Project* Use your school's library or some other reference source to research a company that increased the demand for its product by creative advertising. Write a paper about the company. Use graphs to show how a change in demand is a change in a product's marginal utility.

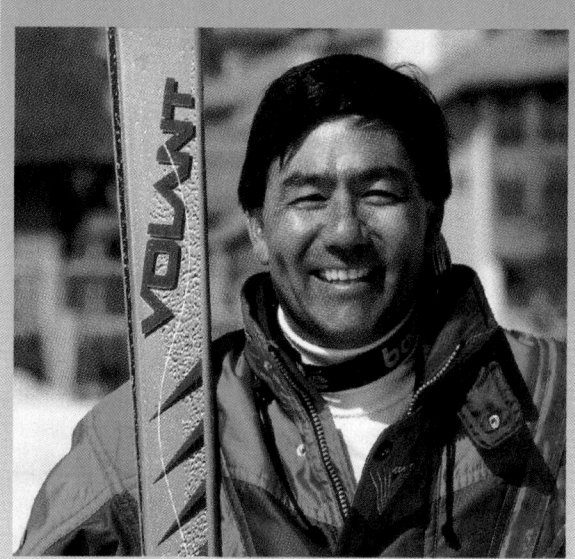

Business Capsule

Courtesy The Volant Ski Corporation, Colorado

Hank Kashiwa, co-founder of Volant Ski Corp., used a video brochure to educate customers about their stainless steel skis. Sales increased in 1993 to 20,000 pairs of skis.

7.5 Extrema of Functions of Two Variables

Relative Extrema ■ *The First-Partials Test for Relative Extrema* ■
The Second-Partials Test for Relative Extrema ■ *Applications of Extrema*

Relative Extrema

Earlier in the text, you learned how to use derivatives to find the relative minimum and relative maximum values of a function of a single variable. In this section, you will learn how to use partial derivatives to find the relative minimum and relative maximum values of a function of two variables.

Relative Extrema of a Function of Two Variables

Let f be a function defined on a region containing (x_0, y_0). The number $f(x_0, y_0)$ is a **relative maximum** of f if there is a circular region R centered at (x_0, y_0) such that

$$f(x, y) \leq f(x_0, y_0) \qquad f(x_0, y_0) \text{ is a relative maximum.}$$

for all (x, y) in R. The number $f(x_0, y_0)$ is a **relative minimum** of f if there is a circular region R centered at (x_0, y_0) such that

$$f(x, y) \geq f(x_0, y_0) \qquad f(x_0, y_0) \text{ is a relative minimum.}$$

for all (x, y) in R.

Graphically, you can think of a point on a surface as a relative maximum if it is at least as high as all "nearby" points on the surface, and you can think of a point on a surface as a relative minimum if it is at least as low as all "nearby" points on the surface. Several relative maxima and relative minima are shown in Figure 7.25.

As in single-variable calculus, you need to distinguish between relative extrema and absolute extrema of a function of two variables. The number $f(x_0, y_0)$ is an absolute maximum of f in the region R if it is greater than or equal to all other function values in the region. For instance, the function

$$f(x, y) = -(x^2 + y^2)$$

graphs as a paraboloid, opening downward, with vertex at $(0, 0, 0)$. The number $f(0, 0) = 0$ is an absolute maximum of the function over the entire xy-plane. An absolute minimum of f in a region is defined similarly.

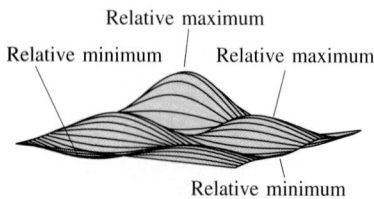

Relative maximum

Relative minimum   Relative maximum

Relative minimum

FIGURE 7.25 Relative Extrema

The First-Partials Test for Relative Extrema

To locate the relative extrema of a function of two variables, you can use a procedure that is similar to the First-Derivative Test used for functions of a single variable.

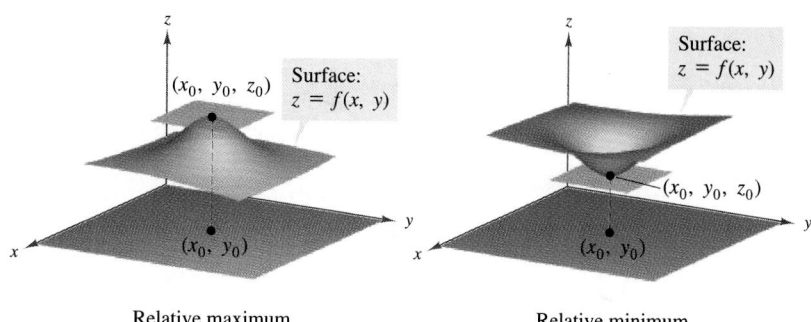

Relative maximum   Relative minimum

FIGURE 7.26

Surface: $z = f(x, y)$

Saddle point at $(0, 0, 0)$:

$f_x(0, 0) = f_y(0, 0) = 0$

FIGURE 7.27

First-Partials Test for Relative Extrema

If $f(x_0, y_0)$ is a relative extremum of f on an open region R in the xy-plane, and the first partial derivatives of f exist in R, then

$$f_x(x_0, y_0) = 0 \quad \text{and} \quad f_y(x_0, y_0) = 0,$$

as shown in Figure 7.26.

Note An *open* region in the xy-plane is similar to an open interval on the real number line. For instance, the region R consisting of the interior of the circle $x^2 + y^2 = 1$ is an open region. If the region R consists of the interior of the circle *and* the points on the circle, then it would be a *closed* region.

A point (x_0, y_0) is a **critical point** of f if $f_x(x_0, y_0)$ or $f_y(x_0, y_0)$ is undefined or if

$$f_x(x_0, y_0) = 0 \quad \text{and} \quad f_y(x_0, y_0) = 0. \qquad \textit{Critical point}$$

The First-Partials Test states that if the first partial derivatives exist, then you need only examine values of $f(x, y)$ at critical points to find the relative extrema. As is true for a function of a single variable, however, the critical points of a function of two variables do not always yield relative extrema. For instance, the point $(0, 0)$ is a critical point of the surface shown in Figure 7.27, but $f(0, 0)$ is not a relative extremum of the function. Such points are called **saddle points** of the function.

EXAMPLE 1 *Finding Relative Extrema*

Find the relative extrema of

$$f(x, y) = 2x^2 + y^2 + 8x - 6y + 20.$$

Solution

Begin by finding the first partial derivatives of f.

$$f_x(x, y) = 4x + 8 \quad \text{and} \quad f_y(x, y) = 2y - 6$$

Because these partial derivatives are defined for all points in the xy-plane, the only critical points are those for which both first partial derivatives are 0. To locate these points, set $f_x(x, y)$ and $f_y(x, y)$ equal to 0, and solve the resulting system of equations.

$4x + 8 = 0$	*Set $f_x(x, y)$ equal to 0.*
$2y - 6 = 0$	*Set $f_y(x, y)$ equal to 0.*

The solution of this system is $x = -2$ and $y = 3$. Therefore, the point $(-2, 3)$ is the only critical number of f. From the graph of the function, as shown in Figure 7.28, you can see that this critical point yields a relative minimum of the function. Thus, the function has only one relative extremum, which is

$$f(-2, 3) = 3. \qquad \qquad \textit{Relative minimum} \qquad \blacksquare$$

Example 1 shows a relative minimum occurring at one type of critical point—the type for which both $f_x(x, y)$ and $f_y(x, y)$ are zero. The next example shows a relative maximum that occurs at the other type of critical point—the type for which either $f_x(x, y)$ or $f_y(x, y)$ is undefined.

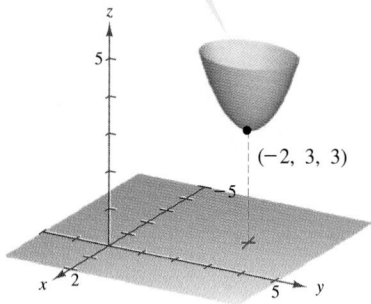

Surface:
$f(x, y) = 2x^2 + y^2 + 8x - 6y + 20$

$(-2, 3, 3)$

FIGURE 7.28

EXAMPLE 2 *Finding Relative Extrema*

Find the relative extrema of

$$f(x, y) = 1 - (x^2 + y^2)^{1/3}.$$

Solution

Begin by finding the first partial derivatives of f.

$$f_x(x, y) = -\frac{2x}{3(x^2 + y^2)^{2/3}} \quad \text{and} \quad f_y(x, y) = -\frac{2y}{3(x^2 + y^2)^{2/3}}$$

These partial derivatives are defined for all points in the xy-plane *except* the point $(0, 0)$. Thus, $(0, 0)$ is a critical point of f. Moreover, this is the only critical point because there are no other values of x and y for which either partial is undefined or for which both partials are 0. From the graph of the function, as shown in Figure 7.29, you can see that this critical point yields a relative maximum of the function. Thus, the function has only one relative extremum, which is

$$f(0, 0) = 1. \qquad \qquad \textit{Relative maximum} \qquad \blacksquare$$

Surface:
$f(x, y) = 1 - (x^2 + y^2)^{1/3}$

$(0, 0, 1)$

FIGURE 7.29 $f_x(x, y)$ and $f_y(x, y)$ are undefined at $(0, 0)$.

TECHNOLOGY

Classifying Extrema with a Graphing Utility

The First-Partials Test tells you that the relative extrema of a function $z = f(x, y)$ can occur only at the critical points of the function. The test does not, however, give you a method for determining whether a critical point actually yields a relative minimum, a relative maximum, or neither. Once you have located the critical points of a function, you can use technology to find the relative extrema graphically. Four examples of surfaces are shown below. Try using the graphs and the given critical numbers to classify the relative extrema.

Surface: $f(x, y) = x^2 - 2x + y^2 + 4y + 5$

Critical point: $(1, -2)$

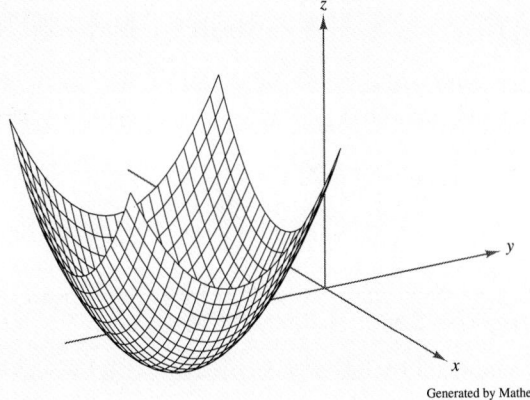

Generated by Mathematica

Surface: $f(x, y) = \sqrt{x^2 + y^2}$

Critical point: $(0, 0)$

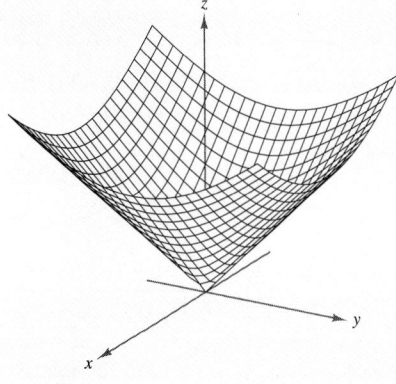

Generated by Mathematica

Surface: $f(x, y) = \dfrac{1}{1 + x^2 + y^2}$

Critical point: $(0, 0)$

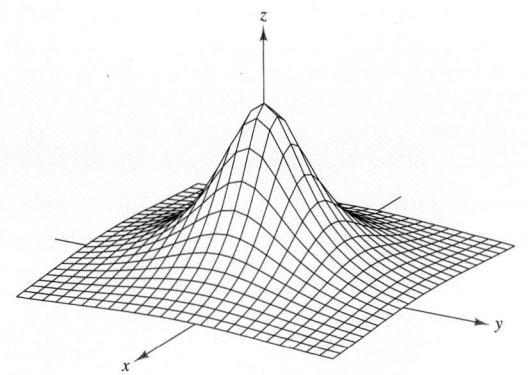

Generated by Mathematica

Surface: $f(x, y) = 8xye^{-x^2 - y^2}$

Critical points: $(0, 0), \left(\pm\dfrac{1}{\sqrt{2}}, \pm\dfrac{1}{\sqrt{2}} \right), \left(\pm\dfrac{1}{\sqrt{2}}, \mp\dfrac{1}{\sqrt{2}} \right)$

Generated by Mathematica

The Second-Partials Test for Relative Extrema

For functions such as those in Examples 1 and 2, you can determine the *type* of extrema at the critical points by sketching the graph of the function. For more complicated functions, a graphical approach is not so easy to use. The **Second-Partials Test** is an analytical test that can be used to determine whether a critical number yields a relative minimum, a relative maximum, or neither.

Second-Partials Test

If f has continuous first and second partial derivatives in an open region and there exists a point (a, b) in the region such that $f_x(a, b) = 0$ and $f_y(a, b) = 0$, then the quantity

$$d = f_{xx}(a, b) f_{yy}(a, b) - [f_{xy}(a, b)]^2$$

can be used as follows.

1. $f(a, b)$ is a relative minimum if $d > 0$ and $f_{xx}(a, b) > 0$.
2. $f(a, b)$ is a relative maximum if $d > 0$ and $f_{xx}(a, b) < 0$.
3. $(a, b, f(a, b))$ is a saddle point if $d < 0$.
4. The test gives no information if $d = 0$.

Note If $d > 0$, then $f_{xx}(a, b)$ and $f_{yy}(a, b)$ must have the same sign. Thus, you can replace $f_{xx}(a, b)$ with $f_{yy}(a, b)$ in the first two parts of the test.

EXAMPLE 3 Applying the Second-Partials Test

Find the relative extrema and saddle points of $f(x, y) = xy - \frac{1}{4}x^4 - \frac{1}{4}y^4$.

Solution

Begin by finding the critical points of f. Because

$$f_x(x, y) = y - x^3 \quad \text{and} \quad f_y(x, y) = x - y^3$$

are defined for all points in the xy-plane, the only critical points are those for which both first partial derivatives are 0. By solving the equations $y - x^3 = 0$ and $x - y^3 = 0$ simultaneously, you can determine that the critical points are $(1, 1)$, $(-1, -1)$, and $(0, 0)$. Furthermore, because

$$f_{xx}(x, y) = -3x^2, \quad f_{yy}(x, y) = -3y^2, \quad \text{and} \quad f_{xy}(x, y) = 1,$$

you can use the quantity $d = f_{xx}(a, b) f_{yy}(a, b) - [f_{xy}(a, b)]^2$ to classify the critical points as follows.

Critical Point	d	$f_{xx}(x, y)$	Conclusion
$(1, 1)$	$(-3)(-3) - 1 = 8$	-3	Relative maximum
$(-1, -1)$	$(-3)(-3) - 1 = 8$	-3	Relative maximum
$(0, 0)$	$(0)(0) - 1 = -1$	0	Saddle point

The graph of f is shown in Figure 7.30.

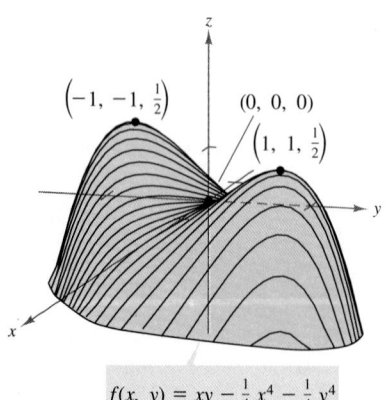

$f(x, y) = xy - \frac{1}{4}x^4 - \frac{1}{4}y^4$

FIGURE 7.30

Applications of Extrema

Real Life

EXAMPLE 4 *Finding a Maximum Profit*

Note In Example 4, you can check that the two products are substitutes by observing that x_1 increases as p_2 increases and x_2 increases as p_1 increases.

A company makes two substitute products whose demand functions are

$$x_1 = 200(p_2 - p_1) \qquad\qquad \textit{Demand for Product 1}$$
$$x_2 = 500 + 100p_1 - 180p_2, \qquad \textit{Demand for Product 2}$$

where p_1 and p_2 are the prices per unit (in dollars) and x_1 and x_2 are the numbers of units sold. The costs of producing the two products are \$0.50 and \$0.75 per unit, respectively. Find the prices that will yield a maximum profit.

Solution
The cost and revenue functions are as follows.

$$\begin{aligned}
C &= 0.5x_1 + 0.75x_2 & \textit{Cost}\\
&= 0.5(200)(p_2 - p_1) + 0.75(500 + 100p_1 - 180p_2) & \textit{Substitute.}\\
&= 375 - 25p_1 - 35p_2 & \textit{Simplify.}\\
R &= p_1 x_1 + p_2 x_2 & \textit{Revenue}\\
&= p_1(200)(p_2 - p_1) + p_2(500 + 100p_1 - 180p_2) & \textit{Substitute.}\\
&= -200p_1{}^2 - 180p_2{}^2 + 300p_1 p_2 + 500p_2 & \textit{Simplify.}
\end{aligned}$$

This implies that the profit function is

$$\begin{aligned}
P &= R - C & \textit{Profit}\\
&= -200p_1{}^2 - 180p_2{}^2 + 300p_1 p_2 + 500p_2 - (375 - 25p_1 - 35p_2)\\
&= -200p_1{}^2 - 180p_2{}^2 + 300p_1 p_2 + 25p_1 + 535p_2 - 375.
\end{aligned}$$

The maximum profit occurs when the two first partial derivatives are zero.

$$\frac{\partial P}{\partial p_1} = -400p_1 + 300p_2 + 25 = 0$$

$$\frac{\partial P}{\partial p_2} = 300p_1 - 360p_2 + 535 = 0$$

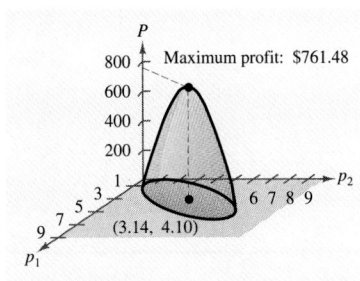

FIGURE 7.31

By solving this system simultaneously, you can conclude that the solution is $p_1 = \$3.14$ and $p_2 = \$4.10$. From the graph of the function shown in Figure 7.31, you can see that this critical number yields a maximum. Thus, the maximum profit is

$$P = P(3.14, 4.10) = \$761.48.$$

Note In Example 4, to convince yourself that the maximum profit is \$761.48, try substituting other prices into the profit function. For each pair of prices, you will obtain a profit that is less than \$761.48. For instance, if $p_1 = \$2$ and $p_2 = \$3$, then the profit is $P = P(2, 3) = \$660.00$.

Real Life

EXAMPLE 5 *Finding a Maximum Volume*

Consider all possible rectangular boxes that are resting on the xy-plane with one vertex at the origin and the opposite vertex in the plane $6x + 4y + 3z = 24$, as shown in Figure 7.32. Of all such boxes, which has the greatest volume?

Solution

Because one vertex of the box lies in the plane given by $6x + 4y + 3z = 24$ or $z = \frac{1}{3}(24 - 6x - 4y)$, you can write the volume of the box as

$$V = xyz \qquad\qquad\qquad Volume = (width)(length)(height)$$
$$= xy \left(\tfrac{1}{3}\right)(24 - 6x - 4y) \qquad Substitute\ for\ z.$$
$$= \tfrac{1}{3}(24xy - 6x^2y - 4xy^2). \qquad Simplify.$$

To find the critical numbers, set the first partial derivatives equal to zero.

$$V_x = \tfrac{1}{3}(24y - 12xy - 4y^2) \qquad Partial\ with\ respect\ to\ x$$
$$= \tfrac{1}{3}y(24 - 12x - 4y) \qquad\quad Factor.$$
$$= 0 \qquad\qquad\qquad\qquad\quad Set\ equal\ to\ 0.$$

$$V_y = \tfrac{1}{3}(24x - 6x^2 - 8xy) \qquad Partial\ with\ respect\ to\ y$$
$$= \tfrac{1}{3}x(24 - 6x - 8y) \qquad\quad Factor.$$
$$= 0 \qquad\qquad\qquad\qquad\quad Set\ equal\ to\ 0.$$

The four solutions of this system are $(0, 0)$, $(0, 6)$, $(4, 0)$, and $\left(\frac{4}{3}, 2\right)$. Using the Second-Partials Test, you can determine that the maximum volume occurs when the width is $x = \frac{4}{3}$ and the length is $y = 2$. For these values, the height of the box is

$$z = \tfrac{1}{3}\left[24 - 6\left(\tfrac{4}{3}\right) - 4(2)\right] = \tfrac{8}{3}.$$

Thus, the maximum volume is

$$V = xyz = \left(\tfrac{4}{3}\right)(2)\left(\tfrac{8}{3}\right) = \tfrac{64}{9} \text{ cubic units.}$$

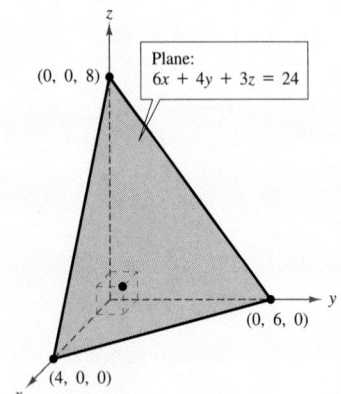

Plane:
$6x + 4y + 3z = 24$

$(0, 0, 8)$

$(0, 6, 0)$

$(4, 0, 0)$

FIGURE 7.32

Discussion Problem   **Using the Second-Partials Test**

In Example 5, explain why you can disregard the three critical numbers $(0, 0)$, $(0, 6)$, and $(4, 0)$. Then use the second partial derivatives

$$V_{xx}(x, y) = -4y$$
$$V_{yy}(x, y) = -\tfrac{8}{3}x$$
$$V_{xy}(x, y) = \tfrac{1}{3}(24 - 12x - 8y)$$

to explain why the critical number $\left(\frac{4}{3}, 2\right)$ yields a maximum.

Warm Up

The following warm-up exercises involve skills that were covered in earlier sections. You will use these skills in the exercise set for this section.

In Exercises 1–6, solve the system of equations.

1. $\begin{cases} 5x = 15 \\ 3x - 2y = 5 \end{cases}$

2. $\begin{cases} \frac{1}{2}y = 3 \\ -x + 5y = 19 \end{cases}$

3. $\begin{cases} x + y = 5 \\ x - y = -3 \end{cases}$

4. $\begin{cases} 2x - 4y = 14 \\ 3x + y = 7 \end{cases}$

5. $\begin{cases} x^2 + x = 0 \\ 2yx + y = 0 \end{cases}$

6. $\begin{cases} 3y^2 + 6y = 0 \\ xy + x + 2 = 0 \end{cases}$

In Exercises 7–10, find all first and second partial derivatives of the function.

7. $z = 4x^3 - 3y^2$

8. $z = 2x^2 - 3xy + y^2$

9. $z = x^4 - \sqrt{xy} + 2y$

10. $z = xe^{xy}$

E X E R C I S E S 7.5   means that technology can help you solve or check the exercise(s).

In Exercises 1–4, find any critical points and relative extrema of the function.

1. $f(x, y) = x^2 - y^2 + 4x - 8y - 11$

2. $f(x, y) = x^2 + y^2 + 2x - 6y + 6$

3. $f(x, y) = \sqrt{x^2 + y^2 + 1}$

4. $f(x, y) = \sqrt{25 - (x - 2)^2 - y^2}$

In Exercises 5–20, examine each function for relative extrema and saddle points.

5. $f(x, y) = (x - 1)^2 + (y - 3)^2$

6. $f(x, y) = 9 - (x - 3)^2 - (y + 2)^2$

7. $f(x, y) = 2x^2 + 2xy + y^2 + 2x - 3$

8. $f(x, y) = -x^2 - 5y^2 + 8x - 10y - 13$

9. $f(x, y) = -5x^2 + 4xy - y^2 + 16x + 10$

10. $f(x, y) = x^2 + 6xy + 10y^2 - 4y + 4$

11. $f(x, y) = 3x^2 + 2y^2 - 12x - 4y + 7$

12. $f(x, y) = -3x^2 - 2y^2 + 3x - 4y + 5$

13. $f(x, y) = x^2 - y^2 + 4x - 4y - 8$

14. $f(x, y) = x^2 - 3xy - y^2$

15. $f(x, y) = xy$

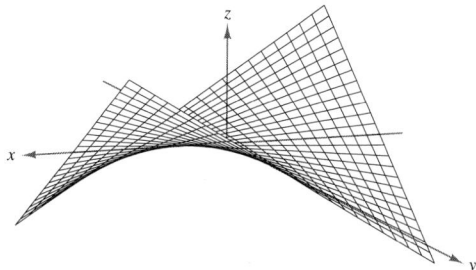

16. $f(x, y) = 12x + 12y - xy - x^2 - y^2$

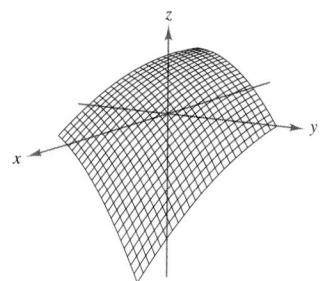

17. $f(x, y) = (x^2 + 4y^2)e^{1-x^2-y^2}$

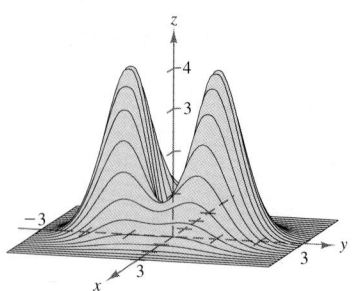

18. $f(x, y) = e^{-(x^2+y^2)}$

19. $f(x, y) = e^{xy}$

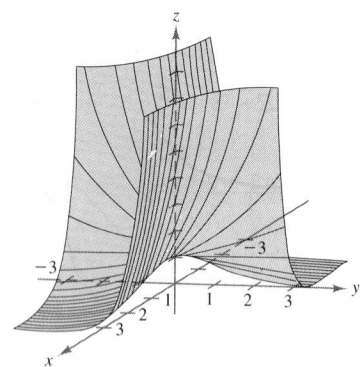

20. $f(x, y) = -\dfrac{4x}{x^2 + y^2 + 1}$

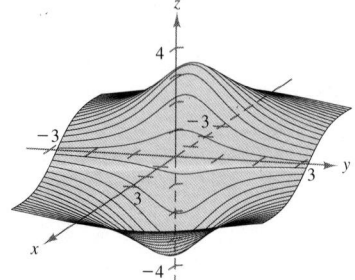

In Exercises 21–24, determine whether there is a relative maximum, a relative minimum, a saddle point, or insufficient information to determine the nature of the function $f(x, y)$ at the critical point (x_0, y_0).

21. $f_{xx}(x_0, y_0) = 16$
$f_{yy}(x_0, y_0) = 4$
$f_{xy}(x_0, y_0) = 8$

22. $f_{xx}(x_0, y_0) = -4$
$f_{yy}(x_0, y_0) = -6$
$f_{xy}(x_0, y_0) = 3$

23. $f_{xx}(x_0, y_0) = -7$
$f_{yy}(x_0, y_0) = 4$
$f_{xy}(x_0, y_0) = 9$

24. $f_{xx}(x_0, y_0) = 20$
$f_{yy}(x_0, y_0) = 8$
$f_{xy}(x_0, y_0) = 9$

In Exercises 25–30, find the critical points and test for relative extrema. List the critical points for which the Second-Partials Test fails.

25. $f(x, y) = (xy)^2$

26. $f(x, y) = \sqrt{x^2 + y^2}$

27. $f(x, y) = x^3 + y^3$

28. $f(x, y) = x^3 + y^3 - 3x^2 + 6y^2 + 3x + 12y + 7$

29. $f(x, y) = x^{2/3} + y^{2/3}$

30. $f(x, y) = (x^2 + y^2)^{2/3}$

In Exercises 31 and 32, find the critical points of the function and from the form of the function determine whether each critical point is a relative maximum or a relative minimum.

31. $f(x, y, z) = (x - 1)^2 + (y + 3)^2 + z^2$

32. $f(x, y, z) = 6 - [x(y + 2)(z - 1)]^2$

True or False In Exercises 33–36, determine whether the statement is true or false. If it is false, explain why or give an example that shows it is false.

33. If $d > 0$ and $f_x(a, b) < 0$, then $f(a, b)$ is a relative minimum.

34. A saddle point always occurs at a critical point.

35. If $f(x, y)$ has a relative maximum at (x_0, y_0, z_0), then $f_x(x_0, y_0) = f_y(x_0, y_0) = 0$.

36. The function $f(x, y) = \sqrt[3]{x^2 + y^2}$ has a relative maximum at the origin.

In Exercises 37–40, find three positive numbers x, y, and z that satisfy the given conditions.

37. The sum is 30 and the product is maximum.

38. The sum is 32 and $P = xy^2z$ is maximum.

39. The sum is 30 and the sum of the squares is minimum.

40. The sum is 1 and the sum of the squares is minimum.

41. *Revenue* A company manufactures two products. The total revenue from x_1 units of product 1 and x_2 units of product 2 is

$$R = -5x_1{}^2 - 8x_2{}^2 - 2x_1x_2 + 42x_1 + 102x_2.$$

Find x_1 and x_2 so as to maximize the revenue.

42. *Revenue* A retail outlet sells two competitive products, the prices of which are p_1 and p_2. Find p_1 and p_2 so as to maximize the total revenue

$$R = 500p_1 + 800p_2 + 1.5p_1p_2 - 1.5p_1{}^2 - p_2{}^2.$$

Revenue In Exercises 43 and 44, find p_1 and p_2 so as to maximize the total revenue $R = x_1p_1 + x_2p_2$ for a retail outlet that sells two competitive products with the given demand functions.

43. $x_1 = 1000 - 2p_1 + p_2, \ x_2 = 1500 + 2p_1 - 1.5p_2$

44. $x_1 = 1000 - 4p_1 + 2p_2, \ x_2 = 900 + 4p_1 - 3p_2$

45. *Profit* A corporation manufactures a product at two locations. The costs of producing x_1 units at location 1 and x_2 units at location 2 are $C_1 = 0.04x_1{}^2 + 5x_1 + 375$ and $C_2 = 0.07x_2{}^2 + 3.1x_2 + 295$, respectively. If the product sells for \$15 per unit, find the quantity that must be produced at each location to maximize the profit

$$P = 15(x_1 + x_2) - C_1 - C_2.$$

46. *Profit* Repeat Exercise 45 for a product that sells for \$50 per unit with cost functions $C_1 = 0.1x_1{}^3 + 20x_1 + 150$ and $C_2 = 0.05x_2{}^3 + 20.6x_2 + 125$.

47. *Profit* A corporation manufactures a product at two locations. The cost functions for producing x_1 units at location 1 and x_2 units at location 2 are

$$C_1 = 0.05x_1{}^2 + 15x_1 + 5400$$

and

$$C_2 = 0.03x_2{}^2 + 15x_2 + 6100,$$

respectively. The demand function for the product is given by

$$p = 225 - 0.4(x_1 + x_2),$$

and therefore the total revenue function is

$$R = [225 - 0.4(x_1 + x_2)](x_1 + x_2).$$

Find the production levels at the two locations that will maximize the profit

$$P = R - C_1 - C_2.$$

48. *Cost* The material for constructing the base of an open box costs 1.5 times as much as the material for constructing the sides. Find the dimensions of the box of largest volume that can be made for a fixed amount of money C.

49. *Volume* Find the dimensions of a rectangular package of largest volume that may be sent by parcel post assuming that the sum of the length and the girth (perimeter of a cross section) cannot exceed 108 inches.

50. *Volume* Show that the rectangular box of given volume and minimum surface area is a cube.

51. *Hardy-Weinberg Law* Common blood types are determined genetically by three alleles A, B, and O. (An allele is any of a group of possible mutational forms of a gene.) A person whose blood type is AA, BB, or OO is homozygous. A person whose blood type is AB, AO, or BO is heterozygous. The Hardy-Weinberg Law states that the proportion P of heterozygous individuals in any given population is

$$P(p, q, r) = 2pq + 2pr + 2qr,$$

where p represents the percent of allele A in the population, q represents the percent of allele B in the population, and r represents the percent of allele O in the population. Use the fact that $p + q + r = 1$ (the sum of the three must equal 100%) to show that the maximum proportion of heterozygous individuals in any population is $\frac{2}{3}$.

52. *Stocking a Lake* A lake is to be stocked with smallmouth and largemouth bass. Let x represent the number of smallmouth bass and y represent the number of largemouth bass in the lake. The weight of each fish is dependent on the population densities. After a 6-month period, the weight of a single smallmouth bass is

$$W_1 = 3 - 0.002x - 0.005y,$$

and the weight of a single largemouth bass is

$$W_2 = 4.5 - 0.003x - 0.004y.$$

Assuming no fish die during the 6-month period, how many smallmouth and largemouth bass should be stocked in the lake so that the *total* weight T of bass in the lake is a maximum?

7.6 Lagrange Multipliers

Lagrange Multipliers with One Constraint ■
Lagrange Multipliers with Two Constraints

Lagrange Multipliers with One Constraint

In Example 5 in Section 7.5, you were asked to find the dimensions of the rectangular box of maximum volume that would fit in the first octant beneath the plane $6x + 4y + 3z = 24$, as shown again in Figure 7.33. Another way of stating this problem is to say that you are asked to find the maximum of

$$V = xyz \qquad \qquad \textit{Objective function}$$

subject to the constraint

$$6x + 4y + 3z - 24 = 0. \qquad \textit{Constraint}$$

This type of problem is called a **constrained optimization** problem. In Section 7.5, you answered this question by solving for z in the constraint equation and then rewriting V as a function of two variables.

In this section, you will study a different (and often better) way to solve constrained optimization problems. This involves the use of variables called **Lagrange multipliers,** named after the French mathematician Joseph Louis Lagrange (1736–1813).

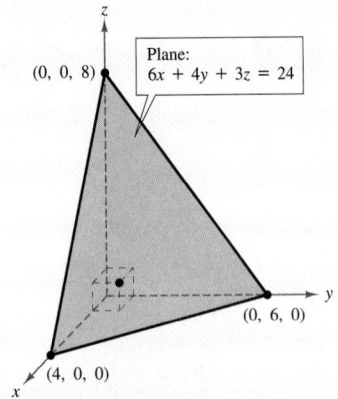

Plane:
$6x + 4y + 3z = 24$

$(0, 0, 8)$

$(0, 6, 0)$

$(4, 0, 0)$

FIGURE 7.33

Method of Lagrange Multipliers

If $f(x, y)$ has a maximum or minimum subject to the constraint $g(x, y) = 0$, then it will occur at one of the critical numbers of the function F defined by

$$F(x, y, \lambda) = f(x, y) - \lambda g(x, y).$$

The variable λ (the lowercase Greek letter lambda) is called a **Lagrange multiplier.** For functions of three variables, F has the form

$$F(x, y, z, \lambda) = f(x, y, z) - \lambda g(x, y, z).$$

The method of Lagrange multipliers gives you a way of finding critical points but does not tell you whether these points yield minimums, maximums, or neither. To make this distinction, you must rely on the context of the problem.

EXAMPLE 1 *Using Lagrange Multipliers: One Constraint*

Find the maximum of

$$V = xyz \qquad\qquad \textit{Objective function}$$

subject to the constraint

$$6x + 4y + 3z - 24 = 0. \qquad\qquad \textit{Constraint}$$

Solution

First, let $f(x, y, z) = xyz$ and $g(x, y, z) = 6x + 4y + 3z - 24$. Then, define a new function F by

$$\begin{aligned} F(x, y, z, \lambda) &= f(x, y, z) - \lambda g(x, y, z) \\ &= xyz - \lambda(6x + 4y + 3z - 24). \end{aligned}$$

To find the critical numbers of F, set the partial derivatives of F with respect to x, y, z, and λ equal to zero and obtain

$$\begin{aligned} F_x(x, y, z, \lambda) &= yz - 6\lambda = 0 \\ F_y(x, y, z, \lambda) &= xz - 4\lambda = 0 \\ F_z(x, y, z, \lambda) &= xy - 3\lambda = 0 \\ F_\lambda(x, y, z, \lambda) &= -6x - 4y - 3z + 24 = 0. \end{aligned}$$

Solving for λ in the first equation and substituting into the second and third equations produces the following.

$$xz - 4\left(\frac{yz}{6}\right) = 0 \quad \longrightarrow \quad y = \frac{3}{2}x$$

$$xy - 3\left(\frac{yz}{6}\right) = 0 \quad \longrightarrow \quad z = 2x$$

Next, substitute these values for y and z into the equation $F_\lambda(x, y, z, \lambda) = 0$ and solve for x.

$$F_\lambda(x, y, z, \lambda) = 0$$

$$-6x - 4\left(\tfrac{3}{2}x\right) - 3(2x) + 24 = 0$$

$$-18x = -24$$

$$x = \tfrac{4}{3}$$

Using this x-value, you can conclude that the critical values are $x = \tfrac{4}{3}$, $y = 2$, and $z = \tfrac{8}{3}$, which implies that the maximum is

$$V = xyz \qquad\qquad \textit{Objective function}$$

$$= \left(\frac{4}{3}\right)(2)\left(\frac{8}{3}\right) \qquad\qquad \textit{Substitute values of x, y, and z.}$$

$$= \frac{64}{9} \text{ cubic units.} \qquad\qquad \textit{Maximum volume}$$

Note Example 1 shows how Lagrange multipliers can be used to solve the same problem that was solved in Example 5 in Section 7.5.

Real Life

EXAMPLE 2 *Finding a Maximum Production*

For many industrial applications, a simple robot costs as much as a year's wages and benefits for three workers. Thus, manufacturers must carefully balance the amount of money spent on labor and capital.

A manufacturer's production is modeled by the Cobb-Douglas function

$$f(x, y) = 100x^{3/4}y^{1/4}, \qquad \textit{Objective function}$$

where x represents the units of labor and y represents the units of capital. Each labor unit costs \$150 and each capital unit costs \$250. The total expenses for labor and capital cannot exceed \$50,000. Find the maximum production level.

Solution

As total labor and capital expenses cannot exceed \$50,000, the constraint is

$$150x + 250y = 50,000 \qquad \textit{Constraint}$$
$$150x + 250y - 50,000 = 0. \qquad \textit{Standard form}$$

To find the maximum production level, begin by writing the function

$$F(x, y, \lambda) = 100x^{3/4}y^{1/4} - \lambda(150x + 250y - 50,000).$$

Next, set the partial derivatives of this function equal to zero.

$$F_x(x, y, \lambda) = 75x^{-1/4}y^{1/4} - 150\lambda = 0 \qquad \textit{Equation 1}$$
$$F_y(x, y, \lambda) = 25x^{3/4}y^{-3/4} - 250\lambda = 0 \qquad \textit{Equation 2}$$
$$F_\lambda(x, y, \lambda) = -150x - 250y + 50,000 = 0 \qquad \textit{Equation 3}$$

The strategy for solving such a system must be customized to the particular system. In this case, you can solve for λ in the first equation, substitute into the second, solve for x, substitute into the third equation, and solve for y.

$$75x^{-1/4}y^{1/4} - 150\lambda = 0 \qquad \textit{Equation 1}$$
$$\lambda = \tfrac{1}{2}x^{-1/4}y^{1/4} \qquad \textit{Solve for } \lambda.$$
$$25x^{3/4}y^{-3/4} - 250(\tfrac{1}{2})x^{-1/4}y^{1/4} = 0 \qquad \textit{Substitute in Equation 2.}$$
$$25x - 125y = 0 \qquad \textit{Multiply by } x^{1/4}y^{3/4}.$$
$$x = 5y \qquad \textit{Solve for } x.$$
$$-150(5y) - 250y + 50,000 = 0 \qquad \textit{Substitute in Equation 3.}$$
$$-1000y = -50,000 \qquad \textit{Simplify.}$$
$$y = 50 \qquad \textit{Solve for } y.$$

Using this value for y, it follows that $x = 5(50) = 250$. Thus, the maximum production level of

$$f(250, 50) = 100(250)^{3/4}(50)^{1/4} \qquad \textit{Substitute for x and y.}$$
$$\approx 16,719 \text{ units} \qquad \textit{Maximum production}$$

occurs when $x = 250$ units of labor and $y = 50$ units of capital. ∎

Economists call the Lagrange multiplier obtained in a production function the **marginal productivity of money.** For instance, in Example 2, the marginal productivity of money when $x = 250$ and $y = 50$ is

$$\lambda = \tfrac{1}{2}x^{-1/4}y^{1/4} = \tfrac{1}{2}(250)^{-1/4}(50)^{1/4} \approx 0.334.$$

This means that if one additional dollar is spent on production, approximately 0.334 additional units of the product can be produced.

Real Life

EXAMPLE 3 *Finding a Maximum Production*

In Example 2, suppose that $70,000 is available for labor and capital. What is the maximum number of units that can be produced?

Solution
You could rework the entire problem, as demonstrated in Example 2. However, because the only change in the problem is the availability of additional money to spend on labor and capital, you can use the fact that the marginal productivity of money is

$$\lambda \approx 0.334.$$

Because an additional $20,000 is available and the maximum production in Example 2 was 16,719 units, you can conclude that the maximum production is now

$$16,719 + (0.334)(20,000) \approx 23,400 \text{ units.}$$

Try using the procedure demonstrated in Example 2 to confirm this result.

▦ TECHNOLOGY

You can use a three-dimensional graphing utility to confirm graphically the results of Examples 2 and 3. Begin by graphing the surface $f(x, y) = 100x^{3/4}y^{1/4}$. Then graph the vertical plane given by $150x + 250y = 50,000$. As shown at the right, the maximum production level corresponds to the highest point on the intersection of the surface and the plane.

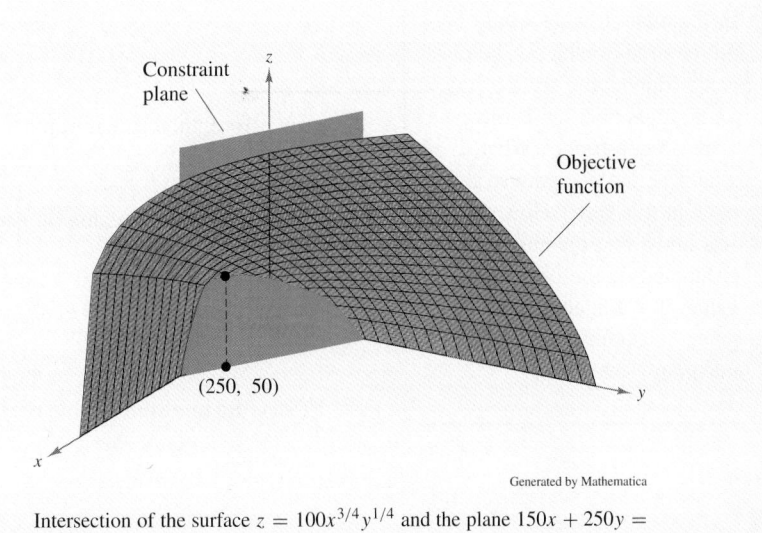

Generated by Mathematica

Intersection of the surface $z = 100x^{3/4}y^{1/4}$ and the plane $150x + 250y = 50,000$.

EXAMPLE 4 *Optimizing with Four Variables*

Find the minimum of the function

$$f(x, y, z, w) = x^2 + y^2 + z^2 + w^2 \qquad \textit{Objective function}$$

subject to the constraint

$$3x + 2y - 4z + w - 3 = 0. \qquad \textit{Constraint}$$

Solution

Begin by forming the function

$$F(x, y, z, w, \lambda) = x^2 + y^2 + z^2 + w^2 - \lambda(3x + 2y - 4z + w - 3).$$

Next, set the five partial derivatives of F equal to zero.

$F_x(x, y, z, w, \lambda) = 2x - 3\lambda = 0$	*Equation 1*
$F_y(x, y, z, w, \lambda) = 2y - 2\lambda = 0$	*Equation 2*
$F_z(x, y, z, w, \lambda) = 2z + 4\lambda = 0$	*Equation 3*
$F_w(x, y, z, w, \lambda) = 2w - \lambda = 0$	*Equation 4*
$F_\lambda(x, y, z, w, \lambda) = -3x - 2y + 4z - w + 3 = 0$	*Equation 5*

For this system, you can solve the first four equations in terms of λ.

$$2x - 3\lambda = 0 \quad \longrightarrow \quad x = \tfrac{3}{2}\lambda$$
$$2y - 2\lambda = 0 \quad \longrightarrow \quad y = \lambda$$
$$2z + 4\lambda = 0 \quad \longrightarrow \quad z = -2\lambda$$
$$2w - \lambda = 0 \quad \longrightarrow \quad w = \tfrac{1}{2}\lambda$$

Substituting these values into the fifth equation allows you to solve for λ.

$$-3x - 2y + 4z - w + 3 = 0$$
$$-3\left(\tfrac{3}{2}\lambda\right) - 2(\lambda) + 4(-2\lambda) - \left(\tfrac{1}{2}\lambda\right) = -3$$
$$-15\lambda = -3$$
$$\lambda = \tfrac{1}{5}$$

Therefore, the critical numbers are

$$x = \tfrac{3}{10}, \quad y = \tfrac{1}{5}, \quad z = -\tfrac{2}{5}, \quad \text{and} \quad w = \tfrac{1}{10},$$

and the minimum value of f subject to the given constraint is

$$f\left(\tfrac{3}{10}, \tfrac{1}{5}, -\tfrac{2}{5}, \tfrac{1}{10}\right) = \left(\tfrac{3}{10}\right)^2 + \left(\tfrac{1}{5}\right)^2 + \left(-\tfrac{2}{5}\right)^2 + \left(\tfrac{1}{10}\right)^2 \quad \textit{Substitute.}$$
$$= \tfrac{9}{100} + \tfrac{1}{25} + \tfrac{4}{25} + \tfrac{1}{100} \quad \textit{Simplify.}$$
$$= \tfrac{3}{10}. \quad \textit{Minimum value}$$

Thus, the minimum value of $f(x, y, z, w)$ is $\tfrac{3}{10}$.

Discovery

In Example 4, what would be the minimum value of the objective function $f(x, y, z, w) = x^2 + y^2 + z^2 + w^2$ if there were no constraint? What would be the maximum value of f in this case? How do you know that the answer to Example 4 is the minimum value of f subject to the given constraint, and not the maximum value?

In Example 4 in Section 7.5, you found the maximum profit for two substitute products whose demand functions are

$$x_1 = 200(p_2 - p_1) \qquad \text{\textit{Demand for Product 1}}$$
$$x_2 = 500 + 100p_1 - 180p_2. \qquad \text{\textit{Demand for Product 2}}$$

With this model, the total demand, $x_1 + x_2$, is completely determined by the prices p_1 and p_2. In many real-life situations, this assumption is too simplistic: regardless of the prices of the substitute brands, the annual total demands for some products, such as toothpaste, are relatively constant. In such situations, the total demand is **limited,** and variations in price do not affect the total demand as much as they affect the market share of the substitute brands.

EXAMPLE 5 *Finding the Maximum Profit*

Real Life

A company makes two substitute products whose demand functions are

$$x_1 = 200(p_2 - p_1) \qquad \text{\textit{Demand for Product 1}}$$
$$x_2 = 500 + 100p_1 - 180p_2, \qquad \text{\textit{Demand for Product 2}}$$

where p_1 and p_2 are the prices per unit (in dollars) and x_1 and x_2 are the numbers of units sold. The costs of producing the two products are $0.50 and $0.75 per unit, respectively. The total demand is limited to 200 units per year. Find the prices that will yield a maximum profit.

Solution
From Example 4 in Section 7.5, the profit function is modeled by

$$P = -200p_1{}^2 - 180p_2{}^2 + 300p_1p_2 + 25p_1 + 535p_2 - 375.$$

The total demand for the two products is

$$x_1 + x_2 = 200(p_2 - p_1) + 500 + 100p_1 - 180p_2$$
$$= -100p_1 + 20p_2 + 500.$$

Because the total demand is limited to 200 units,

$$-100p_1 + 20p_2 + 500 = 200. \qquad \text{\textit{Constraint}}$$

Using Lagrange multipliers, you can determine that the maximum profit occurs when $p_1 = \$3.94$ and $p_2 = \$4.69$. This corresponds to an annual profit of $712.21.

Note The constrained optimization problem in Example 5 is represented graphically in Figure 7.34. The graph of the objective function is a paraboloid and the graph of the constraint is a vertical plane. In the "unconstrained" optimization problem on page 495, the maximum profit occurred at the vertex of the paraboloid. In this "constrained" problem, however, the maximum profit corresponds to the highest point on the curve that is the intersection of the paraboloid and the vertical "constraint" plane.

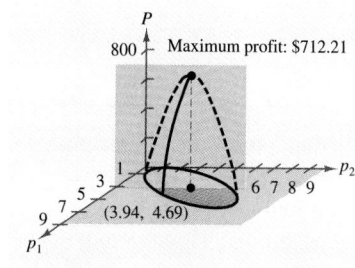

FIGURE 7.34

Lagrange Multipliers with Two Constraints

In Examples 1 through 5, each of the optimization problems contained only one constraint. When an optimization problem has two constraints, you need to introduce a second Lagrange multiplier. The customary symbol for this second multiplier is μ, the Greek letter mu.

EXAMPLE 6 *Using Lagrange Multipliers: Two Constraints*

Find the minimum value of

$$f(x, y, z) = x^2 + y^2 + z^2 \qquad\qquad \textit{Objective function}$$

subject to the constraints

$$x + y - 3 = 0 \qquad\qquad \textit{Constraint 1}$$
$$x + z - 5 = 0. \qquad\qquad \textit{Constraint 2}$$

Solution

Begin by forming the function

$$F(x, y, z, \lambda, \mu) = x^2 + y^2 + z^2 - \lambda(x + y - 3) - \mu(x + z - 5).$$

Next, set the five partial derivatives equal to zero, and solve the resulting system of equations for x, y, and z.

$$F_x(x, y, z, \lambda, \mu) = 2x - \lambda - \mu = 0 \qquad \textit{Equation 1}$$
$$F_y(x, y, z, \lambda, \mu) = 2y - \lambda = 0 \qquad \textit{Equation 2}$$
$$F_z(x, y, z, \lambda, \mu) = 2z - \mu = 0 \qquad \textit{Equation 3}$$
$$F_\lambda(x, y, z, \lambda, \mu) = -x - y + 3 = 0 \qquad \textit{Equation 4}$$
$$F_\mu(x, y, z, \lambda, \mu) = -x - z + 5 = 0 \qquad \textit{Equation 5}$$

Solving this system of equations produces $x = \frac{8}{3}$, $y = \frac{1}{3}$, and $z = \frac{7}{3}$. Thus, the minimum value of $f(x, y, z)$ is

$$f\left(\frac{8}{3}, \frac{1}{3}, \frac{7}{3}\right) = \left(\frac{8}{3}\right)^2 + \left(\frac{1}{3}\right)^2 + \left(\frac{7}{3}\right)^2 = \frac{38}{3}.$$

Discussion Problem Solving a System of Equations

Explain how you would solve the system of equations shown in Example 6. Illustrate your description by actually solving the system.

Suppose that in Example 6 you had been asked to find the maximum value of $f(x, y, z)$ subject to the two constraints. How would your answer have been different?

Warm Up

The following warm-up exercises involve skills that were covered in earlier sections. You will use these skills in the exercise set for this section.

In Exercises 1–6, solve the system of linear equations.

1. $\begin{cases} 4x - 6y = 3 \\ 2x + 3y = 2 \end{cases}$

2. $\begin{cases} 6x - 6y = 5 \\ -3x - y = 1 \end{cases}$

3. $\begin{cases} 5x - y = 25 \\ x - 5y = 15 \end{cases}$

4. $\begin{cases} 4x - 9y = 5 \\ -x + 8y = -2 \end{cases}$

5. $\begin{cases} 2x - y + z = 3 \\ 2x + 2y + z = 4 \\ -x + 2y + 3z = -1 \end{cases}$

6. $\begin{cases} -x - 4y + 6z = -2 \\ x - 3y - 3z = 4 \\ 3x + y + 3z = 0 \end{cases}$

In Exercises 7–10, find all first partial derivatives.

7. $f(x, y) = x^2 y + xy^2$

8. $f(x, y) = 25(xy + y^2)^2$

9. $f(x, y, z) = x(x^2 - 2xy + yz)$

10. $f(x, y, z) = z(xy + xz + yz)$

EXERCISES 7.6

 means that technology can help you solve or check the exercise(s).

In Exercises 1–12, use Lagrange multipliers to find the indicated extrema. In each case, assume that x and y are positive.

Objective Function	*Constraint*
1. Maximize $f(x, y) = xy$	$x + y = 10$
2. Maximize $f(x, y) = xy$	$2x + y = 4$
3. Minimize $f(x, y) = x^2 + y^2$	$x + y - 4 = 0$
4. Minimize $f(x, y) = x^2 + y^2$	$-2x - 4y + 5 = 0$
5. Maximize $f(x, y) = x^2 - y^2$	$y - x^2 = 0$
6. Maximize $f(x, y) = x^2 - y^2$	$x - 2y + 6 = 0$
7. Maximize $f(x, y) = 3x + xy + 3y$	$x + y = 25$
8. Maximize $f(x, y) = 3x + y + 10$	$x^2 y = 6$
9. Maximize $f(x, y) = \sqrt{6 - x^2 - y^2}$	$x + y - 2 = 0$
10. Minimize $f(x, y) = \sqrt{x^2 + y^2}$	$2x + 4y - 15 = 0$
11. Maximize $f(x, y) = e^{xy}$	$x^2 + y^2 - 8 = 0$
12. Minimize $f(x, y) = 2x + y$	$xy = 32$

In Exercises 13–18, use Lagrange multipliers to find the indicated extrema. In each case, assume that x, y, and z are positive.

13. Minimize $f(x, y, z) = 2x^2 + 3y^2 + 2z^2$

 Constraint: $x + y + z - 24 = 0$

14. Maximize $f(x, y, z) = xyz$

 Constraint: $x + y + z - 6 = 0$

15. Minimize $f(x, y, z) = x^2 + y^2 + z^2$

 Constraint: $x + y + z = 1$

16. Minimize $f(x, y) = x^2 - 8x + y^2 - 12y + 48$

 Constraint: $x + y = 8$

17. Maximize $f(x, y, z) = x + y + z$

 Constraint: $x^2 + y^2 + z^2 = 1$

18. Maximize $f(x, y, z) = x^2 y^2 z^2$

 Constraint: $x^2 + y^2 + z^2 = 1$

In Exercises 19 and 20, use Lagrange multipliers with the objective function

$$f(x, y, z, w) = 2x^2 + y^2 + z^2 + 2w^2$$

with the given constraints to find the indicated extrema. In each case, assume that x, y, z, and w are nonnegative.

19. Maximize $f(x, y, z, w)$

Constraint: $2x + 2y + z + w = 2$

20. Maximize $f(x, y, z, w)$

Constraint: $x + y + 2z + 2w = 4$

In Exercises 21–24, use Lagrange multipliers to find the indicated extrema of f subject to two constraints. In each case, assume x, y, and z are nonnegative.

21. Maximize $f(x, y, z) = xyz$

Constraints: $x + y + z = 24$, $x - y + z = 12$

22. Minimize $f(x, y, z) = x^2 + y^2 + z^2$

Constraints: $x + 2z = 4$, $x + y = 8$

23. Maximize $f(x, y, z) = xyz$

Constraints: $x^2 + z^2 = 5$, $x - 2y = 0$

24. Maximize $f(x, y, z) = xy + yz$

Constraints: $x + 2y = 6$, $x - 3z = 0$

In Exercises 25–28, find three positive numbers x, y, and z that satisfy the given conditions.

25. The sum is 120 and the product is maximum.

26. The sum is 120 and the sum of the squares is minimum.

27. The sum is S and the product is maximum.

28. The sum is S and the sum of the squares is minimum.

In Exercises 29–32, find the minimum distance from the curve or surface to the specified point. (*Hint:* Start by minimizing the square of the distance.)

29. Line: $x + 2y = 5$, $(0, 0)$

Minimize $d^2 = x^2 + y^2$.

30. Circle: $(x - 4)^2 + y^2 = 4$, $(0, 10)$

Minimize $d^2 = x^2 + (y - 10)^2$.

31. Plane: $x + y + z = 1$, $(2, 1, 1)$

Minimize $d^2 = (x - 2)^2 + (y - 1)^2 + (z - 1)^2$.

32. Cone: $z = \sqrt{x^2 + y^2}$, $(4, 0, 0)$

Minimize $d^2 = (x - 4)^2 + y^2 + z^2$.

33. *Volume* Find the dimensions of the rectangular package of largest volume subject to the constraint that the sum of the length and the girth cannot exceed 108 inches (see figure). (*Hint:* Maximize $V = xyz$ subject to the constraint $x + 2y + 2z = 108$.)

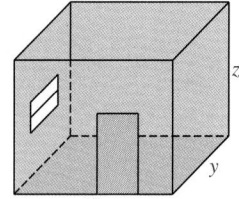

FIGURE FOR 33   FIGURE FOR 34

34. *Cost* In redecorating an office, the cost for new carpeting is five times the cost of wallpapering a wall. Find the dimensions of the largest office that can be redecorated for a fixed cost C (see figure). (*Hint:* Maximize $V = xyz$ subject to $5xy + 2xz + 2yz = C$.)

35. *Cost* A cargo container (in the shape of a rectangular solid) must have a volume of 480 cubic feet. Use Lagrange multipliers to find the dimensions of the container of this size that has a minimum cost, if the bottom will cost $5 per square foot to construct and the sides and top will cost $3 per square foot to construct.

36. *Cost* A manufacturer has an order for 1000 units that can be produced at two locations. Let x_1 and x_2 be the numbers of units produced at the two plants. Find the number of units that should be produced at each plant to minimize the cost if the cost function is given by

$$C = 0.25x_1^2 + 25x_1 + .05x_2^2 + 12x_2.$$

37. *Cost* A manufacturer has an order for 2000 units that can be produced at two locations. Let x_1 and x_2 be the numbers of units produced at the two plants. The cost function is modeled by

$$C = 0.25x_1^2 + 10x_1 + 0.15x_2^2 + 12x_2.$$

Find the number of units that should be produced at each plant to minimize the cost.

38. *Hardy-Weinberg Law* Repeat Exercise 51 in Section 7.5 using Lagrange multipliers—that is, maximize

$$P(p, q, r) = 2pq + 2pr + 2qr$$

subject to the constraint

$$p + q + r = 1.$$

39. *Least-Cost Rule* The production function for a company is

$$f(x, y) = 100x^{0.25}y^{0.75},$$

where x is the number of units of labor and y is the number of units of capital. Suppose that labor costs $48 per unit, capital costs $36 per unit, and management sets a production goal of 20,000 units.

(a) Find the numbers of units of labor and capital needed to meet the production goal while minimizing the cost.

(b) Show that the conditions of part (a) are met when

$$\frac{\text{Marginal productivity of labor}}{\text{Marginal productivity of capital}} = \frac{\text{unit price of labor}}{\text{unit price of capital}}.$$

This proportion is called the **Least-Cost Rule** (or Equimarginal Rule).

40. *Least-Cost Rule* Repeat Exercise 39 for the production function

$$f(x, y) = 100x^{0.6}y^{0.4}.$$

41. *Production* The production function for a company is

$$f(x, y) = 100x^{0.25}y^{0.75},$$

where x is the number of units of labor and y is the number of units of capital. Suppose that labor costs $48 per unit and capital costs $36 per unit. The total cost of labor and capital is limited to $100,000.

(a) Find the maximum production level for this manufacturer.

(b) Find the marginal productivity of money.

(c) Use the marginal productivity of money to find the maximum number of units that can be produced if $125,000 is available for labor and capital.

42. *Production* Repeat Exercise 41 for the production function

$$f(x, y) = 100x^{0.06}y^{0.04}.$$

43. *Bacteria Culture* A microbiologist must prepare a culture medium in which to grow a certain type of bacteria. The percent of salt contained in this medium is $S = 12xyz$, where x, y, and z are the nutrient solutions to be mixed in the medium. For the bacteria to grow, the medium must be 13% salt. The nutrient solutions cost $1, $2, and $3 per liter. How much of each nutrient solution should be used to minimize the cost of the culture medium?

44. *Bacteria Culture* Repeat Exercise 43 for a salt-content model of

$$S = 0.01x^2y^2z^2.$$

45. *Investment Strategy* An investor is considering three different stocks in which to invest $300,000. The average annual dividends for the stocks are

Dow Chemicals (D)   3.9%

CIGNA Corp. (C)   4.5%

Pennzoil Company (P)   4.0%.

The amount invested in Pennzoil must follow the equation

$$3000D - 3000C + P^2 = 0.$$

How much should be invested in each stock to yield a maximum of dividends?

46. *Research Project* Use your school's library or some other reference source to write a paper about two different types of investment options available. Find examples of each type and find data about their dividends for the past 10 years. What are the similarities and differences between the two types?

Least Squares Regression Analysis

Measuring the Accuracy of a Mathematical Model ■
Least Squares Regression Line ■ *Least Squares Regression Quadratic*

Measuring the Accuracy of a Mathematical Model

When seeking a mathematical model to fit real-life data, you should try to find a model that is both as *simple* and as *accurate* as possible. For instance, a simple linear model for the points shown in Figure 7.35 is

$$f(x) = 1.8566x - 5.0246. \qquad \text{\textit{Linear model}}$$

However, Figure 7.36 shows that by choosing a slightly more complicated quadratic model,

$$g(x) = 0.1996x^2 - 0.7281x + 1.3749, \qquad \text{\textit{Quadratic model}}$$

you can obtain significantly greater accuracy.

FIGURE 7.35

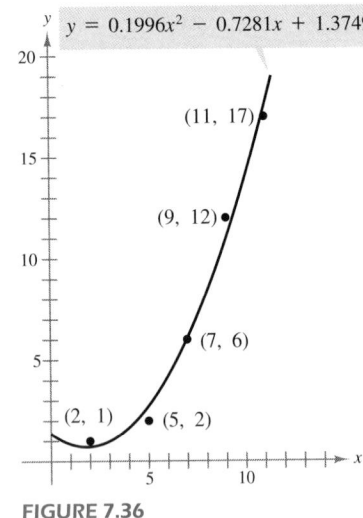

FIGURE 7.36

To measure how well the model $y = f(x)$ fits a collection of points, sum the squares of the differences between the actual y-values and the model's y-values. This sum is called the **sum of the squared errors** and is denoted by S. Graphically, S is the sum of the squares of the vertical distances between the graph of f and the given points in the plane, as shown in Figure 7.37.

$$S = d_1^2 + d_2^2 + d_3^2$$

FIGURE 7.37

Definition of the Sum of the Squared Errors

The **sum of the squared errors** for the model $y = f(x)$ with respect to the points $(x_1, y_1), (x_2, y_2), \ldots, (x_n, y_n)$ is given by

$$S = [f(x_1) - y_1]^2 + [f(x_2) - y_2]^2 + \cdots + [f(x_n) - y_n]^2.$$

EXAMPLE 1 *Finding the Sum of the Squared Errors*

Find the sum of the squared errors for the linear and quadratic models

$$f(x) = 1.8566x - 5.0246. \qquad \textit{Linear model}$$

$$g(x) = 0.1996x^2 - 0.7281x + 1.3749 \qquad \textit{Quadratic model}$$

(see Figures 7.35 and 7.36) with respect to the points

$$(2, 1), (5, 2), (7, 6), (9, 12), (11, 17).$$

Solution

Begin by evaluating each model at the given x-values, as shown in Table 7.1.

TABLE 7.1

x	2	5	7	9	11
Actual y-values	1	2	6	12	17
Linear model, $f(x)$	-1.3114	4.2584	7.9716	11.6848	15.3980
Quadratic model, $g(x)$	0.7171	2.7244	6.0586	10.9896	17.5174

For the linear model f, the sum of the squared errors is

$$S = (-1.3114 - 1)^2 + (4.2584 - 2)^2 + (7.9716 - 6)^2$$
$$+ (11.6848 - 12)^2 + (15.3980 - 17)^2$$
$$\approx 16.9959.$$

Similarly, the sum of the squared errors for the quadratic model g is

$$S = (0.7171 - 1)^2 + (2.7244 - 2)^2 + (6.0586 - 6)^2$$
$$+ (10.9896 - 12)^2 + (17.5174 - 17)^2$$
$$\approx 1.8968.$$

Note In Example 1, note that the sum of the squared errors for the quadratic model is less than the sum of the squared errors for the linear model, which confirms that the quadratic model is a better fit.

Least Squares Regression Line

The sum of the squared errors can be used to determine which of several models is the best fit for a collection of data. In general, if the sum of the squared errors of f is less than the sum of the squared errors of g, then f is said to be a better fit for the data than g. In regression analysis, you consider all possible models of a certain type. The one that is defined to be the best-fitting model is the one with the least sum of the squared errors. Example 2 shows how to use the optimization techniques described in Section 7.5 to find the best-fitting linear model for a collection of data.

EXAMPLE 2 *Finding the Best Linear Model*

Find the values of a and b so that the linear model

$$f(x) = ax + b$$

has a minimum sum of the squared errors for the points

$$(-3, 0), (-1, 1), (0, 2), (2, 3).$$

Solution

The sum of the squared errors is

$$S = [f(x_1) - y_1]^2 + [f(x_2) - y_2]^2 + [f(x_3) - y_3]^2 + [f(x_4) - y_4]^2$$
$$= (-3a + b - 0)^2 + (-a + b - 1)^2 + (b - 2)^2 + (2a + b - 3)^2$$
$$= 14a^2 - 4ab + 4b^2 - 10a - 12b + 14.$$

To find the values of a and b for which S is a minimum, you can use the techniques described in Section 7.5. That is, find the partial derivatives of S.

$$\frac{\partial S}{\partial a} = 28a - 4b - 10 \qquad\qquad \textit{Differentiate with respect to a.}$$

$$\frac{\partial S}{\partial b} = -4a + 8b - 12 \qquad\qquad \textit{Differentiate with respect to b.}$$

Next, set each partial derivative equal to zero.

$$28a - 4b - 10 = 0 \qquad\qquad \textit{Set } \partial S/\partial a \textit{ equal to 0.}$$
$$-4a + 8b - 12 = 0 \qquad\qquad \textit{Set } \partial S/\partial b \textit{ equal to 0.}$$

The solution of this system of linear equations is

$$a = \frac{8}{13} \quad \text{and} \quad b = \frac{47}{26}.$$

Thus, the best-fitting linear model for the given points is

$$f(x) = \frac{8}{13}x + \frac{47}{26}.$$

The graph of this model is shown in Figure 7.38.

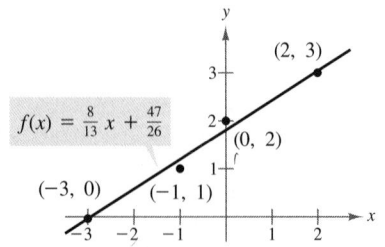

$f(x) = \frac{8}{13}x + \frac{47}{26}$

FIGURE 7.38

The line in Example 2 is called the **least squares regression line** for the given data. The solution shown in Example 2 can be generalized to find a formula for the least squares regression line, as follows. Consider the linear model

$$f(x) = ax + b$$

and the points $(x_1, y_1), (x_2, y_2), \ldots, (x_n, y_n)$. The sum of the squared errors is

$$S = \sum_{i=1}^{n} [f(x_i) - y_i]^2 = \sum_{i=1}^{n} (ax_i + b - y_i)^2.$$

To minimize S, set the partial derivatives $\partial S / \partial a$ and $\partial S / \partial b$ equal to zero and solve for a and b. The results are summarized below.

The Least Squares Regression Line

The **least squares regression line** for the points

$$(x_1, y_1), (x_2, y_2), \ldots, (x_n, y_n)$$

is $y = ax + b$, where

$$a = \frac{n \sum_{i=1}^{n} x_i y_i - \sum_{i=1}^{n} x_i \sum_{i=1}^{n} y_i}{n \sum_{i=1}^{n} x_i^2 - \left(\sum_{i=1}^{n} x_i \right)^2} \quad \text{and} \quad b = \frac{1}{n} \left(\sum_{i=1}^{n} y_i - a \sum_{i=1}^{n} x_i \right).$$

In the formula for the least squares regression line, note that if the x-values are symmetrically spaced about zero, then

$$\sum_{i=1}^{n} x_i = 0$$

and the formulas for a and b simplify to

$$a = \frac{n \sum_{i=1}^{n} x_i y_i}{n \sum_{i=1}^{n} x_i^2} \quad \text{and} \quad b = \frac{1}{n} \sum_{i=1}^{n} y_i.$$

Note also that only the *development* of the least squares regression line involves partial derivatives. The *application* of this formula is simply a matter of computing the values of a and b—a task that is performed much more simply on a calculator or a computer than by hand.

Discovery

Graph the three points $(2, 2)$, $(2, 1)$, and $(2.1, 1.5)$ and visually estimate the least squares regression line for this data. Now use the formulas on this page or a graphing utility to show that the equation of the line is actually $y = 1.5$. In general, the least squares regression line for "nearly vertical" data can be quite unusual. Show that by interchanging the roles of x and y, you can obtain a better linear approximation.

Real
Life

EXAMPLE 3 *Modeling Median Income*

The median income y (in thousands of dollars) for American households from 1981 through 1990 is listed in Table 7.2. Find the least squares regression line for the data and use the result to predict the median income for an American household in 1995. *(Source: U.S. Bureau of Census)*

TABLE 7.2

Year	1981	1982	1983	1984	1985	1986	1987	1988	1989	1990
y	19.1	20.2	21.0	22.4	23.6	24.9	26.1	27.2	28.9	29.9

Solution

Let t represent the year, with $t = 1$ corresponding to 1981. Then, you need to find the linear model that best fits the points

$$(1, 19.1), (2, 20.2), (3, 21.0), (4, 22.4), (5, 23.6),$$
$$(6, 24.9), (7, 26.1), (8, 27.2), (9, 28.9), \text{ and } (10, 29.9).$$

Using a calculator with a built-in least squares program, you can determine that the best-fitting line is

$$y = 1.22t + 17.6.$$

With this model, you can predict the 1995 median income to be

$$y = 1.22(15) + 17.6 = 35.9,$$

or $35,900 per year. This result is shown graphically in Figure 7.39. ■

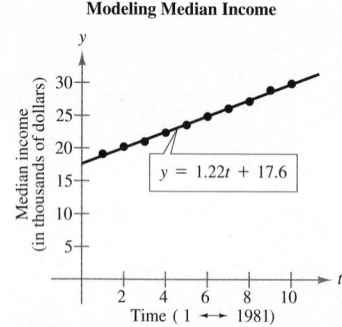

Modeling Median Income

$y = 1.22t + 17.6$

Median income (in thousands of dollars)

Time (1 ↔ 1981)

FIGURE 7.39

▦ TECHNOLOGY

Most graphing utilities have a built-in linear regression program. For instance, the steps for finding the linear regression model in Example 3 on a *TI-81* are shown at the right. Steps for other calculators are given in Appendix D. When you run such a program, the "*r*-value" gives a measure of how well the model fits the data. The closer the value of $|r|$ is to 1, the better the fit. For the data in Example 3, $r \approx 0.9987$, which implies that the model is a very good fit.

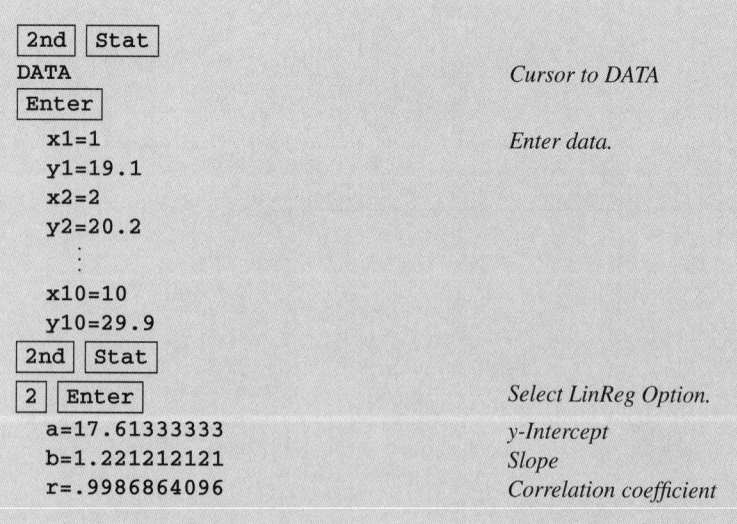

2nd	Stat		
DATA			*Cursor to DATA*
Enter			
x1=1			*Enter data.*
y1=19.1			
x2=2			
y2=20.2			
⋮			
x10=10			
y10=29.9			
2nd	Stat		
2	Enter		*Select LinReg Option.*
a=17.61333333			*y-Intercept*
b=1.221212121			*Slope*
r=.9986864096			*Correlation coefficient*

Least Squares Regression Quadratic

When using regression analysis to model data, remember that the least squares regression line provides only the best *linear* model for a set of data. It does not necessarily provide the best possible model. For instance, in Example 1, you saw that the quadratic model was a better fit than the linear model.

Regression analysis can be performed with many different types of models, such as exponential or logarithmic models. The following development shows how to find the best-fitting quadratic model for a collection of data points. Consider a quadratic model of the form

$$f(x) = ax^2 + bx + c.$$

The sum of the squared errors for this model is

$$S = \sum_{i=1}^{n} [f(x_i) - y_i]^2 = \sum_{i=1}^{n} (ax_i^2 + bx_i + c - y_i)^2.$$

To find the values of a, b, and c that minimize S, set the three partial derivatives, $\partial S/\partial a$, $\partial S/\partial b$, and $\partial S/\partial c$, equal to zero.

$$\frac{\partial S}{\partial a} = \sum_{i=1}^{n} 2x_i^2(ax_i^2 + bx_i + c - y_i) = 0$$

$$\frac{\partial S}{\partial b} = \sum_{i=1}^{n} 2x_i(ax_i^2 + bx_i + c - y_i) = 0$$

$$\frac{\partial S}{\partial c} = \sum_{i=1}^{n} 2(ax_i^2 + bx_i + c - y_i) = 0$$

By expanding this system, you obtain the result given in the following summary.

Least Squares Regression Quadratic

The **least squares regression quadratic** for the points

$$(x_1, y_1), (x_2, y_2), \dots, (x_n, y_n)$$

is $y = ax^2 + bx + c$, where a, b, and c are the solutions of the following system of equations.

$$a\sum_{i=1}^{n} x_i^4 + b\sum_{i=1}^{n} x_i^3 + c\sum_{i=1}^{n} x_i^2 = \sum_{i=1}^{n} x_i^2 y_i$$

$$a\sum_{i=1}^{n} x_i^3 + b\sum_{i=1}^{n} x_i^2 + c\sum_{i=1}^{n} x_i = \sum_{i=1}^{n} x_i y_i$$

$$a\sum_{i=1}^{n} x_i^2 + b\sum_{i=1}^{n} x_i + cn = \sum_{i=1}^{n} y_i$$

EXAMPLE 4 *Modeling the Average Price of a Home*   *Real Life*

The average price y (in thousands of dollars) of a new one-family house in the United States from 1965 to 1991 is listed in Table 7.3. Find the least squares regression quadratic for this data and use the result to predict the average home price for an American household in 1998. *(Source: U.S. Bureau of Census)*

TABLE 7.3

Year	1965	1970	1975	1980	1985	1988	1990	1991
y	21.5	26.6	42.6	76.4	100.8	138.3	149.8	147.2

Solution

Let t represent the year, with $t = 65$ corresponding to 1965. Then, you need to find the quadratic model that best fits the points

$$(65, 21.5), (70, 26.6), (75, 42.6), (80, 76.4),$$
$$(85, 100.8), (88, 138.3), (90, 149.8), \text{ and } (91, 147.2)$$

Using a computer or calculator with a built-in least squares program, you can determine that the best-fitting quadratic model is

$$y = 601.9 - 19.12t + 0.156t^2.$$

With this model, you can predict the 1998 average home price to be

$$y = 601.9 - 19.12(98) + 0.156(98)^2 \approx 226.4,$$

or $226,400 per year. This result is shown graphically in Figure 7.40. ▬

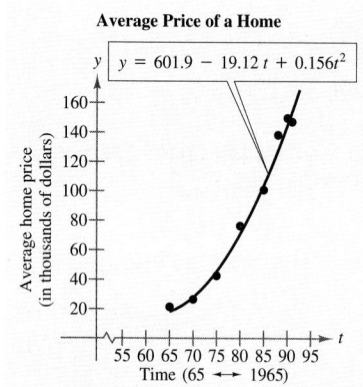

Average Price of a Home

$y = 601.9 - 19.12\,t + 0.156t^2$

Average home price (in thousands of dollars)

Time (65 ↔ 1965)

FIGURE 7.40

Discussion Problem   **Least Squares Regression Analysis**

Most graphing utilities, such as a *TI-81* or *Casio fx-7700g*, have several built-in least squares regression programs. Try entering the points

$$(65, 21.5), (70, 26.6), (75, 42.6), (80, 76.4),$$
$$(85, 100.8), (88, 138.3), (90, 149.8), \text{ and } (91, 147.2)$$

from Example 4 in a graphing utility. Then run one of the regression programs for the points. The quadratic model in Example 4 has a correlation coefficient of $r \approx 0.994$. Can you find a model, such as an exponential model or power model

$$y = ab^x \qquad\qquad \textit{Exponential model}$$
$$y = ax^b, \qquad\qquad \textit{Power model}$$

that has a better correlation coefficient?

Warm Up

The following warm-up exercises involve skills that were covered in earlier sections. You will use these skills in the exercise set for this section.

In Exercises 1 and 2, evaluate the expression.

1. $(2.5 - 1)^2 + (3.25 - 2)^2 + (4.1 - 3)^2$ **2.** $(1.1 - 1)^2 + (2.08 - 2)^2 + (2.95 - 3)^2$

In Exercises 3 and 4, find the partial derivatives of S.

3. $S = a^2 + 6b^2 - 4a - 8b - 4ab + 6$ **4.** $S = 4a^2 + 9b^2 - 6a - 4b - 2ab + 8$

In Exercises 5–10, evaluate the summation.

5. $\displaystyle\sum_{i=1}^{5} i$ **6.** $\displaystyle\sum_{i=1}^{6} 2i$ **7.** $\displaystyle\sum_{i=1}^{4} \frac{1}{i}$ **8.** $\displaystyle\sum_{i=1}^{3} i^2$ **9.** $\displaystyle\sum_{i=1}^{6} (2 - i)^2$ **10.** $\displaystyle\sum_{i=1}^{5} (30 - i^2)$

E X E R C I S E S   7.7

 means that technology can help you solve or check the exercise(s).

In Exercises 1–4, (a) use the method of least squares to find the least squares regression line, and (b) calculate the sum of the squared errors.

1.

2.

3.

4.

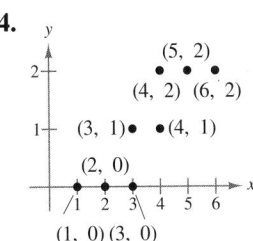

In Exercises 5–14, find the least squares regression line for the given points.

5. $(-2, 0), (-1, 1), (0, 1), (1, 2), (2, 3)$

6. $(-4, -1), (-2, 0), (2, 4), (4, 5)$

7. $(-2, 2), (2, 6), (3, 7)$

8. $(-5, 1), (1, 3), (2, 3), (2, 5)$

9. $(-3, 4), (-1, 2), (1, 1), (3, 0)$

10. $(-10, 10), (-5, 8), (3, 6), (7, 4), (5, 0)$

11. $(0, 0), (1, 1), (3, 4), (4, 2), (5, 5)$

12. $(1, 0), (3, 3), (5, 6)$

13. $(0, 6), (4, 3), (5, 0), (8, -4), (10, -5)$

14. $(5, 2), (0, 0), (2, 1), (7, 4), (10, 6), (12, 6)$

In Exercises 15–18, use partial derivatives to find the values of a and b such that the linear model $f(x) = ax + b$ has a minimum sum of the squared errors for the points.

15. $(-2, -1), (0, 0), (2, 3)$

16. $(-3, 0), (-1, 1), (1, 1), (3, 2)$

17. $(-2, 4), (-1, 1), (0, -1), (1, -3)$

18. $(-5, -3), (-4, -2), (-2, -1), (-1, 1)$

In Exercises 19–22, find the least squares regression quadratic for the given points. Then plot the points and sketch the graph of the least squares quadratic.

19. $(-2, 0), (-1, 0), (0, 1), (1, 2), (2, 5)$

20. $(-4, 5), (-2, 6), (2, 6), (4, 2)$

21. $(1, 0), (2, 1), (3, 7), (4, 13)$

22. $(0, 10), (1, 9), (2, 6), (3, 0)$

In Exercises 23–26, use a computer with a built-in least squares program to find a model (linear and quadratic) for the data. State which model best fits the data.

23. $(-4, 1), (-3, 2), (-2, 2), (-1, 4), (0, 6), (1, 8), (2, 9)$

24. $(-1, -4), (0, -3), (1, -3), (2, 0), (4, 5), (6, 9), (9, 3)$

25. $(0, 769), (1, 677), (2, 601), (3, 543), (4, 489), (5, 411)$

26. $(1, 10.3), (2, 14.2), (3, 18.9), (4, 23.7), (5, 29.1), (6, 35)$

27. *Demand* A store manager wants to know the demand for a product as a function of price. The daily sales for three different prices of the product are listed in the table.

Price, x	$1.00	$1.25	$1.50
Demand, y	450	375	330

(a) Find the least squares regression line for the data.
(b) Estimate the demand when the price is $1.40.
(c) What price will create a demand of 500 products?

28. *Demand* A hardware retailer wants to know the demand for a tool as a function of price. The monthly sales for four different prices of the tool are listed in the table.

Price, x	$25	$30	$35	$40
Demand, y	82	75	67	55

(a) Find the least squares regression line for the data.
(b) Estimate the demand when the price is $32.95.
(c) What price will yield a demand of 83 tools?

29. *Crop Yield* A farmer used four test plots to determine the relationship between wheat yield in bushels per acre and the amount of fertilizer in hundreds of pounds per acre. The results are given in the table.

Fertilizer, x	1.0	1.5	2.0	2.5
Yield, y	35	44	50	56

(a) Find the least squares regression line for the data.
(b) Estimate the yield for a fertilizer application of 160 pounds per acre.

30. *Carcinogen Contamination* After contamination by a carcinogen, people in different geographic regions were assigned an exposure index that represented the degree of contamination. Using the following data, find a least squares regression line to estimate the mortality per 100,000 people for a given exposure.

Exposure, x	1.35	2.67	3.93	5.14	7.43
Mortality, y	118.5	135.2	167.3	197.6	204.7

31. *Infant Mortality* To study the number of infant deaths per 1000 live births in the United States, a medical researcher obtains the following data. *(Source: Department of Health and Human Services)*

Year	1950	1960	1970	1980	1988	1991
Deaths, y	29.2	26.0	20.0	12.6	10.0	9.0

(a) Find the least squares regression line for the data and use it to estimate the number of infant deaths in 1998. Let $t = 0$ represent 1970.
(b) Find the least squares regression quadratic for the data and use it to estimate the number of infant deaths in 1998.

32. *Population Growth* The table gives the approximate world population (in billions) for five different years.

Year	1800	1850	1900	1950	1990
t	-2	-1	0	1	1.8
Population, y	0.9	1.1	1.5	2.4	5.2

(a) During the 1800s, population growth was almost linear. Find a least squares regression line for those years and use it to estimate the population in 1875.
(b) Find a least squares regression quadratic for the data from 1850 through 1990 and use it to estimate the population in the year 2000.
(c) Even though the rate of growth of the population has begun to decline, most demographers believe the population size will pass the eight billion mark sometime in the next 50 years. What do you think?

33. *Engine Design* After developing a new turbocharger for an automobile engine, the following experimental data was obtained for speed in miles per hour at 2-second intervals.

Time, x	0	2	4	6	8	10
Speed, y	0	15	30	50	65	70

(a) Find a least squares regression quadratic for the data.
(b) Use the model to estimate the speed after 5 seconds.

34. *New York Stock Exchange* The daily average of shares traded (in thousands) on the NYSE for selected years is listed in the table. *(Source: New York Stock Exchange)*

Year	1970	1975	1980	1985	1990
Shares	11,564	18,551	44,871	109,169	156,777

(a) Find a least squares regression quadratic that models the data.

(b) Use the model to estimate the number of shares that will be traded in 2000.

In Exercises 35–38, use a graphing utility to find any model that best fits the data points.

35. $(1, 13)$, $(2, 16.5)$, $(4, 24)$, $(5, 28)$, $(8, 39)$, $(11, 50.25)$, $(17, 72)$, $(20, 85)$

36. $(1, 5.5)$, $(3, 7.75)$, $(6, 15.2)$, $(8, 23.5)$, $(11, 46)$, $(15, 110)$

37. $(1, 1.5)$, $(2.5, 8.5)$, $(5, 13.5)$, $(8, 16.7)$, $(9, 18)$, $(20, 22)$

38. $(0, 0.5)$, $(1, 7.6)$, $(3, 60)$, $(4.2, 117)$, $(5, 170)$, $(7.9, 380)$

In Exercises 39–42, plot the points and determine whether the data has positive, negative, or no correlation. Then use a graphing utility to find the value of r and confirm your result. The number r is called the **correlation coefficient.** It is a measure of how well the model fits the data. Correlation coefficients vary between -1 and 1, and the closer $|r|$ is to 1, the better the model.

39. $(1, 4)$, $(2, 6)$, $(3, 8)$, $(4, 11)$, $(5, 13)$, $(6, 15)$

40. $(1, 7.5)$, $(2, 7)$, $(3, 7)$, $(4, 6)$, $(5, 5)$, $(6, 4.9)$

41. $(1, 3)$, $(2, 6)$, $(3, 2)$, $(4, 3)$, $(5, 9)$, $(6, 1)$

42. $(0.5, 2)$, $(0.75, 1.75)$, $(1, 3)$, $(1.5, 3.2)$, $(2, 3.7)$, $(2.6, 4)$

True or False In Exercises 43–46, determine whether the statement is true or false. Explain your reasoning.

43. Data that is modeled by $y = 3.29x - 4.17$ has a negative correlation.

44. Data that is modeled by $y = -0.238x + 25$ has a negative correlation.

45. If the correlation coefficient $r \approx -0.98781$, the model is a good fit.

46. A correlation coefficient of $r \approx 0.201$ implies that the data has no correlation.

$r = 0.981$

Positive Correlation

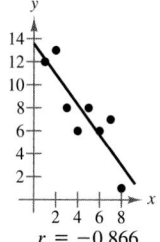

$r = -0.866$

Negative Correlation

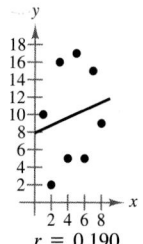

$r = 0.190$

No Correlation

Case Study: Projecting Retail Sales

The Regional Economic Analysis Division (READ) of the Bureau of Economic Analysis is a unit of the U.S. Department of Commerce. READ is responsible for developing and interpreting the regional economic accounts of the United States. READ develops methods for estimating gross state product; maintains and improves regional economic projections; and develops analytical techniques for regional economic impact studies.

READ performs regional economic impact analyses, which estimate the effect of a particular event or change in policy on a state's economy. In these analyses, one of the techniques READ economists use to estimate the mathematical relationships among economic variables is regression analysis.

For instance, READ analysts estimate that the total amount spent in eating and drinking establishments in Ohio depends primarily on the number of adults in the state and their level of disposable (after tax) personal income. When either of these variables increases, there are more dollars spent on eating and drinking in Ohio restaurants and bars.

Using annual data on these three variables for the 1970 to 1991 period, READ has used multiple least squares regression methods, a variation of the least squares regression line discussed in Section 7.7, to determine that the actual relationship is:

$$\text{Sales} = -8092.1 + 0.0385 \cdot \text{Income} + 1.1815 \cdot \text{Population}$$

where:

■ Sales is retail sales of Ohio eating and drinking establishments, in millions of dollars,

■ Income is disposable personal income of Ohioans, in millions of dollars, and

■ Population is the adult (18+) population of Ohio, in thousands.

This regression equation shows that an increase of \$1 million in Ohio income will result in \$38,500 more spent in Ohio's Red Lobsters, TGIFridays, and other restaurants and bars ($0.0385 \cdot \$1,000,000$). Similarly, if the state's adult population increases by a thousand, there will be \$1,181,500 more spent in Ohio's eating and drinking places.

In the business world, it is useful to have an idea of the impact that forces outside a firm's control will have on its business. If projections of Ohio income and population are available, this equation will give an expected value for retail sales in eating and drinking establishments for future years. These types of equations could be quite useful to firms in their planning process. The relationship estimated above could give guidance to those in the restaurant business, as well as to firms that supply restaurants with food, drink, and equipment.

Actual and Estimated Sales

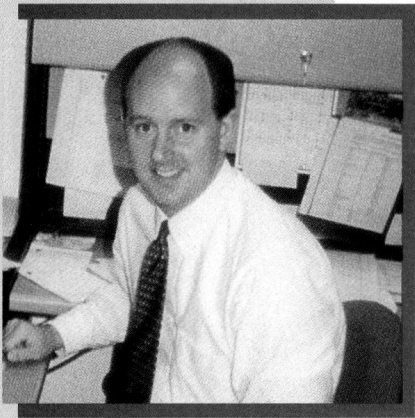

Clifford H. Woodruff is a regional economist for the Regional Economic Analysis Division of the Bureau of Economic Analysis ■

What Would You Do?

1. If you were in the business of manufacturing and selling restaurant equipment such as commercial refrigerators, stoves, tables, and chairs in Ohio, what would you do if economists were predicting a recession for the coming year? A recession typically means higher unemployment and lower income levels. Suppose a predicted recession is expected to lead to a 7% overall reduction in income of Ohioans for a certain year while population remains constant. Use the regression equation to show how this decrease will affect the sales figure that would normally be predicted for this year.

2. If Ohio universities plan to substantially increase their admissions of out-of-state students, such that another 5000 students would be arriving in the state next fall, what effect would you expect this to have on the restaurant business? If you ran a restaurant near a college campus, which of the following scenarios would you prefer (if all other factors remained the same) and why? Make a mathematical argument and explain all calculations.

(A) An increase in out-of-state admissions of 8000 students

OR

(B) An increase in out-of-state admissions of 4500 where each student is given a $50 grant (considered as income) as a reward for enrolling in Ohio.

3. Why are both the population and income variables needed in this equation? Why couldn't we simply use one or the other to generate the estimates of sales? Can you think of other variables that affect restaurant sales, which might be added to the regression equation to improve its ability to predict?

Double Integrals and Area in the Plane

Double Integrals ■ *Finding Area with a Double Integral*

Double Integrals

In Section 7.4, you learned that it is meaningful to differentiate functions of several variables by differentiating with respect to one variable at a time while holding the other variables constant. It should not be surprising to learn that you can *integrate* functions of two or more variables using a similar procedure. For instance, if you are given the partial derivative

$$f_x(x, y) = 2xy, \qquad \text{\textit{Partial with respect to x}}$$

then, by holding y constant, you can integrate with respect to x to obtain

$$\int f_x(x, y)\, dx = f(x, y) = x^2 y + C(y).$$

This procedure is called **partial integration with respect to x.** Note that the "constant of integration" $C(y)$ is assumed to be a function of y, because y is fixed during integration with respect to x. Similarly, if you are given the partial derivative

$$f_y(x, y) = x^2 + 2, \qquad \text{\textit{Partial with respect to y}}$$

then, by holding x constant, you can integrate with respect to y to obtain

$$\int f_y(x, y)\, dy = f(x, y) = x^2 y + 2y + C(x).$$

In this case, the "constant of integration" $C(x)$ is assumed to be a function of x, because x is fixed during integration with respect to y.

To evaluate a definite integral of a function of two or more variables, you can apply the Fundamental Theorem of Calculus to one variable while holding the others constant, as follows.

$$\int_1^{2y} 2xy\, dx = x^2 y \Big]_1^{2y} = (2y)^2 y - (1)^2 y = 4y^3 - y.$$

x is the variable of integration and y is fixed.

Replace x by the limits of integration.

The result is a function of y.

Note that you omit the constant of integration, just as you do for a definite integral of a function of one variable.

EXAMPLE 1 *Finding Partial Integrals*

a. $\int_{1}^{x} (2x^2 y^{-2} + 2y)\, dy = \left[\dfrac{-2x^2}{y} + y^2\right]_{1}^{x}$ Hold x constant.

$$= \left(\dfrac{-2x^2}{x} + x^2\right) - \left(\dfrac{-2x^2}{1} + 1\right)$$

$$= 3x^2 - 2x - 1$$

b. $\int_{y}^{5y} \sqrt{x - y}\, dx = \left[\dfrac{2}{3}(x - y)^{3/2}\right]_{y}^{5y}$ Hold y constant.

$$= \dfrac{2}{3}[(5y - y)^{3/2} - (y - y)^{3/2}]$$

$$= \dfrac{16}{3}y^{3/2} \quad = \dfrac{8}{3}y^{3/2} \;\; ?$$

In Example 1a, note that the definite integral defines a function of x and can *itself* be integrated. An "integral of an integral" is called a **double integral.** With a function of two variables, there are two types of double integrals.

$$\int_{a}^{b}\int_{g_1(x)}^{g_2(x)} f(x, y)\, dy\, dx = \int_{a}^{b}\left[\int_{g_1(x)}^{g_2(x)} f(x, y)\, dy\right] dx$$

$$\int_{a}^{b}\int_{g_1(y)}^{g_2(y)} f(x, y)\, dx\, dy = \int_{a}^{b}\left[\int_{g_1(y)}^{g_2(y)} f(x, y)\, dx\right] dy$$

Notice that the difference between these two types is the order in which the integration is performed, $dy\, dx$ or $dx\, dy$.

EXAMPLE 2 *Evaluating a Double Integral*

$$\int_{1}^{2}\int_{0}^{x} (2xy + 3)\, dy\, dx = \int_{1}^{2}\left[\int_{0}^{x} (2xy + 3)\, dy\right] dx$$

$$= \int_{1}^{2}\left[xy^2 + 3y\right]_{0}^{x} dx$$

$$= \int_{1}^{2} (x^3 + 3x)\, dx$$

$$= \left[\dfrac{x^4}{4} + \dfrac{3x^2}{2}\right]_{1}^{2}$$

$$= \left(\dfrac{2^4}{4} + \dfrac{3(2^2)}{2}\right) - \left(\dfrac{1^4}{4} + \dfrac{3(1^2)}{2}\right)$$

$$= \dfrac{33}{4}$$

⊞ TECHNOLOGY

A symbolic integration utility, such as *Derive, Maple,* or *Mathematica,* can be used to evaluate double integrals. To do this, you need to enter the integrand, then integrate twice—once with respect to one of the variables and then with respect to the other variable. For instance, when *Derive* is used to evaluate the integral in Example 2, you obtain the following.

1: **2xy + 3**

2: $\int_{0}^{x}$ **(2xy + 3) dy**

3: $\int_{1}^{2}\int_{0}^{x}$ **(2xy + 3) dy dx**

4: $\dfrac{33}{4}$

Finding Area with a Double Integral

One of the simplest applications of a double integral is finding the area of a plane region. For instance, consider the region R that is bounded by

$$a \leq x \leq b \quad \text{and} \quad g_1(x) \leq y \leq g_2(x).$$

Using the techniques described in Section 5.5, you know that the area of R is

$$\int_a^b [g_2(x) - g_1(x)]\, dx.$$

This same area is also given by the double integral

$$\int_a^b \int_{g_1(x)}^{g_2(x)} dy\, dx$$

because

$$\int_a^b \int_{g_1(x)}^{g_2(x)} dy\, dx = \int_a^b \left[y \right]_{g_1(x)}^{g_2(x)} dx$$

$$= \int_a^b [g_2(x) - g_1(x)]\, dx.$$

Figure 7.41 shows the two basic types of plane regions whose areas can be determined by a double integral.

Note In Figure 7.41, note that the horizontal or vertical orientation of the narrow rectangle indicates the order of integration. The "outer" variable of integration always corresponds to the width of the rectangle. Notice also that the outer limits of integration for a double integral are constant, whereas the inner limits may be functions of the outer variable.

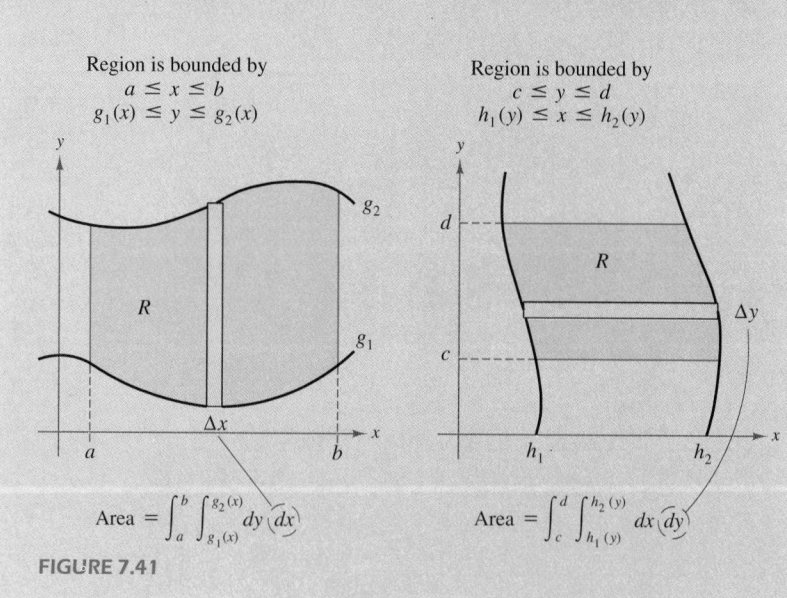

Determining Area in the Plane by Double Integrals

Region is bounded by
$$a \leq x \leq b$$
$$g_1(x) \leq y \leq g_2(x)$$

Region is bounded by
$$c \leq y \leq d$$
$$h_1(y) \leq x \leq h_2(y)$$

$$\text{Area} = \int_a^b \int_{g_1(x)}^{g_2(x)} dy\, dx$$

$$\text{Area} = \int_c^d \int_{h_1(y)}^{h_2(y)} dx\, dy$$

FIGURE 7.41

EXAMPLE 3 *Finding Area by a Double Integral*

Use a double integral to find the area of the rectangular region shown in Figure 7.42.

Solution

The bounds for x are $1 \le x \le 5$ and the bounds for y are $2 \le y \le 4$. Therefore, the area of the region is

$$\int_1^5 \int_2^4 dy\, dx = \int_1^5 \left[y \right]_2^4 dx \qquad \text{\textit{Integrate with respect to } y.}$$

$$= \int_1^5 (4 - 2)\, dx \qquad \text{\textit{Apply Fundamental Theorem.}}$$

$$= \int_1^5 2\, dx \qquad \text{\textit{Simplify.}}$$

$$= \left[2x \right]_1^5 \qquad \text{\textit{Integrate with respect to } x.}$$

$$= 10 - 2 \qquad \text{\textit{Apply Fundamental Theorem.}}$$

$$= 8. \qquad \text{\textit{Simplify.}}$$

You can confirm this by noting that the rectangle is two units by four units.

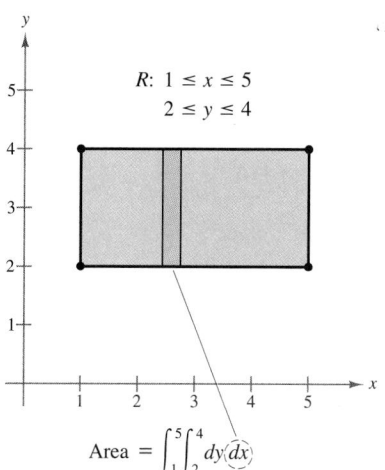

$R: 1 \le x \le 5$
$\quad\ 2 \le y \le 4$

$\text{Area} = \int_1^5 \int_2^4 dy\, dx$

FIGURE 7.42

EXAMPLE 4 *Finding Area by a Double Integral*

Use a double integral to find the area of the region bounded by the graphs of $y = x^2$ and $y = x^3$.

Solution

As shown in Figure 7.43, the two graphs intersect when $x = 0$ and $x = 1$. Choosing x to be the outer variable, the bounds for x are $0 \le x \le 1$ and the bounds for y are $x^3 \le y \le x^2$. This implies that the area of the region is

$$\int_0^1 \int_{x^3}^{x^2} dy\, dx = \int_0^1 \left[y \right]_{x^3}^{x^2} dx \qquad \text{\textit{Integrate with respect to } y.}$$

$$= \int_0^1 (x^2 - x^3)\, dx \qquad \text{\textit{Apply Fundamental Theorem.}}$$

$$= \left[\frac{x^3}{3} - \frac{x^4}{4} \right]_0^1 \qquad \text{\textit{Integrate with respect to } x.}$$

$$= \frac{1}{3} - \frac{1}{4} \qquad \text{\textit{Apply Fundamental Theorem.}}$$

$$= \frac{1}{12}. \qquad \text{\textit{Simplify.}}$$

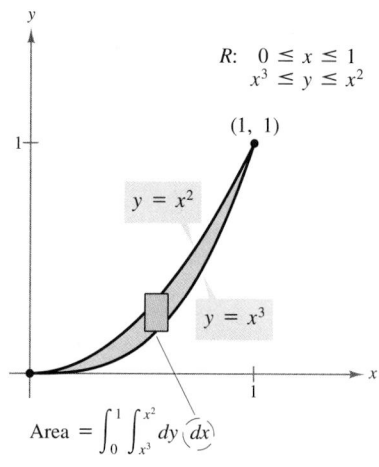

$R: \ 0 \le x \le 1$
$\quad\ x^3 \le y \le x^2$

$(1, 1)$

$y = x^2$

$y = x^3$

$\text{Area} = \int_0^1 \int_{x^3}^{x^2} dy\, dx$

FIGURE 7.43

In setting up double integrals, the most difficult task is likely to be determining the correct limits of integration. This can be simplified by making a sketch of the region R and identifying the appropriate bounds for x and y.

EXAMPLE 5 *Changing the Order of Integration*

For the double integral

$$\int_0^2 \int_{y^2}^4 dx \, dy,$$

a. sketch the region R whose area is represented by the integral,
b. rewrite the integral so that x is the outer variable, and
c. show that both orders of integration yield the same value.

Solution

a. From the limits of integration, you know that

$$y^2 \leq x \leq 4, \qquad\qquad \textit{Variable bounds for x}$$

which means that the region R is bounded on the left by the parabola $x = y^2$ and on the right by the line $x = 4$. Furthermore, because

$$0 \leq y \leq 2, \qquad\qquad \textit{Constant bounds for y}$$

you know that the region lies above the x-axis, as shown in Figure 7.44.

b. If you interchange the order of integration so that x is the outer variable, then x will have constant bounds of integration given by $0 \leq x \leq 4$. Solving for y in the equation $x = y^2$ implies that the bounds for y are $0 \leq y \leq \sqrt{x}$, as shown in Figure 7.45. Thus, with x as the outer variable, the integral can be written as

$$\int_0^4 \int_0^{\sqrt{x}} dy \, dx.$$

c. Both integrals yield the same value.

$$\int_0^2 \int_{y^2}^4 dx \, dy = \int_0^2 \Big[x\Big]_{y^2}^4 dy = \int_0^2 (4 - y^2) \, dy = \left[4y - \frac{y^3}{3}\right]_0^2 = \frac{16}{3}$$

$$\int_0^4 \int_0^{\sqrt{x}} dy \, dx = \int_0^4 \Big[y\Big]_0^{\sqrt{x}} dx = \int_0^4 \sqrt{x} \, dx = \left[\frac{2}{3} x^{3/2}\right]_0^4 = \frac{16}{3}$$

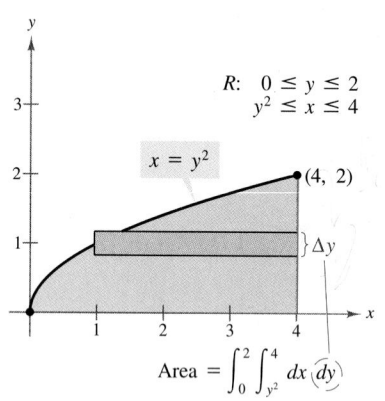

$R: \quad 0 \leq y \leq 2$
$\qquad y^2 \leq x \leq 4$

$x = y^2$

$(4, 2)$

$\} \Delta y$

$\text{Area} = \int_0^2 \int_{y^2}^4 dx \, (dy)$

FIGURE 7.44

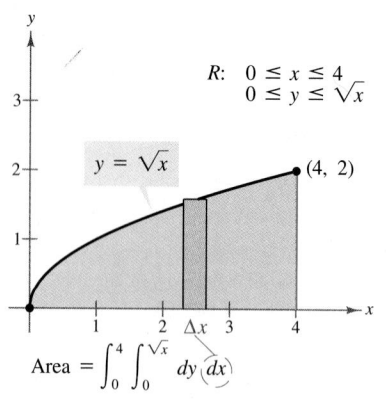

$R: \quad 0 \leq x \leq 4$
$\qquad 0 \leq y \leq \sqrt{x}$

$y = \sqrt{x}$

$(4, 2)$

Δx

$\text{Area} = \int_0^4 \int_0^{\sqrt{x}} dy \, (dx)$

FIGURE 7.45

To designate a double integral or an area of a region without specifying a particular order of integration, you can use the symbol

$$\int_R \int dA,$$

where $dA = dx \, dy$ or $dA = dy \, dx$.

EXAMPLE 6 *Finding Area by a Double Integral*

Use a double integral to calculate the area denoted by

$$\int_R \int dA,$$

where R is the region bounded by $y = x$ and $y = x^2 - x$.

Solution

Begin by sketching the region R, as shown in Figure 7.46. From the sketch, you can see that vertical rectangles of width dx are more convenient than horizontal ones. Therefore, x is the outer variable of integration and its constant bounds are $0 \le x \le 2$. This implies that the bounds for y are $x^2 - x \le y \le x$, and the area is given by

$$\int_R \int dA = \int_0^2 \int_{x^2-x}^x dy\,dx$$

$$= \int_0^2 \Big[y\Big]_{x^2-x}^x dx$$

$$= \int_0^2 [x - (x^2 - x)]\,dx$$

$$= \int_0^2 (2x - x^2)\,dx$$

$$= \Big[x^2 - \frac{x^3}{3}\Big]_0^2$$

$$= 4 - \frac{8}{3}$$

$$= \frac{4}{3}.$$

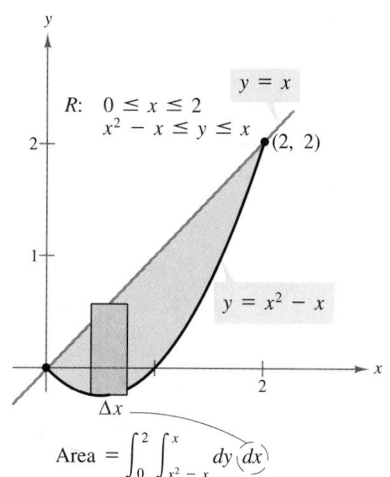

R: $0 \le x \le 2$
$x^2 - x \le y \le x$

$y = x$

$(2, 2)$

$y = x^2 - x$

Δx

Area $= \int_0^2 \int_{x^2-x}^x dy\,(dx)$

FIGURE 7.46

As you are working the exercises for this section, you should be aware that the primary uses of double integrals will be discussed in Section 7.9. We have introduced double integrals by way of areas in the plane so that you can gain practice in finding the limits of integration. When setting up a double integral, remember that your first step should be to sketch the region R. After doing this, you have two choices of integration orders: $dx\,dy$ or $dy\,dx$.

Discussion Problem   **Sketching Regions in the Plane**

Sketch the region represented by the double integral.

a. $\int_0^4 \int_0^y dx\,dy$ **b.** $\int_0^4 \int_0^x dy\,dx$ **c.** $\int_0^4 \int_{x^2}^x dy\,dx$

Warm Up   The following warm-up exercises involve skills that were covered in earlier sections. You will use these skills in the exercise set for this section.

In Exercises 1–6, evaluate the definite integral.

1. $\displaystyle\int_0^1 dx$

2. $\displaystyle\int_1^4 2x^2\,dx$

3. $\displaystyle\int_1^2 (x^3 - 2x + 4)\,dx$

4. $\displaystyle\int_1^2 \frac{2}{7x^2}\,dx$

5. $\displaystyle\int_0^2 \frac{2x}{x^2+1}\,dx$

6. $\displaystyle\int_0^2 xe^{x^2+1}\,dx$

In Exercises 7–10, sketch the region bounded by the graphs of the equations.

7. $y = x, \ y = 0, \ x = 0, \ x = 3$

8. $y = x, \ y = 3, \ y = 0, \ x = 0$

9. $y = 4 - x^2, \ y = 0, \ x = 0, \ x = 2$

10. $y = x^2, \ y = 4x, \ x = 0, \ x = 4$

EXERCISES 7.8 means that technology can help you solve or check the exercise(s).

In Exercises 1–10, evaluate the partial integral.

1. $\displaystyle\int_0^x (2x - y)\,dy$

2. $\displaystyle\int_x^{x^2} \frac{y}{x}\,dy$

3. $\displaystyle\int_1^{2y} \frac{y}{x}\,dx$

4. $\displaystyle\int_0^{e^y} y\,dx$

5. $\displaystyle\int_0^{\sqrt{9-x^2}} x^2 y\,dy$

6. $\displaystyle\int_{x^2}^{\sqrt{x}} (x^2 + y^2)\,dy$

7. $\displaystyle\int_{e^y}^y \frac{y\ln x}{x}\,dx$

8. $\displaystyle\int_{-\sqrt{1-y^2}}^{\sqrt{1-y^2}} (x^2+y^2)\,dx$

9. $\displaystyle\int_0^{x^3} ye^{-y/x}\,dy$

10. $\displaystyle\int_y^3 \frac{xy}{\sqrt{x^2+1}}\,dx$

In Exercises 11–24, evaluate the double integral.

11. $\displaystyle\int_0^2 \int_0^1 (x - y)\,dy\,dx$

12. $\displaystyle\int_0^2 \int_0^2 (6 - x^2)\,dy\,dx$

13. $\displaystyle\int_0^4 \int_0^3 xy\,dy\,dx$

14. $\displaystyle\int_0^1 \int_0^x \sqrt{1 - x^2}\,dy\,dx$

15. $\displaystyle\int_0^1 \int_0^{\sqrt{1-y^2}} (x+y)\,dx\,dy$

16. $\displaystyle\int_0^2 \int_{3y^2-6y}^{2y-y^2} 3y\,dx\,dy$

17. $\displaystyle\int_1^2 \int_0^4 (x^2 - 2y^2 + 1)\,dx\,dy$

18. $\displaystyle\int_0^1 \int_y^{2y} (1 + 2x^2 + 2y^2)\,dx\,dy$

19. $\displaystyle\int_0^2 \int_0^{\sqrt{1-y^2}} -5xy\,dx\,dy$

20. $\displaystyle\int_0^4 \int_0^x \frac{2}{(x+1)(y+1)}\,dy\,dx$

21. $\displaystyle\int_0^2 \int_0^{4-x^2} x^3\,dy\,dx$

22. $\displaystyle\int_0^a \int_0^{a-x} (x^2 + y^2)\,dy\,dx$

23. $\displaystyle\int_0^\infty \int_0^\infty e^{-(x+y)/2}\,dy\,dx$

24. $\displaystyle\int_0^\infty \int_0^\infty xye^{-(x^2+y^2)}\,dx\,dy$

In Exercises 25–32, sketch the region R whose area is given by the double integral. Then change the order of integration and show that both orders yield the same area.

25. $\displaystyle\int_0^1 \int_0^2 dy\,dx$

26. $\displaystyle\int_1^2 \int_2^4 dx\,dy$

27. $\displaystyle\int_0^1 \int_{2y}^2 dx\,dy$

28. $\displaystyle\int_0^4 \int_0^{\sqrt{x}} dy\,dx$

29. $\displaystyle\int_0^2 \int_{x/2}^1 dy\,dx$

30. $\displaystyle\int_0^4 \int_{\sqrt{x}}^2 dy\,dx$

31. $\displaystyle\int_0^1 \int_{y^2}^{\sqrt[3]{y}} dx\,dy$

32. $\displaystyle\int_{-2}^2 \int_0^{4-y^2} dx\,dy$

In Exercises 33 and 34, evaluate the double integral. Note that it is necessary to change the order of integration.

33. $\displaystyle\int_0^3 \int_y^3 e^{x^2} dx\,dy$

34. $\displaystyle\int_0^2 \int_x^2 e^{-y^2} dy\,dx$

In Exercises 35–40, use a double integral to find the area of the specified region.

35.

36.

37.

38.

39.

40.

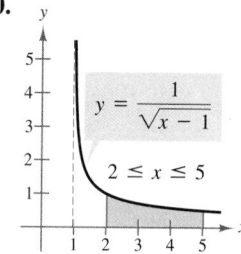

In Exercises 41–46, use a double integral to find the area of the region bounded by the graphs of the equations.

41. $y = 25 - x^2,\ y = 0$

42. $y = x^{3/2},\ y = x$

43. $5x - 2y = 0,\ x + y = 3,\ y = 0$

44. $xy = 9,\ y = x,\ y = 0,\ x = 9$

45. $y = x,\ y = 2x,\ x = 2$

46. $y = x^2 + 2x + 1,\ y = 3(x + 1)$

In Exercises 47–52, use a symbolic integration utility to evaluate the double integral.

47. $\displaystyle\int_0^1 \int_0^2 e^{-x^2-y^2} dx\,dy$

48. $\displaystyle\int_0^3 \int_0^{x^2} \sqrt{x}\sqrt{1+x}\,dy\,dx$

49. $\displaystyle\int_1^2 \int_0^x e^{xy}\,dy\,dx$

50. $\displaystyle\int_1^2 \int_y^{2y} \ln(x + y)\,dx\,dy$

51. $\displaystyle\int_0^1 \int_x^1 \sqrt{1-x^2}\,dy\,dx$

52. $\displaystyle\int_0^4 \int_0^y \frac{2}{(x+1)(y+1)}\,dx\,dy$

True or False In Exercises 53 and 54, determine whether the statement is true or false. Explain your reasoning.

53. Changing the order of integration will sometimes change the value of a double integral.

54. $\displaystyle\int_2^5 \int_1^6 x\,dy\,dx = \int_1^6 \int_2^5 x\,dx\,dy$

Applications of Double Integrals

Volume of a Solid Region ■
Average Value of a Function over a Region

Volume of a Solid Region

In Section 7.8, you used double integrals as an alternative way to find the area of a plane region. In this section, you will study the primary uses of double integrals—to find the volume of a solid region and to find the average value of a function.

Consider a function $z = f(x, y)$ that is continuous and nonnegative over a region R. Let S be the solid region that lies between the xy-plane and the surface

$$z = f(x, y) \qquad \text{Surface lying above the } xy\text{-plane}$$

directly above the region R, as shown in Figure 7.47. You can find the volume of S by integrating $f(x, y)$ over the region R.

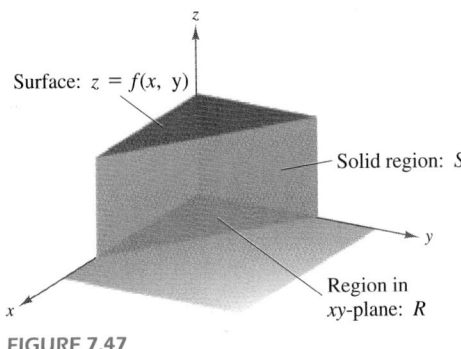

FIGURE 7.47

Determining Volume by Double Integrals

If R is a bounded region in the xy-plane and f is continuous and nonnegative over R, then the **volume of the solid** region between the surface $z = f(x, y)$ and R is given by the double integral

$$\int_R \int f(x, y)\, dA,$$

where $dA = dx\, dy$ or $dA = dy\, dx$.

EXAMPLE 1 *Finding the Volume of a Solid*

Find the volume of the solid region bounded in the first octant by the plane

$$z = 2 - x - 2y.$$

Solution

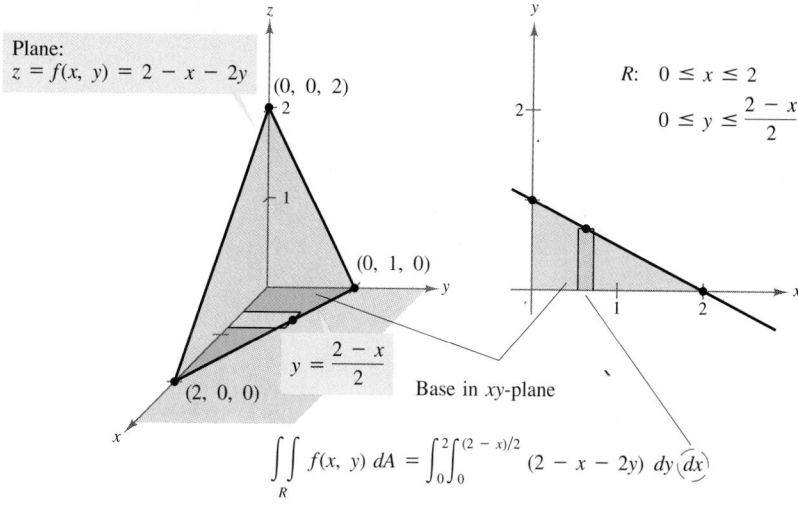

Plane:
$z = f(x, y) = 2 - x - 2y$
(0, 0, 2)

(0, 1, 0)

$y = \dfrac{2 - x}{2}$

(2, 0, 0)   Base in *xy*-plane

R: $0 \le x \le 2$
$0 \le y \le \dfrac{2 - x}{2}$

$$\iint_R f(x, y)\, dA = \int_0^2 \int_0^{(2-x)/2} (2 - x - 2y)\, dy\, dx$$

FIGURE 7.48

Note Example 1 uses $dy\,dx$ as the order of integration. Try using the other order, $dx\,dy$, as indicated in Figure 7.49, to find the volume of the region.

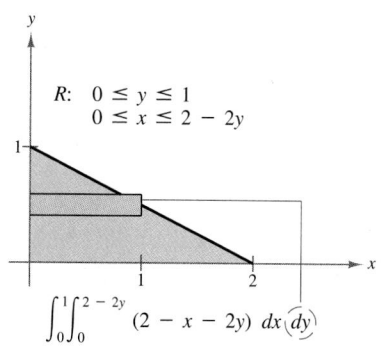

R: $0 \le y \le 1$
$0 \le x \le 2 - 2y$

$$\int_0^1 \int_0^{2-2y} (2 - x - 2y)\, dx\, dy$$

FIGURE 7.49

To set up the double integral for the volume, it is helpful to sketch both the solid and the region R in the xy-plane. In Figure 7.48, you can see that the region R is bounded by the lines $x = 0$, $y = 0$, and $y = \frac{1}{2}(2 - x)$. One way to set up the double integral is to choose x as the outer variable. With that choice, the constant bounds for x are $0 \le x \le 2$ and the variable bounds for y are $0 \le y \le \frac{1}{2}(2 - x)$. Thus, the volume of the solid region is

$$V = \int_0^2 \int_0^{(2-x)/2} (2 - x - 2y)\, dy\, dx$$

$$= \int_0^2 \left[(2 - x)y - y^2 \right]_0^{(2-x)/2} dx$$

$$= \int_0^2 \left[(2 - x)\left(\frac{1}{2}\right)(2 - x) - \left[\frac{1}{2}(2 - x)\right]^2 \right] dx$$

$$= \frac{1}{4} \int_0^2 (2 - x)^2\, dx$$

$$= \left[-\frac{1}{12}(2 - x)^3 \right]_0^2$$

$$= \frac{2}{3}.$$

In Example 1, the order of integration was arbitrary. Although the example used x as the outer variable, you could just as easily have used y as the outer variable. The next example describes a situation in which one order of integration is more convenient than the other.

EXAMPLE 2 *Comparing Different Orders of Integration*

Find the volume under the surface $f(x, y) = e^{-x^2}$, bounded by the xz-plane and the planes $y = x$ and $x = 1$, as shown in Figure 7.50.

Solution

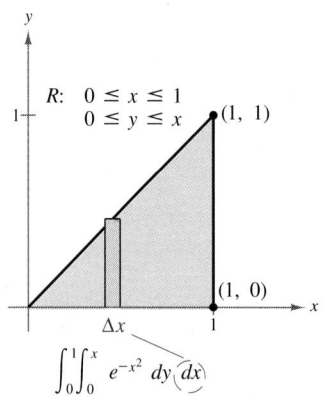

$$\int_0^1 \int_0^x e^{-x^2} \, dy \, dx$$

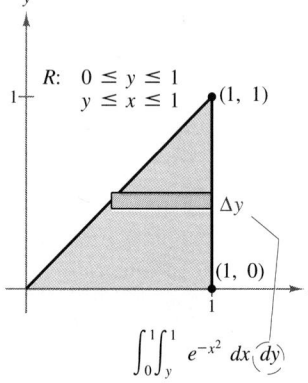

$$\int_0^1 \int_y^1 e^{-x^2} \, dx \, dy$$

FIGURE 7.51

In the xy-plane, the bounds of region R are the lines $y = 0$, $x = 1$, and $y = x$. The two possible orders of integration are indicated in Figure 7.51. If you attempt to evaluate the two double integrals shown in the figure, you will discover that the one on the right involves finding the antiderivative of e^{-x^2}, which you know is not an elementary function. The integral on the left, however, can be easily evaluated, as follows.

$$
\begin{aligned}
V &= \int_0^1 \int_0^x e^{-x^2} \, dy \, dx \\
&= \int_0^1 \left[e^{-x^2} y \right]_0^x dx \\
&= \int_0^1 x e^{-x^2} \, dx \\
&= \left[-\frac{1}{2} e^{-x^2} \right]_0^1 \\
&= -\frac{1}{2} \left(\frac{1}{e} - 1 \right)
\end{aligned}
$$

FIGURE 7.50

Guidelines for Finding the Volume of a Solid

1. Write the equation of the surface in the form $z = f(x, y)$ and sketch the solid region.
2. Sketch the region R in the xy-plane and determine the order and limits of integration.
3. Evaluate the double integral

$$\int_R \int f(x, y) \, dA$$

using the order and limits determined in the second step.

The first step above suggests that you sketch the three-dimensional solid region. This is a good suggestion, but, it is not always feasible and is not as important as making a sketch of the two-dimensional region R.

EXAMPLE 3 *Finding the Volume of a Solid*

Find the volume of the solid bounded above by the surface

$$f(x, y) = 6x^2 - 2xy$$

and below by the plane region R shown in Figure 7.52.

Solution

Because the region R is bounded by the parabola $y = 3x - x^2$ and the line $y = x$, the limits for y are $x \le y \le 3x - x^2$. The limits for x are $0 \le x \le 2$, and the volume of the solid is

$$V = \int_0^2 \int_x^{3x-x^2} (6x^2 - 2xy) \, dy \, dx$$

$$= \int_0^2 \left[6x^2 y - xy^2 \right]_x^{3x-x^2} dx$$

$$= \int_0^2 [(18x^3 - 6x^4 - 9x^3 + 6x^4 - x^5) - (6x^3 - x^3)] \, dx$$

$$= \int_0^2 (4x^3 - x^5) \, dx$$

$$= \left[x^4 - \frac{x^6}{6} \right]_0^2$$

$$= \frac{16}{3}.$$

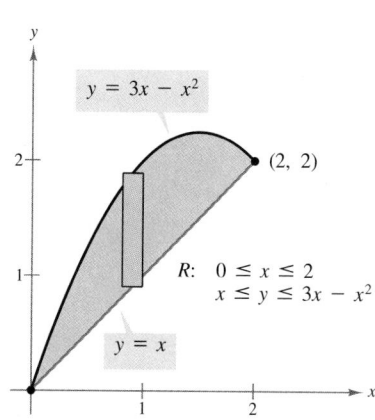

$y = 3x - x^2$

(2, 2)

$R: \quad 0 \le x \le 2$
$\quad\quad x \le y \le 3x - x^2$

$y = x$

FIGURE 7.52

A *population density function* $p = f(x, y)$ is a model that describes density (in people per square unit) of a region. To find the population of a region R, evaluate the double integral

$$\int_R \int f(x, y) \, dA.$$

EXAMPLE 4 *Finding a City's Population*

The population density (in people per square mile) of the city shown in Figure 7.53 can be modeled by

$$f(x, y) = \frac{50,000}{x + |y| + 1},$$

where x and y are measured in miles. Approximate the city's population. What is the city's average population density?

Solution

Because the model involves the absolute value of y, it follows that the population density is symmetrical about the x-axis. Thus, the population in the first quadrant is equal to the population in the fourth quadrant. This means that you can find the total population by doubling the population in the first quadrant.

$$
\begin{aligned}
\text{Population} &= 2\int_0^4 \int_0^5 \frac{50,000}{x + y + 1} \, dy \, dx \\
&= 100,000 \int_0^4 \left[\ln(x + y + 1) \right]_0^5 dx \\
&= 100,000 \int_0^4 [\ln(x + 6) - \ln(x + 1)] \, dx \\
&= 100,000 \Bigg[(x + 6) \ln(x + 6) - (x + 6) \\
&\qquad\qquad - (x + 1) \ln(x + 1) + (x + 1) \Bigg]_0^4 \\
&= 100,000 \Bigg[(x + 6) \ln(x + 6) - (x + 1) \ln(x + 1) - 5 \Bigg]_0^4 \\
&= 100,000[10 \ln(10) - 5 \ln(5) - 5 - 6 \ln(6) + 5] \\
&\approx 422,810 \ \text{people}
\end{aligned}
$$

Thus, the city's population is about 422,810. Because the city covers a region 4 miles wide and 10 miles long, its area is 40 square miles. Thus, the average population density is

$$\text{Average population density} = \frac{422,810}{40}$$

$$\approx 10,570 \text{ people per square mile.}$$

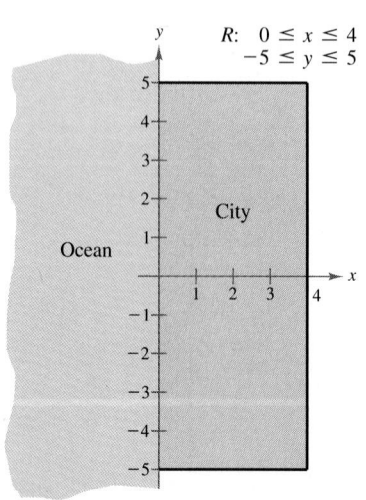

R: $0 \le x \le 4$
      $-5 \le y \le 5$

City

Ocean

FIGURE 7.53

Average Value of a Function over a Region

Average Value of a Function over a Region

If f is integrable over the plane region R with area A, then its **average value** over R is

$$\text{Average value} = \frac{1}{A} \int_R \int f(x, y) \, dA.$$

Real Life

EXAMPLE 5 *Finding the Average Profit*

A manufacturer determines that the profit for selling x units of one product and y units of a second product is

$$P = -(x - 200)^2 - (y - 100)^2 + 5000.$$

The weekly sales for product 1 vary between 150 and 200 units and the weekly sales for product 2 vary between 80 and 100 units. Estimate the average weekly profit for the two products.

Solution

Because $150 \leq x \leq 200$ and $80 \leq y \leq 100$, you can estimate the weekly profit to be the average of the profit function over the rectangular region shown in Figure 7.54. Because the area of this rectangular region is $(50)(20) = 1000$, it follows that the average profit V is

$$V = \frac{1}{1000} \int_{150}^{200} \int_{80}^{100} [-(x - 200)^2 - (y - 100)^2 + 5000] \, dy \, dx$$

$$= \frac{1}{1000} \int_{150}^{200} \left[-(x - 200)^2 y - \frac{(y - 100)^3}{3} + 5000y \right]_{80}^{100} dx$$

$$= \frac{1}{1000} \int_{150}^{200} \left[-20(x - 200)^2 - \frac{292,000}{3} \right] dx$$

$$= \frac{1}{3000} \left[-20(x - 200)^3 + 292,000x \right]_{150}^{200}$$

$$\approx \$4033.$$

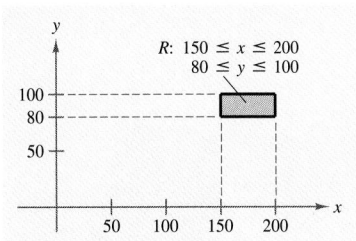

R: $150 \leq x \leq 200$
$80 \leq y \leq 100$

FIGURE 7.54

Discussion Problem   ### Finding an Average Value

What is the average value of the constant function $f(x, y) = 100$ over a region R? Explain your reasoning.

Warm Up

The following warm-up exercises involve skills that were covered in earlier sections. You will use these skills in the exercise set for this section.

In Exercises 1–4, sketch the region that is described.

1. $0 \le x \le 2,\ 0 \le y \le 1$

2. $1 \le x \le 3,\ 2 \le y \le 3$

3. $0 \le x \le 4,\ 0 \le y \le 2x - 1$

4. $0 \le x \le 2,\ 0 \le y \le x^2$

In Exercises 5–10, evaluate the double integral.

5. $\displaystyle\int_0^1 \int_1^2 dy\, dx$

6. $\displaystyle\int_0^3 \int_1^3 dx\, dy$

7. $\displaystyle\int_0^1 \int_0^x x\, dy\, dx$

8. $\displaystyle\int_0^4 \int_1^y y\, dx\, dy$

9. $\displaystyle\int_1^3 \int_x^{x^2} 2\, dy\, dx$

10. $\displaystyle\int_0^1 \int_x^{-x^2+2} dy\, dx$

EXERCISES 7.9

means that technology can help you solve or check the exercise(s).

In Exercises 1–6, sketch the region of integration and evaluate the double integral.

1. $\displaystyle\int_0^2 \int_0^1 (3x + 4y)\, dy\, dx$

2. $\displaystyle\int_{-a}^a \int_{-\sqrt{a^2-x^2}}^{\sqrt{a^2-x^2}} dy\, dx$

3. $\displaystyle\int_0^1 \int_y^{\sqrt{y}} x^2 y^2\, dx\, dy$

4. $\displaystyle\int_0^6 \int_{y/2}^3 (x + y)\, dx\, dy$

5. $\displaystyle\int_0^1 \int_0^{\sqrt{1-x^2}} y\, dy\, dx$

6. $\displaystyle\int_0^2 \int_0^{4-x^2} xy^2\, dy\, dx$

In Exercises 7–10, set up the integral for both orders of integration and use the more convenient order to evaluate the integral over the region R.

Integral	Region R
7. $\displaystyle\int_R \int xy\, dA$	Rectangle with vertices at $(0, 0)$, $(0, 5)$, $(3, 5)$, $(3, 0)$
8. $\displaystyle\int_R \int \frac{y}{x^2 + y^2}\, dA$	Triangle bounded by $y = x$, $y = 2x$, $x = 2$
9. $\displaystyle\int_R \int \frac{y}{1 + x^2}\, dA$	Region bounded by $y = 0$, $y = \sqrt{x}$, $x = 4$
10. $\displaystyle\int_R \int x\, dA$	Semicircle bounded by $y = \sqrt{25 - x^2}$ and $y = 0$

In Exercises 11 and 12, evaluate the double integral. Note that it is necessary to change the order of integration.

11. $\displaystyle\int_0^1 \int_{y/2}^{1/2} e^{-x^2}\, dx\, dy$

12. $\displaystyle\int_0^{\ln 10} \int_{e^x}^{10} \frac{1}{\ln y}\, dy\, dx$

In Exercises 13–24, use a double integral to find the volume of the specified solid.

13.

14.

15.

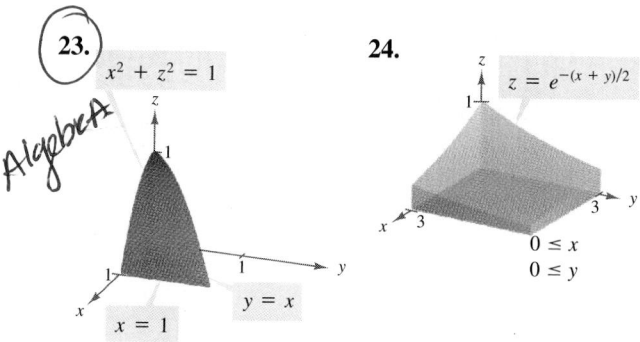

$z = 8 - x - y$

$y = x$ $y = 3$

16.

$z = 6$

$y = x$

$x = 2$

17.

$2x + 3y + 4z = 12$

18.

$x + y + z = 1$

19.

$z = 1 - xy$

$y = x$ $y = 1$

20.

$z = 4 - y^2$

$y = x$ $y = 2$

21.

$z = 4 - x^2 - y^2$

$-1 \le x \le 1$
$-1 \le y \le 1$

22.

$z = \dfrac{1}{(x + 1)^2 (y + 1)^2}$

$0 \le x$
$0 \le y$

23.

$x^2 + z^2 = 1$

$y = x$

$x = 1$

24.

$z = e^{-(x + y)/2}$

$0 \le x$
$0 \le y$

In Exercises 25–28, use a double integral to find the volume of the solid bounded by the graphs of the equations.

25. $z = xy, z = 0, y = 0, y = 4, x = 0, x = 1$

26. $z = x, z = 0, y = x, y = 0, x = 0, x = 4$

27. $z = x^2, z = 0, x = 0, x = 2, y = 0, y = 4$

28. $z = x + y, x^2 + y^2 = 4$ (first octant)

In Exercises 29–32, find the average value of $f(x, y)$ over the region R.

Integral	*Region R*
29. $f(x, y) = x$	Rectangle with vertices $(0, 0)$, $(4, 0)$, $(4, 2)$, $(0, 2)$
30. $f(x, y) = xy$	Rectangle with vertices $(0, 0)$, $(4, 0)$, $(4, 2)$, $(0, 2)$
31. $f(x, y) = x^2 + y^2$	Square with vertices $(0, 0)$, $(2, 0)$, $(2, 2)$, $(0, 2)$
32. $f(x, y) = e^{x+y}$	Triangle with vertices $(0, 0)$, $(0, 1)$, $(1, 1)$

33. *Average Revenue* A company sells two products whose demand functions are

$$x_1 = 500 - 3p_1 \quad \text{and} \quad x_2 = 750 - 2.4p_2.$$

Therefore, the total revenue is given by

$$R = x_1 p_1 + x_2 p_2.$$

Estimate the average revenue if the price p_1 varies between $50 and $75 and the price p_2 varies between $100 and $150.

34. *Average Weekly Profit* A firm's weekly profit in marketing two products is given by

$$P = 192x_1 + 576x_2 - x_1^2 - 5x_2^2 - 2x_1x_2 - 5000,$$

where x_1 and x_2 represent the numbers of units of each product sold weekly. Estimate the average weekly profit if x_1 varies between 40 and 50 units and x_2 varies between 45 and 50 units.

Chapter Summary and Study Tips

After studying this chapter, you should have acquired the following skills. The exercise numbers are keyed to the Review Exercises that begin on page 540. Answers to odd–numbered Review Exercises are given in the back of the text.

■ Plot points in space. (*Section 7.1*)   Review Exercises 1, 2

■ Find the distance between two points in space. (*Section 7.1*)   Review Exercises 3, 4

$$d = \sqrt{(x_2 - x_1)^2 + (y_2 - y_1)^2 + (z_2 - z_1)^2}$$

■ Find the midpoints of line segments in space. (*Section 7.1*)   Review Exercises 5, 6

$$\text{Midpoint} = \left(\frac{x_1 + x_2}{2}, \frac{y_1 + y_2}{2}, \frac{z_1 + z_2}{2} \right)$$

■ Write the standard forms of the equations of spheres. (*Section 7.1*)   Review Exercises 7–10

$$(x - h)^2 + (y - k)^2 + (z - l)^2 = r^2$$

■ Find the centers and radii of spheres. (*Section 7.1*)   Review Exercises 11, 12

■ Sketch the coordinate plane traces of spheres. (*Section 7.1*)   Review Exercises 13, 14

■ Sketch planes in space. (*Section 7.2*)   Review Exercises 15–18

■ Classify quadric surfaces in space. (*Section 7.2*)   Review Exercises 19–26

■ Evaluate functions of several variables. (*Section 7.3*)   Review Exercises 27, 28

■ Find the domains and ranges of functions of several variables. (*Section 7.3*)   Review Exercises 29, 30

■ Sketch the level curves of functions of two variables. (*Section 7.3*)   Review Exercises 31–34

■ Use functions of several variables to answer questions about real life. (*Section 7.3*)   Review Exercises 35–38

■ Find the first partial derivatives of functions of several variables. (*Section 7.4*)   Review Exercises 39–48

$$\frac{\partial z}{\partial x} = \lim_{\Delta x \to 0} \frac{f(x + \Delta x, y) - f(x, y)}{\Delta x}$$

$$\frac{\partial z}{\partial y} = \lim_{\Delta y \to 0} \frac{f(x, y + \Delta y) - f(x, y)}{\Delta y}$$

■ Find the slopes of surfaces in the *x*- or *y*-direction. (*Section 7.4*)   Review Exercises 49–52

■ Find the second partial derivatives of functions of several variables. (*Section 7.4*)   Review Exercises 53–56

■ Use partial derivatives to answer questions about real life. (*Section 7.4*)   Review Exercises 57, 58

■ Find the relative extrema of functions of two variables. (*Section 7.5*)   Review Exercises 59–66

■ Use relative extrema to answer questions about real life. (*Section 7.5*)   Review Exercises 67, 68

■ Use Lagrange multipliers to find extrema of functions of several variables. (*Section 7.6*)   Review Exercises 69–74

■ Use Lagrange multipliers to answer questions about real life. (*Section 7.6*)   Review Exercises 75, 76

*Several student study aids are available with this text. The *Student Solutions Guide* includes detailed solutions to all odd-numbered exercises, as well as practice chapter tests with answers. The *Graphics Calculator Guide* offers instructions on the use of a variety of graphing calculators and computer graphing software. The *Brief Calculus TUTOR* includes additional examples for selected exercises in the text.

■ Find the least squares regression lines, $y = ax + b$, for data. (*Section 7.7*)   Review Exercises 77, 78

$$a = \frac{n\sum_{i=1}^{n} x_i y_i - \sum_{i=1}^{n} x_i \sum_{i=1}^{n} y_i}{n\sum_{i=1}^{n} x_i^2 - \left(\sum_{i=1}^{n} x_i\right)^2}, \qquad b = \frac{1}{n}\left(\sum_{i=1}^{n} y_i - a\sum_{i=1}^{n} x_i\right)$$

■ Use least squares regression lines to model real-life data. (*Section 7.7*)   Review Exercises 79, 80

■ Find the least squares regression quadratics for data. (*Section 7.7*)   Review Exercises 81, 82

■ Evaluate double integrals. (*Section 7.8*)   Review Exercises 83–86

■ Use double integrals to find the areas of regions. (*Section 7.8*)   Review Exercises 87–90

■ Use double integrals to find the volumes of solids. (*Section 7.9*)   Review Exercises 91, 92

$$\text{Volume} = \int_R \int f(x, y)\, dA$$

■ Use double integrals to find the average values of real-life models. (*Section 7.9*)   Review Exercises 93, 94

$$\text{Average value} = \frac{1}{A}\int_R \int f(x, y)\, dA$$

■ **Comparing Two Dimensions with Three Dimensions**   Many of the formulas and techniques in this chapter are generalizations of formulas and techniques used in earlier chapters in the text. Here are several examples.

Two-Dimensional Coordinate System	*Three-Dimensional Coordinate System*
Distance Formula $d = \sqrt{(x_2 - x_1)^2 + (y_2 - y_1)^2}$	*Distance Formula* $d = \sqrt{(x_2 - x_1)^2 + (y_2 - y_1)^2 + (z_2 - z_1)^2}$
Midpoint Formula $\text{Midpoint} = \left(\dfrac{x_1 + x_2}{2}, \dfrac{y_1 + y_2}{2}\right)$	*Midpoint Formula* $\text{Midpoint} = \left(\dfrac{x_1 + x_2}{2}, \dfrac{y_1 + y_2}{2}, \dfrac{z_1 + z_2}{2}\right)$
Equation of Circle $(x - h)^2 + (y - k)^2 = r^2$	*Equation of Sphere* $(x - h)^2 + (y - k)^2 + (z - l)^2 = r^2$
Equation of Line $ax + by = c$	*Equation of Plane* $ax + by + cz = d$
Derivative of $y = f(x)$ $\dfrac{dy}{dx} = \lim_{\Delta x \to 0} \dfrac{f(x + \Delta x) - f(x)}{\Delta x}$	*Partial derivative of $z = f(x, y)$* $\dfrac{\partial z}{\partial x} = \lim_{\Delta x \to 0} \dfrac{f(x + \Delta x, y) - f(x, y)}{\Delta x}$
Area of Region $A = \displaystyle\int_a^b f(x)\, dx$	*Volume of Region* $V = \displaystyle\int_R \int f(x, y)\, dA$

Review Exercises

 means that technology can help you solve or check the exercise(s).

In Exercises 1 and 2, plot the points.

1. $(2, -1, 4)$, $(-1, 3, -3)$ **2.** $(1, -2, -3)$, $(-4, -3, 5)$

In Exercises 3 and 4, find the distance between the two points.

3. $(0, 0, 0)$, $(2, 5, 9)$ **4.** $(-4, 1, 5)$, $(1, 3, 7)$

In Exercises 5 and 6, find the midpoint of the line segment joining the two points.

5. $(2, 6, 4)$, $(-4, 2, 8)$ **6.** $(5, 0, 7)$, $(-1, -2, 9)$

In Exercises 7–10, find the standard form of the equation of the sphere.

7. Center: $(0, 1, 0)$; Radius: 5

8. Center: $(4, -5, 3)$; Radius: 10

9. Diameter endpoints: $(3, 4, 0)$, $(5, 8, 2)$

10. Diameter endpoints: $(-2, 5, 1)$, $(4, -3, 3)$

In Exercises 11 and 12, find the center and radius of the sphere.

11. $x^2 + y^2 + z^2 + 4x - 2y - 8z + 5 = 0$

12. $x^2 + y^2 + z^2 + 4y - 10z - 7 = 0$

In Exercises 13 and 14, sketch the *xy*-trace of the sphere.

13. $(x + 2)^2 + (y - 1)^2 + (z - 3)^2 = 25$

14. $(x - 1)^2 + (y + 3)^2 + (z - 6)^2 = 72$

In Exercises 15–18, find the intercepts and sketch the graph of the plane.

15. $x + 2y + 3z = 6$ **16.** $2y + z = 4$

17. $6x + 3y - 6z = 12$ **18.** $4x - y + 2z = 8$

In Exercises 19–26, identify the surface.

19. $x^2 + y^2 + z^2 - 2x + 4y - 6z + 5 = 0$

20. $16x^2 + 16y^2 - 9z^2 = 0$

21. $x^2 + \dfrac{y^2}{16} + \dfrac{z^2}{9} = 1$ **22.** $-x^2 + \dfrac{y^2}{16} + \dfrac{z^2}{9} = 1$

23. $z = \dfrac{x^2}{9} + y^2$ **24.** $-4x^2 + y^2 + z^2 = 4$

25. $z = \sqrt{x^2 + y^2}$ **26.** $z = 9x + 3y - 5$

In Exercises 27 and 28, find the function values.

27. $f(x, y) = xy^2$

(a) $f(2, 3)$ (b) $f(0, 1)$

(c) $f(-5, 7)$ (d) $f(-2, -4)$

28. $f(x, y) = \dfrac{x^2}{y}$

(a) $f(6, 9)$ (b) $f(8, 4)$

(c) $f(t, 2)$ (d) $f(r, r)$

In Exercises 29 and 30, describe the region R in the *xy*-plane that corresponds to the domain of the function. Then find the range of the function.

29. $f(x, y) = \sqrt{1 - x^2 - y^2}$ **30.** $f(x, y) = \dfrac{1}{x + y}$

In Exercises 31–34, describe the level curves of the function. Sketch the level curves for the given *c*-values.

31. $z = 10 - 2x - 5y$, $c = 0, 2, 4, 5, 10$

32. $z = \sqrt{9 - x^2 - y^2}$, $c = 0, 1, 2, 3$

33. $z = (xy)^2$, $c = 1, 4, 9, 12, 16$

34. $z = 2e^{xy}$, $c = 1, 2, 3, 4, 5$

35. *Average Precipitation* The contour map shown below represents the average yearly precipitation for Iowa. (*Source: U.S. National Oceanic and Atmospheric Administration*)

(a) Discuss the use of color to represent the level curves.

(b) Which part of Iowa receives the most precipitation?

(c) Which part of Iowa receives the least precipitation?

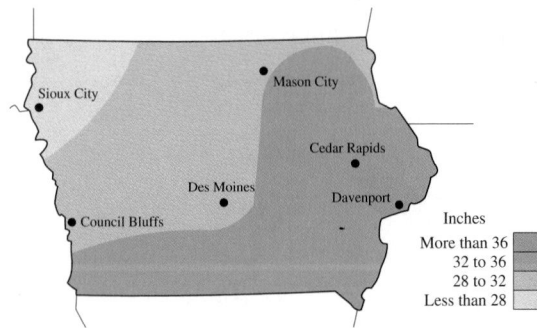

36. *Population Density*   The contour map below represents the population density of New York. (*Source: U.S. Bureau of Census*)

(a) Discuss the use of color to represent the level curves.
(b) Do the level curves correspond to equally spaced population densities?
(c) Describe how to obtain a more detailed contour map.

Persons per
square mile
More than 250
100 to 250
50 to 100
Less than 50

37. *Equation of Exchange*   Economists use an equation of exchange to express the relation among money, prices, and business transactions. This equation can be written as

$$P = \frac{MV}{T},$$

where M is the money supply, V is the velocity of circulation, T is the total number of transactions, and P is the price level. Find P when $M = \$2500$, $V = 6$, and $T = 6000$.

38. *Biomechanics*   The Froude number F, defined as

$$F = \frac{v^2}{gl},$$

where v represents velocity, g represents gravitational acceleration, and l represents stride length, is an example of a "similarity criterion." Find the Froude number of a rabbit whose velocity is 2 meters/sec, gravitational acceleration is 3 m/sec², and stride length is 0.75 meters.

In Exercises 39–48, find the first partial derivatives.

39. $f(x, y) = x^2y + 3xy + 2x - 5y$

40. $f(x, y) = 5x^2 + 4xy - 3y^2$

41. $z = 6x^2\sqrt{y} + 3\sqrt{xy} - 7xy$

42. $z = (xy + 2x + 4y)^2$

43. $f(x, y) = \ln(2x + 3y)$

44. $f(x, y) = \ln\sqrt{2x + 3y}$

45. $f(x, y) = x^2e^y - y^2e^x$

46. $f(x, y) = x^2e^{-2y}$

47. $w = xyz^2$

48. $w = xyz + 2xy - 9xz + 4yz - y^2z + 4z^2$

In Exercises 49–52, find the slope of the surface at the indicated point in (a) the x-direction and (b) the y-direction.

49. $z = 3x - 4y + 9$, $(3, 2, 10)$

50. $z = 4x^2 - y^2$, $(2, 4, 0)$

51. $z = 8 - x^2 - y^2$, $(1, 2, 3)$

52. $z = x^2 - y^2$, $(5, -4, 9)$

In Exercises 53–56, find all second partial derivatives.

53. $f(x, y) = x^3 - 4xy^2 + y^3$

54. $f(x, y) = \dfrac{y}{x + y}$

55. $f(x, y) = \sqrt{64 - x^2 - y^2}$

56. $f(x, y) = x^2e^{-y^2}$

57. *Marginal Cost*   A company manufactures two models of skis: cross-country skis and downhill skis. The cost function for producing x cross-country skis and y downhill skis is

$$C = 15(xy)^{1/3} + 99x + 139y + 2293.$$

Find the marginal costs when $x = 250$ and $y = 175$.

58. *Marginal Revenue*   At a baseball stadium, souvenir caps are sold at two locations. If x_1 and x_2 are the numbers of baseball caps sold at location 1 and location 2, respectively, then the total revenue for the caps is

$$R = 15x_1 + 16x_2 - \frac{1}{10}x_1^2 - \frac{1}{10}x_2^2 - \frac{1}{100}x_1x_2.$$

Given that $x_1 = 50$ and $x_2 = 40$, find the marginal revenue at location 1 and at location 2.

In Exercises 59–66, find any critical points and relative extrema of the function.

59. $f(x, y) = x^2 + 2xy + y^2$

60. $f(x, y) = x^3 - 3xy + y^2$

61. $f(x, y) = x^2 + 6xy + 3y^2 + 6x + 8$

62. $f(x, y) = x + y^2 - e^x$

63. $f(x, y) = x^3 + y^2 - xy$

64. $f(x, y) = y^2 + xy + 3y - 2x + 5$

65. $f(x, y) = x^3 + y^3 - 3x - 3y + 2$

66. $f(x, y) = y^2 - x^2$

67. *Revenue* A company manufactures and sells two products. The demand functions for the products are

$$p_1 = 100 - x_1 \quad \text{and} \quad p_2 = 200 - 0.5x_2.$$

(a) Find the total revenue functions for x_1 and x_2.
(b) Find x_1 and x_2 so that the revenue is maximized.
(c) What is the maximum revenue?

68. *Profit* A company manufactures a product at two locations. The costs of manufacturing x_1 units at plant 1 and x_2 units at plant 2 are

$$C_1 = 0.03x_1^2 + 4x_1 + 300$$
$$C_2 = 0.05x_2^2 + 7x_2 + 175.$$

If the product sells for $10 per unit, find x_1 and x_2 so that the profit, $P = 10(x_1 + x_2) - C_1 - C_2$, is maximized.

In Exercises 69–74, locate any extrema of the functions by using Lagrange multipliers.

69. $f(x, y) = x^2 y$, Constraint: $x + 2y = 2$

70. $f(x, y) = x^2 + y^2$, Constraint: $x + y = 4$

71. $f(x, y, z) = xyz$, Constraint: $x + 2y + z - 4 = 0$

72. $f(x, y, z) = xz + yz$, Constraint: $x + y + z = 6$

73. $f(x, y, z) = x^2 + y^2 + z^2$, Constraints: $x + z = 6$,
$y + z = 8$

74. $f(x, y, z) = xyz$, Constraints: $x + y + z = 32$,
$x - y + z = 0$

75. *Maximum Production Level* The production function for a manufacturer is

$$f(x, y) = 4x + xy + 2y.$$

Assume that the total amount available for labor x and capital y is $2000 and that units of labor and capital cost $20 and $4, respectively. Find the maximum production level for this manufacturer.

76. *Minimum Cost* A manufacturer has an order for 1500 units that can be produced at two locations. Let x_1 and x_2 be the numbers of units produced at the two locations. Find the number that should be produced at each to meet the order and minimize cost if the cost function is

$$C = 0.20x_1^2 + 10x_1 + 0.15x_2^2 + 12x_2.$$

In Exercises 77 and 78, (a) use the method of least squares to find the least squares regression line and (b) calculate the sum of the squared errors.

77. $(-2, -3), (-1, -1), (1, 2), (3, 2)$

78. $(-3, -1), (-2, -1), (0, 0), (1, 1), (2, 1)$

79. *Biotechnology* The biotechnology industry, which includes genetic engineering, has produced over 27 new wonder drugs. The biotechnology industry product sales (in billions of dollars) from 1990 to 1993 are listed in the table. *(Source: Ernst and Young)*

Year	1990	1991	1992	1993
Sales	2.9	4.0	5.9	7.0

(a) Use a graphing utility with a built-in least squares regression program to find a linear model for the data.
(b) Use the model to estimate the product sales of the biotechnology industry in the year 2000.

80. *Federal Employees* The per capita federal government employment decreased steadily from 1966 to 1992. The table lists the number of federal employees per 10,000 people for selected years. *(Source: U.S. Bureau of Census)*

Year	1966	1971	1976	1981	1986	1992
Employees	111	105	102	96	92	89

(a) Find a least squares regression line to model the data.
(b) Use the model to estimate when the number of federal employees per 10,000 will be 80.

In Exercises 81 and 82, find the least squares regression quadratic for the given points. Plot the points and sketch the least squares regression quadratic.

81. $(-1, 9), (0, 7), (1, 5), (2, 6), (4, 23)$

82. $(0, 10), (2, 9), (3, 7), (4, 4), (5, 0)$

In Exercises 83–86, evaluate the double integral.

83. $\displaystyle\int_0^1 \int_0^{1+x} (3x + 2y)\, dy\, dx$

84. $\displaystyle\int_{-2}^2 \int_0^4 (x - y^2)\, dx\, dy$

85. $\displaystyle\int_1^2 \int_1^{2y} \frac{x}{y^2}\,dx\,dy$

86. $\displaystyle\int_0^4 \int_0^{\sqrt{16-x^2}} 2x\,dy\,dx$

In Exercises 87–90, use a double integral to find the area of the region.

87.

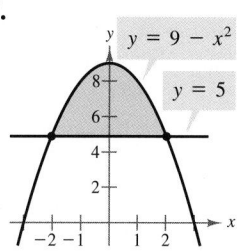

$y = 9 - x^2$

$y = 5$

88.

$y = \dfrac{4}{x}$

89.

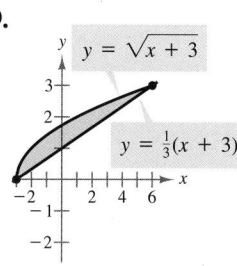

$y = \sqrt{x} + 3$

$y = \frac{1}{3}(x + 3)$

90.

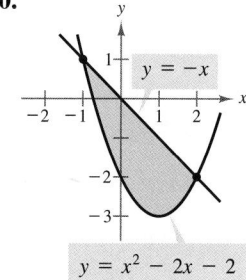

$y = -x$

$y = x^2 - 2x - 2$

91. Find the volume of the solid bounded by the graphs of $z = (xy)^2$, $z = 0$, $y = 0$, $y = 4$, $x = 0$, and $x = 4$.

92. Find the volume of the solid bounded by the graphs of $z = x + y$, $z = 0$, $x = 0$, $x = 3$, $y = x$, and $y = 0$.

93. *Average Elevation*   In a triangular coastal area, the elevation in miles above sea level at the point (x, y) is $f(x, y) = 0.25 - 0.025x - 0.01y$, where x and y are measured in miles (see figure). Find the average elevation of the triangular area.

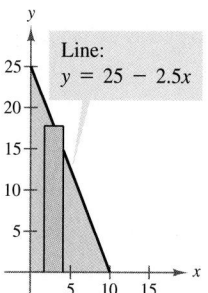

Line:
$y = 25 - 2.5x$

94. *Real Estate Value*   The average value of real estate (in dollars per square foot) for a rectangular section of a city is given by $f(x, y) = 2.5x^{3/2}y^{3/4}$. The section of the city is shown in the figure below. Find the average value of real estate for this section.

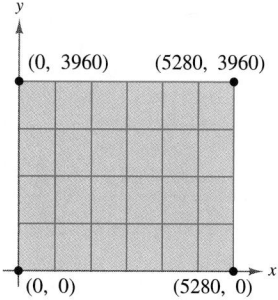

$(0, 3960)$ $(5280, 3960)$

$(0, 0)$ $(5280, 0)$

Sample Post-Graduation Exam Questions

The following questions were taken from certified public accountant (CPA) exams, graduate management admission tests (GMAT), graduate records exams (GRE), actuarial exams, or college-level academic skills tests (CLAST). The answers to the questions are given in the back of the book.

1. What is the derivative of $f(x, y) = y^2(x + y)^3$ with respect to y?
   (a) $6y(x + y)^2$ (b) $y(x + y)^2(2x + 5y)$
   (c) $3y^2(x + y)^2$ (d) $y(x + y)^2(5x + 2y)$

2. Let $f(x, y) = x^2 + y^2 + 6x - 2y + 4$. At which point does f have a relative minimum?
   (a) $(-3, 1, -13)$ (b) $(-3, 1, -6)$
   (c) $(3, 1, -2)$ (d) $(-3, -1, -2)$

For Questions 3–4, use the following excerpts from the 1993 Tax Rate Schedules.

Schedule X–Use if your filing status is **Single**

If the amount on Form 1040, line 37, is over—	But not over—	Enter on Form 1040, line 38	of the amount over—
$0	$22,100	.........15%	$0
22,100	53,500	3,315.00 + 28%	22,100
53,500	115,000	12,107.00 + 31%	53,500
115,100	250,000	31,172.00 + 36%	115,000
250,000	....	79,772.00 + 39.6%	250,000

Schedule Y-1–Use if your filing status is **Married filing jointly** or **Qualifying widow(er)**

If the amount on Form 1040, line 37, is over—	But not over—	Enter on Form 1040, line 38	of the amount over—
$0	$36,900	.........15%	$0
36,900	89,150	5,535.00 + 28%	36,900
89,150	140,000	20,165.00 + 31%	89,150
140,000	250,000	35,928.50 + 36%	140,000
250,000	....	75,528.50 + 39.6%	250,000

3. The tax for a married couple filing jointly whose amount on Form 1040, line 37 is $125,480 is
   (a) $11,262.30   (b) $47,801.50
   (c) $31,427.30   (d) $34,944.80

4. The tax for a single whose amount on Form 1040, line 37 is $1,000,000 is
   (a) $372,528.50   (b) $297,000
   (c) $368,028.50   (d) $376,772

5. If x, y, and z are chosen from the three numbers $\frac{1}{3}$, -2, and 4, what is the largest possible value of the expression $[(x^2 + z)]/(y^2)$?
   (a) 126   (b) 42   (c) 24   (d) 72

6. If $xz = 4y$, then $(x^3)/2$ equals
   (a) $\dfrac{2y^3}{z^3}$ (b) $\dfrac{16y^2}{z^3}$ (c) $\dfrac{32y^3}{z^3}$ (d) $\dfrac{64y^3}{z^3}$

7. Mave Co. calculated the following ratios for one of its profit centers:
   Gross margin 31%, Return on Sales 26%, Capital Turnover .5 times
   What is Mave's return on investment for this profit center?
   (a) 8.5%   (b) 13%   (c) 15.5%   (d) 26%

$$\int_{\infty}^{\infty} \frac{1}{\sigma\sqrt{2\pi}} \; e^{-(x-\mu)^2/2\sigma^2} \, dx = 1$$

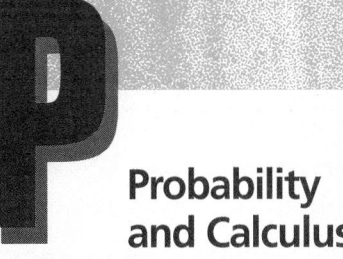

P

Probability and Calculus

P.1 Discrete Probability
P.2 Continuous Random Variables
P.3 Expected Value and Variance
Chapter Summary and Study Tips
Review Exercises

The study of modern probability is often traced to the French mathematician Blaise Pascal. In 1654, Pascal was asked why it was unprofitable to bet even money that double sixes would turn up at least once in 24 tosses of two dice. Pascal answered the question by calculating the probability of double sixes to be 1/36.

At first, probability dealt with sample spaces that contained only finitely many outcomes, such as the number of ways two dice can be tossed. When combined with calculus, however, probability theory was able to analyze problems in which there are infinitely many outcomes. These two outlooks still divide the study of probability into two fields—discrete probability and continuous probability.

Since Pascal's time, the applications of probability have expanded greatly—to fields as diverse as management, quality control, psychology, and biology. Modern work in probability is exemplified by the Japanese quality control expert, Kaoru Ishikawa (1915–1989).

$$P(a \le x \le b) = \int_a^b f(x) \, dx$$

Ishikawa

Discrete Probability

Sample Spaces ■ *Discrete Random Variables* ■ *Discrete Probability* ■
Expected Value ■ *Variance and Standard Deviation*

Sample Spaces

When assigning measurements to the uncertainties of everyday life, people often use ambiguous terminology such as "fairly certain," "probable," and "highly unlikely." Probability theory allows you to remove this ambiguity by assigning a number to the likelihood of the occurrence of an event. This number is called the **probability** that the event will occur. For example, if you toss a fair coin, the probability that it will land heads up is one-half or 0.5.

In probability theory, any happening whose result is uncertain is called an **experiment.** The possible results of the experiment are the **outcomes,** a collection of outcomes is an **event,** and the collection of all possible outcomes is the **sample space** of the experiment. For instance, consider an experiment in which a coin is tossed. The sample space of this experiment consists of two outcomes: either the coin will land heads up (denoted by H) or it will land tails up (denoted by T). Thus, the sample space S is

$$S = \{H, T\}. \qquad \textit{Sample space}$$

In this text, all outcomes of a sample space are assumed to be equally likely. For instance, when a coin is tossed, H and T are assumed to be equally likely.

The Stock Market/© 92 Tom Ives

When a weather forecaster states that there is a 50% chance of thunderstorms, it means that thunderstorms have occurred on half of all days that have had similar weather conditions.

Real Life

EXAMPLE 1 *Finding a Sample Space*

An experiment consists of tossing a six-sided die.

a. What is the sample space?
b. Describe the event corresponding to a number greater than 2 turning up.

Solution

a. The sample space consists of six outcomes, which can be represented by the numbers 1 through 6. That is,

$$S = \{1, 2, 3, 4, 5, 6\}. \qquad \textit{Sample space}$$

Note that each of the outcomes in the sample space is equally likely.

b. The event corresponding to a number greater than 2 turning up is the following subset of S.

$$E = \{3, 4, 5, 6\}. \qquad \textit{Event}$$

Discrete Random Variables

A function that assigns a numerical value to each of the outcomes in a sample space is called a **random variable.** For instance, in the sample space $S = \{HH, HT, TH, TT\}$, the outcomes could be assigned the numbers 2, 1, and 0, depending on the number of heads in the outcome.

Definition of a Discrete Random Variable

Let S be a sample space. A **random variable** is a function x that assigns a numerical value to each outcome in S. If the set of values taken on by the random variable is finite, then the random variable is **discrete.** The number of times a specific value of x occurs is the **frequency** of x and is denoted by $n(x)$.

Real Life

EXAMPLE 2 *Finding Frequencies*

Three coins are tossed. A random variable assigns the number 0, 1, 2, or 3 to each possible outcome, depending on the number of heads that turn up.

$$S = \{HHH, HHT, HTH, HTT, THH, THT, TTH, TTT\}$$

$$\downarrow \quad \downarrow \quad \downarrow \quad \downarrow \quad \downarrow \quad \downarrow \quad \downarrow \quad \downarrow$$

$$3 \quad\ 2 \quad\ 2 \quad\ 1 \quad\ 2 \quad\ 1 \quad\ 1 \quad\ 0$$

Find the frequency of 0, 1, 2, and 3. Then use a bar graph to represent the result.

Solution

To find the frequencies, simply count the number of occurrences of each value of the random variable, as shown in Table P.1.

TABLE P.1

Random variable, x	0	1	2	3
Frequency of x, $n(x)$	1	3	3	1

This table is called a **frequency distribution** of the random variable. The result is shown graphically by the bar graph in Figure P.1. ■

Note In Example 2, note that the sample space consists of *eight* outcomes, each of which is *equally likely*. The sample space does *not* consist of the outcomes "0 heads," "1 head," "2 heads," and "3 heads." You cannot consider these events to be outcomes because they are not equally likely.

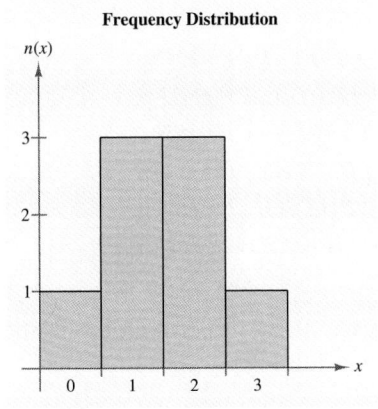

Frequency Distribution

FIGURE P.1

Discrete Probability

The probability of a random variable x is

$$P(x) = \frac{\text{Frequency of } x}{\text{Number of outcomes in } S} = \frac{n(x)}{n(S)}, \qquad \textit{Probability}$$

where $n(S)$ is the number of outcomes in the sample space. By this definition, it follows that the probability of an event must be a number between 0 and 1. That is, $0 \le P(x) \le 1$.

The collection of probabilities corresponding to the values of the random variable is called the **probability distribution** of the random variable. If the range of a discrete random variable consists of m different values $\{x_1, x_2, x_3, \ldots, x_m\}$, then the sum of the probabilities of x_i is 1. This can be written as

$$P(x_1) + P(x_2) + P(x_3) + \cdots + P(x_m) = 1.$$

Real Life

EXAMPLE 3   *Finding a Probability Distribution*

Five coins are tossed. Graph the probability distribution for the random variable giving the number of heads that turn up.

Solution

x	Event	$n(x)$
0	$TTTTT$	1
1	$HTTTT, THTTT, TTHTT, TTTHT, TTTTH$	5
2	$HHTTT, HTHTT, HTTHT, HTTTH, THHTT$ $THTHT, THTTH, TTHHT, TTHTH, TTTHH$	10
3	$HHHTT, HHTHT, HHTTH, HTHHT, HTHTH$ $HTTHH, THHHT, THHTH, THTHH, TTHHH$	10
4	$HHHHT, HHHTH, HHTHH, HTHHH, THHHH$	5
5	$HHHHH$	1

The number of outcomes in the sample space is $n(S) = 32$. The probability of each value of the random variable is shown in Table P.2.

TABLE P.2

Random variable, x	0	1	2	3	4	5
Probability, $P(x)$	$\frac{1}{32}$	$\frac{5}{32}$	$\frac{10}{32}$	$\frac{10}{32}$	$\frac{5}{32}$	$\frac{1}{32}$

A graph of this probability distribution is shown in Figure P.2. Note that values of the random variable are represented by intervals on the x-axis.

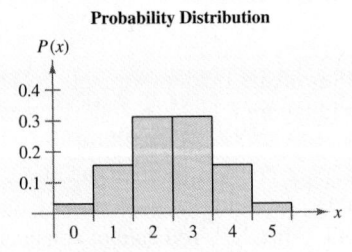

Probability Distribution

FIGURE P.2

Expected Value

Suppose you repeated the coin-tossing experiment in Example 3 several times. On the average, how many heads would you expect to turn up? From Figure P.2, it seems reasonable that the average number of heads would be $2\frac{1}{2}$. This "average" is the **expected value** of the random variable.

Note   Although the expected value of x is denoted by $E(x)$, the mean of x is usually denoted by μ. Because the mean often occurs near the center of the values in the range of the random variable, it is called a **measure of central tendency.**

Definition of Expected Value

If the range of a discrete random variable consists of m different values $\{x_1, x_2, x_3, \ldots, x_m\}$, then the **expected value** of the random variable is

$$E(x) = x_1 P(x_1) + x_2 P(x_2) + x_3 P(x_3) + \cdots + x_m P(x_m).$$

The expected value is also called the **mean** of the random variable.

Real Life

EXAMPLE 4 *Finding an Expected Value*

Five coins are tossed. Find the expected value for the number of heads that will turn up.

Solution
Using the results of Example 3, you have the following.

$$E(x) = \overbrace{(0)\left(\tfrac{1}{32}\right)}^{0\ Heads} + \overbrace{(1)\left(\tfrac{5}{32}\right)}^{1\ Head} + \overbrace{(2)\left(\tfrac{10}{32}\right)}^{2\ Heads} + \overbrace{(3)\left(\tfrac{10}{32}\right)}^{3\ Heads} + \overbrace{(4)\left(\tfrac{5}{32}\right)}^{4\ Heads} + \overbrace{(5)\left(\tfrac{1}{32}\right)}^{5\ Heads}$$
$$= \tfrac{80}{32} = 2.5$$

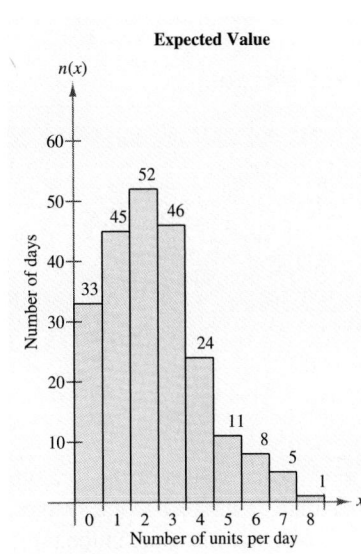

Expected Value

FIGURE P.3

Real Life

EXAMPLE 5 *Finding an Expected Value*

Over a period of 1 year (225 selling days), a sales representative sold between 0 and 8 units per day, as shown in Figure P.3. From this data, what is the average number of units per day the sales representative should expect to sell?

Solution
One way to answer this question is to calculate the expected value for the number of units.

$$E(x) = (0)\left(\tfrac{33}{225}\right) + (1)\left(\tfrac{45}{225}\right) + (2)\left(\tfrac{52}{225}\right) + (3)\left(\tfrac{46}{225}\right) + (4)\left(\tfrac{24}{225}\right)$$
$$+ (5)\left(\tfrac{11}{225}\right) + (6)\left(\tfrac{8}{225}\right) + (7)\left(\tfrac{5}{225}\right) + (8)\left(\tfrac{1}{225}\right)$$
$$= \tfrac{529}{225} \approx 2.35 \text{ units per day}$$

Variance and Standard Deviation

The expected value or mean gives a measure of the average value assigned by a random variable. But the mean doesn't tell the whole story. For instance, all three of the following distributions have a mean of 2.

Distribution 1

Random variable, x	0	1	2	3	4
Frequency of x, $n(x)$	2	2	2	2	2

Distribution 2

Random variable, x	0	1	2	3	4
Frequency of x, $n(x)$	0	3	4	3	0

Distribution 3

Random variable, x	0	1	2	3	4
Frequency of x, $n(x)$	5	0	0	0	5

Even though each distribution has the same mean, the patterns of the distributions are quite different. In the first distribution, each value has the same frequency. In the second, the values are clustered about the mean. In the third distribution, the values are far from the mean. To measure how much the distribution varies from the mean, you can use the concept of **standard deviation.**

Definition of Variance and Standard Deviation

Consider a random variable whose range is $\{x_1, x_2, x_3, \ldots, x_m\}$ with a mean of μ. The **variance** of the random variable is

$$V(x) = (x_1 - \mu)^2 P(x_1) + (x_2 - \mu)^2 P(x_2) + \cdots + (x_m - \mu)^2 P(x_m).$$

The **standard deviation** of the random variable is

$$\sigma = \sqrt{V(x)}$$

(σ is the lowercase Greek letter sigma).

When the standard deviation is small, most of the values of the random variable are clustered near the mean. As the standard deviation becomes larger, the distribution becomes more and more spread out. For instance, in the three distributions above, you would expect the second to have the smallest standard deviation and the third to have the largest. This is confirmed in Example 6.

(a) Mean = 2; standard deviation ≈ 1.41

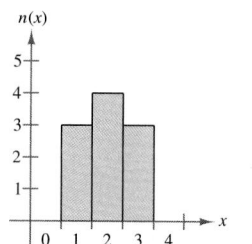
(b) Mean = 2; standard deviation ≈ 0.77

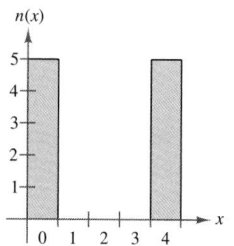
(c) Mean = 2; standard deviation = 2

FIGURE P.4

EXAMPLE 6 *Finding Variance and Standard Deviation*

Find the variance and standard deviation of each of the three distributions shown on page P-6.

Solution

a. For distribution 1, the mean is $\mu = 2$, the variance is

$$V(x) = (0 - 2)^2 \left(\tfrac{2}{10}\right) + (1 - 2)^2 \left(\tfrac{2}{10}\right) + (2 - 2)^2 \left(\tfrac{2}{10}\right)$$
$$+ (3 - 2)^2 \left(\tfrac{2}{10}\right) + (4 - 2)^2 \left(\tfrac{2}{10}\right)$$
$$= 2, \qquad\qquad\qquad \textit{Variance}$$

and the standard deviation is

$$\sigma = \sqrt{2} \approx 1.41. \qquad\qquad \textit{Standard deviation}$$

b. For distribution 2, the mean is $\mu = 2$, the variance is

$$V(x) = (0 - 2)^2 \left(\tfrac{0}{10}\right) + (1 - 2)^2 \left(\tfrac{3}{10}\right) + (2 - 2)^2 \left(\tfrac{4}{10}\right)$$
$$+ (3 - 2)^2 \left(\tfrac{3}{10}\right) + (4 - 2)^2 \left(\tfrac{0}{10}\right)$$
$$= 0.6, \qquad\qquad\qquad \textit{Variance}$$

and the standard deviation is

$$\sigma = \sqrt{0.6} \approx 0.77. \qquad\qquad \textit{Standard deviation}$$

c. For distribution 3, the mean is $\mu = 2$, the variance is

$$V(x) = (0 - 2)^2 \left(\tfrac{5}{10}\right) + (1 - 2)^2 \left(\tfrac{0}{10}\right) + (2 - 2)^2 \left(\tfrac{0}{10}\right)$$
$$+ (3 - 2)^2 \left(\tfrac{0}{10}\right) + (4 - 2)^2 \left(\tfrac{5}{10}\right)$$
$$= 4, \qquad\qquad\qquad \textit{Variance}$$

and the standard deviation is

$$\sigma = \sqrt{4} = 2. \qquad\qquad \textit{Standard deviation}$$

The graphs of the three distributions are shown in Figure P.4. As expected, note that the second distribution has the smallest standard deviation and the third distribution has the largest. ■

Discussion Problem   **Creating Distributions**

a. Create a distribution of 10 numbers whose mean is 2 and whose standard deviation is smaller than any of the standard deviations in Example 6. Is it possible to create a distribution whose standard deviation is 0?

b. Create a distribution of 10 numbers whose mean is 2 and whose standard deviation is larger than any of the standard deviations in Example 6.

Warm Up   The following warm-up exercises involve skills that were covered in earlier sections. You will use these skills in the exercise set for this section.

In Exercises 1 and 2, solve for x.

1. $\dfrac{1}{9} + \dfrac{2}{3} + \dfrac{2}{9} = x$

2. $\dfrac{1}{3} + \dfrac{5}{12} + \dfrac{1}{8} + \dfrac{1}{12} + \dfrac{x}{24} = 1$

In Exercises 3–6, evaluate the expression.

3. $0\left(\frac{1}{16}\right) + 1\left(\frac{3}{16}\right) + 2\left(\frac{8}{16}\right) + 3\left(\frac{3}{16}\right) + 4\left(\frac{1}{16}\right)$

4. $0\left(\frac{1}{12}\right) + 1\left(\frac{2}{12}\right) + 2\left(\frac{6}{12}\right) + 3\left(\frac{2}{12}\right) + 4\left(\frac{1}{12}\right)$

5. $(0-1)^2\left(\frac{1}{4}\right) + (1-1)^2\left(\frac{1}{2}\right) + (2-1)^2\left(\frac{1}{4}\right)$

6. $(0-2)^2\left(\frac{1}{12}\right) + (1-2)^2\left(\frac{2}{12}\right) + (2-2)^2\left(\frac{6}{12}\right) + (3-2)^2\left(\frac{2}{12}\right) + (4-2)^2\left(\frac{1}{12}\right)$

In Exercises 7–10, write the fraction as a percent.

7. $\frac{3}{8}$

8. $\frac{9}{11}$

9. $\frac{13}{24}$

10. $\frac{112}{256}$

E X E R C I S E S   P.1   means that technology can help you solve or check the exercise(s).

In Exercises 1–4, list the elements in the specified set.

1. *Tossing a Coin*   A coin is tossed three times.

  (a) The sample space S
  (b) The event A that at least two heads occur
  (c) The event B that no more than one head occurs

2. *Tossing a Coin*   A coin is tossed. If a head occurs, the coin is tossed again; otherwise, a die is tossed.

  (a) The sample space S
  (b) The event A that a number greater than 3 occurs on the die
  (c) The event B that two heads occur

3. *Selecting an Integer*   An integer is selected from the set of all integers between 1 and 50 that are divisible by 3.

  (a) The sample space S
  (b) The event A that the integer is divisible by 12
  (c) The event B that the integer is a perfect square

4. *Taking a Poll*   Three people are asked their opinions on a political issue. They can answer "In favor" (I), "Opposed" (O), or "Undecided" (U).

  (a) The sample space S
  (b) The event A that at least 2 are in favor
  (c) The event B that no more than 1 is opposed

5. *Election Poll*   Three people have been nominated for president of a college class. From a small poll it is estimated that Jane has a probability of 0.29 of winning and Larry has a probability of 0.47. What is the probability of the third candidate winning the election?

6. *Random Selection*   In a class of 72 students, 44 are girls and of these, 12 are going to college. Of the 28 boys in the class, 9 are going to college. If a student is selected at random from the class, what is the probability that the person chosen is (a) going to college? (b) not going to college? (c) a girl who is not going to college?

7. *Quality Control* A component of a spacecraft has both a main system and a backup system. The probability of at least one of the systems performing satisfactorily throughout the duration of the flight is 0.9855. What is the probability of both of them failing?

8. *Choosing a Card* A card is chosen at random from a standard 52-card deck of playing cards. What is the probability that the card will be black and a face card?

9. *Tossing Coins* Two coins are tossed. A random variable assigns the number 0, 1, or 2 to each possible outcome, depending on the number of heads that turn up. Find the frequencies of 0, 1, and 2.

10. *Tossing Coins* Four coins are tossed. A random variable assigns the number 0, 1, 2, 3, or 4 to each possible outcome, depending on the number of heads that turn up. Find the frequencies of 0, 1, 2, 3, and 4.

11. *True-False Exam* Three students answer a true-false question on an examination. A random variable assigns the number 0, 1, 2, or 3 to each outcome, depending on the number of answers of *true* among the three students. Find the frequencies of 0, 1, 2, and 3.

12. *True-False Exam* Four students answer a true-false question on an examination. A random variable assigns the number 0, 1, 2, 3, or 4 to each outcome, depending on the number of answers of *true* among the four students. Find the frequencies of 0, 1, 2, 3, and 4.

In Exercises 13–16, sketch a graph of the probability distribution and find the required probabilities.

13.

x	0	1	2	3	4
$P(x)$	$\frac{1}{20}$	$\frac{3}{20}$	$\frac{6}{20}$	$\frac{6}{20}$	$\frac{4}{20}$

(a) $P(1 \leq x \leq 3)$ (b) $P(x \geq 2)$

14.

x	0	1	2	3	4
$P(x)$	$\frac{8}{20}$	$\frac{6}{20}$	$\frac{3}{20}$	$\frac{2}{20}$	$\frac{1}{20}$

(a) $P(x \leq 2)$ (b) $P(x > 2)$

15.

x	0	1	2	3	4	5
$P(x)$	0.041	0.189	0.247	0.326	0.159	0.038

(a) $P(x \leq 3)$ (b) $P(x > 3)$

16.

x	0	1	2	3
$P(x)$	0.027	0.189	0.441	0.343

(a) $P(1 \leq x \leq 2)$ (b) $P(x < 2)$

17. *Boy or Girl?* Consider a couple that has four children. Assume that it is equally likely that each child is a girl or a boy.

(a) Complete the set to form the sample space consisting of 16 elements.

$S = \{gggg, gggb, ggbg, \ldots\}$

(b) Complete the table, in which the random variable x is the number of girls in the family.

x	0	1	2	3	4
$P(x)$					

(c) Use the table in part (b) to sketch the graph of the probability distribution.

(d) Use the table in part (b) to find the probability of having at least one boy.

18. *Tossing Dice* Consider the experiment of tossing a six-sided die twice.

(a) Complete the set to form the sample space of 36 elements. Note that each element is an ordered pair in which the entries are the numbers of points on the first and second tosses, respectively.

$S = \{(1, 1), (1, 2), \ldots, (2, 1), (2, 2), \ldots\}$

(b) Complete the table, in which the random variable x is the sum of the number of points.

x	2	3	4	5	6	7	8	9	10	11	12
$P(x)$											

(c) Use the table in part (b) to sketch the graph of the probability distribution.

(d) Use the table in part (b) to find $P(5 \leq x \leq 9)$.

In Exercises 19–22, find $E(x)$, $V(x)$, and σ for the given probability distribution.

19.

x	1	2	3	4	5
$P(x)$	$\frac{1}{16}$	$\frac{3}{16}$	$\frac{8}{16}$	$\frac{3}{16}$	$\frac{1}{16}$

20.

x	1	2	3	4	5
$P(x)$	$\frac{4}{10}$	$\frac{2}{10}$	$\frac{2}{10}$	$\frac{1}{10}$	$\frac{1}{10}$

21.

x	-3	-1	0	3	5
$P(x)$	$\frac{1}{5}$	$\frac{1}{5}$	$\frac{1}{5}$	$\frac{1}{5}$	$\frac{1}{5}$

22.

x	$-\$5000$	$-\$2500$	$\$300$
$P(x)$	0.008	0.052	0.940

Tossing Dice In Exercises 23 and 24, find the mean and variance of the discrete random variable x.

23. x is (a) the number of points when a four-sided die is tossed once and (b) the sum of the points when the four-sided die is tossed twice.

24. x is the number of heads when a coin is tossed four times.

25. *Revenue* A publishing company introduces a new weekly magazine that sells for $1.50 on the newsstand. The marketing group of the company estimates that sales x in thousands will be approximated by the following probability function.

x	10	15	20	30	40
P(x)	0.25	0.30	0.25	0.15	0.05

(a) Find $E(x)$ and σ.
(b) Find the expected revenue.

26. *Personal Income* In a certain section of a large city, the probability distribution of the random variable x, the annual income of a family in thousands of dollars, is given in the following table.

x	30	40	50	60	80
P(x)	0.10	0.20	0.50	0.15	0.05

Find $E(x)$ and σ.

27. *Insurance* An insurance company needs to determine the annual premium required to break even on fire protection policies with a face value of $90,000. If x is the claim size on these policies and the analysis is restricted to the losses $30,000, $60,000, and $90,000, then the probability distribution of x is given by the following table.

x	0	30,000	60,000	90,000
P(x)	0.995	0.0036	0.0011	0.0003

What premium should customers be charged for the company to break even?

28. *Insurance* An insurance company needs to determine the annual premium required to break even for collision protection for cars with a value of $10,000. If x is the claim size on these policies and the analysis is restricted to the losses $1,000, $5,000, and $10,000, then the probability distribution of x is given by the following table.

x	0	1,000	5,000	10,000
P(x)	0.936	0.040	0.020	0.004

What premium should customers be charged for the company to break even?

Games of Chance If x is the net gain to a player in a game of chance, then E(x) is usually negative. This value gives the average amount per game the player can expect to lose over the long run. In Exercises 29 and 30, find the expected net gain to the player for one play of the specified game.

29. In roulette, the wheel has the 38 numbers 00, 0, 1, 2, . . . , 34, 35, and 36, marked on equally spaced slots. If a player bets $1 on a number and wins, then the player keeps the dollar and receives an additional 35 dollars. Otherwise, the dollar is lost.

30. A service organization is selling $2 raffle tickets as part of a fund-raising program. The first prize is a boat valued at $2950, and the second prize is a camping tent valued at $400. In addition to the first and second prizes, there are 25 $20 gift certificates to be awarded. The number of tickets sold is 3000.

31. *Market Analysis* After considerable market study, a sporting goods company has decided on two possible cities in which to open a new store. Management estimates that city 1 will yield $20 million in revenues if successful and will lose $4 million if not, whereas city 2 will yield $50 million in revenues if successful and lose $9 million if not. City 1 has a 0.3 probability of being successful and city 2 has a 0.2 probability of being successful. In which city should the sporting goods company open the new store with respect to the expected return from each store?

32. Repeat Exercise 31 if the probabilities of city 1 and city 2 being successful are 0.4 and 0.25, respectively.

33. Use a graphing utility to find the mean and standard deviation of the following data, which gives the ages of 50 residents of a long-term-care nursing facility.

62, 64, 66, 66, 68, 69, 69, 70, 70, 70,
71, 72, 72, 72, 72, 73, 73, 74, 74, 75,
75, 75, 75, 76, 76, 77, 77, 77, 77, 77,
77, 78, 78, 79, 79, 79, 80, 81, 81, 83,
84, 84, 87, 88, 89, 91, 94, 94, 97, 98

34. Use a graphing utility to find the mean and standard deviation of the following data, which gives the number of hours of overtime for 60 employees of a particular company during a given week.

0.0, 0.0, 0.0, 0.0, 0.0, 0.5, 0.5, 1.0, 1.0, 1.0,
2.0, 2.0, 2.0, 2.0, 2.0, 2.0, 2.0, 2.5, 2.5, 2.5,
3.0, 3.0, 3.0, 3.0, 3.0, 3.0, 3.0, 4.0, 4.0, 4.0,
4.0, 4.5, 4.5, 5.0, 5.0, 5.0, 5.0, 5.0, 6.0, 6.0,
6.5, 6.5, 6.5, 7.0, 7.0, 7.0, 7.0, 8.0, 8.0, 8.0,
8.0, 8.0, 8.0, 8.0, 8.0, 8.5, 8.5, 8.5, 9.0, 9.5

EXAMPLE 1 *Verifying a Probability Density Function*

Show that $f(x) = 12x(1 - x)^2$ is a probability density function over the interval $[0, 1]$.

Solution

Begin by observing that f is continuous and nonnegative on the interval $[0, 1]$.

$$f(x) = 12x(1 - x)^2 \geq 0, \qquad 0 \leq x \leq 1 \quad \textit{Nonnegative}$$

Next, evaluate the following integral.

$$\int_0^1 12x(1 - x)^2 \, dx = 12 \int_0^1 (x^3 - 2x^2 + x) \, dx$$

$$= 12 \left[\frac{x^4}{4} - \frac{2x^3}{3} + \frac{x^2}{2} \right]_0^1$$

$$= 12 \left(\frac{1}{4} - \frac{2}{3} + \frac{1}{2} \right)$$

$$= 1$$

Because this value is 1, you can conclude that f is a probability density function over the interval $[0, 1]$. The graph of f is shown in Figure P.6.

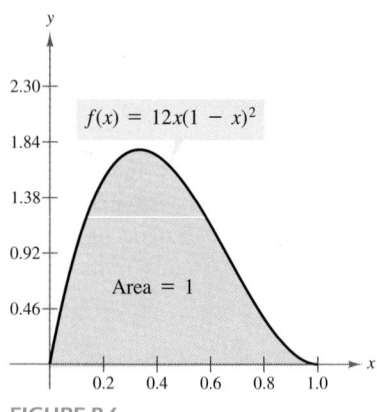

FIGURE P.6

The next example deals with an infinite interval and its corresponding improper integral.

EXAMPLE 2 *Verifying a Probability Density Function*

Show that $f(t) = 0.1e^{-0.1t}$ is a probability density function over the infinite interval $[0, \infty)$.

Solution

Begin by observing that f is continuous and nonnegative on the interval $[0, \infty)$.

$$f(t) = 0.1e^{-0.1t} \geq 0, \qquad 0 \leq t \qquad \textit{Nonnegative}$$

Next, evaluate the following integral.

$$\int_0^\infty 0.1e^{-0.1t} \, dt = \lim_{b \to \infty} \left[-e^{-0.1t} \right]_0^b$$

$$= \lim_{b \to \infty} (-e^{-0.1b} + 1)$$

$$= 1$$

Because this value is 1, you can conclude that f is a probability density function over the interval $[0, \infty)$. The graph of f is shown in Figure P.7.

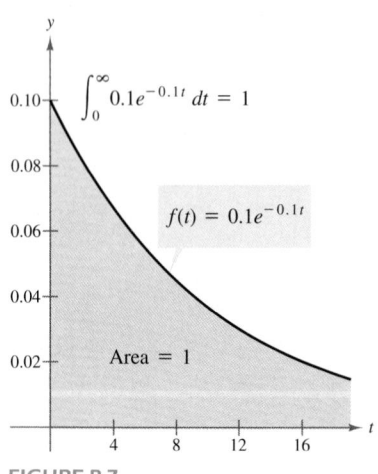

FIGURE P.7

Continuous Random Variables ∎ *Applications*

Continuous Random Variables

In many applications of probability, it is useful to consider a random variable whose range is an interval on the real line. Such a random variable is called **continuous.** For instance, the random variable that measures the height of a person in a population is continuous.

To define the probability of an event involving a continuous random variable, you cannot simply count the number of ways the event can occur (as you can with a discrete random variable). Rather, you need to define a function f called a **probability density function.**

Definition of a Probability Density Function

Consider a function f of a continuous random variable x whose range is the interval $[a, b]$. The function is a **probability density function** if it is nonnegative and continuous on the interval $[a, b]$ and if

$$\int_a^b f(x)\, dx = 1.$$

The probability that x lies in the interval $[c, d]$ is

$$P(c \leq x \leq d) = \int_c^d f(x)\, dx,$$

as shown in Figure P.5. If the range of the continuous random variable is an infinite interval, then the integrals are improper integrals.

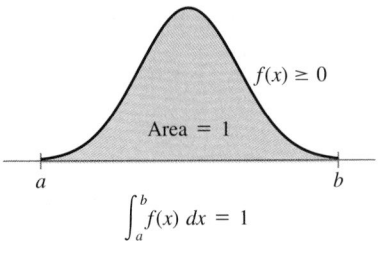

$$\int_a^b f(x)\, dx = 1$$

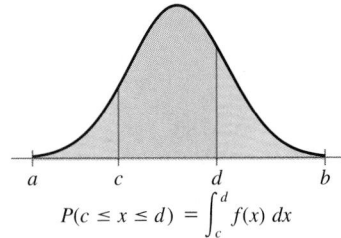

$$P(c \leq x \leq d) = \int_c^d f(x)\, dx$$

FIGURE P.5 Probability Density Function

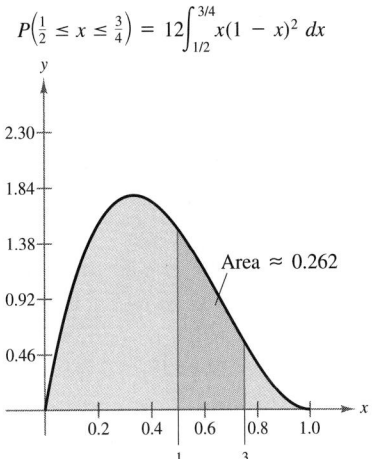

$$P\left(\tfrac{1}{2} \le x \le \tfrac{3}{4}\right) = 12\int_{1/2}^{3/4} x(1-x)^2\, dx$$

FIGURE P.8

EXAMPLE 3 *Finding a Probability*

For the probability density function in Example 1,

$$f(x) = 12x(1-x)^2,$$

find the probability that x lies in the interval $\tfrac{1}{2} \le x \le \tfrac{3}{4}$.

Solution

$$P\left(\tfrac{1}{2} \le x \le \tfrac{3}{4}\right) = 12\int_{1/2}^{3/4} x(1-x)^2\, dx$$

$$= 12\int_{1/2}^{3/4} (x^3 - 2x^2 + x)\, dx$$

$$= 12\left[\frac{x^4}{4} - \frac{2x^3}{3} + \frac{x^2}{2}\right]_{1/2}^{3/4}$$

$$= 12\left[\frac{\left(\tfrac{3}{4}\right)^4}{4} - \frac{2\left(\tfrac{3}{4}\right)^3}{3} + \frac{\left(\tfrac{3}{4}\right)^2}{2} - \frac{\left(\tfrac{1}{2}\right)^4}{4} + \frac{2\left(\tfrac{1}{2}\right)^3}{3} - \frac{\left(\tfrac{1}{2}\right)^2}{2}\right]$$

$$\approx 0.262$$

Therefore, the probability that x lies in the interval $\left[\tfrac{1}{2}, \tfrac{3}{4}\right]$ is approximately 0.262 or 26.2%, as indicated in Figure P.8. ■

   In Example 3, note that if you had been asked to find the probability that x lies in any of the intervals $\tfrac{1}{2} < x < \tfrac{3}{4}$, $\tfrac{1}{2} \le x < \tfrac{3}{4}$, or $\tfrac{1}{2} < x \le \tfrac{3}{4}$, you would have obtained the same solution as that given in the example. In other words, the inclusion of either endpoint adds nothing to the probability. This demonstrates an important difference between discrete and continuous random variables. For a continuous random variable, the probability that x will be precisely one value (such as 0.5) is considered to be zero, because

$$P(0.5 \le x \le 0.5) = \int_{0.5}^{0.5} f(x)\, dx = 0.$$

You should not interpret this result to mean that it is impossible for the continuous random variable x to have the value 0.5. It simply means that the probability that x will have this *exact* value is insignificant.

EXAMPLE 4 *Finding a Probability*

Consider a probability density function defined over the interval $[0, 5]$. If the probability that x lies in the interval $[0, 2]$ is 0.7, what is the probability that x lies in the interval $[2, 5]$?

Solution

Because the probability that x lies in the interval $[0, 5]$ is 1, you can conclude that the probability that x lies in the interval $[2, 5]$ is $1 - 0.7 = 0.3$. ■

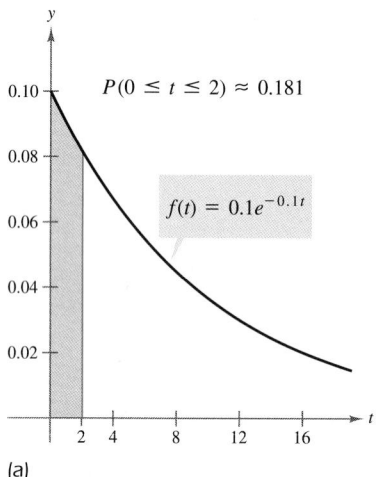

P(0 ≤ t ≤ 2) ≈ 0.181

$f(t) = 0.1e^{-0.1t}$

(a)

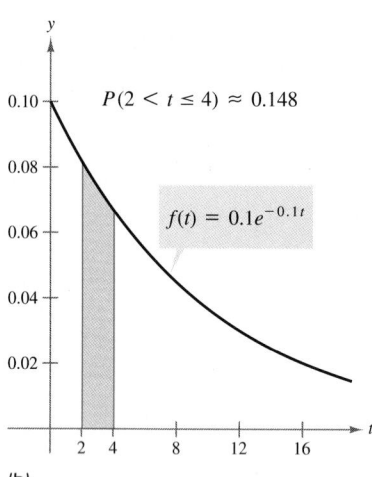

P(2 < t ≤ 4) ≈ 0.148

$f(t) = 0.1e^{-0.1t}$

(b)

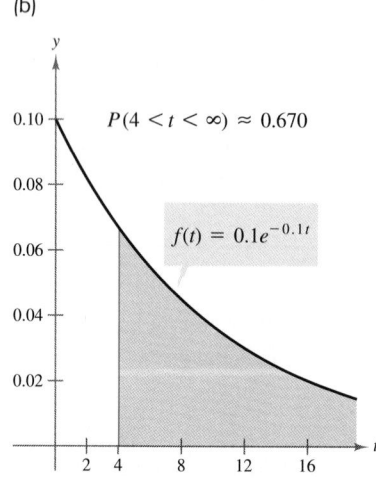

P(4 < t < ∞) ≈ 0.670

$f(t) = 0.1e^{-0.1t}$

(c)

FIGURE P.9

Applications

Real Life

EXAMPLE 5 *Modeling the Lifetime of a Product*

The usable lifetime (in years) of a product is modeled by the probability density function

$$f(t) = 0.1e^{-0.1t}, \qquad 0 \le t < \infty.$$

Find the probability that a randomly selected unit will have a lifetime falling in the given interval.

a. No more than 2 years
b. More than 2 years, but no more than 4 years
c. More than 4 years

Solution

a. The probability that the unit will last no more than 2 years is

$$P(0 \le t \le 2) = 0.1\int_0^2 e^{-0.1t}\,dt$$

$$= \left[-e^{-0.1t}\right]_0^2$$

$$= -e^{-0.2} + 1$$

$$\approx 0.181.$$

b. The probability that the unit will last more than 2 years, but no more than 4 years, is

$$P(2 < t \le 4) = 0.1\int_2^4 e^{-0.1t}\,dt$$

$$= \left[-e^{-0.1t}\right]_2^4$$

$$= -e^{-0.4} + e^{-0.2}$$

$$\approx 0.148.$$

c. The probability that the unit will last more than 4 years is

$$P(4 < t < \infty) = 0.1\int_4^\infty e^{-0.1t}\,dt$$

$$= \lim_{b \to \infty} \left[-e^{-0.1t}\right]_4^b$$

$$= \lim_{b \to \infty} (-e^{-0.1b} + e^{-0.4})$$

$$= e^{-0.4}$$

$$\approx 0.670.$$

These three probabilities are illustrated graphically in Figure P.9. Note that the sum of the three probabilities is 1.

Real
Life

EXAMPLE 6 *Modeling Weekly Demand*

The weekly demand for a product is modeled by the probability density function

$$f(x) = \frac{1}{36}(-x^2 + 6x), \qquad 0 \le x \le 6,$$

where x is the number of units sold (in thousands). What are the minimum and maximum weekly sales? Find the probability that the sales for a randomly chosen week will be between 2000 and 4000 units.

Solution
Because $0 \le x \le 6$, the weekly sales vary between a minimum of 0 and a maximum of 6000 units. The probability is given by the integral

$$P(2 \le x \le 4) = \frac{1}{36}\int_2^4 (-x^2 + 6x)\, dx$$

$$= \frac{1}{36}\left[-\frac{x^3}{3} + 3x^2 \right]_2^4$$

$$= \frac{1}{36}\left(-\frac{64}{3} + 48 + \frac{8}{3} - 12 \right)$$

$$= \frac{13}{27}$$

$$\approx 0.481.$$

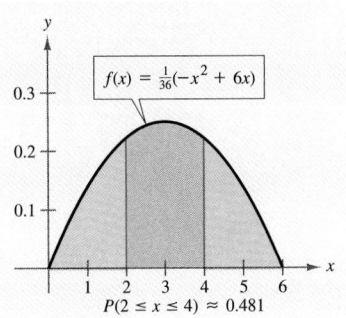

$f(x) = \frac{1}{36}(-x^2 + 6x)$

$P(2 \le x \le 4) \approx 0.481$

FIGURE P.10

Thus, the probability that the weekly sales will be between 2000 and 4000 units is about 0.481 or 48.1%, as indicated in Figure P.10. ■

Discussion Problem   *Modeling Population Heights*

Which of the following probability density functions do you think is a better model of the heights of American women (ages 18–24)? Explain your reasoning.

(a)   (b)   (c)

Use the model to estimate the average height of American women.

Warm Up

The following warm-up exercises involve skills that were covered in earlier sections. You will use these skills in the exercise set for this section.

In Exercises 1–4, determine whether f is continuous and nonnegative on the given interval.

1. $f(x) = \dfrac{1}{x}$, $[1, 4]$

2. $f(x) = x^2 - 1$, $[0, 1]$

3. $f(x) = 3 - x$, $[1, 5]$

4. $f(x) = e^{-x}$, $[0, 1]$

In Exercises 5–10, evaluate the definite integral.

5. $\displaystyle\int_0^4 \frac{1}{4}\, dx$

6. $\displaystyle\int_1^3 \frac{1}{4}\, dx$

7. $\displaystyle\int_0^2 \frac{2-x}{2}\, dx$

8. $\displaystyle\int_1^2 \frac{2-x}{2}\, dx$

9. $\displaystyle\int_0^\infty 0.4e^{-0.4t}\, dt$

10. $\displaystyle\int_0^\infty 3e^{-3t}\, dt$

E X E R C I S E S   P.2   means that technology can help you solve or check the exercise(s).

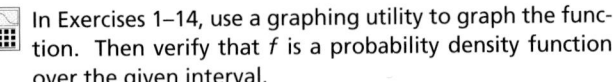 In Exercises 1–14, use a graphing utility to graph the function. Then verify that f is a probability density function over the given interval.

1. $f(x) = \frac{1}{8}$, $[0, 8]$

2. $f(x) = \frac{1}{5}$, $[0, 5]$

3. $f(x) = \dfrac{4-x}{8}$, $[0, 4]$

4. $f(x) = \dfrac{x}{18}$, $[0, 6]$

5. $f(x) = 6x(1-x)$, $[0, 1]$

6. $f(x) = \dfrac{x(6-x)}{36}$, $[0, 6]$

7. $f(x) = \frac{1}{5}e^{-x/5}$, $[0, \infty)$

8. $f(x) = \frac{1}{6}e^{-x/6}$, $[0, \infty)$

9. $f(x) = \dfrac{3x}{8}\sqrt{4 - x^2}$, $[0, 2]$

10. $f(x) = 12x^2(1-x)$, $[0, 1]$

11. $f(x) = \frac{4}{27}x^2(3-x)$, $[0, 3]$

12. $f(x) = \frac{2}{9}x(3-x)$, $[0, 3]$

13. $f(x) = \frac{1}{3}e^{-x/3}$, $[0, \infty)$ **14.** $f(x) = \frac{1}{4}$, $[8, 12]$

In Exercises 15–20, find the constant k so that the function f is a probability density function over the given interval.

15. $f(x) = kx$, $[1, 4]$

16. $f(x) = kx^3$, $[0, 4]$

17. $f(x) = k(4 - x^2)$, $[-2, 2]$

18. $f(x) = k\sqrt{x}(1 - x)$, $[0, 1]$

19. $f(x) = ke^{-x/2}$, $[0, \infty)$

20. $f(x) = \dfrac{k}{b - a}$, $[a, b]$

In Exercises 21–26, sketch the graph of the probability density function over the indicated interval and find the indicated probabilities.

21. $f(x) = \frac{1}{10}$, $[0, 10]$

   (a) $P(0 < x < 6)$ (b) $P(4 < x < 6)$

   (c) $P(8 < x < 10)$ (d) $P(x \geq 2)$

22. $f(x) = \dfrac{x}{50}$, $[0, 10]$

   (a) $P(0 < x < 6)$ (b) $P(4 < x < 6)$

   (c) $P(8 < x < 10)$ (d) $P(x \geq 2)$

23. $f(x) = \frac{3}{16}\sqrt{x}$, $[0, 4]$

   (a) $P(0 < x < 2)$ (b) $P(2 < x < 4)$

   (c) $P(1 < x < 3)$ (d) $P(x \leq 3)$

24. $f(x) = \dfrac{5}{4(x+1)^2}$, $[0, 4]$

   (a) $P(0 < x < 2)$ (b) $P(2 < x < 4)$

   (c) $P(1 < x < 3)$ (d) $P(x \leq 3)$

25. $f(t) = \frac{1}{3}e^{-t/3}$, $[0, \infty)$

   (a) $P(t < 2)$ (b) $P(t \geq 2)$

   (c) $P(1 < t < 4)$ (d) $P(t = 3)$

26. $f(t) = \frac{3}{256}(16 - t^2)$, $[-4, 4]$

   (a) $P(t < -2)$ (b) $P(t > 2)$

   (c) $P(-1 < t < 1)$ (d) $P(t > -2)$

27. *Transportation* Buses arrive and depart from a college every 30 minutes. The probability density function for the waiting time t (in minutes) for a person arriving at the bus stop is

$$f(t) = \tfrac{1}{30}, \ [0, 30].$$

Find the probability that the person will wait (a) no more than 5 minutes, and (b) at least 18 minutes.

28. *Learning Theory* The time t (in hours) required for a new employee to successfully learn to operate a machine in a manufacturing process is described by the probability density function

$$f(t) = \tfrac{5}{324}t\sqrt{9 - t}, \ [0, 9].$$

Find the probability that a new employee will learn to operate the machine (a) in less than 3 hours, and (b) in more than 4 hours but less than 8 hours.

In Exercises 29–32, find the required probabilities using the **exponential density function**

$$f(t) = \frac{1}{\lambda}e^{-t/\lambda}, \ [0, \infty).$$

29. *Waiting Time* The waiting time (in minutes) for service at the checkout at a grocery store is exponentially distributed with $\lambda = 3$. Find the probability of waiting (a) less than 2 minutes, (b) more than 2 minutes but less than 4 minutes, and (c) at least 2 minutes.

30. *Useful Life* The lifetime (in years) of a battery is exponentially distributed with $\lambda = 5$. Find the probability that the lifetime of a given battery will be (a) less than 6 years, (b) more than 2 years but less than 6 years, and (c) more than 8 years.

31. *Waiting Time* The length of time (in hours) required to unload trucks at a depot is exponentially distributed with $\lambda = \frac{3}{4}$. What proportion of the trucks can be unloaded in less than 1 hour?

32. *Useful Life* The time (in years) until failure of a component in a machine is exponentially distributed with $\lambda = 3.5$. A manufacturer has a large number of these machines and plans to replace the components in all the machines during regularly scheduled maintenance periods. How much time should elapse between maintenance periods if at least 90% of the components are to remain working throughout the period?

33. *Demand* The weekly demand x (in tons) for a certain product is a continuous random variable with the density function

$$f(x) = \tfrac{1}{36}xe^{-x/6}, \ [0, \infty).$$

Find the following.

   (a) $P(x < 6)$ (b) $P(6 < x < 12)$

   (c) $P(x > 12) = 1 - P(x \leq 12)$

34. *Demand* Given the conditions of Exercise 33, determine the number of tons that should be ordered each week so that the demand can be met for 90% of the weeks.

35. *Learning Theory* The probability density function for the percentage of recall in a certain learning experiment is found to be

$$f(x) = \tfrac{15}{4}x\sqrt{1 - x}, \ [0, 1].$$

What is the probability that a randomly chosen individual in the experiment will recall (a) between 0% and 25%, and (b) between 50% and 75%, of the material?

36. *Metallurgy* The probability density function for the percent of iron in ore samples taken from a certain region is

$$f(x) = \tfrac{1155}{32}x^3(1 - x)^{3/2}, \ [0, 1].$$

Find the probability that a sample will contain (a) from 0% to 25% iron and (b) from 50% to 100% iron.

37. The probability of obtaining 49, 50, or 51 heads when a fair coin is tossed 100 times is

$$P(49 \leq x \leq 51) \approx \int_{48.5}^{51.5} \frac{1}{5\sqrt{2\pi}}e^{-(x-50)^2/50}dx.$$

Use a computer or graphing utility and Simpson's Rule (with $n = 12$) to approximate this integral.

Expected Value and Variance

Expected Value ■ *Variance and Standard Deviation* ■ *Median* ■
Special Probability Density Functions

Expected Value

In Section P.1, you studied the concepts of expected value, mean, variance, and standard deviation for *discrete* random variables. In this section, you will extend these concepts to *continuous* random variables.

Definition of Expected Value

If f is a probability density function for a continuous random variable x over the interval $[a, b]$, then the **expected value** or **mean** of x is

$$\mu = E(x) = \int_a^b xf(x)\,dx.$$

EXAMPLE 1 *Finding Average Weekly Demand*

Real Life

In Example 6 in Section P.2, the weekly demand for a product was modeled by the probability density function

$$f(x) = \frac{1}{36}(-x^2 + 6x), \qquad 0 \le x \le 6.$$

Find the expected weekly demand for this product.

Solution

$$\begin{aligned}
\mu = E(x) &= \frac{1}{36}\int_0^6 x(-x^2 + 6x)\,dx \\
&= \frac{1}{36}\int_0^6 (-x^3 + 6x^2)\,dx \\
&= \frac{1}{36}\left[\frac{-x^4}{4} + 2x^3\right]_0^6 \\
&= 3
\end{aligned}$$

From Figure P.11, you can see that an expected value of 3 seems reasonable because the region is symmetric about the line $x = 3$.

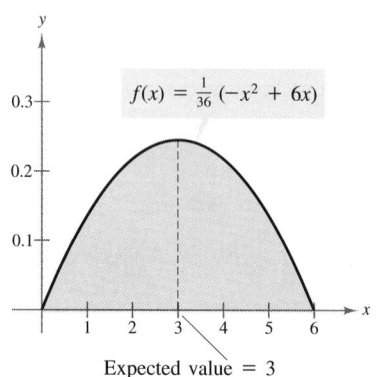

$f(x) = \frac{1}{36}(-x^2 + 6x)$

Expected value $= 3$

FIGURE P.11

Variance and Standard Deviation

Standard deviation = 1.0

Standard deviation = 1.5

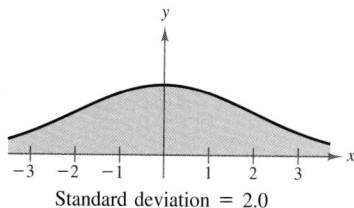

Standard deviation = 2.0

FIGURE P.12

Definition of Variance and Standard Deviation

If f is a probability density function for a continuous random variable x over the interval $[a, b]$, then the **variance** of x is

$$V(x) = \int_a^b (x - \mu)^2 f(x)\, dx,$$

where μ is the mean of x. The **standard deviation** of x is

$$\sigma = \sqrt{V(x)}.$$

Recall from Section P.1 that distributions that are clustered about the mean tend to have smaller standard deviations than distributions that are more dispersed. For instance, all three of the probability density distributions shown in Figure P.12 have a mean of $\mu = 0$, but they have different standard deviations. Because the first distribution is clustered more toward the mean, its standard deviation is the smallest of the three.

EXAMPLE 2 *Finding Variance and Standard Deviation*

Find the variance and standard deviation for the probability density function

$$f(x) = 2 - 2x, \qquad 0 \le x \le 1.$$

Solution

Begin by finding the mean.

$$\mu = \int_0^1 x(2 - 2x)\, dx = \frac{1}{3} \qquad\qquad \textit{Mean}$$

Next, apply the formula for variance.

$$\begin{aligned}
V(x) &= \int_0^1 \left(x - \frac{1}{3}\right)^2 (2 - 2x)\, dx \\
&= \int_0^1 \left(-2x^3 + \frac{10x^2}{3} - \frac{14x}{9} + \frac{2}{9}\right) dx \\
&= \left[-\frac{x^4}{2} + \frac{10x^3}{9} - \frac{7x^2}{9} + \frac{2x}{9}\right]_0^1 \\
&= \frac{1}{18} \qquad\qquad \textit{Variance}
\end{aligned}$$

Finally, you can conclude that the standard deviation is

$$\sigma = \sqrt{\frac{1}{18}} \approx 0.236. \qquad\qquad \textit{Standard deviation}$$

The integral for variance can be difficult to evaluate. The following alternative formula is often simpler.

Alternative Formula for Variance

If f is a probability density function for a continuous random variable x over the interval $[a, b]$, then the **variance** of x is

$$V(x) = \int_a^b x^2 f(x)\, dx - \mu^2,$$

where μ is the mean of x.

EXAMPLE 3   *Using the Alternative Formula*

Find the standard deviation of the probability density function

$$f(x) = \frac{2}{\pi(x^2 - 2x + 2)}, \qquad 0 \le x \le 2.$$

What percent of the distribution lies within one standard deviation of the mean?

Solution

Begin by using a symbolic integrator to find the mean.

$$\mu = \int_0^2 \left(\frac{2}{\pi(x^2 - 2x + 2)} \right)(x)\, dx$$

$$= 1 \qquad\qquad\qquad\qquad\qquad\qquad\qquad\qquad \textit{Mean}$$

Next, use a symbolic integrator to find the variance.

$$V(x) = \int_0^2 \left(\frac{2}{\pi(x^2 - 2x + 2)} \right)(x^2)\, dx - 1^2$$

$$\approx 0.273 \qquad\qquad\qquad\qquad\qquad\qquad \textit{Variance}$$

This implies that the standard deviation is

$$\sigma = \sqrt{0.273} \approx 0.522. \qquad\qquad\qquad \textit{Standard deviation}$$

To find the percent of the distribution that lies within one standard deviation of the mean, integrate the probability density function between $\mu - \sigma = 0.478$ and $\mu + \sigma = 1.522$.

$$\int_{0.478}^{1.522} \frac{2}{\pi(x^2 - 2x + 2)}\, dx \approx 0.613$$

Thus, about 61.3% of the distribution lies within one standard deviation of the mean. This result is illustrated in Figure P.13.

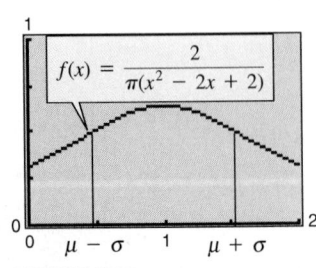

$$f(x) = \frac{2}{\pi(x^2 - 2x + 2)}$$

FIGURE P.13

Median

The mean of a probability density function is an example of a **measure of central tendency.** Another useful measure of central tendency is the **median.**

Definition of Median

If f is a probability density function for a continuous random variable x over the interval $[a, b]$, then the **median** of x is the number m such that

$$\int_a^m f(x)\,dx = 0.5.$$

Real Life

EXAMPLE 4 *Comparing Mean and Median*

In Example 5 in Section P.2, the probability density function

$$f(t) = 0.1e^{-0.1t}, \qquad 0 \le t < \infty$$

was used to model the usable lifetime of a product. Find the mean and median usable lifetime.

Solution

Using integration by parts or a symbolic integrator, you can find the mean to be

$$\mu = \int_0^\infty 0.1te^{-0.1t}\,dt$$

$$= 10 \text{ years}. \qquad\qquad \textit{Mean}$$

The median is given by

$$\int_0^m 0.1e^{-0.1t}\,dt = 0.5$$

$$-e^{-0.1m} + 1 = 0.5$$

$$e^{-0.1m} = 0.5$$

$$-0.1m = \ln 0.5$$

$$m = -10 \ln 0.5$$

$$m \approx 6.93 \text{ years}. \qquad\qquad \textit{Median}$$

From this, you can see that the mean and median of a probability distribution can be quite different. Using the mean, the "average" lifetime of a product is 10 years, but using the median, the "average" lifetime is 6.93 years. In Figure P.14, note that half of the products have usable lifetimes of 6.93 years or less.

Usable Lifetime of a Product

Area $= \frac{1}{2}$

$f(t) = 0.1e^{-0.1t}$

Area $= \frac{1}{2}$

Median ≈ 6.93

Time (in years)

FIGURE P.14

Special Probability Density Functions

The remainder of this section describes three common types of probability density functions: uniform, exponential, and normal. The **uniform probability density function** is defined by

$$f(x) = \frac{1}{b-a}, \qquad a \le x \le b. \qquad \textit{Uniform probability density function}$$

This probability density function represents a continuous random variable for which each outcome is equally likely.

EXAMPLE 5 *Analyzing a Probability Density Function*

Find the expected value and standard deviation for the uniform probability density function

$$f(x) = \frac{1}{8}, \qquad 0 \le x \le 8.$$

Solution
The expected value (or mean) is

$$\mu = \int_0^8 \frac{1}{8} x \, dx$$

$$= \left[\frac{x^2}{16} \right]_0^8$$

$$= 4. \qquad \qquad \textit{Expected value}$$

The variance is

$$V(x) = \int_0^8 \frac{1}{8} x^2 \, dx - 4^2$$

$$= \left[\frac{x^3}{24} \right]_0^8 - 16$$

$$\approx 5.333. \qquad \qquad \textit{Variance}$$

The standard deviation is

$$\sigma = \sqrt{5.333}$$

$$\approx 2.309. \qquad \qquad \textit{Standard deviation}$$

The graph of f is shown in Figure P.15.

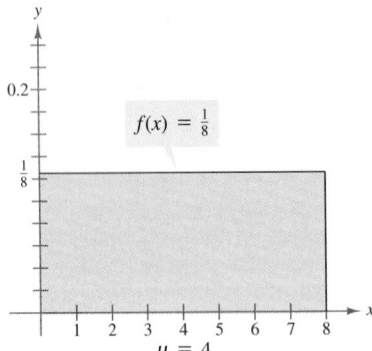

FIGURE P.15 Uniform Probability Density Function

Note Try showing that the mean and variance of the general uniform probability density function $f(x) = 1/(b-a)$ is $\mu = \frac{1}{2}(a+b)$ and $V(x) = \frac{1}{12}(b-a)^2$.

The second special type of probability density function is an **exponential probability density function** and has the form

$$f(x) = ae^{-ax}, \qquad 0 \leq x < \infty.$$

Exponential probability density function, a > 0

The probability density function in Example 4 is of this type. Try showing that this function has a mean of $1/a$ and a variance of $1/a^2$.

The third special type of probability density function (and the most widely used) is the **normal probability density function** given by

$$f(x) = \frac{1}{\sigma\sqrt{2\pi}}e^{-(x-\mu)^2/2\sigma^2}, \qquad -\infty < x < \infty.$$

Normal probability density function

The expected value for this function is μ and the standard deviation is σ. Figure P.16 shows the graph of a typical normal probability density function.

A normal probability density function for which $\mu = 0$ and $\sigma = 1$ is called a **standard normal probability density function.**

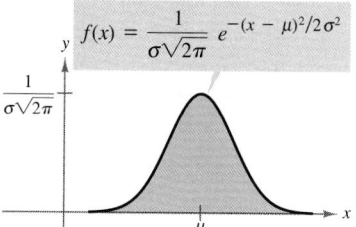

$$f(x) = \frac{1}{\sigma\sqrt{2\pi}}e^{-(x-\mu)^2/2\sigma^2}$$

FIGURE P.16   Normal Probability Density Function

The SAT and GMAT standardized tests are published by the College Entrance Examination Board. On each test, scores vary between 200 and 800. The mean tends to be around 500 and the standard deviation tends to be around 100.

Real Life

EXAMPLE 6 *Finding a Probability*

In 1990, the scores for the *Graduate Management Admission Test* (GMAT) could be modeled by a normal probability density function with a mean of $\mu = 490$ and a standard deviation of $\sigma = 110$. If you select a person who took the GMAT in 1990, what is the probability that the person scored between 600 and 700? What is the probability that the person scored between 700 and 800?

Solution

Using a calculator or computer, you can find the first probability to be

$$P(600 \leq x \leq 700) = \int_{600}^{700} \frac{1}{110\sqrt{2\pi}}e^{-(x-490)^2/2(110)^2} \, dx$$
$$\approx 0.13.$$

Thus, the probability of choosing a person who scored between 600 and 700 is about 13%. In a similar way, you can find the probability of choosing a person who scored between 700 and 800 to be

$$P(700 \leq x \leq 800) = \int_{700}^{800} \frac{1}{110\sqrt{2\pi}}e^{-(x-490)^2/2(110)^2} \, dx$$
$$\approx 0.026,$$

or about 2.6%.

Note   In Example 6, note that probabilities connected with normal distributions must be evaluated with a table of values or with a symbolic integration utility.

TECHNOLOGY   *Using the Normal Probability Density Function*

The *standard* normal probability density function is

$$f(x) = \frac{1}{\sqrt{2\pi}} e^{-x^2/2}.$$

For this function, the mean is $\mu = 0$ and the standard deviation is $\sigma = 1$. This function does not have an antiderivative that is an elementary function. It does, however, have an antiderivative, which is denoted by $\frac{1}{2}\text{ERF}(x/\sqrt{2})$. Symbolic integration utilities such as *Derive*, *Mathematica*, and *Maple* use built-in programs that can evaluate this function. Here are some examples.

a. The probability that a random value is between 0 and 1.02 is

$$P(0 \leq x \leq 1.02) = \int_0^{1.02} \frac{1}{\sqrt{2\pi}} e^{-x^2/2}\, dx$$

$$= \frac{1}{2}\text{ERF}\left(\frac{1.02}{\sqrt{2}}\right) - \frac{1}{2}\text{ERF}(0)$$

$$\approx 0.3461.$$

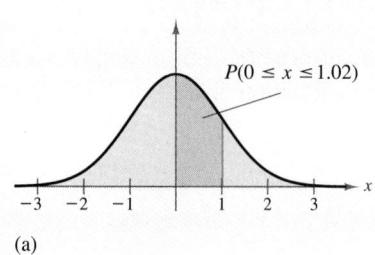

(a)

b. The probability that a random value is between -1.43 and 0 is

$$P(-1.43 \leq x \leq 0) = \int_{-1.43}^{0} \frac{1}{\sqrt{2\pi}} e^{-x^2/2}\, dx$$

$$= \frac{1}{2}\text{ERF}(0) - \frac{1}{2}\text{ERF}\left(\frac{-1.43}{\sqrt{2}}\right)$$

$$\approx 0.4236.$$

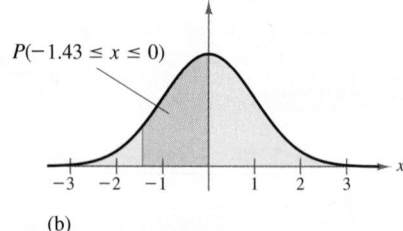

(b)

c. The probability that a random value is between 0.14 and 1.23 is

$$P(0.14 \leq x \leq 1.23) = \int_{0.14}^{1.23} \frac{1}{\sqrt{2\pi}} e^{-x^2/2}\, dx$$

$$= \frac{1}{2}\text{ERF}\left(\frac{1.23}{\sqrt{2}}\right) - \frac{1}{2}\text{ERF}\left(\frac{0.14}{\sqrt{2}}\right)$$

$$\approx 0.3350.$$

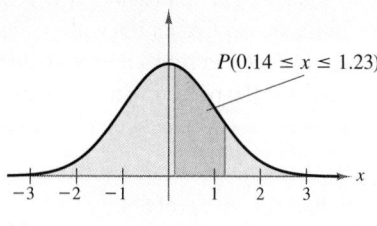

(c)

d. The probability that a random value is greater than or equal to 0.76 is

$$P(0.76 \leq x < \infty) = \int_{0.76}^{\infty} \frac{1}{\sqrt{2\pi}} e^{-x^2/2}\, dx$$

$$= \frac{1}{2} - \frac{1}{2}\text{ERF}\left(\frac{0.76}{\sqrt{2}}\right)$$

$$\approx 0.2236.$$

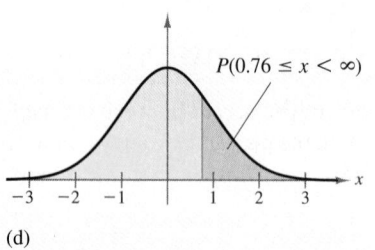

(d)

Graphical representations of these four probabilities are shown in the figure at left.

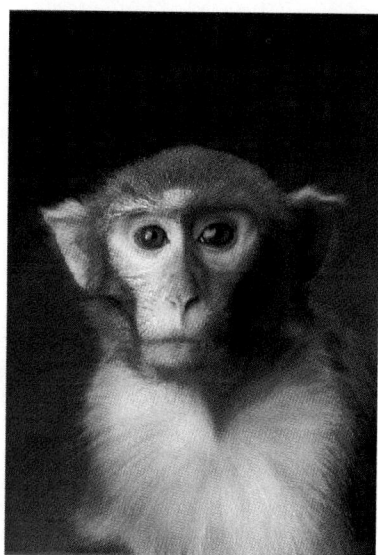

Allstock/© G. Robert Bishop/HMS Group

In addition to being popular zoo animals, rhesus monkeys are commonly used in medical and behavioral research. Research on rhesus monkeys led to the discovery of the *Rh factor* in human red blood cells.

Real Life

EXAMPLE 7 *Modeling Body Weight*

The weight of adult male rhesus monkeys is normally distributed with a mean of 15 pounds and a standard deviation of 3 pounds. In a typical population of adult male rhesus monkeys, what percent of the monkeys would have a weight that is within one standard deviation of the mean?

Solution

For this population, the normal probability density function is

$$f(x) = \frac{1}{3\sqrt{2\pi}} e^{-(x-15)^2/18}.$$

The probability that a randomly chosen adult male monkey will weigh between 12 and 18 pounds (that is, within 3 pounds of 15 pounds) is

$$P(12 \le x \le 18) = \int_{12}^{18} \frac{1}{3\sqrt{2\pi}} e^{-(x-15)^2/18} \, dx$$

$$\approx 0.683.$$

Thus, about 68% of the adult male monkeys have weights that lie within one standard deviation of the mean, as shown in Figure P.17.

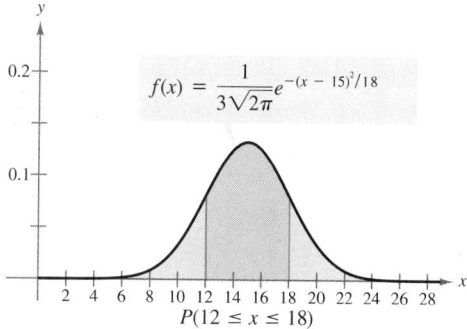

FIGURE P.17

The result that is described in Example 7 can be generalized to all normal distributions. That is, in any normal distribution, the probability that x lies within one standard deviation of the mean is about 68%. For normal distributions, 95.4% of the x-values lie within two standard deviations of the mean, and almost all (99.7%) of the x-values lie within three standard deviations of the mean.

Discussion Problem   *Exploring Normal Distributions*

In a normal distribution, what percent of the x-values lie within 1.5 standard deviations of the mean? What percent lie within 0.5 standard deviation of the mean?

Warm Up

The following warm-up exercises involve skills that were covered in earlier sections. You will use these skills in the exercise set for this section.

In Exercises 1–4, solve for *m*.

1. $\int_0^m \frac{1}{10}\, dx = 0.5$

2. $\int_0^m \frac{1}{16}\, dx = 0.5$

3. $\int_0^m \frac{1}{3}e^{-t/3}\, dt = 0.5$

4. $\int_0^m \frac{1}{9}e^{-t/9}\, dt = 0.5$

In Exercises 5–8, evaluate the definite integral.

5. $\int_0^2 \frac{x^2}{2}\, dx$

6. $\int_1^2 x(4 - 2x)\, dx$

7. $\int_2^5 x^2 \left(\frac{1}{3}\right) dx - \left(\frac{7}{2}\right)^2$

8. $\int_2^4 x^2 \left(\frac{4 - x}{2}\right) dx - \left(\frac{8}{3}\right)^2$

In Exercises 9 and 10, find the indicated probability using the given probability density function.

9. $f(x) = \frac{1}{8}$, $[0, 8]$;   (a) $P(x \le 2)$,   (b) $P(3 < x < 7)$

10. $f(x) = 6x - 6x^2$, $[0, 1]$;   (a) $P\left(x \le \frac{1}{2}\right)$,   (b) $P\left(\frac{1}{4} \le x \le \frac{3}{4}\right)$

EXERCISES   P.3   means that technology can help you solve or check the exercise(s).

In Exercises 1–10, use the given probability density function over the indicated interval to find (a) the mean, (b) the variance, and (c) the standard deviation of the random variable. Sketch the graph of the density function, and then locate the mean on the graph.

1. $f(x) = \frac{1}{8}$, $[0, 8]$

2. $f(x) = \frac{1}{4}$, $[0, 4]$

3. $f(t) = \frac{t}{18}$, $[0, 6]$

4. $f(x) = \frac{4}{3x^2}$, $[1, 4]$

5. $f(x) = 6x(1 - x)$, $[0, 1]$

6. $f(x) = \frac{3}{32}x(4 - x)$, $[0, 4]$

7. $f(x) = \frac{5}{2}x^{3/2}$, $[0, 1]$

8. $f(x) = \frac{3}{16}\sqrt{4 - x}$, $[0, 4]$

9. $f(x) = \frac{4}{3(x + 1)^2}$, $[0, 3]$

10. $f(x) = \frac{1}{18}\sqrt{9 - x}$, $[0, 9]$

In Exercises 11 and 12, find the median of the exponential probability density function.

11. $f(t) = \frac{1}{9}e^{-t/9}$, $[0, \infty)$

12. $f(t) = \frac{2}{5}e^{-2t/5}$, $[0, \infty)$

In Exercises 13–18, identify the probability density function. Then find the mean, variance, and standard deviation without integrating.

13. $f(x) = \frac{1}{10}$, $[0, 10]$

14. $f(x) = \frac{1}{9}$, $[0, 9]$

15. $f(x) = \frac{1}{8}e^{-x/8}$, $[0, \infty)$

16. $f(x) = \frac{5}{3}e^{-5x/3}$, $[0, \infty)$

17. $f(x) = \frac{1}{11\sqrt{2\pi}}e^{-(x-100)^2/242}$, $(-\infty, \infty)$

18. $f(x) = \frac{1}{6\sqrt{2\pi}}e^{-(x-30)^2/72}$, $(-\infty, \infty)$

In Exercises 19–24, use a symbolic differentiation utility to find the mean, standard deviation, and indicated probability.

Function	*Probability*
19. $f(x) = \dfrac{1}{\sqrt{2\pi}}e^{-x^2/2}$	$P(0 \le x \le 0.85)$
20. $f(x) = \dfrac{1}{\sqrt{2\pi}}e^{-x^2/2}$	$P(-1.21 \le x \le 1.21)$
21. $f(x) = \frac{1}{6}e^{-x/6}$	$P(x \ge 2.23)$
22. $f(x) = \frac{3}{4}e^{-3x/4}$	$P(x \ge 0.27)$
23. $f(x) = \dfrac{1}{2\sqrt{2\pi}}e^{-(x-8)^2/8}$	$P(3 \le x \le 13)$
24. $f(x) = \dfrac{1}{1.5\sqrt{2\pi}}e^{-(x-2)^2/4.5}$	$P(-2.5 \le x \le 2.5)$

 25. Let x be a random variable that is normally distributed with a mean of 60 and a standard deviation of 12. Find the required probabilities using a symbolic integration utility.
(a) $P(x > 64)$ (b) $P(x > 70)$
(c) $P(x < 70)$ (d) $P(33 < x < 65)$

26. Let x be a random variable that is normally distributed with a mean of 75 and a standard deviation of 12. Find the required probabilities using a symbolic integration utility.
(a) $P(x > 69)$ (b) $P(x < 99)$
(c) $P(x < 57)$ (d) $P(63 < x < 78)$

27. *Arrival Time* The arrival time t of a bus at a bus stop is uniformly distributed between the times of 10:00 A.M. and 10:10 A.M.
(a) Find the mean and standard deviation of the random variable t.
(b) What is the probability that you will miss the bus if you arrive at the bus stop at 10:03 A.M.?

28. *Arrival Time* Repeat Exercise 27 for a bus that arrives between the times of 10:00 A.M. and 10:05 A.M.

29. *Useful Life* The time t until failure of an appliance is exponentially distributed with a mean of 2 years.
(a) Find the probability density function for the random variable t.
(b) Find the probability that the appliance will fail in less than 1 year.

30. *Arrival Time* The time t between arrivals of customers at a gasoline station is exponentially distributed with a mean of 2 minutes.
(a) Find the probability density function for the random variable t.
(b) If a customer has just arrived, determine the probability that it will be more than 3 minutes before the next arrival.

31. *Waiting Time* The waiting time t for service at a customer service desk in a department store is exponentially distributed with a mean of 5 minutes.
(a) Find the probability density function for the random variable t.
(b) Find the probability that t is within one standard deviation of the mean.

32. *Service Time* The service time t for a customer at the service desk in a department store is exponentially distributed with a mean of 3.5 minutes.
(a) Find the probability density function for the random variable t.
(b) Find the probability that t is within one standard deviation of the mean.

33. *Standardized Test Scores* The scores on a national exam are normally distributed with a mean of 150 and a standard deviation of 16. You scored 174 on the exam.
(a) How far, in standard deviations, did your score exceed the national mean?
(b) What percent of those who took the exam had scores lower than yours?

34. *Useful Life* The length of life of a battery is normally distributed with a mean of 400 hours and a standard deviation of 24 hours. You purchased one of the batteries and its useful life was 340 hours.
(a) How far, in standard deviations, did the useful life of your battery fall short of the expected life?
(b) What percent of all other batteries of this type have useful lives that exceed yours?

35. *Demand* The daily demand x for a certain product (in hundreds of pounds) is a random variable with the probability density function
$$f(x) = \tfrac{1}{36}x(6 - x), \quad [0, 6].$$
(a) Determine the expected value and the standard deviation of demand.
(b) Determine the median of the random variable.
(c) Find the probability that x is within one standard deviation of the mean.

36. *Demand* Repeat Exercise 35 for a probability density function of
$$f(x) = \tfrac{3}{256}(x - 2)(10 - x), \quad [2, 10].$$

37. *Learning Theory* The percent recall x in a learning experiment is a random variable with the probability density function
$$f(x) = \tfrac{15}{4}x\sqrt{1 - x}, \quad [0, 1].$$
Determine the mean and variance of random variable x.

38. *Metallurgy* The percent of iron x in samples of ore is a random variable with the probability density function

$$f(x) = \tfrac{1155}{32}x^3(1 - x)^{3/2}, \quad [0, 1].$$

Determine the expected percent of iron in each ore sample.

39. *Demand* The daily demand x for a certain product (in thousands of units) is a random variable with the probability density function

$$f(x) = \tfrac{1}{25}xe^{-x/5}, \quad [0, \infty).$$

(a) Determine the expected daily demand.
(b) Find $P(x \le 4)$.

40. *Recovery Time* The time t (in days) until recovery after a certain medical procedure is a random variable with the probability density function

$$f(t) = \frac{1}{2\sqrt{t - 2}}, \quad [3, 6].$$

(a) Find the probability that a patient selected at random will take more than 4 days to recover.
(b) Determine the expected time for recovery.

In Exercises 41–46, find the mean and median.

41. $f(x) = \tfrac{1}{11}$ $[0, 11]$

42. $f(x) = 0.04$ $[0, 25]$

43. $f(x) = 4(1 - 2x)$ $\left[0, \tfrac{1}{2}\right]$

44. $f(x) = \tfrac{4}{3} - \tfrac{2}{3}x$ $[0, 3]$

45. $f(x) = \tfrac{1}{5}e^{-x/5}$ $[0, \infty)$

46. $f(x) = \tfrac{2}{3}e^{-2x/3}$ $[0, \infty)$

47. *Cost of Electricity* The daily cost of electricity x in a city is a random variable with the probability density function

$$f(x) = 0.28e^{-0.28x}, \quad 0 \le x < \infty.$$

Find the median daily cost of electricity.

48. *Coupon Sales* The number of coupons used by a customer in a grocery store is a random variable with the probability density function

$$f(x) = \frac{2x + 1}{10}, \quad 1 \le x \le 2.$$

Find the expected number of coupons a customer will use.

49. *Demand* The daily demand x for water (in millions of gallons) in a town is a random variable with the probability density function

$$f(x) = \tfrac{1}{9}xe^{-x/3}, \quad [0, \infty).$$

(a) Determine the expected value and the standard deviation of the demand.
(b) Find the probability that the demand is greater than 4 million gallons on a given day.

50. *Useful Life* The length of life of an electrical component is normally distributed with a mean of 5.3 years and a standard deviation of 0.8 year. How long should this component be guaranteed if the producer does not want to replace any more than 10% of the components during the time covered by the guarantee?

51. *Machine Precision* An automatic filling machine fills cans so that the weights are normally distributed with a mean of μ and a standard deviation of σ. The value of μ can be controlled by settings on the machine, but σ depends on the precision and design of the machine. For a particular substance, $\sigma = 0.15$ ounce. If 12-ounce cans are being filled, determine the setting for μ so that no more than 5% of the cans weigh less than the stated weight.

52. *Useful Life* A storage battery has an expected lifetime of 4.5 years with a standard deviation of 0.5 year. Assume that the useful lives of these batteries are normally distributed. Use a computer or calculator and Simpson's Rule (with $n = 12$) to approximate the probability that a given battery will last for 4 to 5 years.

53. *Wages* The employees of a large corporation are paid an average wage of $12.30 per hour with a standard deviation of $1.50. Assume that these wages are normally distributed. Use a computer or calculator and Simpson's Rule (with $n = 10$) to approximate the percent of employees that earn hourly wages of $9.00 to $12.00.

54. *Profit* The weekly profit x (in thousands of dollars) of a store is normally distributed with $\mu = 8$ and $\sigma = 3$. Use a symbolic integration utility to find $P(8 < x < 11)$.

55. *Intelligence Quotient* The IQs of students in a school are normally distributed with a mean of 110 and a standard deviation of 10. Use a symbolic integration utility to find the probability that a student selected at random will have an IQ within one standard deviation of the mean.

Chapter Summary and Study Tips

After studying this chapter, you should have acquired the following skills. The exercise numbers are keyed to the Review Exercises that begin on page P–30. Answers to odd-numbered Review Exercises are given in the back of the text.

- Describe sample spaces for experiments. (*Section P.1*)   Review Exercises 1–4
- Assign values to discrete random variables. (*Section P.1*)   Review Exercises 5, 6
- Form frequency distributions for discrete random variables. (*Section P.1*)   Review Exercises 7, 8
- Find the probabilities of events for discrete random variables. (*Section P.1*)   Review Exercises 9–12

$$P(x) = \frac{\text{Frequency of } x}{\text{Number of outcomes in } S} = \frac{n(x)}{n(S)}$$

- Find the expected values or means of discrete random variables. (*Section P.1*)   Review Exercises 13–16

$$\mu = E(x) = x_1 P(x_1) + x_2 P(x_2) + x_3 P(x_3) + \cdots + x_m P(x_m).$$

- Find the variances and standard deviations of discrete random variables. (*Section P.1*)   Review Exercises 17–20

$$V(x) = (x_1 - \mu)^2 P(x_1) + \cdots + (x_m - \mu)^2 P(x_m), \qquad \sigma = \sqrt{V(x)}$$

- Verify continuous probability density functions. (*Section P.2*)   Review Exercises 21–24
- Use continuous probability density functions to find probabilities. (*Section P.2*)   Review Exercises 25–28

$$P(c \leq x \leq d) = \int_c^d f(x)\, dx$$

- Use continuous probability density functions to answer questions about real life. (*Section P.2*)   Review Exercises 29–32
- Find the means of continuous probability density functions. (*Section P.3*)   Review Exercises 33–36

$$\mu = E(x) = \int_a^b x f(x)\, dx$$

- Find the variances and standard deviations of continuous probability density functions. (*Section P.3*)   Review Exercises 37–40

$$V(x) = \int_a^b (x - \mu)^2 f(x)\, dx, \qquad \sigma = \sqrt{V(x)}$$

- Find the medians of continuous probability density functions. (*Section P.3*)   Review Exercises 41–44
- Use special probability density functions to answer questions about real life. (*Section P.3*)   Review Exercises 45–50
- Using Technology   Integrals that arise with continuous probability density functions tend to be difficult to evaluate by hand. When evaluating such integrals, we suggest that you use a symbolic integration utility such as *Derive*, *Mathematica*, or *Maple*, or that you use a numerical integration technique such as Simpson's Rule with a programmable calculator.

*Several student study aids are available with this text. The *Student Solutions Guide* includes detailed solutions to all odd-numbered exercises, as well as practice chapter tests with answers. The *Graphics Calculator Guide* offers instructions on the use of a variety of graphing calculators and computer graphing software. The *Brief Calculus TUTOR* includes additional examples for selected exercises in the text.

Review Exercises

 means that technology can help you solve or check the exercise(s).

In Exercises 1–4, describe the sample space of the experiment.

1. A month of the year is chosen for a vacation.

2. A letter from the word *calculus* is selected.

3. A student must answer three questions from a selection of four essay questions.

4. A winner in a game show must choose two out of five prizes.

5. Three numbers are drawn in a lottery. Each number is a digit from 0 to 9. Find the sample space giving the number of 7's drawn.

6. As cans of soft drink are filled on the production line, four are randomly selected and labeled with an "S" if the weight is satisfactory and a "U" if the weight is unsatisfactory. Find the sample space giving the satisfactory/unsatisfactory classification of each can.

In Exercises 7 and 8, complete the table to form the frequency distribution of the random variable *x*. Then construct a bar graph to represent the result.

7. A computer randomly selects a three-digit bar code. Each digit can be 0 or 1, and *x* is the number of 1's in the bar code.

x	0	1	2	3
$n(x)$				

8. A cat has a litter of four kittens. Let *x* represent the number of male kittens.

x	0	1	2	3	4
$n(x)$					

In Exercises 9 and 10, sketch a graph of the given probability distribution and find the required probabilities.

9.

x	1	2	3	4	5
$P(x)$	$\frac{1}{18}$	$\frac{7}{18}$	$\frac{5}{18}$	$\frac{3}{18}$	$\frac{2}{18}$

(a) $P(2 \le x \le 4)$ (b) $P(x \ge 3)$

10.

x	-2	-1	1	3	5
$P(x)$	$\frac{1}{11}$	$\frac{2}{11}$	$\frac{4}{11}$	$\frac{3}{11}$	$\frac{1}{11}$

(a) $P(x < 0)$ (b) $P(x > 1)$

11. *Tossing Dice* Consider an experiment in which two six-sided dice are tossed. Find the indicated probability.

(a) The probability that the total is 8.
(b) The probability that the total is greater than 4.
(c) The probability that doubles are thrown.
(d) The probability of getting double sixes.

12. *Selecting a Card* Consider an experiment in which one card is randomly selected from a standard deck of 52 playing cards. Find the probability of

(a) selecting a face card.
(b) selecting a card that is not a face card.
(c) selecting a black card that is not a face card.
(d) selecting a card whose value is 6 or less.

13. *Quiz Scores* An instructor gave a 25-point quiz to 52 students. Use the following frequency distribution of quiz scores to find the mean quiz score.

Score	9	10	11	12	13	14	15	16	17
Frequency	1	0	1	0	0	0	3	4	7

Score	18	19	20	21	22	23	24	25
Frequency	3	0	9	11	6	3	0	4

14. *Cost Increases* A small business uses three different materials, A, B, and C, to create a particular product. The following table gives the cost and the percent increase of the cost of each of the three materials. Find the mean percent increase of the three products.

Material	Percent Increase	Cost of Supplies
A	8%	$650
B	23%	$375
C	16%	$800

15. *Revenue* A publishing company introduces a new weekly newspaper that sells for 75 cents. The marketing group of the company estimates that sales *x* (in thousands) will be approximated by the following probability function.

x	10	15	20	30	40
$P(x)$	0.10	0.20	0.50	0.15	0.05

(a) Find $E(x)$.   (b) Find the expected revenue.

16. *Game of Chance* A service organization is selling $3 raffle tickets as part of a fund-raising program. The first and second prizes are $2000 and $1000, respectively. In addition to the first and second prizes, there are 50 $20 gift certificates to be awarded. The number of tickets sold is 2000. Find the expected net gain to the player when one ticket is purchased.

17. *Sales Volume* A company sells five different models of personal computers. During one month the sales for the five models were as follows.

Model 1   24 sold at $1200 each
Model 2   12 sold at $1500 each
Model 3   35 sold at $2000 each
Model 4   5 sold at $2200 each
Model 5   4 sold at $3000 each

Find the variance and standard deviation of the prices.

18. *Textbook Prices* A school buys multiple copies of five different mathematics textbooks. The quantities and prices per book are as follows.

Geometry   12 copies at $54 each
Algebra   45 copies at $45 each
Precalculus   25 copies at $52 each
Calculus   20 copies at $60 each
Statistics   15 copies at $65 each

Find the variance and standard deviation of the prices.

19. *Car Ownership* A random survey of households recorded the number of cars per household. The results of the survey are shown in the table.

x	0	1	2	3	4	5
$P(x)$	0.10	0.28	0.39	0.17	0.04	0.02

Find the variance and standard deviation of x.

20. *Number of Children* The probability distribution for the number of children in a sample of families is given in the following table.

x	0	1	2	3	4
$P(x)$	0.12	0.31	0.43	0.12	0.02

Find the variance and standard deviation of x.

In Exercises 21–24, use a graphing utility to graph the function. Then verify that f is a probability density function.

21. $f(x) = \frac{1}{8}(4 - x)$, $[0, 4]$

22. $f(x) = \frac{3}{4}x^2(2 - x)$, $[0, 2]$

23. $f(x) = \dfrac{1}{4\sqrt{x}}$, $[1, 9]$

24. $f(x) = 8.75x^{3/2}(1 - x)$, $[0, 1]$

In Exercises 25–28, find the indicated probability for the probability density function.

25. $f(x) = \frac{1}{50}(10 - x)$, $[0, 10]$, $P(0 < x < 2)$

26. $f(x) = \frac{1}{36}(9 - x^2)$, $[-3, 3]$, $P(-1 < x < 2)$

27. $f(x) = \dfrac{2}{(x + 1)^2}$, $[0, 1]$, $P\left(0 < x < \dfrac{1}{2}\right)$

28. $f(x) = \dfrac{3}{128}\sqrt{x}$, $[0, 16]$, $P(4 < x < 9)$

29. *Transportation* Buses arrive and depart from a college every 20 minutes. The probability density function for the waiting time t (in minutes) for a person arriving at the bus stop is

$$f(t) = \tfrac{1}{20}, [0, 20].$$

Find the probability that the person will wait (a) no more than 10 minutes, and (b) at least 15 minutes.

30. *Learning Theory* The time t (in hours) required for a new employee to successfully learn to operate a machine in a manufacturing process is described by the probability density function

$$f(t) = \tfrac{5}{324}t\sqrt{9 - t}, [0, 9].$$

Find the probability that a new employee will learn to operate the machine in less than 4 hours.

31. *Recovery Time* The time t (in days) until recovery after a certain medical procedure is a random variable with the probability density function

$$f(t) = \dfrac{1}{4\sqrt{t - 4}}, [5, 13].$$

Find the probability that a patient selected at random will take more than 8 days to recover.

32. *Demand* The monthly demand x (in kilograms) for a certain product is a random variable with density function

$$f(x) = \tfrac{1}{64}xe^{-x/8}.$$

Find the probability that the demand is at least 9 kilograms for a randomly selected month.

In Exercises 33–36, find the mean of the continuous probability density function.

33. $f(x) = \dfrac{1}{5}$, $[0, 5]$ **34.** $f(x) = \dfrac{8-x}{32}$, $[0, 8]$

35. $f(x) = \tfrac{1}{6}e^{-x/6}$, $[0, \infty)$ **36.** $f(x) = 0.3e^{-0.3x}$, $[0, \infty)$

In Exercises 37–40, find the variance and standard deviation of the continuous probability density function.

37. $f(x) = \tfrac{2}{9}x(3 - x)$, $[0, 3]$

38. $f(x) = \tfrac{3}{16}\sqrt{x}$, $[0, 4]$

39. $f(x) = \tfrac{1}{2}e^{-x/2}$, $[0, \infty)$

40. $f(x) = 0.8e^{-0.8x}$, $[0, \infty)$

In Exercises 41–44, find the median of the continuous probability density function.

41. $f(x) = 6x(1 - x)$, $[0, 1]$

42. $f(x) = 12x^2(1 - x)$, $[0, 1]$

43. $f(x) = 0.25e^{-x/4}$, $[0, \infty)$

44. $f(x) = \tfrac{5}{6}e^{-5x/6}$, $[0, \infty)$

45. *Waiting Time* The waiting time t (in minutes) for service at the checkout at a grocery store is exponentially distributed with the probability density function

$$f(t) = \tfrac{1}{3}e^{-t/3}, [0, \infty).$$

Find the probability of waiting (a) less than 2 minutes, and (b) more than 2 minutes but less than 4 minutes.

46. *Useful Life* The lifetime t (in hours) of a mechanical unit is exponentially distributed with the following density function.

$$f(t) = \tfrac{1}{350}e^{-t/350}, [0, \infty).$$

Find the probability that a given unit chosen at random will perform satisfactorily for more than 400 hours.

47. *Botany* In a botany experiment, plants are grown in a nutrient solution. The heights of the plants are found to be normally distributed with a mean of 42 centimeters and a standard deviation of 3 centimeters. Find the probability that a plant in the experiment is at least 50 centimeters tall.

48. *Wages* The distribution of hourly wages for the workers in a certain company is normally distributed with a mean of $14.50 and a standard deviation of $1.40. (a) What percent of the workers receive an hourly wage between $13 and $15, inclusive? (b) The highest 10% of the hourly wages is greater than what amount?

49. *Meteorology* The monthly rainfall x in a certain state is normally distributed with a mean of 3.75 inches and a standard deviation of 0.5 inch. Use Simpson's Rule (with $n = 12$) to approximate the probability that in a randomly selected month the rainfall is between 3.5 and 4 inches.

50. *Demand* The weekly demand x (in tons) for a certain product is a continuous random variable with the density function

$$f(x) = \tfrac{1}{25}xe^{-x/5}, [0, \infty).$$

Use a symbolic integration utility to find (a) $P(x < 5)$, (b) $P(5 < x < 10)$, and (c) $P(x > 10) = 1 - P(x \le 10)$.

$$y = \frac{1}{u(x)} \int Q(x)\, u(x)\, dx$$

D

Differential Equations

Differential equations—equations that involve the derivatives of a function—provided much of the motivation for the early development of calculus. Many of the early classic problems in calculus, such as the pendulum problem and the vibrating string problem, could be modeled as differential equations.

For instance, the pendulum problem, which was solved by James Bernoulli in 1690, is to find a curve along which a pendulum takes the same time to make a complete oscillation whether it swings through a wide or a small arc.

Throughout history, problem solving has been the driving force of most mathematical discoveries. In the words of the American mathematician Mary Ellen Rudin (1924–), "I'm a problem solver . . . if a problem can be stated in a simple form that I can really understand, then I have this feeling that I should be able to solve it."

$$y' + P(x)y = Q(x)$$

Rudin

General Solution of a Differential Equation

A **differential equation** is an equation involving a differentiable function and one or more of its derivatives. For instance,

$$y' + 2y = 0 \qquad\qquad \textit{Differential equation}$$

is a differential equation. A function $y = f(x)$ is a **solution** of a differential equation if the equation is satisfied when y and its derivatives are replaced by $f(x)$ and its derivatives. For instance,

$$y = e^{-2x} \qquad\qquad \textit{Solution of differential equation}$$

is a solution of the differential equation given above. To see this, substitute for y and $y' = -2e^{-2x}$ in the original equation.

$$y' + 2y = -2e^{-2x} + 2(e^{-2x}) = 0 \qquad \textit{Substitute for } y \textit{ and } y'.$$

In the same way, you can show that $y = 2e^{-2x}$, $y = -3e^{-2x}$, and $y = \frac{1}{2}e^{-2x}$ are also solutions of the differential equation. In fact, each function given by

$$y = Ce^{-2x}, \qquad\qquad \textit{General solution}$$

where C is a real number, is a solution of the equation. This family of solutions is called the **general solution** of the differential equation.

EXAMPLE 1 *Checking Solutions*

Show that (a) $y = Ce^x$ and (b) $y = Ce^{-x}$ are solutions of the differential equation $y'' - y = 0$.

Solution

a. Because $y' = Ce^x$ and $y'' = Ce^x$, it follows that

$$y'' - y = Ce^x - Ce^x = 0.$$

Hence, $y = Ce^x$ *is* a solution.

b. Because $y' = -Ce^{-x}$ and $y'' = Ce^{-x}$, it follows that

$$y'' - y = Ce^{-x} - Ce^{-x} = 0.$$

Hence, $y = Ce^{-x}$ is also a solution. ■

Particular Solutions and Initial Conditions

A **particular solution** of a differential equation is any solution that is obtained by assigning specific values to the constants in the general equation.*

Geometrically, the general solution of a differential equation is a family of graphs called **solution curves.** For instance, the general solution of the differential equation $xy' - 2y = 0$ is

$$y = Cx^2. \qquad \textit{General solution}$$

Figure D.1 shows several solution curves of this differential equation.

Particular solutions of a differential equation are obtained from **initial conditions** placed on the unknown function and its derivatives. For instance, in Figure D.1, suppose you wanted to find the particular solution whose graph passes through the point $(1, 3)$. This initial condition can be written as

$$y = 3 \quad \text{when} \quad x = 1. \qquad \textit{Initial condition}$$

Substituting these values into the general solution produces $3 = C(1)^2$, which implies that $C = 3$. Thus, the particular solution is

$$y = 3x^2. \qquad \textit{Particular solution}$$

FIGURE D.1

EXAMPLE 2 *Finding a Particular Solution*

Verify that

$$y = Cx^3 \qquad \textit{General solution}$$

is a solution of the differential equation $xy' - 3y = 0$ for any value of C. Then find the particular solution determined by the initial condition

$$y = 2 \quad \text{when} \quad x = -3. \qquad \textit{Initial condition}$$

Solution
The derivative of $y = Cx^3$ is $y' = 3Cx^2$. Substituting into the differential equation produces

$$xy' - 3y = x(3Cx^2) - 3(Cx^3) = 0.$$

Thus, $y = Cx^3$ is a solution for any value of C. To find the particular solution, substitute $x = -3$ and $y = 2$ into the general solution to obtain $2 = C(-3)^3$ or $C = -\frac{2}{27}$. This implies that the particular solution is

$$y = -\frac{2}{27}x^3. \qquad \textit{Particular solution}$$

---

*Some differential equations have solutions other than those given by their general solutions. These are called **singular solutions.** In our brief discussion of differential equations, we will not discuss singular solutions.

Real
Life

EXAMPLE 3 *Finding a Particular Solution*

You are working in the marketing department of a company that is producing a new product to be sold nationally. You determine that a maximum of 10 million units of the product could be sold in a year. You hypothesize that the rate of growth of the sales x (in millions of units) is proportional to the difference between the maximum sales and the current sales. As a differential equation, this hypothesis can be written as

$$\frac{dx}{dt} = k(10 - x), \quad 0 \le x \le 10.$$

Rate of change of x ↑ is proportional to ↑ the difference between 10 and x.

The general solution of this differential equation is

$$x = 10 - Ce^{-kt}, \qquad\qquad \text{\textit{General solution}}$$

where t is the time in years. After 1 year, 250,000 units have been sold. Sketch the graph of the sales function over a 10-year period.

Solution

Because the product is new, you can assume that $x = 0$ when $t = 0$. Thus, you have *two* initial conditions.

$$x = 0 \quad \text{when} \quad t = 0 \qquad \text{\textit{First initial condition}}$$
$$x = 0.25 \quad \text{when} \quad t = 1 \qquad \text{\textit{Second initial condition}}$$

Substituting the first initial condition into the general solution produces

$$0 = 10 - Ce^{-k(0)},$$

which implies that $C = 10$. Substituting the second initial condition into the general solution produces

$$0.25 = 10 - 10e^{-k(1)},$$

which implies that $k = \ln \frac{40}{39} \approx 0.0253$. Thus, the particular solution is

$$x = 10 - 10e^{-0.0253t}. \qquad \text{\textit{Particular solution}}$$

Table D.1 shows the annual sales during the first 10 years, and the graph of the solution is shown in Figure D.2.

TABLE D.1

t	1	2	3	4	5	6	7	8	9	10
x	0.25	0.49	0.73	0.96	1.19	1.41	1.62	1.83	2.04	2.24

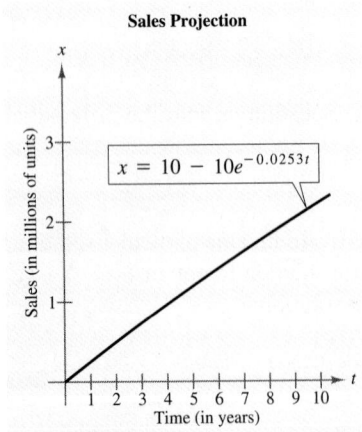

Sales Projection

$x = 10 - 10e^{-0.0253t}$

Sales (in millions of units)

Time (in years)

FIGURE D.2

In the first three examples in this section, each solution was given in explicit form, such as $y = f(x)$. Sometimes you will encounter solutions for which it is more convenient to write the solution in implicit form, as illustrated in Example 4.

EXAMPLE 4 *Sketching Graphs of Solutions*

Verify that

$$2y^2 - x^2 = C \qquad \text{\textit{General solution}}$$

is a solution of the differential equation $2yy' - x = 0$. Then sketch the particular solutions represented by $C = 0$, $C = \pm 1$, and $C = \pm 4$.

Solution

To verify the given solution, differentiate both sides with respect to x.

$$2y^2 - x^2 = C \qquad \text{\textit{Given general solution}}$$
$$4yy' - 2x = 0 \qquad \text{\textit{Differentiate with respect to }x.}$$
$$2yy' - x = 0 \qquad \text{\textit{Divide both sides by 2.}}$$

Because the third equation is the given differential equation, you can conclude that $2y^2 - x^2 = C$ is a solution. The particular solutions represented by $C = 0$, $C = \pm 1$, and $C = \pm 4$ are shown in Figure D.3.

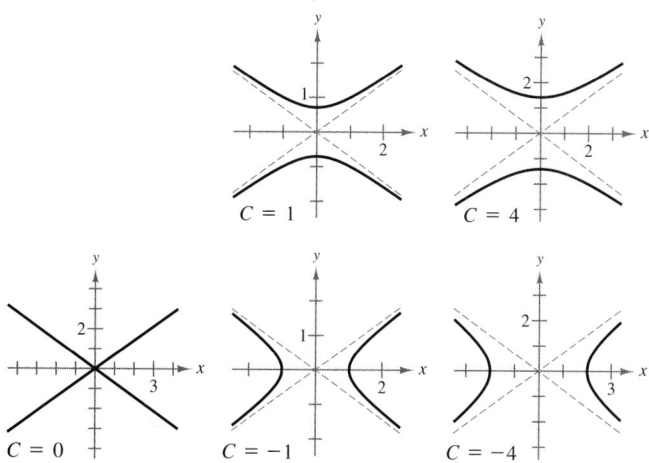

FIGURE D.3   Graphs of Five Particular Solutions

Discussion Problem   *Writing a Differential Equation*

Write a differential equation that has the family of circles $x^2 + y^2 = C$ as a general solution.

Warm Up

The following warm-up exercises involve skills that were covered in earlier sections. You will use these skills in the exercise set for this section.

In Exercises 1–4, find the first and second derivatives of the function.

1. $y = 3x^2 + 2x + 1$

2. $y = -2x^3 - 8x + 4$

3. $y = -3e^{2x}$

4. $y = -3e^{x^2}$

In Exercises 5–8, use implicit differentiation to find dy/dx.

5. $x^2 + y^2 = 2x$

6. $2x - y^3 = 4y$

7. $xy^2 = 3$

8. $3xy + x^2y^2 = 10$

In Exercises 9 and 10, solve for k.

9. $0.5 = 9 - 9e^{-k}$

10. $14.75 = 25 - 25e^{-2k}$

E X E R C I S E S   D.1 means that technology can help you solve or check the exercise(s).

In Exercises 1–10, verify that the function is a solution of the differential equation.

Solution	Differential Equation
1. $y = x^3 + 5$	$y' = 3x^2$
2. $y = 2x^3 - x + 1$	$y' = 6x^2 - 1$
3. $y = e^{-2x}$	$y' + 2y = 0$
4. $y = 3e^{x^2}$	$y' - 2xy = 0$
5. $y = 2x^3$	$y' - \dfrac{3}{x}y = 0$
6. $y = 4x^2$	$y' - \dfrac{2}{x}y = 0$
7. $y = x^2$	$x^2y'' - 2y = 0$
8. $y = \dfrac{1}{x}$	$xy'' + 2y' = 0$
9. $y = 2e^{2x}$	$y'' - y' - 2y = 0$
10. $y = e^{x^3}$	$y'' - 3x^2y' - 6xy = 0$

In Exercises 11–28, verify that the function is a solution of the differential equation for any value of C.

Solution	Differential Equation
11. $y = \dfrac{1}{x} + C$	$\dfrac{dy}{dx} = -\dfrac{1}{x^2}$
12. $y = \sqrt{4 - x^2} + C$	$\dfrac{dy}{dx} = -\dfrac{x}{\sqrt{4 - x^2}}$
13. $y = Ce^{4x}$	$\dfrac{dy}{dx} = 4y$
14. $y = Ce^{-4x}$	$\dfrac{dy}{dx} = -4y$
15. $y = Ce^{-t/3} + 7$	$3\dfrac{dy}{dt} + y - 7 = 0$
16. $y = Ce^{-t} + 10$	$y' + y - 10 = 0$
17. $y = Cx^2 - 3x$	$xy' - 3x - 2y = 0$
18. $y = x \ln x^2 + 2x^{3/2} + Cx$	$y' - \dfrac{y}{x} = 2 + \sqrt{x}$
19. $y = x^2 + 2x + \dfrac{C}{x}$	$xy' + y = x(3x + 4)$
20. $y = C_1 + C_2e^x$	$y'' - y' = 0$

Solution	Differential Equation
21. $y = C_1 e^{x/2} + C_2 e^{-2x}$	$2y'' + 3y' - 2y = 0$
22. $y = C_1 e^{4x} + C_2 e^{-x}$	$y'' - 3y' - 4y = 0$
23. $y = \dfrac{bx^4}{4-a} + Cx^a$	$y' - \dfrac{ay}{x} = bx^3$
24. $y = \dfrac{x^3}{5} - x + C\sqrt{x}$	$2xy' - y = x^3 - x$
25. $y = \dfrac{2}{1 + Ce^{x^2}}$	$y' + 2xy = xy^2$
26. $y = x(\ln x + C)$	$x + y - xy' = 0$
27. $y = x \ln x + Cx + 4$	$x(y' - 1) - (y - 4) = 0$
28. $y = Ce^{x - x^2}$	$y' + (2x - 1)y = 0$

In Exercises 29–32, use implicit differentiation to verify that the equation is a solution of the differential equation for any value of C.

Solution	Differential Equation
29. $x^2 + y^2 = Cy$	$y' = \dfrac{2xy}{x^2 - y^2}$
30. $y^2 + 2xy - x^2 = C$	$(x + y)y' - x + y = 0$
31. $x^2 + xy = C$	$x^2 y'' - 2(x + y) = 0$
32. $x^2 - y^2 = C$	$y^3 y'' + x^2 - y^2 = 0$

In Exercises 33–36, determine whether the function is a solution of the differential equation $y^{(4)} - 16y = 0$.

33. $y = e^{-2x}$ **34.** $y = 5 \ln x$

35. $y = \dfrac{4}{x}$ **36.** $y = 4e^{2x}$

In Exercises 37–40, determine whether the function is a solution of the differential equation $y''' - 3y' + 2y = 0$.

37. $y = \dfrac{2}{9} xe^{-2x}$ **38.** $y = 4e^x + \dfrac{2}{9} xe^{-2x}$

39. $y = xe^x$ **40.** $y = x \ln x$

In Exercises 41–48, verify that the general solution satisfies the differential equation. Then find the particular solution that satisfies the initial condition.

41. General solution: $y = Ce^{-2x}$
Differential equation: $y' + 2y = 0$
Initial condition: $y = 3$ when $x = 0$

42. General solution: $2x^2 + 3y^2 = C$
Differential equation: $2x + 3yy' = 0$
Initial condition: $y = 2$ when $x = 1$

43. General solution: $y = C_1 + C_2 \ln |x|, \quad x > 0$
Differential equation: $xy'' + y' = 0$
Initial condition: $y = 5$ and $y' = 0.5$ when $x = 1$

44. General solution: $y = C_1 x + C_2 x^3$
Differential equation: $x^2 y'' - 3xy' + 3y = 0$
Initial condition: $y = 0$ and $y' = 4$ when $x = 2$

45. General solution: $y = C_1 e^{4x} + C_2 e^{-3x}$
Differential equation: $y'' - y' - 12y = 0$
Initial condition: $y = 5$ and $y' = 6$ when $x = 0$

46. General solution: $y = Ce^{x - x^2}$
Differential equation: $y' + (2x - 1)y = 0$
Initial condition: $y = 2$ when $x = 1$

47. General solution: $y = e^{2x/3}(C_1 + C_2 x)$
Differential equation: $9y'' - 12y' + 4y = 0$
Initial condition: $y = 4$ when $x = 0$
$y = 0$ when $x = 3$

48. General solution: $y = (C_1 + C_2 x + \frac{1}{12} x^4)e^{2x}$
Differential equation: $y'' - 4y' + 4y = x^2 e^{2x}$
Initial condition: $y = 2$ and $y' = 1$ when $x = 0$

In Exercises 49–52, the general solution of the differential equation is given. Sketch the graph of the particular solutions that correspond to the given values of C.

General Solution	C-values
49. $y = Cx^2$	$1, 2, 4$
$xy' - 2y = 0$	
50. $4y^2 - x^2 = C$	$0, \pm1, \pm4$
$4yy' - x = 0$	
51. $y = C(x + 2)^2$	$0, \pm1, \pm2$
$(x + 2)y' - 2y = 0$	
52. $y = Ce^{-x}$	$0, \pm1, \pm2$
$y' + y = 0$	

In Exercises 53–58, use integration to find the general solution of the differential equation.

53. $\dfrac{dy}{dx} = 3x^2$ **54.** $\dfrac{dy}{dx} = \dfrac{1}{1 + x}$

55. $\dfrac{dy}{dx} = \dfrac{x + 3}{x}$ **56.** $\dfrac{dy}{dx} = \dfrac{1}{x^2 - 1}$

57. $\dfrac{dy}{dx} = x\sqrt{x - 3}$ **58.** $\dfrac{dy}{dx} = xe^x$

In Exercises 59–62, you are shown the graphs of some of the solutions of the differential equation. Find the particular solution whose graph passes through the indicated point.

59. $y^2 = Cx^3$
$2xy' - 3y = 0$

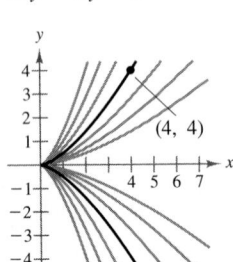

60. $2x^2 - y^2 = C$
$yy' - 2x = 0$

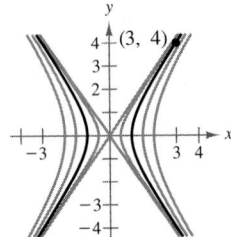

61. $y = Ce^x$
$y' - y = 0$

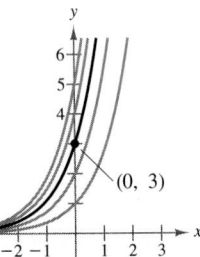

62. $y^2 = 2Cx$
$2xy' - y = 0$

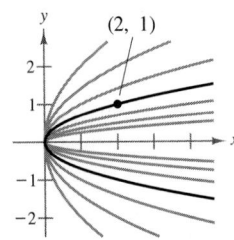

63. *Population Growth* The limiting capacity of the habitat of a wildlife herd is 750. The growth rate dN/dt of the herd is proportional to the unutilized opportunity for growth, as described by the differential equation

$$\frac{dN}{dt} = k(750 - N).$$

The general solution of this differential equation is $N = 750 - Ce^{-kt}$. When $t = 0$, the population of the herd is 100. After 2 years, the population has grown to 160.

(a) Write the population function N as a function of t.
(b) Use a graphing utility to graph the population function.
(c) What is the population of the herd after 4 years?

64. *Investment Growth* The rate of growth of an investment is proportional to the amount in the investment at any time t. That is

$$\frac{dA}{dt} = kA.$$

The initial investment is \$1000, and after 10 years the balance is \$3320.12. The general solution is $A = Ce^{kt}$. What is the particular solution?

65. *Marketing* You are working in the marketing department of a computer software company. Your marketing team determines that a maximum of 30,000 units of a new product can be sold in a year. You hypothesize that the rate of growth of the sales x is proportional to the difference between the maximum sales and the current sales. That is,

$$\frac{dx}{dt} = k(30{,}000 - x).$$

The general solution of this differential equation is $x = 30{,}000 - Ce^{-kt}$, where t is the time in years. During the first year, 2000 units are sold. Complete the table showing the number of units sold in subsequent years.

Year, t	2	4	6	8	10
Units, x					

66. *Marketing* In Exercise 65, suppose that the maximum annual sales is 50,000 units. How does this change the sales shown in the table?

True or False In Exercises 67 and 68, determine whether the statement is true or false. Explain.

67. A differential equation can have more than one solution.

68. If $y = f(x)$ is a solution of a differential equation, then $y = f(x) + C$ is also a solution.

69. Show that $y = a + Ce^{k(1-b)t}$ is a solution of the differential equation

$$y = a + b(y - a) + \frac{1}{k}\frac{dy}{dt},$$

where k is a constant.

70. The function $y = Ce^{kx}$ is a solution of the differential equation

$$\frac{dy}{dx} = 0.07y.$$

Is it possible to determine C or k without being given additional information? Explain your reasoning.

71. *Snow Removal* Assume that the rate of change in the number of miles s of road cleared per hour by a snowplow is inversely proportional to the depth h of the snow. This rate of change is described by the differential equation

$$\frac{ds}{dh} = \frac{k}{h}.$$

Show that

$$s = 25 - \frac{13}{\ln 3}\ln\frac{h}{2}$$

is a solution of this differential equation.

$A = 1000\,e^{-12t}$

Separation of Variables

Separation of Variables ■ *Applications*

Separation of Variables

The simplest type of differential equation is one of the form

$$y' = f(x).$$

You know that this type of equation can be solved by integration to obtain

$$y = \int f(x)\,dx.$$

In this section, you will learn how to use integration to solve another important family of differential equations—those in which the variables can be separated. This technique is called **separation of variables.**

Separation of Variables

If f and g are continuous functions, then the differential equation

$$\frac{dy}{dx} = f(x)g(y)$$

has a general solution of

$$\int \frac{1}{g(y)}\,dy = \int f(x)\,dx + C.$$

Essentially, the technique of separation of variables is just what its name implies. For a differential equation involving x and y, you separate the x's to one side and the y's to the other. After separating variables, integrate both sides to obtain the general solution. Here is an example.

$$\frac{dy}{dx} = \frac{x}{y^2 + 1} \qquad \text{\textit{Differential equation}}$$

$$(y^2 + 1)\,dy = x\,dx \qquad \text{\textit{Separate variables.}}$$

$$\int (y^2 + 1)\,dy = \int x\,dx \qquad \text{\textit{Integrate both sides.}}$$

$$\frac{y^3}{3} + y = \frac{x^2}{2} + C \qquad \text{\textit{General solution}}$$

EXAMPLE 1 *Solving a Differential Equation*

Find the general solution of the differential equation

$$\frac{dy}{dx} = \frac{x}{y}.$$

Solution

Begin by separating variables, then integrate both sides.

$$\frac{dy}{dx} = \frac{x}{y} \qquad\qquad \textit{Differential equation}$$

$$y\,dy = x\,dx \qquad\qquad \textit{Separate variables.}$$

$$\int y\,dy = \int x\,dx \qquad\qquad \textit{Integrate both sides.}$$

$$\frac{y^2}{2} = \frac{x^2}{2} + C_1 \qquad\qquad \textit{Find antiderivatives.}$$

$$y^2 = x^2 + C \qquad\qquad \textit{Multiply both sides by 2.}$$

Note After finding the general solution of a differential equation, you should use the techniques demonstrated in Section D.1 to check the solution. For instance, in Example 1 you can check the solution by differentiating the equation $y^2 = x^2 + C$ to obtain $2yy' = 2x$ or $y' = x/y$.

Thus, the general solution is $y^2 = x^2 + C$. Note that C_1 is used as a temporary constant of integration in anticipation of multiplying both sides of the equation by 2 to produce the constant C. ▬

EXAMPLE 2 *Solving a Differential Equation*

Find the general solution of the differential equation

$$e^y \frac{dy}{dx} = 2x.$$

Use a graphing utility to sketch several solutions.

Solution

Begin by separating variables, then integrate both sides.

$$e^y \frac{dy}{dx} = 2x \qquad\qquad \textit{Differential equation}$$

$$e^y\,dy = 2x\,dx \qquad\qquad \textit{Separate variables.}$$

$$\int e^y\,dy = \int 2x\,dx \qquad\qquad \textit{Integrate both sides.}$$

$$e^y = x^2 + C \qquad\qquad \textit{Find antiderivatives.}$$

By taking the natural logarithms of both sides, you can write the general solution as

$$y = \ln(x^2 + C). \qquad\qquad \textit{General Solution}$$

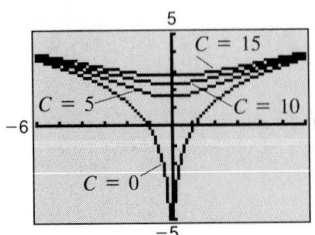

FIGURE D.4

The graphs of the particular solutions given by $C = 0$, $C = 5$, $C = 10$, and $C = 15$ are shown in Figure D.4. ▬

EXAMPLE 3 *Finding a Particular Solution*

Solve the differential equation

$$xe^{x^2} + yy' = 0$$

subject to the initial condition $y = 1$ when $x = 0$.

Solution

$xe^{x^2} + yy' = 0$	*Differential equation*
$y\dfrac{dy}{dx} = -xe^{x^2}$	*Subtract xe^{x^2} from both sides.*
$y\,dy = -xe^{x^2}\,dx$	*Separate variables.*
$\displaystyle\int y\,dy = \int -xe^{x^2}\,dx$	*Integrate both sides.*
$\dfrac{y^2}{2} = -\dfrac{1}{2}e^{x^2} + C_1$	*Find antiderivatives.*
$y^2 = -e^{x^2} + C$	*Multiply both sides by 2.*

To find the particular solution, substitute the initial condition values to obtain $(1)^2 = -e^{(0)^2} + C$. This implies that $1 = -1 + C$, or $C = 2$. Thus, the particular solution that satisfies the initial condition is

$y^2 = -e^{x^2} + 2.$	*Particular solution*

Real Life

EXAMPLE 4 *Solving a Differential Equation*

Example 3 in Section D.1 uses the differential equation

$$\frac{dx}{dt} = k(10 - x)$$

to model the sales of a new product. Solve this differential equation.

Note In Example 4, the context of the original model indicates that $(10 - x)$ is positive. Thus, when you integrate $1/(10 - x)$, you can write $-\ln(10 - x)$, rather than $-\ln|10 - x|$.

Also note in Example 4 that the solution agrees with the one that was given in Example 3 in the previous section.

Solution

$\dfrac{dx}{dt} = k(10 - x)$	*Differential equation*
$\dfrac{1}{10 - x}\,dx = k\,dt$	*Separate variables.*
$\displaystyle\int \dfrac{1}{10 - x}\,dx = \int k\,dt$	*Integrate both sides.*
$-\ln(10 - x) = kt + C_1$	*Find antiderivatives.*
$\ln(10 - x) = -kt - C_1$	*Multiply both sides by -1.*
$10 - x = e^{-kt - C_1}$	*Exponentiate both sides.*
$x = 10 - Ce^{-kt}$	*Solve for x.*

Applications

EXAMPLE 5 *Modeling National Income*

Let y represent the national income, a represent the income spent on necessities, and b represent the percent of the remaining income spent on luxuries. A commonly used economic model that relates these three quantities is

$$\frac{dy}{dt} = k(1 - b)(y - a),$$

where t is the time in years. Assume that b is 75%, and solve the resulting differential equation.

Solution

Because b is 75%, it follows that $(1 - b)$ is 0.25. Thus, you can solve the differential equation as follows.

$$\frac{dy}{dt} = k(0.25)(y - a) \qquad \textit{Differential equation}$$

$$\frac{1}{y - a}\,dy = 0.25k\,dt \qquad \textit{Separate variables.}$$

$$\int \frac{1}{y - a}\,dy = \int 0.25k\,dt \qquad \textit{Integrate both sides.}$$

$$\ln(y - a) = 0.25kt + C_1 \qquad \textit{Find antiderivatives, given } y - a > 0.$$

$$y - a = Ce^{0.25kt} \qquad \textit{Exponentiate both sides.}$$

$$y = a + Ce^{0.25kt} \qquad \textit{Add } a \textit{ to both sides.}$$

The graph of this solution is shown in Figure D.5. In the figure, note that the national income is spent in three ways.

$$\text{(National income)} = \text{(necessities)} + \text{(luxuries)} + \text{(capital investment)}$$

Tony Stone Images/Marcus Brooke

Corporate profits in the United States are closely monitored by New York City's Wall Street executives. Corporate profits, however, represent only about 6.8% of the national income. In 1991 the national income was over $4.5 trillion. Of this, almost 75% was employee compensation.

FIGURE D.5

EXAMPLE 6 *Using Graphical Information*

Find the equation of the graph that has the following characteristics.

1. At each point (x, y) on the graph, the slope is $-x/2y$.
2. The graph passes through the point $(2, 1)$.

Solution

Using the information about the slope of the graph, you can write the differential equation

$$\frac{dy}{dx} = -\frac{x}{2y}.$$

Using the given point on the graph, you can determine the initial condition $y = 1$ when $x = 2$.

$$\frac{dy}{dx} = -\frac{x}{2y} \qquad\qquad \text{Differential equation}$$

$$2y\,dy = -x\,dx \qquad\qquad \text{Separate variables.}$$

$$\int 2y\,dy = \int -x\,dx \qquad\qquad \text{Integrate both sides.}$$

$$y^2 = -\frac{x^2}{2} + C_1 \qquad\qquad \text{Find antiderivatives.}$$

$$2y^2 = -x^2 + C \qquad\qquad \text{Multiply both sides by 2.}$$

$$x^2 + 2y^2 = C \qquad\qquad \text{Simplify.}$$

Applying the initial condition yields

$$(2)^2 + 2(1)^2 = C,$$

which implies that $C = 6$. Therefore, the equation that satisfies the two given conditions is

$$x^2 + 2y^2 = 6. \qquad\qquad \text{Particular solution}$$

As shown in Figure D.6, the graph of this equation is an ellipse. ▬

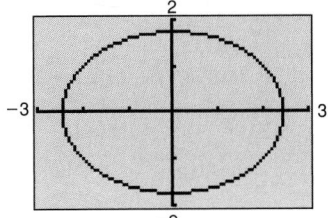

FIGURE D.6

Discussion Problem   Classifying Differential Equations

In which of the following differential equations can the variables be separated?

a. $\dfrac{dy}{dx} = \dfrac{3x}{y}$

b. $\dfrac{dy}{dx} = \dfrac{3x}{y} + 1$

c. $x^2\dfrac{dy}{dx} = \dfrac{3x}{y}$

d. $\dfrac{dy}{dx} = \dfrac{3x + y}{y}$

Warm Up

The following warm-up exercises involve skills that were covered in earlier sections. You will use these skills in the exercise set for this section.

In Exercises 1–6, find the indefinite integral and check your result by differentiating.

1. $\int x^{3/2}\, dx$

2. $\int (t^3 - t^{1/3})\, dt$

3. $\int \dfrac{2}{x-5}\, dx$

4. $\int \dfrac{y}{2y^2+1}\, dy$

5. $\int e^{2y}\, dy$

6. $\int xe^{1-x^2}\, dx$

In Exercises 7–10, solve the equation for C or k.

7. $(3)^2 - 6(3) = 1 + C$

8. $(-1)^2 + (-2)^2 = C$

9. $10 = 2e^{2k}$

10. $(6)^2 - 3(6) = e^{-k}$

EXERCISES D.2   means that technology can help you solve or check the exercise(s).

In Exercises 1–6, decide whether the variables in the differential equation can be separated.

1. $\dfrac{dy}{dx} = \dfrac{x}{y+3}$

2. $\dfrac{dy}{dx} = \dfrac{x+1}{x}$

3. $\dfrac{dy}{dx} = \dfrac{1}{x} + 1$

4. $\dfrac{dy}{dx} = \dfrac{x}{x+y}$

5. $\dfrac{dy}{dx} = x - y$

6. $x\dfrac{dy}{dx} = \dfrac{1}{y}$

In Exercises 7–26, use separation of variables to find the general solution of the differential equation.

7. $\dfrac{dy}{dx} = 2x$

8. $\dfrac{dy}{dx} = x^2 y$

9. $\dfrac{dy}{dx} = \dfrac{1}{x}$

10. $(y+1)\dfrac{dy}{dx} = 2x$

11. $3y^2\dfrac{dy}{dx} = 1$

12. $(1+y)\dfrac{dy}{dx} - 4x = 0$

13. $y' - xy = 0$

14. $y' - y = 5$

15. $\dfrac{dy}{dt} = \dfrac{e^t}{4y}$

16. $\dfrac{dy}{dx} = \sqrt{\dfrac{x}{y}}$

17. $e^y\dfrac{dy}{dt} = 3t^2 + 1$

18. $\dfrac{dy}{dx} = \dfrac{x^2+2}{3y^2}$

19. $(2+x)y' = 2y$

20. $xy' = y$

21. $\dfrac{dy}{dx} = \sqrt{1-y}$

22. $y' - y(x+1) = 0$

23. $y' = (2x-1)(y+3)$

24. $e^x(y'+1) = 1$

25. $y' = \dfrac{x}{y} - \dfrac{x}{1+y}$

26. $yy' - 2xe^x = 0$

In Exercises 27–32, use the given initial condition to find the particular solution of the differential equation.

Differential Equation	Initial Condition
27. $yy' - e^x = 0$	$y = 4$ when $x = 0$
28. $\sqrt{x} + \sqrt{y}\,y' = 0$	$y = 4$ when $x = 1$
29. $x(y+4) + y' = 0$	$y = -5$ when $x = 0$
30. $dP - 6P\, dt = 0$	$P = 5$ when $t = 0$
31. $\dfrac{dy}{dx} = x^2(1+y)$	$y = 3$ when $x = 0$
32. $dT + k(T-70)\, dt = 0$	$T = 140$ when $t = 0$

In Exercises 33 and 34, find an equation for the graph that passes through the point and has the specified slope. Then graph the equation.

33. Point: $(-1, 1)$; Slope: $y' = \dfrac{6x}{5y}$

34. Point: $(8, 2)$; Slope: $y' = \dfrac{2y}{3x}$

Velocity In Exercises 35 and 36, solve the differential equation to find velocity v as a function of time if $v = 0$ when $t = 0$. The differential equation models the motion of two people on a toboggan after consideration of the force of gravity, friction, and air resistance.

35. $12.5\dfrac{dv}{dt} = 43.2 - 1.25v$

36. $12.5\dfrac{dv}{dt} = 43.2 - 1.75v$

Newton's Law of Cooling In Exercises 37–39, use Newton's Law of Cooling, which states that the rate of change in the temperature T of an object is proportional to the difference between the temperature T of the object and the temperature T_0 of the surrounding environment. This is described by the differential equation

$$\frac{dT}{dt} = k(T - T_0).$$

37. A steel ingot whose temperature is $1500°F$ is placed in a room whose temperature is a constant $90°F$. One hour later, the temperature of the ingot is $1120°F$. What is the ingot's temperature 5 hours after it is placed in the room?

38. A room is kept at a constant temperature of $70°F$. An object placed in the room cools from $350°F$ to $150°F$ in 45 minutes. How long will it take for the object to cool to a temperature of $80°F$?

39. Food at a temperature of $70°F$ is placed in a freezer that is set at $0°F$. After 1 hour, the temperature of the food is $48°F$.

    (a) Find the temperature of the food after it has been in the freezer 6 hours.

    (b) How long will it take the food to cool to a temperature of $10°F$?

40. *Cell Growth* The rate of growth of a spherical cell with volume V is proportional to its surface area S. For a sphere, the surface area and volume are related by $S = kV^{2/3}$. Thus, a model for the cell's growth is

$$\frac{dV}{dt} = kV^{2/3}.$$

Solve this differential equation.

41. *Learning Theory* The management of a factory has found that a worker can produce at most 30 units per day. The number of units N per day produced by a new employee will increase at a rate proportional to the difference between 30 and N. This is described by the differential equation

$$\frac{dN}{dt} = k(30 - N),$$

where t is the time in days. Solve this differential equation.

42. *Sales* The rate of increase in sales S (in thousands of units) of a product is proportional to the current level of sales and inversely proportional to the square of the time t. This is described by the differential equation

$$\frac{dS}{dt} = \frac{kS}{t^2},$$

where t is the time in years. The saturation point for the market is 50,000 units. That is, the limit of S as $t \to \infty$ is 50. After 1 year, 10,000 units have been sold. Find S as a function of the time t.

43. *Pareto's Law* According to the economist Vilfredo Pareto (1848–1923), the rate of decrease of the number of people y in a stable economy having an income of at least x dollars is directly proportional to the number of such people and inversely proportional to their income x. This is modeled by the differential equation

$$\frac{dy}{dx} = -k\frac{y}{x}.$$

Solve this differential equation.

44. *Pareto's Law* In 1991, 9.9 million people in the United States earned over \$75,000 and 55.8 million people earned over \$25,000 (see figure). Assume that Pareto's Law holds and use the result of Exercise 43 to determine the number of people (in millions) who earned (a) over \$10,000 and (b) over \$250,000. *(Source: U.S. Bureau of Census)*

First-Order Linear Differential Equations ■ Applications

First-Order Linear Differential Equations

Definition of a First-Order Linear Differential Equation

A **first-order linear differential equation** is an equation of the form

$$y' + P(x)y = Q(x),$$

where P and Q are functions of x. An equation that is written in this form is said to be in **standard form.**

Note   The term "first-order" refers to the fact that the highest-order derivative of y in the equation is the first derivative.

To solve a linear differential equation, write it in standard form to identify the functions $P(x)$ and $Q(x)$. Then integrate $P(x)$ and form the expression

$$u(x) = e^{\int P(x)\,dx},$$ *Integrating factor*

which is called an **integrating factor.** The general solution of the equation is

$$y = \frac{1}{u(x)} \int Q(x)u(x)\,dx.$$ *General solution*

EXAMPLE 1   *Solving a Linear Differential Equation*

Find the general solution of $y' + y = e^x$.

Solution

For this equation, $P(x) = 1$ and $Q(x) = e^x$. Thus, the integrating factor is

$$u(x) = e^{\int dx} = e^x.$$ *Integrating factor*

This implies that the general solution is

$$y = \frac{1}{e^x} \int e^x(e^x)\,dx$$

$$= e^{-x}\left(\frac{1}{2}e^{2x} + C\right)$$

$$= \frac{1}{2}e^x + Ce^{-x}.$$ *General solution*

In Example 1, the differential equation was given in standard form. For equations that are not written in standard form, you should first convert to standard form so that you can identify the functions $P(x)$ and $Q(x)$.

EXAMPLE 2 *Solving a Linear Differential Equation*

Find the general solution of

$$xy' - 2y = x^2.$$

Assume $x > 0$.

Solution

Begin by writing the equation in standard form.

$$y' - \left(\frac{2}{x}\right)y = x \qquad\qquad \textit{Standard form, } y' + P(x)y = Q(x)$$

In this form, you can see that $P(x) = -2/x$ and $Q(x) = x$. Thus,

$$\int P(x)\,dx = -\int \frac{2}{x}\,dx = -2\ln x = -\ln x^2,$$

which implies that the integrating factor is

$$u(x) = e^{\int P(x)\,dx} = e^{-\ln x^2} = \frac{1}{x^2}. \qquad \textit{Integrating factor}$$

This implies that the general solution is

$$y = \frac{1}{u(x)}\int Q(x)u(x)\,dx \qquad\qquad \textit{Form of general solution}$$

$$= \frac{1}{1/x^2}\int x\left(\frac{1}{x^2}\right)\,dx \qquad\qquad \textit{Substitute.}$$

$$= x^2 \int \frac{1}{x}\,dx \qquad\qquad \textit{Simplify.}$$

$$= x^2(\ln x + C). \qquad\qquad \textit{General solution}$$

Discovery

Solve for y' in the differential equation in Example 2. Use this equation for y' to determine the slope of y at the points $(1, 0)$ and $(e^{-1/2}, -1/2e)$. Now graph the particular solution $y = x^2 \ln x$ and estimate the slope at $x = 1$ and $x = e^{-1/2}$. What happens to the slope of y as x approaches zero?

Guidelines for Solving a Linear Differential Equation

1. Write the equation in standard form

$$y' + P(x)y = Q(x).$$

2. Find the integrating factor $u(x) = e^{\int P(x)\,dx}$.

3. Evaluate the following integral to find the general solution

$$y = \frac{1}{u(x)}\int Q(x)u(x)\,dx.$$

Using a Symbolic Integrator

From Example 2, you can see that it can be difficult to solve a linear differential equation. Fortunately, the task is greatly simplified by symbolic integrators such as *Derive*, *Maple*, and *Mathematica*. For instance, to use *Derive* to solve the linear differential equation in Example 1, begin by writing the equation in standard form to identify $P(x) = 1$ and $Q(x) = e^x$. Then use the command

LINEAR1_GEN (p, q, x, y, c),

as shown below. Notice that you obtain the same solution that was obtained in Example 1.

1: LINEAR1_GEN (1, $\hat{e}^x$, x, y, c)   *Author.*

2: $y = \dfrac{\hat{e}^x}{2} + c\hat{e}^{-x}$ *Simplify.*

Similarly, you can solve the differential equation in Example 2 as follows.

1: LINEAR1_GEN $\left(-\dfrac{2}{x},\ x,\ x,\ y,\ c\right)$ *Author.*

2: $y = x^2 LN(x) + cx^2$ *Simplify.*

To use *Derive* to find a particular solution, use the command

LINEAR1 (p, q, x, y, x_0, y_0),

where (x_0, y_0) is the initial condition. For instance, in Example 1, suppose you are given the initial condition that $y = 4$ when $x = 0$. You can solve for the particular solution as follows.

1: LINEAR1 (1, $\hat{e}^x$, x, y, 0, 4)   *Author.*

2: $y = \dfrac{\hat{e}^x}{2} + \dfrac{7\hat{e}^{-x}}{2}$ *Simplify.*

Applications

During the 1980s, American families continued their trend of becoming a country of "nonsavers." In 1983, 62% of all American families had savings accounts. By 1989, only 44% did.

Real Life

EXAMPLE 3 *Finding a Balance*

You are setting up a "continuous annuity" trust fund. For 20 years, money is continuously transferred from your checking account to the trust fund at the rate of $1000 per year (about $2.74 per day). The account earns 8%, compounded continuously. What is the balance in the account after 20 years?

Solution
Let A represent the balance after t years. The balance increases in two ways: with interest *and* with additional deposits. The rate at which the balance is changing can therefore be modeled by

$$\frac{dA}{dt} = \underbrace{0.08A}_{Interest} + \underbrace{1000}_{Deposits}.$$

In standard form, this linear differential equation is

$$\frac{dA}{dt} - 0.08A = 1000, \qquad\qquad Standard\ form$$

which implies that $P(t) = -0.08$ and $Q(t) = 1000$. The general solution is

$$R = -12{,}500 + Ce^{0.08t}. \qquad\qquad General\ solution$$

Because $A = 0$ when $t = 0$, you can determine that $C = 12{,}500$. Thus, the revenue after 20 years is

$$A = -12{,}500 + 12{,}500e^{0.08(20)}$$
$$\approx -12{,}500 + 61{,}912.91$$
$$= \$49{,}412.91.$$

Discussion Problem   ## Why an Integrating Factor Works

When both sides of the first-order linear differential equation

$$y' + P(x)y = Q(x)$$

are multiplied by the integrating factor $e^{\int P(x)\,dx}$, you obtain

$$y'e^{\int P(x)\,dx} + P(x)e^{\int P(x)\,dx}y = Q(x)e^{\int P(x)\,dx}.$$

Show that the left side is the derivative of $ye^{\int P(x)\,dx}$, which implies that the general solution is given by

$$ye^{\int P(x)\,dx} = \int Q(x)e^{\int P(x)\,dx}\,dx.$$

Warm Up   The following warm-up exercises involve skills that were covered in earlier sections. You will use these skills in the exercise set for this section.

In Exercises 1–4, simplify the expression.

1. $e^{-x}(e^{2x} + e^x)$

2. $\dfrac{1}{e^{-x}}(e^{-x} + e^{2x})$

3. $e^{-\ln x^3}$

4. $e^{2\ln x + x}$

In Exercises 5–10, find the indefinite integral.

5. $\displaystyle\int e^x(2 + e^{-2x})\,dx$

6. $\displaystyle\int e^{2x}(xe^x + 1)\,dx$

7. $\displaystyle\int \dfrac{1}{2x + 5}\,dx$

8. $\displaystyle\int \dfrac{x + 1}{x^2 + 2x + 3}\,dx$

9. $\displaystyle\int (4x - 3)^2\,dx$

10. $\displaystyle\int x(1 - x^2)^2\,dx$

E X E R C I S E S   D.3   means that technology can help you solve or check the exercise(s).

In Exercises 1–6, write the linear differential equation in standard form.

1. $x^3 - 2x^2 y' + 3y = 0$

2. $y' - 5(2x - y) = 0$

3. $xy' + y = xe^x$

4. $xy' + y = x^3 y$

5. $y + 1 = (x - 1)y'$

6. $x = x^2(y' + y)$

In Exercises 7–18, solve the differential equation.

7. $\dfrac{dy}{dx} + 3y = 6$

8. $\dfrac{dy}{dx} + 5y = 15$

9. $\dfrac{dy}{dx} + y = e^{-x}$

10. $\dfrac{dy}{dx} + 3y = e^{-3x}$

11. $\dfrac{dy}{dx} + \dfrac{y}{x} = 3x + 4$

12. $\dfrac{dy}{dx} + \dfrac{2y}{x} = 3x + 1$

13. $y' + 5xy = x$

14. $y' + 5y = e^{5x}$

15. $(x - 1)y' + y = x^2 - 1$

16. $x^3 y' + 2y = e^{1/x^2}$

17. $xy' + y = x^2 + 1$

18. $xy' + y = x^2 \ln x$

In Exercises 19–22, solve for y in two ways.

19. $y' + y = 4$

20. $y' + 10y = 5$

21. $y' - 2xy = 2x$

22. $y' + 4xy = x$

In Exercises 23–30, find the particular solution that satisfies the initial condition.

Differential Equation	*Initial Condition*
23. $y' + y = 6e^x$	$y = 3$ when $x = 0$
24. $y' + 3x^2 y = 3x^2$	$y = 6$ when $x = 0$
25. $xy' + y = 0$	$y = 2$ when $x = 2$
26. $y' + (2x - 1)y = 0$	$y = 2$ when $x = 1$
27. $y' + y = x$	$y = 4$ when $x = 0$
28. $y' + 2y = e^{-2x}$	$y = 4$ when $x = 1$
29. $xy' - 2y = -x^2$	$y = 5$ when $x = 1$
30. $x^2 y' - 4xy = 10$	$y = 10$ when $x = 1$

31. *Sales* The rate of change (in thousands of units) in sales S is modeled by

$$\frac{dS}{dt} = 0.2(100 - S) + 0.2t,$$

where t is the time in years. Solve this differential equation and use the result to complete the table.

t	0	1	2	3	4	5	6	7	8	9	10
S	0										

Applications of Differential Equations

Applications of Differential Equations

Real Life

EXAMPLE 1 *Modeling Advertising Awareness*

A new product is introduced through an advertising campaign to a population of 1 million potential customers. The rate at which the population hears about the product is assumed to be proportional to the number of people who are not yet aware of the product. By the end of 1 year, half of the population has heard of the product. How many will have heard of it by the end of 2 years?

Solution

Let y be the number (in millions) of people at time t who have heard of the product. This means that $(1 - y)$ is the number of people who have not heard, and dy/dt is the rate at which the population hears about the product. From the given assumption, you can write the following differential equation.

$$\frac{dy}{dt} = k(1 - y)$$

Rate of change of y ⟶ is proportional to ⟶ the difference between 1 and y.

Using separation of variables *or* a symbolic integration utility, you can find the general solution to be

$$y = 1 - Ce^{-kt}. \qquad \textit{General solution}$$

To solve for the constants C and k, use the initial conditions. That is, because $y = 0$ when $t = 0$, you can determine that $C = 1$. Similarly, because $y = 0.5$ when $t = 1$, it follows that $0.5 = 1 - e^{-k}$, which implies that $k = \ln 2 \approx 0.693$. Therefore the particular solution is

$$y = 1 - e^{-0.693t}. \qquad \textit{Particular solution}$$

This model is shown graphically in Figure D.7. Using the model, you can determine that the number of people who have heard of the product after 2 years is

$$y = 1 - e^{-0.693(2)} \approx 0.75 \text{ or } 750{,}000 \text{ people.} \qquad \blacksquare$$

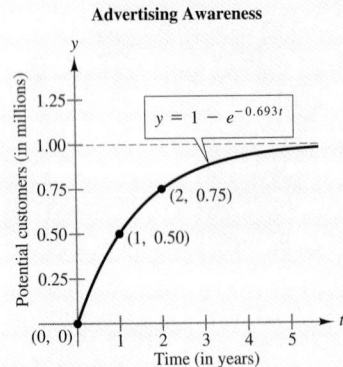

Advertising Awareness

$y = 1 - e^{-0.693t}$

(2, 0.75)

(1, 0.50)

(0, 0)

Potential customers (in millions)

Time (in years)

FIGURE D.7

Real Life

EXAMPLE 2 *Modeling a Chemical Reaction*

During a chemical reaction, substance A is converted into substance B at a rate that is proportional to the square of the amount of A. When $t = 0$, 60 grams of A are present, and after 1 hour ($t = 1$), only 10 grams of A remain unconverted. How much of A is present after 2 hours?

Solution

Let y be the unconverted amount of substance A at any time t. From the given assumption about the conversion rate, you can write the following differential equation.

$$\frac{dy}{dt} = ky^2$$

Rate of change of y is propor-tional to   the square of y.

Using separation of variables *or* a symbolic integration utility, you can find the general solution to be

$$y = \frac{-1}{kt + C}.$$ *General solution*

To solve for the constants C and k, use the initial conditions. That is, because $y = 60$ when $t = 0$, you can determine that $C = -\frac{1}{60}$. Similarly, because $y = 10$ when $t = 1$, it follows that

$$10 = \frac{-1}{k - (1/60)},$$

which implies that $k = -\frac{1}{12}$. Therefore the particular solution is

$$y = \frac{-1}{(-1/12)t - (1/60)}$$ *Substitute for k and C.*

$$= \frac{60}{5t + 1}.$$ *Particular solution*

Using the model, you can determine that the unconverted amount of substance A after 2 hours is

$$y = \frac{60}{5(2) + 1} \approx 5.45 \text{ grams.}$$

In Figure D.8, note that the chemical conversion is occurring rapidly during the first hour. Then, as more and more of substance A has been converted, the conversion rate slows down.   ▬

Chemical Reaction

Amount (in grams) / Time (in hours)

$(0, 60)$

$y = \dfrac{60}{5t + 1}$

$(1, 10)$ $(2, 5.45)$

FIGURE D.8

Note   In Example 2, the rate of conversion was assumed to be proportional to the *square* of the unconverted amount. How would the result change if the rate of conversion were assumed to be proportional to the unconverted amount?

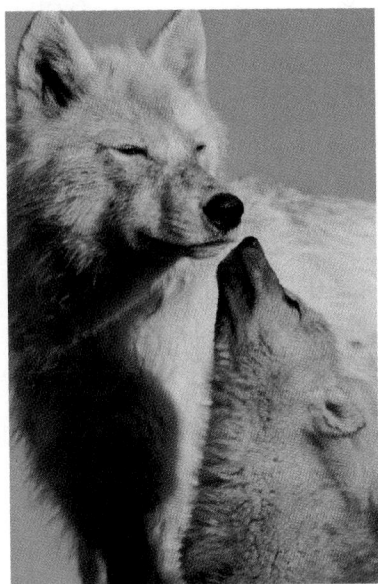

Allstock/© Jim Brandenburg

During the second half of the 20th century, wolves disappeared from most of the middle and northern areas of the United States. Recently, however, wolf populations have been reappearing in several north-ern national parks.

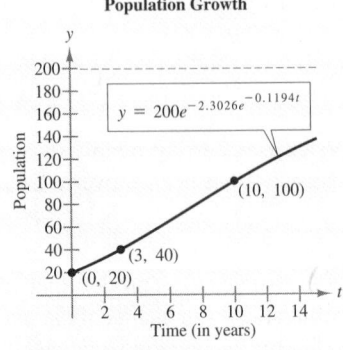

Population Growth

$y = 200e^{-2.3026e^{-0.1194t}}$

(10, 100)

(3, 40)

(0, 20)

Time (in years)

Population

FIGURE D.9

Earlier in the text, you studied two models for population growth: *expo-nential growth*, which assumes that the rate of change of y is proportional to y, and *logistics growth*, which assumes that the rate of change of y is proportional to y and $L - y$, where L is the population limit.

The next example describes a third type of growth model called a **Gompertz growth model.** This model assumes that the rate of change of y is proportional to y and the natural log of L/y, where L is the population limit.

Real Life

EXAMPLE 3 *Modeling Population Growth*

A population of 20 wolves has been introduced to a national park. The forest service estimates that the maximum population the park can sustain is 200 wolves. After 3 years, the population is estimated to be 40 wolves. If the population follows a Gompertz growth model, how many wolves will be in the park in 10 years?

Solution

Let y be the number of wolves at any time t. From the given assumption about the rate of growth of the population, you can write the following differential equation.

$$\frac{dy}{dt} = ky \ln \frac{200}{y}$$

Rate of change of y is propor-tional to   the product of y and   the log of the ratio of 200 and y.

Using separation of variables *or* a symbolic integration utility, you can find the general solution to be

$$y = 200e^{-Ce^{-kt}}.$$ *General solution*

To solve for the constants C and k, use the initial conditions. That is, because $y = 20$ when $t = 0$, you can determine that $C = \ln 10 \approx 2.3026$. Similarly, because $y = 40$ when $t = 3$, it follows that

$$40 = 200e^{-2.3026e^{-3k}},$$

which implies that $k \approx 0.1194$. Therefore, the particular solution is

$$y = 200e^{-2.3026e^{-0.1194t}}.$$ *Particular solution*

Using the model, you can estimate the wolf population in 10 years to be

$$y = 200e^{-2.3026e^{-0.1194(10)}} \approx 100 \text{ wolves.}$$

In Figure D.9, note that after 10 years the population has reached about half of the estimated maximum population. Try checking the growth model to see that it yields $y = 20$ when $t = 0$ and $y = 40$ when $t = 3$. ■

In genetics, a commonly used hybrid selection model is based on the differential equation

$$\frac{dy}{dt} = ky(1 - y)(a - by).$$

In this model, y represents the portion of the population that has a certain characteristic and t represents the time (measured in generations). The numbers a, b, and k are constants that depend on the genetic characteristic that is being studied.

Real Life

EXAMPLE 4 *Modeling Hybrid Selection*

You are studying a population of beetles to determine how quickly characteristic D will pass from one generation to the next. At the beginning of your study ($t = 0$), you find that half the population has characteristic D. After four generations ($t = 4$), you find that 80% of the population has characteristic D. Use the hybrid selection model above with $a = 2$ and $b = 1$ to find the percent of the population that will have characteristic D in 10 generations.

Solution

Using $a = 2$ and $b = 1$, the differential equation for the hybrid selection model is

$$\frac{dy}{dt} = ky(1 - y)(2 - y).$$

Using separation of variables *or* a symbolic integration utility, you can find the general solution to be

$$\frac{y(2 - y)}{(1 - y)^2} = Ce^{2kt}. \qquad \text{\textit{General solution}}$$

To solve for the constants C and k, use the initial conditions. That is, because $y = 0.5$ when $t = 0$, you can determine that $C = 3$. Similarly, because $y = 0.8$ when $t = 4$, it follows that

$$\frac{0.8(1.2)}{(0.2)^2} = 3e^{8k},$$

which implies that $k = \frac{1}{8} \ln 8 \approx 0.2599$. Therefore the particular solution is

$$\frac{y(2 - y)}{(1 - y)^2} = 3e^{0.5199t}. \qquad \text{\textit{Particular solution}}$$

Using the model, you can estimate the percent of the population that will have characteristic D in 10 years to be given by

$$\frac{y(2 - y)}{(1 - y)^2} = 3e^{0.5199(10)}.$$

Using a symbolic algebra utility, you can solve this equation for y to obtain $y \approx 0.96$. The graph of the model is shown in Figure D.10.

Hybrid Selection

$y = 1.0$

(4, 0.8)

$\dfrac{y(2 - y)}{(1 - y)^2} = 3e^{0.5199t}$

(0, 0.5)

Percent of population

Time (in generations)

FIGURE D.10

Real Life

EXAMPLE 5 *Modeling a Chemical Mixture*

A tank contains 40 gallons of a solution composed of 90% water and 10% alcohol. A second solution containing half water and half alcohol is added to the tank at the rate of 4 gallons per minute. At the same time, the tank is being drained at the rate of 4 gallons per minute, as shown in Figure D.11. Assuming that the solution is stirred constantly, how much alcohol will be in the tank after 10 minutes?

Solution

Let y be the number of gallons of alcohol in the tank at any time t. The *percent* of alcohol in the 40-gallon tank at any time is $y/40$. Moreover, because 4 gallons are being drained each minute, the rate of change of y is

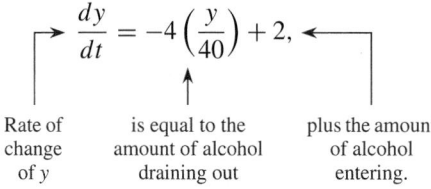

$$\frac{dy}{dt} = -4\left(\frac{y}{40}\right) + 2,$$

| Rate of change of y | is equal to the amount of alcohol draining out | plus the amount of alcohol entering. |

where 2 represents the number of gallons of alcohol entering each minute in the 50% solution. In standard form, this linear differential equation is

$$y' + \frac{1}{10}y = 2. \qquad \textit{Standard form}$$

Using an integrating factor *or* a symbolic integration utility, you can find the general solution to be

$$y = 20 + Ce^{-t/10}. \qquad \textit{General solution}$$

Because $y = 4$ when $t = 0$, you can conclude that $C = -16$. Thus, the particular solution is

$$y = 20 - 16e^{-t/10}. \qquad \textit{Particular solution}$$

Using this model, you can determine that the amount of alcohol in the tank when $t = 10$ is

$$y = 20 - 16e^{-(10)/10}$$
$$\approx 14.1 \text{ gallons.}$$

4 gal/min

4 gal/min

FIGURE D.11

Discussion Problem Extending the Example

Sketch the particular solution obtained in Example 5. Describe the rate of change of the amount of alcohol in the tank. Does the amount approach 0 as t increases? Explain your reasoning.

Warm Up   The following warm-up exercises involve skills that were covered in earlier sections. You will use these skills in the exercise set for this section.

In Exercises 1–4, use separation of variables to find the general solution of the differential equation.

1. $\dfrac{dy}{dx} = 3x$

2. $2y\dfrac{dy}{dx} = 3$

3. $\dfrac{dy}{dx} = 2xy$

4. $\dfrac{dy}{dx} = \dfrac{x - 4}{4y^3}$

In Exercises 5–8, use an integrating factor to solve the first-order linear differential equation.

5. $y' + 2y = 4$

6. $y' + 2y = e^{-2x}$

7. $y' + xy = x$

8. $xy' + 2y = x^2$

In Exercises 9 and 10, write the equation that models the statement.

9. The rate of change of y with respect to x is proportional to the square of x.

10. The rate of change of x with respect to t is proportional to the difference of x and t.

E X E R C I S E S   D.4   means that technology can help you solve or check the exercise(s).

In Exercises 1–6, assume that the rate of change of y is proportional to y. Solve the resulting differential equation $dy/dx = ky$ and find the particular solution that passes through the points.

1. $(0, 1)$, $(3, 2)$

2. $(0, 4)$, $(1, 6)$

3. $(0, 4)$, $(4, 1)$

4. $(0, 60)$, $(5, 30)$

5. $(2, 2)$, $(3, 4)$

6. $(1, 4)$, $(2, 1)$

7. *Growth of an Investment* The rate of growth of an investment is proportional to the amount A of the investment at any time t. An investment of \$2000 increases to a value of \$2983.65 in 5 years. Find its value after 10 years.

8. *Population Growth* The rate of change of population of a city is proportional to the population P at any time t. In 1993, the population is 400,000, and the constant of proportionality is 0.015. Estimate the population of the city in the year 2000.

9. *Sales Increase* The rate of change in sales S (in thousands of units) of a new product is proportional to the difference between L and S (in thousands of units) at any time t. When $t = 0$, $S = 0$. Write and solve the differential equation for this sales model.

10. *Sales Increase* Use the result of Exercise 9 to write S as a function of t if (a) $L = 100$, $S = 25$ when $t = 2$, and (b) $L = 500$, $S = 50$ when $t = 1$.

In Exercises 11–14, the rate of change of y is proportional to the product of y and the difference of L and y. Solve the resulting differential equation $dy/dx = ky(L - y)$ and find the particular solution that passes through the given points for the indicated value of L.

11. $L = 20$; $(0, 1)$, $(5, 10)$

12. $L = 100$; $(0, 10)$, $(5, 30)$

13. $L = 5000$; $(0, 250)$, $(25, 2000)$

14. $L = 1000$; $(0, 100)$, $(4, 750)$

15. *Logistics Growth* At any time t, the rate of growth of the population N of deer in a state park is proportional to the product of N and $L - N$, where $L = 500$ is the maximum number of deer the park can maintain. When $t = 0$, $N = 100$, and when $t = 4$, $N = 200$. Write N as a function of t.

16. *Logistics Growth* The rate of change in sales S (in thousands of units) of a new product is proportional to the product of S and $L - S$. L (in thousands of units) is the estimated maximum level of sales, and $S = 10$ when $t = 0$. Write and solve the differential equation for this sales model.

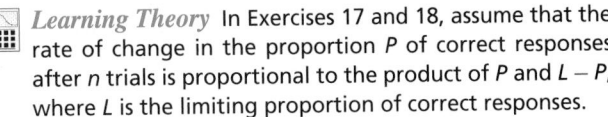 *Learning Theory* In Exercises 17 and 18, assume that the rate of change in the proportion P of correct responses after n trials is proportional to the product of P and $L - P$, where L is the limiting proportion of correct responses.

17. Write and solve the differential equation for this learning theory model.

18. Use the solution of Exercise 17 to write P as a function of n, and then use a graphing utility to graph the solution.

   (a) $L = 1.00$
       $P = 0.50$ when $n = 0$
       $P = 0.85$ when $n = 4$.
   (b) $L = 0.80$
       $P = 0.25$ when $n = 0$
       $P = 0.60$ when $n = 10$.

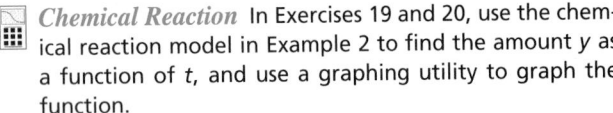 *Chemical Reaction* In Exercises 19 and 20, use the chemical reaction model in Example 2 to find the amount y as a function of t, and use a graphing utility to graph the function.

19. $y = 45$ grams when $t = 0$; $y = 4$ grams when $t = 2$

20. $y = 75$ grams when $t = 0$; $y = 12$ grams when $t = 1$

In Exercises 21 and 22, use the Gompertz growth model described in Example 3 to find the growth function, and sketch its graph.

21. $L = 500$; $y = 100$ when $t = 0$; $y = 150$ when $t = 2$

22. $L = 5000$; $y = 500$ when $t = 0$; $y = 625$ when $t = 1$

23. *Gompertz Growth Model* A population of eight beavers has been introduced to a new wetlands area. Biologists estimate that the maximum population the wetlands can sustain is 60 beavers. After 3 years, the population is 15 beavers. If the population follows a Gompertz growth model, how many beavers will be in the wetlands in 10 years?

24. *Gompertz Growth Model* A population of 30 rabbits has been introduced in a new region. It is estimated that the maximum population the region can sustain is 400 rabbits. After 1 year, the population is estimated to be 90 rabbits. If the population follows a Gompertz growth model, how many rabbits will be present after 3 years?

In Exercises 25 and 26, use the hybrid selection model in Example 4 to find the percent of the population that has the indicated characteristic.

25. *Hybrid Selection* You are studying a population of mayflies to determine how quickly characteristic A will pass from one generation to the next. At the start of the study, half the population has characteristic A. After four generations, 75% of the population has characteristic A. Find the percent of the population that will have characteristic A after 10 generations. (Assume $a = 2$ and $b = 1$.)

26. *Hybrid Selection* A research team is studying a population of snails to determine how quickly characteristic B will pass from one generation to the next. At the start of the study, 40% of the snails have characteristic A. After five generations, 80% of the population have characteristic A. Find the percent of the population that will have characteristic A after eight generations. (Assume $a = 2$ and $b = 1$.)

27. *Mixture* A 100-gallon tank is full of a solution containing 25 pounds of a concentrate. Starting at time $t = 0$, distilled water is admitted to the tank at the rate of 5 gallons per minute, and the well-stirred solution is withdrawn at the same rate.

   (a) Find the amount Q of the concentrate in the solution as a function of t. (*Hint:* $Q' + Q/20 = 0$)

   (b) Find the time when the amount of concentrate in the tank reaches 15 pounds.

28. *Mixture* A 200-gallon tank is half full of distilled water. At time $t = 0$, a solution containing 0.5 pounds of concentrate per gallon enters the tank at the rate of 5 gallons per minute, and the well-stirred mixture is withdrawn at the same rate. Find the amount Q of concentrate in the tank after 30 minutes. (*Hint:* $Q' + Q/20 = \frac{5}{2}$)

29. *Snow Removal* Assume that the rate of change in the number of miles s of road cleared per hour by a snowplow is inversely proportional to the height h of snow. That is,

$$\frac{ds}{dh} = \frac{k}{h}.$$

Find s as a function of h if $s = 25$ miles when $h = 2$ inches and $s = 12$ miles when $h = 6$ inches ($2 \leq h \leq 15$).

30. *Evaporation* A wet towel hung from a clothesline to dry loses moisture through evaporation at a rate proportional to its moisture content. If after 1 hour the towel has lost 40% of its original moisture content, after how long will it have lost 80%?

31. *Growth Rate* Let x and y be the sizes of two internal organs of a particular mammal at time t. Empirical data indicate that the relative growth rates of these two organs are equal, and hence we have

$$\frac{1}{x}\frac{dx}{dt} = \frac{1}{y}\frac{dy}{dt}.$$

Use this differential equation to write y as a function of x.

32. *Population Growth* When predicting population growth, demographers must consider birth and death rates as well as the net change caused by the difference between the rates of immigration and emigration. Let P be the population at time t and N be the net increase per unit time due to the difference between immigration and emigration. Thus, the rate of growth of the population is given by

$$\frac{dP}{dt} = kP + N, \qquad N \text{ is constant.}$$

Solve this differential equation to find P as a function of time.

33. *Investment Growth* A large corporation starts at time $t = 0$ to invest part of its receipts at a rate of P dollars per year in a fund for future corporate expansion. Assume that the fund earns r percent interest per year compounded continuously. Thus, the rate of growth of the amount A in the fund is given by

$$\frac{dA}{dt} = rA + P,$$

where $A = 0$ when $t = 0$. Solve this differential equation for A as a function of t.

Investment Growth In Exercises 34–36, use the result of Exercise 33.

34. Find A for the following.

(a) $P = \$100{,}000$, $r = 12\%$, and $t = 5$ years
(b) $P = \$250{,}000$, $r = 15\%$, and $t = 10$ years

35. Find P if the corporation needs $\$120{,}000{,}000$ in 8 years and the fund earns $16\frac{1}{4}\%$ interest compounded continuously.

36. Find t if the corporation needs $\$800{,}000$ and it can invest $\$75{,}000$ per year in a fund earning 13% interest compounded continuously.

Mixture In Exercises 37–39, a medical researcher wants to determine the concentration C (in moles per liter) of a tracer drug injected into a moving fluid. Solve this problem by considering a single-compartment dilution model (see figure). Assume that the fluid is continuously mixed and that the volume of fluid in the compartment is constant.

Flow R (pure)

Volume V

Tracer injected

Flow R (concentration C)

FIGURE FOR 37–39

37. If the tracer is injected instantaneously at time $t = 0$, then the concentration of the fluid in the compartment begins diluting according to the differential equation

$$\frac{dC}{dt} = \left(-\frac{R}{V}\right)C, \qquad C = C_0 \text{ when } t = 0.$$

(a) Solve this differential equation to find the concentration as a function of time.
(b) Find the limit of C as $t \to \infty$.

38. Use the solution of the differential equation in Exercise 37 to find the concentration as a function of time, and use a graphing utility to graph the function.

(a) $V = 2$ liters, $R = 0.5$ L/min, and $C_0 = 0.6$ mol/L
(b) $V = 2$ liters, $R = 1.5$ L/min, and $C_0 = 0.6$ mol/L

39. In Exercises 37 and 38, it was assumed that there was a single initial injection of the tracer drug into the compartment. Now consider the case in which the tracer is continuously injected (beginning at $t = 0$) at the rate of Q mol/min. Considering Q to be negligible compared with R, use the differential equation

$$\frac{dC}{dt} = \frac{Q}{V} - \left(\frac{R}{V}\right)C, \qquad C = 0 \text{ when } t = 0.$$

(a) Solve this differential equation to find the concentration as a function of time.
(b) Find the limit of C as $t \to \infty$.

Chapter Summary and Study Tips

After studying this chapter, you should have acquired the following skills. **The exercise numbers are keyed to the Review Exercises that begin on page D-31. Answers to odd-numbered Review Exercises are given in the back of the text.**

■ Verify that an equation is a solution of a differential equation. (*Section D.1*)   Review Exercises 1–8

■ Use initial conditions to find particular solutions. (*Section D.1*)   Review Exercises 9–16

■ Use particular solutions to answer questions about real life. (*Section D.1*)   Review Exercises 17, 18

■ Solve differential equations whose variables are separable. (*Section D.2*)   Review Exercises 19–24

   Separable variables: $\dfrac{dy}{dx} = f(x)g(y)$

■ Use separable variable differential equations to answer questions about real life. (*Section D.2*)   Review Exercises 25, 26

■ Solve first-order linear differential equations. (*Section D.3*)   Review Exercises 27–34

   First-order linear: $y' + P(x)y = Q(x)$

   Integrating factor: $u(x) = e^{\int P(x)\,dx}$

   General solution: $y = \dfrac{1}{u(x)} \displaystyle\int Q(x)u(x)\,dx$

■ Use first-order linear differential equations to answer questions about real life. (*Section D.3*)   Review Exercises 35, 36

■ Use differential equations to model real-life problems. (*Section D.4*)   Review Exercises 37–40.

■ **Checking Solutions**   Much of the work involved in finding a particular solution of a differential equation is in solving for the constant (or constants) that occur in the general solution. Because it is easy to make a calculation error, it is a good idea to check the particular solution to see that it satisfies the initial condition(s). For instance, the general solution of $y' = k(y + 4)$ is

   $y = -4 + Ce^{kx}.$ *General solution*

   With the initial conditions of $y = 0$ when $x = 0$ and $y = 20$ when $x = 1$, the particular solution is

   $y = -4 + 4e^{1.792x}.$ *Particular solution*

   You can check this by evaluating y when $x = 0$ and $x = 1$ to see that you obtain $y = 0$ and $y = 20$, respectively.

■ **Modeling Real Life**   When setting up a differential equation that models a real-life situation, remember that the rate of change of a quantity is represented as a derivative. For instance, if you are modeling the rate of change of y with respect to time, then you should be using the derivative dy/dt.

*Several student study aids are available with this text. The *Student Solutions Guide* includes detailed solutions to all odd-numbered exercises, as well as practice chapter tests with answers. The *Graphics Calculator Guide* offers instructions on the use of a variety of graphing calculators and computer graphing software. The *Brief Calculus TUTOR* includes additional examples for selected exercises in the text.

Review Exercises

 means that technology can help you solve or check the exercise(s).

In Exercise 1–8, verify that y is a solution of the given differential equation.

Solution	*Equation*	*Solution*	*Equation*
1. $y = 3x^{2/3}$	$\frac{3}{2}xy' - y = 0$	**5.** $y = C(x-4)^2$	$\frac{dy}{dx} - \frac{2y}{x} = \frac{4}{x}\frac{dy}{dx}$
2. $y = e^{(1-3x)}$	$y' + 3y = 0$	**6.** $y = \sqrt{x^2 - 16} + C$	$y'\sqrt{x^2 - 16} = x$
3. $y = -\frac{1}{3} + Ce^{-3/x}$	$y' - \frac{3y}{x^2} = \frac{1}{x^2}$	**7.** $y = e^{x^3}(x + C)$	$\frac{dy}{dx} - 3x^2 y = e^{x^3}$
4. $y = Cx^{3/2}$	$\frac{3}{2}y - xy' = 0$	**8.** $y = Ce^{-(x-2)^2/2}$	$y' + xy = 2y$

In Exercises 9–16, verify that the general solution satisfies the given differential equation. Then find the particular solution that satisfies the initial condition.

General Solution	*Differential Equation*	*Initial Condition*
9. $y = Ce^{-x/5}$	$5y' + y = 0$	$y = 5$ when $x = 0$
10. $y = Ce^{3x^2}$	$y' - 6xy = 0$	$y = 2$ when $x = 0$
11. $y = \frac{1}{2}e^x + Ce^{-x}$	$y' + y = e^x$	$y = \frac{3}{2}$ when $x = 0$
12. $y = 5 + Ce^{-3x^2}$	$y + \frac{y'}{6x} = 5$	$y = -1$ when $x = 0$
13. $y = x^2 + 2x + \frac{C}{x}$	$\frac{dy}{dx} + \frac{y}{x} = 3x + 4$	$y = 3$ when $x = 1$
14. $y = Cx^3$	$xy' - 3y = 0$	$y = 5$ when $x = 1$
15. $y = \frac{x^3 - 3x + C}{3(x-1)}$	$(x-1)y' + y = x^2 - 1$	$y = 4$ when $x = 2$
16. $y = x^4 + Cx^3 - \frac{x}{2}$	$y' - \frac{3}{x}y = x^3 + 1$	$y = 1$ when $x = 1$

17. *Population Growth* A population of fruit flies is modeled by
$$\frac{dy}{dt} = ky.$$
  (a) Show that the solution to the differential equation is $y = Ce^{kt}$.
  (b) There were 180 fruit flies after 2 days and 300 after 4 days. How many were there after 10 days?

18. *Sales* The monthly sales S of a product can be modeled by
$$\frac{dS}{dt} = k(900,000 - S).$$
  (a) Show that the solution to the differential equation is $S = 900,000 - Ce^{-kt}$.
  (b) The sales are 0 when $t = 0$ and $\$100,000$ when $t = 6$. When will the sales reach $\$500,000$?

In Exercises 19–24, find the general solution of the differential equation.

19. $yy' - 3x^2 = 0$

20. $y' + xy = 0$

21. $y' = x^2y^2 - 9x^2$

22. $(x-3)y' = y + 2$

23. $xyy' - (1 + 2y^2 + y^4) = 0$

24. $\frac{y'}{x} - \frac{e^{x^2}}{y+1} = 0$

25. *Chemical Reaction*   In a chemical reaction, a compound changes into another compound at a rate proportional to the unchanged amount, according to the model

$$\frac{dy}{dt} = ky.$$

(a) Solve the differential equation.

(b) If initially there are 20 grams of the original compound and 16 grams remain after 1 hour, when will 75% of the compound be changed?

26. *X-Ray Absorption*   The absorption of x-rays through a body is proportional to the density ρ of the body and to the intensity I, according to the model

$$\text{Absorption} = \frac{dI}{dr} = -k\rho I,$$

where r is the depth of penetration. Solve for I as a function of r. (Assume that the intensity is I_0 when $r = 0$.)

In Exercises 27–34, solve the first-order linear differential equation.

27. $\dfrac{dy}{dx} + 6y = 9$

28. $\dfrac{dy}{dx} + 2y = e^{5x}$

29. $\dfrac{dy}{dx} - xy = 6x$

30. $\dfrac{dy}{dx} - 3x^2 y = e^{x^3}$

31. $\dfrac{dy}{dx} - \dfrac{3y}{x^2} = \dfrac{1}{x^2}$

32. $\dfrac{dy}{dx} - \dfrac{y}{x} = \dfrac{x+2}{x}$

33. $2xy' - y = x^3 - x$

34. $xy' - y = x^4$

35. *Investment*   Let $A(t)$ be the amount in a fund earning interest at the annual rate of r, compounded continuously. If a continuous cash flow of P dollars per year is withdrawn from the fund, then the rate of decrease of A is given by the differential equation

$$\frac{dA}{dt} = rA - P,$$

where $A = A_0$ when $t = 0$.

(a) Solve this equation for A as a function of t.

(b) Use the result of part (a) to find A when $A_0 = \$2{,}000{,}000$, $r = 7\%$, $P = \$250{,}000$, and $t = 5$ years.

(c) Find A_0 if a retired person wants a continuous cash flow of \$40,000 per year for 20 years. Assume that the person's investment will earn 8%, compounded continuously.

36. *Spread of a Disease*   An infectious disease spreads through a large population according to the model

$$y' = \frac{1 - y}{4},$$

where y is the percent of the population exposed to the disease, and t is the time in years.

(a) Solve this differential equation, assuming $y(0) = 0$.

(b) Find the number of years it takes for half of the population to have been exposed to the disease.

(c) Find the percentage of the population that has been exposed to the disease after 4 years.

37. *Barometric Pressure*   The barometric pressure y (in inches of mercury) at an altitude of x miles above sea level decreases at a rate proportional to the current pressure according to the model

$$\frac{dy}{dx} = -0.2y,$$

where $y = 29.92$ inches when $x = 0$. Find the barometric pressure at the top of Mt. St. Helens (8364 feet) and at the top of Mt. McKinley (20,320 feet).

38. *Sales*   A company introduces a new product for which it is believed that the limit on yearly sales is 500,000 units. Sales are expected to increase at a rate proportional to the product of sales and the difference between sales and the upper limit. Initial and second-year sales are 10,000 and 100,000 units, respectively.

(a) Estimate third-year sales.

(b) During what year will sales surpass 400,000 units?

39. *Population Growth*   The rate of growth in the number N of chickens on a poultry farm varies at a rate directly proportional to N and $(L - N)$, where L is the limiting size of the flock.

(a) Write a differential equation to model the situation.

(b) Suppose a farm had 500 chickens when $t = 0$ and 1000 chickens when $t = 4$. If $L = 5000$, how large will the flock be when $t = 8$?

40. *Forensic Science*   Police discover the body of a murder victim at 10:00 P.M. At that time, the temperature of the body is 87°F. One hour later, the temperature is 86°F. The temperature in the room is 70°. Use Newton's Law of Cooling to estimate the time that the victim was murdered.

$$\sum_{n=0}^{\infty} ar^n = \frac{a}{1-r}$$

S Series and Taylor Polynomials

To a great extent, mathematics is the study of patterns. In no other branch of mathematics is this more evident than in the study of sequences and series. Sequences of numbers, such as the patterns observed in the movement of the sun, moon, and planets, have intrigued humans since ancient times.

The study of infinite sequences and series has been a part of calculus from its inception. The representation of a function by an infinite series was part of Newton's early development of calculus.

Today, sequences and series continue to be a vital part of mathematics. In fact, with high-speed computers, sequences and series have become even more useful. This was evidenced by the Polish mathematician Benoit Mandelbrot (1924–), when he discovered the Mandelbrot fractal in the 1970s.

$$S = a + ar + ar^2 + ar^3 + \cdots$$

Mandelbrot

Michael Marsland/Yale University Office of Public Affairs

Sequences

In mathematics, the word "sequence" is used in much the same way as it is in ordinary English. When you say that a collection of objects or events is "in sequence," you mean that the collection is ordered so that it has a first member, second member, third member, and so on. Mathematically, a sequence is defined as a function whose domain is the set of positive integers. For instance, the equation $a_n = 2^n$ defines the following sequence.

$$a_1, \; a_2, \; a_3, \; a_4, \; \ldots, \; a_n, \; \ldots$$
$$\downarrow \quad \downarrow \quad \downarrow \quad \downarrow \qquad \qquad \downarrow$$
$$2, \quad 4, \quad 8, \quad 16 \; , \ldots, \; 2^n, \; \ldots$$

Note Occasionally it is convenient to begin subscripting a sequence with zero (or some other integer). In such cases, you can write

$$a_0, a_1, a_2, \ldots, a_n, \ldots.$$

Definition of a Sequence

A **sequence** $\{a_n\}$ is a function whose domain is the set of positive integers. The function values $a_1, a_2, a_3, \ldots, a_n, \ldots$ are the **terms** of the sequence.

EXAMPLE 1 *Finding Terms of a Sequence*

a. The first four terms of the sequence whose nth term is $a_n = 2n + 1$ are

$$a_1, \qquad \qquad a_2, \qquad \qquad a_3, \qquad \qquad a_4$$
$$\downarrow \qquad \qquad \downarrow \qquad \qquad \downarrow \qquad \qquad \downarrow$$
$$2(1) + 1 = 3, \quad 2(2) + 1 = 5, \quad 2(3) + 1 = 7, \quad 2(4) + 1 = 9.$$

b. The first four terms of the sequence whose nth term is $b_n = \dfrac{3}{n+1}$ are

$$b_1, \qquad \qquad b_2, \qquad \qquad b_3, \qquad \qquad b_4$$
$$\downarrow \qquad \qquad \downarrow \qquad \qquad \downarrow \qquad \qquad \downarrow$$
$$\frac{3}{(1)+1} = \frac{3}{2}, \quad \frac{3}{(2)+1} = \frac{3}{3}, \quad \frac{3}{(3)+1} = \frac{3}{4}, \quad \frac{3}{(4)+1} = \frac{3}{5}.$$ ■

The Limit of a Sequence

The primary concern of this chapter is sequences whose terms approach a limiting value. Such sequences are said to **converge;** sequences that have no limit are said to **diverge.** For instance, the terms of the sequence

$$\frac{1}{2}, \frac{1}{4}, \frac{1}{8}, \frac{1}{16}, \ldots, \frac{1}{2^n}, \ldots$$

approach 0 as n increases. You can write this limit as

$$\lim_{n \to \infty} a_n = \lim_{n \to \infty} \frac{1}{2^n} = 0.$$

Although there are technical differences, you can for the most part operate with limits of sequences just as you did with limits of continuous functions in Section 3.6. For instance, to evaluate the limit of the sequence whose nth term is

$$a_n = \frac{2n}{n+1},$$

you can write

$$\lim_{n \to \infty} \frac{2n}{n+1} = \lim_{n \to \infty} \frac{2}{1 + (1/n)} \qquad \textit{Divide numerator and denominator by n.}$$

$$= \frac{2}{1 + 0} \qquad \textit{Take limit as } n \to \infty.$$

$$= 2. \qquad \textit{Limit of sequence}$$

EXAMPLE 2 *Finding the Limit of a Sequence*

a. The terms of the sequence whose nth term is $a_n = 3 + (-1)^n$ oscillate between 2 and 4.

$$a_1 = 2, \ a_2 = 4, \ a_3 = 2, \ a_4 = 4, \ldots$$

Thus, the limit as $n \to \infty$ does not exist, and the sequence diverges.

b. The limit of the sequence whose nth term is $a_n = n/(1 - 2n)$ is

$$\lim_{n \to \infty} \frac{n}{1 - 2n} = \lim_{n \to \infty} \frac{1}{(1/n) - 2} \qquad \textit{Divide numerator and denominator by n.}$$

$$= -\frac{1}{2}. \qquad \textit{Take limit as } n \to \infty.$$

Thus, the sequence converges to $-\frac{1}{2}$.

c. The limit of the sequence whose nth term is $a_n = 2^n/(2^n - 1)$ is

$$\lim_{n \to \infty} \frac{2^n}{2^n - 1} = \lim_{n \to \infty} \frac{1}{1 - (1/2^n)} \qquad \textit{Divide numerator and denominator by } 2^n.$$

$$= 1. \qquad \textit{Take limit as } n \to \infty.$$

Thus, the sequence converges to 1.

In this chapter you will learn that many important sequences in calculus involve factorials. If n is a positive integer, then ***n* factorial** is defined as

$$n! = 1 \cdot 2 \cdot 3 \cdot 4 \cdots (n-1) \cdot n. \qquad \text{\textit{n factorial}}$$

As a special case, 0! is defined to be 1.

$$0! = 1$$
$$1! = 1$$
$$2! = 1 \cdot 2 = 2$$
$$3! = 1 \cdot 2 \cdot 3 = 6$$
$$4! = 1 \cdot 2 \cdot 3 \cdot 4 = 24$$

Factorials follow the same conventions for order of operations as exponents. That is, just as $2x^3$ and $(2x)^3$ imply different orders of operations, $2n!$ and $(2n)!$ imply the following orders.

$$2n! = 2(n!) = 2(1 \cdot 2 \cdot 3 \cdot 4 \cdots n)$$
$$(2n)! = 1 \cdot 2 \cdot 3 \cdot 4 \cdots n \cdot (n+1) \cdots (2n)$$

Try evaluating $n!$ for several values of n. You will find that n doesn't have to be very large before $n!$ becomes huge. For instance, $10! = 3{,}628{,}800$.

EXAMPLE 3 *Finding the Limit of a Sequence*

Find the limit of the sequence whose nth term is $a_n = \dfrac{(-1)^n}{n!}$.

Solution

One way to determine the limit is to write several terms of the sequence and look for a pattern.

$$
\begin{array}{cccccc}
a_1, & a_2, & a_3, & a_4, & a_5, & a_6 \\
\downarrow & \downarrow & \downarrow & \downarrow & \downarrow & \downarrow \\
-\dfrac{1}{1}, & \dfrac{1}{2}, & -\dfrac{1}{6}, & \dfrac{1}{24}, & -\dfrac{1}{120}, & \dfrac{1}{720}
\end{array}
$$

From these terms, it is clear that the denominator is increasing without bound while the numerator is bounded. Thus, you can write

$$\lim_{n \to \infty} \frac{(-1)^n}{n!} = 0.$$

This result is shown graphically in Figure S.1. Note that the terms of the sequence oscillate between positive and negative values.   ▬

Note   Try using a symbolic algebra utility such as *Derive*, *Mathematica*, or *Maple* to evaluate the limit in Example 3.

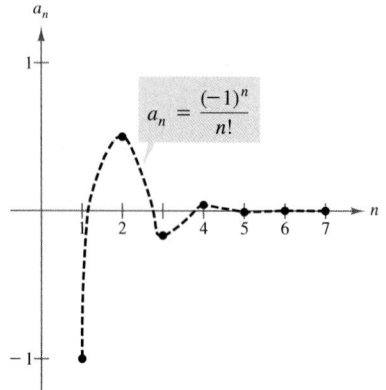

$$a_n = \frac{(-1)^n}{n!}$$

FIGURE S.1

Pattern Recognition for Sequences

Often, the terms of a sequence are generated by a procedure that does not explicitly identify the nth term of the sequence. In such circumstances, you need to discover a *pattern* in the sequence and find a formula for the nth term.

EXAMPLE 4 *Finding a Pattern for a Sequence*

Consider the function $f(x) = e^{x/3}$. Determine the convergence or divergence of the sequence whose nth term is

$$a_n = f^{(n-1)}(0),$$

where $f^{(0)}(x) = f(x)$ and $f^{(n)}$ is the nth derivative of f.

Solution

Begin by calculating several derivatives of f and evaluating the results for $x = 0$, as shown in Table S.1.

TABLE S.1

n	1	2	3	4	5	6	$\ldots$	n
$f^{(n-1)}(x)$	$e^{x/3}$	$\dfrac{e^{x/3}}{3}$	$\dfrac{e^{x/3}}{3^2}$	$\dfrac{e^{x/3}}{3^3}$	$\dfrac{e^{x/3}}{3^4}$	$\dfrac{e^{x/3}}{3^5}$	$\ldots$	$\dfrac{e^{x/3}}{3^{n-1}}$
$f^{(n-1)}(0)$	1	$\dfrac{1}{3}$	$\dfrac{1}{3^2}$	$\dfrac{1}{3^3}$	$\dfrac{1}{3^4}$	$\dfrac{1}{3^5}$	$\ldots$	$\dfrac{1}{3^{n-1}}$

From this table, you can see that the pattern is

$$a_n = \frac{1}{3^{n-1}}.$$

Therefore, you can write

$$\lim_{n \to \infty} \frac{1}{3^{n-1}} = 0,$$

which means that the sequence converges to 0.

Searching for a pattern for the nth term of a sequence can be difficult. It helps to consider the following patterns.

nth Term	*Terms*	*Type of Sequence*
$(-1)^n$	$-1,\ 1,\ -1,\ 1,\ -1,\ 1,\ -1,\ 1,\ \ldots$	*Changes in sign*
$(-1)^{n+1}$	$1,\ -1,\ 1,\ -1,\ 1,\ -1,\ 1,\ -1,\ \ldots$	*Changes in sign*
$an + b$	$a + b,\ 2a + b,\ 3a + b,\ 4a + b,\ \ldots$	*Arithmetic*
a^n	$a,\ a^2,\ a^3,\ a^4,\ a^5,\ a^6,\ \ldots$	*Geometric*
$n!$	$1,\ 2,\ 6,\ 24,\ 120,\ 720,\ \ldots$	*Factorial*
n^p	$1,\ 2^p,\ 3^p,\ 4^p,\ 5^p,\ 6^p,\ \ldots$	*Power*

Discovery

Determine the first eight terms of the sequence whose nth term is

$$a_n = \left(1 + \frac{1}{n}\right)^n.$$

What is the limit of this sequence? How does this sequence relate to the definition of the number e given on page 262?

Without a specific rule for the nth term of a sequence, it is not possible to determine the convergence or divergence of the sequence—knowing the first several terms is not enough. For instance, the first three terms of the following four sequences are identical. Yet, from their nth terms, you can see that two of the sequences converge to 0, one converges to $\frac{1}{9}$, and one diverges.

$$\{a_n\} = \left\{ \frac{1}{2}, \frac{1}{4}, \frac{1}{8}, \frac{1}{16}, \dots, \frac{1}{2^n}, \dots \right\}$$

$$\{b_n\} = \left\{ \frac{1}{2}, \frac{1}{4}, \frac{1}{8}, \frac{1}{15}, \dots, \frac{6}{(n+1)(n^2-n+6)}, \dots \right\}$$

$$\{c_n\} = \left\{ \frac{1}{2}, \frac{1}{4}, \frac{1}{8}, \frac{7}{62}, \dots, \frac{n^2-3n+3}{9n^2-25n+18}, \dots \right\}$$

$$\{d_n\} = \left\{ \frac{1}{2}, \frac{1}{4}, \frac{1}{8}, 0, \dots, \frac{-n(n+1)(n-4)}{6(n^2+3n-2)}, \dots \right\}$$

Thus, if only the first several terms of a sequence are given, there are many possible patterns that can be used to write a formula for the nth term. In such a situation, remember that your decision as to whether the sequence converges or diverges depends on your description of the nth term.

EXAMPLE 5 *Finding a Pattern for a Sequence*

Determine an nth term for the sequence

$$-\frac{1}{1}, \frac{3}{2}, -\frac{7}{6}, \frac{15}{24}, -\frac{31}{120}, \dots$$

Solution

Begin by observing that the numerators are one less than 2^n. Thus, you can generate the numerators by the rule

$$2^n - 1, \qquad n = 1, 2, 3, 4, 5, \dots$$

Factoring the denominators produces

$$1 = 1!$$
$$2 = 1 \cdot 2 = 2!$$
$$6 = 1 \cdot 2 \cdot 3 = 3!$$
$$24 = 1 \cdot 2 \cdot 3 \cdot 4 = 4!$$
$$120 = 1 \cdot 2 \cdot 3 \cdot 4 \cdot 5 = 5!$$

Thus, the denominators can be represented by $n!$. Finally, because the signs alternate, you can write

$$a_n = (-1)^n \left(\frac{2^n - 1}{n!} \right)$$

as one possible formula for the nth term of this sequence.

Applications

Interest rates on savings accounts are related to inflation rates. Throughout most of this century, the United States experienced very little inflation. In fact, from 1915 to 1940, the average annual inflation rate was only 1.3%. From 1940 to 1970, the average annual inflation rate was about 3.5%, and from 1970 to 1992, the average annual inflation rate was 6.0%.

There are many applications of sequences in business and economics. The next example involves the balance in an account for which the interest is compounded monthly. The terms of the sequence are the balances at the end of the first month, the end of the second month, and so on.

Real Life

EXAMPLE 6 *Finding Balances*

A deposit of $1000 is made in an account that earns 6% interest, compounded monthly. Find a sequence that represents the monthly balances.

Solution
Because an annual interest rate of 6% compounded monthly corresponds to a monthly rate of 0.5%, the balance after 1 month is

$$A_1 = 1000 + 1000(0.005) = 1000(1.005).$$

After 2 months, the balance is

$$A_2 = 1000(1.005)(1.005) = 1000(1.005)^2.$$

Continuing this pattern, you can determine that the balance after n months is

$$A_n = 1000(1.005)^n.$$

This implies that the first several terms of the sequence are

$$1000(1.005),\ 1000(1.005)^2,\ 1000(1.005)^3,\ 1000(1.005)^4,\ \ldots$$

or

$$\$1005.00,\ \$1010.03,\ \$1015.08,\ \$1020.15,\ \ldots.$$

Note that this sequence is of the form $P[1 + (r/12)]^n$, which agrees with the formula for the balance in an account.   ■

Discussion Problem   Determining Convergence or Divergence

Find a formula for the nth term of the sequence. Then, based on your formula, decide whether the sequence converges or diverges.

a. $\dfrac{1}{1},\ \dfrac{1}{2},\ \dfrac{1}{3},\ \dfrac{1}{4},\ \dfrac{1}{5},\ \ldots$

b. $\dfrac{2}{2},\ \dfrac{4}{8},\ \dfrac{6}{26},\ \dfrac{8}{80},\ \dfrac{10}{242},\ \ldots$

c. $\dfrac{3}{1},\ \dfrac{5}{3},\ \dfrac{7}{5},\ \dfrac{9}{7},\ \dfrac{11}{9},\ \ldots$

Warm Up

The following warm-up exercises involve skills that were covered in earlier sections. You will use these skills in the exercise set for this section.

In Exercises 1–6, find the indicated limit.

1. $\lim\limits_{x \to \infty} \dfrac{1}{x^3}$

2. $\lim\limits_{x \to \infty} \dfrac{1}{x^2 - 4}$

3. $\lim\limits_{x \to \infty} \dfrac{2x^2}{x^2 + 1}$

4. $\lim\limits_{x \to \infty} \dfrac{x^3 - 1}{x^2 + 2}$

5. $\lim\limits_{x \to \infty} e^{-2x}$

6. $\lim\limits_{x \to \infty} \dfrac{1}{2^{x-1}}$

In Exercises 7–10, simplify the expression.

7. $\dfrac{n^2 - 4}{n^2 + 2n}$

8. $\dfrac{n^2 + n - 12}{n^2 - 16}$

9. $\dfrac{3}{n} + \dfrac{1}{n^3}$

10. $\dfrac{1}{n-1} + \dfrac{1}{n+2}, \quad n \geq 2$

E X E R C I S E S   S.1   means that technology can help you solve or check the exercise(s).

In Exercises 1–8, write out the first five terms of the specified sequence.

1. $a_n = 2^n$

2. $a_n = \dfrac{n}{n+1}$

3. $a_n = \left(-\dfrac{1}{2}\right)^n$

4. $a_n = \dfrac{n-1}{n^2+2}$

5. $a_n = \dfrac{3^n}{n!}$

6. $a_n = 5 - \dfrac{1}{n} + \dfrac{1}{n^2}$

7. $a_n = \dfrac{(-1)^n}{n^2}$

8. $a_n = \dfrac{3n!}{(n-1)!}$

In Exercises 9–26, determine the convergence or divergence of the sequence. If the sequence converges, find its limit.

9. $a_n = \dfrac{5}{n}$

10. $a_n = \dfrac{n}{2}$

11. $a_n = \dfrac{n+1}{n}$

12. $a_n = \dfrac{1}{n^{3/2}}$

13. $a_n = \dfrac{n^2 + 3n - 4}{2n^2 + n - 3}$

14. $a_n = \dfrac{\sqrt{n}}{\sqrt{n+1}}$

15. $a_n = \dfrac{n^2 - 25}{n+5}$

16. $a_n = 1 + (-1)^n$

17. $a_n = \dfrac{1 + (-1)^n}{n}$

18. $a_n = \dfrac{n!}{n}$

19. $a_n = 3 - \dfrac{1}{2^n}$

20. $a_n = \dfrac{n}{\sqrt{n^2 + 1}}$

21. $a_n = \dfrac{3^n}{4^n}$

22. $a_n = (0.5)^n$

23. $a_n = \dfrac{(n+1)!}{n!}$

24. $a_n = \dfrac{(n-2)!}{n!}$

25. $a_n = (-1)^n \left(\dfrac{n}{n+1}\right)$

26. $a_n = \dfrac{n-1}{n} - \dfrac{n}{n-1}, \quad n \geq 2$

In Exercises 27 and 28, use the graph of the sequence to decide whether the sequence converges. Then verify your result analytically.

27.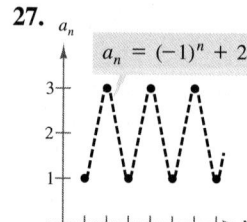

$a_n = (-1)^n + 2$

28.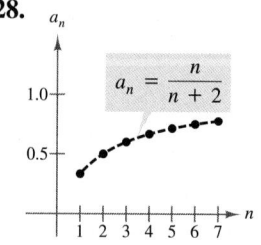

$a_n = \dfrac{n}{n + 2}$

In Exercises 29–42, write an expression for the *n*th term of the given sequence.

29. $1, 4, 7, 10, \ldots$

30. $3, 7, 11, 15, \ldots$

31. $-1, 4, 9, 14, \ldots$

32. $1, \frac{1}{4}, \frac{1}{9}, \frac{1}{16}, \ldots$

33. $\frac{2}{3}, \frac{3}{4}, \frac{4}{5}, \frac{5}{6}, \ldots$

34. $2, \frac{3}{3}, \frac{4}{5}, \frac{5}{7}, \frac{6}{9}, \ldots$

35. $2, -1, \frac{1}{2}, -\frac{1}{4}, \frac{1}{8}, \ldots$

36. $\frac{1}{3}, \frac{2}{9}, \frac{4}{27}, \frac{8}{81}, \ldots$

37. $2, 1 + \frac{1}{2}, 1 + \frac{1}{3}, 1 + \frac{1}{4}, \ldots$

38. $1 + \frac{1}{2}, 1 + \frac{1}{4}, 1 + \frac{1}{8}, 1 + \frac{1}{16}, \ldots$

39. $-2, 2, -2, 2, \ldots$

40. $2, -4, 6, -8, 10, \ldots$

41. $1, \frac{1}{2}, \frac{1}{6}, \frac{1}{24}, \frac{1}{120}, \ldots$

42. $1, x, \dfrac{x^2}{2}, \dfrac{x^3}{6}, \dfrac{x^4}{24}, \dfrac{x^5}{120}, \ldots$

In Exercises 43–46, write the next two terms of the arithmetic sequence.

43. $2, 5, 8, 11, \ldots$

44. $\frac{7}{2}, 4, \frac{9}{2}, 5, \ldots$

45. $1, \frac{5}{3}, \frac{7}{3}, 3, \ldots$

46. $\frac{1}{2}, \frac{5}{4}, 2, \frac{11}{4}, \ldots$

In Exercises 47–50, write the next two terms of the geometric sequence.

47. $3, -\frac{3}{2}, \frac{3}{4}, -\frac{3}{8}, \ldots$

48. $5, 10, 20, 40, \ldots$

49. $2, 6, 18, 54, \ldots$

50. $9, 6, 4, \frac{8}{3}, \ldots$

In Exercises 51–54, determine whether the sequence is arithmetic or geometric, and write the *n*th term of the sequence.

51. $20, 10, 5, \frac{5}{2}, \ldots$

52. $100, 92, 84, 76, \ldots$

53. $\frac{8}{3}, \frac{10}{3}, 4, \frac{14}{3}, \ldots$

54. $378, -126, 42, -14, \ldots$

In Exercises 55 and 56, give an example of a sequence satisfying the given condition. (There is more than one correct answer.)

55. A sequence that converges to $\frac{3}{4}$

56. A sequence that converges to 100

57. *Compound Interest* Consider the sequence $\{A_n\}$, whose *n*th term is given by $A_n = P[1 + (r/12)]^n$, where P is the principal, A_n is the amount at compound interest after n months, and r is the annual percentage rate. Find the first ten terms of the sequence for $P = \$9000$ and $r = 0.06$.

58. *Compound Interest* Consider the sequence $\{A_n\}$, whose *n*th term is given by $A_n = P(1 + r)^n$, where P is the principal, A_n is the amount at compound interest after n years, and r is the annual percentage rate. Find the first ten terms of the sequence for $P = \$5000$ and $r = 0.10$.

59. *Individual Retirement Account* A deposit of $2000 is made each year in an account that earns 11% interest compounded annually. The balance after n years is given by

$$A_n = 2000(11)[(1.1)^n - 1].$$

(a) Compute the first six terms of the sequence.

(b) Find the balance after 20 years by finding the 20th term of the sequence.

(c) Find the balance after 40 years by finding the 40th term of the sequence.

60. *Population Growth* Consider an idealized population with the characteristic that each population member produces one offspring at the end of every time period. If each population member has a lifespan of three time periods and the population begins with ten newborn members, then the following table gives the population during the first five time periods.

	Time Period				
Age Bracket	1	2	3	4	5
0–1	10	10	20	40	70
1–2		10	10	20	40
2–3			10	10	20
Total	10	20	40	70	130

The sequence for the total population has the property that

$$S_n = S_{n-1} + S_{n-2} + S_{n-3}, \qquad n > 3.$$

Find the total population during the next five time periods.

61. *Hospital Costs* The average cost per day for a semiprivate hospital room from 1980 to 1990 is approximated by the model

$$a_n = 127.42 + 17.37n, \qquad n = 0, 1, 2, \ldots, 10,$$

where a_n is the average cost in dollars and n is the year, with $n = 0$ corresponding to 1980. Find the terms of this finite sequence and construct a bar graph that represents the sequence. Use the model to predict the cost in 1995. *(Source: American Hospital Association)*

62. *Federal Debt* It took more than 200 years for the United States to accumulate a $1 trillion debt. Then it took just 8 years to get to $3 trillion. The federal debt during the decade of the 1980s is approximated by the model

$$a_n = 0.917e^{0.087n}, \qquad n = 0, 1, 2, \ldots, 10,$$

where a_n is the debt in trillions and n is the year, with $n = 0$ corresponding to 1980. Find the terms of this finite sequence and construct a bar graph that represents the sequence. *(Source: Treasury Department)*

63. *Investment* A deposit of $100 is made each month in an account that earns 6% interest compounded monthly. The balance in the account after n months is given by

$$A_n = 100(201)[(1.005)^n - 1].$$

(a) Compute the first six terms of this sequence.

(b) Find the balance after 5 years by computing the 60th term of the sequence.

(c) Find the balance after 20 years by computing the 240th term of the sequence.

64. The sum of the first n positive integers is given by

$$S_n = \frac{n(n+1)}{2}, \qquad n = 1, 2, 3, \ldots.$$

(a) Compute the first five terms of this sequence and verify that each term gives the correct sum.

(b) Find the sum of the first 50 positive integers.

65. The sum of the squares of the first n positive integers is given by

$$S_n = \frac{n(n+1)(2n+1)}{6}, \qquad n = 1, 2, 3, \ldots.$$

(a) Compute the first five terms of the sequence and verify that each term gives the correct sum.

(b) Find the sum of the squares of the first 20 positive integers.

66. *Bouncing Ball* A ball is dropped from a height of 12 feet, and on each rebound it rises to $\frac{2}{3}$ its previous height.

(a) Write an expression for the height of the nth rebound.

(b) Determine the convergence or divergence of this sequence. If it converges, find the limit.

67. *Governmental Expenditures* A government program that currently costs taxpayers $1.3 billion per year is to be cut back by 15% per year.

(a) Write an expression for the amount budgeted for this program after n years.

(b) Compute the budget amounts for the first four years.

(c) Determine the convergence or divergence of the sequence of reduced budgets. If the sequence converges, find its limit.

68. *Price Increases* If the average price of a new car increases $5\frac{1}{2}$% per year and the average price is currently $13,000, then the average price after n years is

$$P_n = \$13,000(1.055)^n.$$

Compute the average price for the first five years of increases.

69. Consider the sequence whose nth term a_n is given by

$$a_n = \left(1 + \frac{1}{n}\right)^n.$$

Demonstrate that the terms of this sequence approach e by finding a_1, a_{10}, a_{100}, a_{1000}, and $a_{10,000}$.

70. *Drilling Costs* A well-drilling company charges $16 for drilling the first foot of a well, $16.10 for drilling the second foot, $16.20 for the third foot, and so on. Determine the cost of drilling a 100-foot well.

71. *Job Offer* A person accepts a position with a company at a salary of $32,800 for the first year. The person is guaranteed a raise of 5% per year for the first four years. Determine the person's salary during the fourth year of employment.

Sigma Notation ■ *Infinite Series* ■ *The nth-Term Test for Divergence* ■
Geometric Series ■ *Applications*

Sigma Notation

In this section, you will study infinite summations. The decimal representation of $\frac{1}{3}$ is a simple example of an infinite summation.

$$\frac{1}{3} = 0.33333\ldots$$

$$= 0.3 + 0.03 + 0.003 + 0.0003 + 0.00003 + \cdots$$

$$= \frac{3}{10} + \frac{3}{10^2} + \frac{3}{10^3} + \frac{3}{10^4} + \frac{3}{10^5} + \cdots$$

$$= \sum_{n=1}^{\infty} \frac{3}{10^n}$$

The last notation is called **sigma notation** or **summation notation.**

Note Although i, j, k, and n are commonly used as indices of summation, any letter can be used. Moreover, the upper and lower limits of summation can be any two integers.

Sigma Notation

The finite sum $a_1 + a_2 + a_3 + \cdots + a_N$ can be written as

$$\sum_{i=1}^{N} a_i.$$

The letter i is the **index of summation,** and 1 and N are the lower and upper limits of summation.

EXAMPLE 1 *Using Sigma Notation*

Sum	*Σ Notation*
a. $1 + 2 + 3 + 4 + 5 + 6$	$\sum_{i=1}^{6} i$
b. $3(1) + 3\left(\frac{1}{2}\right) + 3\left(\frac{1}{2}\right)^2 + \cdots + 3\left(\frac{1}{2}\right)^N$	$\sum_{k=0}^{N} 3\left(\frac{1}{2}\right)^k$

Infinite Series

The infinite summation

$$\sum_{n=1}^{\infty} a_n = a_1 + a_2 + a_3 + a_4 + \cdots$$

is called an **infinite series.** The **sequence of partial sums** of the series is denoted by

$$S_1 = a_1, \quad S_2 = a_1 + a_2, \quad S_3 = a_1 + a_2 + a_3, \quad \ldots.$$

Convergence and Divergence of an Infinite Series

Consider the infinite series $a_1 + a_2 + a_3 + \cdots$. If the sequence of partial sums $\{S_n\}$ converges to S, then the infinite series **converges** to S. This limit is denoted by

$$\lim_{n \to \infty} S_n = \sum_{n=1}^{\infty} a_n = S,$$

and S is called the **sum of the series.** If the limit of the sequence of partial sums $\{S_n\}$ does not exist, then the series **diverges.**

EXAMPLE 2   *Determining Convergence and Divergence*

a. The infinite series

$$\sum_{n=1}^{\infty} \frac{1}{2^n} = \frac{1}{2} + \frac{1}{4} + \frac{1}{8} + \frac{1}{16} + \cdots$$

has the following partial sums.

$$S_1 = \frac{1}{2}, \quad S_2 = \frac{3}{4}, \quad S_3 = \frac{7}{8}, \quad S_4 = \frac{15}{16}, \quad \ldots, \quad S_n = \frac{2^n - 1}{2^n}.$$

Because the limit of $\{S_n\}$ is 1, it follows that the infinite series converges and its sum is 1. Thus, you can write

$$\sum_{n=1}^{\infty} \frac{1}{2^n} = \frac{1}{2} + \frac{1}{4} + \frac{1}{8} + \frac{1}{16} + \cdots = 1.$$

b. The infinite series

$$\sum_{n=1}^{\infty} 1 = 1 + 1 + 1 + 1 + \cdots$$

diverges because the sequence of partial sums $\{S_n\}$ diverges. ▬

TECHNOLOGY

Symbolic algebra utilities, such as *Derive*, *Mathematica*, and *Maple*, can be used to evaluate infinite sums. For instance, you can use *Derive* to evaluate the sum in Example 2a by typing the command SUM(1/2∧n,n,1,INF) and simplifying, as follows.

$$1: \ \sum_{n=1}^{\infty} \frac{1}{2^n}$$

$$2: \ 1$$

The following properties are useful in determining the sums of infinite series.

Properties of Infinite Series

For the convergent infinite series

$$\sum_{n=1}^{\infty} a_n = A \quad \text{and} \quad \sum_{n=1}^{\infty} b_n = B,$$

the following properties are true.

1. $\displaystyle\sum_{n=1}^{\infty} ca_n = c\sum_{n=1}^{\infty} a_n = cA$

2. $\displaystyle\sum_{n=1}^{\infty} (a_n + b_n) = \sum_{n=1}^{\infty} a_n + \sum_{n=1}^{\infty} b_n = A + B$

Discovery

Determine the first eight terms of the sequence of partial sums for the infinite series

$$\sum_{n=0}^{\infty} \frac{1}{n!}.$$

What is the limit of this sequence of partial sums? You will discover later in this chapter that this infinite series converges to the number e.

EXAMPLE 3 *Using Properties of Infinite Series*

Find the sums of the infinite series.

a. $\displaystyle\sum_{n=1}^{\infty} \frac{5}{2^n}$ **b.** $\displaystyle\sum_{n=1}^{\infty} \left(\frac{1}{2^n} + \frac{1}{2^{n+1}} \right)$

Solution

For each infinite series, use the result of Example 2a.

$$\sum_{n=1}^{\infty} \frac{1}{2^n} = 1$$

a. Using Property 1 of infinite series, you can write

$$\sum_{n=1}^{\infty} \frac{5}{2^n} = 5\sum_{n=1}^{\infty} \frac{1}{2^n} = 5(1) = 5.$$

b. Begin by noting that

$$\sum_{n=1}^{\infty} \frac{1}{2^{n+1}} = \sum_{n=1}^{\infty} \frac{1}{2}\left(\frac{1}{2^n} \right) = \frac{1}{2}\sum_{n=1}^{\infty} \frac{1}{2^n} = \frac{1}{2}(1) = \frac{1}{2}.$$

Now, you can use Property 2 of infinite series to write

$$\sum_{n=1}^{\infty} \left(\frac{1}{2^n} + \frac{1}{2^{n+1}} \right) = \sum_{n=1}^{\infty} \frac{1}{2^n} + \sum_{n=1}^{\infty} \frac{1}{2^{n+1}} = 1 + \frac{1}{2} = \frac{3}{2}.$$

The nth-Term Test for Divergence

The two primary questions regarding an infinite series are as follows.

1. Does the series converge or does it diverge?
2. If the series converges, to what value does it converge?

A simple test for divergence gives a partial answer to the first question.

Note Be sure you see that the nth-Term Test is a test for *divergence*, not for convergence. That is, if the nth term does not converge to 0, then you know that the series diverges. If the nth term does converge to 0, the series may or may not converge.

---

nth-Term Test for Divergence

Consider the infinite series $\sum_{n=1}^{\infty} a_n$. If

$$\lim_{n\to\infty} a_n \neq 0,$$

then the series diverges.

EXAMPLE 4 *Testing for Divergence*

a. By the nth-Term Test, the infinite series

$$\sum_{n=1}^{\infty} 2^n = 2 + 4 + 8 + 16 + \cdots$$

diverges, because

$$\lim_{n\to\infty} 2^n = \infty.$$

b. The nth-Term Test tells you nothing about the infinite series

$$\sum_{n=1}^{\infty} \frac{1}{2^n} = \frac{1}{2} + \frac{1}{4} + \frac{1}{8} + \frac{1}{16} + \cdots.$$

because

$$\lim_{n\to\infty} \frac{1}{2^n} = 0.$$

From Example 2a, you know that this series converges. The point here is that you cannot deduce this from the nth-Term Test.

c. The infinite series

$$\sum_{n=1}^{\infty} \frac{n!}{2n! + 1} = \frac{1}{3} + \frac{2}{5} + \frac{6}{13} + \frac{24}{49} + \frac{120}{241} + \cdots$$

diverges because

$$\lim_{n\to\infty} \frac{n!}{2n! + 1} = \lim_{n\to\infty} \frac{1}{2 + (1/n!)} = \frac{1}{2 + 0} = \frac{1}{2}.$$

Geometric Series

If a is a nonzero real number, then the infinite series

Note Note that the first term of this series is $ar^0 = a$. If the index had begun with $n = 1$, the first term would have been $ar^1 = ar$.

$$\sum_{n=0}^{\infty} ar^n = a + ar + ar^2 + \cdots + ar^n + \cdots$$ *Geometric series*

is called a **geometric series** with ratio r.

Nth Partial Sum of a Geometric Series

The Nth partial sum of the geometric series $\displaystyle\sum_{n=0}^{\infty} ar^n$ is

$$S_N = \frac{a(1 - r^{N+1})}{1 - r}, \qquad r \neq 1.$$

EXAMPLE 5 *Finding an Nth Partial Sum*

Find the 3rd, 5th, and 10th partial sums of the geometric series

$$\sum_{n=0}^{\infty} 3\left(\frac{1}{4}\right)^n = 3 + \frac{3}{4} + \frac{3}{4^2} + \frac{3}{4^3} + \cdots.$$

Solution

For this geometric series, $a = 3$ and $r = \frac{1}{4}$. Because the index begins with $n = 0$, the Nth partial sum is

$$S_N = \frac{a(1 - r^{N+1})}{1 - r}$$

$$= \frac{3[1 - (1/4)^{N+1}]}{1 - (1/4)}$$

$$= \frac{3[1 - (1/4)^{N+1}]}{3/4}$$

$$= 4\left[1 - \left(\tfrac{1}{4}\right)^{N+1}\right]$$

$$= 4 - \left(\tfrac{1}{4}\right)^{N}.$$

Using this formula, you can find the 3rd, 5th, and 10th partial sums as follows.

$$S_3 = 4 - \left(\tfrac{1}{4}\right)^3 \approx 3.984 \qquad \text{\textit{3rd partial sum}}$$

$$S_5 = 4 - \left(\tfrac{1}{4}\right)^5 \approx 3.999 \qquad \text{\textit{5th partial sum}}$$

$$S_{10} = 4 - \left(\tfrac{1}{4}\right)^{10} \approx 4.000 \qquad \text{\textit{10th partial sum}}$$

When applying the formula for the Nth partial sum of a geometric series, be sure to check that the index begins with $n = 0$. If it begins with some other number, you will have to adjust S_N accordingly. Here is an example.

$$\sum_{n=1}^{10} ar^n = -a + \sum_{n=0}^{10} ar^n = -a + \frac{a(1 - r^{11})}{1 - r}$$

The same type of adjustment is used in the next example.

Real Life

EXAMPLE 6 *Finding an Annuity Balance*

A deposit of $50 is made every month for 2 years into a savings account that pays 6%, compounded monthly. What is the balance in the account at the end of 2 years?

Solution

From the formula for compound interest, after 24 months, the money that was deposited the first month will have become

$$A_{24} = 50 \left(1 + \frac{0.06}{12}\right)^{24} = 50(1.005)^{24}.$$

Similarly, after 23 months, the money deposited the second month will have become

$$A_{23} = 50 \left(1 + \frac{0.06}{12}\right)^{23} = 50(1.005)^{23}.$$

Continuing this process, you can find that the total balance resulting from the 24 deposits will be

$$A = A_1 + A_2 + \cdots + A_{24}$$

$$= \sum_{n=1}^{24} A_n = \sum_{n=1}^{24} 50(1.005)^n.$$

Noting that the index begins with $n = 1$, you can use the formula for the Nth partial sum to find the balance.

$$A = \sum_{n=1}^{24} 50(1.005)^n$$

$$= -50 + \sum_{n=0}^{24} 50(1.005)^n$$

$$= -50 + \frac{50(1 - 1.005^{25})}{1 - 1.005}$$

$$\approx \$1277.96$$

The growth of this account is shown graphically in Figure S.2.

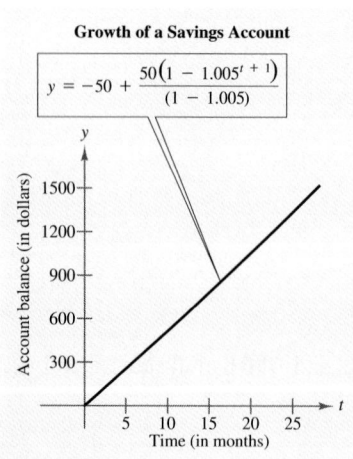

Growth of a Savings Account

$$y = -50 + \frac{50(1 - 1.005^{t+1})}{(1 - 1.005)}$$

Account balance (in dollars)

Time (in months)

FIGURE S.2

Note You can apply the test for convergence or divergence of an infinite geometric series regardless of the beginning value of the index of summation. If the series converges, however, then the formula for its sum is only valid for geometric series whose index begins at $n = 0$.

Convergence of an Infinite Geometric Series

Consider the infinite geometric series $\sum\limits_{n=0}^{\infty} ar^n$.

1. If $|r| \geq 1$, the series *diverges*.
2. If $|r| < 1$, the series *converges* and its sum is $\dfrac{a}{1-r}$.

EXAMPLE 7 *Determining Convergence and Divergence*

Decide whether each series converges or diverges.

a. $\sum\limits_{n=0}^{\infty} \left(-\dfrac{1}{2}\right)^n$ b. $\sum\limits_{n=0}^{\infty} \left(\dfrac{3}{2}\right)^n$ c. $\sum\limits_{n=1}^{\infty} \dfrac{4}{3^n}$

Solution

a. For this infinite geometric series, $a = 1$ and $r = -\dfrac{1}{2}$. Because $|r| < 1$, it follows that the series converges. Moreover, because the index begins with $n = 0$, you can apply the formula for the sum of an infinite geometric series to conclude that

$$\sum_{n=0}^{\infty} \left(-\frac{1}{2}\right)^n = \frac{a}{1-r} = \frac{1}{1-(-1/2)} = \frac{1}{3/2} = \frac{2}{3}.$$

b. For this infinite geometric series, $a = 1$ and $r = \dfrac{3}{2}$. Because $|r| > 1$, it follows that the series diverges.

c. By rewriting the infinite geometric series as

$$\sum_{n=1}^{\infty} 4\left(\frac{1}{3}\right)^n,$$

you can see that $a = 4$ and $r = \dfrac{1}{3}$. Because $|r| < 1$, the series converges. To find the sum of the series, note that the index begins with $n = 1$, then adjust the formula for the sum as follows.

$$\sum_{n=1}^{\infty} 4\left(\frac{1}{3}\right)^n = -4 + \sum_{n=0}^{\infty} 4\left(\frac{1}{3}\right)^n$$

$$= -4 + \frac{4}{1-(1/3)}$$

$$= -4 + \frac{4}{2/3}$$

$$= -4 + 6$$

$$= 2$$

Thus, the series converges to 2.

Applications

Microwave ovens were first marketed in the early 1970s. From that time until the mid-1980s, the number of units sold each year increased. From the mid-1980s to the early 1990s, the annual sales stabilized to about 11 million units per year.

Real Life

EXAMPLE 8 *Modeling Market Stabilization*

A manufacturer sells 10,000 units of a product each year. In any given year, each unit has a 10% chance of breaking. That is, after 1 year you expect only 9000 of the previous year's 10,000 units to still be in use. During the next year, this number will drop by an additional 10% to 8100, and so on. How many units will be in use after 20 years? Is the number of units in use stabilizing? If so, what is the stabilization point?

Solution

You can model this situation with a geometric series, as follows.

End of Year	Number of Units in Use
0	10,000
1	$10,000 + 10,000(0.9)$
2	$10,000 + 10,000(0.9) + 10,000(0.9)^2$
3	$10,000 + 10,000(0.9) + 10,000(0.9)^2 + 10,000(0.9)^3$

After 20 years, the number of units in use will be

$$\sum_{n=0}^{20} 10,000(0.9)^n = \frac{10,000[1 - (0.9)^{21}]}{1 - 0.9} \approx 89,058.$$

As indicated in Figure S.3, the number of units in use is approaching a stabilization point of

$$\sum_{n=0}^{\infty} 10,000(0.9)^n = \frac{10,000}{1 - 0.9} = 100,000 \text{ units.}$$

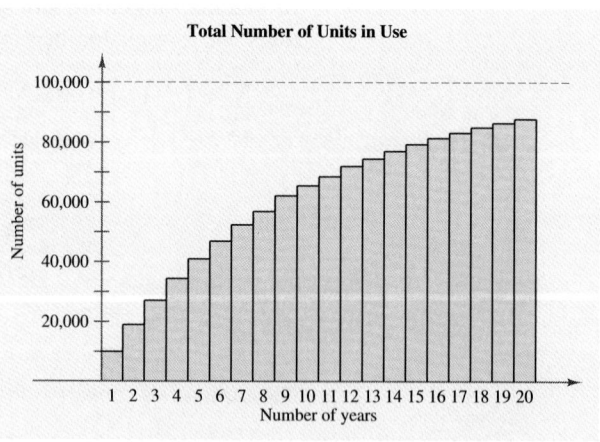

Total Number of Units in Use

FIGURE S.3

Real
Life

EXAMPLE 9 *Modeling a Bouncing Ball*

A ball is dropped from a height of 6 feet and begins to bounce. The height of each bounce is $\frac{3}{4}$ that of the previous bounce, as shown in Figure S.4. Find the total distance traveled by the ball.

Solution

When the ball hits the ground the first time, it has traveled a distance of

$$D_1 = 6.$$

Between the first and second times it hits the ground, it has traveled an additional distance of

$$D_2 = \underbrace{6\left(\frac{3}{4}\right)}_{Up} + \underbrace{6\left(\frac{3}{4}\right)}_{Down} = 12\left(\frac{3}{4}\right).$$

Between the second and third times the ball hits the ground, it has traveled an additional distance of

$$D_3 = \underbrace{6\left(\frac{3}{4}\right)\left(\frac{3}{4}\right)}_{Up} + \underbrace{6\left(\frac{3}{4}\right)\left(\frac{3}{4}\right)}_{Down} = 12\left(\frac{3}{4}\right)^2.$$

Continuing this process, you obtain a total distance traveled of

$$D = 6 + 12\left(\frac{3}{4}\right) + 12\left(\frac{3}{4}\right)^2 + \cdots$$

$$= -6 + 12 + 12\left(\frac{3}{4}\right) + 12\left(\frac{3}{4}\right)^2 + \cdots$$

$$= -6 + \sum_{n=0}^{\infty} 12\left(\frac{3}{4}\right)^n$$

$$= -6 + \frac{12}{1 - (3/4)}$$

$$= -6 + 48$$

$$= 42 \text{ feet.}$$

Thus, the ball travels a total distance of 42 feet.

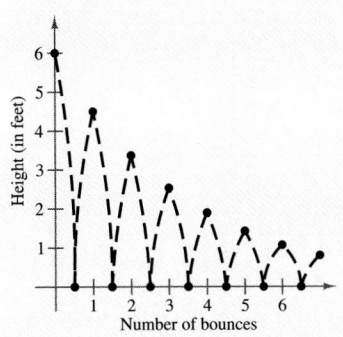

Distance Traveled by a Bouncing Ball

Height (in feet)

Number of bounces

FIGURE S.4

Discussion Problem   *Modeling a Bouncing Ball*

In Example 9, how much farther would the ball have traveled if the height of each bounce had been $\frac{7}{8}$ that of the previous bounce? Explain your reasoning.

Warm Up

The following warm-up exercises involve skills that were covered in earlier sections. You will use these skills in the exercise set for this section.

In Exercises 1 and 2, add the fractions.

1. $\frac{1}{2} + \frac{1}{3} + \frac{1}{4} + \frac{1}{5}$

2. $1 + \frac{3}{4} + \frac{4}{6} + \frac{5}{8}$

In Exercises 3–6, evaluate the expression.

3. $\dfrac{1 - \left(\frac{1}{2}\right)^5}{1 - \frac{1}{2}}$

4. $\dfrac{3\left[1 - \left(\frac{1}{3}\right)^4\right]}{1 - \frac{1}{3}}$

5. $\dfrac{2\left[1 - \left(\frac{1}{4}\right)^3\right]}{1 - \frac{1}{4}}$

6. $\dfrac{\frac{1}{2}\left[1 - \left(\frac{1}{2}\right)^5\right]}{1 - \frac{1}{2}}$

In Exercises 7–10, find the limit.

7. $\displaystyle\lim_{n\to\infty} \frac{3n}{4n + 1}$

8. $\displaystyle\lim_{n\to\infty} \frac{3n}{n^2 + 1}$

9. $\displaystyle\lim_{n\to\infty} \frac{n!}{n! - 3}$

10. $\displaystyle\lim_{n\to\infty} \frac{2n! + 1}{4n! - 1}$

E X E R C I S E S   S.2   means that technology can help you solve or check the exercise(s).

In Exercises 1–4, find the first five terms of the sequence of partial sums.

1. $\displaystyle\sum_{n=1}^{\infty} \frac{1}{n^2} = 1 + \frac{1}{4} + \frac{1}{9} + \frac{1}{16} + \frac{1}{25} + \cdots$

2. $\displaystyle\sum_{n=1}^{\infty} (-1)^{n+1} \frac{3^n}{2^{n-1}} = 3 - \frac{9}{2} + \frac{27}{4} - \frac{81}{8} + \frac{243}{16} - \cdots$

3. $\displaystyle\sum_{n=1}^{\infty} \frac{3}{2^{n-1}} = 3 + \frac{3}{2} + \frac{3}{4} + \frac{3}{8} + \frac{3}{16} + \cdots$

4. $\displaystyle\sum_{n=1}^{\infty} \frac{(-1)^{n+1}}{n!} = 1 - \frac{1}{2} + \frac{1}{6} - \frac{1}{24} + \frac{1}{120} - \cdots$

In Exercises 5–12, verify that the infinite series diverges.

5. $\displaystyle\sum_{n=1}^{\infty} \frac{n}{n + 1} = \frac{1}{2} + \frac{2}{3} + \frac{3}{4} + \frac{4}{5} + \cdots$

6. $\displaystyle\sum_{n=1}^{\infty} \frac{n}{2n + 3} = \frac{1}{5} + \frac{2}{7} + \frac{3}{9} + \frac{4}{11} + \cdots$

7. $\displaystyle\sum_{n=1}^{\infty} \frac{n^2}{n^2 + 1} = \frac{1}{2} + \frac{4}{5} + \frac{9}{10} + \frac{16}{17} + \cdots$

8. $\displaystyle\sum_{n=1}^{\infty} \frac{n}{\sqrt{n^2 + 1}} = \frac{1}{\sqrt{2}} + \frac{2}{\sqrt{5}} + \frac{3}{\sqrt{10}} + \frac{4}{\sqrt{17}} + \cdots$

9. $\displaystyle\sum_{n=0}^{\infty} 3\left(\frac{3}{2}\right)^n = 3 + \frac{9}{2} + \frac{27}{4} + \frac{81}{8} + \cdots$

10. $\displaystyle\sum_{n=0}^{\infty} 5\left(-\frac{3}{2}\right)^n = 5 - \frac{15}{2} + \frac{45}{4} - \frac{135}{8} + \cdots$

11. $\displaystyle\sum_{n=0}^{\infty} 1000(1.055)^n = 1000 + 1055 + 1113.025 + \cdots$

12. $\displaystyle\sum_{n=0}^{\infty} 2(-1.03)^n = 2 - 2.06 + 2.1218 - \cdots$

In Exercises 13–16, verify that the geometric series converges.

13. $\sum_{n=0}^{\infty} 2\left(\frac{3}{4}\right)^n = 2 + \frac{3}{2} + \frac{9}{8} + \frac{27}{32} + \frac{81}{128} + \cdots$

14. $\sum_{n=0}^{\infty} 2\left(-\frac{1}{2}\right)^n = 2 - 1 + \frac{1}{2} - \frac{1}{4} + \frac{1}{8} - \cdots$

15. $\sum_{n=0}^{\infty} (0.9)^n = 1 + 0.9 + 0.81 + 0.729 + \cdots$

16. $\sum_{n=0}^{\infty} (-0.6)^n = 1 - 0.6 + 0.36 - 0.216 + \cdots$

In Exercises 17–30, find the sum of the convergent series.

17. $\sum_{n=0}^{\infty} \left(\frac{1}{2}\right)^n = 1 + \frac{1}{2} + \frac{1}{4} + \frac{1}{8} + \cdots$

18. $\sum_{n=0}^{\infty} 2\left(\frac{2}{3}\right)^n = 2 + \frac{4}{3} + \frac{8}{9} + \frac{16}{27} + \cdots$

19. $\sum_{n=0}^{\infty} \left(-\frac{1}{2}\right)^n = 1 - \frac{1}{2} + \frac{1}{4} - \frac{1}{8} + \cdots$

20. $\sum_{n=0}^{\infty} 2\left(-\frac{2}{3}\right)^n = 2 - \frac{4}{3} + \frac{8}{9} - \frac{16}{27} + \cdots$

21. $\sum_{n=0}^{\infty} 2\left(\frac{1}{\sqrt{2}}\right)^n = 2 + \sqrt{2} + 1 + \frac{1}{\sqrt{2}} + \cdots$

22. $\sum_{n=0}^{\infty} 4\left(\frac{1}{4}\right)^n = 4 + 1 + \frac{1}{4} + \frac{1}{16} + \cdots$

23. $1 + 0.1 + 0.01 + 0.001 + \cdots$

24. $8 + 6 + \frac{9}{2} + \frac{27}{8} + \cdots$

25. $2 - \frac{2}{3} + \frac{2}{9} - \frac{2}{27} + \cdots$ **26.** $4 - 2 + 1 - \frac{1}{2} + \cdots$

27. $\sum_{n=0}^{\infty} \left(\frac{1}{2^n} - \frac{1}{3^n}\right)$ **28.** $\sum_{n=0}^{\infty} [(0.7)^n + (0.9)^n]$

29. $\sum_{n=0}^{\infty} \left(\frac{1}{3^n} + \frac{1}{4^n}\right)$ **30.** $\sum_{n=0}^{\infty} [(0.4)^n - (0.8)^n]$

In Exercises 31–40, determine the convergence or divergence of the series.

31. $\sum_{n=1}^{\infty} \frac{n+10}{10n+1}$ **32.** $\sum_{n=0}^{\infty} \frac{4}{2^n}$

33. $\sum_{n=1}^{\infty} \frac{n!+1}{n!}$ **34.** $\sum_{n=1}^{\infty} \frac{n+1}{2n-1}$

35. $\sum_{n=1}^{\infty} \frac{3n-1}{2n+1}$ **36.** $\sum_{n=0}^{\infty} \frac{1}{4^n}$

37. $\sum_{n=0}^{\infty} (1.075)^n$ **38.** $\sum_{n=1}^{\infty} \frac{2^n}{100}$

39. $\sum_{n=0}^{\infty} \frac{3}{4^n}$ **40.** $\sum_{n=0}^{\infty} n!$

In Exercises 41–44, the repeating decimal is expressed as a geometric series. Find the sum of the geometric series and write the decimal as the ratio of two integers.

41. $0.6\overline{66} = 0.6 + 0.06 + 0.006 + 0.0006 + \cdots$

42. $0.23\overline{23} = 0.23 + 0.0023 + 0.000023 + \cdots$

43. $0.81\overline{81} = 0.81 + 0.0081 + 0.000081 + \cdots$

44. $0.21\overline{21} = 0.21 + 0.0021 + 0.000021 + \cdots$

45. *Sales* A company produces a new product for which it estimates the annual sales to be 8000 units. Suppose that in any given year 10% of the units (regardless of age) will become inoperative.

(a) How many units will be in use after n years?
(b) Find the market stabilization level of the product.

46. *Sales* Repeat Exercise 45 with the assumption that 25% of the units will become inoperative each year.

47. *Bouncing Ball* A ball is dropped from a height of 16 feet. Each time it drops h feet, it rebounds $0.64h$ feet. Find the total distance traveled by the ball.

48. *Bouncing Ball* The ball in Exercise 47 takes the following times for each fall. (t is measured in seconds.)

$s_1 = -16t^2 + 16,$ $s_1 = 0$ if $t = 1$
$s_2 = -16t^2 + 16(0.64),$ $s_2 = 0$ if $t = 0.8$
$s_3 = -16t^2 + 16(0.64)^2,$ $s_3 = 0$ if $t = (0.8)^2$
$s_4 = -16t^2 + 16(0.64)^3,$ $s_4 = 0$ if $t = (0.8)^3$
$\vdots$ $\vdots$
$s_n = -16t^2 + 16(0.64)^{n-1},$ $s_n = 0$ if $t = (0.8)^{n-1}$

Beginning with s_2, the ball takes the same amount of time to bounce up as to fall, and thus the total elapsed time before the ball comes to rest is

$$t = 1 + 2\sum_{n=1}^{\infty} (0.8)^n.$$

Find the total time it takes for the ball to come to rest.

49. *Annuity* A deposit of $100 is made at the beginning of each month for 5 years into an account that pays 10% interest compounded monthly. What is the balance A in the account at the end of the 5 years?

$$A = 100\left(1 + \frac{0.10}{12}\right) + \cdots + 100\left(1 + \frac{0.10}{12}\right)^{60}$$

50. *Annuity* A deposit of P dollars is made every month for t years into an account that pays an annual interest rate of r compounded monthly. Let $N = 12t$ be the total number of deposits. Show that the balance in the account after t years is

$$A = P\left[\left(1 + \frac{r}{12}\right)^N - 1\right]\left(1 + \frac{12}{r}\right).$$

51. *Multiplier Effect* The annual spending by tourists in a resort city is 100 million dollars. Approximately 75% of that revenue is again spent in the resort city, and of that amount approximately 75% is again spent in the resort city. If this pattern continues, write the geometric series that gives the total amount of spending generated by the 100 million dollars and find the sum of the series.

52. *Area* Find the fraction of the total area of the square that is eventually shaded if the pattern of shading shown in the accompanying figure is continued. (Note that the sides of the shaded corner squares are one-fourth those of the squares in which they are placed.)

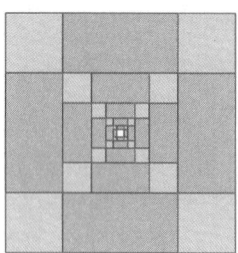

53. *Wages* Suppose that an employer offered to pay you 1 cent the first day, and then double your wages each day thereafter. Find your total wages for working 20 days.

54. *Probability* A fair coin is tossed until a head appears. The probability that the first head appears on the nth toss is given by $P = \left(\frac{1}{2}\right)^n$ where $n \geq 1$. Show that

$$\sum_{n=1}^{\infty}\left(\frac{1}{2}\right)^n = 1.$$

55. *Probability* Use a symbolic algebra utility to estimate the expected number of tosses required until the first head occurs in the experiment in Exercise 54.

56. *Number of Ancestors* The number of direct ancestors a person has had is given by

$$2 + 2^2 + 2^3 + 2^4 + \cdots + 2^n + \cdots.$$

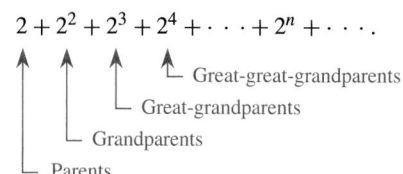

This formula is valid *provided* the person has no common ancestors. (A common ancestor is one to whom you are related in more than one way. For example, one of your great-grandmothers on your father's side might also be one of your great-grandmothers on your mother's side (see figure). How many direct ancestors have you had who have lived since the year 1 A.D.? Assume that the average time between generations was 25 years (resulting in 80 generations) so that the total is given by

$$2 + 2^2 + 2^3 + 2^4 + \cdots + 2^{80}.$$

Considering your total, is it reasonable to assume that you have had no common ancestors in the past 2000 years?

Have you had common ancestors?

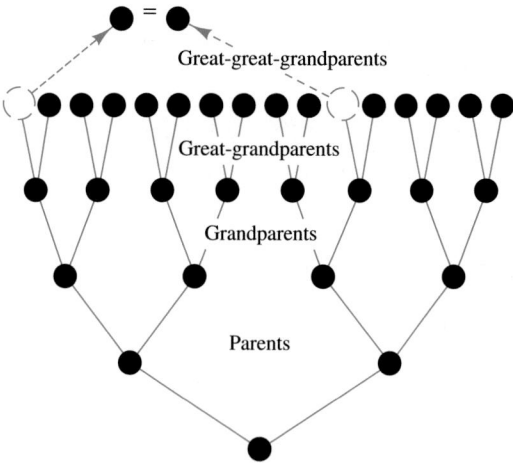

In Exercises 57–62, use a symbolic algebra utility to evaluate the summation.

57. $\displaystyle\sum_{n=1}^{\infty} n^2 \left(\frac{1}{2}\right)^n$

58. $\displaystyle\sum_{n=1}^{\infty} 2n^3 \left(\frac{1}{5}\right)^n$

59. $\displaystyle\sum_{n=1}^{\infty} \frac{n!}{(n!)^2}$

60. $\displaystyle\sum_{n=1}^{\infty} n \left(\frac{4}{11}\right)^n$

61. $\displaystyle\sum_{n=1}^{\infty} e^2 \left(\frac{1}{e}\right)^n$

62. $\displaystyle\sum_{n=1}^{\infty} \ln 2 \left(\frac{1}{8}\right)^{2n}$

p-Series
and the Ratio Test

p-Series ■ *The Ratio Test*

p-Series

In Section S.2, you studied geometric series. In this section you will study another common type of series called a **p-series.**

Definition of a p-Series

Let p be a positive constant. An infinite series of the form

$$\sum_{n=1}^{\infty} \frac{1}{n^p} = \frac{1}{1^p} + \frac{1}{2^p} + \frac{1}{3^p} + \cdots$$

is called a **p-series.** If $p = 1$, then the series

$$\sum_{n=1}^{\infty} \frac{1}{n} = 1 + \frac{1}{2} + \frac{1}{3} + \cdots$$

is called the **harmonic series.**

EXAMPLE 1 *Classifying p-Series*

a. The infinite series

$$\sum_{n=1}^{\infty} \frac{1}{n^3} = \frac{1}{1^3} + \frac{1}{2^3} + \frac{1}{3^3} + \cdots$$

is a p-series with $p = 3$.

b. The infinite series

$$\sum_{n=1}^{\infty} \frac{1}{\sqrt{n}} = \frac{1}{1^{1/2}} + \frac{1}{2^{1/2}} + \frac{1}{3^{1/2}} + \cdots$$

is a p-series with $p = \frac{1}{2}$.

c. The infinite series

$$\sum_{n=1}^{\infty} \frac{1}{3^n} = \frac{1}{3^1} + \frac{1}{3^2} + \frac{1}{3^3} + \cdots$$

is *not* a p-series. (It is a geometric series.)

Some infinite p-series converge and others diverge. With the following test, you can determine the convergence or divergence of a p-series.

Test for Convergence of a p-Series

Consider the p-series

$$\sum_{n=1}^{\infty} \frac{1}{n^p} = \frac{1}{1^p} + \frac{1}{2^p} + \frac{1}{3^p} + \cdots .$$

1. The series diverges if $0 < p \le 1$.
2. The series converges if $p > 1$.

Discovery

It is surprising that the harmonic series

$$\sum_{n=1}^{\infty} \frac{1}{n} = 1 + \frac{1}{2} + \frac{1}{3} + \cdots$$

diverges even though its individual terms approach zero. Convince yourself that this series diverges by showing that

$$1 + \frac{1}{2} > \frac{1}{2}$$
$$\frac{1}{3} + \frac{1}{4} > \frac{1}{2}$$
$$\frac{1}{5} + \cdots + \frac{1}{8} > \frac{1}{2}$$
$$\frac{1}{9} + \cdots + \frac{1}{16} > \frac{1}{2}.$$

EXAMPLE 2 *Determining Convergence or Divergence*

Determine whether the p-series converges or diverges.

a. $\displaystyle\sum_{n=1}^{\infty} \frac{1}{n^{0.9}}$ **b.** $\displaystyle\sum_{n=1}^{\infty} \frac{1}{n}$ **c.** $\displaystyle\sum_{n=1}^{\infty} \frac{1}{n^{1.1}}$

Solution

a. For the p-series

$$\sum_{n=1}^{\infty} \frac{1}{n^{0.9}} = \frac{1}{1^{0.9}} + \frac{1}{2^{0.9}} + \frac{1}{3^{0.9}} + \cdots ,$$

$p = 0.9$. Because $p \le 1$, you can conclude that the series diverges.

b. For the p-series

$$\sum_{n=1}^{\infty} \frac{1}{n} = \frac{1}{1} + \frac{1}{2} + \frac{1}{3} + \cdots ,$$

$p = 1$, which means that the series is the *harmonic series*. Because $p \le 1$, you can conclude that the series diverges.

c. For the p-series

$$\sum_{n=1}^{\infty} \frac{1}{n^{1.1}} = \frac{1}{1^{1.1}} + \frac{1}{2^{1.1}} + \frac{1}{3^{1.1}} + \cdots ,$$

$p = 1.1$. Because $p > 1$, you can conclude that the series converges.

In Example 2, notice that the p-Series Test tells you only whether the series diverges or converges. It does not give a formula for the sum of a convergent p-series. To approximate such a sum, you can use a computer to evaluate several partial sums. More is said about this on page S-25.

Approximating the Sum of a p-Series

It can be shown that the sum S of a convergent p-series differs from its Nth partial sum by no more than

$$\frac{1}{(p-1)N^{p-1}}.$$ *Maximum error*

When p is greater than or equal to 3, this means that you can approximate the sum of the convergent p-series by adding several of the terms. For instance, because

$$\sum_{n=1}^{10} \frac{1}{n^3} \approx 1.19753$$ *10th partial sum*

and $1/[(2)(10^2)] = 0.005$, you can conclude that the sum of the infinite p-series with $p = 3$ is between 1.19753 and $(1.19753 + 0.005)$ or 1.20253. For convergent p-series in which p is less than 3, you need to add more and more terms of the series to obtain a reasonable approximation of the sum. For instance, when $p = 2$, you can use a computer to find the following sums.

$$\sum_{n=1}^{10} \frac{1}{n^2} \approx 1.54977$$ *10th partial sum*

$$\sum_{n=1}^{100} \frac{1}{n^2} \approx 1.63498$$ *100th partial sum*

$$\sum_{n=1}^{1000} \frac{1}{n^2} \approx 1.64393$$ *1000th partial sum*

Because $1/[(1)(1000)] = 0.001$, you can conclude that the partial sum S_{1000} is within 0.001 of the actual sum of the series.

When p is close to 1, approximating the sum of the series becomes difficult. For instance, consider the following partial sums.

$$\sum_{n=1}^{10} \frac{1}{n^{1.1}} \approx 2.680155$$ *10th partial sum*

$$\sum_{n=1}^{100} \frac{1}{n^{1.1}} \approx 4.278024$$ *100th partial sum*

$$\sum_{n=1}^{1000} \frac{1}{n^{1.1}} \approx 5.572827$$ *1000th partial sum*

Because $1/[(0.1)(1000^{0.1})] \approx 5$, you can see that even the partial sum S_{1000} is not very close to the actual sum of the series.

The Ratio Test

At this point, you have studied two convergence tests: one for a geometric series and one for a p-series. The next test is more general—it can be applied to infinite series that do not happen to be geometric or p-series.

The Ratio Test

Let $\displaystyle\sum_{n=1}^{\infty} a_n$ be an infinite series with nonzero terms.

1. The series converges if $\displaystyle\lim_{n\to\infty} \left| \frac{a_{n+1}}{a_n} \right| < 1$.

2. The series diverges if $\displaystyle\lim_{n\to\infty} \left| \frac{a_{n+1}}{a_n} \right| > 1$.

3. The test is inconclusive if $\displaystyle\lim_{n\to\infty} \left| \frac{a_{n+1}}{a_n} \right| = 1$.

Note   Although the Ratio Test is listed with an index that begins with $n = 1$, it can be applied to an infinite series with a beginning index of $n = 0$ (or any other integer).

The Ratio Test is particularly useful for series that converge rapidly. Series involving factorial or exponential functions are frequently of this type.

EXAMPLE 3 *Using the Ratio Test*

Determine the convergence or divergence of the infinite series

$$\sum_{n=0}^{\infty} \frac{2^n}{n!} = \frac{1}{1} + \frac{2}{1} + \frac{4}{2} + \frac{8}{6} + \frac{16}{24} + \frac{32}{120} + \cdots .$$

Solution
Using the Ratio Test with $a_n = 2^n/n!$, you obtain

$$\lim_{n\to\infty} \left| \frac{a_{n+1}}{a_n} \right| = \lim_{n\to\infty} \left[\frac{2^{n+1}}{(n+1)!} \div \frac{2^n}{n!} \right]$$

$$= \lim_{n\to\infty} \left[\frac{2^{n+1}}{(n+1)!} \cdot \frac{n!}{2^n} \right]$$

$$= \lim_{n\to\infty} \frac{2}{n+1}$$

$$= 0.$$

Because this limit is less than 1, you can apply the Ratio Test to conclude that the series converges. Using a computer, you can approximate the sum of the series to be $S \approx S_{10} \approx 7.39$.   ▬

Example 3 tells you something about the rates at which the sequences $\{2^n\}$ and $\{n!\}$ increase as n approaches infinity. For example, in Table S.2, you can see that although the factorial sequence $\{n!\}$ has a slow start, it quickly overpowers the exponential sequence $\{2^n\}$.

TABLE S.2

n	0	1	2	3	4	5	6	7	8	9
2^n	1	2	4	8	16	32	64	128	256	512
$n!$	1	1	2	6	24	120	720	5040	40,320	362,880

From this table, you can also see that the sequence $\{n\}$ approaches infinity more slowly than the sequence $\{2^n\}$. This is further demonstrated in Example 4.

EXAMPLE 4 *Using the Ratio Test*

Determine the convergence or divergence of the infinite series

$$\sum_{n=1}^{\infty} \frac{n}{2^n} = \frac{1}{2} + \frac{2}{4} + \frac{3}{8} + \frac{4}{16} + \frac{5}{32} + \frac{6}{64} + \cdots.$$

Solution

Using the Ratio Test with $a_n = n/2^n$, you obtain

$$\lim_{n \to \infty} \left| \frac{a_{n+1}}{a_n} \right| = \lim_{n \to \infty} \left(\frac{n+1}{2^{n+1}} \div \frac{n}{2^n} \right)$$

$$= \lim_{n \to \infty} \left(\frac{n+1}{2^{n+1}} \cdot \frac{2^n}{n} \right)$$

$$= \lim_{n \to \infty} \frac{n+1}{2n}$$

$$= \frac{1}{2}.$$

Because this limit is less than 1, you can apply the Ratio Test to conclude that the series converges. Using a computer, you can determine that the sum of the series is $S = 2$.   ▬

When applying the Ratio Test, remember that if the limit of $|a_{n+1}/a_n|$ as $n \to \infty$ is 1, then the test does not tell you whether the series converges or diverges. This type of result often occurs with series that converge or diverge slowly. For instance, when you apply the Ratio Test to the harmonic series in which $a_n = 1/n$, you obtain

$$\lim_{n \to \infty} \left| \frac{a_{n+1}}{a_n} \right| = \lim_{n \to \infty} \frac{1/(n+1)}{1/n} = \lim_{n \to \infty} \frac{n}{n+1} = 1.$$

Thus, from the Ratio Test, you cannot conclude that the harmonic series diverges. From the *p*-Series Test, you know it diverges.

EXAMPLE 5 *Using the Ratio Test*

Determine the convergence or divergence of the infinite series

$$\sum_{n=1}^{\infty} \frac{2^n}{n^2} = \frac{2}{1} + \frac{4}{4} + \frac{8}{9} + \frac{16}{16} + \frac{32}{25} + \frac{64}{36} + \cdots .$$

Solution

Using the Ratio Test with $a_n = 2^n/n^2$, you obtain

$$\lim_{n\to\infty} \left| \frac{a_{n+1}}{a_n} \right| = \lim_{n\to\infty} \left[\frac{2^{n+1}}{(n+1)^2} \div \frac{2^n}{n^2} \right]$$

$$= \lim_{n\to\infty} \left[\frac{2^{n+1}}{(n+1)^2} \cdot \frac{n^2}{2^n} \right]$$

$$= \lim_{n\to\infty} 2 \left(\frac{n}{n+1} \right)^2$$

$$= 2.$$

Because this limit is greater than 1, you can apply the Ratio Test to conclude that the series diverges.   ■

Summary of Tests of Series

Test	Series	Converges	Diverges
nth-Term	$\sum_{n=1}^{\infty} a_n$		$\lim_{n\to\infty} a_n \neq 0$
Geometric	$\sum_{n=0}^{\infty} ar^n$	$\|r\| < 1$	$\|r\| \geq 1$
p-Series	$\sum_{n=1}^{\infty} \frac{1}{n^p}$	$p > 1$	$0 < p \leq 1$
Ratio	$\sum_{n=1}^{\infty} a_n$	$\lim_{n\to\infty} \left\| \frac{a_{n+1}}{a_n} \right\| < 1$	$\lim_{n\to\infty} \left\| \frac{a_{n+1}}{a_n} \right\| > 1$

Discussion Problem   Comparing Tests

Determine whether each infinite series converges or diverges. Explain your reasoning.

a. $\displaystyle\sum_{n=1}^{\infty} \frac{5}{n!}$ **b.** $\displaystyle\sum_{n=1}^{\infty} \frac{5}{2^n}$ **c.** $\displaystyle\sum_{n=1}^{\infty} \frac{5}{n^2}$

Warm Up

The following warm-up exercises involve skills that were covered in earlier sections. You will use these skills in the exercise set for this section.

In Exercises 1–4, simplify the expression.

1. $\dfrac{n!}{(n+1)!}$

2. $\dfrac{(n+1)!}{n!}$

3. $\dfrac{3^n}{n+1} \cdot \dfrac{n}{3^n}$

4. $\dfrac{(n+1)^2}{(n+1)!} \cdot \dfrac{n!}{n^2}$

In Exercises 5–8, find the indicated limit.

5. $\displaystyle \lim_{n \to \infty} \dfrac{(n+1)^2}{n^2}$

6. $\displaystyle \lim_{n \to \infty} \dfrac{5^{n+1}}{5^n}$

7. $\displaystyle \lim_{n \to \infty} \left(\dfrac{5}{n+1} \div \dfrac{5}{n} \right)$

8. $\displaystyle \lim_{n \to \infty} \left(\dfrac{(n+1)^3}{3^{n+1}} \div \dfrac{n^3}{3^n} \right)$

In Exercises 9 and 10, decide whether the series is geometric.

9. $\displaystyle \sum_{n=1}^{\infty} \dfrac{1}{4^n}$

10. $\displaystyle \sum_{n=1}^{\infty} \dfrac{1}{n^4}$

E X E R C I S E S   S.3   means that technology can help you solve or check the exercise(s).

In Exercises 1–6, determine whether the series is a p-series.

1. $\displaystyle \sum_{n=1}^{\infty} \dfrac{1}{n^2}$

2. $\displaystyle \sum_{n=1}^{\infty} \dfrac{1}{\sqrt{n}}$

3. $\displaystyle \sum_{n=1}^{\infty} \dfrac{1}{3^n}$

4. $\displaystyle \sum_{n=1}^{\infty} n^{-3/4}$

5. $\displaystyle \sum_{n=1}^{\infty} \dfrac{1}{n^n}$

6. $\displaystyle \sum_{n=1}^{\infty} \dfrac{1}{n+1}$

In Exercises 7–16, determine the convergence or divergence of the given p-series.

7. $\displaystyle \sum_{n=1}^{\infty} \dfrac{1}{n^3}$

8. $\displaystyle \sum_{n=1}^{\infty} \dfrac{1}{n^{1/3}}$

9. $\displaystyle \sum_{n=1}^{\infty} \dfrac{1}{\sqrt[3]{n}}$

10. $\displaystyle \sum_{n=1}^{\infty} \dfrac{1}{n^{4/3}}$

11. $\displaystyle \sum_{n=1}^{\infty} \dfrac{1}{n^{1.03}}$

12. $\displaystyle \sum_{n=1}^{\infty} \dfrac{1}{n^{\pi}}$

13. $1 + \dfrac{1}{\sqrt{2}} + \dfrac{1}{\sqrt{3}} + \dfrac{1}{\sqrt{4}} + \cdots$

14. $1 + \frac{1}{4} + \frac{1}{9} + \frac{1}{16} + \frac{1}{25} + \cdots$

15. $1 + \dfrac{1}{2\sqrt{2}} + \dfrac{1}{3\sqrt{3}} + \dfrac{1}{4\sqrt{4}} + \cdots$

16. $1 + \frac{1}{2} + \frac{1}{3} + \frac{1}{4} + \frac{1}{5} + \cdots$

In Exercises 17–30, use the Ratio Test to determine the convergence or divergence of the given series.

17. $\displaystyle \sum_{n=0}^{\infty} \dfrac{3^n}{n!}$

18. $\displaystyle \sum_{n=1}^{\infty} n \left(\dfrac{2}{3} \right)^n$

19. $\displaystyle \sum_{n=0}^{\infty} \dfrac{n!}{3^n}$

20. $\displaystyle \sum_{n=1}^{\infty} n \left(\dfrac{3}{2} \right)^n$

21. $\displaystyle\sum_{n=1}^{\infty} \frac{n}{4^n}$

22. $\displaystyle\sum_{n=1}^{\infty} \frac{n^2}{2^n}$

23. $\displaystyle\sum_{n=1}^{\infty} \frac{2^n}{n^5}$

24. $\displaystyle\sum_{n=0}^{\infty} (-1)^n e^{-n}$

25. $\displaystyle\sum_{n=0}^{\infty} \frac{(-1)^n 2^n}{n!}$

26. $\displaystyle\sum_{n=0}^{\infty} \frac{4n}{n!}$

27. $\displaystyle\sum_{n=0}^{\infty} \frac{4^n}{3^n + 1}$

28. $\displaystyle\sum_{n=0}^{\infty} \frac{3^n}{n + 1}$

29. $\displaystyle\sum_{n=0}^{\infty} \frac{n5^n}{n!}$

30. $\displaystyle\sum_{n=1}^{\infty} \frac{2n!}{n^5}$

In Exercises 31–34, approximate the sum of the given convergent series using the indicated number of terms. Estimate the maximum error of your approximation.

31. $\displaystyle\sum_{n=1}^{\infty} \frac{1}{n^3}$, four terms

32. $\displaystyle\sum_{n=1}^{\infty} \frac{1}{n^4}$, four terms

33. $\displaystyle\sum_{n=1}^{\infty} \frac{1}{n^{3/2}}$, ten terms

34. $\displaystyle\sum_{n=1}^{\infty} \frac{1}{n^{10}}$, three terms

In Exercises 35 and 36, verify that the Ratio Test is inconclusive for the p-series.

35. $\displaystyle\sum_{n=1}^{\infty} \frac{1}{n^{3/2}}$

36. $\displaystyle\sum_{n=1}^{\infty} \frac{1}{n^3}$

In Exercises 37–48, test for convergence or divergence using any appropriate test from this chapter. Identify the test used.

37. $\displaystyle\sum_{n=1}^{\infty} \frac{2n}{n + 1}$

38. $\displaystyle\sum_{n=1}^{\infty} \frac{10}{3\sqrt[3]{n^2}}$

39. $\displaystyle\sum_{n=1}^{\infty} \frac{1}{n\sqrt[3]{n}}$

40. $\displaystyle\sum_{n=0}^{\infty} \left(\frac{5}{6}\right)^n$

41. $\displaystyle\sum_{n=0}^{\infty} \frac{(-1)^n 2^n}{3^n}$

42. $\displaystyle\sum_{n=2}^{\infty} \ln n$

43. $\displaystyle\sum_{n=1}^{\infty} \left(\frac{1}{n^2} - \frac{1}{n^3}\right)$

44. $\displaystyle\sum_{n=1}^{\infty} \frac{n3^n}{n!}$

45. $\displaystyle\sum_{n=0}^{\infty} \left(\frac{5}{4}\right)^n$

46. $\displaystyle\sum_{n=1}^{\infty} n(0.4)^n$

47. $\displaystyle\sum_{n=1}^{\infty} \frac{n!}{3^{n-1}}$

48. $\displaystyle\sum_{n=1}^{\infty} \frac{1}{n^{0.95}}$

In Exercises 49 and 50, use a computer to confirm the sum of the convergent series.

49. $\displaystyle\sum_{n=1}^{\infty} \frac{1}{n^2} = \frac{\pi^2}{6}$

50. $\displaystyle\sum_{n=1}^{\infty} \frac{1}{(2n)^2} = \frac{\pi^2}{24}$

51. *Research Expenses* The table lists the research and development expenses at universities for environmental sciences (in millions of dollars) for the years 1989 to 1992. (*Source: U.S. National Science Foundation*)

Year	1989	1990	1991	1992
Amount	1.01	1.065	1.12	1.18

(a) Use an infinite series to model the data.
(b) Can you determine whether the series is converging or diverging by using the Ratio Test? Explain.

52. *Research Project* Use your school's library or some other reference source to find data about a college or university that can be modeled by a series. Write a summary about your findings, including a description of the convergence or divergence of the series, and how it was determined.

Power Series ■ *Radius of Convergence of a Power Series* ■
Taylor and Maclaurin Series ■ *A Basic List of Power Series*

Power Series

In the previous two sections, you studied infinite series whose terms are constants. In this section, you will study infinite series that have variable terms. Specifically, you will study a type of infinite series that is called a **power series.** Informally, you can think of a power series as a "very long" polynomial.

Note The index of a power series usually begins with $n = 0$. In such cases, we use the convention that $(x - c)^0 = 1$ even if $x = c$.

Definition of Power Series

An infinite series of the form

$$\sum_{n=0}^{\infty} a_n x^n = a_0 + a_1 x + a_2 x^2 + a_3 x^3 + \cdots + a_n x^n + \cdots$$

is called a **power series** in x. An infinite series of the form

$$\sum_{n=0}^{\infty} a_n (x - c)^n = a_0 + a_1 (x - c) + a_2 (x - c)^2 + \cdots$$
$$+ a_n (x - c)^n + \cdots$$

is called a **power series centered at c.**

EXAMPLE 1 *Writing Power Series*

a. The following power series is centered at 0.

$$\sum_{n=0}^{\infty} \frac{x^n}{n!} = 1 + x + \frac{x^2}{2!} + \frac{x^3}{3!} + \cdots$$

b. The following power series is centered at 1.

$$\sum_{n=1}^{\infty} \frac{(x - 1)^n}{n} = (x - 1) + \frac{(x - 1)^2}{2} + \frac{(x - 1)^3}{3} + \cdots$$

c. The following power series is centered at -1.

$$\sum_{n=1}^{\infty} \frac{(x + 1)^n}{n} = (x + 1) + \frac{(x + 1)^2}{2} + \frac{(x + 1)^3}{3} + \cdots$$

Radius of Convergence of a Power Series

A power series in x can be viewed as a function of x,

$$f(x) = \sum_{n=0}^{\infty} a_n (x - c)^n,$$

where the **domain** of f is the set of all x for which the power series converges. Determining this domain is one of the primary problems associated with power series. Every power series converges at its center c, because

$$f(c) = \sum_{n=0}^{\infty} a_n (c - c)^n = a_0(1) + 0 + 0 + \cdots = a_0.$$

Thus, c is always in the domain of f. It can happen that the domain of f consists only of the single number c. In fact, this is one of the three basic types of domains of power series, as indicated in Figure S.5.

Single point:
$R = 0$

All reals:
$R = \infty$

$(c - R, c + R)$

FIGURE S.5   Three Types of Domains

Convergence of a Power Series

For a power series centered at c, precisely one of the following is true.

1. The series converges only at $x = c$.
2. The series converges for all x.
3. There exists a positive real number R such that the series converges for $|x - c| < R$ and diverges for $|x - c| > R$.

In the third type of domain, the number R is called the **radius of convergence** of the power series. For the first and second types of domains, the radii of convergence are considered to be 0 and ∞, respectively.

In the third case, the series converges in the interval $(c - R, c + R)$ and diverges in the intervals $(-\infty, c - R)$ and $(c + R, \infty)$. Determining the convergence or divergence at the endpoints $c - R$ and $c + R$ can be difficult, and, except for simple cases, we will leave the endpoint question open. To find the radius of convergence of a power series, you can use the following test.

Radius of Convergence of a Power Series

The radius of convergence R of a power series centered at c is

$$R = \lim_{n \to \infty} \left| \frac{a_n}{a_{n+1}} \right|, \qquad 0 \le R \le \infty.$$

EXAMPLE 2 *Finding the Radius of Convergence*

Find the radius of convergence of the power series

$$\sum_{n=0}^{\infty} \frac{x^n}{n!}.$$

Solution

For this power series, $a_n = 1/n!$. Thus, by the test for the radius of convergence of a power series, you can write

$$\lim_{n\to\infty}\left|\frac{a_n}{a_{n+1}}\right| = \lim_{n\to\infty}\left|\frac{1/n!}{1/(n+1)!}\right|$$

$$= \lim_{n\to\infty}\left|\frac{(n+1)!}{n!}\right|$$

$$= \lim_{n\to\infty}(n+1)$$

$$= \infty.$$

Because the radius of convergence is infinite, you can conclude that the power series converges for all real values of x.   ▬

EXAMPLE 3 *Finding the Radius of Convergence*

Find the radius of convergence of the power series

$$\sum_{n=0}^{\infty} \frac{(-1)^n (x+1)^n}{2^n}.$$

Solution

For this power series, $a_n = (-1)^n/2^n$. Thus, by the test for the radius of convergence of a power series, you can write

$$\lim_{n\to\infty}\left|\frac{a_n}{a_{n+1}}\right| = \lim_{n\to\infty}\left|\frac{(-1)^n/2^n}{(-1)^{n+1}/2^{n+1}}\right|$$

$$= \lim_{n\to\infty}\left|\frac{2^{n+1}}{2^n}\right|$$

$$= \lim_{n\to\infty}2$$

$$= 2.$$

Because the radius of convergence is 2 and the center of the series is $c = -1$, you can conclude that the power series converges in the interval

$$(-1-2, -1+2) = (-3, 1).$$ ▬

Note It is possible to show that the power series in Example 3 diverges at both of the endpoints of its interval of convergence. Can you see how?

Taylor and Maclaurin Series

The problem of finding a power series for a given function is answered by **Taylor's Theorem,** named after the English mathematician Brook Taylor (1685–1731). This theorem shows how to use derivatives of a function f to write the power series for f.

Note The power series listed at the right is called the **Taylor series** for $f(x)$ centered at c. If the series is centered at 0, it is called a **Maclaurin series**, after the Scottish mathematician Colin Maclaurin (1698–1746).

Taylor's Theorem

If f is represented by a power series centered at c, then the power series has the following form.

$$f(x) = \sum_{n=0}^{\infty} \frac{f^{(n)}(c)(x-c)^n}{n!}$$

$$= f(c) + \frac{f'(c)(x-c)}{1!} + \frac{f''(c)(x-c)^2}{2!} + \frac{f'''(c)(x-c)^3}{3!} + \cdots$$

EXAMPLE 4 *Finding a Maclaurin Series*

Find the power series for $f(x) = e^x$, centered at 0. What is the radius of convergence of the series?

Solution

Begin by finding several derivatives of f and evaluating each at $c = 0$.

$f(x) = e^x$	$f(0) = 1$	*Original function*
$f'(x) = e^x$	$f'(0) = 1$	*1st derivative*
$f''(x) = e^x$	$f''(0) = 1$	*2nd derivative*
$f'''(x) = e^x$	$f'''(0) = 1$	*3rd derivative*
$f^{(4)}(x) = e^x$	$f^{(4)}(0) = 1$	*4th derivative*
$f^{(5)}(x) = e^x$	$f^{(5)}(0) = 1$	*5th derivative*

From this pattern, you can see that $f^{(n)}(0) = 1$. Thus, by Taylor's Theorem,

$$e^x = f(0) + f'(0)x + \frac{f''(0)x^2}{2!} + \frac{f'''(0)x^3}{3!} + \cdots$$

$$= 1 + x + \frac{x^2}{2!} + \frac{x^3}{3!} + \cdots$$

$$= \sum_{n=0}^{\infty} \frac{x^n}{n!}.$$

From Example 2, you know that this series has an infinite radius of convergence. In other words, it converges for all values of x.

EXAMPLE 5 *Finding a Taylor Series*

Find the power series for $f(x) = 1/x$, centered at 1. Then use the result to evaluate $f(\frac{1}{2})$.

Solution

Successive differentiation of $f(x)$ produces the following.

$f(x) = x^{-1}$	$f(1) = 1 = 0!$	*Original function*
$f'(x) = -x^{-2}$	$f'(1) = -1 = -(1!)$	*1st derivative*
$f''(x) = 2x^{-3}$	$f''(1) = 2 = 2!$	*2nd derivative*
$f'''(x) = -6x^{-4}$	$f'''(1) = -6 = -(3!)$	*3rd derivative*
$f^{(4)}(x) = 24x^{-5}$	$f^{(4)}(1) = 24 = 4!$	*4th derivative*
$f^{(5)}(x) = -120x^{-6}$	$f^{(5)}(1) = -120 = -(5!)$	*5th derivative*

From this pattern, you can see that $f^{(n)}(1) = (-1)^n n!$. Thus, by Taylor's Theorem, you can write

$$\frac{1}{x} = f(1) + f'(1)(x-1) + \frac{f''(1)(x-1)^2}{2!} + \frac{f'''(1)(x-1)^3}{3!} + \cdots$$

$$= 1 - (x-1) + \frac{2!(x-1)^2}{2!} - \frac{3!(x-1)^3}{3!} + \frac{4!(x-1)^4}{4!} - \cdots$$

$$= 1 - (x-1) + (x-1)^2 - (x-1)^3 + (x-1)^4 - \cdots$$

$$= \sum_{n=0}^{\infty} (-1)^n (x-1)^n.$$

To evaluate the series when $x = \frac{1}{2}$, you can substitute $\frac{1}{2}$ for x and use the formula for the sum of a geometric series.

$$f\left(\frac{1}{2}\right) = \sum_{n=0}^{\infty} (-1)^n \left(\frac{1}{2} - 1\right)^n$$

$$= \sum_{n=0}^{\infty} \left(\frac{1}{2}\right)^n$$

$$= \frac{1}{1 - (1/2)}$$

$$= 2$$

In Example 5, the radius of convergence of the series is $R = 1$, and its interval of convergence is

$$(0, 2). \qquad \textit{Interval of convergence}$$

(It is possible to show that the series diverges when $x = 0$ and when $x = 2$.) Figure S.6 compares the graphs of $f(x) = 1/x$ and the graph of the Taylor series for f. In the figure, note that the domains are different. In other words, the power series in Example 5 only represents f in the interval $(0, 2)$.

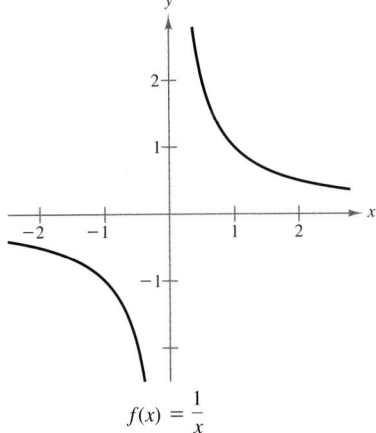

$$f(x) = \frac{1}{x}$$

Domain: all $x \neq 0$

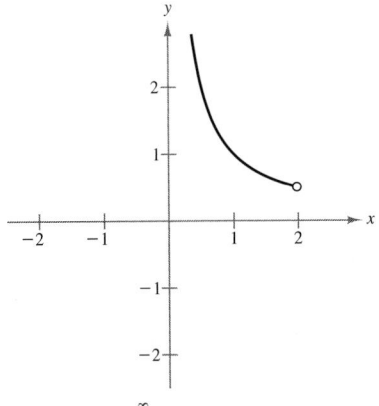

$$f(x) = \sum_{n=0}^{\infty} (-1)^n (x-1)^n$$

Domain: $0 < x < 2$

FIGURE S.6

EXAMPLE 6 *Finding a Maclaurin Series*

Find the Maclaurin series for each of the functions.

a. $f(x) = e^{x^2}$ **b.** $f(x) = e^{-x^2}$

Solution

a. To use Taylor's Theorem directly, you would have to calculate successive derivatives of $f(x) = e^{x^2}$. By calculating the first two,

$$f'(x) = 2xe^{x^2}$$

and

$$f''(x) = (4x^2 + 2)e^{x^2},$$

you can see that this task would be very tedious. Fortunately, there is a simpler way to find the power series. From Example 4, you already know that the Maclaurin series for e^x is

$$e^x = 1 + x + \frac{x^2}{2!} + \frac{x^3}{3!} + \frac{x^4}{4!} + \cdots.$$

Thus, to find the Maclaurin series for e^{x^2}, you can simply substitute x^2 for x in the series for e^x. Doing this produces

$$e^{x^2} = 1 + x^2 + \frac{(x^2)^2}{2!} + \frac{(x^2)^3}{3!} + \frac{(x^2)^4}{4!} + \cdots$$

$$= 1 + x^2 + \frac{x^4}{2!} + \frac{x^6}{3!} + \frac{x^8}{4!} + \cdots$$

$$= \sum_{n=0}^{\infty} \frac{x^{2n}}{n!}.$$

b. Using a similar approach, you can find the Maclaurin series for e^{-x^2} by substituting $-x^2$ for x in the series for e^x. Doing this produces

$$e^{-x^2} = 1 + (-x^2) + \frac{(-x^2)^2}{2!} + \frac{(-x^2)^3}{3!} + \frac{(-x^2)^4}{4!} + \cdots$$

$$= 1 - x^2 + \frac{x^4}{2!} - \frac{x^6}{3!} + \frac{x^8}{4!} - \cdots$$

$$= \sum_{n=0}^{\infty} \frac{(-1)^n x^{2n}}{n!}.$$

Why are we interested in power series? The reason is that power series share many of the desirable properties of polynomials—they can be easily differentiated and easily integrated. This means that if you wanted to integrate a function such as $f(x) = e^{x^2}$ (which doesn't have an elementary antiderivative), you could represent the function with a power series and then integrate the power series.

A Basic List of Power Series

Example 6 illustrates an important point in determining power series representations of functions. Though Taylor's Theorem is applicable to a wide variety of functions, it is often tedious to use because of the complexity of finding derivatives. The most practical use of Taylor's Theorem is in developing power series for a *basic list* of elementary functions. Then from the basic list, you can determine power series for other functions by the operations of addition, subtraction, multiplication, division, differentiation, integration, and composition with known power series.

Power Series for Elementary Functions

$$\frac{1}{x} = 1 - (x-1) + (x-1)^2 - (x-1)^3 + (x-1)^4 - \cdots + (-1)^n(x-1)^n + \cdots, \qquad 0 < x < 2$$

$$\frac{1}{x+1} = 1 - x + x^2 - x^3 + x^4 - x^5 + \cdots + (-1)^n x^n + \cdots, \qquad -1 < x < 1$$

$$\ln x = (x-1) - \frac{(x-1)^2}{2} + \frac{(x-1)^3}{3} - \frac{(x-1)^4}{4} + \cdots + \frac{(-1)^{n-1}(x-1)^n}{n} + \cdots, \qquad 0 < x \le 2$$

$$e^x = 1 + x + \frac{x^2}{2!} + \frac{x^3}{3!} + \frac{x^4}{4!} + \cdots + \frac{x^n}{n!} + \cdots, \qquad -\infty < x < \infty$$

$$(1+x)^k = 1 + kx + \frac{k(k-1)x^2}{2!} + \frac{k(k-1)(k-2)x^3}{3!} + \frac{k(k-1)(k-2)(k-3)x^4}{4!} + \cdots, \qquad -1 < x < 1$$

The last series in the list above is called a **binomial series.** Example 7 illustrates the use of such a series.

EXAMPLE 7 *Using the Basic List of Power Series*

Find the power series for $g(x) = \sqrt[3]{1+x}$, centered at 0.

Solution
Using the binomial series

$$(1+x)^k = 1 + kx + \frac{k(k-1)x^2}{2!} + \frac{k(k-1)(k-2)x^3}{3!} + \cdots$$

with $k = \frac{1}{3}$, you can write

$$(1+x)^{1/3} = 1 + \frac{x}{3} - \frac{2x^2}{3^2 2!} + \frac{2 \cdot 5 x^3}{3^3 3!} - \frac{2 \cdot 5 \cdot 8 x^4}{3^4 4!} + \cdots,$$

which converges for $-1 < x < 1$.

EXAMPLE 8 *Using the Basic List of Power Series*

Find power series for each of the functions.

a. $f(x) = 1 + 2e^x$, centered at 0
b. $f(x) = e^{2x+1}$, centered at 0
c. $f(x) = \ln 2x$, centered at 1

Solution

a. To find the power series for this function, you can multiply the series for e^x by 2 and add 1.

$$1 + 2e^x = 1 + 2\left(1 + x + \frac{x^2}{2!} + \frac{x^3}{3!} + \frac{x^4}{4!} + \cdots\right)$$

$$= 1 + 2 + 2x + \frac{2x^2}{2!} + \frac{2x^3}{3!} + \frac{2x^4}{4!} + \cdots$$

$$= 1 + \sum_{n=0}^{\infty} \frac{2x^n}{n!}$$

b. To find the power series for $e^{2x+1} = e^{2x}e$, you can substitute $2x$ for x into the series for e^x and multiply the result by e.

$$e^{2x+1} = e^{2x}e$$

$$= e\left[1 + (2x) + \frac{(2x)^2}{2!} + \frac{(2x)^3}{3!} + \frac{(2x)^4}{4!} + \cdots\right]$$

$$= e\sum_{n=0}^{\infty} \frac{2^n x^n}{n!}$$

c. To find the power series for $\ln 2x$, substitute $2x$ for x in the series for $\ln x$.

$$\ln 2x = (2x - 1) - \frac{(2x-1)^2}{2} + \frac{(2x-1)^3}{3} - \frac{(2x-1)^4}{4} + \cdots$$

$$= \sum_{n=1}^{\infty} \frac{(-1)^{n-1}(2x-1)^n}{n}$$

▬

Discussion Problem   **Using the Basic List of Power Series**

Explain how to use a power series from the basic list to find the power series for each of the following functions.

a. $f(x) = 3 - 5e^{-x}$, centered at 0

b. $f(x) = \dfrac{2}{x-2}$, centered at 3

c. $f(x) = \ln \dfrac{4}{x}$, centered at 1

Warm Up

The following warm-up exercises involve skills that were covered in earlier sections. You will use these skills in the exercise set for this section.

In Exercises 1–4, find $f(g(x))$ and $g(f(x))$.

1. $f(x) = x^2$, $g(x) = x - 1$

2. $f(x) = 3x$, $g(x) = 2x + 1$

3. $f(x) = \sqrt{x + 4}$, $g(x) = x^2$

4. $f(x) = e^x$, $g(x) = x^2$

In Exercises 5–8, find $f'(x)$, $f''(x)$, $f'''(x)$, and $f^{(4)}(x)$.

5. $f(x) = 5e^x$

6. $f(x) = \ln x$

7. $f(x) = 3e^{2x}$

8. $f(x) = \ln 2x$

In Exercises 9 and 10, simplify the expression.

9. $\dfrac{3^n}{n!} \div \dfrac{3^{n+1}}{(n+1)!}$

10. $\dfrac{n!}{(n+2)!} \div \dfrac{(n+1)!}{(n+3)!}$

EXERCISES S.4

 means that technology can help you solve or check the exercise(s).

In Exercises 1–4, write the first five terms of the power series.

1. $\displaystyle\sum_{n=0}^{\infty} \left(\frac{x}{4}\right)^n$

2. $\displaystyle\sum_{n=1}^{\infty} \frac{(-1)^n (x-2)^n}{3^n}$

3. $\displaystyle\sum_{n=0}^{\infty} \frac{(-1)^{n+1}(x+1)^n}{n!}$

4. $\displaystyle\sum_{n=0}^{\infty} \frac{(-1)^n n x^n}{n!}$

In Exercises 5–24, find the radius of convergence for the given series.

5. $\displaystyle\sum_{n=0}^{\infty} \left(\frac{x}{2}\right)^n$

6. $\displaystyle\sum_{n=0}^{\infty} \left(\frac{x}{k}\right)^n$

7. $\displaystyle\sum_{n=1}^{\infty} \frac{(-1)^n x^n}{3n}$

8. $\displaystyle\sum_{n=1}^{\infty} (-1)^{n+1} n x^n$

9. $\displaystyle\sum_{n=0}^{\infty} \frac{(-1)^n x^n}{n!}$

10. $\displaystyle\sum_{n=0}^{\infty} \frac{(3x)^n}{n!}$

11. $\displaystyle\sum_{n=0}^{\infty} n! \left(\frac{x}{2}\right)^n$

12. $\displaystyle\sum_{n=0}^{\infty} \frac{(-1)^n x^n}{(n+1)(n+2)}$

13. $\displaystyle\sum_{n=1}^{\infty} \frac{(-1)^{n+1} x^n}{4^n}$

14. $\displaystyle\sum_{n=0}^{\infty} \frac{(-1)^n n! (x-4)^n}{3^n}$

15. $\displaystyle\sum_{n=1}^{\infty} \frac{(-1)^{n+1}(x-5)^n}{n 5^n}$

16. $\displaystyle\sum_{n=0}^{\infty} \frac{(x-2)^{n+1}}{(n+1)3^{n+1}}$

17. $\displaystyle\sum_{n=0}^{\infty} \frac{(-1)^{n+1}(x-1)^{n+1}}{n+1}$

18. $\displaystyle\sum_{n=1}^{\infty} \frac{(-1)^{n+1}(x-c)^n}{n c^n}$

19. $\displaystyle\sum_{n=1}^{\infty} \frac{(x-c)^{n-1}}{c^{n-1}}$, $\quad 0 < c$

20. $\displaystyle\sum_{n=1}^{\infty} \frac{(-1)^{n+1} x^{2n-1}}{2n-1}$

21. $\displaystyle\sum_{n=1}^{\infty} \frac{n}{(n+1)!} (-2x)^{n-1}$

22. $\displaystyle\sum_{n=0}^{\infty} \frac{(-1)^n x^{2n}}{n!}$

23. $\displaystyle\sum_{n=0}^{\infty} \frac{x^{2n+1}}{(2n+1)!}$

24. $\displaystyle\sum_{n=0}^{\infty} \frac{n! x^n}{(n+1)!}$

In Exercises 25–32, apply Taylor's Theorem to find the power series (centered at c) for the given function, and find the radius of convergence.

Function	Center
25. $f(x) = e^x$	$c = 0$
26. $f(x) = e^{-x}$	$c = 0$
27. $f(x) = e^{2x}$	$c = 0$
28. $f(x) = e^{-2x}$	$c = 0$
29. $f(x) = \dfrac{1}{x+1}$	$c = 0$
30. $f(x) = \dfrac{1}{2-x}$	$c = 0$
31. $f(x) = \sqrt{x}$	$c = 2$
32. $f(x) = \sqrt{x}$	$c = 4$

In Exercises 33–36, apply Taylor's Theorem to find the binomial series (centered at $c = 0$) for the given function, and find the radius of convergence.

33. $f(x) = \dfrac{1}{(1+x)^3}$ **34.** $f(x) = \sqrt{1+x}$

35. $f(x) = \dfrac{1}{\sqrt{1+x}}$ **36.** $f(x) = \sqrt[3]{1+x}$

In Exercises 37–40, find the radius of convergence of (a) $f(x)$, (b) $f'(x)$, (c) $f''(x)$, and (d) $\int f(x)\,dx$.

37. $f(x) = \displaystyle\sum_{n=0}^{\infty} \left(\frac{x}{2}\right)^n$

38. $f(x) = \displaystyle\sum_{n=1}^{\infty} \frac{x^n}{n5^n}$

39. $f(x) = \displaystyle\sum_{n=0}^{\infty} \frac{(x+1)^{n+1}}{n+1}$

40. $f(x) = \displaystyle\sum_{n=1}^{\infty} \frac{(-1)^{n+1}(x-1)^n}{n}$

In Exercises 41–52, find the power series for the function using the suggested method. Use the basic list of power series for elementary functions provided in this section.

41. Use the power series for e^x.
$$f(x) = e^{x^3}$$

42. Use the series found in Exercise 41.
$$f(x) = e^{-x^3}$$

43. Differentiate the series found in Exercise 41.
$$f(x) = 3x^2 e^{x^3}$$

44. Use the power series for e^x and e^{-x}.
$$f(x) = \frac{e^x + e^{-x}}{2}$$

45. Use the power series for $1/(1+x)$.
$$f(x) = \frac{1}{1+x^4}$$

46. Use the power series for $\dfrac{1}{1+x}$.
$$f(x) = \frac{2x}{1+x}$$

47. Integrate the power series for $\dfrac{1}{1+x}$.
$$f(x) = \ln(1+x^2)$$

48. Integrate the series for $1/(1+x)$.
$$f(x) = \ln(1+x)$$

49. Integrate the series for $1/x$.
$$f(x) = \ln x$$

50. Differentiate the series found in Exercise 44.
$$f(x) = \frac{e^x - e^{-x}}{2}$$

51. Differentiate the series for $-1/x$.
$$f(x) = \frac{1}{x^2}$$

52. Differentiate the power series for e^x term by term and use the resulting series to show that
$$\frac{d}{dx}[e^x] = e^x.$$

In Exercises 53 and 54, use the Taylor series for the exponential function to approximate the expression to four decimal places.

53. $e^{1/2}$ **54.** e^{-1}

In Exercises 55 and 56, use a symbolic algebra utility and 50 terms of the given series to approximate the function
$$f(x) = \sum_{n=1}^{\infty} \frac{(-1)^{n+1}(x-1)^n}{n}, \qquad 0 < x \le 2.$$

55. $f(0.5)$ (Actual sum is $\ln 0.5$.)

56. $f(1.5)$ (Actual sum is $\ln 1.5$.)

S.5 Taylor Polynomials

Taylor Polynomials and Approximation ■ *Taylor's Theorem with Remainder* ■
Applications to Probability

Taylor Polynomials and Approximation

In Section S.4, you saw that it is sometimes possible to obtain an *exact* power series representation of a function. For example, the function $f(x) = e^{-x}$ can be represented exactly by the power series

$$e^{-x} = \sum_{n=0}^{\infty} \frac{(-1)^n}{n!} x^n$$

$$= 1 - x + \frac{x^2}{2} - \frac{x^3}{3!} + \frac{x^4}{4!} - \cdots + \frac{(-1)^n x^n}{n!} + \cdots.$$

The problem with using this power series is that the exactness of its representation depends on the summation of an infinite number of terms. In practice, this is not feasible, and you must be content with a finite summation that approximates the function rather than representing it exactly. For instance, consider the following sequence of partial sums.

$$S_0(x) = 1 \qquad\qquad \text{0th-degree Taylor polynomial}$$

$$S_1(x) = 1 - x \qquad\qquad \text{1st-degree Taylor polynomial}$$

$$S_2(x) = 1 - x + \frac{x^2}{2} \qquad\qquad \text{2nd-degree Taylor polynomial}$$

$$S_3(x) = 1 - x + \frac{x^2}{2} - \frac{x^3}{3!} \qquad\qquad \text{3rd-degree Taylor polynomial}$$

$$\vdots$$

$$S_n(x) = 1 - x + \frac{x^2}{2} - \cdots + \frac{(-1)^n x^n}{n!} \qquad \text{nth-degree Taylor polynomial}$$

Each of these polynomial approximations of e^{-x} is a **Taylor polynomial** for e^{-x}. As n approaches infinity, the graphs of these Taylor polynomials become closer and closer approximations to the graph of $f(x) = e^{-x}$.

For example, Figure S.7 on page S-42 shows the graphs of S_1, S_2, S_3, and S_4. Notice in the figure that the closer x is to the center of convergence ($x = 0$ in this case), the better the polynomial approximates e^{-x}. This conclusion is reinforced by Table S.3 on the next page. From Section S.4, you know that the power series for e^{-x} converges for *all* x. From Figure S.7 and Table S.3, however, you can see that the farther x is from 0, the more terms you need to obtain a good approximation.

TABLE S.3

x	0	0.5	1.0	1.5	2.0
$S_1 = 1 - x$	1	0.5000	0	-0.5000	-1.0
$S_2 = 1 - x + \dfrac{x^2}{2}$	1	0.6250	0.5000	0.6250	1.0
$S_3 = 1 - x + \dfrac{x^2}{2} - \dfrac{x^3}{3!}$	1	0.6042	0.3333	0.0625	-0.3333
$S_4 = 1 - x + \dfrac{x^2}{2} - \dfrac{x^3}{3!} + \dfrac{x^4}{4!}$	1	0.6068	0.3750	0.2734	0.3333
e^{-x}	1	0.6065	0.3679	0.2231	0.1353

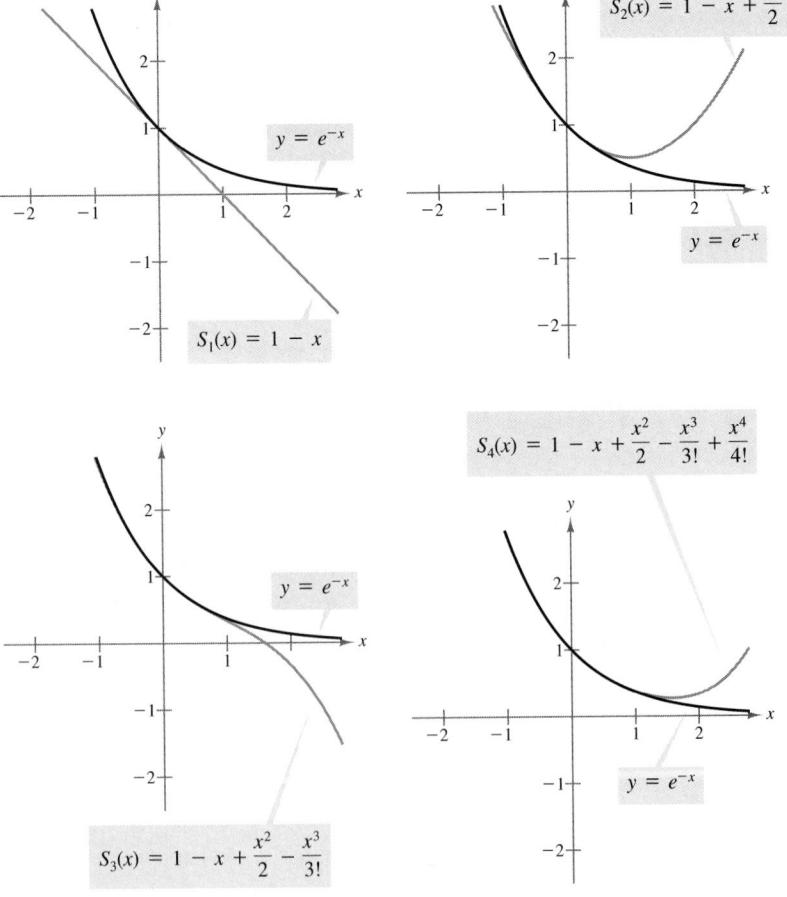

FIGURE S.7

TECHNOLOGY

Finding Taylor Polynomials

Symbolic differentiation utilities, such as *Derive*, *Mathematica*, and *Maple*, are programmed to find Taylor polynomials. For instance, to use *Derive* to find the 5th-degree Taylor polynomial for $f(x) = e^{-x}$, you can enter the following.

1: TAYLOR($\hat{e}^{-x}$, x, 0, 5)	*Author.*
2: $-\dfrac{x^5}{120} + \dfrac{x^4}{24} - \dfrac{x^3}{6} + \dfrac{x^2}{2} - x + 1$	*Simplify.*

After finding this polynomial, you can use a graphing utility to compare the graphs of this Taylor polynomial with the graph of $f(x) = e^{-x}$, as shown below.

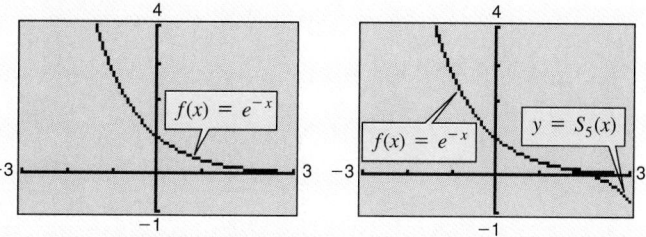

When you use technology to find a Taylor polynomial whose center is not 0, you can obtain polynomials whose forms differ from the standard form. For instance, *Derive* computes the 5th-degree Taylor polynomial of $f(x) = \ln x$, centered at 1, to be

$$S_5(x) = \frac{(x-1)(12x^4 - 63x^3 + 137x^2 - 163x + 137)}{60}.$$

The graph of this Taylor polynomial is compared with the graph of $f(x) = \ln x$ below.

EXAMPLE 1 *Finding Taylor Polynomials*

Find a Taylor polynomial that is a reasonable approximation for

$$f(x) = e^{-x^2}$$

in the interval $[-1, 1]$. What degree of Taylor polynomial should you use?

Solution

To begin, you need to define what constitutes a "reasonable" approximation. Suppose you decide that you want the values of $S_n(x)$ and e^{-x^2} to differ by no more than 0.01 in the interval $[-1, 1]$. To answer the question, you can compute Taylor polynomials of higher and higher degree and then graphically compare them with $f(x) = e^{-x^2}$. For instance, the 4th-, 6th-, and 8th-degree Taylor polynomials for f are as follows.

$$S_4(x) = 1 - x^2 + \frac{x^4}{2} \qquad \textit{4th-degree Taylor polynomial}$$

$$S_6(x) = 1 - x^2 + \frac{x^4}{2} - \frac{x^6}{6} \qquad \textit{6th-degree Taylor polynomial}$$

$$S_8(x) = 1 - x^2 + \frac{x^4}{2} - \frac{x^6}{6} + \frac{x^8}{24} \qquad \textit{8th-degree Taylor polynomial}$$

To compare $S_4(x)$ and e^{-x^2} graphically, sketch both graphs on the same viewing rectangle, as shown in Figure S.8. Then, use the trace feature of the graphing utility to compare the y-values at -1 and 1. When you do this, you will find that the y-values differ by more than 0.01.

Next, perform the same comparison with $S_6(x)$ and e^{-x^2}. With these two graphs, the y-values still differ by more than 0.01 in the interval $[-1, 1]$. Finally, by graphically comparing $S_8(x)$ and e^{-x^2}, you can determine that their graphs differ by less than 0.01 in the interval $[-1, 1]$. To convince yourself of this, try evaluating e^{-x^2} and $S_8(x)$ when $x = \pm 1$. You should obtain the values 0.368 and 0.375, which differ by 0.007.

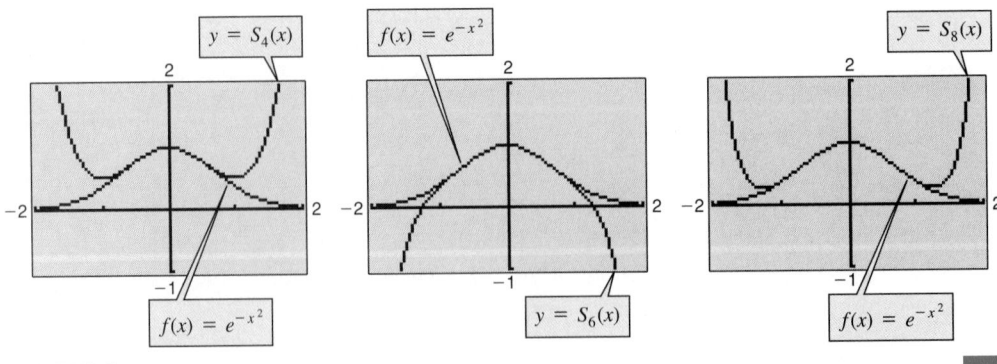

FIGURE S.8

Taylor's Theorem with Remainder

In Example 1, you studied a graphical procedure for determining how well a Taylor polynomial approximates a function f. The following theorem gives you an analytic procedure for determining this.

Taylor's Theorem with Remainder

Let f have derivatives up through order $n+1$ for every x in an interval I containing c. Then for all x in I, $f(x) = S_n(x) + R_n$, where $S_n(x)$ is the nth-degree Taylor polynomial for f and R_n is given by

$$R_n = \frac{f^{(n+1)}(z)}{(n+1)!}(x-c)^{n+1}$$

for some number z between c and x. The value R_n is called the **nth remainder** of $f(x)$.

Although this theorem appears to give a formula for the exact remainder, note that it does not specify which value of z should be used to find R_n. In other words, the practical application of this theorem lies not in calculating R_n, but in finding bounds for R_n.

EXAMPLE 2 *Using a Taylor Polynomial Approximation*

Approximate $e^{-0.75}$ by a 4th-degree Taylor polynomial and determine the maximum error of the approximation.

Solution

Using the 4th-degree Taylor polynomial for e^{-x}, you have the following.

$$e^{-x} \approx 1 - x + \frac{x^2}{2} - \frac{x^3}{3!} + \frac{x^4}{4!}$$

$$e^{-0.75} \approx 1 - 0.75 + \frac{(0.75)^2}{2} - \frac{(0.75)^3}{3!} + \frac{(0.75)^4}{4!} \approx 0.474$$

By Taylor's Theorem with Remainder, the error in this approximation is

$$R_4 = -\frac{e^{-z}}{5!}(0.75)^5, \qquad 0 \le z \le 0.75.$$

Because e^{-z} has a maximum value of 1 in the interval $[0, 0.75]$, it follows that

$$|R_4| \le \frac{1}{5!}(0.75)^5 \approx 0.002.$$

Thus, the approximation is off by at most 0.002.   ▬

Earlier in the text, you looked at different ways to approximate a definite integral: the Midpoint Rule, the Trapezoidal Rule, and Simpson's Rule. The next example shows how you can use a power series to approximate a definite integral.

EXAMPLE 3 *Approximating a Definite Integral*

Use the 8th-degree Taylor polynomial for e^{-x^2} to approximate the definite integral

$$\int_0^1 e^{-x^2}\, dx.$$

Solution
The 8th-degree Taylor polynomial for e^{-x^2} is

$$S_8(x) = 1 - x^2 + \frac{x^4}{2} - \frac{x^6}{6} + \frac{x^8}{24}.$$

Using this polynomial, you can write the following approximation.

$$\int_0^1 e^{-x^2}\, dx \approx \int_0^1 S_8(x)\, dx$$

$$= \int_0^1 \left(1 - x^2 + \frac{x^4}{2} - \frac{x^6}{6} + \frac{x^8}{24}\right) dx$$

$$= \left[x - \frac{x^3}{3} + \frac{x^5}{5(2)} - \frac{x^7}{7(6)} + \frac{x^9}{9(24)}\right]_0^1$$

$$= 1 - \frac{1}{3} + \frac{1}{10} - \frac{1}{42} + \frac{1}{216}$$

$$\approx 0.747$$

This result is shown graphically in Figure S.9. Try comparing this result with that obtained using a symbolic integration utility. When we did this, we obtained a value of 0.746824. Thus, the approximation has an error of less than 0.001.

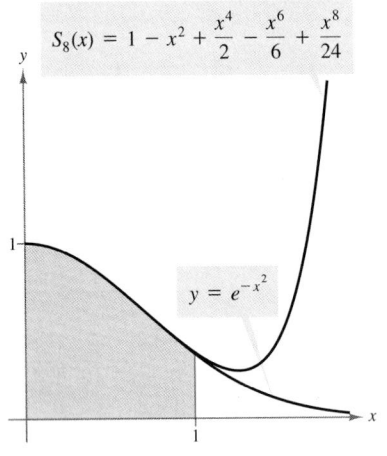

$$S_8(x) = 1 - x^2 + \frac{x^4}{2} - \frac{x^6}{6} + \frac{x^8}{24}$$

$$y = e^{-x^2}$$

FIGURE S.9

When using a Taylor polynomial to approximate a function on an interval, remember that as you move farther away from the center of the Taylor polynomial, you must use a polynomial of higher and higher degree to obtain a given accuracy. For definite integrals, it helps to locate the center of the Taylor polynomial at the midpoint of the interval of integration. For instance, if you want to approximate the definite integral

$$\int_0^2 e^{-x^2}\, dx,$$

you could use a Taylor polynomial centered at 1. If you try this with an 8th-degree Taylor polynomial, you will obtain an approximation of 0.882.

Applications to Probability

Many applications of probability involve experiments in which the sample space is

$$S = \{0, 1, 2, 3, 4, \ldots\}. \qquad \textit{Sample space}$$

As is always true in probability, the sum of the probabilities of the various outcomes is 1. That is, if $P(n)$ is the probability that n will occur, then

$$\sum_{n=0}^{\infty} P(n) = P(0) + P(1) + P(2) + P(3) + \cdots$$

$$= 1.$$

The next example shows how this concept is used in a coin-tossing experiment.

Real Life

EXAMPLE 4 *Finding Probabilities*

A fair coin is tossed until a head turns up. The possible outcomes are

$$\{\overset{0}{H}, \overset{1}{TH}, \overset{2}{TTH}, \overset{3}{TTTH}, \overset{4}{TTTTH}, \ldots\},$$

where the random variable assigned to each outcome is the number of tails that have consecutively appeared before tossing a head (which automatically ends the experiment). Show that the sum of the probabilities in this experiment is 1.

Solution
The probability that 0 tails will appear is $\frac{1}{2}$. The probability that exactly 1 tail will appear is $(\frac{1}{2})^2$. The probability that exactly 2 tails will appear is $(\frac{1}{2})^3$, and so on. Thus, the sum of the probabilities is given by a geometric series.

$$\sum_{n=0}^{\infty} P(n) = P(0) + P(1) + P(2) + P(3) + \cdots$$

$$= \sum_{n=0}^{\infty} \left(\frac{1}{2}\right)^{n+1} \qquad \textit{Geometric series}$$

$$= \sum_{n=0}^{\infty} \frac{1}{2}\left(\frac{1}{2}\right)^{n} \qquad a = \tfrac{1}{2} \text{ and } r = \tfrac{1}{2}$$

$$= \frac{a}{1-r} \qquad \textit{Sum of a geometric series}$$

$$= \frac{1/2}{1-1/2}$$

$$= 1$$

Thus, the sum of the probabilities is 1. This result is shown graphically in Figure S.10.

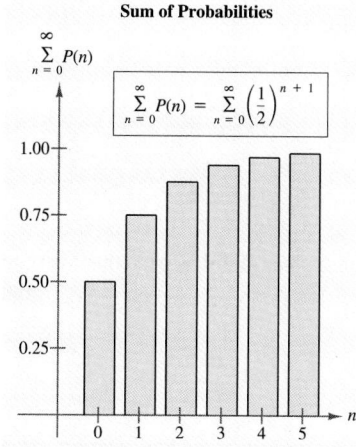

Sum of Probabilities

$$\sum_{n=0}^{\infty} P(n) = \sum_{n=0}^{\infty} \left(\frac{1}{2}\right)^{n+1}$$

FIGURE S.10

The **expected value** of a random variable whose range is $\{0, 1, 2, \ldots\}$ is

$$\text{Expected value} = \sum_{n=0}^{\infty} n P(n) = 0 P(0) + 1 P(1) + 2 P(2) + \cdots.$$

This formula is demonstrated in Example 5.

Real Life

EXAMPLE 5 *Finding an Expected Value*

Find the expected value for the coin-tossing experiment in Example 4.

Solution

Using the probabilities from Example 4, you can write

$$\text{Expected value} = \sum_{n=0}^{\infty} n P(n)$$

$$= \sum_{n=0}^{\infty} n \left(\tfrac{1}{2}\right)^{n+1}$$

$$= 0 \left(\tfrac{1}{2}\right) + 1 \left(\tfrac{1}{2}\right)^2 + 2 \left(\tfrac{1}{2}\right)^3 + 3 \left(\tfrac{1}{2}\right)^4 + \cdots.$$

This series is not geometric, so to find its sum you need to resort to a different tactic. Using the binomial series given in Section S.4, you can write

$$(1 - x)^{-2} = 1 + 2x + 3x^2 + 4x^3 + \cdots,$$

which implies that

$$\left(1 - \tfrac{1}{2}\right)^{-2} = 1 + 2 \left(\tfrac{1}{2}\right) + 3 \left(\tfrac{1}{2}\right)^2 + 4 \left(\tfrac{1}{2}\right)^3 + \cdots$$

$$= \left(\tfrac{1}{2}\right)^{-2}$$

$$= 4.$$

Thus, you can conclude that the expected value is

$$\text{Expected value} = 1 \left(\tfrac{1}{2}\right)^2 + 2 \left(\tfrac{1}{2}\right)^3 + 3 \left(\tfrac{1}{2}\right)^4 + \cdots$$

$$= \left(\tfrac{1}{2}\right)^2 \left[1 + 2 \left(\tfrac{1}{2}\right) + 3 \left(\tfrac{1}{2}\right)^2 + 4 \left(\tfrac{1}{2}\right)^3 + \cdots\right]$$

$$= \tfrac{1}{4}(4)$$

$$= 1.$$

This means that if the experiment were conducted many times, the average number of tails that would occur would be 1. ■

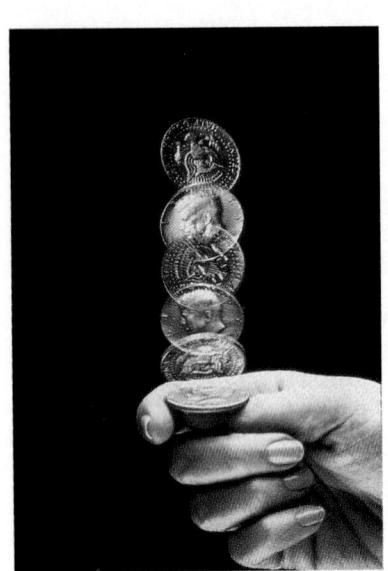

The Stock Market/©91 Al Francekevich

An experiment consists of tossing a fair coin repeatedly until the coin finally lands "heads up." Each time the experiment is performed, the number of tosses necessary to obtain "heads" is counted. If this experiment is performed hundreds of times, the average number of tosses per experiment will be 2.

Discussion Problem   Extending the Example

In Example 5, suppose that the coin is unbalanced so that the probability of landing heads up is 0.6. How does this alter the expected value?

Warm Up

The following warm-up exercises involve skills that were covered in earlier sections. You will use these skills in the exercise set for this section.

In Exercises 1–6, find a power series representation for the function.

1. $f(x) = e^{3x}$ **2.** $f(x) = e^{-3x}$ **3.** $f(x) = \dfrac{4}{x}$

4. $f(x) = \ln 5x$ **5.** $f(x) = (1+x)^{1/4}$ **6.** $f(x) = \sqrt{1+x}$

In Exercises 7–10, evaluate the definite integral.

7. $\displaystyle\int_0^1 (1 - x + x^2 - x^3 + x^4)\, dx$ **8.** $\displaystyle\int_0^{1/2} \left(1 + \frac{x}{3} - \frac{x^2}{9} + \frac{5x^3}{27} \right) dx$

9. $\displaystyle\int_1^2 \left[(x-1) - \frac{(x-1)^2}{2} + \frac{(x-1)^3}{3} \right] dx$

10. $\displaystyle\int_1^{3/2} \left[1 - (x-1) + (x-1)^2 - (x-1)^3 \right] dx$

E X E R C I S E S   S.5

 means that technology can help you solve or check the exercise(s).

In Exercises 1–6, find the Taylor polynomial (centered at 0) of degree (a) 1, (b) 2, (c) 3, and (d) 4.

1. $f(x) = e^x$ **2.** $f(x) = \ln(x+1)$

3. $f(x) = \sqrt{x+1}$ **4.** $f(x) = \dfrac{1}{(x+1)^2}$

5. $f(x) = \dfrac{x}{x+1}$ **6.** $f(x) = \dfrac{4}{x+1}$

In Exercises 7 and 8, complete the table using the given Taylor polynomials as approximations to the function f.

7.

x	0	$\frac{1}{4}$	$\frac{1}{2}$	$\frac{3}{4}$	1
$f(x) = e^{x/2}$					
$1 + \dfrac{x}{2}$					
$1 + \dfrac{x}{2} + \dfrac{x^2}{8}$					
$1 + \dfrac{x}{2} + \dfrac{x^2}{8} + \dfrac{x^3}{48}$					
$1 + \dfrac{x}{2} + \dfrac{x^2}{8} + \dfrac{x^3}{48} + \dfrac{x^4}{384}$					

8.

x	0	$\frac{1}{4}$	$\frac{1}{2}$	$\frac{3}{4}$
$f(x) = \ln(x^2 + 1)$				
x^2				
$x^2 - \dfrac{x^4}{2}$				
$x^2 - \dfrac{x^4}{2} + \dfrac{x^6}{3}$				
$x^2 - \dfrac{x^4}{2} + \dfrac{x^6}{3} - \dfrac{x^8}{4}$				

In Exercises 9 and 10, find the Taylor polynomial (centered at 0) of degree (a) 2, (b) 4, (c) 6, and (d) 8.

9. $f(x) = \dfrac{1}{1+x^2}$ **10.** $f(x) = e^{-x^2}$

In Exercises 11 and 12, use a symbolic differentiation utility to find the 4th-degree Taylor polynomial (centered at 0).

11. $f(x) = \dfrac{1}{x^2+1}$ **12.** $f(x) = xe^x$

In Exercises 13–16, match the Taylor polynomial approximation of the function $f(x) = e^{-x^2/2}$ with its graph. [The graphs are labeled (a)–(d)].

13. $y = -\frac{1}{2}x^2 + 1$ **14.** $y = \frac{1}{8}x^4 - \frac{1}{2}x^2 + 1$

15. $y = e^{-1/2}[(x + 1) + 1]$

16. $y = e^{-1/2}\left[\frac{1}{3}(x - 1)^3 - (x - 1) + 1\right]$

(a)   (b)

(c)   (d)

      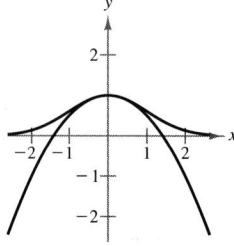

In Exercises 17–20, use a sixth-degree Taylor polynomial centered at c for the function f to obtain the required approximation.

Function	Approximation
17. $f(x) = e^{-x}$, $c = 0$	$f\left(\frac{1}{2}\right)$
18. $f(x) = x^2 e^{-x}$, $c = 0$	$f\left(\frac{1}{4}\right)$
19. $f(x) = \ln x$, $c = 2$	$f\left(\frac{3}{2}\right)$
20. $f(x) = \sqrt{x}$, $c = 4$	$f(5)$

In Exercises 21–24, use a sixth-degree Taylor polynomial centered at 0 to approximate the integral.

Function	Approximation
21. $f(x) = e^{-x^2}$	$\displaystyle\int_0^1 e^{-x^2}\,dx$
22. $f(x) = \ln(x^2 + 1)$	$\displaystyle\int_{-1/4}^{1/4} \ln(x^2 + 1)\,dx$

Function	Approximation
23. $f(x) = \dfrac{1}{\sqrt{1 + x^2}}$	$\displaystyle\int_0^{1/2} \frac{1}{\sqrt{1 + x^2}}\,dx$
24. $f(x) = \dfrac{1}{\sqrt[3]{1 + x^2}}$	$\displaystyle\int_0^{1/2} \frac{1}{\sqrt[3]{1 + x^2}}\,dx$

In Exercises 25 and 26, determine the degree of the Taylor polynomial centered at c required to approximate f in the given interval to an accuracy of ± 0.001.

Function	Interval
25. $f(x) = e^x$, $c = 1$	$[0, 2]$
26. $f(x) = \dfrac{1}{x}$, $c = 1$	$\left[1, \dfrac{3}{2}\right]$

In Exercises 27 and 28, determine the maximum error guaranteed by Taylor's Remainder Theorem when a given fifth-degree Taylor polynomial is used to approximate f in the indicated interval.

27. $f(x) = e^{-x}$, $[0, 1]$ **28.** $f(x) = \dfrac{1}{x}$, $\left[1, \dfrac{3}{2}\right]$

29. *Profit* Let n be a random variable representing the number of units of a certain commodity sold per day in a given store. The probability distribution of n is given in the table.

n	0	1	2	3	4, . . .
$P(n)$	$\frac{1}{2}$	$\left(\frac{1}{2}\right)^2$	$\left(\frac{1}{2}\right)^3$	$\left(\frac{1}{2}\right)^4$	$\left(\frac{1}{2}\right)^5$, ...

(a) Show that $\displaystyle\sum_{n=0}^{\infty} P(n) = 1$.

(b) Find the expected value of the random variable n.

(c) If there is a \$10 profit on each unit sold, what is the expected daily profit on this commodity?

30. Repeat Exercise 29 for the probability distribution for n that is given in the table below.

n	0	1	2	3, . . .
$P(n)$	$\frac{1}{2}\left(\frac{2}{3}\right)$	$\frac{1}{2}\left(\frac{2}{3}\right)^2$	$\frac{1}{2}\left(\frac{2}{3}\right)^3$	$\frac{1}{2}\left(\frac{2}{3}\right)^4$, ...

Newton's Method

Newton's Method ■ *Convergence of Newton's Method*

Newton's Method

Finding the zeros of a function is a fundamental problem in algebra and in calculus. Sometimes this problem can be solved algebraically. For instance, you can find the zeros of the quadratic function

$$f(x) = 2x^2 - 13x + 1$$

by applying the Quadratic Formula to the equation $2x^2 - 13x + 1 = 0$. In real life, however, you often encounter functions whose zeros cannot be found so easily. In such cases, you can use various approximation methods to find the zeros. One such method, called **Newton's Method,** is described in this section.

Consider a function f, such as the one whose graph is shown in Figure S.11. An actual zero of the function is $x = c$. To approximate this zero, choose x_1 close to c and form the first-degree Taylor polynomial centered at x_1.

$$S_1(x) = f(x_1) + f'(x_1)(x - x_1) \qquad \textit{1st-degree Taylor polynomial}$$

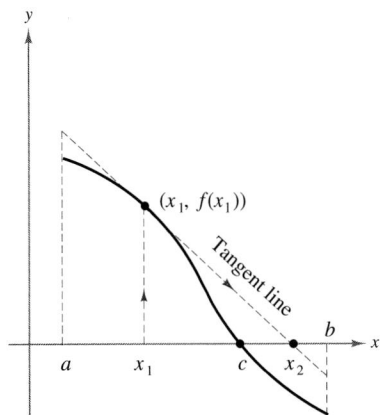

FIGURE S.11 The x-intercept of the tangent line approximates the zero of f.

Graphically, you can interpret this polynomial as the equation of the tangent line to the graph of f at the point $(x_1, f(x_1))$. Newton's Method is based on the assumption that this tangent line will cross the x-axis at about the same point as the graph of f crosses the x-axis. With this assumption, set $S_1(x)$ equal to zero, solve for x

$$f(x_1) + f'(x_1)(x - x_1) = 0$$

$$x - x_1 = -\frac{f(x_1)}{f'(x_1)}$$

$$x = x_1 - \frac{f(x_1)}{f'(x_1)},$$

and use the resulting value as a new, and hopefully better, approximation for the actual zero c. Thus, from the approximation x_1, you form a second approximation

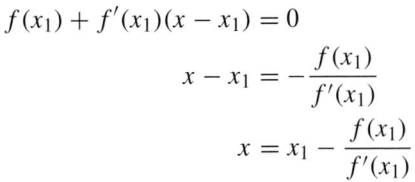

If you want to obtain an even better approximation, you can use x_2 to calculate x_3. Repeated application of this process is called Newton's Method.

Newton's Method

Let c be a zero of f and let f be differentiable on an open interval that contains c. To approximate c, use the following steps.

1. Make an initial approximation x_1 "close to" c.

2. Determine a new approximation using the formula

$$x_{n+1} = x_n - \frac{f(x_n)}{f'(x_n)}.$$

3. If $|x_n - x_{n+1}|$ is less than the desired accuracy, let x_{n+1} serve as a final approximation. Otherwise, return to step 2 and calculate a new approximation.

Each calculation of a successive approximation is called an **iteration.**

EXAMPLE 1   *Using Newton's Method*

Use three iterations of Newton's Method to approximate a zero of

$$f(x) = x^2 - 2.$$

Use $x_1 = 1$ as the initial guess.

Solution

The first derivative of f is $f'(x) = 2x$. Thus, the iterative formula for Newton's method is

$$x_{n+1} = x_n - \frac{f(x_n)}{f'(x_n)} = x_n - \frac{x_n{}^2 - 2}{2x_n}.$$

The calculations for three iterations are shown in Table S.4. The first iteration is depicted graphically in Figure S.12.

TABLE S.4

n	x_n	$f(x_n)$	$f'(x_n)$	$\dfrac{f(x_n)}{f'(x_n)}$	$x_n - \dfrac{f(x_n)}{f'(x_n)}$
1	1.000000	−1.000000	2.000000	−0.500000	1.500000
2	1.500000	0.250000	3.000000	0.083333	1.416667
3	1.416667	0.006945	2.833334	0.002451	1.414216
4	1.414216				

Thus, the approximation is $x = 1.414216$. For this particular function, you can easily determine the exact zero to be $\sqrt{2} \approx 1.414214$. Thus, after only three iterations of Newton's Method, you can obtain an approximation that is within 0.000002 of the actual root.

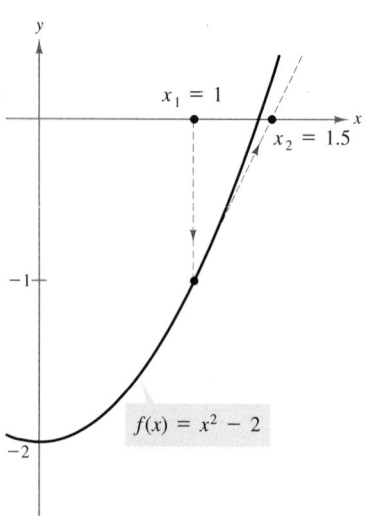

FIGURE S.12

EXAMPLE 2 *Using Newton's Method*

Use Newton's Method to approximate the zeros of

$$f(x) = 2x^3 + x^2 - x + 1.$$

Continue the iterations until two successive approximations differ by less than 0.001.

Solution

Begin by sketching the graph of f and observing that it has only one real zero, which occurs near $x_1 = -1.2$, as shown in Figure S.13. Three iterations of Newton's Method are shown in Table S.5.

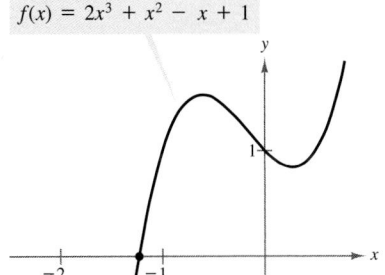

$f(x) = 2x^3 + x^2 - x + 1$

FIGURE S.13

TABLE S.5

n	x_n	$f(x_n)$	$f'(x_n)$	$\dfrac{f(x_n)}{f'(x_n)}$	$x_n - \dfrac{f(x_n)}{f'(x_n)}$
1	-1.20000	0.18400	5.24000	0.03511	-1.23511
2	-1.23511	-0.00771	5.68276	-0.00136	-1.23375
3	-1.23375	-0.00001	5.66533	-0.00000	-1.23375
4	-1.23375				

Thus, you can estimate the zero of f to be -1.23375.

EXAMPLE 3 *Using Newton's Method*

Use Newton's Method to approximate the zeros of $f(x) = e^x + x$. Continue the iterations until two successive approximations differ by less than 0.001.

Solution

Begin by sketching the graph of f and observing that it has only one real zero, which occurs near $x_1 = -0.5$, as shown in Figure S.14. Three iterations of Newton's Method are shown in Table S.6.

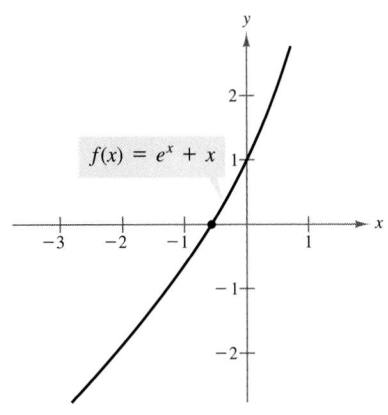

$f(x) = e^x + x$

FIGURE S.14

TABLE S.6

n	x_n	$f(x_n)$	$f'(x_n)$	$\dfrac{f(x_n)}{f'(x_n)}$	$x_n - \dfrac{f(x_n)}{f'(x_n)}$
1	-0.500000	0.106531	1.606531	0.066311	-0.566311
2	-0.566311	0.001305	1.567616	0.000832	-0.567143
3	-0.567143	0.000000	1.567143	0.000000	-0.567143
4	-0.567143				

Thus, you can estimate the zero of f to be -0.567143.

TECHNOLOGY

Programming Newton's Method

Technology can be used in a variety of ways to approximate zeros of functions. Earlier in the text, you saw how the zoom feature of a graphing calculator can be used to approximate a zero graphically.

Another way to use technology to approximate the zeros of a function is to program Newton's Method into a graphing utility. For instance, the following steps show how to program Newton's Method into a *TI-81* or *TI-82* graphing calculator. See Appendix D for other calculators.

```
Pgrm1:NEWTON
```

`:Disp ''ENTER APPROXIMATION''`	*Prompt user for approximation.*
`:Input X`	*Input approximation.*
`:(Xmax-Xmin)/100→D`	*Define value of delta.*
`:1→N`	*Initialize counter.*
`:Lbl 1`	*Begin loop.*
* `:X-Y₁/NDeriv(Y₁,D)→R`	*Compute new root.*
`:If abs(X-R)≤abs(X/1E10)`	*Compare approximations.*
`:Goto 2`	*If test is true, go to 2.*
`:R→X`	*Otherwise, continue iterations.*
`:N+1→N`	*Increase counter by 1.*
`:Goto 1`	*End loop.*
`:Lbl 2`	*Begin printout.*
`:Disp ''ROOT=''`	
`:Disp R`	*Display approximate zero.*
`:Disp ''ITER=''`	
`:Disp N`	*Display number of iterations.*

Before running the program, enter the function as Y_1. Then graph the function and estimate one of its zeros. When you run the program, you will be prompted to enter the estimate as X. After two successive approximations differ by less than 0.0000000001, the program will display the refined approximation.

For instance, to use the program to approximate the zero of the function in Example 3,

$$f(x) = e^x + x,$$

begin by graphing the function, as shown at the left. Then run the program and enter -0.5 as the initial approximation. The calculator will display a refined approximation of -0.5671432904.

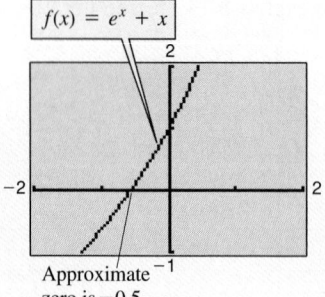

$f(x) = e^x + x$

Approximate zero is -0.5.

*On a *TI-82*, use `:X-Y₁/nDeriv(Y₁,X,D)→R`

Convergence of Newton's Method

When, as in Examples 1, 2, and 3, the approximations approach a zero of a function, Newton's Method is said to **converge.** You should know, however, that Newton's Method does not always converge. Two situations in which it may not converge are as follows.

1. If $f'(x_n) = 0$ for some n. (See Figure S.15.)
2. If $\lim\limits_{n \to \infty} x_n$ does not exist. (See Figure S.16.)

The type of problem illustrated in Figure S.15 can usually be overcome with a better choice for x_1. The problem illustrated in Figure S.16, however, is usually more serious. For instance, Newton's Method does not converge for any choice of x_1 (other than the actual zero) for the function

$$f(x) = x^{1/3}.$$

Try running the program listed on the previous page to approximate the zero of this function. If you do, you will find that the program fails.

FIGURE S.15

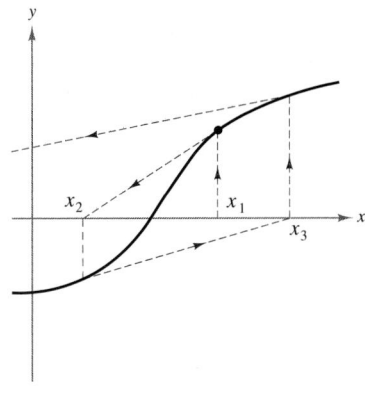

FIGURE S.16

EXAMPLE 4   *Finding a Point of Intersection*

Estimate the point of intersection of the graphs of

$$y = e^{-x^2} \quad \text{and} \quad y = x,$$

as shown in Figure S.17. Use Newton's Method and continue the iterations until two successive approximations differ by less than 0.0001.

Solution

The point of intersection of the two graphs occurs when $e^{-x^2} = x$, which implies that

$$0 = x - e^{-x^2}.$$

To use Newton's Method, let

$$f(x) = x - e^{-x^2}$$

and employ the iterative formula

$$x_{n+1} = x_n - \frac{f(x_n)}{f'(x_n)} = x_n - \frac{x_n - e^{-x_n^2}}{1 + 2x_n e^{-x_n^2}}.$$

Table S.7 shows three iterations of Newton's Method beginning with an initial approximation of $x_1 = 0.5$.

TABLE S.7

n	x_n	$f(x_n)$	$f'(x_n)$	$\dfrac{f(x_n)}{f'(x_n)}$	$x_n - \dfrac{f(x_n)}{f'(x_n)}$
1	0.500000	−0.27880	1.77880	−0.15673	0.65673
2	0.65673	0.00706	1.85331	0.00381	0.65292
3	0.65292	0.00000	1.85261	0.00000	0.65292
4	0.65292				

Thus, you can estimate that the point of intersection occurs when $x \approx 0.65292$. ∎

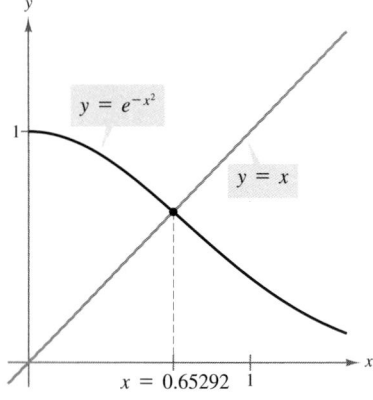

FIGURE S.17

Discussion Problem   Exploring Newton's Method Graphically

Use a graphing utility to sketch the graph of

$$f(x) = x^{1/3}.$$

On the same viewing rectangle, graph the tangent line to the graph of f at the point $(1, 1)$. If you used $x_1 = 1$ as an initial approximation, what value would Newton's Method yield as the second approximation? Answer the question graphically.

Warm Up

The following warm-up exercises involve skills that were covered in earlier sections. You will use these skills in the exercise set for this section.

In Exercises 1–4, evaluate f and f' at the indicated x-value.

1. $f(x) = x^2 - 2x - 1$, $x = 2.4$ **2.** $f(x) = x^3 - 2x^2 + 1$, $x = -0.6$

3. $f(x) = e^{2x} - 2$, $x = 0.35$ **4.** $f(x) = e^{x^2} - 7x + 3$, $x = 1.4$

In Exercises 5–8, solve for x.

5. $|x - 5| \le 0.1$ **6.** $|4 - 5x| \le 0.01$

7. $\left|2 - \dfrac{x}{3}\right| \le 0.01$ **8.** $|2x + 7| \le 0.01$

In Exercises 9 and 10, find the point(s) of intersection of the graphs of the two equations.

9. $y = x^2 - x - 2$ **10.** $y = x^2$
    $y = 2x - 1$ $y = x + 1$

E X E R C I S E S   S.6   means that technology can help you solve or check the exercise(s).

In Exercises 1 and 2, complete one iteration of Newton's Method for the function using the indicated initial estimate.

Function	*Initial Estimate*
1. $f(x) = x^2 - 5$	$x_1 = 2.2$
2. $f(x) = 3x^2 - 2$	$x_1 = 1$

In Exercises 3–12, approximate the indicated zero(s) of the function. Use Newton's Method, continuing until two successive approximations differ by less than 0.001.

3. $f(x) = x^3 + x - 1$ **4.** $f(x) = x^5 + x - 1$

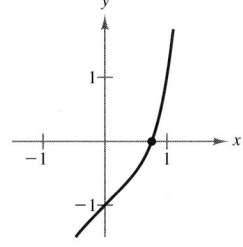

5. $y = 5\sqrt{x - 1} - 2x$

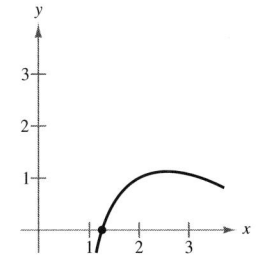

6. $f(x) = \ln x - \dfrac{1}{x}$

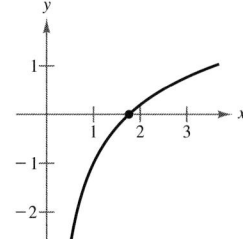

7. $f(x) = \ln x + x$

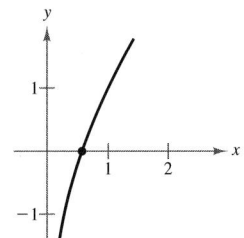

8. $y = e^{3x}(3 - x) - 1$

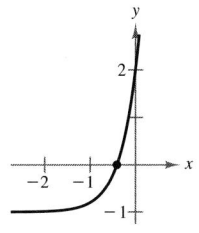

9. $f(x) = e^{-x^2} - x^2$

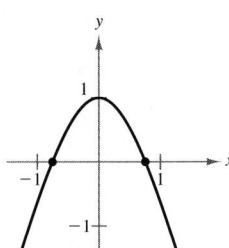

10. $y = x^4 + x^3 - 1$

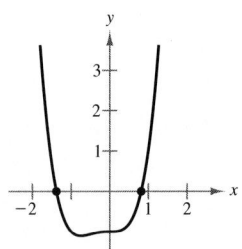

11. $f(x) = x^3 - 27x - 27$

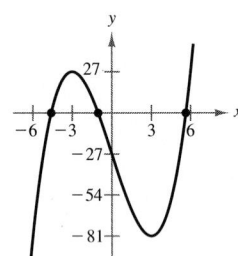

12. $y = x^3 - x^2 + 3$

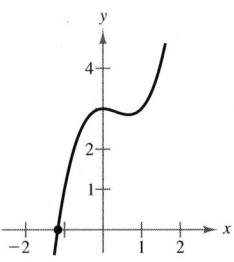

In Exercises 13–16, approximate, to three decimal places, the x-value of the point of intersection of the graphs.

13. $f(x) = 4 - x$,
    $g(x) = \ln x$

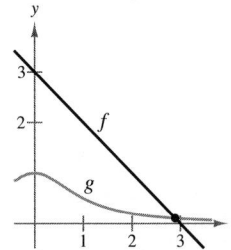

14. $f(x) = 2x + 1$,
    $g(x) = \sqrt{x + 4}$

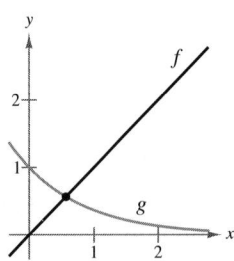

15. $f(x) = 3 - x$,
    $g(x) = \dfrac{1}{x^2 + 1}$

16. $f(x) = x$
    $g(x) = e^{-x}$

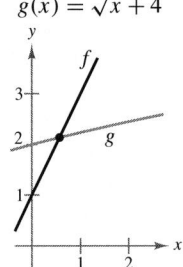

In Exercises 17–20, apply Newton's Method using the indicated initial estimate. Then explain why the method fails.

17. $y = 2x^3 - 6x^2 + 6x - 1$, $x_1 = 1$

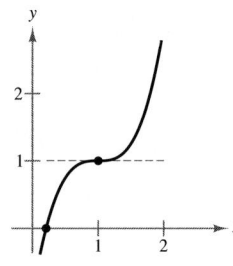

18. $y = 4x^3 - 12x^2 + 12x - 3$, $x_1 = \frac{3}{2}$

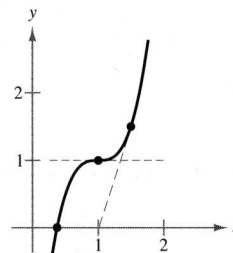

19. $y = -x^3 + 3x^2 - x + 1$, $x_1 = 1$

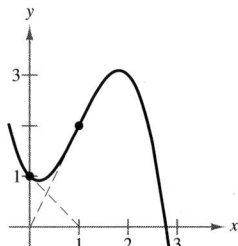

20. $y = x^3 - 2x - 2$, $x_1 = 0$

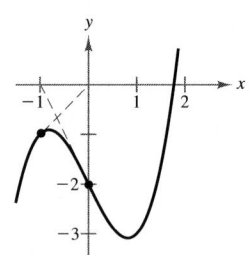

In Exercises 21 and 22, use Newton's Method to obtain a general rule for approximating the required radical.

21. $\sqrt{a}$ [*Hint:* Consider $f(x) = x^2 - a$.]

22. $\sqrt[n]{a}$ [*Hint:* Consider $f(x) = x^n - a$.]

In Exercises 23–26, use the results of Exercises 21 and 22 to approximate the indicated radical to three decimal places.

23. $\sqrt{7}$ **24.** $\sqrt{5}$

25. $\sqrt[4]{6}$ **26.** $\sqrt[3]{15}$

27. Use Newton's Method to show that the equation

$$x_{n+1} = x_n(2 - ax_n)$$

can be used to approximate $1/a$ if x_1 is an initial guess of the reciprocal of a. Note that this method of approximating reciprocals uses only the operations of multiplication and subtraction. [*Hint:* Consider $f(x) = (1/x) - a$.]

28. Use the result of Exercise 27 to approximate $\frac{1}{11}$ to three decimal places.

29. *Optimal Time* A man is in a boat 2 miles from the nearest point on the coast (see figure). He is to go to a point Q, which is 3 miles down the coast and 1 mile inland. If he can row at 3 mi/hr and walk at 4 mi/hr, toward what point on the coast should he row in order to reach point Q in the least time?

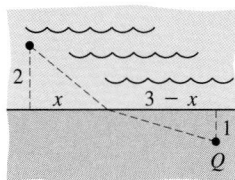

30. *Average Cost* A company estimates that the cost in dollars of producing x units of a product is given by the model

$$C = 0.0001x^3 + 0.02x^2 + 0.4x + 800.$$

Find the production level that minimizes the average cost per unit.

31. *Chemical Concentration* The concentration C of a antibiotic in the bloodstream t hours after injection into muscle tissue is

$$C = \frac{3t^2 + t}{50 + t^3}.$$

When is the concentration the greatest?

32. *Cost* The ordering and transportation cost C of the components used in manufacturing a product is

$$C = 100\left(\frac{200}{x^2} + \frac{x}{x + 30}\right), \qquad 1 \le x,$$

where C is measured in thousands of dollars and x is the order size in hundreds. Find the order size that minimizes the costs.

33. *Forestry* The value of a tract of timber is

$$V(t) = 100{,}000e^{0.8\sqrt{t}},$$

where t is the time in years, with $t = 0$ corresponding to 1990. If money earns interest at a rate of $r = 10\%$ compounded continuously, then the present value of the timber at any time t is given by

$$A(t) = V(t)e^{-0.10t}.$$

Assume the cost of maintenance of the timber to be a constant cash flow at the rate of $1000 per year. Then the total present value of this cost for t years is

$$C(t) = \int_0^t 1000e^{-0.10u}\,du,$$

and the net present value of the tract of timber is

$$P(t) = A(t) - C(t).$$

Find the year when the timber should be harvested to maximize the present value function P.

34. *Forestry* Repeat Exercise 33 for

$$V(t) = 100{,}000e^{0.9\sqrt{t}}.$$

In Exercises 35–40, use a graphing utility to approximate all the real zeros of the function by Newton's Method. Graph the function to make the initial estimate of a zero.

35. $f(x) = \frac{1}{4}x^3 - 3x^2 + \frac{3}{4}x - 2$

36. $f(x) = \frac{1}{2}x^3 - \frac{11}{3}x^2 + \frac{10}{3}x + \frac{32}{3}$

37. $f(x) = -x^4 + 5x^2 - 5$

38. $f(x) = \frac{4}{11}x^4 + \frac{3}{7}x^2 - 2$

39. $f(x) = x^2 - \ln x - \frac{3}{2}$

40. $f(x) = 0.16e^{x^2} - 4.1x^3 + 6.8$

Chapter Summary and Study Tips

After studying this chapter, you should have acquired the following skills. The exercise numbers are keyed to the Review Exercises that begin on page S-62. Answers to odd-numbered Review Exercises are given in the back of the text.

▪   Find the terms of sequences. (*Section S.1*)   Review Exercises 1–4

▪   Determine the convergence or divergence of sequences. Find the limits of conver-   Review Exercises 5–12
gent sequences. (*Section S.1*)

▪   Find patterns for sequences. (*Section S.1*)   Review Exercises 13–16

▪   Use sequences to answer questions about real life. (*Section S.1*)   Review Exercises 17, 18

▪   Find the partial sums of sequences. (*Section S.2*)   Review Exercises 19–22
$$S_1 = a_1, \ S_2 = a_1 + a_2, \ S_3 = a_1 + a_2 + a_3, \ \ldots$$

▪   Determine the convergence or divergence of infinite series. (*Section S.2*)   Review Exercises 23–26

▪   Use the nth-Term Test to show that series diverge. (*Section S.2*)   Review Exercises 27–30

The series $\displaystyle\sum_{n=1}^{\infty} a_n$ diverges if $\displaystyle\lim_{n\to\infty} a_n \neq 0$.

▪   Find the Nth partial sums of geometric series. (*Section S.2*)   Review Exercises 31–34
$$S_N = \frac{a(1 - r^{N+1})}{1 - r}, \qquad r \neq 1.$$

▪   Determine the convergence or divergence of geometric series. (*Section S.2*)   Review Exercises 35–38

If $|r| \geq 1$, the series *diverges*.

If $|r| < 1$, the series *converges* and its sum is $\dfrac{a}{1 - r}$.

▪   Use geometric series to model real life. (*Section S.2*)   Review Exercises 39, 40

▪   Determine the convergence or divergence of p-series. (*Section S.3*)   Review Exercises 41–44

The series diverges if $0 < p \leq 1$.

The series converges if $p > 1$.

▪   Use technology to approximate the sums of convergent p-series. (*Section S.3*)   Review Exercises 45–48

▪   Use the Ratio Test to determine the convergence or divergence of series.   Review Exercises 49–54
(*Section S.3*)

The series converges if $\displaystyle\lim_{n\to\infty} \left| \frac{a_{n+1}}{a_n} \right| < 1$.

The series diverges if $\displaystyle\lim_{n\to\infty} \left| \frac{a_{n+1}}{a_n} \right| > 1$.

▪   Find the radii of convergence of power series. (*Section S.4*)   Review Exercises 55–58

▪   Use Taylor's Theorem to find power series for functions. (*Section S.4*)   Review Exercises 59–62
$$f(x) = \sum_{n=0}^{\infty} \frac{f^{(n)}(c)(x - c)^n}{n!} = f(c) + \frac{f'(c)(x - c)}{1!} + \frac{f''(c)(x - c)^2}{2!} + \cdots$$

*Several student study aids are available with this text. The *Student Solutions Guide* includes detailed solutions to all odd-numbered exercises, as well as practice chapter tests with answers. The *Graphics Calculator Guide* offers instructions on the use of a variety of graphing calculators and computer graphing software. The *Brief Calculus TUTOR* includes additional examples for selected exercises in the text.

- Use the basic list of power series to find power series for functions. (*Section S.4*) —
- Find Taylor polynomials for functions. (*Section S.5*) —
- Use Taylor polynomials to approximate functions. (*Section S.5*) —
- Determine the maximum errors of approximations using Taylor polynomials. (*Section S.5*) —
- Approximate definite integrals using Taylor polynomials. (*Section S.5*) —
- Use Taylor polynomials to model probabilities. (*Section S.5*) —
- Use Newton's Method to approximate the zeros of functions. (*Section S.6*) —

$$x_{n+1} = x_n - \frac{f(x_n)}{f'(x_n)}$$

- Use Newton's Method to approximate the points of intersection of graphs. (*Section S.6*) —

- **Using the List of Basic Power Series**   To be efficient at finding Taylor series or Taylor polynomials, learn how to use the following basic list.

$$\frac{1}{x} = 1 - (x-1) + (x-1)^2 - (x-1)^3 + (x-1)^4 - \cdots + (-1)^n (x-1)^n + \cdots, \qquad 0 < x < 2$$

$$\frac{1}{x+1} = 1 - x + x^2 - x^3 + x^4 - x^5 + \cdots + (-1)^n x^n + \cdots, \qquad -1 < x < 1$$

$$\ln x = (x-1) - \frac{(x-1)^2}{2} + \frac{(x-1)^3}{3} - \frac{(x-1)^4}{4} + \cdots + \frac{(-1)^{n-1}(x-1)^n}{n} + \cdots, \qquad 0 < x \le 2$$

$$e^x = 1 + x + \frac{x^2}{2!} + \frac{x^3}{3!} + \frac{x^4}{4!} + \cdots + \frac{x^n}{n!} + \cdots, \qquad -\infty < x < \infty$$

$$(1+x)^k = 1 + kx + \frac{k(k-1)x^2}{2!} + \frac{k(k-1)(k-2)x^3}{3!} + \frac{k(k-1)(k-2)(k-3)x^4}{4!} + \cdots, \qquad -1 < x < 1$$

- **Using Technology to Approximate Zeros**   Newton's Method is only one way that technology can be used to approximate the zeros of a function. Another way is to use the zoom and trace features of a graphing utility, as shown below. (Compare this with the procedure described on page S-54.)

Original screen

Screen after zooming four times

Review Exercises

 means that technology can help you solve or check the exercise(s).

In Exercises 1–4, write out the first five terms of the specified sequence. (Begin with $n = 1$.)

1. $a_n = \left(-\dfrac{1}{3}\right)^n$

2. $a_n = \dfrac{n-2}{n^2+2}$

3. $a_n = \dfrac{4^n}{n!}$

4. $a_n = \dfrac{(-1)^n}{n^3}$

In Exercises 5–12, determine the convergence or divergence of the given sequence. If the sequence converges, find its limit.

5. $a_n = \dfrac{2n+3}{n^2}$

6. $a_n = \dfrac{1}{\sqrt{n}}$

7. $a_n = \dfrac{n^3}{n^2+1}$

8. $a_n = 10e^{-n}$

9. $a_n = 5 + \dfrac{1}{3^n}$

10. $a_n = \dfrac{n}{\sqrt{n^2+1}}$

11. $a_n = \dfrac{1}{n^{4/3}}$

12. $a_n = \dfrac{(n-1)!}{(n+1)!}$

In Exercises 13–16, find the general term of the given sequence.

13. $\dfrac{1}{3}, \dfrac{2}{6}, \dfrac{3}{9}, \dfrac{4}{12}, \dots$

14. $\dfrac{1}{2}, \dfrac{2}{5}, \dfrac{3}{10}, \dfrac{4}{17}, \dots$

15. $\dfrac{1}{3}, -\dfrac{2}{9}, \dfrac{4}{27}, -\dfrac{8}{81}, \dots$

16. $1, \dfrac{2}{5}, \dfrac{4}{25}, \dfrac{8}{125}, \dfrac{16}{625}, \dots$

17. *Sales Increases* A mail-order company sells \$15,000 worth of products during its first year. The company's goal is to increase sales by \$10,000 each year for 9 years.

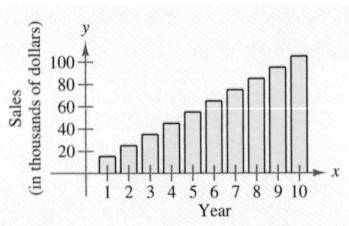

(a) Write an expression for the amount of sales during the nth year.

(b) Compute the total sales for the first 5 years that the mail-order company is in business.

18. *Number of Logs* Logs are stacked in a pile, as shown in the figure. The top row has 15 logs and the bottom row has 21 logs.

FIGURE FOR 18

(a) Write an expression for the number of logs in the nth row.

(b) Use the expression in part (a) to verify the number of logs in each row.

In Exercises 19–22, find the first five terms of the sequence of partial sums for the infinite series.

19. $\displaystyle\sum_{n=0}^{\infty} \left(\dfrac{3}{2}\right)^n$

20. $\displaystyle\sum_{n=1}^{\infty} \dfrac{(-1)^{n+1}}{2n}$

21. $\displaystyle\sum_{n=1}^{\infty} \dfrac{(-1)^{n+1}}{(2n)!}$

22. $\displaystyle\sum_{n=1}^{\infty} \dfrac{1}{n^2}$

In Exercises 23–26, determine the convergence or divergence of the infinite series.

23. $\displaystyle\sum_{n=1}^{\infty} \dfrac{n^2+1}{n(n+1)}$

24. $\displaystyle\sum_{n=0}^{\infty} \left(\dfrac{1}{3}\right)^n$

25. $\displaystyle\sum_{n=0}^{\infty} 2(0.25)^{n+1}$

26. $\displaystyle\sum_{n=1}^{\infty} \dfrac{\sqrt{n^3}}{n}$

In Exercises 27–30, use the nth-Term Test to verify that the series diverges.

27. $\displaystyle\sum_{n=1}^{\infty} \dfrac{2n}{n+5}$

28. $\displaystyle\sum_{n=1}^{\infty} \dfrac{n^3}{1-n^3}$

29. $\displaystyle\sum_{n=0}^{\infty} \left(\dfrac{5}{4}\right)^n$

30. $\displaystyle\sum_{n=0}^{\infty} 3\left(-\dfrac{4}{3}\right)^n$

In Exercises 31–34, find the Nth partial sum of the series.

31. $\displaystyle\sum_{n=0}^{\infty} \left(\dfrac{1}{5}\right)^n$

32. $\displaystyle\sum_{n=0}^{\infty} 3\left(\dfrac{1}{6}\right)^n$

33. $\displaystyle\sum_{n=0}^{\infty} \left(\dfrac{1}{2^n} + \dfrac{1}{4^n}\right)$

34. $\displaystyle\sum_{n=0}^{\infty} 2\left(\dfrac{1}{\sqrt{3}}\right)^n$

In Exercises 35–38, decide whether the series converges or diverges. If it converges, find its sum.

35. $\sum_{n=0}^{\infty} = \frac{1}{4}(4)^n$

36. $\sum_{n=0}^{\infty} = 4\left(-\frac{1}{4}\right)^n$

37. $\sum_{n=0}^{\infty} = [(0.5)^n + (0.2)^n]$

38. $\sum_{n=0}^{\infty} = [(1.5)^n + (0.2)^n]$

39. *Bouncing Ball* A ball is dropped from a height of 8 feet. Each time it drops h feet, it rebounds $0.7h$ feet.

(a) Write a model for the distance traveled by the ball.
(b) Find the total distance traveled by the ball.

40. *Marketing* A company estimates the annual sales of a new product to be 8000 units. Each year, 15% of the units that have been sold become inoperative. Thus, after 1 year 8000 are in use, after 2 years $[8000 + 0.85(8000)]$ units are in use, and so on. How many units will be in use after n years?

In Exercises 41–44, determine the convergence or divergence of the p-series.

41. $\sum_{n=1}^{\infty} \frac{1}{n^4}$

42. $\sum_{n=1}^{\infty} 2n^{-2/3}$

43. $\sum_{n=1}^{\infty} \frac{1}{n\sqrt[4]{n}}$

44. $\sum_{n=1}^{\infty} \frac{1}{n^e}$

In Exercises 45–48, approximate the sum of the given convergent series using the indicated number of terms. Include an estimate of the maximum error for your approximation.

45. $\sum_{n=1}^{\infty} \frac{1}{n^6}$, four terms

46. $\sum_{n=1}^{\infty} \frac{1}{n^3}$, six terms

47. $\sum_{n=1}^{\infty} \frac{1}{n^{5/4}}$, six terms

48. $\sum_{n=1}^{\infty} \frac{1}{n^{12}}$, four terms

In Exercises 49–54, use the Ratio Test to determine the convergence or divergence of the given series.

49. $\sum_{n=1}^{\infty} \frac{n4^n}{n!}$

50. $\sum_{n=0}^{\infty} \frac{n!}{4^n}$

51. $\sum_{n=1}^{\infty} \frac{(-1)^n 3^n}{n}$

52. $\sum_{n=1}^{\infty} \frac{2^n}{n}$

53. $\sum_{n=1}^{\infty} \frac{n2^n}{n!}$

54. $\sum_{n=0}^{\infty} \frac{2n}{1-4^n}$

In Exercises 55–58, find the radius of convergence of the power series.

55. $\sum_{n=0}^{\infty} \frac{(-1)^n (x-2)^n}{(n+1)^2}$

56. $\sum_{n=0}^{\infty} (2x)^n$

57. $\sum_{n=0}^{\infty} n!(x-3)^n$

58. $\sum_{n=0}^{\infty} \frac{(x-2)^n}{2^n}$

In Exercises 59–62, apply Taylor's Theorem to find the power series for $f(x)$ centered at c.

59. $f(x) = e^{-0.5x}$, $c = 0$

60. $f(x) = \frac{1}{\sqrt{x}}$, $c = 1$

61. $f(x) = \frac{1}{x}$, $c = -1$

62. $f(x) = \sqrt[4]{1+x}$, $c = 0$

In Exercises 63–66, use the basic list of power series for elementary functions in Section S.4 to find the series representation of $f(x)$. Assume the series is centered at 0.

63. $f(x) = \ln(x+2)$

64. $f(x) = e^{2x+1}$

65. $f(x) = (1+x^2)^2$

66. $f(x) = \frac{1}{x^3+1}$

In Exercises 67–70, use a sixth-degree Taylor polynomial to approximate the function in the given interval.

67. $f(x) = \frac{1}{(x+3)^2}$, $[-1, 1]$ **68.** $f(x) = e^{x+1}$, $[-2, 2]$

69. $f(x) = \ln(x+2)$, $[0, 2]$ **70.** $f(x) = \sqrt{x+2}$, $[-1, 1]$

In Exercises 71–74, use a sixth-degree Taylor polynomial centered at c for the function f to obtain the desired approximation.

71. $f(x) = e^{x^2}$, $c = 1$, approximate $f(1.25)$

72. $f(x) = \frac{1}{\sqrt{x}}$, $c = 1$, approximate $f(1.15)$

73. $f(x) = \ln(1+x)$, $c = 1$, approximate $f(1.5)$

74. $f(x) = e^{x-1}$, $c = 0$, approximate $f(1.75)$

In Exercises 75 and 76, determine the maximum error guaranteed by Taylor's Remainder Theorem when the given 5th-degree polynomial is used to approximate f in the indicated interval.

75. $f(x) = \dfrac{2}{x}$, $\left[1, \dfrac{3}{2}\right]$,

$P_5(x) = 2[1 - (x - 1) + (x - 1)^2 - (x - 1)^3$

$\qquad\qquad + (x - 1)^4 - (x - 1)^5]$

76. $f(x) = e^{-2x}$, $[0, 1]$,

$P_5(x) = 1 - 2x + \dfrac{(2x)^2}{2!} - \dfrac{(2x)^3}{3!} + \dfrac{(2x)^4}{4!} - \dfrac{(2x)^5}{5!}$

In Exercises 77–80, use a sixth-degree Taylor polynomial centered at 0 to approximate the definite integral.

77. $\displaystyle\int_0^{0.3} \sqrt{1 + x^3}\, dx$ **78.** $\displaystyle\int_0^{0.5} e^{-x^2}\, dx$

79. $\displaystyle\int_0^{.75} \ln(x^2 + 1)\, dx$ **80.** $\displaystyle\int_0^{0.5} \sqrt{1 + x}\, dx$

Production In Exercises 81 and 82, let n be a random variable representing the number of units produced per hour from one of three machines. Find the expected value of the random variable n, and determine the expected production costs if each unit costs $23.00 to make.

81. $P(n) = \left(\dfrac{1}{3}\right)^{n+1}$ **82.** $P(n) = \dfrac{1}{2}\left(\dfrac{1}{3}\right)^{n+1}$

 In Exercises 83–86, use Newton's Method to approximate to three decimal places the zero(s) of the given function.

83. $f(x) = 2x^3 + 3x - 1$ **84.** $f(x) = x^3 + 2x + 1$

85. $f(x) = \ln 3x + x$ **86.** $f(x) = e^x - 3$

In Exercises 87–90, apply Newton's Method to approximate to three decimal places the x-value of the point of intersection of the graphs of the given equations.

87. $f(x) = x^5$, $g(x) = x + 3$

88. $f(x) = 2 - x$, $g(x) = x^5 + 2$

89. $f(x) = x^3$, $g(x) = e^{-x}$

90. $f(x) = 2x^2$, $g(x) = 5e^{-x}$

$$\int \cos x \, dx = \sin x + C$$

Trigonometric Functions

Trigonometric functions have a dual history. The oldest use of trigonometric functions involves "solving" a right triangle. This type of use is common in navigation and engineering.

A more recent use of trigonometric functions takes advantage of their periodic nature to model quantities that have repetitive patterns, such as seasons of the year and blood pressure. With this second use, the six trigonometric functions are viewed as functions of a real variable. As such, the trigonometric functions have graphs, derivatives, integrals, and infinite series.

Today, the use of mathematical functions to model real-life phenomena is common in economics, science, and engineering. For instance, the Hispanic American David Cardús (1922–) is a renowned biomathematician who uses mathematics to model biological phenomena.

$$\frac{d}{dx}[\sin x] = \cos x$$

Cardús

Angles and Degree Measure

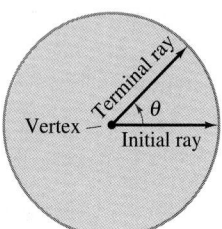

FIGURE T.1 Standard Position of an Angle

As shown in Figure T.1, an **angle** has three parts: an **initial ray, a terminal ray,** and a **vertex.** An angle is in **standard position** if its initial ray coincides with the positive x-axis and its vertex is at the origin.

Figure T.2 shows the degree measures of several common angles. Note that θ (the lowercase Greek letter theta) is used to represent an angle and its measure. Angles whose measures are between $0°$ and $90°$ are **acute,** and angles whose measures are between $90°$ and $180°$ are **obtuse.** An angle whose measure is $90°$ is a **right** angle and an angle whose measure is $180°$ is a **straight** angle.

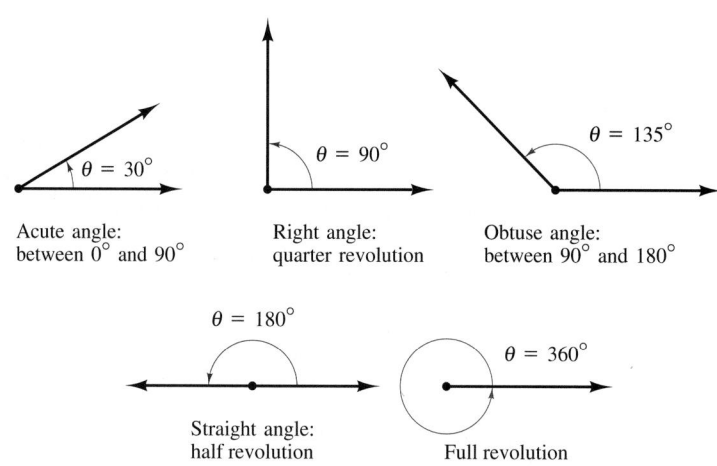

FIGURE T.2

Positive angles are measured *counterclockwise* beginning with the initial ray. Negative angles are measured *clockwise.* For instance, Figure T.3 shows an angle whose measure is $-45°$.

Merely knowing where an angle's initial and terminal rays are located does not allow you to assign a measure to the angle. To measure an angle, you must know how the terminal ray was revolved. For example, Figure T.3 shows that the angle measuring $-45°$ has the same terminal ray as the angle measuring $315°$. Such angles are called **coterminal.**

FIGURE T.3 Coterminal Angles

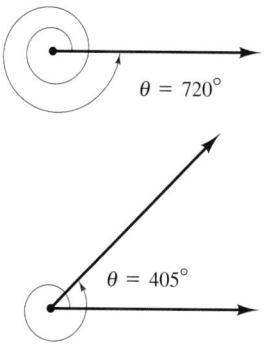

FIGURE T.4

Although it may seem strange to consider angle measures that are larger than 360°, such angles have very useful applications in trigonometry. An angle that is larger than 360° is one whose terminal ray has revolved more than one full revolution counterclockwise. Figure T.4 shows two angles measuring more than 360°. In a similar way, you can generate an angle whose measure is less than −360° by revolving a terminal ray more than one full revolution clockwise.

EXAMPLE 1 *Finding Coterminal Angles*

For each angle, find a coterminal angle θ such that $0° \leq \theta < 360°$.

a. 450°   **b.** 750°   **c.** −160°   **d.** −390°

Solution

a. To find an angle coterminal to 450°, subtract 360°, as shown in Figure T.5(a).

$$\theta = 450° - 360° = 90°$$

b. To find an angle that is coterminal to 750°, subtract 2(360°), as shown in Figure T.5(b).

$$\theta = 750° - 2(360°) = 750° - 720° = 30°$$

c. To find an angle coterminal to −160°, add 360°, as shown in Figure T.5(c).

$$\theta = -160° + 360° = 200°$$

d. To find an angle that is coterminal to −390°, add 2(360°), as shown in Figure T.5(d).

$$\theta = -390° + 2(360°) = -390° + 720° = 330°$$

FIGURE T.5

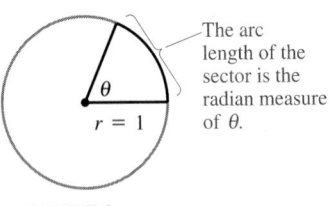

The arc length of the sector is the radian measure of θ.

FIGURE T.6

Radian Measure

A second way to measure angles is in terms of radians. To assign a radian measure to an angle θ, consider θ to be the central angle of a circular sector of radius 1, as shown in Figure T.6. The radian measure of θ is then defined to be the length of the arc of the sector. Recall that the circumference of a circle is given by

$$\text{Circumference} = (2\pi)(\text{radius}).$$

Thus, the circumference of a circle of radius 1 is simply 2π, and you can conclude that the radian measure of an angle measuring $360°$ is 2π. In other words,

$$360° = 2\pi \text{ radians} \quad \text{or} \quad 180° = \pi \text{ radians}.$$

Figure T.7 gives the radian measures of several common angles.

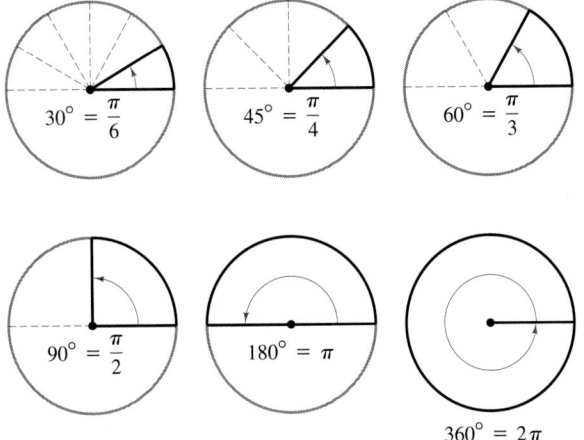

FIGURE T.7 Radian Measure for Several Common Angles

It is important for you to be able to convert back and forth between the degree and radian measures of an angle. You should remember the conversions for the common angles shown in Figure T.7. For other conversions, you can use the following conversion rule.

Angle Measure Conversion Rule

The degree measure and radian measure of an angle are related by the equation

$$180° = \pi \text{ radians}.$$

Section 1 ■ Radian Measure of Angles **T-5**

Discovery

Most calculators and graphing utilities have both degree and radian modes. Learn how to use your calculator to convert from degrees to radians, and vice versa.

For example, on the *TI-81*, you can verify Example 2 as follows. Set the calculator to radian mode and enter 135. From the MATH menu, select the degree symbol (item 6), and press ENTER. The radian measure 2.35619449 will be displayed. (*Note:* $3\pi/4 = 2.35619449$)

EXAMPLE 2 *Converting from Degrees to Radians*

Convert each degree measure to radian measure.

a. $135°$ **b.** $40°$ **c.** $540°$ **d.** $-270°$

Solution

To convert from degree measure to radian measure, multiply the degree measure by $(\pi \text{ radians})/180°$.

a. $135° = (135 \text{ degrees}) \left(\dfrac{\pi \text{ radians}}{180 \text{ degrees}} \right) = \dfrac{3\pi}{4} \text{ radians}$

b. $40° = (40 \text{ degrees}) \left(\dfrac{\pi \text{ radians}}{180 \text{ degrees}} \right) = \dfrac{2\pi}{9} \text{ radians}$

c. $540° = (540 \text{ degrees}) \left(\dfrac{\pi \text{ radians}}{180 \text{ degrees}} \right) = 3\pi \text{ radians}$

d. $-270° = (-270 \text{ degrees}) \left(\dfrac{\pi \text{ radians}}{180 \text{ degrees}} \right) = -\dfrac{3\pi}{2} \text{ radians}$

Although it is common to list radian measure in multiples of π, this is not necessary. For instance, if the degree measure of an angle is $79.3°$, the radian measure is

$$79.3° = (79.3 \text{ degrees}) \left(\dfrac{\pi \text{ radians}}{180 \text{ degrees}} \right) \approx 1.384 \text{ radians}.$$

EXAMPLE 3 *Converting from Radians to Degrees*

Convert each radian measure to degree measure.

a. $-\dfrac{\pi}{2}$ **b.** $\dfrac{7\pi}{4}$ **c.** $\dfrac{11\pi}{6}$ **d.** $\dfrac{9\pi}{2}$

Solution

To convert from radian measure to degree measure, multiply the radian measure by $180°/(\pi \text{ radians})$.

a. $-\dfrac{\pi}{2} \text{ radians} = \left(-\dfrac{\pi}{2} \text{ radians} \right) \left(\dfrac{180 \text{ degrees}}{\pi \text{ radians}} \right) = -90°$

b. $\dfrac{7\pi}{4} \text{ radians} = \left(\dfrac{7\pi}{4} \text{ radians} \right) \left(\dfrac{180 \text{ degrees}}{\pi \text{ radians}} \right) = 315°$

c. $\dfrac{11\pi}{6} \text{ radians} = \left(\dfrac{11\pi}{6} \text{ radians} \right) \left(\dfrac{180 \text{ degrees}}{\pi \text{ radians}} \right) = 330°$

d. $\dfrac{9\pi}{2} \text{ radians} = \left(\dfrac{9\pi}{2} \text{ radians} \right) \left(\dfrac{180 \text{ degrees}}{\pi \text{ radians}} \right) = 810°$

Triangles

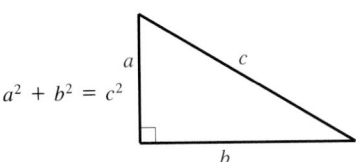

$$a^2 + b^2 = c^2$$

FIGURE T.8

A Summary of Rules About Triangles

1. The sum of the angles of a triangle is $180°$.
2. The sum of the two acute angles of a right triangle is $90°$.
3. **Pythagorean Theorem** The sum of the squares of the legs of a right triangle is equal to the square of the hypotenuse, as shown in Figure T.8.
4. **Similar Triangles** If two triangles are similar (have the same angle measures), then the ratios of the corresponding sides are equal, as shown in Figure T.9.
5. The area of a triangle is equal to one-half the base times the height. That is, $A = \frac{1}{2}bh$.
6. Each angle of an equilateral triangle measures $60°$.
7. Each acute angle of an isosceles right triangle measures $45°$.

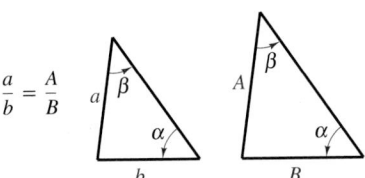

$$\frac{a}{b} = \frac{A}{B}$$

FIGURE T.9

EXAMPLE 4 *Finding the Area of a Triangle*

Find the area of an equilateral triangle with 1-foot sides.

Solution
To use the formula $A = \frac{1}{2}bh$, you must first find the height of the triangle, as shown in Figure T.10. To do this, apply the Pythagorean Theorem to the shaded portion of the triangle.

$$h^2 + \left(\frac{1}{2}\right)^2 = 1^2 \qquad \textit{Pythagorean Theorem}$$

$$h^2 = \frac{3}{4} \qquad \textit{Simplify.}$$

$$h = \frac{\sqrt{3}}{2} \qquad \textit{Solve for } h.$$

Thus, the area of the triangle is

$$A = \frac{1}{2}bh = \frac{1}{2}(1)\left(\frac{\sqrt{3}}{2}\right) = \frac{\sqrt{3}}{4} \text{ square feet.}$$

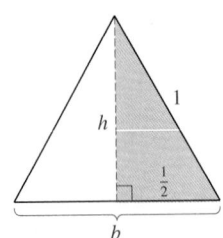

FIGURE T.10

Discussion Problem Developing a Formula

Develop a formula for the area of an equilateral triangle whose sides each have a length of s.

Warm Up

The following warm-up exercises involve skills that were covered in earlier sections. You will use these skills in the exercise set for this section.

In Exercises 1 and 2, find the area of the triangle.

1. Base: 10 cm; height: 7 cm   **2.** Base: 4 in.; height: 6 in.

In Exercises 3–6, let a, b, and c represent the lengths of the legs and hypotenuse, respectively, of a right triangle. Solve for the missing side length.

3. $a = 5, b = 12$ **4.** $a = 3, c = 5$

5. $a = 8, c = 17$ **6.** $b = 8, c = 10$

In Exercises 7–10, use the given information to determine whether the figure is a right triangle, an isosceles triangle, or an equilateral triangle. (a, b, and c represent the side lengths.)

7. $a = 4, b = 4, c = 4$ **8.** $a = 1, b = 1, c = 2$

9. $a = 12, b = 16, c = 20$ **10.** $a = 1, b = 1, c = \sqrt{2}$

E X E R C I S E S   T.1   means that technology can help you solve or check the exercise(s).

In Exercises 1–4, determine two coterminal angles (one positive and one negative) for the given angle. Give the answers in degrees.

1. (a)

(b) $\theta = -41°$

2. (a)

$\theta = 45°$

$\theta = -120°$

(b)

$\theta = 390°$

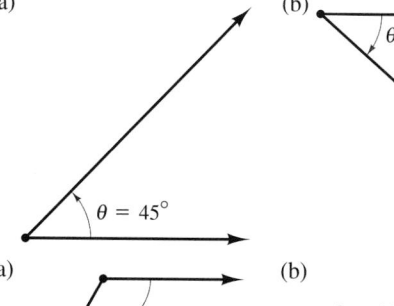

3. (a)

$\theta = 300°$

(b) $\theta = 740°$

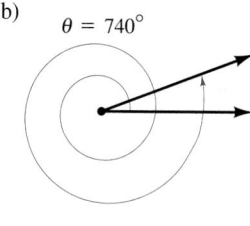

4. (a) $\theta = -420°$

(b) $\theta = 230°$

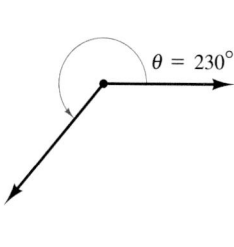

In Exercises 5–8, determine two coterminal angles (one positive and one negative) for the given angle. Give the answers in radians.

5. (a) (b)

6. (a) (b)

7. (a) (b)

8. (a) (b)

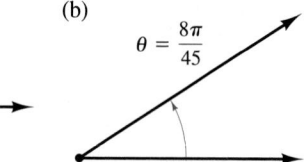

In Exercises 9–16, express the angle in radian measure as a multiple of π.

9. $30°$

10. $150°$

11. $315°$

12. $120°$

13. $-30°$

14. $-240°$

15. $-270°$

16. $144°$

In Exercises 17–24, express the angle in degree measure.

17. $\dfrac{3\pi}{2}$

18. $\dfrac{7\pi}{6}$

19. $-\dfrac{7\pi}{12}$

20. $\dfrac{\pi}{9}$

21. $\dfrac{11\pi}{2}$

22. $-\dfrac{7\pi}{4}$

23. $-\dfrac{11\pi}{30}$

24. $\dfrac{43\pi}{60}$

In Exercises 25–32, solve the triangle for the indicated side and/or angle.

25.

26.

27.

28.

29.

30.

31.

32.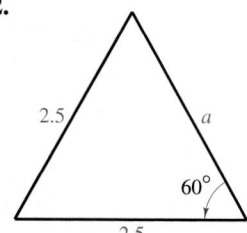

In Exercises 33–36, find the area of the equilateral triangle with sides of length *s*.

33. $s = 6$ in.

34. $s = 8$ m

35. $s = 5$ ft

36. $s = 12$ cm

True or False In Exercises 37–40, determine whether the statement is true or false. Explain your reasoning.

37. An angle whose measure is $75°$ is obtuse.

38. $\theta = -35°$ is coterminal to $325°$.

39. A right triangle can have one angle whose measure is $89°$.

40. An angle whose measure is π radians is a straight angle.

41. *Height* A person 6 feet tall standing 16 feet from a streetlight casts a shadow 8 feet long (see figure). What is the height of the streetlight?

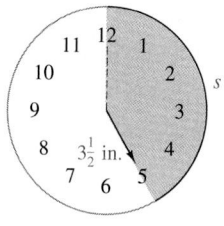

FIGURE FOR 43   FIGURE FOR 44

45. *Distance* A man bends his elbow through $75°$. The distance from his elbow to the tip of his index finger is $18\frac{3}{4}$ inches (see figure).

(a) Find the radian measure of this angle.

(b) Find the distance the tip of the index finger moves.

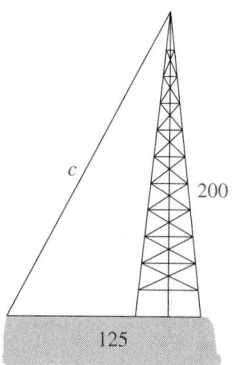

FIGURE FOR 41   FIGURE FOR 42

42. *Length* A guy wire is stretched from a broadcasting tower at a point 200 feet above the ground to an anchor 125 feet from the base (see figure). How long is the wire?

43. Let *r* represent the radius of a circle, θ the central angle (measured in radians), and *s* the length of the arc subtended by the angle (see figure). Use the relationship $\theta = s/r$ to complete the table.

r	8 ft	15 in.	85 cm		
s	12 ft			96 in.	8642 mi
θ		1.6	$\dfrac{3\pi}{4}$	4	$\dfrac{2\pi}{3}$

44. *Arc Length* The minute hand on a clock is $3\frac{1}{2}$ inches long (see figure). Through what distance does the tip of the minute hand move in 25 minutes?

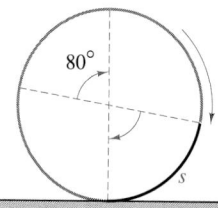

FIGURE FOR 45   FIGURE FOR 46

46. *Distance* A tractor tire that is 5 feet in diameter (*d*) is partially filled with a liquid ballast for additional traction. To check the air pressure, the tractor operator rotates the tire until the valve stem is at the top so that the liquid will not enter the gauge. On a given occasion, the operator notes that the tire must be rotated $80°$ to have the stem in the proper position (see figure).

(a) Find the radian measure of this rotation.

(b) How far must the tractor be moved to get the valve stem in the proper position?

47. *Latitude* Assuming that the earth is a sphere of radius 4000 miles, what is the difference in latitude of two cities, one of which is 325 miles due north of the other? (Latitude lines on the earth run parallel to the equator and measure the angles from the equator to points north or south of the equator.)

48. *Wheel Revolutions* A car is moving at the rate of 45 mi/hr (66 ft/sec), and the diameter of each wheel is 2 feet. Find the number of revolutions per minute that the wheels make and the number of radians per second generated by a line segment from the center to the circumference of each wheel.

The Trigonometric Functions

The Trigonometric Functions ■ *Trigonometric Identities* ■
Evaluating Trigonometric Functions ■ *Solving Trigonometric Equations*

The Trigonometric Functions

There are two common approaches to the study of trigonometry. In one case the trigonometric functions are defined as ratios of two sides of a right triangle. In the other case these functions are defined in terms of a point on the terminal side of an arbitrary angle. The first approach is the one generally used in surveying, navigation, and astronomy, where a typical problem involves a triangle, three of whose six parts (sides and angles) are known and three of which are to be determined. The second approach is the one normally used in science, economics, and biology, where the periodic nature of the trigonometric functions is emphasized. In the following definition, the six trigonometric functions are defined from both viewpoints.

FIGURE T.11

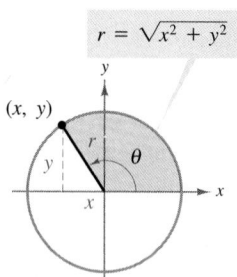

FIGURE T.12

Definition of the Trigonometric Functions

Right Triangle Definition: $0 < \theta < \dfrac{\pi}{2}$. (See Figure T.11.)

$$\sin\theta = \frac{\text{opp.}}{\text{hyp.}} \qquad \csc\theta = \frac{\text{hyp.}}{\text{opp.}}$$

$$\cos\theta = \frac{\text{adj.}}{\text{hyp.}} \qquad \sec\theta = \frac{\text{hyp.}}{\text{adj.}}$$

$$\tan\theta = \frac{\text{opp.}}{\text{adj.}} \qquad \cot\theta = \frac{\text{adj.}}{\text{opp.}}$$

Circular Function Definition: θ is any angle in standard position and (x, y) is a point on the terminal ray of the angle. (See Figure T.12.)

$$\sin\theta = \frac{y}{r} \qquad \csc\theta = \frac{r}{y}$$

$$\cos\theta = \frac{x}{r} \qquad \sec\theta = \frac{r}{x}$$

$$\tan\theta = \frac{y}{x} \qquad \cot\theta = \frac{x}{y}$$

The full names of the trigonometric functions are **sine, cosecant, cosine, secant, tangent,** and **cotangent.**

Trigonometric Identities

In the second definition of the six trigonometric functions, the value of r is always positive. From this, it follows that the signs of the trigonometric functions are determined from the signs of x and y, as shown in Figure T.13.

The following trigonometric identities are also direct consequences of the definitions.

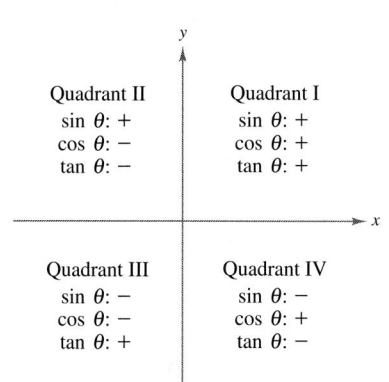

Quadrant II
$\sin\theta$: +
$\cos\theta$: −
$\tan\theta$: −

Quadrant I
$\sin\theta$: +
$\cos\theta$: +
$\tan\theta$: +

Quadrant III
$\sin\theta$: −
$\cos\theta$: −
$\tan\theta$: +

Quadrant IV
$\sin\theta$: −
$\cos\theta$: +
$\tan\theta$: −

FIGURE T.13

$$\csc\theta = \frac{1}{\sin\theta} \qquad \sec\theta = \frac{1}{\cos\theta} \qquad \cot\theta = \frac{1}{\tan\theta}$$

$$\tan\theta = \frac{\sin\theta}{\cos\theta} \qquad \cot\theta = \frac{\cos\theta}{\sin\theta}$$

Furthermore, because

$$\sin^2\theta + \cos^2\theta = \left(\frac{y}{r}\right)^2 + \left(\frac{x}{r}\right)^2 = \frac{x^2 + y^2}{r^2} = \frac{r^2}{r^2} = 1,$$

you can obtain the Pythagorean Identity $\sin^2\theta + \cos^2\theta = 1$. Other trigonometric identities are listed below. In the list, ϕ is the lowercase Greek letter phi.

Note The symbol $\sin^2\theta$ is used to represent $(\sin\theta)^2$.

Trigonometric Identities

Pythagorean Identities

$\sin^2\theta + \cos^2\theta = 1$

$\tan^2\theta + 1 = \sec^2\theta$

$\cot^2\theta + 1 = \csc^2\theta$

Sum or Difference of Two Angles

$\sin(\theta \pm \phi) = \sin\theta\cos\phi \pm \cos\theta\sin\phi$

$\cos(\theta \pm \phi) = \cos\theta\cos\phi \mp \sin\theta\sin\phi$

$\tan(\theta \pm \phi) = \dfrac{\tan\theta \pm \tan\phi}{1 \mp \tan\theta\tan\phi}$

Double Angle

$\sin 2\theta = 2\sin\theta\cos\theta$

$\cos 2\theta = 2\cos^2\theta - 1 = 1 - 2\sin^2\theta$

Reduction Formulas

$\sin(-\theta) = -\sin\theta$

$\cos(-\theta) = \cos\theta$

$\tan(-\theta) = -\tan\theta$

$\sin\theta = -\sin(\theta - \pi)$

$\cos\theta = -\cos(\theta - \pi)$

$\tan\theta = \tan(\theta - \pi)$

Half Angle

$\sin^2\theta = \frac{1}{2}(1 - \cos 2\theta)$

$\cos^2\theta = \frac{1}{2}(1 + \cos 2\theta)$

Although an angle can be measured in either degrees or radians, in calculus radian measure is preferred. Thus, all angles in the remainder of this chapter are assumed to be measured in radians unless marked otherwise. In other words, when we write sin 3, we mean the sine of 3 radians, and when we write sin 3°, we mean the sine of 3 degrees.

Evaluating Trigonometric Functions

There are two common methods of evaluating trigonometric functions: decimal approximations using a calculator and exact evaluations using trigonometric identities and formulas from geometry. The next three examples illustrate the second method.

EXAMPLE 1 *Evaluating Trigonometric Functions*

Evaluate the sine, cosine, and tangent of $\pi/3$.

Solution

Begin by drawing the angle $\theta = \pi/3$ in standard position, as shown in Figure T.14. Because $\pi/3$ radians is $60°$, you can imagine an equilateral triangle with sides of length 1 and θ as one of its angles. Because the altitude of the triangle bisects its base, you know that $x = \frac{1}{2}$. Thus, using the Pythagorean Theorem, you have

$$ y = \sqrt{r^2 - x^2} = \sqrt{1 - \left(\tfrac{1}{2}\right)^2} = \sqrt{\tfrac{3}{4}} = \frac{\sqrt{3}}{2}. $$

Now, using $x = \frac{1}{2}$, $y = \frac{1}{2}\sqrt{3}$, and $r = 1$, you can find the values of the sine, cosine, and tangent as follows.

$$ \sin \frac{\pi}{3} = \frac{y}{r} = \frac{\frac{1}{2}\sqrt{3}}{1} = \frac{\sqrt{3}}{2} $$

$$ \cos \frac{\pi}{3} = \frac{x}{r} = \frac{\frac{1}{2}}{1} = \frac{1}{2} $$

$$ \tan \frac{\pi}{3} = \frac{y}{x} = \frac{\frac{1}{2}\sqrt{3}}{\cdot\frac{1}{2}} = \sqrt{3} $$

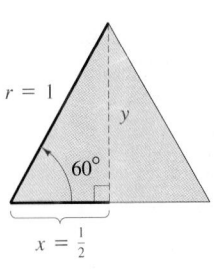

FIGURE T.14

The sines, cosines, and tangents of several common angles are listed in Table T.1. You should remember, or be able to derive, these values.

TABLE T.1

Degree measure of θ	0	30°	45°	60°	90°
Radian measure of θ	0	$\dfrac{\pi}{6}$	$\dfrac{\pi}{4}$	$\dfrac{\pi}{3}$	$\dfrac{\pi}{2}$
$\sin \theta$	0	$\dfrac{1}{2}$	$\dfrac{\sqrt{2}}{2}$	$\dfrac{\sqrt{3}}{2}$	1
$\cos \theta$	1	$\dfrac{\sqrt{3}}{2}$	$\dfrac{\sqrt{2}}{2}$	$\dfrac{1}{2}$	0
$\tan \theta$	0	$\dfrac{1}{\sqrt{3}}$	1	$\sqrt{3}$	undefined

To extend the use of the values in Table T.1 to angles in quadrants other than the first quadrant, you can use the concept of a reference angle, as shown in Figure T.15, together with the appropriate quadrant sign. The **reference angle** for an angle θ is the smallest positive angle between the terminal side of θ and the x-axis. For instance, the reference angle for $135°$ is $45°$ and the reference angle for $210°$ is $30°$.

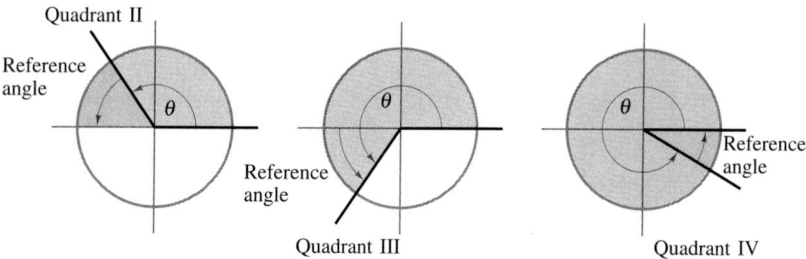

Reference angle: $\pi - \theta$ Reference angle: $\theta - \pi$ Reference angle: $2\pi - \theta$

FIGURE T.15

EXAMPLE 2 *Evaluating Trigonometric Functions*

Evaluate the following.

a. $\sin \dfrac{3\pi}{4}$ **b.** $\tan 330°$ **c.** $\cos \dfrac{7\pi}{6}$

Solution

a. Because the reference angle for $3\pi/4$ is $\pi/4$ and the sine is positive in the second quadrant, you can write

$$\sin \frac{3\pi}{4} = \sin \frac{\pi}{4} \qquad \text{\textit{Reference angle}}$$

$$= \frac{\sqrt{2}}{2}. \qquad \text{\textit{See Figure T.16(a).}}$$

b. Because the reference angle for $330°$ is $30°$ and the tangent is negative in the fourth quadrant, you can write

$$\tan 330° = - \tan 30° \qquad \text{\textit{Reference angle}}$$

$$= -\frac{1}{\sqrt{3}}. \qquad \text{\textit{See Figure T.16(b).}}$$

c. Because the reference angle for $7\pi/6$ is $\pi/6$ and the cosine is negative in the third quadrant, you can write

$$\cos \frac{7\pi}{6} = - \cos \frac{\pi}{6} \qquad \text{\textit{Reference angle}}$$

$$= -\frac{\sqrt{3}}{2}. \qquad \text{\textit{See Figure T.16(c).}}$$

(a)

(b)

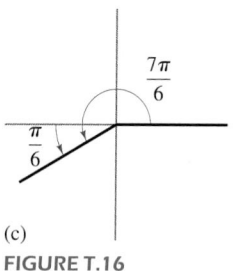

(c)

FIGURE T.16

EXAMPLE 3 *Evaluating Trigonometric Functions*

Evaluate the following.

a. $\sin\left(-\dfrac{\pi}{3}\right)$ **b.** $\sec 60°$ **c.** $\cos 15°$

d. $\sin 2\pi$ **e.** $\cot 0°$ **f.** $\tan\dfrac{9\pi}{4}$

Solution

a. By the reduction formula, $\sin(-\theta) = -\sin\theta$,

$$\sin\left(-\frac{\pi}{3}\right) = -\sin\frac{\pi}{3} = -\frac{\sqrt{3}}{2}.$$

b. By the reciprocal formula, $\sec\theta = 1/\cos\theta$,

$$\sec 60° = \frac{1}{\cos 60°} = \frac{1}{1/2} = 2.$$

c. By the difference formula, $\cos(\theta - \phi) = \cos\theta\cos\phi + \sin\theta\sin\phi$,

$$
\begin{aligned}
\cos 15° &= \cos(45° - 30°)\\
&= (\cos 45°)(\cos 30°) + (\sin 45°)(\sin 30°)\\
&= \left(\frac{\sqrt{2}}{2}\right)\left(\frac{\sqrt{3}}{2}\right) + \left(\frac{\sqrt{2}}{2}\right)\left(\frac{1}{2}\right)\\
&= \frac{\sqrt{6}+\sqrt{2}}{4}.
\end{aligned}
$$

d. Because the reference angle for 2π is 0,

$$\sin 2\pi = \sin 0 = 0.$$

e. Using the reciprocal formula, $\cot\theta = 1/\tan\theta$, and the fact that $\tan 0 = 0$, you can conclude that $\cot 0°$ is undefined.

f. Because the reference angle for $9\pi/4$ is $\pi/4$ and the tangent is positive in the first quadrant,

$$\tan\frac{9\pi}{4} = \tan\frac{\pi}{4} = 1.$$

                                                                       ■

Examples 1, 2, and 3 all involve standard angles such as $\pi/6$. To evaluate trigonometric functions involving nonstandard angles, you should use a calculator. When doing this, remember to set the calculator to the proper mode—either degree mode or radian mode. Furthermore, most calculators have only three trigonometric functions: sine, cosine, and tangent. To evaluate the other three functions, you should combine these keys with the reciprocal key. For instance, you can evaluate the secant of $\pi/7$ as follows.

Function	Calculator Steps	Display
$\dfrac{\pi}{7}$		1.109916264

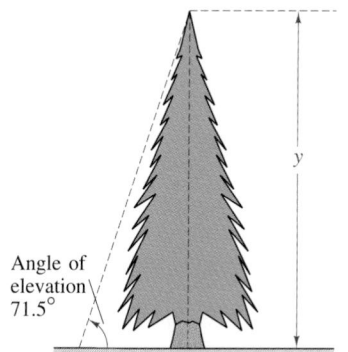

Angle of
elevation
71.5°

y

$x = 50$

FIGURE T.17

Real
Life

EXAMPLE 4 *Solving a Right Triangle*

A surveyor is standing 50 feet from the base of a large tree. The surveyor measures the angle of elevation to the top of the tree as 71.5°. How tall is the tree?

Solution

Referring to Figure T.17, you can see that

$$\tan 71.5° = \frac{y}{x},$$

where $x = 50$ and y is the height of the tree. Thus, you can determine the height of the tree to be

$$y = (x)(\tan 71.5°) \approx (50)(2.98868) \approx 149.4 \text{ feet.}$$ ■

Real
Life

EXAMPLE 5 *Calculating Peripheral Vision*

To measure the extent of your peripheral vision, stand 1 foot from the corner of a room, facing the corner. Have a friend move an object along the wall until you can just barely see it. If the object is 2 feet from the corner, as shown in Figure T.18, what is the total angle of your peripheral vision?

Solution

Let α represent the total angle of your peripheral vision. As shown in Figure T.19, you can model the physical situation with an isosceles right triangle whose legs are $\sqrt{2}$ feet and whose hypotenuse is 2 feet. In the triangle, the angle θ is given by

$$\tan \theta = \frac{y}{x} = \frac{\sqrt{2}}{\sqrt{2} - 1} \approx 3.414.$$

Using the inverse tangent function of a calculator, you can determine that $\theta \approx 73.7°$. Thus, $\alpha/2 \approx 180° - 73.7° = 106.3°$, which implies that $\alpha \approx 212.6°$. In other words, the total angle of your peripheral vision is about 212.6°.

Some occupations, such as that of a commercial pilot, require excellent vision, including good depth perception and good peripheral vision.

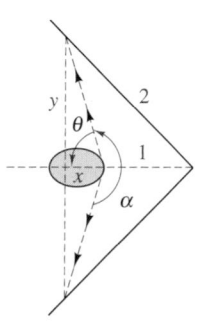

y 2

θ

1

x

α

FIGURE T.18

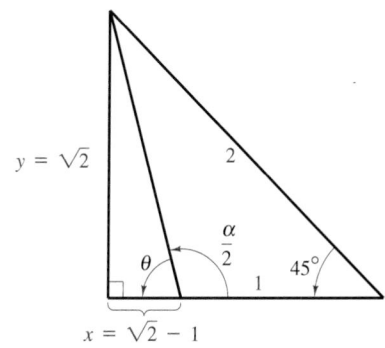

$y = \sqrt{2}$

2

θ $\dfrac{\alpha}{2}$

1   45°

$x = \sqrt{2} - 1$

FIGURE T.19   ▬

Solving Trigonometric Equations

An important part of the study of trigonometry is learning how to solve trigonometric equations. For example, consider the equation

$$\sin\theta = 0.$$

You know $\theta = 0$ is one solution. Also, in Example 3d, you saw that $\theta = 2\pi$ is another solution. But these are not the only solutions. In fact, this equation has infinitely many solutions! Any one of the following values of θ will work.

$$\ldots, -3\pi, -2\pi, -\pi, 0, \pi, 2\pi, 3\pi, \ldots$$

To simplify the situation, we usually restrict the search for solutions to the interval $0 \le \theta \le 2\pi$, as indicated in Example 6.

EXAMPLE 6 *Solving Trigonometric Equations*

Solve for θ in each equation. Assume $0 \le \theta \le 2\pi$.

a. $\sin\theta = -\dfrac{\sqrt{3}}{2}$ **b.** $\cos\theta = 1$ **c.** $\tan\theta = 1$

Solution

a. To solve the equation $\sin\theta = -\sqrt{3}/2$, first note that

$$\sin\frac{\pi}{3} = \frac{\sqrt{3}}{2}.$$

Because the sine is negative in the third and fourth quadrants, it follows that you are seeking values of θ in these quadrants that have a reference angle of $\pi/3$. The two angles fitting these criteria are

$$\theta = \pi + \frac{\pi}{3} = \frac{4\pi}{3} \quad \text{and} \quad \theta = 2\pi - \frac{\pi}{3} = \frac{5\pi}{3},$$

as indicated in Figure T.20.

b. To solve $\cos\theta = 1$, observe that $\cos 0 = 1$ and note that in the interval $[0, 2\pi]$, the only angles whose reference angles are 0 are 0, π, and 2π. Of these, 0 and 2π have cosines of 1. (The cosine of π is -1.) Thus, the equation has two solutions:

$$\theta = 0 \quad \text{and} \quad \theta = 2\pi.$$

c. Because $\tan\pi/4 = 1$ and the tangent is positive in the first and third quadrants, it follows that the two solutions are

$$\theta = \frac{\pi}{4} \quad \text{and} \quad \theta = \pi + \frac{\pi}{4} = \frac{5\pi}{4}.$$

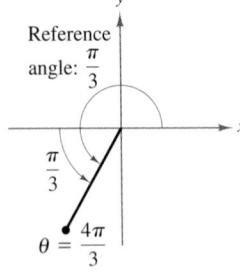

Reference angle: $\dfrac{\pi}{3}$

$\dfrac{\pi}{3}$

$\theta = \dfrac{4\pi}{3}$

Quadrant III

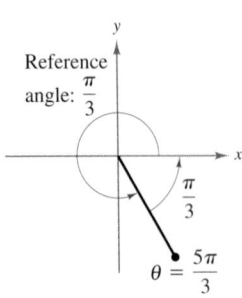

Reference angle: $\dfrac{\pi}{3}$

$\dfrac{\pi}{3}$

$\theta = \dfrac{5\pi}{3}$

Quadrant IV

FIGURE T.20

EXAMPLE 7 *Solving a Trigonometric Equation*

Solve the equation for θ.

$$\cos 2\theta = 2 - 3\sin\theta, \qquad 0 \le \theta \le 2\pi.$$

Solution

You can use the double angle identity

$$\cos 2\theta = 1 - 2\sin^2\theta$$

to rewrite the given equation, as follows.

$$\cos 2\theta = 2 - 3\sin\theta$$
$$1 - 2\sin^2\theta = 2 - 3\sin\theta$$
$$0 = 2\sin^2\theta - 3\sin\theta + 1$$
$$0 = (2\sin\theta - 1)(\sin\theta - 1)$$

For $2\sin\theta - 1 = 0$, you have $\sin\theta = \frac{1}{2}$, which has solutions of

$$\theta = \frac{\pi}{6} \quad \text{and} \quad \theta = \frac{5\pi}{6}.$$

For $\sin\theta - 1 = 0$, you have $\sin\theta = 1$, which has a solution of

$$\theta = \frac{\pi}{2}.$$

Thus, for $0 \le \theta \le 2\pi$, the three solutions are

$$\theta = \frac{\pi}{6}, \quad \frac{\pi}{2}, \quad \text{and} \quad \frac{5\pi}{6}.$$

Note In Example 7, note that the expression $2\sin^2\theta - 3\sin\theta + 1$ is a quadratic in $\sin\theta$, and as such can be factored. For instance, if you let $x = \sin\theta$, then the quadratic factors as

$$2x^2 - 3x + 1 = (2x - 1)(x - 1).$$

TECHNOLOGY

A calculator can be used to solve equations of the form

$\sin\theta = a, \quad -\frac{\pi}{2} \le \theta \le \frac{\pi}{2}$

$\cos\theta = a, \quad 0 \le \theta \le \pi$

$\tan\theta = a, \quad -\frac{\pi}{2} < \theta < \frac{\pi}{2}.$

For instance, on the *TI-81* or *TI-82*, you can solve the equation $\sin\theta = \frac{1}{2}$ by first setting the calculator to radian mode and then entering

| 2nd | SIN | .5 |

to obtain 0.5235987756 (which is a decimal approximation of $\pi/6$). Note, however, that the calculator displays only one solution—the solution that occurs in the interval $-\pi/2 \le \theta \le \pi/2$. To obtain the other solutions, you need to use your knowledge of trigonometry.

Discussion Problem Solving Trigonometric Equations

For each equation, find all solutions in the interval $0 \le \theta \le 2\pi$.

a. $\sin\theta = 1$ **b.** $\cos\theta = -\frac{1}{2}$

c. $\tan\theta = 0$ **d.** $\sec\theta = 2$

e. $\csc\theta = \dfrac{2}{\sqrt{3}}$ **f.** $\cot\theta = -1$

$\mathcal{Warm\ Up}$ The following warm-up exercises involve skills that were covered in earlier sections. You will use these skills in the exercise set for this section.

In Exercises 1–4, convert the angle to radian measure.

1. $135°$ **2.** $-210°$

3. $-100°$ **4.** $540°$

In Exercises 5–8, solve for *x*.

5. $x^2 - x = 0$ **6.** $2x^2 - x = 1$

7. $x^2 - 2x = -1$ **8.** $x^2 - 5x = -6$

In Exercises 9 and 10, solve for *t*.

9. $\dfrac{2\pi}{24}(t - 4) = \dfrac{\pi}{2}$ **10.** $\dfrac{2\pi}{365}(t - 10) = \dfrac{\pi}{4}$

E X E R C I S E S   T.2   means that technology can help you solve or check the exercise(s).

In Exercises 1–6, determine all six trigonometric functions for the angle θ.

1.

$(3, 4)$

2.

$(8, -15)$

3.

$(-12, -5)$

4.

$(1, -1)$

5.

$(-\sqrt{3}, 1)$

6.

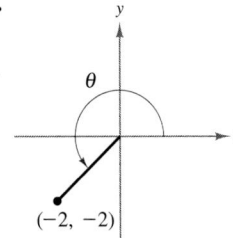

$(-2, -2)$

In Exercises 7–12, find the indicated trigonometric function from the given one.

7. Given $\sin\theta = \frac{1}{2}$, find $\csc\theta$.

8. Given $\sin\theta = \frac{1}{3}$, find $\tan\theta$.

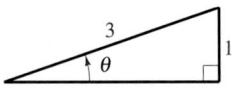

9. Given $\cos\theta = \frac{4}{5}$, find $\cot\theta$.

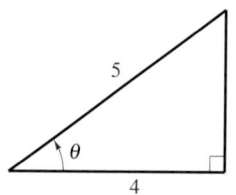

5

4

θ

10. Given $\sec\theta = \frac{13}{5}$, find $\cot\theta$.

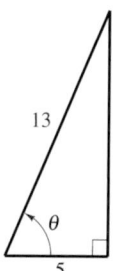

13

5

θ

11. Given $\cot\theta = \frac{15}{8}$, find $\sec\theta$.

8

15

θ

12. Given $\tan\theta = \frac{1}{2}$, find $\sin\theta$.

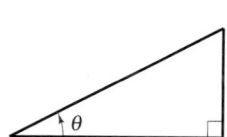

1

2

θ

In Exercises 13–18, sketch a right triangle corresponding to the trigonometric function of the angle θ and find the other five trigonometric functions of θ.

13. $\sin\theta = \frac{1}{3}$

14. $\cot\theta = 5$

15. $\sec\theta = 2$

16. $\cos\theta = \frac{5}{7}$

17. $\tan\theta = 3$

18. $\csc\theta = 4.25$

In Exercises 19–24, determine the quadrant in which θ lies.

19. $\sin\theta < 0$, $\cos\theta > 0$

20. $\sin\theta > 0$, $\cos\theta < 0$

21. $\sin\theta > 0$, $\sec\theta > 0$

22. $\cot\theta < 0$, $\cos\theta > 0$

23. $\csc\theta > 0$, $\tan\theta < 0$

24. $\cos\theta > 0$, $\tan\theta < 0$

In Exercises 25–32, evaluate the sines, cosines, and tangents of the angles *without* using a calculator.

25. (a) $60°$

(b) $-\dfrac{2\pi}{3}$

26. (a) $\dfrac{\pi}{4}$

(b) $\dfrac{5\pi}{4}$

27. (a) $-\dfrac{\pi}{6}$

(b) $150°$

28. (a) $-\dfrac{\pi}{2}$

(b) $\dfrac{\pi}{2}$

29. (a) $225°$

(b) $-225°$

30. (a) $300°$

(b) $330°$

31. (a) $750°$

(b) $510°$

32. (a) $\dfrac{10\pi}{3}$

(b) $\dfrac{17\pi}{3}$

In Exercises 33–40, use a calculator to evaluate the trigonometric functions to four decimal places.

33. (a) $\sin 12°$

(b) $\csc 12°$

34. (a) $\sec 225°$

(b) $\sec 135°$

35. (a) $\tan\dfrac{\pi}{9}$

(b) $\tan\dfrac{10\pi}{9}$

36. (a) $\cot 1.35$

(b) $\tan 1.35$

37. (a) $\cos(-110°)$

(b) $\cos 250°$

38. (a) $\tan 240°$

(b) $\cot 210°$

39. (a) $\csc 2.62$

(b) $\csc 150°$

40. (a) $\sin(-0.65)$

(b) $\sin 5.63$

In Exercises 41–46, find two values of θ corresponding to the given functions. List the measure of θ in radians ($0 \le \theta \le 2\pi$). Do not use a calculator.

41. (a) $\sin\theta = \frac{1}{2}$

(b) $\sin\theta = -\frac{1}{2}$

42. (a) $\cos\theta = \dfrac{\sqrt{2}}{2}$

(b) $\cos\theta = -\dfrac{\sqrt{2}}{2}$

43. (a) $\csc\theta = \dfrac{2\sqrt{3}}{3}$

(b) $\cot\theta = -1$

44. (a) $\sec\theta = 2$

(b) $\sec\theta = -2$

45. (a) $\tan\theta = -1$

(b) $\cot\theta = -\sqrt{3}$

46. (a) $\sin\theta = \dfrac{\sqrt{3}}{2}$

(b) $\sin\theta = -\dfrac{\sqrt{3}}{2}$

In Exercises 47–56, solve the equation for θ ($0 \le \theta \le 2\pi$). For some of the equations you should use the trigonometric identities listed in this section.

47. $2\sin^2\theta = 1$

48. $\tan^2\theta = 3$

49. $\tan^2\theta - \tan\theta = 0$

50. $2\cos^2\theta - \cos\theta = 1$

51. $\sin 2\theta - \cos\theta = 0$

52. $\sec\theta\csc\theta = 2\csc\theta$

53. $\sin\theta = \cos\theta$

54. $\cos 2\theta + 3\cos\theta + 2 = 0$

55. $\cos^2\theta + \sin\theta = 1$

56. $\cos\dfrac{\theta}{2} - \cos\theta = 1$

In Exercises 57–62, solve for x, y, or r as indicated.

57. Solve for y.

58. Solve for x.

59. Solve for x.

60. Solve for r.

61. Solve for r.

62. Solve for x.

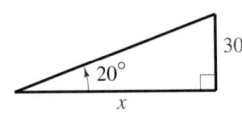

63. *Length* A 20-foot ladder leaning against the side of a house makes a $75°$ angle with the ground (see figure). How far up the side of the house does the ladder reach?

FIGURE FOR 63

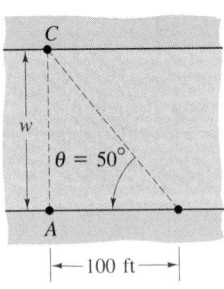

FIGURE FOR 64

64. *Width* A biologist wants to know the width w of a river in order to properly set instruments to study the pollutants in the water. From point A the biologist walks downstream 100 feet and sights to point C. From this sighting it is determined that $\theta = 50°$ (see figure). How wide is the river?

65. *Distance* From a 150-foot observation tower on the coast, a Coast Guard officer sights a boat in difficulty. The angle of depression of the boat is $3°$ (see figure). How far is the boat from the shoreline?

66. *Angle Measure* A ramp $17\frac{1}{2}$ feet in length rises to a loading platform that is $3\frac{1}{2}$ feet off the ground (see figure). Find the angle that the ramp makes with the ground.

67. *Average Temperature* The average daily temperature (in degrees Fahrenheit) for a certain city is given by

$$T = 45 - 23 \cos\left[\frac{2\pi}{365}(t - 32)\right],$$

where t is the time in days, with $t = 1$ corresponding to January 1. Find the average temperature on the following dates.

(a) January 1   (b) July 4 ($t = 185$)

68. *Sales* A company that produces a seasonal product forecasts monthly sales over the next 2 years to be

$$S = 23.1 + 0.442t + 4.3 \sin\frac{\pi t}{6},$$

where S is measured in thousands of units and t is the time in months, with $t = 1$ representing January 1987. Predict sales for the following months.

(a) February 1987   (b) February 1988
(c) September 1987   (d) September 1988

In Exercises 69 and 70, use a graphing utility to complete the table. Then graph the function.

x	0	2	4	6	8	10
$f(x)$						

69. $f(x) = \dfrac{2}{5}x + 2 \sin\dfrac{\pi x}{5}$

70. $f(x) = \dfrac{1}{2}(5 - x) + 3 \cos\dfrac{\pi x}{5}$

Graphs of Trigonometric Functions

Graphs of Trigonometric Functions ■ *Limits of Trigonometric Functions* ■
Applications

Graphs of Trigonometric Functions

When you are sketching the graph of a trigonometric function, it is common to
use x (rather than θ) as the independent variable. On the simplest level, you
can sketch the graph of a function such as

$$f(x) = \sin x$$

by constructing a table of values, plotting the resulting points, and connecting
them with a smooth curve, as shown in Figure T.21. Some examples of values
are shown in Table T.2.

TABLE T.2

x	0	$\dfrac{\pi}{6}$	$\dfrac{\pi}{4}$	$\dfrac{\pi}{3}$	$\dfrac{\pi}{2}$	$\dfrac{2\pi}{3}$	$\dfrac{3\pi}{4}$	$\dfrac{5\pi}{6}$	π
$\sin x$	0.00	0.50	0.71	0.87	1.00	0.87	0.71	0.50	0.00

In Figure T.21, note that the maximum value of $\sin x$ is 1 and the minimum
value is -1. The **amplitude** of the sine function (or the cosine function) is
defined to be half of the difference between its maximum and minimum values.
Thus, the amplitude of $f(x) = \sin x$ is 1.

The periodic nature of the sine function becomes evident when you observe
that as x increases beyond 2π, the graph repeats itself over and over, continuously oscillating about the x-axis. The **period** of the function is the distance
(on the x-axis) between successive cycles. Thus, the period of $f(x) = \sin x$ is
2π.

FIGURE T.21

Figure T.22, shown below, shows the graphs of at least one cycle of all six trigonometric functions.

FIGURE T.22   Graphs of the Six Trigonometric Functions

Familiarity with the graphs of the six basic trigonometric functions allows you to sketch graphs of more general functions such as

$$y = a \sin bx \quad \text{and} \quad y = a \cos bx.$$

Note that the function $y = a \sin bx$ oscillates between $-a$ and a and hence has an amplitude of

$$|a|. \qquad\qquad \textit{Amplitude of } y = a \sin bx$$

Furthermore, because $bx = 0$ when $x = 0$ and $bx = 2\pi$ when $x = 2\pi/b$, it follows that the function $y = a \sin bx$ has a period of

$$\frac{2\pi}{|b|}. \qquad\qquad \textit{Period of } y = a \sin bx$$

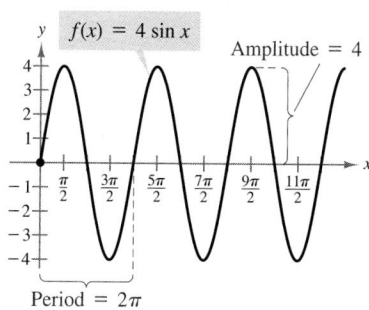

$f(x) = 4 \sin x$

Amplitude = 4

Period = 2π

FIGURE T.23

EXAMPLE 1 *Graphing a Trigonometric Function*

Sketch the graph of

$$f(x) = 4 \sin x.$$

Solution

The graph of $f(x) = 4 \sin x$ has the following characteristics.

Amplitude: 4

Period: 2π

Three cycles of the graph are shown in Figure T.23, starting with the point $(0, 0)$. ▬

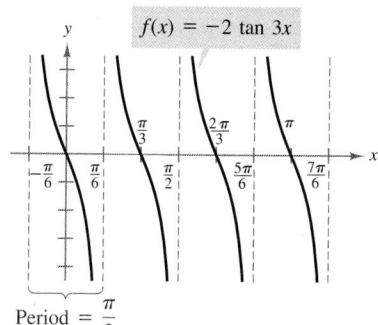

y

$(0, 3)$

Amplitude = 3

Period = π

$f(x) = 3 \cos 2x$

FIGURE T.24

EXAMPLE 2 *Graphing a Trigonometric Function*

Sketch the graph of

$$f(x) = 3 \cos 2x.$$

Solution

The graph of $f(x) = 3 \cos 2x$ has the following characteristics.

Amplitude: 3

Period: $\dfrac{2\pi}{2} = \pi$

Almost three cycles of the graph are shown in Figure T.24, starting with the maximum point $(0, 3)$. ▬

$f(x) = -2 \tan 3x$

Period = $\dfrac{\pi}{3}$

FIGURE T.25

EXAMPLE 3 *Graphing a Trigonometric Function*

Sketch the graph of

$$f(x) = -2 \tan 3x.$$

Solution

The graph of this function has a period of $\pi/3$. The vertical asymptotes of this tangent function occur at

$$x = \ldots, \underbrace{-\frac{\pi}{6}, \frac{\pi}{6}}, \frac{\pi}{2}, \frac{5\pi}{6}, \ldots.$$

$$\text{Period} = \frac{\pi}{3}$$

Several cycles of the graph are shown in Figure T.25, starting with the vertical asymptote $x = -\pi/6$. ▬

Graphing Trigonometric Functions

A graphing utility allows you to explore the effects of the constants a, b, c, and d on the graph of a function of the form

$$f(x) = a \sin[b(x - c)] + d.$$

After trying several values for these constants, you can see that a determines the amplitude, b determines the period, c determines the horizontal shift, and d determines the vertical shift. Four examples are shown below. In each case, the graph of f is compared with the graph of $y = \sin x$. For instance, in the first graph, notice that, relative to the graph of $y = \sin x$, the graph of f is shifted $\pi/2$ units to the right, stretched vertically by a factor of 2, and shifted up one unit. Similarly, in the second graph, notice that, relative to the graph of $y = \sin x$, the graph of f is shifted $\pi/2$ units to the right, stretched horizontally by a factor of one-half, stretched vertically by a factor of 3, and shifted down two units.

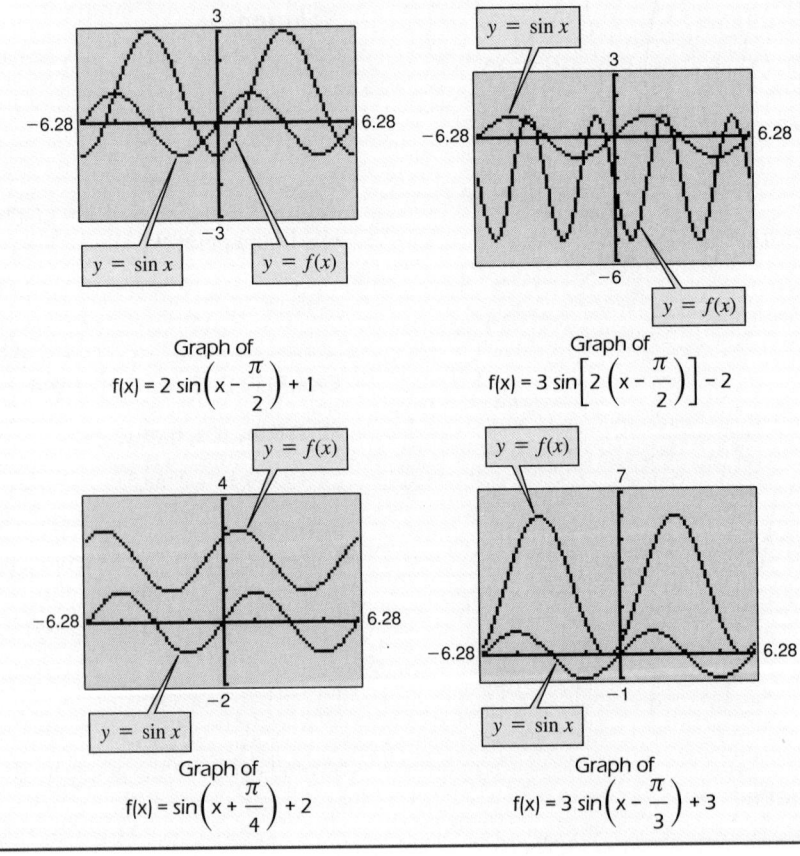

Graph of
$$f(x) = 2 \sin\left(x - \frac{\pi}{2}\right) + 1$$

Graph of
$$f(x) = 3 \sin\left[2\left(x - \frac{\pi}{2}\right)\right] - 2$$

Graph of
$$f(x) = \sin\left(x + \frac{\pi}{4}\right) + 2$$

Graph of
$$f(x) = 3 \sin\left(x - \frac{\pi}{3}\right) + 3$$

Limits of Trigonometric Functions

The sine and cosine functions are continuous over the entire real line. Thus, you can use direct substitution to evaluate a limit such as

$$\lim_{x \to 0} \sin x = \sin 0 = 0.$$

When direct substitution with a trigonometric limit yields an indeterminate form, you can rely on technology to help evaluate the limit. The next example examines the limit of a function that you will encounter again in Section T.4.

EXAMPLE 4 *Evaluating a Trigonometric Limit*

Use a calculator to evaluate the function

$$f(x) = \frac{\sin x}{x}$$

at several x-values near $x = 0$. Then use the result to estimate the limit

$$\lim_{x \to 0} \frac{\sin x}{x}.$$

Use a graphing utility (set in radian mode) to confirm your result.

Solution
Table T.3 shows several values of the function at x-values near zero. (Note that the function is undefined when $x = 0$.)

TABLE T.3

x	-0.20	-0.15	-0.10	-0.05	0.05	0.10	0.15	0.20
$\dfrac{\sin x}{x}$	0.9933	0.9963	0.9983	0.9996	0.9996	0.9983	0.9963	0.9933

From the table, it appears that the limit is 1. That is

$$\lim_{x \to 0} \frac{\sin x}{x} = 1.$$

Figure T.26 shows the graph of $f(x) = (\sin x)/x$. From this graph, it appears that $f(x)$ get closer and closer to 1 as x approaches 0 (from either side).

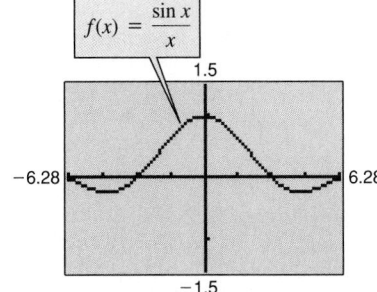

FIGURE T.26

Try using the technique illustrated in Example 4 to evaluate the limit

$$\lim_{x \to 0} \frac{\sin 5x}{5x}.$$

Can you hypothesize the limit of the general form

$$\lim_{x \to 0} \frac{\sin nx}{nx},$$

where n is a positive integer?

Applications

There are many examples of periodic phenomena in both business and biology. Many businesses have cyclical sales patterns, and plant growth is affected by the day-night cycle. The following example describes the cyclical pattern followed by many types of predator-prey populations, such as coyotes and rabbits or owls and mice.

Real Life

EXAMPLE 5 *Modeling Predator-Prey Cycles*

The population P of a predator at time t (in months) is modeled by

$$P = 10{,}000 + 3000 \sin \frac{2\pi t}{24},$$

and the population p of its primary food source (its prey) is modeled by

$$p = 15{,}000 + 5000 \cos \frac{2\pi t}{24}.$$

Graph both models on the same set of axes and explain the oscillations in the size of each population.

Solution

Each function has a period of 24 months. The predator population has an amplitude of 3000 and oscillates about the line $y = 10{,}000$. The prey population has an amplitude of 5000 and oscillates about the line $y = 15{,}000$. The graphs of the two models are shown in Figure T.27. The cycles of this predator-prey population are explained by the following diagram.

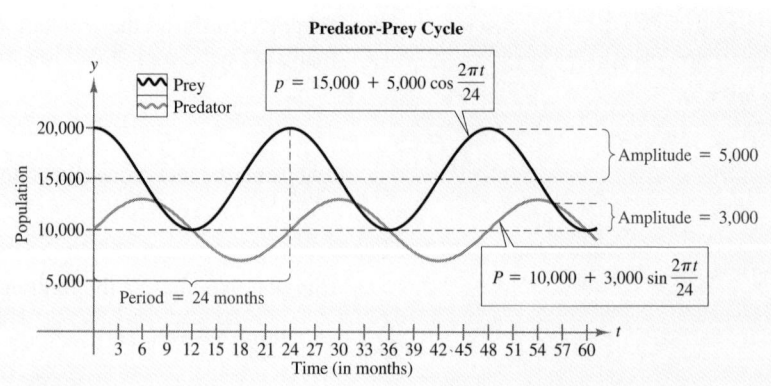

FIGURE T.27

Real
Life

EXAMPLE 6 *Modeling Biorhythms*

A popular theory that attempts to explain the ups and downs of everyday life states that each of us has three cycles which begin at birth. These three cycles can be modeled by sine waves

$$\text{Physical (23 days):} \quad P = \sin \frac{2\pi t}{23}$$

$$\text{Emotional (28 days):} \quad E = \sin \frac{2\pi t}{28}$$

$$\text{Intellectual (33 days):} \quad I = \sin \frac{2\pi t}{33},$$

where t is the number of days since birth. Consider a person who was born on July 20, 1964. Describe the person's biorhythms during the month of September 1984.

Solution

Figure T.28 shows the person's biorhythms during the month of September 1984. Note that September 1, 1984 was the 7349th day of the person's life.

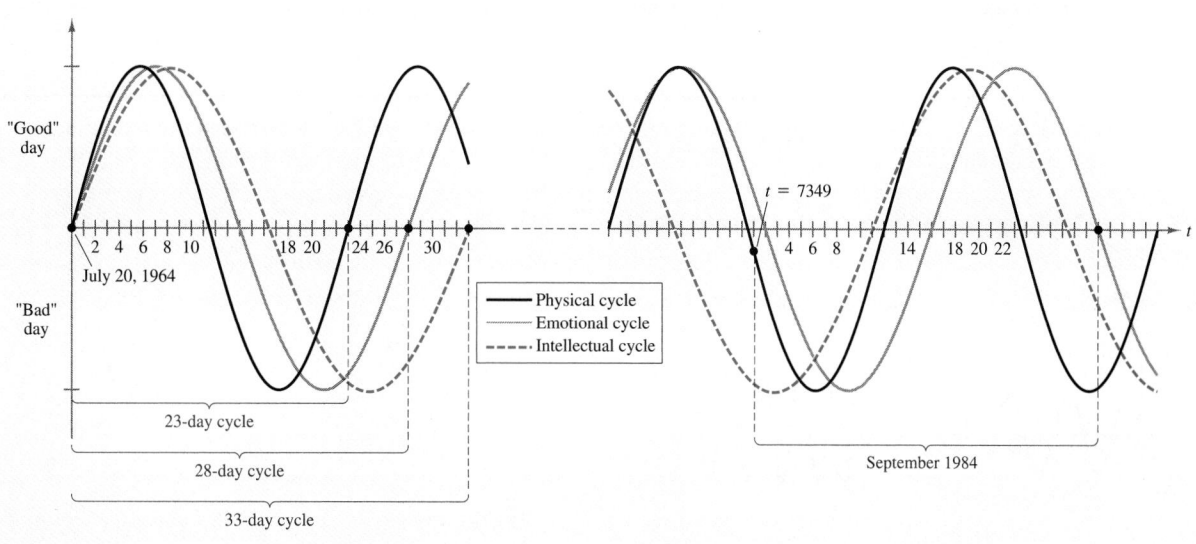

FIGURE T.28

Discussion Problem   *Biorhythms*

Consider a person who was born on August 16, 1978. Describe the person's biorhythms during the month of April 1995.

Warm Up

The following warm-up exercises involve skills that were covered in earlier sections. You will use these skills in the exercise set for this section.

In Exercises 1 and 2, find the indicated limit.

1. $\lim\limits_{x \to 2} (x^2 + 4x + 2)$

2. $\lim\limits_{x \to 3} (x^3 - 2x^2 + 1)$

In Exercises 3–6, evaluate the trigonometric function without using a calculator.

3. $\cos \dfrac{\pi}{2}$

4. $\tan \dfrac{5\pi}{4}$

5. $\sin \dfrac{11\pi}{6}$

6. $\cos \dfrac{5\pi}{3}$

In Exercises 7–10, use a calculator to evaluate the trigonometric function to four decimal places.

7. $\cos 15°$

8. $\sin 275°$

9. $\sin 103°$

10. $\tan 327°$

E X E R C I S E S   T.3 means that technology can help you solve or check the exercise(s).

In Exercises 1–14, determine the period and amplitude of the function.

1. $y = 2 \sin 2x$

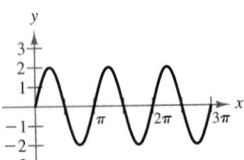

2. $y = 3 \cos 3x$

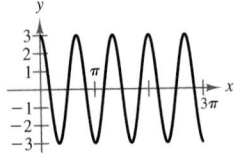

3. $y = \dfrac{3}{2} \cos \dfrac{x}{2}$

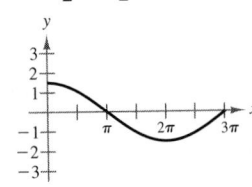

4. $y = -2 \sin \dfrac{x}{3}$

5. $y = \dfrac{1}{2} \cos \pi x$

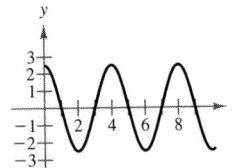

6. $y = \dfrac{5}{2} \cos \dfrac{\pi x}{2}$

7. $y = -2 \sin x$

8. $y = -\cos \dfrac{2x}{3}$

9. $y = -2 \sin 10x$

10. $y = \frac{1}{3} \sin 8x$

11. $y = \frac{1}{2} \sin \frac{2x}{3}$

12. $y = 5 \cos \frac{x}{4}$

13. $y = 3 \sin 4\pi x$

14. $y = \frac{2}{3} \cos \frac{\pi x}{10}$

In Exercises 15–20, find the period of the function.

15. $y = 5 \tan 2x$

16. $y = 7 \tan 2\pi x$

17. $y = 3 \sec 5x$

18. $y = \csc 4x$

19. $y = \cot \frac{\pi x}{6}$

20. $y = 5 \tan \frac{2\pi x}{3}$

In Exercises 21–26, match the trigonometric function with the correct graph and give the period of the function. [The graphs are labeled (a)–(f).]

21. $y = \sec 2x$

22. $y = \frac{1}{2} \csc 2x$

23. $y = \cot \frac{\pi x}{2}$

24. $y = -\sec x$

25. $y = 2 \csc \frac{x}{2}$

26. $y = \tan \frac{x}{2}$

(a)

(b)

(c)

(d)

(e)

(f)

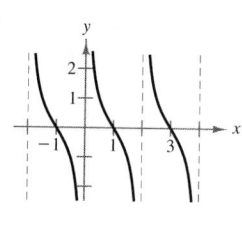

In Exercises 27–46, sketch the graph of the function.

27. $y = \sin \frac{x}{2}$

28. $y = 4 \sin \frac{x}{3}$

29. $y = 2 \cos \frac{2x}{3}$

30. $y = \frac{3}{2} \cos \frac{2x}{3}$

31. $y = -2 \sin 6x$

32. $y = -3 \cos 4x$

33. $y = \cos 2\pi x$

34. $y = \frac{3}{2} \sin \frac{\pi x}{4}$

35. $y = -\sin \frac{2\pi x}{3}$

36. $y = 10 \cos \frac{\pi x}{6}$

37. $y = 2 \tan x$

38. $y = 2 \cot x$

39. $y = \cot 2x$

40. $y = 3 \tan \pi x$

41. $y = \csc \frac{2x}{3}$

42. $y = \csc \frac{x}{3}$

43. $y = 2 \sec 2x$

44. $y = \sec \pi x$

45. $y = \csc 2\pi x$

46. $y = -\tan x$

In Exercises 47–50, complete the table (using a calculator set in radian mode) to estimate $\lim\limits_{x \to 0} f(x)$.

x	-0.1	-0.01	-0.001	0.001	0.01	0.1
$f(x)$						

47. $f(x) = \dfrac{1 - \cos x}{x}$

48. $f(x) = \dfrac{\sin 2x}{\sin 3x}$

49. $f(x) = \dfrac{\sin x}{5x}$

50. $f(x) = \dfrac{3(1 - \cos x)}{x}$

True or False In Exercises 51–54, determine whether the statement is true or false. Explain your reasoning.

51. The amplitude of $f(x) = -3 \cos 2x$ is -3.

52. The period of $f(x) = 5 \cot \left(-\dfrac{4x}{3} \right)$ is $\dfrac{3\pi}{2}$.

53. $\lim\limits_{x \to 0} \dfrac{\sin 5x}{3x} = \dfrac{5}{3}$.

54. One solution of $\tan \dfrac{x}{2} = 1$ is $\dfrac{5\pi}{4}$.

55. *Respiratory Cycle* For a person at rest, the velocity v in liters per second of air flow into and out of the lungs during a respiratory cycle is

$$v = 0.9 \sin \frac{\pi t}{3},$$

where t is the time in seconds. Inhalation occurs when $v > 0$, and exhalation occurs when $v < 0$.

(a) Find the time for one full respiratory cycle.
(b) Find the number of cycles per minute.
(c) Sketch the graph of the velocity function.

56. *Respiratory Cycle* After exercising for a few minutes, a person has a respiratory cycle for which the velocity of air flow is approximated by

$$y = 1.75 \sin \frac{\pi t}{2}.$$

Use this model to repeat Exercise 55.

 57. *Piano Tuning* When tuning a piano, a technician strikes a tuning fork for the A above middle C and sets up wave motion that can be approximated by

$$y = 0.001 \sin 880\pi t,$$

where t is the time in seconds.

(a) What is the period p of this function?
(b) What is the frequency f of this note ($f = 1/p$)?
(c) Sketch the graph of this function.

 58. *Blood Pressure* The function

$$P = 100 - 20 \cos \frac{5\pi t}{3}$$

approximates the blood pressure P in millimeters of mercury at time t in seconds for a person at rest.

(a) Find the period of the function.
(b) Find the number of heartbeats per minute.
(c) Sketch the graph of the pressure function.

 59. *Predator-Prey Cycle* The population P of a predator at time t (in months) is modeled by

$$P = 8000 + 2500 \sin \frac{2\pi t}{24},$$

and the population p of its prey is modeled by

$$p = 12{,}000 + 4000 \cos \frac{2\pi t}{24}.$$

Graph both models on the same set of axes and explain the oscillations in the size of each population.

 60. *Predator-Prey Cycle* The population P of a predator at time t (in months) is modeled by

$$P = 5700 + 1200 \sin \frac{2\pi t}{24},$$

and the population p of its prey is modeled by

$$p = 9800 + 2750 \cos \frac{2\pi t}{24}.$$

Graph both models on the same set of axes and explain the oscillations in the size of each population.

Sales In Exercises 61 and 62, sketch the graph of the sales function over 1 year where S is sales in thousands of units and t is the time in months, with $t = 1$ corresponding to January.

61. $S = 22.3 - 3.4 \cos \dfrac{\pi t}{6}$

62. $S = 74.50 + 43.75 \sin \dfrac{\pi t}{6}$

63. *Biorhythms* For the person born on July 20, 1964, use the biorhythm cycles given in Example 6 to calculate this person's three energy levels on December 25, 2000.

64. *Biorhythms* Use your birthday and the concept of biorhythms as given in Example 6 to calculate your three energy levels on December 25, 2000.

In Exercises 65 and 66, use a graphing utility to graph the functions on the same coordinate axes where $0 \leq x \leq 2$.

65. (a) $y = \dfrac{4}{\pi} \sin \pi x$

     (b) $y = \dfrac{4}{\pi} \left(\sin \pi x + \dfrac{1}{3} \sin 3\pi x \right)$

66. (a) $y = \dfrac{1}{2} - \dfrac{4}{\pi^2} \cos \pi x$

     (b) $y = \dfrac{1}{2} - \dfrac{4}{\pi^2} \left(\cos \pi x + \dfrac{1}{9} \cos 3\pi x \right)$

In Exercises 67 and 68, use a graphing utility to graph the function f and find $\lim\limits_{x \to 0} f(x)$.

67. $f(x) = \dfrac{\sin x}{x}$

68. $f(x) = \dfrac{\sin 5x}{\sin 2x}$

69. *Sales* Sales S, in thousands of units, of a seasonal product is modeled by

$$S = 58.3 + 32.5 \cos \frac{\pi t}{6},$$

where t is the time in months, with $t = 1$ corresponding to January and $t = 12$ corresponding to December.

(a) Use a graphing utility to graph S.
(b) Determine the months when sales exceed 75,000 units.

T.4 Derivatives of Trigonometric Functions

Derivatives of Trigonometric Functions ■
Relative Extrema of Trigonometric Functions ■ *Applications*

Derivatives of Trigonometric Functions

In the previous section, you looked at two important trigonometric limits:

$$\lim_{\Delta x \to 0} \frac{\sin \Delta x}{\Delta x} = 1 \quad \text{and} \quad \lim_{\Delta x \to 0} \frac{1 - \cos \Delta x}{\Delta x} = 0.$$

These two limits are used in the following development of the derivative of the sine function.

$$\frac{d}{dx}[\sin x] = \lim_{\Delta x \to 0} \frac{\sin(x + \Delta x) - \sin x}{\Delta x}$$

$$= \lim_{\Delta x \to 0} \frac{\sin x \cos \Delta x + \cos x \sin \Delta x - \sin x}{\Delta x}$$

$$= \lim_{\Delta x \to 0} \left(\cos x \frac{\sin \Delta x}{\Delta x} - \sin x \frac{1 - \cos \Delta x}{\Delta x} \right)$$

$$= \cos x \left(\lim_{\Delta x \to 0} \frac{\sin \Delta x}{\Delta x} \right) - \sin x \left(\lim_{\Delta x \to 0} \frac{1 - \cos \Delta x}{\Delta x} \right)$$

$$= (\cos x)(1) - (\sin x)(0)$$

$$= \cos x.$$

This differentiation rule is illustrated graphically in Figure T.29. Note that the *slope* of the sine curve determines the *value* of the cosine curve. The Chain Rule version of this differentiation rule is

$$\frac{d}{dx}[\sin u] = \cos u \frac{du}{dx}.$$

The Chain Rule versions of the differentiation rules for all six trigonometric functions are listed below.

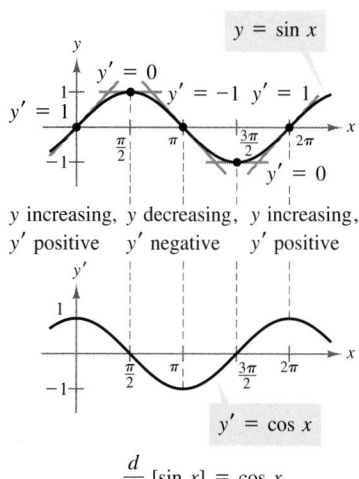

y increasing, y decreasing, y increasing,
y' positive y' negative y' positive

$$\frac{d}{dx}[\sin x] = \cos x$$

FIGURE T.29

Note To help you remember these differentiation rules, note that each trigonometric function that begins with a "c" has a negative sign in its derivative.

Derivatives of Trigonometric Functions

$$\frac{d}{dx}[\sin u] = \cos u \frac{du}{dx} \qquad \frac{d}{dx}[\cos u] = -\sin u \frac{du}{dx}$$

$$\frac{d}{dx}[\tan u] = \sec^2 u \frac{du}{dx} \qquad \frac{d}{dx}[\cot u] = -\csc^2 u \frac{du}{dx}$$

$$\frac{d}{dx}[\sec u] = \sec u \tan u \frac{du}{dx} \qquad \frac{d}{dx}[\csc u] = -\csc u \cot u \frac{du}{dx}$$

EXAMPLE 1 *Differentiating Trigonometric Functions*

Differentiate each function.

a. $y = \sin 2x$ **b.** $y = \cos(x - 1)$ **c.** $y = \tan 3x$

Solution

a. Letting $u = 2x$, you have the following.

$$\frac{dy}{dx} = \cos u \frac{du}{dx} = \cos 2x \frac{d}{dx}[2x] = (\cos 2x)(2) = 2\cos 2x$$

b. Letting $u = x - 1$, you can see that $u' = 1$. Thus, the derivative is simply

$$\frac{dy}{dx} = -\sin(x - 1).$$

c. Letting $u = 3x$, you have $u' = 3$, which implies that

$$\frac{dy}{dx} = 3\sec^2 3x.$$

EXAMPLE 2 *Differentiating a Trigonometric Function*

Differentiate $f(x) = \cos 3x^2$.

Solution

Letting $u = 3x^2$, you obtain

$$f'(x) = -\sin u \frac{du}{dx} \qquad\qquad \textit{Use Cosine Rule.}$$

$$= -\sin 3x^2 \frac{d}{dx}[3x^2] \qquad\qquad \textit{Substitute } 3x^2 \textit{ for } u.$$

$$= -(\sin 3x^2)(6x)$$

$$= -6x\sin 3x^2. \qquad\qquad \textit{Simplify.}$$

TECHNOLOGY

When you use a symbolic differentiation utility, such as *Derive*, *Mathematica*, or *Maple*, to differentiate trigonometric functions, you can easily obtain results that appear to be different from those you would obtain by hand. For instance, *Derive*'s answer to the function in Example 3 is

$$f'(x) = 12\tan(3x)^3 + 12\tan(3x)^5.$$

How does this result compare with that given in Example 3?

EXAMPLE 3 *Differentiating a Trigonometric Function*

Differentiate

$$f(x) = \tan^4 3x.$$

Solution

By the Power Rule, you can write

$$\frac{d}{dx}[(\tan 3x)^4] = 4(\tan 3x)^3 \frac{d}{dx}[\tan 3x]$$

$$= 4(\tan^3 3x)(3)(\sec^2 3x)$$

$$= 12\tan^3 3x \sec^2 3x.$$

EXAMPLE 4 *Differentiating a Trigonometric Function*

Differentiate $y = \csc \dfrac{x}{2}$.

Solution

$$y = \csc \frac{x}{2} \qquad\qquad\qquad \textit{Original function}$$

$$\frac{dy}{dx} = -\csc\frac{x}{2}\cot\frac{x}{2}\frac{d}{dx}\left[\frac{x}{2}\right] \qquad \textit{Apply Cosecant Rule.}$$

$$= -\frac{1}{2}\csc\frac{x}{2}\cot\frac{x}{2} \qquad\qquad \textit{Simplify.} \qquad \blacksquare$$

EXAMPLE 5 *Differentiating a Trigonometric Function*

Differentiate $f(t) = \sqrt{\sin 4t}$.

Solution

Begin by rewriting the function in rational exponent form. Then apply the General Power Rule to find the derivative.

$$f(t) = (\sin 4t)^{1/2} \qquad\qquad \textit{Rewrite with rational exponent.}$$

$$f'(t) = \left(\frac{1}{2}\right)(\sin 4t)^{-1/2}\frac{d}{dt}[\sin 4t] \qquad \textit{Apply General Power Rule.}$$

$$= \left(\frac{1}{2}\right)(\sin 4t)^{-1/2}(4\cos 4t)$$

$$= \frac{2\cos 4t}{\sqrt{\sin 4t}} \qquad\qquad\qquad \textit{Simplify.} \qquad \blacksquare$$

EXAMPLE 6 *Differentiating a Trigonometric Function*

Differentiate $y = x\sin x$.

Solution

Using the Product Rule, you can write

$$y = x\sin x \qquad\qquad\qquad \textit{Original function}$$

$$\frac{dy}{dx} = x\frac{d}{dx}[\sin x] + \sin x\frac{d}{dx}[x] \qquad \textit{Apply Product Rule.}$$

$$= x\cos x + \sin x. \qquad\qquad \textit{Simplify.} \qquad \blacksquare$$

Note   Notice that all of the differentiation rules that you learned in earlier chapters in the text can be applied to trigonometric functions. For instance, Example 5 uses the General Power Rule and Example 6 uses the Product Rule.

Relative Extrema of Trigonometric Functions

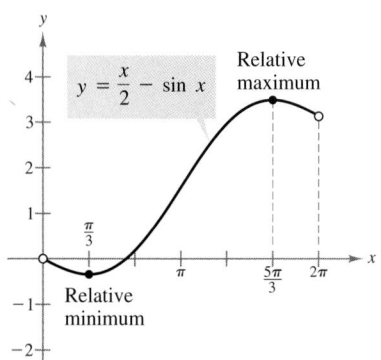

FIGURE T.30

EXAMPLE 7 *Finding Relative Extrema*

Find the relative extrema of

$$y = \frac{x}{2} - \sin x$$

on the interval $(0, 2\pi)$.

Solution

To find the relative extrema of the function, begin by finding its critical numbers. The derivative of y is

$$\frac{dy}{dx} = \frac{1}{2} - \cos x.$$

By setting the derivative equal to 0, you obtain $\cos x = \frac{1}{2}$. Therefore, in the interval $(0, 2\pi)$, the critical numbers are $x = \pi/3$ and $x = 5\pi/3$. Using the First-Derivative Test, you can conclude that $\pi/3$ yields a relative minimum and $5\pi/3$ yields a relative maximum, as shown in Figure T.30. ▬

Note   Recall that the critical numbers of a function $y = f(x)$ are the x-values for which $f'(x) = 0$ or $f'(x)$ is undefined.

EXAMPLE 8 *Finding Relative Extrema*

Find the relative extrema of $f(x) = 2 \sin x - \cos 2x$ on the interval $(0, 2\pi)$.

Solution

$f(x) = 2 \sin x - \cos 2x$	*Original function*
$f'(x) = 2 \cos x + 2 \sin 2x$	*Differentiate.*
$0 = 2 \cos x + 2 \sin 2x$	*Set derivative equal to 0.*
$0 = 2 \cos x + 4 \cos x \sin x$	*Identity:* $\sin 2x = 2 \cos x \sin x$
$0 = 2(\cos x)(1 + 2 \sin x)$	*Factor.*

From this, you can see that the critical numbers occur when $\cos x = 0$ and when $\sin x = -\frac{1}{2}$. Thus, in the interval $(0, 2\pi)$, the critical numbers are

$$x = \frac{\pi}{2}, \ \frac{3\pi}{2}, \ \frac{7\pi}{6}, \ \frac{11\pi}{6}.$$

Using the First-Derivative Test, you can determine that $(\pi/2, 3)$ and $(3\pi/2, -1)$ are relative maxima, and $\left(7\pi/6, -\frac{3}{2}\right)$ and $\left(11\pi/6, -\frac{3}{2}\right)$ are relative minima, as shown in Figure T.31. ▬

FIGURE T.31

TECHNOLOGY

Graphing Trigonometric Functions

Because of the difficulty of solving some trigonometric equations, it can be difficult to find the critical numbers of a trigonometric function. For instance, consider the function

$$f(x) = 2\sin x - \cos 3x.$$

Setting the derivative of this function equal to zero produces

$$f'(x) = 2\cos x + 3\sin 3x = 0.$$

This equation is difficult to solve analytically. Hence, it is difficult to find the relative extrema of f analytically. With a graphing utility, however, you can easily sketch the graph of f and use the zoom feature to estimate the relative extrema. In the graph shown below, notice that the function has three relative minima and three relative maxima in the interval $(0, 2\pi)$.

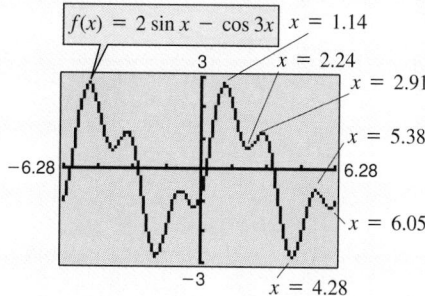

Once you have obtained rough approximations for the relative extrema, you can further refine the approximations by applying other approximation techniques to the equation

$$f'(x) = 2\cos x + 3\sin 3x = 0.$$

For instance, if you use Newton's Method to approximate this equation's solutions in the interval $(0, 2\pi)$, you obtain

    1.1410,   2.2357,   2.9065,   4.2826,   5.3773,   and   6.0481.

Try using technology to locate the relative extrema of the function

$$f(x) = 2\sin x - \cos 4x.$$

How many relative extrema does this function have in the interval $(0, 2\pi)$?

Applications

EXAMPLE 9 *Modeling Seasonal Sales*

A fertilizer manufacturer finds that the sales of one of its fertilizer brands follows a seasonal pattern that can be modeled by

$$F = 100{,}000 \left[1 + \sin \frac{2\pi(t-60)}{365} \right],$$

where F is the amount sold (in pounds) and t is the time (in days), with $t = 1$ representing January 1, as shown in Figure T.32. On which day of the year is the maximum amount of fertilizer sold?

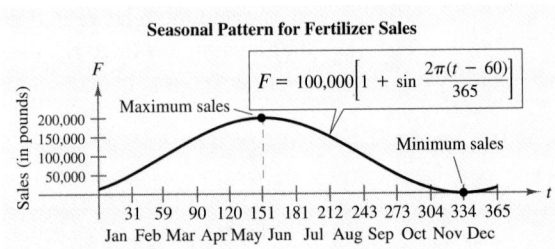

Seasonal Pattern for Fertilizer Sales

$$F = 100{,}000 \left[1 + \sin \frac{2\pi(t-60)}{365} \right]$$

Maximum sales

Minimum sales

Sales (in pounds): 200,000 150,000 100,000 50,000

31 59 90 120 151 181 212 243 273 304 334 365
Jan Feb Mar Apr May Jun Jul Aug Sep Oct Nov Dec

FIGURE T.32

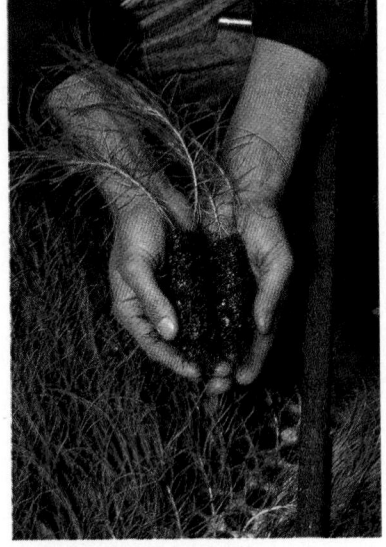

The Stock Market/© 92 Peter Beck

In 1990, the agricultural industry in the United States spent over $7 billion on fertilizers. Fertilizers are used to aid the growth of almost all agricultural products. For instance, fertilizers were used in the bedding soil of these pine seedlings which are being used in a reforestation project.

Solution

The derivative of the model is

$$\frac{dF}{dt} = 100{,}000 \left(\frac{2\pi}{365} \right) \cos \frac{2\pi(t-60)}{365}.$$

Setting this derivative equal to zero produces

$$\cos \frac{2\pi(t-60)}{365} = 0.$$

Because the cosine is zero at $\pi/2$ and $3\pi/2$, you obtain the following.

$$\frac{2\pi(t-60)}{365} = \frac{\pi}{2} \qquad\qquad \frac{2\pi(t-60)}{365} = \frac{3\pi}{2}$$

$$t - 60 = \frac{365}{4} \qquad\qquad t - 60 = \frac{3(365)}{4}$$

$$t = \frac{365}{4} + 60 \qquad\qquad t = \frac{3(365)}{4} + 60$$

$$t \approx 151 \qquad\qquad\qquad t \approx 334$$

The 151st day of the year is May 31 and the 334th day of the year is November 30. From the graph in Figure T.32, you can see that, according to the model, the maximum sales occur on May 31. ▬

Real Life

EXAMPLE 10 *Modeling Temperature Change*

The temperature T (in degrees Fahrenheit) during a given 24-hour period can be modeled by

$$T = 70 + 15 \sin \frac{\pi(t-8)}{12},$$

where t is the time (in hours), with $t = 0$ corresponding to midnight, as shown in Figure T.33. Find the rate at which the temperature is changing at 6 A.M.

FIGURE T.33

Solution

The rate of change of the temperature is given by the derivative

$$\frac{dT}{dt} = \frac{15\pi}{12} \cos \frac{\pi(t-8)}{12}.$$

Because 6 A.M. corresponds to $t = 6$, the rate of change at 6 A.M. is

$$\begin{aligned}
\frac{dT}{dt} &= \frac{15\pi}{12} \cos \left(\frac{-2\pi}{12} \right) \\
&= \frac{5\pi}{4} \cos \left(-\frac{\pi}{6} \right) \\
&= \frac{5\pi}{4} \left(\frac{\sqrt{3}}{2} \right) \\
&\approx 3.4° \text{ per hour.}
\end{aligned}$$

Discussion Problem   **Modeling Temperature Changes**

In Example 10, when does the minimum temperature occur? When does the maximum temperature occur? Suppose that each occurs 1 hour later. How would this change the model?

Warm Up

The following warm-up exercises involve skills that were covered in earlier sections. You will use these skills in the exercise set for this section.

In Exercises 1–4, find the derivative of the function.

1. $f(x) = 3x^3 - 2x^2 + 4x - 7$ 　　　**2.** $g(x) = (x^3 + 4)^4$

3. $f(x) = (x - 1)(x^2 + 2x + 3)$ 　　**4.** $g(x) = \dfrac{2x}{x^2 + 5}$

In Exercises 5 and 6, find the relative extrema of the function.

5. $f(x) = x^2 + 4x + 1$ 　　　　　**6.** $f(x) = \frac{1}{3}x^3 - 4x + 2$

In Exercises 7–10, solve the trigonometric equation for x where $0 \le x \le 2\pi$.

7. $\sin x = \dfrac{\sqrt{3}}{2}$ 　　　　　　　**8.** $\cos x = -\dfrac{1}{2}$

9. $\cos \dfrac{x}{2} = 0$ 　　　　　　　**10.** $\sin \dfrac{x}{2} = -\dfrac{\sqrt{2}}{2}$

EXERCISES T.4 means that technology can help you solve or check the exercise(s).

In Exercises 1–24, find the derivative of the function.

1. $y = x^2 - \cos x$ 　　　　　**2.** $y = 5 + \sin x$

3. $y = \frac{1}{2} - 3\sin x$ 　　　　**4.** $g(t) = \pi \cos t$

5. $f(x) = 4\sqrt{x} + 3\cos x$ 　　**6.** $f(x) = \sin x + \cos x$

7. $f(t) = t^2 \cos t$ 　　　　　**8.** $f(x) = (x + 1)\cos x$

9. $g(t) = \dfrac{\cos t}{t}$ 　　　　　**10.** $f(x) = \dfrac{\sin x}{x}$

11. $y = \tan x + x^2$ 　　　　**12.** $y = \ln|\sec x + \tan x|$

13. $y = 5x \sec x$ 　　　　　**14.** $y = e^{-x} \sin x$

15. $y = \sin 4x$ 　　　　　　**16.** $y = \cos 3x$

17. $y = \csc x^2$ 　　　　　　**18.** $y = \sin \pi x$

19. $y = \frac{1}{2} \csc 2x$ 　　　　**20.** $y = \csc^2 x$

21. $y = x \sin \dfrac{1}{x}$ 　　　　**22.** $y = x^2 \sin \dfrac{1}{x}$

23. $y = 3 \tan 4x$ 　　　　　**24.** $y = \tan e^x$

In Exercises 25–40, find the derivative of the function and simplify your answer by using the trigonometric identities listed in Section T.2.

25. $y = \cos^2 x$ 　　　　　　**26.** $y = \frac{1}{4} \sin^2 2x$

27. $y = \cos^2 x - \sin^2 x$ 　　**28.** $y = \sin x \cos x$

29. $y = \dfrac{\cos x}{\sin x}$ 　　　　　**30.** $y = \dfrac{x}{2} + \dfrac{\sin 2x}{4}$

31. $y = \ln|\sin x|$ 　　　　　**32.** $y = -\ln|\cos x|$

33. $y = \ln|\csc x^2 - \cot x^2|$ 　**34.** $y = x + \cot x$

35. $y = \tan x - x$ 　　　　　**36.** $y = \dfrac{\sec^7 x}{7} - \dfrac{\sec^5 x}{5}$

37. $y = \sqrt{\sin x}$ 　　　　　**38.** $y = \ln(\sin^2 x)$

39. $y = \frac{1}{2}(x \tan x - \sec x)$ 　**40.** $y = \ln|\cot x|$

In Exercises 41 and 42, use implicit differentiation to find dy/dx and evaluate the derivative at the indicated point.

Function	*Point*
41. $\sin x + \cos 2y = 1$	$\left(\dfrac{\pi}{2}, \dfrac{\pi}{4}\right)$
42. $\tan(x + y) = x$	$(0, 0)$

In Exercises 43–46, show that the function satisfies the differential equation.

Function	*Differential Equation*
43. $y = 2\sin x + 3\cos x$	$y'' + y = 0$
44. $y = \dfrac{10 - \cos x}{x}$	$xy' + y = \sin x$
45. $y = \cos 2x + \sin 2x$	$y'' + 4y = 0$
46. $y = e^x(\cos \sqrt{2}x + \sin \sqrt{2}x)$	$y'' - 2y' + 3y = 0$

In Exercises 47–52, find the slope of the tangent line to the given sine function at the origin. Compare this value with the number of complete cycles in the interval $[0, 2\pi]$.

47. $y = \sin \dfrac{5x}{4}$

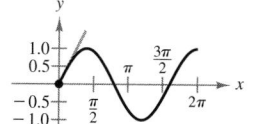

48. $y = \sin \dfrac{5x}{2}$

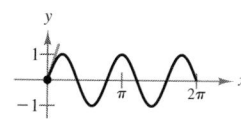

49. $y = \sin 2x$

50. $y = \sin \dfrac{3x}{2}$

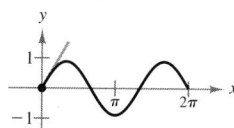

51. $y = \sin x$

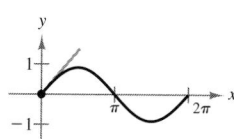

52. $y = \sin \dfrac{x}{2}$

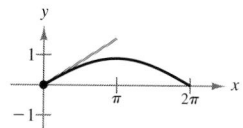

In Exercises 53 and 54, find an equation of the tangent line to the graph of the function at the indicated point.

Function	*Point*
53. $f(x) = \tan x$	$\left(-\dfrac{\pi}{4}, -1\right)$
54. $f(x) = \sec x$	$\left(\dfrac{\pi}{3}, 2\right)$

In Exercises 55–60, determine the relative extrema of the function on the interval $(0, 2\pi)$. Use a graphing utility to confirm your result.

55. $y = 2\sin x + \sin 2x$ **56.** $y = 2\sin x + \cos 2x$

57. $y = x - 2\sin x$ **58.** $y = e^{-x}\sin x$

59. $y = e^{-x}\cos x$ **60.** $y = \sec \dfrac{x}{2}$

61. *Sales* Sales of electricity in the United States have had both an increasing annual sales pattern and a seasonal monthly sales pattern. For the years 1983–1985, sales can be approximated by the model

$$S = 180.60 + 0.55t + 13.60\cos\frac{\pi t}{3},$$

where S is the number of sales (per month) in billions of kilowatt hours and t is the time in months, with $t = 1$ corresponding to January 1983 (see figure).

(a) Find the relative extrema of this function for the years 1983 and 1984.

(b) Use this model to determine the sales in August 1985. (Use $t = 31.5$.)

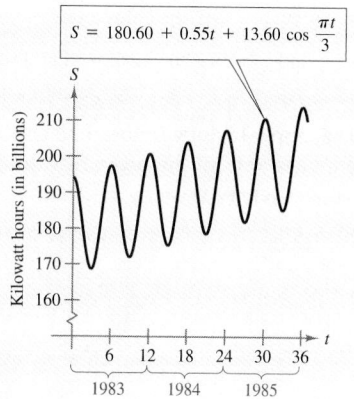

62. *Plant Growth Rate* Plants do not grow at constant rates during a normal 24-hour period because their growth is affected by sunlight. Suppose that the growth of a certain plant species in a controlled environment is given by the model

$$h = 0.2t + 0.03 \sin 2\pi t,$$

where h is the height of the plant in inches and t is the time in days, with $t = 0$ corresponding to midnight (see figure). During what time of day is the rate of growth of this plant

(a) the greatest?   (b) the least?

Time (in days)

63. *Average Temperature* The normal average daily temperature in degrees Fahrenheit for a certain city is given by

$$T = 55 - 21 \cos \frac{2\pi(t - 32)}{365},$$

where t is the time in days, with $t = 1$ corresponding to January 1. Find the expected date of

(a) the warmest day.   (b) the coldest day.

64. For $f(x) = \sec^2 x$ and $g(x) = \tan^2 x$, show that $f'(x) = g'(x)$.

In Exercises 65 and 66, apply Taylor's Theorem to verify the power series centered at $c = 0$ for the given function, and find the radius of convergence.

65. $\sin x = x - \dfrac{x^3}{3!} + \dfrac{x^5}{5!} - \dfrac{x^7}{7!} + \cdots + \dfrac{(-1)^n x^{2n+1}}{(2n+1)!} + \cdots$

66. $\cos x = 1 - \dfrac{x^2}{2!} + \dfrac{x^4}{4!} - \dfrac{x^6}{6!} + \cdots + \dfrac{(-1)^n x^{2n}}{(2n)!} + \cdots$

In Exercises 67 and 68, use the power series for $\sin x$ to find the power series of the given function.

67. $f(x) = \sin x^2$ **68.** $g(x) = \dfrac{\sin x}{x}$

In Exercises 69 and 70, use the power series for $\cos x$ to find the power series of the given function.

69. $h(x) = \cos 2x$ **70.** $f(x) = \cos \sqrt{x}$

In Exercises 71 and 72, differentiate the appropriate power series to verify the given derivative formulas.

71. $\dfrac{d}{dx}[\sin x] = \cos x$ **72.** $\dfrac{d}{dx}[\cos x] = -\sin x$

In Exercises 73–78, use a graphing utility (a) to graph f and f' on the same coordinate axes over the specified interval, (b) to find the critical numbers of f, and (c) to find the interval(s) on which f' is positive and the interval(s) on which it is negative. Note the behavior of f in relation to the sign of f'.

Function	*Interval*
73. $f(t) = t^2 \sin t$	$(0, 2\pi)$
74. $f(x) = \dfrac{x}{2} + \cos \dfrac{x}{2}$	$(0, 4\pi)$
75. $f(x) = \sin x - \frac{1}{3} \sin 3x + \frac{1}{5} \sin 5x$	$(0, \pi)$
76. $f(x) = x \sin x$	$(0, \pi)$
77. $f(x) = \sqrt{2x} \sin x$	$(0, 2\pi)$
78. $f(x) = 4e^{-0.5x} \sin \pi x$	$(0, 4)$

In Exercises 79 and 80, use Newton's Method to approximate the real zeros of the function in the interval $[0, 10]$.

79. $f(x) = x \sin x - \cos 2x$ **80.** $f(x) = x \cos x - \sin 2x$

In Exercises 81–86, use a graphing utility to find the relative extrema of the trigonometric function. Let $0 < x < 2\pi$.

81. $f(x) = \dfrac{x}{\sin x}$

82. $f(x) = \dfrac{x^2 - 2}{\sin x} - 5x$

83. $f(x) = \ln x \cos x$

84. $f(x) = \ln x \sin x$

85. $f(x) = \sin(0.1x^2)$

86. $f(x) = \sin \sqrt{x}$

Integrals of Trigonometric Functions

The Six Basic Trigonometric Integrals ■ *Other Trigonometric Integrals* ■ *Application*

The Six Basic Trigonometric Integrals

For each trigonometric differentiation rule, there is a corresponding integration rule. For instance, corresponding to the differentiation rule

$$\frac{d}{dx}[\cos u] = -\sin u \frac{du}{dx}$$

is the integration rule

$$\int \sin u \, du = -\cos u + C.$$

The following list contains the integration formulas that correspond to the six basic trigonometric differentiation rules.

Integrals Involving Trigonometric Functions

Differentiation Rule	Integration Rule
$\dfrac{d}{dx}[\sin u] = \cos u \dfrac{du}{dx}$	$\displaystyle\int \cos u \, du = \sin u + C$
$\dfrac{d}{dx}[\cos u] = -\sin u \dfrac{du}{dx}$	$\displaystyle\int \sin u \, du = -\cos u + C$
$\dfrac{d}{dx}[\tan u] = \sec^2 u \dfrac{du}{dx}$	$\displaystyle\int \sec^2 u \, du = \tan u + C$
$\dfrac{d}{dx}[\sec u] = \sec u \tan u \dfrac{du}{dx}$	$\displaystyle\int \sec u \tan u \, du = \sec u + C$
$\dfrac{d}{dx}[\cot u] = -\csc^2 u \dfrac{du}{dx}$	$\displaystyle\int \csc^2 u \, du = -\cot u + C$
$\dfrac{d}{dx}[\csc u] = -\csc u \cot u \dfrac{du}{dx}$	$\displaystyle\int \csc u \cot u \, du = -\csc u + C$

Note Note that this list gives you formulas for integrating only two of the six trigonometric functions: the sine function and the cosine function. The list does not show you how to integrate the other four trigonometric functions. Rules for doing that are discussed later in this section.

EXAMPLE 1 *Integrating a Trigonometric Function*

Evaluate the integral $\int 2\cos x\,dx$.

Solution

Let $u = x$. Then $du = dx$.

$$\int 2\cos x\,dx = 2\int \cos x\,dx \qquad \text{\textit{Constant Multiple Rule}}$$

$$= 2\int \cos u\,du \qquad \text{\textit{Substitute for x and dx.}}$$

$$= 2\sin u + C \qquad \text{\textit{Integrate.}}$$

$$= 2\sin x + C \qquad \text{\textit{Substitute for u.}}$$

EXAMPLE 2 *Integrating a Trigonometric Function*

Evaluate the integral $\int 3x^2 \sin x^3\,dx$.

Solution

Let $u = x^3$. Then $du = 3x^2\,dx$.

$$\int 3x^2 \sin x^3\,dx = \int (\sin x^3)3x^2\,dx \qquad \text{\textit{Rewrite integrand.}}$$

$$= \int \sin u\,du \qquad \text{\textit{Substitute for } x^3 \text{ and } 3x^2\,dx.}$$

$$= -\cos u + C \qquad \text{\textit{Integrate.}}$$

$$= -\cos x^3 + C \qquad \text{\textit{Substitute for u.}}$$

EXAMPLE 3 *Integrating a Trigonometric Function*

Evaluate the integral $\int \sec 3x \tan 3x\,dx$.

Solution

Let $u = 3x$. Then $du = 3\,dx$.

$$\int \sec 3x \tan 3x\,dx = \frac{1}{3}\int (\sec 3x \tan 3x)3\,dx \qquad \begin{array}{l}\textit{Multiply and}\\ \textit{divide by 3.}\end{array}$$

$$= \frac{1}{3}\int \sec u \tan u\,du \qquad \begin{array}{l}\textit{Substitute for 3x and}\\ \textit{3 dx.}\end{array}$$

$$= \frac{1}{3}\sec u + C \qquad \textit{Integrate.}$$

$$= \frac{1}{3}\sec 3x + C \qquad \textit{Substitute for u.}$$

▦ TECHNOLOGY

If you have access to a symbolic integration utility, such as *Derive*, *Mathematica*, or *Maple*, try using it to integrate the functions in Examples 1, 2, and 3. Does your utility give the same results that are given in the examples?

EXAMPLE 4 *Integrating a Trigonometric Function*

Evaluate the integral $\int e^x \sec^2 e^x\, dx$.

Solution

Let $u = e^x$. Then $du = e^x\, dx$.

$$\int e^x \sec^2 e^x\, dx = \int (\sec^2 e^x)e^x\, dx \qquad \text{\textit{Rewrite integrand.}}$$

$$= \int \sec^2 u\, du \qquad \text{\textit{Substitute for } } e^x \text{ \textit{and} } e^x\, dx.$$

$$= \tan u + C \qquad \text{\textit{Integrate.}}$$

$$= \tan e^x + C \qquad \text{\textit{Substitute for } } u.$$

■

The next two examples use the General Power Rule for integration and the Log Rule for integration. Recall from Chapter 5 that these rules are

$$\int u^n \frac{du}{dx}\, dx = \frac{u^{n+1}}{n+1} + C, \qquad n \neq -1 \qquad \text{\textit{General Power Rule}}$$

and

$$\int \frac{du/dx}{u}\, dx = \ln|u| + C. \qquad \text{\textit{Log Rule}}$$

The key to using these two rules is identifying the proper substitution u. For instance, in the next example, the proper choice for u is $\sin 4x$.

EXAMPLE 5 *Using the General Power Rule*

Evaluate the integral $\int \sin^2 4x \cos 4x\, dx$.

Solution

Let $u = \sin 4x$. Then $du/dx = 4\cos 4x$.

$$\int \sin^2 4x \cos 4x\, dx = \frac{1}{4}\int \overbrace{(\sin 4x)^2}^{u^2}\overbrace{(4\cos 4x)}^{du/dx}\, dx$$

$$= \frac{1}{4}\int u^2\, du$$

$$= \frac{1}{4}\frac{u^3}{3} + C$$

$$= \frac{1}{4}\frac{(\sin 4x)^3}{3} + C$$

$$= \frac{1}{12}\sin^3 4x + C$$

EXAMPLE 6 *Using the Log Rule*

Evaluate the integral $\displaystyle\int \frac{\sin x}{\cos x}\,dx$.

Solution

Let $u = \cos x$. Then $du/dx = -\sin x$.

$$\int \frac{\sin x}{\cos x}\,dx = -\int \frac{-\sin x}{\cos x}\,dx \qquad \text{Rewrite integrand.}$$

$$= -\int \frac{du/dx}{u}\,dx \qquad \text{Substitute for } \cos x \text{ and } -\sin x.$$

$$= -\ln|u| + C \qquad \text{Log Rule}$$

$$= -\ln|\cos x| + C \qquad \text{Substitute for } u. \quad \blacksquare$$

EXAMPLE 7 *Evaluating a Definite Integral*

Evaluate the definite integral $\displaystyle\int_0^{\pi/4} \cos 2x\,dx$.

Solution

$$\int_0^{\pi/4} \cos 2x\,dx = \left[\frac{1}{2}\sin 2x\right]_0^{\pi/4}$$

$$= \frac{1}{2} - 0$$

$$= \frac{1}{2} \qquad\qquad \blacksquare$$

EXAMPLE 8 *Finding Area by Integration*

Find the area of the region bounded by the x-axis and one arc of the graph of $y = \sin x$.

Solution

As indicated in Figure T.34, this area is given by

$$\text{Area} = \int_0^{\pi} \sin x\,dx$$

$$= \left[-\cos x\right]_0^{\pi}$$

$$= -(-1) - (-1)$$

$$= 2.$$

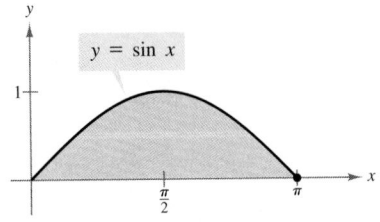

FIGURE T.34

Thus, the region has an area of 2. $\quad \blacksquare$

Other Trigonometric Integrals

At the beginning of this section, the integration rules for the sine and cosine functions were listed. Now, using the result of Example 6, you have an integration rule for the tangent function. That rule is

$$\int \tan x \, dx = \int \frac{\sin x}{\cos x} \, dx = -\ln|\cos x| + C.$$

Integration formulas for the other three trigonometric functions can be developed in a similar way. For instance, to integrate the secant function, you can write the following.

$$\int \sec x \, dx = \int \frac{\sec x (\sec x + \tan x)}{\sec x + \tan x} \, dx$$

$$= \int \frac{\sec^2 x + \sec x \tan x}{\sec x + \tan x} \, dx \qquad \textit{Use substitution with}$$
$$\qquad\qquad\qquad\qquad\qquad\qquad\qquad \textit{u} = \sec x + \tan x$$

$$= \ln|\sec x + \tan x| + C$$

These formulas, and integration formulas for the other two trigonometric functions, are summarized below.

Integrals of Trigonometric Functions

$$\int \tan u \, du = -\ln|\cos u| + C \qquad \int \sec u \, du = \ln|\sec u + \tan u| + C$$

$$\int \cot u \, du = \ln|\sin u| + C \qquad \int \csc u \, du = \ln|\csc u - \cot u| + C$$

EXAMPLE 9 *Integrating a Trigonometric Function*

Evaluate the integral $\int \tan 4x \, dx$.

Solution
Let $u = 4x$. Then $du = 4 \, dx$.

$$\int \tan 4x \, dx = \frac{1}{4} \int (\tan 4x) 4 \, dx \qquad\qquad \textit{Rewrite integrand.}$$

$$= \frac{1}{4} \int \tan u \, du \qquad\qquad \textit{Substitute for } 4x \textit{ and } 4 \, dx.$$

$$= -\frac{1}{4} \ln|\cos u| + C \qquad\qquad \textit{Tangent Rule}$$

$$= -\frac{1}{4} \ln|\cos 4x| + C \qquad\qquad \textit{Substitute for u.}$$

Application

In the next example, recall that the average value of a function f over an interval $[a, b]$ is given by

$$\frac{1}{b-a}\int_{a}^{b} f(x)\, dx.$$

Real Life

EXAMPLE 10 *Finding an Average Temperature*

The temperature T (in degrees Fahrenheit) during a 24-hour period can be modeled by

$$T = 72 + 18 \sin \frac{\pi(t-8)}{12},$$

where t is the time (in hours), with $t = 0$ representing midnight. Find the average temperature during the 4-hour period from noon to 4 P.M.

Solution

To find the average temperature A, use the formula for the average value of a function over an interval.

$$A = \frac{1}{4}\int_{12}^{16}\left[72 + 18\sin\frac{\pi(t-8)}{12}\right] dt$$

$$= \frac{1}{4}\left[72t + 18\left(\frac{12}{\pi}\right)\left(-\cos\frac{\pi(t-8)}{12}\right)\right]_{12}^{16}$$

$$= \frac{1}{4}\left[72(16) + 18\left(\frac{12}{\pi}\right)\left(\frac{1}{2}\right) - 72(12) + 18\left(\frac{12}{\pi}\right)\left(\frac{1}{2}\right)\right]$$

$$= \frac{1}{4}\left(288 + \frac{216}{\pi}\right)$$

$$= 72 + \frac{54}{\pi} \approx 89.2°$$

Thus, the average temperature is 89.2°, as indicated in Figure T.35. ▪

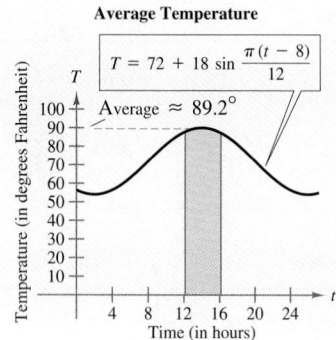

Average Temperature

$T = 72 + 18 \sin \dfrac{\pi(t-8)}{12}$

Average ≈ 89.2°

Temperature (in degrees Fahrenheit)

Time (in hours)

FIGURE T.35

Discussion Problem   *Finding Average Temperature*

Use the temperature model in Example 10 to find the average temperature during the given time intervals. What can you conclude?

a. From midnight to the following midnight

b. From midnight to noon

c. From noon to midnight

Warm Up

The following warm-up exercises involve skills that were covered in earlier sections. You will use these skills in the exercise set for this section.

In Exercises 1–4, evaluate the trigonometric function.

1. $\cos\dfrac{5\pi}{4}$

2. $\sin\left(-\dfrac{\pi}{3}\right)$

3. $\tan\dfrac{5\pi}{6}$

4. $\sec\pi$

In Exercises 5–8, simplify the expression using the trigonometric identities.

5. $\sin x \sec x$

6. $\cos^2 x(\sec^2 x - 1)$

7. $\sec x \sin\left(\dfrac{\pi}{2} - x\right)$

8. $\cot x \sec x$

In Exercises 9 and 10, evaluate the definite integral.

9. $\displaystyle\int_0^4 \left(x^2 + 3x - 4\right) dx$

10. $\displaystyle\int_0^2 x(4 - x^2)\, dx$

E X E R C I S E S   T.5 means that technology can help you solve or check the exercise(s).

In Exercises 1–34, evaluate the integral.

1. $\displaystyle\int (2\sin x + 3\cos x)\, dx$

2. $\displaystyle\int (t^2 - \sin t)\, dt$

3. $\displaystyle\int (1 - \csc t \cot t)\, dt$

4. $\displaystyle\int (\theta^2 + \sec^2\theta)\, d\theta$

5. $\displaystyle\int (\csc^2\theta - \cos\theta)\, d\theta$

6. $\displaystyle\int (\sec y \tan y - \sec^2 y)\, dy$

7. $\displaystyle\int \sin 2x\, dx$

8. $\displaystyle\int \cos 6x\, dx$

9. $\displaystyle\int x \cos x^2\, dx$

10. $\displaystyle\int x \sin x^2\, dx$

11. $\displaystyle\int \sec^2 \dfrac{x}{2}\, dx$

12. $\displaystyle\int \csc^2 \dfrac{x}{2}\, dx$

13. $\displaystyle\int \tan 3x\, dx$

14. $\displaystyle\int \csc 2x \cot 2x\, dx$

15. $\displaystyle\int \tan^3 x \sec^2 x\, dx$

16. $\displaystyle\int \sqrt{\cot x}\, \csc^2 x\, dx$

17. $\displaystyle\int \cot \pi x\, dx$

18. $\displaystyle\int \tan 5x\, dx$

19. $\displaystyle\int \csc 2x\, dx$

20. $\displaystyle\int \sec \dfrac{x}{2}\, dx$

21. $\displaystyle\int \dfrac{\sec^2 2x}{\tan 2x}\, dx$

22. $\displaystyle\int \dfrac{\sin x}{\cos^2 x}\, dx$

23. $\displaystyle\int \dfrac{\sec x \tan x}{\sec x - 1}\, dx$

24. $\displaystyle\int \dfrac{\cos t}{1 + \sin t}\, dt$

25. $\displaystyle\int \dfrac{\sin x}{1 + \cos x}\, dx$

26. $\displaystyle\int \dfrac{\sin \sqrt{x}}{\sqrt{x}}\, dx$

27. $\displaystyle\int \dfrac{\csc^2 x}{\cot^3 x}\, dx$

28. $\displaystyle\int \dfrac{1 - \cos\theta}{\theta - \sin\theta}\, d\theta$

29. $\displaystyle\int e^x \sin e^x\, dx$

30. $\displaystyle\int e^{\sin x} \cos x\, dx$

31. $\displaystyle\int e^{-x} \tan e^{-x}\, dx$

32. $\displaystyle\int e^{\sec x} \sec x \tan x\, dx$

33. $\displaystyle\int (\sin 2x + \cos 2x)^2\, dx$

34. $\displaystyle\int (\csc 2\theta - \cot 2\theta)^2\, d\theta$

In Exercises 35–38, evaluate the integral.

35. $\int x \cos x \, dx$

36. $\int x \sin x \, dx$

37. $\int x \sec^2 x \, dx$

38. $\int \theta \sec \theta \tan \theta \, d\theta$

In Exercises 39–46, evaluate the definite integral.

39. $\int_0^{\pi/4} \cos \dfrac{4x}{3} \, dx$

40. $\int_0^{\pi/2} \sin 2x \, dx$

41. $\int_{\pi/2}^{2\pi/3} \sec^2 \dfrac{x}{2} \, dx$

42. $\int_0^{\pi/2} (x + \cos x) \, dx$

43. $\int_{\pi/12}^{\pi/4} \csc 2x \cot 2x \, dx$

44. $\int_0^{\pi/8} \sin 2x \cos 2x \, dx$

45. $\int_0^1 \tan(1 - x) \, dx$

46. $\int_0^{\pi/4} \sec x \tan x \, dx$

In Exercises 47–52, determine the area of the region.

47. $y = \cos \dfrac{x}{4}$

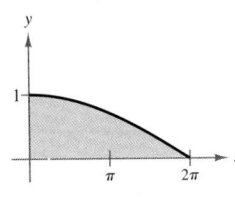

48. $y = \tan x$

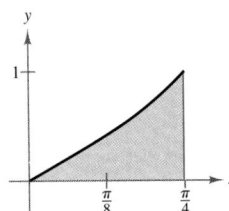

49. $y = x + \sin x$

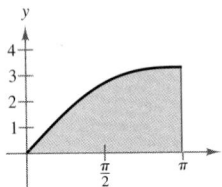

50. $y = 2 \sin x + \sin 2x$

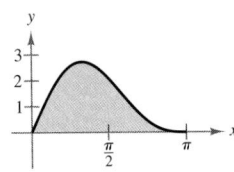

51. $y = \sin x + \cos 2x$

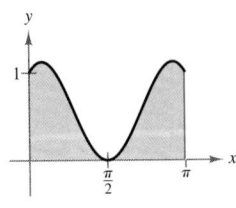

52. $y = x \sin x$

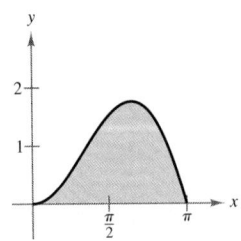

In Exercises 53 and 54, find the volume of the solid generated by revolving the region bounded by the graphs of the given equations about the x-axis.

53. $y = \sec x,\ y = 0,\ x = 0,\ x = \dfrac{\pi}{4}$

54. $y = \csc x,\ y = 0,\ x = \dfrac{\pi}{6},\ x = \dfrac{5\pi}{6}$

In Exercises 55 and 56, find the general solution to the first-order linear differential equation.

55. $y' + 2y = \sin x$

56. $y' \cos^2 x + y = 1$

57. Use a Taylor polynomial of degree 6 to approximate the integral of $(\sin x)/x$ over the interval $[0, \pi/2]$.

58. Use a Taylor polynomial of degree 12 to approximate the integral of $\cos x^2$ over the interval $[0, 1]$.

59. Approximate the definite integral
$$\int_0^{\pi/2} f(x) \, dx, \qquad f(x) = \begin{cases} \dfrac{\sin x}{x}, & x > 0 \\ 1, & x = 0 \end{cases}$$
by letting $n = 4$ and using

(a) the Trapezoidal Rule   (b) Simpson's Rule.

60. Approximate the integral in Exercise 58 by letting $n = 4$ and using

(a) the Trapezoidal Rule   (b) Simpson's Rule.

61. *Average Value* The minimum stockpile level of gasoline in the United States can be approximated by the model
$$Q = 217 + 13 \cos \dfrac{\pi(t - 3)}{6},$$
where Q is measured in millions of barrels of gasoline and t is the time in months, with $t = 1$ corresponding to January. Find the average minimum level given by this model during

(a) the first quarter $(0 \le t \le 3)$
(b) the second quarter $(3 \le t \le 6)$
(c) the entire year $(0 \le t \le 12)$.

62. *Sales* The sales of a seasonal product are given by the model
$$S = 74.50 + 43.75 \sin \dfrac{\pi t}{6},$$
where S is measured in thousands of units and t is the time in months, with $t = 1$ corresponding to January. Find the average sales during

(a) the first quarter $(0 \le t \le 3)$
(b) the second quarter $(3 \le t \le 6)$
(c) the entire year $(0 \le t \le 12)$.

63. *Air-Conditioning Cost* Suppose that the temperature in degrees Fahrenheit is given by

$$T = 72 + 12 \sin \frac{\pi(t-8)}{12},$$

where t is the time in hours, with $t = 0$ representing midnight. Furthermore, suppose that it costs $0.10 to cool a particular house 1° for 1 hour.

(a) Find the cost C of cooling this house if the thermostat is set at 72° and the cost is given by

$$C = 0.1 \int_{8}^{20} \left[72 + 12 \sin \frac{\pi(t-8)}{12} - 72 \right] dt.$$

(b) Find the savings realized by resetting the thermostat to 78° by evaluating the integral

$$C = 0.1 \int_{10}^{18} \left[72 + 12 \sin \frac{\pi(t-8)}{12} - 78 \right] dt.$$

64. *Respiratory Cycle* For a person at rest, the velocity v in liters per second of air flow into and out of the lungs during a respiratory cycle is approximated by

$$v = 0.9 \sin \frac{\pi t}{3},$$

where t is the time in seconds. Find the volume in liters of air inhaled during one cycle by integrating this function over the interval $[0, 3]$.

65. *Respiratory Cycle* After exercising for a few minutes, a person has a respiratory cycle for which the velocity of air flow is approximated by

$$v = 1.75 \sin \frac{\pi t}{2}.$$

How much does the lung capacity of a person increase as a result of exercising? In other words, how much more air is inhaled during a cycle after exercising than is inhaled during a cycle at rest? (See Exercise 64.) (Note that the cycle is shorter and you must integrate over the interval $[0, 2]$.)

66. *Sales* In Example 9 in Section T-4, the sales of a seasonal product were approximated by the model

$$F = 100,000 \left[1 + \sin \frac{2\pi(t-60)}{365} \right],$$

where F was measured in pounds and t was the time in days, with $t = 1$ representing January 1. The manufacturer of this product wants to set up a manufacturing schedule to produce a uniform amount each day. What should this amount be? (Assume that there are 200 production days during the year.)

In Exercises 67–70, use a graphing utility and Simpson's Rule to approximate the integral.

Integral	n
67. $\displaystyle\int_{0}^{\pi/2} \sqrt{x} \sin x \, dx$	$n = 8$
68. $\displaystyle\int_{0}^{\pi/2} \cos \sqrt{x} \, dx$	$n = 8$
69. $\displaystyle\int_{0}^{\pi} \sqrt{1 + \cos^2 x} \, dx$	$n = 20$
70. $\displaystyle\int_{0}^{2} (4 + x + \sin \pi x) \, dx$	$n = 20$

T.6

L'Hôpital's Rule

Indeterminate Forms and Limits ■ *L'Hôpital's Rule*

Indeterminate Forms and Limits

In Sections 1.5 and 3.6, you studied limits such as

$$\lim_{x \to 1} \frac{x^2 - 1}{x - 1} \quad \text{and} \quad \lim_{x \to \infty} \frac{2x + 1}{x + 1}.$$

In those sections, you discovered that direct substitution can produce an **indeterminate form** such as $0/0$ or ∞/∞. For instance, if you substitute $x = 1$ into the first limit, you obtain

$$\lim_{x \to 1} \frac{x^2 - 1}{x - 1} = \frac{0}{0}, \qquad\qquad \textit{Indeterminate form}$$

which tells you nothing about the limit. To find the limit, you can factor and cancel, as follows.

$$\lim_{x \to 1} \frac{x^2 - 1}{x - 1} = \lim_{x \to 1} \frac{(x - 1)(x + 1)}{x - 1} \qquad\qquad \textit{Factor.}$$

$$= \lim_{x \to 1} \frac{\cancel{(x - 1)}(x + 1)}{\cancel{x - 1}} \qquad\qquad \textit{Cancel.}$$

$$= \lim_{x \to 1} (x + 1) \qquad\qquad \textit{Simplify.}$$

$$= 1 + 1 \qquad\qquad \textit{Direct substitution}$$

$$= 2 \qquad\qquad \textit{Simplify.}$$

For the second limit, direct substitution produces the indeterminate form ∞/∞, which again tells you nothing about the limit. To evaluate this limit, you can divide the numerator and denominator by x. Then you can use the fact that the limit of $1/x$, as $x \to \infty$, is 0.

$$\lim_{x \to \infty} \frac{2x + 1}{x + 1} = \lim_{x \to \infty} \frac{2 + (1/x)}{1 + (1/x)} \qquad\qquad \begin{array}{l}\textit{Divide numerator and} \\ \textit{denominator by } x.\end{array}$$

$$= \frac{2 + 0}{1 + 0} \qquad\qquad \textit{Evaluate limits.}$$

$$= 2 \qquad\qquad \textit{Simplify.}$$

Algebraic techniques such as these tend to work well as long as the function itself is algebraic. To find the limit of other types of functions, such as exponential functions or trigonometric functions, you generally need to use a different approach.

EXAMPLE 1 *Approximating a Limit*

Evaluate the limit

$$\lim_{x \to 0} \frac{e^{3x} - 1}{x}.$$

Solution

When evaluating a limit, you can choose from three basic approaches. That is, you can attempt to find the limit *analytically*, *graphically*, or *numerically*. For this particular limit, it is not clear how to use an analytical approach because direct substitution yields an indeterminate form.

$$\lim_{x \to 0} \frac{e^{3x} - 1}{x} = \lim_{x \to 0} \frac{e^{3(0)} - 1}{0} = \frac{0}{0} \qquad \textit{Indeterminate form}$$

Using a graphical approach, graph the function, as shown in Figure T.36. Then use the zoom and trace features to estimate the limit. Using a numerical approach, you can construct a table, such as that shown in Table T.4.

TABLE T.4

x	−0.01	−0.001	−0.0001	0	0.0001	0.001	0.01
$\dfrac{e^{3x} - 1}{x}$	2.9554	2.9955	2.9996		3.0005	3.0045	3.0455

From the values in the table, it appears that the limit is 3. Thus, from either a graphical or a numerical approach, you can approximate the limit to be

$$\lim_{x \to 0} \frac{e^{3x} - 1}{x} = 3.$$

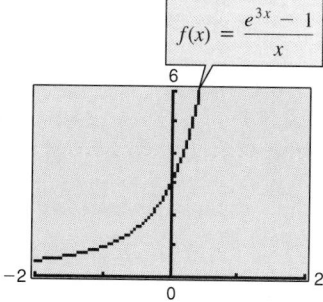

$$f(x) = \frac{e^{3x} - 1}{x}$$

FIGURE T.36

EXAMPLE 2 *Approximating a Limit*

Evaluate the limit $\displaystyle\lim_{x \to 0} \frac{\sin 4x}{x}$.

Solution

As in Example 1, it is not clear how to use an analytical approach because direct substitution yields an indeterminate form.

$$\lim_{x \to 0} \frac{\sin 4x}{x} = \lim_{x \to 0} \frac{\sin 4(0)}{0} = \frac{0}{0} \qquad \textit{Indeterminate form}$$

Using a graphical approach, you can graph the function, as shown in Figure T.37. Then, using the zoom and trace features, you can estimate the limit to be 4. A numerical approach would lead to the same conclusion. Thus, using either a graphical or a numerical approach, you can approximate the limit to be

$$\lim_{x \to 0} \frac{\sin 4x}{x} = 4.$$

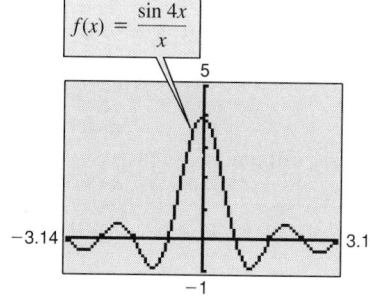

$$f(x) = \frac{\sin 4x}{x}$$

FIGURE T.37

L'Hôpital's Rule

L'Hôpital's Rule, which is named after the French mathematician Guillaume Francois Antoine de L'Hôpital (1661–1704), describes an analytical approach for evaluating limits.

L'Hôpital's Rule

Let (a, b) be an interval that contains c. Let f and g be differentiable in (a, b), except possibly at c. If the limit of $f(x)/g(x)$ as x approaches c produces the indeterminate form $0/0$ or ∞/∞, then

$$\lim_{x \to c} \frac{f(x)}{g(x)} = \lim_{x \to c} \frac{f'(x)}{g'(x)}$$

provided the limit on the right exists or is infinite. The indeterminate form ∞/∞ comes in four forms: ∞/∞, $(-\infty)/\infty$, $\infty/(-\infty)$, and $(-\infty)/(-\infty)$. L'Hôpital's Rule can be applied to each of these forms.

EXAMPLE 3 *Using L'Hôpital's Rule*

Evaluate the limit

$$\lim_{x \to 0} \frac{e^{3x} - 1}{x}.$$

Solution

In Example 1, it was shown that the limit appears to be 3. Because direct substitution produces the indeterminate form $0/0$, you can apply L'Hôpital's Rule to obtain the same result.

$$\lim_{x \to 0} \frac{e^{3x} - 1}{x} = \lim_{x \to 0} \frac{\dfrac{d}{dx}[e^{3x} - 1]}{\dfrac{d}{dx}[x]} \qquad \textit{Apply L'Hôpital's Rule.}$$

$$= \lim_{x \to 0} \frac{3e^{3x}}{1} \qquad \textit{Differentiate numerator and denominator separately.}$$

$$= \frac{3e^{3(0)}}{1} \qquad \textit{Direct substitution}$$

$$= 3 \qquad \textit{Simplify.} \qquad ■$$

Note   Be sure you see that L'Hôpital's Rule involves $f'(x)/g'(x)$, *not* the derivative of the quotient $f(x)/g(x)$.

EXAMPLE 4 *Using L'Hôpital's Rule*

Evaluate the limit

$$\lim_{x \to 0} \frac{\sin 4x}{x}.$$

Note You *cannot* apply L'Hôpital's Rule unless direct substitution produces the indeterminate form $0/0$ or ∞/∞. For instance, if you were to apply L'Hôpital's Rule to the limit

$$\lim_{x \to 0} \frac{x}{e^x},$$

you would incorrectly conclude that the limit is 1. Can you see why this is incorrect?

Solution
In Example 2, it was shown that the limit appears to be 4. Because direct substitution produces the indeterminate form $0/0$

$$\lim_{x \to 0} \frac{\sin 4x}{x} = \frac{0}{0}, \qquad \text{\textit{Indeterminate form}}$$

you can apply L'Hôpital's Rule to obtain the same result.

$$\lim_{x \to 0} \frac{\sin 4x}{x} = \lim_{x \to 0} \frac{\dfrac{d}{dx}[\sin 4x]}{\dfrac{d}{dx}[x]} \qquad \text{\textit{Apply L'Hôpital's Rule.}}$$

$$= \lim_{x \to 0} \frac{4 \cos 4x}{1} \qquad \text{\textit{Differentiate numerator and denominator separately.}}$$

$$= \frac{4 \cos[4(0)]}{1} \qquad \text{\textit{Direct substitution}}$$

$$= 4 \qquad \text{\textit{Simplify.}}$$

EXAMPLE 5 *Using L'Hôpital's Rule*

Evaluate the limit

$$\lim_{x \to \infty} \frac{e^x}{e^{2x} + 1}.$$

Note Another form of L'Hôpital's Rule states that if the limit of $f(x)/g(x)$ as x approaches ∞ or $-\infty$ produces the indeterminate form $0/0$ or ∞/∞, then

$$\lim_{x \to \infty} \frac{f(x)}{g(x)} = \lim_{x \to \infty} \frac{f'(x)}{g'(x)}.$$

This form is used in Example 5.

Solution
Because direct substitution produces the indeterminate form ∞/∞

$$\lim_{x \to \infty} \frac{e^x}{e^{2x} + 1} = \frac{\infty}{\infty}, \qquad \text{\textit{Indeterminate form}}$$

you can apply L'Hôpital's Rule, as follows.

$$\lim_{x \to \infty} \frac{e^x}{e^{2x} + 1} = \lim_{x \to \infty} \frac{\dfrac{d}{dx}[e^x]}{\dfrac{d}{dx}[e^{2x} + 1]} \qquad \text{\textit{Apply L'Hôpital's Rule.}}$$

$$= \lim_{x \to \infty} \frac{e^x}{2e^{2x}} \qquad \text{\textit{Differentiate numerator and denominator separately.}}$$

$$= \lim_{x \to \infty} \frac{1}{2e^x} \qquad \text{\textit{Simplify.}}$$

$$= 0 \qquad \text{\textit{Evaluate limit.}}$$

Sometimes it is necessary to apply L'Hôpital's Rule more than once to remove an indeterminate form. This is illustrated in Example 6.

EXAMPLE 6 *Using L'Hôpital's Rule Repeatedly*

Evaluate the limit $\displaystyle\lim_{x \to -\infty} \frac{x^2}{e^{-x}}$.

Solution

Because direct substitution results in the indeterminate form ∞/∞

$$\lim_{x \to -\infty} \frac{x^2}{e^{-x}} = \frac{\infty}{\infty}, \qquad\qquad\qquad \textit{Indeterminate form}$$

you can apply L'Hôpital's Rule, as follows.

$$\lim_{x \to -\infty} \frac{x^2}{e^{-x}} = \lim_{x \to -\infty} \frac{\dfrac{d}{dx}[x^2]}{\dfrac{d}{dx}[e^{-x}]} \qquad\qquad \textit{Apply L'Hôpital's Rule.}$$

$$= \lim_{x \to -\infty} \frac{2x}{-e^{-x}} \qquad\qquad \begin{array}{l}\textit{Differentiate numerator and}\\ \textit{denominator separately.}\end{array}$$

$$= \frac{-\infty}{-\infty} \qquad\qquad\qquad \textit{Indeterminate form}$$

After one application of L'Hôpital's Rule, you still obtain an indeterminate form. In such cases, you can try L'Hôpital's Rule again, as follows.

$$\lim_{x \to -\infty} \frac{2x}{-e^{-x}} = \lim_{x \to -\infty} \frac{\dfrac{d}{dx}[2x]}{\dfrac{d}{dx}[-e^{-x}]} \qquad\qquad \textit{Apply L'Hôpital's Rule.}$$

$$= \lim_{x \to -\infty} \frac{2}{e^{-x}} \qquad\qquad \begin{array}{l}\textit{Differentiate numerator and}\\ \textit{denominator separately.}\end{array}$$

$$= 0 \qquad\qquad\qquad \textit{Evaluate limit.}$$

Thus, you can conclude that the limit is 0. ■

Note Remember that even in those cases in which L'Hôpital's Rule can be applied to determine a limit, it is still a good idea to confirm the result graphically or numerically. For instance, Table T.5 provides a numerical confirmation of the limit in Example 6.

TABLE T.5

x	-2	-4	-6	-8	-10	-12
$\dfrac{x^2}{e^{-x}}$	0.5413	0.2931	0.0892	0.0215	0.0045	0.0008

L'Hôpital's Rule can be used to compare the rate of growth of two functions. For instance, consider the limit in Example 5

$$\lim_{x \to \infty} \frac{e^x}{e^{2x} + 1} = 0.$$

Both of the functions $f(x) = e^x$ and $g(x) = e^{2x} + 1$ approach infinity as $x \to \infty$. However, because the quotient $f(x)/g(x)$ approaches 0 as $x \to \infty$, it follows that the denominator is growing much more rapidly than the numerator.

EXAMPLE 7 *Comparing Rates of Growth*

Each of the following functions approaches infinity as x approaches infinity. Which function has the most rapid rate of growth?

a. $f(x) = x$ **b.** $g(x) = e^x$ **c.** $h(x) = \ln x$

Solution

Using L'Hôpital's Rule, you can show that each of the following limits is 0.

$$\lim_{x \to \infty} \frac{x}{e^x} = \lim_{x \to \infty} \frac{\frac{d}{dx}[x]}{\frac{d}{dx}[e^x]} = \lim_{x \to \infty} \frac{1}{e^x} = 0$$

$$\lim_{x \to \infty} \frac{\ln x}{x} = \lim_{x \to \infty} \frac{\frac{d}{dx}[\ln x]}{\frac{d}{dx}[x]} = \lim_{x \to \infty} \frac{1}{x} = 0$$

$$\lim_{x \to \infty} \frac{\ln x}{e^x} = \lim_{x \to \infty} \frac{\frac{d}{dx}[\ln x]}{\frac{d}{dx}[e^x]} = \lim_{x \to \infty} \frac{1}{xe^x} = 0$$

From this, you can conclude that $h(x) = \ln x$ has the slowest rate of growth, $f(x) = x$ has the next fastest, and $g(x) = e^x$ has the fastest. This conclusion is confirmed graphically in Figure T.38.

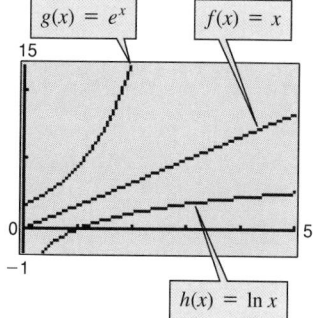

FIGURE T.38

Discussion Problem   *Comparing Rates of Growth*

Each of the following functions approaches infinity as x approaches infinity. In each pair, which function has the more rapid rate of growth?

a. $f(x) = e^x$, $g(x) = e^{\sqrt{x}}$ **c.** $f(x) = \tan \dfrac{\pi x}{2x + 1}$, $g(x) = x$

b. $f(x) = \sqrt{x^3 + 1}$, $g(x) = x$

Warm Up

The following warm-up exercises involve skills that were covered in earlier sections. You will use these skills in the exercise set for this section.

In Exercises 1–4, find the indicated limit.

1. $\lim\limits_{x \to \infty} (x^2 - 10x + 1)$

2. $\lim\limits_{x \to \infty} \dfrac{x+1}{x^2}$

3. $\lim\limits_{x \to \infty} \dfrac{2x^2 - 5x + 7}{3x^2 + 12x + 4}$

4. $\lim\limits_{x \to \infty} \dfrac{x^2 - 5}{2x + 7}$

In Exercises 5–8, find the first derivative of the function.

5. $f(x) = \cos x^2$

6. $f(x) = \sin(5x - 1)$

7. $f(x) = \sec 4x$

8. $f(x) = \tan(x^2 - 2)$

In Exercises 9 and 10, find the second derivative of the function.

9. $f(x) = \sin(2x + 3)$

10. $f(x) = \tan x$

E X E R C I S E S   T.6   means that technology can help you solve or check the exercise(s).

In Exercises 1–6, decide whether the limit produces an indeterminate form.

1. $\lim\limits_{x \to 0} \dfrac{2x + \sqrt{x}}{x}$

2. $\lim\limits_{x \to \infty} \dfrac{x^2 + 4x - 3}{7x^2 + 2}$

3. $\lim\limits_{x \to -\infty} \dfrac{4}{x^2 + e^x}$

4. $\lim\limits_{x \to 0} \dfrac{\sin x}{e^x}$

5. $\lim\limits_{x \to \infty} \dfrac{2xe^{2x}}{3e^x}$

6. $\lim\limits_{x \to \infty} \dfrac{\ln x}{x}$

In Exercises 7–10, complete the table to estimate the limit numerically.

7. $\lim\limits_{x \to 0} \dfrac{e^{-x} - 1}{3x}$

x	−0.1	−0.01	−0.001	0	0.001	0.01	0.1
$f(x)$							

8. $\lim\limits_{x \to 3} \dfrac{x^2 + x - 12}{x^2 - 9}$

x	2.9	2.99	2.999	3	3.001	3.01	3.1
$f(x)$							

9. $\lim\limits_{x \to 0} \dfrac{\sin x}{5x}$

x	−0.1	−0.01	−0.001	0	0.001	0.01	0.1
$f(x)$							

10. $\lim\limits_{x \to 0} \dfrac{\cos 2x - 1}{6x}$

x	−0.1	−0.01	−0.001	0	0.001	0.01	0.1
$f(x)$							

In Exercises 11–14, use a graphing utility to find the indicated limit graphically.

11. $\lim\limits_{x \to \infty} \dfrac{\ln x}{x^2}$

12. $\lim\limits_{x \to \infty} \dfrac{e^x}{x^2}$

13. $\lim\limits_{x \to 2} \dfrac{x^2 - x - 2}{x^2 - 5x + 6}$

14. $\lim\limits_{x \to 1} \dfrac{x^2 + 3x - 4}{x^2 + 2x - 3}$

In Exercises 15–40, use L'Hôpital's Rule to find the limit. You may need to use L'Hôpital's Rule repeatedly.

15. $\displaystyle\lim_{x\to 0}\frac{e^{-x}-1}{x}$

16. $\displaystyle\lim_{x\to 3}\frac{x^2+x-12}{x^2-9}$

17. $\displaystyle\lim_{x\to 0}\frac{\sin x}{5x}$

18. $\displaystyle\lim_{x\to 0}\frac{\cos 2x-1}{6x}$

19. $\displaystyle\lim_{x\to\infty}\frac{\ln x}{x^2}$

20. $\displaystyle\lim_{x\to\infty}\frac{e^x}{x^2}$

21. $\displaystyle\lim_{x\to 2}\frac{x^2-x-2}{x^2-5x+6}$

22. $\displaystyle\lim_{x\to 1}\frac{x^2+3x-4}{x^2+2x-3}$

23. $\displaystyle\lim_{x\to 0}\frac{2x+1-e^x}{x}$

24. $\displaystyle\lim_{x\to 0}\frac{2x-1+e^{-x}}{3x}$

25. $\displaystyle\lim_{x\to\infty}\frac{\ln x}{e^x}$

26. $\displaystyle\lim_{x\to\infty}\frac{3x}{e^x}$

27. $\displaystyle\lim_{x\to\infty}\frac{4x^2+2x-1}{3x^2-7}$

28. $\displaystyle\lim_{x\to\infty}\frac{3x^2+5}{2x^2-11}$

29. $\displaystyle\lim_{x\to\infty}\frac{1-x}{e^x}$

30. $\displaystyle\lim_{x\to 0}\frac{e^{3x}-1}{2x}$

31. $\displaystyle\lim_{x\to 1}\frac{\ln x}{x^2-1}$

32. $\displaystyle\lim_{x\to 2}\frac{\ln(x-1)}{x-2}$

33. $\displaystyle\lim_{x\to 0}\frac{\sin 2x}{\sin 5x}$

34. $\displaystyle\lim_{x\to\frac{\pi}{2}}\frac{2\cos x}{3\cos x}$

35. $\displaystyle\lim_{x\to 0}\frac{\sin x}{e^x-1}$

36. $\displaystyle\lim_{x\to\pi}\frac{\cos(x/2)}{x-\pi}$

37. $\displaystyle\lim_{x\to\infty}\frac{x}{\sqrt{x^2+1}}$

38. $\displaystyle\lim_{x\to 0}\frac{\sqrt{4-x^2}-2}{x}$

39. $\displaystyle\lim_{x\to\infty}\frac{e^{3x}}{x^3}$

40. $\displaystyle\lim_{x\to\infty}\frac{x^2}{e^x\ln x}$

In Exercises 41–48, find the limit. (*Hint:* L'Hôpital's Rule does not apply in every case.)

41. $\displaystyle\lim_{x\to\infty}\frac{x^2+2x+1}{x^2+3}$

42. $\displaystyle\lim_{x\to\infty}\frac{3x^3-7x+5}{4x^3+2x-11}$

43. $\displaystyle\lim_{x\to-1}\frac{x^3+3x^2-6x-8}{2x^3-3x^2-5x+6}$

44. $\displaystyle\lim_{x\to 0}\frac{2x^3-x^2-3x}{x^4+2x^3-9x^2-18x}$

45. $\displaystyle\lim_{x\to 3}\frac{\ln(x-2)}{x-2}$

46. $\displaystyle\lim_{x\to-1}\frac{\ln(x+2)}{x+2}$

47. $\displaystyle\lim_{x\to 1}\frac{2\ln x}{e^x}$

48. $\displaystyle\lim_{x\to 0}\frac{\sin\pi x}{x}$

In Exercises 49–54, use L'Hôpital's Rule to compare the rate of growth of the numerator and the denominator.

49. $\displaystyle\lim_{x\to\infty}\frac{x^2}{e^{4x}}$

50. $\displaystyle\lim_{x\to\infty}\frac{x^3}{e^{2x}}$

51. $\displaystyle\lim_{x\to\infty}\frac{(\ln x)^4}{x}$

52. $\displaystyle\lim_{x\to\infty}\frac{(\ln x)^2}{x^4}$

53. $\displaystyle\lim_{x\to\infty}\frac{(\ln x)^n}{x^m}$

54. $\displaystyle\lim_{x\to\infty}\frac{x^m}{e^{nx}}$

55. Complete the table to show that x eventually "overpowers" $(\ln x)^5$.

x	10	10^2	10^3	10^4	10^5	10^6
$\dfrac{(\ln x)^5}{x}$						

56. Complete the table to show that e^x eventually "overpowers" x^6.

x	1	2	4	8	12	20	30
$\dfrac{e^x}{x^6}$							

In Exercises 57–60, L'Hôpital's Rule is used incorrectly. Describe the error.

57. $\displaystyle\lim_{x\to 0}\frac{e^{3x}-1}{e^x}=\lim_{x\to 0}\frac{3e^{3x}}{e^x}=\lim_{x\to 0}3e^{2x}=3$

58. $\displaystyle\lim_{x\to 0}\frac{\sin\pi x+1}{x}=\lim_{x\to 0}\frac{\pi\cos\pi x}{1}=\pi$

59. $\displaystyle\lim_{x\to 1}\frac{e^x-1}{\ln x}=\lim_{x\to 1}\frac{e^x}{(1/x)}=\lim_{x\to 1}xe^x=e$

60. $\displaystyle\lim_{x\to\infty}\frac{e^{-x}}{1-e^{-x}}=\lim_{x\to\infty}\frac{-e^{-x}}{e^{-x}}=\lim_{x\to\infty}-1=-1$

In Exercises 61–64, use a graphing utility to (a) graph the function and (b) find the limit (if it exists).

61. $\displaystyle\lim_{x\to 2}\frac{x-2}{\ln(3x-5)}$

62. $\displaystyle\lim_{x\to\infty}\frac{x^4}{e^x}$

63. $\displaystyle\lim_{x\to-2}\frac{\sqrt{x^2-4}-5}{x+2}$

64. $\displaystyle\lim_{x\to 0}\frac{3\tan x}{5x}$

True or False In Exercises 65–68, determine whether the statement is true or false. Explain your reasoning.

65. $\lim\limits_{x\to 0} \dfrac{x^2 + 3x - 1}{x + 1} = \lim\limits_{x\to 0} \dfrac{2x + 3}{1} = 3$

66. $\lim\limits_{x\to\infty} \dfrac{x}{1 - x} = \lim\limits_{x\to\infty} \dfrac{1}{-1} = 1$

67. If
$$\lim_{x\to\infty} \frac{f(x)}{g(x)} = 0,$$
then $g(x)$ has a more rapid growth rate than $f(x)$.

68. If $\lim\limits_{x\to\infty} \dfrac{f(x)}{g(x)} = 1$, then $g(x) = f(x)$.

69. Show that L'Hôpital's Rule fails for the limit
$$\lim_{x\to\infty} \frac{x}{\sqrt{x^2 + 1}}.$$
What is the limit?

 70. Use a graphing utility to graph
$$f(x) = \frac{x^k - 1}{k}$$
for $k = 1, 0.1$, and 0.01. Then find
$$\lim_{k\to 0^+} \frac{x^k - 1}{k}.$$

 71. *Sales Growth* The growth in sales for the years 1986 through 1992 for two major toy companies is modeled by

$f(t) = 1289.75 + 17.22t^2 + 1.67e^t$ *Hasbro*

$g(t) = 2419.55 + 774.58t,$ *Toys R Us*

where $t = 0$ corresponds to 1986. *(Source: Hasbro; Toys R Us)*

(a) Which company has the faster rate of growth of sales?

(b) Use a graphing utility to graph the models f and g for $0 \le x \le 10$. If the rate of growth of the sales of each company continues according to the model, when will the sales of the faster growing company exceed the sales of the slower growing company?

72. ***Research Project*** Use your school's library or some other reference source to gather data on the sales growth of two competing companies. Model the data for both companies, and determine which company is growing at a faster rate. Write a short paper that describes your findings, including the factors that account for the growth of the faster growing company.

— *Business Capsule* ——————

Anne States Photography

Toy companies depend on innovative ideas to increase sales. In 1990, Larami Corp. marketed the Super Soaker, created by Atlanta toy inventor Lonnie Johnson. By 1993, 27 million Super Soakers had been sold, making it the most popular water gun in American retail history.

Chapter Summary and Study Tips

After studying this chapter, you should have acquired the following skills. The exercise numbers are keyed to the Review Exercises that begin on page T-61. Answers to odd-numbered Review Exercises are given in the back of the text.

■ Find coterminal angles. (*Section T.1*)   Review Exercises 1–4

■ Convert from degree to radian measure and from radian to degree measure.   Review Exercises 5–12
   (*Section T.1*)

   π radians = $180°$

■ Use formulas relating to triangles. (*Section T.1*)   Review Exercises 13–16

■ Use formulas relating to triangles to solve real-life problems. (*Section T.1*)   Review Exercises 17, 18

■ Find the reference angles for given angles. (*Section T.2*)   Review Exercises 19–22

■ Evaluate trigonometric functions exactly. (*Section T.2*)   Review Exercises 23–30

   Right Triangle Definition: $0 < \theta < \dfrac{\pi}{2}$.

   $$\sin\theta = \frac{\text{opp.}}{\text{hyp.}} \qquad \cos\theta = \frac{\text{adj.}}{\text{hyp.}} \qquad \tan\theta = \frac{\text{opp.}}{\text{adj.}}$$

   $$\csc\theta = \frac{\text{hyp.}}{\text{opp.}} \qquad \sec\theta = \frac{\text{hyp.}}{\text{adj.}} \qquad \cot\theta = \frac{\text{adj.}}{\text{opp.}}$$

   Circular Function Definition: θ is any angle in standard position and (x, y) is a point on the terminal ray of the angle.

   $$\sin\theta = \frac{y}{r} \qquad \cos\theta = \frac{x}{r} \qquad \tan\theta = \frac{y}{x}$$

   $$\csc\theta = \frac{r}{y} \qquad \sec\theta = \frac{r}{x} \qquad \cot\theta = \frac{x}{y}$$

■ Use a calculator to approximate values of trigonometric functions. (*Section T.2*)   Review Exercises 31–34

■ Solve right triangles. (*Section T.2*)   Review Exercises 35–38

■ Solve trigonometric equations. (*Section T.2*)   Review Exercises 39–44

■ Use right triangles to solve real-life problems. (*Section T.2*)   Review Exercises 45, 46

■ Sketch graphs of trigonometric functions. (*Section T.3*)   Review Exercises 47–54

■ Use trigonometric functions to model real-life situations. (*Section T.3*)   Review Exercises 55, 56

■ Find derivatives of trigonometric functions. (*Section T.4*)   Review Exercises 57–68

   $$\frac{d}{dx}[\sin u] = \cos u \frac{du}{dx} \qquad\qquad \frac{d}{dx}[\cos u] = -\sin u \frac{du}{dx}$$

   $$\frac{d}{dx}[\tan u] = \sec^2 u \frac{du}{dx} \qquad\qquad \frac{d}{dx}[\cot u] = -\csc^2 u \frac{du}{dx}$$

   $$\frac{d}{dx}[\sec u] = \sec u \tan u \frac{du}{dx} \qquad\qquad \frac{d}{dx}[\csc u] = -\csc u \cot u \frac{du}{dx}$$

* Several student study aids are available with this text. The *Student Solutions Guide* includes detailed solutions to all odd-numbered exercises, as well as practice chapter tests with answers. The *Graphics Calculator Guide* offers instructions on the use of a variety of graphing calculators and computer graphing software. The *Brief Calculus TUTOR* includes additional examples for selected exercises in the text.

▪   Analyze the graphs of trigonometric functions. (*Section T.4*)

▪   Use relative extrema to solve real-life problems. (*Section T.4*)

▪   Solve trigonometric integrals. (*Section T.5*)

$$\int \cos u \, du = \sin u + C \qquad \int \sin u \, du = -\cos u + C$$

$$\int \sec^2 u \, du = \tan u + C \qquad \int \sec u \tan u \, du = \sec u + C$$

$$\int \csc^2 u \, du = -\cot u + C \qquad \int \csc u \cot u \, du = -\csc u + C$$

$$\int \tan u \, du = -\ln|\cos u| + C \qquad \int \sec u \, du = \ln|\sec u + \tan u| + C$$

$$\int \cot u \, du = \ln|\sin u| + C \qquad \int \csc u \, du = \ln|\csc u - \cot u| + C$$

▪   Find the areas of regions in the plane. (*Section T.5*)

▪   Use trigonometric integrals to solve real-life problems. (*Section T.5*)

▪   Use L'Hôpital's Rule to evaluate limits. (*Section T.6*)

▪   Compare the rates of growth of two functions. (*Section T.6*)

▪   Degree and Radian Modes   When using a computer or calculator to evaluate or graph a trigonometric function, be sure that you use the proper mode: radian mode or degree mode.

▪   Checking the Form of an Answer   Because of the abundance of trigonometric identities, solutions of problems in this chapter can take a variety of forms. For instance, the expressions $-\ln|\cot x| + C$ and $\ln|\tan x| + C$ are equivalent. Thus, when you are checking your solutions with those given in the back of the text, remember that your solution might be correct—even if its form doesn't agree precisely with that given in the text.

▪   Using Technology   Throughout this chapter, remember that technology can help you *graph* trigonometric functions, *evaluate* trigonometric functions, *differentiate* trigonometric functions, and *integrate* trigonometric functions. Consider, for instance, the difficulty of sketching the graph of the function below *without* using a graphing utility.

Review Exercises

 means that technology can help you solve or check the exercise(s).

In Exercises 1–4, sketch the angle in standard position and list one positive and one negative coterminal angle.

1. $\dfrac{11\pi}{4}$ **2.** $\dfrac{2\pi}{9}$

3. $110°$ **4.** $-405°$

In Exercises 5–8, convert the degree measure to radian measure.

5. $210°$ **6.** $-75°$

7. $-480°$ **8.** $810°$

In Exercises 9–12, convert the radian measure to degree measure.

9. $\dfrac{7\pi}{3}$ **10.** $\dfrac{9\pi}{10}$

11. $-\dfrac{3\pi}{5}$ **12.** $-\dfrac{21\pi}{9}$

In Exercises 13–16, solve the triangle for the indicated side and/or angle.

13.

14.

15.

16.
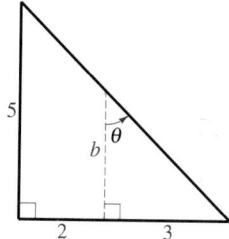

17. *Height* A ladder of length 16 feet leans against the side of a house. The bottom of the ladder is 4.4 feet from the house (see figure). Find the height h of the top of the ladder.

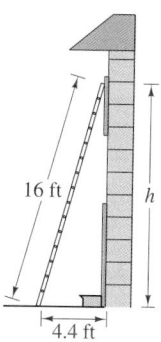

18. *Length* To stabilize a 75-foot tower for a radio antenna, a guy wire must be attached from the top of the tower to an anchor 50 ft from the base. How long is the wire?

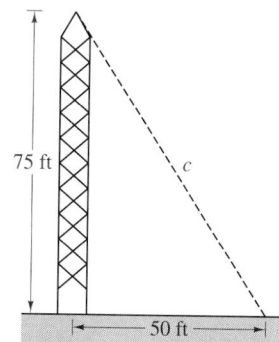

In Exercises 19–22, find the reference angle for the given angle.

19. $\dfrac{18\pi}{3}$

20. $-\dfrac{6\pi}{5}$

21. $252°$

22. $640°$

In Exercises 23–30, evaluate the trigonometric function without using a calculator.

23. $\cos 45°$

24. $\sin 240°$

25. $\tan \dfrac{\pi}{3}$

26. $\csc \dfrac{\pi}{4}$

27. $\sin \dfrac{5\pi}{3}$

28. $\cot \left(-\dfrac{5\pi}{6}\right)$

29. $\sec (-180°)$

30. $\cos \left(-\dfrac{4\pi}{3}\right)$

In Exercises 31–34, use a calculator to evaluate the trigonometric function. Round to four decimal places.

31. $\tan 33°$

32. $\sec \dfrac{12\pi}{5}$

33. $\sin \left(-\dfrac{\pi}{9}\right)$

34. $\cos 105°$

In Exercises 35–38, solve for x, y, or r as indicated.

35.

36.

37.

38.

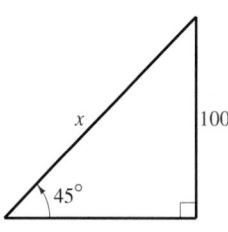

In Exercises 39–44, solve the trigonometric equation.

39. $2\cos x + 1 = 0$

40. $2\sin^2 x = 1$

41. $2\sin^2 x + 3\sin x + 1 = 0$

42. $\cos^3 x = \cos x$

43. $\sec^2 x - \sec x - 2 = 0$

44. $2\sec^2 x + \tan^2 x - 3 = 0$

45. *Height* The length of a shadow of a tree is 125 feet when the angle of elevation of the sun is 33° (see figure). Approximate the height h of the tree.

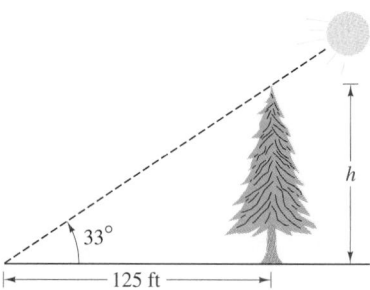

46. *Distance Between Towns* A passenger in an airplane flying at 35,000 feet sees two towns directly to the left of the airplane. The angles of depression to the towns are 32° and 76° (see figure). How far apart are the towns?

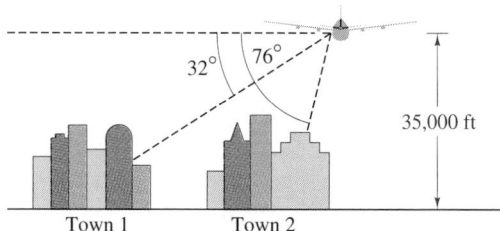

In Exercises 47–54, graph the trigonometric function.

47. $y = 2\cos 6x$

48. $y = \sin 2\pi x$

49. $y = \dfrac{1}{3}\tan x$

50. $y = \cot \dfrac{x}{2}$

51. $y = 3\sin \dfrac{2x}{5}$

52. $y = 8\cos \left(-\dfrac{x}{4}\right)$

53. $y = \sec 2\pi x$

54. $y = 3\csc 2x$

55. *Sales* The daily sales S (in thousands of units) of a seasonal product is modeled by

$$S = 74 + \frac{3}{365}t + 40\sin \frac{2\pi t}{365},$$

where t is the time in days, with $t = 1$ corresponding to January 1. Graph this model over a 1-year period.

56. *Sales* The daily sales S (in hundreds of units) of a seasonal product is modeled by

$$S = 25 + \frac{2}{365}t + 20\sin \frac{2\pi t}{365},$$

where t is the time in days, with $t = 1$ corresponding to January 1. Graph this model over a 1-year period.

In Exercises 57–68, find the derivative of the function.

57. $y = \sin 5\pi x$

58. $y = \tan(4x - \pi)$

59. $y = -x \tan x$

60. $y = \csc 3x + \cot 3x$

61. $y = \dfrac{\cos x}{x^2}$

62. $y = \dfrac{\cos(x-1)}{x-1}$

63. $y = 3 \sin^2 4x + x$

64. $y = x \cos x - \sin x$

65. $y = 2 \csc^3 x$

66. $y = \sec^2 2x$

67. $y = e^x \cot x$

68. $y = \frac{1}{2} e^{\sin 2x}$

In Exercises 69–72, find the relative extrema of the function on the interval $(0, 2\pi)$.

69. $f(x) = \dfrac{x}{2} + \cos x$

70. $f(x) = \sin x \cos x$

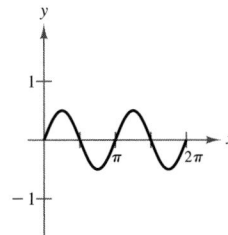

71. $f(x) = \sin^2 x + \sin x$ **72.** $f(x) = \dfrac{\cos x}{1 + \sin^2 x}$

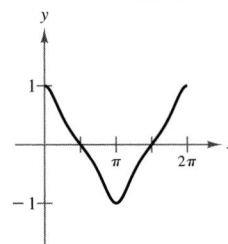

73. *Sales* Refer to the model given in Exercise 55.

(a) Find the maximum daily sales of the product. On what day of the year does the maximum daily sales occur?

(b) Find the minimum daily sales of the product. On what day of the year does the minimum daily sales occur?

74. *Sales* Refer to the model given in Exercise 56.

(a) Find the maximum daily sales of the product. On what day of the year does the maximum daily sales occur?

(b) Find the minimum daily sales of the product. On what day of the year does the minimum daily sales occur?

In Exercises 75–82, evaluate the integral.

75. $\displaystyle \int (3 \sin x - 2 \cos x)\, dx$

76. $\displaystyle \int \csc 2x \cot 2x\, dx$

77. $\displaystyle \int \sin^3 x \cos x\, dx$

78. $\displaystyle \int x \cos x^2\, dx$

79. $\displaystyle \int_0^\pi (1 + \sin x)\, dx$

80. $\displaystyle \int_{-\pi/6}^{\pi/6} \sec^2 x\, dx$

81. $\displaystyle \int_{-\pi/3}^{\pi/3} 4 \sec x \tan x\, dx$

82. $\displaystyle \int_{-\pi/2}^{\pi/2} (2x + \cos x)\, dx$

In Exercises 83–86, find the area of the region.

83. $y = \sin 2x$

84. $y = \cot x$

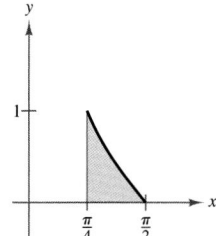

85. $y = 2 \sin x + \cos 3x$

86. $y = 2 \cos x + \cos 2x$

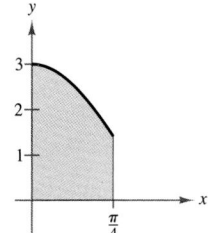

87. *Energy Consumption* Domestic energy consumption in the United States is seasonal. Assume that consumption is approximated by the model

$$Q = 6.9 + \cos \frac{\pi(2t - 1)}{12},$$

where Q is the total consumption (in quadrillion BTUs) and t is the time in months, with $0 < t \le 1$ corresponding to January (see figure). Find the average consumption rate of domestic energy during a year.

88. *Average Sales* The monthly sales (in millions of units) of a seasonal product can be modeled by

$$S = 15 + 6 \sin \frac{\pi(t - 8)}{6},$$

where t is the time in months, with $0 < t \le 1$ corresponding to January. Find the average monthly sales (a) during a year, and (b) from July through December.

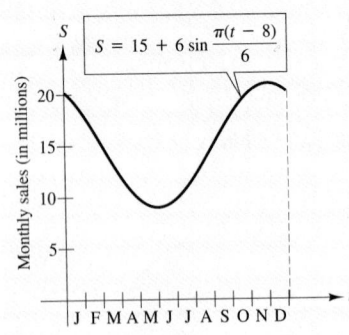

In Exercises 89–96, find the limit. Use L'Hôpital's Rule when necessary.

89. $\lim\limits_{x \to 1} \dfrac{3x - 1}{5x + 5}$

90. $\lim\limits_{x \to 2} \dfrac{x^2 + 2x + 11}{x^3 + 4}$

91. $\lim\limits_{x \to 1} \dfrac{x^3 - x^2 + 4x - 4}{x^3 - 6x^2 + 5x}$

92. $\lim\limits_{x \to 2} \dfrac{4x^2 + 13x - 42}{3x^2 - 23x + 34}$

93. $\lim\limits_{x \to 0} \dfrac{\sin \pi x}{\sin 2\pi x}$

94. $\lim\limits_{x \to 0} \dfrac{\cos^2 x - 1}{\sin x}$

95. $\lim\limits_{x \to 0} \dfrac{\sin^2 x}{e^x}$

96. $\lim\limits_{x \to \infty} \dfrac{e^{5x}}{x^2}$

97. Given

$$\lim\limits_{x \to \infty} \frac{f(x)}{g(x)} = 0,$$

what can you say about the rates of growth of f and g?

98. Given

$$\lim\limits_{x \to \infty} \frac{f(x)}{g(x)} = \infty,$$

what can you say about the rates of growth of f and g?

Appendix A

Alternate Introduction to the Fundamental Theorem of Calculus

In this appendix we use a summation process to provide an alternate development of the definite integral. It is intended that this supplement follow Section 5.3 in the text. If used, this appendix should replace the material preceding Example 2 in Section 5.4.

Area of a Region in the Plane

We begin by showing how the area of a region in the plane can be approximated by the use of rectangles.

EXAMPLE 1   Using Rectangles to Approximate the Area of a Region

Use the four rectangles indicated in Figure A.1 to approximate the area of the region lying between the graph of

$$f(x) = \frac{x^2}{2}$$

and the x-axis, between $x = 0$ and $x = 4$.

SOLUTION

We can find the heights of the rectangles by evaluating the function f at each of the midpoints of the subintervals

$$[0, 1], \quad [1, 2], \quad [2, 3], \quad [3, 4].$$

Since the width of each rectangle is 1, the sum of the areas of the four rectangles is

$$S = \overset{\text{width}}{\overbrace{(1)}} \, \overset{\text{height}}{\overbrace{f\left(\frac{1}{2}\right)}} + \overset{\text{width}}{\overbrace{(1)}} \, \overset{\text{height}}{\overbrace{f\left(\frac{3}{2}\right)}} + \overset{\text{width}}{\overbrace{(1)}} \, \overset{\text{height}}{\overbrace{f\left(\frac{5}{2}\right)}} + \overset{\text{width}}{\overbrace{(1)}} \, \overset{\text{height}}{\overbrace{f\left(\frac{7}{2}\right)}}$$

$$= \frac{1}{8} + \frac{9}{8} + \frac{25}{8} + \frac{49}{8}$$

$$= \frac{84}{8} = 10.5.$$

Thus, we approximate the area of the given region to be 10.5.

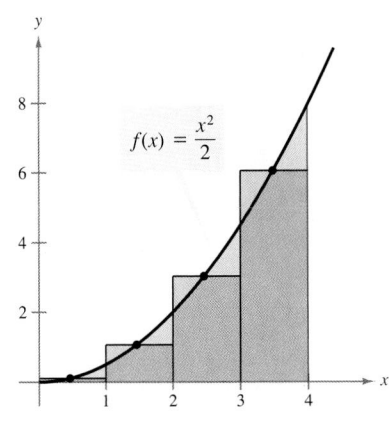

FIGURE A.1

$f(x) = \dfrac{x^2}{2}$

A1

REMARK The approximation technique used in Example 1 is called the **Midpoint Rule.** We will say more about the Midpoint Rule in Section 5.6.

We can generalize the procedure illustrated in Example 1. Let f be a continuous function defined on the closed interval $[a, b]$. To begin, we partition the interval into n subintervals, each of width $\Delta x = (b - a)/n$, as follows.

$$a = x_0 < x_1 < x_2 < \cdots < x_{n-1} < x_n = b$$

In each subinterval $[x_{i-1}, x_i]$ we choose an arbitrary point c_i and form the sum

$$S = f(c_1)\Delta x + f(c_2)\Delta x + \cdots + f(c_{n-1})\Delta x + f(c_n)\Delta x.$$

This type of summation is called a **Riemann sum,** and is often written using summation notation as follows.

$$S = \sum_{i=1}^{n} f(c_i)\Delta x$$

For the Riemann sum in Example 1, the interval is $[a, b] = [0, 4]$, the number of subintervals is $n = 4$, the width of each interval is $\Delta x = 1$, and the point c_i in each subinterval is its midpoint. Thus, we can write the approximation in Example 1 as

$$S = \sum_{i=1}^{n} f(c_i)\Delta x = \sum_{i=1}^{4} f(c_i)(1) = \frac{1}{8} + \frac{9}{8} + \frac{25}{8} + \frac{49}{8} = \frac{84}{8}.$$

EXAMPLE 2 Using a Riemann Sum to Approximate Area

Use a Riemann sum to approximate the area of the region bounded by the graph of $f(x) = -x^2 + 2x$ and the x-axis, for $0 \le x \le 2$. In the Riemann sum, let $n = 6$ and choose c_i to be the left endpoint of each subinterval.

SOLUTION

We subdivide the interval $[0, 2]$ into six subintervals, each of width

$$\Delta x = \frac{2 - 0}{6} = \frac{1}{3},$$

as shown in Figure A.2. Since c_i is the left endpoint of each subinterval, the Riemann sum is given by

$$S = \sum_{i=1}^{n} f(c_i)\Delta x$$

$$= \left[f(0) + f\left(\frac{1}{3}\right) + f\left(\frac{2}{3}\right) + f(1) + f\left(\frac{4}{3}\right) + f\left(\frac{5}{3}\right)\right]\left(\frac{1}{3}\right)$$

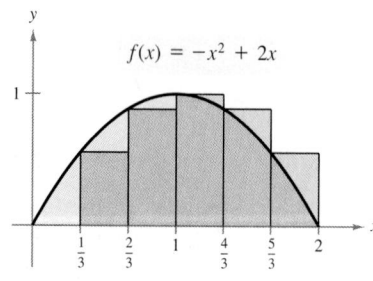

FIGURE A.2

$$= \left[0 + \frac{5}{9} + \frac{8}{9} + 1 + \frac{8}{9} + \frac{5}{9} \right]\left(\frac{1}{3}\right)$$

$$= \frac{35}{27}.$$

Example 2 illustrates an important point. If a function f is continuous and nonnegative over the interval $[a, b]$, then the Riemann sum

$$S = \sum_{i=1}^{n} f(c_i)\Delta x$$

can be used to approximate the area of the region bounded by the graph of f and the x-axis, between $x = a$ and $x = b$. Moreover, for a given interval, as the number of subintervals increases, the approximation to the actual area will improve. We illustrate this in the next two examples by using Riemann sums to approximate the area of a triangle.

EXAMPLE 3   Approximating the Area of a Triangle

Use a Riemann sum to approximate the area of the triangular region bounded by the graph of $f(x) = 2x$ and the x-axis, $0 \le x \le 3$. Use a partition of six subintervals and choose c_i to be the left endpoint of each subinterval.

SOLUTION

We subdivide the interval $[0, 3]$ into six subintervals, each of width

$$\Delta x = \frac{3 - 0}{6} = \frac{1}{2},$$

as shown in Figure A.3. Since c_i is the left endpoint of each subinterval, the Riemann sum is given by

$$S = \sum_{i=1}^{n} f(c_i)\Delta x$$

$$= \left[f(0) + f\left(\frac{1}{2}\right) + f(1) + f\left(\frac{3}{2}\right) + f(2) + f\left(\frac{5}{2}\right) \right]\left(\frac{1}{2}\right)$$

$$= [0 + 1 + 2 + 3 + 4 + 5]\left(\frac{1}{2}\right)$$

$$= \frac{15}{2}.$$

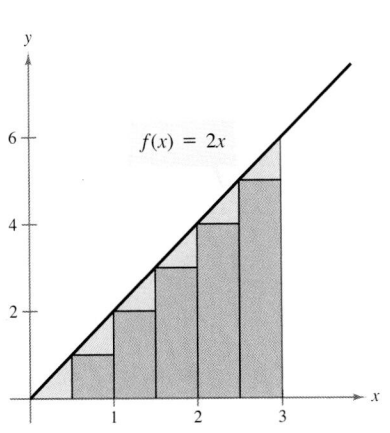

FIGURE A.3

The approximations in Examples 2 and 3 are called **left Riemann sums,** because we chose c_i to be the left endpoint of each subinterval. If we had used the right endpoints in Example 3, the **right Riemann sum** would have been $\frac{21}{2}$. (Try verifying this.) Note that the exact area of the triangular region in Example 3 is

$$\text{Area} = \frac{1}{2}(\text{base})(\text{height}) = \frac{1}{2}(3)(6) = 9.$$

Thus, the left Riemann sum gives us an approximation that is less than the actual area, and the right Riemann sum gives us an approximation that is greater than the actual area.

In Example 4, we will show that the approximation improves as the number of subintervals increases.

EXAMPLE 4   Increasing the Number of Subintervals

Let $f(x) = 2x$ for $0 \leq x \leq 3$. Use a computer to determine the left and right Riemann sums for $n = 10$, $n = 100$, and $n = 1000$ subintervals.

SOLUTION

A basic computer program for this problem is as follows.

```
10   INPUT; N
20   DELTA=3/N
30   LSUM=0: RSUM=0
40   FOR I=1 TO N
50   LC=(I-1)*DELTA: RC=I*DELTA
60   LSUM=LSUM+2*LC*DELTA: RSUM=RSUM+2*RC*DELTA
70   NEXT
80   PRINT "LEFT RIEMANN SUM: "; LSUM
90   PRINT "RIGHT RIEMANN SUM: "; RSUM
100  END
```

After running this program for $n = 10$, $n = 100$, and $n = 1000$, we obtained the results shown in Table A.1.

TABLE A.1

n	Left Riemann Sum	Right Riemann Sum
10	8.100	9.900
100	8.910	9.090
1000	8.991	9.009

From the results of Example 4, it appears that the Riemann sums are approaching the limit 9 as n approaches infinity. It is this observation that motivates the following definition of a **definite integral.** In this definition, we consider the partition of $[a, b]$ into n subintervals of equal width $\Delta x = (b - a)/n$ as follows.

$$a = x_0 < x_1 < x_2 < \cdots < x_{n-1} < x_n = b$$

Moreover, we consider c_i to be an arbitrary point in the ith subinterval $[x_{i-1}, x_i]$. To say that the number of subintervals n tends to infinity is equivalent to saying that the width, Δx, of the subintervals tends to zero.

Definition of Definite Integral

If f is a continuous function defined on the closed interval $[a, b]$, then the **definite integral of f on $[a, b]$** is

$$\int_a^b f(x)\, dx = \lim_{\Delta x \to 0} \sum_{i=1}^{n} f(c_i)\Delta x = \lim_{n \to \infty} \sum_{i=1}^{n} f(c_i)\Delta x.$$

If f is continuous and nonnegative on the interval $[a, b]$, then the definite integral of f on $[a, b]$ gives the area of the region bounded by the graph of f, the x-axis, and the vertical lines $x = a$ and $x = b$.

Evaluation of a definite integral by its limit definition can be difficult. However, there are times when we can solve a definite integral by recognizing that it represents the area of a common type of geometric figure.

EXAMPLE 5   The Areas of Common Geometric Figures

Sketch the region corresponding to each of the following definite integrals. Then evaluate each definite integral using a geometric formula.

a. $\displaystyle\int_1^3 4\, dx$ **b.** $\displaystyle\int_0^3 (x + 2)\, dx$ **c.** $\displaystyle\int_{-2}^2 \sqrt{4 - x^2}\, dx$

SOLUTION

A sketch of each region is shown in Figure A.4 (page A6).

a. The region associated with this definite integral is a rectangle of height 4 and width 2. Moreover, since the function $f(x) = 4$ is continuous and nonnegative on the interval $[1, 3]$, we can conclude that the area of the rectangle is given by the definite integral. Thus, the value of the definite integral is

$$\int_1^3 4\, dx = 4(2) = 8.$$

b. The region associated with this definite integral is a trapezoid with an altitude of 3 and parallel bases of lengths 2 and 5. The formula for the area of a trapezoid is $\frac{1}{2}h(b_1 + b_2)$, and so we have

$$\int_0^3 (x + 2)\, dx = \frac{1}{2}(3)(2 + 5) = \frac{21}{2}.$$

c. The region associated with this definite integral is a semicircle of radius 2. Thus, the area is $\frac{1}{2}\pi r^2$, and we have

$$\int_{-2}^2 \sqrt{4 - x^2}\, dx = \frac{1}{2}\pi(2^2) = 2\pi.$$

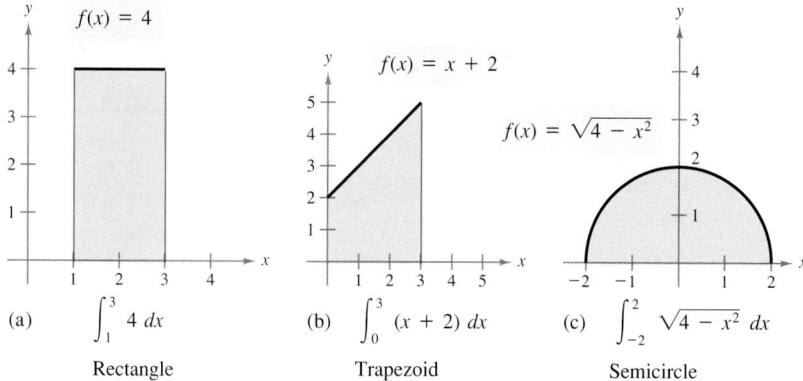

(a) $\int_1^3 4\, dx$

Rectangle

(b) $\int_0^3 (x + 2)\, dx$

Trapezoid

(c) $\int_{-2}^2 \sqrt{4 - x^2}\, dx$

Semicircle

FIGURE A.4

For some simple functions it is possible to evaluate definite integrals by the Riemann sum definition. In the next example, we will use the fact that the sum of the first n integers is given by the formula

$$1 + 2 + \cdots + n = \sum_{i=1}^n i = \frac{n(n + 1)}{2} \qquad \textit{See Exercise 27.}$$

to compute the area of the triangular region of Examples 3 and 4.

EXAMPLE 6   Evaluating a Definite Integral by Its Definition

Evaluate the definite integral $\displaystyle\int_0^3 2x\, dx$.

SOLUTION

Let $\Delta x = (b - a)/n = 3/n$, and choose c_i to be the right endpoint of each subinterval, $c_i = 3i/n$. Then we have

$$\int_0^3 2x \, dx = \lim_{\Delta x \to 0} \sum_{i=1}^{n} f(c_i)\Delta x$$

$$= \lim_{n \to \infty} \sum_{i=1}^{n} 2\left(i\frac{3}{n}\right)\left(\frac{3}{n}\right)$$

$$= \lim_{n \to \infty} \frac{18}{n^2} \sum_{i=1}^{n} i$$

$$= \lim_{n \to \infty} \left(\frac{18}{n^2}\right)\left(\frac{n(n+1)}{2}\right)$$

$$= \lim_{n \to \infty} \left(9 + \frac{9}{n}\right).$$

This limit can be evaluated in the same way that we calculated horizontal asymptotes in Section 3.6. In particular, as n approaches infinity, we see that $9/n$ approaches 0, and the above limit is 9. Thus, we conclude that

$$\int_0^3 2x \, dx = 9.$$

From Example 6, you can see that it can be difficult to evaluate the definite integral of even a simple function by using Riemann sums. A computer can help in calculating these sums for large values of n, but this procedure would only give an approximation of the definite integral. Fortunately, the **Fundamental Theorem of Calculus** provides a technique for evaluating definite integrals using antiderivatives, and for this reason it is often thought to be the most important theorem in calculus. In the remainder of this appendix, we will show how derivatives and integrals are related via the Fundamental Theorem of Calculus.

To simplify the discussion, we will assume that f is a continuous non-negative function defined on the interval $[a, b]$. Let $A(x)$ be the area of the region under the graph of f from a to x, as indicated in Figure A.5. The area under the shaded region in Figure A.6 is thus $A(x + \Delta x) - A(x)$.

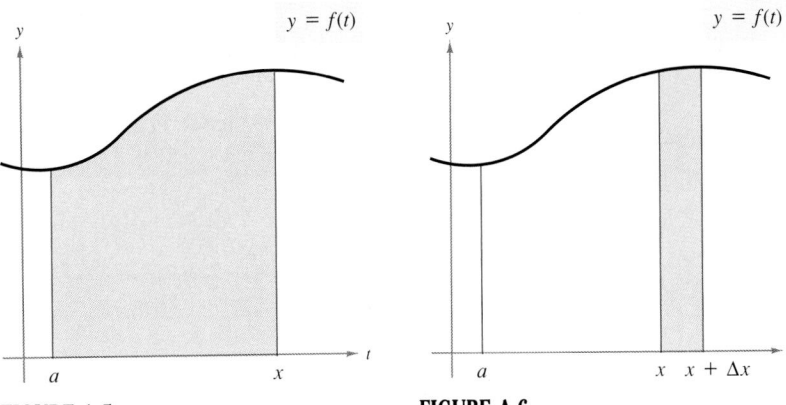

FIGURE A.5

FIGURE A.6

If Δx is small, then this area is approximately given by the area of the rectangle of height $f(x)$ and width Δx. Thus, we have $A(x + \Delta x) - A(x) \approx f(x)\Delta x$. Dividing by Δx produces

$$f(x) \approx \frac{A(x + \Delta x) - A(x)}{\Delta x}.$$

By taking the limit as Δx approaches 0, we see that

$$f(x) = \lim_{\Delta x \to 0} \frac{A(x + \Delta x) - A(x)}{\Delta x} = A'(x)$$

and we have established the fact that the area function $A(x)$ is an antiderivative of f. Although we assumed that f is continuous and nonnegative, this development is valid if the function f is simply continuous on the closed interval $[a, b]$. We use this result in the proof of the Fundamental Theorem of Calculus.

Fundamental Theorem of Calculus

If f is a continuous function on the closed interval $[a, b]$, then

$$\int_a^b f(x)\, dx = F(b) - F(a),$$

where F is any function such that $F'(x) = f(x)$.

Proof

From the previous discussion, we know that

$$\int_a^x f(x)\, dx = A(x)$$

and in particular

$$A(a) = \int_a^a f(x)\, dx = 0 \quad \text{and} \quad A(b) = \int_a^b f(x)\, dx.$$

If F is *any* antiderivative of f, then we know that F differs from A by a constant. That is, $A(x) = F(x) + C$. Hence,

$$\int_a^b f(x)\, dx = A(b) - A(a) = [F(b) + C] - [F(a) + C] = F(b) - F(a).$$

You are now ready to continue Section 5.4, on page 342, just after the statement of the Fundamental Theorem of Calculus.

APPENDIX A · EXERCISES

In Exercises 1–6, use the left Riemann sum and the right Riemann sum to approximate the area of the given region using the indicated number of subintervals.

1. $y = \sqrt{x}$

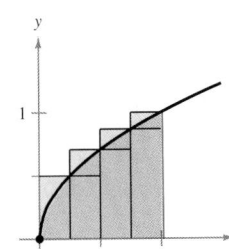

2. $y = \sqrt{x} + 1$

3. $y = \dfrac{1}{x}$

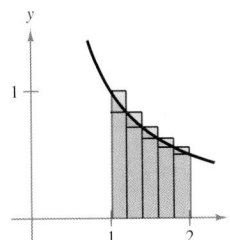

4. $y = \dfrac{1}{x - 2}$

5. $y = \sqrt{1 - x^2}$

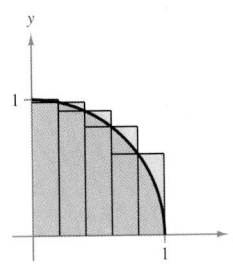

6. $y = \sqrt{x} + 1$

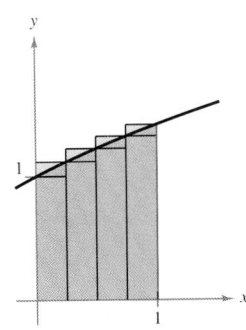

7. Repeat Exercise 1 using the midpoint Riemann sum.

8. Repeat Exercise 2 using the midpoint Riemann sum.

9. Consider a triangle of area 2 bounded by the graphs of $y = x$, $y = 0$, and $x = 2$.
   (a) Sketch the graph of the region.

(b) Divide the interval $[0, 2]$ into n equal subintervals and show that the endpoints are

$$0 < 1\left(\frac{2}{n}\right) < \cdots < (n - 1)\left(\frac{2}{n}\right) < n\left(\frac{2}{n}\right).$$

(c) Show that the left Riemann sum is

$$S_L = \sum_{i=1}^{n}\left[(i - 1)\left(\frac{2}{n}\right)\right]\left(\frac{2}{n}\right).$$

(d) Show that the right Riemann sum is

$$S_R = \sum_{i=1}^{n}\left[i\left(\frac{2}{n}\right)\right]\left(\frac{2}{n}\right).$$

(e) Complete the following table.

n	5	10	50	100
Left sum S_L				
Right sum S_R				

(f) Show that $\lim\limits_{n\to\infty} S_L = \lim\limits_{n\to\infty} S_R = 2$.

10. Consider a trapezoid of area 4 bounded by the graphs of $y = x$, $y = 0$, $x = 1$, and $x = 3$.
   (a) Sketch the graph of the region.
   (b) Divide the interval $[1, 3]$ into n equal subintervals and show that the endpoints are

$$1 < 1 + 1\left(\frac{2}{n}\right) < \cdots < 1 + (n - 1)\left(\frac{2}{n}\right) < 1 + n\left(\frac{2}{n}\right).$$

(c) Show that the left Riemann sum is

$$S_L = \sum_{i=1}^{n}\left[1 + (i - 1)\left(\frac{2}{n}\right)\right]\left(\frac{2}{n}\right).$$

(d) Show that the right Riemann sum is

$$S_R = \sum_{i=1}^{n}\left[1 + i\left(\frac{2}{n}\right)\right]\left(\frac{2}{n}\right).$$

(e) Complete the following table.

n	5	10	50	100
Left sum S_L				
Right sum S_R				

(f) Show that $\lim\limits_{n\to\infty} S_L = \lim\limits_{n\to\infty} S_R = 4$.

In Exercises 11–16, set up a definite integral that yields the area of the given region. (Do not evaluate the integral.)

11. $f(x) = 3$

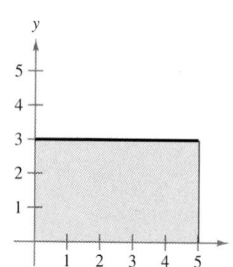

12. $f(x) = 4 - 2x$

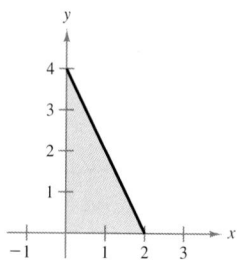

13. $f(x) = 4 - |x|$

14. $f(x) = x^2$

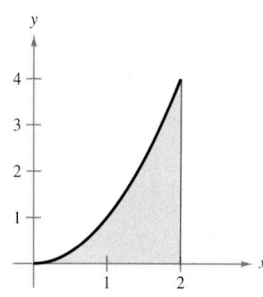

15. $f(x) = 4 - x^2$

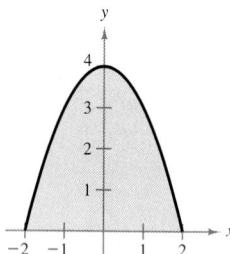

16. $f(x) = \dfrac{1}{x^2 + 1}$

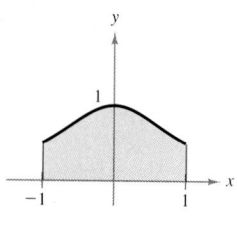

In Exercises 17–26, sketch the region whose area is indicated by the given definite integral. Then use a geometric formula to evaluate the integral.

17. $\displaystyle\int_0^3 4\, dx$

18. $\displaystyle\int_{-a}^a 4\, dx$

19. $\displaystyle\int_0^4 x\, dx$

20. $\displaystyle\int_0^4 \frac{x}{2}\, dx$

21. $\displaystyle\int_0^2 (2x + 5)\, dx$

22. $\displaystyle\int_0^5 (5 - x)\, dx$

23. $\displaystyle\int_{-1}^1 (1 - |x|)\, dx$

24. $\displaystyle\int_{-a}^a (a - |x|)\, dx$

25. $\displaystyle\int_{-3}^3 \sqrt{9 - x^2}\, dx$

26. $\displaystyle\int_{-r}^r \sqrt{r^2 - x^2}\, dx$

27. Show that $\displaystyle\sum_{i=1}^n i = \frac{n(n + 1)}{n}$. Hint: Add the following two sums.

$$S = 1 + 2 + 3 + \cdots + (n - 2) + (n - 1) + n$$
$$S = n + (n - 1) + (n - 2) + \cdots + 3 + 2 + 1$$

28. Use the Riemann sum definition of the definite integral and the result of Exercise 27 to evaluate $\int_1^2 x\, dx$.

Appendix B

Reference Tables

REFERENCE TABLE 1   The Greek Alphabet

Letter		Name	Letter		Name	Letter		Name
A	α	Alpha	I	ι	Iota	P	ρ	Rho
B	β	Beta	K	κ	Kappa	Σ	σ	Sigma
Γ	γ	Gamma	Λ	λ	Lambda	T	τ	Tau
Δ	δ	Delta	M	μ	Mu	Υ	υ	Upsilon
E	ε	Epsilon	N	ν	Nu	Φ	ϕ	Phi
Z	ζ	Zeta	Ξ	ξ	Xi	X	χ	Chi
H	η	Eta	O	o	Omicron	Ψ	ψ	Psi
Θ	θ	Theta	Π	π	Pi	Ω	ω	Omega

REFERENCE TABLE 2   The Number of Each Day in the Year

Day of Month	Jan.	Feb.	Mar.	Apr.	May	June	July	Aug.	Sept.	Oct.	Nov.	Dec.	Day of Month
1	1	32	60	91	121	152	182	213	244	274	305	335	1
2	2	33	61	92	122	153	183	214	245	275	306	336	2
3	3	34	62	93	123	154	184	215	246	276	307	337	3
4	4	35	63	94	124	155	185	216	247	277	308	338	4
5	5	36	64	95	125	156	186	217	248	278	309	339	5
6	6	37	65	96	126	157	187	218	249	279	310	340	6
7	7	38	66	97	127	158	188	219	250	280	311	341	7
8	8	39	67	98	128	159	189	220	251	281	312	342	8
9	9	40	68	99	129	160	190	221	252	282	313	343	9
10	10	41	69	100	130	161	191	222	253	283	314	344	10
11	11	42	70	101	131	162	192	223	254	284	315	345	11
12	12	43	71	102	132	163	193	224	255	285	316	346	12
13	13	44	72	103	133	164	194	225	256	286	317	347	13
14	14	45	73	104	134	165	195	226	257	287	318	348	14
15	15	46	74	105	135	166	196	227	258	288	319	349	15
16	16	47	75	106	136	167	197	228	259	289	320	350	16
17	17	48	76	107	137	168	198	229	260	290	321	351	17
18	18	49	77	108	138	169	199	230	261	291	322	352	18
19	19	50	78	109	139	170	200	231	262	292	323	353	19
20	20	51	79	110	140	171	201	232	263	293	324	354	20
21	21	52	80	111	141	172	202	233	264	294	325	355	21
22	22	53	81	112	142	173	203	234	265	295	326	356	22
23	23	54	82	113	143	174	204	235	266	296	327	357	23
24	24	55	83	114	144	175	205	236	267	297	328	358	24
25	25	56	84	115	145	176	206	237	268	298	329	359	25
26	26	57	85	116	146	177	207	238	269	299	330	360	26
27	27	58	86	117	147	178	208	239	270	300	331	361	27
28	28	59	87	118	148	179	209	240	271	301	332	362	28
29	29	*	88	119	149	180	210	241	272	302	333	363	29
30	30	—	89	120	150	181	211	242	273	303	334	364	30
31	31	—	90	—	151	—	212	243	—	304	—	365	31

*On leap year, Feb. 29 is day 60 and the number of each day after Feb. 29 is increased by one.

REFERENCE TABLE 3   Units of Measurement of Length

English System: Inch (in), Foot (ft), Yard (yd), Mile (mi)

1 mi = 5280 ft	1 mi = 1760 yd
1 yd = 3 ft	1 ft = 12 in

Metric System: Millimeter (mm), Centimeter (cm), Meter (m), Kilometer (km)

1 km = 1000 m	1 m = 100 cm
1 m = 1000 mm	1 cm = 10 mm

Conversion Factors (six significant figures)

Metric to English	English to Metric
1 mm = 0.0393701 in	1 in = 25.4000 mm
1 cm = 0.393701 in	1 in = 2.54000 cm
1 m = 3.28084 ft	1 ft = 0.304800 m
1 m = 1.09361 yd	1 yd = 0.914400 m
1 km = 0.621371 mi	1 mi = 1.60934 km

Miscellaneous

1 fathom = 6 ft
1 astronomical unit = 93,000,000 mi (average distance between earth and sun)
1 light year = 5,800,000,000,000 mi (distance traveled by light in one year)

REFERENCE TABLE 4   Units of Measurement of Area

English System: Square Inch (in^2), Square Foot (ft^2), Square Yard (yd^2), Acre, Square Mile (mi^2)

1 mi^2 = 640 acres	1 acre = 43,560 ft^2
1 yd^2 = 9 ft^2	1 ft^2 = 144 in^2

Metric System: Square Centimeter (cm²), Square Meter (m²), Square Kilometer (km²)

$1 \text{ km}^2 = 1,000,000 \text{ m}^2$ $1 \text{ m}^2 = 10,000 \text{ cm}^2$

Conversion Factors (six significant figures)

Metric to English	English to Metric
$1 \text{ cm}^2 = 0.155000 \text{ in}^2$	$1 \text{ in}^2 = 6.45160 \text{ cm}^2$
$1 \text{ m}^2 = 10.7640 \text{ ft}^2$	$1 \text{ ft}^2 = 0.0929030 \text{ m}^2$
$1 \text{ m}^2 = 1.19599 \text{ yd}^2$	$1 \text{ yd}^2 = 0.836127 \text{ m}^2$
$1 \text{ km}^2 = 0.386102 \text{ mi}^2$	$1 \text{ mi}^2 = 2.58999 \text{ km}^2$

Miscellaneous

1 square mile = 1 section = 4 quarters

REFERENCE TABLE 5   Units of Measurement of Volume

English System: Cubic Inch (in³), Cubic Foot (ft³), Cubic Yard (yd³), Fluid Ounce (fl oz), Pint (pt), Quart (qt), Gallon (gal)

$1 \text{ yd}^3 = 27 \text{ ft}^3$	$1 \text{ ft}^3 = 1728 \text{ in}^3$
$1 \text{ gal} = 4 \text{ qt}$	$1 \text{ qt} = 2 \text{ pt}$
$1 \text{ qt} = 32 \text{ fl oz}$	$1 \text{ pt} = 16 \text{ fl oz}$
$1 \text{ gal} = 231 \text{ in}^3$	$1 \text{ ft}^3 = 7.48052 \text{ gal}$

Metric System: Cubic Centimeter (cm³), Cubic Meter (m³), Milliliter (cc), Liter

$1 \text{ m}^3 = 1000 \text{ liters}$	$1 \text{ liter} = 1000 \text{ cc}$
$1 \text{ cm}^3 = 1 \text{ cc}$	

Conversion Factors (six significant figures)

Metric to English	English to Metric
$1 \text{ cm}^3 = 0.0610237 \text{ in}^3$	$1 \text{ in}^3 = 16.3871 \text{ cm}^3$
$1 \text{ m}^3 = 35.3147 \text{ ft}^3$	$1 \text{ ft}^3 = 0.0283168 \text{ m}^3$
$1 \text{ m}^3 = 1.30795 \text{ yd}^3$	$1 \text{ yd}^3 = 0.764555 \text{ m}^3$

REFERENCE TABLE 5   (Continued)

Miscellaneous

1 gallon = 5 fifths   1 fifth = 0.757 liter
1 quart = 4 cups   1 cup = 16 tablespoons
1 tablespoon = 3 teaspoons (cooking)
1 tablespoon = 4 teaspoons (medical)
1 barrel (bl) = 42 gallons (petroleum)

REFERENCE TABLE 6   Units of Measurement of Mass and Force

English System (Force or Weight): Ounce (oz), Pound (lb), Ton

1 ton = 2000 lb   1 lb = 16 oz

Metric System (Mass): Gram (g), Kilogram (kg), Metric Ton

1 metric ton = 1000 kg   1 kg = 1000 g

Conversion Factors (six significant figures at sea level)

Metric to English	English to Metric
1 g = 0.0352740 oz	1 oz = 28.3495 g
1 kg = 2.20462 lb	1 lb = 0.453592 kg
1 metric ton = 1.10231 ton	1 ton = 0.907185 metric ton

REFERENCE TABLE 7   Units of Measurement of Time

Second (sec), Minute (min), Hour (hr)

1 hr = 60 min   1 min = 60 sec

Calendar Units: Day, Week, Month, Year (yr)

1 yr = 365 days (366 days on leap year)
1 yr = 365.256 mean solar days
1 yr = 12 months
1 week = 7 days
1 day = 24 hr

REFERENCE TABLE 8 Units of Measurement of Temperature

Fahrenheit (F), Celsius (C), Kelvin or Absolute (K)

Celsius to Fahrenheit

$$°F = \frac{9}{5}°C + 32$$

Fahrenheit to Celsius

$$°C = \frac{5}{9}°F - 32$$

Celsius to Kelvin
$$°K = °C + 273.15$$

Kelvin to Celsius
$$°C = °K - 273.15$$

Freezing temperature for water = 32° F = 0° C
Boiling temperature for water = 212° F = 100° C
Absolute zero temperature = 0° K = −273.15° C = −459.67° F
  (0° K is, by definition, the coldest possible temperature, at which there is no molecular activity.)

REFERENCE TABLE 9 Miscellaneous Units and Number Constants

1 dozen (doz) = 12 units   1 gross = 12 dozen units
1 score = 20 units

$\pi \approx 3.1415926535$ $e \approx 2.7182818284$

Equatorial radius of the earth = 3963.34 mi = 6378.388 km
Polar radius of the earth = 3949.99 mi = 6356.912 km
Acceleration due to gravity at sea level = 32.1726 ft/sec^2
Speed of sound at sea level (standard atmosphere) = 1116.45 ft/sec
Speed of light in vacuum = 186,284 mi/sec
Density of water: 1 ft^3 = 62.425 lb

REFERENCE TABLE 10 Algebra

Operations with Exponents

1. $x^n x^m = x^{n+m}$ 2. $\dfrac{x^n}{x^m} = x^{n-m}$ 3. $(xy)^n = x^n y^n$

4. $\left(\dfrac{x}{y}\right)^n = \dfrac{x^n}{y^n}$ 5. $(x^n)^m = x^{nm}$ 6. $-x^n = -(x^n)$

7. $cx^n = c(x^n)$ 8. $x^{n^m} = x^{(n^m)}$

Exponents and Radicals (n and m are positive integers)

1. $x^n = \underbrace{x \cdot x \cdot x \cdots x}_{n \text{ factors}}$ 2. $x^0 = 1, \; x \neq 0$

3. $x^{-n} = \dfrac{1}{x^n}, \; x \neq 0$ *4. $\sqrt[n]{x} = a \;\Longrightarrow\; x = a^n$

5. $x^{1/n} = \sqrt[n]{x}$ 6. $x^{m/n} = (x^{1/n})^m = (\sqrt[n]{x})^m$
$\qquad\qquad\qquad\qquad\qquad\quad x^{m/n} = (x^m)^{1/n} = \sqrt[n]{x^m}$

7. $\sqrt[2]{x} = \sqrt{x}$

Operations with Fractions

1. $\dfrac{a}{b} + \dfrac{c}{d} = \dfrac{a}{b}\left(\dfrac{d}{d}\right) + \dfrac{c}{d}\left(\dfrac{b}{b}\right) = \dfrac{ad}{bd} + \dfrac{bc}{bd} = \dfrac{ad + bc}{bd}$

2. $\dfrac{a}{b} - \dfrac{c}{d} = \dfrac{a}{b}\left(\dfrac{d}{d}\right) - \dfrac{c}{d}\left(\dfrac{b}{b}\right) = \dfrac{ad}{bd} - \dfrac{bc}{bd} = \dfrac{ad - bc}{bd}$

3. $\left(\dfrac{a}{b}\right)\left(\dfrac{c}{d}\right) = \dfrac{ac}{bd}$

4. $\dfrac{a/b}{c/d} = \left(\dfrac{a}{b}\right)\left(\dfrac{d}{c}\right) = \dfrac{ad}{bc}$

$\quad \dfrac{a/b}{c} = \dfrac{a/b}{c/1} = \left(\dfrac{a}{b}\right)\left(\dfrac{1}{c}\right) = \dfrac{a}{bc}$

5. $\dfrac{\cancel{a}b}{\cancel{a}c} = \dfrac{b}{c}$

$\quad \dfrac{ab + ac}{ad} = \dfrac{\cancel{a}(b + c)}{\cancel{a}d} = \dfrac{b + c}{d}$

*If n is even, the principal nth root is defined to be positive.

Quadratic Formula

$$ax^2 + bx + c = 0 \quad \Longrightarrow \quad x = \frac{-b \pm \sqrt{b^2 - 4ac}}{2a}$$

Factors and Special Products

1. $x^2 - a^2 = (x - a)(x + a)$

2. $x^3 - a^3 = (x - a)(x^2 + ax + a^2)$

3. $x^3 + a^3 = (x + a)(x^2 - ax + a^2)$

4. $x^4 - a^4 = (x - a)(x + a)(x^2 + a^2)$

Factoring by Grouping

$$acx^3 + adx^2 + bcx + bd = ax^2(cx + d) + b(cx + d) = (ax^2 + b)(cx + d)$$

Binomial Theorem

1. $(x + a)^2 = x^2 + 2ax + a^2$

2. $(x - a)^2 = x^2 - 2ax + a^2$

3. $(x + a)^3 = x^3 + 3ax^2 + 3a^2x + a^3$

4. $(x - a)^3 = x^3 - 3ax^2 + 3a^2x - a^3$

5. $(x + a)^4 = x^4 + 4ax^3 + 6a^2x^2 + 4a^3x + a^4$

6. $(x - a)^4 = x^4 - 4ax^3 + 6a^2x^2 - 4a^3x + a^4$

7. $(x + a)^n = x^n + nax^{n-1} + \dfrac{n(n - 1)}{2!}a^2x^{n-2} + \dfrac{n(n - 1)(n - 2)}{3!}a^3x^{n-3} +$

   $\cdots + na^{n-1}x + a^n$

8. $(x - a)^n = x^n - nax^{n-1} + \dfrac{n(n - 1)}{2!}a^2x^{n-2} - \dfrac{n(n - 1)(n - 2)}{3!}a^3x^{n-3} +$

   $\cdots \pm na^{n-1}x \mp a^n$

Miscellaneous

1. If $ab = 0$, then $a = 0$ or $b = 0$.

2. If $ac = bc$ and $c \neq 0$, then $a = b$.

3. Factorial: $0! = 1$, $1! = 1$, $2! = 2 \cdot 1$, $3! = 3 \cdot 2 \cdot 1$, $4! = 4 \cdot 3 \cdot 2 \cdot 1$, etc.

REFERENCE TABLE 10 (Continued)

Sequences

1. Arithmetic: $a, a + b, a + 2b, a + 3b, a + 4b, a + 5b, \ldots$

2. Geometric: $ar^0, ar^1, ar^2, ar^3, ar^4, ar^5, \ldots$

$$ar^0 + ar^1 + ar^2 + ar^3 + \cdots + ar^n = \frac{a(1 - r^{n+1})}{1 - r}$$

3. General Harmonic: $\dfrac{1}{a}, \dfrac{1}{a + b}, \dfrac{1}{a + 2b}, \dfrac{1}{a + 3b}, \dfrac{1}{a + 4b}, \dfrac{1}{a + 5b}, \ldots$

4. Harmonic: $\dfrac{1}{1}, \dfrac{1}{2}, \dfrac{1}{3}, \dfrac{1}{4}, \dfrac{1}{5}, \ldots$

5. p-Sequence: $\dfrac{1}{1^p}, \dfrac{1}{2^p}, \dfrac{1}{3^p}, \dfrac{1}{4^p}, \dfrac{1}{5^p}, \ldots$

Series

$$\frac{1}{x} = 1 - (x - 1) + (x - 1)^2 - (x - 1)^3 + (x - 1)^4 - \cdots + (-1)^n(x - 1)^n + \cdots, \quad 0 < x < 2$$

$$\frac{1}{1 + x} = 1 - x + x^2 - x^3 + x^4 - x^5 + \cdots + (-1)^n x^n + \cdots, \qquad\qquad -1 < x < 1$$

$$\ln x = (x - 1) - \frac{(x - 1)^2}{2} + \frac{(x - 1)^3}{3} - \frac{(x - 1)^4}{4} + \cdots + \frac{(-1)^{n-1}(x - 1)^n}{n} + \cdots, \quad 0 < x \leq 2$$

$$e^x = 1 + x + \frac{x^2}{2!} + \frac{x^3}{3!} + \frac{x^4}{4!} + \frac{x^5}{5!} + \cdots + \frac{x^n}{n!} + \cdots, \qquad\qquad -\infty < x < \infty$$

$$\sin x = x - \frac{x^3}{3!} + \frac{x^5}{5!} - \frac{x^7}{7!} + \cdots, \qquad\qquad -\infty < x < \infty$$

$$\cos x = 1 - \frac{x^2}{2!} + \frac{x^4}{4!} - \frac{x^6}{6!} + \cdots, \qquad\qquad -\infty < x < \infty$$

$$(1 + x)^k = 1 + kx + \frac{k(k - 1)x^2}{2!} + \frac{k(k - 1)(k - 2)x^3}{3!} + \frac{k(k - 1)(k - 2)(k - 3)x^4}{4!} + \cdots, \quad -1 < x < 1*$$

$$(1 + x)^{-k} = 1 - kx + \frac{k(k + 1)x^2}{2!} - \frac{k(k + 1)(k + 2)x^3}{3!} + \frac{k(k + 1)(k + 2)(k + 3)x^4}{4!} - \cdots, \quad -1 < x < 1*$$

*The convergence at $x = \pm 1$ depends on the value k.

REFERENCE TABLE 11   Table of Square Roots and Cube Roots

n	$\sqrt{n}$	$\sqrt[3]{n}$	n	$\sqrt{n}$	$\sqrt[3]{n}$	n	$\sqrt{n}$	$\sqrt[3]{n}$
1	1.00000	1.00000	51	7.14143	3.70843	101	10.0499	4.65701
2	1.41421	1.25992	52	7.21110	3.73251	102	10.0995	4.67233
3	1.73205	1.44225	53	7.28011	3.75629	103	10.1489	4.68755
4	2.00000	1.58740	54	7.34847	3.77976	104	10.1980	4.70267
5	2.23607	1.70998	55	7.41620	3.80295	105	10.2470	4.71769
6	2.44949	1.81712	56	7.48331	3.82586	106	10.2956	4.73262
7	2.64575	1.91293	57	7.54983	3.84850	107	10.3441	4.74746
8	2.82843	2.00000	58	7.61577	3.87088	108	10.3923	4.76220
9	3.00000	2.08008	59	7.68115	3.89300	109	10.4403	4.77686
10	3.16228	2.15443	60	7.74597	3.91487	110	10.4881	4.79142
11	3.31662	2.22398	61	7.81025	3.93650	111	10.5357	4.80590
12	3.46410	2.28943	62	7.87401	3.95789	112	10.5830	4.82028
13	3.60555	2.35133	63	7.93725	3.97906	113	10.6301	4.83459
14	3.74166	2.41014	64	8.00000	4.00000	114	10.6771	4.84881
15	3.87298	2.46621	65	8.06226	4.02073	115	10.7238	4.86294
16	4.00000	2.51984	66	8.12404	4.04124	116	10.7703	4.87700
17	4.12311	2.57128	67	8.18535	4.06155	117	10.8167	4.89097
18	4.24264	2.62074	68	8.24621	4.08166	118	10.8628	4.90487
19	4.35890	2.66840	69	8.30662	4.10157	119	10.9087	4.91868
20	4.47214	2.71442	70	8.36660	4.12129	120	10.9545	4.93242
21	4.58258	2.75892	71	8.42615	4.14082	121	11.0000	4.94609
22	4.69042	2.80204	72	8.48528	4.16017	122	11.0454	4.95968
23	4.79583	2.84387	73	8.54400	4.17934	123	11.0905	4.97319
24	4.89898	2.88450	74	8.60233	4.19834	124	11.1355	4.98663
25	5.00000	2.92402	75	8.66025	4.21716	125	11.1803	5.00000
26	5.09902	2.96250	76	8.71780	4.23582	126	11.2250	5.01330
27	5.19615	3.00000	77	8.77496	4.25432	127	11.2694	5.02653
28	5.29150	3.03659	78	8.83176	4.27266	128	11.3137	5.03968
29	5.38516	3.07232	79	8.88819	4.29084	129	11.3578	5.05277
30	5.47723	3.10723	80	8.94427	4.30887	130	11.4018	5.06580
31	5.56776	3.14138	81	9.00000	4.32675	131	11.4455	5.07875
32	5.65685	3.17480	82	9.05539	4.34448	132	11.4891	5.09164
33	5.74456	3.20753	83	9.11043	4.36207	133	11.5326	5.10447
34	5.83095	3.23961	84	9.16515	4.37952	134	11.5758	5.11723
35	5.91608	3.27107	85	9.21954	4.39683	135	11.6190	5.12993
36	6.00000	3.30193	86	9.27362	4.41400	136	11.6619	5.14256
37	6.08276	3.33222	87	9.32738	4.43105	137	11.7047	5.15514
38	6.16441	3.36198	88	9.38083	4.44796	138	11.7473	5.16765
39	6.24500	3.39121	89	9.43398	4.46475	139	11.7898	5.18010
40	6.32456	3.41995	90	9.48683	4.48140	140	11.8322	5.19249
41	6.40312	3.44822	91	9.53939	4.49794	141	11.8743	5.20483
42	6.48074	3.47603	92	9.59166	4.51436	142	11.9164	5.21710
43	6.55744	3.50340	93	9.64365	4.53065	143	11.9583	5.22932
44	6.63325	3.53035	94	9.69536	4.54684	144	12.0000	5.24148
45	6.70820	3.55689	95	9.74679	4.56290	145	12.0416	5.25359
46	6.78233	3.58305	96	9.79796	4.57886	146	12.0830	5.26564
47	6.85565	3.60883	97	9.84886	4.59470	147	12.1244	5.27763
48	6.92820	3.63424	98	9.89949	4.61044	148	12.1655	5.28957
49	7.00000	3.65931	99	9.94987	4.62606	149	12.2066	5.30146
50	7.07107	3.68403	100	10.0000	4.64159	150	12.2474	5.31329

REFERENCE TABLE 11   (Continued)

n	$\sqrt{n}$	$\sqrt[3]{n}$	n	$\sqrt{n}$	$\sqrt[3]{n}$	n	$\sqrt{n}$	$\sqrt[3]{n}$
151	12.2882	5.32507	168	12.9615	5.51785	185	13.6015	5.69802
152	12.3288	5.33680	169	13.0000	5.52877	186	13.6382	5.70827
153	12.3693	5.34848	170	13.0384	5.53966	187	13.6748	5.71848
154	12.4097	5.36011	171	13.0767	5.55050	188	13.7113	5.72865
155	12.4499	5.37169	172	13.1149	5.56130	189	13.7477	5.73879
156	12.4900	5.38321	173	13.1529	5.57205	190	13.7840	5.74890
157	12.5300	5.39469	174	13.1909	5.58277	191	13.8203	5.75897
158	12.5698	5.40612	175	13.2288	5.59344	192	13.8564	5.76900
159	12.6095	5.41750	176	13.2665	5.60408	193	13.8924	5.77900
160	12.6491	5.42884	177	13.3041	5.61467	194	13.9284	5.78896
161	12.6886	5.44012	178	13.3417	5.62523	195	13.9642	5.79889
162	12.7279	5.45136	179	13.3791	5.63574	196	14.0000	5.80879
163	12.7671	5.46256	180	13.4164	5.64622	197	14.0357	5.81865
164	12.8062	5.47370	181	13.4536	5.65665	198	14.0712	5.82848
165	12.8452	5.48481	182	13.4907	5.66705	199	14.1067	5.83827
166	12.8841	5.49586	183	13.5277	5.67741	200	14.1421	5.84804
167	12.9228	5.50688	184	13.5647	5.68773			

REFERENCE TABLE 12 Exponential Tables

x	e^x	e^{-x}	x	e^x	e^{-x}	x	e^x	e^{-x}
0.0	1.0000	1.0000	3.5	33.115	0.0302	7.0	1096.63	0.0009
0.1	1.1052	0.9048	3.6	36.598	0.0273	7.1	1211.97	0.0008
0.2	1.2214	0.8187	3.7	40.447	0.0247	7.2	1339.43	0.0007
0.3	1.3499	0.7408	3.8	44.701	0.0224	7.3	1480.30	0.0007
0.4	1.4918	0.6703	3.9	49.402	0.0202	7.4	1635.98	0.0006
0.5	1.6487	0.6065	4.0	54.598	0.0183	7.5	1808.04	0.0006
0.6	1.8221	0.5488	4.1	60.340	0.0166	7.6	1998.20	0.0005
0.7	2.0138	0.4966	4.2	66.686	0.0150	7.7	2208.35	0.0005
0.8	2.2255	0.4493	4.3	73.700	0.0136	7.8	2440.60	0.0004
0.9	2.4596	0.4066	4.4	81.451	0.0123	7.9	2697.28	0.0004
1.0	2.7183	0.3679	4.5	90.017	0.0111	8.0	2980.96	0.0003
1.1	3.0042	0.3329	4.6	99.484	0.0101	8.1	3294.47	0.0003
1.2	3.3201	0.3012	4.7	109.95	0.0091	8.2	3640.95	0.0003
1.3	3.6693	0.2725	4.8	121.51	0.0082	8.3	4023.87	0.0002
1.4	4.0552	0.2466	4.9	134.29	0.0074	8.4	4447.07	0.0002
1.5	4.4817	0.2231	5.0	148.41	0.0067	8.5	4914.77	0.0002
1.6	4.9530	0.2019	5.1	164.02	0.0061	8.6	5431.66	0.0002
1.7	5.4739	0.1827	5.2	181.27	0.0055	8.7	6002.91	0.0002
1.8	6.0496	0.1653	5.3	200.34	0.0050	8.8	6634.24	0.0002
1.9	6.6859	0.1496	5.4	221.41	0.0045	8.9	7331.97	0.0001
2.0	7.3891	0.1353	5.5	244.69	0.0041	9.0	8103.08	0.0001
2.1	8.1662	0.1225	5.6	270.43	0.0037	9.1	8955.29	0.0001
2.2	9.0250	0.1108	5.7	298.87	0.0033	9.2	9897.13	0.0001
2.3	9.9742	0.1003	5.8	330.30	0.0030	9.3	10938.02	0.0001
2.4	11.023	0.0907	5.9	365.04	0.0027	9.4	12088.38	0.0001
2.5	12.182	0.0821	6.0	403.43	0.0025	9.5	13359.73	0.0001
2.6	13.464	0.0743	6.1	445.86	0.0022	9.6	14764.78	0.0001
2.7	14.880	0.0672	6.2	492.75	0.0020	9.7	16317.61	0.0001
2.8	16.445	0.0608	6.3	544.57	0.0018	9.8	18033.74	0.0001
2.9	18.174	0.0550	6.4	601.85	0.0017	9.9	19930.37	0.0001
3.0	20.086	0.0498	6.5	665.14	0.0015	10.0	22026.47	0.0000
3.1	22.198	0.0450	6.6	735.10	0.0014			
3.2	24.533	0.0408	6.7	812.41	0.0012			
3.3	27.113	0.0369	6.8	897.85	0.0011			
3.4	29.964	0.0334	6.9	992.27	0.0010			

REFERENCE TABLE 13 Natural Logarithmic Tables

	0.00	0.01	0.02	0.03	0.04	0.05	0.06	0.07	0.08	0.09
1.0	0.0000	0.0100	0.0198	0.0296	0.0392	0.0488	0.0583	0.0677	0.0770	0.0862
1.1	0.0953	0.1044	0.1133	0.1222	0.1310	0.1398	0.1484	0.1570	0.1655	0.1740
1.2	0.1823	0.1906	0.1989	0.2070	0.2151	0.2231	0.2311	0.2390	0.2469	0.2546
1.3	0.2624	0.2700	0.2776	0.2852	0.2927	0.3001	0.3075	0.3148	0.3221	0.3293
1.4	0.3365	0.3436	0.3507	0.3577	0.3646	0.3716	0.3784	0.3853	0.3920	0.3988
1.5	0.4055	0.4121	0.4187	0.4253	0.4318	0.4383	0.4447	0.4511	0.4574	0.4637
1.6	0.4700	0.4762	0.4824	0.4886	0.4947	0.5008	0.5068	0.5128	0.5188	0.5247
1.7	0.5306	0.5365	0.5423	0.5481	0.5539	0.5596	0.5653	0.5710	0.5766	0.5822
1.8	0.5878	0.5933	0.5988	0.6043	0.6098	0.6152	0.6206	0.6259	0.6313	0.6366
1.9	0.6419	0.6471	0.6523	0.6575	0.6627	0.6678	0.6729	0.6780	0.6831	0.6881
2.0	0.6931	0.6981	0.7031	0.7080	0.7129	0.7178	0.7227	0.7275	0.7324	0.7372
2.1	0.7419	0.7467	0.7514	0.7561	0.7608	0.7655	0.7701	0.7747	0.7793	0.7839
2.2	0.7885	0.7930	0.7975	0.8020	0.8065	0.8109	0.8154	0.8198	0.8242	0.8286
2.3	0.8329	0.8372	0.8416	0.8459	0.8502	0.8544	0.8587	0.8629	0.8671	0.8713
2.4	0.8755	0.8796	0.8838	0.8879	0.8920	0.8961	0.9002	0.9042	0.9083	0.9123
2.5	0.9163	0.9203	0.9243	0.9282	0.9322	0.9361	0.9400	0.9439	0.9478	0.9517
2.6	0.9555	0.9594	0.9632	0.9670	0.9708	0.9746	0.9783	0.9821	0.9858	0.9895
2.7	0.9933	0.9969	1.0006	1.0043	1.0080	1.0116	1.0152	1.0188	1.0225	1.0260
2.8	1.0296	1.0332	1.0367	1.0403	1.0438	1.0473	1.0508	1.0543	1.0578	1.0613
2.9	1.0647	1.0682	1.0716	1.0750	1.0784	1.0818	1.0852	1.0886	1.0919	1.0953
3.0	1.0986	1.1019	1.1053	1.1086	1.1119	1.1151	1.1184	1.1217	1.1249	1.1282
3.1	1.1314	1.1346	1.1378	1.1410	1.1442	1.1474	1.1506	1.1537	1.1569	1.1600
3.2	1.1632	1.1663	1.1694	1.1725	1.1756	1.1787	1.1817	1.1848	1.1878	1.1909
3.3	1.1939	1.1969	1.2000	1.2030	1.2060	1.2090	1.2119	1.2149	1.2179	1.2208
3.4	1.2238	1.2267	1.2296	1.2326	1.2355	1.2384	1.2413	1.2442	1.2470	1.2499
3.5	1.2528	1.2556	1.2585	1.2613	1.2641	1.2669	1.2698	1.2726	1.2754	1.2782
3.6	1.2809	1.2837	1.2865	1.2892	1.2920	1.2947	1.2975	1.3002	1.3029	1.3056
3.7	1.3083	1.3110	1.3137	1.3164	1.3191	1.3218	1.3244	1.3271	1.3297	1.3324
3.8	1.3350	1.3376	1.3403	1.3429	1.3455	1.3481	1.3507	1.3533	1.3558	1.3584
3.9	1.3610	1.3635	1.3661	1.3686	1.3712	1.3737	1.3762	1.3788	1.3813	1.3838
4.0	1.3863	1.3888	1.3913	1.3938	1.3962	1.3987	1.4012	1.4036	1.4061	1.4085
4.1	1.4110	1.4134	1.4159	1.4183	1.4207	1.4231	1.4255	1.4279	1.4303	1.4327
4.2	1.4351	1.4375	1.4398	1.4422	1.4446	1.4469	1.4493	1.4516	1.4540	1.4563
4.3	1.4586	1.4609	1.4633	1.4656	1.4679	1.4702	1.4725	1.4748	1.4770	1.4793
4.4	1.4816	1.4839	1.4861	1.4884	1.4907	1.4929	1.4951	1.4974	1.4996	1.5019
4.5	1.5041	1.5063	1.5085	1.5107	1.5129	1.5151	1.5173	1.5195	1.5217	1.5239
4.6	1.5261	1.5282	1.5304	1.5326	1.5347	1.5369	1.5390	1.5412	1.5433	1.5454
4.7	1.5476	1.5497	1.5518	1.5539	1.5560	1.5581	1.5602	1.5623	1.5644	1.5665
4.8	1.5686	1.5707	1.5728	1.5748	1.5769	1.5790	1.5810	1.5831	1.5851	1.5872
4.9	1.5892	1.5913	1.5933	1.5953	1.5974	1.5994	1.6014	1.6034	1.6054	1.6074
5.0	1.6094	1.6114	1.6134	1.6154	1.6174	1.6194	1.6214	1.6233	1.6253	1.6273
5.1	1.6292	1.6312	1.6332	1.6351	1.6371	1.6390	1.6409	1.6429	1.6448	1.6467
5.2	1.6487	1.6506	1.6525	1.6544	1.6563	1.6582	1.6601	1.6620	1.6639	1.6658
5.3	1.6677	1.6696	1.6715	1.6734	1.6752	1.6771	1.6790	1.6808	1.6827	1.6845
5.4	1.6864	1.6882	1.6901	1.6919	1.6938	1.6956	1.6974	1.6993	1.7011	1.7029

REFERENCE TABLE 13   (Continued)

	0.00	0.01	0.02	0.03	0.04	0.05	0.06	0.07	0.08	0.09
5.5	1.7047	1.7066	1.7084	1.7102	1.7120	1.7138	1.7156	1.7174	1.7192	1.7210
5.6	1.7228	1.7246	1.7263	1.7281	1.7299	1.7317	1.7334	1.7352	1.7370	1.7387
5.7	1.7405	1.7422	1.7440	1.7457	1.7475	1.7492	1.7509	1.7527	1.7544	1.7561
5.8	1.7579	1.7596	1.7613	1.7630	1.7647	1.7664	1.7681	1.7699	1.7716	1.7733
5.9	1.7750	1.7766	1.7783	1.7800	1.7817	1.7834	1.7851	1.7867	1.7884	1.7901
6.0	1.7918	1.7934	1.7951	1.7967	1.7984	1.8001	1.8017	1.8034	1.8050	1.8066
6.1	1.8083	1.8099	1.8116	1.8132	1.8148	1.8165	1.8181	1.8197	1.8213	1.8229
6.2	1.8245	1.8262	1.8278	1.8294	1.8310	1.8326	1.8342	1.8358	1.8374	1.8390
6.3	1.8405	1.8421	1.8437	1.8453	1.8469	1.8485	1.8500	1.8516	1.8532	1.8547
6.4	1.8563	1.8579	1.8594	1.8610	1.8625	1.8641	1.8656	1.8672	1.8687	1.8703
6.5	1.8718	1.8733	1.8749	1.8764	1.8779	1.8795	1.8810	1.8825	1.8840	1.8856
6.6	1.8871	1.8886	1.8901	1.8916	1.8931	1.8946	1.8961	1.8976	1.8991	1.9006
6.7	1.9021	1.9036	1.9051	1.9066	1.9081	1.9095	1.9110	1.9125	1.9140	1.9155
6.8	1.9169	1.9184	1.9199	1.9213	1.9228	1.9242	1.9257	1.9272	1.9286	1.9301
6.9	1.9315	1.9330	1.9344	1.9359	1.9373	1.9387	1.9402	1.9416	1.9430	1.9445
7.0	1.9459	1.9473	1.9488	1.9502	1.9516	1.9530	1.9544	1.9559	1.9573	1.9587
7.1	1.9601	1.9615	1.9629	1.9643	1.9657	1.9671	1.9685	1.9699	1.9713	1.9727
7.2	1.9741	1.9755	1.9769	1.9782	1.9796	1.9810	1.9824	1.9838	1.9851	1.9865
7.3	1.9879	1.9892	1.9906	1.9920	1.9933	1.9947	1.9961	1.9974	1.9988	2.0001
7.4	2.0015	2.0028	2.0042	2.0055	2.0069	2.0082	2.0096	2.0109	2.0122	2.0136
7.5	2.0149	2.0162	2.0176	2.0189	2.0202	2.0215	2.0229	2.0242	2.0255	2.0268
7.6	2.0281	2.0295	2.0308	2.0321	2.0334	2.0347	2.0360	2.0373	2.0386	2.0399
7.7	2.0412	2.0425	2.0438	2.0451	2.0464	2.0477	2.0490	2.0503	2.0516	2.0528
7.8	2.0541	2.0554	2.0567	2.0580	2.0592	2.0605	2.0618	2.0631	2.0643	2.0656
7.9	2.0669	2.0681	2.0694	2.0707	2.0719	2.0732	2.0744	2.0757	2.0769	2.0782
8.0	2.0794	2.0807	2.0819	2.0832	2.0844	2.0857	2.0869	2.0882	2.0894	2.0906
8.1	2.0919	2.0931	2.0943	2.0956	2.0968	2.0980	2.0992	2.1005	2.1017	2.1029
8.2	2.1041	2.1054	2.1066	2.1078	2.1090	2.1102	2.1114	2.1126	2.1138	2.1150
8.3	2.1163	2.1175	2.1187	2.1199	2.1211	2.1223	2.1235	2.1247	2.1258	2.1270
8.4	2.1282	2.1294	2.1306	2.1318	2.1330	2.1342	2.1353	2.1365	2.1377	2.1389
8.5	2.1401	2.1412	2.1424	2.1436	2.1448	2.1459	2.1471	2.1483	2.1494	2.1506
8.6	2.1518	2.1529	2.1541	2.1552	2.1564	2.1576	2.1587	2.1599	2.1610	2.1622
8.7	2.1633	2.1645	2.1656	2.1668	2.1679	2.1691	2.1702	2.1713	2.1725	2.1736
8.8	2.1748	2.1759	2.1770	2.1782	2.1793	2.1804	2.1815	2.1827	2.1838	2.1849
8.9	2.1861	2.1872	2.1883	2.1894	2.1905	2.1917	2.1928	2.1939	2.1950	2.1961
9.0	2.1972	2.1983	2.1994	2.2006	2.2017	2.2028	2.2039	2.2050	2.2061	2.2072
9.1	2.2083	2.2094	2.2105	2.2116	2.2127	2.2138	2.2148	2.2159	2.2170	2.2181
9.2	2.2192	2.2203	2.2214	2.2225	2.2235	2.2246	2.2257	2.2268	2.2279	2.2289
9.3	2.2300	2.2311	2.2322	2.2332	2.2343	2.2354	2.2364	2.2375	2.2386	2.2396
9.4	2.2407	2.2418	2.2428	2.2439	2.2450	2.2460	2.2471	2.2481	2.2492	2.2502
9.5	2.2513	2.2523	2.2534	2.2544	2.2555	2.2565	2.2576	2.2586	2.2597	2.2607
9.6	2.2618	2.2628	2.2638	2.2649	2.2659	2.2670	2.2680	2.2690	2.2701	2.2711
9.7	2.2721	2.2732	2.2742	2.2752	2.2762	2.2773	2.2783	2.2793	2.2803	2.2814
9.8	2.2824	2.2834	2.2844	2.2854	2.2865	2.2875	2.2885	2.2895	2.2905	2.2915
9.9	2.2925	2.2935	2.2946	2.2956	2.2966	2.2976	2.2986	2.2996	2.3006	2.3016

REFERENCE TABLE 14   Properties of Logarithms

Inverse Properties

1. $\ln e^x = x$

2. $e^{\ln x} = x$

Properties of Logarithms

1. $\ln 1 = 0$

2. $\ln e = 1$

3. $\ln xy = \ln x + \ln y$

4. $\ln \dfrac{x}{y} = \ln x - \ln y$

5. $\ln x^y = y \ln x$

6. $\log_a x = \dfrac{\ln x}{\ln a}$

REFERENCE TABLE 15   Geometry

Triangles

1. General triangle

    Sum of triangles $\alpha + \beta + \theta = 180°$

    Area $= \dfrac{1}{2}(\text{base})(\text{height}) = \dfrac{1}{2}bh$

 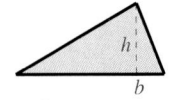

2. Similar triangles

    $\dfrac{a}{b} = \dfrac{A}{B}$

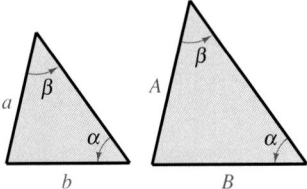

3. Right triangle

    $c^2 = a^2 + b^2$ (Pythagorean Theorem)

    Sum of acute angles $\alpha + \beta = 90°$

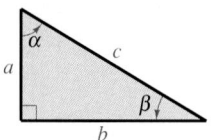

4. Equilateral triangle

    Height $= h = \dfrac{\sqrt{3}\,s}{2}$

    Area $= \dfrac{\sqrt{3}\,s^2}{4}$

 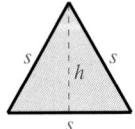

5. Isosceles right triangle

$$\text{Area} = \frac{s^2}{2}$$

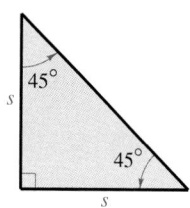

Quadrilaterals (Four-Sided Figures)

1. Rectangle

$$\text{Area} = (\text{length})(\text{height}) = bh$$

2. Square

$$\text{Area} = (\text{side})^2 = s^2$$

3. Parallelogram

$$\text{Area} = bh$$

4. Trapezoid

$$\text{Area} = \frac{1}{2}h(a + b)$$

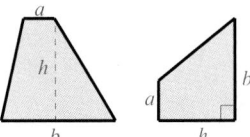

Circles and Ellipses

1. Circle

$$\text{Area} = \pi r^2$$

$$\text{Circumference} = 2\pi r$$

2. Sector of circle (θ in radians)

$$\text{Area} = \frac{\theta r^2}{2}$$

$$s = r\theta$$

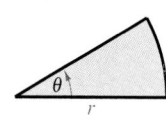

REFERENCE TABLE 15   (Continued)

3. Circular ring

$$\text{Area} = \pi(R^2 - r^2)$$

4. Ellipse

$$\text{Area} = \pi ab$$

$$\text{Circumference} \approx 2\pi\sqrt{\frac{a^2 + b^2}{2}}$$

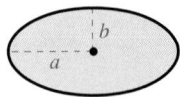

Solid Figures

1. Cone (A = area of base)

$$\text{Volume} = \frac{Ah}{3}$$

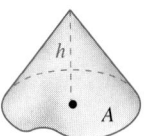

2. Right circular cone

$$\text{Volume} = \frac{\pi r^2 h}{3}$$

$$\text{Lateral surface area} = \pi r\sqrt{r^2 + h^2}$$

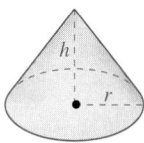

3. Frustum of right circular cone

$$\text{Volume} = \frac{\pi(r^2 + rR + R^2)h}{3}$$

$$\text{Lateral surface area} = \pi s(R + r)$$

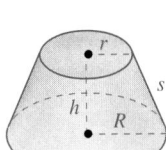

4. Right circular cylinder

$$\text{Volume} = \pi r^2 h$$

$$\text{Lateral surface area} = 2\pi rh$$

5. Sphere

$$\text{Volume} = \frac{4}{3}\pi r^3$$

$$\text{Surface area} = 4\pi r^2$$

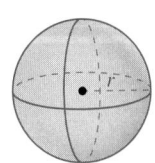

REFERENCE TABLE 16   Trigonometry

Definitions of the Six Trigonometric Functions

Right triangle definition: $0 < \theta < \pi/2$

$$\sin \theta = \frac{\text{opp.}}{\text{hyp.}} \qquad \csc \theta = \frac{\text{hyp.}}{\text{opp.}}$$

$$\cos \theta = \frac{\text{adj.}}{\text{hyp.}} \qquad \sec \theta = \frac{\text{hyp.}}{\text{adj.}}$$

$$\tan \theta = \frac{\text{opp.}}{\text{adj.}} \qquad \cot \theta = \frac{\text{adj.}}{\text{opp.}}$$

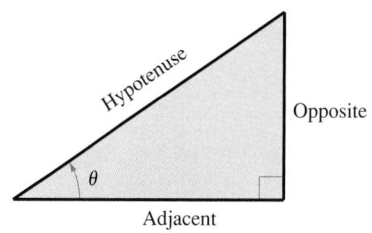

Circular function definition: θ is any angle and (x, y) is a point on the terminal ray of the angle.

$$\sin \theta = \frac{y}{r} \qquad \csc \theta = \frac{r}{y}$$

$$\cos \theta = \frac{x}{r} \qquad \sec \theta = \frac{r}{x}$$

$$\tan \theta = \frac{y}{x} \qquad \cot \theta = \frac{x}{y}$$

$$r = \sqrt{x^2 + y^2}$$

Signs of the Trigonometric Functions by Quadrant

Quadrant	sin	cos	tan	cot	sec	csc
I	+	+	+	+	+	+
II	+	−	−	−	−	+
III	−	−	+	+	−	−
IV	−	+	−	−	+	−

REFERENCE TABLE 16   (Continued)

Values of Trigonometric Functions at Common Angles

Degrees	0°	30°	45°	60°	90°
Radians	0	$\dfrac{\pi}{6}$	$\dfrac{\pi}{4}$	$\dfrac{\pi}{3}$	$\dfrac{\pi}{2}$
$\sin \theta$	0	$\dfrac{1}{2}$	$\dfrac{\sqrt{2}}{2}$	$\dfrac{\sqrt{3}}{2}$	1
$\cos \theta$	1	$\dfrac{\sqrt{3}}{2}$	$\dfrac{\sqrt{2}}{2}$	$\dfrac{1}{2}$	0
$\tan \theta$	0	$\dfrac{1}{\sqrt{3}}$	1	$\sqrt{3}$	undefined

Trigonometric Identities

Reciprocal identities

$$\sin \theta = \frac{1}{\csc \theta} \qquad \cos \theta = \frac{1}{\sec \theta} \qquad \tan \theta = \frac{1}{\cot \theta}$$

$$\csc \theta = \frac{1}{\sin \theta} \qquad \sec \theta = \frac{1}{\cos \theta} \qquad \cot \theta = \frac{1}{\tan \theta}$$

$$\tan \theta = \frac{\sin \theta}{\cos \theta} \qquad \cot \theta = \frac{\cos \theta}{\sin \theta}$$

Pythagorean identities

$$\sin^2 \theta + \cos^2 \theta = 1 \qquad \tan^2 \theta + 1 = \sec^2 \theta \qquad \cot^2 \theta + 1 = \csc^2 \theta$$

Reduction formulas

$$\sin(-\theta) = -\sin \theta \qquad \cos(-\theta) = \cos \theta \qquad \tan(-\theta) = -\tan \theta$$
$$\sin \theta = -\sin(\theta - \pi) \qquad \cos \theta = -\cos(\theta - \pi) \qquad \tan \theta = \tan(\theta - \pi)$$

Sum or difference of two angles

$$\sin(\theta \pm \phi) = \sin\theta\cos\phi \pm \cos\theta\sin\phi$$
$$\cos(\theta \pm \phi) = \cos\theta\cos\phi \mp \sin\theta\sin\phi$$
$$\tan(\theta \pm \phi) = \frac{\tan\theta \pm \tan\phi}{1 \mp \tan\theta\tan\phi}$$
$$\sin(\theta + \phi)\sin(\theta - \phi) = \sin^2\theta - \sin^2\phi$$
$$\cos(\theta + \phi)\cos(\theta - \phi) = \cos^2\theta - \sin^2\phi$$

Double-angle identities

$$\sin 2\theta = 2\sin\theta\cos\theta$$
$$\cos 2\theta = 2\cos^2\theta - 1 = 1 - 2\sin^2\theta$$
$$\tan 2\theta = \frac{2\tan\theta}{1 - \tan^2\theta}$$

Multiple-angle identities

$$\sin 3\theta = 3\sin\theta - 4\sin^3\theta$$
$$\cos 3\theta = -3\cos\theta + 4\cos^3\theta$$
$$\tan 3\theta = \frac{3\tan\theta - \tan^2\theta}{1 - 3\tan^2\theta}$$
$$\sin 4\theta = 4\sin\theta\cos\theta - 8\sin^3\theta\cos\theta$$
$$\cos 4\theta = 8\cos^4\theta - 8\cos^2\theta + 1$$
$$\tan 4\theta = \frac{4\tan\theta - 4\tan^3\theta}{1 - 6\tan^2\theta + \tan^4\theta}$$

Half-angle identities

$$\sin^2\theta = \frac{1}{2}(1 - \cos 2\theta)$$
$$\cos^2\theta = \frac{1}{2}(1 + \cos 2\theta)$$

Product identities

$$\sin\theta\sin\phi = \frac{1}{2}\cos(\theta - \phi) - \frac{1}{2}\cos(\theta + \phi)$$
$$\cos\theta\cos\phi = \frac{1}{2}\cos(\theta - \phi) + \frac{1}{2}\cos(\theta + \phi)$$
$$\cos\theta\sin\phi = \frac{1}{2}\sin(\theta - \phi) + \frac{1}{2}\sin(\theta + \phi)$$

REFERENCE TABLE 17   Tables of Trigonometric Functions

1 degree ≈ 0.01745 radians
1 radian ≈ 57.29578 degrees

For $0 \leqslant \theta \leqslant 45$, read from upper left.
For $45 \leqslant \theta \leqslant 90$, read from lower right.
For $90 \leqslant \theta \leqslant 360$, use the identities:

θ	Quadrant II	Quadrant III	Quadrant IV
$\sin \theta$	$\sin(180 - \theta)$	$-\sin(\theta - 180)$	$-\sin(360 - \theta)$
$\cos \theta$	$-\cos(180 - \theta)$	$-\cos(\theta - 180)$	$\cos(360 - \theta)$
$\tan \theta$	$-\tan(180 - \theta)$	$\tan(\theta - 180)$	$-\tan(360 - \theta)$
$\cot \theta$	$-\cot(180 - \theta)$	$\cot(\theta - 180)$	$-\cot(360 - \theta)$

Degrees	Radians	sin	cos	tan	cot		
0° 00′	.0000	.0000	1.0000	.0000	—	1.5708	90° 00′
10	.0029	.0029	1.0000	.0029	343.774	1.5679	50
20	.0058	.0058	1.0000	.0058	171.885	1.5650	40
30	.0087	.0087	1.0000	.0087	114.589	1.5621	30
40	.0116	.0116	.9999	.0116	85.940	1.5592	20
50	.0145	.0145	.9999	.0145	68.750	1.5563	10
1° 00′	.0175	.0175	.9998	.0175	57.290	1.5533	89° 00′
10	.0204	.0204	.9998	.0204	49.104	1.5504	50
20	.0233	.0233	.9997	.0233	42.964	1.5475	40
30	.0262	.0262	.9997	.0262	38.188	1.5446	30
40	.0291	.0291	.9996	.0291	34.368	1.5417	20
50	.0320	.0320	.9995	.0320	31.242	1.5388	10
2° 00′	.0349	.0349	.9994	.0349	28.636	1.5359	88° 00′
10	.0378	.0378	.9993	.0378	26.432	1.5330	50
20	.0407	.0407	.9992	.0407	24.542	1.5301	40
30	.0436	.0436	.9990	.0437	22.904	1.5272	30
40	.0465	.0465	.9989	.0466	21.470	1.5243	20
50	.0495	.0494	.9988	.0495	20.206	1.5213	10
3° 00′	.0524	.0523	.9986	.0524	19.081	1.5184	87° 00′
10	.0553	.0552	.9985	.0553	18.075	1.5155	50
20	.0582	.0581	.9983	.0582	17.169	1.5126	40
30	.0611	.0610	.9981	.0612	16.350	1.5097	30
40	.0640	.0640	.9980	.0641	15.605	1.5068	20
50	.0669	.0669	.9978	.0670	14.924	1.5039	10
4° 00′	.0698	.0698	.9976	.0699	14.301	1.5010	86° 00′
10	.0727	.0727	.9974	.0729	13.727	1.4981	50
20	.0756	.0756	.9971	.0758	13.197	1.4952	40
30	.0785	.0785	.9969	.0787	12.706	1.4923	30
40	.0814	.0814	.9967	.0816	12.251	1.4893	20
50	.0844	.0843	.9964	.0846	11.826	1.4864	10
5° 00′	.0873	.0872	.9962	.0875	11.430	1.4835	85° 00′
10	.0902	.0901	.9959	.0904	11.059	1.4806	50
20	.0931	.0929	.9957	.0934	10.712	1.4777	40
30	.0960	.0958	.9954	.0963	10.385	1.4748	30
40	.0989	.0987	.9951	.0992	10.078	1.4719	20
50	.1018	.1016	.9948	.1022	9.788	1.4690	10
6° 00′	.1047	.1045	.9945	.1051	9.514	1.4661	84° 00′
10	.1076	.1074	.9942	.1080	9.255	1.4632	50
20	.1105	.1103	.9939	.1110	9.010	1.4603	40
30	.1134	.1132	.9936	.1139	8.777	1.4573	30
40	.1164	.1161	.9932	.1169	8.556	1.4544	20
50	.1193	.1190	.9929	.1198	8.345	1.4515	10
7° 00′	.1222	.1219	.9925	.1228	8.144	1.4486	83° 00′
10	.1251	.1248	.9922	.1257	7.953	1.4457	50
20	.1280	.1276	.9918	.1287	7.770	1.4428	40
30	.1309	.1305	.9914	.1317	7.596	1.4399	30
40	.1338	.1334	.9911	.1346	7.429	1.4370	20
50	.1367	.1363	.9907	.1376	7.269	1.4341	10
		cos	sin	cot	tan	Radians	Degrees

Degrees	Radians	sin	cos	tan	cot		
8°00′	.1396	.1392	.9903	.1405	7.115	1.4312	82°00′
10	.1425	.1421	.9899	.1435	6.968	1.4283	50
20	.1454	.1449	.9894	.1465	6.827	1.4254	40
30	.1484	.1478	.9890	.1495	6.691	1.4224	30
40	.1513	.1507	.9886	.1524	6.561	1.4195	20
50	.1542	.1536	.9881	.1554	6.435	1.4166	10
9°00′	.1571	.1564	.9877	.1584	6.314	1.4137	81°00′
10	.1600	.1593	.9872	.1614	6.197	1.4108	50
20	.1629	.1622	.9868	.1644	6.084	1.4079	40
30	.1658	.1650	.9863	.1673	5.976	1.4050	30
40	.1687	.1679	.9858	.1703	5.871	1.4021	20
50	.1716	.1708	.9853	.1733	5.769	1.3992	10
10°00′	.1745	.1736	.9848	.1763	5.671	1.3963	80°00′
10	.1774	.1765	.9843	.1793	5.576	1.3934	50
20	.1804	.1794	.9838	.1823	5.485	1.3904	40
30	.1833	.1822	.9833	.1853	5.396	1.3875	30
40	.1862	.1851	.9827	.1883	5.309	1.3846	20
50	.1891	.1880	.9822	.1914	5.226	1.3817	10
11°00′	.1920	.1908	.9816	.1944	5.145	1.3788	79°00′
10	.1949	.1937	.9811	.1974	5.066	1.3759	50
20	.1978	.1965	.9805	.2004	4.989	1.3730	40
30	.2007	.1994	.9799	.2035	4.915	1.3701	30
40	.2036	.2022	.9793	.2065	4.843	1.3672	20
50	.2065	.2051	.9787	.2095	4.773	1.3643	10
12°00′	.2094	.2079	.9781	.2126	4.705	1.3614	78°00′
10	.2123	.2108	.9775	.2156	4.638	1.3584	50
20	.2153	.2136	.9769	.2186	4.574	1.3555	40
30	.2182	.2164	.9763	.2217	4.511	1.3526	30
40	.2211	.2193	.9757	.2247	4.449	1.3497	20
50	.2240	.2221	.9750	.2278	4.390	1.3468	10
13°00′	.2269	.2250	.9744	.2309	4.331	1.3439	77°00′
10	.2298	.2278	.9737	.2339	4.275	1.3410	50
20	.2327	.2306	.9730	.2370	4.219	1.3381	40
30	.2356	.2334	.9724	.2401	4.165	1.3352	30
40	.2385	.2363	.9717	.2432	4.113	1.3323	20
50	.2414	.2391	.9710	.2462	4.061	1.3294	10
14°00′	.2443	.2419	.9703	.2493	4.011	1.3265	76°00′
10	.2473	.2447	.9696	.2524	3.962	1.3235	50
20	.2502	.2476	.9689	.2555	3.914	1.3206	40
30	.2531	.2504	.9681	.2586	3.867	1.3177	30
40	.2560	.2532	.9674	.2617	3.821	1.3148	20
50	.2589	.2560	.9667	.2648	3.776	1.3119	10
15°00′	.2618	.2588	.9659	.2679	3.732	1.3090	75°00′
10	.2647	.2616	.9652	.2711	3.689	1.3061	50
20	.2676	.2644	.9644	.2742	3.647	1.3032	40
30	.2705	.2672	.9636	.2773	3.606	1.3003	30
40	.2734	.2700	.9628	.2805	3.566	1.2974	20
50	.2763	.2728	.9621	.2836	3.526	1.2945	10
16°00′	.2793	.2756	.9613	.2867	3.487	1.2915	74°00′
10	.2822	.2784	.9605	.2899	3.450	1.2886	50
20	.2851	.2812	.9596	.2931	3.412	1.2857	40
30	.2880	.2840	.9588	.2962	3.376	1.2828	30
40	.2909	.2868	.9580	.2994	3.340	1.2799	20
50	.2938	.2896	.9572	.3026	3.305	1.2770	10
17°00′	.2967	.2924	.9563	.3057	3.271	1.2741	73°00′
10	.2996	.2952	.9555	.3089	3.237	1.2712	50
20	.3025	.2979	.9546	.3121	3.204	1.2683	40
30	.3054	.3007	.9537	.3153	3.172	1.2654	30
40	.3083	.3035	.9528	.3185	3.140	1.2625	20
50	.3113	.3062	.9520	.3217	3.108	1.2595	10
		cos	sin	cot	tan	Radians	Degrees

Degrees	Radians	sin	cos	tan	cot		
18°00′	.3142	.3090	.9511	.3249	3.078	1.2566	72°00′
10	.3171	.3118	.9502	.3281	3.047	1.2537	50
20	.3200	.3145	.9492	.3314	3.018	1.2508	40
30	.3229	.3173	.9483	.3346	2.989	1.2479	30
40	.3258	.3201	.9474	.3378	2.960	1.2450	20
50	.3287	.3228	.9465	.3411	2.932	1.2421	10
19°00′	.3316	.3256	.9455	.3443	2.904	1.2392	71°00′
10	.3345	.3283	.9446	.3476	2.877	1.2363	50
20	.3374	.3311	.9436	.3508	2.850	1.2334	40
30	.3403	.3338	.9426	.3541	2.824	1.2305	30
40	.3432	.3365	.9417	.3574	2.798	1.2275	20
50	.3462	.3393	.9407	.3607	2.773	1.2246	10
20°00′	.3491	.3420	.9397	.3640	2.747	1.2217	70°00′
10	.3520	.3448	.9387	.3673	2.723	1.2188	50
20	.3549	.3475	.9377	.3706	2.699	1.2159	40
30	.3578	.3502	.9367	.3739	2.675	1.2130	30
40	.3607	.3529	.9356	.3772	2.651	1.2101	20
50	.3636	.3557	.9346	.3805	2.628	1.2072	10
21°00′	.3665	.3584	.9336	.3839	2.605	1.2043	69°00′
10	.3694	.3611	.9325	.3872	2.583	1.2014	50
20	.3723	.3638	.9315	.3906	2.560	1.1985	40
30	.3752	.3665	.9304	.3939	2.539	1.1956	30
40	.3782	.3692	.9293	.3973	2.517	1.1926	20
50	.3811	.3719	.9283	.4006	2.496	1.1897	10
22°00′	.3840	.3746	.9272	.4040	2.475	1.1868	68°00′
10	.3869	.3773	.9261	.4074	2.455	1.1839	50
20	.3898	.3800	.9250	.4108	2.434	1.1810	40
30	.3927	.3827	.9239	.4142	2.414	1.1781	30
40	.3956	.3854	.9228	.4176	2.394	1.1752	20
50	.3985	.3881	.9216	.4210	2.375	1.1723	10
23°00′	.4014	.3907	.9205	.4245	2.356	1.1694	67°00′
10	.4043	.3934	.9194	.4279	2.337	1.1665	50
20	.4072	.3961	.9182	.4314	2.318	1.1636	40
30	.4102	.3987	.9171	.4348	2.300	1.1606	30
40	.4131	.4014	.9159	.4383	2.282	1.1577	20
50	.4160	.4041	.9147	.4417	2.264	1.1548	10
24°00′	.4189	.4067	.9135	.4452	2.246	1.1519	66°00′
10	.4218	.4094	.9124	.4487	2.229	1.1490	50
20	.4247	.4120	.9112	.4522	2.211	1.1461	40
30	.4276	.4147	.9100	.4557	2.194	1.1432	30
40	.4305	.4173	.9088	.4592	2.177	1.1403	20
50	.4334	.4200	.9075	.4628	2.161	1.1374	10
25°00′	.4363	.4226	.9063	.4663	2.145	1.1345	65°00′
10	.4392	.4253	.9051	.4699	2.128	1.1316	50
20	.4422	.4279	.9038	.4734	2.112	1.1286	40
30	.4451	.4305	.9026	.4770	2.097	1.1257	30
40	.4480	.4331	.9013	.4806	2.081	1.1228	20
50	.4509	.4358	.9001	.4841	2.066	1.1199	10
26°00′	.4538	.4384	.8988	.4877	2.050	1.1170	64°00′
10	.4567	.4410	.8975	.4913	2.035	1.1141	50
20	.4596	.4436	.8962	.4950	2.020	1.1112	40
30	.4625	.4462	.8949	.4986	2.006	1.1083	30
40	.4654	.4488	.8936	.5022	1.991	1.1054	20
50	.4683	.4514	.8923	.5059	1.977	1.1025	10
27°00′	.4712	.4540	.8910	.5095	1.963	1.0996	63°00′
10	.4741	.4566	.8897	.5132	1.949	1.0966	50
20	.4771	.4592	.8884	.5169	1.935	1.0937	40
30	.4800	.4617	.8870	.5206	1.921	1.0908	30
40	.4829	.4643	.8857	.5243	1.907	1.0879	20
50	.4858	.4669	.8843	.5280	1.894	1.0850	10
		cos	sin	cot	tan	Radians	Degrees

REFERENCE TABLE 17   (Continued)

Degrees	Radians	sin	cos	tan	cot		
28°00′	.4887	.4695	.8829	.5317	1.881	1.0821	62°00′
10	.4916	.4720	.8816	.5354	1.868	1.0792	50
20	.4945	.4746	.8802	.5392	1.855	1.0763	40
30	.4974	.4772	.8788	.5430	1.842	1.0734	30
40	.5003	.4797	.8774	.5467	1.829	1.0705	20
50	.5032	.4823	.8760	.5505	1.816	1.0676	10
29°00′	.5061	.4848	.8746	.5543	1.804	1.0647	61°00′
10	.5091	.4874	.8732	.5581	1.792	1.0617	50
20	.5120	.4899	.8718	.5619	1.780	1.0588	40
30	.5149	.4924	.8704	.5658	1.767	1.0559	30
40	.5178	.4950	.8689	.5696	1.756	1.0530	20
50	.5207	.4975	.8675	.5735	1.744	1.0501	10
30°00′	.5236	.5000	.8660	.5774	1.732	1.0472	60°00′
10	.5265	.5025	.8646	.5812	1.720	1.0443	50
20	.5294	.5050	.8631	.5851	1.709	1.0414	40
30	.5323	.5075	.8616	.5890	1.698	1.0385	30
40	.5352	.5100	.8601	.5930	1.686	1.0356	20
50	.5381	.5125	.8587	.5969	1.675	1.0327	10
31°00′	.5411	.5150	.8572	.6009	1.664	1.0297	59°00′
10	.5440	.5175	.8557	.6048	1.653	1.0268	50
20	.5469	.5200	.8542	.6088	1.643	1.0239	40
30	.5498	.5225	.8526	.6128	1.632	1.0210	30
40	.5527	.5250	.8511	.6168	1.621	1.0181	20
50	.5556	.5275	.8496	.6208	1.611	1.0152	10
32°00′	.5585	.5299	.8480	.6249	1.600	1.0123	58°00′
10	.5614	.5324	.8465	.6289	1.590	1.0094	50
20	.5643	.5348	.8450	.6330	1.580	1.0065	40
30	.5672	.5373	.8434	.6371	1.570	1.0036	30
40	.5701	.5398	.8418	.6412	1.560	1.0007	20
50	.5730	.5422	.8403	.6453	1.550	.9977	10
33°00′	.5760	.5446	.8387	.6494	1.540	.9948	57°00′
10	.5789	.5471	.8371	.6536	1.530	.9919	50
20	.5818	.5495	.8355	.6577	1.520	.9890	40
30	.5847	.5519	.8339	.6619	1.511	.9861	30
40	.5876	.5544	.8323	.6661	1.501	.9832	20
50	.5905	.5568	.8307	.6703	1.492	.9803	10
34°00′	.5934	.5592	.8290	.6745	1.483	.9774	56°00′
10	.5963	.5616	.8274	.6787	1.473	.9745	50
20	.5992	.5640	.8258	.6830	1.464	.9716	40
30	.6021	.5664	.8241	.6873	1.455	.9687	30
40	.6050	.5688	.8225	.6916	1.446	.9657	20
50	.6080	.5712	.8208	.6959	1.437	.9628	10
35°00′	.6109	.5736	.8192	.7002	1.428	.9599	55°00′
10	.6138	.5760	.8175	.7046	1.419	.9570	50
20	.6167	.5783	.8158	.7089	1.411	.9541	40
30	.6196	.5807	.8141	.7133	1.402	.9512	30
40	.6225	.5831	.8124	.7177	1.393	.9483	20
50	.6254	.5854	.8107	.7221	1.385	.9454	10
36°00′	.6283	.5878	.8090	.7265	1.376	.9425	54°00′
10	.6312	.5901	.8073	.7310	1.368	.9396	50
20	.6341	.5925	.8056	.7355	1.360	.9367	40
30	.6370	.5948	.8039	.7400	1.351	.9338	30
40	.6400	.5972	.8021	.7445	1.343	.9308	20
50	.6429	.5995	.8004	.7490	1.335	.9279	10
		cos	sin	cot	tan	Radians	Degrees

Degrees	Radians	sin	cos	tan	cot		
37°00′	.6458	.6018	.7986	.7536	1.327	.9250	53°00′
10	.6487	.6041	.7969	.7581	1.319	.9221	50
20	.6516	.6065	.7951	.7627	1.311	.9192	40
30	.6545	.6088	.7934	.7673	1.303	.9163	30
40	.6574	.6111	.7916	.7720	1.295	.9134	20
50	.6603	.6134	.7898	.7766	1.288	.9105	10
38°00′	.6632	.6157	.7880	.7813	1.280	.9076	52°00′
10	.6661	.6180	.7862	.7860	1.272	.9047	50
20	.6690	.6202	.7844	.7907	1.265	.9018	40
30	.6720	.6225	.7826	.7954	1.257	.8988	30
40	.6749	.6248	.7808	.8002	1.250	.8959	20
50	.6778	.6271	.7790	.8050	1.242	.8930	10
39°00′	.6807	.6293	.7771	.8098	1.235	.8901	51°00′
10	.6836	.6316	.7753	.8146	1.228	.8872	50
20	.6865	.6338	.7735	.8195	1.220	.8843	40
30	.6894	.6361	.7716	.8243	1.213	.8814	30
40	.6923	.6383	.7698	.8292	1.206	.8785	20
50	.6952	.6406	.7679	.8342	1.199	.8756	10
40°00′	.6981	.6428	.7660	.8391	1.192	.8727	50°00′
10	.7010	.6450	.7642	.8441	1.185	.8698	50
20	.7039	.6472	.7623	.8491	1.178	.8668	40
30	.7069	.6494	.7604	.8541	1.171	.8639	30
40	.7098	.6517	.7585	.8591	1.164	.8610	20
50	.7127	.6539	.7566	.8642	1.157	.8581	10
41°00′	.7156	.6561	.7547	.8693	1.150	.8552	49°00′
10	.7185	.6583	.7528	.8744	1.144	.8523	50
20	.7214	.6604	.7509	.8796	1.137	.8494	40
30	.7243	.6626	.7490	.8847	1.130	.8465	30
40	.7272	.6648	.7470	.8899	1.124	.8436	20
50	.7301	.6670	.7451	.8952	1.117	.8407	10
42°00′	.7330	.6691	.7431	.9004	1.111	.8378	48°00′
10	.7359	.6713	.7412	.9057	1.104	.8348	50
20	.7389	.6734	.7392	.9110	1.098	.8319	40
30	.7418	.6756	.7373	.9163	1.091	.8290	30
40	.7447	.6777	.7353	.9217	1.085	.8261	20
50	.7476	.6799	.7333	.9271	1.079	.8232	10
43°00′	.7505	.6820	.7314	.9325	1.072	.8203	47°00′
10	.7534	.6841	.7294	.9380	1.066	.8174	50
20	.7563	.6862	.7274	.9435	1.060	.8145	40
30	.7592	.6884	.7254	.9490	1.054	.8116	30
40	.7621	.6905	.7234	.9545	1.048	.8087	20
50	.7650	.6926	.7214	.9601	1.042	.8058	10
44°00′	.7679	.6947	.7193	.9657	1.036	.8029	46°00′
10	.7709	.6967	.7173	.9713	1.030	.7999	50
20	.7738	.6988	.7153	.9770	1.024	.7970	40
30	.7767	.7009	.7133	.9827	1.018	.7941	30
40	.7796	.7030	.7112	.9884	1.012	.7912	20
50	.7825	.7050	.7092	.9942	1.006	.7883	10
45°00′	.7854	.7071	.7071	1.0000	1.000	.7854	45°00′
		cos	sin	cot	tan	Radians	Degrees

REFERENCE TABLE 18   Plane Analytic Geometry

Distance Between (x_1, y_1) and (x_2, y_2)

$$d = \sqrt{(x_2 - x_1)^2 + (y_2 - y_1)^2}$$

Midpoint Between (x_1, y_1) and (x_2, y_2)

$$\text{Midpoint} = \left(\frac{x_1 + x_2}{2}, \frac{y_1 + y_2}{2} \right)$$

Slope of Line Passing Through (x_1, y_1) and (x_2, y_2)

$$m = \frac{y_2 - y_1}{x_2 - x_1}$$

Slopes of Parallel Lines

$$m_1 = m_2$$

Slopes of Perpendicular Lines

$$m_1 = -\frac{1}{m_2}$$

Equations of Lines

Point-slope form: $y - y_1 = m(x - x_1)$ General form: $Ax + By + C = 0$
Vertical line: $x = a$ Horizontal line: $y = b$

Equations of Circles [Center: (h, k), Radius: r]

Standard form: $(x - h)^2 + (y - k)^2 = r^2$
General form: $Ax^2 + Ay^2 + Dx + Ey + F = 0$

REFERENCE TABLE 18 (Continued)

Equations of Parabolas [Vertex: (h, k)]

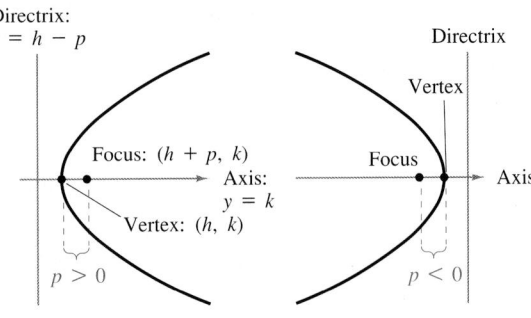

$$(x - h)^2 = 4p(y - k)$$ $$(y - k)^2 = 4p(x - h)$$

(a) Vertical axis: $p > 0$ (b) Vertical axis: $p < 0$ (c) Horizontal axis: $p > 0$ (d) Horizontal axis: $p < 0$

Equations of Ellipses [Center: (h, k)]

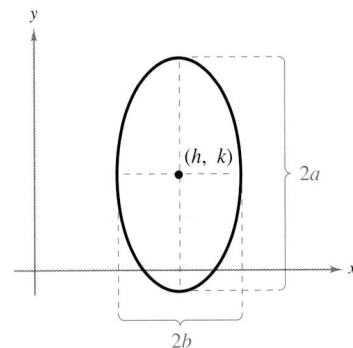

$$\frac{(x - h)^2}{a^2} + \frac{(y - k)^2}{b^2} = 1$$ $$\frac{(x - h)^2}{b^2} + \frac{(y - k)^2}{a^2} = 1$$

Equations of Hyperbolas [Center: (h, k)]

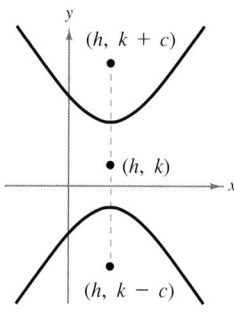

$$\frac{(x - h)^2}{a^2} - \frac{(y - k)^2}{b^2} = 1$$ $$\frac{(y - k)^2}{a^2} - \frac{(x - h)^2}{b^2} = 1$$

REFERENCE TABLE 19   Solid Analytic Geometry

Distance Between (x_1, y_1, z_1) and (x_2, y_2, z_2)

$$d = \sqrt{(x_2 - x_1)^2 + (y_2 - y_1)^2 + (z_2 - z_1)^2}$$

Midpoint Between (x_1, y_1, z_1) and (x_2, y_2, z_2)

$$\text{Midpoint} = \left(\frac{x_1 + x_2}{2}, \frac{y_1 + y_2}{2}, \frac{z_1 + z_2}{2} \right)$$

Equation of Plane

$$Ax + By + Cz + D = 0$$

Equation of Sphere [Center: (h, k, l), Radius: r]

$$(x - h)^2 + (y - k)^2 + (z - l)^2 = r^2$$

REFERENCE TABLE 20   Differentiation Formulas

1. $\dfrac{d}{dx}[cu] = cu'$

2. $\dfrac{d}{dx}[u \pm v] = u' \pm v'$

3. $\dfrac{d}{dx}[uv] = uv' + vu'$

4. $\dfrac{d}{dx}\left[\dfrac{u}{v}\right] = \dfrac{vu' - uv'}{v^2}$

5. $\dfrac{d}{dx}[c] = 0$

6. $\dfrac{d}{dx}[u^n] = nu^{n-1}u'$

7. $\dfrac{d}{dx}[x] = 1$

8. $\dfrac{d}{dx}[|u|] = \dfrac{u}{|u|}(u'), \; u \neq 0$

9. $\dfrac{d}{dx}[\ln u] = \dfrac{u'}{u}$

10. $\dfrac{d}{dx}[e^u] = e^u u'$

11. $\dfrac{d}{dx}[\sin u] = (\cos u)u'$

12. $\dfrac{d}{dx}[\cos u] = -(\sin u)u'$

13. $\dfrac{d}{dx}[\tan u] = (\sec^2 u)u'$

14. $\dfrac{d}{dx}[\cot u] = -(\csc^2 u)u'$

15. $\dfrac{d}{dx}[\sec u] = (\sec u \tan u)u'$

16. $\dfrac{d}{dx}[\csc u] = -(\csc u \cot u)u'$

REFERENCE TABLE 21 Integration Formulas

Forms Involving u^n

1. $\displaystyle\int u^n \, du = \frac{u^{n+1}}{n+1} + C, \; n \neq -1$

2. $\displaystyle\int \frac{1}{u} \, du = \ln |u| + C$

Forms Involving $a + bu$

3. $\displaystyle\int \frac{u}{a+bu} \, du = \frac{1}{b^2}[bu - a \ln |a + bu|] + C$

4. $\displaystyle\int \frac{u}{(a+bu)^2} \, du = \frac{1}{b^2}\left[\frac{a}{a+bu} + \ln |a + bu|\right] + C$

5. $\displaystyle\int \frac{u}{(a+bu)^n} \, du = \frac{1}{b^2}\left[\frac{-1}{(n-2)(a+bu)^{n-2}} + \frac{a}{(n-1)(a+bu)^{n-1}}\right] + C, \; n \neq 1, 2$

6. $\displaystyle\int \frac{u^2}{a+bu} \, du = \frac{1}{b^3}\left[-\frac{bu}{2}(2a - bu) + a^2 \ln |a + bu|\right] + C$

7. $\displaystyle\int \frac{u^2}{(a+bu)^2} \, du = \frac{1}{b^3}\left[bu - \frac{a^2}{a+bu} - 2a \ln |a + bu|\right] + C$

8. $\displaystyle\int \frac{u^2}{(a+bu)^3} \, du = \frac{1}{b^3}\left[\frac{2a}{a+bu} - \frac{a^2}{2(a+bu)^2} + \ln |a + bu|\right] + C$

9. $\displaystyle\int \frac{u^2}{(a+bu)^n} \, du = \frac{1}{b^3}\left[\frac{-1}{(n-3)(a+bu)^{n-3}} + \frac{2a}{(n-2)(a+bu)^{n-2}} - \frac{a^2}{(n-1)(a+bu)^{n-1}}\right] + C, \; n \neq 1, 2, 3$

10. $\displaystyle\int \frac{1}{u(a+bu)} \, du = \frac{1}{a} \ln \left|\frac{u}{a+bu}\right| + C$

11. $\displaystyle\int \frac{1}{u(a+bu)^2} \, du = \frac{1}{a}\left[\frac{1}{a+bu} + \frac{1}{a} \ln \left|\frac{u}{a+bu}\right|\right] + C$

12. $\displaystyle\int \frac{1}{u^2(a+bu)} \, du = -\frac{1}{a}\left[\frac{1}{u} + \frac{b}{a} \ln \left|\frac{u}{a+bu}\right|\right] + C$

13. $\displaystyle\int \frac{1}{u^2(a+bu)^2} \, du = -\frac{1}{a^2}\left[\frac{a + 2bu}{u(a+bu)} + \frac{2b}{a} \ln \left|\frac{u}{a+bu}\right|\right] + C$

Forms Involving $\sqrt{a + bu}$

14. $\displaystyle \int u^n \sqrt{a + bu}\, du = \frac{2}{b(2n + 3)} \left[u^n(a + bu)^{3/2} - na \int u^{n-1} \sqrt{a + bu}\, du \right]$

15. $\displaystyle \int \frac{1}{u\sqrt{a + bu}}\, du = \frac{1}{\sqrt{a}} \ln \left| \frac{\sqrt{a + bu} - \sqrt{a}}{\sqrt{a + bu} + \sqrt{a}} \right| + C,\, 0 < a$

16. $\displaystyle \int \frac{1}{u^n \sqrt{a + bu}}\, du = \frac{-1}{a(n - 1)} \left[\frac{\sqrt{a + bu}}{u^{n-1}} + \frac{(2n - 3)b}{2} \int \frac{1}{u^{n-1}\sqrt{a + bu}}\, du \right],\, n \ne 1$

17. $\displaystyle \int \frac{\sqrt{a + bu}}{u}\, du = 2\sqrt{a + bu} + a \int \frac{1}{u\sqrt{a + bu}}\, du$

18. $\displaystyle \int \frac{\sqrt{a + bu}}{u^n}\, du = \frac{-1}{a(n - 1)} \left[\frac{(a + bu)^{3/2}}{u^{n-1}} + \frac{(2n - 5)b}{2} \int \frac{\sqrt{a + bu}}{u^{n-1}}\, du \right],\, n \ne 1$

19. $\displaystyle \int \frac{u}{\sqrt{a + bu}}\, du = -\frac{2(2a - bu)}{3b^2}\sqrt{a + bu} + C$

20. $\displaystyle \int \frac{u^n}{\sqrt{a + bu}}\, du = \frac{2}{(2n + 1)b} \left[u^n \sqrt{a + bu} - na \int \frac{u^{n-1}}{\sqrt{a + bu}}\, du \right]$

Forms Involving $u^2 - a^2,\, 0 < a$

21. $\displaystyle \int \frac{1}{u^2 - a^2}\, du = -\int \frac{1}{a^2 - u^2}\, du = \frac{1}{2a} \ln \left| \frac{u - a}{u + a} \right| + C$

22. $\displaystyle \int \frac{1}{(u^2 - a^2)^n}\, du = \frac{-1}{2a^2(n - 1)} \left[\frac{u}{(u^2 - a^2)^{n-1}} + (2n - 3) \int \frac{1}{(u^2 - a^2)^{n-1}}\, du \right],\, n \ne 1$

Forms Involving $\sqrt{u^2 \pm a^2},\, 0 < a$

23. $\displaystyle \int \sqrt{u^2 \pm a^2}\, du = \frac{1}{2}[u\sqrt{u^2 \pm a^2} \pm a^2 \ln |u + \sqrt{u^2 \pm a^2}|] + C$

24. $\displaystyle \int u^2\sqrt{u^2 \pm a^2}\, du = \frac{1}{8}[u(2u^2 \pm a^2)\sqrt{u^2 \pm a^2} - a^4 \ln |u + \sqrt{u^2 \pm a^2}|] + C$

25. $\displaystyle \int \frac{\sqrt{u^2 + a^2}}{u}\, du = \sqrt{u^2 + a^2} - a \ln \left| \frac{a + \sqrt{u^2 + a^2}}{u} \right| + C$

26. $\displaystyle \int \frac{\sqrt{u^2 \pm a^2}}{u^2}\, du = \frac{-\sqrt{u^2 \pm a^2}}{u} + \ln |u + \sqrt{u^2 \pm a^2}| + C$

REFERENCE TABLE 21   (Continued)

27. $\displaystyle\int \frac{1}{\sqrt{u^2 \pm a^2}}\, du = \ln\left|u + \sqrt{u^2 \pm a^2}\right| + C$

28. $\displaystyle\int \frac{1}{u\sqrt{u^2 + a^2}}\, du = \frac{-1}{a}\ln\left|\frac{a + \sqrt{u^2 + a^2}}{u}\right| + C$

29. $\displaystyle\int \frac{u^2}{\sqrt{u^2 \pm a^2}}\, du = \frac{1}{2}\left[u\sqrt{u^2 \pm a^2} \mp a^2 \ln\left|u + \sqrt{u^2 \pm a^2}\right|\right] + C$

30. $\displaystyle\int \frac{1}{u^2\sqrt{u^2 \pm a^2}}\, du = \mp \frac{\sqrt{u^2 \pm a^2}}{a^2 u} + C$

31. $\displaystyle\int \frac{1}{(u^2 \pm a^2)^{3/2}}\, du = \frac{\pm u}{a^2\sqrt{u^2 \pm a^2}} + C$

Forms Involving $\sqrt{a^2 - u^2},\ 0 < a$

32. $\displaystyle\int \frac{\sqrt{a^2 - u^2}}{u}\, du = \sqrt{a^2 - u^2} - a\ln\left|\frac{a + \sqrt{a^2 - u^2}}{u}\right| + C$

33. $\displaystyle\int \frac{1}{u\sqrt{a^2 - u^2}}\, du = \frac{-1}{a}\ln\left|\frac{a + \sqrt{a^2 - u^2}}{u}\right| + C$

34. $\displaystyle\int \frac{1}{u^2\sqrt{a^2 - u^2}}\, du = \frac{-\sqrt{a^2 - u^2}}{a^2 u} + C$

35. $\displaystyle\int \frac{1}{(a^2 - u^2)^{3/2}}\, du = \frac{u}{a^2\sqrt{a^2 - u^2}} + C$

Forms Involving e^u

36. $\displaystyle\int e^u\, du = e^u + C$

37. $\displaystyle\int u e^u\, du = (u - 1)e^u + C$

38. $\displaystyle\int u^n e^u\, du = u^n e^u - n\int u^{n-1} e^u\, du$

39. $\displaystyle\int \frac{1}{1 + e^u}\, du = u - \ln(1 + e^u) + C$

40. $\displaystyle\int \frac{1}{1 + e^{nu}}\, du = u - \frac{1}{n}\ln(1 + e^{nu}) + C$

Forms Involving ln u

41. $\displaystyle\int \ln u \; du = u[-1 + \ln u] + C$

42. $\displaystyle\int u \ln u \; du = \frac{u^2}{4}[-1 + 2 \ln u] + C$

43. $\displaystyle\int u^n \ln u \; du = \frac{u^{n+1}}{(n+1)^2}[-1 + (n+1) \ln u] + C, \; n \neq -1$

44. $\displaystyle\int (\ln u)^2 \; du = u[2 - 2 \ln u + (\ln u)^2] + C$

45. $\displaystyle\int (\ln u)^n \; du = u(\ln u)^n - n \int (\ln u)^{n-1} \; du$

Forms Involving sin u or cos u

46. $\displaystyle\int \sin u \; du = -\cos u + C$

47. $\displaystyle\int \cos u \; du = \sin u + C$

48. $\displaystyle\int \sin^2 u \; du = \frac{1}{2}(u - \sin u \cos u) + C$

49. $\displaystyle\int \cos^2 u \; du = \frac{1}{2}(u + \sin u \cos u) + C$

50. $\displaystyle\int \sin^n u \; du = -\frac{\sin^{n-1} u \cos u}{n} + \frac{n-1}{n} \int \sin^{n-2} u \; du$

51. $\displaystyle\int \cos^n u \; du = \frac{\cos^{n-1} u \sin u}{n} + \frac{n-1}{n} \int \cos^{n-2} u \; du$

52. $\displaystyle\int u \sin u \; du = \sin u - u \cos u + C$

53. $\displaystyle\int u \cos u \; du = \cos u + u \sin u + C$

54. $\displaystyle\int u^n \sin u \; du = -u^n \cos u + n \int u^{n-1} \cos u \; du$

55. $\displaystyle\int u^n \cos u \; du = u^n \sin u - n \int u^{n-1} \sin u \; du$

56. $\displaystyle\int \frac{1}{1 \pm \sin u} \; du = \tan u \mp \sec u + C$

57. $\displaystyle\int \frac{1}{1 \pm \cos u} \; du = -\cot u \pm \csc u + C$

58. $\displaystyle\int \frac{1}{\sin u \cos u} \; du = \ln |\tan u| + C$

REFERENCE TABLE 21 (Continued)

Forms Involving tan u, cot u, sec u, csc u

59. $\displaystyle\int \tan u \, du = -\ln |\cos u| + C$

60. $\displaystyle\int \cot u \, du = \ln |\sin u| + C$

61. $\displaystyle\int \sec u \, du = \ln |\sec u + \tan u| + C$

62. $\displaystyle\int \csc u \, du = \ln |\csc u - \cot u| + C$

63. $\displaystyle\int \tan^2 u \, du = -u + \tan u + C$

64. $\displaystyle\int \cot^2 u \, du = -u - \cot u + C$

65. $\displaystyle\int \sec^2 u \, du = \tan u + C$

66. $\displaystyle\int \csc^2 u \, du = -\cot u + C$

67. $\displaystyle\int \tan^n u \, du = \frac{\tan^{n-1} u}{n - 1} - \int \tan^{n-2} u \, du, \; n \neq 1$

68. $\displaystyle\int \cot^n u \, du = -\frac{\cot^{n-1} u}{n - 1} - \int (\cot^{n-2} u) \, du, \; n \neq 1$

69. $\displaystyle\int \sec^n u \, du = \frac{\sec^{n-2} u \tan u}{n - 1} + \frac{n - 2}{n - 1} \int \sec^{n-2} u \, du, \; n \neq 1$

70. $\displaystyle\int \csc^n u \, du = -\frac{\csc^{n-2} u \cot u}{n - 1} + \frac{n - 2}{n - 1} \int \csc^{n-2} u \, du, \; n \neq 1$

71. $\displaystyle\int \frac{1}{1 \pm \tan u} \, du = \frac{1}{2}(u \pm \ln |\cos u \pm \sin u|) + C$

72. $\displaystyle\int \frac{1}{1 \pm \cot u} \, du = \frac{1}{2}(u \mp \ln |\sin u \pm \cos u|) + C$

73. $\displaystyle\int \frac{1}{1 \pm \sec u} \, du = u + \cot u \mp \csc u + C$

74. $\displaystyle\int \frac{1}{1 \pm \csc u} \, du = u - \tan u \pm \sec u + C$

REFERENCE TABLE 22 Formulas from Business

Basic Terms

x = number of units produced (or sold)
p = price per unit
R = total revenue from selling x units
C = total cost of producing x units
$\overline{C}$ = average cost per unit
P = total profit from selling x units

Basic Equations

$$R = xp \qquad \overline{C} = \frac{C}{x} \qquad P = R - C$$

Demand Function: $p = f(x)$ = price required to sell x units

$$\eta = \frac{p/x}{dp/dx} = \text{price elasticity of demand}$$

(If $|\eta| < 1$, the demand is inelastic. If $|\eta| > 1$, the demand is elastic.)

Typical Graphs of Revenue, Cost, and Profit Functions

The low prices required to sell more units eventually result in a decreasing revenue.

Revenue Function

As x increases, the average cost per unit decreases.

Cost Function

The break-even point occurs when $R = C$.

Profit Function

REFERENCE TABLE 22   (Continued)

Marginals

$$\frac{dR}{dx} = \text{marginal revenue} \approx \text{the } \textit{extra} \text{ revenue for selling one additional unit}$$

$$\frac{dC}{dx} = \text{marginal cost} \approx \text{the } \textit{extra} \text{ cost of producing one additional unit}$$

$$\frac{dP}{dx} = \text{marginal profit} \approx \text{the } \textit{extra} \text{ profit for selling one additional unit}$$

Revenue Function

REFERENCE TABLE 23   Formulas from Finance

Basic Terms

P = amount of deposit
r = interest rate
n = number of times interest is compounded per year
t = number of years
A = balance after t

Compound Interest Formulas

1. Balance when interest is compounded n times per year

$$A = P\left(1 + \frac{r}{n}\right)^{nt}$$

2. Balance when interest is compounded continuously

$$A = Pe^{rt}$$

Balance of an Increasing Annuity after n Deposits per Year of P for t Years

$$A = P\left[\left(1 + \frac{r}{n}\right)^{nt} - 1\right]\left(1 + \frac{n}{r}\right)$$

Initial Deposit for a Decreasing Annuity with n Withdrawals per Year of W for t Years

$$P = W\left(\frac{n}{r}\right)\left[1 - \left(\frac{1}{1 + [r/n]}\right)^{nt}\right]$$

Monthly Installment M for a Loan of P Dollars over t Years at $r\%$ Interest

$$M = P\left[\frac{r/12}{1 - \left(\frac{1}{1 + [r/12]}\right)^{12t}}\right]$$

REFERENCE TABLE 24 Standard Normal Distribution (z-scores)

					Hundredths Digit for z-score					
z	0.00	0.01	0.02	0.03	0.04	0.05	0.06	0.07	0.08	0.09
0.0	0.0000	0.0040	0.0080	0.0120	0.0160	0.0199	0.0239	0.0279	0.0319	0.0359
0.1	0.0398	0.0438	0.0478	0.0517	0.0557	0.0596	0.0636	0.0675	0.0714	0.0753
0.2	0.0793	0.0832	0.0871	0.0910	0.0948	0.0987	0.1026	0.1064	0.1103	0.1141
0.3	0.1179	0.1217	0.1255	0.1293	0.1331	0.1368	0.1406	0.1443	0.1480	0.1517
0.4	0.1554	0.1591	0.1628	0.1664	0.1700	0.1736	0.1772	0.1808	0.1844	0.1879
0.5	0.1915	0.1950	0.1985	0.2019	0.2054	0.2088	0.2123	0.2157	0.2190	0.2224
0.6	0.2257	0.2291	0.2324	0.2357	0.2389	0.2422	0.2454	0.2486	0.2517	0.2549
0.7	0.2580	0.2611	0.2642	0.2673	0.2704	0.2734	0.2764	0.2794	0.2823	0.2852
0.8	0.2881	0.2910	0.2939	0.2967	0.2995	0.3023	0.3051	0.3078	0.3106	0.3133
0.9	0.3159	0.3186	0.3212	0.3238	0.3264	0.3289	0.3315	0.3340	0.3365	0.3389
1.0	0.3413	0.3438	0.3461	0.3485	0.3508	0.3531	0.3554	0.3577	0.3599	0.3621
1.1	0.3643	0.3665	0.3686	0.3708	0.3729	0.3749	0.3770	0.3790	0.3810	0.3830
1.2	0.3849	0.3869	0.3888	0.3907	0.3925	0.3944	0.3962	0.3980	0.3997	0.4015
1.3	0.4032	0.4049	0.4066	0.4082	0.4099	0.4115	0.4131	0.4147	0.4162	0.4177
1.4	0.4192	0.4207	0.4222	0.4236	0.4251	0.4265	0.4279	0.4292	0.4306	0.4319
1.5	0.4332	0.4345	0.4357	0.4370	0.4382	0.4394	0.4406	0.4418	0.4429	0.4441
1.6	0.4452	0.4463	0.4474	0.4484	0.4495	0.4505	0.4515	0.4525	0.4535	0.4545
1.7	0.4554	0.4564	0.4573	0.4582	0.4591	0.4599	0.4608	0.4616	0.4625	0.4633
1.8	0.4641	0.4649	0.4656	0.4664	0.4671	0.4678	0.4686	0.4693	0.4699	0.4706
1.9	0.4713	0.4719	0.4726	0.4732	0.4738	0.4744	0.4750	0.4756	0.4761	0.4767
2.0	0.4772	0.4778	0.4783	0.4788	0.4793	0.4798	0.4803	0.4808	0.4812	0.4817
2.1	0.4821	0.4826	0.4830	0.4834	0.4838	0.4842	0.4846	0.4850	0.4854	0.4857
2.2	0.4861	0.4864	0.4868	0.4871	0.4875	0.4878	0.4881	0.4884	0.4887	0.4890
2.3	0.4893	0.4896	0.4898	0.4901	0.4904	0.4906	0.4909	0.4911	0.4913	0.4916
2.4	0.4918	0.4920	0.4922	0.4925	0.4927	0.4929	0.4931	0.4932	0.4934	0.4936
2.5	0.4938	0.4940	0.4941	0.4943	0.4945	0.4946	0.4948	0.4949	0.4951	0.4952
2.6	0.4953	0.4955	0.4956	0.4957	0.4959	0.4960	0.4961	0.4962	0.4963	0.4964
2.7	0.4965	0.4966	0.4967	0.4968	0.4969	0.4970	0.4971	0.4972	0.4973	0.4974
2.8	0.4974	0.4975	0.4976	0.4977	0.4977	0.4978	0.4979	0.4979	0.4980	0.4981
2.9	0.4981	0.4982	0.4982	0.4983	0.4984	0.4984	0.4985	0.4985	0.4986	0.4986
3.0	0.4987	0.4987	0.4987	0.4988	0.4988	0.4989	0.4989	0.4989	0.4990	0.4990

Tenths Digit for z-score

Appendix C

Graphing Utilities

Introduction

In Section 1.2, you studied the point-plotting method for sketching the graph of an equation. One of the disadvantages of the point-plotting method is that in order to get a good idea about the shape of a graph, you need to plot *many* points. With only a few points, you could badly misrepresent the graph. For instance, consider the equation

$$y = \frac{1}{30}x(39 - 10x^2 + x^4).$$

Suppose you plotted only five points: $(-3, -3)$, $(-1, -1)$, $(0, 0)$, $(1, 1)$, and $(3, 3)$, as shown in Figure A.7. From these five points, you might assume that the graph of the equation is a straight line. This, however, is not correct. By plotting several more points you can see that the actual graph is not straight at all! (See Figure A.8.)

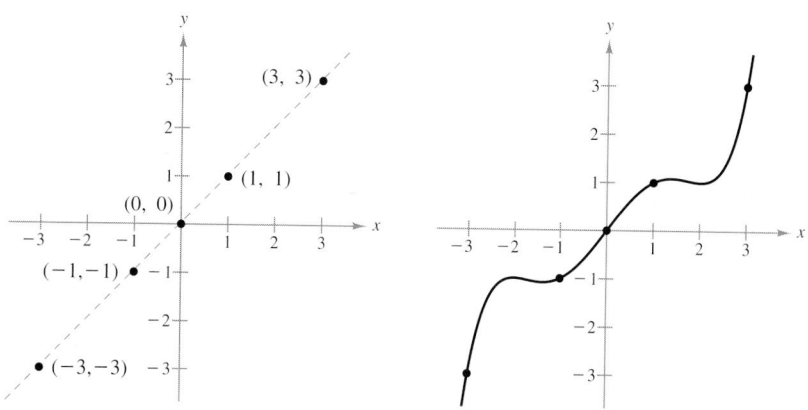

FIGURE A.7   **FIGURE A.8**

Thus, the point-plotting method leaves us with a dilemma. On the one hand, the method can be very inaccurate if only a few points are plotted. But, on the other hand, it is very time consuming to plot a dozen (or more) points. Technology can help us solve this dilemma. Plotting several (even several hundred) points in a rectangular coordinate system is something that a graphing utility can do easily.

The point-plotting method is the method used by *all* graphing packages for computers and *all* graphing calculators. Each computer or calculator screen is made up of a grid of hundreds or thousands of small areas called **pixels.** Screens that have many pixels per inch are said to have a higher **resolution** than screens that don't have as many. For instance, the screen shown in Figure A.9(a) has a higher resolution than the screen shown in Figure A.9(b). Note that the "graph" of the line on the first screen looks more like a line than the "graph" on the second screen.

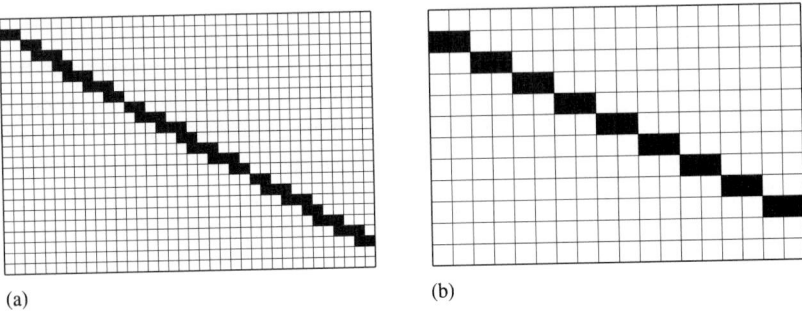

(a)   (b)

FIGURE A.9

Screens on most graphing calculators have 48 pixels per inch. Screens on computer monitors typically have between 32 and 100 pixels per inch.

EXAMPLE 1   Using Pixels to Sketch a Graph

Use the grid shown in Figure A.10 to sketch a graph of $y = \frac{1}{2}x^2$. Each pixel on the grid must be either on (shaded black) or off (unshaded).

SOLUTION

To shade the grid, we use the following rule. If a pixel contains a plotted point of the graph, then it will be "on"; otherwise, the pixel will be "off." Using this rule, the graph of the curve looks like that shown in Figure A.11.

FIGURE A.10

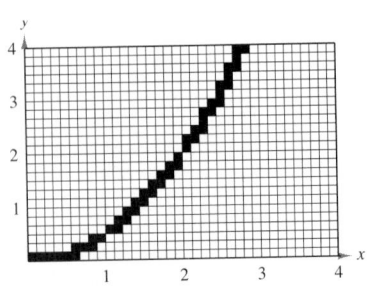

FIGURE A.11

Basic Graphing

There are many different types of graphing utilities—graphing calculators and software packages for computers. The procedures used to draw a graph are similar for most of these utilities.

Basic Graphing Steps for a Graphing Utility

To draw the graph of an equation involving x and y with a graphing utility, use the following steps.

1. Rewrite the equation so that y is isolated on the left side of the equation.
2. Set the boundaries of the viewing rectangle by entering the minimum and maximum x-values and the minimum and maximum y-values.
3. Enter the equation in the form $y =$ (expression involving x). Read the user's guide that accompanies your graphing utility to see how the equation should be entered.
4. Activate the graphing utility.

EXAMPLE 2 Sketching the Graph of an Equation

Sketch the graph of $2y + x^3 = 4x$.

SOLUTION

To begin, solve the given equation for y in terms of x.

$$2y + x^3 = 4x \qquad \text{\textit{Given equation}}$$

$$2y = -x^3 + 4x \qquad \text{\textit{Subtract } } x^3 \text{ \textit{from both sides.}}$$

$$y = -\frac{1}{2}x^3 + 2x \qquad \text{\textit{Divide both sides by 2.}}$$

Set the viewing rectangle so that $-10 \le x \le 10$ and $-10 \le y \le 10$. (On some graphing utilities, this is the default setting.) Next, enter the equation into the graphing utility.

$$Y = -X \wedge 3/2 + 2 * X$$

Finally, activate the graphing utility. The display screen should look like that shown in Figure A.12.

FIGURE A.12

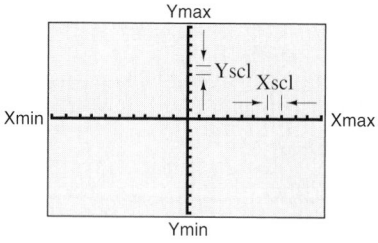

FIGURE A.13

In Figure A.12, notice that the calculator screen does not label the tick marks on the x-axis or the y-axis. To see what the tick marks represent, check the values in the utility's "range."

Range

Xmin $= -10$	*The minimum x-value is -10.*
Xmax $= 10$	*The maximum x-value is 10.*
Xscl $= 1$	*The x-scale is 1 unit per tick mark.*
Ymin $= -10$	*The minimum y-value is -10.*
Ymax $= 10$	*The maximum y-value is 10.*
Yscl $= 1$	*The y-scale is 1 unit per tick mark.*
Xres $= 1$	*The x-resolution is 1 plotted point per pixel.*

These settings are summarized visually in Figure A.13.

EXAMPLE 3   Graphing an Equation Involving Absolute Value

Sketch the graph of $y = |x - 3|$.

SOLUTION

This equation is already written so that y is isolated on the left side of the equation, so you can enter the equation as follows.

$$Y = \text{abs}(X - 3)$$

After activating the graphing utility, its screen should look like the one shown in Figure A.14.

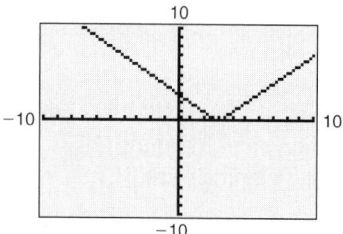

FIGURE A.14

Special Features

In order to be able to use your graphing calculator to its best advantage, you must be able to determine a proper viewing rectangle and use the zoom feature. The next two examples show how this is done.

EXAMPLE 4   Determining a Viewing Rectangle

Sketch the graph of $y = x^2 + 12$.

SOLUTION

Begin as usual by entering the equation.

$$Y = X \wedge 2 + 12$$

Activate the graphing utility. If you used a viewing rectangle in which $-10 \leq x \leq 10$ and $-10 \leq y \leq 10$, then no part of the graph will appear on the screen, as shown in Figure A.15(a). The reason for this is that the lowest point on the graph of $y = x^2 + 12$ occurs at the point $(0, 12)$. With the viewing rectangle in Figure A.15(a), the largest y-value is 10. In other words, none of the graph is visible on a screen whose y-values range between -10 and 10.

To be able to see the graph, change Ymax $= 10$ to Ymax $= 30$ and Yscl $= 1$ to Yscl $= 5$. Now activate the graphing utility and you will obtain the graph shown in Figure A.15(b). On this graph, note that each tick mark on the y-axis represents 5 units because you changed the y-scale to 5. Also note that the highest point on the y-axis is now 30 because you changed the maximum value of y to 30.

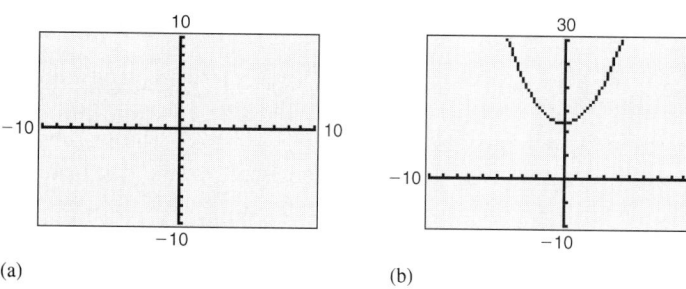

(a)   (b)

FIGURE A.15

EXAMPLE 5   Using the Zoom Feature

Sketch the graph of $y = x^3 - x^2 - x$. How many x-intercepts does this graph have?

SOLUTION

Begin by drawing the graph on a "standard" viewing rectangle, as shown in Figure A.16(a). (See page A52.) From the display screen, it is clear that the graph has at least one intercept (just to the left of $x = 2$), but it is difficult to determine whether the graph has other intercepts. To obtain a better view of the graph near $x = -1$, you can use the zoom feature of the graphing utility. The redrawn screen is shown in Figure A.16(b). From this screen you can tell that the graph has three x-intercepts whose x-coordinates are approximately -0.6, 0, and 1.6.

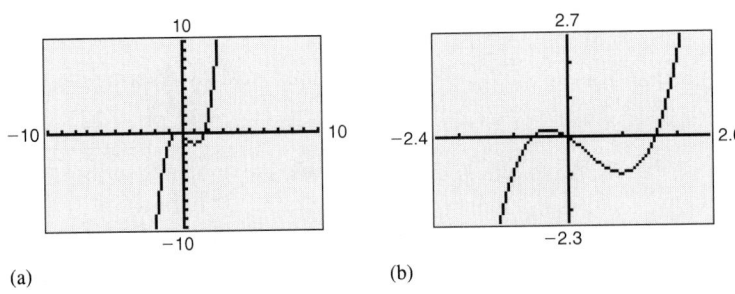

(a)   (b)

FIGURE A.16

EXAMPLE 6   Sketching More Than One Graph on the Same Screen

Sketch the graphs of $y = -\sqrt{36 - x^2}$ and $y = \sqrt{36 - x^2}$ on the same screen.

SOLUTION

To begin, enter both equations into the graphing utility.

$$Y = \sqrt{(36 - X \wedge 2)}$$
$$Y = -\sqrt{(36 - X \wedge 2)}$$

Then, activate the graphing utility to obtain the graph shown in Figure A.17(a). Notice that the graph should be the upper and lower parts of the circle given by $x^2 + y^2 = 6^2$. The reason it doesn't look like a circle is that, with the standard settings, the tick marks on the x-axis are farther apart than the tick marks on the y-axis. To correct this, change the viewing rectangle so that $-15 \le x \le 15$. The redrawn screen is shown in Figure A.17(b). Notice that on this screen the graph appears to be more circular.

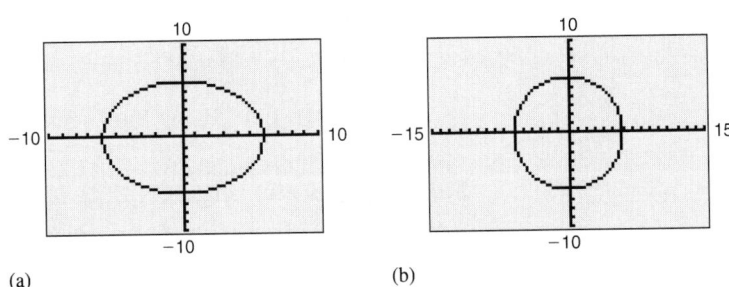

(a)   (b)

FIGURE A.17

Numerical Differentiation

Most graphing utilities have a built-in capability for approximating the derivative of a function $y = f(x)$ at a point x. If your graphing utility does not have this capability, you can use the program provided in Appendix D. On the Texas Instruments calculators (TI-81, TI-82, and TI-85), this numerical approximation is based on the formula

$$f'(x) \approx \frac{f(x + \delta) - f(x - \delta)}{2\delta}$$

where delta (δ) is a small positive number. On some other calculators, such as the Sharp EL 9200 and 9300, this approximation is based on the more familiar formula

$$f'(x) \approx \frac{f(x + \delta) - f(x)}{\delta}.$$

In both cases, the approximation usually becomes more accurate as δ gets closer to zero.

EXAMPLE 7   Approximating the Derivative at a Point

Approximate the derivative of $y = 2x^3 + 1$ at the point $x = 4$. Use $\delta = 0.001$.

SOLUTION

To begin, locate the appropriate command—such as NDeriv(, nDeriv(, nDer(, or $\frac{d}{dx}$(—or menu item on your graphing utility. Notice the format of the command and the arguments. The format required for a numerical derivative varies among different graphing calculators and computers. For example, the command format on the TI-81, having two arguments, is NDeriv(expression,δ), and on the TI-82 it is nDeriv(expression,variable, value,δ). Input the appropriate arguments and activate the command. For instance, entering

nDeriv(2X∧3+1,X,4,.001)

on the TI-82 gives 96.000002. For some graphing utilities, such as the TI-81, you will need to store the value 4 as the X variable, and then use the command for the numerical derivative, as shown below.

4 Sto X

NDeriv(2X∧3+1,.001)

Your answer should be close to the exact answer $f'(4) = 96$.   ▬

REMARK   For some graphing utilities, the numerical derivative capability can be found in the MATH, CALC, or MATH CALC menu. Consult your user's manual or the Graphing Technology Guide that accompanies this text.

EXAMPLE 8 Using the Derivative of a Function

Graph the function $y = 3x - x^3$ on the standard viewing rectangle.

a. Approximate the derivative at $x = -3$, $x = 0$, $x = 1$ and $x = 3$.

b. What do the signs of the derivative values tell you about the shape of the graph of f at these points?

c. Where does f have horizontal tangent lines?

SOLUTION

The graph of $y = 3x - x^3$ is shown in Figure A.18.

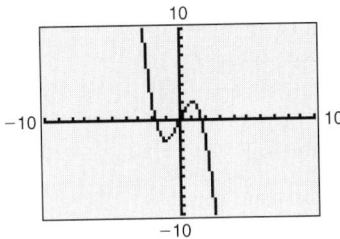

FIGURE A.18

a. Using the numerical derivative key on the graphing utility, you can obtain the following derivative approximations.

$$f'(-3) \approx -24$$
$$f'(0) \approx 3$$
$$f'(1) \approx 0$$
$$f'(3) \approx -24$$

b. The signs of these derivative values indicate that the graph of f is decreasing at $x = -3$, increasing at $x = 0$, and decreasing at $x = 3$. Furthermore, the graph has a horizontal tangent line at $x = 1$.

c. You have already observed that f has a horizontal tangent line at $x = 1$. From the shape of the graph, it appears that there is another horizontal tangent line near $x = -1$. You can use your graphing utility to confirm this by showing that the numerical derivative at $x = -1$ is 0. ■

Most graphing utilities have a built-in algorithm for approximating definite integrals. If your calculator does not have this capability, you can use the programs for Simpson's Rule provided in Appendix D or Section 6.5.

EXAMPLE 9 Numerical Integration

Use your graphing utility to approximate the area under the curve of $y = \sqrt{16 - x^4}$ between $x = -2$ and $x = 2$.

SOLUTION

The graph of the region is indicated in Figure A.19.

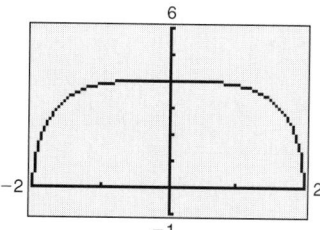

FIGURE A.19

The area is given by the definite integral

$$\int_{-2}^{2} \sqrt{16 - x^4}\, dx.$$

To approximate this integral, you should find the appropriate integration key on your graphing utility. Most commands require that you enter the function, the variable of integration, the lower limit of integration, and the upper limit of integration. For example, on the TI-85, you can use the following command from the CALC menu.

fnint($\sqrt{\,}$(16−X∧4),X,−2,2)

The answer should be approximately 13.98.

Discussion
Problem

Sketch the graph of $y = x^2 - 12x$, using $-10 \le x \le 10$ and $-10 \le y \le 10$. The graph appears to be a straight line, as shown in the figure. However, this is misleading because the screen doesn't show an important portion of the graph. Can you find a range setting that reveals a better view of this graph?

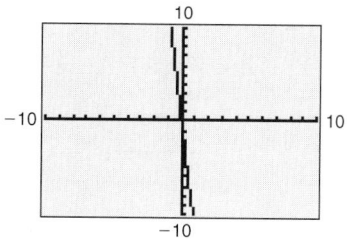

Warm Up

A Misleading Graph

In Exercises 1–10, solve for y in terms of x.

1. $3x + y = 4$

2. $x - y = 0$

3. $2x + 3y = 2$

4. $4x - 5y = -2$

5. $3x + 4y - 5 = 0$

6. $-2x - 3y + 6 = 0$

7. $x^2 + y - 4 = 0$

8. $-2x^2 + 3y + 2 = 0$

9. $x^2 + y^2 = 4$

10. $x^2 - y^2 = 9$

APPENDIX C · EXERCISES

In Exercises 1–20, use a graphing utility to sketch the graph of the equation. Use a setting on each graph of $-10 \leq x \leq 10$ and $-10 \leq y \leq 10$.

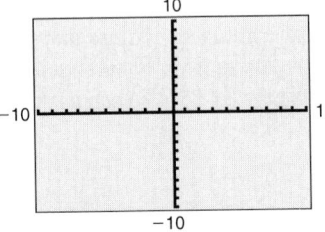

```
RANGE
Xmin=-10
Xmax=10
Xscl=1
Ymin=-10
Ymax=10
Yscl=1
Xres=1
```

1. $y = x - 5$

2. $y = -x + 4$

3. $y = -\frac{1}{2}x + 3$

4. $y = \frac{2}{3}x + 1$

5. $2x - 3y = 4$

6. $x + 2y = 3$

7. $y = \frac{1}{2}x^2 - 1$

8. $y = -x^2 + 6$

9. $y = x^2 - 4x - 5$

10. $y = x^2 - 3x + 2$

11. $y = -x^2 + 2x + 1$

12. $y = -x^2 + 4x - 1$

13. $2y = x^2 + 2x - 3$

14. $3y = -x^2 - 4x + 5$

15. $y = |x + 5|$

16. $y = \frac{1}{2}|x - 6|$

17. $y = \sqrt{x^2 + 1}$

18. $y = 2\sqrt{x^2 + 2} - 4$

19. $y = \frac{1}{5}(-x^3 + 16x)$

20. $y = \frac{1}{8}(x^3 + 8x^2)$

In Exercises 21–30, use a graphing utility to match the equation with its graph. [The graphs are labeled (a), (b), (c), (d), (e), (f), (g), (h), (i), and (j).]

21. $y = x$

22. $y = -x$

23. $y = x^2$

24. $y = -x^2$

25. $y = x^3$

26. $y = -x^3$

27. $y = |x|$

28. $y = -|x|$

29. $y = \sqrt{x}$

30. $y = -\sqrt{x}$

(a)

(b)

(c)

(d)

(e)

(f)

(g)

(h)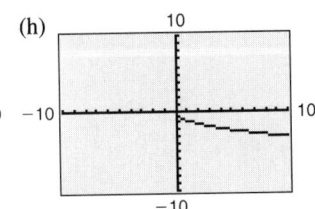

(i)

(j)

In Exercises 31–34, use a graphing utility to sketch the graph of the equation. Use the indicated setting.

31. $y = -2x^2 + 12x + 14$ **32.** $y = -x^2 + 5x + 6$

```
RANGE
Xmin=-5
Xmax=10
Xscl=1
Ymin=-5
Ymax=35
Yscl=5
Xres=1
```

```
RANGE
Xmin=-8
Xmax=4
Xscl=1
Ymin=-5
Ymax=15
Yscl=5
Xres=1
```

33. $y = x^3 + 6x^2$ **34.** $y = -x^3 + 16x$

```
RANGE
Xmin=-10
Xmax=5
Xscl=1
Ymin=-4
Ymax=36
Yscl=3
Xres=1
```

```
RANGE
Xmin=-6
Xmax=6
Xscl=1
Ymin=-25
Ymax=25
Yscl=5
Xres=1
```

In Exercises 35–38, find a setting on a graphing utility such that the graph of the equation agrees with the graph shown.

35. $y = -x^2 - 4x + 20$ **36.** $y = x^2 + 12x - 8$

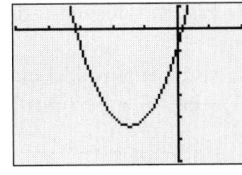

37. $y = -x^3 + x^2 + 2x$ **38.** $y = x^3 + 3x^2 - 2x$

In Exercises 39–42, use a graphing utility to find the number of x-intercepts of the equation.

39. $y = \frac{1}{8}(4x^2 - 32x + 65)$

40. $y = \frac{1}{4}(-4x^2 + 16x - 15)$

41. $y = 4x^3 - 20x^2 - 4x + 61$

42. $y = \frac{1}{4}(2x^3 + 6x^2 - 4x + 1)$

In Exercises 43–46, use a graphing utility to sketch the graphs of the equations on the same screen. Using a "square setting," what geometrical shape is bounded by the graphs?

43. $y = |x| - 4$
     $y = -|x| + 4$

44. $y = x + |x| - 4$
     $y = x - |x| + 4$

45. $y = -\sqrt{25 - x^2}$
     $y = \sqrt{25 - x^2}$

46. $y = 6$
     $y = -\sqrt{3}x - 4$
     $y = \sqrt{3}x - 4$

Ever Been Married?   In Exercises 47–50, use the following models, which relate ages to the percentages of American males and females who have never been married.

$$y = \frac{0.36 - 0.0056x}{1 - 0.0817x + 0.00226x^2}, \quad \begin{array}{l} \text{Males} \\ 20 \le x \le 50 \end{array}$$

$$y = \frac{100}{8.944 - 0.886x + 0.249x^2}, \quad \begin{array}{l} \text{Females} \\ 20 \le x \le 50 \end{array}$$

In these models, y is the percentage of the population (in decimal form) who have never been married and x is the age of the person. (*Source:* U.S. Bureau of the Census)

47. Use a graphing utility to sketch the graphs of both equations giving the percentages of American males and females who have never been married. Use the following range settings.

```
RANGE
Xmin=20
Xmax=50
Xscl=5
Ymin=0
Ymax=1
Yscl=0.1
Xres=1
```

48. Write a short paragraph describing the relationship between the two graphs that were plotted in Exercise 47.

49. Suppose an American male is chosen at random from the population. If the person is 25 years old, what is the probability that he has never been married?

50. Suppose an American female is chosen at random from the population. If the person is 25 years old, what is the probability that she has never been married?

Earnings and Dividends In Exercises 51–54, use the following model, which approximates the relationship between dividends per share and earnings per share for the Pall Corporation between 1982 and 1989.

$$y = -0.166 + 0.502x - 0.0953x^2, \qquad 0.25 \le x \le 2$$

In this model, y is the dividends per share (in dollars) and x is the earnings per share (in dollars). (*Source:* Standard ASE Stock Reports)

51. Use a graphing utility to sketch the graph of the model that gives the dividend per share in terms of the earnings per share. Use the following range settings.

```
RANGE
Xmin=0
Xmax=2
Xscl=0.25
Ymin=0
Ymax=0.5
Yscl=0.1
Xres=1
```

52. According to the given model, what size dividend would the Pall Corporation pay if the earnings per share were $1.30?

53. Use the trace feature on your graphing utility to estimate the earnings per share that would produce a dividend per share of $0.25. The choices are labeled (a), (b), (c), and (d). (Find the y-value that is as close to 0.25 as possible. The x-value that is displayed will then be the approximate earnings per share that would produce a dividend per share of $0.25.)
   (a) $1.00   (b) $1.03   (c) $1.06   (d) $1.09

54. The **Payout Ratio** for a stock is the ratio of the dividend per share to earnings per share. Use the model to find the payout ratio for an earnings per share of (a) $0.75, (b) 1.00, and (c) $1.25.

In Exercises 55–58, use a graphing utility to approximate the derivative of the function f at the indicated x-values. What does the value of the derivative tell you about the shape of the graph of f? Verify your answer by graphing the function f on an appropriate viewing rectangle.

55. $f(x) = 4x^4 - x^{1/3} + 1$; $x = -1$, $x = 1$, $x = 3$

56. $f(x) = (x - 2)^3 - 48\sqrt{x}$; $x = 1$, $x = 4$, $x = 6$

57. $f(x) = \dfrac{x^2 - 1}{x^2 + 1}$; $x = -2$, $x = 0$, $x = 2$

58. $f(x) = \dfrac{x^2 + 3}{x - 1}$; $x = -2$, $x = -1$, $x = 2$

In Exercises 59 and 60, use your graphing utility to graph the function f on the indicated domain, and visually estimate the x-values at which the graph of f has a horizontal tangent. Verify your answers by numerically approximating the derivative at these x-values.

59. $f(x) = x\sqrt{x + 2}$, $-2 \le x \le 5$

60. $f(x) = x^3 - 2x^2 + 1$, $-5 \le x \le 5$

61. Use your graphing utility to approximate the derivative of $f(x) = |x|$ at various positive and negative x-values. Does the derivative of f exist at $x = 0$? What is $f'(0)$ according to your graphing utility?

62. Use your graphing utility to approximate the derivative of $f(x) = x^{1/3}$ at various positive and negative x-values. Does the derivative of f exist at $x = 0$? What is $f'(0)$ according to your graphing utility?

In Exercises 63–66, use the numerical integration capability of your graphing utility to approximate the integral.

63. $\displaystyle\int_0^4 \sqrt{25 - x^2}\, dx$

64. $\displaystyle\int_0^1 \dfrac{1}{\sqrt{4 - x}}\, dx$

65. $\displaystyle\int_{-2}^2 \dfrac{4 + x^3}{x^2 - 16}\, dx$

66. $\displaystyle\int_0^3 \dfrac{x^{2/3}}{x + 4}\, dx$

67. Find the area under the curve $y = e^{-x^2}$ between $x = 0$ and $x = 5$.

68. Use the numerical integration capability of your graphing utility to approximate the value of the constant b that satisfies $\displaystyle\int_1^b \dfrac{1}{x}\, dx = 1$.

Appendix D

Programs

Programs for the Texas Instruments TI-81 and TI-82 graphing calculators are given in several sections in the text. This appendix contains translations of these programs for the TI-85, Casio *fx*-7700, Casio *fx*-9700, and Sharp EL 9200/9300, arranged by calculator model. Similar programs can be written for other brands and models of graphics calculators.

Enter a program in your calculator, then refer to the text discussion and apply the program as appropriate. The following section references are provided to help you locate the text discussions of the programs and their uses:

Evaluating Functions	Section 1.4
Midpoint Rule	Section 5.6
Simpson's Rule	Section 6.5
Linear Regression	Section 7.7
Newton's Method	Section S.6

Also included at the beginning of this appendix are the steps for finding a linear regression model using the TI-82. Within the Casio *fx*-7700 section is an additional program that performs numerical differentiation at a point.

Texas Instruments TI-82:   **Linear Regression**

Here are the steps for finding a linear regression model in the Modeling Median Income example.

STAT 4 L_1 , L_2	*Clear lists L_1 and L_2.*
STAT 1	*Reach the list editor.*
1, 2, ..., 10	*Enter data in list L_1.*
19.1, 20.2, ..., 29.9	*Enter data in list L_2.*
STAT CALC 3	*Set 2-variable statistics with Xlist L_1, Ylist L_2, and frequency 1.*
STAT CALC 5	*Select linear regression option.*
a = 1.221212121	*Slope.*
b = 17.61333333	*y-Intercept.*
r = .9986864096	*Correlation coefficient.*

Texas Instruments TI-85: **Evaluating Functions**

This program evaluates a function that has been stored as y1.

PROGRAM:Evaluate
:Repeat 1<0   *Start a continuous loop (press ON to break).*
:Input x   *Ask for input.*
:Disp y1   *Calculate the value of the function.*
:End   *End loop.*

Texas Instruments TI-85: **Midpoint Rule**

This program uses the Midpoint Rule to approximate the definite integral $\int_a^b f(x)dx$. You must store the expression $f(x)$ as y1 before executing the program. The program itself will prompt you for the limits a and b and for the number of subintervals n.

PROGRAM:Midpoint
:Disp "Lower Limit"   *Prompt for value of a.*
:Input A   *Input value of a.*
:Disp "Upper Limit"   *Prompt for value of b.*
:Input B   *Input value of b.*
:Disp "n divisions"   *Prompt for value of n.*
:Input N   *Input value of n.*
:0→S   *Initialize sum of areas.*
:(B-A)/N→W   *Calculate width of subinterval.*
:1→J   *Initialize counter.*
:While J≤N   *Begin conditional loop.*
:A+(J-1)∗W→L   *Calculate left endpoint.*
:A+J∗W→R   *Calculate right endpoint.*
:(L+R)/2→x   *Calculate midpoint of subinterval.*
:S+W∗y1→S   *Add area to sum.*
:J+1→J   *Increase counter.*
:End   *End loop.*
:Disp "Approximation"
:Disp S   *Display approximation.*

Texas Instruments TI-85:   **Simpson's Rule**

This program uses Simpson's Rule to approximate the definite integral $\int_a^b f(x)dx$. You must store the expression $f(x)$ as y1 before executing the program. The program itself will prompt you for the limits a and b and for *half* the number of subintervals you want to use.

```
PROGRAM:Simpson
:Disp "Lower Limit"              Prompt for value of a.
:Input A                         Input value of a.
:Disp "Upper Limit"              Prompt for value of b.
:Input B                         Input value of b.
:Disp "n/2 divisions"            Prompt for value of n/2.
:Input D                         Input value of n/2.
:0→S                             Initialize sum of areas.
:(B-A)/(2D)→W                    Calculate width of subinterval.
:1→J                             Initialize counter.
:While J≤D                       Begin conditional loop.
:A+2(J-1)*W→L                    Calculate left endpoint.
:A+2J*W→R                        Calculate right endpoint.
:(L+R)/2→M                       Calculate midpoint of subinterval.
:L→x
:y1→L                            Evaluate f(x) at left endpoint.
:M→x
:y1→M                            Evaluate f(x) at midpoint.
:R→x
:y1→R                            Evaluate f(x) at right endpoint.
:W*(L+4M+R)/3+S→S                Add area by Simpson's Rule to sum.
:J+1→J                           Increase counter.
:End                             End loop.
:Disp "Approximation"
:Disp S                          Display approximation.
```

Texas Instruments TI-85:   **Linear Regression**

Here are the steps for finding a linear regression model in the Modeling Median Income example.

STAT EDIT	*Set X as xlist Name and Y as ylist Name.*
CLRxy	*Clear any previous data.*
x1 = 1 y1 = 19.1	*Enter data.*
x2 = 2 y2 = 20.2	
⋮	
x10 = 10 y10 = 29.9	
STAT CALC LINR	*Calculate linear regression model.*
a = 17.6133333333	*y-Intercept.*
b = 1.22121212121	*Slope.*
corr = .998686409604	*Correlation coefficient.*

Texas Instruments TI-85:   **Newton's Method**

This program uses Newton's Method to approximate the zeros of a function. You must store the expression $f(x)$ as y1 before executing the program. Then graph the function to estimate one of its zeros. The program will prompt you for this estimate.

PROGRAM:Newton	
:Disp "Enter Approximation"	*Prompt user for approximation.*
:Input x	*Input approximation.*
:1→N	*Initialize counter.*
:x-y1/der1(y1,x)→R	*Compute new root.*
:While abs (x-R)>1E-10	*Begin conditional loop.*
:R→x	*Continue the iteration.*
:x-y1/der1(y1,x)→R	*Compute new root.*
:N+1→N	*Increase counter by 1.*
:End	*End loop.*
:Disp "Root="	
:Disp R	*Display approximate zero.*
:Disp "Iter="	
:Disp N	*Display number of iterations.*

Casio *fx*-7700:   **Evaluating Functions**

This program evaluates a function that has been stored in function memory location f_1.

EVALUATE	
Lbl 1	*Begin loop.*
"X="?→X	*Prompt for input.*
"F(X)=":f₁ ◢	*Display the value of the function, then pause.*
Goto 1	*End loop.*

Casio *fx*-7700:   **Midpoint Rule**

This program uses the Midpoint Rule to approximate the definite integral $\int_a^b f(x)\,dx$. You must store the expression $f(x)$ as f_1 before executing the program. The program itself will prompt you for the limits a and b and for the number of subintervals n.

MIDPOINT	
"LOWER LIMIT"?→A	*Prompt for value of a.*
"UPPER LIMIT"?→B	*Prompt for value of b.*
"N DIVISIONS"?→N	*Prompt for value of n.*
0→S	*Initialize sum of areas.*
(B-A)÷N→W	*Calculate width of subinterval.*
1→J	*Initialize counter.*
Lbl 1	*Begin loop.*
A+(J-1)W→L	*Calculate left endpoint.*
A+JW→R	*Calculate right endpoint.*
(L+R)÷2→X	*Calculate midpoint of subinterval.*
S+Wf₁→S	*Add area to sum.*
J+1→J	*Increase counter.*
J≤N⇒Goto 1	*Test counter and end loop.*
"APPROXIMATION"	
S	*Display approximation.*

Casio *fx*-7700:   **Simpson's Rule**

This program uses Simpson's Rule to approximate the definite integral $\int_a^b f(x)dx$. You must store the expression $f(x)$ as f_1 before executing the program. The program itself will prompt you for the limits a and b and for *half* the number of subintervals you want to use.

SIMPSON	
"LOWER LIMIT"?→A	*Prompt for value of a.*
"UPPER LIMIT"?→B	*Prompt for value of b.*
"N÷2 DIVISIONS"?→D	*Prompt for value of n/2.*
0→S	*Initialize sum of areas.*
(B-A)÷(2D)→W	*Calculate width of subinterval.*
1→J	*Initialize counter.*
Lbl 1	*Begin loop.*
A+2(J-1)W→L	*Calculate left endpoint.*
A+2JW→R	*Calculate right endpoint.*
(L+R)÷2→M	*Calculate midpoint of subinterval.*
L→X	
f_1→L	*Evaluate f(x) at left endpoint.*
M→X	
f_1→M	*Evaluate f(x) at midpoint.*
R→X	
f_1→R	*Evaluate f(x) at right endpoint.*
W(L+4M+R)÷3+S→S	*Add area by Simpson's Rule to sum.*
J+1→J	*Increase counter.*
J≤D⇒Goto 1	*Test counter and end loop.*
"APPROXIMATION"	
S	*Display approximation.*

Casio *fx*-7700:   **Linear Regression**

Here are the steps for finding a linear regression model in the Modeling Median Income example.

MODE ÷ MODE 4	*Set the calculator for linear regression.*
MODE MODE 1	*Prepare to store statistical data.*
EDIT ERS YES	*Erase any previous data.*
1 , 19.1	*Enter data.*
2 , 20.2	
⋮	
10 , 29.9	
CAL REG	*Calculate the regression model.*
A = 17.61333333	*y-Intercept.*
B = 1.221212121	*Slope.*
r = 0.9986864096	*Correlation coefficient.*

Casio *fx*-7700:   **Newton's Method**

The main program here uses Newton's Method to approximate the zeros of a function. You must store the expression $f(x)$ as f_1 before executing the program. Then graph the function to estimate one of its zeros. The program will prompt you for this estimate.

The Newton's Method program calls on another program to calculate numerical derivatives. This program also requires the expression $f(x)$ to have been stored as f_1. In the code below, program NEWTON believes NDERIV is stored as program 0. You may store NDERIV in any location, just include the correct address within NEWTON.

NEWTON

"ENTER APPROXIMATION"?→X	*Prompt user for approximation.*
1→N	*Initialize counter.*
Prog 0	*Call program 0 (NDERIV) to calculate the numerical derivative.*
X-f_1÷Y→R	*Compute new root.*
Lbl 1	*Begin loop.*
R→X	*Continue the iteration.*
Prog 0	*Call program 0 (NDERIV) to calculate the numerical derivative.*
X-f_1÷Y→R	*Compute new root.*
N+1→N	*Increase counter by 1.*
Abs (X-R)≥1E-10⇒Goto 1	*End loop.*
"ROOT="	
R◢	*Display approximate zero.*
"ITER="	
N	*Display number of iterations.*

NDERIV

.001→D	*Define value of delta.*
X→A	*Store x.*
A+D→X	*Calculate upper value.*
f_1→B	*Evaluate the function.*
A-D→X	*Calculate lower value.*
f_1→C	*Evaluate the function.*
(B-C)÷2D→Y	*Calculate the symmetric difference to approximate the numerical derivative.*
A→X	*Restore x.*

Casio *fx*-7700:   **Numerical Differentiation**

This program performs numerical differentiation at a point. You must store the expression to be differentiated $f(x)$ as f_1 and store the value of x for which the approximation is to be computed before executing the program.

DERIVATIVE

.001↦D	*Set $\Delta x = 0.001$ for approximating derivatives.*
X+D↦X	*Evaluate $(x + \Delta x)$.*
f_1↦B	*Evaluate $f(x + \Delta x)$.*
X-D↦X	*Evaluate $(x - \Delta x)$.*
f_1↦C	*Evaluate $f(x - \Delta x)$.*
(B-C)/2D↦Y	*Evaluate $[f(x + \Delta x) - f(x - \Delta x)] / 2\Delta x$.*
Y	*Display approximate numerical derivative.*

Casio *fx*-9700:   **Evaluating Functions**
_____

This program evaluates a function that has been stored in function memory location f_1.

EVALUATE↵
Lbl 1↵   *Begin loop.*
"X="?→X↵   *Ask for input.*
"F(X)=":f_1 ◢   *Display the value of the function, then pause.*
Goto 1   *End loop.*

Casio *fx*-9700:   **Midpoint Rule**
_____

This program uses the Midpoint Rule to approximate the definite integral $\int_a^b f(x)\,dx$. You must store the expression $f(x)$ as f_1 before executing the program. The program itself will prompt you for the limits a and b and for the number of subintervals n.

MIDPOINT↵
"LOWER LIMIT"?→A↵   *Prompt for value of a.*
"UPPER LIMIT"?→B↵   *Prompt for value of b.*
"N DIVISIONS"?→N↵   *Prompt for value of n.*
0→S↵   *Initialize sum of areas.*
(B-A)÷N→W↵   *Calculate width of subinterval.*
1→J↵   *Initialize counter.*
Lbl 1↵   *Begin loop.*
A+(J-1)W→L↵   *Calculate left endpoint.*
A+JW→R↵   *Calculate right endpoint.*
(L+R)÷2→X↵   *Calculate midpoint of subinterval.*
S+Wf_1→S↵   *Add area to sum.*
J+1→J↵   *Increase counter.*
J≤N⇒Goto 1↵   *Test counter and end loop.*
"APPROXIMATION"↵
S   *Display approximation.*

Casio *fx*-9700:   **Simpson's Rule**

This program uses Simpson's Rule to approximate the definite integral $\int_a^b f(x)dx$. You must store the expression $f(x)$ as f_1 before executing the program. The program itself will prompt you for the limits a and b and for *half* the number of subintervals you want to use.

SIMPSON↵
"LOWER LIMIT"?→A↵   *Prompt for value of a.*
"UPPER LIMIT"?→B↵   *Prompt for value of b.*
"N÷2 DIVISIONS"?→D↵   *Prompt for value of n/2.*
0→S↵   *Initialize sum of areas.*
(B-A)÷(2D)→W↵   *Calculate width of subinterval.*
1→J↵   *Initialize counter.*
Lbl 1↵   *Begin loop.*
A+2(J-1)W→L↵   *Calculate left endpoint.*
A+2JW→R↵   *Calculate right endpoint.*
(L+R)÷2→M↵   *Calculate midpoint of subinterval.*
L→X↵
f₁→L↵   *Evaluate f(x) at left endpoint.*
M→X↵
f₁→M↵   *Evaluate f(x) at midpoint.*
R→X↵
f₁→R↵   *Evaluate f(x) at right endpoint.*
W(L+4M+R)÷3+S→S↵   *Add area by Simpson's Rule to sum.*
J+1→J↵   *Increase counter.*
J≤D⇒Goto 1↵   *Test counter and end loop.*
"APPROXIMATION"↵
S   *Display approximation.*

Casio *fx*-9700:	**Linear Regression**

Here are the steps for finding a linear regression model in the Modeling Median Income example.

MENU 4	*Set the calculator for regression.*
SETUP	*Set the model to linear.*
EDIT ERS YES	*Erase any previous data.*
1 , 19.1	*Enter data.*
2 , 20.2	
&#8942;	
10 , 29.9	
REG	*Calculate the regression model.*
A = 17.6133333333	*y-Intercept.*
B = 1.22121212121	*Slope.*
r = 0.998686409604	*Correlation coefficient.*

Casio *fx*-9700:	**Newton's Method**

This program uses Newton's Method to approximate the zeros of a function. You must store the expression $f(x)$ as f_1 before executing the program. Then graph the function to estimate one of its zeros. The program will prompt you for this estimate.

NEWTON↵	
"ENTER APPROXIMATION"?→X↵	*Prompt user for approximation.*
1→N↵	*Initialize counter.*
X-f_1÷d/dx(f_1,X)→R↵	*Compute new root.*
Lbl 1↵	*Begin loop.*
R→X↵	*Continue the iteration.*
X-f_1÷d/dx(f_1,X)→R↵	*Compute new root.*
N+1→N↵	*Increase counter by 1.*
Abs (X-R)≥1E-10⇒Goto 1 ↵	*End loop.*
"ROOT="↵	
R◢	*Display approximate zero.*
"ITER="↵	
N	*Display number of iterations.*

Sharp EL 9200/9300:   **Evaluating Functions**

This program evaluates a function that is entered within the program itself.

evaluate
Label 1   *Begin loop.*
Input x   *Ask for input.*
y= *insert expression here*   *Calculate the value of the function, written in the local variable* x.
Print y   *Display the value of the function.*
Goto 1   *End loop.*

Sharp EL 9200/9300:   Midpoint Rule

This program uses the Midpoint Rule to approximate the definite integral $\int_a^b f(x)dx$. Before running it, you must enter an expression $f(x)$ for the integrand just once in the program itself. The program will prompt you for the limits a and b and for the number of subintervals n.

The program includes a subroutine to evaluate the function $f(x)$. It is placed at the beginning of the program for convenient access when you are changing the integrand.

midpoint	
Goto start	*Jump over the next three lines.*
Label eval	*Begin subroutine.*
y= *f(x)*	*Enter the integrand here as an expression in the local variable* x.
Return	*Continue the main program from where this subroutine was called.*
Label start	*Jumping point for* Goto *command above; start of main program.*
Print "Lower Limit	*Prompt for value of a.*
Input a	*Input value of a.*
Print "Upper Limit	*Prompt for value of b.*
Input b	*Input value of b.*
Print "n divisions	*Prompt for value of n.*
Input n	*Input value of n.*
s=0	*Initialize sum of areas.*
w=(b-a)/n	*Calculate width of subinterval.*
j=1	*Initialize counter.*
Label 1	*Begin loop.*
l=a+(j-1)∗w	*Calculate left endpoint.*
r=a+j∗w	*Calculate right endpoint.*
x=(l+r)/2	*Calculate midpoint of subinterval.*
Gosub eval	*Evaluate the function.*
s=s+w∗y	*Add area to sum.*
j=j+1	*Increase counter.*
If j<=n Goto 1	*Test counter and end loop.*
Print "Approximation	
Print s	*Display approximation.*

Sharp EL 9200/9300:   **Simpson's Rule**

This program uses Simpson's Rule to approximate the definite integral $\int_a^b f(x)dx$. Before running it, you must enter an expression $f(x)$ for the integrand just once in the program itself. The program will prompt you for the limits a and b and for *half* the number of subintervals you want to use.

The program includes a subroutine to evaluate the function $f(x)$. It is placed at the beginning of the program for convenient access when you are changing the integrand.

simpson	
Goto start	*Jump over the next three lines.*
Label eval	*Begin subroutine.*
y= *f(x)*	*Enter the integrand here as an expression in the local variable x.*
Return	*Continue the main program from where this subroutine was called.*
Label start	*Jumping point for* Goto *command above; start of main program.*
Print "Lower Limit	*Prompt for value of a.*
Input a	*Input value of a.*
Print "Upper Limit	*Prompt for value of b.*
Input b	*Input value of b.*
Print "n/2 divisions	*Prompt for value of n/2.*
Input d	*Input value of n/2.*
s=0	*Initialize sum of areas.*
w=(b-a)/(2d)	*Calculate width of subinterval.*
j=1	*Initialize counter.*
Label 1	*Begin loop.*
l=a+2(j-1)*w	*Calculate left endpoint.*
r=a+2j*w	*Calculate right endpoint.*
m=(l+r)/2	*Calculate midpoint of subinterval.*
x=l	
Gosub eval	*Evaluate f(x) at left endpoint.*
l=y	
x=m	
Gosub eval	*Evaluate f(x) at midpoint.*
m=y	
x=r	
Gosub eval	*Evaluate f(x) at right endpoint.*
r=y	
s=w*(l+4m+r)/3+s	*Add area by Simpson's Rule to sum.*
j=j+1	*Increase counter.*
If j<=d Goto 1	*Test counter and end loop.*
Print "Approximation	
Print s	*Display approximation.*

Sharp EL 9200/9300:   **Linear Regression**

Here are the steps for finding a linear regression model in the Modeling Median Income example.

Statistics   *Press the statistics mode key.*
MENU DEL ALL DATA   *Delete any previous data.*
TWO VARIABLE X,Y   *Select the data format for linear regression.*
   x = 1 y = 19.1   *Enter data.*
   x = 2 y = 20.2
      ⋮
   x = 10 y = 29.9
MENU STAT REG   *Calculate linear regression model.*
   a = 17.61333333   *y-Intercept.*
   b =1.221212121   *Slope.*
   r = 0.998686409   *Correlation coefficient.*

Sharp EL 9200/9300:   **Newton's Method**

This program uses Newton's Method to approximate the zeros of a function. First graph the function to estimate one of its zeros. The program will prompt you for this estimate.

Before running the program, you must enter the expression $f(x)$ twice within the program itself. Take care that you use the correct variable, local x or global X, each time.

The program includes a subroutine to evaluate the function $f(x)$. Next is a second subroutine to calculate the numerical derivative of the function for the current value of x. They are placed at the beginning of the program for convenient access when you are changing the function.

newton	
Goto start	*Jump over the next six lines.*
Label eval	*Begin subroutine.*
y= _f(x)_	*Enter the function here as an expression in the local variable* x.
Return	*Continue the main program from where this subroutine was called.*
Label nderiv	*Begin subroutine.*
d=d/dx(_f(X)_,x)	*Enter the function here as an expression in the global variable* X.
Return	*Continue the main program from where this subroutine was called.*
Label start	*Jumping point for* Goto *command above; start of main program.*
Print "Enter Approximation	*Prompt user for approximation.*
Input x	*Input approximation.*
n=1	*Initialize counter.*
Gosub eval	*Evaluate the function.*
Gosub nderiv	*Calculate the numerical derivative.*
r=x-y/d	*Compute new root.*
Label 1	*Begin loop.*
x=r	*Continue the iteration.*
Gosub eval	*Evaluate the function.*
Gosub nderiv	*Calculate the numerical derivative.*
r=x-y/d	*Compute new root.*
n=n+1	*Increase counter by 1.*
If abs (x-r)>=1E-10 Goto 1	*Compare approximations and try to end loop.*
Print "Root	
Print r	*Display approximate zero.*
Print "Iter	
Print n	*Display number of iterations.*

Appendix E

Computer Algebra Systems

Throughout the text, explanations of how to use Computer Algebra Systems (CAS) to accomplish certain calculus tasks are given in Technology Notes. In instances where commands are presented for illustration, the commands are often given for the CAS package *Derive*. To help you become acquainted with the rudiments of using a CAS, the following pages contain introductory instructions for *Derive*, as well as for two other popular Computer Algebra Systems, *Maple* and *Mathematica*.

Introduction to Derive

The purpose of this introduction is to illustrate some basic *Derive* commands and demonstrate the use of the different windows and modes of the software. You should be working at the computer terminal. To begin, enter the Author mode (all expressions should be entered in this mode), type

   3+4,

and press the Enter (or Return) key. *Derive* will display this line on the screen. To simplify the expression, press S (for Simplify). The program will then prompt you to check the line number of the expression that you are simplifying. Press Enter again, and 7 should appear on the line beneath 3+4. *Derive* will label each expression in the window with a line number. Here are some basic commands in *Derive*. Note that you can use the Escape key to return to a previous command line.

1. Author 2*(4−1)^3 and press Enter. Simplify will give the answer, 54.
2. *Derive* can calculate limits. Author LIM(x+3,x,1) and Simplify will give 4.
3. *Derive* can differentiate and integrate symbolically. For instance, DIF(SIN(x),x) will Simplify to COS(x).
4. You can enter and simplify an expression by pressing Ctrl-Enter after you have typed it in the Author window. For example, Author INT(x^(1/2),x) and press Ctrl-Enter. The answer $\dfrac{2x^{3/2}}{3}$ will appear in the window.
5. *Derive* can calculate definite integrals as well: INT(x^(1/2)1,4) will Simplify to 14/3.
6. *Derive* can integrate numerically. Author the expression 4/(x^2+1) and press Enter. Then type C (for Calculus), type I (for Integrate), and press

Enter again. Now respond with x as the variable of integration, 0 as the lower limit of integration, and tab to 1 as the upper limit. Entering this expression and pressing X (for approXimation) will give 3.14159 as the numerical approximation of this definite integral.

7. Both two- and three-dimensional graphs are no problem for the Plot command. Author the expression $x^5 - x$, press Enter, and then type P (for Plot). You should now be in the 2D-Plot window. You can plot the function by pressing P again, and you can adjust the domain and range by changing the Scale or using the Zoom function. Pressing A will take you back to the Algebra window. Now Author $4 - x^2 - 2*y^2$, press Enter, and type P. You should be in the 3D-Plot window. You can plot the surface by pressing P again. (It takes *Derive* a little time to prepare a 3D plot.)

8. *Derive* can calculate important mathematical constants to any degree of accuracy. Author PI, press Enter, and then type O (for Options) and P (for Precision). Change the number of digits to 50 and Escape to the Algebra window. Type X (for approXimation) and press Enter. *Derive* will give all 50 digits of the constant pi.

9. You can Quit *Derive* by typing Q, and answering yes.

For additional information, consult either the *Derive User Manual* or the on-line HELP command and menu.

Introduction to Maple

The purpose of this introduction is to illustrate the basic *Maple* commands. You should be working at the computer terminal. To begin, type the sum

> 3+4;

and press the Enter key. Note that you need to end the line with a semicolon. Your computer should respond with the answer 7. Continue with the commands below, typing them to the right of the > symbol.

1. Let's try some simple arithmetic.

> 2*(4−1)^3;
                    54

2. *Maple* can calculate limits.

> limit(x+3,x=1);
                    4

3. *Maple* can differentiate and integrate symbolically.

> diff(sin(x),x);
                    cos(x)

```
> int(x^(1/2),x);
                2/3x ³/²
> int(x^(1/2),x=1..4);
                14/3
```

4. *Maple* can integrate numerically as well. The use of the Int command with a capital I avoids any attempt at symbolic integration, and is usually faster.

```
> evalf(Int(4/(1+x^2),x=0..1));
                3.141592654
```

5. We can conveniently graph functions with *Maple*. You might need to define the graphics mode using the command: plotsetup(tek,xterm);.

```
> plot(x^5−x,x=−10..10);
                        (you will see the graph of the function.)
```

You can use a letter to define a function. Let's illustrate this shortcut by plotting the above function again with a different range of *y*-values.

```
> f:=x^5−x;
> plot(f,x=−10..10,y=−10..10);
                        (you will see the same function with a different
                        y-scale.)
```

6. *Maple* knows all the important mathematical constants to any degree of accuracy.

```
> evalf(Pi,50);
                3.14159. . . (you will see 50 digits of pi.)
```

7. For more information, consult the *Maple* documentation. There is also extensive on-line help available. For instance, here is how to learn more about the numerical capabilities of *Maple*.

```
> help(evalf);
```

Introduction to Mathematica

The purpose of this introduction is to illustrate the basic *Mathematica* commands. You should be working at the computer terminal. To begin, type the sum

    3+4

and press the Enter key. Your computer should respond with the answer 7. Continue with the commands below. You should type in whatever you see after the *In*[]:= symbol, press the Enter key, and *Mathematica* will produce the output after the *Out*[ ]:= symbol. The numbers in the brackets will increase as you continue your session.

1. *Mathematica* can evaluate expressions such as $2(4 - 1)^3$.

   In[2]:= 2 * (4 − 1)^3
   Out[2]:= 54

2. *Mathematica* can calculate limits.
   In[3]:= Limit[x + 3,x− > 1]
   Out[3]:= 4

3. *Mathematica* can differentiate and integrate symbolically.

   In[4]: = D[Sin[x],x]
   Out[4]: = Cos[x]
   In[5]: = Integrate[Sqrt[x],x]
   Out[5]: = 2x$^{3/2}$/3
   In[6]: = Integrate[Sqrt[x], {x, 1, 4}]
   Out[6]: = 14/3

4. *Mathematica* can numerically approximate integrals as well.

   In[7]: = NIntegrate[4/(1 + x^2), {x, 0, 1}]
   Out[7]: = 3.14159

5. *Mathematica* can produce two- and three-dimensional graphs.

   In[8]: = Plot[x^5 − x, {x, −10, 10}]
   Out[8]: = (you will see the graph of the function.)

   Let's graph the previous function again with a different range.

   In[9]: = Show[%,PlotRange − > {−1, 1}]
   Out[9]: = (the range of the preceding graph has been altered.)
   In[10]: = Plot3D[4 − x^2 − 2y^2, {x, −2, 2}, {y, −1, 1}]
   Out[10]: = (you will see a three-dimensional surface.)

6. *Mathematica* knows all the important mathematical constants to any degree of accuracy.

   In[11]: = N[Pi,50]
   Out[11]: = 3.14159. . . (you will see 50 digits of pi.)

7. *Mathematica* can solve equations.

   In[12]: = FindRoot[Cos[x], ==x, {x, 1}]
   Out[12]: = {x− > 0.739085}

8. For more information, consult the *Mathematica* documentation. There is also extensive on-line help available. For instance, here is how to learn more about the logarithm function.

   In[13]: = ? Log

Answers to Odd-Numbered Exercises

CHAPTER 0

SECTION 0.1 (page 0–7)

1. Rational **3.** Irrational **5.** Rational
7. Rational **9.** Irrational
11. (a) Yes **(b)** No **(c)** Yes **(d)** No
13. (a) Yes **(b)** No **(c)** No **(d)** Yes
15. $x \geq 12$ **17.** $x < -\frac{1}{2}$

19. $x \geq \frac{1}{2}$ **21.** $x > 1$

23. $-\frac{1}{2} < x < \frac{7}{2}$ **25.** $-\frac{3}{4} < x < -\frac{1}{4}$

27. $x > 6$ **29.** $-3 \leq x \leq 1$

31. $-3 \leq x \leq 2$

33. $r > 12.5\%$
35. $x \geq 36$ units
37. Length of side $\geq 10\sqrt{5}$
39. (a) False **(b)** True **(c)** True
(d) True if $ab < 0$ and false if $ab > 0$

SECTION 0.2 (page 0–12)

1. (a) -51 **(b)** 51 **(c)** 51
3. (a) -14.99 **(b)** 14.99 **(c)** 14.99 **5.** 14
7. 1.25 **9.** $-5 < x < 5$

11. $x < -6$ and $x > 6$ **13.** $-7 < x < 3$

15. $x \leq -7$ or $x \geq 13$ **17.** $x < 6$ or $x > 14$

19. $4 < x < 5$ **21.** $a - b \leq x \leq a + b$

23. $|x| \leq 2$ **25.** $|x| > 2$ **27.** $|x - 4| \leq 2$
29. $|x - 2| > 2$ **31.** $|x - 4| < 2$
33. $|y - a| \leq 2$ **35.** $65.8 \leq h \leq 71.2$
37. $175{,}000 \leq x \leq 225{,}000$
39. (a) $|4750 - a| \leq 500$, $|4750 - a| \leq 237.50$
(b) At variance
41. (a) $|20{,}000 - a| \leq 500$, $|20{,}000 - a| \leq 1000$
(b) At variance

SECTION 0.3 (page 0–18)

1. -24 **3.** $\frac{1}{2}$ **5.** 3 **7.** 44
9. 5 **11.** 9
13. $\frac{1}{2}$ **15.** $\frac{1}{4}$ **17.** 908.3483 **19.** -5.3601
21. $5x^6$ **23.** $24y^{10}$ **25.** $10x^4$ **27.** $7x^5$
29. $\frac{4}{3}(x + y)^2$ **31.** $3x$ **33.** $4x^4$
35. (a) $2\sqrt{2}$ **(b)** $3\sqrt{2}$
37. (a) $2x\sqrt[3]{2x^2}$ **(b)** $2|x|z\sqrt[4]{2z}$
39. (a) $\dfrac{5\sqrt{3}|x|}{y^2}$ **(b)** $(x - y)\sqrt{5(x - y)}$
41. $x \geq 1$ **43.** $(-\infty, \infty)$
45. $(-\infty, 1)$ and $(1, \infty)$ **47.** $x > 3$
49. $1 \leq x \leq 5$ **51.** $\$25{,}760.55$ **53.** $\$4765.56$

SECTION 0.4 (page 0–24)

1. $\frac{1}{2}, -\frac{1}{3}$ **3.** $\frac{3}{2}$ **5.** $-2 \pm \sqrt{3}$

7. $(x-2)^2$ **9.** $(2x+1)^2$ **11.** $(x+2)(x-1)$

13. $(3x-2)(x-1)$ **15.** $(x-2y)^2$

17. $(3+y)(3-y)(9+y^2)$

19. $(x-2)(x^2+2x+4)$

21. $(y+4)(y^2-4y+16)$

23. $(x-3)(x^2+3x+9)$

25. $(x-4)(x-1)(x+1)$ **27.** $(2x-3)(x^2+2)$

29. $(x-2)(2x^2-1)$ **31.** $0, 5$ **33.** ± 3

35. $\pm\sqrt{3}$ **37.** $0, 6$ **39.** $-2, 1$ **41.** $2, 3$

43. -4 **45.** ± 2 **47.** $1, \pm 2$

49. $x \le 3$ or $x \ge 4$ **51.** $-2 \le x \le 2$

53. $(x+2)(x^2-2x+4)$

55. $(x-1)(2x^2+x-1)$ **57.** ± 1

59. $1, 2, 3$ **61.** $1, \pm\frac{1}{2}$ **63.** 4 **65.** 2000 units

SECTION 0.5 (page 0-32)

1. $\dfrac{x+5}{x-1}$ **3.** $\dfrac{5x-1}{x^2+2}$ **5.** $\dfrac{4x-3}{x^2}$

7. $\dfrac{x-6}{x^2-4}$ **9.** $\dfrac{2}{x-3}$

11. $\dfrac{(A+B)x+3(A-2B)}{(x-6)(x+3)}$ **13.** $-\dfrac{(x-1)^2}{x(x^2+1)}$

15. $\dfrac{x+2}{(x+1)^{3/2}}$ **17.** $-\dfrac{3t}{2\sqrt{1+t}}$

19. $-\dfrac{x^2+3}{(x+1)(x-2)(x-3)}$

21. $\dfrac{(A+C)x^2-(A-B-2C)x-(2A+2B-C)}{(x+1)^2(x-2)}$

23. $\dfrac{x(x^2+2)}{(x+1)^{3/2}}$ **25.** $\dfrac{2}{x^2\sqrt{x^2+2}}$

27. $\dfrac{1}{2\sqrt{x}(x+1)^{3/2}}$ **29.** $\dfrac{\sqrt{3}}{3}$ **31.** $\dfrac{2}{3\sqrt{2}}$

33. $\dfrac{x\sqrt{x}-4}{x-4}$ **35.** $\dfrac{y}{6\sqrt{y}}$ **37.** $\dfrac{49\sqrt{x^2-9}}{x+3}$

39. $\dfrac{\sqrt{14}+2}{2}$ **41.** $\dfrac{x(5+\sqrt{3})}{11}$ **43.** $\sqrt{6}-\sqrt{5}$

45. $\dfrac{1}{x(\sqrt{3}+\sqrt{2})}$ **47.** $\dfrac{2x-1}{2x+\sqrt{4x-1}}$

49. \$232.68

CHAPTER 1

SECTION 1.1 (page 8)

Warm Up

1. $3\sqrt{5}$ **2.** $2\sqrt{5}$ **3.** $\frac{1}{2}$ **4.** -2

5. $5\sqrt{3}$ **6.** $-\sqrt{2}$ **7.** $x=-3, x=9$

8. $y=-8, y=4$ **9.** $x=19$ **10.** $y=1$

1. $a=4$, $b=3$, **3.** $a=10$, $b=3$,
$c=5$ $c=\sqrt{109}$
$4^2+3^2=5^2$ $10^2+3^2=(\sqrt{109})^2$

5. $d=2\sqrt{5}$ **7.** $d=2\sqrt{10}$
Midpoint: $(4, \ 3)$ Midpoint: $\left(-\frac{1}{2}, \ -2\right)$

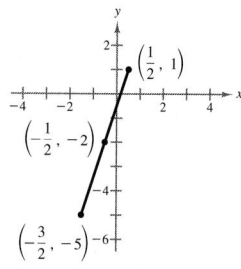

9. $d=2\sqrt{37}$ **11.** $d=\sqrt{8-2\sqrt{3}}$
Midpoint: $(3, \ 8)$ Midpoint: $\left(0, \ \dfrac{\sqrt{3}+1}{2}\right)$

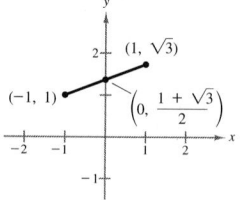

13. $d_1 = \sqrt{45}, d_2 = \sqrt{20},$
$d_3 = \sqrt{65}$

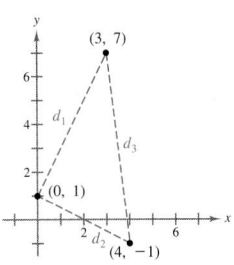

15. $d_1 = d_2 = d_3 = d_4$
$= \sqrt{5}$

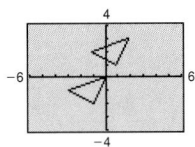

17. Collinear, because
$d_1 + d_2 = d_3$
$2\sqrt{5} + \sqrt{5} = 3\sqrt{5}$

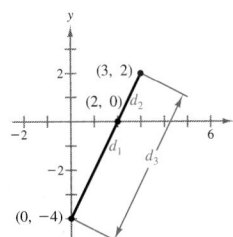

19. Not collinear, because
$d_1 + d_2 \neq d_3$
$d_1 = \sqrt{18}, d_2 = \sqrt{41}$
$d_3 = \sqrt{113}$

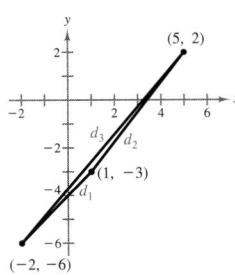

21. $x = 4, -2$ **23.** $y = \pm\sqrt{55}$

25. $\left(\dfrac{3x_1 + x_2}{4}, \dfrac{3y_1 + y_2}{4}\right), \left(\dfrac{x_1 + x_2}{2}, \dfrac{y_1 + y_2}{2}\right),$
$\left(\dfrac{x_1 + 3x_2}{4}, \dfrac{y_1 + 3y_2}{4}\right)$

27. **(a)** $\left(\frac{7}{4}, -\frac{7}{4}\right), \left(\frac{5}{2}, -\frac{3}{2}\right), \left(\frac{13}{4}, -\frac{5}{4}\right)$
  (b) $\left(-\frac{3}{2}, -\frac{9}{4}\right), \left(-1, -\frac{3}{2}\right), \left(-\frac{1}{2}, -\frac{3}{4}\right)$

29. **(a)** 16.76 ft   **(b)** 1341.04 ft^2

31.

33. **(a)** 2900   **(b)** 2450   **(c)** 2970   **(d)** 3270

35. **(a)** 1.42 million   **(b)** 1.04 million
  (c) 0.85 million   **(d)** 1.13 million

37. **(a)** Revenue: \$4372.0 million
      Profit: \$390.95 million

39. **(a)** $(-1, 2), (1, 1), (2, 3)$
  (b)

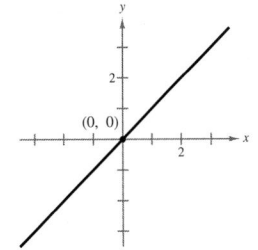

SECTION 1.2 (page 21)

Warm Up

1. $y = \frac{1}{5}(x + 12)$ **2.** $y = x - 15$

3. $y = \dfrac{1}{x^3 + 2}$

4. $y = \pm\sqrt{x^2 + x - 6} = \pm\sqrt{(x + 3)(x - 2)}$

5. $y = -1 \pm \sqrt{9 - (x - 2)^2}$

6. $y = 5 \pm \sqrt{81 - (x + 6)^2}$

7. $(x - 2)(x - 1)$ **8.** $(x + 3)(x + 2)$

9. $\left(y - \frac{3}{2}\right)^2$ **10.** $\left(y - \frac{7}{2}\right)^2$

1. **(a)** Not a solution point   **(b)** Solution point
  (c) Solution point

3. **(a)** Not a solution point   **(b)** Solution point
  (c) Not a solution point

5. c   **6.** d   **7.** b   **8.** f   **9.** a   **10.** e

11. $(0, -3), \left(\frac{3}{2}, 0\right)$ **13.** $(0, -2), (-2, 0), (1, 0)$

15. $(0, 0), (-3, 0), (3, 0)$ **17.** $(-2, 0), (0, 2)$

19. $(0, 0)$

21.

23.

25.

27.

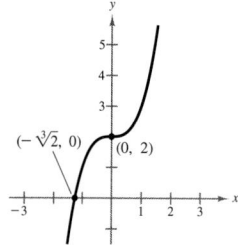

47. $(x-1)^2 + (y+3)^2 = 4$

29.

31.

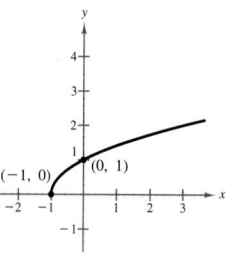

49. $(x+2)^2 + (y+3)^2 = 16$

33.

35.

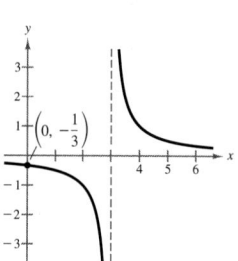

51. $\left(x-\frac{1}{2}\right)^2 + \left(y-\frac{1}{2}\right)^2 = 2$

37.

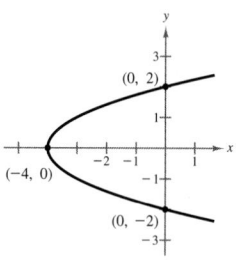

53. $\left(x+\frac{1}{2}\right)^2 + \left(y+\frac{5}{4}\right)^2 = \frac{9}{4}$

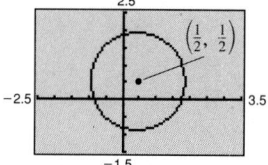

39. $x^2 + y^2 - 9 = 0$

41. $x^2 + y^2 - 4x + 2y - 11 = 0$

43. $x^2 + y^2 + 2x - 4y = 0$

45. $x^2 + y^2 - 6y = 0$

55. $(1, 1)$ **57.** $(5, 2)$ **59.** $(-1, -2), (2, 1)$

61. $(0, 0), (\sqrt{2}, 2\sqrt{2}), (-\sqrt{2}, -2\sqrt{2})$

63. $(-1, 0), (0, 1), (1, 0)$

65. (a) $C = 11.8x + 5000$; $R = 19.3x$
 (b) 667 units
 (c) 680 units

67. 50,000 units   **69.** 193 units

71. (a)

Year	1982	1985	1987
Model	1384.30	1583.14	1819.70

Year	1988	1989	1990
Model	1969.18	2139.46	2330.54

 (b) $3597.94 million

73. (a)

Year	1980	1985	1990
Salary	15,848.32	24,097.00	31,963.44

Year	1991	1994
Salary	33,527.71	38,209.43

 (c) $47,537.98

75. $(3, 1)$ **77.** $(-2, 0), (1, 3)$ **79.** $(-2, 5), (2, 5)$

81. $(0, 5.36)$

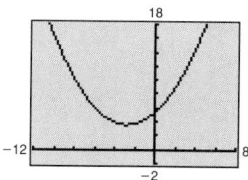

83. $(0, -4.3), (1.9749, 0), (-1.7097, 0), (12.7349, 0)$

85. $(1.4780, 0), (12.8553, 0), (0, 2.3875)$

87. $(0, 0.4167)$

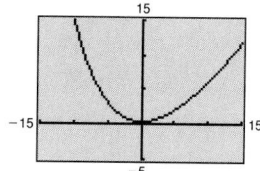

SECTION 1.3   (page 35)

1. 1   **3.** 0   **5.** -3

7. $m = 3$ **9.** $m = 0$

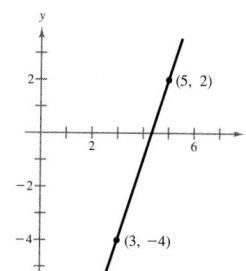

11. m is undefined   **13.** $m = 0$

 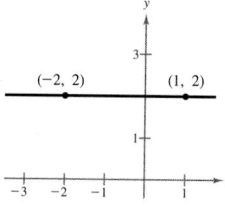

15. $(0, 1), (1, 1), (3, 1)$ **17.** $(7, -6), (5, -2), (4, 0)$
19. $(0, 10), (2, 4), (3, 1)$
21. $(-8, 0), (-8, 2), (-8, 3)$ **23.** $m = -\frac{1}{5}, (0, 4)$

25. $m = \frac{7}{5}, (0, -3)$

27. m is undefined; no y-intercept.

29. $y = 2x - 5$ **31.** $3x + y = 0$

     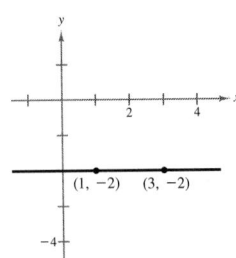

33. $x - 2 = 0$ **35.** $y + 2 = 0$

     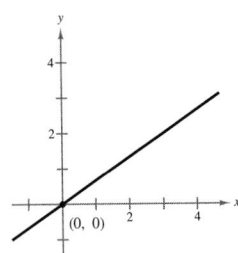

37. $3x - 4y + 12 = 0$ **39.** $2x - 3y = 0$

     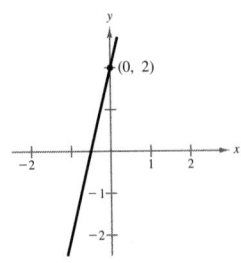

41. $3x + y - 1 = 0$ **43.** $4x - y + 2 = 0$

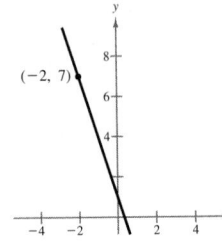

45. $9x - 12y + 8 = 0$

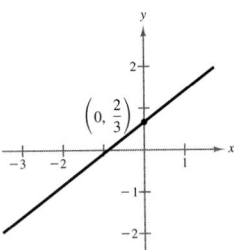

47. The points are not collinear.   **49.** $x - 3 = 0$

51. **(a)** $x + y + 1 = 0$ **(b)** $x - y + 5 = 0$

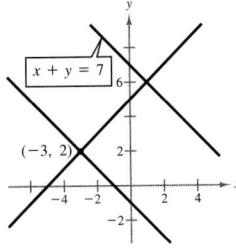

53. **(a)** $3x + 4y + 2 = 0$ **(b)** $4x - 3y + 36 = 0$

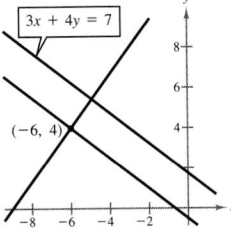

55. **(a)** $y = 0$ **(b)** $x + 1 = 0$

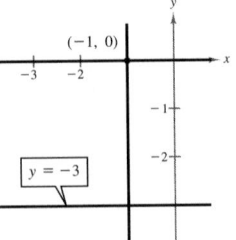

57. (a) $2x - 3y + 1 = 0$ **(b)** $3x + 2y - 5 = 0$

59.   **61.**

63.   **65.**

     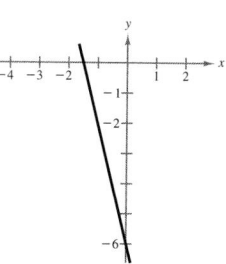

67. $F = \frac{9}{5}C + 32$ **69.** $C = 0.25x + 100$

71. (a) $S = 1700t + 26{,}300$ **(b)** \$34,800
(c) Salary increases by the same amount (\$1700) each year.
(d) Salary increases by the same percent each year. Yes, as your salary increases, the amount of your raise increases.

73. (a) $y = -205t + 1025,\ 0 \le t \le 5$
(b)

(c) \$410.00   **(d)** 2.07 years

75. (a) $C = 14.75t + 26{,}500$ **(b)** $R = 25t$
(c) $P = 10.25t - 26{,}500$ **(d)** 2585.4 hr
77. $x \le 24$ units   **79.** $x \le 70$ units

     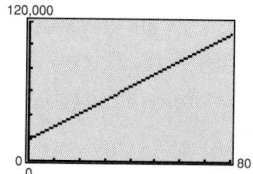

81. $x \le 275$ units

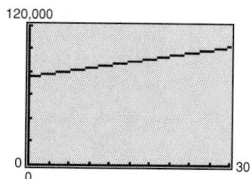

83. (a) $W = 2000 + 0.07S$
(b) $W = 2300 + 0.05S$
(c) $(15{,}000,\ 3050)$

The point of intersection signifies that if your sales were \$15,000, then both sides would yield wages of \$3050.

(d) No. You will make more money (if sales are \$20,000) at your current job ($W = \$3400$) than in the offered job ($W = \$3300$).

SECTION 1.4   (page 47)

Warm Up

1. 20   **2.** 10   **3.** $x^2 + x - 6$

4. $x^3 + 9x^2 + 26x + 30$ **5.** $\dfrac{1}{x}$ **6.** $\dfrac{2x - 1}{x}$

7. $y = -2x + 17$ **8.** $y = \frac{6}{5}x^2 + \frac{1}{5}$

9. $y = 3 \pm \sqrt{5 + (x + 1)^2}$ **10.** $y = \pm\sqrt{4x^2 + 2}$

1. (a) -3 (b) -9 (c) $2x - 5$ (d) $2\Delta x - 1$

3. (a) 2 (b) 18 (c) $\frac{1}{2}c^2$
  (d) $\frac{1}{2}x^2 + x\Delta x + \frac{1}{2}(\Delta x)^2$

5. (a) 1 (b) -1 (c) 1
  (d) $\dfrac{|x-1|}{(x-1)} = \begin{cases} -1, & x < 1 \\ 1, & x > 1 \end{cases}$

7. 3 **9.** $3 + \Delta x$ **11.** $3x^2 + 3x\Delta x + (\Delta x)^2 - 1$

13. y is not a function of x.   **15.** y is a function of x.

17. y is a function of x.   **19.** y is not a function of x.

21. Domain: $(-\infty, \infty)$ **23.** Domain: $\left[\frac{3}{2}, \infty\right)$
  Range: $(-\infty, \infty)$ Range: $[0, \infty)$

25. Domain: $(-\infty, 0) \cup (0, \infty)$
  Range: $(0, \infty)$

27.

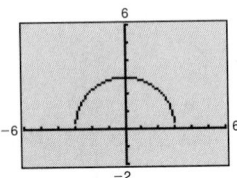

Domain: $[-3, 3]$
Range: $[0, 3]$

29.

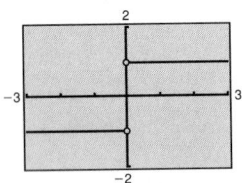

Domain: $(-\infty, 0) \cup (0, \infty)$
Range: $y = -1$ or $y = 1$

31.

Domain: $(-\infty, -4) \cup (-4, \infty)$
Range: $(-\infty, 1) \cup (1, \infty)$

33. y is a function of x.   **35.** y is not a function of x.

37. y is a function of x.

39. (a) $2x$ (b) $(x + 1)(x - 1) = x^2 - 1$
  (c) $\dfrac{x + 1}{x - 1}$ (d) x (e) x

41. (a) $3x^2 - 1$ (b) $2x^4 - 2x^2$ (c) $\dfrac{2x^2}{x^2 - 1}$
  (d) $2x^4 - 4x^2 + 2$ (e) $4x^4 - 1$

43. (a) $x^2 + 5 + \sqrt{1 - x}$ (b) $(x^2 + 5)\sqrt{1 - x}$
  (c) $\dfrac{x^2 + 5}{\sqrt{1 - x}}$ (d) $6 - x, 1 \geq x$
  (e) Not defined

45. (a) $\dfrac{1}{x} + \dfrac{1}{x^2} = \dfrac{x + 1}{x^2}$ (b) $\dfrac{1}{x^3}$ (c) x
  (d) x^2 (e) x^2

47. $f(g(x)) = \left(\sqrt[3]{x}\right)^3 = x$
  $g(f(x)) = \sqrt[3]{x^3} = x$

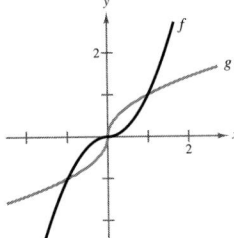

49. $f(g(x)) = 5\left(\dfrac{x - 1}{5}\right) + 1 = x$
  $g(f(x)) = \dfrac{5x + 1 - 1}{5} = x$

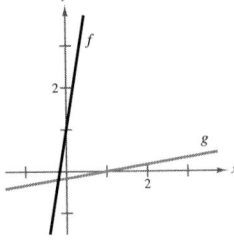

51. $f(g(x)) = \sqrt{x^2 + 4 - 4} = x, x \geq 0$
$g(f(x)) = (\sqrt{x-4})^2 + 4 = x, x \geq 4$

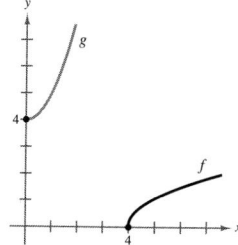

53. $f(x) = 2x - 3, f^{-1}(x) = \dfrac{x+3}{2}$

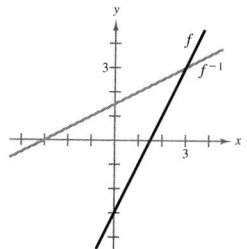

55. $f(x) = x^5, f^{-1}(x) = \sqrt[5]{x}$

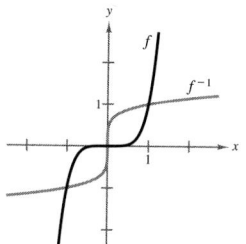

57. $f(x) = \sqrt{9 - x^2}, f'(x) = \sqrt{9 - x^2}, 0 \leq x \leq 3$

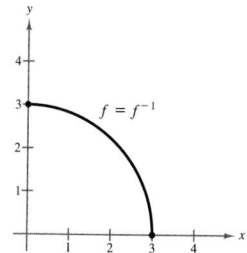

59. $f(x) = x^{2/3}, f^{-1}(x) = x^{3/2}, x \geq 0$

61.

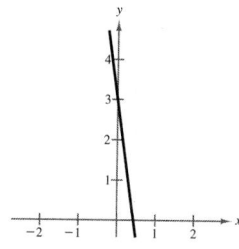

$f(x)$ is one-to-one.
$f^{-1}(x) = \dfrac{3 - x}{7}$

63.

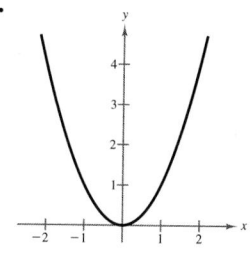

$f(x)$ is not one-to-one.

65.

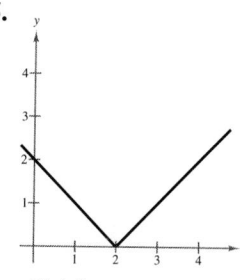

$f(x)$ is not one-to-one.

67. **(a)** 0   **(b)** 0   **(c)** -1 **(d)** $\sqrt{15}$
(e) $\sqrt{x^2 - 1}$ **(f)** $x - 1, x \geq 0$

69. The data fits the function
(b) $g(x) = cx^2$ with $c = -2$.

71. The data fits the function
(d) $r(x) = c/x$ with $c = 32$.

73. (a)

(b)

(c)

(d)

(e)

(f)

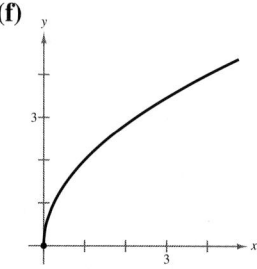

75. $V(x) = 2500x + 750,000$

77. (a) $x = \dfrac{1475}{p} - 100$ **(b)** 47.5 units

79. (a)

(b) (25, 14)
(c) $0 \le x < 25$
(d) $x > 25$

81. (a) $C = 98,000 + 12.30x$
(b) $R = 17.98x$
(c) $P = 5.68x - 98,000$

83.

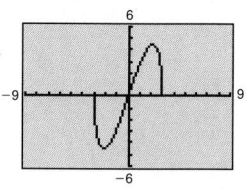

Zeros: $x = 0, \pm 3$
$f(x)$ is not one-to-one.

85.

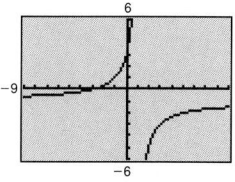

Zeros: $t = -3$
$g(t)$ is one-to-one.

87.

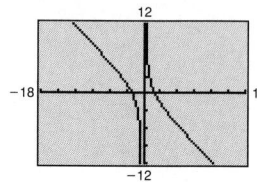

Zeros: $x = \pm 2$
$f(x)$ is not one-to-one.

SECTION 1.5 (page 60)

Warm Up

1. (a) 7 **(b)** $c^2 - 3c + 3$
   (c) $x^2 + 2xh + h^2 - 3x - 3h + 3$
2. (a) -4 **(b)** 10 **(c)** $3t^2 + 4$
3. h **4.** 4
5. Domain: $(-\infty, 0) \cup (0, \infty)$
   Range: $(-\infty, 0) \cup (0, \infty)$

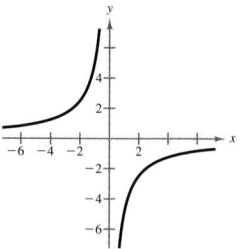

Warm Up *(continued)*

6. Domain: $[-5, 5]$ **7.** Domain: $(-\infty, \infty)$
Range: $[0, 5]$ Range: $[0, \infty)$

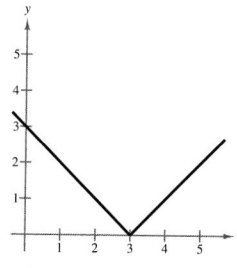

8. Domain: $(-\infty, 0) \cup (0, \infty)$
Range: $-1, 1$

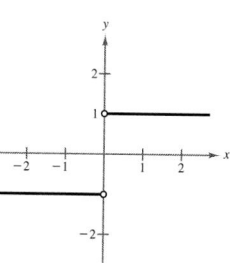

9. y is not a function of x.
10. y is a function of x.

1.

x	1.9	1.99	1.999	2
$f(x)$	13.5	13.95	13.995	?

x	2.001	2.01	2.1
$f(x)$	14.005	14.05	14.5

$\lim\limits_{x \to 2} (5x + 4) = 14$

3.

x	1.9	1.99	1.999	2
$f(x)$	0.2564	0.2506	0.2501	?

x	2.001	2.01	2.1
$f(x)$	0.2499	0.2494	0.2439

$\lim\limits_{x \to 2} \dfrac{x - 2}{x^2 - 4} = \dfrac{1}{4}$

5.

x	-0.1	-0.01	-0.001	0
$f(x)$	0.2911	0.2889	0.2887	?

x	0.001	0.01	0.1
$f(x)$	0.2887	0.2884	0.2863

$\lim\limits_{x \to 0} \dfrac{\sqrt{x + 3} - \sqrt{3}}{x} \approx 0.2887$

$\left(\text{The actual limit is } \dfrac{1}{2\sqrt{3}}. \right)$

7.

x	1.5	1.9	1.99	1.999	2
$f(x)$	0.3780	0.1601	0.0501	0.0158	?

$\lim\limits_{x \to 2} \dfrac{2 - x}{\sqrt{4 - x^2}} = 0$

9. (a) 1   **(b)** 3   **11. (a)** 1   **(b)** 3
13. (a) 12   **(b)** 27   **(c)** $\frac{1}{3}$
15. (a) 1   **(b)** 1   **(c)** 1
17. (a) 0   **(b)** 0   **(c)** 0
19. (a) 3   **(b)** -3 **(c)** Limit does not exist.
21. 4   **23.** -3 **25.** -4 **27.** 2   **29.** -1
31. $\frac{2}{3}$ **33.** -2 **35.** Limit does not exist.   **37.** $\frac{1}{10}$
39. 12   **41.** Limit does not exist.   **43.** -1
45. 2   **47.** 2   **49.** $3x^2$ **51.** $2t - 5$

53. $\dfrac{1}{2\sqrt{2}}$ **55.** $-\infty$ **57.** $-\infty$ **59.** ∞

61. 4   **63.** Limit does not exist.

65. $-\dfrac{17}{9} \approx -1.8889$ **67.** Yes. 1814.02

SECTION 1.6   (page 71)

> **Warm Up**
>
> **1.** $\dfrac{x+4}{x-8}$ **2.** $\dfrac{x+1}{x-3}$ **3.** $\dfrac{x+2}{2(x-3)}$
>
> **4.** $\dfrac{x-4}{x-2}$ **5.** $x = 0, -7$ **6.** $x = -5, 1$
>
> **7.** $x = -\frac{2}{3}, -2$ **8.** $x = 0, 3, -8$
>
> **9.** 13   **10.** -1

1. Continuous   **3.** Not continuous $(x \neq \pm 2)$
5. $(-\infty, \infty)$ **7.** $(-\infty, -1) \cup (-1, \infty)$
9. $(-\infty, \infty)$ **11.** $(-\infty, 1) \cup (1, \infty)$
13. $(-\infty, \infty)$ **15.** $(-\infty, 4) \cup (4, 5) \cup (5, \infty)$
17. $(-\infty, 1) \cup (1, \infty)$ **19.** $(-\infty, \infty)$
21. $(-\infty, 2) \cup (2, \infty)$ **23.** $(-\infty, \infty)$
25. $(-\infty, -1) \cup (-1, \infty)$
27. Continuous on all intervals $(c, c+1)$,
where c is an integer.
29. Continuous on all intervals $(c, c+1)$,
where c is an integer.
31. $(1, \infty)$ **33.** Continuous
35. Nonremovable discontinuity at $x = 2$
37. Removable discontinuity at $x = 4$

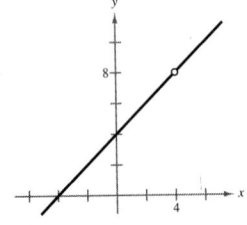

39. Removable discontinuity at $x = 0$

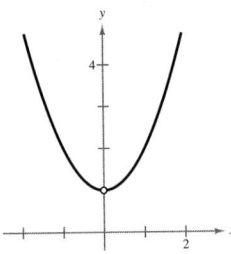

41. Continuous on $(-\infty, 0) \cup (0, \infty)$

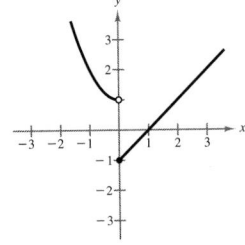

43. $a = 2$
45. Not continuous at $x = 2$ and $x = -1$.

47. $(-\infty, \infty)$
49. Continuous on all intervals $\left(\dfrac{c}{2}, \dfrac{c+1}{2}\right)$,
where c is an integer.
51. The graph of $f(x) = \dfrac{x^2 + x}{x}$ appears to be continuous on $[-4, 4]$, but f is not continuous at $x = 0$.

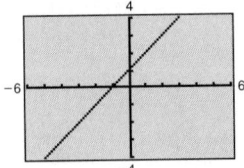

53. (a) Graph has nonremovable discontinuities at
$t = \frac{1}{4}, \frac{1}{2}, \frac{3}{4}, 1, \frac{5}{4}, \ldots$

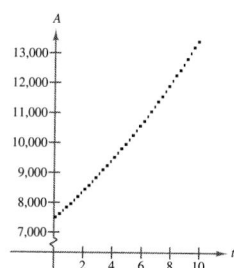

(b) $11,379.17

55. (a)
$$C(t) = \begin{cases} 1.04, & 0 < t \le 2 \\ 1.04 + 0.36\,[\![t - 1]\!], & t > 2, t \text{ is not an integer} \\ 1.04 + 0.36(t - 2), & t > 2, t \text{ is an integer} \end{cases}$$

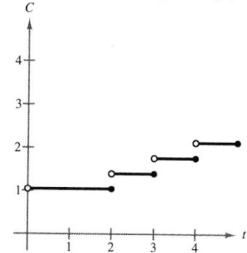

C is not continuous at $t = 2, 3, 4, \ldots$

(b) $3.56

57. (a)

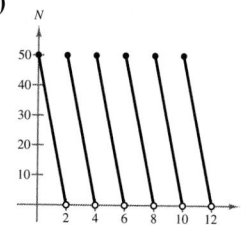

Nonremovable discontinuities at $t = 2, 4, 6, 8, \ldots$
(b) Every two months

CHAPTER 1 REVIEW EXERCISES   (page 76)

1. a   **2.** c   **3.** b   **4.** d
5. $\sqrt{29}$ **7.** $3\sqrt{2}$ **9.** $(7, 4)$ **11.** $(-8, 6)$

13. The taller bars in the book represent revenues. The middle bars represent costs. The smaller bars in front represent profits, because $P = R - C$.

15. $(4, 7), (5, 8), (8, 10)$

17.

19.

21.

23.
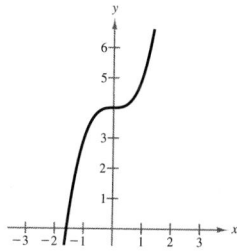

25. $(0, -3), \left(-\frac{3}{4}, 0\right)$ **27.** $x^2 + y^2 = 9$

29. $(x - 3)^2 + (y + 4)^2 = 25$
Center: $(3, -4)$
Radius: 5

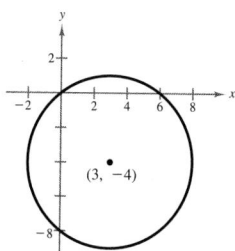

31. $(1, 1)$ **33.** $(0, 0), (1, 1), (-1, -1)$
35. (a) $C = 200 + 10x; R = 14x$
(b) 50 shirts

37. Slope: -3
  y-intercept: $(0, -2)$

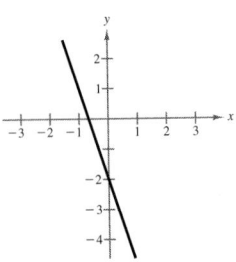

39. Slope: 0 (horizontal line)
  y-intercept: $\left(0, -\frac{5}{3}\right)$

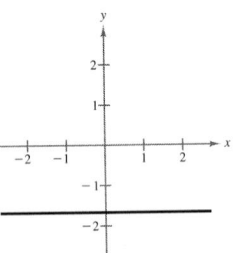

41. Slope: $-\frac{2}{5}$
  y-intercept: $(0, -1)$

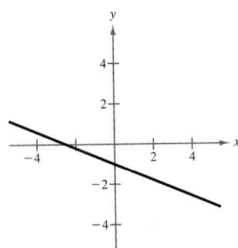

43. $\frac{6}{7}$ **45.** $\frac{20}{21}$
47. $y = -2x + 5$

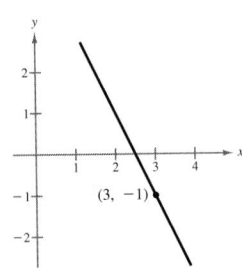

49. (a) $y = \frac{7}{8}x + \frac{69}{8}$ (b) $y = -2x$
  (c) $y = -2x$ (d) $y = -\frac{2}{3}x + 4$
51. (a) $x = -10p + 1070$ (b) 725 units
  (c) 650 units
53. y is a function of x. **55.** y is not a function of x.
57. (a) 7 (b) $3x + 7$ (c) $10 + 3\Delta x$
59. Domain: $(-\infty, \infty)$ **61.** Domain: $[-1, \infty)$
  Range: $\left[-\frac{1}{4}, \infty\right)$ Range: $[0, \infty)$

63. Domain: $(-\infty, \infty)$
  Range: $(-\infty, 3]$

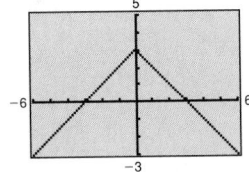

65. (a) $x^2 + 2x$ (b) $x^2 - 2x + 2$
  (c) $2x^3 - x^2 + 2x - 1$ (d) $\dfrac{1 + x^2}{2x - 1}$
  (e) $4x^2 - 4x + 2$ (f) $2x^2 + 1$
67. $f^{-1}(x) = \frac{2}{3}x$
69. $f(x)$ does not have an inverse. **71.** 7 **73.** 49
75. $\frac{10}{3}$ **77.** Limit does not exist. **79.** $-\frac{1}{4}$
81. $-\infty$ **83.** Limit does not exist.
85. $3x^2 - 1$ **87.** 0.5774
89. False **90.** True **91.** False
92. True **93.** False **94.** True
95. $(-\infty, -4) \cup (-4, \infty)$
97. $(-\infty, -1) \cup (-1, \infty)$
99. Continuous on all intervals of the form $(c, c+1)$,
  where c is an integer
101. $(-\infty, 0) \cup (0, \infty)$ **103.** $a = 2$

105. (a)

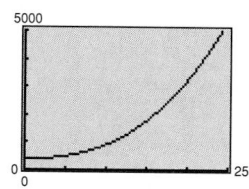

(b)

t	0	5	10
Debt	381	542	909
Model	358.78	494.63	917.48

t	15	20	21
Debt	1817	3206	3599
Model	1777.33	3224.18	3597.19

(c) $5408.03 billion

SAMPLE POST-GRAD EXAM QUESTIONS (page 80)

1. (e)   **2.** (d)   **3.** (b)   **4.** (b)
5. (a)   **6.** (c)   **7.** (e)   **8.** (b)

CHAPTER 2

SECTION 2.1 (page 90)

> **Warm Up**
>
> **1.** $x = 2$ **2.** $y = 2$ **3.** $2x$ **4.** $3x^2$
> **5.** $\dfrac{1}{x^2}$ **6.** $2x$ **7.** $(-\infty, 1) \cup (1, \infty)$
> **8.** $(-\infty, \infty)$ **9.** $(-\infty, 0) \cup (0, \infty)$
> **10.** $(-\infty, -4) \cup (-4, 3) \cup (3, \infty)$

1.

3.

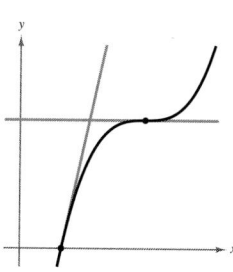

5. $m = 1$ **7.** $m = 0$ **9.** $m = -\frac{1}{3}$
11. 1990: $m \approx 20$
1992: $m \approx 4$
13. $f(x) = 3$
1. $f(x + \Delta x) = 3$
2. $f(x + \Delta x) - f(x) = 0$
3. $\dfrac{f(x + \Delta x) - f(x)}{\Delta x} = 0$
4. $\lim\limits_{\Delta x \to 0} \dfrac{f(x + \Delta x) - f(x)}{\Delta x} = 0$
15. $f(x) = -5x + 3$
1. $f(x + \Delta x) = -5x - 5\Delta x + 3$
2. $f(x + \Delta x) - f(x) = -5\Delta x$
3. $\dfrac{f(x + \Delta x) - f(x)}{\Delta x} = -5$
4. $\lim\limits_{\Delta x \to 0} \dfrac{f(x + \Delta x) - f(x)}{\Delta x} = -5$
17. $f(x) = x^2$
1. $f(x + \Delta x) = x^2 + 2x\Delta x + (\Delta x)^2$
2. $f(x + \Delta x) - f(x) = 2x\Delta x + (\Delta x)^2$
3. $\dfrac{f(x + \Delta x) - f(x)}{\Delta x} = 2x + \Delta x$
4. $\lim\limits_{\Delta x \to 0} \dfrac{f(x + \Delta x) - f(x)}{\Delta x} = 2x$
19. $6x - 5$
21. $h(t) = \sqrt{t - 1}$
1. $h(t + \Delta t) = \sqrt{t + \Delta t - 1}$
2. $h(t + \Delta t) - h(t) = \sqrt{t + \Delta t - 1} - \sqrt{t - 1}$
3. $\dfrac{h(t + \Delta t) - h(t)}{\Delta t} = \dfrac{1}{\sqrt{t + \Delta t - 1} + \sqrt{t - 1}}$
4. $\lim\limits_{\Delta t \to 0} \dfrac{h(t + \Delta t) - h(t)}{\Delta t} = \dfrac{1}{2\sqrt{t - 1}}$
23. $f(t) = t^3 - 12t$
1. $f(t + \Delta t) = t^3 + 3t^2\Delta t + 3t(\Delta t)^2$
$\qquad\qquad + (\Delta t)^3 - 12t - 12\Delta t$
2. $f(t + \Delta t) - f(t) = 3t^2\Delta t + 3t(\Delta t)^2$
$\qquad\qquad + (\Delta t)^3 - 12\Delta t$
3. $\dfrac{f(t + \Delta t) - f(t)}{\Delta t} = 3t^2 + 3t\Delta t + (\Delta t)^2 - 12$
4. $\lim\limits_{\Delta t \to 0} \dfrac{f(t + \Delta t) - f(t)}{\Delta t} = 3t^2 - 12$
25. $-\dfrac{2}{x^3}$

27. $f'(x) = -2$
$f'(2) = -2$

29. $f'(x) = -1$
$f'(0) = -1$

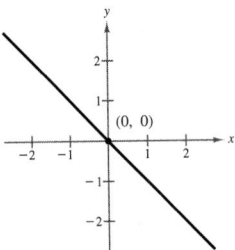

31. $f'(x) = 2x$
$f'(2) = 4$

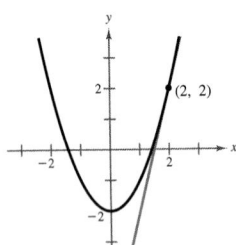

33. $f'(x) = 3x^2$
$f'(2) = 12$

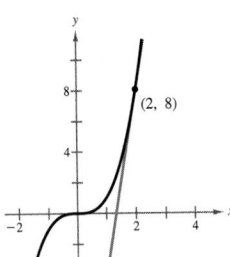

35. $f'(x) = \dfrac{1}{2\sqrt{x+1}}$
$f'(3) = \frac{1}{4}$

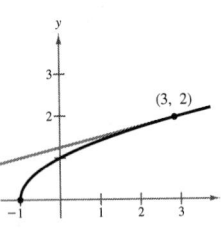

37. $f'(x) = 3x^2 + 2$
$f'(1) = 5$

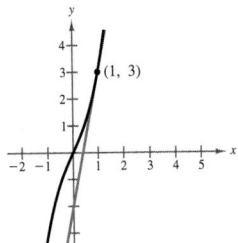

39. $y = 2x - 2$

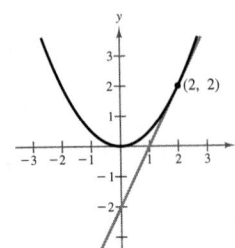

41. $y = -6x - 3$

43. $y = \dfrac{x}{4} + 2$

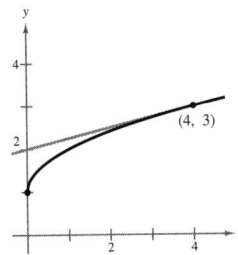

45. $y = -x + 1$ **47.** $y = -6x + 8$
$y = -6x - 8$

49. $x \neq -3$ (node)
51. $x \neq -1$ (nonremovable discontinuity)
53. $x \neq 3$ (cusp)   **55.** $x > 1$
57. $x \neq 0$ (nonremovable discontinuity)
59.

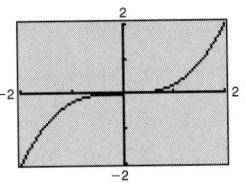

x	-2	$-\frac{3}{2}$	-1	$-\frac{1}{2}$
$f(x)$	-2	-0.8438	-0.25	-0.0313
$f'(x)$	3	1.6875	0.75	0.1875

x	0	$\frac{1}{2}$	1	$\frac{3}{2}$	2
$f(x)$	0	0.0313	0.25	0.8438	2
$f'(x)$	0	0.1875	0.75	1.6875	3

61. True
62. False. $f(x) = |x|$ is continuous, but not differentiable, at $x = 0$.
63. True   **64.** True

65. $f'(x) = 2x - 4$

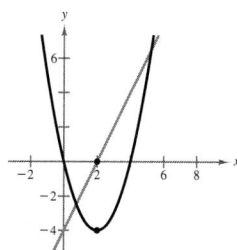

The *x*-intercept of the derivative indicates a point of horizontal tangency for f.

SECTION 2.2   (page 102)

Warm Up

1. (a) 8   **(b)** 16   **(c)** $\frac{1}{2}$

2. (a) $\frac{1}{36}$ **(b)** $\frac{1}{32}$ **(c)** $\frac{1}{64}$

3. $4x(3x^2 + 1)$ **4.** $\frac{3}{2}x^{1/2}(x^{3/2} - 1)$

5. $\frac{1}{4x^{3/4}}$ **6.** $x^2 - \frac{1}{x^{1/2}} + \frac{1}{3x^{2/3}}$

7. $0, -\frac{2}{3}$ **8.** $0, \pm 1$

9. $-10, 2$ **10.** $-2, 12$

---

1. (a) 2   **(b)** $\frac{1}{2}$ **3. (a)** -1 **(b)** $-\frac{1}{3}$

5. 0   **7.** 1   **9.** $2x$ **11.** $-6t + 2$

13. $3t^2 - 2$ **15.** $\frac{16}{3}t^{1/3}$ **17.** $\frac{2}{\sqrt{x}}$

19. $-\frac{8}{x^3} + 4x$

21. Function: $y = \dfrac{1}{4x^3}$

Rewrite: $y = \dfrac{1}{4}x^{-3}$

Derivative: $y' = \dfrac{-3}{4}x^{-4}$

Simplify: $y' = -\dfrac{3}{4x^4}$

23. Function: $y = \dfrac{1}{(4x)^3}$

Rewrite: $y = \dfrac{1}{64}x^{-3}$

Derivative: $y' = -\dfrac{3}{64}x^{-4}$

Simplify: $y' = -\dfrac{3}{64x^4}$

25. Function: $y = \dfrac{\sqrt{x}}{x}$

Rewrite: $y = x^{-1/2}$

Derivative: $y' = -\dfrac{1}{2}x^{-3/2}$

Simplify: $y' = -\dfrac{1}{2x^{3/2}}$

27. $-\dfrac{1}{x^2}, -1$ **29.** $\dfrac{4}{3t^2}, \dfrac{16}{3}$ **31.** $8x + 4, 4$

33. $\dfrac{2(x^3 + 2)}{x^2}$ **35.** $2x - 2 + \dfrac{8}{x^5}$ **37.** $\dfrac{2x^3 - 6}{x^3}$

39. $3x^2 + 1$ **41.** $\dfrac{4}{5x^{1/5}}$ **43.** $\dfrac{1}{3x^{2/3}} + \dfrac{1}{5x^{4/5}}$

45. $y = 2x - 2$

47. $(0, -1), \left(-\dfrac{\sqrt{6}}{2}, \dfrac{5}{4}\right), \left(\dfrac{\sqrt{6}}{2}, \dfrac{5}{4}\right)$

49. No horizontal tangents

51. (a)

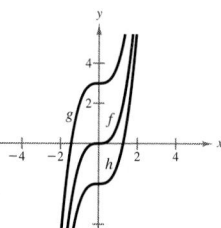

(b) $f'(1) = g'(1)$
$= h'(1)$
$= 3$

(c)

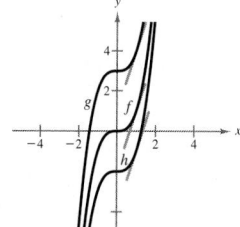

53. (a) 3   **(b)** 6   **(c)** −3   **(d)** 6

55. (a) 1990: −4.5   **(c)** Billions of dollars per year
1992: 6.27

57. $P = 0.40x - 250$

59. $(-0.267, 1.577), (1.2, 0)$

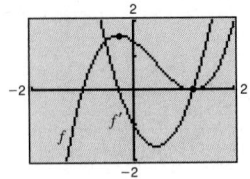

SECTION 2.3   (page 116)

Warm Up

1. 3   **2.** −7   **3.** $y' = 8x - 2$

4. $y' = -9t^2 + 4t$ **5.** $s' = -32t + 24$

6. $y' = -32x + 54$ **7.** $A' = -\frac{3}{5}r^2 + \frac{3}{5}r + \frac{1}{2}$

8. $y' = 2x^2 - 4x + 7$ **9.** $y' = 12 - \dfrac{x}{2500}$

10. $y' = 74 - \dfrac{3x^2}{10,000}$

1. (a) $2.5 billion per year
(b) −$0.714 billion per year
(c) $5.8 billion per year
(d) $2.2 billion per year

3. Average rate: 2
Instantaneous rates: $f'(1) = 2, f'(2) = 2$

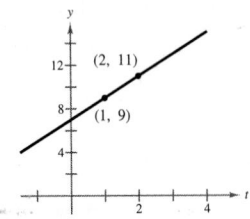

5. Average rate: −1
Instantaneous rates: $h'(0) = 0, h'(1) = -2$

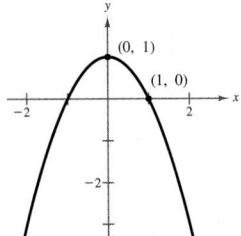

7. Average rate: 2.1
Instantaneous rates: $f'(1) = 2, f'(1.1) = 2.2$

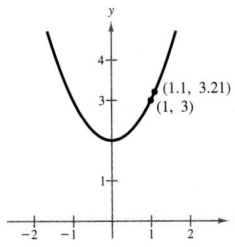

9. Average rate: $-\frac{1}{4}$
Instantaneous rates: $f'(1) = -1, f'(4) = -\frac{1}{16}$

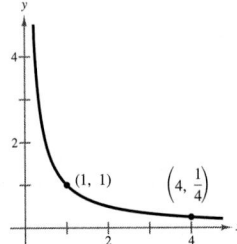

11. Average rate: 1
Instantaneous rates: $g'(1) = 2, g'(9) = \frac{2}{3}$

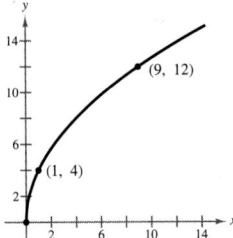

13. (a) Average rate: $\frac{11}{27}$

Instantaneous rates: $E'(0) = \frac{1}{3}$, $E'(1) = \frac{4}{9}$

(b) Average rate: $\frac{11}{27}$

Instantaneous rates: $E'(1) = \frac{4}{9}$, $E'(2) = \frac{1}{3}$

(c) Average rate: $\frac{5}{27}$

Instantaneous rates: $E'(2) = \frac{1}{3}$, $E'(3) = 0$

(d) Average rate: $-\frac{7}{27}$

Instantaneous rates: $E'(3) = 0$, $E'(4) = -\frac{5}{9}$

15. (a) -80 ft/sec

(b) $s'(2) = -64$ ft/sec, $s'(3) = -96$ ft/sec

(c) $\dfrac{\sqrt{555}}{4} \approx 5.89$ sec

(d) $-8\sqrt{555} \approx -188.5$ sec

17. (a) $s'(0) = 0$ ft/sec   **(b)** $s'(1) = 15$ ft/sec

(c) $s'(4) = 30$ ft/sec   **(d)** $s'(9) = 45$ ft/sec

19. 1.47   **21.** $470 - \frac{1}{2}x$ **23.** $50 - x$

25. $-18x^2 + 16x + 200$ **27.** $-4x + 72$

29. $-\frac{1}{2000}x + 12.2$ **31. (a)** 64.998   **(b)** 65

33. (a) 0.584   **(b)** 0.6

35. (a) 37.40   **(b)** 79.80   **(c)** 14.83

(d) -48.40

37. (a) $R = 5x - 0.001x^2$

(b) $P = 3.5x - 0.001x^2 - 35$

(c)

x	600	1200	1800	2400	3000
$\dfrac{dR}{dx}$	3.8	2.6	1.4	0.2	-1.0
$\dfrac{dP}{dx}$	2.3	1.1	-0.1	-1.3	-2.5
P	1705	2725	3025	2605	1465

39. (a) $P = -0.0003x^2 + 17.8x - 85,000$

(b) 5.8 dollars

43. $C(351) - C(350) \approx -1.91$

$\dfrac{dC}{dQ} = -1.93$ when $Q = 350$.

45. $C = \dfrac{16,500}{x}$

$\dfrac{dC}{dx} = -\dfrac{16,500}{x^2}$

x	10	15	20	25
C	\$1650	\$1100	\$825	\$660
$\dfrac{dC}{dx}$	-165	-73.33	-41.25	-26.40

x	30	35	40
C	\$550	\$471.43	\$412.50
$\dfrac{dC}{dx}$	-18.33	-13.47	-10.31

The driver who gets 15 miles per gallon would benefit more from a 1 mile per gallon increase in fuel efficiency. The rate of change is much larger when $x = 15$.

47.

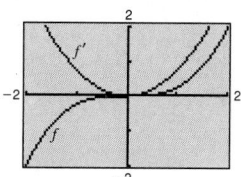

f has a horizontal tangent at $x = 0$.

SECTION 2.4   (page 130)

Warm Up

1. $2(3x^2 + 7x + 1)$ **2.** $4x^2(6 - 5x^2)$

3. $\dfrac{23}{(2x+7)^2}$ **4.** $-\dfrac{x^2 + 8x + 4}{(x^2 - 4)^2}$

5. $\dfrac{4x^3 - 3x^2 + 3}{x^2}$ **6.** $\dfrac{x^2 - 2x + 4}{(x - 1)^2}$

7. 11   **8.** 0   **9.** $-\frac{1}{4}$ **10.** $\frac{17}{4}$

1. $f'(x) = 15x^4 - 2x$ **3.** $f'(x) = 2x^2$

$f'(1) = 13$ $f'(0) = 0$

5. $g'(x) = 3x^2 - 12x + 11$
$g'(4) = 11$

7. $h'(x) = -\dfrac{5}{(x-5)^2}$
$h'(6) = -5$

9. $f'(t) = \dfrac{2t^2 + 3}{3t^2}$
$f'(2) = \dfrac{11}{12}$

11. Function: $y = \dfrac{x^2 + 2x}{x}$
Rewrite: $y = x + 2$
Derivative: $y' = 1$
Simplify: $y' = 1$

13. Function: $y = \dfrac{7}{3x^3}$
Rewrite: $y = \dfrac{7}{3}x^{-3}$
Derivative: $y' = -7x^{-4}$
Simplify: $y' = -\dfrac{7}{x^4}$

15. Function: $y = \dfrac{4x^2 - 3x}{8\sqrt{x}}$
Rewrite: $y = \dfrac{1}{2}x^{3/2} - \dfrac{3}{8}x^{1/2}$
Derivative: $y' = \dfrac{3}{4}x^{1/2} - \dfrac{3}{16}x^{-1/2}$
Simplify: $y' = \dfrac{3}{4}\sqrt{x} - \dfrac{3}{16\sqrt{x}}$

17. Function: $y = \dfrac{x^2 - 4x + 3}{x - 1}$
Rewrite: $y = x - 3,\ x \neq 1$
Derivative: $y' = 1,\ x \neq 1$
Simplify: $y' = 1,\ x \neq 1$

19. $10x^4 + 12x^3 - 3x^2 - 18x - 15$
21. $28t^6 - 42t^5 - 15t^4 - 8t + 7$
23. $6p^2(p^3 - 2)$
25. $\dfrac{5}{6x^{1/6}} + \dfrac{1}{x^{2/3}}$
27. $-\dfrac{5}{(2x - 3)^2}$
29. $\dfrac{2}{(x + 1)^2}$
31. $\dfrac{3(x^4 + 1)}{x^2}$
33. $-\dfrac{1}{(t + 3)^2}$
35. $\dfrac{x - 1}{2x^{3/2}}$
37. $\dfrac{2x^3 + 11x^2 - 8x - 17}{(x + 4)^2}$

39. $15x^4 - 48x^3 - 33x^2 - 32x - 20$
41. $y = \dfrac{1}{4}x + \dfrac{1}{2}$
43. $y = -x - 2$
45. $(0,\ 0)$ and $(2,\ 4)$
47. $(0,\ 0)$ and $(\sqrt[3]{-4},\ -2.117)$
49.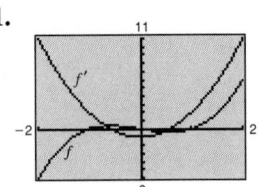
51.
53. -1.87
55. (a) -0.480 (b) 0.120 (c) 0.015
57. 31.55 bacteria/hr
59. (a) $p = \dfrac{4000}{\sqrt{x}}$
(b) $C = 250x + 10,000$
(c) $P = 4000\sqrt{x} - 250x - 10,000$

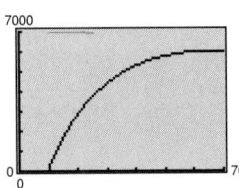

$\$500$ per unit
61. d
63. (a) -38.125
(b) -10.37
(c) -3.80
Increasing the order size reduces the cost per item.

SECTION 2.5   (page 140)

Warm Up

1. $(1 - 5x)^{2/5}$ **2.** $(2x - 1)^{3/4}$
3. $(4x^2 + 1)^{-1/2}$ **4.** $(x - 6)^{-1/3}$
5. $x^{1/2}(1 - 2x)^{-1/3}$ **6.** $(2x)^{-1}(3 - 7x)^{3/2}$
7. $(x - 2)(3x^2 + 5)$ **8.** $(x - 1)(5\sqrt{x} - 1)$
9. $(x^2 + 1)^2(4 - x - x^3)$
10. $(3 - x^2)(x - 1)(x^2 + x + 1)$

$y = f(g(x))$	$u = g(x)$	$y = f(u)$
1. $y = (6x - 5)^4$	$u = 6x - 5$	$y = u^4$
3. $y = (4 - x^2)^{-1}$	$u = 4 - x^2$	$y = u^{-1}$
5. $y = \sqrt{5x - 2}$	$u = 5x - 2$	$y = \sqrt{u}$
7. $y = \dfrac{1}{3x + 1}$	$u = 3x + 1$	$y = u^{-1}$

9. c **10.** d **11.** b **12.** a

13. $6(2x - 7)^2$ **15.** $12x(x^2 - 1)^2$

17. $-6(4 - 2x)^2$ **19.** $6x(6 - x^2)(2 - x^2)$

21. $\dfrac{4x}{3(x^2 - 9)^{1/3}}$ **23.** $\dfrac{1}{2\sqrt{t + 1}}$

25. $\dfrac{4t + 5}{2\sqrt{2t^2 + 5t + 2}}$ **27.** $\dfrac{6x}{(9x^2 + 4)^{2/3}}$

29. $-\dfrac{2x}{\sqrt{4 - x^2}}$ **31.** $-\dfrac{x}{(25 + x^2)^{3/2}}$

33. $\dfrac{4x^2}{(4 - x^3)^{7/3}}$

35. $y = \frac{8}{3}x - \frac{7}{3}$ or $3y - 8x + 7 = 0$

37. $f'(x) = \dfrac{1 - 3x^2 - 4x^{3/2}}{2\sqrt{x}(x^2 + 1)^2}$

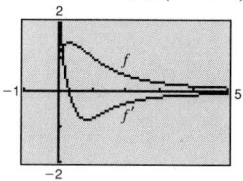

The zero of $f'(x)$ corresponds to the point on the graph of $f(x)$ where the tangent line is horizontal.

39. $f'(x) = -\dfrac{(\sqrt{(x + 1)}/x)}{2x(x + 1)}$

$f'(x)$ has no zeros.

41. $-\dfrac{1}{(x - 2)^2}$ **43.** $\dfrac{72}{(3 - t)^3}$

45. $-\dfrac{9x^2}{(x^3 - 4)^2}$ **47.** $-\dfrac{1}{2(x + 2)^{3/2}}$

49. $-\dfrac{3x^2}{(x^3 - 1)^{4/3}}$ **51.** $\dfrac{3(x + 1)}{\sqrt{2x + 3}}$

53. $\dfrac{t(5t - 8)}{2\sqrt{t - 2}}$ **55.** $x^2(x - 4)(5x - 12)$

57. $\dfrac{5t^2 + 8t - 9}{2\sqrt{t + 2}}$ **59.** $-\dfrac{3}{4\sqrt{3 - 2x}\,x^{3/2}}$

61. $\dfrac{3t(t^2 + 3t - 2)}{(t^2 + 2t - 1)^{3/2}}$ **63.** $-\dfrac{1}{x^2(x^3 + 1)^{2/3}}$

65. $\dfrac{2(6 - 5x)(5x^2 - 12x + 5)}{(x^2 - 1)^3}$

67. **(a)** \$74.00 per 1% **(b)** \$81.59 per 1%
   (c) \$89.94 per 1%

69.

t	0	1	2	3	4
$\dfrac{dN}{dt}$	0	177.78	44.44	10.82	3.29

The rate of growth of N is decreasing

71. **(a)** $V = \dfrac{10{,}000}{\sqrt[3]{t + 1}}$
   (b) $-\$1322.83$ per year
   (c) $-\$524.97$ per year

SECTION 2.6 (page 147)

> ### Warm Up
>
> **1.** $t = 0, \frac{3}{2}$ **2.** $t = -2, 7$ **3.** $t = -2, 10$
>
> **4.** $t = \dfrac{9 \pm 3\sqrt{10{,}249}}{32}$ **5.** $\dfrac{dy}{dx} = 6x^2 + 14x$
>
> **6.** $\dfrac{dy}{dx} = 8x^3 + 18x^2 - 10x - 15$
>
> **7.** $\dfrac{dy}{dx} = \dfrac{2x(x + 7)}{(2x + 7)^2}$ **8.** $\dfrac{dy}{dx} = -\dfrac{6x^2 + 10x + 15}{(2x^2 - 5)^2}$
>
> **9.** Domain: $(-\infty, \infty)$ **10.** Domain: $[7, \infty)$
>   Range: $[-4, \infty)$ Range: $[0, \infty)$

1. 0   **3.** 2   **5.** $2t - 8$ **7.** $\dfrac{4}{9t^{7/3}}$

9. $48x^2 - 16$ **11.** $\dfrac{4}{9x^{2/3}}$ **13.** $\dfrac{4}{(x-1)^3}$

15. $12x^2 + 24x + 16$ **17.** $60x^2 - 72x$

19. $120x + 360$ **21.** $-\dfrac{9}{2x^5}$

23. $-\dfrac{3}{8(4-x)^{5/2}}$ **25.** $4x$ **27.** $\dfrac{2}{x^2}$

29. 2   **31.** $f''(x) = 6(x-3) = 0$ when $x = 3$.

33. $f''(x) = 2(3x+4) = 0$ when $x = -\frac{4}{3}$.

35. $f''(x) = 36(x^2 - 1) = 0$ when $x = \pm 1$.

37. $f''(x) = \dfrac{2x(x+3)(x-3)}{(x^2+3)^3}$

$= 0$ when $x = 0$ or $x = \pm 3$.

39. (a) $s(t) = -16t^2 + 144t$
   (b) $v(t) = -32t + 144$
     $a(t) = -32$
   (c) 4.5 sec, 324 ft
   (d) -144 ft/sec, which is the same speed as the initial velocity.

41.

t	0	10	20	30
$\dfrac{ds}{dt}$	0	45	60	67.5
$\dfrac{d^2s}{dt^2}$	9.00	2.25	1.00	0.56

t	40	50	60
$\dfrac{ds}{dt}$	72	75	77.14
$\dfrac{d^2s}{dt^2}$	0.36	0.25	0.18

As t increases, the velocity of the car increases at a diminishing rate (acceleration decreases).

43.

The degrees of the successive derivatives decrease by 1.

45.

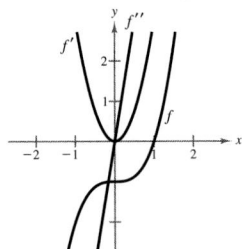

47. False. The product rule is $[f(x)g(x)]'$
   $= f'(x)g(x) + f(x)g'(x)$.

48. True   **49.** True   **50.** True

51. True   **52.** True

53. False. Let $f(x) = x^2$ and $g(x) = x^2 + 1$.

SECTION 2.7   (page 154)

Warm Up

1. $y = x^2 - 2x$ **2.** $y = \dfrac{x-3}{4}$

3. $y = 1, x \neq -6$ **4.** $y = -4, x \neq \pm\sqrt{3}$

5. $y = \pm\sqrt{5 - x^2}$ **6.** $y = \pm\sqrt{6 - x^2}$

7. $\frac{8}{3}$ **8.** $-\frac{1}{2}$ **9.** $\frac{5}{7}$ **10.** 1

1. $-\dfrac{y}{x}$ **3.** $-\dfrac{x}{y}$ **5.** $-\dfrac{1}{5}$ **7.** $-\dfrac{x}{y}, 0$

9. $-\dfrac{y}{x+1}, -\dfrac{1}{4}$ **11.** $\dfrac{2x}{3y^2}, \dfrac{4}{3}$

13. $\dfrac{y - 3x^2}{2y - x}, \dfrac{1}{2}$ **15.** $\dfrac{1 - 3x^2 y^3}{3x^3 y^2 - 1}, -1$

17. $-\sqrt{\dfrac{y}{x}}, -\dfrac{5}{4}$ **19.** $-\sqrt[3]{\dfrac{y}{x}}, -\dfrac{1}{2}$

21. $\dfrac{2xy - y^2 - x^2}{2xy - x^2}, -\dfrac{1}{8}$ **23.** $3x, 3$

25. $-\dfrac{4x}{9y}, -\dfrac{\sqrt{5}}{3}$ **27.** $-\dfrac{x}{y}, \dfrac{4}{3}$

29. $-\dfrac{9x}{16y}, -\dfrac{\sqrt{3}}{4}$

31. At $(5, 12)$: $5x + 12y - 169 = 0$
At $(-12, 5)$: $12x - 5y + 169 = 0$

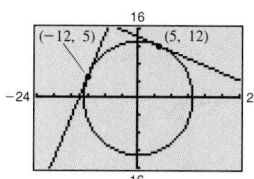

33. At $(1, \sqrt{5})$: $15x - 2\sqrt{5}\, y - 5 = 0$
At $(1, -\sqrt{5})$: $15x + 2\sqrt{5}\, y - 5 = 0$

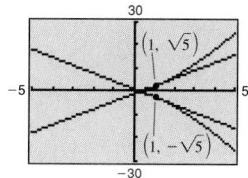

35. $\dfrac{1}{0.024x^3 + 0.04x}$ **37.** $-\dfrac{x^2}{100}$

39. (a) -2

(b)

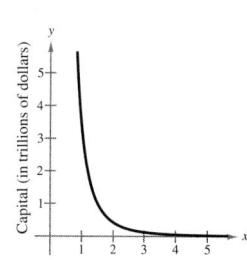

As more labor is used, less capital is available.
As more capital is used, less labor is available.

SECTION 2.8   (page 162)

> **Warm Up**
>
> **1.** $A = \pi r^2$ **2.** $V = \frac{4}{3}\pi r^3$ **3.** $S = 6s^2$
>
> **4.** $V = s^3$ **5.** $V = \frac{1}{3}\pi r^2 h$ **6.** $A = \frac{1}{2}bh$
>
> **7.** $-\dfrac{x}{y}$ **8.** $\dfrac{2x - 3y}{3x}$ **9.** $-\dfrac{2x + y}{x + 2}$
>
> **10.** $-\dfrac{y^2 - y + 1}{2xy - 2y - x}$

1. (a) 62 **(b)** $\frac{32}{85}$ **3. (a)** $-\frac{5}{8}$ **(b)** $\frac{3}{2}$

5. (a) 24π in.^{2}/min   **(b)** 96π in.^{2}/min

7. If $\dfrac{dr}{dt}$ is constant, $\dfrac{dA}{dt} = 2\pi r \dfrac{dr}{dt}$
and thus is proportional to r.

9. (a) $\dfrac{5}{\pi}$ ft/min   **(b)** $\dfrac{5}{4\pi}$ ft/min

11. $\dfrac{4}{45\pi}$ ft/min   **13. (a)** 9 cm^3/sec   **(b)** 900 cm^3/sec

15. (a) -12 cm/min   **(b)** 0 cm/min   **(c)** 4 cm/min
(d) 12 cm/min

17. (a) $-\frac{7}{12}$ ft/sec   **(b)** $-\frac{3}{2}$ ft/sec   **(c)** $-\frac{48}{7}$ ft/sec

19. (a) -750 mi/hr   **(b)** 20 min

21. -8.33 ft/sec   **23.** 650 per week

25. (a) 53.88 million per year
(b) 165 million per year

CHAPTER 2 REVIEW EXERCISES   (page 166)

1. -2 **3.** 0

5. $t = 7$: slope ≈ 600 million per year (revenues are increasing)
$t = 10$: slope ≈ -700 million per year (revenues are decreasing)

7. -3 **9.** $\dfrac{1}{4}$ **11.** 7 **13.** $-\dfrac{1}{(x - 5)^2}$

15. -5 **17.** $\frac{1}{6}$ **19.** $y = -2x + 6$ **21.** 1

23. 0 **25.** 0 **27.** $5x^4$ **29.** $\dfrac{1}{2\sqrt{x}}$ **31.** $12x^3$

33. $-\dfrac{4}{3t^3}$ **35.** $44x^3 - 10x$ **37.** $\dfrac{x + 1}{2x^{3/2}}$

39. Average rate of change: 4
Instantaneous rate of change when $x = 0$: 3
Instantaneous rate of change when $x = 1$: 5

41. (a) 82.82 million per year
(b) 1986: -12.18 million per year
1990: -790.82 million per year
(c) Revenues were decreasing in 1986 and 1990, but grew during the period 1987–1989.

43. (a) $s(t) = -16t^2 + 276$ **(b)** -32 ft/sec
(c) $t = 2$: -64 ft/sec   **(d)** 4.15 sec
$t = 3$: -96 ft/sec
(e) 132.8 ft/sec

45. $R = 27.50x$ **47.** $\dfrac{dC}{dx} = 320$
$C = 15x + 2500$
$P = 12.50 - 2500$

49. $\dfrac{dR}{dx} = \dfrac{35(x-4)}{2(x-2)^{3/2}}$

51. $\dfrac{dP}{dx} = -0.0006x^2 + 12x - 1$ **53.** $15x^2(1 - x^2)$

55. $16x^3 - 33x^2 + 12x$ **57.** $-\dfrac{2(3x^2 - 5x - 3)}{(x^2 + 1)^2}$

59. $\dfrac{4t^5 - 4t^3 + 2t^2 + 1}{t^2(t^3 - 1)^2}$ **61.** $30x(5x^2 + 2)^2$

63. $-\dfrac{1}{(x+1)^{3/2}}$ **65.** $\dfrac{2x^2 + 1}{\sqrt{x^2 + 1}}$

67. $\dfrac{2t^2 + t + 1}{\sqrt{t^2 + 1}}$ **69.** $32x(1 - 4x^2)$

71. $18x^5(x+1)(2x+3)^2$ **73.** $x(x-1)^4(7x - 2)$

75. $\dfrac{3(9t + 5)}{2\sqrt{3t + 1}(1 - 3t)^3}$

77. (a) $t = 1$: -6.63 $t = 3$: -6.5
$t = 5$: -4.33 $t = 10$: -1.36
(b)

The rate of decrease is approaching zero.

79. 6 **81.** $-\dfrac{120}{x^6}$ **83.** $\dfrac{35x^{3/2}}{2}$ **85.** $\dfrac{2}{x^{2/3}}$

87. (a) $s(t) = -16t^2 + 5t + 30$ **(b)** 1.534 sec
(c) -44.09 ft/sec   **(d)** -32 ft/sec^2

89. $-\dfrac{2x + 3y}{3(x + y^2)}$ **91.** $\dfrac{x}{y}$ **93.** $\dfrac{3x^2 - 2xy + y}{x^2 - x + 4y}$

95. $-\dfrac{4y^{1/2}}{9x^{2/3}}$ **97.** $\dfrac{1}{64}$ ft/min

SAMPLE POST-GRAD EXAM QUESTIONS   (page 170)

1. (c)   **2.** (b)   **3.** (b)
4. (a)   **5.** (c)   **6.** (a)

CHAPTER 3

SECTION 3.1   (page 179)

Warm Up

1. $x = 0$, $x = 8$ **2.** $x = 0$, $x = 24$
3. $x = \pm 5$ **4.** $x = 0$ **5.** $(-\infty, 3) \cup (3, \infty)$
6. $(-\infty, 1)$ **7.** $(-\infty, -2) \cup (-2, 5) \cup (5, \infty)$
8. $\left(-\sqrt{3}, \sqrt{3}\right)$
9. $x = -2$: $-\dfrac{103}{3}$ **10.** $x = -2$: $-\dfrac{7}{9}$
$x = 0$: $\dfrac{1}{3}$ $x = 0$: 3
$x = 2$: -13 $x = 2$: $-\dfrac{1}{3}$

1. $f'(-1) = -\dfrac{8}{25}$ **3.** $f'(-3) = -\dfrac{2}{3}$
$f'(0) = 0$ $f'(-2)$ undefined
$f'(1) = \dfrac{8}{25}$ $f'(-1) = \dfrac{2}{3}$

5. Increasing on $(-\infty, -1)$
Decreasing on $(-1, \infty)$

7. Increasing on $(-1, 0)$ and $(1, \infty)$
Decreasing on $(-\infty, -1)$ and $(0, 1)$

9. No critical numbers
Increasing on $(-\infty, \infty)$

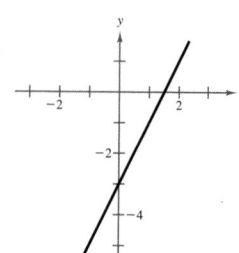

11. Critical number: $x = 1$
Increasing on $(-\infty, 1)$
Decreasing on $(1, \infty)$

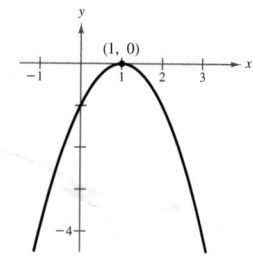

13. Critical number: $x = \frac{5}{2}$
Decreasing on $\left(-\infty, \frac{5}{2}\right)$
Increasing on $\left(\frac{5}{2}, \infty\right)$

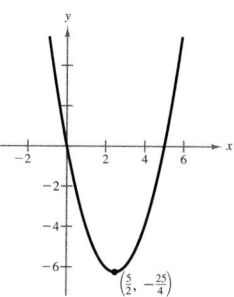

15. Critical numbers: $x = 0, x = 4$
Increasing on $(-\infty, 0)$ and $(4, \infty)$
Decreasing on $(0, 4)$

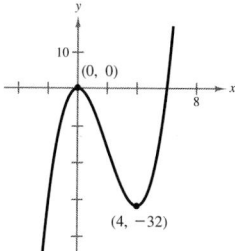

17. Critical number: $x = -1$
Decreasing on $(-\infty, \infty)$

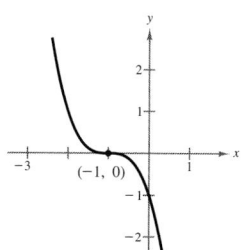

19. Critical number: $x = 1$
Increasing on $(-\infty, 1)$
Decreasing on $(1, \infty)$

21. Critical numbers: $x = -1, x = -\frac{5}{3}$
Increasing on $\left(-\infty, -\frac{5}{3}\right)$ and $(-1, \infty)$
Decreasing on $\left(-\frac{5}{3}, -1\right)$

23. Critical number: $x = 0$
Decreasing on $(-\infty, 0)$
Increasing on $(0, \infty)$

25. Critical numbers: $x = 0, x = \frac{3}{2}$
Decreasing on $\left(-\infty, \frac{3}{2}\right)$
Increasing on $\left(\frac{3}{2}, \infty\right)$

27. Domain: $(-\infty, 3]$
Critical numbers: $x = 2, x = 3$
Increasing on $(-\infty, 2)$
Decreasing on $(2, 3)$

29. Critical numbers: $x = 2, x = -2$
Decreasing on $(-\infty, -2)$ and $(2, \infty)$
Increasing on $(-2, 2)$

31. Critical numbers: $x = -1, x = 1$
Discontinuity: $x = 0$
Increasing on $(-\infty, -1)$ and $(1, \infty)$
Decreasing on $(-1, 0)$ and $(0, 1)$

33. No critical numbers
Discontinuities: $x = \pm 4$
Increasing on $(-\infty, -4), (-4, 4)$, and $(4, \infty)$

35. Critical number: $x = 0$
Increasing on $(-\infty, 0)$
Decreasing on $(0, \infty)$

37. (a) Decreasing on $[1, 4.10)$
Increasing on $(4.10, \infty)$
(b)

(c) $C = 900$ when $x = 2$ and $x = 15$.
Use an order size of $x = 4$, which will minimize the cost C.

39. Moving upward on $(0, 3)$
Moving downward on $(3, 6)$

41. (a)

(b) Increasing on $(0, 18.9)$
Decreasing on $(18.9, 21)$

43. (a)

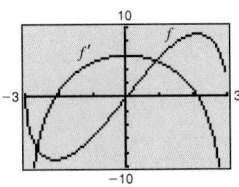

(b) $x = \pm\dfrac{3\sqrt{2}}{2}$

(c) $f' > 0$ on $\left(-\dfrac{3\sqrt{2}}{2}, \dfrac{3\sqrt{2}}{2}\right)$

$f' < 0$ on $\left(-3, -\dfrac{3\sqrt{2}}{2}\right), \left(\dfrac{3\sqrt{2}}{2}, 3\right)$

f is decreasing when $f' < 0$, and f is increasing when $f' > 0$.

SECTION 3.2   (page 189)

> **Warm Up**
>
> **1.** $0, \pm\frac{1}{2}$ **2.** $-2, 5$ **3.** 1 **4.** $0, 125$
> **5.** Negative   **6.** Positive
> **7.** Positive   **8.** Negative
> **9.** Increasing   **10.** Decreasing

1. Relative maximum: $(1, 5)$
3. Relative minimum: $(3, -9)$
5. Relative maximum: $\left(\frac{2}{3}, \frac{28}{9}\right)$
   Relative minimum: $(1, 3)$
7. No relative extrema
9. Relative maximum: $(0, 15)$
   Relative minimum: $(4, -17)$
11. Relative minimum: $\left(\frac{3}{2}, -\frac{27}{16}\right)$
13. No relative extrema
15. Relative minimum: $(0, 0)$
17. Relative maximum: $(-1, -2)$
   Relative minimum: $(1, 2)$
19. Relative maximum: $(0, 4)$
21. Minimum: $(2, 2)$ **23.** Maximum: $(0, 5)$
   Maximum: $(-1, 8)$ Minimum: $(3, -13)$

25. Minima: $(-1, -4)$ and $(2, -4)$
   Maxima: $(0, 0)$ and $(3, 0)$
27. Minimum: $(0, 0)$ **29.** Maximum: $(2, 1)$
   Maximum: $(-1, 5)$ Minimum: $(0, \frac{1}{3})$
31.

33.

Maximum: $(5, 7)$ Maximum: $(1, 4.7)$
Minimum: $(2.69, -5.55)$ Minimum: $(0.44, -1.06)$
35. Absolute minimum: $(0, 0)$
   Absolute maximum: $(1, 2)$
37. Absolute minimum: $(2, 1)$
39. $\left| f''\left(\dfrac{\sqrt{3}}{3}\right) \right| = \dfrac{40\sqrt{3}}{3}$
41. $\left| f^{(4)}\left(\frac{1}{2}\right) \right| = 360$ **43.** 82 units   **45.** \$2.10
47. 1981
   There were approximately 95 males for every 100 females in 1981.

SECTION 3.3   (page 198)

> **Warm Up**
>
> **1.** $f''(x) = 48x^2 - 54x$
> **2.** $g''(s) = 12s^2 - 18s + 2$
> **3.** $g''(x) = 56x^6 + 120x^4 + 72x^2 + 8$
> **4.** $f''(x) = \dfrac{4}{9(x-3)^{2/3}}$
> **5.** $h''(x) = \dfrac{15}{2x^5}$ **6.** $f''(x) = -\dfrac{42}{(3x+2)^3}$
> **7.** $x = \pm\dfrac{\sqrt{3}}{3}$ **8.** $x = 0, 3$ **9.** $t = \pm 4$
> **10.** $x = 0, \pm 5$

1. Concave upward on $(-\infty, \infty)$
3. Concave upward on $\left(-\infty, -\frac{1}{2}\right)$
   Concave downward on $\left(-\frac{1}{2}, \infty\right)$

5. Concave upward on $(-\infty, -2)$ and $(2, \infty)$
   Concave downward on $(-2, 2)$
7. Relative maximum: $(3, 9)$
9. Relative minimum: $(5, 0)$
11. Relative maximum: $(1, 3)$
    Relative minimum: $(\frac{7}{3}, 1.\overline{814})$
13. Relative minimum: $(3, -25)$
15. Relative minimum: $(0, -3)$
17. Relative maximum: $(-2, -4)$
    Relative minimum: $(2, 4)$
19. Sign of $f'(x)$ on $(0, 2)$ is positive.
    Sign of $f''(x)$ on $(0, 2)$ is positive.
21. Sign of $f'(x)$ on $(0, 2)$ is negative.
    Sign of $f''(x)$ on $(0, 2)$ is negative.
23. $(3, 0)$ 25. $(1, 0), (3, -16)$
27. No inflection points   29. $\left(\frac{3}{2}, -\frac{1}{16}\right), (2, 0)$
31. Relative maximum: $(-2, 16)$
    Relative minimum: $(2, -16)$
    Point of inflection: $(0, 0)$

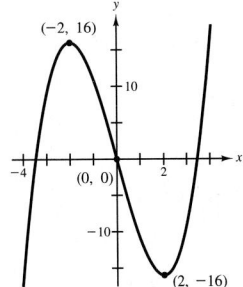

33. Point of inflection: $(2, 8)$

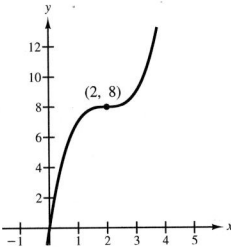

35. Relative maximum: $(0, 0)$
    Relative minima: $(\pm 2, -4)$
    Points of inflection: $\left(\pm\dfrac{2}{\sqrt{3}}, -\dfrac{20}{9}\right)$

35. (*continued*)

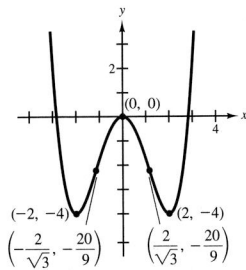

37. Relative maximum: $(-1, 0)$
    Relative minimum: $(1, -4)$
    Point of inflection: $(0, -2)$

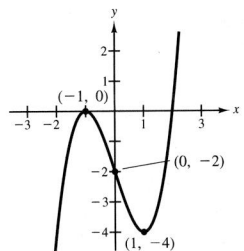

39. Relative minimum: $(-2, -2)$

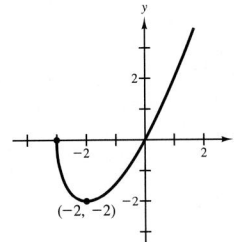

41. Relative maximum: $(0, 4)$
    Points of inflection: $\left(\pm\dfrac{\sqrt{3}}{3}, 3\right)$

43.

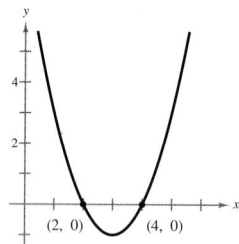

45. (a) f': Positive on $(-\infty, 0)$

f: Increasing on $(-\infty, 0)$

(b) f': Negative on $(0, \infty)$

f: Decreasing on $(0, \infty)$

(c) f': Not increasing

f: Not concave upward

(d) f': Decreasing on $(-\infty, \infty)$

f: Concave downward on $(-\infty, \infty)$

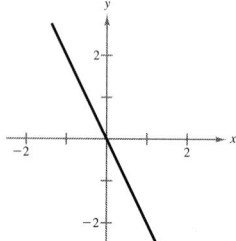

47. $(200, 320)$ **49.** $(3, 36)$ **51.** 100 units

53. $x = 50$ units   **55.** 8:30 P.M.

57. $\sqrt{3} \approx 1.732$ years   **59.**

61.

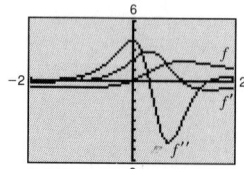

Relative maximum: $(1, 2)$

Relative minimum: $(-1, -\frac{2}{3})$

Points of inflection: $(-1.88, -0.59)$,

$(0.35, 0.90), (1.53, 1.69)$

63.

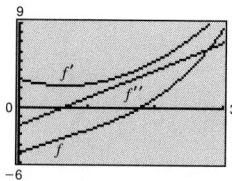

Relative maximum: $(3, 8.5)$

Relative minimum: $(0, -5)$

Point of inflection: $\left(\frac{2}{3}, -3.2963\right)$

65.

SECTION 3.4   (page 207)

Warm Up

1. $x + \frac{1}{2}y = 12$ **2.** $2xy = 24$ **3.** $xy = 24$

4. $\sqrt{(x_2 - x_1)^2 + (y_2 - y_1)^2} = 10$

5. $x = -3$ **6.** $x = -\frac{2}{3}, 1$ **7.** $x = \pm 5$

8. $x = 4$ **9.** $x = \pm 1$ **10.** $x = \pm 3$

1. 55 and 55   **3.** 9, 18   **5.** $\sqrt{192}$ and $\sqrt{192}$

7. 1   **9. (a)** 99 in.^{3} **(b)** 125 in.^{3} **(c)** 117 in.^{3}

11. Length = width = 25 ft   **13.** $x = 25$ ft, $y = \frac{100}{3}$ ft

15. 16 in.^{3} **17.** $x = 5$ m, $y = \frac{10}{3}$ m

19. Length: 50 m, width: $\dfrac{100}{\pi}$ m

21. $x = 3$, $y = \frac{3}{2}$

23. Length: $2x = \dfrac{10}{\sqrt{2}} \approx 7.07$

Width: $y = \dfrac{5}{\sqrt{2}} \approx 3.54$

25. $r \approx 1.51$ in., $h = 2r \approx 3.02$ in.

27. $\left(\pm\sqrt{\frac{5}{2}}, \frac{7}{2}\right)$

29. 18 in. $\times$ 18 in. $\times$ 36 in.

31. Radius: $\dfrac{8}{\pi + 4}$

Side of square: $\dfrac{16}{\pi + 4}$

33. $x = 1$ mi   **35.** $w = 8\sqrt{3}$ in., $h = 8\sqrt{6}$ in.

37. $10\sqrt{2} \times 5\sqrt{2}$

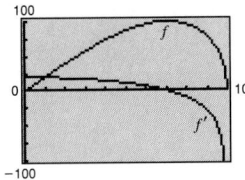

SECTION 3.5   (page 217)

> Warm Up
>
> **1.** 1   **2.** 1.2   **3.** 2   **4.** $\frac{1}{2}$
>
> **5.** $\dfrac{dC}{dx} = 1.2 + 0.006x$ **6.** $\dfrac{dP}{dx} = 0.02x + 11$
>
> **7.** $\dfrac{dR}{dx} = 14 - \dfrac{x}{1000}$ **8.** $\dfrac{dR}{dx} = 3.4 - \dfrac{x}{750}$
>
> **9.** $\dfrac{dP}{dx} = -1.4x + 7$ **10.** $\dfrac{dC}{dx} = 4.2 + 0.003x^2$

1. 2000 units   **3.** 200 units   **5.** 80 units

7. 200 units   **9.** $60   **11.** $69.68   **13.** 3 units

15. (a) $80   (b) $45.93

17. Maximum profit: $10,000

Point of diminishing returns: $5833.33

19. 200 units   **21.** $50

23. Line should run from the power station to a point across the river $3/(2\sqrt{7}) \approx 0.57$ mi downstream.

25. 77.46 mph

27. $-\frac{17}{3}$, elastic   **29.** $-\frac{1}{3}$, inelastic

31. $-\frac{3}{2}$, elastic

33. (a) -6.83% (b) -1.37 (c) $-\frac{4}{3}$

(d) $R = 20p - 2p^3$, $x = \frac{40}{3}$, $p = \sqrt{\frac{10}{3}} \approx \$1.83$

35. (a) $-\dfrac{14}{9}$ (b) $x = \dfrac{32}{3}$, $p = \dfrac{4\sqrt{3}}{3}$

37. No, $\eta = -\frac{1}{3}$, demand is inelastic

39. (a) 1987

(b) 1994

(c) 1987: $6006.6 million

1994: $8050.6 million

(d)

41. (a) Demand function   (b) Cost function

(c) Revenue function   (d) Profit function

SECTION 3.6   (page 230)

> Warm Up
>
> **1.** 3   **2.** 1   **3.** -11 **4.** 4   **5.** 0   **6.** 1
>
> **7.** $\overline{C} = \dfrac{150}{x} + 3$ **8.** $\overline{C} = \dfrac{1900}{x} + 1.7 + 0.002x$
>
> $\dfrac{dC}{dx} = 3$ $\dfrac{dC}{dx} = 1.7 + 0.004x$
>
> **9.** $\overline{C} = 0.005x + 0.5 + \dfrac{1375}{x}$
>
> $\dfrac{dC}{dx} = 0.01x + 0.5$
>
> **10.** $\overline{C} = \dfrac{760}{x} + 0.05$
>
> $\dfrac{dC}{dx} = 0.05$

1. Vertical: $x = 0$ **3.** Vertical: $x = -1$, $x = 2$

Horizontal: $y = 1$ Horizontal: $y = 1$

5. Vertical: $x = -1$, $x = 1$ **7.** Vertical: $x = \pm 2$

Horizontal: none   Horizontal: $y = \frac{1}{2}$

9. f   **10.** b   **11.** c   **12.** a   **13.** e

14. d   **15.** ∞ **17.** $-\infty$ **19.** $-\infty$

21. $-\infty$ **23.** $\frac{2}{3}$ **25.** 0   **27.** $-\infty$

29. ∞ **31.** 5

33.

x	10^0	10^1	10^2	10^3
$f(x)$	2.000	0.348	0.101	0.032

x	10^4	10^5	10^6
$f(x)$	0.010	0.003	0.001

$$\lim_{x \to \infty} \frac{x+1}{x\sqrt{x}} = 0$$

35.

x	-10^6	-10^4	-10^2	10^0
$f(x)$	-2	-2	-1.9996	0.8944

x	10^2	10^4	10^6
$f(x)$	1.9996	2	2

$$\lim_{x \to -\infty} \frac{2x}{\sqrt{x^2+4}} = -2, \quad \lim_{x \to \infty} \frac{2x}{\sqrt{x^2+4}} = 2$$

37.   **39.**

41.   **43.**

45.   **47.**

49.   **51.**

53.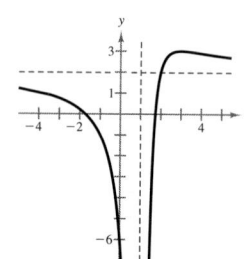

55. **(a)** \$47.05, \$5.92   **(b)** \$1.35
57. **(a)** \$176 million   **(b)** \$528 million
   (c) \$1584 million   **(d)** ∞
59. a **61.** **(a)** 5 years: 153   **(b)** 400
            10 years: 215
            25 years: 294
63. Horizontal asymptotes: $y = \pm\frac{3}{2}$

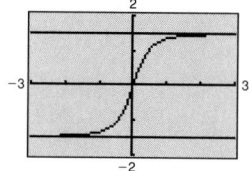

SECTION 3.7   (page 240)

Warm Up

1. Vertical: $x = 0$ **2.** Vertical: $x = 2$
   Horizontal: $y = 0$ Horizontal: $y = 0$
3. Vertical: $x = -3$ **4.** Vertical: $x = 1, x = 3$
   Horizontal: $y = 40$ Horizontal: $y = 1$
5. Decreasing on $(-\infty, -2)$
   Increasing on $(-2, \infty)$
6. Increasing on $(-\infty, -4)$
   Decreasing on $(-4, \infty)$

Warm Up *(continued)*

7. Increasing on $(-\infty, -1)$ and $(1, \infty)$
   Decreasing on $(-1, 1)$
8. Decreasing on $(-\infty, 0)$ and $\left(\sqrt[3]{2}, \infty\right)$
   Increasing on $\left(0, \sqrt[3]{2}\right)$
9. Increasing on $(-\infty, 1)$ and $(1, \infty)$
10. Decreasing on $(-\infty, -3)$ and $\left(\frac{1}{3}, \infty\right)$
    Increasing on $\left(-3, \frac{1}{3}\right)$

1.

3.

5.

7.

9.

11.

13.

15.

17.

19.

21.

23.

25.

27.

29.
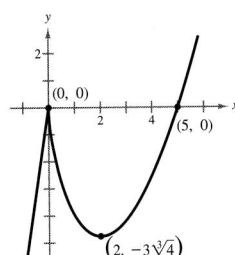

31. Domain: $(-\infty, 2)$, $(2, \infty)$

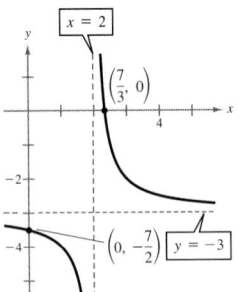

33. Domain: $(-\infty, -1)$, $(-1, 1)$, $(1, \infty)$

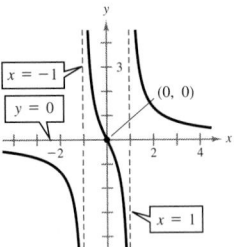

35. Domain: $(-\infty, 4]$ **37.** Domain: $(-\infty, 0)$, $(0, \infty)$

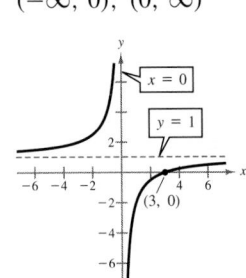

39. Domain: $(-\infty, 1)$, $(1, \infty)$

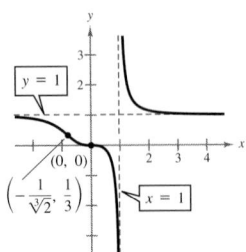

41. $f(x) = -x^3 + x^2 + x + 1$ **43.** $f(x) = x^3 + 1$

45.

47.

49.

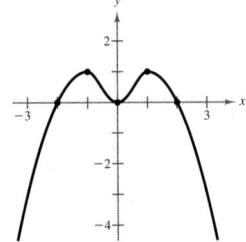

51. (a) $C = 0.24s + \dfrac{900}{s}$, $40 \le s \le 65$

(b)

53.

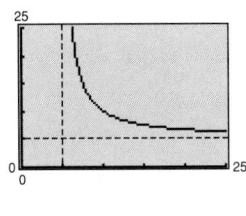

SECTION 3.8   (page 248)

Warm Up

1. $\dfrac{dC}{dx} = 0.18x$ **2.** $\dfrac{dR}{dx} = 1.25 + 0.03\sqrt{x}$

3. $\dfrac{dP}{dx} = -\dfrac{0.01}{\sqrt[3]{x^2}} + 1.4$ **4.** $\dfrac{dA}{dx} = \dfrac{\sqrt{3}}{2}x$

5. $\dfrac{dC}{dr} = 2\pi$ **6.** $\dfrac{dS}{dr} = 8\pi r$

7. $A = \pi r^2$ **8.** $A = x^2$

9. $V = x^3$ **10.** $V = \frac{4}{3}\pi r^3$

1. $6x \, dx$ **3.** $12(4x - 1)^2 \, dx$ **5.** $\dfrac{x}{\sqrt{x^2 + 1}} \, dx$

7. $\dfrac{1 - 2x^2}{\sqrt{1 - x^2}} \, dx$ **9.** $\dfrac{-8}{(1 - 3x)^2} \, dx$

11. 0.1005 **13.** -0.013245

15. $dy = 0.3$ **17.** $dy = -0.04$

      $\Delta y = 0.331$ $\Delta y \approx -0.0394$

19.

$dx = \Delta x$	dy	Δy	$\Delta y - dy$	$\dfrac{dy}{\Delta x}$
1.000	4.000	5.000	1.000	0.800
0.500	2.000	2.250	0.250	0.889
0.100	0.400	0.410	0.010	0.976
0.010	0.040	0.040	0.000	0.998
0.001	0.004	0.004	0.000	1.000

21.

$dx = \Delta x$	dy	Δy	$\Delta y - dy$	$\dfrac{dy}{\Delta x}$
1.000	80.000	211.000	131.000	0.379
0.500	40.000	65.656	25.656	0.609
0.100	8.000	8.841	0.841	0.905
0.010	0.800	0.808	0.008	0.990
0.001	0.080	0.080	0.000	0.999

23. (a) $\Delta p = -0.25 = dp$ **(b)** $\Delta p = -0.25 = dp$

25. $\$5.20$ **27.** $-\$1250$

29. $R = -\frac{1}{3}x^2 + 100x$, $\$6$

31. $P = -\frac{1}{2000}x^2 + 23x - 275,000; \; -\$5$

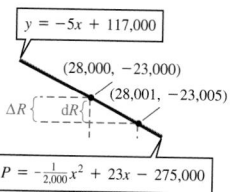

33. (a) $d\,A = 2x \, \Delta x, \; \Delta A = 2x \, \Delta x + (\Delta x)^2$

(b)

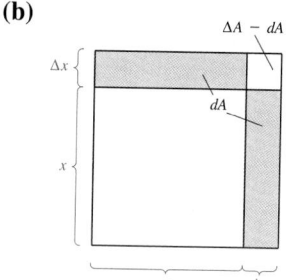

35. $\pm\frac{5}{2}\pi$ in.^{2}, $\pm\frac{1}{40}$

37. $\pm 2.88\pi$ in.^{3}, ± 0.01 **39.** $\$1160$

CHAPTER 3 REVIEW EXERCISES   (page 252)

1. $x = 1$ **3.** $x = 0, x = 1$

5. Increasing on $\left(-\frac{1}{2}, \infty\right)$

    Decreasing on $\left(-\infty, -\frac{1}{2}\right)$

7. Increasing on $(-\infty, 3) \cup (3, \infty)$

9. (a) $(0.23, 6.15)$

(b) $(0, 0.23)$, $(6.15, 12)$

(c) Maximum daily temperature is rising from early January to early June

(d)

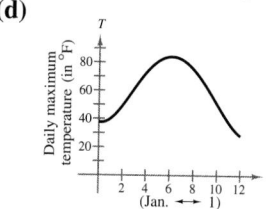

11. Relative maximum: $(0, -2)$

     Relative minimum: $(1, -4)$

13. Relative minimum: $(8, -52)$

15. Relative maxima: $(-1, 1)$, $(1, 1)$

     Relative minimum: $(0, 0)$

17. Relative maximum: $(0, 6)$

19. Relative maximum: $(0, 0)$
Relative minimum: $(4, 8)$

21. Maximum: $(0, 6)$
Minimum: $\left(-\frac{5}{2}, -\frac{1}{4}\right)$

23. Maxima: $(-2, 17)$, $(4, 17)$
Minima: $(-4, -15)$, $(2, -15)$

25. Maximum: $(2, 26)$
Minimum: $(1, -1)$

27. Maximum: $(1, 1)$
Minimum: $(-1, -1)$

29. (a) $253, 1990
(b) $176.08, 1984

31. Concave upward: $(2, \infty)$
Concave downward: $(-\infty, -2)$

33. Concave upward: $\left(-\dfrac{2}{\sqrt{3}}, \dfrac{2}{\sqrt{3}}\right)$
Concave downward: $\left(-\infty, -\dfrac{2}{\sqrt{3}}\right)$ and $\left(\dfrac{2}{\sqrt{3}}, \infty\right)$

35. $(0, 0)$, $(4, -128)$

37. $(0, 0)$, $(1.0652, 4.5244)$, $(2.5348, 3.5246)$

39. Relative maximum: $\left(-\sqrt{3}, 6\sqrt{3}\right)$
Relative minimum: $\left(\sqrt{3}, -6\sqrt{3}\right)$

41. Relative maximum: $(-4, 0)$
Relative minimum: $(-2, -108)$

43. $\left(50, 166\frac{2}{3}\right)$ **45.** 13, 13

47. (a) $54,607
(b) $5000

49. (a) $x = 3$
(b) $x = \sqrt{3}$

51. $N = 85$ (maximizes revenue)   **53.** 125

55. Elastic for $x > 0$

57. Vertical asymptote: $x = 4$
Horizontal asymptote: $y = 2$

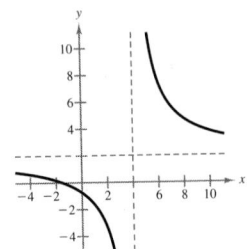

59. Vertical asymptote: $x = 0$
Horizontal asymptote: $y = -3$

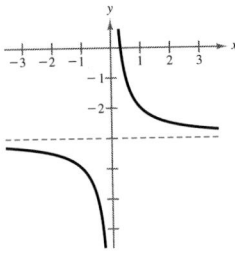

61. Vertical asymptotes: $x = 1, x = 4$
Horizontal asymptote: $y = 0$

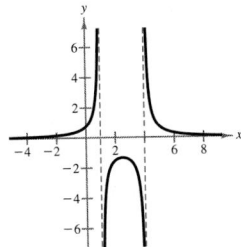

63. $-\infty$ **65.** $\frac{5}{2}$ **67.** $-\infty$

69. (a)

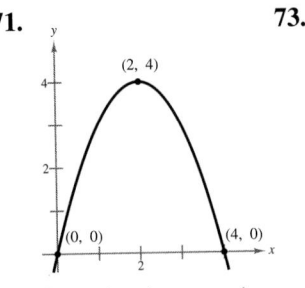

(b) $\displaystyle\lim_{s \to \infty} T = 0.37$

71.

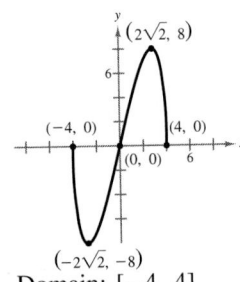

Domain: $(-\infty, \infty)$

73.

Domain: $[-4, 4]$

75.

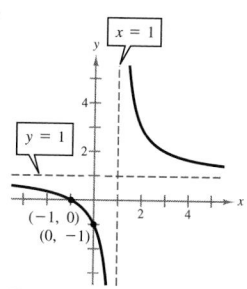

Domain: $(-\infty, 1)\cup(1, \infty)$

77.

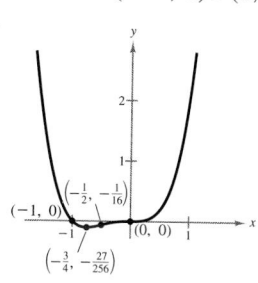

Domain: $(-\infty, \infty)$

79.

Domain: $(-\infty, \infty)$

81. $dy = 12x\,dx$ **83.** $dy = \dfrac{5}{3x^{4/3}}\,dx$ **85.** \$800

87. \$15.25   **89.** $dS = \pm 1.8\pi$ in.^{2}
$dV = \pm 8.1\pi$ in.^{3}

SAMPLE POST-GRAD EXAM QUESTIONS   (page 256)

1. (b)   **2.** (a)   **3.** (c)   **4.** (d)
5. (b)   **6.** (a)

CHAPTER 4

SECTION 4.1   (page 266)

Warm Up

1. Continuous on $(-\infty, \infty)$
2. Removable discontinuity at $x = 4$
3. 0   **4.** 0   **5.** 4   **6.** $\frac{1}{2}$ **7.** $\frac{3}{2}$
8. 6   **9.** 0   **10.** 0

1. (a) 625   (b) 9   (c) $16\sqrt{2}$ (d) 9
(e) 125   (f) 4

3. (a) 3125   (b) $\frac{1}{5}$ (c) 625   (d) $\frac{1}{125}$

5. (a) $\frac{1}{5}$ (b) 27   (c) 5   (d) 4096
7. (a) e^7 (b) e^{12} (c) $\dfrac{1}{e^6}$ (d) 1
9. 4   **11.** -2 **13.** 2   **15.** 16   **17.** $-\frac{1}{3}$
19. 9   **21.** e   **23.** e   **24.** c
25. a   **26.** f   **27.** d   **28.** b
29. $f(x) = 6^x$ **31.** $f(x) = 5^{-x}$

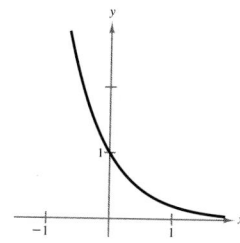

33. $y = 3^{-x^2}$ **35.** $y = 3^{-|x|}$

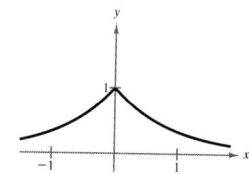

37. $s(t) = \dfrac{3^{-t}}{4}$ **39.** $h(x) = e^{x-2}$

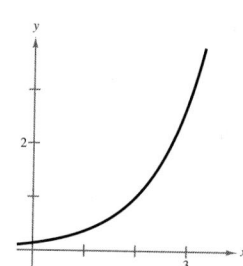

41. $N(t) = 500e^{-0.2t}$ **43.** $g(x) = \dfrac{2}{1 + e^{x^2}}$

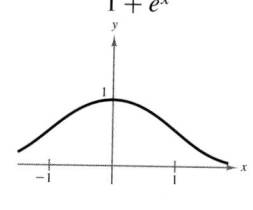

45.

n	1	2	4	12
A	1343.92	1346.86	1348.35	1349.35

n	365	Continuous Compounding
A	1349.84	1349.86

47.

n	1	2	4	12
A	3262.04	3290.66	3305.28	3315.15

n	365	Continuous Compounding
A	3319.95	3320.12

49.

t	1	10	20
P	96,078.94	67,032.00	44,932.90

t	30	40	50
P	30,119.42	20,189.65	13,533.53

51.

t	1	10	20
P	95,132.82	60,716.10	36,864.45

t	30	40	50
P	22,382.66	13,589.88	8251.24

53. (a) \$849.53
(b) \$421.12
$\lim\limits_{x \to \infty} p = 0$

55. (a) 0.1535   (b) 0.4866   (c) 0.8111

57. (a)
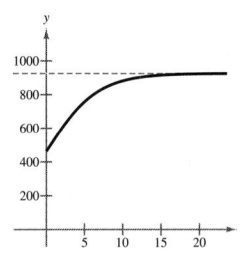
(b) $\lim\limits_{t \to \infty} \dfrac{925}{1 + e^{-0.3t}} = 925$

59. (a) 0.731   (b) 11
(c) $\lim\limits_{n \to \infty} \dfrac{0.83}{1 + e^{-0.2n}} = 0.83$

61.
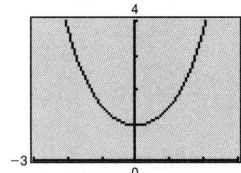
No horizontal asymptotes.
Continuous on the entire real line.

63.
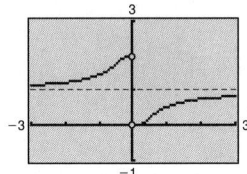
Horizontal asymptote: $y = 1$.
Discontinuous at $x = 0$.

SECTION 4.2   (page 275)

Warm Up

1. $\dfrac{1}{2}e^x(2x^2 - 1)$ 2. $\dfrac{e^x(x + 1)}{x}$

3. $e^x(x - e^x)$ 4. $e^{-x}(e^{2x} - x)$

5. $-\dfrac{6}{7x^3}$ 6. $6x - \dfrac{1}{6}$

7. $6(2x^2 - x + 6)$ 8. $\dfrac{t + 2}{2t^{3/2}}$

Warm Up *(continued)*

9. Relative maximum: $\left(-\dfrac{4\sqrt{3}}{3}, \dfrac{16\sqrt{3}}{9} \right)$

Relative minimum: $\left(\dfrac{4\sqrt{3}}{3}, -\dfrac{16\sqrt{3}}{9} \right)$

10. Relative maximum: $(0, 5)$

Relative minima: $(-1, 4),\ (1, 4)$

1. 3   **3.** -1 **5.** $4e^{4x}$

7. $2(x-1)e^{-2x+x^2}$ **9.** $-\dfrac{e^{1/x}}{x^2}$ **11.** $\dfrac{e^{\sqrt{x}}}{2\sqrt{x}}$

13. $e^{4x}(4x^2 + 2x + 4)$

15. $3(e^x - e^{-x})(e^{-x} + e^x)^2$

17. $-\dfrac{2(e^x - e^{-x})}{(e^x + e^{-x})^2}$ **19.** $xe^x + e^x + 4e^{-x}$

21. $\dfrac{dy}{dx} = \dfrac{1}{2}(-x - 1 - 2y)\ \left(\text{Equivalently, } \dfrac{dy}{dx} = -\dfrac{1}{2} \right)$

23. $6(3e^{3x} + 2e^{-2x})$ **25.** $5e^{-x} - 50e^{-5x}$

27. No relative extrema

No points of inflection

Horizontal asymptote to the right: $y = \frac{1}{2}$

Horizontal asymptote to the left: $y = 0$

Vertical asymptote: $x \approx -0.693$

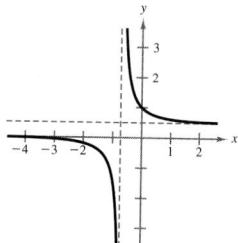

29. Relative minimum: $(0, 0)$

Relative maximum: $(2, 4e^{-2})$

Points of inflection: $(2 - \sqrt{2}, 0.191),$

$(2 + \sqrt{2}, 0.384)$

31.

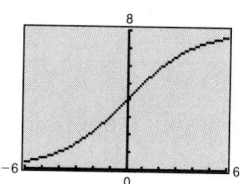

Asymptotes: $y = 0, y = 8$

33. (a)

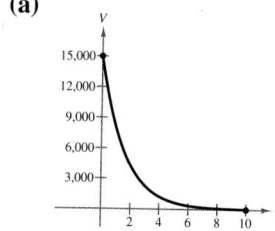

(b) $-\$5028.84$/year

(c) $-\$406.89$/year

(d) In this model, the initial rate of depreciation is greater than in a linear model.

35. (a)

(b) 80.3%

(c) $x \approx 1.1$ or approximately 1100 egg masses

37. (a) $\$433.31$/year   **(b)** $\$890.22$/year

(c) $\$21{,}839.26$/year

39. $t = 5 : 14.44$

$t = 10 : 3.63$

$t = 25 : 0.58$

41.

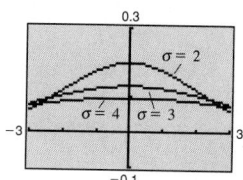

For larger σ, the graph becomes flatter.

SECTION 4.3 (page 283)

Warm Up

1. $\frac{1}{4}$ 2. 64   3. 1   4. $81e^4$
5. $x > -4$ 6. Any real number x
7. $x < -1$ and $x > 1$ 8. $x > 5$
9. $3462.03   10. $3374.65

---

1. $e^{0.6931\ldots} = 2$ 3. $e^{-1.6094\ldots} = 0.2$
5. $\ln 1 = 0$ 7. $\ln(0.0498\ldots) = -3$
9. c   10. d   11. b   12. a
13.

15.

17.

19.

21.

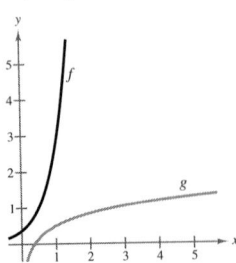

23. x^2 25. $5x + 2$ 27. $\sqrt{x}$
29. (a) 1.7917   (b) 0.4055   (c) 4.3944
    (d) 0.5493
31. $\ln 2 - \ln 3$ 33. $\ln x + \ln y + \ln z$
35. $\frac{1}{2} \ln(x^2 + 1)$

37. $\ln 2 + \ln x - \frac{1}{2} \ln(x + 1) - \frac{1}{2} \ln(x - 1)$
39. $\ln 3 + \ln x + \ln(x + 1) - 2 \ln(2x + 1)$
41. $\ln \dfrac{x - 2}{x + 2}$ 43. $\ln \dfrac{x^3 y^2}{z^4}$

45. $\ln \left[\dfrac{x(x + 3)}{x + 4} \right]^3$ 47. $\ln \left[\dfrac{x(x^2 + 1)}{x + 1} \right]^{3/2}$

49. $\ln \dfrac{(x - 1)^3}{x(x + 1)^2}$

51. $x = 4$ 53. $x = 1$
55. $x = \ln 4 - 1 \approx 0.3863$

57. $t = \dfrac{\ln 7 - \ln 3}{-0.2} \approx -4.2365$

59. $x = \dfrac{\ln 15}{2 \ln 5} \approx 0.8413$

61. $t = \dfrac{\ln 2}{\ln 1.07} \approx 10.2448$

63. $t = \dfrac{\ln 3}{12 \ln[1 + (0.07/12)]} \approx 15.740$

65. $t = -\ln \frac{4}{5} \approx 0.2231$
67. (a) 14.21 years   (b) 13.88 years
    (c) 13.87 years   (d) 13.86 years
69.

r	2%	4%	6%	8%
t	54.93	27.47	18.31	13.73

r	10%	12%	14%
t	10.99	9.16	7.85

71. 1999   73. 9370 years   75. 12,451 years
77. (a) 80   (b) 57.5   (c) 10 months
79.

x	y	$\dfrac{\ln x}{\ln y}$	$\ln \dfrac{x}{y}$	$\ln x - \ln y$
1	2	0	-0.6931	-0.6931
3	4	0.7925	-0.2877	-0.2877
10	5	1.4307	0.6931	0.6931
4	0.5	-2.0000	2.0794	2.0794

81.

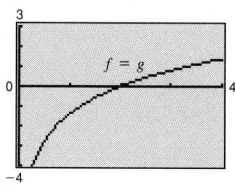

SECTION 4.4 (page 292)

> **Warm Up**
>
> **1.** $2\ln(x+1)$ **2.** $\ln x + \ln(x+1)$
> **3.** $\ln x - \ln(x+1)$ **4.** $3[\ln x - \ln(x-3)]$
> **5.** $\ln 4 + \ln x + \ln(x-7) - 2\ln x$
> **6.** $3\ln x + \ln(x+1) - \frac{1}{2}\ln(x-2)$
> **7.** $-\dfrac{y(y+y^x \ln y)}{x(y+y^x)}$ **8.** $-\dfrac{-3+2xy-y^2}{x(x-2y)}$
> **9.** $-12x + 2$ **10.** $-\dfrac{6}{x^4}$

1. 3   **3.** 2   **5.** $\dfrac{3}{2}$ **7.** $\dfrac{2}{x}$ **9.** $\dfrac{1}{x}$

11. $\dfrac{2(x^3-1)}{x(x^3-4)}$ **13.** $\dfrac{3}{x}(\ln x)^5$ **15.** $1 + \ln x$

17. $\dfrac{2x^2-1}{x(x^2-1)}$ **19.** $\dfrac{1-x^2}{x(x^2+1)}$ **21.** $\dfrac{2}{1-x^2}$

23. $\dfrac{1}{1-x^2}$ **25.** $\dfrac{1-2\ln x}{x^3}$ **27.** $-\dfrac{4}{x(4+x^2)}$

29. $\dfrac{2x}{2x^2-3}$ **31.** $e^{-x}\left(\dfrac{1}{x} - \ln x\right)$ **33.** $2x$

35. $e^{x(\ln 2)}$ **37.** $\dfrac{1}{\ln 4}\ln x$ **39.** 2

41. -0.63093 **43.** 1.49136 **45.** $(\ln 3)3^x$

47. $\dfrac{1}{x\ln 2}$ **49.** $(2\ln 4)4^{2x-3}$ **51.** $\dfrac{3}{(3x+7)\ln 3}$

53. $2x(\ln 10)10^{x^2}$ **55.** $2^x(1+x\ln 2)$ **57.** $\dfrac{2xy}{3-2y^2}$

59. $\dfrac{y(1-6x^2)}{1+y}$ **61.** $\dfrac{1}{2x}$ **63.** $(\ln 5)^2 5^x$

65. $2,\ y = 2x - 1$ **67.** $-\frac{8}{5},\ y = -\frac{8}{5}x - 4$

69. $\dfrac{1}{\ln 2},\ y = \dfrac{1}{\ln 2}x - \dfrac{1}{\ln 2}$

71. Relative minimum: $(1, 1)$

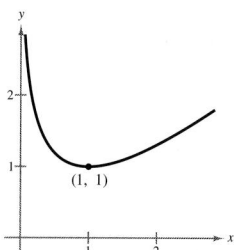

73. Relative maximum: $\left(e, \dfrac{1}{e}\right)$

Point of inflection: $\left(e^{3/2}, \dfrac{3}{2e^{3/2}}\right)$

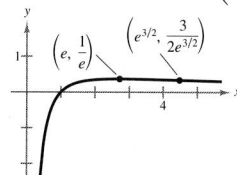

75. Relative minimum: $\left(\dfrac{1}{\sqrt{e}}, -\dfrac{1}{2e}\right)$

Point of inflection: $\left(\dfrac{1}{e^{3/2}}, -\dfrac{3}{2e^3}\right)$

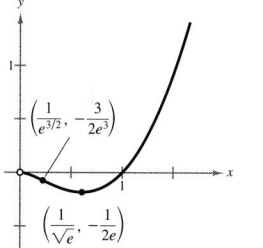

77. $-\dfrac{1}{p},\ -\dfrac{1}{10}$

79. $-\dfrac{1000p}{(p^2+1)[\ln(p^2+1)]^2},\ -4.65$

81. $p = 1000e^{-x}$

$\dfrac{dp}{dx} = -1000e^{-x}$

$p = 10,\ \dfrac{dp}{dx} = -10$

$\dfrac{dp}{dx}$ and $\dfrac{dx}{dp}$ are reciprocals of each other.

83. $e^{8/3} \approx 14.39$

85. (a)

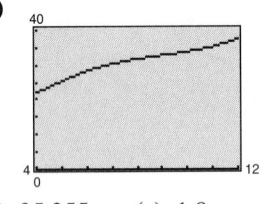

(b) 35,255   **(c)** 1.8

SECTION 4.5   (page 301)

Warm Up

1. $-\frac{1}{4} \ln 2$ **2.** $\frac{1}{5} \ln \frac{10}{3}$ **3.** $\frac{1}{3} \ln \frac{25}{16}$

4. $\frac{1}{20} \ln \frac{11}{16}$ **5.** $7.36e^{0.23t}$ **6.** $-33.6e^{-1.4t}$

7. $1.296e^{0.072t}$ **8.** $-0.025e^{-0.001t}$

9. 4   **10.** 12
---

1. $y = 2e^{0.1014t}$ **3.** $y = 4e^{-0.4159t}$

5. $y = 0.6687e^{0.4024t}$

7. $y = 10e^{2t}$, exponential growth

9. $y = 30e^{-4t}$, exponential decay

11. *Isotope: Ra^{226}*
   Half-life (in years): 1620
   Initial quantity: 10 grams
   Amount after 1000 years: 6.52 grams
   Amount after 10,000 years: 0.14 gram

13. *Isotope: C^{14}*
   Half-life (in years): 5730
   Initial quantity: 6.70 grams
   Amount after 1000 years: 5.94 grams
   Amount after 10,000 years: 2.00 grams

15. *Isotope: Pu^{239}*
   Half-life (in years): 24,360
   Initial quantity: 2.16 grams
   Amount after 1000 years: 2.10 grams
   Amount after 10,000 years: 1.63 grams

17. 68%   **19.** $\dfrac{5730(\ln 20 - \ln 3)}{\ln 2} \approx 15,682.8$ years

21. (a) 1350   **(b)** $\dfrac{5 \ln 2}{\ln 3} \approx 3.15$ hr   **(c)** No.

23. *Initial investment:* $1000
   Annual rate: 12%
   Time to double: 5.78 years
   Amount after 10 years: $3320.12
   Amount after 25 years: $20,085.54

25. *Initial investment:* $750
   Annual rate: 8.94%
   Time to double: 7.75 years
   Amount after 10 years: $1833.67
   Amount after 25 years: $7009.86

27. *Initial investment:* $500
   Annual rate: 9.50%
   Time to double: 7.30 years
   Amount after 10 years: $1292.85
   Amount after 25 years: $5375.51

29. (b) 6.17%

31.

Number of compoundings/yr	4	12
Effective yield	5.095%	5.116%

Number of compoundings/yr	365	Continuous
Effective yield	5.127%	5.127%

35. (a) $1061.0 million   **(b)** $874.9 million

37. (a) $S(t) = 30e^{-1.7918/t}$
   (b) $30e^{-0.35836} = 20.9646$ or 20,965 units
   (c)

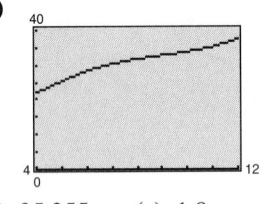

39. (a) $N(t) = 30(1 - e^{-0.0502t})$
   (b) $t = \dfrac{\ln 6}{0.0502} \approx 36$ days

41. (a) $C = \dfrac{45}{e^{1000[\ln(45/40)/(-200)]}} \approx 81.0915$

$k = \dfrac{\ln(45/40)}{-200} \approx -0.0005889$

(b) $x = \dfrac{200}{\ln(9/8)} \approx 1698$ units

$p = 45\left(\dfrac{9}{8}\right)^5 \dfrac{1}{e} \approx \$29.83$

43. 2078

45. (a) $I = e^{8.3 \ln 10} \approx 199{,}526{,}231.5$

(b) The intensity is squared when R is doubled.

(c) $\dfrac{1}{I \ln 10}$

CHAPTER 4 REVIEW EXERCISES (page 308)

1. 1024   **3.** $\frac{1}{625}$ **5.** 1

7. $\frac{1}{6}$ **9.** 4   **11.** $\frac{1}{2}$

13. 1950: 2492.4 million shares
1970: 14,677.0 million shares
1990: 86,428.2 million shares

15.   **17.**

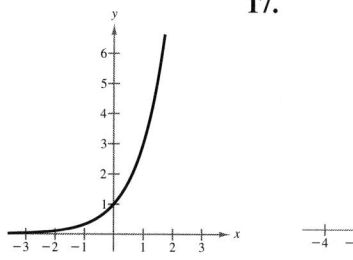

19. $7500

21. $f(2) \approx 5.4366$ **23.** $g(17) \approx 0.4005$

25. (a)

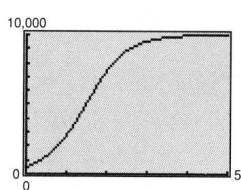

(b) $P \approx 1049$ fish

(c) Yes, P approaches 10,000 fish as t approaches ∞.

(d) The population is increasing most rapidly at the inflection point, which occurs around $t = 15$ months.

27.

n	1	2	4	12
A	$1216.65	$1218.99	$1220.19	$1221.00

n	365	Continuous Compounding
A	$1221.39	$1221.40

29. (b)

31. 1970: $A \approx 22.48$ years
1980: $A \approx 24.96$ years
1990: $A \approx 28.75$ years

33. $8xe^{x^2}$ **35.** $\dfrac{1 - 2x}{e^{2x}}$ **37.** $4e^{2x}$

39. $\dfrac{-10e^{2x}}{(1 + e^{2x})^2}$

41. No relative extrema
No points of inflection
$y = 0$ is a horizontal asymptote

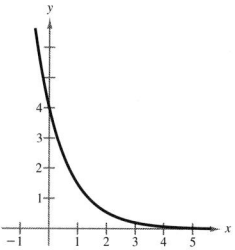

43. (2, 1.847) is a relative minimum.
No points of inflection.
$y = 0$ is a horizontal asymptote.
$x = 0$ is a vertical asymptote.

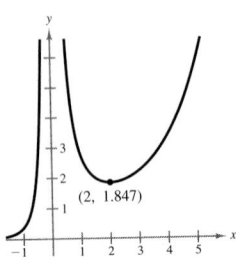

45. $e^{2.4849} \approx 12$ **47.** $\ln 4.4817 \approx 1.5$

49.   **51.**

 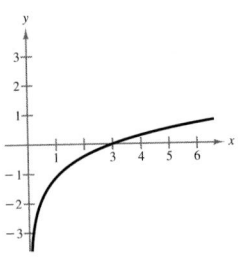

53. $\ln x + \frac{1}{2} \ln(x - 1)$

55. $3[\ln(1 - x) - \ln 3 - \ln x]$

57. 3   **59.** 1   **61.** $\dfrac{3 + \sqrt{13}}{2} \approx 3.3028$ **63.** $\dfrac{1}{4}$

65. (a)

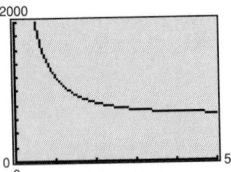

(b) A 30-year term has a smaller monthly payment, but takes more time to pay off, than a 20-year term.

67. $\dfrac{2}{x}$ **69.** $\sqrt{\ln x} + \dfrac{1}{2\sqrt{\ln x}}$

71. $\dfrac{1 - 3 \ln x}{x^4}$ **73.** $-2x$

75. No relative extrema   **77.** No relative extrema
No points of inflection   No points of inflection

 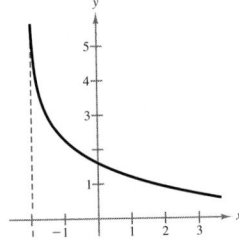

79. 2   **81.** 0   **83.** 1.4307   **85.** 1.5

87. $\dfrac{2}{(2x - 1) \ln 3}$ **89.** $-\dfrac{2}{x \ln 2}$

91. (a) $t = 2$: \$11,250   **(b)** $t = 1$:
  -4315.23 dollars/year
  $t = 4$:
  -1820.49 dollars/year

  (c) $t \approx 4.8$ years

93. $y = 500e^{-0.01277t}$ **95.** 27.9 yrs
97. \$667.4 million

SAMPLE POST-GRAD EXAM QUESTIONS (page 312)

1. (b)   **2.** (c)   **3.** (a)   **4.** (c)
5. (d)   **6.** (a)   **7.** (b)

CHAPTER 5

SECTION 5.1   (page 322)

Warm Up

1. $x^{-1/2}$ **2.** $(2x)^{4/3}$ **3.** $5^{1/2}x^{3/2} + x^{5/2}$

4. $x^{-1/2} + x^{-2/3}$ **5.** $(x + 1)^{5/2}$ **6.** $x^{1/6}$

7. -12 **8.** -10 **9.** 14   **10.** 14

9. $6x + C$

$$\frac{d}{dx}[6x + C] = 6$$

11. $t^3 + C$

$$\frac{d}{dt}[t^3 + C] = 3t^2$$

13. $-\dfrac{5}{2x^2} + C$

15. $u + C$

$$\frac{d}{du}[u + C] = 1$$

17. $\frac{2}{5}x^{5/2} + C$

$$\frac{d}{dx}\left[\frac{2}{5}x^{5/2} + C\right] = x^{3/2}$$

	Given	Rewrite	Integrate	Simplify
19.	$\displaystyle\int \sqrt[3]{x}\, dx$	$\displaystyle\int x^{1/3}\, dx$	$\dfrac{x^{4/3}}{4/3} + C$	$\frac{3}{4}x^{4/3} + C$
21.	$\displaystyle\int \dfrac{1}{x\sqrt{x}}\, dx$	$\displaystyle\int x^{-3/2}\, dx$	$\dfrac{x^{-1/2}}{-1/2} + C$	$-\dfrac{2}{\sqrt{x}} + C$
23.	$\displaystyle\int \dfrac{1}{2x^3}\, dx$	$\dfrac{1}{2}\displaystyle\int x^{-3}\, dx$	$\dfrac{1}{2}\left(\dfrac{x^{-2}}{-2}\right) + C$	$-\dfrac{1}{4x^2} + C$

25.

27. $\dfrac{x^4}{4} + 2x + C$

29. $\frac{6}{7}x^{7/3} + \frac{3}{2}x^2 - x + C$

31. $\frac{3}{5}x^{5/3} + C$

33. $-\dfrac{1}{2x^2} + C$

35. $-\dfrac{1}{4x} + C$

37. $t - \dfrac{2}{t} + C$

39. $\frac{3}{4}u^4 + \frac{1}{2}u^2 + C$

41. $2x^3 - \frac{11}{2}x^2 + 5x + C$

43. $\frac{2}{7}y^{7/2} + C$

45. $f(x) = 2x^{3/2} + 3x - 1$

47. $f(x) = 2x^3 - 3x^2$

49. $f(x) = -\dfrac{1}{x^2} + \dfrac{1}{x} + \dfrac{1}{2}$

51. $y = -\frac{5}{2}x^2 - 2x + 2$

53. $f(x) = 4x^{3/2} - 10x + 10$

55. $f(x) = x^2 + x + 4$

57. $f(x) = \frac{9}{4}x^{4/3}$

59. $C = 85x + 5500$

61. $C = \frac{1}{10}\sqrt{x} + 4x + 750$

63. $R = 225x - \frac{3}{2}x^2, \ p = 225 - \frac{3}{2}x$

65. $P = -9x^2 + 1650x$

67. 56.25 feet

69. $v_0 = 40\sqrt{22} \approx 187.617$ ft/sec

71. **(a)** $C = x^2 - 12x + 125$

(b) \$2025

$\overline{C} = x - 12 + \dfrac{125}{x}$

(c) \$125 is fixed. \$1900 is variable.

73. $S = -\dfrac{0.175}{3}t^3 + 0.2t^2 + 0.81t + 16.7,$ 16.16 quadrillion Btu's

SECTION 5.2   (page 331)

Warm Up

1. $\frac{1}{2}x^4 + x + C$

2. $\frac{3}{2}x^2 + \frac{2}{3}x^{3/2} - 4x + C$

3. $-\dfrac{1}{x} + C$

4. $-\dfrac{1}{6t^2} + C$

5. $\frac{4}{7}t^{7/2} + \frac{2}{5}t^{5/2} + C$

6. $\frac{4}{5}x^{5/2} - \frac{2}{3}x^{3/2} + C$

7. $-\dfrac{5(x-2)^4}{16}$

8. $-\dfrac{1}{12(x-1)^2}$

9. $9(x^2 + 3)^{2/3}$

10. $-\dfrac{5}{(1-x^3)^{1/2}}$

$\displaystyle\int u^n \frac{du}{dx}\, dx$	u	$\dfrac{du}{dx}$
1. $\displaystyle\int (5x^2 + 1)^2 (10x)\, dx$	$5x^2 + 1$	$10x$
3. $\displaystyle\int \sqrt{1 - x^2}(-2x)\, dx$	$1 - x^2$	$-2x$
5. $\displaystyle\int \left(4 + \frac{1}{x^2}\right)\left(\frac{-2}{x^3}\right) dx$	$4 + \dfrac{1}{x^2}$	$-\dfrac{2}{x^3}$

7. $\frac{1}{5}(1 + 2x)^5 + C$

9. $\frac{2}{3}(5x^2 - 4)^{3/2} + C$

11. $\frac{1}{5}(x - 1)^5 + C$

13. $\frac{1}{16}(x^2 - 1)^8 + C$

15. $-\dfrac{1}{3(1 + x^3)} + C$

17. $-\dfrac{1}{2(x^2 + 2x - 3)} + C$

19. $\sqrt{x^2 - 4x + 3} + C$

21. $-\frac{15}{8}(1 - x^2)^{4/3} + C$

23. $4\sqrt{1 + x^2} + C$

25. $-3\sqrt{2x + 3} + C$

27. $-\frac{1}{2}\sqrt{1-x^4}+C$ **29.** $\sqrt{2x}+C$

31. $\frac{1}{6}(x^3+3x)^2+C$ **33.** $\frac{1}{48}(6x^2-1)^4+C$

35. $-\frac{2}{45}(2-3x^3)^{5/2}+C$ **37.** $\sqrt{x^2+25}+C$

39. $\frac{2}{3}\sqrt{x^3+3x+4}+C$

41. $\frac{1}{6}(2x-1)^3+C_1=\frac{4}{3}x^3-2x^2+x+C_2$

$\left(\text{Answers differ by a constant: } C_2=C_1-\frac{1}{6}\right)$

43. $\dfrac{1}{2}\dfrac{(x^2-1)^3}{3}+C_1=\dfrac{1}{6}x^6-\dfrac{1}{2}x^4+\dfrac{1}{2}x^2+C_2$

$\left(\text{Answers differ by a constant: } C_2=C_1-\frac{1}{6}\right)$

45. $\frac{1}{3}[5-(1-x^2)^{3/2}]$

47. (a) $C=8\sqrt{x+1}+18$

(b)

49. $x=\frac{1}{3}(p^2-25)^{3/2}+24$

51. $x=\dfrac{6000}{\sqrt{p^2-16}}+3000$

53. $V=\dfrac{200{,}000}{t+1}+300{,}000,\ \ \$340{,}000$

55. (a) $Q=(x-19{,}999)^{0.95}+19{,}999$

(b)

x	20,000	50,000
Q	20,000	37,916.56
$x-Q$	0	12,083.44

x	100,000	150,000
Q	65,491.59	92,151.16
$x-Q$	34,508.41	57,848.84

55. *(continued)*

(c)

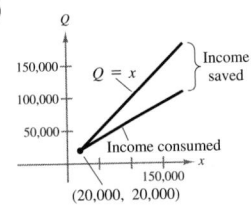

57. $-\frac{2}{3}x^{3/2}+\frac{2}{3}(x+1)^{3/2}+C$

SECTION 5.3   (page 338)

> **Warm Up**
>
> **1.** $\left(\frac{5}{2},\infty\right)$ **2.** $(-\infty,2)\cup(3,\infty)$
>
> **3.** $x+2-\dfrac{2}{x+2}$ **4.** $x-2+\dfrac{1}{x-4}$
>
> **5.** $x+8+\dfrac{2x-4}{x^2-4x}$ **6.** $x^2-x-4+\dfrac{20x+22}{x^2+5}$
>
> **7.** $\dfrac{1}{4}x^4-\dfrac{1}{x}+C$ **8.** $\dfrac{1}{2}x^2+2x+C$
>
> **9.** $\dfrac{1}{2}x^2-\dfrac{4}{x}+C$ **10.** $-\dfrac{1}{x}-\dfrac{3}{2x^2}+C$

1. $e^{2x}+C$ **3.** $\frac{1}{4}e^{4x}+C$ **5.** $-\frac{9}{2}e^{-x^2}+C$

7. $\frac{5}{3}e^{x^3}+C$ **9.** $\frac{1}{3}e^{x^3+3x^2-1}+C$ **11.** $-5e^{2-x}+C$

13. $-\frac{1}{2}e^{2/x}+C$ **15.** $2e^{\sqrt{x}}+C$

17. $\ln|x+1|+C$ **19.** $-\frac{1}{2}\ln|3-2x|+C$

21. $\ln\sqrt{x^2+1}+C$ **23.** $\frac{1}{3}\ln|x^3+1|+C$

25. $\frac{1}{2}\ln|x^2+6x+7|+C$ **27.** $\ln|\ln x|+C$

29. $-\ln(1+e^{-x})+C$ **31.** $2\ln|5-e^{2x}|+C$

33. $e^x+2x-e^{-x}+C$ **35.** $-\frac{2}{3}(1-e^x)^{3/2}+C$

37. $-\dfrac{1}{x-1}+C$ **39.** $\dfrac{x^2}{2}-4\ln|x|+C$

41. $\dfrac{x^2}{4}-4\ln|x|+C$ **43.** $2\ln(e^x+1)+C$

45. $\frac{1}{2}x^2 + 3x + 8 \ln |x - 1| + C$

47. $\frac{1}{2}x^2 + 5x + 8 \ln |x - 1| + C$

49. $\ln |e^x + x| + C$

51. (a) $P(t) = 1000[1 + \ln(1 + 0.25t)^{12}]$
    (b) $P(3) \approx 7715$ (c) $t \approx 6$ days

53. (a) $p = -50e^{-x/500} + 45.06$
    (b)
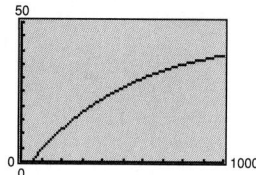

The price increases as the demand increases.
    (c) 387

55. (a) $T = 9.292t^{5/2} - 2.63t^3 - 44.71e^{-t} + 348.81$
    (b) $T \approx 339$ million transactions

SECTION 5.4   (page 348)

Warm Up

1. $\frac{3}{2}x^2 + 7x + C$ **2.** $\frac{2}{5}x^{5/2} + \frac{4}{3}x^{3/2} + C$

3. $\frac{1}{5} \ln |x| + C$ **4.** $-\dfrac{1}{6e^{6x}}$ **5.** $-\dfrac{8}{5}$

6. $-\frac{62}{3}$ **7.** $0.008x^{5/2} + 29{,}500x + C$

8. $x^2 + 9000x + C$ **9.** $25{,}000x - 0.005x^2 + C$

10. $0.01x^3 + 4600x + C$

1. Area $= 6$

3. Area $= \frac{35}{2}$

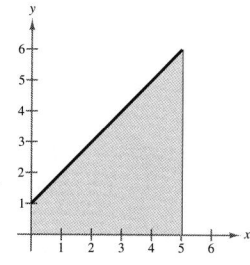

5. $\frac{1}{6}$ **7.** $\frac{8}{5}$ **9.** 6   **11.** 1

13. 0   **15.** $\frac{14}{3}$ **17.** $\frac{1}{3}$ **19.** -4

21. $\frac{22}{3}$ **23.** $-\frac{27}{20}$ **25.** 2

27. $\frac{1}{2}(1 - e^{-2}) \approx 0.432$ **29.** $\dfrac{e^3 - e}{3} \approx 5.789$

31. 4   **33.** 4   **35.** $\frac{1}{2} \ln 5 - \frac{1}{2} \ln 8 \approx -0.235$

37. $2 \ln(2 + e^3) - 2 \ln 3 \approx 3.993$

39. Area $= 10$ **41.** Area $= \frac{1}{4}$

43. Area $= \ln 9$ **45.** 10

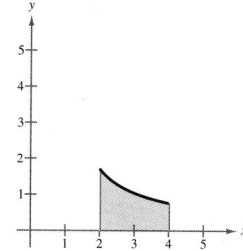

47. $4 + 5 \ln 5 \approx 12.047$

49. (a) 11   (b) 5   (c) -32 (d) -1

51. Average $= \frac{14}{3}$

$$x = \pm\frac{2\sqrt{3}}{3} \approx \pm 1.155$$

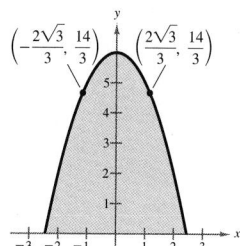

53. Average $= \frac{4}{3}$

$$x = \sqrt{2 + \frac{2\sqrt{5}}{3}} \approx 1.868$$

$$x = \sqrt{2 - \frac{2\sqrt{5}}{3}} \approx 0.714$$

55. Average $= -\frac{2}{3}$

$$x = \frac{4 + 2\sqrt{3}}{3} \approx 2.488$$

$$x = \frac{4 - 2\sqrt{3}}{3} \approx 0.179$$

57. Even   **59.** Neither odd nor even

61. (a) $\frac{8}{3}$ (b) $\frac{16}{3}$ (c) $-\frac{8}{3}$ **63.** $6.75

65. $22.50   **67.** $3.97   **69.** $2500   **71.** $1250

73. (a) $137,000 (b) $214,720.93 (c) $338,393.53

75. $3082.95   **77.** (a) $R = 4.648t^{3/2} - \frac{2}{15}t^3 + 45.2$

(b) $61.82 billion

79. $\frac{2}{3}\sqrt{7} - \frac{1}{3}$ **81.** $\frac{39}{200}$

SECTION 5.5 (page 357)

Warm Up

1. $-x^2 + 3x + 2$ **2.** $-2x^2 + 4x + 4$

3. $-x^3 + 2x^2 + 4x - 5$ **4.** $x^3 - 6x - 1$

5. $(0, 4), (4, 4)$ **6.** $(1, -3), (2, -12)$

7. $(-3, 9), (2, 4)$ **8.** $(-2, -4), (0, 0), (2, 4)$

9. $(1, -2), (5, 10)$ **10.** $(1, e)$

---

1. 36   **3.** 9   **5.** $\frac{3}{2}$ **7.** $e - 2$

9.

11. Area $= \frac{32}{3}$

13. Area $= \frac{1}{6}$

15. Area $= 2$

17. Area $= \frac{125}{6}$

19. Area $= 2$

21. Area $= \frac{3}{2}$

23. Area $= \frac{64}{3}$

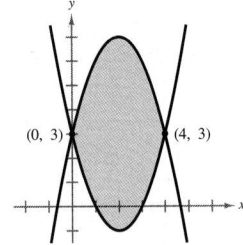

25. Area $= \frac{9}{2}$ **27.** Area $= 9$

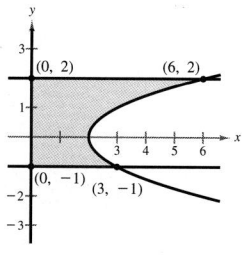

29. Area $= (2e + \ln 2) - 2e^{1/2} \approx 2.832$

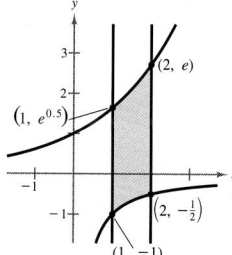

31. Area $= \frac{9}{2}$ **33.** Area $= -\frac{1}{2}e^{-1} + \frac{1}{2}$
≈ 0.316

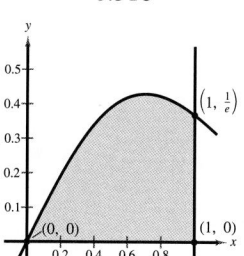

35. 8

37. Point of equilibrium: $(80, 10)$
Consumer surplus $= 1600$
Producer surplus $= 400$

39. Point of equilibrium: $(100, 200)$
Consumer surplus $= 5000$
Producer surplus $= 5000$

41. Point of equilibrium: $(50, 150)$
Consumer surplus ≈ 1666.67
Producer surplus $= 1250$

43. Point of equilibrium: $\left(266\frac{2}{3}, 16\frac{2}{3}\right)$
Consumer surplus ≈ 4444.44
Producer surplus ≈ 888.89

45. Point of equilibrium: $(300, 500)$
Consumer surplus $= 50,000$
Producer surplus $\approx 25,497$

47. A typical demand function is decreasing, whereas a typical supply function is increasing.

49. R_1, $4.16 billion   **51.** $501 million

53. Consumer surplus $= \$700,000$
Producer surplus $= \$1,375,000$

55. $333.33 million   **57.** 648

SECTION 5.6   (page 367)

Warm Up
1. $\frac{1}{6}$ **2.** $\frac{3}{20}$ **3.** $\frac{7}{40}$ **4.** $\frac{13}{12}$ **5.** $\frac{61}{30}$
6. $\frac{53}{18}$ **7.** $\frac{2}{3}$ **8.** $\frac{4}{7}$ **9.** 0   **10.** 5

1. Midpoint Rule: 2
Exact area: 2

3. Midpoint Rule: 0.6730
Exact area: $\frac{2}{3} \approx 0.6667$

5. Midpoint Rule: 4.6250
Exact area:
$\frac{14}{3} \approx 4.6667$

7. Midpoint Rule: 17.2500
Exact area:
$\frac{52}{3} \approx 17.3333$

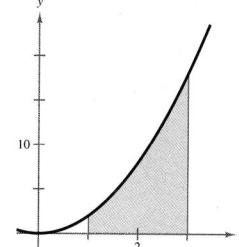

9. Midpoint Rule: 2.7266
Exact area: $\frac{11}{4} = 2.75$

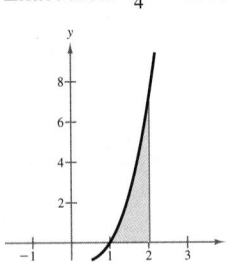

11. Midpoint Rule: 0.5703
Exact area:
$\frac{7}{12} \approx 0.5833$

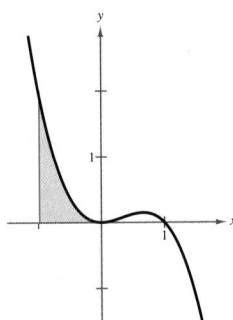

13. Midpoint Rule: 0.0859
Exact area: $\frac{1}{12} \approx 0.0833$

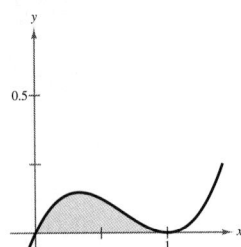

15. Area ≈ 54.6667,
$n = 40$

17. Midpoint Rule: 1.5
Exact area: 1.5

19.

Number of subintervals	2	4	6
Approximations	13.0375	12.7357	12.6591

Number of subintervals	8	10
Approximations	12.6267	12.6096

21.

Number of subintervals	2	4	6
Approximations	3.1523	3.2202	3.2320

Number of subintervals	8	10
Approximations	3.2361	3.2380

23. Exact: 4
Trapezoidal Rule: 4.0625
Midpoint Rule: 3.9688
Midpoint Rule is better in this example.

25. 1.1167   **27.** 1.55

29.

n	Midpoint Rule	Trapezoidal Rule
4	15.3965	15.6055
8	15.4480	15.5010
12	15.4578	15.4814
16	15.4613	15.4745
20	15.4628	15.4713

31. 4.8103   **33.** 916.25 ft

SECTION 5.7   (page 374)

Warm Up

1. 0, 2   **2.** 0, 2   **3.** 0, 2, -2 **4.** -1, 2
5. 2, 4   **6.** 1, 5   **7.** 53.5982   **8.** 1.9459
9. 3.3934   **10.** 1.3896

1. $\frac{16\pi}{3}$ **3.** $\frac{15\pi}{2}$ **5.** $\frac{512\pi}{15}$ **7.** $\frac{32\pi}{15}$

9. $\frac{\pi}{3}$ **11.** $\pi\left(\ln 2 - \frac{2}{3}\right) \approx 0.0832$

13. $\frac{128\pi}{5}$ **15.** $\frac{\pi}{2}(e^2 - 1)$ **17.** 8π

19. $\frac{2}{3}\pi$ **21.** $\frac{\pi}{4}$ **23.** $\frac{256\pi}{15}$ **25.** 18π

27. $V = \pi \int_{-r}^{r} (r^2 - x^2)\,dx = \frac{4\pi r^3}{3}$ **29.** 48π

31. (a) 1,256,637 ft^3 **33.** 58.5598
(b) 2513 fish

CHAPTER 5 REVIEW EXERCISES (page 378)

1. $16x + C$ **3.** $\frac{2}{3}x^3 + \frac{5}{2}x^2 + C$ **5.** $x^{2/3} + C$

7. $\frac{3}{7}x^{7/3} + \frac{3}{2}x^2 + C$ **9.** $f(x) = \frac{3}{2}x^2 + x - 2$

11. $f(x) = \frac{1}{6}x^4 - 8x + \frac{33}{2}$

13. (a) 2.5 sec **(b)** 100 ft **(c)** 1.25 sec **(d)** 75 ft

15. $x + 5x^2 + \frac{25}{3}x^3 + C$ or $\frac{1}{15}(1 + 5x)^3 + C_1$

17. $\frac{2}{5}\sqrt{5x - 1} + C$ **19.** $\frac{1}{2}x^2 - x^4 + C$

21. $\frac{1}{4}(x^4 - 2x)^2 + C$ **23. (a)** 30.5 board-feet
(b) 125.2 board-feet

25. $-e^{-3x} + C$ **27.** $\frac{1}{2}e^{x^2 - 2x} + C$

29. $-\frac{1}{3}\ln|1 - x^3| + C$ **31.** $\frac{2}{3}x^{3/2} + 2x + 2x^{1/2} + C$

33. $A = 4$ **35.** $A = \frac{8}{3}$ **37.** $A = 2\ln 2$

39. 16   **41.** 0   **43.** 2   **45.** $\frac{1}{8}$ **47.** 3.899

49. 0   **51.** \$700.25   **53.** Average value: $\frac{8}{5}$
$x = \frac{29}{4}$

55. Average value: $\frac{1}{3}(-1 + e^3) \approx 6.362$,
$x \approx 3.150$

57. \$520.54   **59.** $\displaystyle\int_{-2}^{2} 6x^5\,dx = 0$
(Odd function)

61. $\displaystyle\int_{-2}^{-1} \frac{4}{x^2}\,dx = \int_{1}^{2} \frac{4}{x^2}\,dx = 2$
(Symmetric about y-axis)

63. Area $= \frac{25}{3}$ **65.** Area $= \frac{3}{2}$

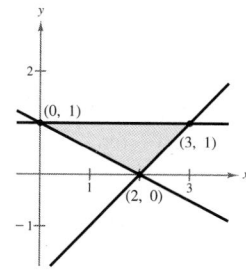

67. Area $= \frac{4}{15}$ **69.** Area $= \frac{64}{3}$

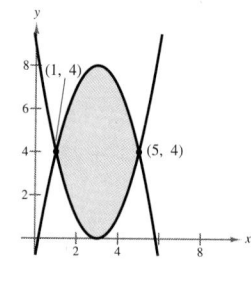

71. Consumer surplus: 11,250   **73.** 3.85 pounds
Producer surplus: 14,062.5

75. $n = 4$: 13.3203   **77.** $n = 4$: 0.7867
$n = 20$: 13.7167 $n = 20$: 0.7855

79. $\pi \ln 4 \approx 4.355$ **81.** $\dfrac{\pi}{2}(e^2 - e^{-2}) \approx 11.394$

83. $\dfrac{56\pi}{3}$ **85.** $\dfrac{2\pi}{35}$ **87.** $\dfrac{5\pi}{16}\sqrt{15}$

SAMPLE POST-GRAD EXAM QUESTIONS (page 382)

1. (d)   **2.** (b)   **3.** (c)   **4.** (b)
5. (a)   **6.** (b)   **7.** (d)   **8.** (d)

CHAPTER 6

SECTION 6.1 (page 390)

Warm Up

1. $5x + C$ **2.** $\frac{2}{5}x^{5/2} + C$

3. $\frac{1}{4}(x^2 + 1)^4 + C$ **4.** $e^{6x} + C$

5. $\ln|2x + 1| + C$ **6.** $-e^{-x^2} + C$

7. $x(x - 1)(2x - 1)$ **8.** $3x(x + 4)^2(x + 8)$

9. $(x + 21)(x + 7)^{-1/2}$ **10.** $x(x + 5)^{-2/3}$

1. $\frac{1}{5}(x-2)^5 + C$ **3.** $\frac{2}{9-t} + C$

5. $\frac{2}{3}(1+x)^{3/2} + C$ **7.** $\ln(3x^2 + x)^2 + C$

9. $-\frac{1}{10(5x+1)^2} + C$ **11.** $2(x+1)^{1/2} + C$

13. $-\frac{1}{3}\ln|1 - e^{3x}| + C$

15. $\frac{1}{2}x^2 + x + \ln|x-1| + C$

17. $\frac{1}{3}(x^2 + 4)^{3/2} + C$ **19.** $\frac{1}{5}e^{5x} + C$

21. $\frac{-1}{2(x+1)^2} + \frac{1}{3(x+1)^3} + C$

23. $\frac{1}{9}\left[\ln|3x-1| - \frac{1}{3x-1}\right] + C$

25. $\frac{1}{6}(1-x)^6 - \frac{1}{5}(1-x)^5 + C$

27. $\frac{1}{2}\ln|x^2 - 2x| + C$

29. $\frac{2}{5}(x-3)^{5/2} + 2(x-3)^{3/2} + C$

31. $-\frac{2}{3}(1-x)^{3/2} + \frac{4}{5}(1-x)^{5/2} - \frac{2}{7}(1-x)^{7/2} + C$

33. $\frac{1}{20}(2x-1)^{5/2} + \frac{1}{6}(2x-1)^{3/2} - \frac{3}{4}(2x-1)^{1/2} + C$

35. $\frac{3}{28}(t+1)^{4/3}(4t-3) + C$

37. $2(\sqrt{t}-1) + 2\ln|\sqrt{t}-1| + C$

39. $4\sqrt{t} + \ln t + C$ **41.** $\frac{26}{3}$

43. $\frac{3}{2}(e-1) \approx 2.577$ **45.** $\ln 2 - \frac{1}{2} \approx 0.193$

47. $\frac{13}{320}$ **49.** $\frac{144}{5}$ **51.** $\frac{1209}{28}$ **53.** $\frac{16}{15}\sqrt{2}$

55. $\frac{4}{3}$ **57.** $\frac{4\pi}{15} \approx 0.838$ **59.** $\frac{1}{2}$

61. (a) 0.547   **63.** $24,520.95
(b) 0.586

65. 5.8849

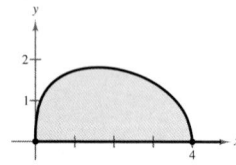

SECTION 6.2   (page 399)

Warm Up

1. $12x^3 + 2$ **2.** $\frac{1}{2}x + \frac{1}{8}$ **3.** $\frac{4x^2 + 2}{x^3 + x}$

4. $3x^2 e^{x^3}$ **5.** $e^x(x^2 + 2x)$ **6.** $-\frac{4}{(x-3)^2}$

7. $\frac{63}{3}$ **8.** $\frac{4}{3}$ **9.** $\frac{32}{3}$ **10.** 8

1. $\frac{1}{3}xe^{3x} - \frac{1}{9}e^{3x} + C$

3. $-x^2 e^{-x} - 2xe^{-x} - 2e^{-x} + C$

5. $x \ln 2x - x + C$

7. $\frac{1}{4}e^{4x} + C$ **9.** $\frac{e^{4x}}{16}(4x - 1) + C$

11. $\frac{1}{2}e^{x^2} + C$ **13.** $x^2 e^x - 2e^x x + 2e^x$

15. $x^3 e^x - 3x^2 e^x + 6xe^x - 6e^x + C$

17. $\frac{1}{4}x^4 \ln x - \frac{1}{16}x^4 + C$

19. $\frac{1}{2}t^2 \ln(t+1) - \frac{1}{2}\ln(t+1) - \frac{1}{4}(t-1)^2 + C$

21. $\frac{x^2}{2}(\ln x)^2 - \frac{x^2}{2}\ln x + \frac{x^2}{4} + C$ **23.** $\frac{1}{3}(\ln x)^3 + C$

25. $\frac{2}{3}x(x-1)^{3/2} - \frac{4}{15}(x-1)^{5/2} + C$

27. $(x^2 - 1)e^x - 2xe^x + 2e^x + C = (x-1)^2 e^x + C$

29. $\frac{e^{2x}}{4(2x+1)} + C$ **31.** $e - 2 \approx 0.718$

33. $\frac{5}{36}e^6 + \frac{1}{36} \approx 56.060$

35. $\frac{2}{3}x(2x-3)^{3/2} - \frac{2}{15}(2x-3)^{5/2} + C$

37. $\frac{2}{5}x(4+5x)^{1/2} - \frac{4}{75}(4+5x)^{3/2} + C$

39. $\displaystyle\int x^n \ln x \, dx = \frac{x^{n+1}}{n+1}\ln x - \int \frac{x^n}{n+1}\,dx$

$$= \frac{x^{n+1}}{n+1}\ln x - \frac{x^{n+1}}{(n+1)^2} + C$$

$$= \frac{x^{n+1}}{(n+1)^2}[-1 + (n+1)\ln x] + C$$

41. $\dfrac{e^{5x}}{125}(25x^2 - 10x + 2) + C$ **43.** $-\dfrac{1}{x} - \dfrac{\ln x}{x} + C$

45. $1 - 5e^{-4} \approx 0.908$ **47. (a)** 2

  (b) $4\pi(e - 2) \approx 9.026$

49. $\dfrac{3}{128} - \dfrac{379}{128}e^{-8} \approx 0.022$

51. $\dfrac{1,171,875}{256}\pi \approx 14,381.070$

53. (a) Increase **(b)** 113,212 units **(c)** 11,321 per year

55. (a) $3.2 \ln 2 - 0.2 \approx 2.018$

  (b) $12.8 \ln 4 - 7.2 \ln 3 - 1.8 \approx 8.035$

57. $18,126.92 **59.** $1,332,474.72 **61.** $4103.07

63. (a) $1,200,000 **(b)** $1,094,142.26

65. 4.254 **67.** $45,957.78 **69.** Yes; $81,241.19

SECTION 6.3 (page 411)

Warm Up

1. $(x - 4)(x + 3)$ **2.** $(x - 5)(x + 5)$

3. $x(x - 2)(x + 1)$ **4.** $x(x - 2)^2$

5. $(x - 2)(x - 1)^2$ **6.** $(x - 3)(x - 1)^2$

7. $\dfrac{1}{x - 2} + x$ **8.** $\dfrac{1}{1 - x} + 2x - 2$

9. $\dfrac{2}{2 - x} + x^2 - x - 2$ **10.** $\dfrac{6}{x - 1} + x + 4$

1. $\dfrac{5}{x - 5} - \dfrac{3}{x + 5}$ **3.** $\dfrac{9}{x - 3} - \dfrac{1}{x}$

5. $\dfrac{1}{x - 5} + \dfrac{3}{x + 2}$ **7.** $\dfrac{3}{x} - \dfrac{5}{x^2}$

9. $\dfrac{1}{3(x - 2)} + \dfrac{1}{(x - 2)^2}$

11. $\dfrac{8}{x + 1} - \dfrac{1}{(x + 1)^2} + \dfrac{2}{(x + 1)^3}$

13. $\dfrac{1}{2} \ln \left| \dfrac{x - 1}{x + 1} \right| + C$

15. $\dfrac{1}{4} \ln |4x + 1| - \dfrac{1}{4} \ln |4 - x| + C$

17. $-\ln |x| + \ln |3x - 1| + C$

19. $\ln |x| - \ln |2x + 1| + C$

21. $\ln |x - 1| - \ln |x + 2| + C$

23. $\dfrac{3}{2} \ln |2x - 1| - 2 \ln |x + 1| + C$

25. $5 \ln |x - 2| - \ln |x + 2| - 3 \ln |x| + C$

27. $\dfrac{1}{2}[3 \ln |x - 4| - \ln |x|] + C$

29. $-3 \ln |x - 1| - \dfrac{1}{x - 1} + C$

31. $\dfrac{1}{2}\left[5 \ln |x + 1| - \ln |x| + \dfrac{3}{x + 1} \right] + C$

33. $\dfrac{1}{6} \ln \dfrac{4}{7} \approx -0.093$ **35.** $-\dfrac{4}{5} + 2 \ln \dfrac{5}{3} \approx 0.222$

37. $\dfrac{1}{2} - \ln 2 \approx -0.193$ **39.** $\dfrac{5}{2} - \dfrac{11}{3} \ln 2 \approx -0.042$

41. $\dfrac{1}{5} \ln |e^x - 1| - \dfrac{1}{5} \ln |e^x + 4| + C$

43. $\dfrac{1}{4} \ln \left(\sqrt{4 + x^2} - 2 \right) - \dfrac{1}{4} \ln \left(\sqrt{4 + x^2} + 2 \right) + C$

45. $-\dfrac{2}{3(\sqrt{3x} + 2)} + C$ **47.** $12 - \dfrac{7}{2} \ln 7 \approx 5.1893$

49. $5 \ln 2 - \ln 5 \approx 1.8563$ **51.** $\dfrac{1}{2a}\left(\dfrac{1}{a + x} + \dfrac{1}{a - x} \right)$

53. $\dfrac{1/a}{x} + \dfrac{1/a}{a - x}$ **55.** $\dfrac{\pi}{165}\left[136 - 33 \ln \dfrac{11}{3} \right] \approx 1.7731$

57. $\pi\left[\dfrac{1}{3} + \dfrac{1}{4} \ln 3 \right] \approx 1.9100$

59. $y = \dfrac{1000}{1 + 9e^{-0.1656t}}$

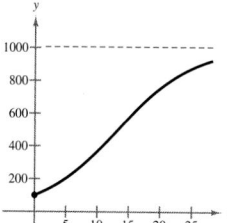

61. $1.077 thousand   **63.** 1467.85 thousand

SECTION 6.4 (page 422)

Warm Up

1. $x^2 + 8x + 16$ **2.** $x^2 + x + \frac{1}{4}$

3. $x^2 - 2x + 1$ **4.** $x^2 - \frac{2}{3}x + \frac{1}{9}$

5. $\frac{2}{x} - \frac{2}{x+2}$ **6.** $-\frac{3}{4x} + \frac{3}{4(x-4)}$

7. $\frac{3}{2(x-2)} - \frac{2}{x^2} - \frac{3}{2x}$

8. $-\frac{3}{x+1} + \frac{2}{x-2} + \frac{4}{x}$ **9.** $2e^x(x-1) + C$

10. $x^3 \ln x - \frac{x^3}{3} + C$

---

1. $\frac{1}{9}\left(\frac{2}{2+3x} + \ln |2 + 3x|\right) + C$

3. $\frac{2(3x-4)}{27}\sqrt{2+3x} + C$

5. $\ln\left(x^2 + \sqrt{x^4 - 9}\right) + C$

7. $\frac{1}{2}(x^2 - 1)e^{x^2} + C$

9. $\frac{1}{2}(x^2 + 1)[-1 + \ln(x^2 + 1)] + C$

11. $\ln\left|\frac{x}{1+x}\right| + C$ **13.** $-\frac{1}{3}\ln\left|\frac{3 + \sqrt{x^2 + 9}}{x}\right| + C$

15. $-\frac{1}{2}\ln\left|\frac{2 + \sqrt{4 - x^2}}{x}\right| + C$

17. $\frac{1}{4}x^2(-1 + 2\ln x) + C$ **19.** $3x^2 - \ln(1 + e^{3x^2}) + C$

21. $\frac{1}{4}\left(x^2\sqrt{x^4 - 4} - 4\ln\left|x^2 + \sqrt{x^4 - 4}\right|\right) + C$

23. $\frac{1}{27}\left[\frac{4}{2+3t} - \frac{4}{2(2+3t)^2} + \ln |2 + 3t|\right] + C$

25. $\frac{1}{\sqrt{3}}\ln\left|\frac{\sqrt{3+s} - \sqrt{3}}{\sqrt{3+s} + \sqrt{3}}\right| + C$

27. $\frac{1}{8}\left[\frac{-1}{2(3+2x)^2} + \frac{6}{3(3+2x)^3} - \frac{9}{4(3+2x)^4}\right] + C$

29. $-\frac{\sqrt{1-x^2}}{x} + C$ **31.** $\frac{1}{9}x^3(-1 + 3\ln x) + C$

33. $\frac{1}{27}\left[3x - \frac{25}{3x-5} + 10\ln |3x - 5|\right] + C$

35. $\frac{1}{4}\left[x(x^2 + 2)\sqrt{x^2 + 4} - 8\ln\left|x + \sqrt{x^2 + 4}\right|\right] + C$

37. $\frac{1}{2}[4x - \ln(1 + e^{4x})] + C$

39. $\frac{1}{9}[3\ln x - 4\ln |4 + 3\ln x|] + C$

41. $\frac{5\sqrt{5}}{3}$ **43.** $12\ln\left(\frac{2e^2}{1+e^2}\right) \approx 6.7946$

45. $(x^2 - 2x + 2)e^x + C$ **47.** $-\left[\frac{1}{x} + \ln\left|\frac{x}{x+1}\right|\right] + C$

49. (a) $(x+3)^2 - 9$ (b) $(x-4)^2 - 7$
(c) $(x^2 + 1)^2 - 6$ (d) $4 - (x+1)^2$

51. $\frac{1}{2\sqrt{17}}\ln\left|\frac{(x+3) - \sqrt{17}}{(x+3) + \sqrt{17}}\right| + C$

53. $-\ln\left|\frac{1 + \sqrt{x^2 - 2x + 2}}{x - 1}\right| + C$

55. $\frac{1}{8}\ln\left|\frac{x-3}{x+1}\right| + C$

57. $\frac{1}{2}\ln |x^2 + 1 + \sqrt{x^4 + 2x^2 + 2}| + C$

59. $\frac{40}{3}$ **61.** 42.58   **63.** \$1138.43

SECTION 6.5 (page 431)

Warm Up

1. $\frac{2}{x^3}$ **2.** $-\frac{96}{(2x+1)^4}$ **3.** $-\frac{12}{x^4}$

4. $6x - 4$ **5.** $16e^{2x}$ **6.** $e^{x^2}(4x^2 + 2)$

7. (3, 18)   **8.** (1, 8)   **9.** $n < -5\sqrt{10}$

$n > 5\sqrt{10}$

10. $n < -5,\ n > 5$

	Exact value	Trapezoidal Rule	Simpson's Rule
1.	2.6667	2.7500	2.6667
3.	8.4000	9.0625	8.4167
5.	4.0000	4.0625	4.0000
7.	0.5000	0.5090	0.5004
9.	0.6931	0.6970	0.6933
11.		6.25	6.00
13.		0.342	0.372
15.		0.749	0.771
17.		0.772	0.780
19.		1.88	1.89

21. $21,831.20   **23.** $678.36

25. $0.3413 = 34.13\%$ **27.** 89,500 ft^2

29. (a) 2

   (b) $\dfrac{2^5}{180(4^4)}(24) \approx 0.017$

31. (a) $\dfrac{5e}{64} \approx 0.212$

   (b) $\dfrac{13e}{1024} \approx 0.035$

33. (a) $n = 101$ **35. (a)** $n = 3280$
   (b) $n = 8$ **(b)** $n = 60$

37. 19.5215   **39.** 3.6558

41. Exact value: $\displaystyle\int_0^1 x^3\,dx = \dfrac{x^4}{4}\bigg]_0^1 = \dfrac{1}{4}$

   Simpson's Rule:

   $\displaystyle\int_0^1 x^3\,dx = \dfrac{1}{6}\left[0^3 + 4\left(\dfrac{1}{2}\right)^3 + 1^3\right] = \dfrac{1}{4}$

43. 416.1 ft

45. 58.876 grams
   (Simpson's Rule with $n = 100$)

47. 1876 subscribers (Simpson's Rule with $n = 100$)

SECTION 6.6   (page 442)

Warm Up

1. 9   **2.** 3   **3.** $-\dfrac{1}{8}$

4. Limit does not exist.

5. Limit does not exist.   **6.** -4

7. (a) $\dfrac{32}{3}b^3 - 16b^2 + 8b - \dfrac{4}{3}$ **(b)** $-\dfrac{4}{3}$

8. (a) $\dfrac{b^2 - b - 11}{(b-2)^2(b-5)}$ **(b)** $\dfrac{11}{20}$

9. (a) $\ln\left(\dfrac{5 - 3b^2}{b+1}\right)$ **(b)** $\ln 5 \approx 1.609$

10. (a) $e^{-3b^2}(e^{6b^2} + 1)$ **(b)** 2

1. 1   **3.** 1   **5.** Diverges   **7.** Diverges

9. Diverges   **11.** Diverges   **13.** 0   **15.** 4

17. 6   **19.** Diverges   **21.** 6   **23.** Diverges

25. 0   **27.** $\ln\left(4 + \sqrt{7}\right) - \ln 3 \approx 0.7954$

29.

x	1	10
xe^{-x}	0.3679	0.0005

x	25	50
xe^{-x}	0.0000	0.0000

31.

x	1	10
$x^2 e^{-(1/2)x}$	0.6065	0.6738

x	25	50
$x^2 e^{-(1/2)x}$	0.0023	0.0000

33. 2   **35.** $\dfrac{1}{4}$ **37. (a)** $4,637,228   **(b)** $5,555,556

39. (a) $748,367.34   **41. (a)** 1   **43. (a)** 0.111
   (b) $808,030.14   **(b)** $\dfrac{\pi}{3}$ **(b)** 0.194
   (c) $900,000.00   **(c)** 0.052

CHAPTER 6 REVIEW EXERCISES   (page 446)

1. $t + C$ **3.** $\dfrac{(x+5)^4}{4} + C$

5. $\dfrac{1}{10}e^{10x} + C$ **7.** $\dfrac{1}{5}\ln|x| + C$

9. $\dfrac{1}{3}(x^2+4)^{3/2} + C$ **11.** $2\ln(3 + e^x) + C$

13. $\dfrac{(x-2)^5}{5} + \dfrac{(x-2)^4}{2} + C$

15. $\dfrac{2}{15}(x+1)^{3/2}(3x-2) + C$

17. $\dfrac{4}{5}(x-3)^{3/2}(x+2) + C$

19. $-\dfrac{2}{15}(1-x)^{3/2}(3x+7) + C$

21. $\dfrac{26}{15}$ **23.** $\dfrac{412}{15}$ **25. (a)** 0.696 **(b)** 0.693

27. $2\sqrt{x}\ \ln x - 4\sqrt{x} + C$ **29.** $xe^x - 2e^x + C$

31. $x^2e^{2x} - xe^{2x} + \dfrac{1}{2}e^{2x} + C$ **33.** $\$45,317.31$

35. $\$432,979.25$ **37.** $\dfrac{1}{5}\ln|x| - \dfrac{1}{5}\ln|x+5| + C$

39. $\ln|x-5| + 3\ln|x+2| + C$

41. $x - \dfrac{25}{8}\ln|x+5| + \dfrac{9}{8}\ln|x-3| + C$

43. (a) $y = \dfrac{10{,}000}{1 + 7e^{-0.098652t}}$

(b)

Time, t	0	3	6
Sales, y	1250	1611	2052

Time, t	12	24
Sales, y	3182	6039

(c) $t \approx 31$ weeks

45. $\sqrt{x^2+25} - 5\ln\left|\dfrac{5 + \sqrt{x^2+25}}{x}\right| + C$

47. $\dfrac{1}{4}\ln\left|\dfrac{x-2}{x+2}\right| + C$ **49.** $\dfrac{8}{3}$

51. $2\sqrt{1+x} + \ln\left|\dfrac{\sqrt{1+x} - 1}{\sqrt{1+x} + 1}\right| + C$

53. $(x-5)^3e^{x-5} - 3(x-5)^2e^{x-5} + 6(x-6)e^{x-5} + C$

55. $\dfrac{1}{10}\ln\left|\dfrac{x-3}{x+7}\right| + C$

57. $\dfrac{1}{2}\Big[(x-5)\sqrt{(x-5)^2 - 5^2}$

$\qquad + 25\ln\left|(x-5) + \sqrt{(x-5)^2 - 5^2}\right|\Big] + C$

59. 0.705 **61.** 0.741 **63.** 0.376 **65.** 0.289

67. 2.29 **69.** 0.001 **71.** 1 **73.** Diverges

75. 2 **77.** 2 **79. (a)** $\$494,525.28$

$\qquad\qquad\qquad\qquad\qquad$ **(b)** $\$833,333.33$

81. (a) 0.25 **(b)** 0.79×10^{-5}

SAMPLE POST-GRAD EXAM QUESTIONS   (page 450)

1. (c)   **2.** (a)   **3.** (b)   **4.** (d)

5. (d)   **6.** (b)   **7.** (a)   **8.** (c)

CHAPTER 7

SECTION 7.1   (page 458)

Warm Up

1. $2\sqrt{5}$ **2.** 5 **3.** 8 **4.** 8 **5.** $(4, 7)$

6. $(1, 0)$ **7.** $(0, 3)$ **8.** $(-1, 1)$

9. $(x-2)^2 + (y-3)^2 = 4$

10. $(x-1)^2 + (y-4)^2 = 25$

1.   **3.**

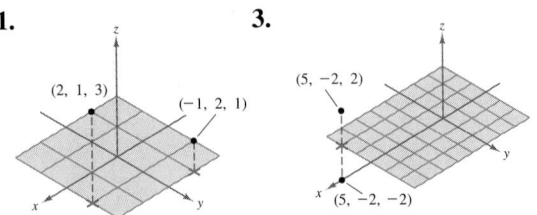

5. $3\sqrt{2}$ **7.** $\sqrt{206}$ **9.** $(2, -5, 3)$

11. $\left(\dfrac{1}{2}, \dfrac{1}{2}, -1\right)$ **13.** $(6, -3, 5)$ **15.** $(1, 2, 1)$

17. $3, 3\sqrt{5}, 6$; right triangle

19. $2, 2\sqrt{5}, 2\sqrt{2}$; the triangle is neither right nor isosceles.

21. $x^2 + (y-2)^2 + (z-2)^2 = 4$

23. $\left(x - \frac{3}{2}\right)^2 + (y-2)^2 + (z-1)^2 = \frac{21}{4}$

25. $(x-1)^2 + (y-1)^2 + (z-5)^2 = 9$

27. $(x-1)^2 + (y-3)^2 + z^2 = 10$

29. Center: $(1, -3, -4)$
Radius: 5

31. Center: $(0, 4, 0)$
Radius: 4

33. Center: $(1, 3, 2)$
Radius: $\dfrac{5}{\sqrt{2}} = \dfrac{5\sqrt{2}}{2}$

35. Center: $\left(\frac{1}{3}, -1, 0\right)$
Radius: 1

37.

39.

41. (a)

(b)

43. (a)

(b)
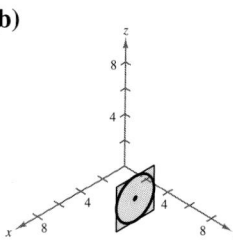

45. $(3, 3, 3)$

SECTION 7.2 (page 468)

Warm Up

1. $(4, 0)$, $(0, 3)$ **2.** $\left(-\frac{4}{3}, 0\right)$, $(0, -8)$

3. $(1, 0)$, $(0, -2)$ **4.** $(-5, 0)$, $(0, -5)$

5. $(x-1)^2 + (y-2)^2 + (z-9)^2 + 1 = 0$

6. $(x-4)^2 + (y+2)^2 - (z+3)^2 = 0$

7. $(x+1)^2 + (y-1)^2 - z = 0$

8. $(x-3)^2 + (y+5)^2 + (z+13)^2 = 1$

9. $x^2 - y^2 + z^2 = \frac{1}{4}$ **10.** $x^2 - y^2 + z^2 = 4$

1.

3.

5.

7.

9.

11.

13.

15.

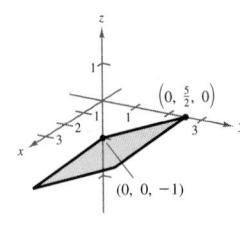

17. Perpendicular   **19.** Parallel   **21.** Parallel

23. Neither parallel nor perpendicular   **25.** $\dfrac{6\sqrt{14}}{7}$

27. $\dfrac{\sqrt{6}}{6}$ **29.** c   **30.** e   **31.** f   **32.** g

33. d   **34.** b   **35.** a   **36.** h

37. Trace in xy-plane $(z = 0)$: $y = x^2$ (parabola)
Trace in plane $y = 1$: $x^2 - z^2 = 1$ (hyperbola)
Trace in yz-plane $(x = 0)$: $y = -z^2$ (parabola)

39. Trace in xy-plane $(z = 0)$: $\dfrac{x^2}{4} + y^2 = 1$ (ellipse)

Trace in xz-plane $(y = 0)$: $\dfrac{x^2}{4} + z^2 = 1$ (ellipse)

Trace in yz-plane $(x = 0)$: $y^2 + z^2 = 1$ (circle)

41. Ellipsoid   **43.** Hyperboloid of one sheet

45. Elliptic paraboloid   **47.** Hyperbolic paraboloid

49. Hyperboloid of two sheets   **51.** Elliptic cone

53. Hyperbolic paraboloid   **55.** Sphere

57.

59.

SECTION 7.3   (page 476)

Warm Up

1. 11   **2.** -16 **3.** 7

4. 4   **5.** $(-\infty, \infty)$

6. $(-\infty, -3) \cup (-3, 0) \cup (0, \infty)$

7. $[5, \infty)$ **8.** $\left(-\infty, -\sqrt{5}\,\right] \cup \left[\sqrt{5}, \infty\right)$

9. 55.0104   **10.** 6.9165

1. (a) $\dfrac{3}{2}$ **(b)** $-\dfrac{1}{4}$ **(c)** 6   **(d)** $\dfrac{5}{y}$ **(e)** $\dfrac{x}{2}$ **(f)** $\dfrac{5}{t}$

3. (a) 5   **(b)** $3e^2$ **(c)** $2e^{-1}$ **(d)** $5e^y$ **(e)** xe^2 **(f)** te^t

5. (a) $\dfrac{2}{3}$ **(b)** 0   **7. (a)** 90π **(b)** 50π

9. (a) 20,655   **(b)** 1,397,673   **11. (a)** 0   **(b)** 6

13. (a) $x^2 + 2x\Delta x + (\Delta x)^2 - 2y$ **(b)** -2, $\Delta y \neq 0$

15. Domain: all points (x, y) inside and on the circle $x^2 + y^2 = 16$
Range: $[0, 4]$

17. Domain: all points (x, y) such that $y \neq 0$
Range: $(0, \infty)$

19. All points inside and on the ellipse $9x^2 + y^2 = 9$

21. All points (x, y) such that $y \neq 0$

23. All points (x, y) such that $x \neq 0$ and $y \neq 0$

25. All points (x, y) such that $y \geq 0$

27. The half-plane below the line $y = -x + 4$

29. (b)   **30. (d)**   **31. (a)**   **32. (c)**

33.

35.

37.

39.

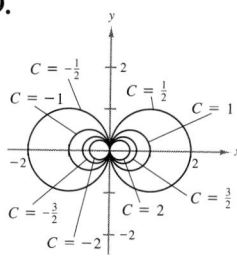

41. 135,540 units   **43.** $21,960

45. (a) $1250   (b) $925

47.

I \ R	0	0.03	0.05
0	$2593.74	$1929.99	$1592.33
0.28	$2004.23	$1491.34	$1230.42
0.35	$1877.14	$1396.77	$1152.40

49. (a) $13.287 billion
   (b) The variable x has greater influence because its coefficient is larger.

SECTION 7.4 (page 487)

Warm Up

1. $\dfrac{x}{\sqrt{x^2+3}}$ **2.** $-6x(3-x^2)^2$

3. $e^{2t+1}(2t+1)$ **4.** $\dfrac{e^{2x}(2-3e^{2x})}{\sqrt{1-e^{2x}}}$

5. $-\dfrac{2}{3-2x}$ **6.** $\dfrac{3(t^2-2)}{2t(t^2-6)}$

7. $-\dfrac{10x}{(4x-1)^3}$ **8.** $-\dfrac{(x+2)^2(x^2+8x+27)}{(x^2-9)^3}$

9. $f'(2)=8$ **10.** $f'(2)=\dfrac{7}{2}$

1. $f_x(x,\,y)=2$
    $f_y(x,\,y)=-3$

3. $f_x(x,\,y)=\dfrac{5}{2\sqrt{x}}$
    $f_y(x,\,y)=-12y$

5. $f_x(x,\,y)=y$
    $f_y(x,\,y)=x$

7. $\dfrac{\partial z}{\partial x}=\sqrt{y}$
    $\dfrac{\partial z}{\partial y}=\dfrac{x}{2\sqrt{y}}$

9. $f_x(x,\,y)=\dfrac{x}{\sqrt{x^2+y^2}}$
    $f_y(x,\,y)=\dfrac{y}{\sqrt{x^2+y^2}}$

11. $\dfrac{\partial z}{\partial x}=2xe^{2y}$
    $\dfrac{\partial z}{\partial y}=2x^2e^{2y}$

13. $h_x(x,\,y)=-2xe^{-(x^2+y^2)}$
    $h_y(x,\,y)=-2ye^{-(x^2+y^2)}$

15. $\dfrac{\partial z}{\partial x}=\dfrac{2x}{x^2+y^2}$
    $\dfrac{\partial z}{\partial y}=\dfrac{2y}{x^2+y^2}$

17. $\dfrac{\partial z}{\partial x}=\dfrac{3y-x}{x^2-y^2}$
    $\dfrac{\partial z}{\partial y}=\dfrac{y-3x}{x^2-y^2}$

19. $f_x(x,\,y)=3xye^{x-y}(2+x)$

21. $g_x(x,\,y)=3y^2e^{y-x}(1-x)$ **23.** 9

25. $f_x(x,\,y)=6x+y$, 13, $f_y(x,\,y)=x-2y$, 0

27. $f_x(x,\,y)=-\dfrac{y^2}{(x-y)^2}$, $-\dfrac{1}{4}$
    $f_y(x,\,y)=\dfrac{x^2}{(x-y)^2}$, $\dfrac{1}{4}$

29. $w_x=\dfrac{x}{\sqrt{x^2+y^2+z^2}}$, $\dfrac{2}{3}$
    $w_y=\dfrac{y}{\sqrt{x^2+y^2+z^2}}$, $-\dfrac{1}{3}$
    $w_z=\dfrac{z}{\sqrt{x^2+y^2+z^2}}$, $\dfrac{2}{3}$

31. $w_x=\dfrac{x}{x^2+y^2+z^2}$, $\dfrac{3}{25}$
    $w_y=\dfrac{y}{x^2+y^2+z^2}$, 0
    $w_z=\dfrac{z}{x^2+y^2+z^2}$, $\dfrac{4}{25}$

33. $w_x = 2z^2 + 3yz,\ 2$

$w_y = 3xz - 12yz,\ 30$

$w_z = 4xz + 3xy - 6y^2,\ -1$

35. $w_x = \dfrac{y - x - 3z}{(x + y + z)^3},\ -\dfrac{7}{125}$ **37.** $(-6, 4)$

$w_y = -2\dfrac{x + 2z}{(x + y + z)^3},\ -\dfrac{12}{125}$

$w_z = 2\dfrac{y - z}{(x + y + z)^3},\ -\dfrac{2}{125}$

39. $(1, 1)$ **41. (a)** 2   **(b)** -3 **43. (a)** 6   **(b)** -18

45. (a) $-\dfrac{3}{4}$ **(b)** 0   **47. (a)** -2 **(b)** -2

49. $\dfrac{\partial^2 z}{\partial y \partial x} = \dfrac{\partial^2 z}{\partial x \partial y}$ **51.** $\dfrac{\partial^2 z}{\partial y \partial x} = \dfrac{\partial^2 z}{\partial x \partial y} = ye^{2xy}$

$= -2$

53. $\dfrac{\partial^2 z}{\partial x^2} = 6x$ **55.** $\dfrac{\partial^2 z}{\partial x^2} = 24x$

$\dfrac{\partial^2 z}{\partial y^2} = -8$ $\dfrac{\partial^2 z}{\partial y^2} = 6x - 24y$

$\dfrac{\partial^2 z}{\partial y \partial x} = \dfrac{\partial^2 z}{\partial x \partial y} = 0$ $\dfrac{\partial^2 z}{\partial y \partial x} = \dfrac{\partial^2 z}{\partial x \partial y} = 6y$

57. $\dfrac{\partial^2 z}{\partial x^2} = -2$ **59.** $\dfrac{\partial^2 z}{\partial x^2} = \dfrac{2y^2}{(x - y)^3}$

$\dfrac{\partial^2 z}{\partial y^2} = -2$ $\dfrac{\partial^2 z}{\partial y^2} = \dfrac{2x^2}{(x - y)^3}$

$\dfrac{\partial^2 z}{\partial y \partial x} = \dfrac{\partial^2 z}{\partial x \partial y} = 0$ $\dfrac{\partial^2 z}{\partial y \partial x} = \dfrac{\partial^2 z}{\partial x \partial y}$

$= -\dfrac{2xy}{(x - y)^3}$

61. $\dfrac{\partial^2 z}{\partial x^2} = \dfrac{y^2}{(x^2 + y^2)^{3/2}}$

$\dfrac{\partial^2 z}{\partial y^2} = \dfrac{x^2}{(x^2 + y^2)^{3/2}}$

$\dfrac{\partial^2 z}{\partial y \partial x} = \dfrac{\partial^2 z}{\partial x \partial y} = -\dfrac{xy}{(x^2 + y^2)^{3/2}}$

63. $\dfrac{\partial^2 z}{\partial x^2} = 0$

$\dfrac{\partial^2 z}{\partial y^2} = 2xe^{-y^2}(2y^2 - 1)$

$\dfrac{\partial^2 z}{\partial y \partial x} = \dfrac{\partial^2 z}{\partial x \partial y} = -2ye^{-y^2}$

65. $w_x = 6xy - 5yz$ **67.** $w_x = \dfrac{y(y + z)}{(x + y + z)^2}$

$w_y = 3x^2 - 5xz + 10z^2$ $w_y = \dfrac{x(x + z)}{(x + y + z)^2}$

$w_z = -5xy + 20yz$ $w_z = -\dfrac{xy}{(x + y + z)^2}$

69. At $(120, 160)$: $\dfrac{\partial C}{\partial x} \approx 154.77$

At $(120, 160)$: $\dfrac{\partial C}{\partial y} \approx 193.33$

71. (a) $f_x(x,\ y) = 60\left(\dfrac{y}{x}\right)^{0.4},\ \ f_x(1000, 500) \approx 45.47$

(b) $f_y(x,\ y) = 40\left(\dfrac{x}{y}\right)^{0.6},\ \ f_x(1000, 500) \approx 60.63$

73. (a) Complementary

(b) Substitute

(c) Complementary

75. An increase in either price will cause a decrease in the number of applicants.

77. (a) $U_x = -10x + y$ **(b)** $U_y = x - 6y$

(c) When $x = 2$ and $y = 3$, $U_x = -17$ and $U_y = -16$. The person should consume one more unit of good y, because the rate of decrease of satisfaction is less for y.

(d)

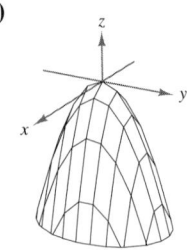

SECTION 7.5 (page 497)

Warm Up

1. $(3, 2)$ **2.** $(11, 6)$ **3.** $(1, 4)$ **4.** $(3, -2)$
5. $(0, 0)$, $(-1, 0)$ **6.** $(-2, 0)$, $(2, -2)$

7. $\dfrac{\partial z}{\partial x} = 12x^2 \qquad \dfrac{\partial^2 z}{\partial y^2} = -6$

$\dfrac{\partial z}{\partial y} = -6y \qquad \dfrac{\partial^2 z}{\partial x \partial y} = 0$

$\dfrac{\partial^2 z}{\partial x^2} = 24x \qquad \dfrac{\partial^2 z}{\partial y \partial x} = 0$

8. $\dfrac{\partial z}{\partial x} = 4x - 3y \qquad \dfrac{\partial^2 z}{\partial y^2} = 2$

$\dfrac{\partial z}{\partial y} = 2y - 3x \qquad \dfrac{\partial^2 z}{\partial x \partial y} = -3$

$\dfrac{\partial^2 z}{\partial x^2} = 4 \qquad \dfrac{\partial^2 z}{\partial y \partial x} = -3$

9. $\dfrac{\partial z}{\partial x} = 4x^3 - \dfrac{\sqrt{xy}}{2x} \qquad \dfrac{\partial^2 z}{\partial y^2} = \dfrac{\sqrt{xy}}{4y^2}$

$\dfrac{\partial z}{\partial y} = -\dfrac{\sqrt{xy}}{2y} + 2 \qquad \dfrac{\partial^2 z}{\partial x \partial y} = -\dfrac{\sqrt{xy}}{4xy}$

$\dfrac{\partial^2 z}{\partial x^2} = 12x^2 + \dfrac{\sqrt{xy}}{4x^2} \qquad \dfrac{\partial^2 z}{\partial y \partial x} = -\dfrac{\sqrt{xy}}{4xy}$

10. $\dfrac{\partial z}{\partial x} = e^{xy}(xy + 1) \qquad \dfrac{\partial^2 z}{\partial y^2} = x^3 e^{xy}$

$\dfrac{\partial z}{\partial y} = x^2 e^{xy} \qquad \dfrac{\partial^2 z}{\partial x \partial y} = xe^{xy}(xy + 2)$

$\dfrac{\partial^2 z}{\partial x^2} = ye^{xy}(xy + 2) \qquad \dfrac{\partial^2 z}{\partial y \partial x} = xe^{xy}(xy + 2)$

1. Critical point: $(-2, -4)$
No relative extrema
$(-2, -4, 1)$ is a saddle point.
3. Critical point: $(0, 0)$
Relative minimum: $(0, 0, 1)$
5. Relative minimum: $(1, 3, 0)$
7. Relative minimum: $(-1, 1, -4)$
9. Relative maximum: $(8, 16, 74)$

11. Relative minimum: $(2, 1, -7)$
13. Saddle point: $(-2, -2, -8)$
15. Saddle point: $(0, 0, 0)$
17. Relative maxima: $(0, \pm1, 4)$
Relative minimum: $(0, 0, 0)$
Saddle points: $(\pm1, 0, 1)$
19. Saddle point: $(0, 0, 1)$
21. Insufficient information
23. $f(x_0, y_0)$ is a saddle point.
25. Relative minima: $(a, 0, 0)$, $(0, b, 0)$
Second-Partials Test fails at $(a, 0)$ and $(0, b)$.
27. Saddle point: $(0, 0, 0)$
Second-Partials Test fails at $(0, 0)$.
29. Relative minimum: $(0, 0, 0)$
Second-Partials Test fails at $(0, 0)$.
31. Relative minimum: $(1, -3, 0)$
33. False. (a, b) must be a critical point.
34. True **35.** False. The function need not have partial derivatives.
36. False. The origin is a minimum. **37.** 10, 10, 10
39. 10, 10, 10 **41.** $x_1 = 3$, $x_2 = 6$
43. $p_1 = 2500$, $p_2 = 3000$ **45.** $x_1 = 125$, $x_2 = 85$
47. $x_1 \approx 94$, $x_2 \approx 157$ **49.** $36 \times 18 \times 18$ in. **51.** Proof

SECTION 7.6 (page 507)

Warm Up

1. $\left(\dfrac{7}{8}, \dfrac{1}{12}\right)$ **2.** $\left(-\dfrac{1}{24}, -\dfrac{7}{8}\right)$ **3.** $\left(\dfrac{55}{12}, -\dfrac{25}{12}\right)$
4. $\left(\dfrac{22}{23}, -\dfrac{3}{23}\right)$ **5.** $\left(\dfrac{5}{3}, \dfrac{1}{3}, 0\right)$ **6.** $\left(\dfrac{14}{19}, -\dfrac{10}{19}, -\dfrac{32}{57}\right)$
7. $f_x = 2xy + y^2$ **8.** $f_x = 50y^2(x + y)$
$f_y = x^2 + 2xy \qquad f_y = 50y(x + y)(x + 2y)$
9. $f_x = 3x^2 - 4xy + yz$
$f_y = -2x^2 - xz$
$f_z = xy$
10. $f_x = yz + z^2$
$f_y = xz + z^2$
$f_z = xy + 2xz + 2yz$

1. $f(5, 5) = 25$ **3.** $f(2, 2) = 8$

5. $f\left(\dfrac{\sqrt{2}}{2}, \dfrac{1}{2}\right) = \dfrac{1}{4}$ **7.** $f\left(\dfrac{25}{2}, \dfrac{25}{2}\right) = 231.25$

9. $f(1, 1) = 2$ **11.** $f(2, 2) = e^4$

13. $f(9, 6, 9) = 432$ **15.** $f\left(\tfrac{1}{3}, \tfrac{1}{3}, \tfrac{1}{3}\right) = \tfrac{1}{3}$

17. $f\left(\dfrac{1}{\sqrt{3}}, \dfrac{1}{\sqrt{3}}, \dfrac{1}{\sqrt{3}}\right) = \sqrt{3}$

19. $f\left(\tfrac{4}{15}, \tfrac{8}{15}, \tfrac{4}{15}, \tfrac{2}{15}\right) = \tfrac{8}{15}$ **21.** $f(9, 6, 9) = 486$

23. $f\left(\sqrt{\dfrac{10}{3}}, \dfrac{1}{2}\sqrt{\dfrac{10}{3}}, \sqrt{\dfrac{5}{3}}\right) = \dfrac{5\sqrt{15}}{9}$

25. $40, 40, 40$ **27.** $\dfrac{S}{3}, \dfrac{S}{3}, \dfrac{S}{3}$

29. $\sqrt{5}$ **31.** $\sqrt{3}$ **33.** $36 \times 18 \times 18$ in.

35. Length = Width = $\sqrt[3]{360} \approx 7.1$ ft

Height = $\dfrac{480}{360^{2/3}} \approx 9.5$ ft

37. $x_1 = 752.5, \ x_2 = 1247.5$
To minimize cost, let $x_1 = 753$ units and
$x_2 = 1247$ units.

39. $x = 50\sqrt{2} \approx 71$

$y = 200\sqrt{2} \approx 283$

41. **(a)** $f\left(\dfrac{3125}{6}, \dfrac{6250}{3}\right) \approx 147{,}314$
(b) 1.473
(c) $184{,}142$

43. $x = \sqrt[3]{0.065} \approx 0.402$

$y = \tfrac{1}{2}\sqrt[3]{0.065} \approx 0.201$

$z = \tfrac{1}{3}\sqrt[3]{0.065} \approx 0.134$

45. Stock D: \$147,000
Stock C: \$150,000
Stock P: \$3000

SECTION 7.7   (page 517)

Warm Up

1. 5.0225 **2.** 0.0189

3. $S_a = 2a - 4 - 4b$ **4.** $S_a = 8a - 6 - 2b$

$ \ S_b = 12b - 8 - 4a$ $ \ S_b = 18b - 4 - 2a$

5. 15 **6.** 42 **7.** $\tfrac{25}{12}$

8. 14 **9.** 31 **10.** 95

---

1. **(a)** $y = \tfrac{3}{4}x + \tfrac{4}{3}$ **(b)** $\tfrac{1}{6}$

3. **(a)** $y = -2x + 4$ **(b)** 2 **5.** $y = \tfrac{7}{10}x + \tfrac{7}{5}$

7. $y = x + 4$ **9.** $y = -\tfrac{13}{20}x + \tfrac{7}{4}$

11. $y = \tfrac{37}{43}x + \tfrac{7}{43}$ **13.** $y = -\tfrac{175}{148}x + \tfrac{945}{148}$

15. $y = x + \tfrac{2}{3}$ **17.** $y = -2.3x - 0.9$

19. $y = \tfrac{3}{7}x^2 + \tfrac{6}{5}x + \tfrac{26}{35}$

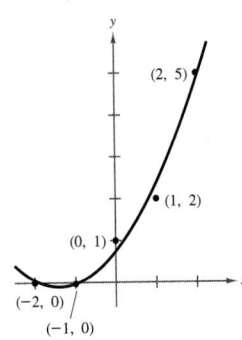

21. $y = 1.25x^2 - 1.75x + 0.25$

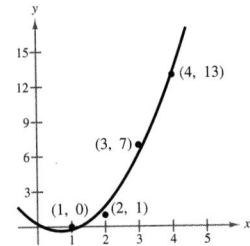

23. Linear: $y = 1.4286x + 6$
Quadratic: $y = 0.1190x^2 + 1.6667x + 5.6429$

25. Linear: $y = -68.9143x + 753.9524$
Quadratic: $y = 2.8214x^2 - 83.0214x + 763.3571$

27. **(a)** $y = -240x + 685$ **29.** **(a)** $y = 13.8x + 22.1$
(b) 349 **(b)** 44.18 bushels/acre
(c) \$0.77

31. **(a)** $y = -0.5267t + 19.4677, \ \approx 4.7$ deaths
(b) $y = -0.000545t^2 - 0.5255t + 19.5881,$
≈ 4.4 deaths

33. **(a)** $y = -\tfrac{25}{112}x^2 + \tfrac{541}{56}x - \tfrac{25}{14}$ **(b)** 40.9 mph

35. Linear: $y = 3.7569x + 9.0347$
Quadratic: $y = 0.006316x^2 + 3.6252x + 9.4282$

37. Linear: $y = 0.9374x + 6.2582$
Quadratic: $y = -0.08715x^2 + 2.8159x + 0.3975$

39. Positive correlation, $r = 0.9981$

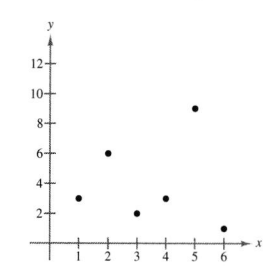

41. No correlation, $r = 0$

43. False, the slope is positive.
44. True **45.** True **46.** True

SECTION 7.8 (page 528)

Warm Up

1. 1 **2.** 42 **3.** $\frac{19}{4}$ **4.** $\frac{1}{7}$

5. ln 5 **6.** $\frac{e}{2}(e^4 - 1) \approx 72.8474$

7.

8.

9.

10.
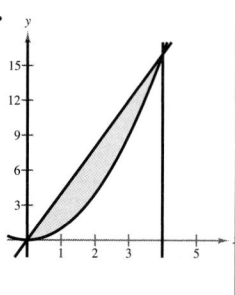

1. $\dfrac{3x^2}{2}$ **3.** $y \ln |2y|$ **5.** $\dfrac{x^2}{2}(9 - x^2)$

7. $\frac{1}{2}y[(\ln y)^2 - y^2]$ **9.** $x^2(1 - e^{-x^2} - x^2 e^{-x^2})$

11. 1 **13.** 36 **15.** $\frac{2}{3}$ **17.** $\frac{20}{3}$ **19.** 5

21. $\frac{16}{3}$ **23.** 4

25. $\displaystyle\int_0^1 \int_0^2 dy\,dx = \int_0^2 \int_0^1 dx\,dy = 2$

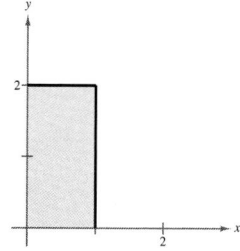

27. $\displaystyle\int_0^1 \int_{2y}^2 dx\,dy = \int_0^2 ds \int_0^{x/2} dy\,dx = 1$

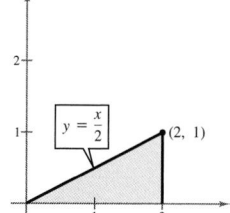

29. $\displaystyle\int_0^2 \int_{x/2}^1 dy\,dx = \int_0^1 \int_0^{2y} dx\,dy = 1$

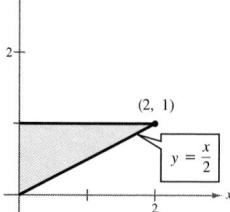

31. $\int_0^1 \int_{y^2}^{\sqrt[3]{y}} dx\,dy = \int_0^1 \int_{x^3}^{\sqrt{x}} dy\,dx = \frac{5}{12}$

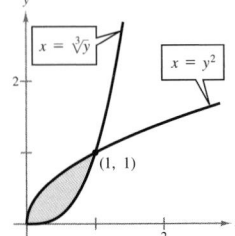

33. $\frac{1}{2}(e^9 - 1) \approx 4051.042$ **35.** 24 **37.** $\frac{16}{3}$

39. $\frac{8}{3}$ **41.** $\frac{500}{3}$ **43.** $\frac{75}{4}$ **45.** 2 **47.** 0.6588

49. 8.1747 **51.** 0.4521 **53.** False

55. True, the region is a rectangle.

SECTION 7.9 *(page 536)*

Warm Up

1.

2.

3.

4.

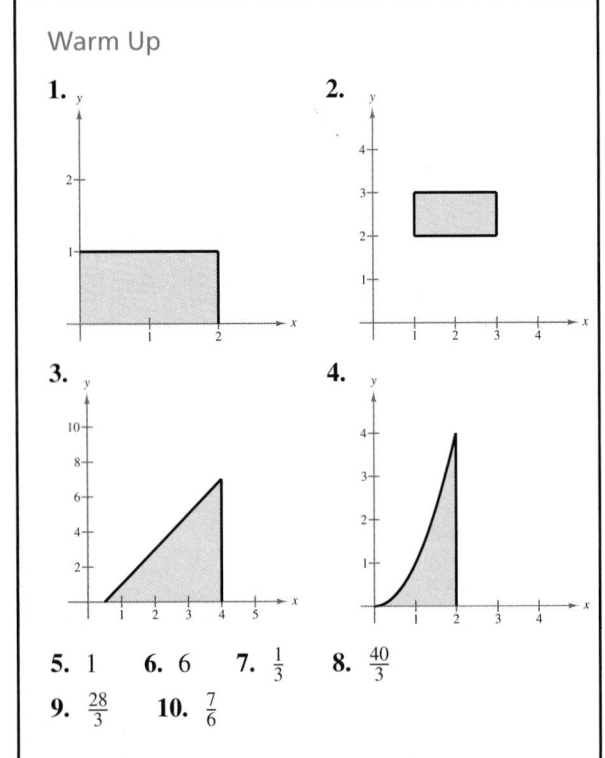

5. 1 **6.** 6 **7.** $\frac{1}{3}$ **8.** $\frac{40}{3}$

9. $\frac{28}{3}$ **10.** $\frac{7}{6}$

1. 10

3. $\frac{1}{54}$

5. $\frac{1}{3}$

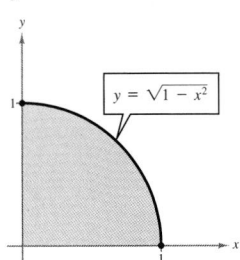

7. $\int_0^3 \int_0^5 xy\,dy\,dx = \int_0^5 \int_0^3 xy\,dx\,dy = \frac{225}{4}$

9. $\int_0^4 \int_0^{\sqrt{x}} \frac{y}{1+x^2}\,dy\,dx = \int_0^2 \int_{y^2}^4 \frac{y}{1+x^2}\,dx\,dy$
$= \frac{1}{4}\ln 17 \approx 0.708$

11. $\int_0^{1/2} \int_0^{2x} e^{-x^2}\,dy\,dx = 0.2212$ **13.** 4

15. 22.5 **17.** 12 **19.** $\frac{3}{8}$ **21.** $\frac{40}{3}$ **23.** $\frac{1}{3}$

25. 4 **27.** $\frac{32}{3}$ **29.** 2 **31.** $\frac{8}{3}$ **33.** $75,125

CHAPTER 7 REVIEW EXERCISES *(page 540)*

1.

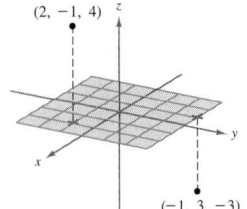

3. $\sqrt{110}$

5. $(-1, 4, 6)$ **7.** $x^2 + (y-1)^2 + z^2 = 25$

9. $(x - 4)^2 + (y - 6)^2 + (z - 1)^2 = 6$

11. Center: $(-2, 1, 4)$, radius: 4

13.

15.

17.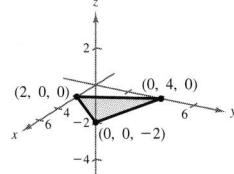

19. Sphere

21. Ellipsoid   **23.** The graph is an elliptic paraboloid.

25. Top half of a circular cone

27. (a) 18   **29.** The domain is the set of all
    (b) 0   points inside or on the circle
    (c) -245 $x^2 + y^2 = 1$, and the range is
    (d) -32 $[0, 1]$.

31. The level curves are   **33.** The level curves are
    lines of slope $-\frac{2}{5}$.   hyperbolas.

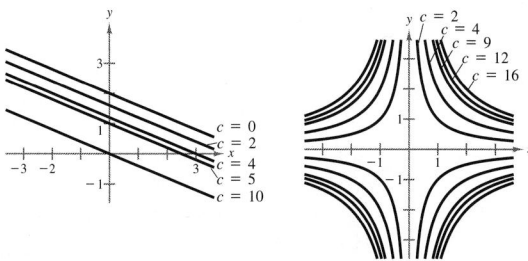

35. (a) The level curves represent lines of equal rainfall
        and separate the four colors.
    (b) The small eastern portion containing Davenport
    (c) the northwestern portion containing Sioux City

37. \$2.50   **39.** $f_x = 2xy + 3y + 2$

$$f_y = x^2 + 3x - 5$$

41. $z_x = 12x\sqrt{y} + \dfrac{3}{2}\sqrt{\dfrac{y}{x}} - 7y$ **43.** $f_x = \dfrac{2}{2x + 3y}$

$$z_y = \dfrac{3x^2}{\sqrt{y}} + \dfrac{3}{2}\sqrt{\dfrac{x}{y}} - 7x \qquad f_y = \dfrac{3}{2x + 3y}$$

45. $f_x = 2xe^y - y^2 e^x$ **47.** $w_x = yz^2$

$$f_y = x^2 e^y - 2ye^x \qquad\quad w_y = xz^2$$

$$w_z = 2xyz$$

49. (a) $z_x = 3$ **51.** (a) $z_x = -2x$
    (b) $z_y = -4$ At $(1, 2, 3)$, $z_x = -2$.
                         (b) $z_y = -2y$
                            At $(1, 2, 3)$, $z_y = -4$.

53. $f_{xx} = 6x$

$$f_{yy} = -8x + 6y$$

$$f_{xy} = f_{yx} = -8y$$

55. $f_{xx} = \dfrac{y^2 - 64}{(64 - x^2 - y^2)^{3/2}}$

$$f_{yy} = \dfrac{x^2 - 64}{(64 - x^2 - y^2)^{3/2}}$$

$$f_{xy} = f_{yx} = \dfrac{-xy}{(64 - x^2 - y^2)^{3/2}}$$

57. $C_x(250, 175) \approx 99.70$

$$C_y(250, 175) \approx 140.01$$

59. Relative minimum: $(x, -x, 0)$

61. Saddle point: $\left(\frac{3}{2}, -\frac{3}{2}, 12.5\right)$

63. Relative minimum: $\left(\frac{1}{6}, \frac{1}{12}, -\frac{1}{432}\right)$
    Saddle point: $(0, 0, 0)$

65. Relative minimum: $(1, 1, -2)$
    Relative maximum: $(-1, -1, 6)$
    Saddle points: $(1, -1, 2)$, $(-1, 1, 2)$

67. (a) $R = -x_1^2 - \frac{1}{2}x_2^2 + 100x_1 + 200x_2$
    (b) $x_1 = 50$, $x_2 = 200$
    (c) \$22,500.00

69. $\left(\frac{4}{3}, \frac{1}{3}, \frac{16}{27}\right)$, $(0, 1, 0)$

71. At $\left(\frac{4}{3}, \frac{2}{3}, \frac{4}{3}\right)$, the relative maximum value is $\frac{32}{27}$.

73. At $\left(\frac{4}{3}, \frac{10}{3}, \frac{14}{3}\right)$, the relative minimum is $34\frac{2}{3}$.

75. $f(49.4, 253) \approx 13{,}202$ **77.** (a) $y = \frac{60}{59}x - \frac{15}{59}$
                                          (b) 2.746

79. (a) $S = 1.42t + 2.82$ ($t = 0$ is 1990.)
(b) $17.02 billion

81. $y = 1.71x^2 - 2.57x + 5.56$

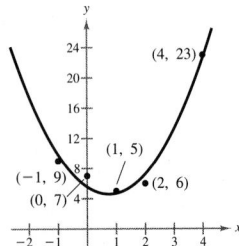

83. $\frac{29}{6}$ **85.** $\frac{7}{4}$

87. $\int_{-2}^{2} \int_{5}^{9-x^2} dy\, dx = \int_{5}^{9} \int_{-\sqrt{9-y}}^{\sqrt{9-y}} dx\, dy = \frac{32}{3}$

89. $\frac{9}{2}$ **91.** $\frac{4096}{9}$ **93.** 0.0833 mile

SAMPLE POST-GRAD EXAM QUESTIONS   (page 544)

1. (b)   **2. (b)**   **3. (c)**   **4. (d)**
5. (a)   **6. (c)**   **7. (b)**

CHAPTER P

SECTION P.1   (page P-8)

Warm Up

1. 1   **2.** 1   **3.** 2   **4.** 2   **5.** $\frac{1}{2}$ **6.** 1
7. 37.50%   **8.** $81\frac{9}{11}\%$ **9.** $54\frac{1}{6}\%$
10. 43.75%

1. (a) $S = \{HHH, HHT, HTH, HTT, THH,$
$\quad THT, TTH, TTT\}$
(b) $A = \{HHH, HHT, HTH, THH\}$
(c) $B = \{HTT, THT, TTH, TTT\}$
3. (a) $S = \{3, 6, 9, 12, 15, 18, 21, 24, 27, 30, 33,$
$\quad 36, 39, 42, 45, 48\}$
(b) $A = \{12, 24, 36, 48\}$
(c) $B = \{9, 36\}$

5. 0.24   **7.** 0.0145   **9.**

Random variable	0	1	2
Frequency	1	2	1

11.

Random variable	0	1	2	3
Frequency	1	3	3	1

13. (a) $\frac{3}{4}$ **(b)** $\frac{4}{5}$ **15. (a)** 0.803   **(b)** 0.197

    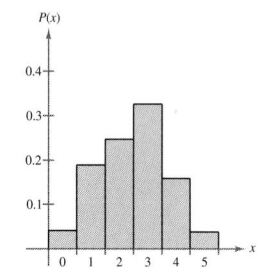

17. (a) $S = \{gggg, gggb, ggbg, gbgg, bggg, ggbb,$
$\quad gbgb, gbbg, bgbg, bbgg, bggb, gbbb,$
$\quad bgbb, bbgb, bbbg, bbbb\}$
(b)

x	0	1	2	3	4
$P(x)$	$\frac{1}{16}$	$\frac{4}{16}$	$\frac{6}{16}$	$\frac{4}{16}$	$\frac{1}{16}$

(c)   **(d)** $\frac{15}{16}$

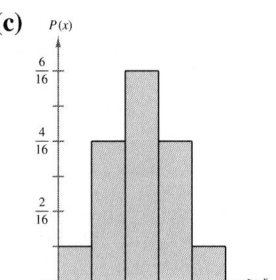

19. $E(x) = 3$ **21.** $E(x) = 0.8$
$V(x) = 0.875$ $V(x) = 8.16$
$\sigma = 0.9354$ $\sigma = 2.8566$

23. (a) Mean: 2.5   **25. (a)** $E(x) = 18.5$
Variance: 1.25 $\sigma = 8.0777$
(b) Mean: 5   **(b)** $27,750
Variance: 2.5

27. $201   **29.** $−$0.0526   **31.** City 1

33. Mean: 77.3
   Standard deviation: 8.198

SECTION P.2   (page P-16)

1. $\displaystyle\int_0^8 \frac{1}{8}\,dx = \left[\frac{1}{8}x\right]_0^8 = 1$

3. $\displaystyle\int_0^4 \frac{4-x}{8}\,dx = \left[\frac{1}{2}x - \frac{1}{16}x^2\right]_0^4 = 1$

5. $\displaystyle\int_0^2 \frac{3}{8}x\sqrt{4-x^2}\,dx = \left[-\frac{(4-x^2)^{3/2}}{8}\right]_0^2 = 1$

7. $\displaystyle\int_0^\infty \frac{1}{5}e^{-x/5}\,dx = \lim_{b\to\infty}\left[-e^{-x/5}\right]_0^b = 1$

9. $\displaystyle\int_0^1 6x(1-x)\,dx = \left[3x^2 - 2x^3\right]_0^1 = 1$

11. $\displaystyle\int_0^3 \frac{4}{27}x^2(3-x)\,dx = \frac{4}{27}\left[x^3 - \frac{x^4}{4}\right]_0^3 = 1$

13. $\displaystyle\int_0^\infty \frac{1}{3}e^{-x/3}\,dx = \lim_{b\to\infty}\left[-e^{-x/3}\right]_0^b = 1$

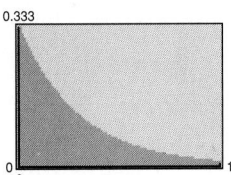

15. $\frac{15}{2}$ **17.** $\frac{3}{32}$ **19.** $\frac{1}{2}$

21. (a) $\frac{3}{5}$ (b) $\frac{1}{5}$ (c) $\frac{1}{5}$ (d) $\frac{4}{5}$

23. (a) $\dfrac{\sqrt{2}}{4} \approx 0.354$

(b) $1 - \dfrac{\sqrt{2}}{4} \approx 0.646$

(c) $\frac{1}{8}(3\sqrt{3} - 1) \approx 0.525$

(d) $\dfrac{3\sqrt{3}}{8} \approx 0.650$

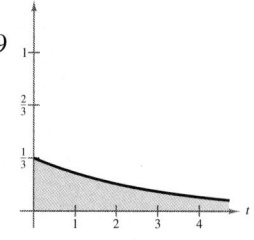

25. (a) $e^{-0/3} - e^{-2/3} \approx 0.4866$
(b) $e^{-2/3} - 0 \approx 0.5134$
(c) $e^{-1/3} - e^{-4/3} \approx 0.4529$
(d) 0

27. (a) $\frac{1}{6}$
(b) $\frac{2}{5}$

29. (a) $1 - e^{-2/3} \approx 0.487$
(b) $e^{-2/3} - e^{-4/3} \approx 0.250$
(c) $e^{-2/3} \approx 0.513$

31. $1 - e^{-4/3} \approx 0.736$

33. (a) $-\frac{1}{6}(12e^{-1} - 6) \approx 0.264$
(b) $2e^{-1} - 3e^{-2} \approx 0.330$
(c) $1 - (1 - 3e^{-2}) \approx 0.406$

35. (a) 0.107 (b) 0.353 **37.** 0.236

SECTION P.3   (page P-26)

Warm Up

1. 5 **2.** 8 **3.** $3 \ln |2|$ **4.** $9 \ln |2|$
5. $\frac{4}{3}$ **6.** $\frac{4}{3}$ **7.** $\frac{3}{4}$ **8.** $\frac{2}{9}$
9. (a) $\frac{1}{4}$ (b) $\frac{1}{2}$ **10.** (a) $\frac{1}{2}$ (b) $\frac{11}{16}$

---

1. (a) 4 (b) $\frac{16}{3}$

(c) $\dfrac{4}{\sqrt{3}} = \dfrac{4\sqrt{3}}{3}$

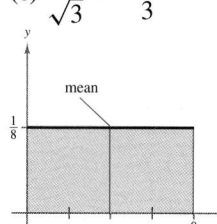

3. (a) 4 (b) 2 (c) $\sqrt{2}$

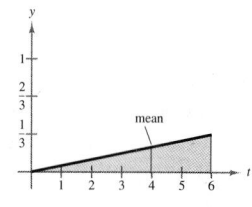

5. (a) $\frac{1}{2}$ (b) $\frac{1}{20}$

(c) $\dfrac{1}{2\sqrt{5}} = \dfrac{\sqrt{5}}{10}$

7. (a) $\frac{5}{7}$ (b) $\frac{20}{441}$

(c) $\dfrac{2\sqrt{5}}{21}$

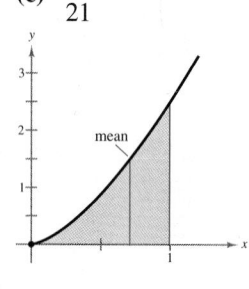

9. (a) $\frac{4}{3} \ln 4 - 1 \approx 0.848$
(b) $4 - \left(\frac{4}{3} \ln 4\right)^2 \approx 0.583$
(c) $\sqrt{4 - \left(\frac{4}{3} \ln 4\right)^2} \approx 0.764$

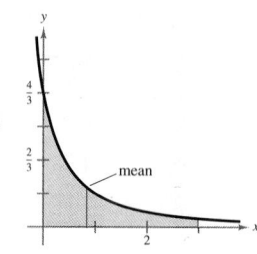

11. $-9 \ln \frac{1}{2} \approx 6.238$

13. Uniform density function
Mean: 5
Variance: $\frac{25}{3}$
Standard deviation: $\dfrac{5\sqrt{12}}{6} \approx 2.887$

15. Exponential density function
Mean: 8
Variance: 64
Standard deviation: 8

17. Normal density function
Mean: 100
Variance: 121
Standard deviation: 11

19. Mean: 0
Standard deviation: 1
$P(0 \leq x \leq 0.85) \approx 0.3023$

21. Mean: 6
Standard deviation: 6
$P(x \geq 2.23) \approx 0.6896$

23. Mean: 8
Standard deviation: 2
$P(3 \leq x \leq 13) \approx 0.9876$

25. (a) $P(x > 64) \approx 0.3694$
(b) $P(x > 70) \approx 0.2023$
(c) $P(x < 70) \approx 0.7977$
(d) $P(33 < x < 65) \approx 0.6493$

27. (a) Mean: 10:05 A.M.
Standard deviation: $\dfrac{5\sqrt{3}}{3} \approx 2.9$ min
(b) $\frac{3}{10}$

29. (a) $f(t) = \frac{1}{2}e^{-t/2}$
(b) $P(0 < t < 1) = 1 - e^{-1/2} \approx 0.3935$

31. (a) $f(t) = \frac{1}{5}e^{-t/5}$ (b) $0.865 = 86.5\%$

33. (a) 1.5 standard deviations   (b) 0.9332

35. (a) $\mu = 3$, $\sigma = \dfrac{3\sqrt{5}}{5} \approx 1.342$
(b) 3   (c) $0.626 = 62.6\%$

37. $\mu = \frac{4}{7}$
$V(x) = \frac{8}{147}$

39. (a) 10
(b) $P(x \leq 4) \approx 0.1912$

41. Mean: $\frac{11}{2}$ = median

43. Mean: $\frac{1}{6}$ **45.** Mean: 5
Median: 0.1465   Median: $5 \ln 2 \approx 3.4657$

47. $\dfrac{1}{-0.28} \ln 0.5 \approx 2.4755$

49. (a) Expected value: 6
Standard deviation: $3\sqrt{2} \approx 4.243$
(b) 0.615

51. $\mu \approx 12.25$ **53.** 40.68%   **55.** 68.28%

CHAPTER P REVIEW EXERCISES   (page P-30)

1. $S = \{$January, February, March, April, May, June, July, August, September, October, November, December$\}$

3. If the equations are numbered 1, 2, 3, and 4, $S = \{123, 124, 134, 234\}$.

5. $S = \{0, 1, 2, 3\}$

7.

x	0	1	2	3
$n(x)$	1	3	3	1

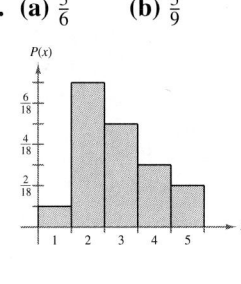

9. (a) $\frac{5}{6}$ (b) $\frac{5}{9}$

11. (a) $\frac{5}{36}$ (b) $\frac{5}{6}$ (c) $\frac{1}{6}$ (d) $\frac{1}{36}$

13. 19.5   **15.** (a) 20.5   (b) $15,375

17. $V(x) = 218{,}243.7500$
$\sigma \approx 467.1657$

19. $V(x) \approx 1.1611$
$\sigma \approx 1.0775$

21. $\displaystyle\int_0^4 \frac{1}{8}(4 - x)\,dx = \left[\frac{1}{2}x - \frac{x^2}{16}\right]_0^4 = (2 - 1) = 1$

23. $\displaystyle\int_1^9 \frac{1}{4\sqrt{x}}\,dx = \frac{1}{4}\left[2\sqrt{x}\right]_1^9 = 1$

25. $\frac{9}{25}$ **27.** $\frac{2}{3}$ **29.** (a) $\frac{1}{2}$ (b) $\frac{1}{4}$

31. $\frac{1}{2}$ **33.** 2.5   **35.** 6

37. Variance: $\frac{9}{20}$

Standard deviation: $\dfrac{3}{2\sqrt{5}}$

39. Variance: 4
Standard deviation: 2

41. $\frac{1}{2}$ **43.** 2.7726   **45.** (a) 0.4866   (b) 0.2498

47. 0.00383   **49.** 0.3829

CHAPTER D

SECTION D.1   (page D-6)

Warm Up

1. $y' = 6x + 2$ **2.** $y' = -6x^2 - 8$
$y'' = 6$ $y'' = -12x$

3. $y' = -6e^{2x}$ **4.** $y' = -6xe^{x^2}$
$y'' = -12e^{2x}$ $y'' = -6e^{x^2}(2x^2 + 1)$

5. $\dfrac{1-x}{y}$ **6.** $\dfrac{2}{3y^2+4}$ **7.** $-\dfrac{y}{2x}$

8. $-\dfrac{y}{x}$ **9.** $k = 2\ln 3 - \ln\dfrac{17}{2} \approx 0.0572$

10. $k = \ln 10 - \dfrac{\ln 41}{2} \approx 0.4458$

---

1. $y' = 3x^2$

3. $y' = -2e^{-2x}$ and
$y' + 2y = -2e^{-2x} + 2(e^{-2x}) = 0$

5. $y' = 6x^2$ and
$y' - \dfrac{3}{x}y = 6x^2 - \dfrac{3}{x}(2x^3) = 0$

7. $y'' = 2$ and
$x^2 y'' - 2y = x^2(2) - 2(x^2) = 0$

9. $y' = 4e^{2x}$, $y'' = 8e^{2x}$, and
$y'' - y' - 2y = 8e^{2x} - 4e^{2x} - 2(2e^{2x}) = 0$

11. $\dfrac{dy}{dx} = -\dfrac{1}{x^2}$ **13.** $\dfrac{dy}{dx} = 4Ce^{4x} = 4y$

15. $\dfrac{dy}{dt} = -\dfrac{1}{3}Ce^{-t/3}$ and

$3\dfrac{dy}{dt} + y - 7 = 3\left(-\dfrac{1}{3}Ce^{-t/3}\right) + (Ce^{-t/3} + 7) - 7$

$= 0$

17. $xy' - 3x - 2y = x(2Cx - 3) - 3x - 2(Cx^2 - 3x)$
$= 0$

19. $xy' + y = x\left(2x + 2 - \dfrac{C}{x^2}\right) + \left(x^2 + 2x + \dfrac{C}{x}\right)$

$= x(3x + 4)$

21. $2y'' + 3y' - 2y = 2\left(\dfrac{1}{4}C_1 e^{x/2} + 4C_2 e^{-2x}\right)$

$+ 3\left(\dfrac{1}{2}C_1 e^{x/2} - 2C_2 e^{-2x}\right)$

$- 2(C_1 e^{x/2} + C_2 e^{-2x}) = 0$

23.

$y' - \dfrac{ay}{x} = \left(\dfrac{4bx^3}{4-a} + aCx^{a-1}\right) - \dfrac{a}{x}\left(\dfrac{bx^4}{4-a} + Cx^a\right)$

$= bx^3$

25. $y' + 2xy = -\dfrac{4Cxe^{x^2}}{(1 - Ce^{x^2})^2} + 2x\left(\dfrac{2}{1 + Ce^{x^2}}\right) = xy^2$

27. $y' = \ln x + 1 + C$ and
$x(y' - 1) - (y - 4) = x(\ln x + 1 + C - 1)$
$- (x \ln x + Cx + 4 - 4) = 0$

29. Implicit differentiation: $2x + 2yy' = Cy'$

$y' = \dfrac{2x}{C - 2y} = \dfrac{2xy}{Cy - 2y^2}$

$= \dfrac{2xy}{(x^2 + y^2) - 2y^2} = \dfrac{2xy}{x^2 - y^2}$

31. $x + y = \dfrac{C}{x}$

$y'' = \dfrac{2C}{x^3}$

$x^2 y'' - 2(x + y) = \dfrac{2C}{x} - \dfrac{2C}{x} = 0$

33. Solution   **35.** Not a solution

37. Not a solution   **39.** Solution

41. $y = 3e^{-2x}$ **43.** $y = 5 + \ln \sqrt{|x|}$

45. $y = 3e^{4x} + 2e^{-3x}$ **47.** $y = \frac{4}{3}(3 - x)e^{2x/3}$

49. $y = Cx^2$ **51.** $y = C(x + 2)^2$

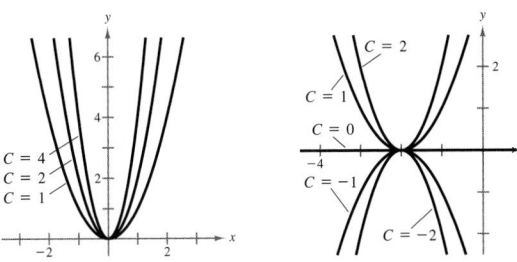

53. $y = x^3 + C$ **55.** $y = x + 3\ln|x| + C$

57. $y = \frac{2}{5}(x - 3)^{3/2}(x + 2) + C$

59. $y^2 = \frac{1}{4}x^3$ **61.** $y = 3e^x$

63. **(a)** $N = 750 - 650e^{-0.0484t}$

(b)

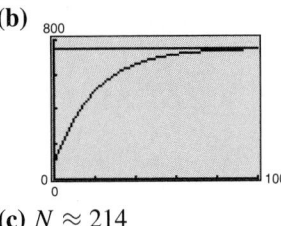

(c) $N \approx 214$

65.

Year, t	2	4	6	8	10
Units, x	3867	7235	10,169	12,725	14,951

67. True

68. False. From Example 1, $y = e^x$ is a solution of $y'' - y = 0$, but $y = e^x + 1$ is not.

71. Because
$$\frac{ds}{dh} = -\frac{13}{\ln 3}\left(\frac{1/2}{h/2}\right) = -\frac{13}{\ln 3}\frac{1}{h} \text{ and } -\frac{13}{\ln 3}$$
is a constant, we can conclude that the equation is a solution to $ds/dh = k/h$ where $k = -13/(\ln 3)$.

SECTION D.2   (page D-14)

Warm Up

1. $\frac{2}{5}x^{5/2} + C$ **2.** $\frac{1}{4}t^4 - \frac{3}{4}t^{4/3} + C$

3. $2\ln|x - 5| + C$ **4.** $\frac{1}{4}\ln|2y^2 + 1| + C$

5. $\frac{1}{2}e^{2y} + C$ **6.** $-\frac{1}{2}e^{1-x^2} + C$ **7.** $C = -10$

8. $C = 5$ **9.** $k = \dfrac{\ln 5}{2} \approx 0.8047$

10. $k = -2\ln 3 - \ln 2 \approx -2.8904$

1. Yes
$(y + 3)\,dy = x\,dx$

3. Yes
$dy = \left(\dfrac{1}{x} + 1\right)dx$

5. No. The variables cannot be separated.

7. $y = x^2 + C$

9. $y = \ln|x| + C$ **11.** $y = \sqrt[3]{x + C}$

13. $y = Ce^{x^2/2}$ **15.** $y^2 = \frac{1}{2}e^t + C$

17. $y = \ln|t^3 + t + C|$ **19.** $y = C(2 + x)^2$

21. $y = 1 - \left(C - \dfrac{x}{2}\right)^2$ **23.** $y = -3 + Ce^{x^2-x}$

25. $3y^2 + 2y^3 = 3x^2 + C$ **27.** $y^2 = 2e^x + 14$

29. $y = -4 - e^{-x^2/2}$ **31.** $y = 4e^{x^2} - 1$

33. $5y^2 = 6x^2 - 1$ or $6x^2 - 5y^2 = 1$

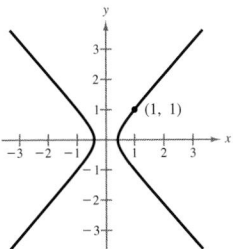

35. $v = 34.56(1 - e^{-0.1t})$ **37.** $T \approx 383.298°$

39. **(a)** $T \approx 7.277°$ **(b)** $t \approx 5.158$ hr

41. $N = 30 + Ce^{-kt}$ **43.** $y = Cx^{-k}$

SECTION D.3   (page D-20)

1. $y' + \dfrac{-3}{2x^2}y = \dfrac{x}{2}$ **3.** $y' + \dfrac{1}{x}y = e^x$

5. $y' + \dfrac{1}{1-x}y = \dfrac{1}{x-1}$ **7.** $y = 2 + Ce^{-3x}$

9. $y = e^{-x}(x + C)$ **11.** $y = x^2 + 2x + \dfrac{C}{x}$

13. $y = \dfrac{1}{5} + Ce^{-(5/2)x^2}$ **15.** $y = \dfrac{x^3 - 3x + C}{3(x - 1)}$

17. $y = \dfrac{x^2}{3} + 1 + \dfrac{C}{x}$ **19.** $y = Ce^{-x} + 4$

21. $y = Ce^{x^2} - 1$ **23.** $y = 3e^x$ **25.** $xy = 4$

27. $y = 5e^{-x} + x - 1$ **29.** $y = x^2(5 - \ln|x|)$

31. $S = t + 95(1 - e^{-t/5})$

t	0	1	2	3	4	5
S	0	18.22	33.32	45.86	56.31	65.05

t	6	7	8	9	10
S	72.39	78.57	83.82	88.30	92.14

33. $p = 400 - 3x$ **35.** $p = 15(4 + e^{-t})$

37. (a) $A = \dfrac{P}{r^2}(e^{rt} - rt - 1)$

(b) $A \approx \$34{,}543{,}402$

SECTION D.4   (page D-4)

1. $y = e^{(x \ln 2)/3} \approx e^{0.2310x}$ **3.** $y = 4e^{-(x \ln 4)/4}$
$\approx 4e^{-0.3466x}$

5. $y = \dfrac{1}{2}e^{(\ln 2)x} \approx \dfrac{1}{2}e^{0.6931x}$ **7.** $\$4451.08$

9. $S = L(1 - e^{-kt})$ **11.** $y = \dfrac{20}{1 + 19e^{-0.5889x}}$

13. $y = \dfrac{5000}{1 + 19e^{-0.10156x}}$ **15.** $N = \dfrac{500}{1 + 4e^{-0.2452t}}$

17. $\dfrac{dP}{dn} = kP(L - P)$, $P = \dfrac{CL}{e^{-Lkn} + C}$

19. $y = \dfrac{360}{8 + 41t}$ **21.** $y = 500e^{-1.6094e^{-0.1451t}}$

   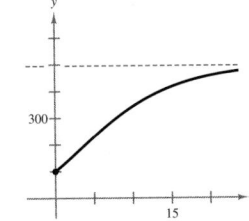

23. 34 beavers   **25.** 92%   **27. (a)** $Q = 25e^{-t/20}$
(b) 10.2 min

29. $s = 25 - \dfrac{13 \ln (h/2)}{\ln 3}$, $2 \le h \le 15$

31. $y = Cx$ **33.** $A = \dfrac{P}{r}(e^{rt} - 1)$

35. $\$7{,}305{,}295.15$ **37. (a)** $C = C_0 e^{-Rt/V}$ **(b)** 0

39. (a) $C(t) = \dfrac{Q}{R}(1 - e^{-Rt/V})$ **(b)** $\dfrac{Q}{R}$

CHAPTER D REVIEW EXERCISES (page D-31)

1. $\frac{3}{2}xy' - y = \frac{3}{2}x(2x^{-1/3}) - y = 3x^{2/3} - 3x^{2/3} = 0$

3. $y' - \dfrac{3y}{x^2} = \dfrac{3C}{x^2}e^{-3/x} - \dfrac{3}{x^2}\left(-\dfrac{1}{3} + Ce^{-3/x}\right) = \dfrac{1}{x^2}$

5. $y' - \dfrac{2y}{x} = 2C(x-4) - 2\left[\dfrac{C(x-4)^2}{x}\right]$

$= 2C(x-4)\left(1 - \dfrac{x-4}{x}\right)$

$= 2C(x-4)\left(\dfrac{4}{x}\right) = \dfrac{4}{x}\dfrac{dy}{dx}$

7. $\dfrac{dy}{dx} - 3x^2y = e^{x^3} + 3x^2y - 3x^2y = e^{x^3}$

9. $y = 5e^{-x/5}$ **11.** $y = \frac{1}{2}e^x + e^{-x}$

13. $y = x^2 + 2x$ **15.** $y = \dfrac{x^3 - 3x + 10}{3(x-1)}$

17. (a) $y' = Cke^{kt} = ky$ (b) 1389 flies

19. $2x^3 - y^2 = C$ **21.** $y = \dfrac{3(1 + Ce^{2x^3})}{1 - Ce^{2x^3}}$

23. $2(y^2 + 1)(\ln|x| + C) + 1 = 0$

25. (a) $y = Ce^{kt}$ (b) $t = \dfrac{\ln 0.25}{\ln 0.8} \approx 6.2$ hr

27. $y = \frac{3}{2} + Ce^{-6x}$ **29.** $y = -6 + Ce^{x^2/2}$

31. $y = -\frac{1}{3} + Ce^{-3/x}$

33. $y = \frac{1}{5}x^3 - x + C\sqrt{x}$

35. (a) $A = \dfrac{P}{r} + \left(A_0 - \dfrac{P}{r}\right)e^{rt}$

(b) $A \approx \$1{,}341{,}465.28$
(c) $A_0 \approx \$399{,}051.74$

37. Mt. St. Helens: $y = 21.796$ in.
Mt. McKinley: $y = 13.859$ in.

39. (a) $\dfrac{dN}{dt} = kN(L - N)$

(b) $N \approx 1800$ chickens

CHAPTER S

SECTION S.1   (page S-8)

> **Warm Up**
>
> **1.** 0 **2.** 0 **3.** 2 **4.** ∞ **5.** 0 **6.** 0
>
> **7.** $\dfrac{n-2}{n}$ **8.** $\dfrac{n-3}{n-4}$ **9.** $\dfrac{3n^2+1}{n^3}$
>
> **10.** $\dfrac{2n+1}{(n-1)(n+2)}$

1. 2, 4, 8, 16, 32   **3.** $-\frac{1}{2}, \frac{1}{4}, -\frac{1}{8}, \frac{1}{16}, -\frac{1}{32}$

5. $3, \frac{9}{2}, \frac{27}{6}, \frac{81}{24}, \frac{243}{120}$ **7.** $-1, \frac{1}{4}, -\frac{1}{9}, \frac{1}{16}, -\frac{1}{25}$

9. Converges to 0   **11.** Converges to 1

13. Converges to $\frac{1}{2}$ **15.** Diverges

17. Converges to 0   **19.** Converges to 3

21. Converges to 0   **23.** Diverges   **25.** Diverges

27. Diverges   **29.** $3n - 2$ **31.** $5n - 6$

33. $\dfrac{n+1}{n+2}$ **35.** $\dfrac{(-1)^{n-1}}{2^{n-2}}$ **37.** $\dfrac{n+1}{n}$

39. $2(-1)^n$ **41.** $\dfrac{1}{n!}$ **43.** 2, 5, 8, 11, 14, 17, . . .

45. $1, \frac{5}{3}, \frac{7}{3}, 3, \frac{11}{3}, \frac{13}{3}, \ldots$

47. $3, -\frac{3}{2}, \frac{3}{4}, -\frac{3}{8}, \frac{3}{16}, -\frac{3}{32}, \ldots$

49. 2, 6, 18, 54, 162, 486, . . .

51. Geometric, $20(\frac{1}{2})^{n-1}$ **53.** Arithmetic, $\frac{2}{3}n + 2$

55. $\dfrac{3n+1}{4n}$

57. 9045.00, 9090.23, 9135.68, 9181.35, 9227.26, 9273.40, 9319.76, 9366.36, 9413.20, 9460.26

59. (a)

Year	1	2	3
Balance	$2200	$4620	$7282

Year	4	5	6
Balance	$10,210.20	$13,431.22	$16,974.34

59. *(continued)*

    (b) $126,005.00   **(c)** $973,703.62

61. $387.97

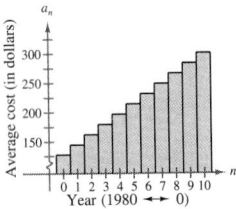

63. (a)

Year	1	2	3
Balance	$100.50	$201.50	$303.01

Year	4	5	6
Balance	$405.03	$507.55	$610.59

    (b) $7011.89   **(c)** $46,435.11

65. (a) $S_1 = 1$ **(b)** $S_{20} = 2870$

    $S_2 = 5$

    $S_3 = 14$

    $S_4 = 30$

    $S_5 = 55$

67. (a) $1.3(0.85)^n$

    (b)

Year	1	2
Budget amount	$1.105 billion	$0.939 billion

Year	3	4
Budget amount	$0.798 billion	$0.679 billion

    (c) Converges to 0

69. $a_1 = 2$ **71.** $37,970.10

    $a_{10} = 2.5937$

    $a_{100} = 2.7048$

    $a_{1000} = 2.7169$

    $a_{10,000} = 2.7181$

SECTION S.2   (page S-20)

Warm Up

1. $\frac{77}{60}$ **2.** $\frac{73}{24}$ **3.** $\frac{31}{16}$ **4.** $\frac{40}{9}$ **5.** $\frac{21}{8}$

6. $\frac{31}{32}$ **7.** $\frac{3}{4}$ **8.** 0 **9.** 1 **10.** $\frac{1}{2}$

---

1. $S_1 = 1$ **3.** $S_1 = 3$

    $S_2 = \frac{5}{4} = 1.25$ $S_2 = \frac{9}{2} = 4.5$

    $S_3 = \frac{49}{36} \approx 1.361$ $S_3 = \frac{21}{4} = 5.25$

    $S_4 = \frac{205}{144} \approx 1.424$ $S_4 = \frac{45}{8} = 5.625$

    $S_5 = \frac{5269}{3600} \approx 1.464$ $S_5 = \frac{93}{16} = 5.8125$

5. nth-Term Test: $\lim\limits_{n \to \infty} \dfrac{n}{n+1} = 1 \neq 0$

7. nth-Term Test: $\lim\limits_{n \to \infty} \dfrac{n^2}{n^2+1} = 1 \neq 0$

9. Geometric series: $r = \frac{3}{2} > 1$

11. Geometric series: **13.** $r = \frac{3}{4} < 1$

    $r = 1.055 > 1$

15. $r = 0.9 < 1$ **17.** 2 **19.** $\frac{2}{3}$

21. $4 + 2\sqrt{2} \approx 6.828$ **23.** $\frac{10}{9}$ **25.** $\frac{3}{2}$ **27.** $\frac{1}{2}$

29. $\dfrac{17}{6}$ **31.** $\lim\limits_{n \to \infty} \dfrac{n+10}{10n+1} = \dfrac{1}{10} \neq 0$; diverges

33. $\lim\limits_{n \to \infty} \dfrac{n!+1}{n!} = 1 \neq 0$; diverges

35. $\lim\limits_{n \to \infty} \dfrac{3n-1}{2n+1} = \dfrac{3}{2} \neq 0$; diverges

37. Geometric series: $r = 1.075 > 1$; diverges

39. Geometric series: $r = \frac{1}{4} < 1$; converges   **41.** $\frac{2}{3}$

43. $\frac{9}{11}$ **45. (a)** $80,000(1 - 0.9^n)$ **47.** 72.89 ft

              (b) $80,000$

49. 7808.24 **51.** $\displaystyle\sum_{n=0}^{\infty} 100(0.75)^n = \$400$ million

53. $10,485.75$ **55.** 2 **57.** 6

59. $e - 1 \approx 1.7183$ **61.** $\dfrac{e^2}{e-1} \approx 4.3003$

SECTION S.3 (page S-29)

Warm Up

1. $\dfrac{1}{n+1}$ **2.** $n+1$ **3.** $\dfrac{n}{n+1}$ **4.** $\dfrac{n+1}{n^2}$

5. 1 **6.** 5 **7.** 1 **8.** $\frac{1}{3}$

9. Geometric series **10.** Not a geometric series

1. p-series **3.** Not a p-series **5.** Not a p-series

7. Converges **9.** Diverges **11.** Converges

13. Diverges **15.** Converges **17.** Converges

19. Diverges **21.** Converges **23.** Diverges

25. Converges **27.** Diverges **29.** Converges

31. 1.1777, the error is less than $\frac{1}{32}$.

33. 1.9953, the error is less than $\dfrac{2}{\sqrt{10}} \approx 0.6325$.

35. $\displaystyle\lim_{n\to\infty}\left|\dfrac{a_{n+1}}{a_n}\right| = \lim_{n\to\infty}\dfrac{1/[(n+1)^{3/2}]}{1/(n^{3/2})}$
$$= \lim_{n\to\infty}\left(\dfrac{n}{n+1}\right)^{3/2} = 1$$

37. Diverges, nth-Term Test

39. Converges, p-series

41. Converges, Geometric Series Test

43. Converges, p-series

45. Diverges, Geometric Series Test

47. Diverges, Ratio Test

49. $\displaystyle\sum_{n=1}^{100}\dfrac{1}{n^2} \approx 1.635$, $\dfrac{\pi^2}{6} \approx 1.644934$

51. (a) $\displaystyle\sum_{k=1}^{n}[1.00 + 0.06(k-1)]$

(b) No, $\displaystyle\lim_{k\to\infty}\dfrac{1.00 + 0.06(k)}{1.00 + 0.06(k-1)} = 1$

SECTION S.4 (page S-39)

Warm Up

1. $f(g(x)) = (x-1)^2$ **2.** $f(g(x)) = 6x + 3$
   $g(f(x)) = x^2 - 1$ $g(f(x)) = 6x + 1$

3. $f(g(x)) = \sqrt{x^2 + 4}$
   $g(f(x)) = x + 4$, $x \geq -4$

4. $f(g(x)) = e^{x^2}$ **5.** $f'(x) = 5e^x$
   $g(f(x)) = e^{2x}$ $f''(x) = 5e^x$
                          $f'''(x) = 5e^x$
                          $f^{(4)}(x) = 5e^x$

6. $f'(x) = \dfrac{1}{x}$ **7.** $f'(x) = 6e^{2x}$
   $f''(x) = -\dfrac{1}{x^2}$ $f''(x) = 12e^{2x}$
   $f'''(x) = \dfrac{2}{x^3}$ $f'''(x) = 24e^{2x}$
   $f^{(4)}(x) = -\dfrac{6}{x^4}$ $f^{(4)}(x) = 48e^{2x}$

8. $f'(x) = \dfrac{1}{x}$ **9.** $\dfrac{n+1}{3}$ **10.** $\dfrac{n+3}{n+1}$
   $f''(x) = -\dfrac{1}{x^2}$
   $f'''(x) = \dfrac{2}{x^3}$
   $f^{(4)}(x) = -\dfrac{6}{x^4}$

1. $\displaystyle\sum_{n=0}^{\infty}\left(\dfrac{x}{4}\right)^n = 1 + \dfrac{x}{4} + \left(\dfrac{x}{4}\right)^2 + \left(\dfrac{x}{4}\right)^3 + \left(\dfrac{x}{4}\right)^4 + \cdots$

3. $\displaystyle\sum_{n=0}^{\infty}\dfrac{(-1)^{n+1}(x+1)^n}{n!}$
$$= -1 + (x+1) - \dfrac{(x+1)^2}{2} + \dfrac{(x+1)^3}{6}$$
$$- \dfrac{(x+1)^4}{24} + \cdots$$

5. 2   **7.** 1   **9.** ∞ **11.** 0   **13.** 4

15. 5   **17.** 1   **19.** c **21.** ∞ **23.** ∞

25. $\displaystyle\sum_{n=0}^{\infty}\frac{x^n}{n!}$, $R = \infty$ **27.** $\displaystyle\sum_{n=0}^{\infty}\frac{(2x)^n}{n!}$, $R = \infty$

29. $\displaystyle\sum_{n=0}^{\infty}(-1)^n x^n$, $R = 1$

31. $\sqrt{2} + \frac{1}{4}\sqrt{2}(x-2)$

$\displaystyle + \sum_{n=2}^{\infty}\frac{(-1)^{n+1}1\cdot 3\cdots(2n-3)}{2^{2n}n!}\sqrt{2}\,(x-2)^n$

$R = 2$

33. $\displaystyle\sum_{n=0}^{\infty}(-1)^n\frac{(n+2)(n+1)}{2}x^n$, $R = 1$

35. $1 + \displaystyle\sum_{n=1}^{\infty}\frac{(-1)^n 1\cdot 3\cdot 5\cdots(2n-1)}{2^n n!}x^n$, $R = 1$

37. $R = 2$ (all parts)   **39.** $R = 1$ (all parts)

41. $\displaystyle\sum_{n=0}^{\infty}\frac{x^{3n}}{n!}$ **43.** $3\displaystyle\sum_{n=0}^{\infty}\frac{x^{3n+2}}{n!}$

45. $\displaystyle\sum_{n=0}^{\infty}(-1)^n x^{4n}$ **47.** $\displaystyle\sum_{n=0}^{\infty}\frac{(-1)^n x^{2n+2}}{n+1}$

49. $\displaystyle\sum_{n=0}^{\infty}\frac{(-1)^n(x-1)^{n+1}}{n+1}$

51. $\displaystyle\sum_{n=1}^{\infty}(-1)^{n+1}n(x-1)^{n-1}$

53. 1.6487   **55.** -0.6931

SECTION S.5 (page S-49)

Warm Up

1. $\displaystyle\sum_{n=0}^{\infty}\frac{3^n x^n}{n!}$ **2.** $\displaystyle\sum_{n=0}^{\infty}\frac{(-1)^n 3^n x^n}{n!}$

3. $4\displaystyle\sum_{n=0}^{\infty}(-1)^n(x-1)^n$

Warm Up *(continued)*

4. $\ln 5 + \displaystyle\sum_{n-1}^{\infty}\frac{(-1)^{n-1}(x-1)^n}{n}$

5. $1 + \dfrac{x}{4} - \dfrac{3x^2}{4^2 2!} + \dfrac{3\cdot 7x^3}{4^3 3!} - \dfrac{3\cdot 7\cdot 11x^4}{4^4 4!} + \cdots$

6. $1 + \dfrac{x}{2} - \dfrac{x^2}{2^2 2!} + \dfrac{1\cdot 3x^3}{2^3 3!} - \dfrac{1\cdot 3\cdot 5x^4}{2^4 4!} + \cdots$

7. $\frac{47}{60}$ **8.** $\frac{311}{576}$ **9.** $\frac{5}{12}$ **10.** $\frac{77}{192}$

---

1. **(a)** $S_1(x) = 1 + x$ **(b)** $S_2(x) = 1 + x + \dfrac{x^2}{2}$

(c) $S_3(x) = 1 + x + \dfrac{x^2}{2} + \dfrac{x^3}{6}$

(d) $S_4(x) = 1 + x + \dfrac{x^2}{2} + \dfrac{x^3}{6} + \dfrac{x^4}{24}$

3. **(a)** $S_1(x) = 1 + \dfrac{x}{2}$ **(b)** $S_2(x) = 1 + \dfrac{x}{2} - \dfrac{x^2}{8}$

(c) $S_3(x) = 1 + \dfrac{x}{2} - \dfrac{x^2}{8} + \dfrac{x^3}{16}$

(d) $S_4(x) = 1 + \dfrac{x}{2} - \dfrac{x^2}{8} + \dfrac{x^3}{16} - \dfrac{5x^4}{128}$

5. **(a)** $S_1(x) = x$
(b) $S_2(x) = x - x^2$
(c) $S_3(x) = x - x^2 + x^3$
(d) $S_4(x) = x - x^2 + x^3 - x^4$

7.

x	0	0.25	0.50	0.75	1.00
$f(x)$	1.0000	1.1331	1.2840	1.4550	1.6487
$S_1(x)$	1.0000	1.1250	1.2500	1.3750	1.5000
$S_2(x)$	1.0000	1.1328	1.2813	1.4453	1.6250
$S_3(x)$	1.0000	1.1331	1.2839	1.4541	1.6458
$S_4(x)$	1.0000	1.1331	1.2840	1.4549	1.6484

9. (a) $S_2(x) = 1 - x^2$
  (b) $S_4(x) = 1 - x^2 + x^4$
  (c) $S_6(x) = 1 - x^2 + x^4 - x^6$
  (d) $S_8(x) = 1 - x^2 + x^4 - x^6 + x^8$

11. $S_4(x) = 1 - x^2 + x^4$ **13.** (d)

14. (c)   **15.** (a)   **16.** (b)   **17.** 0.607

19. 0.4055   **21.** 0.74286   **23.** 0.481

25. 7   **27.** $\dfrac{1}{6!} \approx 0.00139$ **29. (b)** 1   **(c)** \$10

SECTION S.6   (page S-57)

Warm Up

1. $f(2.4) = -0.04$ **2.** $f(-0.6) = 0.064$
  $f'(2.4) = 2.8$ $f'(-0.6) = 3.48$

3. $f(0.35) = 0.01$ **4.** $f(1.4) = 0.30$
  $f'(0.35) = 4.03$ $f'(1.4) = 12.88$

5. $4.9 \le x \le 5.1$ **6.** $0.798 \le x \le 0.802$

7. $5.97 \le x \le 6.03$ **8.** $-3.505 \le x \le -3.495$

9. $\left(\dfrac{\sqrt{13}+3}{2}, \sqrt{13}+2 \right), \left(\dfrac{3-\sqrt{13}}{2}, 2-\sqrt{13} \right)$

10. $\left(\dfrac{1-\sqrt{5}}{2}, \dfrac{3-\sqrt{5}}{2} \right), \left(\dfrac{1+\sqrt{5}}{2}, \dfrac{3+\sqrt{5}}{2} \right)$

---

1. 2.2364   **3.** 0.682   **5.** 1.25   **7.** 0.567

9. ± 0.753 **11.** $-4.596, -1.042, 5.638$

13. 2.926   **15.** 2.893   **17.** $f'(x_1) = 0$

19. $1 = x_1 = x_3 = \ldots$ **21.** $x_{n+1} = \dfrac{x_n{}^2 + a}{2x_n}$
  $0 = x_2 = x_4 = \ldots$

23. 2.646   **25.** 1.565   **29.** $x \approx 1.563$ mi

31. $t \approx 4.486$ hr   **33.** 15.9 yr

35. 11.8033

37. $\pm 1.9021, \pm 1.1756$ **39.** 1.3385, 0.2359

CHAPTER S REVIEW EXERCISES   (page S-62)

1. $-\frac{1}{3}, \frac{1}{9}, -\frac{1}{27}, \frac{1}{81}, -\frac{1}{243}$ **3.** $4, 8, 10\frac{2}{3}, 10\frac{2}{3}, \frac{128}{15}$

5. Converges to 0   **7.** Diverges

9. Converges to 5   **11.** Converges to 0

13. $\dfrac{n}{3n}$ or $\dfrac{1}{3}$, $\quad n \ne 0$

15. $(-1)^n \dfrac{2^n}{3^{n+1}}$, $\quad n = 0, 1, 2, \ldots$

17. (a) $15{,}000 + 10{,}000(n-1)$ **(b)** \$175,000

19. $S_0 = 1$ **21.** $S_1 = \frac{1}{2} = 0.5$
  $S_1 = \frac{5}{2} = 2.5$ $\quad S_2 = \frac{11}{24} \approx 0.4583$
  $S_2 = \frac{19}{4} = 4.75$ $\quad S_3 = \frac{331}{720} \approx 0.4597$
  $S_3 = \frac{65}{8} = 8.125$ $\quad S_4 = \frac{18{,}535}{40{,}320} \approx 0.4597$
  $S_4 = \frac{211}{16} = 13.1875$ $\quad S_5 = \frac{1{,}668{,}151}{3{,}628{,}800} \approx 0.4597$

23. Diverges   **25.** Converges

27. $\displaystyle \lim_{n \to \infty} \dfrac{2n}{n+5} = 2 \ne 0$ **29.** $\displaystyle \lim_{n \to \infty} \left(\dfrac{5}{4} \right)^n = \infty \ne 0$

31. $\frac{5}{4} \left[1 - \left(\frac{1}{5} \right)^{n+1} \right]$

33. $2 \left[1 - \left(\frac{1}{2} \right)^{n+1} \right] + \frac{4}{3} \left[1 - \left(\frac{1}{4} \right)^{n+1} \right]$

35. Diverges   **37.** Converges to $\frac{13}{4}$

39. (a) $D = -8 + 16 + 16(0.7) + 16(0.7)^2 + \cdots$
(b) $\frac{136}{3}$ ft

41. Converges   **43.** Converges

45. 1.0172, Error $< \dfrac{1}{(5)4^5} \approx 1.9531 \times 10^{-4}$

47. 2.17857, Error $< \dfrac{1}{(1/4)(7)^{1/4}} < 2.4592$

49. Converges   **51.** Diverges   **53.** Converges

55. $R = 1$ **57.** $R = 0$ **59.** $\displaystyle\sum_{n-0}^{\infty} \left(-\frac{1}{2}\right)^n \frac{x^n}{n!}$

61. $-\displaystyle\sum_{n=0}^{\infty} (x+1)^n$ **63.** $\ln 2 + \displaystyle\sum_{n=1}^{\infty} (-1)^{n+1} \frac{(x/2)^n}{n}$

65. $1 + 2x^2 + x^4$

67. $\frac{1}{9} - \frac{2}{27}x + \frac{1}{27}x^2 - \frac{4}{243}x^3 + \frac{5}{729}x^4 - \frac{2}{729}x^5 + \frac{7}{6561}x^6$

69. $\ln 3 + \frac{1}{3}(x-1) - \frac{1}{18}(x-1)^2 + \frac{1}{81}(x-1)^3$
$\qquad - \frac{1}{324}(x-1)^4 + \frac{1}{1215}(x-1)^5 - \frac{1}{4374}(x-1)^6$

71. 4.7705   **73.** 0.9163   **75.** $\frac{1}{32}$ **77.** 0.301

79. 0.1233   **81.** 0.25, \$5.75   **83.** 0.313

85. 0.258   **87.** 1.341   **89.** 0.773

CHAPTER T

SECTION T.1   (page T-7)

Warm Up

1. 35 cm^2 **2.** 12 in.^{2} **3.** $c = 13$

4. $b = 4$ **5.** $b = 15$ **6.** $a = 6$

7. Equilateral triangle   **8.** Isosceles triangle

9. Right triangle   **10.** Isosceles triangle and right triangle

1. (a) $405°$, $-315°$
(b) $319°$, $-401°$

3. (a) $660°$, $-60°$
(b) $20°$, $-340°$

5. (a) $\dfrac{19\pi}{9}$, $-\dfrac{17\pi}{9}$
(b) $\dfrac{8\pi}{3}$, $-\dfrac{4\pi}{3}$

7. (a) $\dfrac{7\pi}{4}$, $-\dfrac{\pi}{4}$
(b) $\dfrac{28\pi}{15}$, $-\dfrac{32\pi}{15}$

9. $\dfrac{\pi}{6}$ **11.** $\dfrac{7\pi}{4}$ **13.** $-\dfrac{\pi}{6}$ **15.** $-\dfrac{3\pi}{2}$

17. $270°$ **19.** $-105°$ **21.** $990°$ **23.** $-66°$

25. $c = 10$, $\theta = 60°$ **27.** $a = 4\sqrt{3}$, $\theta = 30°$

29. $\theta = 40°$ **31.** $s = \sqrt{3}$, $\theta = 60°$

33. $9\sqrt{3}$ in.^{2} **35.** $\dfrac{25\sqrt{2}}{4}$ ft^2

37. False. An obtuse angle is between $90°$ and $180°$.

38. True, $-35° + 360° = 325°$.

39. True. The angles would be $90°$, $89°$, and $1°$.

40. True   **41.** 18 ft

43.

r	8 ft	15 in.	85 cm	24 in.	$\dfrac{12{,}963}{\pi}$ mi
s	12 ft	24 in.	200.28 cm	96 in.	8642 mi
θ	1.5	1.6	$\dfrac{3\pi}{4}$	4	$\dfrac{2\pi}{3}$

45. (a) $\dfrac{5\pi}{12}$ (b) 7.8125π in.   **47.** $4.655°$

SECTION T.2   (page T-18)

Warm Up

1. $\dfrac{3\pi}{4}$ **2.** $-\dfrac{7\pi}{6}$ **3.** $-\dfrac{5\pi}{9}$ **4.** 3π

5. $x = 0$, $x = 1$ **6.** $x = -\frac{1}{2}$, $x = 1$

7. $x = 1$ **8.** $x = 2$, $x = 3$

9. $t = 10$ **10.** $t = \dfrac{445}{8}$

1. $\sin\theta = \frac{4}{5},$ $\csc\theta = \frac{5}{4}$
$\cos\theta = \frac{3}{5},$ $\sec\theta = \frac{5}{3}$
$\tan\theta = \frac{4}{3},$ $\cot\theta = \frac{3}{4}$

3. $\sin\theta = -\frac{5}{13},$ $\csc\theta = -\frac{13}{5}$
$\cos\theta = -\frac{12}{13}$ $\sec\theta = -\frac{13}{12}$
$\tan\theta = \frac{5}{12},$ $\cot\theta = \frac{12}{5}$

5. $\sin\theta = \frac{1}{2},$ $\csc\theta = 2$
$\cos\theta = -\frac{\sqrt{3}}{2},$ $\sec\theta = -\frac{2\sqrt{3}}{3}$
$\tan\theta = -\frac{\sqrt{3}}{3},$ $\cot\theta = -\sqrt{3}$

7. $\csc\theta = 2$ **9.** $\cot\theta = \frac{4}{3}$ **11.** $\sec\theta = \frac{17}{15}$

13. $\sin\theta = \frac{1}{3},$ $\csc\theta = 3$
$\cos\theta = \frac{2\sqrt{2}}{3},$ $\sec\theta = \frac{3\sqrt{2}}{4}$
$\tan\theta = \frac{\sqrt{2}}{4},$ $\cot\theta = 2\sqrt{2}$

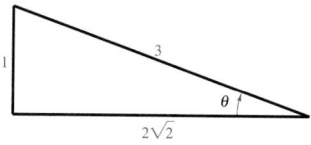

15. $\sin\theta = \frac{\sqrt{3}}{2},$ $\csc\theta = \frac{2\sqrt{3}}{3}$
$\cos\theta = \frac{1}{2},$ $\sec\theta = 2$
$\tan\theta = \sqrt{3},$ $\cot\theta = \frac{\sqrt{3}}{3}$

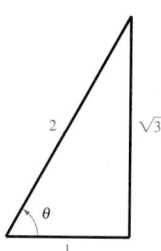

17. $\sin\theta = \frac{3\sqrt{10}}{10},$ $\csc\theta = \frac{\sqrt{10}}{3}$
$\cos\theta = \frac{\sqrt{10}}{10},$ $\sec\theta = \sqrt{10}$
$\tan\theta = 3,$ $\cot\theta = \frac{1}{3}$

19. Quadrant IV **21.** Quadrant I **23.** Quadrant II

25. (a) $\sin 60° = \frac{\sqrt{3}}{2}$ (b) $\sin\left(-\frac{2\pi}{3}\right) = -\frac{\sqrt{3}}{2}$
$\cos 60° = \frac{1}{2}$ $\cos\left(-\frac{2\pi}{3}\right) = -\frac{1}{2}$
$\tan 60° = \sqrt{3}$ $\tan\left(-\frac{2\pi}{3}\right) = \sqrt{3}$

27. (a) $\sin\left(-\frac{\pi}{6}\right) = -\frac{1}{2}$ (b) $\sin 150° = \frac{1}{2}$
$\cos\left(-\frac{\pi}{6}\right) = \frac{\sqrt{3}}{2}$ $\cos 150° = -\frac{\sqrt{3}}{2}$
$\tan\left(-\frac{\pi}{6}\right) = -\frac{\sqrt{3}}{3}$ $\tan 150° = -\frac{\sqrt{3}}{3}$

29. (a) $\sin 225° = -\frac{\sqrt{2}}{2}$ (b) $\sin(-225°) = \frac{\sqrt{2}}{2}$
$\cos 225° = -\frac{\sqrt{2}}{2}$ $\cos(-225°) = -\frac{\sqrt{2}}{2}$
$\tan 225° = 1$ $\tan(-225°) = -1$

31. (a) $\sin 750° = \frac{1}{2}$ (b) $\sin 510° = \frac{1}{2}$
$\cos 750° = \frac{\sqrt{3}}{2}$ $\cos 510° = -\frac{\sqrt{3}}{2}$
$\tan 750° = \frac{\sqrt{3}}{3}$ $\tan 510° = -\frac{\sqrt{3}}{3}$

33. (a) 0.2079   **35. (a)** 0.3640   **37. (a)** −0.3420
 (b) 4.8097   **(b)** 0.3640   **(b)** −0.3420

39. (a) 2.0070   **41. (a)** $\dfrac{\pi}{6}, \dfrac{5\pi}{6}$ **43. (a)** $\dfrac{\pi}{3}, \dfrac{2\pi}{3}$
 (b) 2.0000   **(b)** $\dfrac{7\pi}{6}, \dfrac{11\pi}{6}$ **(b)** $\dfrac{3\pi}{4}, \dfrac{7\pi}{4}$

45. (a) $\dfrac{3\pi}{4}, \dfrac{7\pi}{4}$ **(b)** $\dfrac{5\pi}{6}, \dfrac{11\pi}{6}$

47. $\dfrac{\pi}{4}, \dfrac{3\pi}{4}, \dfrac{5\pi}{4}, \dfrac{7\pi}{4}$ **49.** $0, \dfrac{\pi}{4}, \pi, \dfrac{5\pi}{4}, 2\pi$

51. $\dfrac{\pi}{6}, \dfrac{\pi}{2}, \dfrac{5\pi}{6}, \dfrac{3\pi}{2}$ **53.** $\dfrac{\pi}{4}, \dfrac{5\pi}{4}$

55. $0, \dfrac{\pi}{2}, \pi, 2\pi$ **57.** $\dfrac{100\sqrt{3}}{3}$ **59.** $\dfrac{25\sqrt{3}}{3}$

61. 15.5572   **63.** $20 \sin 75° \approx 19.32$ ft

65. $150 \cot 3° \approx 2862.2$ ft   **67. (a)** 25.2°F
                                            (b) 65.1°F

69.

x	0	2	4	6	8	10
$f(x)$	0	2.7021	2.7756	1.2244	1.2979	4

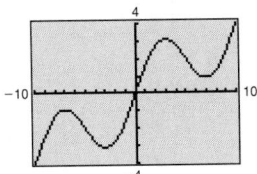

SECTION T.3 (page T-28)

Warm Up

1. 14   **2.** 10   **3.** 0   **4.** 1
5. $-\frac{1}{2}$ **6.** $\frac{1}{2}$ **7.** 0.9659   **8.** −0.9962
9. 0.9744   **10.** −0.6494

1. Period: π **3.** Period: 4π **5.** Period: 2
 Amplitude: 2   Amplitude: $\frac{3}{2}$ Amplitude: $\frac{1}{2}$

7. Period: 2π **9.** Period: $\dfrac{\pi}{5}$ **11.** Period: 3π
 Amplitude: 2   Amplitude: 2   Amplitude: $\frac{1}{2}$

13. Period: $\dfrac{1}{2}$ **15.** Period: $\dfrac{\pi}{2}$ **17.** Period: $\dfrac{2\pi}{5}$
 Amplitude: 3

19. Period: 6

21. c; Period: π **22.** e; Period: π

23. f; Period: 1   **24.** a; Period: 2π

25. b; Period: 4π **26.** d; Period: 2π

27.

29.

31.

33.

35.

37.

39.

41.

43.

45.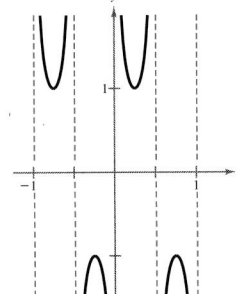

47.

x	-0.1	-0.01	-0.001
$f(x)$	-0.0500	-0.0050	-0.0005

x	0.001	0.01	0.1
$f(x)$	0.0005	0.0050	0.0500

$$\lim_{x\to0}\frac{1-\cos x}{x}=0$$

49.

x	-0.1	-0.01	-0.001
$f(x)$	0.1997	0.2000	0.2000

x	0.001	0.01	0.1
$f(x)$	0.2000	0.2000	0.1997

$$\lim_{x\to0}\frac{\sin x}{5x}=\frac{1}{5}$$

51. False, the amplitude is 3 (must be positive).

52. False, the period is $\dfrac{\pi}{4/3}=\dfrac{3\pi}{4}$.

53. True, $\displaystyle\lim_{x\to0}\frac{\sin 5x}{3x}=\frac{5}{3}\left(\lim_{x\to0}\frac{\sin 5x}{5x}\right)=\frac{5}{3}(1)=\frac{5}{3}.$

54. False,
$$\tan\left(\frac{5\pi/4}{2}\right)\neq1.$$

55. **(a)** 6 sec **(b)** 10
(c)

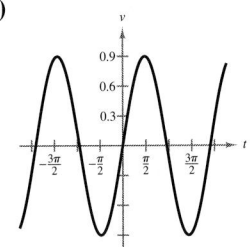

57. **(a)** $\dfrac{1}{440}$ **(b)** 440
(c)

59.

61.

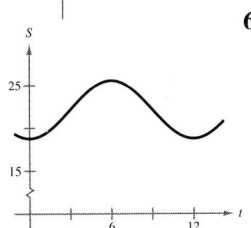

63. $P(13{,}673)\approx0.1362$
$E(13{,}673)\approx0.9010$
$I(13{,}673)\approx0.8660$

65.

67. $\displaystyle\lim_{x\to0}\frac{\sin x}{x}=1$

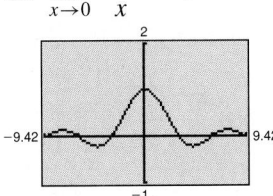

69. January, February, November, December

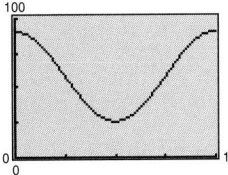

SECTION T.4 (page T-38)

1. $2x + \sin x$ 3. $-3\cos x$ 5. $\dfrac{2}{\sqrt{x}} - 3\sin x$

7. $-t^2 \sin t + 2t \cos t$ 9. $-\dfrac{t \sin t + \cos t}{t^2}$

11. $\sec^2 x + 2x$ 13. $5\sec x(x \tan x + 1)$

15. $4\cos 4x$ 17. $-2x \csc x^2 \cot x^2$

19. $-\csc 2x \cot 2x$ 21. $\sin \dfrac{1}{x} - \dfrac{1}{x} \cos \dfrac{1}{x}$

23. $12 \sec^2 4x$ 25. $-2\cos x \sin x = -\sin 2x$

27. $-4\cos x \sin x = -2\sin 2x$ 29. $-\csc^2 x$

31. $\dfrac{1}{\sin x} \cos x = \cot x$ 33. $2x \csc x^2$

35. $\sec^2 x - 1 = \tan^2 x$ 37. $\dfrac{\cos x}{2\sqrt{\sin x}}$

39. $\dfrac{1}{2}(x \sec^2 x + \tan x - \sec x \tan x)$ 41. $\dfrac{\cos x}{2 \sin 2y}, 0$

43. $y'' + y = (-2\sin x - 3\cos x)$
    $+ (2\sin x + 3\cos x) = 0$

45. $y'' + 4y = (-4\cos 2x - 4\sin 2x)$
    $+ 4(\cos 2x + \sin 2x) = 0$

47. $\dfrac{5}{4}$ 49. 2   51. 1   53. $y = 2x + \left(\dfrac{\pi}{2} - 1\right)$

55. Relative maximum: $\left(\dfrac{\pi}{3}, \dfrac{3\sqrt{3}}{2}\right)$

    Relative minimum: $\left(\dfrac{5\pi}{3}, -\dfrac{3\sqrt{3}}{2}\right)$

57. Relative minima: $\left(\dfrac{\pi}{3}, \dfrac{\pi}{3} - \sqrt{3}\right)$

    Relative maxima: $\left(\dfrac{5\pi}{3}, \dfrac{5\pi}{3} + \sqrt{3}\right)$

59. Relative maximum: $\left(\dfrac{7\pi}{4}, 0.0029\right)$

    Relative minimum: $\left(\dfrac{3\pi}{4}, -0.0670\right)$

61. **(a)** Relative minima:
       $(3.0369, 168.68)$, $(9.0369, 171.98)$,
       $(15.0369, 175.28)$, $(21.0369, 178.58)$
       Relative maxima:
       $(0.0369, 194.21)$, $(6.0369, 197.51)$,
       $(12.0369, 200.81)$, $(18.0369, 204.11)$
    (b) $\$197.93$

63. **(a)** $t = 214.5$ (August 2 and 3)
    (b) $t = 32$ (February 1)

65. $\displaystyle\sum_{n=0}^{\infty} \dfrac{(-1)^n x^{2n+1}}{(2n+1)!}$, $R = \infty$

67. $\displaystyle\sum_{n=0}^{\infty} \dfrac{(-1)^n x^{4n+2}}{(2n+1)!}$ 69. $\displaystyle\sum_{n=0}^{\infty} \dfrac{(-1)^n (2x)^{2n}}{(2n)!}$

73. **(a)**

(b) 0, 2.2889, 5.0870
(c) $f' > 0$ on $(0, 2.2889)$, $(5.0870, 2\pi)$
       $f' < 0$ on $(2.2889, 5.0870)$

75. (a)

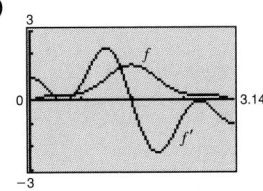

(b) 0.5236, $\pi/2$, 2.6180
(c) $f' > 0$ on $(0, 0.5236)$, $(0.5236, \pi/2)$
$\quad\; f' < 0$ on $(\pi/2, 2.6180)$, $(2.6180, \pi)$

77. (a)

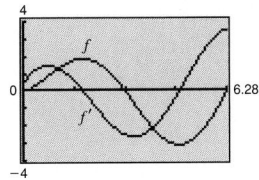

(b) 1.8366, 4.8158
(c) $f' > 0$ on $(0, 1.8366)$, $(4.8158, 2\pi)$
$\quad\; f' < 0$ on $(1.8366, 4.8158)$

79. 0.6080, 2.8457, 6.4323, 9.3196
81. Relative maximum: 4.49, -4.60
83. Relative maximum: $(1.27, \; 0.07)$
Relative minimum: $(3.38, \; -1.18)$
85. Relative maximum: $(3.96, \; 1)$

SECTION T.5 (page T-47)

Warm Up

1. $-\dfrac{\sqrt{2}}{2}$ **2.** $-\dfrac{\sqrt{3}}{2}$ **3.** $-\dfrac{\sqrt{3}}{3}$ **4.** -1

5. $\tan x$ **6.** $\sin^2 x$ **7.** 1

8. $\csc x$ **9.** $\dfrac{88}{3}$ **10.** 4

---

1. $-2\cos x + 3\sin x + C$ **3.** $t + \csc t + C$
5. $-\cot\theta - \sin\theta + C$ **7.** $-\frac{1}{2}\cos 2x + C$

9. $\dfrac{1}{2}\sin x^2 + C$ **11.** $2\tan\dfrac{x}{2} + C$
13. $-\frac{1}{3}\ln|\cos 3x| + C$ **15.** $\frac{1}{4}\tan 4x + C$
17. $\dfrac{1}{\pi}\ln|\sin\pi x| + C$
19. $\frac{1}{2}\ln|\csc 2x - \cot 2x| + C$ **21.** $\frac{1}{2}\ln|\tan 2x| + C$
23. $\ln|\sec x - 1| + C$ **25.** $-\ln|1 + \cos x| + C$
27. $\frac{1}{2}\tan^2 x + C$ **29.** $-\cos e^x + C$
31. $\ln|\cos e^{-x}| + C$ **33.** $x - \frac{1}{4}\cos 4x + C$
35. $x\sin x + \cos x + C$ **37.** $x\tan x + \ln|\cos x| + C$
39. $\dfrac{3\sqrt{3}}{8} \approx 0.6495$ **41.** $2(\sqrt{3} - 1) \approx 1.4641$
43. $\frac{1}{2}$ **45.** $\ln(\cos 0) - \ln(\cos 1) \approx 0.6156$
47. 4 **49.** $\dfrac{\pi^2}{2} + 2 \approx 6.9348$ **51.** 2
53. π **55.** $y = \frac{1}{5}(2\sin x - \cos x) + Ce^{-2x}$
57. 1.3707 **59. (a)** 1.3655 **(b)** 1.3708
61. (a) 225.28 million barrels **(b)** 225.28 million barrels
(c) 217 million barrels
63. (a) $C \approx \$9.17$ **(b)** $C \approx \$3.14$, savings $\approx \$6.03$
65. 0.5093 liter **67.** 0.9777 **69.** 3.8202

SECTION T.6 (page T-56)

Warm Up

1. ∞ **2.** 0 **3.** $\frac{2}{3}$ **4.** ∞
5. $-2x\sin x^2$ **6.** $5\cos(5x - 1)$
7. $4\sec(4x)\tan(4x)$ **8.** $2x\sec^2(x - 2)$
9. $-4\sin(2x + 3)$ **10.** $2\sec^2 x\tan x$

---

1. Yes **3.** No **5.** Yes

7.

x	-0.1	-0.01	-0.001
$f(x)$	-0.35	-0.335	-0.3335

x	0.001	0.01	0.1
$f(x)$	-0.3332	-0.332	-0.32

$$\lim_{x \to 0} \frac{e^{-x} - 1}{3x} = -\frac{1}{3}$$

9.

x	-0.1	-0.01	-0.001
$f(x)$	0.1997	0.2	0.2

x	0.001	0.01	0.1
$f(x)$	0.2	0.2	0.1997

$$\lim_{x \to 0} \frac{\sin x}{5x} = \frac{1}{5}$$

11. 0   **13.** -3 **15.** -1 **17.** $\frac{1}{5}$ **19.** 0

21. -3 **23.** 1   **25.** 0   **27.** $\frac{4}{3}$

29. 0   **31.** $\frac{1}{2}$ **33.** $\frac{2}{5}$ **35.** 1

37. ∞ **39.** ∞ **41.** 1   **43.** 0

45. 0   **47.** 0   **49.** 0   **51.** 0   **53.** 0

55.

x	10	10^2	10^3
$\dfrac{(\ln x)^5}{x}$	6.47	20.71	15.73

x	10^4	10^5	10^6
$\dfrac{(\ln x)^5}{x}$	6.63	2.02	0.503

$$\lim_{x \to \infty} \frac{(\ln x)^5}{x} = 0$$

57. The limit of the denominator is not 0.

59. The limit of the numerator is not 0.

61. (a)   **(b)** $\frac{1}{3}$

63. (a) 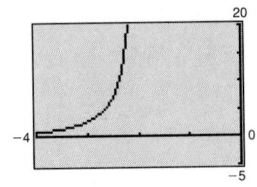   **(b)** Limit does not exist.

65. False, $\displaystyle\lim_{x \to 0} \frac{x^2 + 3x - 1}{x + 1} = \frac{-1}{1} = -1$

66. False, $\displaystyle\lim_{x \to \infty} \frac{x}{1 - x} = -1$ **67.** True

68. False. For example, $\displaystyle\lim_{x \to \infty} \frac{x + 1}{x} = 1$, but $x + 1 \neq x$.

69. $\displaystyle\lim_{x \to \infty} \frac{x}{\sqrt{x^2 + 1}} = \lim_{x \to \infty} \frac{\sqrt{x^2 + 1}}{x} = \lim_{x \to \infty} \frac{x}{\sqrt{x^2 + 1}}$

$\displaystyle\lim_{x \to \infty} \frac{x}{\sqrt{x^2 + 1}} = \lim_{x \to \infty} \frac{1}{\sqrt{1 + (1/x^2)}} = 1$

71. (a) Hasbro   **(b)** 1994

(c)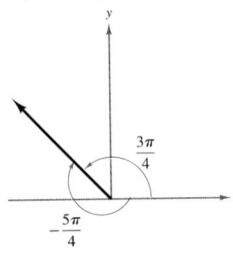

CHAPTER T REVIEW EXERCISES   (page T-61)

1. $\dfrac{3\pi}{4}, -\dfrac{5\pi}{4}$ **3.** $470°, -250°$

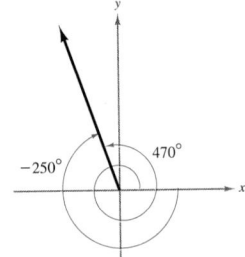

5. $\dfrac{7\pi}{6}$ **7.** $-\dfrac{8\pi}{3}$ **9.** $420°$ **11.** $-108°$

13. $b = 4\sqrt{3}, \ \theta = 60°$

15. $a = \dfrac{5\sqrt{3}}{2}, \ c = 5, \ \theta = 60°$

17. 15.38 ft   **19.** 0 **21.** $72°$ **23.** $\dfrac{\sqrt{2}}{2}$

25. $\sqrt{3}$ **27.** $-\dfrac{\sqrt{3}}{2}$ **29.** -1 **31.** 0.6494

33. -0.3420 **35.** $r \approx 146.19$ **37.** $x \approx 68.69$

39. $\dfrac{2\pi}{3} + 2k\pi, \ \dfrac{4\pi}{3} + 2k\pi$

41. $\dfrac{7\pi}{6} + 2k\pi, \ \dfrac{3\pi}{2} + 2k\pi, \ \dfrac{11\pi}{6} + 2k\pi$

43. $\dfrac{\pi}{3} + 2k\pi, \ \pi + 2k\pi, \ \dfrac{5\pi}{3} + 2k\pi$ **45.** 81.18 ft

47.   **49.**

51.   **53.**

55. 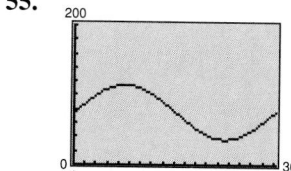   **57.** $5\pi \cos 5\pi x$

59. $-x \sec^2 x - \tan x$ **61.** $\dfrac{-x \sin x - 2 \cos x}{x^3}$

63. $24 \sin 4x \cos 4x + 1 = 12 \sin 8x + 1$

65. $-6 \csc^3 x \cot x$ **67.** $e^x (\cot x - \csc^2 x)$

69. Relative maximum: $(0.523, \ 1.128)$
Relative minimum: $(2.616, \ 0.443)$

71. Relative maxima: $\left(\dfrac{\pi}{2}, \ 2\right), \ \left(\dfrac{3\pi}{2}, \ 0\right)$
Relative minima: $\left(\dfrac{7\pi}{6}, \ -\dfrac{1}{4}\right), \ \left(\dfrac{11\pi}{6}, \ -\dfrac{1}{4}\right)$

73. (a) $\$114.75$ thousand, 92
(b) $\$36.25$ thousand, 273

75. $-3 \cos x - 2 \sin x + C$ **77.** $\frac{1}{4} \sin^4 x + C$

79. $\pi + 2$ **81.** 0 **83.** 1

85. $\frac{5}{3}$ **87.** 6.9 quads

89. $\frac{1}{5}$ **91.** $-\frac{5}{4}$ **93.** $\frac{1}{2}$ **95.** 0

97. $g(x)$ grows faster than $f(x)$.

APPENDIX A   (page A9)

1. Left Riemann sum: 0.518
Right Riemann sum: 0.768

3. Left Riemann sum: 0.746
Right Riemann sum: 0.646

5. Left Riemann sum: 0.859
Right Riemann sum: 0.659

7. Midpoint Rule: 0.673

9.

n	5	10	50	100
Left sum, S_L	1.6	1.8	1.96	1.98
Right sum, S_R	2.4	2.2	2.04	2.02

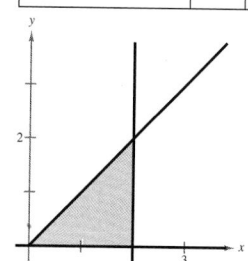

11. $\displaystyle\int_0^5 3\,dx$

13. $\displaystyle\int_{-4}^4 (4 - |x|)\,dx = \int_{-4}^0 (4 + x)\,dx + \int_0^4 (4 - x)\,dx$

15. $\displaystyle\int_{-2}^2 (4 - x^2)\,dx$

17. $A = 12$

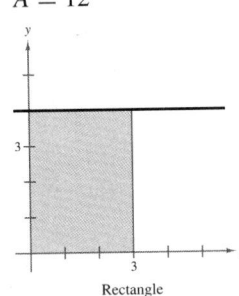

Rectangle

19. $A = 8$

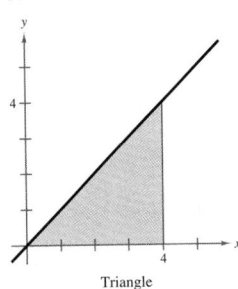

Triangle

21. $A = 14$

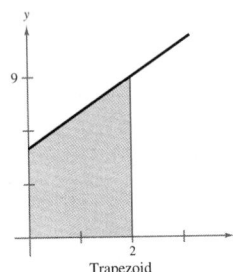

Trapezoid

23. $A = 1$

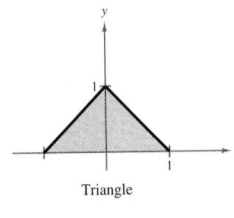

Triangle

25. $A = \dfrac{9\pi}{2}$

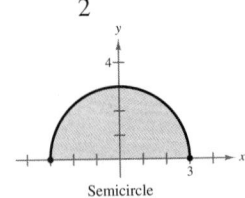

Semicircle

APPENDIX C (page A56)

Warm Up

1. $y = 4 - 3x$ **2.** $y = x$

3. $y = \frac{2}{3}(1 - x)$ **4.** $y = \frac{2}{3}(2x + 1)$

5. $y = \frac{1}{4}(5 - 3x)$ **6.** $y = \frac{2}{3}(-x + 3)$

7. $y = 4 - x^2$ **8.** $y = \frac{2}{3}(x^2 - 1)$

9. $y = \pm\sqrt{4 - x^2}$ **10.** $y = \pm\sqrt{x^2 - 9}$

1.

3.

5.

7.

9.

11.

13. **15.**

17. **19.**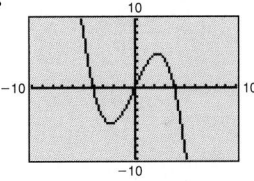

21. (d) **23.** (a) **25.** (i) **27.** (j) **29.** (e)

31. **33.**

35.
```
RANGE
Xmin=-10
Xmax=10
Xscl=1
Ymin=-12
Ymax=30
Yscl=6
Xres=1
```
37.
```
RANGE
Xmin=-5
Xmax=5
Xscl=1
Ymin=-3.75
Ymax=3.75
Yscl=.75
Xres=1
```

39. No intercepts **41.** Three x-intercepts

43. Square **45.** Circle

47. **49.** 0.59

51. 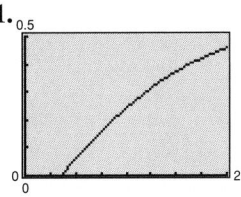 **53.** (b)

55. $f'(1) \approx -16.333$, decreasing
$f'(1) \approx 15.667$, increasing
$f'(3) \approx 431.840$, increasing

57. $f'(-2) \approx -0.320$, decreasing
$f'(0) \approx 0$, horizontal tangent
$f'(2) \approx 0.320$, increasing

59. 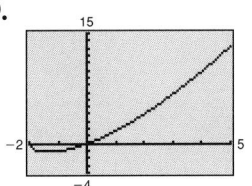 **61.** $f'(0)$ does not exist.

63. 17.591 **65.** -1.099 **67.** 0.886

Index

CREATING A VIEWING RECTANGLE

Each of the viewing rectangles shows portions of the graph of $y = 0.1x^4 - x^3 + 2x^2$.
The first viewing rectangle shows the most complete graph of the equation.

  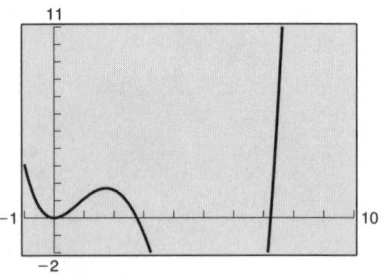

SHIFTS AND REFLECTIONS OF GRAPHS OF FUNCTIONS

  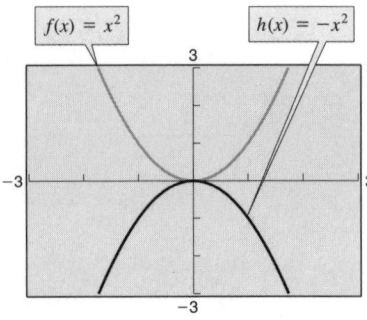

Vertical shift upward: 2 units *Horizontal shift to the right: 2 units* *Reflection*

MAINTAINING GEOMETRIC PERSPECTIVE WITH A SQUARE VIEWING RECTANGLE

To maintain a proper geometric perspective for graphs such as perpendicular lines and circles, use a viewing rectangle
with a "square setting" in which the ticks on the horizontal and vertical axes are equally spaced.

 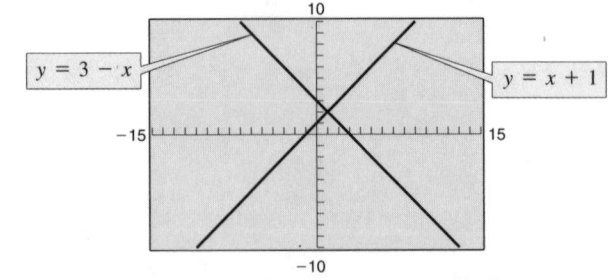

Nonsquare setting: Lines do not appear to be perpendicular *Square setting: Lines appear perpendicular*

 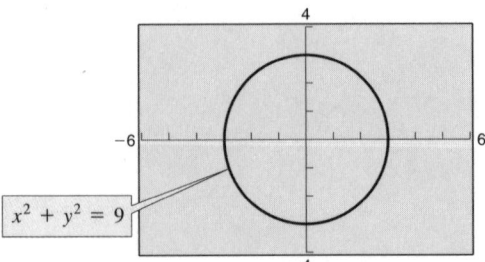

Nonsquare setting: Circle does not appear to be circular *Square setting: Circle appears circular*